NON-LEAGUE DIRECTORY 1993

EDITOR: JAMES WRIGHT

Published by:

Tony Williams

ISBN 1-869833-50-3

Typeset by:

Midnight Oil.

Printed by:

Richard Clay, Bungay.

Distributed by:

Little Red Witch Book Distribution, 24a Queen Square, North Curry, Taunton TA3 6LE.

Cover photograph:

Wimborne Town goalkeeper Kevin Leonard palms the ball away as his side head for a sensational victory in the F.A. Vase Final at Wembley.

Photo: Dave West.

EDITORIAL PREFACE

Well here it is - the 15th edition. Bigger than ever before, and, above all, earlier! We have always stated that we want to get the book out for the start of the season, and this time we have just about succeeded in that at least it hits the printer before the season kicks off. The fact that the computers have behaved this summer (and I have learned through bitter experience to be more disciplined in 'backing-up' data'!) has helped the operation run far more smoothly than it did twelve months ago. So, I hope you enjoy reading the Directory as much as I have enjoyed compiling it, and that you find it a useful and informative companion for the current campaign.

James Wright

PUBLISHER:
Tony Williams

EDITOR:
James Wright

EDITORIAL ADDRESS:
**Football Directories, 24a Queen Square, North Curry, TAUNTON, Somerset
TA3 6LE
(Tel: 0823 490469.   Fax: 0823 490281)**

EDITORIAL ASSISTANTS:
Steve Whitney, Keith Rye, Michael Williams.

EXECUTIVE EDITORIAL COMMITTEE:
**Tony Williams, James Wright, Steve Whitney,
Adrian Titcombe, Steve Clark.**

SENIOR PHOTOGRAPHERS:
Eric Marsh, Colin Stevens, Dennis Nicholson, Dave West, Gavin Ellis, Mick Cheney, Francis Short, Paul Dennis, Mike Floate, Roger Turner, Ged Rule, Keith Gillard, David Collins, Victor Robertson, Neil Whittington, Nick Robinson, Steve Daniels, Martin Wray, Elaine Sarjeant, Keith Clayton, Richard Brock, Don Fowler, Paul Barber, Derrick Kinsey, Alan Watson, Barry Lockwood, Rob Ruddock, Paul Williamson, John Diamond, Alan Monument, Ray Frith.

CONTRIBUTORS:
Leo Hoenig (County Cup Reviews), Mike Ford (League Tables & County Cup Results), Paul Marsh (Statistics), Ian Runham (Wirral Programme Club), Anthony Davie (Junior Cups), Bob Coalbran (West Midlands Programme Club), Peter Hunter (GMV Conference), Nick Robinson (Diadora League), Dennis Strudwick (Beazer Homes League), Duncan Bayley (H.F.S. Loans League), Malcolm Stammers (Welsh Football), Rex Bennett (Channel Islands), Wally Goss (Amateur Football Alliance), Rod Harrington (League Tables), Linda Whitehead (Women's Football), Mike Simmonds (Schools), Jeremy Biggs, Bill Mitchell, Trevor Bailey (Sunday Football), David Phillips (Isle of Man), Robert Errington, Gareth Davies (North Wales Football), Rob Kelly, Peter Bentley, Mike Josling, Steve Carr, Paul Vanes, Paul Bates, Malcolm Parkes, Basil Stallard, Nigel Webster (Police), Mike Wilson (Diadora statistics), Kerry Miller, Howard Watts, Leslie G Moore (Ten Year Records).
All League and Senior Club Secretaries.

Sincere apologies to anyone inadvertently ommitted, but so many people have helped out that I'm sure some-one has been missed.

ACKNOWLEDGEMENTS

A book this size couldn't possibly be completed without the tireless work and co-operation of numerous parties. We are again indebted to:

Jean Bastin, Typecast.

Although she has been extremely busy over the last few months typesetting a number of the other publications that now come under the Football Diretories banner, she has still found time to set some of the more intricate statistics that are beyond our humble means.

Richard Clays, Bungay.

Perhaps it is too early to thank them, but they have never let us down in the past and we are quite sure they will come up trumps this time!

The Football Association.

Steve Clark and Sue Ball have been brilliant all season providing details for the F.A. competitions, which as you will see dominate a large chunk of this book, and our grateful thanks go to them.

The League Secretaries.

One of my main aims in taking over the editorship was to extend coverage to smaller leagues which in the past have received only superficial cover in the Directory. I therefore contacted many more secretaries than previously, and as you will see the response was very good. As for the more senior leagues, most seem to be now (after fifteen years) well versed in providing information. This is very gratifying, makes our onerous task that much easier, and our thanks go to them for their co-operation.

The Club Secretaries

By writing individually to the secretaries (or our club contacts) of all senior clubs this year we had a response rate of well over 90%. Thank you very much indeed! During the coming season I may well be sending out a questionaire to all Pyramid clubs in an etempt to standardise the club information which as you will see varies considerably from league to league. I apologise for constantly badgering club officials for information but they always rise to occasion and know it is appreciated by the fans.

ISCA Reprographics (Exeter).

Although we have worked with ISCA on various projects over the years this is the first time we have inflicted upon them the hundreds of photos that need 'bromiding' at this time of year. They have come through their baptisum of fire with flying colours and our thanks go to them.

Character Graphics (Taunton).

As last year, Character Graphics in Taunton have stepped in during the last couple of days during the production of the Directory to provide our last minute bromides. It is reassuring to know they are on our doorstep and our thanks go to them.

All Photographers.

These are a group of people we can not thank enough for their enthusiasm and dedication. Without their help neither this Directory nor 'Team Talk' would be possible. Need we say more. One of the most heartening things to have emerged is that the photographic 'team' is expanding all the time; we have received many photos from new but talented photographers throughout the season.

All Contributors.

League and Club secretaries provide the bulk of information for this book, but there are a number of enthusiasts who provide specialist information and our thanks go to them for their continued help.

CONTENTS

INTRODUCTION

This is my first year of editing the Non-League Directory, and it has certainly been a great thrill to co-ordinate a publication I have been an avid reader of for years.

While great attention has been paid to extending the coverage, the lay-out of the book is essentially the same as is has been for several years now. However some notes of explanation are perhaps necessary:

Roughly speaking the book is divided into six main sections:

'THE FRONT' (Photos, F.A. Competitions, etc)

THE G.M.V. CONFERENCE (pages 135 - 288)

THE DIADORA LEAGUE AND ITS FEEDERS (pages 289 - 458)

THE BEAZER HOMES LEAGUE AND ITS FEEDERS (pages 459 - 730)

THE H.F.S. LOANS LEAGUE AND ITS FEEDERS (pages 731 - 899)

'THE BACK' (Misc. competitions, Wales, Scotland, etc)

Although there has been an increase in size, and a substantial increase in quantity, the task of compiling the book has, quite honestly, been far simpler than last year when I was 'House Editor'. A number of factors contributed to this. Firstly, last year I was putting a lot of information on the machine 'afresh' in the format I wanted it. This year has been more a case of updating pages that were already filed down and that I was happy with. Secondly, it has been an immense help having Steve Whitney working in the office. I was able to off-load the Conference section on to him, and with his newly founded type-setting skills, he completed that, enabling me to 'forget' about one large section of the book. Steve also compiled all the squad details for the major clubs, which was a terrific help. Keith Rye was again brilliant with the pasting up of pages, and keeping a north eye on the 'state of play', and my colleague Mike Williams bailed me out with some of the more difficult late type-setting in the final fortnight.

The end result is that we have managed to get the Directory out for the start of September. This is something I feel is particularly important; people wish to know all the details and statistics of the previous season as soon as possible, and also need to have the information on league constitutions, club personnel, groundshare arrangements etc, to hand at the start of the season. Therefore, from now on I certainly hope that we will always be able to get the book out by the start of the campaign.

A few points about some of the terms and styles used in the book for anyone who has not seen an earlier edition:

1) Playing squads for Beazer, H.F.S. and Diadora League clubs - these are up-to-date as from Mid-July. Each player's previous clubs, in reverse chronological order, are listed after his name.

2) We have again reproduced club programme covers on each one-club page. To give some indication of their relative merit we have annotated them with the mark they received in the West Midlands Programme Club's (W.M.P.C.C.) annual programme survey. The rating is a mark out of forty points arrived at by judging the following criteria; cover (maximun 5 points), content (max 10), print (max 5), value (max 10), Bonus marks (max 10 - for match details on cover, teams on outside, use of colour photos, glossy paper throughout, neatly trimmed pages, editorial endeavour). We stress that all the ratings refer to last season's issues, and one issue only; therefore a club should not take offence if its programme did not score particularly highly.

3) Abbreviations; even with 1,072 pages to play with, I had to resort to some abbreviations in order to cram all the stuff in, particularly in some club 'Honours' sections. Most of these are self-explanatory. 'Lg' has been used as a standard abbreviation of 'League', 'R-up' for 'Runners-up', 'Snr' for 'Senior', 'Jnr' for Junior. Words such as 'winners' and 'champions' are assumed. Thus an example 'Honours' line reading; *Northern Lg 53-54 (R-up 32-33, Div 2 67-68), Northumberland Snr Cup R-up 89-90* – would mean that the club in question won the Northern League in 1953-54, were Runners-up in 1932-33, won Division Two in 1967-68, and were Northumberland Senior Cup Finalists in 1989-90. In some honours lists, clubs' best F.A. Trophy and F.A. Vase runs are included.

4) I have always felt the Directory lacked a proper index. This time, with the help of a clever little programme that sorts files alphabetically, I have knocked one up, and it should contain all Pyramid clubs who are featured in the book.

Finally, comments are always appreciated, as are contributions. If you feel your league or club's coverage in the Directory should be improved please do not hesitate to contact me at the address on page 3.

Enjoy the season,   **James Wright**

PUBLISHER'S FOREWARD

It seems a very long time ago that I managed to get the support of Alan Smith of The Queen Anne Press Division of MacDonald and Jane's, who plublished the first Non-League Football book in 1978-79 as 'A Playfair Annual'. It cost 70p and contained 256 pages in a pocket book format with just four pages of photos in the centre.

Leatherhead and Spennymoor United featured on the cover (they were FA Trophy Semi-Finalists) and in a coverage of leagues, all, of course individual self contained units outside any pyramid system, it was interesting to see that the top of the Cheshire County League (independant of the Northern Premier League) were Marine, Stalybridge Celtic and Witton Albion. Tradition dies hard in the North West!

After two years MacDonald & Janes lost interest in the Annual and I published the 1980-81 edition myself.

Geoff Peters at Carreras Rothmans then suggested The Non-League Football Yearbook should come under The Rothmans Publications banner and we enjoyed a happy couple of years together before Queen Anne Press, under the influence of Robert Maxwell, linked with Rothmans and as expected, the chairman didn't show much concern for either Mr Peters or our publication.

So back it reverted to me and at this stage I was lucky to be introduced to Tony Bagley a director of Newnes Books. He was an ex-referee who supported the idea for Non-league and Football League Club Directories.

Sadly, after the first year Tony tragically died and Newnes, who were linking with Hamlyns at the time, did not take up the offer of publishing either title again.

By this time I had moved to Somerset and as the Non-League book had now acheived such loyal support from the football world outisde the Football League it wasn't surprising that we have expanded and indeed haven't looked back.

We continue to have a great deal of fun producing our pubications and as I move over to concentrate on publishing a list of exciting titles I am thrilled that James Wright bothered to contact us with a request for work.

This persistance and luck in his timing, saw him start will us over two years ago and although not a player, his love of football, non-league clubs and 'the family' involved in Pyramid competitions throughout the country, is so strong and sincere that I have the utmost confidence that 'The Non-League Football Club Directory' will get better and better every year.

It certainly could not be in better hands!

Tony Williams.

PYRAMID PRINCIPLES CAN
HELP THOSE IN 'HIGHER PLACES'

The 1991-92 season was dominated at Non-League level by the superb championship race in the G.M.Vauxhall Conference where Colchester United and Wycombe Wanderers fought out a magnificent battle which the U's won on the last day of the season by goal difference.

This left the pyramid world with mixed feelings:

Like the supporters of Lincoln City and Darlington before them the Colchester following never really accepted the different atmosphere of the Conference and often the determination of all opposition to put them in their place didn't help relationships!

Full marks to all of them getting back to the Football League so quickly and it is interesting to hear their spokesmen saying they had all really enjoyed the experience and the atmosphere of the game at this level.

It is quite clear these emotions are natural <u>providing they had successfully 'escaped'</u> but I wonder what the supporters of the club involved really think (perhaps this is a good feature for Team Talk?).

Do they really prefer to be escorted to the away grounds by police?
Do they enjoy standing in segregated and usually open areas of the ground?
Do they appreciate the fact they can't relax with a drink and a snack with rival supporters at the ground?

Hopefully a few of the real strengths of pyramid football; such as the spirit of the game, strong but healthy competetive, rivalry the entertaining of officials, players and supporters, the care of your supporters and the image of your club and the game in general, have rubbed off on clubs who briefly glimpsed this different world.

It is interesting to see that Wimbledon and Barnet have kept their independent club character which undoubtedly gives a breath of fresh air to a scene which must be so depressed with the muddled negotiating of those involved in The Premier League and The Football League.

When you are priviliged to be present at an occasion like the FA Vase Final at Wembley you realise the strengths of 'real' football in this country.

When I say 'real' football I mean the sort of occasion when you can see the enjoyment and pride of two little clubs appearing at the great stadium.

The work put in by both sets of club officials to make the day a success.
The quality of the play without fear or the negative attitudes often adopted by more sophisticated senior outfits.
The spirit in which the supporters used the game as a celebration and a party rather than an argument or war.
The colour, the humour, the fun and the goals gave us a magnificent day.

This is why we are all in love with the game. If our involvement gives us half the satisfaction that the 1992 Vase Final gave we will be lucky, but the common denominater at most non-league games is that everyone present is 'giving' to the game. They are not there purely for financial reward, or as 'hangers on' or 'takers' they generally love the sport and are loyally dedicated to their clubs.

It is with this in mind that I must mention my fear for the future at the very top.

I have supported The Football Association and its very genuine care for the whole of football (including the 95% outside The Football League) since I first started writing, compiling and organising sponsorship in the sixties.

Recently, the idea of the FA gaining money to pass down to its huge membership through the control of the Prmeier League seemed a great idea.

However, we do need to know just how <u>the game</u> is benefitting from the Football Association's more commerical outlook.

In previous years we at Football Directories have done all we can to promote what we consider to be the good points of non-league football.

It is the football world for which The Football Association are responsible and hopefully through our promotion of all the FA Competitions, it's England Semi-Professional squad and the successful setting up of the Pyramid of Football Leagues, that world is now understood and known better, thanks to our publications.

So we were saddened to hear that the FA's Publications Department were a little worried by time and support given to us by the FA's staff (who indeed have always been enthusiastically helpful at all times) and the use of the FA's official logos which had all been given to Football Directories without expecting any financial return.

We have taken the FA credits off this years publications to avoid causing embarrasment but of course we'll continue to promote the FA Competitions and Internationals in the same way.

Poor Bruce Barlow who has worked so hard to produce the Non league videos in recent seasons also found that he now has to find £150 a minute for non-league clubs FA Cup footage compared with £50 a minute last year as the FA have pulled off an excellent deal by selling their film rights but the new agents understandably need to recoup their investment.

This is all acceptable sensible business but where does it leave the non-league game and itssupporters or indeed those who are working hard (and not exactly making a fortune!) by promoting the game they love?

To repeat: we do need to know how the extra money coming into football's heirarchy is going to benefit those at lower levels throughout the game who give it so much.

We read about brilliant deals for the FA Premier League Clubs Chairman but in this new world of high powered commercial promotion of the game who else is benefitting and how?

Tony Williams.

THE SEMI-PROFESSIONAL FOOTBALL AWARDS 1991-92

PLAYER OF THE YEAR

Tommy Killick

* * * * *

INDIVIDUAL MERIT AWARDS

Gordon Rayner
James Bowdidge
Tony Ricketts
Paul Cavell
Roly Howard

* * * * *

REGIONAL CLUB AWARDS

NORTH EAST	**Blyth Spartans**
NORTH WEST	**Stalybridge Celtic**
MIDLANDS	**Bromsgrove Rovers**
EAST of ENGLAND	**Colchester United**
HOME COUNTIES NORTH	**Stevenage Borough**
HOME COUNTIES SOUTH	**Hastings Town**
WEST of ENGLAND	**Wimborne Town**
F.A. CUP	**Farnborough Town**

PLAYER OF THE YEAR

Tommy Killick
(Wimborne Town)

The selection of the Non-league Player of the Year for 1991-92 is made from the lower levels of the game for the first time.

The F.A. Vase Final was probably one of the finest examples of what football means to so many followers of the game throughout the country.

Two semi-professional clubs, Wimborne Town from the Jewson Wessex League and Guiseley, newly promoted to the HFS Loans League Division One, gave an uninhibited display of attacking football in a happy carnival atmosphere which brought eight goals and victory to the 'underdog' from Dorset.

The victory was inspired by the intelligent striker's display of Tommy Killick who tore the Guiseley defence to pieces with his mobility, speed and skill. Tommy is representative of hundreds of potentially good players throughout the middle order of Pyramid League clubs, but he took his chances on his special day, and despite warnings from his doctor, he played, rose to the occasion, scored two goals, inspired a 5-3 victory and showed the football world just what talent exists in depth throughout non-league football.

Tommy Killick wins the Award and represents a huge world of footballers at Wimborne's level. Hopefully many will be inspired by his achievement.

INDIVIDUAL
MERIT AWARDS 1991-92

Gordon Rayner (Guiseley Manager)

Gordon could be forgiven for thinking that football managership isn't too difficult a job! His two seasons in charge of Guiseley have brought all round success including promotion into the HFS Loans League from The Northern Counties East, and two exciting trips to Wembley in the F.A. Vase.

To reach the Final twice is an achievement in itself, but for Guiseley to play their part in two 'spectactulars' producing eight goal finals in consecutive years, must be a special record that will be hard to emulate.

Gordon deserves special recognition for building the Guiseley squad that brought the club such credit.

James Bowdidge (Chairman, Colchester United)

When you get relegated from The Football League, have problems regarding a home of your own on which to play, then fail to get promotion back to the League and your manager leaves - how do you feel?

Fairly insecure, I should imagine! But the Colchester United chairman kept cool, kept his players full time and was rewarded with a thrilling non-league 'double'. The F.A. Trophy and Conference Championship with a place back in the big time - Congratulations.

Tony Ricketts (Bath City Player Manager)

Many managers find themselves in charge of clubs going through difficult times, with little money and limited support. However, anyone who has watched Tony Ricketts play will know of his determination and spirit that lifts his playing colleagues, so perhaps Bath City's excellent season in the Conference with such limited resources will not be to big a surprise.

He developed a fine club spirit in which his small and unglamourous squad played to their full potential and achieved results that were a credit to all involved.

Paul Cavell (Dagenham & Redbridge)

Strikers are always likely to become heros as their names feature in the goalscoring credits and there is nothing to challenge the thrill of 'hitting the back of the net'. However thoroughbred workers who act as team men and score goals are a bit special and if they are also good clubman, then the manager knows he has a 'gem'.

Paul Cavell is such a player. He finished top of the Conference scoring charts last season, won his first England Semi-Professional Cap and has developed into a superb all round footballer.

Roly Howard (Marine Manager)

Once again Roly proved what a shrewd manager he has become by taking his side to the F.A. Trophy Semi-Final, challenging Stalybridge Celtic all the way for the HFS title and looking often the HFS Loans League Representative XI which soundly beat the F.A.XI.

Roly's knowledge of local players is second to none and it would be fitting if Marine can improve their ground facilities and win a place in the Conference. One of Britain's very best managers would then be given a new and exciting challenge which he would relish.

REGIONAL CLUB AWARDS 1991-92

North East - Blyth Spartans

Despite a constant battle against financial problems, Blyth Spartans held their own in the Northern League championship, beat North Shields in The Northumberland Cup and developed their own local talent in a very tough season in which the famous 'Spartans' were not allowed to disappear.

North West - Stalybridge Celtic

To win a major competition by fourteen points says a great deal for the all round strength of a club and Stalybridge Celtic's domination of the HFS championship race brings great credit to all involved. They have earned their first taste of Conference football and it's good to see this famous name back at the top.

Midlands - Bromsgrove Rovers

A gradual upgrading of their challenge in the Beazer Premier League saw Bromsgrove Rovers surpress their previous near misses and time their challenge to perfection to win the 1992 championship. Their ground had been steadily improved over the years and the clubs all round planning deserved its just rewards.

East of England - Colchester United

Colchester United showed a truly professional attitude to their Conference campaign and few would begrudge them their chmaionship success. A good all round squad was well drilled and will take the good wishes of non-league football with them into The Barclays League.

Home Counties North - Stevenage Borough

Steady improvement each year, having resurrected the club to represent Stevenage, has seen Borough' attract excellent support, conduct itself impressively and stride forward relentlessley its aim to reach the top of the pyramid. Stevenage Borough is a fine example to all the little clubs with similar ambitions.

Home Counties South - Hastings Town

Another town with a history of football clubs coming and going is Hastings. But after a superb season in which the 'Town' team stormed through to promotion, the local supporters thoroughly enjoyed watching a club that jad obviously been well prepared for its confident step up into senior competition.

West of England - Wimborne Town

Wimborne Town became Dirset's first ever club to play at Wemlbey and anyone watching the warm up before the game realised that the club weren't there by accident. Every player on the books was involved, kitted out smartly and working as a unit. The team then brought great credit to their area, their League and to football in general in a memorable Vase success achieved with style and spirit.

F.A. CUP
TEAM OF THE YEAR

After hanging on to beat Torquay United in a thrilling cup tie, shown by Sky Television, Farnborough Town deserved the National coverage that followed two heroic battles with West Ham United.

Once again a Non-League club showed that it wasn't old fashioned 'kick them off the park' cup spirit that brought success. Like Woking, the quality of play was impressive and how good it was to hear the wonderful common sense football talk of Farnborough Town's long serving hero - manager Ted Pearce. Some senior managers could certainly learn a thing or two from Ted.

PREVIOUS AWARD WINNERS

Player of the Year

1983-84	Brian Thompson (Maidstone United)
1984-85	Alan Cordice (Wealdstone)
1985-86	Jeff Johnson (Altrincham)
1986-87	Mark Carter (Runcorn)
1987-88	David Howell (Enfield)
1988-89	Steve Butler (Maidstone United)
1989-90	Phil Gridelet (Barnet)
1990-91	Mark West (Wycombe Wanderers)

Individual Merit Awards

1978-79

Jim Arnold (Stafford Rangers)
Tony Jennings (Enfield)
Bily Kellock (Kettering)
Chris Tudor (Almondsbury Greenway)
Howard Wilkinson (England S-Pro Manager)

1979-80

Ted Hardy (Manager of Enfield)
Leo Skeete (Stamford)
Mark Newsom (Maidstone Utd)
Dave Ryan (Northwich Victoria)

1980-81

Tony Sanders (Manager of Altrincham)
Larry Pritchard (Sutton Utd)
Terry Moore (Bishop's Stortford)
Colin Williams (Northwich Victoria)
Keith Wright (England S-Pro Manager)

1981-82

Mickey Burns (Forest Green Rovers)
Barry Howard (Altrincham)
John Williams (Manager of Runcorn)
Keith Barrett (Enfield)
Graham Bennett (Bangor City)

1982-83

John Watson (Maidstone Utd)
John Davison (Altrincham)
John Barley (Maidstone Utd)
Ken Jones (Northwich Victoria)
Tommy Dixon (Blyth Spartans)
Bill Dellow (Secretary of Southern League)

1983-84

Paul Culpin (Nuneaton Borough)
Tommy Robson (Stamford)
Mark Newsom (Maidstone Utd)
Dave Ryan (Northwich Victoria)

1984-85

Paul Culpin (Nuneaton Borough)
David Howells (Enfield)
Paul & Lee Joinson (Halesowen Town)

1985-86

Kim Casey (Kidderminster H)
Paul Shirtliff (Frickley Athletic)
Cyril Whiteside (Chairman of Clitheroe FC)
Barrie Williams (Manager of Sutton Utd)

1986-87

Paul Davies (Kidderminster H)
Barry Fry (Manager of Barnet)
Peter Hunter (Secretary of GMV Conference)
Jim Thompson (Chairman of Maidstone Utd)
(Special 'Pyramid' creation award)

1987-88

Kevin Verity (England S-Pro Manager)
Steve Burr (Macclesfield)
Bill McCullough (Chairman of Barrow)

1988-89

Barrie Williams (Manager of Sutton Utd)
Stan Storton (Manager of Telford Utd)
Mickey Roberts (Macclesfield Town)
Nigel Ransom (Welling United)

1989-90

Gary Wager (Merthyr Tydfil)
Ray Wilkie (Manager of Barrow)
Gordon Bartlett (Manager of Yeading)
Gary Simpson (Altrincham)

1990-91

Dereck Brown (Woking)
Frank Northwood (Manager of Gresley Rovers)
Ted Pearce (Manager of Farnborough Town)
Noel White (Liverpool and The Football Association)

PAST CLUB AWARDS

1977-1978

Team of the Year: Blyth Spartans
Special Merit Award: Enfield
FA Cup Award: Blyth Spartans
FA Vase Merit Award: Barton Rovers

1978-1979

Team of the Year: Barking
Special Merit Award: Worcester City
FA Cup Award: Altrincham
FA Vase Merit Award: Billericay Town

1979-1980

Team of the Year: Dagenham
Special Merit Awards: Altrincham &
Stamford
FA Cup Award: Harlow Town
FA Vase Merit Award: Guisborough
Town

1980-1981

Team of the Year: Altrincham
Special Merit Awards: Bishop's
Stortford, Runcorn & Slough
FA Cup Award: Enfield
FA Vase Merit Award: Willenhall

1981-1982

Team of the Year: Leytonstone &
Ilford
Special Merit Awards: Shepshed
Charterhouse, Enfield, Runcorn &
Wealdstone
FA Cup Award: Altrincham
FA Vase Merit Award: Rainworth MW

1982-1983

Team of the Year: England Semi-Pro
team
Special Merit Awards: Enfield, Sutton
Utd, Gateshead & Harrow Borough
FA Cup Award: Bishop's Stortford
FA Vase Merit Award: Harry Rudge
(Sec. Halesowen)

1983-1984

North East: Whitby Town
North West: South Liverpool
Midlands: Shepshed Charterhouse
East of England: Stansted
Home Counties: Maidstone Utd
West & Wales: Exmouth Town

1984-1985

North East: Bishop Auckland
North West: Fleetwood Town
Midlands: Telford United
East of England: Boston United
Home Counties: Wealdstone
West & Wales: Exmouth Town

1985-1986

North East: Gateshead
North West: Altrincham
Midlands: Kidderminster Harriers
East of England: Wisbech Town
Home Counties: Enfield
West & Wales: Barry Town

1986-1987

North East: Scarborough
North West: Macclesfield
Midlands: Burton Albion

East of England: Fareham Town
Home Counties: Barnet
West & Wales: Merthyr Tydfil

1987-1988

North East: Blyth Spartans
North West: Colne Dynamoes
Midlands: Kettering
East of England: Lincoln City
Home Counties: Bashley & Barnet
West & Wales: Yeovil Town

1988-1989

North East: Bishop Auckland
North West: Hyde United
Midlands: Tamworth
East of England: Kettering Town
Home Counties North: Leytonstone-Ilford
Home Counties South: Maidstone United
West & Wales: Merthyr Tydfil

1989-1990

North East: Darlington
North West: Colne Dynamoes
Midlands: Leek Town
East of England: Wivenhoe Town
Home Counties North: Barnet
Home Counties South: Welling United
West & Wales: Newport AFC
FA Cup Team of the Year: Whitley Bay

1990-1991

North East: Guiseley
North West: Witton Albion
Midlands: Stourbridge
East of England: Colchester United
Home Counties North: Barnet
Home Counties South: Littlehampton Town
West of England: Gloucester City
FA Cup Team of the Year: Woking

Non-League Photos of the Year

As many of you have appreciated, the quality and variety of photos sent in by our regular photographers to Team Talk (the only national monthly magazine featuring football in the 'pyramid' competitions) are probably best displayed in colour.

We will be featuring the best contributions again this season, but as usual we would like to pay tribute in this Directory to all those football mad enthusiasts who travel through all weathers to take superb action photos. We really do appreciate them.

The Photo of the Year captures the superb action of a really brave header from Gretna's Chris Pickford as he dives in front of the covering Langley Park defenders during a Northern League match. Alan Watson sends a regular supply of superb photos from the North East and this effort wins him this years award.

Every year spectacular goalkeepers and forwards with exciting volleys and headers give photographers their best chances to impress but our first eight photos are general goalmouth scenes that have been very well presented.

Fisher Athletic goalkeeper Stephen Banks makes a brillant save from Dover Athletic's Colin Blewden.
Photo: Alan Coomes.

Margate's Tony Harwood snatches a late winner at Whyteleaf despite a fine rugby tackle. Photo: Dennis Nicholson.

Ron Duggins sent us this exciting picture of a last minute winner by Matlock's Everton Marsh against Solihull Borough.

A really impressive photo shows the concentration and tension of the packed crowd as Wimborne attack in their FA Vase semi-final against Bamber Bridge. Photo Action Prints.

Another double act by Gretna's Chris Pickard and photographer Alan Watson. This time it's a goal at Langley Park.

Not much action; but a beautiful view of an excellent free kick well presented by Neil Whittington. Gale is the scorer for Histon in his sides 3-0 victory at Chatteris.

Hot Shots

Sudbury Town's Dean Barker shoots just wide in the home FA Vase semi-final against Guiseley. Photo: Clive Pearson.

Paul Barber catches Tamworth's Kevan Kane in perfect shooting action against Solihull Borough.

Guiseley's Alan Roberts powers in a shot at Sudbury in the Fa Vase Semi-final. Photo: Dennis Nicholson.

Dartford's experienced John Leslie scores with a beautifully balanced and controlled volley but 'The Darts' lost 1-3 at home to Moor Green. Photo: Keith Gillard.

Bath City's R.Cousins shows all the grace and skill of his ice skating namesake as he shoots spectacularly against Dorking in the FA Trophy. Photo: Paul Dennis.

A super action shot by Rob Ruddock who travelled from Merseyside to see Stalybridge Celtic and their ace goalscorer Chris Camden take on Harrow Borough in the FA Trophy.

Everbody's favourites

Goalkeepers are usually popular characters and the photos on these pages show some exciting goalmouth action. Here Andrew Mollitt captures a fine save by Leek Town's Bob Aslin from Morecombe's Jimmy Brown.

Andy McDonald the Selsey keeper is beaten by this Malden Vale shot which hits the post and gives Vale an equalizer from the rebound. He had the last laugh however as Selsey won 2-1. Photo: Graham Cotterill.

Despite conceding five goals at Hampton, Eastbourne Town goalkeeper Ian Stringer had a great game and Dennis Nicholson shows us one of his magnificent saves.

The save of the season? A Marine defender pressured by two Kettering Town players in the FA trophy heads towards his own goal. But Kevin O'Brien hurls himself backwards and sideways to scoop the ball to safety. Congratulations to Kevn and photographer Mick Cheney.

Whatever you do - Do it with style!

Supporting your club

Above: Wimborne Town supporters before their home semi-final against Bamber Bridge. Photo: Keith Clayton.

Below: Two youngsters at Fleetwood Town. Photo: Paul Daniels.

'Postitional play'

Above: Chertsey goalkeeper Alan Henley goes the wrong way against Bamber Bridge. Photo: Graham Cottrill.

Below: Croydon's defence can't reach a Gosport header in the FA Trophy. Photo: Dave West.

'Pitch preparation'

Above: Smoke screen: Photo: Dennis Nicholson.

Below: No lines - just arrows! Photo: Eric Marsh.

This could be a foul ref!

Above: Yeovil Town's top scorer Micky Spencer falls after a Walsall tackle. Photo: Paul Dennis.

Below: Somersham's Mark Furness goes up and over a Potton United leg. Photo: Gavin Ellis.

'Picking your vantage point'

Above: Beleive it or not, this photo was taken at Tonbridge when their attendance record was broken when Yeovil were the visitors in the FA Cup. Photo: Tim Lancaster.

Below: Wimborne supporters overspill at their home Vase Semi-Final. Photo: Keith Clayton.

Create your own style

Above: Too hot to handle? Ade Gurdler saves for Pagham at Bexhill. Photo: Roger Turner.

Right: I'll celebrate on my own. Hastings Town Andy Blondrage has scored the winner against Ashford Town. Photo: T.S.Blackman.

Below: I don't usually take throw-ins! Dartford's Jason Shaw tries a new style against Gloucester (or does he normaly play rugby?). Photo: Keith Clayton.

ID MOTORS

Balance + Movement + Poise = Style

Above: Bashly celebrate a Leroy Whale (No.9) goal against Cambridge City. Photo: Keith Clayton.

Left: Tom McGinty congratulates Mark Boyland (No.9) after a goal at Fisher Athletic. Photo: Alan Coomes.

Below: Look ref he's got his fingers in my ear! (Oxford City v 61 FC.)

Stylish mascots bring good luck. Gretna (Freddie Sheckley), Ricky Cook (West Ham United) and Sally O'Brien (Farnborough Town), Craig Hackett (Halesowen Town) and particularly Robert Barden (Crawley) prove the point. Photos by Alan Watson, Eric Marsh (Twice) and Paul Dennis.

Did you see that.....

A one armed man was playing for Alma Swanley.
Photo: Mike Floate.

The lovely Wycombe Wanderers new ground was on fire. Photo: Paul Dennis.

...Marine have a row of entertainment boxes.

Two aliens were watching the Aylesbury United v Newport AFC match.

Sometimes we worry about our photographers!
Why did they take these photos?

Above: Was it the matching hair styles?
The mishaped halo?
or just the action?
The players are Wren of Bowers United and Saggers of Southend Manor.
Below: Your guess is as good as ours!

A possible new photographic competition

To find how many players can be fitted into a possible Team Talk front cover.

Entry One: Woking v Harrow Borough (a mere six players and no ball) - A good photo from Stephen Harris.

Entry Two: Grays v Enfield. Nine players (we think) challenge for a corner in the home goalmouth. Photo: Paul Dennis.

INTERNATIONAL &
F.A. REPRESENTATIVE
FOOTBALL

A quiet season

England's only Semi-Professional International of the season was contested against Wales at Aberystwyth Town FC on Tuesday 3rd March, and England collected their first victory over the Welsh since 1989 with a very convincing display.

The English line-up, spearheaded by joint Conference top-scorers Paul Cavell and Terry Robbins, had a very attacking look to it, and after an initial scare when Bob Colville made a forceful run down the right and pulled across a low centre that begged to be tapped home, they bossed the opening half.

The strong Redbridge Forest contingent was the source of most good things for England. In the seventh minute Paul Watts hit a shot just over from nearly forty yards, then three minutes later Cavell outstripped the Welsh defence and squared the ball low across the box to clubmate Paul Richardson who slammed it against the the underside of the bar. England's next chance fell to Delwyn Humphreys in the 14th minute. The Kidderminster forward shot just over after a strong run, but it was his last contribution as he was immediately replaced by Gary Abbott who thus joined his Welling team-mate Robbins up front alongside Cavell. Cavell continued to be the star performer of the first half. In the 35th minute he picked up the ball inside his own half and hared down the right to the Welsh goalline before cutting the ball back into the path of Bobby Mayes. The Redbridge midfielder hit a powerful drive that Jon Roberts did well to get his body behind. Cavell again beat the Welsh defence for pace just before the interval but, with Roberts off his line, he lobbed over.

Despite some lively running by Ceri Williams, Wales had been able to offer little in attack, their only shot being a tame effort from Dave Webley, easily fielded by John McKenna, just before the break. It took only two minutes of the second period for England to grab the goal that had until then somehow eluded them. A free-kick was rolled short to Mayes who hit a wicked curler round the wall. The ball skidded cruelly off the wet turf in front of an unfortunate Roberts and squirmed in.

Fiercely proud of their recent impressive record against England, the Welsh came far more into the game, and won a string of corners. However they did not seriously threaten the visiting 'keeper (Ryan Price, who had replaced McKenna just before the hour mark) until Barry Town's experienced forward Paul Giles came on to make a late impact.

Although not as dominant as during the opening 45 minutes, England remained well in command with the Redbridge Forest players outstanding. Mayes and Cavell continued to wreak havoc with surging runs, but 'Man of the Match' was probably Paul Richardson who ran the midfield throughout the evening.

There was just one goal in it, but on the whole it was a very encouraging display by the England side, and at the end the only complaint seemed to be that there are just not enough of these games; for Wales this was their only fixture of the season, and England have just the faint possibility of a fixture against Northern Ireland on the horizon. Finally, congratulations to Aberystwyth Town Football Club who handled the event so smoothly.

James Wright.

F.A. Representative Match Committee

Messrs J Barter, E A Brown, C Geary, Gp Capt P W Hilton, C Jones, Major T C Knight, K Marsden, B W Mulrenan, W Wilson.

WALES v. ENGLAND '92

(Played at Aberystwyth Town FC, Tuesday 3rd March 1992)

WALES (0) 0

1. Jon Roberts (Barry Town)
2. Iain Williams (Bangor City)
3. Phil Williams (Newport AFC)
4. Terry Boyle (Merthyr Tydfil)
5. Elfyn Edwards (Macclesfield Town)
6. Steve Williams (Barry Town)
7. Mark Tucker (Merthyr Tydfil)
8. Dave Webley (Merthyr Tydfil)
9. Bob Colville (Guiseley)
10. Andy Beattie (Merthyr Tydfil)
11. Ceri Williams (Merthyr Tydfil)

12. Trevor Ball (Colwyn B.) (For 1, 89m)
13. John Lewis (Abergavenny) (Unused)
14. Paul Giles (Barry Town) (For 3, 82m)
15. Phil Green (Newport) (For 9, 68m)
16. Mark Price (Newport) (Unused)

Manager: Tony Jennings

Referee: Rodger Gifford (Llanbradach)
Linesmen: A C Howells (Port Talbot)

ENGLAND (0) 1

1. John McKenna (Boston United)
2. Paul Shirtliff (Boston United)
3. Paul Watts (Redbridge Forest)
4. Paul Nicol (Kettering Town)
5. Steve Conner (Redbridge Forest)
6. Delwyn Humphreys (Kidderminster)
7. Paul Richardson (Redbridge Forest)
8. Mark Golley (Welling United)
9. Bobby Mayes (Redbridge Forest)
10. Terry Robbins (Welling United)
11. Paul Cavell (Redbridge Forest)

12. Jim Wigmore (Farnborough) (Unused)
13. Ryan Price (Stafford) (For 1, 57m)
14. Simon Read (Farnboro.) (For 10, 83m)
15. Gary Abbott (Welling) (For 6, 14m)

Scorer: Mayes (46 minutes)

Manager: Lyn Jones

G D Lewis (Caersws)

The victorious England side pictured before their win at Aberystwyth.

Lyn Jones' gallant Welsh side, beaten by England for the first time since 1989.

42

FOUR NATIONS TOURNAMENTS 1979-87
and other Internationals

1979 (England)
Knock - out basis, England won final.

S/Final	England	5 v 1	Scotland
S/Final	Holland	3 v 0	Italy
3rd Place	Scotland	1 v 2	Italy
Final	England	1 v 0	Holland

1980 (Holland)	P	W	D	L	F	A	PTS
Scotland	3	2	1	0	7	2	5
England	3	2	0	1	6	5	4
Italy	3	0	2	1	2	4	2
Holland	3	0	1	2	3	7	1

1981 (Italy)	P	W	D	L	F	A	PTS
England	3	1	2	0	3	1	4
Italy	3	1	2	0	2	1	4
Scotland	3	0	3	0	2	2	3
Holland	3	0	1	2	2	5	1

1982 (Scotland)	P	W	D	L	F	A	PTS
Scotland	3	1	2	0	5	4	4
England	3	1	2	0	2	1	4
Italy	3	0	2	1	4	6	2
Holland	3	1	0	2	5	5	2

1983 (England)	P	W	D	L	F	A	PTS
England	3	3	0	0	10	1	6
Scotland	3	1	1	1	7	6	3
Holland	3	1	1	1	6	11	3
Italy	3	0	0	3	3	8	0

1984 (Italy)	P	W	D	L	F	A	PTS
Italy	3	2	1	0	4	1	5
England	3	1	1	1	5	4	3
Holland	3	1	1	1	8	8	3
Scotland	3	0	1	2	2	6	1

1985 (Holland)	P	W	D	L	F	A	PTS
Scotland	3	2	0	1	4	4	4
England	3	1	1	1	6	5	3
Italy	3	1	1	1	4	4	3
Holland	3	1	0	2	4	5	2

1986 (Scotland)
Competition cancelled - Italy withdrew.

1987 (Scotland)	P	W	D	L	F	A	PTS
Italy	3	2	1	0	6	3	5
England	3	2	0	1	7	3	4
Scotland	3	1	0	2	4	6	2
Holland	3	0	1	2	0	5	1

OVERALL FOUR NATIONS TROPHY RECORD

	P	W	D	L	F	A	PTS
England	23	13	6	4	45	21	32
Italy	23	7	9	7	27	31	23
Scotland	23	7	8	8	33	37	22
Holland	23	5	5	13	31	47	15

OTHER RESULTS

v. WALES

		Eng.	Wales
1984	Newtown	1	2
1985	Telford	1	0
1986	Merthyr	1	3
1987	Gloucester	2	2
1988	Rhyl	2	0
1989	Kidderminster	2	0
1990	Merthyr	0	0
1991	Stafford	1	2
1992	Aberystwyth	1	0

v. REPUBLIC OF IRELAND

		Eng.	Ire.
1986	Kidderminster	2	1
1986	Nuneaton	2	1
1990	Dublin	2	1
1990	Cork	3	0

v. GIBRALTAR

		Eng.	Gib.
1982	Gibraltar	3	2

v. ITALY

		Eng.	Italy
1989	La Spezia	1	1
1990	Solerno	0	2
1991	Kettering	0	0

ENGLAND'S Overall International Record					
W	D	P	L	F	A
39	21	10	8	68	38

Semi-Professional International Caps
FOR ENGLAND 1979-1992 (MAX 40)

Gary Abbott (Welling) 87 v I.(Sub), S.(Sub) (2), 92 W.(Sub) (3)

David Adamson (Boston Utd) 79 v S.H., 80 v I.S.H. (5)

Tony Agana (Weymouth) 86 v R.I. (1)

Jim Arnold (Stafford Rangers) 79 v S.H. (2)

Noel Ashford (Enfield & Redbridge For) 82 v G.H.S., 83 v I.H.S., 84 v W.H.S.I., 85 v W.I.(Sub), 86 v Rep.Ireland, R.I., 87 v W.(Sub), I.H.S., 90 v W.R.I (2), 91 v I.(Sub). (22)

John Askey (Macclesfield) 90 v W, (1)

Paul Bancroft (Kidderminster) 89 v I.W, 90 v I.W.R.I (2), 91 v W. (9)

Keith Barrett (Enfield) 81 v H.S.I., 82 v G.I.H.S., 83 v I.H.S., 84 v W.(Sub) H.S., 85 v I.H.S. (16)

Mark Beeney (Maidstone) 89 v I.(Sub) (1)

Colin Brazier (Kidderminster) 87 v W. (1)

Steve Brooks (Cheltenham) 88 v W.(Sub), 90 v W.RI(2 1Sub). (4)

David Buchanan (Blyth) 86 v R.I.(Sub) R.I. (2)

Steve Butler (Maidstone) 88 v W., 89 v I.W. (3)

Mark Carter (Runcorn & Barnet) 87 v W.I.H.S., 88 v W., 89 v I.W., 90 v I.R.I (2), 91 v I.W(Sub). (11)

Kim Casey (Kidderminster) 86 v W.R.I,R.I.(Sub), 87 v W.I. (5)

Paul Cavell (Redbridge) 92 v W. (1)

Kevin Charlton (Telford) 85 v W.I. (2)

Andrew Clarke (Barnet) 90 v R.I (2), (2)

David Clarke (Blyth Spartans) 80 v I.S.(Sub)H, 81 v H.S.I., 82 v I.H.S., 83 v H.S., 84 v H.S.I. (14)

Gary Clayton (Burton) 86 v R.I. (1)

Robert Codner (Barnet) 88 v W. (1)

Steve Conner (Dartford & Redbridge F.) 90 v I , 91 v I.W. (3), 92 v W (4)

David Constantine (Altrincham) 85 v I.H.S., 86 v W (4)

Robbie Cooke (Kettering) 89 v W.(Sub), 90 v I., (2)

Alan Cordice (Wealdstone) 83 v I.H.S., 84 v W.S.(Sub), I.(Sub), 85 v I.H.S. (9)

Paul Cuddy (Altrincham) 87 v I.H.S. (3)

Paul Culpin (Nuneaton B.) 84 v W., 85 v W.(Sub) I.H.S. (2)

Paul Davies (Kidderminster) 86 v W., 87 v W.I.S., 88 v W., 89 v W. (6)

John Davison (Altrincham) 79 v S.H., 80 v I.S., 81 v H.S.I., 82 v G.I.H.S., 83 v I.H.S., 84 v W.H.I.S., 85 v I.H.S., 86 v W.R.I. R.I. (24)

John Denham (Northwich Victoria) 80 v H. (1)

Peter Densmore (Runcorn) 88 v W., 89 v I. (2)

Phil Derbyshire (Mossley) 83 v H.(Sub)S.(Sub) (2)

Mick Doherty (Weymouth) 86 v W.(Sub) (1)

Mick Farrelly (Altrincham) 87 v I.H.S. (3)

Trevor Finnegan (Weymouth) 81 v H.S. (2)

Paul Furlong (Enfield) 90 v I.I.R.(2), 91 v I.W. (5)

John Glover (Maidstone Utd) 85 v W.I.H.S. (4)

Mark Golley (Sutton) 87 v H.(Sub)S., 88 v W., 89 v I.W., (5), 92 v W (6)

Phil Gridelet (Hendon + Barnet) 89 v I.W. 90 v W.I.R(2), (5)

Steve Hancock (Macclesfield) 90 v W. (1)

Andy Hessenthaler (Dartford) 90 v I. (1)

Kenny Hill (Maidstone Utd) 80 v I.S.H. (3)

Mark Hone (Welling) 90 v I (1)

Gary Hooley (Frickley) 85 v W. (1)

Keith Houghton (Blyth Spartans) 79 v S. (1)

Barry Howard (Altrincham) 81 v H.S.I., 82 v G.I.H.S. (7)

David Howell (Enfield) 85 v H.(Sub)S.(Sub), 86 v W.R.I., 87 v W.I.H.S., 88 v W., 89 v I.W., 90 v I.W.R.I(2), (15)

Delwyn Humphreys (Kidderminster H) 91 v W(Sub). (1), 92 v W (2)

Steve Humphries (Barnet) 87 v H.(Sub) (1)

Nicky Ironton (Enfield) 83 v H.(Sub), 84 v W.(2)

Tony Jennings (Enfield) 79 v S.H., 80 v I.S.H., 81 v H.S.I., 82 v G.I.H.S. (12)

Jeff Johnson (Altrincham) 81 v S.I., 82 v G.I.H.S., 83 v I.H.S., 84 v H.S.I., 84 v I.H.S, 86 v W.(Sub)R.I.(2), (17)

Tom Jones (Weymouth) 87 v W. (1)

Anton Joseph (Telford Utd + Kidderminster) 84 v S.(Sub), 85 v W.I.H.S., 86 v W.(Sub), 87 v W.I.(Sub)H., 88 v W., 89 v I.W., 90 v I.R.I(2), (14)

Mike Lake (Macclesfield) 89 v I. (1)

Andy Lee (Telford/Witton) 89 v I(Sub), 91 v I.W. (3)

Kenny Lowe (Barnet) 91 v I.W. (2)

John McKenna (Boston Utd) 88 v W.(Sub), 90 v I.R.I(2), 91 v I.W. (6), 92 v W (7)

Bobby Mayes (Redbridge) 92 v W (1)

Paul Mayman (Northwich Vic) 80 v I.S. (2)

Stewart Mell (Burton) 85 v W. (1)

Neil Merrick (Weymouth) 80 v I.(Sub)S. (2)

Trevor Morley Nuneaton Bor.) 84 v W.H.S.I., 85 v W.S.(Sub) (6)

Les Mutrie (Blyth Spartans) 79 v S.H., 80 v I.S.H. (5)

Mark Newson (Maidstone U.) 84 v W.H.S.I., 85 v W. (5)

Doug Newton (Burton) 85 v W.H.S. (3)

Paul Nicol (Kettering T) 91 v I.W. (2), 92 v W (3)

Steve Norris (Telford) 88 v W.(Sub) (1)

Eamon O'Keefe (Mossley) 79 v S.H. (2)

Frank Ovard (Maidstone) 81 v H.(Sub)S.(Sub)I.(Sub) (3)

Andy Pape (Harrow + Enfield) 85 v W.(Sub)H.S., 86 v W.(Sub) R.I. 87 v W.I.H.S., 88 v W., 89 v I.W., 90 v I.W.E. (15)

Brian Parker (Yeovil Town) 80 v S. (1)

Trevor Peake (Nuneaton Bor.) 79 v S.H. (2)

David Pearce (Harrow Bor) 84 v I.(Sub) (1)

Brendan Phillips (Nuneaton B., Kettering) 79 v S.H., 80 v S.(Sub)H. (4)

Gary Philips (Barnet) 82 v G. (1)

Ryan Price (Stafford) 92 v W(Sub) (1)

Simon Read (Farnborough) 92 v W.(Sub) (1)

Carl Richards (Enfield) 86 v R.I. (1)

Paul Richardson (Redbridge) 92 v W (1)

Derek Richardson (Maidstone U.) 83 v I., 84 v W., 86 v R.I. (4)

Terry Robbins (Welling) 92 v W (1)

Peter Robinson (Blyth S.) 83 vI.H.S., 84 v W.I., 85 v W (6)

John Rogers (Altrincham) 81 v H.S.I., 82 v I.(Sub)S. (5)

Paul Rogers (Sutton) 89 v W., 90 v I.R.I(2), 91 v I.W. (6)

Neil Sellars (Scarborough) 81 v H.S.I., 82 v G.H.(Sub)S., 83 v I.H.S. (5)

Peter Shearer (Cheltenham) 89 v I.(Sub) (1)

Paul Shirtliff (Frickley & Boston) 86 v R.I.(2), 87 v W.I.H., 88 v W., 89 v I.W., 90 v I.W.R.I.(2), (12), 92 v W. (13)

Paul Showler (Altrincham) 91 v I(Sub).W. (2)

Gordon Simmonite (Boston Utd) 79 v S.(Sub)H.(Sub), 80 v I.S.H. (5)

Gary Simpson (Stafford) 86 v R.I.(2), 87 v I.H.S., 90 v I.W.R.I.(2), (9)

Glenn Skivington (Barrow) 90 v I.W.RI, 91 v I.W. (5)

Alan Smith (Alvechurch) 82 v G.I.S. (3)

Ian Smith (Mossley) 80 v I.S.H.(Sub) (3)

Ossie Smith (Runcorn) 84 v W.(1)

Tim Smithers (Nuneaton), 85 v W.(Sub)I., 86 v W. (3)

Mickey Stephens (Sutton Utd), 82 v G.S.(Sub), 86 v W.R.I.R.I.(Sub) (5)

Bob Stockley (Nuneaton Bor.) 80 v H. (1)

Peter Taylor (Maidstone) 84 v H.S.I. (3)

Shaun Teale (Weymouth) 88 v W. (1)

Brian Thompson (Yeovil & Maidstone) 79 v S.H., 81 v H.S.I., 82 v I.H.S., 83 v I.H.S, 84 v W.H.S.I (4)

Kevin Todd (Berwick Rangers) 91 v W. (1)

Tony Turner (Telford) 85 v W. (1)

David Waite (Enfield) 82 v G. (1)

Paul Walker (Blyth) 86 v W.R.I.(Sub), 87 v S.(Sub) (4)

Mark Ward (Northwich Victoria) 83 v S.(Sub) (1)

John Watson (Wealdstone, Scarborough & Maidstone) 79 v S.(Sub)H., 80 v I.S.H., 81 v H.S.I., 82 v I.H.S., 83 v I.H.S., 84 v W.(Sub)H.S.I. (18)

Paul Watts (Redbridge Forest) 89 v W., 90 v I.RI(2), 91 v I, (5), 92 v W (6)

Mark West (Wycombe W) 91 v W. (1)

Barry Whitbread (Runcorn & Altrincham) 79 v S.H., 80 v I.S.H., 81 v I. (6)

Russ Wilcox (Frickley) 86 v W.R.I (2)

Colin Williams (Scarborough & Telford) 81 H.S., 82 v I.H.S. (12)

Roger Willis (Barnet) 91 v I(Sub). (1)

Paul Wilson (Frickley) 86 v W. (1)

F.A. REPRESENTATIVE MATCHES 1991 - 1992

5th November 1991
Bromsgrove Rovers FC

F. A. XI   2 v 1   BRITISH STUDENTS
Davies (2)

Green (Kidderminster H.) sub **Acton** (Telford United), **Willets** (Cheltenham), **Brighton** (Bromsgrove Rovers), **Barnett** (Kidderminster H.) sub **Weir** (Kidderminster H.), **Brindley** (Telford United), **Stott** (Bromsgrove Rovers), **Taylor** (Moor Green), **Howell** (Kidderminster H.), **Whitehouse** (Kidderminster H.) sub Davies, **Lilwall** (Kidderminster H.) sub Gillet, **Humphreys** (Kidderminster H.).

19th November 1991
Marine FC

F. A. XI   1 v 3   HFS LOANS LGE
O'Connor   Camden (2), Ross

Farrelly (Macclesfield T.), **Lee** (Altrincham), **Chilton** (Altrincham), **McNeillis** (Witton Albion), **Hancock** (Northwich V.) sub **Rowlands** (Altrincham), **Anderson** (Witton Albion), **O'Connor** (Northwich V.), **Anderson** (Witton Albion), **McKenna** (Altrincham), **Hanlon** (Macclesfield T.)

21st January 1992
Aylesbury United

F. A. XI   7 v 1   DIADORA LEAGUE
Abbott (5), Fielder, Read   Hobson

Hyde (Wycombe W.), **Hone** (Welling United) sub **Robbins** (Welling United), **Conner** (Redbrdige F.), **Creaser** (Wycombe W.), **Watts** (Redbridge F.), **Fielder** (Slough T.), **Golley** (Welling United) sub **Jacques** (Redbridge F.), **Guppy** (Wycombe W.), **Abbott** (Welling United), **Mayes** (Redbridge F.), **Read** (Farnborough T.).

21st January 1992
Ossett Albion

F. A. XI   1 v 1   COMBINED SERVICES
Tilly

Game abandoned after 60 minutes

Price (Stafford R.), **Shirtliff** (Boston U.), **Watson** (Gainsborough T.) sub **Farrar** (Emley), **Simpson** (Stafford R.), **Nicol** (Kettering T.), **Hardy** (Boston U.), **Tilly** (Matlock Town) sub **Brown** (Kettering T.), **Richardson** (Redbridge F.), **Cavell** (Redbridge F.), **Brown** (Kettering T.) sub **Jones** (Boston U.), **Devlin** (Stafford R.).

MISCELLANEOUS PHOTOS

Bishop's Stortford (striped shirts) take on Boreham Wood in the F.A. Trophy Qualifying Rounds.

Milton Keynes based Shenley & Loughton FC pictured before a local cup tie. Photo - James Wright.

Pirton FC, of the Campri South Midlands League Premier Division. Photo - Gavin Ellis.

THE FOOTBALL ASSOCIATION CHALLENGE CUP

REVIEW 1991-92
Featuring Non-League Clubs.

F.A. CHALLENGE CUP COMMITTEE 1992-93

Messrs W T Annable, P D Bloom, E A Brown (V.C.), R I Burr, W G Halsey, G M Holmes, W G McKeag (C), T Myatt, Dr J O'Hara, P Rushton, S Seymour, M D B Sinclair.

F.A. CHALLENGE CUP

Farnborough - Heroes of 91-92

The F.A. Cup kicked off in glorious sunshine on the last day of August. The first goal of the competition was scored by **Wellingborough Town**'s John Cowper who found the net within a minute at **Willenhall Town**, but his side conceded six goals in the last 89 minutes! Heroes of the day were West Midlands League Division One outfit **Ilkeston Town** who ruined **Grantham Town**'s ground opening celebrations by scoring a staggering 5-1 win over John Robertson's men who were enjoying a 100% start to their Beazer campaign.

The First Qualifying Round, on September 14th, brought the first Conference casualties, **Northwich Victoria**, who were dumped out by local rivals **Eastwood Hanley**. The next giants to fall were **Macclesfield Town** who went down at home to Central Midlands side **Borrowash Victoria** in the Second Qualifying Round, and it was another side from Borrowash's League, **Lincoln United**, who were one of the surprise packages of the year. They battled their way right through the qualifying competition, ousting H.F.S. Premier Division sides **Frickley Athletic** and **Leek Town** en route, to a big pay day away to Huddersfield Town in the First Round Proper.

One of the main stories of this year's Cup was the appearance of a Scottish club in the First Round for the first time in living memory. **Gretna** progressed through four qualifying rounds, notching a sensational win over unbeaten H.F.S. Premier Division leaders **Stalybridge Celtic**, to earn a memorable home tie with Rochdale. Before the 'Match of the Day' cameras they held the Fourth Division promotion chasers before bowing out in the replay at Spotland.

Another side deserving of the utmost praise were **Tiverton Town** of the Great Mills Western League who reached the First Round Proper for the second consecutive season. In the First Qualifying Round they surprised **Dover Athletic** at Ladysmead, but they were eventually humbled by Fourth Division high-flyers Barnet. Other memorable Qualifying Round results were recorded by **Winsford United** who beat **Altrincham**, **Bridlington Town** who won at **Barrow**, **Guiseley** who beat **Bishop Auckland** to reach the First Round for the first time in their history, and **Weymouth** who forgot their recent problems by crushing **Cheltenham Town** 4-0.

The First Round Proper kicked off in memorable style when **Hayes** scored two late goals to record a sensational win over Fulham at Craven Cottage in a match put forward to the Friday night. The following day was not so prolific for Non-League clubs. The best result of the day was achieved by **Crawley Town** who thumped Northampton Town 4-2, but sadly these two giantkillers were paired together in the next round, Crawley triumphing 2-0 in Middlesex. Perennial Cup fighters **Telford United** created a stir by beating local rivals Stoke City in a replay thus avenging a defeat by the Potters in the corresponding round twelve months earlier, whilst other Non-League heroes were **Enfield**, **Witton Albion** and **Yeovil Town** who won at Aldershot, Halifax Town and Walsall respectively.

Colchester United made a piece of F.A. Cup history they did not want. They became the first Non-League club to be knocked out on penalties going down 4-2 at St James Park after three and a half hours of football against Exeter City had failed to yield a goal.

The accolade of the longest run in this season's competition was shared with Crawley Town, who eventually lost in front of a sell-out crowd at Brighton, by **Kettering Town**. The Poppies started out in the First Qualifying Round at Wisbech Town. They followed this with homes wins over **Braintree Town** and **Heybridge Swifts** and excellent away triumphs at **Stafford Rangers**, **Wycombe Wanderers** and Maidstone United taking them to a Third Round visit to Kenny Dalglish's Blackburn Rovers where they were not disgraced by a 1-4 defeat.

Heroes of '91, **Woking**, were again blessed by the good fortune of a passage to the Third Round Proper without encountering a Barclays League club. Hereford United became the third League club to visit Kingfield in the Cup following Swansea City in 1978 and Charlton Athletic in 1926. Woking dominated the match but could not get the decisive break, and they ultimately capitulated to an extra-time goal in front of a packed Edgar Street crowd.

So enter **Farnborough Town**, F.A. Cup 'Team of the Year'. Ted Pearce's men cruised to the Second Round disposing of **Salisbury** and **Halesowen Town** and bagging thirteen goal in the process. They were denied a first win over League opposition when they conceded a late equaliser to Torquay at Plainmoor, but nothing could stop them ten days later on their home patch, even when the Gulls pulled back three goals after 'Boro had led 4-0. Farnborough were awarded with a home draw against West Ham United, but chose to switch the tie to Upton Park where Dean Coney's late penalty secured them a 1-1 draw and a lucrative replay, also in East London. On a memorable night Simon Read and Andy Bye went close to putting the Conference side ahead, but the Hammers eventually scraped home with a fortunate goal from Morley in the dying seconds.

James Wright

PRELIMINARY ROUND

154 Ties. Matches Played: 182
Home wins: 94 **Draws:** 30 **Away wins:** 38 (2 walkovers)
Best Attendance: 1,402 - Grantham Town v Ilkeston Town
Total Attendance: 26,060 (8 gates unknown) **Average Attendance:** 150
Largest Home Win: Yeading 8, Rayners Lane 0
Best Away Win: Sholing Sports 0, Maidenhead United 6
Result of the Round: Croydon Athletic 2, Hythe Town 1

Saturday 31st August 1991   Res Att

(* **Denotes extra time played**)

Brandon Utd v Shotton Com.   7-1 103
Palmer 32 37 65,   Kirtley 85
Robertson 43,
Lamb 70 74,Muckle 75

Darwen v Hebburn   1-1   96
Hanson 35   Caisley 13

Hebburn v Darwen (4-9-91)   2-1
Tinmouth 53 63   Heyes 15

Esh Winning v Netherfield   1-3   55
Jackson 37   Borrowdale 67 90,Kennedy 90

Alnwick T. v Chester-le-Street 4-3 85
Thompson 5,   Stronach 29,Robertson 65,
Anderson 30,   Calvert 89
Coxford 73 84

Consett v Willington   5-0 120
R Butler 15,Sugden 17,Staff 44,G Butler 83,Robson
85

Clitheroe v Langley Park   4-4   90
Keighley 30 63,   McElwee 10,Gibson 18,
Hey 35,Young 55   Gardner 70,Woodward 76

Langley v C'roe (at C'roe 3-9-91) 1-1
McElwee 101   Young 107

L1ey v C'roe (at Consett 9-9-91) 1-0
                   McDonald 50

Bridlington T. v Evenwood T. 5-1 225
Norbury 4 49,   Pigg 12
Hopkinson 6,
Radford 25,Brown 89

Ashington v Crook Town   3-1   58
Humble 21 50,   Errington 85
Harmison 53

Prudhue E.E. v Bedlington Terr. 0-2 55
                   Mordue 24 secs,Pegg 12

Garforth Town v Whickham   4-1   92
McMahon 2,Glossop 11,   Kiddiz 7
Ottley 29,Winslow (pen) 90

Darlington CB v Horden CW   3-2   31
Mohan,Morrigan,   Hurst 17,Cockburn 80
Laffy

Spennymoor v Easington Colliery 1-0 116
Corkain 48

Stockton v Billingham Town   2-4   47
Lockington 35,   McHale 12 45,Moneshan 24,
May 90   Rowntree 68

Gt Harwood T. v Eccleshill Utd 6-0
Dunn 15,Smith 50,Baker 52 68,Mullen 66,Rogerson
84

Durham City v South Bank   4-0   82
Hogan 31 36 60,Hixon 78

Penrith v Ferryhill Athletic 1-0 103
Batey 37

Washington v Shildon (at Shild.) 1-3 100
Brannigan 85   Adams 9,Sowden 59,M Egie 78

B'pool Wren Rovers v Thackley 3-2   97
Scorers undisclosed   Taylor 70,Daykin 75

W Auckland T. v Denaby Utd   3-5* 90
Stanger 15,McKimm 72,   Downing 23,Mozley 45,
Barrigan 83   Margetts 73 101,Kay 115

Seaham RS v Peterlee Newtown 3-2   70
McDonald 30 65 90   Kirby 80, Own Goal

Sheffield v Congleton Town   2-0   67
Morgan (OG)46,Stafford 64

Burscough W/O Leyland DAF withdrew

Irlam Town v Curzon Ashton   0-0   30

Curzon A. v Irlam T. (2-9-91) 4-1 152
Sanders 28,Bartholomew 87   Platts
Wroe 89,Ridings 90

Knowsley Utd v Atherton LR   5-1   67
Gibiliru 35 39,McConville(pen) 61,   Mather 57
Drury 86, Siddell 88

Prescot AFC v Chadderton   3-2   94
Burns 25,Warriner 43,   Lucas 53,Hession 88
Richards 68

Newtown v Glossop   4-2 176
Curtis 40,Howatt 46,   Scott 37 50
Birch 80,Vincent 83

Liversedge v Maine Road   3-1 108
Murphy 58,Nicholson 71 90   Turner 22

Salford City v Warrington Town 0-0 115

Warrington v Salford (3-9-91) 1-0 194
Dunn 68

Ashton United v Rhyl   0-0 320

Rhyl v Ashton United (3-9-91) 1-0 435
Deeley 48

Radcliffe Borough v Nantwich T. 0-1 129
                  Askey (pen) 25

Newcastle T. v Ossett Albion 2-0 142
Pestridge 48, Ritchie 61

Harworth Cl v Matlby MW   2-1   90
Farrer 50 51   Evans 66

Lancaster City v Winsford Utd 1-5 139
McCrae 32   Thomas,Esdaile,Sheridan,Blackwood(2)

Armthorpe Welf. v Vauxhall GM 1-1   47
Parker 42   Carroll 52

Vauxhall v Armthorpe (3-9-91) 1-2   28
Cotton 34   Johnson 20,Edmonds 68

Worksop Town v Brigg Town   3-1 118
Thorpe 21,Booker 73,Clark 88   Tucker 89

Ossett Town v Nth Ferriby Utd 2-0 185
Gerrard 68,Leadbitter 75

Rossendale Utd v Heanor Town 2-4 220
Green 87,   Preston 17,Checkley 54 89,
Stafford 90   Gillott 93

Arnold T. v Belper (at Belper) 0-2 222
                   Goddard 42 45

Grantham Town v Ilkeston T.   1-5 1402
Hurst 54   Harbottle 13 89(pen),
                 Culley 27,Burrell 49 79

Res Att

Eastwood T. v Farsley C. 2-4 179
Osborne 22, Howey 16,Doig 38,
Copeland 75(pen) Allen 59 65

St Helens v Borrowash Victoria 1-3 90
Gavin 19 Stacey 16 28,Wilkinson 78

Holbeach Utd v Hinckley Ath. 2-3 56
Gregory 42, Potter 40 76,
Simmons 72 Fawcett 47

Rocester v Oakham United 1-3 125
Shelley 65 Nicholson 35,Farby 80,Bramley 90

Dudley T. v Lincoln United 1-4 143
Baker 36 Ward 69,Park 71 81,Tomlinson(OG)

Sandwell Boro v Alfreton Town 1-2 45
Lowe 70 Stevenson 61,Millington 90

Boston v Harrogate Town 2-3 65
Cook 21,Rodwell 41 Annan 5 53,Brown 85

Irthlingboro D. v Wednesfield 2-2 72
Birch 7,Paine 62 Wells 53,Morgan 88

Wednesfield v I. Diam. (4-9-91) 3-3 140
Moore 35 44, Schiavi 24,Bendon 30,
Morgan Thompson 78

I. Diam. v Wednesfield (9-9-91) 1-2 174
Birch 90 Wells 2,King 57

Tamworth v Lye Town 2-2 778
Ross 16,Perry 44 Shaw 77,Young 90

Lye Town v Tamworth (3-9-91) 1-3 379
Stokes 5 Cartwright 36,Smith 59,Morris 67

Oldbury United v Blakenall 2-3
Scorer undisclosed Keeling 46,Conniff 63(OG)

Solihull Boro v Spalding Utd 1-0 99
Powell 27

Hinckley v Bridgnorth Town 2-4 90
Ison 57, Harris 32,Taylor 35,
Kempin 87 Own Goal 42,Yates 45

RC Warwick v Rushall Olym. 2-1
White 5,Titterton 22 McRobbie 80

Stourbridge v L. Buckby (1-9-91) 1-0 446
Ingram 87

Hinckley T. v Boldmere St Mich. 3-1 153
Donaldson 17 27,Wilcox 25 Clifton 43

Willenhall T. v Wellingboro' T. 6-1 110
Savage 6,Edwards 30 70 78 83 Cowper 2

Hednesford v N'hampton Spen. 1-1 470
O'Connor 13 Inwood 17

N'hampton v Hednesford (3-9-91) 1-1 146
Briggs 80 King 70

Hednesford v N'hampton (9-9-91) 1-0 771
Burr 88

Stamford Town v Paget Rgrs 2-1 130
Tilley 36,Hollis 42 Christopher 47

Walsall Wood v Raunds Town 1-1 97
Thompson 9 Murphy 43

Raunds v Walsall Wood (3-9-91) 3-1 122
Lewis 26,Frost 48,O'Keefe 90 Thompson 75

Banbury U. v Stratford Town 4-1 226
Mitchell 10(pen),Own Goal 31, Beechey 5
Hewitson 81,Pearce 87

Highgate United v Chasetown 0-3 45
Dixon 9 90,Collins 78

Malvern v Halesowen Harriers 3-2 66
Bullock 2,Walker 12, Madeley 46,
Carter 19 Merchant 80

Tring Town v Hemel Hempstead 0-3 70
Maxwell 15,Lowe 60,Bartlett 65

Clafont St P. v Flackwell Hth 2-0 60
Darlington 58,Hippolyte 90

Evesham Utd v Rothwell Town 3-1 153
Rawle 74 82,Candy 92 McIlroy 65

Rushden Town v Friar Lane OB 3-2 222
Heard 11,Jeffrey 66, Parker 33,
Green 90 Plens 44

Edgware Town v Southall 4-0 138
Kidd 2,Murphy 37,Thompson 61,Mangan 73

Waltham Abbey v Stevenage Boro. 0-1 219
Cardines 50

Desboro' T W/O Vauxhall Mtrs withdrew

Braintree Town v Bury Town 2-1 275
England 17,Hollocks 86(pen) Lee 55

Mirrless Blackstone v Gt Yarmouth 2-1 80
Hardy 15,Hand 76 Cockrill 37

Aveley v Felixstowe Town 2-0 95
Driscoll 55,Hoyce 60

Barton Rovers v Bourne Town 3-4 138
Camp 41 44 60 Langford 4,Munton 16,
Blythe 77,Spreadborough 88

Wisbech v Burnham Ramblers 4-3 316
Williams 8 12, Hatcher 44 59,
Garwood 27,Garner 46 Corfield 66

Collier Row v Saffron Walden T. 2-2 95
Samuels 66,Mansfield 75 Keys 40 44

Saffron WT v Collier R. (3-91-91) 2-3 125
Mercer 3,Oldfield 20 Whiteley 22,Braithwaite,
Own Goal

Leyton Wingate v Eynesbury Rvrs 6-0 107
Steppings 7 18,John 14 46,Morlby 50,Fishenden 60

Hitchin Town v Tiptree United 1-1 343
Quarman 51 Jay 1(pen)

Tiptree Utd v Hitchin (3-9-91) 1-0 143
Lee 49

Purfleet v Gorleston 3-1 79
Matthews 37,Wood 49,Thompson 59 Prior 85

King's Lynn v Haverhill Rovers 5-2 411
Sharman 40,Own Goal 44, Abery 52,
Gallagher 72 84,Howard 80 Suddery 56

March Town Utd v Histon 1-1 175
Richards 23 Haylock 12

Histon v March T. Utd (3-9-91) 2-1* 128
Crisp 99,Munn 103 Bailey 100

Walthamstow P. v Langford 3-2 59
Tredgold 70 88,Francas 78 Phelan 7 58

Arlesey Town v Clapton 0-1 55
Mason 70

Sudbury Town v Barking 2-2 425
Smith 9,Parnell 75 Benstock 41,Lane 72

Barking v Sudbury Town (3-9-91) 2-2 202
Portway 21,Lane 118 Smith 40,Cutting 94

Sudbury Town v Barking (9-9-91) 2-1 591
Smith 47,Barker 62 Hoy 38

Letchworth GC. v Potton Utd 1-1 99
Rutherford 48 Seekings 47

Potton Utd v Letchworth (4-9-91) 2-0 155
Own Goal 35,Albone 47

Haringey Borough v Watton Utd 5-0
Campbell 44,Henry 61,Milton 65 85,Roberts 81

East Thurrock Utd v Royston T. 1-0 123
Innell 36

Canvey Is. v Harwich & Parkeston 0-2 130
Harvey 24,Hepburn 55

Rainham v Lowestoft Town (at L'toft) 0-1 179
McKechnie 46

Barkingside v Baldock Town 1-1 45
Hutton 73 Sharpe 33

Baldock v Barkingside (3-9-91) 5-0 215
Roberts 44 83,Sharp 46,Williams 58 72

52

Curzon Ashton attack the Irlam goal during their 4-1 replay win. Photo - Colin Stevens.

Dulwich Hamlet's Willie Lillington is denied by a fine save by Harefield's Andy Hopping. Photo - Dave West.

Haringey's Michael Milton, scorer of two goals, prepares to beat Death of Watton United. Photo - Francis Short.

(* Denotes extra time played)

Ware v Milton Keynes Boro. 5-1 149
Own Goal 31,Pugh 39 82, *Drewe 17*
Alzapiedi 42 66

Ford United v Hornchurch 2-1 63
Lord 42,Wood 65 *Murcott 73*

Halstead Town v Hoddesdon T. 3-2 120
Curtis 13,Bibby 16, *Robbins 33,*
Taylor 90 *Cummins 64*

Basildon Utd v Brimsdown Rvrs 0-1* 51
Freeman 106

Wolverton v Uxbridge 1-0 93
Mason 79

Witham Town v Welwyn Garden C-1 102
Elliott 2,McBean 71,Ellis 88 *Lawrence 80*

Newmarket T. v Biggleswade T. 1-1 103
Sinclair 12 *Chadwick 35*

Big'wade v Newmarket *(3-9-91)* 2-2 186
Graves 65,Wright 100 *Kearns 17 114*

Big'wade v Newmarket *(9-9-91)* 1-0 271
Hay 68

Leighton T. v Kingsbury Town 3-2 120
McGuinness 4 17, *Quinn 49,*
Downey 85 *Suthers 80*

Croydon v Darenth Heathside 3-0 66
Boyton 13 36, Norris 14 *(at Darenth)*

Yeading v Rayners Lane 8-0 108
Welsh 30 50 72 85,Whiskey 36 42 80,Sawyers 65

Cheshunt v Tilbury 0-3 52
Henry 85,Phillips 10 67

Burnham v Feltham & Hounslow 1-1 95
Dodds 62 *Hargie 19 (at Windsor)*

F. & H'low v Burnham *(4-9-91)* 0-4 210
Ferguson 10,Chandler 17,Lindo 23,Cook 75

Beckenham v Wingate & Finch. 1-0 43
Crouch 33

Egham Town v Wembley 0-1 76
Witter 88

Dulwich v Harefield *(1-9-91)* 2-1 107
Akers 44,Murrock 72 *Pettifer 44 (at Tooting)*

Hertford Town v Northwood 3-2 82
Beyner 2 23, *Vincent 28,*
Whitehead 81 *Blackman 61*

Horsham YMCA v Erith & Belv. 1-2 58
Smith 11 *Bartley 62 87*

Shoreham v Sheppey United 0-3 65
Kenny 57,Wilson 87,Talbot 88

Molesey v Ringmer 4-0 25
Vidal 10 26,Mann 35

Corinthian v Merstham 6-0 44
Arnold 41,Penton 54 76,Mitchell 66,Clark
74,Allchorn 79

Chertsey Town v Worthing 2-2 143
Walcott 44,Ellerker 46Anderson 30,Own Goal 40

Worthing v Chertsey T. *(3-9-91)* 4-1 215
Lambert 17,Clarke 46, *Walcott 49*
Boxall 63,Anderson 90

Chichester City v Chipstead 1-3 70
Ashburner 43 *Paterson 17 51,Wright 49*

Faversham T. v Eastbourne T. 0-0

E'bourne T. v Fav'ham *(4-9-91)* 0-4 214
(at E'bourne Utd) *Barton 50,Carpenter 60 88*

Whyteleafe v Ashford Town 2-0 131
Cox 31,Sheridan 52

Tunbridge Wells v Burgess Hill 0-2 131
Williams 35, Own Goal 83

Canterbury City v Arundel 1-0 61
Clout 19

Leatherhead v Corinthian Casuals 3-1 130
Steffe 64,Russell 73,Own Goal 90 *Clark 61*

Cove v Slade Green 2-1 74
Newbury 60,Thompson 89 *Bryan 15*

Chatham Town v Steyning Town 1-3 77
Doe 70 *Paine 55,Salter 65 85*

Lewes v Three Bridges 4-3 104
Rice 4 13 75, *Lever 39,*
Freeman 36 *Malthouse 47 89*

Met. Police v Hastings Town 2-4 72
Mario 35 37 *White 27 90,Miles 52,Blondrage 73*

Tooting & Mitcham Utd v Redhill 2-0 178
Cowan 53,Dennington 65

Whitstable v Eastbourne Utd 0-1 204
Campbell 37

Hampton v Haywards Hth Town 3-0 143
Beadle 58,Ewing 86,Reed 90

Hythe Town v Croydon Ath. 4-4 253
Arger 16 19, *Gall 8 85,Ndah 22,*
Allon 45 65 *Embley 66*

Croydon A. v Hythe *(3-9-91)* 2-1 91
James 17,Ndah 35 *Ross 35*

Langney Sports v Southwick 0-1 179
Smyth 10

Lancing v Wick 4-1 139
Towell 14 69,Herbert 89,Milton 90 *Banks 42*

Epsom & Ewell v Walton & Hersham 1-5 143
Tweedy 79 *Holman 44,Jones 50,*
Horner 56,Wingfield 73

Oakwood v Havant Town 0-3 50
Sherry 2,Tate 86(pen) 88

Newbury Town v Horndean 1-0 78
Sheehan 44

Selsey v Malden Vale 2-1 105
Rishman 42,Benham 80 *Burke 50*

Bracknell Town v Portfield 2-2 50
McCrady 52,Smith 75 *Standing 40 70*

Portfield v Bracknell *(4-9-91)* 2-1* 114
Forry 62,Vickers 118 *Freer 55*

Buckingham Town v Abingdon U. 1-0 137
Blencowe 23

Sholing Spts v Maidenhead Utd 0-6 127
Bale 13,Hall 45 80,Mooney 71 86,Thomas 73

Totton AFC v AFC Lymington 2-2 126
Pitter 30,Hitchcock 84(pen) *Rankin 31,Kelly 35*

Lymington v Totton *(4-9-91)* 3-2 119
Rankin 9,Perrett 21,Adams 55 *Pitter 33 76*

Horsham v Hungerford Town 2-1 115
Forrset 26,Dunk 85 *Jell 41*

Bournemouth v Abingdon Town 1-2 92
Munday 68 *Herbert 69,Varney 88*

Calne Town v Westbury United 1-2 105
Scorer Undisclosed *Lunt 20,Fielding 30*

Fareham Town v Thatcham Town 1-5 112
Taylor 76 *Fearon 24,McCartney 32,*
Baker 33 37,Laing 76

Thame United v Eastleigh 1-1 156
Watson 57 *Stanhope 69*

Eastleigh v Thame Utd *(3-9-91)* 0-2 156
Thomas 42,Hayward 65

Chard Town v Witney Town 1-2 149
West 76 *Mills 11 79*

Cwmbran Town v Paulton Rvrs 1-0 78
Jolosa 2

Glastonbury v Keynsham Town 1-0 80
McCartney 74

Gosport Borough v Clevedon   1-3 158
Own Goal 45   Panes 42,Lee 69,Taylor 71

Melksham T. v Welton Rovers   1-1 186
Sinclair 18   Horwood 88

Barry Town v Ton Pentre   3-1 381
Burrows 31,Matthews 62,Evans 74 Own Goal 82

Welton v Melksham T. (2-9-91)   1-2 170
Spalding 70   Dixon 15,Sinclair 40

Radstock Town v Devizes T.   0-2 65
Webb 40 58

Dawlish T. v Maesteg Park   1-2 84
Bath 35   Webber 80,Fraser 88

Bridgend T. v Chippenham T.   2-0 55
Evans 44 80

St Blazey v Minehead   0-3 97
Morgan 35 37,Lewis 55

Yate Town v Bristol M.F.   4-1 241
Thaws 8 40 47,Thompson 46   Waring 39

Clandown v Ilfracombe T.   1-3 24
Taylor 89   Mackie 39,Saunders 58,Slade 68

Frome Town v Exmouth Town   3-1 87
Ford 20,Parsons 29 89   Dodd 50

Torrington v Barnstaple Town   3-1
Saunders 48,Tregedon 70,Pitts 74   Williams 52

Shortwood U. v Weston-s-Mare   3-0 156
Bell 37,Lewis 51,Finan 61

Bideford v Falmouth Town   2-3 185
Cansfield 2,   Leonce 60,Hodge 76,
Nancekivel 63   Gardner 90

Lee Mooney fires in Maidenhead's sixth at Sholing in the Preliminary Round. Photo - John Holloway.

Bob Horn (stripes) goes close for Chichester City, but his side still lost 0-3 to Chipstead. Photo - Dennis Nicholson.

Malden Vale attackers outnumber Selsey defenders but cannot make this attack count. Photo - Graham Cotterill.

Hastings' Paul Giles finds a gap in the Metropolitan Police defence at Imber Court. Photo - Roger Turner.

Simon Jolley, later sent off, punches clear during Hythe's defeat at Croydon Athletic. Photo - Dave West.

FIRST QUALIFYING ROUND

144 **Ties. Matches Played:** 168
Home wins: 81 (Inc. 1 replayed tie) **Draws:** 23 **Away wins:** 64
Best Attendance: 1,017 - Wisbech Town v Kettering Town
Total Attendance: 43,084 (1 gate unknown) **Average Attendance:** 258
Largest Home Win: 6-0; Dover v Chipstead, Saltash v Ilfracombe.
Best Away Win: Melksham Town 1, Worcester City 8
Result of the Round: Eastwood Hanley 2, Northwich Victoria 1

Saturday 14th September 1991	Res	Att

(* Denotes extra time played)

Workington v Gateshead   0-1   193
O'Brien 25

Alnwick Town v Brandon United   1-1   135
Moscrop 62   Lamb 85

Brandon v Alnwick Town *(18-9-91)* 0-1   182
Mullen 34

Netherfield v Billingham Syn.   3-2   130
Fleming 49,Tottoh 53,   Malone 10,
Borrowdale 86   Allen 20

Newcastle Blue Star v Hebburn   5-1   169
McCarthy 5 42, Storey 12,   Caiseley
Nicholson 75,Haley 89

Annfield Plain v North Shields   0-4   120
Howie 30 85,Nicholson 60 72

Ashington v Consett   0-4   106
Staff 12,McLeod 39,Brown 55,Sugden 66

Bridlington T. v Blyth Spartans   3-1   316
Radford 19,Connor 59,Brown 75   Bond 20 63

Northallerton v Langley Park   1-0   71
Crane 10

Cleator Moor Celtic v Gretna   0-7   142
Nelson 10,Pickford 11 57 60 88,
O'Hagan 50,Wilson 52

Spennymoor Utd v Bedlington T. 0-1   154
Donaldson 52

Darlington CB v Murton   1-3   66
Hewitt 36   Watson 70,Evans 71,Laws 85

Whitby Town v Garforth Town   0-1   244
Woods 14

Dunston FB v Guisborough T.   1-0   140
Coyles 70

Penrith v Billingham Town   4-2   121
Savage 16,Monaghan 25,   Roulston 46,
Gardner 43,Gate 52   McGarry 56

Durham City v Tow Law Town   1-0   100
Holden 43(pen)

Morecambe v Gt Harwood Town 1-0   402
Holden 35

Norton & S'ton Anc. v Guiseley   0-4   89
Elliott 32 77,Nagy 81,Roberts 89

Seaham Red Star v Shildon   3-0   70
Gamble 61,McDonald 88,Gibb 89
(Replay ordered - SRS ineligible player)

Shildon v Seaham RS *(28-9-91)* 2-1   126
Howell 28,Adams 78   Robinson 87

Denaby Utd v Harrogate RA   1-0   123
Mozley 83

Fleetwood T. v B'pool Rovers   3-2   298
Walmesley 14,Madden 43,Smith 65Diggle 17 82

Prescot AFC v Accrington Stan.   0-5   300
Lyons 20 80 87,Grimshaw 60,Owen 75

Knowsley United v Sheffield   2-0   106
Siddell 41,Saunders 89

Curzon Ashton v Bangor City   1-1   121
Priest 53   Evans 20

Bangor v Curzon Ashton *(17-9-91)* 1-2   305
Lloyd 27   Liptrot 37,McKiernan 75

Buxton v Burscough   4-2   355

Caernarfon Town v Colwyn Bay   1-1   342
McGuire 28   Williscroft 50

Colwyn B. v Caernarfon *(17-9-91)* 2-1   795
Own Goal 1,Donnelly 88   Edwards 84

Rhyl v Newtown   1-0   317
Roberts 38

Warrington Town v Hyde United   1-0   290
Meachin 72

Marine v Liversedge   4-0   220
Haw 12,Grant 43,Murray 65 89

Flixton v Mossley   1-1   174
Higgins 9   Burke 32

Mossley v Flixton *(17-9-91)* 2-1   376
Bowler 78,Haydock 88   Higgins 22(pen)

Winsford United v Nantwich Town 3-0   386
Hall,Cameron,Blackwood

Harworth Cl v Droylsden   0-1
Kershaw 61

Bootle v Newcastle Town   2-1   50
Williams 39 64   Lawton 46

Eastwood Hanley v Northwich Vic. 2-1   321
Bates 38(pen),Twiggs 63   Buxton 73

Heanor Town v Armthorpe Welfare 0-2   167
Lucas 15 27

Ossett Town v Southport   0-1   270
Livens 68

Stalybridge Celtic v Worksop Town 4-0   403
Scores undisclosed

Skelmersdale U. v Macclesfield T. 0-4   417
Shepherd 7,Heesom 14,Dawson 37,Askey 61

Borrowash Vic. v Belper Town   2-0   173
Wilkinson 55,Bookbinder 89

Farsley Celtic v Emley   0-1   425
Broadbent 59

Horwich RMI v Ilkeston Town   1-0   161
Redshaw 85

Harrogate Town v Frickley Ath.   2-2   358
Phillpott 31 84   Fuller 32 Woodhead 38

F'ley v H'gate *(at H'gate 17-9-91)* 3-3   429
Owen 44 (pen),   Phillott 10 17,
Parker 57,Fuller 81   Wright 79

Frickley v Harrogate Town *(23-9-91)* 3-2   382
Parker 2,Fuller 33,   Greenough 9,
Own Goal 75   Sumner 78

Alfreton T. v Hinckley Athletic   1-0   199
McCarthy 57

Lincoln U. v Gainsboro' Tr. 3-1 319
Goddard 48,Cromble 66,Ward 70 Kaye 30

Goole Town v Oakham Utd 0-1 231
Nicholson 17

Bridgnorth T. v Matlock T. 1-2 150
Balshaw 66 Richardson 79,Vaughan 87

Solihull v Wednesfield (15-9-91) 3-0 209
Wright 19,Burton 70 78

Blakenall v Boston United 1-2 498
Lees 4 Cavell 12,Jones 81

Moor Green v Tamworth 0-3 757
Busst 21(own goal), Smith 80,Eccleston 85

West Mids Police v Burton A. 0-1 250
Machin 45

Willenhall T. v RC Warwick 2-1 150
Minton 52,Stevens 77 Hathaway 78

Hinckley Town v Leicester Utd 2-0 238
Donaldson 88,Symonds 90

Shepshed Alb. v Stourbridge 2-0 291
Korpaw 33,Glover 34

Chasetown v Bilston Town 0-0 114

Bilston v Chasetown (17-9-91) 0-1 107
Dixon 78

Banbury Utd v Hednesford T. 2-1 258
Stratford 60,McDowell 71 O'Connor 13

Raunds Town v Gresley Rvrs 1-1 162
Murphy 58 Barry 76(pen)

Gresley v Raunds T. (17-9-91) 2-0 644
Acklam 72 73

VS Rugby v Stamford Town 2-0 550
Rosegreen 4 22

APV Peterboro' C. v Alvechurch 0-0 47

A'church v APV P'boro (17-9-91) 3-2 181
Dearn 30, Watkins 27
Richardson 44 61 Scotcher 33

Evesham Utd v Malvern Town 2-4 328
Jones 8, Coppin 5 67 84,
Ridlington 12 Carter 50

Chalfont St P. v Nuneaton B. 0-4 250
Gocan 29,Cottrill 34,Simpson 56,Carty 80

Corby Town v Hemel Hempstead 1-0 287
Murphy 13

Bedworth Utd v Bromsgrove Rvrs 0-2 264
Omeara 17,Hanks 48

Desborough T. v Rushden Town 2-4 200
Woolmer 23, Belfon 46 90,
Barrett 72 Jeffrey 70,Green 79

Stevenage B. v Sutton Coldfield 0-2 464
Smith 14,Biddle 75

Redditch Utd v Edgware Town 5-1 182
L Joinson 22 88,Campbell 47, Managan 46
Stanton 76 84

Wisbech T. v Kettering Town 0-3 1017
Brown 21 54,Christie 25

Bourne Town v Braintree Town 0-3 256
Own Goal 10,England 78,Coghlan 89

Aveley v Heybridge Swifts 0-2 102
Nihill 12,Kerr 84

B. Stortford v Mirrlees B'stone 1-1 242
Hopkins 28 Locke 70

Mirrlees B. v B. S'ford (17-9-91) 2-0 204
Secondie 11,Shard 55

King's Lynn v Cambridge City 3-3 816
Creane 27 70, Gawthrop 50 59,
Rippin 52 Ryan 73

Cambridge v K. Lynn (18-9-91) 1-2* 369
Grogan 22 Boyers 8 110

Purfleet v Collier Row 2-2 86
Spiteri 59,Wood 71 Braithwaite 76,Samuels 80

Collier R. v Purfleet (18-9-91) 0-1 164
Brett 32

Tiptree United v Dagenham 1-0 163
Lee 22

Harlow v Leyton Wingate (at Ware) 4-1 61
Gayle 24,St Hilaire 60, Steppings 12
Head 55,Margerrison 80(pen)

Clacton Town v Billericay Town 1-2 230
Edwards 15 Jenkins 2,Jones 26

Sudbury Town v Histon 1-0 504
Bain 35

Clapton v Chelmsford City 1-5 195
Pitts 8 Jones 12,Greene 24 40 62,Groom 64

Enfield v Walthamstow Pennant 4-0 412
Westley 16 47 78, Salmon 68

Lowestoft Town v Boreham Wood 2-1 214
Bowler 76,Pratt 87 Bourne 62

Harwich & Parkeston v Potton U. 2-1 280
Kemp 17 85 Cox 16

East Thurrock U. v Grays Ath. 1-1 457
Wallace 45 Cherry 75(pen)

Grays v East Thurrock (17-9-91) 2-1 503
Stittle 60,Whittingham 70 Wallace 40

Redbridge F. v Haringey Boro' 5-0 244
Mayles 32,Broom 53 56,Garvey 61,Davidson 67

Stowmarket Town v Hendon 1-4 180
Bennett 47(pen) Clark 18,Duffield 21(pen)
Birch 51,Davies 86

Halstead T. v Baldock Town 2-3 240
Cutnore 47,Barker 87 Bone 43 61,Williams 47

Ford Utd v Wivenhoe Town 3-1 98
St Pier 24 38 87 Scorer undisclosed

Dartford v Ware (15-9-91) 5-1 631
Quail 14 85,Leslie 35, Brett 51
Barlow 43(pen),Sheringham 45

Thetford T. v St Albans City 0-2 131
Storey 23,Clark 32

Biggleswade v Brimsdown R. 1-2* 74
Lepore 85 Montague 70 96

Witham Town v Wealdstone 1-3 220
McBean 32 Kelly 21,Wilson 59,Donnellan 87

Chesham United v Wolverton 5-1 564
Dawber 43,Barnes 87,Banton 48 66 82 Marshall 70

Tilbury v Leighton Town 1-1 63
Phillips 88(pen) Dempsey 53

Leighton v Tilbury (17-9-91) 1-0 380
Larkins 87

Yeading v Ruislip Manor 3-1 222
Whiskey 45,Sawyers 50 63 Waugh 1

Slough Town v Croydon 2-2 524
Pluckrose 25,O'Connor 70 Norris 10 72

Croydon v Slough T. (16-9-91) 0-3 246
Anderson 60,Stanley 73,McKinnon 85

Hertford v Staines Town 2-0 112
Pacquette 59,Whitehead 88

Dulwich v Burnham (at 15-9-91) 1-0 138
Lillington 57

Wembley v Windsor & Eton 1-2 126
Lawrence 84 Evans 36,Bates 37

Fisher Ath. v Beckenham Town 4-0 203
Samsom 1(pen) 87,Underwood 53,Grice 90

David Evans (half obsured) puts Bangor ahead at Curzon Ashton. Photo - Alan Monument.

Paul Sharp of Mirrlees Blackstone is closed down by the Bishop's Stortford defence. Photo - Mike Floate.

Camberley's Mark Watson makes a spectacular save in his side's home defeat against Marlow. Photo - Eric Marsh.

Banstead Ath. v Wokingham T.   1-2 121
Bell 85   *Noad 22,Carter 36*

Corinthian v Erith & Belvedere   1-3 109
Mitchell 74   *Booth 15 45,Young 69*

Molesey v Crawley Town   1-5 154
Roffe 8   *Oakes 6,Venables 36 87,*
                     Gallagher 42,Whittingdon 44

Hailsham Town v Sheppey Utd 1-1 146
Hutchinson 64   *Farnie 34*

Sheppey U. v Hailsham *(17-9-91)* 4-1 182
Fulton 53 66 92,Wilson 88   *Kemp 52*

Whitehawk v Bromley   0-2 135
              Campbell 76(pen), Brown 87

Whyteleafe v Worthing   1-2 112
Sheridan 11   *Barnard 45 60*

Faversham T. v Carshalton A.   3-2 208
Little 20,Rudd 68,Walsh 75   *Bolton 40 76*

Dover Athletic v Chipstead   6-0 809
Rogers 17 30 42 79,Blenden 53 72

Steyning Town v Bognor Regis 0-1 197
                     Cormack 20

Cove v Burgess Hill Town   1-1   74
Thompson 36   *Strange 49*

Burgess Hill T. v Cove *(18-9-91)* 4-0 164
Williams 20,Carr 50,Fernley 65,Strange 75

Leatherhead v Dorking   1-2 370
Lawler 82(pen)   *Hanlan 20 72*

Gravesend & N. v Canterbury C. 2-1 336
Franco 59 90   *King 83*

Herne Bay v Kingstonian   0-2 301
                  Pearce 82,Vines 84

Eastbourne United v Lewes   1-4 107
Campbell 83   *Russell 22,Rice 36,Crooks 47 80*

Tooting & Mitcham v Margate   2-1 255
Cowan 44,Taylor 65   *Toms 2*

Peacehaven & T. v Hastings T. 2-1 355
Coade 69,Ingledew 78   *Miles 79*

Walton & H'ham v Littlehampton 1-1 247
Holman 17   *Bennett 75*

Littlehampton v Walton. *(18-9-91)* 2-1 391
                Styles 79   Bennett 40 73

Lancing v Hampton   1-3 135
Gurney 16   Beadle 68,Jenkins 75,Thompson 82

Southwick v Sittingbourne   1-3 111
King 35   *Bourne 17,Julian 58,Jordan 90*

Tonbridge v Croydon Athletic 2-1 352
Thompson 6,Clark 42   *Prosper 60*

Camberley Town v Marlow   1-3   92
Lloyd 65   *Mikurenda 57,Jack 86 89*

Portfield v Havant Town   1-2 160
Clarke 75   *Tate 23(pen) 60*

Selsey v Andover   2-1 112
Davies 30,Smith 89   *Thomson 62*

Romsey Town v Newbury Town 2-1 256
Wood 54,White 78   *Leader 9*

Pagham v Basingstoke Town   1-3 210
Darney 70   Johnson 45,Lucas 59,Hickman 90

Horsham v Buckingham Town 1-0 225
Dunk 10

AFC Lymington v Bashley   2-4 433
Holloway 51,   *Lovell 9,Whale 45*
Rankin 75   *Baird 56,Gowans 89*

Newport IOW v Maidenhead Utd 0-3 443
              Muir 49,Laryea 74 88

Swanage T. & H. v Waterlooville 1-1 118
Turrell 88   *Elley 75*

Waterlooville v Swanage *(17-9-91)* 2-0 151
Own Goal 43,Burns 75

Thame United v Abingdon Town 2-0 335
Hayward 53,Thomas 60

Thatcham Town v Salisbury   1-1 321
Duncan 43   *Green 51*

Salisbury v Thatcham *(18-9-91)* 3-0 221
Cranmer 58,Gomersall 70,Phillips 78

Poole Town v Westbury United   3-1 169
Morley 25,Bartlett 76,Coombes 78 *Lunt 77*

Brockenhurst v Dorchester Town 1-2 230
Diles 35   *Green 25 80*

Clevedon Town v Witney Town 2-2 140
Perrett 30 32   *O'Loughlin 1,Teggart 54*

Witney Town v Clevedon *(17-9-91)* 1-0 176
Leach 62

Glastonbury v Trowbridge Town 0-4 381
          Adams 17,Jackson 75,Dennison 72 84

Mangotsfield Utd v Cwmbran Town 4-2 171
Micciche 35,Towler 60,   *Thomas 84*
Tanner 64,Brown 79   *Powell 89*

Wimborne Town v Weymouth   1-2 302
Bridle 80   *Cook 10,Bourne 78*

Yate Town v Barry Town   0-3 327
              John 17,Giles 20 24

Bridgend Town v Cheltenham Town 3-3 110
Phillips 25,   *Purdie 30,Willetts 67(pen),*
Perrett 39 76   *Owen 87*

Cheltenham v Bridgend *(18-9-91)* 5-0 480
Buckland 3 39 51,Casey 20 62

Taunton Town v Devizes Town   2-0 237
Own Goal 41,Hunt 45

Stroud v Bath City   1-3 272
Shrimpston 43   *Withey 8,*
                Randall 19(pen),Brown 62

Maesteg Park v Frome Town   4-0   54
Williams 38,McCarthy 60,Radford 62 75

Melksham Town v Worcester City 1-8 245
Harvey 10   *Kearns 24 40 60,Singleton 29,*
             Robinson 31 48,Bridge 78,Jones 81

Gloucester City v Shortwood Utd 4-1 744
Penny 32,Own Goal 34,   *Gobey 71*
Meacham 39,Noble 45

St Austell v Liskeard Athletic   2-3 122
Cook 59,   *Mildon 75,Wilmott 83,*
Davidson 65   *Swiggs 85*

Falmouth Town v Minehead   2-0 393
Torrance 70,Rapsey 73

Torrington v Tiverton Town   2-2 378
Nicholls 17,Pitts 87   *Hynds 48,Smith 88*

Tiverton v Torrington *(18-9-91)* 3-2* 438
Smith 57,Jones 97,   *Nicholls 30,*
Hynds 105   *Gilbert 118*

Saltash Utd v Ilfracombe Town   6-0 143
Norton 5,Fallon 26 30,Fadida 48,Edwards 75,Rowe 78

The start of Crawley's long run - Craig Whittington scores their third at Molesey. Photo - Colin Stevens.

Hastings' Keith Miles skips a tackle during his side's surprise defeat at Peacehaven. Photo - Roger Turner.

The Minehead defence under intense second half pressure in their defeat at Falmouth Town. Photo - Ray Frith.

SECOND QUALIFYING ROUND

72 Ties. Matches Played: 93
Home wins: 53   **Draws:** 21   **Away wins:** 19
Best Attendance: 1,609 - Kettering Town v Braintree Town
Total Attendance: 37,560   **Average Attendance:** 404
Largest Home Win: Cheltenham Town 8, Taunton Town 0
Best Away Win: Tiptree United 0, Harlow Town 6
Result of the Round: Macclesfield Town 1, Borrowash Victoria 2

Saturday 28th September 1991   Res Att

(* Denotes extra time played)

Gateshead v Alnwick Town   6-0   232
Bell 6 52 80,Butler 30 64,Emson 65

Netherfield v Newcastle B.S.   2-1   188
Ward 60,Galley 76   McCarthy 36

North Shields v Consett   3-1   142
Wardrobe 80,McKenzie 85,   McLeod 47
Woodcock 89

Bridlington T. v Northallerton T.   4-0   257
Norbury 40 55,Radford 49,Norman 73

Gretna v Bedlington Terriers   3-1   101
McCartney 2,Pickford 55,Fell 63   Pegg 88

Murton v Garforth Town   3-1   93
Adamson 25,Evans 78,Laws 81   Jackson 52

Dunston FB v Penrith   2-2   131
Cockburn 20,Bensley 50   Scorers undisclosed

Penrith v Dunston FB *(2-10-91)*   6-6   283
Gate 15 40,   Bensley 14,Kendal 24,
Gardner 26,   Halliday 38,
Frankland 47,Graham 47, · Richmond 68 86,
Mitchinson 108   Cockburn 117

Penrith v Dunston FB *(2-10-91)*   2-1   517
18,Graham 96   Frankland
Bensley 3

Durham City v Morecambe   1-4   213
Bragan 8   Brown,McMahon,Coleman,Holden

Guiseley v Shildon   5-1   662
Colville 54,B Roberts 66 77,   Adams 90
A Roberts 69

Denaby Utd v Fleetwood Town   1-0   180
Mozley 75

Accrington S. v Knowsley Utd   2-2   92
Hughes 30,Bondswell 85   Scorers undisclosed

Knowsley v Accrington *(1-10-91)*   2-1* 343
Siddell 38,Jackson 120   Bondswell 63

Curzon Ashton v Buxton   1-0   203
Diamond 85

Colwyn Bay v Rhyl   2-0   785
Donnelly 2,Roberts 53

Warrington Town v Marine   0-0   317

Marine v Warrington *(1-10-91)*   1-0   217
Grant 66

Mossley v Winsford United   1-1   342
Bowler 43   Cameron 55

Winsford Utd v Mossley *(2-10-91)* 6-0 359
Scorers undisclosed

Droylsden v Bootle   1-1   239
Kershaw 36   Foley 89

Bootle v Droylsden   1-3   212
Darby 11   Booth 33 47,Wright 57

Eastwood Han. v Armthorpe W.   3-2   117
Wheaton 22,Bates 34(pen),   Miller 12,
Twigg 85   Lucas 85

Southport v Stalybridge C.   1-2   417
Camble 31   Bennett 21,Smith 67

Emley v Horwich RMI   4-2   378
Cooper 21,Broadbent 44,   Lloyd 3,
Tunnacliffe 33 62   Haddon 77

Frichley Athletic v Alfreton Town   4-1   360
Fuller 27,Woodhead 37,   Newton 77
Parker 46,Deane 59

Lincoln Utd v Oakham United   2-0   200
Ward 12,Goddard 61

Matlock Town v Solihull Borough   2-1   342
Sheppard 45,Marsh 90   Clayton 28

Boston United v Tamworth   1-1   1375
Jones 15   Perry 38

Tamworth v Boston U. *(1-10-91)*   1-0* 1215
Green 111

Burton Albion v Willenhall Town   4-1   401
Cordner 47 64 66,Sallis 67   Edwards 6

Hinckley Town v Shepshed Albion   3-3   281
Own Goal 38,   Dakin 21 90,
Massey 71 88   Roderick 32

Shepshed v Hinckley Town *(1-10-91)* 3-2 392
Dakin 2 56,Watts 24   Steer 51,Akeredolli 86

Chasetown v Banbury United   1-1   147
Collins 61   Hamilton 61

Banbury Utd v Chasetown *(1-10-91)* 1-2* 326
Hamilton 111   Langston 94,Dixon 115

Gresley Rovers v VS Rugby   3-3   774
Denby 33,Acklam 43,   Land 34(OG),Reed 56(pen),
Weston 59   Boyland 87

VS Rugby v Gresley *(2-10-91)*   3-0   707
Rosegreen 57 71,Crawley 83

Alvechurch v Malvern Town   3-0   81
Hart 13,Richardson 22 62

Nuneaton Borough v Corby Town   2-2   667
Simpson 82,Twipper 89   Murphy 17,Edwards 58

Nuneaton B. v Corby *(2-10-91)*   1-0* 392
Keeble 111

Bromsgrove Rovers v Rushden Town 1-0 472
Richardson 75

Sutton Coldfield v Redditch U.   1-3   173
Caulfield 85   Judd 25 58,Lee 90

Kettering Town v Braintree Town   3-1 1609
Graham 11,Jones 16,Hill 72   Hollocks 9

Heybridge v Mirrlees Blackstone   1-1   142
Adcock 46   Secondie 80

M. Blackstone v Heybridge *(2-10-91)* 0-1 350
Nihill 48

King's Lynn v Purfleet   4-2   749
Matthews 9(pen),   Gallagher 9 87,
Blakebrough 72   O'Keefe 17,McNally 89

Tiptree Utd v Harlow Town   0-6   79
Battram 10 40 55,Muller(OG),St Hilaire 18,Durant 80

Billericay Town v Sudbury Town   3-1   472
Jones 12 64 85   Powell 87

Graham Broadbrent of Emley gets in a header under pressure from Ian Lloyd of Horwich. Photo - Barry Lockwood.

Worksop's Ian Clark outjumps a Stalybridge defender during the 0-4 defeat at Bower Fold. Photo - John Hanson.

Dennis Gascoyne puts Thame two up in their shock replay win at home to Waterlooville. Photo - Steve Daniels.

(* Denotes extra time played)

Chelmsford City v Enfield   1-1   605
Mosely 82(OG)   *Keen 26*

Enfield v Chelmsford *(1-10-91)*   2-1   665
Kane 29,Westley 72   *Stead 63*

Lowestoft v Harwich & Parkeston 1-0   277
McKechnie 19

Grays A. v Redbridge Forest   3-1   344
Crown 55,Whittingham 66,   *Own Goal 50*
Brown 69

Hendon v Baldock Town   1-2   209
Das 60   *Sharp 58,Williams 87*

Ford United v Dartford   0-1   323
     Bensted 65

St Albans C. v Brimsdown R.   1-1   338
Cox 60   *Sullivan 90*

Brimsdown v St Albans *(1-10-91)* 2-0   338
Sullivan 65,Dennis 85

Wealdstone v Chesham United   2-4   745
Blackman 50,   *Cosby 1,Ryan 24,*
Hedge 57   *Goldstone 60(pen),Banton 80*

Berkhamsted T. v Leighton Town 2-0   243
Jeffrey 19,Roach 81

Yeading v Slough Town   0-0   475
Slough Town v Yeading *(1-10-91)* 1-0   722
Anderson 88

Hertford Town v Dulwich H.   2-1   134
Whitehead 67 90   *Murrock 11*

Windsor & Eton v Fisher Ath.   3-2   226
Gilman 2,Williams 13,   *Norman 18,*
Woods 51   *Sansom 86*

Wokingham v Erith & Belvedere 1-2   277
Murphy 27   *Cappuccio 46(pen),Booth 60*

Crawley T. v Sheppey Utd   2-0   241
Whittington 14 77

Bromley v Worthing   3-1   413
Brown 5,Campbell 44,Morgan 80   *Nye*

Faversham T. v Dover Ath.   0-0 1157
Dover v Faversham *(1-10-91)*   2-1 1232
Rogers 33,Blewden 81   *Legg 86*

Bognor Regis v Burgess Hill T.   1-2   211
Pullen 75   *Fernley 16,Strange 30*

Dorking v Gravesnd & N'fleet   3-4   185
Grainger 6 20,   *Watkins 22 61,*
Hanlan 75   *Cotier 47,Parkin 51(pen)*

Kingstonian v Lewes   3-2   367
Vines 30,Pearce 66,Harlow 75   *Crooks 13 86*

Tooting & M. v Peacehaven & T.2-0   255
Moss 34,Stevens 41

Littlehampton T. v Hampton   1-3   225
Guille 20   *Jenkins 13,Own Goal 26,Beadle 76*

Sittingbourne v Tonbridge AFC   1-2   641
Wallace 18(OG)   *Wallace 60,Thompson 68*

Marlow v Havant Town   2-1   190
Watkins 46,Caesar 67   *Tate 52(pen)*

Selsey v Romsey Town   1-6   120
Fear(2),White(2),Long,Brockway   *Rishman 86*

Basingstoke Town v Horsham   1-1   261
Clark 5   *Lucas 25*
Horsham v Baingstoke *(1-10-91)* 2-1*   387
Gunn 2,Somers 103   *Chambers 49*

Bashley v Maidenhead United   1-1   205
Lovell 9   *Creighton 25*
Maidenhead v Bashley *(1-10-91)*   1-0   252
Araguez 28

Waterlooville v Thame United   3-3   147
Clements 46,   *Rayson 43 82,*
Burnside 48,Burns 89   *Edwards 79*
Thame v Waterlooville *(1-10-91)*   3-2   320
Rayson 4 99(pen),   *Burns 55,*
Gascoyne 6   *Clements 73*

Salisbury v Poole Town   2-0   220
Smith 40(pen),Chalk 67

Dorchester T. v Witney Town   3-2   458
Mills 29,Clarke 37   *Green 1 30,Diaz 66*

Trowbridge v Mangotsfield U.   3-0   455
Harris 20,Adams 65,Iddles 80

Weymouth v Barry Town   1-1   584
Cook 88   *Matthews 36*
Barry T. v Weymouth *(1-10-92)*   2-3   455
Evans 45,Williams 59   *Cook 12 118,Pugh 88*

Cheltenham T. v Taunton Town   8-0   473
Jordan 12 28,Buckland 25,Casey 30 76 80,Stobart
44,Willetts 88

Bath City v Maesteg Park   5-2   316
Randall 14 27(pen),Boyle,   *Williams 24,*
Ricketts 62,Gill 81   *Bewiamous 83*

Worcester C. v Gloucester City   2-1   904
Robinson 84,Williams 89   *Eaton 44*

Liskeard Ath. v Falmouth Town   5-1   286
Swiggs 8 83(pen),   *Torrance 60*
Juniper 65 70,Ferris 75

Tiverton Town v Saltash United   0-0   278
Saltash U. v Tiverton *(2-10-91)*   1-2   379
Rowe 39   *Scott 40,Charlesworth 68*

Accrington's Andy Bondswell (10) heads a late equaliser in Stanley's 2-2 draw with Knowsley. Photo - Colin Stevens.

Ford United keeper Mark Baker saves a second half penalty in the 0-1 defeat against Dartford. Photo - Dave West.

Romsey Town attack strongly during their 6-1 trouncing of Selsey. Photo - Eric Marsh.

Eastwood Hanley's Richard Johnson clutches a cross as his team lose to Stalybridge. Photo - Colin Stevens.

Grays Athletic No.9 Tommy Williams gives his side a 9th minute lead at Lowestoft Town. Photo - Francis Short.

Ashley Carr of Burgess Hill takes on two Gravesend & Northfleet defenders at Leyland Park. Photo - Roger Turner.

THIRD QUALIFYING ROUND

36 Ties. Matches Played: 45
Home wins: 15 Draws: 9 Away wins: 21
Best Attendance: 1,587 - Kettering Town v Heybridge Swifts
Total Attendance: 28,071 **Average Attendance:** 638
Largest Home Win: Weymouth 4, Cheltenham Town 0
Best Away Win: Thame United 0, Salisbury 4
Result of the Round: Weymouth 4, Cheltenham Town 0

Saturday 12th October 1991   Res Att

Gateshead v Netherfield   0-0 282

Netherfield v G'head *(15-10-91)*   0-3 867
Saddington 48,Leishman 67 70

Nth Shields v Bridlington Town   0-2 237
Hopkinson 2,Bishop 69

Gretna v Murton   3-0 143
O'Hagan 20,Armstrong 60,Nelson 62

Penrith v Morecambe   0-3 559
Coleman,Brennan,McInery

Guiseley v Denaby United   1-1 691
Tennison 86   Downing 2

Denaby U. v Guiseley *(16-10-91)*   1-2 735
Downing 87   Roberts 14 67

Knowsley Utd v Curzon Ashton   2-0 329
Siddell 65 78

Colwyn Bay v Marine   4-3 651
Williams 8,Williscroft 15, Roche 55, Murray 73,
Jones 36 52   Gautrey 89

Winsford Utd v Droylsden   3-2 681
Mayfield 18,Edey 67,   Blair 26(pen),
Blackwood 71   Johnson 83

Eastwood H. v Stalybridge   1-2 382
Hulme 25   Aspinall 53,Camden 62

Borrowash Victoria v Emley   0-3 391
Broadbent 37 89,Balmer 49

Frickley Ath. v Lincoln Utd   0-0 477

Lincoln v Frickley *(15-10-91)*   3-2 802
Park 45,Ward 49   Barnsley 10,
Goddard 60   Heaney 75

Matlock Town v Tamworth   0-2 1149
Eccleston 60,Perry 64

Burton A. v Shepshed Albion   3-2 704
Redfern 2,Bottomley 36, Corpell 36,
Straw 38   Rowe 89

Chasetown v V.S. Rugby   0-0 492

V.S. Rugby v C'town *(16-10-91)*   3-0 605
Rosegreen 5,Shearer 28 38

Alvechurch v Corby Town   2-0 217
Richardson 69 72

Bromsgrove R. v Redditch Utd   2-0 1050
Crisp 47,Cooper 88

Kettering v Heybridge Swifts   3-0 1587
Hill 4(OG),Graham 27,Brown 80

King's Lynn v Harlow Town   2-3 1305
Sharman 30,Rawcliffe 57Durant 3,Battram 11 59

Billericay Town v Enfield   1-3 979
Mosely 28(OG)   Westley 24 92,Warmington 65

(* Denotes extra time played)

Lowestoft Town v Grays Athletic   1-2 679
Youngman 58   Williams 15,Whittingham 80

Baldock Town v Dartford   2-2 628
Templeton 44,   Leslie 43,
Springett 44   Barlow 81(pen)

Dartford v Baldock *(15-10-91)*   1-2 701
Prutton 75   Cuffie 48,Allinson 115

Brimsdown Rovers v Chesham Utd   2-2 412
Taylor 25 43   Barnes 10,Walton 80

Chesham v Brimsdown *(16-10-91)*   2-1 585
Attrell 25,Dawber 82   Moore 75

Berkhamsted T. v Slough Town   1-4 612
Hobbs 35   Anderson 27(pen),
Donnellan 88,McKinnon 51 63

Hertford Town v Windsor & Eton   1-2 280
Pacquette 90   Williams 56,Woods 90

Erith & Belvedere v Crawley Town   1-2 400
Cappuccio 63   Cooper 68,Gallagher 81

Bromley v Dover Athletic   0-3 1010
Little 11,Blewden 51,Rogers 84

Burgess Hill v Gravesend & N'fleet   0-1 341
Fordread 57

Kingstoniand v Tooting & Mitcham   0-0

Tooting v Kingstonian *(15-10-91)*   2-3 517
Taylor 6,Loughlin 17   Erimo(2),Pearce

Hampton v Tonbridge   2-2 529
Ewing 27,Jenkins 39   Own Goal 80,Collins 90

Tonbridge v Hampton *(15-10-91)*   2-1 814
Jenkins 9
(Abandoned (floodlight failure) 81 mins)

Tonbridge v Hampton *(21-10-91)*   3-0 1274
Finch,Graham,Clarke (all in extra time)

Marlow v Romsey Town   2-0 315
Hooper 81,Regan 87

Horsham v Maidenhead United   1-1 535
Forrest 59   Muir 89

Maidenhead v Horsham *(15-10-91)*   0-1 383
Dunk 28

Thame United v Salisbury   0-4 420
Smith 24 26,Gomershall 41,O'Donnell 62

Dorchester Town v Trowbridge Town   1-0 805
Diaz 4

Weymouth v Cheltenham Town   4-0 1176
Browne 60,Cook 69,Clifford 74 81

Bath City v Worcester City   1-2 813
Rickett 9   Kearns 52 56

Liskeard Ath. v Tiverton T.   1-3 1402
Swiggs 18   Jones 1,Annuniata 43,Saunders 44

Ollie Kearns equalises from the spot during Worcester's surprise win at Bath City. Photo - Alan Casse.

Bromley's Grary Campbell shoots for goal, but his side went down 0-3 against Dover Athletic. Photo - Dave West.

Gateshead's Derek Bell fails to score with this header in the home draw against Netherfield. Photo - Alan Watson.

FOURTH QUALIFYING ROUND

28 Ties **Matches Played:** 37
Home wins: 16 **Draws:** 9 **Away wins:** 12
Best Attendance: 3,427 - Crawley Town v Horsham
Total Attendance: 39,637 **Average Attendance:** 1,071
Largest Home Win: Colchester United 5, Burton Albion 0
Best Away Win: Salisbury 1, Farnborough Town 7
Result of the Round: Gretna 3, Stalybridge Celtic 2

Saturday 26th October 1991

WHITLEY B. (1)1 *(Chandler 34)* **WITTON A.** (1)4 *(McNeilis 34, John Connor 65 86,Stewart 89(p)* Att: 443
W.Bay: Young, Embleton, Carver (Shaw 59), Brigg, Teasdale, Scott, Dawson, Lees, Chandler, Sokoluk (Robertson 71), Johnson. *Witton:* Mason, James Connor, Coathup, Cuddy, McNeilis, Anderson, Stewart, Lutkevitch (Dyson 89), McCliskie, Grimshaw, John Connor. Uused sub: Edwards.

GUISELEY (1)2 *(Sams 6(OG),Wilkinson 71)* **BISHOP AUCKLAND** (0)1 *(Harnett 88)* Att: 964
Guiseley: Maxted, Atkinson, Hogarth, Tetley, Bottomley, Morgan, David Roberts, Tennison (Wilkinson 67), Elliott (Noteman 78), Annan, Billy Roberts. *B Auckland:* Sams, Deacey, Petitjean (Fothergill 76), Gavin Liddle (Watson 82), Magee, Lobb, Glen Liddle, Harnett, Robinson, Thompson, Walker.

RUNCORN (0)1 *(Shaughnessy 49)* **GATESHEAD** (0)0 Att: 734
Runcorn: Paladino, Byrne, Mullen, Carroll, Hill, Redman, Brabin, Harold, Shaughnessy (Hagan 89), Saunders, Withers. Unused sub: Hawtin. *G'head:* Smith, Farrelly, Saddington, Forrest, Corner, Halliday, Bell (Emson 67), Veart, Guthrie, Leishman, Butler. Unused sub: Davies.

BARROW (0)0 **BRIDLINGTON TOWN** (1)1 *(Norbury 21)* Att: 1268
Barrow: McDonnell, Slater, Chilton, Skivington, Messenger, Doolan, Wheatley (Atkinson 89), Todhunter, Brown (McNall 76), Procter, Doherty. *Brid'ton:* Ingham, Brentano, Smith, Noteman, Warburton, Stevenson, Bishop, Archer, Norbury, Radford, Harvey. Unused sub: Brown, Burdett.

TELFORD UNITED (0)1 *(Langford 63)* **KNOWSLEY UNITED** (0)0 Att: 743
Telford: Acton, Humphreys, Parrish, Dyson, Nelson, Whittington, Myers, Grainger, Bendow, Langford, Worrall. Unused subs: Cooke, Brown. *Knowsley:* Johnston, O'Brien, Tyrell, Orr, Jackson, Barton, Fagan, McConville (Doolan 45), Siddell, Saunders, Hand (Drury 80).

COLWYN BAY (0)0 **MORECAMBE** (1)2 *(Coleman 30 70)* Att: 781
Colwyn Bay: Darcy, Tinson, Roberts, Williams, Cooke (Bryn A Jones 70), Chaloner, Steve Jones, Brett, Woods, Donnelly, Williscoft. Unused sub: Rush. *M'cambe:* Allison, Tomlinson, Armstrong, Parrilon, Miller, Cain, Holden, McMahon, Coleman, Brown, Lodge (Horrocks 82). Unused sub: Gaffney.

CHORLEY (1)2 *(Rutter 24,Ross 85(p))* **EMLEY** (1)2 *(Bramald 47,Broadbent 89)* Att: 664
Chorley: Christie, Ward, Wills, Moss, Rutter, Griffiths, Halliday, Gough, Ross, Houston, Henshaw (Williams 80). Unused sub: Salisbury. *Emley:* Dennis, Bramald, Smith, Mellor, Codd, Farrar, Burrows, Broadbent, Green, Cooper, Balmer (Duke 70). Unused sub: Wilson.

EMLEY (0)1 *(Burrows 68)* **CHORLEY** (0)1 *(Murray 84)* 28-10-91. Att: 1151
(Match abandoned (fog) after 90 minutes)
Emley: Dennis, Hopley, Smith, Mellor, Codd, Farrar, Burrows, Broadbent (Duke 57), Green (Wilson 76), Cooper, Balmer. *Chorley:* As 1st match, but unused subs Williams & Storton.

CHORLEY (0)0 **EMLEY** (0)1 *(Wright 47)* 4-11-91. Att: 1380.
Chorley: Christie, Ward, Wills, Moss, Rutter, Griffiths, Halliday, Gough (Howard 68), Ross, Houston, Murray. Unused sub: Williams. *Emley:* Dennis, Bramald, Smith, Mellor, Codd, Farrar, Burrows, Wilson, Wright, Cooper, Duke. Unused subs: Balmer, Joyce.

LEEK TOWN (0)0 **LINCOLN UNITED** (1)2 *(Alan Paril 41,Goddard 84)* Att: 720
Leek: Simpson, Norris, Clowes, Anderson, Sutton, Holmes, Myatt, Somerville (Smith 18), Devaney, Snow, Fisher. Unused sub: Bainbride. *Lincoln:* Waby, North, Dye, Crombie, Ward, Stuart Paril, Steven Brown (Hinchliffe 75), Alan Paril, Goddard, Ward, Carter.

GRETNA (1)3 *(Armstrong 25,Pickford 55 61)* **STALYBRIDGE C.** (0)2 *(Camden 60,Brown 88)* Att: 449
Gretna: Leeming, John Wilson, McCartney, Goodrick, O'Hagan, Irwin, Carruthers, Pickford, Nelson, Moat. Unused subs: Mulholland, Mark Wilson. *S'bridge:* Hughes, Bennett, Blackman, Dixon, Aspinall, Booth (Bauress 60), Brown, Higginbottom (O'Connell 65), Camden, Smith, Sharratt.

WINSFORD UNITED (2)3 *(Blackwood 2 6,Cameron 74)* **ALTRINCHAM** (0)2 *(Shaw 52(p) 90(p)* Att: 1133
Winsfordn: Kendrick, Lloyd, Whitney, Edey, Taylor, Esdaille, Finch (Thomas 65), Hall, Cameron, Blackwood (Maynard 84), Sheridan. *A'cham:* Wealands, Lee, Densmore, Rowlands, Reid (Hughes 79), Anderson, Shaw, Daws, Brady, McKenna, Lewis. Unused sub: Wiggans.

WELLING UNITED (2)5 *(Abbott 19 41 49 66 90)* **ALVECHURCH** (0)1 *(Hart 89)* Att: 704
Welling: Barron, Clemmence (Hone 70), Robinson, Brown (Glover 78), Ransom, Berry, White, Burgess, Abbott, Robbins, Reynolds. *A'church:* Biggs, Barry Williams, Brian Williams, Dearn, Hart, Chappell, Eastoe (Fullerton 80), Allbutt (Angoy 17), Richardson, Hallam, Robinson.

COLCHESTER (1)5 *(McDonough 2,McGavin 52 80,Restarick 86,Kinsella 90)* **BURTON A.** (0)0 Att: 2,147
Colchester: Barrett, Donald, Phillips, Kinsella, English, Elliott, Collins (Restarick 78), Bennett, McDonough (Abrahams 75), McGavin, Smith. *Burton:* Goodwin, Bottomley, Foster, Straw, Geelan, Simms, Davies, Simon Redfern, Lycett, David Redfern (Cordner 62), Hall (Sallis 53).

KETTERING TOWN 0 **STAFFORD RANGERS** 0 Att: 1785
K'ring: Bastock, Huxford (Jones 62), Keast, Nicol, Price, Slack, Graham, Brown, Christie, Banscroft, Hill. Unused sub: Bloodworth. *Stafford:* Price, Pearson, Bradshaw, Simpson, Mower, Booth (Newman 40), Wilson, Wood, Tuohy, Whte, Palgrave. Unused sub: Lindsey.

STAFFORD RANGERS (0)0 **KETTERING TOWN** (0)2 *(Christie 71,Jones 87)* 29-10-91. Att: 1070
Stafford: Price, Pearson, Mower (Withe 19), Simpson, Essex, Palgrave, Wilson, Wood, Newman (Lindsey 76), Devlin. *K'ring:* As 1st match, but Jones replaced Christie (80 mins).

Steve McGavin puts over a cross as his Colchester side head to a convincing win over Burton. Photo - Paul Dennis.

Steve Brentano makes a vital tackle on Barrow's Gary Messenger during Bridlington's famous win. Photo - Ged Rule.

Sutton's Mark Costello heads clear a rare Weymouth attack at Gander Green Lane. Photo - Dave West.

70

GRAVESEND & NORTHFLEET (1)1 *(Cotter 11)* **HARLOW TOWN** (0)1 *(Head 69)* Att: 405
G & N: Cadmore, Cooper, Wells, Smart, Graves, Ironton (Flint 28), Franco, Perry, Watkins (Pring 78), Fordred, Cotter. *Harlow:* Mallett, Armstrong, Burns, Chinn, Gleeson, Durant, Emmanuel, Chinn (Porter 74), Battram, Margerrison, Head.

HARLOW TOWN (1)1 *(Battram 7)* **GRAVESEND & NORTHFLEET** (0)0 28-10-91. Att: 706
Harlow: Mallett, Armstrong (Porter 60), Burns, Gleeson, Durant, Emmanuel, Chinn (Barry 70), Battram, Gayle, Margerrison, Head. G & N: Cadmore, Cooper, Wells, Smart (Christie 85), Graves, Perry, Franco, Flint, Pring, Fordred (Watkins 80), Cotter.

GRAYS ATHLETIC (0)0 **ATHERSTONE UNITED** (1)2 *(Brain 44,Green 59)* Att: 517
Grays: Delf, Fox, Brown, Timson, Ward, Crumpton (Tuohy 65), Campbell, Sammons, Williams, Whittingham, Crown. Unused sub: Stittle. *Atherstone:* Starkey, Everitt, Upton, Olner, Jackson, Redgate, Aubrey, Green, Randle, Brain, Williams. Unused subs: Shilton, Greene.

ENFIELD (1)2 *(Robinson 42,Brush 85)* **V.S. RUGBY** (0)1 *(Crawley 51)* Att: 682
Enfield: McCutcheon, Smart, Mason, Keen, Pearce, Brush, Mosely, Kane, Manderson, Robinson, Westley. Unused subs: Turner, Heald. *Rugby:* Martin, Niblett (Clarke 23), McGinty, Halton, Coe, Reed, Shearer, Bradder, Rosegreen, Crawley, Fitzpatrick. Unused sub: Jones.

TAMWORTH (0)0 **BROMSGROVE ROVERS** (0)1 *(Crisp 62)* Att: 1546
T'worth: Leake, Mulholland, Finn, Keogh, Hayward, Ross, Parker (Kane 67), Perry (Cartwright 75), Smith, Gordon, Green. *B'grove:* Cooksey, Skelding, O'Meara, Richardson, Durkin, O'Connor, Daly, Stott, Cunningham, Crisp, Brighton. Unused subs: Hanks, Cooper.

BALDOCK TOWN (1)1 *(Fergusson 19)* **HALESOWEN TOWN** (0)1 *(Flynn 65)* Att: 923
B'dock: Bozier, Kearns, Stanton, Ward, Bruce, Templeton (Roberts 85), Marshall, Bone (Sharpe 65), Fergusson, Cuffie, Allinson. *H'owen:* Rowe, Abell (Edwards 60), Whittingham, Smith, Vowles, Bradley, Hazlewood, Flynn, Bennett (Goodall 85), Shilvock, Harrison.

HALESOWEN TOWN (0)1 *(Shilvock 81)* **BALDOCK TOWN** (0)0 29-10-91. Att: 1219
H'owen: Rowe, Whittingham, Edwards, Smith, Vowles, Bradley, Hazlewood, Flynn, Bennett, Shilvock, Harrison. Unused subs: Attwood, Goodall. *B'dock:* Bozier, Kearns, Stanton, Ward, Bruce, Bone (Phillips 68), Marshall, Barry, Fergusson (Sharp 81), Cuffie, Allinson.

AYLESBURY UNITED (0)1 *(Collins 78)* **CHESHAM UNITED** (0)1 *(Cosby 69)* Att: 1288
A'bury: Garner, Day, Ashby, Benning, Hutter, Wright, Mason, Davies, Hercules, Collins, Robinson. Unused subs: Williams, Lambert. *Chesham:* Lomas (Walton 46), Goldstone, Ryan, May (Cosby 46), Barnes, Bateman, Dawber, Attrell, Banton, Mitchell, Norman.

CHESHAM UNITED (0)1 *(Banton 35)* **AYLESBURY UTD** (1)3 *(Collins 10,Hercules 65 85)*9-10-91. Att: 1436
Chesham: Lomas, Goldstone, Ryan, May, Barnes, Bateman, Cosby, Abebowale, Banton, Mitchell, Norman (Attrell 63). Unused sub: Walton. *A'bury:* As 1st match. Lambert replaced Wright (86 mins).

TIVERTON TOWN (1)1 *(Jones 13)* **DOVER ATHLETIC** (0)0 Att: 756
Tiverton: Nott, Stuart, Saunders, Rogers, Short, Steele (Annunziata 55), Scott, Smith, Jones, Downs, Rogers. Unused sub: Greening. *Dover:* Munden, Harrop, Bartlett, Dixon, O'Connell, McDonald, Jackson, Dyer, Rogers, Little (Ambrose 79), Blewden. Unused sub: Cordice.

MERTHYR TYDFIL (1)1 *(Williams 10)* **WINDSOR & ETON** (1)1 *(Richards 10)* Att: 521
Merthyr: Wager, Tucker, James, Boyle, Lewis, Rogers, D'Auria, Webley, Hemming, Beattie, Cerri Williams. Unused subs: Mark Williams, Hutchison. *Windsor:* Mitchell, Connor, Walters, White, Richards, Woods, Williams, Bates, Evans, Gilman, Franks (Reynolds 85). Unused sub: Gold.

WINDSOR & ETON (0)1 *(Gilman 79)* **MERTHYR TYDFIL** (0)0 4-11-91. Att: 736
Windsor: As 1st match, but no subs used. *Merthyr:* As 1st match, but Williams unused & Hutchison on for Webley (60 mins).

WORCESTER CITY (0)1 *(Tomlinson 53)* **MARLOW** (0)2 *(Regan 76,Harman 88)* Att: 928
Worcester: Dudley, Sullivan, Heywood, Lyttle (Bridge 81), Bywater, Baverstock, Jones, Wright (Tomlinson 45), Kearns, Robinson, Tester. *Marlow:* Ellis, Hannigan, Mikurenda (Jack 45), Kevin Stone, Hubbick, Harman, Lay, Regan, Watkins, George, Martin Stone (West 74).

TONBRIDGE (1)1 *(Baber 41)* **YEOVIL TOWN** (2)2 *(Spencer 3,Shail 11)* Att: 1463
T'bridge: Thompson, Wallace, Bower, Hume, Finch, Baber, Graham, Clarke, Thomson, Mawson, Collins. Unused subs: Tucker, Norris. *Yeovil:* Fry, Harrower, Batty, Shail (Dixon 22), Rutter, Cooper, McDermott, Carroll, Wilson, Spencer, Conning. Unused sub: Mark Boulton.

HAYES (0)1 *(Stephen 81)* **DORCHESTER TOWN** (0)0 Att: 277
Hayes: O'Reilly, Kelly, Keen, Myers, Leather, Cox, Clarke, Benning, Seabrook, Stephen, Dixon (Day 70). Unused sub: Hayward. *D'hester:* Judd, Morrell, White, Coates, Thorpe (Sayers 85), Powell, Green, Diaz, Townsend, Masters, Manson. Unused sub: Borthwick.

SALISBURY (0)1 *(Gomersall 65)* **FARNBORO.** (3)7 *(Doherty 1,Read 31 45 64 82,Horton 48 89)* Att: 808
S'bury: Coombe, Loveridge, Mulkern, Pearson, Cranmer, Green, Woods (Gomersall 45), Sanders, Chalk, Smith, Payne (Phillips 76). *F'boro:* Power, Stemp, Baker, Broome, Bye, Wigmore, Rogers (Hanchard 61), Doherty, Holmes, Read, Horton. Unused sub: Lovell.

HORSHAM 0 CRAWLEY TOWN 0 Att: 2208
Horsham: Green, Wren, Chaplin, Cooke, Breach, Clark, Stepney, Dunk, Gunn, Somers, Walters. Unused subs: Forrest, Bailey. *Crawley:* Winterton, Davis, Powell, Wickens, Vessey, Hulme, Venables (Oakes 80), Webber, Cooper, Whitington, Gallagher. Unused sub: Vansittart.

CRAWLEY TOWN (2)3 *(Gallagher 2,Cant 36,Hulme 90)* **HORSHAM** (0)0 29-10-91. Att: 3427
Crawley: Winterton, Webber, Powell, Wickens, Vessey, Cant, Venables, Hulme, Cooper, Whitington, Gallagher. Unused subs: Davis, Oakes. *H'ham:* As 1st match, Forrest replaced Gunn (57 mins), Bailey replaced Walters (75).

SLOUGH TOWN (1)2 *(Davidson 34(OG),Mallinson 67)* **KINGSTONIAN** (0)1 *(Vines 65)* Att: 990
Slough: Bunting, Stacey, Puckrose, Hill, Anderson, Turkington (Dell 45), Fielder, McKinnon, Whitby, Thompson, Mallinson. Unused sub: Joseph. *K'nian:* Blake, Pearson, Davidson, Eriemo, Hick, Kempton (Galliers 70), Harlow, Gbogidi, Pearce, Barrowcliffe, Smart (Vines 55).

WEYMOUTH (1)1 *(Cook 16)* **SUTTON UNITED** (0)1 *(Davidson 52)* Att: 1576
W'mouth: Weaver, Fullbrook, Gibson, Bourne, Kidd, Pugh, Diaz, Shaw, Clifford (Flint 74), Cook, Browne. Unused sub: King. *Sutton:* McCann, Dawson, Davidson, Golley, Costello, Hemsley, Rogers, Evans, Brown (Smith 75), Massey, Griffiths. Unused sub: Priddle.

SUTTON UNITED (1)3 *(Massey 40(p),Griffiths 68, Golley 78)* **WEYMOUTH** (0)0 29-10-91. Att: 1037
Sutton: As 1st match, but subs unused. *W'mouth:* Weaver, Bourne (Ford 61), Gibson, Flint, Kidd, Pugh, Diaz, Shaw, Clifford, Cook, Browne. Unused sub: King.

Tonbridge's Ian Mawson outpaces Yeovil's Paul Batty in front of a record gate at Longmead. Photo - Mike Floate.

Jon Graham and Phil Brown celebrate the goals that sent Kettering to a shock win at Wycombe. Photo - Eric Marsh.

Horsham 'keeper Duncan Green bravely denies Crawley's Craig Wittington at Queen Street. Photo - Roger Turner.

FIRST ROUND PROPER

27 Ties Matches Played: 37 (Matches involving Non-League clubs)
Home wins: 15 **Draws:** 11 **Away wins:** 11
Best Attendance: 11,082 - W.B.A. v Marlow
Total Attendance: 194,726 **Average Attendance:** 5,263
Largest Home Win: 7-0; W.B.A. v Marlow, Peterborough v Harlow Town
Best Away Win: 0-3; Runcorn v Tranmere, Emley v Bolton
Result of the Round: Fulham 0, Hayes 2

Saturday 16th November 1991

ALDERSHOT (0)0 **ENFIELD** (0) 1 (Brush 70)   Att: 2384
Enfield: McCutcheon, N Keen (Smart 70), Mason, M Keen, Pearce, Brush, Mosely, Kane, Manderson, Robinson (Vance 85),Westley.

ATHERSTONE UNITED 0 **HEREFORD UNITED** 0   Att: 2589
Atherstone: Starkey, Everitt, Upton, Randle, Jackson, Redgate, Olner, Green, Tolley, I Brain, Williams. Unused sub: Greene,

HEREFORD UNITED (1)3 (Lowndes 31, Brain 72 84) **ATHERSTONE UTD** (0)0   26-11-91. Att: 3479
Atherstone: As first game. Wilson replaced Brain (46 mins) and Shilton replaced Williams (71).

BARNET (2)5 (Bull 22, Naylor 36, Carter 63, Evans 68, Showler 81) **TIVERTON** (0)0   Att: 3964
Tiverton: Nott, Stuart, Greening, Rogers (Annunziata 45), Short, Steele, Scott, Smith, Jones (Charlesworth 76), Down, Saunders

A.F.C. BOURNEMOUTH (0)3 (Bond 62, Mundee 65 80) **BROMSGROVE** (1)1 (O'Meara 17)   Att: 4301
Bromsgrove: Cooksey, Skelding, Brighton, Richardson, O'Meara, O'Connor, Daly, Stott, Hanks (Cunningham 67), Crisp, Cooper.

BRIDLINGTON TOWN (0)1 (Stevenson 67) **YORK CITY** (0)2 (Blackstone 47 87)   Att: 1700
Bridlington: Ingham, Brentano, Smith, Noteman, Warburton, Stevenson, Sellers, Harvey, Norbury, Radford, Hopkinson. Unused subs: Brown, Burdett.

CHESTER CITY (1)1 (Barrow 24) **GUISELEY** (0)0   Att: 1851
Guiseley: Maxted, Atkinson, Hogarth, Tetley, Adams, McKenzie (Wilkinson 84), A Roberts, Colville (Noteman 58), Elliott, Waites, W Roberts.

COLCHESTER UNITED 0 **EXETER CITY** 0   Att: 4965
Colchester: Barratt, Donald, J Cook, Kinsella, English, Elliott, Collins, Bennett, McDonough, McGavin, Smith (Grainger 73). Unused sub: Restarick.

EXETER CITY 0 **COLCHESTER UNITED** 0 (Exeter won 4-2 on penalties)   27-11-91. Att: 4066
Colchester: Barratt, Donald, J Cook, Kinsella, English, Goodwin (Grainger 64), Collins, Bennett (Restarick 108), McDonough, McGavin, Smith.

CRAWLEY (2)4 (Cant 43, Hulme 45, Wittington 49 86) **NORTHAMPTON** (2)2 (Chard 18, Adcock 45)
Crawley: Winterton, Webber, Powell, Wickens, Vessey, Cant, Hulme, Towner, Venables, Whittington, Gallagher. Unused subs: Davis, Cooper.   Att: 3370

EMLEY (0)0 **BOLTON W.** (1)3 (Reeves 39 56, Philliskirk 78) At Huddersfield.   17-11-91. Att: 9035
Emley: Dennis, Bramald, Smith, Wright, Codd, Farrar, Burrows, Broadbent (Wilson 85), Duke, Cooper, Joyce (Green 80).

FULHAM (0)0 **HAYES** (0)2 (Day 64, Stephen 86)   15-11-91. Att: 6404
Hayes: O'Reilly, Kelly, Keen, Hayward, Leather, Cox, Day, Marshall, Seabrook (Clarke 80), Stephen, Dixon (Pope 75).

GRETNA 0 **ROCHDALE** 0   Att: 2307
Gretna: Leeming, Mulholland, McCartney, J Wilson, O'Hgan, Goodrick, Armstrong, Carruthers, Pickford, Nelson, Moat. Unused subs: I Wilson, Fell

ROCHDALE (3)3 (Jones 15, Flounders 44, Milner 23) **GRETNA** (0)1 (Carruthers 83)   27-11-91. Att: 4300
Gretna: Exactly as 1st match.

HALESOWEN (2)2 (Flynn 18, Hazlewood 38) **FARNBOROUGH** (2)2 (Hobson 6, Broome 44)   Att: 1866
Halesowen: Rowe, Whittingham, Edwards, Smith, Vowles, Bradley (Goodall 87), Hazlewood, Flynn, Bennett, Shilvock, Harrison. Unused sub: Attwood. *F'boro:* Power, Stemp, Baker, Broome, Bye, Wigmore, Holmes, Doherty (Horton 63), Hobson, Read, Rogers (Fleming 72).

FARNBOROUGH (2)4 (Read 32 36 84, Coombes 88(p)) **HALESOWEN TOWN** (0)0   26-11-91. Att: 1673
F'boro: Power, Stemp, Baker, Broome, Fleming, Wigmore, Rogers, Hobson (Holmes 80), Coombs, Read (Doherty 80), Horton. *H'owen:* As 1st match. Attwood replaced Edwards (65 mins), Laker replaced Harrison (80).

HUDDERSFIELD (3)7 (O'Regan 17, Donovan 23 87, Stapleton 40, Roberts 53 61, Onuora 59)
LINCOLN UTD (0)0   Att: 6763
Lincoln: Waby, North, Dye, Crombie, P Ward, Park (Hinchcliffe 40), P Brown, Barker, Goddard, W Ward (S Brown 74), Carter.

KETTERING TOWN (0)1 (Christie 71) **WYCOMBE WANDERERS** (0)1 (Carroll 63)   Att: 3371
K'ring: Shoemake, Huxford, Jones, Nicol, Price, Slack, Graham, Brown, Christie, Bancroft (Cotton 45), Hill. Unused sub: Appleby. *Wycombe:* Hyde, Cousins, Stapleton, Crossley, Creaser, Smith, Hutchinson, Deakin, Carroll, Scott, Guppy. Unused subs: Nuttell, West.

WYCOMBE WANDERERS (0)0 **KETTERING TOWN** (0)2 (Brown 69, Graham 83)   27-11-91. Att: 5299
Wycombe: Hyde, Cousins, Stapleton, Crossley, Creaser, Smith (Hutchinson 80), Carroll, Deakin, West, Scott, Guppy. Unused sub: Gooden. *K'ring:* As 1st game - subs unused.

KIDDERMINSTER HARRIERS (0)0 **AYLESBURY UNITED** (0)1 (Davies 87)   Att: 1773
K'minster: Green, Benton, McGrath, Weir, Barnett, Wolsey, Joseph, Howell (Davies 85), Whitehouse, Lilwall, Humphreys. Unused sub: Carroll. *Aylesbury:* Garner, Day, Ashby, Benning, Hutter, Wright, Mason, Davies, Hercules, Collins, Robinson. Unused subs: Cassidy, Williams.

Lincoln United players applaud their fans at the end of their memorable run. Photo - Barry Lockwood.

Welling's Joe Francis crosses whilst Terry Robbins makes a run in the tie at Brisbane Road. Photo - Mike Floate.

Paul Brush (centre) beats John Granville to score Enfield's winner at Aldershot. Photo - Eric Marsh.

LEYTON ORIENT (0)2 *(Howard 78, Cooper 81)* **WELLING UNITED** (1)1 *(Berry 9)* Att: 4858
Welling: Barron, Hone, Clemence, Browne, Ransom, Berry, White, Francis, Abbott, Robbins, Reynolds. Unused subs: Robinson, Glover.

MAIDSTONE UNITED (1)1 *(Thompson 9)* **SUTTON UNITED** (0)0 Att: 2008
Sutton: McCann, Dawson, Gates (Dack 82), Golley, Priddle, Helmsley, Rogers, Beeks, Smith, Griffiths (Feltham 74), Scott.

MORECAMBE (0)0 **HULL CITY** (1)1 *(Wilcox 38)* Att: 3210
M'cambe: Allison, Tomlinson, Armstrong, Parillon, Miller, Lodge, Brown, Dullagan (Holden 70), Coleman, John McMahon (Gaffney 83), Cain.

PETERBOROUGH U. (6)7 *(Cooper 6 18, Riley 19, Sterling 23, Halsall 27, Charlery 39, Culpin 87)*
HARLOW TOWN (0)0 Att: 4341
Harlow: Mallett, Armstrong, Burns, Gleeson, Durant, Emmanuel, St Hilaire (Porter 30), Battram, McLean, Margerrison (Cottington 68), Head.

RUNCORN (0)0 **TRANMERE ROVERS** (1)3 *(Irons 2, Aldridge 46 66)* At Tranmere Att: 6563
Runcorn: Pallidino, Byrne, Mullen, Carroll, Hill, Redman (Imrie 74), Brabin, Harold, Shaughnessy, Saunders, Withers (Hawtin 77).

SLOUGH (1)3 *(Pluckrose 19, Fielder 89, McKinnon 90)* **READING** (0)3 *(Williams 70, Gooding 80, Taylor 85)*
Slough: Bunting, Stacey, Pluckrose, Knight, Anderson, Donellan, Fielder, McKinnon, Thompson, Mallinson.
Unused subs: Dell, Whitby. Att: 3990

READING (2)2 *(Williams 6, Lovell 33)* **SLOUGH TOWN** (0)1 *(Joseph 87)* Att: 6363
Slough: Bunting, Whitby, Pluckrose, Hill, Anderson, Donellan (Stanley 51), Fielder, Dell, Joseph, Thompson, Mallinson. Unused sub: Knight.

STOKE CITY 0 **TELFORD UNITED** 0 Att: 9984
Telford: Acton, Humphreys, Brindley, Dyson, Nelson, Whittington, Myers, Grainger, Benbow, Langford, Parrish. Unused subs: Clarke, Cook.

TELFORD UNITED (1)2 *(Benbow 29 83)* **STOKE CITY** (0)1 *(Beeston 81)* 26-11-91. Att: 4082
Telford: Exactly as 1st match.

WEST BROM. (3)6 *(Strodder 22, Goodman 31, Shakespeare 44 56, McNally 62, Robson 63)*
MARLOW (0)0 Att: 11082
Marlow: Ellis, Franks, Poole (George 45), Stone (Hooper 63), Hubbick, West, Lay, Regan, Watkins, Hannigan, Caesar.

WINDSOR & ETON (1)1 *(Gilman 27)* **WOKING** (0)1 *(Baron 57) (Aban. after 69 mins - fog)* Att: 2640
Windsor: Mitchell, Parkins, Walters, White, Richards, Woods, Williams, Bates, Evans, Gilman, Franks. Unused subs: Connor, Reynolds. *Woking:* Batty, Mitchell, Cowler, Pratt, Baron, Wye S, Brown, Biggins, Milton, Friel, Wye L. Unused subs: Parr, White.

WINDSOR (2)2 *(Gilman 8 40)* **WOKING** (1)4 *(Milton 30, Mitchell 67, Walters 70(OG), Friel 80)*
Windsor: Exactly as 1st match. *Woking:* Batty, Mitchell, Cowler, Pratt, Baron, Wye S, Brown, Biggins, Milton, Friel, Collier. Unused subs: Parr, Mulvaney. 26-11-91. Att: 2534

WITTON ALBION (1)1 *(Thomas 31)* **HALIFAX TOWN** (0)1 *(Hildersley 88)* Att: 2002
Witton: Zelem, Stewart, Coathup, McNeilis, Jim Connor, Anderson, Thomas, Hooton, Lutkevitch (Dyson 79), Grimshaw, Joe Connor. Unused sub: Alford.

HALIFAX (0)1 *(Richardson 115)* **WITTON ALBION** (0)2 *(Thomas 96, Grimshaw 112)* 27-11-91. Att: 2172
Witton: Zelem, Coathup, Hooton, McNeilis, Jim Connor, Anderson (Hill 75), Thomas, Cuddy, Lutkevitch (Alford 110), Grimshaw, Joe Connor.

WREXHAM (1)5 *(Connolly 8, Watkin 71 77 86, Thomas 90)* **WINSFORD** (1)2 *(Esdaile 14, Blackwood 76)*
Winsford: Mayfield, Lloyd, Whitney, Edey, Taylor (Neatis 85), Esdaile, Grant (Hall 72), Thomas, Cameron, Blackwood, Sheriden. Att: 2933

YEOVIL TOWN (0)1 *(Wilson 59)* **WALSALL** (0)1 *(Tolson 79)* Att: 4635
Yeovil: Hervin, Harrower, Rowbotham, Shail, Rutter (Cooper 61), Batty, McDermott, Wallace, Wilson, Spencer, Conning. Unused sub: Pritchard.

WALSALL (0)0 **YEOVIL TOWN** (0)1 *(Cooper 95)* Att: 3869
Yeovil: Hervin, Harrower, Batty, Shail, Rutter, McDermott, Carrol (Cooper 44), Wallace, Wilson, Spencer, Conning. Unused sub: Boulton.

Yeovil striker Paul Wilson gives Walsall keeper Alan McKnight a torrid debut. Photo: Paul Dennis.

Paul Wood nets a penalty to put AFC Bournemouth ahead after they had trailed to Bromsgrove. Photo - Gavin Ellis.

Crawley boss Brian Sparrow with scorers Cliff Cant and Tim Hulme after the Northampton win. Photo - Roger Turner.

Hayes' Colin Day puts this chance wide of the Fulham post, but the visitors went on to win. Photo - Dave West.

SECOND ROUND PROPER

8 Ties **Matches Played:** 9 (Matches involving Non-League clubs)
Home wins: 4 **Draws:** 1 **Away wins:** 4
Best Attendance: 6,736 - Preston North End v Witton Albion
Total Attendance: 35,416 **Average Attendance:** 3,935
Largest Home Win: Woking 3, Yeovil Town 0
Best Away Win: Enfield 1, Barnet 4
Result of the Round: Farnborough Town 4, Torquay United 3

Saturday 7th December 1991

AYLESBURY U. (1)2 *(Hercules 24 61)* **HEREFORD** (2)3 *(Fry 7, Heritage 10, Tomlinson 63(OG))* Att: 3200
Aylesbury: Garner, Tomlinson, Ashby, Benning, Hutter, Wright (Cassidy 89), Mason, Davies, Hercules, Collins, Robinson. Unused sub: Williams.

ENFIELD (0)1 *(Robinson 90)* **BARNET** (1)4 *(Bull 36(p), Carter 60 67 75)* Att: 5120
Enfield: McCutcheon, Smart, Mason, Keen, Pearce (Manderson 64), Brush, Moseley, Kane, Warmington, Robinson, Westley.

HAYES (0)0 **CRAWLEY TOWN** (1)2 *(Hulme 32 86)* Att: 4203
Hayes: O'Reilly, Kelly, Keen, Hayward, Leather, Cocks, Day, Marshall, Seabrook, Pope (Clarke 58), Stephen. Unused sub: Denning.
Crawley: Winterton, Webber, Powell, Wickens, Veysey, Cant, Towner (Davies 79), Hulme, Venables, Whittington, Gallagher. Unused sub: Cooper.

MAIDSTONE UNITED (1)1 *(Henry 14)* **KETTERING TOWN** (1)2 *(Brown 44, Oxbrow 58(OG))* Att: 2750
Kettering: Bastock, Huxford, Jones, Nicol, Price, Slack, Graham, Brown, Christie, Bancroft, Hill. Unused subs: Keast, Cotton.

PRESTON (3)5 *(Shaw 30, Swann 31, Senior 32, Flynn 59, Greenwood 88)* **WITTON ALBION** (0)1 *(Thomas 63)*
Witton: Mason, Coathup (Stewart 52), Hooton, McNeilis, Jim Connor, Anderson, Thomas, Cuddy (McLuskie 70), Lutkevitch, Grimshaw, Joe Connor. Att: 6736

TORQUAY UNITED (0)1 *(Loram 87)* **FARNBOROUGH TOWN** (1)1 *(Read 30)* Att: 2725
Farnborough: Power, Stemp, Baker, Broome, Bye, Wigmore, Rogers, Fleming, Coney, Read, Horton. Unused subs: Holmes, Coombs.

FARNBOROUGH TOWN (2)4 *(Coney 35, Read 41, Dohery 65, Broome 68)*
TORQUAY UNITED (0)3 *(M Holmes 75, Loram 77, Colcombe 85)* Att: 2285
Farnborough: Power, Stemp, Baker, Broome, Bye, Wigmore, Doherty, Holmes, Coney, Read, Horton (Fleming 89). Unused sub: Coombs.

WOKING (1)3 *(Friel 30 72 81)* **YEOVIL TOWN** (0)0 Att: 4500
Woking: L Batty, Mitchell, Cowler, Pratt, Baron, S Wye, Brown, Parr, Milton, Friel, Collier. Unused sub: L Wye, Mulvaney.
Yeovil: Hervin, Harrower, P Batty, Shail, Rutter, Carroll (Henderson 58), McDermott, Wallace, Wilson, Spencer, Conning (Pritchard 75).

WREXHAM (0)1 *(Watkin)* **TELFORD UNITED** (0)0 Att: 3897
Telford: Acton, Humphreys, Brindley, Dyson, Nelson, Whittington, Myers, Grainger, Benbow, Langford, Parrish. Unused subs: Clarke, Cook.

Tony Vessey of Crawley Town holds off Steve Pope of Hayes during the clash of the First Round giantkillers. Photo - Dennis Nicholson.

Cliff Hercules lobs home Aylesbury's first goal in their tie against Hereford United. Photo - Dave West.

Mick Holmes scores for Torquay, but at this stage Farnborough were already four ahead. Photo - Eric Marsh.

Trevor Slack fires over a cross as Kettering record an excellent win at 4th Division Maidstone. Photo - Mike Floate.

THIRD ROUND PROPER

4 Ties **Matches Played:** 6   (Matches involving Non-League clubs)
Home wins: 4 **Draws:** 2 **Away wins:** 0
Best Attendance: 23,869 - West Ham United v Farnborough Town
Total Attendance: 92,349   **Average Attendance:** 15,391
Largest Home Win: Brighton & Hove Albion 5, Crawley Town 0
Best Away Win: N/A
Result of the Round: Farnborough Town 1, West Ham United 1

Saturday 4th January 1991

BLACKBURN R. (1)**4** *(Speedie 33,Newell 59 70,Cowans 64)* **KETTERING T.** (0)1 *(Brown 77)*   Att: 13821
Kettering: Bastock, Huxford (Waller 85), Jones, Nicol, Price, Slack, Keast, Brown, Christie, Bancroft (Graham 60), Hill.

BRIGHTON & H.A. (3)5 *(Chapman 39 59(p),Gall 24, Walker 30, Meade 84)* **CRAWLEY T.** (0)0 Att: 18031
Crawley: Winterton, Webber, Powell, Wickens, Veysey, Venables, Cant, Hulme, Searle, Whittington (Towner 55), Gallagher (Davis 75).

FARNBOROUGH TOWN (0)1 *(Coney 82(p))* **WEST HAM UTD** (0)1 *(Dicks 67)* *(at West Ham)* Att: 23449
Farnborough: Power, Stemp, Baker (Horton 68), Broome, Bye, Wigmore, Doherty (Rogers 76), Holmes, Coney, Read, Fleming.

WEST HAM UNITED (0)1 *(Morley 88)* **FARNBOROUGH TOWN** (0)0   14-1-92. Att: 23869
Farnborough: Power, Stemp, Baker (Rogers 80), Broome, Bye, Wigmore, Doherty, Holmes, Coney, Read, Fleming. Unused sub: Horton.

WOKING 0 HEREFORD UNITED 0   Att: 4500
Woking: Batty, Mitchell, Cowler, Pratt, Baron, S Wye, Brown, Biggins, Milton, Friel, Collier. Unused subs: L Wye, Parr.

HEREFORD UNITED (0)2 *(Narbett 42,Brain 101)* **WOKING** (0)1 *(Pratt 82)*   14-2-91. Att: 8679
Woking: Batty, Mitchell, Cowler, Pratt, Baron, S Wye, Brown (Parr 117), Biggins, Milton, Friel, Collier (L Wye 108).

Andy Bye of Farnborough Town puts West Ham 'keeper Ludo Miklosko under early pressure during the sensational Third Round replay at Upton Park. Photo - Eric Marsh.

Crawley's Grant Gallagher is pursued by Brighton's John Crumlin in the big Sussex derby. Photo - Dave West.

Hereford United become the third League club to visit Woking in the FA Cup. Photo - Eric Marsh.

Mick Doherty hits a shot for Farnborough, with Tony Gale close by, in the Third Round replay. Photo - Francis Short.

F.A CHALLENGE TROPHY

REVIEW 1991-92

F.A. CHALLENGE TROPHY

COLCHESTER EMULATE WEALDSTONE

In winning the Vauxhall F.A. Trophy at Wembley, just eight days after they had sealed the G.M.V. Conference title, Colchester United became only the second club to complete the 'Non-League Double'. Wealdstone, in 1985, were previously the only side to have performed the feat. The U's were blessed with the luck that all cup winners require; in the First Round they found themselves two down after only ten minutes at home to **Kingstonian** and did not equalise until the last minute. They then struggled before edging out **Merthyr** in a replay. However, after that fortune played a backseat role as Colchester swept past **Morecambe, Telford** and **Macclesfield** before avenging their 1991 Quarter-Final disappointment by beating **Witton Albion** in the Final.

The 1991-92 Trophy broke new ground in a number of respects. Firstly, it received sponsorship thus becoming the first F.A. competition to benefit from outside financial backing. On Monday 2nd December, prior to the First Round Proper, Lancaster Gate announced that Vauxhall would be providing a pool of £30,000 to be distributed amongst clubs competing in the 'Vauxhall F.A. Challenge Trophy'. Awards were graded from £6,000 for the winners to £200 for Second Round losers. Secondly, the Final was staged on a Sunday thus allowing far more neutrals than usual to attend. And finally, the Final was televised for the first time, BSkyB doing the honours with an evening highlights programme.

The qualifying rounds in 1991 produced their usual quota of upsets. At the first hurdle **Willenhall Town** were perhaps the star performers. The club had been relegated to the West Midlands League, but they amazingly ousted a **Colwyn Bay** side destined to walk away with the H.F.S. Division One crown. **Bridgend Town** and **Rhyl** however restored Welsh pride with surprise victories over **Poole Town** and **Halesowen Town** respectively. **Sutton Coldfield** were another Midland outfit to raise the eyebrows in qualifying. They beat F.A. Cup heroes **Hayes** and the powerful **Cambridge City** side before ultimately bowing out to **Farnborough** in a tie that was sandwiched between the latter's two meetings with West Ham.

Northern League clubs enjoyed one of their better seasons in recent years. Their star side were **Northallerton Town** who eliminated four H.F.S. Loans League sides (including three from the Premier Division) before eventually succumbing at **Telford** in the Second Round Proper. **Blyth Spartans** and **Billingham Synthonia** also enjoyed memorable results against H.F.S. Premier Division opposition.

Whilst the Trophy ended up at Layer Road, most observers will probably remember the 1991-92 competition as being **Marine**'s year. The unglamorous but immensely popular Merseysiders kicked off in the First Qualifying Round and took three matches to see off the challenge of **Nuneaton Borough**. Subsequent wins at **Goole Town** and **Horwich R.M.I.** led them to a First Round tie at **Stafford Rangers**, and a first Conference scalp. After brushing aside **Wivenhoe Town**, Roly Howard's side then pulled off major shocks against **Kettering Town** (who lose annually to 'minor' sides), and in-form **Redbridge Forest**. In the Semi Final Marine did come back from two down at **Witton Albion**, but were eventually pipped in the second match, their twelfth of the competition.

Another stark feature of the 1991-92 Trophy was its almost total domination by Conference sides. By the time we got to the last sixteen only two leagues were represented; the H.F.S. Loans League with three sides, and the omnipotent G.M.V.C. with the other thirteen. A round later Marine were the only Non-Conference survivors. Holders **Wycombe Wanderers** started their defence with an uninspiring home win over **Salisbury** before coming head-to-head with **Woking** in a veritable clash of the giants at Adams Park. A crowd of nearly 6,000 witnessed Wanderers edge through with a goal from new signing Kim Casey, one of the most celebrated names in the Non-League game. Wycombe then beat **Bath City** after a replay before entertaining, in a tense Quarter Final, **Witton Albion**, the side who had reached the last four as an H.F.S. side twelve months earlier. On the day the Cheshire club proved themselves to have more ambition than their hosts, whose prime concern was the Conference title race. Witton therefore reached a second consecutive Semi Final, and this time made it to Wembley.

As you will read in the report of the match further on in this section, the Final failed to live up to expectation, a pity when you consider that the fanatical support enjoyed by the Essex side, and the Sabbath scheduling, resulted in a large gate. Colchester went two up early in the match through Masters (the first American to appear in a Trophy Final) and Kinsella. Witton fought back through Lutkevitch, but United's prolific striker McGavin sealed victory. It was ironic that Colchester had gone right through their history without a major honour only to clinch two in the last week of 1991-92. Staying on the statistical theme, they also became the first side relegated from the League (out-voted Barrow aside) to succeed in the Trophy.

James Wright

FIRST QUALIFYING ROUND

50 Ties. Matches Played: 61
Home wins: 27 Draws: 12 Away wins: 22 (1 walkover)
Best Attendance: 928 - Halesowen Town v Rhyl
Total Attendance: 17,572 **Average Attendance:** 208
Largest Home Win: Taunton Town 6, Maesteg Park 2
Best Away Win: Alnwick Town 0, Southport 5
Result of the Round: Willenhall Town 3, Colwyn Bay 1

Saturday 21st September 1991   Res Att

Whitby Town v Newcastle BS.   2-1 200
Harland 23,Grady 80   Storey 17

Ferryhill A. v Whitley B.   0-2 124
Chandler 77,Johnson 87

Alnwick Town v Southport   0-5 108
*Camerelli 5,Baines 49,Mooney 54,
Livens 76,Blackhurst 84*

Peterlee Newtown v Murton   0-2   65
Evans 26 39

Workington v Northallerton T.   2-2 131
Caton 16(p) 63(p)   Crane 20,Ball 88

N'allerton v Workington *(24-9-91)*   4-0 163
Heward 21,Robson 34,Woods 47 70

Consett v Shildon   0-3 111
Hill 20,Anderson 23,Cudlip 87

Brandon Utd v Spennymoor Utd 1-1 178
Palmer 65   Corkain 62(p)

Spennymoor v Brandon *(24-9-91)*   1-0 292
Blackburn 39

Whickham v North Shields   1-2 220
Capewell 75   Pyle 81 88

Willenhall Town v Colwyn Bay   3-1 117
*Harrison 42,Blake 74,   Williscroft 12
Edwards 85*

Rhyl v Halesowen Town   1-1 385
Davies 75   Harrison 64

Halesowen Town v Rhyl *(24-9-91)* 1-2 928
Harrison 3   Davies 55,Roberts 70

Moor Green v Radcliffe B.   5-2 258
*Russell 20, Own Goal 40,Busst 46, Doody 63,
Grocutt 60,Rowley 78   Coyne 90*

Goole Town v Warrington Town   2-1 211
Collier 40,Wood 46   Scorer undisclosed

Alvechurch v Gainsboro' Trin.   0-1 116
Kayle 50

Winsford United v Newtown   3-0 246
Blackwood (2),Edey

Dudley Town v Redditch United 5-3 154
*Baker 4 40 81,   Molloy 23, L Joinson 61,
Corniffe 8 76   Campbell 68*

Bromsgrove Rvrs v Bedworth Utd 1-1 479
Stott 85   Wilkins 42

Bedworth v Bromsgrove *(24-9-91)* 1-2 335
Taylor 66(p)   Stott 66,Crisp 82

Nuneaton Borough v Marine   0-0 675

Marine v Nuneaton B. *(24-9-91)*   2-2 237
King 36,Maddock 80   Cottrill 55,Twigger 58

Nuneaton B. v Marine *(30-9-91)*   0-1 730
Maddock 63

Eastwood T. v Caernarfon Town 5-1 152
*Goodwin 25,Copeland 30(p),   Barnett 4
Hall 41 55,Osborne 75*

Worksop Town v Matlock Town   1-1 149
Mainwaring 29   Chambers 60

(* Denotes extra time played)

Matlock v Worksop *(24-9-91)*   3-3 537
*Tilly 50 73,   Clark 19,Mainwaring 35,
Sheppard 90   Haigh 37*

Matlock v Worksop *(30-9-91)*   2-0 614
Tilly 27,Hoyland 35

Grantham Town v Buxton   0-2 879
Dove 20,Daughry 80

Congleton T. v Atherstone Utd   0-3 158
Ward 22 26,Shilton 86

Mossley v Alfreton Town   2-3 259
*Bowler 10,   McCarthy 61,
Hardman 53   Millington 62,Pell 75*

Corby Town v Leyton-Wingate   1-3 254
Genovese 33   Newman 14,OG 25,Stanton 70

Stevenage Boro. v Wembley   2-3 333
*Marshall 15,Hardy 78   Graham 26,Pegg 49,
                                 Lawrence 57*

Chelmsford City v St Albans C.   0-1 542
Wilkinson 78

Vauxhall Motors *(w'drew)* Staines *W/O*

Barking v Rushden Town   4-2 125
*Hoy 31 48,Portway 46,   Kirkup 13,
Murphy 89   Belfon 40*

Hitchin Town v Grays Athletic   2-1 325
Quarman 43,Pearson 61   Whittingham 45

Chalfont St P. v Stourbridge   3-2   80
*Bashir 30,Bushay 65,   Wright 80,
Hippolyte 70   Cartwright 85*

Boreham Wood v Aveley   4-1   90
Anderson 15 52,Bourne 40,Potter 73   Moyce 11

Hayes v Baldock Town   3-1 169
Stephens 36,Keen 61,Dixon 73   Roberts 66

Chesham United v Tamworth   1-0 650
Dawber 11

Yeading v Fareham Town   2-1 122
Dickers 61 78   Maddock 82

Uxbridge v Tooting & Mitcham U.   1-2   96
Toms 79   Loughlin 74,Vassell 87

Molesey v Marlow   2-3   82
*Mann 75,Thomas 82   Stone 23,
                         Watkins 35,Caesan 67*

Andover v Bashley   1-2 207
Odey 48(p)   Hughes 32,Skivington 82

Bromley v Basingstoke Town   3-0 389
McMenemy 3 75,Brown 86

Gosport Borough v Croydon   4-1 130
*Mottashed 18,Gosling 52,   Franklin 28
Goater 82,Pinder 84*

Maidenhead Utd v Canterbury C.   4-0 198
Bale 17,Muir 30,Hall 33,Holder 35

Erith & Bel. v Walton Hersham   3-3 155
*Booth 15,Docker 55,   Styles 27
Daniels 81   Holman 34 74*

Walton v Erith & B. *(24-9-91)*   2-1 172
Wingfield 50,Styles 57   Young 71

83

	Res	Att

Margate v Abingdon Town   1-1   318
Buglione 90   *Bradbury 73*

Abingdon v Margate *(24-9-91)*   0-1   437
       Hales 32

Dorking v Bognor Regis Town   2-1   198
Robson 10,Hanlan 55   *Torpey 80*

Waterlooville v Crawley Town   3-2   197
Hore 30 53 87   *Hulme 47 53*

Trowbridge T. v Dorchester Town 1-1   608
Webb 77   *Flint 90*

Dorchester v T'bridge *(24-9-91)*   3-2   735
Diaz 17 70,Manson 84   *Iddles 23,Abbley 64*

Ton Pentre v Barry Town   2-3   391
Armstrong 48,Haig 69 Mullen 38 42,Williams 45

(* Denotes extra time played)

Taunton Town v Maesteg Park   6-2   245
Souness 18 23 82 89,   *Webber 26,*
Richards 21,Hunt 80   *Williams 51*

Bideford v Newport A.F.C.   0-1   350
      Green 88

Bridgend Town v Poole Town   3-1   60
Jones 34,Famer 60,Brown 63   *Platt 79*

Cwmbran v Salisbury *(at Salisbury)*   0-1   206
      Smith 82(p)

Weston-super-Mare v Saltash Utd   2-2   270
Boulton 72,Adams 88   Kenealy 9,Daly 65

Saltash v Weston-s-M. *(24-9-91)*   5-3*   227
Fallon 15 100,Norton 87,   *Lazenby 46 74,*
Pethick 80 119   *Priest 73*

Croydon's Micky Page jumps on the line but cannot Nigel Mottashed's header going in for Gosport's opening goal. Photo - Dave West.

Substitute Mark Skivington (on the line) claims Bashley's winner away to Andover. Photo - Dennis Nicholson.

SECOND QUALIFYING ROUND

32 Ties. Matches Played: 37
Home wins: 16 **Draws:** 5 **Away wins:** 16
Best Attendance: 648 - Bromsgrove Rovers v Hednesford Town
Total Attendance: 8,714 **Average Attendance:** 236
Largest Home Win: Whitby Town 5, Murton 1
Best Away Win: Alfreton Town 0, Atherstone United 3
Result of the Round: Whitley Bay 2, Northallerton Town 3

Saturday 19th October 1991   Res Att   **(* Denotes extra time played)**

Southport v North Shields   4-1 315
Fuller 53,Menamy 57,   Howie 9
Livens 60,Davey 75

Accrington Stan. v Shildon   5-2 416
Owen 11,McDonald 52,   Adams 30,
Grimshaw 61 71 84   Glenc 78

Northallerton v Whitley Bay   0-0 112

Whitley B. v N'allerton *(22-10-91)* 2-3* 420
Johnson 25,   Woods 55,Ball 88,
Chandler 72   Masden 110

Whitby Town v Murton   5-1 140
Robinson 7 53,Own Goal 75,   Laws 10
Pitman 84,Grady 89

Spennymoor U. v Easington C. 1-2 122
Pidgeon 71   Skirving 58,Martin 66

Bromsgrove R. v Hednesford T. 1-0 648
Daly 28

Goole Town v Marine   1-3 251
Kelly 86(p)   Haw 6,Gautrey 42,Grant 85

Alfreton T. v Atherstone Utd   0-3 197
Olner 26 88,Green 28

Dudley Town v Shepshed Albion 2-1 114
Young 31 77   Oxley 35

Eastwood Town v Rhyl   1-2 111
Osbourne   Scorers undisclosed

Droylsden v Winsford United   1-1 347
Schofield 62   Edey 25

Winsford v Droysden *(23-10-91)* 1-3 454
Scorer undisclosed   Lunt 48,Burns 66,Wood 71

Willenhall Town v Matlock Town 2-3 142
Wainwright 15,Edwards 37   Hoyland(3)

Leicester Utd v Gainsborough T. 1-0 140
Hallam 80

Buxton v Moor Green   1-3 346
Bunter 86   Davies 44,Evans 72,Talbot 87

Chesham United v Leyton-W'gate 1-0 532
Attrell 71

Barking v Chalfont St Peter   0-2 104
Darlington 39 48

Staines Town v Heybridge Sw.   0-1 174
Bewers 26

Sutton United v Hayes   2-0 136
Callfield 44,Sturgeon 48

Bishop's Stortford v Boreham W. 1-1 254

B'ham W. v B. S'ford *(22-10-91)* 0-1 136
Lawford 33(p)

Hitchin Town v St Albans City   2-3 430
Smith 16,McGuire 79   Clark 48 60 64

Wembley v Harlow Town   0-0   58

Harlow v Wembley *(23-10-91)*   0-1   54
Bennett 44

Dorking v Yeading   2-1 155
Hanlan 6 26   Welsh 60

Bromley v Maidnehead United   2-0 266
McMenemy 43,Lovell 62

Bashley v Ashford Town   3-1 207
Ingman 21,Lovell 40,Stagg 88   Stanton 8

Whyteleafe v Margate   1-2 118
Harmsworth 38   Brenton 4,Harwood 90

Waterlooville v Walton & Her.   1-1 135
Boyce 43   Barwick 85

Walton & H. v W'ville *(22-10-91)* 4-0 198
Holman 8 30,Mitchell 13,Wingfield 18

Gosport Borough v Marlow   0-2 133
Regan 23,Watkins 57

Tooting & Mitcham v Dulwich Ham. 3-0 255
Loughlin 28,Collins 73 88

Barry Town v Bridgend Town   2-0 217
Summers 68 88

Newport A.F.C. v Saltash United 5-4 521
Green 7 36 82,   Kenealy 4,Norton 51
Sanderson 56,58   Fallon 70 77

Llanelli v Dorchester Town   1-3 144
Watkeys 63   Manson 13,Townsend 44,Diaz 86

Salisbury v Taunton Town   4-1 212
Smith 21,Green 66 82,   McDonnell 69
Chalk 77

Mark Smith (left) of Hitchin is tackled by Alan Campbell of St Albans during the Saints 3-2 win. Photo - Colin Stevens.

Peter McDonnell scores Taunton Town's only goal in their havey defeat at Salisbury. Photo - Dave West.

Margate's Tony Harwood snatches the winner at Whyteleafe despite a dubious challenge. Photo - Dennis Nicholson.

THIRD QUALIFYING ROUND

32 Ties. Matches Played: 42
Home wins: 21 **Draws:** 10 **Away wins:** 11
Best Attendance: 663 - Slough Town v Margate
Total Attendance: 15,057 **Average Attendance:** 358
Largest Home Win: 4-0; Blyth v Accrington, Fleetwood v Seaham
Best Away Win: 0-3; Tow Law v Bishop Auckland, Rhyl v Southport
Result of the Round: Blyth Spartans 4, Accrington Stanley 0

Saturday 30th November 1991 Res Att **(* Denotes extra time played)**

Chorley v Frickley Athletic 0-2 203
Woodhead 57,Thompson 71

Fleetwood Town v Seaham R.S. 4-0 161
Walmesley 5 72,Thompson 60,Madden 65

Morecambe v Emley 2-2 522
Lodge 60, Broadbent 1,
Brown 75 Hopley 49

Emley v Morecambe (2-12-91) 2-4 512
Wood 14, Miller 29,Holden 41,
Codd 80 Brown 44,McMahon 78

Northallerton v Matlock T. 4-2 141
Woods 52,Kennedy 80, Tilly 4,
Winn 83,Gill 89 Own Goal 43

Tow Law T. v Bishop Auckland 0-3 304
(at Crook Town, 4-11-91)
Deacey 22,Thompson 53,Wiggan 85

Whitby T. v Easington Colliery 1-0 193
Pitman 60

Rhyl v Southport 0-3 334
Blackhurst 20 50,Senior 61

Horwich R.M.I. v Marine 1-3 183
Griffin 4 Haw 14 44,Grant 89

Billingham Synthonia v Droysden 4-1 127
Shearer 21,Banks 45 76 Wagstaffe 2
Parry 65

South Bank v Bangor City 1-1 521
(at Middlesbrough FC)
Birch 88 Lloyd 12

Bangor v South Bank (3-12-91) 1-0 284
Morris 67

Blyth Spartans v Accrington St. 4-0 574
Cameron 16,Bond 22 73 90

Fisher Athletic v Bromsgrove R. 1-1 121
Davenport 45 Denehy 89(Own Goal)

Bromsgrove v Fisher (3-12-91) 2-0 624
Daly 85,Crisp 87

V.S. Rugby v Leicester United 2-1 545
Bradder 42,Rosegreen 72 Bond 55

Dudley Town v Worcester City 2-3 308
Horne 31, Robinson 3,
Wareing 76 Tomlinson 79 90

Wembley v Chalfont St Peter 2-0 54
Hutchinson 41 69

Sutton C'field v Cambridge C. 2-1 184
Smith 24 46 Wilkin 58

Hendon v Wealdstone 0-0 427

Wealdstone v Hendon (4-12-91) 4-1 367
Lowe 1 81, Fowler 31
Wilson 47 63

Harrow Borough v B. Stortford 2-1 285
Pye 60,Ripley 87 Petroli 31

Atherstone Utd v Heybridge Sw. 1-1 345
Randle 17 Pannell 51

Heybridge v Atherstone (3-12-91) 0-1 245
K Green 53

Burton Albion v Chesham United 0-0 503

Chesham v Burton A. (4-12-91) 4-0 539
Richardson 7 47,Gipp 77 78

Moor Green v Boston United 1-3 408
Fearon 45 Howarth 30,McGinley 30,
Tourne 61

Dagenham v St Albans City 3-2 454
Grenfell 56,Warner 70, Danzey 47,
West 86 Hobson 51

Tooting & M. v Walton & Hersham 0-0 239

Walton v Tooting & M. (3-12-91) 2-1 258
Jones 48,Mitchell 58 Falanna 55

Dorking v Barry Town 2-1 256
Grainger 20,Yorke 89 Summers 38

Stroud v Newport AFC 1-3 463
Hams 54 Green 25,Kilgour 43,
Hewitt 78

Windsor & Eton v Sutton United 2-2 353
Evans 2 32 Feltham 44 85

Sutton Utd v Windsor (3-12-91) 4-2 481
Feltham 5,Scott 26 57, Evans 47,
Rogers 80 Messitt 84

Gravesend & Northfeet v Marlow 1-3 383
Parkin 27 Hannigan 51,Regan 53,
Caesar 89

Bromley v Weymouth 1-0 481
Denton 33

Wokingham Town v Salisbury 0-0 357

Salisbury v Wokingham (4-12-91) 1-0 274
Green 74

Slough Town v Margate 0-0 663

Margate v Slough Town (3-12-91) 1-2 482
Harwood 46 Pluckrose 52,Scott 54

Bashley v Carshalton Athletic 2-0 453
Stickler 33,Ingman 72

Kingstonian v Dorchester Town 3-0 446
Cherry 14 55,Vines 65

Fleetwood's Craig Madden rounds Seaham keeper Bottenschien as the Fishermen win 4-0. Photo - Colin Stevens.

Dudley's Steve Carter pulls off a fine save from a header by Worcester striker Ollie Kearns. Photo - Gary Cave.

Dorking's Carey Anderson (left) towers above Barry defenders Ray John and Roger Mullen. Photo - Dave West.

FIRST ROUND PROPER

32 Ties. Matches Played: 43
Home wins: 17 Draws: 11 Away wins: 15
Best Attendance: 2,917 - Wycombe Wanderers v Salisbury
Total Attendance: 37,609 **Average Attendance:** 875
Largest Home Win: Enfield 4, Slough Town 0
Best Away Win: Sutton Coldfield Town 0, Farnborough Town 3
Result of the Round: Northallerton Town 1, Frickley Athletic 0

Saturday 11th January 1992   Res Att

(* Denotes extra time played)

Witton Albion v Billingham Syn. 2-2 725
Thomas 14,Connor 57   Allen 31 50

Billingham S. v Witton *(15-1-92)* 1-2* 245
Lynch 64   Heesom 40,McCluskie 108

Macclesfield v Boston Utd   0-0 833

Boston v Macclesfield *(15-1-92)* 0-2 947
Edwards 22,Lambert 78

Southport v Bishop Auckland   1-0 413
Blackhurst 88

Northwich V. v Hyde *(14-1-92)* 1-0 644
Hemmings 43(p)

Whitby Town v Barrow   0-2 739
McPhillips 2,Gilmore 83

Altrincham v Stlaybridge C.   1-2 1256
Lee 39   Priest 49,Leicester 54

Blyth Spartans v Gateshead   0-0 1488

G'head v Blyth *(at Blyth 14-1-91)* 3-0 920
Dixon 101,Lowery 155,Veart 119

Telford U. v Guisborough Town 2-0 795
Langford 70 88

Frickley A. v Northallerton T. 2-2 310
Hatto 19(p),   Wasden 22,
Healey 56   Kennedy 42

Northallerton T. v Fricley A. 1-0* 359
(at Frickley, 14-1-92)
Laogan 118

Fleetwood Town v Morecambe   1-1 412
Walker 52   Coleman 16

Morecambe v Fleetwood *(14-1-91)*1-0* 454
Cain 118

Bangor City v Gretna   0-0 413

Gretna v Bangor City *(14-1-92)* 1-2 301
Armstrong 85   Morris 54 76

Stafford Rangers v Marine   0-1 718
Ross 15

Leek Town v Runcorn   3-3 789
Smith 50 67 87(p)   Shaughnessy 44,
Smith 57(OG),McCarthy 74

Welling Utd v Dover Athletic   3-2 1606
Brown 10,Robbins 19,   O'Connor 62,
Abbott 21   Ambrose 72

Wycombe Wanderers v Salisbury 2-0 2917
Carroll 40,Scott 61

Woking v Wembley   4-2 2075
Pratt 20,Friel 37(p),   Lawrence 36,
Milton 57,Own Goal   Clark 71

Redbridge F. v Bromsgrove *(12-1-92)* 1-1 623
Garvey 29   Pamphlett 14(OG)

Bromsgrove v Redbridge F. *(14-1-92)* 0-1 995
Walsh 76(p)

Gloucester C. v Harrow Borough 1-2 492
Townsend 43   Fraser 41,Cooper 71

Wivenhoe Town v Marlow   1-0 223
Hannigan 29

Sutton Coldfield v Farnborough T. 0-3 646
Read 59,Dougherty 77(p),Horton 87

Colchester United v Kingstonian 2-2 2724
Restarick 9,English 90   Cherry 5,Tutt 10

Kingstonian v Colchester *(14-1-92)* 2-3 1642
Cherry 52(p) 84(p)   Smith 39,Bennett 73
McGavion 79

V.S. Rugby v Kettering Town   0-1 1790
Hill 52

Bromley v Worcester City   1-0 518
Rawlings 58

Atherstone United v Dorking   1-3 401
K Green 89   Grainger 43 85
Anderson 75

Yeovil Town v Chesham United   3-1 1733
Spencer 17 39,   Goldstone 48
McDermott 87(p)

Walton & H. v Kidderminster H. 0-2 426
Howell 16 29

Merthyr Tydfil v Dartford   1-1 750
Dauria 87   Leslie 90

Dartford v Merthyr T. *(14-1-92)* 1-2 520
M Williams 52(OG)   C Williams 25,
Coates 70

Aylesbury Utd v Newport AFC   3-2 870
Collins 21 42,   Sanderson 60,
Hercules 50   Price 86

Dagenham v Bashley   0-0 549

Bashley v Dagenham *(15-1-92)* 2-0 440

Sutton United v Bath City   1-2 757
Feltham 71   Randall 38,Withey 70

Enfield v Slough Town   4-0 670
Kane 12,Turner 15,Salmon 51,Richards 56

Cheltenham Town v Wealdstone   3-2 768
Purdie 2 34,   Lynch 30,
Smith 75   Donnellan 41

89

Bangor 'keeper Scott Healey foils Gretna's Tony Nelson (left) and Kenny Goodrick. Photo - Alan Watson.

Dagenham's John Warner shields the ball under pressure from Bashley's Steve Ingram. Photo - Dave West.

Richard Cherry scores his second penalty but cannot stop Colchester from beating Kingstonian. Photo - Dave West.

SECOND ROUND PROPER

16 Ties. **Matches Played:** 18
Home wins: 13 **Draws:** 2 **Away wins:** 3
Best Attendance: 5,801 - Wycombe Wanderers v Woking
Lowest Attendance: 405 - Marine v Wivenhoe Town
Total Attendance: 21,835   **Average Attendance:** 1,213
Largest Home Win: Farnborough Town 5, Southport 0
Best Away Win: 1-3; Bromley v Yeovil, Harrow v Stalybridge Celtic
Result of the Round: Morecambe 2, Welling United 1

Saturday 1st February 1991   Res Att

Telford Utd v Northallerton T.   3-0   757
Langford 58,Benbow 80 90

Morecambe v Welling *(4-2-92)*   2-1   833
Holden 15,McInerney 26   Reynolds 50

Runcorn v Kidderminster Harr.   1-1   681
Shaughnessy 41   Davies 85

K'minster v Runcorn *(3-2-91)*   5-2*1189
Davies 23 72,   Saunders 42 44
Howell 91,
Benton 105,Wolsey 119

Gateshead v Barrow   1-0 1129
Lowery 26

Bromley v Yeovil Town   1-3   667
Coles 89   Carroll 10,Spencer 21 90

Macclesfield v Bangor *(4-2-92)*   1-0   631
Hanlon 75

Witton Albion v Aylesbury Utd   1-0   852
Thomas 47

Northwich V. v Cheltenham T.   4-2   701
O'Connor 1,Blain 17 68,   Teggart 13,
Blundell 72   Owen 90

(* Denotes extra time played)

Bashley v Kettering Town   2-3 1065
Lovell 65,   Culpin 36,Broom 70,
Gowens 86   Hill 79

Bath City v Dorking   2-0   601
Withey 54,Mings 79

Harrow Borough v Stalybridge C. 1-3   702
Barnard 90   Leicester 14,
*   Camden 69(p),Bauress 80*

Marine v Wivenhoe Town   3-0   405
Haw 32,Murray 62,Ross 62

Farnborough Town v Southport   5-0 1021
Coney 2,Read 16 89,Bye 23,Horton 73

Merthyr Tydfil v Colchester Utd   0-0 1211

Colchester v Merthyr *(4-2-91)*   1-0 2746
McDonough 90

Wycombe Wanderers v Woking   1-0 5801
Casey 28

Redbridge Forest v Enfield   2-0   843
Broom 49 64

Richard Hill (left) prepares to clear for Kettering pursued by Simon Gowans of Bashley in the New Forest mist. Photo - Francis Short.

Southport's Tony Jarvis (right) tries to beat Mick Doherty as his side slump at Farnborough. Photo - Eric Marsh.

Unmarked Adie Mings rifles home Bath's second goal against Dorking at Twerton Park. Photo - Paul Dennis.

Gateshead 'keeper Simon Smith punches clear a Barrow attack as his side oust the 1990 winners. Photo - Ged Rule.

THIRD ROUND PROPER

8 Ties **Matches Played: 10**
Home wins: 6 **Draws:** 2 **Away wins:** 2
Best Attendance: 3,542 - Wycombe Wanderers v Bath City
Lowest Attendance: 533 - Gateshead v Telford United
Total Attendance: 19,642   **Average Attendance:** 1,964
Largest Home Win: 3-1; Colchester v Morecambe, Yeovil v Kidderminster
Best Away Win: 0-1; Gateshead v Telford, Northwich v Macclesfield
Result of the Round: Marine 2, Kettering Town 1

Saturday 22nd February 1992

COLCHESTER U. (2)3 *(Stewart 12 32,McGavin 67)* **MORECAMBE** (1)1 *(Cain 27)* Att: 3,206
Colchester: Barrett, Donald, Roberts (Masters 24), Kinsella, English, Cook, Collins, Stewart (Dart 65), McDonough, McGavin, Smith. *Morecambe:* Alison, Tomlinson, Armstrong, Parillon, Dullaghan, Lodge, Brown, Lavelle (Holden 60), Coleman, McMahon, Cain. Unused sub: McGowan.

MARINE (0)2 *(Haw 57,Gautrey 67(p))* **KETTERING TOWN** (1)1 *(Keast 44)* Att: 1,111
Marine: O'Brien, Rooney, Proctor, Draper, Johnson, Gautrey, Murray (Grant 75), Haw, Ross, Roche, King. Unused sub: McDonough. *Kettering:* Shoemake, Huxford, Keast, Nicol, Slack, Price, Waller (Christie 56), Brown, Bancroft, Culpin (Graham 56), Hill.

NORTHWICH VICTORIA (0)0 **MACCLESFIELD TOWN** (0)1 *(Hanlon 65)* Att: 1,537
Northwich: Bullock, Locke, Butler, Jones, Hancock, Stringer, Blain, Feeley (Graham 72), Easter, O'Connor, Hemmings. Unused sub: Lenton. *Macclesfield:* S Farrelly, Shepard, Johnson, Edwards, S Farrelly (Ellis 45), Hanlon, Askey, Green, Lambert, Timmons, Dempsey. Unused sub: Clayton.

TELFORD UNITED 0 GATESHEAD 0 Att: 1,027
Telford: Actont, Humphreys, Nelson (Hackett 61), Dyson, Brindley, Whittington, Myers, Fergusson, Benbow, Langford, Parrish. Unused sub: Cooke. *Gateshead:* Smith, Farrey, Veart, Granycome, Corner, Halliday, Scope, Bell, Linacre, Dixon, Butler. Unused sub: Forrest.

GATESHEAD (0)0 **TELFORD UNITED** (1)1 *(Humphreys 37)* (at Blyth 26-2-91). Att: 533
Gateshead: Smith, Farrey, Veart, Granycome, Corner, Halliday, Gourlay, Forrest, Linacre, Dixon (Scope 25), Butler. Unused sub: Bell. *Telford:* Acton, Humphreys, Parrish, Dyson, Brindley, Whittington, Myers, Fergusson, Benbow, Langford, Grainger. Unused subs: Cooke, Hackett.

REDBRIDGE (3)3 *(Welsh 20,Pamphlett 31,Cavell 37)* **FARNBORO.** (0)2 *(Leworthy 66,Coney 73)* Att: 1,353
Redbridge: Bennett, Jacques, Watts, Pamphlett, Corner, Ebdon, Mayes (Riley 87), Richardson, Cavell, Walsh (Broom 87), Blackford. *Farnborough:* Hucker, Turkington, Baker, Broome, Bye, Wigmore, Leworthy, Holmes (Coles 77), Coney, Fleming (Comfort 45), Horton.

WITTON ALBION (0)1 *(Heesom 66)* **STALYBRIDGE CELTIC** (0)0 Att: 1,755
Witton: Mason, Halliday, Heesom, McNeilis, Jim Connor, Anderson, Thomas, Rose, Lutkevitch (Alford 83), Grimshaw, Joe Connor. Unused sub: McCluskie. *Celtic:* Hughes, Bennett, Blackman, Dixon, Edmonds, Bauress, Brown, Priest (Woan 80), Camden, Booth (Filson 87), Leicester.

YEOVIL (2)3 *(Robinson 14,Carroll 44,McDermott 47(p))* **KIDDERMINSTER** (0)1 *(Forsyth 67)* Att: 2,679
Yeovil: Coles, Harrower (Batty 59), Ferns, Shail, Rutter, Conning, Carroll, Wallace, Robinson, Spencer, McDermott. Unused sub: Cooper. *K'minster:* Green, Benton, McGrath, Weir, Gillett, Forsyth, Joseph, Howell, Hadley, Davies, Wolsey. Unused subs: Taylor, Carroll.

BATH CITY (0)1 *(Hedges 62)* **WYCOMBE WANDERERS** (1)1 *(Carroll 17)* 23-2-92. Att: 2,899
Bath: Churchward, Hedges, Dicks, Cousins, Crowley, Brown, Banks, Randall, Withey, Boyle (Singleton 84), Mings. Unused sub: Gill. *Wycombe:* Hyde, Stapleton, Cooper, Cousins, Creaser, Smith, Deakin, Casey, Carroll (Ryan 80), Scott, Guppy. Unused sub: Norman.

WYCOMBE WANDERERS (1)2 *(Carroll 35,Casey 68)* **BATH CITY** (0)0 25-2-92. Att: 3,542
Wycombe: As 1st match, but Ryan on for Carroll after 60 mins. *Bath:* As 1st match, but Singleton on for Cousins (76) and Ricketts unused sub.

Manager Roy McDonough misses from the spot, but Colchester still beat Moreacambe 3-1. Photo - Andrew Mollitt.

Two ex-professionals clash, Telford's Paul Dyson (right) and Gateshead's David Corner. Photo - Paul Dennis.

Keith Proctor of Marine slides in to dispossess Kettering's Phil Brown at Rossett Park. Photo - Rob Ruddock.

Redbridge Forest players celebrate their Third Round victory over Farnborough Town. Photo - Eric Marsh.

QUARTER FINALS

4 Ties **Matches Played:** 5
Home wins: 1 **Draws:** 1 **Away wins:** 3
Best Attendance: 4,636 - Wycombe Wanderers v Witton Albion
Lowest Attendance: 1,150 - Marine v Redbridge Forest
Total Attendance: 15,188 **Average Attendance:** 3,038
Largest Home Win: Colchester United 4, Telford United 0
Best Away Win: 1-2; Wycombe v Witton, Yeovil v Macclesfield
Result of the Round: Redbridge Forest 0, Marine 1

Saturday 14th February 1992

MARINE (0)1 *(Ross 61)* **REDBRIDGE FOREST** (0)1 *(Cavell 84)* Att: 1,150
Marine: O'Brien, Rooney (Hanson 25), Proctor, Draper, Johnson, Gautrey, Grant, Haw, Ross, McDonough, King.
Unused sub: Edward Murray. *Redbridge:* Bennett, Jacques, Watts, Pamphlett, Conner, Ebdon, Mayes,
Richardson (Broom 72), Cavell, Walsh, Blackford (Owers 66).

REDBRIDGE FOREST (0)0 **MARINE** (0)1 *(King 49)* 17-3-92. Att: 1,239
Redbridge: Bennett, Jacques, Watts, Pamphlett, Conner, Ebdon, Mayes, Richardson, (Broom 68), Cavell, Walsh,
Blackford (Owers 57). *Marine:* O'Brien, Roberts, Proctor, Draper, McDonough, Gautrey, Grant, Haw (Hanson 73),
Ross, Murray, King. Unused sub: Trewitt.

YEOVIL TOWN (1)1 *(Wallace 19)* **MACCLESFIELD TOWN** (0)2 *(Green 61, Askey 85)* Att: 4,269
Yeovil: Coles, Harrower, Ferns, Shail, Batty (Cooper 58), Conning, McDermott, Wallace, Robinson (Rutter 86),
Spencer, Carroll. *Macclesfield:* S Farrelly, Shepherd, Johnson, Edwards, M Farrelly, Hanlon, Askey, Green,
Lambert, Timmons, Dempsey. Unused Subs: Clayton, Kendal.

COLCHESTER (1)4 *(McGavin 18, Kinsella 49, Bennett 53, Smith 63)* **TELFORD** (0)0 Att: 3,894
Colchester: Barrett, Donald, Roberts, Kinsella (Collins 72), English, Elliott, Cook, Bennett, McDonough (Stewart
72), McGavin, Smith. *Telford:* Acton, Humphreys, Nelson, Dyson, Brindley, Whittington (Clarke 60), Myers,
Fergusson, Benbow, Langford, Grainger. Unused sub: White.

WYCOMBE WAND. (0)1 *(West 90(pen))* **WITTON ALBION** (0)2 *(Lutkevitch 50, Thomas 88)* Att: 4,636
Wycombe: Hyde, Cousins, Johnson, Kerr, Creaser, Smith, Stapleton, Casey, Carroll, Scott, Guppy (West 64).
Unused sub: Ryan. *Witton:* Mason, Halliday, Heesom, McNeilis, Jim Connor, Anderson, Thomas, Rose, Alford,
Grimshaw, Lutkevitch (Stewart 90). Unused sub: Joe Connor.

*H.F.S. Loans League side Marine produced the shock of the Quarter Finals when they eliminated Redbridge Forest.
Here though they are under pressure with goalkeeper Kevin O'Brien being called into action during the 1-1 draw on
Merseyside. Photo - Colin Stevens.*

SEMI FINALS

2 Ties **Matches Played:** 4
Home wins: 1 **Draws:** 2 **Away wins:** 1
Best Attendance: 5,445 - Colchester Unuted v Macclesfield Town
Total Attendance: 11,337   **Average Attendance:** 2,834
Largest Home Win: Colchester United 3, Macclesfield Town 0
Best Away Win: Marine 1, Witton Albion 4

First Leg: Saturday 4th April 1992
Second Leg: Saturday 11th April 1992

WITTON ALBION (2)2 *(Alford 25 31)*, **MARINE** (1)2 *(Grant 38, Rose 80)*
Att: 2,030.
Witton: Keith Mason, Mike Halliday, Darren Heesom, Gary Stewart, Jim Connor, Stewart Anderson, Karl Thomas, Colin Rose, Carl Alford, Mike Lutkevitch (Jim McCluskie 80), Joe Connor. Unused sub: Lee Coathup.
Marine: Kevin O'Brien, Andy Rooney, Kevin Proctor, Andrew Draper, Keith Johnson, Jon Gautrey, Brendon Grant, Eddie Murray (Paul Dawson 80), Brian Ross, Terry McDonough, Peter King. Unused subs: John Roach.

MARINE (0)1 *(Gautrey 87(p))*, **WITTON** (1)4 *(Thomas 5, McClukie 81, Halliday 89, Lutkevitch 90)*
Att: 2,212.
Marine: Kevin O'Brien, Andy Rooney (Eddie Murray 81), Kevin Proctor, Andrew Draper, Keith Johnson, Jon Gautrey, Brendon Grant, Stephen Haw, Brian Ross, Terry McDonough (Paul Dawson 50), Peter King.
Witton: Keith Mason, Mike Halliday, Lee Coathup, Steve McNeilis, Jim Connor, Stewart Anderson, Karl Thomas (Jim McCluskie 80), Gary Stewart (Colin Rose 86), Carl Alford, Andy Grimshaw, Mike Lutkevitch.

COLCHESTER UNITED (2)3 *(Stewart 22, English 25, McDonough 70(p))*, **MACCLESFIELD TOWN** (0)0
Att: 5,445.
Colchester: Scott Barrett, Warren Donald, Paul Roberts, Mark Kinsella, Tony English, David Martin, Jason Cook (Eamonn Collins 77), Ian Stewart (Gary Bennett 72), Roy McDonough, Steve McGavin, Nicky Smith.
Macc: Steve Farrelly, George Shepherd, Paul Johnson, Mike Farrelly, Elfyn Edwards, Steve Hanlon, John Askey, Andrew Green, Colin Lambert, John Timmons, Mark Dempsey. Unused subs: Paul Clayton, Paul Kendall.

MACCLESFIELD TOWN (1)1 *(Timmons 19)*, **COLCHESTER UNITED** (1)1 *(Cook 45)*
Att: 1,650.
Macc: Steve Farrelly, George Shepherd, Paul Johnson, Elfyn Edwards, Mike Farrelly (Paul Clayton 62), Steve Hanlon, John Askey, Andrew Green, Colin Lambert, John Timmons, Ronnie Ellis (Darren Boughey 34).
Colchester: Scott Barrett, Warren Donald, Paul Roberts, Mark Kinsella, Tony English, Jason Cook, David Martin, Ian Stewart, Roy McDonough (Mike Masters 71), Steve McGavin (Gary Bennett 77), Nicky Smith.

Kevin O'Brien, Marine's long-serving goalkeeper, leaps high above fellow defender Jon Gautrey and safely caught the ball as the Mariners head for an exciting 2-2 result at Witton Albion. Photo - Paul Dennis.

Witton's Carl Thomas (right) sells Andrew Draper a dummy at Wincham Park. Photo - Paul Dennis.

Northern Ireland international Ian Stewart puts Colchester a goal up against Macclesfield. Photo - John Robinson.

Skipper Tony English puts Colchester firmly in control of their first leg with a second. Photo - John Robinson.

F.A. TROPHY FINAL

Colchester United 3 v 1 **Witton Albion**

Masters, Smith, McGavin   Lutkevitch

Attendance: 27,806

Referee: K P Barratt (Coventry)

U's Complete Double

No-one will benefit if one beats about the bush, so let it be said at the outset that this was a thoroughly nasty game, and one which did nothing to enhance the prestige of either the competition or the famous stadium. Neither side would accept blame after the game for all the niggling that scarred the afternoon for a good crowd, but it did appear that Colchester for the most part were the better teams purely in terms of football, and that the referee ended up having to flash cards left, right and centre in order to maintain some sort of control. After ninety minutes the score was Colchester United three goals, one red card and two yellows, Witton Albion one goal and four yellow cards. The former, being the better side, were unlucky not to score more goals, whilst the latter were by no means 'hard done by' in terms of the card vote.

After Barrett, exposed by a bad back pass, had saved well at the feet of Thomas early on, Colchester settled and took a fifth minute lead as a result of a phenomenal throw by Roberts which was headed on by McDonough and nodded bravely home by Masters. There could have been more, but in the nineteenth minute Kinsella, wide on the right, beat the Witton offside trap and squared the ball nicely for McDonough and Smith, both unmarked. The former missed, but Smith did not and his neat shot gave Mason no chance.

The remainder of the half was notable for Colchester pressure with Kinsella missing one easy chance, one bad miss by Thomas (who headed wide) for Witton, and five bookings for various crimes. Witton's Anderson, Grimshaw and Coathup collected three of these, and for Colchester one yellow card went to player manager McDonough and the other to Steve McGavin. In the former's case it appeared that Mr Barratt was penalising the wrong man as Jim Connor seemed to kick the Colchester man's midriff, a view which McGavin obviously shared as his card looked to be 'inspired' by an urge to exact revenge on Connor.

The second half saw Witton making a major effort to play some football and get back in the game, which they did in the 57th minute when Lutkevitch headed home a fine cross by Coathup. However, Colchester's defence was untroubled by some naive attempts to break it down from then onwards. Halliday became Witton's fourth booking, and, when he reacted with a punch to some unsavoury actions by opponents, Jason Cook became the first player to be sent off in a Trophy Final. He had to walk, but deserved some sympathy.

There were nine minutes to go plus some injury time, but Colchester not only held out but also scored a late goal through McGavin who raced clear, through a defence that had pushed forward in desperate attack, to easily beat the unprotected Mason. The better team had therefore won and thus completed a superb Conference and Trophy double.

Bill Mitchell

Colchester: Scott Barrett, Warren Donald, Paul Roberts, Mark Kinsella, Tony English, David Martin, Jason Cook, Mike Masters, Roy McDonough (Gary Bennett 65), Steve McGavin, Nicky Smith. Unused sub: Shaun Elliott.

Witton: Keith Mason, Mike Halliday, Lee Coathup, Steve McNeilis, Jim Connor, Stewart Anderson, Karl Thomas, Colin Rose, Carl Alford, Andy Grimshaw (Joe Connor 67), Mike Lutkevitch (Jim McCluskie 79).

Colourful Colchester fans arrive at Wembley for the big match. Photo - Paul Dennis.

Disappointment etched on their faces, Witton fans still enjoy a first Wembley visit. Photo - Graham Cotterill.

Sponsored by Essex Man's favourite 'read', U's celebrate with the Vauxhall F.A. Trophy. Photo - Ian Morseman.

F.A. TROPHY FINAL

Witton Albion's Colin Rose fires over a cross as Colchester's Nicky Smith lurches in to attempt an interception. Photo - Dennis Nicholson.

Eyes down as Colchester United top-scorer Steve McGavin shields the ball from Witton's Lee Coathup (nearest camera). Photo - Gavin Ellis.

F.A. TROPHY CELEBRATIONS

Ian Phillips, the coach at Colchester United, shares a special moment with some of his club's ecstatic following. Photo - Paul Dennis.

The Colchester United goal-scorers proudly parade the Vauxhall F.A. Trophy. Front left to right: Nicky Smith, Steve McGavin, and Mike Masters. Photo - Paul Dennis.

PAST F.A. CHALLENGE TROPHY FINALS

1970 MACCLESFIELD TOWN 2 (Lyond, B Fidler) **TELFORD UNITED 0**   Ref: K Walker
Macc: Cooke, Sievwright, Bennett, Beaumont, Collins, Roberts, Lyons, B Fidler, Young, Corfield, D Fidler. *Telford:* Irvine, Harris, Croft, Flowers, Coton, Ray, Fudge, Hart, Bentley, Murray, Jagger. *Att:* 28,000.

1971 TELFORD UTD 3 (Owen, Bentley, Fudge) **HILLINGDON BORO. 2** (Reeve, Bishop)   Ref: D Smith
Telford: Irvine, Harris, Croft, Ray, Coton, Carr, Fudge, Owen, Bentley, Jagger, Murray. *H'don:* Lowe, Batt, Langley, Higginson, Newcombe, Moore, Fairchild, Bishop, Reeve, Carter, Knox. *Att:* 29,500.

1972 STAFFORD RANGERS 3 (Williams 2, Cullerton) **BARNET 0**   Ref: P Partridge
Staff: Aleksic, Chadwick, Clayton, Sargeant, Aston, Machin, Cullerton, Chapman, Williams, Bayley, Jones. *Barnet:* McClelland, Lye, Jenkins, Ward, Embrey, King, Powell, Rerry, Flatt, Easton, Plume. *Att:* 24,000.

1973 SCARBOROUGH 2 (Leask, Thompson) **WIGAN ATHLETIC 1** (Rogers) *aet*   Ref: H Hackney
Scarboro: Garrow, Appleton, Shoulder, Dunn, Siddle, Fagan, Donoghue, Franks, Leask (Barmby), Thompson, Hewitt. *Wigan:* Reeves, Morris, Sutherland, Taylor, Jackson, Gillibrand, Clements, Oats (McCunnell), Rogers, King, Worswick. *Att:* 23,000.

1974 MORECAMBE 2 (Richmond, Sutton) **DARTFORD 1** (Cunningham)   Ref: B Homewood
M'cambe: Coates, Pearson, Bennett, Sutton, Street, Baldwin, Done, Webber, Roberts (Galley), Kershaw, Richmond. *D'ford:* Morton, Read, Payne, Carr, Burns, Binks, Light, Glozier, Robinson (Hearne), Cunningham, Halleday. *Att:* 19,000.

1975 MATLOCK TOWN 4 (Oxley, Dawson, T Fenoughty, N Fenoughy) **SCARBOROUGH 0** Ref: K Styles
M'lock: Fell, McKay, Smith, Stuart, Dawson, Swan, Oxley, N Fenoughy, Scott, T Fenoughty, M Fenoughty. *S'boro:* Williams, Hewitt, Rettitt, Dunn, Marshall, Todd, Houghton, Woodall, Davidson, Barnby, Aveyard. *Att:* 21,000.

1976 SCARBOROUGH 3 (Woodall, Abbey, Marshall(p)) **STAFFORD R. 2** (Jones 2) *aet*   Ref: R Challis
S'boro: Barnard, Jackson, Marshall, H Dunn, Ayre (Donoghue), HA Dunn, Dale, Barmby, Woodall, Abbey, Hilley. *S'ford:* Arnold, Ritchie, Richards, Sargeant, Seddon, Morris, Chapman, Lowe, Jones, Hutchinson, Chadwick. *Att:* 21,000.

1977 SCARBOROUGH 2 (Dunn(p), Abbey) **DAGENHAM 1** (Harris)   Ref: G Courtney
S'boro: Chapman, Smith, Marshall (Barmby), Dunn, Ayre, Deere, Aveyard, Donoghue, Woodall, Abbey, Dunn. *D'ham:* Fell, Wellman, P Currie, Dunwell, Moore, W Currie, Harkins, Saul, Fox, Harris, Holder. *Att:* 21,500.

1978 ALTRINCHAM 3 (King, Johnson, Rogers) **LEATHERHEAD 1** (Cook)   Ref: A Grey
A'cham: Eales, Allan, Crossley, Bailey, Owens, King, Morris, Heathcote, Johnson, Rogers, Davidson (Flaherty). *L'head:* Swannell, Cooper, Eaton, Davies, Reid, Malley, Cook, Salkeld, Baker, Boyle (Bailey). *Att:* 20,000.

1979 STAFFORD RANGERS 2 (A Wood 2) **KETTERING TOWN 0**   Ref: D Richardson
S'ford: Arnold, F Wood, Willis, Sargeant, Seddon, Ritchie, Secker, Chapman, A Wood, Cullerton, Chadwick (Jones). *K'ring:* Lane, Ashby, Lee, Eastell, Dixey, Suddards, Flannagan, Kellock, Phipps, Clayton, Evans (Hughes). *Att:* 32,000.

1980 DAGENHAM 2 (Duck, Maycock) **MOSSLEY 1** (Smith)   Ref: K Baker
D'ham: Huttley, Wellman, Scales, Dunwell, Mooore, Durrell, Maycock, Horan, Duck, Kidd, Jones (Holder). *M'ley:* Fitton, Brown, Vaughan, Gorman, Salter, Polliot, Smith, Moore, Skeete, O'Connor, Keelan (Wilson). *Att:* 26,000.

1981 BISHOP'S STORTFORD 1 (Sullivan) **SUTTON UNITED 0**   Ref: J Worrall
S'ford: Moore, Blackman, Brame, Smith (Worrell), Bradford, Abery, Sullivan, Knapman, Radford, Simmonds, Mitchell. *Sutton:* Collyer, Rogers, Green, J Rains, T Rains, Stephens (Sunnucks), Waldon, Pritchard, Cornwell, Parsons. *Att:* 22,578.

1982 ENFIELD 1 (Taylor) **ALTRINCHAM 0**   Ref: B Stevens
Enfield: Jacobs, Barrett, Tone, Jennings, Waite, Ironton, Ashford, Taylor, Holmes, Oliver (Flint), King. *A'cham:* Connaughton, Crossley, Davison, Bailey, Cuddy, King (Whitbread), Allan, Heathcote, Johnson, Rogers, Howard. *Att:* 18.678..

1983 TELFORD UTD 2 (Mather 2) **NORTHWICH VICTORIA 1** (Bennett)   Ref: B Hill
Telford: Charlton, Lewis, Turner, Mayman (Joseph), Walker, Easton, Barnett, Williams, Mather, Hogan, Alcock. *N'wich:* Ryan, Fretwell, Murphy, Jones, Forshaw, Ward, Anderson, Abel (Bennett), Reid, Chesters, Wilson. *Att:* 22,071.

1984 NORTHWICH VICTORIA 1 (Chesters) **BANGOR CITY 1** (Whelan)   *Att:* 14,200. Ref: J Martin
replay at Stoke: NORTHWICH 2 (Chesters(p), Anderson) **BANGOR 1** (Lunn)   *Att:* 5,805
N'wich: Ryan, Fretwell, Dean, Jones, Forshaw (Power 65), Bennett, Anderson, Abel, Reid, Chesters, Wilson. *Bangor:* Letheren, Cavanagh, Gray, Whelan, Banks, Lunn, Urqhart, Morris, Carter, Howat, Sutcliffe (Westwood 105). *Same teams in replay.*

1985 WEALDSTONE 2 (Graham, Holmes) **BOSTON UNITED 1** (Cook)   Ref: J Bray
W'stone: Iles, Perkins, Bowgett, Byatt, Davies, Greenaway, Holmes, Wainwright, Donnellan, Graham (N Cordice 89), A Cordice. *Boston:* Blackwell, Casey, Ladd, Creane, O'Brien, Thommson, Laverick (Mallender 78), Simpsom, Gilbert, Lee, Cook. *Att:* 20,775.

1986 ALTRINCHAM 1 (Farrelly) **RUNCORN 0**   Ref: A Ward
A'cham: Wealands, Gardner, Densmore, Johnson, Farrelly, Conning, Cuddy, Davison, Reid, Ellis, Anderson. Sub: Newton. *Runcorn:* McBride, Lee, Roberts, Jones, Fraser, Smith, S Crompton (A Crompton), Imrie, Carter, Mather, Carrodus. *Att:* 15,700.

1987 KIDDERMINSTER HARRIERS 0 BURTON ALBION 0   *Att:* 23,617. Ref: D Shaw
replay at West Brom: KIDDERMINSTER 2 (Davies 2) **BURTON 1** (Groves)   *Att:* 15,685
K'minster: Arnold, Barton, Boxall, Brazier (sub Hazlewood in rep), Collins (sub Pearson 90 at Wembley), Woodall, McKenzie, O'Dowd, Tuohy, Casey, Davies. sub: Jones. *Burton:* New, Essex, Kamara, Vaughan, Simms, Groves, Bancroft, Land, Dorsett, Redfern, (sub Wood in replay), Gauden. Sub: Patterson.

1988 ENFIELD 0 TELFORD UNITED 0   *Att:* 20,161. Ref: L Dilkes
replay at West Brom: ENFIELD 3 (Furlong 2, Howell) **TELFORD 2** (Biggins, Norris(p))   *Att:* 6,912
Enfield: Pape, Cottington, Howell, Keen (sub Edmonds in rep), Sparrow (sub Hayzleden at Wembley), Lewis (sub Edmonds at Wembley), Harding, Cooper, King, Furlong, Francis. *Telford:* Charlton, McGinty, Storton, Nelson, Wiggins, Mayman (sub Cunningham in rep (sub Hancock)), Sankey, Joseph, Stringer (sub Griffiths at Wembley, Griffiths in rep)), Biggins, Norris.

1989   TELFORD UNITED 1 (Crawley) **MACCLESFIELD TOWN 0**   Ref: T Holbrook
Telford: Charlton, Lee, Brindley, Hancock, Wiggins, Mayman, Grainger, Joseph, Nelson, Lloyd, Stringer. Subs: Crawley, Griffiths. *Macc:* Zelem, Roberts, Tobin, Edwards, Hardman, Askey, Lake, Hanlon, Imrie, Burr, Timmons. Subs: Derbyshire, Kendall. *Att: 18,102.*

1990   BARROW 3 (Gordon 2, Cowperthwaite) **LEEK TOWN 0**   Ref: T Simpson
Barrow: McDonnell, Higgins, Chilton, Skivington, Gordon, Proctor, Doherty (Burgess), Farrell (Gilmore), Cowperthwaite, Lowe, Ferris. *Leek:* Simpson, Elsby (Smith), Pearce, McMullen, Clowes, Coleman (Russell), Mellor, Somerville, Sutton, Millington. *Att: 19,011.*

1991   WYCOMBE WANDERERS 2 (Scott, West) **KIDDERMINSTER HARRIERS 1** (Hadley)   Ref: J Watson
Wycombe: Granville, Crossley, Cash, Cash, Kerr, Creaser, Carroll, Ryan, Stapleton, West, Scott, Guppy (Hutchinson). *K'minster:* Jones, Kurila, McGrath, Weir, Barnett, Forsyth, Joseph (Wilcox), Howell (Whitehouse), Hadley, Lilwall, Humphries. *Att: 34,842.*

Dagenham manager Eddie Presland proudly displays the F.A. Trophy after the 1980 victory over Mossley at Wembley. The success was particularly sweet as the 'Daggers' had suffered three Wembley finals defeats in the seventies; in 1970 and 1971 in the F.A. Amateur Cup, and in 1977 in the Trophy.

F.A. TROPHY
Round by Round Chart

1st Rnd Proper

Team	Score
Sutton Utd	1
Bath City	2
Atherstone Utd	1
Dorking	3
Wycombe Wand	2
Salisbury	0
Woking	4
Wembley	2
Witton Albion	2;2
Billingham Syn	2;1
Aylesbury Utd	3
Newport AFC	2
Gloucester C	1
Harrow Boro	2
Altrincham	1
Stalybridge C	2
Stafford Rgrs	0
Marine	1
Wivenhoe T	1
Marlow	0
Dagenham	0;0
Bashley	0;2
VS Rugby	0
Kettering T	1
Redbridge F	1;1
Bromsgrove R	1;0
Enfield	4
Slough Town	0
Sutton Coldfield	0
Farnborough T	3
Southport	1
Bishop Auckland	0
Merthyr Tydfil	1;2
Dartford	1;1
Colchester Utd	2;3
Kingstonian	2;2
Fleetwood T	1;0
Morecambe	1;1
Welling Utd	3
Dover Athletic	2
Telford Utd	2
Guisborough T	0
Frickley Ath	2;0
Norrthallerton	2;1
Blyth Spartans	0;0
Gateshead	0;3
Whitby Town	0
Barrow	2
Bromley	1
Worcester C	0
Yeovil Town	3
Chesham Utd	1
Leek Town	3;2
Runcorn	3;3
Walton & Her.	0
Kidderminster	2
Northwich Vics	1
Hyde United	0
Cheltenham T	3
Wealdstone	2
Macclesfield T	0;2
Boston United	0;0
Bangor City	0;2
Gretna	0;1

2nd Rnd Proper

Team	Score
Bath City	2
Dorking	0
Wycombe Wand	1
Woking	0
Witton Albion	1
Aylesbury Utd	0
Harrow Boro	1
Stalybridge	3
Marine	3
Wivenhoe T	0
Bashley	2
Kettering T	3
Redbridge F	2
Enfield	0
Farnborough T	5
Southport	0
Merthyr Tydfil	1
Colchester Utd	0;1
Morecambe	2
Welling Utd	1
Telford Utd	3
Northallerton	0
Gateshead	1
Barrow	0
Bromley	1
Yeovil Town	3
Runcorn	1;2
Kidderminster	1;5
Northwich Vics	4
Cheltenham T	2
Macclesfield	1
Bangor City	0

3rd Rnd Proper

Team	Score
Bath City	1;0
Wycombe W	1;2
Witton Albion	1
Stalybridge C	0
Marine	2
Kettering T	1
Redbridge F	3
Farnborough T	2
Colchester Utd	3
Morecambe	1
Telford Utd	0;1
Gateshead	0;0
Yeovil Town	3
Kidderminster	1
Northwich Vics	0
Macclesfield T	1

4th Rnd Proper

Team	Score
Wycombe Wand	1
Witton Albion	2
Marine	0;1
Redbridge F	0;0
Colchester Utd	4
Telford Utd	0
Yeovil Town	1
Macclesfield T	2

Semi-final

Team	Score
Witton Albion	2;4
1st leg at Witton	
Marine	2;1
Colchester Utd	3;1
1st leg at Colchester	
Macclesfield	0;1

Final

Team	Score
Witton Albion	1
Colchester Utd	3

F.A CHALLENGE VASE

REVIEW 1991-92

F.A. CHALLENGE VASE

WIMBORNE BRING GLORY TO DORSET

With a truly oustanding performance at Wembley, Dorset minnows **Wimborne Town** re-ignited the romance of the F.A. Vase when they convincingly beat red-hot favourites and holders **Guiseley** in a memorable final. It was the first time that a Dorset club had ever made the trip to the Twin Towers, and the result firmly put Wimborne's League, the recently formed Jewson Wessex, onto the football map.

The club's marathon run commenced in the First Round when, for a second consecutive season, they won at **Mangotsfield United**. After easing past **Chard** the Magpies first started to raise eyebrows with a home win over in-form Diadora outfit **Horsham**. This was followed by a sensational replay triumph at Beazer Southern District League leaders **Hastings Town**, albeit with the help of some disputable arbitration. The Fifth Round took Nick Jennings' side to **Newcastle Town**, and after escaping from the Potteries with a 1-1 draw they began an amazing sequence of five games without conceding a goal; a run that took them all the way to the hallowed turf. Newcastle were duly despatched in the replay, as were **Diss Town** in a tight Quarter Final that yielded just one goal in 210 minutes. The Semi Final paired Wimborne with fellow giant-killers **Bamber Bridge**, and two second leg goals sufficed on a never-to-be-forgotten afternoon at Cuthbury.

Holders **Guiseley**, enjoying an excellent first season in the H.F.S. Loans League, became progressively hotter favourites as the competition wore on. This was due to their faultless passage to the Semi Finals as strongly fancied teams such as **Gresley**, **Great Harwood**, **Solihull**, **Hythe**, and **Hastings** dropped like flies. In the last four **Guiseley**'s nightmare was realised when they were paired with **Sudbury Town** in a true clash of the titans. Sudbury, inspired by the veteran Brian Talbot, seemed to gain the initiative in a 2-2 draw at Nethermoor, but like true champions the holders pulled out a fabulous display in the return to qualify for Wembley for a second successive year.

Many observers will remember the 1992 Vase for the exploits of Bass North West Counties Division Two side **Bamber Bridge**, bettered only by the achievement of Wimborne. Two years ago this club were playing in the local Preston & District League, and this was their first participation in the Vase. They started their run with a 3-0 win at West Cheshire League side **Ashville** and followed this up with convincing away triumphs at Premier Division counterparts **Prescot** and **St Helens**. The team's phenomenal appetite for goals first drew national attention when Northern Counties East side **Liversedge** were knocked for eight on their own pitch in the Second Round. In their first home tie, 'the Bridge' claimed another Bass Premier scalp in the shape of **Flixton**, and in the second, a replay after a 4-4 draw at Brigg, they drew the first four-figure gate of the 1991-92 Vase. Through to the last sixteen from the Extra-Preliminary Round, Bamber Bridge's success was already remarkable, but it did not stop there. **Newport I.O.W.** made one of the longest trips in Vase history to visit Irongate, and left licking their wounds after a 1-2 defeat, then 'Bridge' travelled south to **Chertsey** to create yet another upset. By now the Preston side had scored a staggering thirty times in the competition, but just when it mattered most the goals dried up and Wimborne Town seized their chance.

As always, numerous other teams deserve recognition for having contributed to making the Vase particularly memorable. Not least amongst these teams were **West Midlands Police**, the reigning Midland Combination champions, who enjoyed an excellent run to the last eight with a very skillful side. In fact, many believe that had the club not had to endure a sapping trip to Glasgow to play a national Police cup match in the days preceding the Quarter Final against Sudbury, they would have progressed further. The Influence Combination enjoyed its most prosperous ever Vase campaign as champions-to-be **Evesham United** also made it through to the last eight. They were eventually overwhelmed by the irresistible Guiseley, but the Robins will savour memories of a fine run. Their most notable victory came in the Fourth Round against 1990 Semi Finalists and 1991 Quarter Finalists, **Hythe Town**. After a 3-3 draw in Kent, Hythe had to travel no fewer than three times to Worcestershire before bowing out. On the occasion of the first trip the replay was frozen off, and at the second time of asking it was abandoned at half-time due to waterlogging.

It was generally a good year for Police sides as, in addition to West Midlands Police, **Metropolitan Police** enjoyed an extended run, classing a 2-1 win at **Sittingbourne** as their most noteworthy success. **Diss Town** were their ultimate conquerors, 2-0 at Imber Court in the Fifth Round. The Norfolk side were another outfit to experience their best ever Vase run, and were only beaten by Wimborne by the very tightest of margins in the Quarter Finals.

Finally, although no comprehensive statistical analysis has been undertaken in our office, it would be hard to believe that this F.A. Vase was not the most prolific ever in terms of goals. Not only did it throw up a second consecutive eight goal Wembley final, but it yielded some eye-catching early round scores. To name but a few, there were two 8-3 scorelines, a 2-7, a 6-4 at **Stapenhill**, and a sixteen goal two match tie between **Redgate Clayton** and **St Dominics**. Most amazing of all was a game at **Northwood** where the home side edged out **Braintree** by the odd goal in thirteen. Who said you have to buy a satellite dish to see top class football entertainment!

James Wright

EXTRA PRELIMINARY ROUND

91 Ties **Matches Played:** 101
Home wins: 55 **Draws:** 11 **Away wins:** 35 (1 Walkover)
Best Attendance: 204; Holwell Sports v Coleshill Town
Total Attendance: 6,401 (1 gate missing) **Average Attendance:** 64
Largest Home Win: St Dominics 7, Redgate Clayton 1
Largest Away Win: Prudhoe East End 2, Dunston Federation B. 7
Result of the Round: Old Salesians 3, Farleigh Rovers 2

Saturday 7th September 1991 Res Att (* Denotes extra time played)

	Res	Att		Res	Att
Heaton Stannington v Marske Utd	0-1	28	Eccleshall v Hamlet S & L	3-1	69
Ponteland Utd v Sunderland IFG Roker	1-3	30	Ramsey Town v St Ives T. *(at St Ives)*	2-1	
Prudhoe East End v Dunston FB	2-7	91	Diss Town v Clarksteel Yaxley	2-0	112
Whitehaven Miners v Newton Aycliffe	0-4	38	Downham Town v Brightlingsea United	1-0	92
Pickering Town v Seaton Delaval ST	4-0	108	Stansted v Sawbridgeworth Town	2-1*	148
Seaton Delaval A. v S'land Vaux Ryhope	2-0	31	Norwich United v Somersham Town	0-2	99
Heswall v Poulton Victoria	4-0	60	Ipswich Wndrs v Wroxham *(at Wroxham)*	1-3	52
General Chemicals v Christleton	3-1	52	Brantham Athletic v Ely City	0-2	64
Merseyside Police v Westhoughton Town	4-0	50	Chatteris Town v Woodbridge Town	1-2	89
Ashville v Bamber Bridge	0-3	80	Long Sutton Athletic v LBC Ortonians	1-2	51
Knypersley V. v Atherton LR *(at A'ton)*	3-4	43	Long Buckby v London Colney	2-2	25
Waterloo Dock v Cheadle Town	3-1	46	London Colney v Long Buckby *(14-9-91)*	1-4	30
Redgate Clayton v St Dominics	4-4	70	Beaconsfield Utd v Milton Keynes Boro	3-1	30
St Dominics v Redgate Clayton *(14-9-91)*	7-1	45	Kempston Rovers v Langford	3-0	68
Newton (WC) v Vauxhall Motors (WC)	1-4	20	Wolverton v Brook House	0-3	62
Ayone v Maghull	3-2	40	Biggleswade Town v Wingate & Finchley	0-1	59
Kidsgrove Athletic *w/o* Leyland DAF *withdrew*			Viking Sports v Amersham Town	3-2	65
Blidworth MW v Brodsworth MW	1-0	22	Waltham Town v Totternhoe	3-2	41
Hatfield Town v Immingham Town	2-3	35	The 61 FC v Cockfosters	1-4	10
Dunkirk v Lincoln United	1-5	175	Potters Bar Town v Pirton	1-0*	72
Radford v Louth United	3-2	26	Stotfold v Bowers United	2-1	51
Priory (Eastwood) v Rossington Main	5-1	25	Winslow United v Rayners Lane	1-3	25
Winterton Rangers v Bradford PA	4-1	113	Brimsdown Rovers v Shillington	2-0	58
Nettleham v Tadcaster Albion	0-0	46	Petersfield United v Bedfont	1-0	75
Tadcaster v Nettleham *(14-9-91)*	0-2	55	Deal Town v Eastbourne Town	1-0	190
Clipstone Welfare v RES Parkgate	1-1	61	Horley Town v Slade Green	0-3	40
RES Parkgate v Clipstone *(14-9-91)*	0-1	30	Ashford Town (Middx) v Hartley Wintney	3-0	50
Yorkshire Amateur v Worsborough Bridge	3-1	45	Old Salesians v Farleigh Rovers	3-2	65
Mickleover RBL v Maltby MW *(at Gresley)*	2-1	106	Godalming Town v Broadbridge Heath	0-1*	36
Liversedge v Kimberley Town	2-1*	87	Cobham v Ash United	5-1	22
Stocksbridge Pk Steels v Bradley Rgrs	2-1*	31	Sherborne Town v Bicester Town	3-2	45
Selby Town v Glasshoughton Welfare	1-4	107	Christchurch v Fleet Town	1-3	42
Shirebrook Colliery v Pontefract Co'ries	2-1*	150	Oxford City v Wantage Town	3-1	110
Hallam v Hall Road Rangers *(at Hall Rd)*	2-2	42	Aerostructures S & S v Milton Utd	0-1	44
Hall Road Rangers v Hallam *(14-9-91)*	1-2*	45	Ryde Sports v Kintbury Rangers	3-2	43
Bloxham Town v Brackley Town	4-0	25	AFC Lymington v Bishops Cleeve	5-0	66
Harrowby United v Heath Hayes	5-2	67	Brockenhurst v BAT	4-0	70
Coleshill Town v Holwell Sports	1-1	56	Flight Refuelling v Harrow Hill	5-1	23
Holwell Sports v Coleshill *(11-9-91)*	3-2	204	Bridgwater Town '84 v Brislington	2-0	169
Oldswinford v Knowle	0-0	30	Cinderford Town v Backwell United	1-1	103
Knowle v Oldswinford *(14-9-91)*	1-0	34	Backwell Utd v Cinderford *(14-9-91)*	2-2	72
Oadby Town v Pelsall Villa	1-0	60	Cinderford v Backwell Utd *(18-9-91)*	4-2	130
West Bromwich Town v Anstey Nomads	2-2	33	Old Georgians v Keynsham Town	0-2	40
Anstey Nomads v West Brom *(14-9-91)*	3-0	103	Fairford Town v Larkhall Athletic	2-3*	50
Northfield Town v Tividale	4-0	68	Clandown v Wotton Rovers	1-1	28
Burton Pk Wanderers v Pegasus Juniors	0-2	15	Wotton Rovers v Clandown *(14-9-91)*	2-1*	45
Wolverhampton Casuals v Westfield	1-0	10	Almondsbury Picksons v Cirencester Town	4-4	52
Meir KA v Lutterworth Town	2-1	55	Cirencester v Almondsbury *(11-9-91)*	0-1	100
Kings Heath v Highfield Rgrs *(at Knowle)*	3-2	42	Bemerton Heath H'quins v Swindon Ath.	2-3*	45
Stourport Swifts v Bolehall Swifts	2-0	52	DRG (FP) v Clanfield	3-4	25
St Andrews v Daventry Town	1-2	82	Truro City v St Austell	0-2	180
Stapenhill v Norton United	6-4	100			

Mark Thomas scores Oxford City's second in their first ever Vase tie, a 3-1 win v. Wantage. Photo - Steve Daniels.

Perrins of West Bromwich Town brings the ball out of defence in the home tie with Anstey. Photo - Paul Williamson.

Peter Goodwin of Farleigh deceives an Old Salesian, but his club were surprisingly beaten. Photo - Francis Short.

PRELIMINARY ROUND

160 Ties **Matches Played:** 181
Home wins: 78 **Draws:** 21 **Away wins:** 82
Best Attendance: 396 - Tiverton Town v Elmore
Total Attendance: 15,928 (2 gates missing) **Average Attendance:** 89
Largest Home Win: Blakenall 8, Mile Oak Rovers & Youth 0
Largest Away Win: Petersfield United 1, Tonbridge AFC 7
Result of the Round: Netherfield 1, Sunderland IFG Roker 2

Saturday 5th October 1991   Res   Att   (* Denotes extra time played)

Match	Res	Att
Evenwood Town v Seaton Delaval Amtrs	1-2	15
Ashington v Penrith	1-2	46
Cleator Moor Celtic v Langley Park	2-6	81
Marske United v West Allotment Celtic	2-1	43
Hebburn v Norton & Stockton Ancients	2-0*	250
West Auckland Town v Washington	2-0	30
Willington v Newton Aycliffe	0-4	22
Annfield Plain v Crook Town	3-1	57
Shotton Comrades v Durham City	0-6	50
Chester-le-Street v Pickering Town	2-1	105
Stockton v Dunston Federation B'ries	1-2	
Horden CW v Darlington CB	6-1	27
Netherfield v Sunderland IFG Roker	1-2*	97
Esh Winning v Bedlington Terriers	1-4	45
Oldham Town v Newcastle Town	1-2	30
Vauxhall GM v Rocester	0-0	21
Rocester v Vauxhall GM (8-10-91)	1-2	131
Irlam Town v Heswall	3-2	49
St Helens Town v Burscough	2-3	80
V'hall Mtrs (WC) v Atherton LR (4-10-91)	1-2	32
Curzon Ashton v Blackpool (Wren) Rovers	0-1	63
Nantwich Town v Wythenshawe Amateurs	1-1	148
Wythenshawe v Nantwich (12-10-91)	2-1	115
Ashton United v Lancaster City	4-0	286
Ayone v Bootle	1-1	27
Bootle v Ayone (8-10-91)	2-3*	140
Chadderton v Flixton	4-6*	102
Formby v General Chemicals	1-1	32
General Chemicals v Formby (9-10-91)	0-0	58
Formby v General Chemicals	0-1	33
Clitheroe v Skelmersdale United	2-1	135
Prescot AFC v Bamber Bridge	1-3*	132
Darwen v St Dominics	1-2	144
Atherton Collieries v Maine Road	1-1	48
Maine Road v Atherton Col. (8-10-91)	3-1	61
Salford City v Merseyside Police	2-0	82
Waterloo Dk v Kidsgrove Ath. (at K'grove)	1-1	80
Kidsgrove v W'loo Dock (12-10-91 at W'loo)	1-1	51
W'loo Dk v K'grove (16-10-91 at Knowsley)	1-1	63
Kidsgrove Athletic v Waterloo Dock	3-1	80
Oakham United v Hallam	1-5*	73
Arnold Town v Lincoln United	0-0	190
Lincoln Utd v Arnold Town (9-10-91)	5-0	334
Denaby United v Thackley	3-4	114
Mickleover RBL v Nettleham	3-2	106
Ossett Albion v Immingham Town	2-5	48
Clipstone Welfare v Winterton Rgrs	0-1	100
Yorkshire Amtrs v Glasshoughton Welfare	2-3	
Armthorpe Welfare v Eccleshill United	4-1	46
Radford v Harworth CI	1-2	25
Brigg v Shirebrook Colliery	6-1	
Priory (E'wood) v Stocksbridge Pk Steels	1-3	47
Sheffield v Fiar Lane Old Boys	2-1	42
Blidworth MW v Liversedge	1-3	23
Ilkeston Town v Belper Town	0-3	174
Stapenhill v Oldbury United	0-2	80
Wellingborough v Northfield Town	1-3	50
Pegasus Juniors v Northampton Spencer	0-1	82
Meir KA v Racing Club Warwick	0-1	35
Eccleshall v Wolverhampton Casuals	2-1	46
Halesowen Harriers v Holwell Sports	4-2	87

Match	Res	Att
Daventry Town v West Mids Police	0-0	110
West Mids Police v Daventry (12-10-91)	0-0	30
West Mids Police v Daventry (17-10-91)	2-1*	60
Hinckley v Sandwell Borough	0-1	48
Bridgnorth T. Irthlingboro Diamonds	4-1	80
Malvern Town v Oadby Town	1-0	52
APV P'boro City v Stratford Town	1-0	33
Highgate Utd v Desborough Town	2-0	45
Blakenall v Mile Oak Rvrs & Youth	8-0	89
Anstey Nomads v Kings Heath	2-1	85
Harrowby Utd v Boldmere St Michaels	1-5	77
Hinckley Town v Walsall Wood	1-0	74
Solihull Borough v Knowle	6-2	102
Rushall Olympic v Stourport Swifts	5-1*	72
Lye Town v Bilston Town	1-1	105
Bilston Town v Lye Town (8-10-91)	5-2	122
Wednesfield v Evesham United	1-3	37
Bloxwich Town v Chasetown	0-0	33
Chasetown v Bloxwich Town (19-10-91)	2-0	79
Clacton Town v Ely City	4-3	79
Canvey Island v Witham Town	0-1	73
Boston v Diss Town	0-1*	68
Eynesbury Rovers v Newmarket Town	0-0	130
Newmarket v Eynesbury Rvrs (8-10-91)	0-0	110
Eynesbury Rvrs v Newmarket Town	0-2*	120
Woodbridge Town v Royston Town	0-1	157
Halstead Town v Basildon United	1-3	182
Ramsey Town v March Town United	1-2	
Mirrlees Blackstone v Lowestoft Town	1-4	104
Tiptree United v Downham Town	3-5	26
Berkhamsted Town v Soham Town Rgrs	1-0	79
Stamford Town v Bourne Town	1-0	214
Gorleston v Sowmarket Town	4-2*	133
Stansted v Barton Rovers	3-0	105
Bury Town v LBC Ortonians	1-0	177
Wroxham v Somersham Town	3-0	114
Watton United v Felixstowe Town	1-2	45
Rayners Lane v Kingsbury Town	0-1*	45
Tilbury v Brook House	5-2	57
Wingate & Finchley v Hornchurch	5-0	106
Waltham Abbey v Leighton Town	1-0	51
Brimsdown Rovers v Viking Sports	0-1	66
Feltham & Hounslow Boro v Wootton BC	5-0	30
Stotfold v Tring Town	2-0	61
Ford United v Metropolitan Police	2-3*	65
Clapton v Haringey Borough	1-3	61
Hertford Town v Beaconsfield United	4-1*	103
Arlesey Town v Rainham Town	4-1	150
Flackwell Heath v Edgware Town	1-4	52
Bracknell Town v Hoddesdon Town	0-1	48
Kempston Rovers v Cockfosters	1-3*	79
Welwyn Garden City v Cheshunt	1-2	40
Hampton v Ruislip Manor	1-1	145
Ruislip Manor v Hampton (7-10-91)	2-3	199
Northwood v Long Buckby	4-1	81
Letchworth GC v Potters Bar Town	1-1	44
Potters Bar v Letchworth GC (12-10-91)	2-1	84
Hemel Hempstead v Barkingside	4-1*	65
Southall v Eton Manor (at Eton Manor)	3-2*	26
Ware v Collier Row	0-2	105
Leatherhead v Burnham	0-2	95
Worthing v Slade Green	1-3	130

	Res	Att		Res	Att
Shoreham v Peacehaven & Telscombe	1-3	94	Newport (IOW) v Oxford City	2-0	286
Corinthian v Deal Town	1-0	31	Sholing Spts v Swanage Town & H'ton	1-2	62
Wick v Haywards Heath Town	4-0	55	Thame United v Horndean	6-0	111
Croydon Athletic v Banstead Athletic	2-4	28	Brockenhurst v Romsey Town	1-2	90
Horsham v Cove	5-1	147	East Cowes Vict. Ath. v Witney Town	1-2	40
Tunbridge Wells v Cobham	7-6*	105	Fleet Town v Banbury United	2-2	69
Old Salesians v Hailsham Town	2-7	50	Banbury United v Fleet Town *(8-10-91)*	1-3	182
Chipstead v Burgess Hill Town	0-4	84	Sherborne Town v First Tower United	2-2	87
Herne Bay v Arundel	8-1	69	First Tower Utd v Sherborne *(19-10-91)*	1-2	75
Sittingbourne v Beckenham Town	3-1	271	Westbury United v Bournemouth	0-1	98
Camberley Town v Southwick	1-2	52	Minehead v Melksham Town	4-1	102
Redhill v Alma Swanley	4-0	72	Calne Town v Odd Down	0-1	43
Pagham v Horsham YMCA	3-1	66	Glastonbury v Mangotsfield United	2-4	75
Broadbridge Heath v Oakwood	0-2	45	Clanfield v Devizes Town	1-3	52
Worthing United v Ringmer	2-1	34	Chard Town v Swindon Athletic	2-0	71
Petersfield United v Tonbridge AFC	1-7	180	Larkhall Athletic v Bristol Manor Farm	1-2	49
Whitehawk v Ashford Town (Middx)	2-1*	108	Wotton Rovers v Keynsham Town	2-3	58
Three Bridges v Darenth Heathside	2-1	28	Cinderford Town v Frome Town	3-0	150
Whitstable Town v Lancing	4-0	103	Shortwood United v Radstock Town	5-2	146
Lewes v Selsey	0-2	62	Bridgwater Town v Chippenham Town	0-2	160
Steyning v Epsom & Ewell	0-3	50	Almondsbury Picksons v Welton Rovers	0-1	62
Egham Town v Malden Vale	0-1	89	Clevedon Town v Flight Refuelling	7-1	110
Portfield v Corinthian Casuals	0-1*	40	Exmouth Town v Liskeard Athletic	1-0	119
Langney Sports v Eastbourne Utd	5-2	270	Tiverton Town v Elmore	3-0	396
Sheppey United v Faversham Town	1-4	135	Torrington v Barnstaple Town	1-1	140
Chichester City v Chatham Town	3-0	27	Barnstaple Town v Torrington *(8-10-91)*	1-2	217
Milton United v Abingdon United	3-0	60	Torpoint Athletic v Ilfracombe Town	1-0	88
Newbury Town v AFC Totton	3-0	76	St Blazey v Crediton United	1-2*	75
AFC Lymington v Ryde Sports	1-0	58	St Austell v Ottery St Mary	2-0	82

Gary Martindale coolly slides home St Dominics's sixth goal in the replay against Redgate. Photo - Rob Ruddock.

March Town United on the defensive during their win at Ramsey Town. Photo - Nigel Upson.

Lowe's penalty completes the scoring in Hemel Hempstead's 4-1 win against Barkingside. Photo - Gavin Ellis.

Slade Green keeper Colin Hart clears as the Kent side record a shock win at Worthing. Photo - Colin Stevens.

Mark Thomas of Oxford City tries to find a way through the Newport I.O.W. defence. Photo - Steve Daniels.

FIRST ROUND

96 Ties **Matches Played: 106**
Home wins: 59 Draws: 10 Away wins: 37
Best Attendance: 348 - Tonbridge AFC v Banstead Athletic
Total Attendance: 8,816 **Average Attendance:** 83
Largest Home Win: 6-0; Faversham v Southwick, Purfleet v Southall
Largest Away Win: 0-6; Exmouth v Newquay, Merstham v Whitstable
Result of the Round: Berkhamsted Town 2, Bury Town 0

Saturday 2nd November 1991	Res	Att	(* Denotes extra time played)	Res	Att
West Auckland Town v Horden CW	1-0	84	King's Lynn v Lowestoft Town	2-1*	344
Durham City v Eppleton CW	2-2	80	Royston Town v March Town United	2-1	54
Eppleton CW v Durham City (9-11-91)	2-2	161	Metropolitan Police v Stotfold	1-1	35
Durham City v Eppleton CW (13-11-91)	2-0	198	Stotfold v Metropolitan Police (6-11-91)	0-2	98
Seaton Delaval Amateurs v Dunston FB	1-2*	64	Burnham Ramblers v Haringey Borough	2-2	63
Bedlington Terriers v Newton Aycliffe	0-1	35	Haringey Boro v Burnham Rblrs (5-11-91)	1-2	38
Penrith v Sunderland IFG Roker	2-1	41	Viking Sports v Feltham & Hounslow B.	3-0	45
Chester-le-Street Town v Langley Park	3-3	54	Collier Row v Wingate & Finchley	1-0	76
Langley Pk v Chester-le-Street (9-11-91)	1-3	97	Purfleet v Southall	6-0	45
Billingham Town v Annfield Plain	4-3*	8	Northwood v Braintree Town	7-6*	120
Hebburn v Marske United	3-2	110	Potters Bar Town v Hampton	0-0	64
Atherton Laburnum Rovers v Clitheroe	3-1	70	Hampton v Potters Bar Town (5-11-91)	4-1	147
Burscough v Irlam Town	5-1	71	Cheshunt v Waltham Abbey	2-1	55
Flixton v Kidsgrove Athletic	1-0	35	Arlesey Town v Hertford Town	1-0	150
Glossop v Newcastle Town	0-1	110	Cockfosters v Kingsbury Town	1-1	65
Wythenshaw Amtrs v Eastwood Hanley	0-2	30	Kingsbury Town v Cockfosters (5-11-91)	1-4	63
Salford City v Vauxhall GM	2-0	55	Hemel Hempstead v Edgware Town	0-2	52
Bamber Bridge v St Dominics	6-1	156	Tilbury v Hoddesdon Town	1-0	31
General Chemicals v Maine Road	0-1	32	Corinthian v Langney Sports	1-3	18
Rossendale United v Ayone	5-2*	175	Peacehaven & Telscombe v Whitehawk	5-0	126
Blackpool (Wren) Rovers v Ashton United	1-2	55	Merstham v Whitstable Town	0-6	48
Lincoln United v Harworth Cl	2-3	180	Wick v Sittingbourne	0-2	75
Hallam v Ossett Town	0-1*	93	Faversham Town v Southwick	6-0	78
Glasshoughton Welfare v Belper Town	0-3	50	Tunbridge Wells v Greenwich Borough	1-2*	148
Garforth Town v Heanor Town	4-1	46	Three Bridges v Burgess Hill Town	3-3	63
Mickleover RBL v Borrowash Victoria	3-4	80	Burgess Hill v Three Bridges (6-11-91)	0-1	109
Liversedge v Rainworth Miners Welfare	3-1*	44	Herne Bay v Hailsham Town	3-1	91
Brigg Town v Stocksbridge Park Steels	5-0	52	Worthing United v Selsey	2-1	40
Armthorpe Welfare v Sheffield	2-4	43	Havant Town v Redhill	3-2	88
Harrogate Town v Winterton Rangers	4-1	163	Pagham v Burnham	1-0	70
Thackley v Immingham Town	3-1	100	Horsham v Oakwood	1-0	155
Sandwell Borough v West Mids Police	1-2*	42	Epsom & Ewell v Chertsey Town	0-2	51
Raunds Town v Bridgnorth Town	1-1	69	Slade Green v Chichester City	4-0	33
Bridgnorth Town v Raunds (9-11-91)	0-2	90	Corinthian-Casuals v Malden Vale	2-3*	45
Eccleshall v Halesowen Harriers	4-2	51	Tonbridge AFC v Banstead Athletic	2-1	348
Chasetown v Northampton Spencer	2-1*	57	Sherborne Town v Thatcham Town	0-2	72
Rothwell Town v Evesham United	1-3	44	AFC Lymington v Newport IOW	0-1	100
Solihull Borough v Paget Rgrs (1-11-91)	4-1	123	Witney Town v Bournemouth	4-3	74
Rushall Olympic v Hinckley Town	2-1	150	Didcot Town v Romsey Town	2-1*	37
Boldmere St Michaels v RC Warwick	0-3	39	Fleet Town v Swanage Town & Herston	4-6*	49
APV Peterborough City v Malvern Town	3-0	30	Thame United v Milton United	3-0	90
Anstey Nomads v Oldbury United	4-0	58	Newbury Town v Eastleigh	3-0	65
Bilston Town v Highgate United	1-0	64	Welton Rovers v Minehead	1-0	52
Northfield v Blakenall	1-3	49	Devizes Town v Chard Town	0-3	38
Newmarket Town v Stamford	5-0	110	Shortwood United v Clevedon Town	3-1	100
Diss Town v Witham Town	3-1	149	Wellington v Cinderford Town	1-3	50
Downham Town v Felixstowe Town	3-3	70	Chippenham Town v Bristol Manor Farm	2-0	35
Felixstowe Town v Downham (5-11-91)	2-0	65	Keynsham Town v Odd Down	1-0	46
Holbeach United v Thetford Town	2-1	70	Mangotsfield United v Wimborne Town	1-2	127
Basildon United v Histon	5-3	42	Torpoint Athletic v St Austell	2-0	58
Wroxham v Clacton Town	3-0	64	Crediton United v Torrington	1-2*	105
Gorleston v Stansted	2-1	133	Falmouth Town v Tiverton Town	1-3*	245
Berkhamsted Town v Bury Town	2-0	63	Exmouth Town v Newquay	0-6	84

112

Jerry Rose runs in to score Newmarket's third of five against past Vase winners Stamford. Photo - Francis Short.

The razor-sharp Chris Sibley scores the only goal of Pagham's fine win against Burnham. Photo - Graham Cotterill.

Sherborne's Dave Mann takes a knock on the head from Thatcham's Steve McCartney. Photo - Dave West.

Blood and guts Vase action as Sittingbourne record a 1st Round win at Wick. Photo - Dennis Nicholson.

Simon Pope heads Havant Town into a 2-1 lead v. Redhill as a team-mate just stays onside. Photo - Paul Dennis.

Tonbridge's excellent Lee Thompson on the ball in the 2-1 win over Banstead Athletic. Photo - Mike Floate.

SECOND ROUND

64 Ties Matches Played: 72
Home Wins: 47 Draws: 8 Away Wins: 17
Best Attendance: 637 - Hastings Town v Langney Sports
Total Attendance: 14,978 (1 gate missing) **Average Attendance:** 211
Largest Home Win: Flixton 8, Borrowash Victoria 3
Largest Away Win: Liversedge 3, Bamber Bridge 8
Result of the Round: Evesham United 3, Buckingham Town 1

Saturday 23rd November 1991	Res	Att	(* Denotes extra time played)	Res	Att
Harrogate Railway Athletic v Penrith	0-1	102	Edgware Town v Basildon United	4-3	211
Great Harwood Town v Farsley Celtic	1-1	231	Burnham Ramblers v East Thurrock Utd	5-3	119
Farsley Celtic v Gt Harwood *(27-11-91)*	4-0	260	Collier Row v Harefield United	4-0	98
Dunston Federation B'ries v Thackley	3-2*	100	Saffron Walden Town v Wroxham	3-1	150
Liversedge v Bamber Bridge	3-8	113	Berkhamsted T. v Harwich & Parkeston	2-1	120
Newton Aycliffe v Hebburn	2-2	108	Metropolitan Police v Royston Town	1-0	45
Hebburn v Newton Aycliffe *(30-11-91)*	2-4*		Gorleston v Hampton	0-2	157
Chester-le-Street Town v Durham City	2-0	253	Haverhill Rovers v Sudbury Town	1-1	539
Bridlington Town v Billingham Town	5-0	214	Sudbury Town v Haverhill Rvrs *(26-11-91)*	2-1*	577
North Ferriby Utd v West Auckland Town	1-0	178	Billericay Town v King's Lynn	4-2	404
Newcastle Town v Sheffield	2-0	80	Horsham v Littlehampton Town	2-2	405
Guiseley v Garforth Town	2-0	601	Littlehampton Town v Horsham *(27-11-91)*	0-1	420
Eastwood Hanley v Harrogate Town	4-1	61	Sittingbourne v Tilbury	4-2*	311
Belper Town v Harworth Colliery Inst.	2-1	160	Malden Vale v Thatcham Town	2-2	91
Ossett Town v Atherton Laburnum Rvrs	3-3	95	Thatcham Town v Malden Vale *(26-11-91)*	2-3	158
Atherton LR v Ossett Town *(26-11-91)*	3-1*	200	Hythe Town v Herne Bay	1-1	334
Flixton v Borrowash Victoria	8-3	92	Herne Bay v Hythe Town *(30-11-91)*	1-2*	216
Knowsley United v Cammell Laird	1-0	282	Chertsey T. v Peacehaven & Telscombe	3-2*	161
Burscough v Rossendale United	2-0	183	Faversham Town v Whitstable Town	1-0	271
Ashton United v Maine Road	2-1	319	Three Bridges v Greenwich Borough	2-0	77
Salford v Brigg Town	0-1	80	Langney Sports v Hastings Town	3-3	498
Eccleshall v Wisbech Town	0-2	268	Hastings Town v Langney Spts *(26-11-91)*	2-1	637
Gresley Rovers v Blakenall	1-0	589	Didcot Town v Worthing United	1-2*	102
Chasetown v Witney Town	3-2*	105	Tonbridge AFC v Thame United	1-6	469
Bilston Town v APV Peterborough City	3-1	105	Pagham v Slade Green	3-0	90
Anstey Nomads v Spalding United	3-2	109	Northwood v Purfleet	3-2	109
Raunds Town v Holbeach United	3-0	97	Chippenham Town v Paulton Rovers	1-3	82
Hinckley Athletic v Hucknall Town	3-2	287	Shortwood United v Bridport	3-1	160
West Mids Police v Rushall Olympic	3-1*	52	Torrington v Keynsham Town	1-0	122
Racing Club Warwick v Solihull Borough	1-3	141	Yate Town v Newbury Town	3-0	215
Evesham United v Buckingham Town	3-1	233	Cinedford Town v Newquay	3-1	250
Potton United v Walthamstow Pennant	0-4	108	Wimborne Town v Chard Town	5-2	210
Diss Town v Viking Sports	4-0	249	Hungerford Town v Torpoint Athletic	2-1	171
Felixstowe Town v Cheshunt	2-0	125	Dawlish Town v Welton Rovers	1-2	64
Arlesey Town v Newmarket Town	0-2	120	Tiverton Town v Swanage Town & H.	2-0	241
Great Yarmouth Town v Cockfosters	2-1	90			

Paul Spittle has to take evasive action as team-mate Chris Fontain fires a shot for Didcot Town during their surprise home defeat at the hands of Worthing United. Photo - Dave West.

Steve Buckle of Felixstowe makes an early headed clearance in the home win over Cheshunt. Photo - Gavin Ellis.

Purfleet's Daren Houlding gets in a cross despite the challenge of Tim Vincent of Northwood. Photo - Francis Short.

Steve Halstead of Newquay heads clear on this occasison, but the Peppermints lost at Cinderford. Photo - Ray Frith.

THIRD ROUND

32 Ties **Matches Played:** 37
Home wins: 16 **Draws:** 5 **Away wins:** 16
Best Attendance: 607 - Farsley Celtic v Guiseley
Total Attendance: 8,378 **Average Attendance:** 226
Largest Home Win: Hungerford Town 4, Faversham Town 1
Best Away Win: Farsley Celtic 2, Guiseley 5
Result of the Round: Newmarket Town 2, Solihull Borough 1

Saturday 14th December 1991 Res Att   (* Denotes extra time played)

Atherton LR v Brigg Town   3-3 150
Stewart 37,   Clay 46,
Pizelis 44 72   McLean 75(p),Crossley 85

Brigg v Atherton LR *(21-1-92)*   3-2 94
Crossley 31,   Edwards 18,
Davis 59,Clay 73   Stewart 43

Farsley Celtic v Guiseley   2-5 607
Taylor 23,   Noteman 16 67,
Hamilton 44   A Roberts 24,
*   Annan 34,B Roberts 65*

Belper v Dunston FB *(21-12-91)* 1-1 212
(Abandoned after 90 mins, waterlogged)
Woolley 61   Halliday 9

Dunston FB v Belper *(28-12-91)* 2-0 193
Gordon 14,Cockburn 78

Bridlington T. v Eastwood Han. 2-3* 153
Hopkinson 63,   Wheaton 30,
Archer 109   Muncey 97,Own Goal 119

Chester-le-Street v Ashton Utd 2-1 175
Morgan 70,   Butterworth 55
Robertson 74

Newton Aycliffe v Burscough   2-4* 120
Bellamy 23,   Hodge 48,
Wood 63   Togher 88 118 119

Bamber Bridge v Flixton   2-1 283
Whittaker 41,   Lomas 47
Baldwin 88

Nth Ferriby Utd v Knowsley Utd 1-2 112
Tidy 62   Siddell 15 26

Newcastle T. v Penrith *(28-12-91)*3-2* 121
Stephenton 30,   Monoghan 57,
Wade 93,   Gardner 91
Bright 110

Anstey N. v Felixstowe *(21-12-91)*2-1 329
Culpin 6,   Fuller 52
Tansley 60

Newmarket v Solihull *(21-12-91)* 2-1* 190
Eden 37,Rose 109   Hawker 77

Collier R. v WM Pol.*(21-12-91)* 2-3* 120
Braithwaite 20,   West 82,
Fiore 44   Hussey 87,Powney 93

Raunds T. v Diss T. *(21-12-91)* 0-2 121
*   Rose 48,Mendham 88*

W'stow P. v Evesham *(21-12-91)* 2-3* 42
Tredgold,   Rawle 22,
Adams   Emms 39,Candy 104

Edgware v Hinckley A. *(21-12-91)*2-1* 226
Chance 18,   Thompson 56
Stanborough 60

Wisbech T. v Gt Yarmouth *(21-12-91)* 2-2 545
Williams 25,   Danby 5,
Lindsay 88   Grealy 19

Gt Yarmouth T. v Wisbech *(28-12-91)* 2-4 330
Cockrill 28,   Lawrence 13 60,
Grealy 42   Lindsay 38,
*   Carr 80*

Berkhamsted T. v Gresley Rovers   1-2* 337
Clover 76   Beresford 88,Evans 102

Burnham R. v Chaestown *(21-12-91)* 2-1 132
Eves 32,   Scorer undiscussed
Harding 85

Billericay T. v Bilston T. *(21-12-91)* 2-0 411
Munday 64 83

Saffron Walden v Sudbury *(21-12-91)* 1-2* 325
Simpson 32   Coe 78,Bain 112

Hastings Town v Torrington   3-0 476
White 2 80,Wynter 78

Tiverton Town v Sittingbourne   2-3 320
Smith 47 60   Bourne 52,Freeman 56 58

Pagham v Hythe Town   1-2 171
Darnley 14   Arter 68 72

Chertsey v Cinderford T. *(21-12-91)* 1-1 147
Hutchins 66   Smith 60

Cinderford T. v Chertsey T. *(28-12-91)* 0-0 285

Cinderford v Chertsey T. *(1-1-92)* 1-2 450
Clutterbuck 31   Ellerker 19,Skerritt 75

Met. Police v Thr. Bridges *(21-12-91)* 2-0 51
McKenzie 46,Adams 65

Welton R. v Malden Vale   2-1 90
Vause 60 75   Collymore 80

Shortwood Utd v Yate T. *(21-12-91)* 2-3 150
Bell 50,   Tilley 5,
Marshall 78   Thompson 38 72

Hungerford v Faversham *(21-12-91)* 4-1 110
Howells 13,   Sainsbury 51
Martin 41,
Brooks 77,Notton 87

Worthing United v Northwood   1-2 155
Waller 10   Edey 40,Nolan 43

Wimborne Town v Horsham   1-0* 243
Sturgess 95

Hampton v Newport IW *(17-12-91)* 0-1 226
*   Greening 72*

Paulton Rvrs v Thame U. *(17-12-91)* 4-2 185
Harding(2),   Thomas 43,
Colbourne(2)   Dark 60

117

Atherton LR (white) clear their lines during a thrilling 3rd Round 3-3 draw against Brigg. Photo - Colin Stevens.

Colin Chance (left) celebrates his opening goal against Hinckley Athletic with Leslie Thompson. Photo - Dave West.

Berkhamsted's outstanding Shaun Walker puts Gresley under pressure on a freezing afternoon. Photo - Dave West.

FOURTH ROUND

16 Ties **Matches Played:** 20
Home wins: 7 **Draws:** 4 **Away wins:** 9
Best Attendance: 1,045 - Bamber Bridge v Brigg Town
Total Attendance: 8,875 (1 gate missing) **Average Gate:** 467
Largest Home Win: 3-1; Newport v Burnham, Edgare v Welton
Best Away Win: Chester-le-Street Town 1, Knowsley United 5
Result of the Round: Newcastle Town 3, Gresley Rovers 2

Saturday 18th January 1992

DUNSTON F.B. (1)1 *(Mulholland 24)*, **GUISELEY** (2) 3 *(Noteman 13 89,B Roberts 44)* Att: 423
Dunston: Boyd, Hillary, Cramman, Wright, Harmison, McDonald, Kendal, Cockburn, Mulholland, Halliday, Bensley (Gordon 74). Unused sub: Brown. *Guiseley:* Maxted, Wright, Hogarth, Tetley, Bottomley, A Roberts, Atkinson (Wilkinson 81), Tennison, Noteman (Colville 90), Annan, B Roberts.

BRIGG TOWN (3)4 *(Ward 17,Clay 38,Allott 44,Davis 105)*,
BAMBER BRIDGE (1)4 *(Whiteman 16 107,Baldwin 86,Lancaster 90)* Att: 404
Brigg: Gawthorpe, Penney, Rogers, Allott, Tucker, Clay, McLean, McLaughlin, Ward, Snee (Roach 65), Crossley (Davis 81). *Bamber Bridge:* Barton, Wilkes, Leaver, Proctor, Baldwin, Crawley (Naughton 56), Brown, Mayers (Lancaster 67), Whiteman, Whittaker, Dagleish.

BAMBER BRIDGE (0)1 *(Whittaker 122)*, **BRIGG TOWN** (0)0 25-1-92. Att: 1,045
Bamber Bridge: Barton, Wilkes, Leaver, Proctor, Baldwin, Brown, Mayers, Whiteman, Whittaker, Naughton. Unused subs: Worden, Crawley. *Brigg:* Gawthorpe, Clay, Rogers, Allott, Tucker, McLean, McLaughlin, Davis, Shrimpton (Roach 70), Crossley, Ward (Snee 109).

NEWCASTLE T. (1)3 *(Wade 2 87,Prestridge 96(p))*, **GRESLEY R.** (1)2 *(Beresford 45(p) 51)* Att: 577
Newcastle: Butler, Chetwyn, Williams, Prestridge, Griffiths, Hagan, Steventon (Bright 74), Lawton, Wade, Ritchie, Beardmore (Chamberlain 85). *Gresley:* Aston, Barry, Dick, Denby, Evans, Minton, Weston, Rathbone (Smith 60), Acklam (Land 85), Beresford, Lovell.

BURSCOUGH (0)0 **EASTWOOD HANLEY** (0)1 *(Muncey 59)* Att: 314
Burscough: Robinson, Doyle, Still, Owen, Winn, Boland (Owers 82), McIlwaine, Hodge, Quinn (Walbank 67), Togher, Rigby. *Eastwood:* Johnson, Jones, France, Bates, Ridley, Martin, Hulme, Woodward (Twigg 83), Muncey, Wheaton, Hughes. Unused sub: Grocott.

CHESTER-LE-STREET TOWN (0)1 *(Dixon 89)*,
KNOWSLEY UNITED (0)5 *(Siddell 65,Drury 100 107,Barton 105,Kilshaw 123)* Att: 305
Chester: Caffry, Smith, Taylor (Fowler 82), Johnson, Dixon, Ferry, S Bone (Robertson 70), Todd, Calvert, McRae, C Bone. *Knowsley:* Johnson, Ventre, Fagan, Orr, Jackson, Barton, Fahy, Kilshaw, Siddell, Bell (Saunders 85), Drury. Unused sub: O'Brien.

EDGWARE TOWN (2)3 *(Newing 16,Flynn 30,Thompson 47)*, **WELTON ROVERS** (0)1 *(Vause 85)* Att: 388
Edgware: Beccles, Brennan, Sheridan, Finnerty, Coleman, Deritis, Kidd, Chance, Thompson (Gulfer 69), Newing (Elliott 75), Flynn. *Welton:* Jelley, Davis, Presley, Gough, McCormack, Athey, Prendiville (White 65), Parker, Bowen, Green (Vause 86), Morgan.

SITTINGBOURNE (1)1 *(Jordan 8)*, **METROPOLITAN POLICE** (1)2 *(Adams 22,Pendry 74)* Att: 400
Sittingbourne: Hough, Tingley, Fenton, Stinson, Carr, Harle, Bourne, Handford, Freeman (White 45), Jordan, Stock. Unused subs: Fletcher. *Police:* Stillwell, Bateman, Carruth, Richardson, Dubberley, Mochan, Adams (B Taylor 30), G Taylor, Nicholson, McKenzie, Pendry. Unused sub: Bogidi.

ANSTEY NOMADS (0)0, **DISS TOWN** (1)1 *(Mendham 2)* Att: 450.
Anstey: Eastom, Deeping, Lint, Warren, Wardle, Tansley, Allen, Ford, Culpin (Poulton 63), Roberts, Goddard (Vilcins 70). *Diss:* Saunders, Massingham, Playford, McNarry, Vincent, Mendham, Smith, Rose (Brown 21), Barber, Metcalf, Carter (Warne 63).

NORTHWOOD (1)1 *(Rogan 12)*, **CHERTSEY TOWN** (2)4 *(Skerritt 9 34, Ellerker 52, Sweales 85)*
Northwood: Lavender, Nolan, Augustine (Gee 65), Curran, Holland, Billins, Rogan, Vincent, McCormack (Baynes 76), Edey, Blackman. *Chertsey:* Henly, Hill, Dilger, Hutchins, Ritchie (Torstan 82), Dearling (Davis 45), Britnell, Ellerker, Hopkins, Skerritt, Sweales.

WIMBORNE (1)3 *(Killick 29,Richardson 108,Allan 108)*, **HASTINGS** (1)3 *(Scott 24, T White 104 113)* Att: 626
Wimborne: Balch, Beacham, Barrett, Allan, Taplin, Ames, Richardson, Bridle, Killick, Sturgess (Turner 105), Lynn. Unused sub: Homer. *Hastings:* Carman, Henderson, Scott, Burt (Petkovic 35), D White, Willard, T White, Blondrage, Giles (Burke 78), Miles, Wynter.

HASTINGS TOWN (0)1 *(Scott 120)*, **WIMBORNE TOWN** (0)2 *(Lynn 95,Turner 116)* 21-1-92. Att: 677
Hastings: Carman, Henderson, Sillett, Scott, D White, Willard (Giles 87), T White (Smith 108), Blondrage, Burke, Miles, Wynter. *Wimborne:* As 1st game. Turner on for Barrett (105), Homer for Richardson (86).

SUDBURY TOWN (3)3 *(Cutmore 18,Ketley 23,Coe 40)*, **NEWMARKET** (0)2 *(Eden 73,Vowden 86)* Att: 785
Sudbury: Mokler, Hudson, Thorpe, Powell, Hubbard, Barker, Bain, Coe, Cutmore (Smith 65), Talbot (Parnell 75), Ketley. *Newmarket:* Black, Marris, Saddington, Morton, Vowden, Hicks, Eden, Pritchart, Sinclair, Kearns, Skelley. Unused subs: Burton, Sturgeon.

PAULTON ROVERS (1)1 *(Harding 43)*, **HUNGERFORD TOWN** (0)3 *(Bailey 67 96,Brooks 119)* Att: 205
Paulton: Scrivens, Isles, White (Chard 80), Taylor, Staines, Tovey (Smith 70), Hooper, Cutler, Colbourne, Harding, Minell. *Hungerford:* Cummins, Bailey, Potter, Payne, Martin, Brayshaw, Howells, Henry, Jell (Tucker 38), Brooks, Tull (Parker 97).

WEST MIDLANDS POLICE (1)4 *(McMenamin 19 60,Powney 52,Scriven 89)*,
WISBECH TOWN (0)3 *(Garwood 54 56,Williams 64)* Att: 320
Police: Carmell, Bradford, Wearing, Powney (Grimshaw 90), Hopcroft, West, Ingram, McMenamin, Scriven, Davison (Hussey 86), Small. *Wisbech:* Herbert, Jones, Lindsay, Garwood, Wiles, S Keir, Williams (Brighty 87), Carr, Lawrence, Nightingale, Rider. Unused sub: H Keir.

BILLERICAY (1)3 *(Taylor 5,A Jones 65,S Jones 73)*, **YATE** (1)4 *(Thaws 38 62 115,Bryant 85)*   Att: 438
B'cay: Cass, Taylor, Roser, Gore (A Jones 46), Keune, Munday, Jenkins, Rendell (Howard 102), S Jones, Flanagan, McDonald.   *Yate:* Stevenson, Brown, Holtham, Bryant, Gardiner, Jones, Hewlett, Grimshaw (Davis 96), Thaws, Thompson, Smith. Unused sub: Corby.

NEWPORT (I.W.) (0)3 *(Greening 77 102,Sampson 103)*, **BURNHAM RAMBLERS** (0)1 *(Howard 87)* Att: 581
Newport: Granger, Phillips, O'Rourke (Sperry 71), Williams, Brown, Jenkins, Greening, Ritchie, Thomas, Deacon, Sampson. Unused sub: Durham. *Burnham:* English, Connelly, Tracey, Cordfield, Eves, Simmonds, Wilkins, Young, Taylor (Walker 80), Clayton, Hatcher (Howard 46).

HYTHE (1)3 *(Jarvis 1(p),Whyman 84,Edwards 96)*, **EVESHAM** (1)3 *(Jones 5,Candy 63 111)*   Att: 279
Hythe: O'Brien, Poestske (Whyman 65), Bull, Lee, Warrilow, Smith, Ross, Edwards, Arter, Carey, Jarvis. Unused sub: Valler. *Evesham:* Taylor, Russell, Jones, K Brown, Hooman, I Brown, Hall (Emms 97), Langford, Rawle (Mullen 88), Sadler, Candy.

EVESHAM UNITED 0, HYTHE TOWN 0 *(Abandoned due waterlogging at half time)*   25-1-92. Att: 720
Evesham: Taylor, Russell, Jones, K Brown, Cotterill, I Brown, Hooman, Langford, Rawle, Sadler, Candy. Unused subs: Emms, Mullen. *Hythe:* O'Brien, Edwards, Bull, Bull, Lee, Warrilow, Smith, Ross, Jarvis, Arter, Carey, Whyman. Unused subs: Poetske, Valler.

EVESHAM UNITED (0)2 *(I Brown 96,Emms 119)*, **HYTHE** (0)0   1-2-92. Att: 636
Evesham: As last game, Emms on for Rawle (68), Mullen for Langford (99). *Hythe:* O'Brien, Smart, Lyons (Bull 105), Lee, Allon, Jarvis (Poetske 105), Ross, Edwards, Arter, Whyman, Carey.

Dave Nolan (right) of Northwood and Marco Ellerker tussle during the 4-1 Chertsey win. Photo - Paul Dennis.

Bill Athey (left), Welton Rovers' cricketing star gets in a tackle as his side lose at Edgware. Photo - Dennis Nicholson.

FIFTH ROUND

8 Ties **Matches Played: 9**
Home wins: 5 Draws: 1 Away wins: 3
Best Attendance: 1,202 - Evesham United v Eastwood Hanley
Total Attendance: 6,092 **Average Attendance:** 677
Largest Home Win: Guiseley 4, Edgware Town 0
Best Away Win: Hungerford Town 0, West Midlands Police 3
Result of the Round: Bamber Bridge 2, Newport (I.W.) 1

Saturday 8th February 1992

CHERTSEY TOWN (0)3 *(Skerritt 77 85,Dearling 90)*, **YATE TOWN** (0)1 *(Thompson 60)* Att: 421.
Chertsey: Henly, Hill, Dilger, Walcott, Ritchie (Davis 2), Richards, Britnell, Ellerker, Hopkins (Dearling 75), Skerritt, Sweales. *Yate:* Stevenson, Brown, Holtham, Bryant, Gardiner (Davis 86), Jones, Hewlett, Grimshaw, Thaws, Thompson, Smith. Unused sub: Cordy.

GUISELEY (2)4 *(Noteman 34 39,B Roberts 78,Colville 88)*, **EDGWARE TOWN** (0)0 Att: 975.
Guiseley: Maxted, Atkinson, Hogarth, Tetley, Morgan, Bottomley, A Roberts, Tennison, Noteman (Colville 70), Annan (Wright 73), B Roberts. *Edgware:* Beccles, Brennan, Sheridan, Finnerty, Coleman (Mangan 45), Deritis (Gulfer 63), Kidd, Walsh, Thompson, Newing, Flynn.

BAMBER BRIDGE (0)2 *(Whittaker 62,Mayers 65)*, **NEWPORT I.W.** (0)1 *(Ritchie 81(p))* Att: 950
Bamber Bridge: Barton, Wilkes, Leaver, Proctor, Baldwin, Brown, Dagleish, Mayers, Whiteman, Whittaker, Naughton (Lancaster 89). Unused sub: Byron. *Newport:* Granger, Phillips, Sperry, Brown, Williams, Durham, Greening, Ritchie, Thomas (Marshall 74), Deacon, Simpson (Taylor 74).

NEWCASTLE TOWN (1)1 *(Bishop 39)*, **WIMBORNE TOWN** (0)1 *(Allan 85)* Att: 425
Newcastle: Butler, Chetwyn, Williams, Topper, Bishop, Hagan, Steventon, Lawton, Wade, Ritchie, Beardmore (Bright 55). Unused sub: Chamberlain. *Wimborne:* Leonard, Langdown, Beacham (Hudspith 75), Allan, Taplin, Ames, Richardson, Bridle, Killick, Sturgess, Lynn (Barrett 83).

WIMBORNE TOWN (0)1 *(Sturgess 70)*, **NEWCASTLE TOWN** (0)0 15-2-92. Att: 912
Wimborne: Leonard, Langdown, Barrett, Allan, Taplin, Ames, Richardson, Bridle, Killick, Sturgess, Lynn. Unused subs: Hudspith, Turner. *Newcastle:* Butler, Chetwyn, Williams, Topper, Griffiths, Hagan, Steventon, Lawton, Wade, Ritchie, Pestridge (Beardmore 75). Unused sub: Chamberlain.

HUNGERFORD TOWN (0)0, **WEST MIDS POLICE** (2)3 *(Powney 1 2,Small 84)* Att: 320
Hungerford: Cummins, Bailey, Potter, Payne, Martin, Brayshaw, Howells, Henry, Tucker (Parker 75), Brooks, Tull (Jell 65). *Police:* Carmell, Bradford, Wearing, Powney, Grimshaw, Davison, Ingram, McMenamin, Scriven, Hussey, Small. Unused subs: Kieran, Brady.

METROPOLITAN POLICE (0)0, **DISS TOWN** (2)2 *(Metcalfe 8 20)* Att: 235
Police: Stillwell, B Taylor, Carruth, Richardson, Dubberley, Mochan, Adams, G Taylor, Nicholson, McKenzie, Pendry (Clarke 74). Unused sub: Bays. *Diss:* Saunders, Massingham, Carter, Vincent, Oliver, Mendham, Smith, Rose (Playford 79), Barber, Metcalfe (Warne 69), Brown.

KNOWSLEY (0)2 *(Gaffney 88,Jackson 89)*, **SUDBURY** (2)4 *(Crane 9,Barker 43,Talbot 52,Bain 65)* Att: 652
Knowsley: Johnston, O'Brien, Tyrell, Orr, Jackson, Barton, Fray, Kilshaw, Saunders (Ventre 50), Bell (Gaffney 80), Drury. *Sudbury:* Mokler, Henry, Crane, Hudson, Talbot, Barker, Bain, Coe, Parnell, Smith, Ketley. Unused subs: Powell, Cutmore

EVESHAM UNITED (1)2 *(Emms 19,Cotterill 55)*, **EASTWOOD HANLEY** (1)1 *(Jones 19)* Att: 1,202.
Evesham: Taylor, Russell, Jones, Hooman, Cotterill, Brown, Emms, Langford (Hall 66), Mullen (Rawle 80), Sadler, Candy. *Eastwood:* Johnson, Jones, France, Bates, Ridley, Martin (Grocott 85), Hulme, Twigg, Muncey, Wheaton, Hughes. Unused sub: Rey.

Sean Small of West Mids Police is tackled by Hungerford's Shaun Till. Photo - Paul Dennis.

121

Keith Bain scores to put Sudbury into an unassailable four goal lead at Knowsley. Photo - Colin Stevens.

Matthew Metcalfe scores his second goal for Diss at Metropolitan Police. Photo - Eric Marsh.

Carlton Walcott makes a powerful run for Chertsey during their win over Yate Town. Photo - V Hardwick.

SIXTH ROUND

4 Ties Matches Played: 5
Home wins: 2 Draws: 1 Away wins: 2
Best Attendance: 1,668 - Guiseley v Evesham United
Total Attendance: 6,561 **Average Attendance:** 1,312
Largest Home Win: Guiseley 4, Evesham United 0
Best Away Win: West Midlands Police 1, Sudbury Town 2
Result of the Round: Chertsey Town 0, Bamber Bridge 1

Saturday 29th February 1992

CHERTSEY TOWN (0)0, **BAMBER BRIDGE** (0)1 *(Proctor 54(p))* Att: 1,121
Chertsey: Alan Henly, Kevin Hill, Rob Dilger, Paul Hutchins, Andy Ritchie, Rodney Richards (Keith Dearling 55), Darren Britnell, Marco Ellerker, Carlton Wallcott, Peter Skerritt, Paul Sweales. Unused sub: Colin Davis.
Bamber Bridge: Stuart Barton, Steve Wilkes, Dave Leaver, Stuart Proctor, Jez Baldwin, Darren Brown, Gary Dalgleish, Kenny Mayers, Dave Whiteman, Andy Whittaker, Willy Naughton. Unused subs: Bob Lancaster, Paul Byron.

GUISELEY (2)4 *(Annan 22(p), Noteman 27 66 88)*, **EVESHAM UNITED** (0)0 Att: 1,668
Guiseley: Paul Maxted, Peter Atkinson, Colin Hogarth, Martin Tetley, David Morgan, Phil Wilson, Alan Roberts, Mark Tennison (Paul Bottomley 73), Ian Noteman, Richard Annan (Robert Colville 61), Billy Roberts.
Evesham: Chris Taylor, Nigel Russell, Richard Hooman, Graham Jones, Sean Cotterill, Ian Brown, Tim Hall (Neil Emms 53), Melvyn Langford, Howard Rawle, (Kevin Mullen 60), Stuart Sadler, Robert Candy.

WEST MIDLANDS POLICE (1)1 *(Davison 3)*, **SUDBURY TOWN** (1)2 *(Bain 38, Davison 47(OG))* Att: 1,072
WM Police: Darren Carmell, Ron Bradford, Matt Wearing, Darren Powney, Peter Grimshaw, Steve Hopcraft (Adam West 34), Gary Ingram, Noel McMenamin, Dave Scriven, (Graham Hussey 82), Gary Davison, Sean Small.
Sudbury: Steve Mokler, Gary Hudson, Andy Crane, Trevor Gunn, Brian Talbot (Kevin Ketley 75), Dean Barker, Keith Bain, Paul Coe, Steve Parnell, Paul Smith (Don Cutmore 82), Mike Henry.

DISS TOWN (0)0, **WIMBORNE TOWN** (0)0 Att: 1,528
Diss: Alan Peatfield, Dave Massingham, Steven Playford, Mark Vincent, Marcus Oliver, Peter Mendham, Gary Smith, Andrew Brown, Richard Barber, Matthew Metcalfe (Dave Warne 68), Chris Rose (Jason Carter 64).
Wimborne: Kevin Leonard, Phil Langdown, Dominic Barrett (Shane Turner 105), Mark Allan (Robbie Beacham 80), Andy Taplin, Trevor Ames, Steve Richardson, Nick Bridle, Tommy Killick, Jamie Sturgess, Simon Lynn.

WIMBORNE TOWN (0)1 *(Allan 52)*, **DISS TOWN** (0)0 7-3-92. Att: 1,172
Wimborne: As first match with Beacham replacing Langdown (24 mins) and Turner replacing Darrett (78).
Diss: Alan Peatfield, Dave Massingham, Steven Playford, John McNarry (Matthew Metcalfe 71), Marcus Oliver, Peter Mendham, Gary Smith (Alan Barnard 59), Mark Vincent, Richard Barber, Dave Warne, Jason Carter.

Bamber Bridge's experienced, Willy Naughton, surges past Chertsey's Kevin Hill. Photo - V Hardwick.

Matthew Matcalfe of Diss shoots for goal watched by Trevor Ames of Wimborne Town. Photo - Francis Short.

Ian Noteman (behind post) slots home Guiseley's final goal as they crush Evesham. Photo - Rob Ruddock.

Keith Dearling (left) of Chertsey battles for possesion with Dave Leaver of Bamber Bridge. Photo - Dave West.

SEMI FINALS

2 Ties **Matches Played: 4**
Home wins: 1 Draws: 2 Away wins: 1
Best Attendance: 3,250 - Wimborne Town v Bamber Bridge
Total Attendance: 10,399   **Average Attendance:** 2,024
Largest Home Win: Wimborne Town 2, Bamber Bridge 0
Best Away Win: Sudbury Town 1, Guiseley 3

First Leg: Saturday 21st March 1992
Second Leg: Saturday 28th March 1992

BAMBER BRIDGE (0)0, **WIMBORNE TOWN** (0)0   Att: 2,020
Bamber Bridge: Stuart Barton, Steve Wilkes, Dave Leaver, Stuart Proctor, Jez Baldwin, Darren Brown, Gary Dagleish, Kenny Mayers, Dave Whiteman (Bob Lancaster 85), Andy Whittaker, Willy Naughton. Unused sub: Neil Murphy.
Wimborne: Kevin Leonard, Robert Beacham, Dominic Barrett (Stephen Hudspith 67), Mark Allan, Andrew Taplin, Trevor Ames, Stephen Richardson, Nicholas Bridle, Brian Wilkins, Jamie Sturgess (Shane Turner 78), Simon Lynn.

WIMBORNE TOWN (1)2 *(Ames 37 80)*, **BAMBER BRIDGE** (0)0   Att: 3,250
Wimborne: Kevin Leonard, Phil Langdown, Robert Beacham, Mark Allan, Andrew Taplin, Trevor Ames, Stephen Richardson, Nicholas Bridle, Brian Wilkins, Jamie Sturgess (Shane Turner 85), Simon Lynn. Unused sub: Dominic Barrett.
Bamber Bridge: Stuart Barton, Steve Wilkes, Dave Leaver, Stuart Proctor, Jez Baldwin, Darren Brown, Nigel Marler (Kenny Mayers 78), Mark Wignall, Gary Dagleish, Andy Whittaker (Paul Byron 65), Willy Naughton.

GUISELEY (1)2 *(B Roberts 25, Colville 96)*, **SUDBURY TOWN** (1)2 *(Phillips 36, Ketley 51)*   Att: 2,142
Guiseley: Paul Maxted, Peter Atkinson, Phil Wilson, Colin Hogarth, Dave Morgan, Vince Brockie, Alan Roberts (Bob Colville 67), Mark Tennison, Richard Annan, Billy Roberts. Unused sub: Lal Corbally.
Sudbury: Steve Mokler, Mike Henry, Andy Crane, Brian Talbot, Trevor Gunn, Dean Barker, Keith Bain, Paul Coe, Stewart Phillips (Dave McCoy 82), Paul Smith, Kevin Ketley. Unused sub: Marty Thorpe.

SUDBURY TOWN (0)1 *(Barker 64)*, **GUISELEY** (0)3 *(Noteman 61 67, Tennison 82)*   Attendance: 2,987
Sudbury: Steve Mokler, Mike Henry, Andy Crane, Brian Talbot (Marty Thorpe 72), Trevor Gunn, Dean Barker, Keith Bain, Paul Coe, Steve Parnell (Don Cutmore 69), Paul Smith, Kevin Ketley.
Guiseley: Paul Maxted, Peter Atkinson, Richard Annan, Colin Hogarth, Dave Morgan, Phil Wilson, Alan Roberts, Mark Tennison, Ian Noteman (Bob Colville 78), Mike Nagy (Vince Brockie 71), Billy Roberts.

Trevor Gunn (left) of Sudbury tussles for possession with Colin Hogarth of Guiseley during the Yorkshire side's impressive 3-1 win in Suffolk. Photo - Nick Butcher.

Wimborne's Robbie Beacham is tackled by Darren Brown in the 0-0 draw at Bamber Bridge. Photo - Colin Stevens.

Billy Roberts of Guiseley (right) pursues Keith Bain of Sudbury in the second leg. Photo - Nick Butcher.

Steve Richardson breaks through the 'Bridge defence as Wimborne win 2-0. Photo - Peter Haynes, Action Prints.

F.A. VASE
Round by Round Chart

3rd Rnd Proper	4th Rnd Proper	5th Rnd Proper	6th Rnd Proper	Semi-final	Final
Worthing Utd 1					
Northwood 2	Northwood 1				
Chertsey 1;0;2	Chertsey Town 4				
Cinderford 1;0;1		Chertsey Town 3			
Billericay T 2		Yate Town 1			
Bilston T 0	Billericay T 3				
Shortwood Utd 2	Yate Town 4				
Yate Town 3			Chertsey T 0		
Atherton LR 3;2			Bamber Bridge 1		
Brigg Town 3;3	Brigg Town 4;0				
Bamber Bridge 2	Bamber Bridge 4;1				
Flixton 1		Bamber Bridge 2			
Hampton 0		Newport IW 1			
Newport IW 1	Newport IW 3				
Burnham Rblrs 2	Burnham Rblrs 1			Bamber Bridge 0;0	
Chasetown 1				1st leg at Bamber B.	
Tiverton T 2				Wimborne Town 0;2	
Sittingbourne 3	Sittingbourne 1				
Met Police 2	Met Police 2				
Three Bridges 0		Met Police 0			
Anstey Nomads 2		Diss Town 2			
Felixstowe T 1	Anstey Nomads 0				
Raunds Town 0	Diss Town 1				
Diss Town 2			Diss Town 0;0		
Newcastle T 3			Wimborne Town 0;1		
Penrith 2	Newcastle T 3				
Berkhamsted T 1	Gresley Rvrs 2				
Gresley Rvrs 2		Newcastle T 0;0			
Hastings T 3		Wimborne T 0;1			
Torrington 0	Hastings Town 3;1				
Wimborne T 1	Wimborne T 3;2				Wimborne 5
Horsham 0					
Belper T 1;0					Guiseley 3
Dunston Feds 1;2	Dunston Feds 1				
Farsley C 2	Guiseley 3				
Guiseley 5		Guiseley 4			
Edgware Town 2		Edgware Town 0			
Hinckley Ath 1	Edgware Town 3				
Welton Rvrs 2	Welton Rvrs 1				
Malden Town 1			Guiseley 4		
Walthamstow P 2			Evesham Utd 0		
Evesham Utd 3	Evesham Utd 3;0;2				
Pagham 1	Hythe Town 3;0;0				
Hythe Town 2		Evesham Utd 2			
Newton Aycliffe 2		Eastwood Han 1			
Burscough 4	Burscough 0				
Bridlington T 2	Eastwood Han 1				
Eastwood Han. 3				Guiseley 2;3	
Paulton Rvrs 4				1st leg at Guiseley	
Thame United 2	Paulton Rvrs 1			Sudbury T 2;1	
Hungerford T 4	Hungerford T 3				
Faversham T 1		Hungerford T 0			
Collier Row 2		West Mids Police 3			
West Mids Police 3	West Mids Police 4				
Wisbech T 2;4	Wisbech Town 3				
Gt Yarmouth T 2;2			West Mids Police 1		
Chester-le-Str. 2			Sudbury T 2		
Ashton United 1	Chester-le-Str. 1				
N Ferriby Utd 1	Knowsley Utd 5				
Knowsley Utd 2		Knowsley Utd 2			
Saffron Walden 1		Sudbury T 4			
Sudbury Town 2	Sudbury T 3				
Newmarket T 2	Newmarket T 2				
Solihull Borough 1					

F.A. VASE FINAL

Wimborne Town 5 v 3 Guiseley

Richardson,
Sturgess 2, Killick 2

Noteman 2, Colville

Attendance: 10,772

Referee: M J Bodenham (Cornwall)

Wimborne dethrone Guiseley

Guiseley, the holders from Yorkshire, had made serene progress to a second final and were looking to their free-scoring forwards to help them to retain their trophy having scored 23 goals in seven Vase matches. The Guiseley danger man was clearly Ian Noteman, who had missed Wembley in 1991, with a personal tally of eleven in the competition. Wimborne, by contrast, had no real Vase form at all prior to this season having never progressed past the Third Round. The Jewson Wessex League side had the more arduous route to the final negociating eleven ties including replays in Rounds Four, Five and Six. Their strength appeared to lie in defence; they had not conceded a goal in their previous five Vase matches. They would be the first Dorset side to contest a Wembley final at any level.

Not surprisingly Guiseley were installed as pre-match favourites. When the teams took the field however, it was the underdogs who enjoyed the bulk of the vocal support, some 7,000 fans having made the journey up the M3 that morning. The early exchanges suggested that Wimborne might be swept aside as Guiseley began like an express train. With forwards swarming around the area, it was no surprise when Noteman claimed the opening goal after a quarter of an hour maintaining his prodigious record. Guiseley had further chances as the Dorset side struggled to get in the game. Noteman and his striking partner Richard Annan were looking very sharp up front, whilst Peter Atkinson at full-back was making several foraging runs up the right hand side. Fortunately for Wimborne, keeper Kevin Leonard was already having a fine match, punching well under pressure and making crucial saves to keep his side in the game.

The unpredictable nature of our national game was never better illustrated than when this final was turned on its head in the space of three minutes. First, on 27 minutes, Wimborne skipper Steve Richardson hit a speculative long range shot which Maxted could only help into the net. The Dorset fans, dejected only moments earlier, were propelled into dreamland minutes later by the goal of the game. Tommy Killick, finding himself in space on the left of the box, swerved over a cross with the outside of his right foot. Jamie Sturgess put away the header with great authority.

This double strike seemed to take the stuffing out of Guiseley for a while. Wimborne, on the rack for so long, now began to boss things and Killick helped himself to the third a few minutes before the interval after the offside trap had been sprung. It was a remarkable comeback for Killick who had suffered a serious knee injury in a Sunday League after the Quarter Final. His pace and elusiveness up front were causing the Yorkshiremen all kinds of problems.

The second half began in similar fashion to the first with Guiseley pressing forward again. To their credit the holders had swallowed their disappointment and were making determined efforts to get back into the game. Their reward came after 51 minutes when, after a goalmouth scramble, Ian Noteman slid in his thirteenth Vase goal of the campaign. The destination of the trophy was once more in the balance. However, after 57 minutes Wimborne spiked the Guiseley guns by reclaiming their two goal advantage, Killick again getting through and finishing coolly from a narrow angle.

It was too early to write off Guiseley and they came back once more. Noteman hammered one shot against the bar with Leonard beaten, but Richardson was playing a captain's role in Wimborne's midfield, and his tenacious performance was one of the best of the day. The match was finally killed twelve minutes from time when Sturgess crashed home his second and Wimborne's fifth. Noteman, so nearly a match winner, was substituted as Guiseley seemed to accept their fate. Killick got through again, but was denied by Maxted who beat out his fierce shot. Then substitute Bob Colville grabbed a deserved last minute consolation goal to leave the final score at 5-3.

For the second successive year the final had yielded eight goals. It was played in excellent spirit reflecting great credit on both winners and losers. How refreshing to see teams committed to attack and trying to play football on such an important occasion. Wimborne deserved to win for battling back after such an inauspicious start. For me, the abiding memory will be Guiseley supporters generously applauding the Wimborne players as they took possession of the Trophy. Yes, football was undoubtedly the winner.

Stephen Roberts

Wimborne: Kevin Leonard, Phil Langdown (Brian Wilkins 55), Robert Beacham, Mark Allan, Andrew Taplin, Trevor Ames, Steve Richardson, Nick Bridle, Tommy Killick, Jamie Sturgess (Jason Lovell 86), Simon Lynn.
Guiseley: Paul Maxted, Peter Atkinson, Colin Hogarth, Martin Tetley (Phil Wilson 68), David Morgan, Vince Brockie, Alan Roberts, Mark Tennison, Ian Noteman (Bob Colville 80), Richard Annan, Billy Roberts.

Dorset fans celebrate a memorable victory. Photo - Paul Dennis.

Scoring heroes. From left to right: Tommy Killick, Jamie Sturgess and Steve Richardson. Photo - Eric Marsh.

The victorious Magpies squad with their prize. Photo - Roger Turner.

Tommy Killick beats Paul Maxted.....

..and finds the net for his second and Guiseley's fifth (Photos - Colin Stevens).....

..and turns away to celebrate. Photo - Alan Coomes.

Guiseley dangerman Ian Noteman is pursued by Wimborne captain Steve Richardson. Photo - Dennis Nicholson.

Peter Atkinson puts over a cross for Guiseley before Robbie Beacham can tackle. Photo - Alan Coomes.

Delighted fans mob Wimborne as they climb the famous steps. Photo - Francis Short.

PAST F.A. CHALLENGE VASE FINALS

1975 HODDESDON T. 2 (Sedgwick 2) **EPSOM & EWELL 1** (Wales)   Att: 9,500. Ref: R Toseland
Hoddesdon: Galvin, Green, Hickey, Maybury, Stevenson, Wilson, Bishop, Picking, Sedgwick, Nathan, Schofield. *Epsom:* Page, Bennett, Webb, Wales, Worby, Jones, O'Connell, Walker, Tuite, Eales, Lee.

1976 BILLERICAY TOWN 1 (Aslett) **STAMFORD 0** *(aet)*   Att: 11,848. Ref: A Robinson
Billericay: Griffiths, Payne, Foreman, Pullin, Bone, Coughlan, Geddes, Aslett, Clayden, Scott, Smith. *Stamford:* Johnson, Kwiatkowski, Marchant, Crawford, Downs, Hird, Barnes, Walpole, Smith, Russell, Broadbent.

1977 BILLERICAY TOWN 1 (Clayden) **SHEFFIELD 1** (Coughlan OG) *(aet)*   Att: 14,000. Ref: J Worrall
B'cay: Griffiths, Payne, Bone, Coughlan, Pullin, Scott, Wakefield, Aslett, Clayden, Woodhouse, McQueen. Sub: Whettell *Shef.:* Wing, Gilbody, Lodge, Hardisty, Watts, Skelton, Kay, Travis, Pugh, Thornhill, Haynes. Sub: Strutt.

Replay at Nottm Forest. BILLERICAY 2 (Aslett, Woodhouse) **SHEFFIELD 1** (Thornhill)   Ref: J Worrall
Billericay: Griffiths, Payne, Pullin, Whettell, Bone, McQueen, Woodhouse, Aslett, Clayden, Scott, Wakefield. *Sheffield:* Wing, Gilbody, Lodge, Strutt, Watts, Skelton, Kay, Travis, Pugh, Thornhill, Haynes. Att: 3,482.

1978 NEWCASTLE BLUE STAR 2 (Dunn, Crumplin) **BARTON ROVERS 0**   Ref: T Morris
Blue Star: Halbert, Feenan, Thompson, Davidson, S Dixon, Beynon, Storey, P Dixon, Crumplin, Callaghan, Dunn. Sub: Diamond. *Barton:* Blackwell, Stephens, Crossley, Evans, Harris, Dollimore, Dunn, Harnaman, Fossey, Turner, Smith. Sub: Cox. Att: 16,858.

1979 BILLERICAY TOWN 4 (Young 3, Clayden) **ALMONDSBURY GREENWAY 1** (Price)   Ref: C Seel
Billericay: Norris, Blackaller, Bingham, Whettell, Bone, Reeves, Pullin, Scott, Clayden, Young, Groom. Sub: Carrigan. *Almondsbury:* Hamilton, Bowers, Scarrett, Sullivan, Tudor, Wookey, Bowers, Shehean, Kerr, Butt, Price. Sub: Kilbaine. Att: 17,500.

1980 STAMFORD 2 (Alexander, McGowan) **GUISBOROUGH TOWN 0**   Ref: Neil Midgley
Stamford: Johnson, Kwiatkowski, Ladd, McGowan, Bliszczak I, Mackin, Broadhurst, Hall, Czarnecki, Potter, Alexander. Sub: Bliszczak S. *Guisborough:* Cutter, Scott, Thornton, Angus, Maltby, Percy, Skelton, Coleman, McElvaney, Sills, Dilworth. Sub: Harrison. Att: 11,500.

1981 WHICKHAM 3 (Scott, Williamson, Peck OG) **WILLENHALL 2** (Smith, Stringer) *(aet)*   Ref: R Lewis
Whickham: Thompson, Scott, Knox, Williamson, Cook, Ward, Carroll, Diamond, Cawthra, Robertson, Turnbull. Sub: Allon. *Willenhall:* Newton, White, Dams, Woodall, Heath, Fox, Peck, Price, Matthews, Smith, Stringer. Sub: Trevor. Att: 12,000.

1982 FOREST GREEN ROVERS 3 (Leitch 2, Norman) **RAINWORTH M.W. 0**   Ref: K Walmsey
Forest Green: Moss, Norman, Day, Turner, Higgins, Jenkins, Guest, Burns, Millard, Leitch, Doughty. Sub: Dangerfield. *Rainworth:* Watson, Hallam, Hodgson, Slater, Sterland, Oliver, Knowles, Raine, Radzi, Reah, Comerfield. Sub: Robinson. Att: 12,500.

1983 V.S. RUGBY 1 (Crawley) **HALESOWEN TOWN 0**   Ref: B Daniels
Rugby: Burton, McGinty, Harrison, Preston, Knox, Evans, Ingram, Setchell, Owen, Beecham, Crawley. Sub: Haskins. *Halesowen:* Coldicott, Penn, Edmonds, Lacey, Randall, Shilvock, Hazelwood, Moss, Woodhouse, P Joinson, L Joinson. Sub: Smith. Att: 13,700.

1984 STANSTED 3 (Holt, Gillard, Reading) **STAMFORD 2** (Waddicore, Allen)   Ref: T Bune
Stansted: Coe, Williams, Hilton, Simpson, Cooper, Reading, Callanan, Holt, Reeves, Doyle, Gillard. Sub: Williams. *Stamford:* Parslow, Smitheringale, Blades, McIlwain, Lyon, Mackin, Genovese, Waddicore, Allen, Robson, Beech. Sub: Chapman. Att: 8,125.

1985 HALESOWEN TOWN 3 (Moss, L Joinson 2) **FLEETWOOD TOWN 1** (Moran)   Ref: C Downey
Halesowen: Caldicott, Penn, Sherwood, Warner, Randle, Heath, Hazelwood, Moss (Smith), Woodhouse, P Joinson, L Joinson. *Fleetwood:* Dobson, Moran, Hadgraft, Strachan, Robinson, Milligan, Hall, Trainor, Taylor (Whitehouse), Cain, Kenneley. Att: 16,715.

1986 HALESOWEN TOWN 3 (Moss 2, L Joinson) **SOUTHALL 0**   Ref: D Scott
Halesowen: Pemberton, Moore, Lacey, Randle (Rhodes), Sherwood, Heath, Penn, Woodhouse, P Joinson, L Joinson, Moss. *Southall:* MacKenzie, James, McGovern, Croad, Holland, Powell (Richmond), Pierre, Richardson, Sweales, Ferdinand, Rowe. Att: 18,340.

1987 ST HELENS 3 (Layhe 2, Rigby) **WARRINGTON TOWN 2** (Reid, Cook)   Ref: T Mills
St Helens: Johnson, Benson, Lowe, Bendon, Wilson, McComb, Collins, (Gledhill), O'Neill, Cummins, Lay, Rigby. Sub: Deakin. *Warrington:* O'Brien, Copeland, Hunter, Gratton, Whalley, Reid, Brownlie (Woodyer), Cook, Kinsey, Looker (Hill), Hughes. Att: 4,254.

1988 COLNE DYNAMOES 1 (Anderson) **EMLEY 0**   Ref: A Seville
Colne: Mason, McFafyen, Westwell, Bentley, Dunn, Roscoe, Rodaway, Whitehead (Burke), Diamond, Anderson, Wood (Coates). *Emley:* Dennis, Fielding, Mellor, Codd, Hirst (Burrows), Gartland (Cook), Carmody, Green, Bramald, Devine, Francis. Att: 15,000.

1989 TAMWORTH 1 (Devaney) **SUDBURY TOWN 1** (Hubbick) *aet*   Ref: C Downey
Tamworth: Belford, Lockett, Atkins, Cartwright, McCormack, Myers, Finn, Devaney, Moores, Gordon, Stanton. Subs: Rathbone, Heaton. *Sudbury:* Garnham, Henry, G Barker, Boyland, Thorpe, Klug, D Barker, Barton, Oldfield, Smith, Hubbick. Subs: Money, Hunt. Att: 26,487.

Replay at Peterborough. TAMWORTH 3 (Stanton 2, Moores) **SUDBURY TOWN 0**
Tamworth: Belford, Lockett, Atkins, Cartwright, Finn, Myers, George, Devaney, Moores, Gordon, Stanton. Sub: Heaton. *Sudbury:* Garnham, Henry, G Barker, Boyland, Thorpe, Klug, D Barker, Barton, Oldfield, Smith, Hubbick. Subs: Money, Hunt. Att: 11,201.

1990 YEADING 0   BRIDLINGTON TOWN 0   Att: 7,932. Ref: R Groves
Replay at Leeds.   YEADING 1 (Sweales) **BRIDLINGTON TOWN 0**   Att: 5,000. Ref: R Groves
Yeading: MacKenzie, Wickens, Turner, Whiskey (sub McCarthy at Wembley), Croad (sub McCarthy in rep), Denton (Schwartz in rep), Matthews, James (sub Charles at Wembley), Sweales, Impey (sub Welsh in rep), Cordery. *Bridlington:* Taylor, Pugh, Freeman, McNeil, Warburton, Brentano, Wilkes (sub Hall at Wembley, Brown in rep), Noteman, Gauden (sub Downing in rep), Whiteman, Brattan (sub Brown at Wembley).

1991 GRESLEY ROVERS 4 (Rathbone, Smith 2, Stokes)
GUISELEY 4 (Tennison 2, Walling, A Roberts)   Ref: C Trussell
Replay at Bramall Lane. GUISELEY 3 (Tennison, Walling, Atkinson) **GRESLEY 1** (Astley) Ref: C Trussell
Guiseley: Maxted, Bottomley (Annan in rep), Hogarth, Tetley, Morgan, McKenzie (sub Bottomley in rep), Atkinson (sub Annan at Wembley), Tennison (sub Noteman in rep), Walling, A Roberts, B Roberts (sub Annan at Wembley). *Gresley:* Aston, Barry, Elliott (sub Adcock at Wembley), Denby, Land, Astley, Stokes (sub Weston in rep), K Smith, Acklam, Rathbone, Lovell (sub Weston at Wembley, Adcock in rep). Att: 11,314 at Wembley, 7,585 at Sheffield.

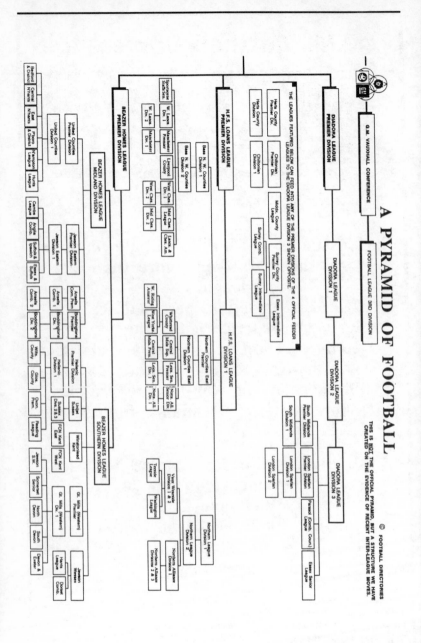

A PYRAMID OF FOOTBALL

© FOOTBALL DIRECTORIES

THIS IS **NOT** THE OFFICIAL PYRAMID, BUT A STRUCTURE WE HAVE CREATED ON THE EVIDENCE OF RECENT INTER-LEAGUE MOVES.

THE LEAGUES FEATURED BELOW CAN FEED INTO ANY OF THE PREMIER DIVISIONS OF THE 4 OFFICIAL FEEDER LEAGUES TO THE DIADORA LEAGUE DIVISION 3 SHOWN OPPOSITE.

G.M. VAUXHALL CONFERENCE

FOOTBALL LEAGUE 3RD DIVISION

DIADORA LEAGUE PREMIER DIVISION

DIADORA LEAGUE DIVISION 1

DIADORA LEAGUE DIVISION 2

DIADORA LEAGUE DIVISION 3

H.F.S. LOANS LEAGUE PREMIER DIVISION

H.F.S. LOANS LEAGUE DIVISION 1

BEAZER HOMES LEAGUE PREMIER DIVISION

BEAZER HOMES LEAGUE MIDLAND DIVISION

BEAZER HOMES LEAGUE SOUTHERN DIVISION

134

G.M. Vauxhall Conference

THE GM VAUXHALL CONFERENCE

President: J C Thompson

Chairman: W J King

Vice-Chairman: B R Lee

Secretary: P D Hunter, 24 Barnehurst Road, Bexleyheath, Kent DA7 6EZ.

NON-LEAGUE TREBLE FOR COLCHESTER UNITED

COLCHESTER UNITED became the first team to emulate the feat achieved by Wealdstone in season 1984/85 by becoming Champions of the Conference and winning the FA Challenge Trophy. Colchester, however, went one better to gain promotion to the Football League, albeit this was not an automatic opportunity to Wealdstone seven seasons ago.

The Conference Championship chase was the closest ever with Colchester becoming champions over Wycombe Wanderers by goal difference. Both clubs finished with a total of 94 points. Kettering Town finished in third place and Merthyr Tydfil, despite their off the field ultimatley successful fight to maintain their future Conference status, finished in a very creditable fourth position.

Wycombe Wanderers finished the season with two trophies, having beaten Barnet to win the Championship Shield and defeating Runcorn in the two-legged Bob Lord Challenge Trophy Final.

The FA Challenge Trophy Final once again featured two Conference clubs. Colchester United defeated the new Conference club Witton Albion in a hard fought final.

The success of Conference clubs in the FA Cup continues with Farnborough Town and Kettering Town reaching the Third Round to play West Ham United and Blackburn Rovers respectively.

Clubs relegated from the Conference are Barrow to the HFS Loans League and Cheltenham Town to the Beazer Homes League. The clubs promoted from the feeder leagues are Bromsgrove Rovers, Stalybridge Celtic and Woking, Champions of the Beazer Homes, HFS Loans and Diadora Leagues respectively.

The Conference continues to maintain its progress in sponsorship, media coverage, reputation and standing outside the FA Premier League and the Football League. Season 1992/93 sees the start of the second season of the current Vauxhall sponsorship, The Mail on Sunday have renewed their sponsorship of the Manager of the Month, Goalscorer of the Month and other Annual Sponsorships. A welcome newcomer to the successful Conference sponsorship team are the Minerva Football Company, with a lucrative ball sponsorship.

The challenge for the championship will be stronger than ever next season for it is interesting to note that season 1992/93 will be the first since the relegation of Lincoln City in 1987 that the Conference constitution will not include a Football League club. With the promotion and relegation restarting at the end of the new season all 22 Semi-Professional clubs have an opportunity to gain promotion to the newly formed Football League Third Division.

Season 1992/93 promises to be an interesting one. Will the new FA Premier League prove to be a success, and will there be any further re-structuring at the Football League level which may affect the Pyramid?

P D Hunter

G.M. Vauxhall Conference

FINAL LEAGUE TABLE 1990-91

	P	Home					Away					Pts
		W	D	L	F	A	W	D	L	F	A	
BARNET	42	13	4	4	50	23	13	5	3	53	29	87
COLCHESTER UNITED	42	16	4	1	41	13	9	6	6	27	22	85
ALTRINCHAM	42	12	6	3	48	22	11	7	3	39	24	82
KETTERING TOWN	42	12	6	3	38	19	11	5	5	29	26	80
WYCOMBE WANDERERS	42	15	3	3	46	17	6	8	7	29	29	74
TELFORD UNITED	42	11	3	7	30	21	9	4	8	32	31	67
MACCLESFIELD TOWN	42	11	4	6	38	22	6	8	7	25	30	63
RUNCORN	42	12	4	5	44	29	4	6	11	25	38	58
MERTHYR TYDFIL	42	9	5	7	37	24	7	4	10	25	37	57
BARROW	42	10	8	3	34	24	5	4	12	25	41	57
WELLING UNITED	42	7	10	4	33	27	6	5	10	22	30	54
NORTHWICH VICTORIA	42	8	7	6	33	30	5	6	10	32	45	52
KIDDERMINSTER HARRIERS	42	8	5	8	33	30	6	5	10	23	37	52
YEOVIL TOWN	42	9	5	7	38	29	4	6	11	20	29	50
STAFFORD RANGERS	42	7	9	5	30	26	5	5	11	18	25	50
CHELTENHAM TOWN	42	8	6	7	29	25	4	6	11	25	47	48
GATESHEAD	42	10	3	8	32	38	4	3	14	20	54	48
BOSTON UNITED	42	9	4	8	40	31	3	7	11	15	38	47
SLOUGH TOWN	42	9	4	8	31	29	4	2	15	20	51	45
BATH CITY	42	9	4	8	39	27	1	8	12	16	34	42
SUTTON UNITED	42	6	6	9	29	33	4	3	14	33	49	39
FISHER ATHLETIC	42	3	9	9	22	30	2	6	13	16	49	30

RESULTS CHART 1991-92

	1	2	3	4	5	6	7	8	9	10	11	12	13	14	15	16	17	18	19	20	21	22
1. Altrincham	#	1-1	4-0	2-4	2-1	1-2	1-1	1-1	1-1	1-1	3-1	1-1	0-1	0-3	2-2	3-7	3-0	2-3	1-2	2-2	0-4	2-1
2. Barrow	0-2	#	2-0	2-2	0-0	1-1	0-1	1-1	0-0	5-1	2-0	2-2	0-2	0-1	2-3	3-4	0-0	3-0	6-1	0-1	0-1	0-0
3. Bath City	3-2	2-1	#	2-0	5-1	0-0	1-2	0-1	1-1	0-1	1-1	0-0	2-0	0-0	3-1	2-1	0-1	1-2	0-3	0-2	1-1	3-1
4. Boston United	2-1	4-1	1-0	#	3-3	0-4	0-1	4-0	1-1	1-2	1-5	2-0	0-2	2-1	2-1	3-1	2-2	1-2	5-1	3-2	2-2	1-3
5. Cheltenham Town	0-2	0-0	1-2	1-1	#	1-1	4-3	3-2	0-3	1-2	2-3	1-2	1-0	0-7	4-1	0-1	0-0	2-1	3-2	0-1	2-1	1-1
6. Colchester Utd	3-3	5-0	5-0	1-0	4-0	#	2-3	2-0	3-1	3-0	2-0	2-0	1-0	1-0	2-1	4-0	2-0	2-0	3-1	3-2	3-0	4-0
7. Farnborough Town	3-0	5-0	1-2	5-0	1-1	0-2	#	3-1	1-3	2-1	4-2	0-0	2-4	1-0	0-2	1-1	1-1	2-2	1-1	1-1	1-3	0-0
8. Gateshead	4-0	1-1	0-1	2-1	2-1	0-2	0-2	#	0-0	0-3	2-0	0-1	2-0	0-1	1-1	2-1	0-0	0-2	1-1	2-1	2-3	1-0
9. Kettering Town	5-0	3-2	2-2	1-3	0-3	2-4	0-5	2-0	#	2-1	2-0	3-1	0-3	3-2	3-0	2-3	2-1	3-0	1-1	1-1	1-1	1-4
10. Kidderminster H.	1-0	1-2	0-1	1-3	2-1	2-2	1-1	5-3	2-3	#	1-1	2-2	1-0	5-1	2-1	3-3	2-1	1-2	1-3	0-1	1-0	1-1
11. Macclesfield Town	1-1	0-1	0-0	0-1	3-3	4-4	1-2	1-0	0-2	0-0	#	3-0	0-0	0-0	3-0	0-1	1-0	2-1	1-2	1-0	3-1	1-2
12. Merthyr Tydfil	3-1	2-1	1-1	2-0	3-1	2-0	1-0	1-4	4-1	2-1	3-2	#	2-1	2-2	2-0	1-2	1-0	2-2	2-1	1-0	1-2	2-2
13. Northwich Victoria	1-2	6-1	1-3	1-1	3-1	1-1	1-1	1-1	4-3	3-1	2-1	4-1	#	0-2	3-0	3-0	1-2	1-1	1-2	3-0	0-1	1-0
14. Redbridge Forest	0-1	2-2	3-1	1-4	1-2	2-1	2-0	2-1	4-0	5-0	0-0	1-1	4-3	#	1-2	4-0	4-3	1-0	2-0	3-1	0-5	0-0
15. Runcorn	2-2	2-2	0-2	2-2	2-1	1-3	1-1	1-1	0-0	4-1	0-0	1-1	3-1	1-0	#	1-0	0-0	0-2	2-2	0-1	1-2	2-2
16. Slough Town	2-3	1-0	2-2	3-1	0-3	2-4	0-5	2-0	0-2	3-1	0-3	0-0	0-1	4-0	1-0	#	2-2	0-3	0-3	2-1	0-1	1-4
17. Stafford Ran.	1-2	0-0	2-0	0-1	2-2	3-3	0-1	1-3	1-2	2-0	1-1	0-0	2-1	2-1	1-0	1-1	#	3-2	0-0	3-2	0-2	0-0
18. Telford United	2-1	4-2	0-2	0-2	2-1	0-3	1-2	1-1	1-1	3-1	0-1	1-2	1-4	3-3	1-0	2-2	4-1	#	2-1	2-1	1-0	1-0
19. Welling United	2-2	5-3	0-5	1-3	1-1	4-1	1-0	2-2	2-3	3-2	2-1	1-2	6-1	2-2	1-2	0-2	1-1	3-1	#	1-1	1-3	1-0
20. Witton Albion	2-0	0-1	2-2	1-0	4-2	2-2	4-1	0-3	1-0	2-1	1-1	3-2	1-1	2-0	1-3	2-1	6-0	1-1	2-2	#	1-2	3-1
21. Wycombe W.	4-2	3-2	1-0	2-1	2-2	1-2	2-1	2-1	1-0	2-0	0-1	4-0	2-0	1-0	1-0	3-0	3-0	6-1	4-0	4-0	#	1-0
22. Yeovil Town	2-1	2-0	1-1	1-1	1-1	0-1	2-2	1-0	0-1	1-1	1-1	2-1	0-1	1-4	1-0	0-1	0-2	3-0	2-1	1-0	#

G.M. Vauxhall Conference

LEADING GOALSCORERS 1991-92

	CONFERENCE	FAC	BLT	FAT	Total
PAUL CAVELL (Redbridge Forest)	29	(1	1	2	33)
TERRY ROBBINS (Welling United)	29	(		1	30)
GARY JONES (Boston United)	27	(2	1	1	31)
ROY McDONOUGH (Colchester United)	26	(1		2	29)
SIMON READ (Farnborough Town)	21	(9	2	3	35)
KARL THOMAS (Witton Albion)	21	(3	1	4	29)
STEVE McGAVIN (Colchester United)	20	(2	2	4	28)
DAVE WEBLEY (Merthyr Tydfil)	20	(			20)
GARY ABBOTT (Welling United)	19	(5		1	25)
KEN McKENNA (Altrincham)	19	(	1		20)
MALCOLM O'CONNOR (Northwich Victoria)	19	(	2	1	22)
PAUL RANDALL (Bath City)	19	(3	2	1	25)
KEITH SCOTT (Wycombe Wanderers)	18	(	1	1	20)
JON GRAHAM (Kettering Town)	17	(3			20)
CERI WILLIAMS (Merthyr Tydfil)	17	(1	1	1	20)
GARY BENNETT (Colchester United)	16	(		2	18)
RICHARD HILL (Kettering Town)	16	(1		2	19)
MICKY SPENCER (Yeovil Town)	16	(1	3	4	24)

The Bob Lord Challenge Trophy

First Round (2 Legs)

BATH CITY Randall 2 (pens)	2	v	1	SLOUGH TOWN Hill	Att: 404
SLOUGH TOWN Knight, Joseph	2	v	0	BATH CITY	Att: 584
CHELTENHAM TOWN Casey 2, Willetts (pen), Kurila (OG)	4	v	2	KIDDERMINSTER HARRIERS Davies, Humphreys	Att: 675
KIDDERMINSTER Howell, Davies, Whitehouse	3	v	1	CHELTENHAM TOWN Fox	Att: 174
FARNBOROUGH TOWN Coombs (pen), Read 2	3	v	2	YEOVIL TOWN Spencer 2	Att: 461
YEOVIL TOWN Carroll 2, Boulton	3	v	0	FARNBOROUGH TOWN	Att: 1,473
GATESHEAD Bell, Corner (pen), Butler	3	v	0	WITTON ALBION	Att: 260
WITTON ALBION McCluskie 2, Thomas, Hill, Lutkevitch	5	v	0	GATESHEAD	Att: 501
NORTHWICH VICTORIA O'Connor 2	2	v	0	STAFFORD RANGERS	Att: 501
STAFFORD RANGERS Pearson	1	v	1	NORTHWICH VICTORIA Vaughan	Att: 540
REDBRIDGE FOREST Conner, Sowerby	2	v	0	BOSTON UNITED	Att: 202
BOSTON UNITED ShirtlifCasey, Cavell, Jones,	4	v	0	REDBRIDGE FOREST	Att: 746

BYES TO SECOND ROUND:

Altrincham, Barrow, Colchester United, Runcorn, Macclesfield Town, Kettering Town, Welling United, Merthyr Tydfil, Telford United, Wycombe Wanderers.

Second Round

ALTRINCHAM Brady 2	2	v	1	BARROW Doherty	Att: 589
COLCHESTER UNITED McGavin Kinsella 2, Collins,	4	v	0	KETTERING TOWN	Att: 1,296
MERTHYR TYDFIL Williams	1	v	3	WYCOMBE WANDERERS Crossley, Hutchinson, Gooden	Att: 526
NORTHWICH VICTORIA Graham 2, Butler	3	v	2	BOSTON UNITED Nesbitt 2	Att: 474
RUNCORN Redman, Hawtin	2	v	2	WITTON ALBION McCluskie 2	Att: 850
WITTON ALBION	0	v	2	RUNCORN Withers, McCarty	Att: 503
SLOUGH TOWN	0	v	1	KIDDERMINSTER HARRIERS Howell	Att: 408
TELFORD UNITED Brindley	1	v	2	MACCLESFIELD TOWN Timmons, Dawson	Att: 597

| YEOVIL TOWN | 2 | v | 0 | WELLING UNITED | Att: 1340 |
| Batty, Spencer | | | | | |

Third Round

COLCHESTER UNITED	2	v	6	WYCOMBE WANDERERS	Att: 919
Restarick, McGavin				West 2, Hutchison 2, Scott, Creaser	
KIDDERMINSTER	1	v	2	YEOVIL TOWN (AET)	Att: 681
Howell				Shail, Carroll	
MACCLESFIELD TOWN	1	v	1	ALTRINCHAM (AET)	Att: 447
Green				Hughes	
ALTRINCHAMN	3	v	1	MACCLESFIELD TOWN	Att: 524
Daws, Anderson, McKenna				Askey	
RUNCORN	2	v	1	NORTHWICH VICTORIA	Att: 558
Withers, McCarty				Graham	

Semi Finals (First & Second Legs)

RUNCORN	2	v	1	ALTRINCHAM	Att: 532
Hill, McCarty				Shaw	
ALTRINCHAM	1	v	3	RUNCORN	Att: 605
Lee				Disley 2, Richards	
YEOVIL TOWN	0	v	0	WYCOMBE WANDERERS	Att: 1,816
WYCOMBE WANDERERS	2	v	0	YEOVIL TOWN	Att: 1,883
Creaser, Greene					

Final (First & Second Legs)

RUNCORN	1	v	0	WYCOMBE WANDERERS	Att: 853
Saunders					
WYCOMBE WANDERERS	2	v	0	RUNCORN	Att: 2,519
Guppy, Carroll					

G.M. Vauxhall Conference

Attendances by Club 1991/92

	Aggregate Attendance 1991/92	Average Gate 1991/92	% Inc. or Dec.	Aggregate Gate 1990/91	Gates over 1,000
WYCOMBE WANDERERS	75,726	3,606	+ 29	2,794	21
COLCHESTER UNITED	73,811	3,514	+ 17	3,003	21
YEOVIL TOWN	44,171	2,103	- 20	2,634	21
KETTERING TOWN	38,997	1,857	- 28	2,563	21
KIDDERMINSTER HARRIERS	27,361	1,302	+ 9	1,197	19
BARROW	26,297	1,252	- 12	1,427	21
BOSTON UNITED	24,636	1,173	- 15	1,372	12
TELFORD UNITED	21,826	1,039	- 12	1,186	11
FARNBOROUGH TOWN	20,485	975	+ 58	616	4
SLOUGH TOWN	19,416	924	- 21	1,168	2
WITTON ALBION	19,182	913	+ 10	829	4
CHELTENHAM TOWN	18,591	885	- 14	1,029	6
STAFFORD RANGERS	18,342	873	- 26	1,174	5
ALTRINCHAM	18,241	868	- 37	1,385	5
WELLING UNITED	17,648	840	- 15	985	3
NORTHWICH VICTORIA	17,228	820	+ 10	748	4
MACCLESFIELD TOWN	15,866	755	- 25	1,001	3
REDBRIDGE FOREST	15,116	719	+114	336	2
BATH CITY	14,785	704	- 20	883	3
MERTHYR TYDFIL	13,658	650	- 21	824	2
RUNCORN	13,219	629	- 14	729	0
GATESHEAD	9,443	449	- 23	586	0

TOTAL CONFERENCE ATTENDANCES 1991/92

Aggregate 1991/92	Average Gate	% Inc or Dec	Gates over 1,000	Gates over 2,000	Clubs with % Inc
564,045	1,221	- 14	41%	14.5%	7

Highest Attendances 1991/92

7,193	Colchester United	v	Barrow	2.5.92
6,303	Colchester United	v	Kettering Town	28.4.92
6,035	Wycombe Wanderers	v	Witton Albion	2.5.92
5,184	Wycombe Wanderers	v	Colchester United	28.9.91
5,162	Wycombe Wanderers	v	Slough Town	1.1.92
5,083	Colchester United	v	Wycombe Wanderers	7.12.91
4,773	Colchester United	v	Redbridge Forest	1.1.92
4,283	Wycombe Wanderers	v	Telford United	12.10.91
4,263	Wycombe Wanderers	v	Bath City	20.4.92

All Time Top Ten Attendances

9,432	Lincoln City v Wycombe W	02.05.88		6,035	Wycombe W v Witton Alb	02.05.92
7,542	Lincoln City v Boston Utd	04.04.88		5,880	Barnet v Darlington	31.03.90
7,221	Colchester Utd v Altrincham	20.04.91		5,822	Boston Utd v Lincoln City	26.12.87
7,193	Colchester Utd v Barrow	02.05.92		5,640	Scarborough v Weymouth	02.05.87
6,303	Colchester Utd v Kettering T	28.04.92		5,525	Darlington v Cheltenham	28.04.90

G.M. Vauxhall Conference
TEN YEAR CLUB RECORD

	82/83	83/84	84/85	85/86	86/87	87/88	88/89	89/90	90/91	91/92
ALTRINCHAM	12	3	5	4	5	14	14	16	3	18
AYLESBURY UNITED	-	-	-	-	-	-	20	-	-	-
BANGOR CITY	13	21	-	-	-	-	-	-	-	-
BARNET	15	9	15	14	2	2	8	2	1	-
BARROW	21	-	18	22	-	-	-	14	10	22
BATH CITY	10	6	4	12	10	20	-	-	20	9
BOSTON UNITED	5	17	17	13	6	16	3	18	18	8
CHELTENHAM TOWN	-	-	-	11	11	13	15	11	16	21
CHORLEY	-	-	-	-	-	-	17	20	-	-
COLCHESTER UNITED	-	-	-	-	-	-	-	-	2	1
DAGENHAM	14	18	19	19	15	22	-	-	-	-
DARLINGTON	-	-	-	-	-	-	-	1	-	-
DARTFORD	-	-	3	21	-	-	-	-	-	-
ENFIELD	1	14	7	1	4	12	13	22	-	-
FARNBOROUGH TOWN	-	-	-	-	-	-	-	21	-	5
FISHER ATHLETIC	-	-	-	-	-	15	18	19	22	-
FRICKLEY ATHLETIC	16	12	11	2	21	-	-	-	-	-
GATESHEAD	-	16	21	-	22	-	-	-	17	14
KETTERING TOWN	19	19	12	9	16	3	2	5	4	3
KIDDERMINSTER HARRIERS	-	10	8	3	12	7	5	13	13	19
LINCOLN CITY	-	-	-	-	-	1	-	-	-	-
MACCLESFIELD TOWN	-	-	-	-	-	11	7	4	7	13
MAIDSTONE UNITED	2	1	13	17	3	9	1	-	-	-
MERTHYR TYDFIL	-	-	-	-	-	-	-	9	9	4
NORTHWICH VICTORIA	8	7	9	16	17	17	10	15	12	11
NUNEATON BOROUGH	11	2	2	18	18	-	-	-	-	-
REDBRIDGE FOREST	-	-	-	-	-	-	-	-	-	7
RUNCORN	4	5	14	6	8	4	6	3	8	16
SCARBOROUGH	9	13	6	15	1	-	-	-	-	-
SLOUGH TOWN	-	-	-	-	-	-	-	-	19	20
STAFFORD RANGERS	22	-	-	7	13	6	19	17	15	17
SUTTON UNITED	-	-	-	-	7	8	12	8	21	-
TELFORD UNITED	6	11	10	8	9	5	16	12	6	6
TROWBRIDGE TOWN	18	22	-	-	-	-	-	-	-	-
WEALDSTONE	3	4	1	10	19	21	-	-	-	-
WELLING UNITED	-	-	-	-	20	19	11	6	11	12
WEYMOUTH	7	15	16	5	14	10	21	-	-	-
WITTON ALBION	-	-	-	-	-	-	-	-	-	10
WORCESTER CITY	17	8	20	-	-	-	-	-	-	-
WYCOMBE WANDERERS	-	-	-	20	-	18	4	10	5	2
YEOVIL TOWN	20	20	22	-	-	-	9	7	14	15

G.M. Vauxhall Conference

PREVIOUS SEASONS' TOP FOUR

Season	Max Pts	Champions Pts		Runners-up Pts		3rd Place Pts		4th Place Pts	
1979/80	76	56	Altrincham	54	Weymouth	49	Worcester C.	45	Boston Utd.
1980/81	76	54	Altrincham	51	Kettering T.	47	Scarborough	45	Northwich V.
1981/82	126	93	Runcorn	86	Enfield	77	Telford Utd.	71	Worcester C.
1982/83	126	84	Enfield	83	Maidstone U.	79	Wealdstone	72*	Runcorn
1983/84	105	70	Maidstone U.	69	Nuneaton Bor.	65	Altrincham	62*	Wealdstone
1984/85	105	62	Wealdstone	58	Nuneaton Bor.	57*	Dartford	57*	Bath City
1985/86	105	76	Enfield	69	Frickley Ath.	67	Kidderminster	63	Altrincham
1986/87	126	91	Scarborough	85	Barnet	73	Maidstone Utd.	70	Enfield
1987/88	126	82	Lincoln City	80	Barnet	75	Kettering Town	74	Runcorn
1988/89	126	84	Maidstone Utd.	76	Kettering Town	74	Boston Utd.	71	Wycombe W.
1989/90	126	87	Darlington	85	Barnet	70	Runcorn	66	Macclesfield T.
1990/91	126	87	Barnet	85	Colchester U.	82	Altrincham	80	Kettering T.
1991/92	126	94	Colchester Utd	94	Wycombe W	73	Kettering Town	68	Merthyr Tydfil

* Indicates position achieved through goal difference.

FOOTBALL LEAGUE MOVEMENTS

1987	Promoted to 4th Div.: **Scarborough**	Relegated to Conference: **Lincoln City**
1988	Promoted to 4th Div.: **Lincoln City**	Relegated to Conference: **Newport County**
1989	Promoted to 4th Div.: **Maidstone United**	Relegated to Conference: **Darlington**
1990	Promoted to 4th Div.: **Darlington**	Relegated to Conference: **Colchester United**
1991	Promoted to 4th Div.: **Barnet**	No relegation from 4th Div.
1992	Promoted to 4th Div.: **Colchester United**	No relegation from 4th Div.

BOB LORD TROPHY

	Winner	Runner-up
1979/80	Northwich Victoria	Altrincham
1980/81	Altrincham	Kettering Town
1981/82	Weymouth	Enfield
1982/83	Runcorn	Scarborough
1983/84	Scarborough	Barnet
1984/85	Runcorn	Maidstone United
1985/86	Stafford Rangers	Barnet
1986/87	Kettering Town	Hendon (Isthmian)
1987/88	Horwich RMI (NPL)	Weymouth
1988/89	Barnet	Hyde United (HFS)
1989/90	Yeovil Town	Kidderminster H.
1990/91	Sutton United	Barrow
1991/92	Wycombe W	Runcorn

CHAMPIONSHIP SHIELD

Conference Champions v Trophy Winners

	Winner	Runner-up
1980	Northwich V	Altrincham
1981	Altrincham	Kettering T.
1982	runcorn	Weymouth
1983	Enfield	Runcorn
1984	Maidstone U.	Scarborough
1985	Runcorn	Wealdstone
1986	Stafford R.	Enfield
1987	Kidderminster H.	Scarborough
1988	Lincoln City	Enfield
1989	Maidstone Utd.	Telford Utd.
1990	Darlington	Barrow
1991	Wycombe W.	Barnet

G.M.A.C. CHALLENGE CUP

(NOW CLUBCALL CUP in which Conference clubs do not compete)

	Winner	Runner-up
1987	Kettering Town	Hendon (Isthmian)
1988	Horwich RMI (NPL)	Weymouth
1989	Barnet	Hyde Utd. (HFS)

G.M. Vauxhall Conference

COMPLETE CLUB RECORD 1979-1992

	No. of Seasons	P	W	D	L	F	A	Pts
ALTRINCHAM #	13	536	233	138	165	849	672	750
A P LEAMINGTON #	3	118	21	32	65	119	234	78
AYLESBURY UNITED	1	40	9	9	22	43	71	36
BANGOR CITY #	4	160	44	45	71	201	273	150
BARNET #	12	494	209	114	174	759	658	688
BARROW #	9	370	108	103	159	452	575	387
BATH CITY #	11	454	161	119	174	587	614	546
BOSTON UNITED #	13	536	213	123	200	831	842	700
CHELTENHAM TOWN	7	292	93	92	107	420	458	358
CHORLEY	2	82	26	12	44	99	138	90
COLCHESTER UNITED	2	84	53	20	11	166	75	179
DAGENHAM	7	294	87	70	137	374	494	307
DARLINGTON	1	42	26	9	7	76	25	87
DARTFORD	3	126	35	31	60	155	199	122
ENFIELD	9	376	169	80	127	672	541	553
FARNBOROUGH TOWN	2	84	28	24	32	128	126	108
FISHER ATHLETIC	4	166	41	46	79	206	283	169
FRICKLEY ATHLETIC	7	290	108	69	113	432	458	337
GATESHEAD	5	210	53	56	111	259	399	202
GRAVESEND & NORTHFLEET #	3	118	40	28	50	148	168	118
KETTERING TOWN #	13	536	216	141	179	813	742	725
KIDDERMINSTER HARRIERS	9	376	152	82	142	638	715	511
LINCOLN CITY	1	42	24	10	8	86	48	82
MACCLESFIELD TOWN	5	208	82	59	67	296	262	305
MAIDSTONE UNITED #	10	410	179	113	118	684	492	589
MERTHYR TYDFIL	3	126	50	37	39	188	180	187
NORTHWICH VICTORIA #	13	536	191	143	202	715	725	658
NUNEATON BOROUGH #	7	286	104	79	103	425	408	333
REDBRIDGE FOREST	1	42	18	9	15	69	56	63
REDDITCH UNITED #	1	38	5	8	25	26	69	18
RUNCORN	11	460	206	127	127	741	576	717
SCARBOROUGH #	8	328	136	101	91	471	393	450
SLOUGH TOWN	2	84	26	12	46	107	162	90
STAFFORD RANGERS #	11	452	132	137	183	571	653	506
SUTTON UNITED	5	208	76	59	73	352	305	287
TELFORD UNITED #	13	536	224	127	185	766	729	737
TROWBRIDGE TOWN	3	126	29	25	72	127	229	109
WEALDSTONE #	8	328	113	99	116	44	443	387
WELLING UNITED	6	250	80	67	103	342	388	307
WEYMOUTH #	10	410	164	102	144	603	553	524
WITTON ALBION	1	42	16	10	16	63	60	58
WORCESTER CITY #	6	244	93	58	93	347	376	288
WYCOMBE WANDERERS	6	250	109	62	79	396	349	382
YEOVIL TOWN #	10	410	126	101	183	548	672	439

- Founder Member of Alliance Premier League in 1979.

(NEWPORT COUNTY - deleted record 29 4 7 18 31 62 19)

Conference Diary
Of Events 1991 - 92

1 - 19 AUGUST

FA Trophy holders **Wycombe Wanderers** are 3-1 favourites to win the title. **Colchester United** are 11-2 second favourites. Stan Allan leaves **Witton Albion** to return to his old club **Altrincham** which leads to **Runcorn** boss Peter O'Brien moving to Witton and John Carroll taking temporary charge at Canal Street. **Northwich Victoria** appoint former Manchester United star Sammy McIlroy as manager and Colchester upgrade Roy McDonough after the departure of Ian Atkins to Birmingham City. **Kidderminster Harriers** goalkeeper Paul Jones joins Wolves for an initial £40,000 deal which could eventually be worth up to £110,000 to the Aggborough club. **Boston United** break their club record transfer fee by signing ex-Kettering Town midfielder Paul Richardson from Barnet for £20,000. Sicilian restaurateur Alex Cuscani becomes the first Italian Chairman in British football by taking command of **Gateshead**. Leeds United offer trials to **Barrow** winger Neil Doherty. Newly promoted **Redbridge Forest** sign a ten-year lease to share Dagenham's Victoria Road ground which has been their 'home' for three seasons. **Kettering Town** appoint veteran striker Ernie Moss as coach. **Colchester United** sell defender Scott Daniels to Exeter City for £50,000 and **Slough Town** break their club transfer record by signing **Farnborough Town** midfielder Colin Fielder for £18,000. **Stafford Rangers** winger Paul Devlin is the latest Conference player to attract Football League interest, reputed to be mighty Liverpool. Ex-Manchester United and Northern Ireland midfielder Norman Whiteside joins **Northwich Victoria** as physio where he teams up with Sammy McIlroy, his former international colleague. **Gateshead** sign the largest sponsorship agreement outside the Football League. Cameron Hall Developments agree a £50,000 deal for each of the next 3 seasons. **Boston United** midfielder Richard Toone scores the first goal of the English domestic season. His goal, scored after just 45 seconds, beat Southampton's Alan Shearer's goal against Spurs by over a minute. Meanwhile, Boston manager Dave Cusack is appointed on a full-time basis.

19 AUG - 2 SEPT

Welling United manager Nicky Brigden gives up his job in retailing to take on the post at Park View Road on a full-time basis. **Yeovil Town** promote Mike McEvoy and Mark Boulton to their professional ranks after completing their YT programme at Huish Park. **Northwich Victoria** striker Malcolm O'Connor becomes the first Conference player to score a hat-trick in the 4-2 win at **Farnborough**. **Redbridge Forest** turn down a bid totalling £100,000 from Watford for midfielder Andy Hessenthaler. **Stafford Rangers** winger Paul Devlin impresses Liverpool during 3 week trial at Anfield. **Bath City** complete construction of their new £250,000 grandstand at Twerton Park. **Telford United** place three experienced players, England Semi-Professional goalkeeper Steve Humphries, defender John McGinty and winger Ian Brown on the transfer list. **Wycombe Wanderers** and Barnet agree to donate the gate receipts from their Championship Shield match to Kevin Durham's Memorial Fund. The player sadly died during the summer having played for both clubs in the league. The Vauxhall Conference apply to the Football Association for permission to use red and yellow cards in senior competative matches.

3 - 16 SEPTEMBER

Leaders **Wycombe Wanderers** set a new Conference record by extending their 100% start to the season to six matches. **Runcorn** appoint John Carroll as manager on a permanent basis following a month as caretaker. **Altrincham** sign **Witton Albion** full-back Andy Lee for a small fee. It will be the England defender's second spell at Moss Lane. **Slough Town** receive planning permission to build a nine hole golf course at Wexham Park. It will be the first of it's kind in British football. **Redbridge Forest** finally sell Andy Hessenthaler to Watford for an initial £65,000 fee - a new club record. The total fee could exceed £100,000. **Yeovil Town** announce plans to build an artificial pitch for community use at Huish Park. The floodlit facility will cost around £150,000. **Stafford Rangers** and Liverpool fail to reach agreement over a fee for the transfer of Paul Devlin and the deal is called off. Latest player to be involved in trials with a First Division club is Rangers' goalkeeper Ryan Price who spends a week with Coventry City. **Runcorn** record their first victory of the season with a 2-0 win over **Farnborough Town**, which leaves only **Kettering Town** and **Gateshead** yet to win a game.

Paul Cavell pictured in early season action for Boston again Merthyr. Cavell later moved to Redbridge Forest along with team-mate Paul Richardson. Photo - Mike Floate.

Kettering somehow manage to keep out this Andy Hessenthaler effort in their 0-4 drubbing at Redbridge Forest. Photo - Dennis Nicholson.

Stafford's highly rated goalkeeper Ryan Price in action at Bath City. Photo - Alan Casse, Avon Press.

Wycombe Wanderers suffer their first defeat of the season, losing 1-0 at home to **Macclesfield Town** in front of a crowd of 3,821, the best in the Conference so far, and **Kettering Town** register their first victory of the campaign by beating **Kidderminster Harriers** 2-1 at Rockingham Road. Five clubs pass the 500 Conference match landmark - founder members **Boston United, Kettering Town, Northwich Victoria, Telford United** and **Altrincham** all reach their half millennium. **Boston** manager Dave Cusack pays £8,000 to Peterborough United for former Ipswich Town defender Chris Swailes whilst **Redbridge Forest** sign Grays Athletic striker Richard Cherry for £9,000. **Wycombe** set a seasonal best attendance record when 5,184 watch the 2-1 home defeat by **Colchester United**, whose winning goal was scored by goalkeeper Scott Barrett in the last minute. **Merthyr Tydfil** call an emergency meeting of the eight Welsh Pyramid clubs to discuss the proposed new League of Wales. **Kettering** defender Richard Huxford joins Newcastle United on trial. Martin O'Neill, manager of leaders **Wycombe**, wins the first Mail on Sunday Manager of the Month award. Red and yellow cards are re-introduced. **Colchester** sign ex-Millwall defender Paul Roberts from Fisher Athletic for £2,000 and **Slough Town** pay **Wycombe** £8,000 for utility player Steve Whitby.

TV entertainer Richard Digance launches a half million pound fund raising initiative to prepare **Yeovil Town** for Football League status. **Stafford Rangers** release former Aston Villa midfielder Des Bremner. The Vauxhall Conference and the Professional Footballers' Association meet to discuss the possibility of a closer working relationship between the two organisations. **Farnborough Town** go to the top of the table, dislodging **Wycombe Wanderers** who have been leading the way all season. **Colchester United** come to the aid of Diadora League Premier Division neighbours Wivenhoe Town by 'lending' them youth coach Steve Foley, who will act as caretaker manager, and several YT players. This follows the resignation of manager Phil Coleman at the struggling Essex club. John Still becomes the latest Conference manager to go full-time as **Redbridge Forest** award him a five-year contract. **Runcorn** sign former Rochdale and Everton midfielder Barry Wellings from Southport. **Stafford Rangers** add ex-Walsall stalwart Kenny Mower to their squad and **Witton Albion** sell long-serving midfielder Paul Lodge to Morecambe. **Wycombe** are now 6-4 on to win the title with **Colchester** at 6-4 against and current leaders **Farnborough** 8-1. **Altrincham** use three different goalkeepers during their Bob Lord Trophy victory over **Barrow**. Steve Roberts, who was making his first appearance of the season, was forced to leave the field after only 10 minutes with a head injury. Defender Martin Lewis took over until Roberts returned, only for the unfortunate keeper to suffer yet another head injury 15 minutes from the end. Harry Wiggins took over between the posts and kept a clean sheet as Altrincham won 2-1.

Northwich Victoria appoint Norman Whiteside as assistant-manager to replace Gordon Clayton, who sadly died three weeks ago. Whiteside will combine the physiotherapist's job with his new role. **Wycombe Wanderers** announce a profit of £45,000 for year ending May 1991. **Gateshead** register their first win of the season, beating **Stafford Rangers** 3-1 at Marston Road. **Slough Town** record the biggest away win of the season so far by winning 7-3 at **Atrincham**. **Colchester United** make their first appearance in the FA Cup Qualifying competition since 1947 with a home tie against Beazer Homes Premier Division side Burton Albion. **Wycombe** sign midfielder John Deakin from Carlisle United and **Redbridge Forest** sign four new players. Goalkeeper Peter Hucker, the former QPR player, arrives from Aldershot, striker Mario Walsh, who has been on loan at **Kettering Town**, joins from **Colchester** and Gary Blackford and Hakan Hayrettin are signed on loan from Barnet. **Welling United** striker Gary Abbott goes into the FA Cup record books by heading all five goals in the Wings' 5-1 win over Alvechurch. **Boston United** defender Chris Swailes, a recent signing from Peterborough United, goes on trial with Newcastle United. **Northwich Victoria** re-sign forward Graham Easter following a spell in Finland.

Redbridge Forest manager John Still continues his rebuilding and signs **Boston United** duo Paul Cavell and Paul Richardson for a 'substantial' five-figure fee and Marcus Ebdon on loan from Peterborough United. Former Spurs and England winger Peter Taylor also agrees to join Forest and play when his committments as assistant-manager at Watford allow. Former Glasgow Rangers and Leicester City boss Jock Wallace stands down as a director of **Colchester United**. **Cheltenham Town**, meanwhile, see their entire Board of Directors stand down following negotiations to strengthen the financial situation at Whaddon Road. **Barrow** become the latest Conference club to launch a YT programme. Sunday football proves a great success at **Kettering Town** as 2,379, their best of the season so far, pay to watch the game against **Bath City** at Rockingham Road. The move to the Sabbath was made to avoid clashing with the Rugby World Cup Final which caused most of the other Conference clubs, who went ahead and played on the Saturday, to record their lowest home gates of the season. **Macclesfield Town** sign former South Liverpool striker Andy Green from Belgian club Binche for £7,000. **Kidderminster Harriers** announce the largest sponsorship deal outside the Football League, securing a £200,000 two-year agreement with brewers Ansells. Dennis Booth, formerly first team coach at Aston Villa, joins **Stafford Rangers** as assistant-manager. **Farnborough Town** break a 14 year attendance record at their Cherrywood Road ground as 3,069 turn up for the top of the table clash with **Colchester United**. **Northwich Victoria**

winger Tony Hemmings is the latest Conference player to attract League attention with Wigan Athletic declaring an interest. The rebuilt **Redbridge Forest** side finally end an 11 match run without a victory by thrashing **Kidderminster** 5-0 at Victoria Road. **Telford United** sign Jason Withe, son of ex-Forest and England striker Peter Withe, from **Stafford** and Gloucester City duo Steve Fergusson and Brendan Hackett.

12 - 25 NOVEMBER

Barrow manager Ray Wilkie is taken ill shortly before the home game against Altrincham - a game which also marked Colin Cowperthwaite's 700th appearance for the Cumbrian club. Barrow appoint Neil McDonald and Alan Cook as caretaker-managers whilst Wilkie is recovering. **Slough Town** sell goalkeeper Phil Burns to Airdrie for £20,000. **Yeovil Town** midfielder Andy Wallace goes on trial at Sheffield United. Long-serving defender John McGinty leaves **Telford United** to join Hednesford Town of the Beazer Homes League Midland Division. Former Northern Ireland and Newcastle United midfielder Tommy Cassidy is appointed as the new manager of **Gateshead** in succession to Tony Lee who resigned following the home defeat by **Bath City**. **Northwich Victoria** turn down a £20,000 bid by Wigan Athletic for Tony Hemmings. **Wycombe Wanderers'** Steve Guppy joins Charlton Athletic on trial. More comings and goings at **Redbridge Forest**. Peterborough United goalkeeper Ian Bennett joins on loan and Adrian Owers signs from Maidstone United on a free transfer. Striker Richard Cherry leaves to join Kingstonian for the same £9,000 fee that manager John Still paid Grays for him just six weeks ago. **Kettering Town's** 10 match unbeaten run ends with a 3-2 home defeat by **Slough Town**. **Merthyr Tydfil** midfielder David D'Auria runs five miles from his broken down car to Pennydarren Park for the home game against **Runcorn**. He arrives on time - only to be ruled unfit to play due to a large blister caused by the run!. **Boston United** sign **Wycombe** striker Mick Nuttell for £10,000 and ex-Aston Villa, Leicester City and Watford defender Steve Sims joins **Stafford Rangers**.

26 NOV - 9 DEC

Derek Mann, General Manager of **Telford United**, leaves to join West Bromwich Albion's management team. The Football Association agree a £30,000 sponsorship deal with Vauxhall Motors for the FA Trophy. **Yeovil Town** reach the FA Cup Second Round for the 21st time, a new record, after beating Walsall in a replay at the Bescot Stadium. **Bath City** release forward David Payne after 8 years service at Twerton Park and over 300 appearances. He joins Weymouth. **Farnborough Town** sign former Queen's Park Rangers, Fulham and Norwich City striker Dean Coney from Hong Kong club Ernest Borel. Amongst the other signings around the Conference is **Cheltenham Town's** capture of Wayne Matthews from Barry Town and Lee Howells from Bristol Rovers, **Northwich Victoria** sign midfielder Andy Feeley from Bury, Chris Hemming joins **Stafford Rangers** from **Merthyr Tydfil** and **Runcorn** add former Horwich RMI striker Darryl McCarty and Scarborough winger Steve Carter to their squad. The Second Round of the FA Cup sees **Kettering Town** beat Fourth Division Maidstone United away and **Farnborough** hold Torquay United to a 1-1 draw at Plainmoor. However, **Witton Albion**, who lost 5-1 at Preston, **Yeovil Town**, beaten 3-0 at Woking and **Telford United**, who lost 1-0 at Wrexham, all bow out. **Northwich Victoria** boss Sammy McIlroy makes a playing comeback in a friendly with Stoke City. **Merthyr Tydfil** continue their opposition to the new League of Wales with the threat of taking legal action against the Welsh FA. **Yeovil** put their entire first team squad on the transfer list. Barnet goalkeeper Steve Berryman signs permanently for **Altrincham** following a period on loan. **Bath City** sign Grantley Dicks, brother of West Ham's Julian, from Paulton Rovers, Paul Evans moves to **Merthyr** from Barry Town and **Stafford** sign winger Darren Roberts from Armitage'90. **Macclesfield Town** goalkeeper Steve Farrelly is the subject of interest from Blackburn Rovers.

10 DEC - 6 JAN 92

Barrow appoint former Altrincham boss John King as team manager following the long-term absence of Ray Wilkie. King is joined by his ex-Altrincham assistant Graham Heathcote. The Bookmakers now make **Colchester United** 6-4 on favourites for the title. **Redbridge Forest** are beaten 1-0 at Runcorn to end their seven match unbeaten run. **Gateshead** sign midfielder Tony Lowery from Mansfield Town, former Hartlepool striker Alan Lamb and full-back Jimmy Robertson from Falkirk. **Yeovil Town** sack goalkeeper David Fry for a breach of club rules. **Farnborough Town** beat Torquay United 4-3 in an FA Cup Second Round replay which is shown live on BSkyB to earn a money spinning tie against First Division West Ham United. The club decide to switch the game to Upton Park. **Stafford Rangers** appoint Dennis Booth as manager in succession to Chris Wright who was sacked. Former Wolves boss Sammy Chapman joins **Telford United** to run the club's scouting system. The Vauxhall Conference renews its agreement with satellite channel Sportscast to feature live matches for the remainder of the season. **Macclesfield Town** receive £10,000 from Sheffield United as part of the transfer arrangement for midfielder Mike Lake after the former Silkman completed 25 first team matches for the First Division club. An eleven match run without a win came to an end for **Witton Albion** when the Cheshire side beat Boston United 1-0. New **Barrow** manager John King signs Phil Power from Chorley, Neil Kelly from **Altrincham** and Crewe striker Terry McPhillips, who joins on loan. **Runcorn** sign Sean Lundon from **Bath City** for a small fee and **Yeovil Town** capture Fulham goalkeeper David Coles. **Farnborough** put up a magnificent showing to hold West Ham to a 1-1 draw at Upton Park in the Third Round of the FA Cup. The Conference's only other representative, **Kettering Town**, bow out, going down 4-1 at Blackburn Rovers.

Redbridge Forest 2, Colchester United 1 - 26/12/91. An unmarked Tony Pamplett head Forest's first half equaliser. Photo - Gavin Ellis.

Colchester United 1, Redbridge Forest 0 - 4/1/92. Redridge defender Steve Conner (left) gets up above Colchester's Roy McDonough and team-mate Bobby Mayes to head clear a corner. Photo - John Robinson.

Welling's Gary Abbott scores his second in another hat-trick, this time in a 5-3 win v Barrow. Photo - Keith Gillard.

7 - 20 JANUARY

Yeovil Town announce that they are to revert back to part-time playing status following a two year experiment employing full-time professionals. **Runcorn** purchase their Canal Street ground from the Commission of New Towns' for £72,500 and have major development plans in mind. **Merthyr Tydfil** present their case to an Appeal Hearing in Llandrindod Wells opposing the new League of Wales. **Wycombe Wanderers** add to their already powerful forward line by signing the prolific Kim Casey for £9,000 from **Cheltenham Town**, who spend £5,000 of the fee to bring Neil Smith from Lincoln City and **Redbridge Forest** pay Barnet £10,000 for midfielder Gary Blackford who has been on loan at Victoria Road for the past two months. **Farnborough Town** finally bow out of the FA Cup to an 89th minute Trevor Morley goal at West Ham. An aggregate attendance of 47,318 watched the two games at Upton Park bringing in gate receipts of over £130,000. Meanwhile, midfielder Brian Broome becomes the club's new appearance record holder, passing Hughie Richardson's 467 game total. **Northwich Victoria** lose winger Gareth Ainsworth to Preston North End and sign Simon Gresty from local club Christleton. **Witton Albion** pay £5,000 to bring **Altrincham** striker Mark Hughes to Wincham Park.

21 JAN - 3 FEB

Cheltenham Town manager Ally Robertson resigns following a run of 11 games without a win. Former Bristol Rovers defender Lyndsay Parsons takes over as caretaker-manager. **Barrow** make their first cash signing in 15 years recruiting defender Paul Rowlands and striker John Brady from **Altrincham**. The deal, which also involved defender Tony Chilton moving in the opposite direction, is valued at an undislosed five-figure fee, beating the club's previous record set in 1977 when Martin Eatough arrived from Morecambe. Gary Blackford, the midfielder recently signed by **Redbridge Forest** from Barnet, is joining Tottenham Hotspur on trial. **Witton Albion** boss Peter O'Brien is admitted to hospital with a jaundice complaint. **Welling United** striker Gary Abbott nets five goals for the second time this season, this time playing for the FA XI against the Diadora League, which was convincingly won 7-1 by the FA side. Former Wolves boss Sammy Chapman leaves **Telford United** after only three weeks. The club have also accepted a £20,000 bid from Barnet for midfielder Paul Grainger. **Wycombe Wanderers** set a new attendance record for the Second Round of the FA Trophy when 5,801 watch the holders defeat Diadora League title favourites Woking 1-0. **Colchester United** sign former Northern Ireland forward Ian Stewart from Aldershot and **Farnborough Town** sign the ex-Tottenham, Portsmouth and Oxford United striker David Leworthy from Reading. Television personality Richard Digance steps down from the Board of Directors at **Yeovil Town**. **Merthyr Tydfil** striker David Webley goes on trial with Swansea City whilst **Stafford Rangers** winger Paul Devlin, who has already had a bid from Liverpool turned down by the club, has gone on trial with Leeds United.

4 - 17 FEBRUARY

Merthyr Tydfil are to retain membership of the Vauxhall Conference following the Appeals Committee's decision to uphold the club's appeal against joining the League of Wales. **Redbridge Forest** midfielder Bobby Mayes turns down the chance to move to West Bromwich Albion after failing to agree terms with the Third Division club. **Farnborough Town** continue their signing of former League players by capturing Aldershot duo goalkeeper Peter Hucker and defender Steve Baker. **Witton Albion** record the biggest win of the season by beating **Stafford Rangers** 6-0 at Wincham Park. The game coincided with the return from illness of manager Peter O'Brien. Vauxhall Conference match referees are to be wired up with lightweight instruments to monitor blood pressure and heart beats. **Slough Town** are taken over by a consortium led by Alan Thorne, former owner of Millwall, his son Byron and Bob Pearson, who managed Millwall for a spell. A crowd of 4,088 turn up for **Barrow** striker Colin Cowperthwaite's testimonial match against Manchester City. Former Torquay United striker Jimmy Smith joins **Cheltenham Town** from Beazer Homes Leaguers Salisbury, where he scored 44 goals last season. **Macclesfield Town** sign the experienced Mick Doherty from **Farnborough** for a small fee. Another experienced player, **Kidderminster Harriers** defender Alan Kurila, has joined Burton Albion as player-coach.

18 FEB - 3 MAR

Winger Paul Devlin, who has had trial periods at Liverpool and Leeds United already this season, signs for Notts County. The fee was thought to be worth around £60,000 to **Stafford Rangers**. Former Northern Ireland and Manchester United midfielder Norman Whiteside has stepped down as assistant manager at **Northwich Victoria** in order to concentrate on his physiotherapy studies. He is succeeded by former Stafford boss Chris Wright. **Wycombe Wanderers**, who have already signed Kim Casey, add Chelmsford City's Dennis Greene and **Slough Town** forward Steve Thompson to their ever-growing list of strikers. Greene, leading scorer for the Beazer Homes League club this season, cost Martin O'Neill a £15,000 fee whilst Thompson joined for a 'substantial' five-figure sum. The Adams Park side reached the final of the Bob Lord Trophy where they will meet **Runcorn**. **Colchester United** are now quoted as 1-2 to win the Conference championship. **Boston United** striker Gary Jones, a bargain £3,000 buy from **Kettering Town** during the summer, registered a hat-trick of hat-tricks with 3 of United's four goals against Gateshead. Jones has now scored 17 goals for the Lincolnshire side. **Kidderminster Harriers** defender Dave Barnett is invited for a one week trial at Barnet with a view to a transfer being completed for the 24-year-old. Barry Fry is still showing interest in **Telford United** midfielder Paul Grainger. The

Third Round of the FA Trophy sees victories for **Colchester** over Morecambe, **Macclesfield Town**, who beat fellow Conference side **Northwich**, **Redbridge Forest** over **Farnborough Town**, **Witton Albion** and **Yeovil Town**. **Kettering Town** are surprisingly beaten at Marine whilst **Telford** and **Gateshead** and **Bath City** and **Wycombe** must try again after drawing. **Redbridge** register the largest victory in the league so far with a 7-0 battering of **Cheltenham Town**. **Northwich** boss Sammy McIlroy plays his first league game of the season and inspires his side to a 4-3 win over **Kettering**, coming back from being three nil down at half-time. Dave Barnett signs for Barnet after his weeks trial. **Kidderminster** will receive a five-figure fee for the centre-half. **Wycombe** sign 34-year-old former Newcastle United, Middlesbrough and Southend defender Peter Johnson from Peterborough United. They progress to the FA Trophy Quarter-Finals by beating **Bath** 2-0 at Adams Park as do **Telford**, who beat **Gateshead** 1-0 in a game played at Blyth Spartans.

4 - 16 MARCH

Former England and Ipswich Town midfielder Brian Talbot has taken over as the new owner of **Kettering Town** along with businessman Mark English. The club are over £100,000 in debt with a large chunk of that being owed to the Inland Revenue. Barnet have withdrawn their interest in **Telford United** midfielder Paul Grainger. Another playing staying put for the moment is Gary Blackford, the **Redbridge Forest** midfielder, who had been on trial with Tottenham Hotspur. England defeat Wales 1-0 in the Semi-Professional International held at Aberystwyth. **Redbridge** provide no less than five of the England side. The Sportscast Channel, which screened live Conference matches, has ceased trading. Former Reading striker David Leworthy nets all four of **Farnborough Town's** goals in the 4-2 win over **Macclesfield Town**. **Gateshead** boss Tommy Cassidy gives five players home debuts against **Welling United**. Steve Cuthbert, Danny Wheatley, Steve Higgins, Neil Grayson and Brian Healey all made their International Stadium bow. **Kettering** sign striker Pat Gavin, defender Lee Howarth and midfielder Gary Butterworth on loan from Peterborough United. **Colchester United**, **Witton Albion** and **Macclesfield Town** are through to the Trophy semi-finals. **Colchester** dismiss **Telford United** 4-0 at Layer Road whilst **Macclesfield** beat **Yeovil Town** 2-1 at Huish Park. Surprise of the round was **Witton's** 2-1 victory at **Wycombe Wanderers** in front of the days best attendance, 4,636. **Redbridge** hold Marine at Rossett Park thanks to a Paul Cavell goal six minutes from time.

17 - 30 MARCH

Kidderminster Harriers announce a profit of £33,709 for the year ending 31 May 1991. That figure does not include the sale of goalkeeper Paul Jones who joined Wolves for £60,000 in the summer. **Redbridge Forest** are out of the FA Trophy after HFS Loans League side Marine win 1-0 at Victoria Road. The Trophy is the one major prize in non-league football that he eluded John Still during his managerial career. Tony Hemmings, the **Northwich Victoria** winger, has gone on trial with Crystal Palace. The Vic's turned down a bid from Wigan Athletic earlier in the season for the 22-year-old. **Welling United** midfielder and assistant manager Ray Burgess makes his 1,000th appearance for the Kent club in the shock 5-0 home defeat by **Bath City**. Transfer deadline day sees the usual flurry of activity with a new registration record of 42 being set. One of the busiest managers on the day is **Stafford Rangers'** Dennis Booth. In an effort to get away from the bottom of the table, Booth signs Aston Villa's former Watford and Derby County winger Nigel Callaghan, ex-Wolves and Stoke defender George Berry from Aldershot and midfielder Paul Jones from **Kettering Town**. The Northamptonshire club are also busy with manager Peter Morris drafting in former Leicester City and Luton striker Marc North from Shepshed, Dean Barker and Stewart Phillips from Sudbury Town, Paul Cox from Notts County, Steve Hardwick from Emley and Brian Talbot, the club's new Chairman! Leaving Rockingham Road is goalkeeper Kevin Shoemake, who joins **Redbridge Forest**, and experienced striker Trevor Christie, to VS Rugby. **Kidderminster Harriers** sign midfielder Paul Grainger from **Telford United** for £10,000 with Richard Forsyth moving in the opposite direction on loan. **Altrincham** suffer their sixth successive defeat in the league, losing 2-1 at home to **Welling United**. The top of the table sees **Colchester United** move three points clear of **Wycombe Wanderers** after a 3-0 win over **Kidderminster** at Layer Road.

31 MAR - 6 APR

Stafford Rangers end an eight week tenancy of bottom spot in the table and are succeeded by **Barrow**. **Kidderminster Harriers** and **Runcorn** also slip into the bottom four. **Welling United** become the seventh Conference club to operate a YT programme, which will begin in earnest during the summer. **Runcorn** take a single goal advantage in the Bob Lord Trophy Final with a Steve Saunders goal against **Wycombe Wanderers** at Canal Street. **Northwich Victoria** strike their first goal in 466 minutes of Conference football with 1-0 win over **Slough Town**. A crowd of 5,633 watch the Under-18 International between England and Eire at **Yeovil Town**. **Colchester United** take an almost impregnable 3-0 lead in the first leg of the FA Trophy semi-final against **Macclesfield Town** at Layer Road. Ian Stewart, Tony English and a penalty from player-boss Roy McDonough net the all-important goals. The all-Northern semi-final between **Witton Albion** and Marine ends all square at 2-2. In the league, **Wycombe** go level on points with **Colchester** after beating **Farnborough Town** 3-1 at Cherrywood Road.

Ray Burgess receives an award to commemerate his 1,000 appearence for Welling United, before their home game against Bath City. Photo - Keith Gillard.

Wycombe Wanderers win the first honour of the season by lifting the Bob Lord Trophy. They overturned a 1-0 deficit to beat **Runcorn** 2-0 at Adams Park in front of a crowd of 2,519 - a record attendance for a Bob Lord Trophy tie. They celebrate further by topping the table after a 4-0 victory over struggling Altrincham. **Colchester United** are now 3 points behind with 7 games to play. **Kidderminster Harriers** end their run of eleven matches without a win with a 2-1- win over **Runcorn**. **Redbridge Forest** convene an EGM to discuss the possible merger with current landlords Dagenham. If both parties agree, a 'new' club called Dagenham and Redbridge will play in the Conference next season. **Farnborough Town** record their biggest away win of the season, beating struggling **Slough Town** 5-0 at Wexham Park. That result meant that the Berkshire side had now lost six matches on the trot. **Altrincham** made a timely end to their run of nine consecutive defeats as they beat **Cheltenham Town** 2-0 at Whaddon Road. The Cheshire club were slipping dangerously close to the relegation places. That defeat though puts Cheltenham in deep trouble at the foot of the table.

Barrow become the first club to be relegated following a home draw with **Yeovil Town**, a result which virtually ensured the Somerset club's Conference status. **Slough Town** continue their slide and extended their run of matches without a win to 12 with a 3-3 draw with **Kidderminster Harriers**. Simon Smith, the **Gateshead** goalkeeper, makes his 350th consecutive appearance for the club against **Macclesfield Town**. **Colchester United** concede their first goal in nine league matches by drawing 4-4 with **Macclesfield Town**. **Redbridge Forest** boss John Still obtains honour number 14 as they beat Chelmsford City 3-0 to win the Essex Senior Cup. **Colchester** go a long way to clinching the title with a 3-1 home win over **Kettering Town**. **Altrincham** are in deep trouble as they lose at home to **Telford United**. **Slough** also lose at **Northwich Victoria**. Two days before the final matches of the season **Wycombe Wanderers** gain a tremendous 5-0 victory at **Redbridge** to really put the pressure on at the top. However, **Colchester** clinch the championship on goal difference on the last Saturday of the 1991/92 campaign with a 5-0 thumping of already relegated **Barrow** at Layer Road in front of a crowd of 7,193. That result ensured that United would stay ahead of **Wycombe** on goal difference despite Wanderers' 4-0 win over **Witton Albion**. Despite beating **Welling United** 3-2, **Cheltenham Town** are relegated. That was due to the fact that **Kidderminster** won 4-0 at **Gateshead**. **Kettering** finish in third spot, their fifth successive top five placing, with **Merthyr Tydfil** securing an excellent fourth place with a last day win at **Telford United**. Both **Colchester** and **Wycombe** break the Conference points record, registering 94 each. That total passes the previous best of 93 set by **Runcorn** ten years ago. The FA Trophy Final at Wembley is a disappointing spectacle despite four goals being scored. A crowd of 27,806 see a niggling game between Conference champions **Colchester United** and **Witton Albion**. American striker Mike Masters put United in front after 5 minutes and Nicky Smith increased the lead on 19 minutes. Mike Lutkevitch pulled one back for Albion after 57 minutes before Jason Cook, the United midfielder, became the first player to be sent-off in a Trophy Final nine minutes from time. However, United not only held out, they increased their lead with a Steve McGavin goal two minutes from the end. So **Colchester** became the first club since Wealdstone in 1985 to win the Conference and Trophy double.

Barrow's John Brady gets in a shot against Yeovil - the Cumbrians' failure to win this game sent them down out of the Conference. Photo - Ged Rule.

John Brady is unsuccessful with another shot, this one blocked, in the above match. Photo - Ged Rule.

Ian Hedges receives the Bath City 'Player of the Year' award. Photo - Alan Casse.

153

Terry Robbins of Welling United, the G.M.V. Conference's joint top scorer in 1991-92, scores his team's goal in a 1-1 draw at home to Witton Albion. Photo - Keith Gillard.

David Leworthy, part of Farnborough Town's exciting forward line, in action against Boston United on 14th March at Cherrywood Road.

GM VAUXHALL CONFERENCE
FIXTURE DATES 1992/93

1. Altrincham
2. Bath City
3. Boston United
4. Bromsgrove Rovers
5. Dagenham & Redbridge
6. Farnborough Town
7. Gateshead
8. Kettering
9. Kidderminster Harriers
10. Macclesfield
11. Merthyr Tydfil

12. Northwich Victoria
13. Runcorn
14. Slough Town
15. Stafford Rangers
16. Stalybridge Celtic
17. Telford
18. Welling United
19. Witton Albion
20. Woking
21. Wycombe Wanderers
22. Yeovil

H/A	1	2	3	4	5	6	7	8	9	10	11	12	13	14	15	16	17	18	19	20	21	22
1	*	06-02	19-09	24-04	14-11	17-10	25-08	26-12	17-11	12-04	29-08	07-11	10-10	16-01	26-09	30-01	20-02	19-12	03-04	06-03	28-11	20-23
2	21-11	*	13-02	20-03	27-03	07-11	30-01	08-12	26-12	06-03	08-09	10-10	28-11	25-08	24-04	19-12	23-01	13-10	29-08	15-09	29-09	12-04
3	13-03	03-10	*	30-01	02-01	23-01	03-04	14-04	29-03	14-11	01-05	12-12	22-08	26-09	02-09	10-02	17-10	26-12	20-03	28-11	09-09	27-02
4	12-12	02-01	25-08	*	06-02	26-12	20-02	23-01	12-04	15-09	28-11	05-09	03-04	13-02	14-11	06-03	03-11	12-09	16-01	01-05	10-10	26-09
5	27-02	17-04	17-11	29-08	*	25-08	16-01	01-05	13-03	17-10	30-01	03-10	31-10	09-02	13-02	20-02	28-11	12-04	19-12	06-10	03-04	26-12
6	01-05	16-01	21-11	10-04	06-03	*	22-08	10-10	05-09	24-04	06-10	28-11	06-02	23-02	27-03	31-10	12-12	03-11	26-09	28-12	31-08	02-01
7	16-09	31-10	06-02	07-11	05-09	05-12	*	27-03	12-12	26-09	17-04	10-04	31-08	27-02	02-01	28-12	03-10	17-10	17-11	23-01	13-03	01-05
8	10-04	20-02	28-12	21-11	29-09	08-09	28-11	*	24-04	29-03	17-10	13-02	30-01	03-11	06-10	03-04	02-01	13-03	27-02	25-08	26-09	12-12
9	22-08	10-04	16-01	28-12	19-09	27-02	14-11	31-08	*	30-01	27-03	01-05	19-12	05-12	20-03	21-11	17-04	03-10	17-10	12-09	31-10	20-02
10	28-12	05-09	29-09	17-04	10-10	19-09	19-12	31-10	10-11	*	16-01	31-08	13-03	21-11	17-11	10-04	13-02	27-02	05-12	27-03	22-08	23-01
11	05-12	31-08	07-11	19-01	22-08	03-04	13-02	23-02	02-01	03-10	*	13-03	24-04	10-04	05-09	14-11	28-12	26-09	23-01	10-10	12-09	02-02
12	06-10	03-04	06-03	01-12	24-04	19-12	26-12	19-09	25-08	13-10	31-10	*	05-12	29-08	23-01	26-09	21-11	14-11	12-04	06-02	27-02	27-03
13	02-01	01-05	27-03	27-02	23-01	29-08	06-10	07-11	26-09	25-08	20-03	15-09	*	17-10	12-04	13-10	29-09	13-02	26-12	12-12	21-11	12-09
14	05-09	02-02	31-10	03-10	31-08	14-11	20-03	22-08	23-01	12-12	26-12	20-02	06-03	*	03-04	06-02	19-09	10-11	24-04	02-01	12-04	13-10
15	10-11	19-09	23-03	05-12	21-11	03-10	10-10	19-12	15-09	06-02	20-02	17-04	28-12	01-05	*	25-08	10-04	29-08	30-03	13-03	30-01	31-10
16	27-03	22-08	10-10	17-10	12-12	13-03	12-04	17-04	13-02	26-12	19-09	02-01	17-11	07-11	27-02	*	31-08	01-05	02-02	29-08	23-01	28-11
17	31-10	27-02	05-12	09-02	20-03	12-09	06-03	15-09	10-10	07-11	12-04	30-01	16-01	19-12	26-12	01-12	*	03-04	25-08	26-09	24-04	29-08
18	23-01	12-12	10-04	27-03	28-12	17-04	24-04	06-02	07-11	28-11	21-11	20-03	19-09	10-10	06-03	05-09	22-08	*	31-10	08-12	02-01	31-08
19	31-08	13-03	05-09	22-08	07-11	20-02	27-10	03-10	28-11	02-01	06-03	28-12	10-04	27-03	24-11	15-09	01-05	30-01	*	13-02	12-12	10-10
20	03-10	05-12	19-12	31-10	01-12	12-04	21-11	20-03	03-04	20-02	27-02	17-10	05-09	30-01	22-08	24-04	30-03	16-01	19-09	*	26-12	19-01
21	17-04	17-10	09-03	19-09	15-02	20-03	29-08	05-12	06-02	01-05	19-12	16-01	20-02	28-12	07-11	03-10	05-09	25-08	24-10	10-04	*	15-09
22	13-02	28-12	24-04	19-12	10-04	30-01	19-09	05-09	06-03	03-04	25-08	22-08	03-10	17-04	17-10	16-01	13-03	05-12	21-11	07-11	09-02	*

ALTRINCHAM

Formed: 1891

President:
Noel White

Chairman:
Bill King

Vice Chairman
Gary Corbett

Directors:
Geoff Lloyd
Peter Jones
John Maunders
John Brindle

Company Secretary:
Gary Corbett

Football Secretary:
Jean Baldwin

Manager:
Gerry Quinn

Club Doctor:
Dr J Jacovelli

Commercial Manager:
Francis Ward

After finishing in third place at the end of the 1990/91 season, Altrincham supporters must have been looking forward to the new campaign with some relish. However, some internal turmoil saw the departure of John King during the summer and former Robins' favourite Stan Allan and another ex-Altrincham player John Davison arrive from neighbours Witton Albion. Allan and Davison had guided Albion into the Conference but gave the chance of seeing the job through at Wincham Park to return to Moss Lane.

It all started reasonably enough and at the turn of the year, Altrincham were actually in fifth place in the table. But a dreadful run which saw only three points secured from seven games saw the departure of Allan on March 25th.

Davison took over temporary charge of team affairs but he couldn't reverse the losing trend, which was the Robins' worst sequence of results since the 1950s. Finally, on April 18th, Cheltenham Town were beaten 2-0 at Whaddon Road to end a run of nine consecutive results. It was certainly a timely victory as relegation for one of the founder members was becoming a distinct possibility.

Cup form was little better. The FA Cup, so often in the past a lifeline to Altrincham's season, ended at their first hurdle, the Fourth Qualifying Round, when nearby HFS Loans League First Division side Winsford United won 3-2. Altrincham also lost in their first game in the FA Trophy when another HFS Loans League club, Stalybridge Celtic, came to Moss Lane and won 2-1. The Bob Lord Trophy gave the club a little joy. After beating Barrow and Macclesfield, Altrincham faced a two-legged semi-final against Runcorn. However, the tie was lost on aggregate to leave the Moss Lane Boardroom trophy cabinet bare.

The club start the 1992/93 campaign with a new manager in former Emley boss Gerry Quinn and it will be interesting to see whether he can bring the glory days back to Moss Lane.

Altrincham F.C. 1991-92. Back Row (L-R): M Carter, C Molloy, H Wiggins, N Daws, M Hughes, G Anderson. Middle: M Holgate, K McKenna, T Miller, S Roberts, J Wealands, A Reid, M Lewis, J Davison. Front: N Shaw, T Edwards, P Rowlands, S Allan, P Densmore, J Brady, N Kelly, S Rudge. Photo: Cliff Hase.

Altrincham

GM Vauxhall Conference: 18th.   FA Cup: 4th Qualifying Round.   FA Trophy: 1st Round.   BL Trophy: Semi-Finalists.

Match No.	Date	Competition	Venue H/A	Opponents	Result	League H/T	Pos.	Goalscorers (Times if known)	Attendance
1	Aug 17	GMVC	H	Kettering	D 1-1	1-1		Reid 32	1293
2	Aug 24	GMVC	H	Yeovil	W 2-1	0-1	8	Daws 57; McKenna 59	937
3	Aug 26	GMVC	A	Telford Utd	L 1-2	0-1	9	McKenna 67	1235
4	Aug 31	GMVC	A	Wycombe W.	L 2-4	1-2	14	Shaw 16; McKenna 49	3245
5	Sep 3	GMVC	H	Barrow	D 1-1	0-1	13	Shaw 58 (pen)	930
6	Sep 7	GMVC	A	Welling Utd	D 2-2	1-2	13	Brady 45; Shaw 56 (pen)	777
7	Sep 14	GMVC	H	Stafford Rangers	W 3-0	2-0	6	Shaw 15,48; Brady 31	1201
8	Sep 21	GMVC	A	Redbridge Forest	W 1-0	0-0	7	Shaw 62	514
9	Sep 24	GMVC	H	Gateshead	D 1-1	0-1	7	Hughes 67	842
10	Sep 28	GMVC	A	Runcorn	D 2-2	1-1	6	Daws 12; Rudge 60	1049
11	Oct 5	GMVC	A	Colchester	D 3-3	1-2	6	McKenna 19; Anderson 49; Brady 76	2849
12	**Oct 8**	**BLT 2**	**H**	**Barrow**	**W 2-1**	**0-0**		**Brady 64,90**	**589**
13	Oct 12	GMVC	A	Farnborough	L 0-3	0-0	9		1113
14	Oct 19	GMVC	H	Slough	L 3-7	2-3	13	Anderson 22; McKenna 36,74	884
15	**Oct 26**	**FAC 4Q**	**A**	**Winsford Utd**	**L 2-3**	**0-2**		**Shaw 52,90 (2 pens)**	**1133**
16	Oct 29	GMVC	H	Witton Albion	D 2-2	1-0	12	Daws 22; o.g. 67	1059
17	Nov 2	GMVC	A	Northwich Victoria	W 2-1	1-1	10	McKenna 32; Brady 62	747
18	Nov 4	GMVC	A	Kidderminster	L 0-1	0-1	12		1128
19	Nov 9	GMVC	H	Boston Utd	L 2-4	1-0	14	Anderson 7; Rowlands 85	908
20	Nov 16	GMVC	A	Barrow	W 2-0	2-0	12	McKenna 21; Edwards 32	1301
21	Nov 23	GMVC	H	Bath City	W 4-0	1-0	6	Anderson 44,65,68 (pen); McKenna 46	771
22	**Nov 26**	**CSC 1**	**A**	**Nantwich**	**W 2-1**	**1-0**		**McKenna; Edwards**	**280**
23	Nov 30	GMVC	H	Merthyr Tydfil	D 1-1	0-0	9	McKenna 70	896
24	Dec 14	GMVC	H	Cheltenham	W 2-1	0-1	5	Shaw 48; Anderson 69	862
25	**Dec 17**	**B LT 3**	**A**	**Macclesfield**	**D 1-1**	**0-0**		**Hughes 90**	**447**
26	Dec 21	GMVC	A	Stafford Rangers	W 2-1	0-1	5	McKenna 50; Hughes 70	680
27	Dec 26	GMVC	H	Macclesfield	D 1-1	0-0	5	McKenna 64	1301
28	Dec 28	GMVC	A	Gateshead	L 0-4	1-0	8		386
29	Jan 1	GMVC	H	Kidderminster	D 1-1	0-1	5	Anderson 75	842
30	Jan 4	GMVC	A	Runcorn	D 2-2	1-1	5	McKenna 14; Daws 57	907
31	**Jan 11**	**FAT 1**	**H**	**Stalybridge Celtic**	**L 1-2**	**1-0**		**Lee 39**	**1256**
32	Jan 18	GMVC	H	Farnborough	D 1-1	0-0	5	Anderson 55	694
33	**Jan 21**	**Gen. Chemicals**			**W 3-0**	**2-0**		**McKenna; McDonald; Edwards**	**306**
34	**Feb 4**	**BLT 3R**	**H**	**Macclesfield**	**W 3-1**	**3-0**		**Daws 13; Anderson 24; McKenna 31**	**524**
35	Feb 8	GMVC	A	Slough	W 3-2	1-0	6	Lewis 12; McDonald 75; McKenna 87	860
36	**Feb 11**	**BLT S/F 1**	**A**	**Runcorn**	**L 1-2**	**1-0**		**Shaw 44**	**532**
37	Feb 15	GMVC	A	Bath City	L 2-3	1-3	8	McKenna 12,80	590
38	**Feb 18**	**BLT S/F 2**	**H**	**Runcorn**	**L 1-3**	**1-3**		**Lee 44**	**605**
39	Feb 28	GMVC	H	Colchester	L 1-2	1-2	12	McKenna 23	905
40	Mar 7	GMVC	A	Merthyr Tydfil	L 1-3	1-1	14	McKenna 42	517
41	Mar 13	GMVC	H	Northwich Victoria	L 0-1	0-1	15		693
42	Mar 21	GMVC	H	Redbridge Forest	L 0-3	0-1	16		479
43	Mar 28	GMVC	H	Welling Utd	L 1-2	1-1	16	McDonald 8	537
44	Apr 4	GMVC	A	Boston Utd	L 1-2	0-1	16	Shaw 58 (pen)	891
45	Apr 11	GMVC	H	Wycombe W.	L 0-4	0-3	17		1166
46	Apr 14	GMVC	A	Witton Albion	L 0-2	0-0	17		825
47	Apr 18	GMVC	A	Cheltenham	W 2-0	1-0	15	Anderson 35; McKenna 68	980
48	Apr 20	GMVC	H	Macclesfield	W 3-1	2-0	15	Edwards 5; Lewis 43; B urns 88	767
49	Apr 25	GMVC	H	Kettering	L 0-5	0-0	16		1347
50	Apr 28	GMVC	H	Telford Utd	L 2-3	2-1	16	Shaw 12; Burns 39	507
51	May 2	GMVC	A	Yeovil	L 1-2	1-1	18	Shaw 31	1919

Best Home Attendance: 1293 v Kettering Town 17.8.91.   Lowest: 497 v Redbridge Forest 21.3.92.   Average Home Attendance: 859

Compared to 1990/91: 1385

Goalscorers League: McKenna 25; Anderson, Shaw 13; Brady, Daws 6; Edwards, McDonald 3; Hughes 4; Lewis 3; Burns, Lee 2; Reid, Rowlands, Rudge 1.

Altrincham

1	2	3	4	5	6	7	8	9	10	11	12	14	Match No.
Wealands	Edwards	Wiggins	Rowlands•	Miller	Anderson	Reid	Daws†	Brady	McKenna	Rudge	Lewis	Carter	1
Wealands	Edwards	Wiggins	Rowlands	Carter†	Anderson	Reid	Daws	Brady	McKenna	Rudge	Densmore	Hughes	2
Wealands	Edwards	Wiggins	Rowlands	Carter†	Anderson•	Reid	Daws	Brady	McKenna	Rudge	Densmore	Hughes	3
Wealands	Edwards•	Wiggins†	Rowlands	Lewis	Reid	Shaw	Daws	Brady	McKenna	Rudge	Hughes	Densmore	4
Wealands	Edwards†	Densmore•	Rowlands	Lewis	Reid	Shaw	Daws	Brady	McKenna	Rudge	Hughes	Wiggins	5
Wealands	Lee•	Densmore	Rowlands	Lewis	Reid	Shaw	Daws	Brady†	McKenna	Rudge	Wiggins	Hughes	6
Wealands	Edwards	Densmore	Rowlands	Lewis	Reid	Shaw	Daws•	Brady†	McKenna†	Rudge	Wiggins	Hughes	7
Wealands	Edwards	Densmore	Rowlands	Lewis	Reid•	Shaw	Daws	Brady†	McKenna†	Rudge	Wiggins	Hughes	8
Wealands	Edwards	Densmore	Rowlands	Lewis†	Reid	Shaw	Daws	Brady†	McKenna	Rudge	Wiggins	Hughes	9
Wealands	Edwards	Densmore	Rowlands	Reid	Anderson	Shaw†	Daws	Brady	Hughes	McKenna	Wiggins	Rudge	10
Wealands	Edwards	Densmore	Rowlands	Reid	Anderson	Rudge	Daws	Brady	Hughes†	McKenna	Wiggins	Lewis	11
Roberts•	**Edwards**	**Densmore**	**Rowlands**	**Lewis†**	**Anderson**	**Rudge**	**Daws**	**Brady**	**Hughes**	**McKenna**	**Wiggins**	**Moreland**	12
Wealands	Edwards	Densmore	Rowlands	Reid	Anderson	Rudge	Daws†	Brady	Hughes	McKenna	Wiggins	Lee	13
Roberts	Lee	Densmore	Rowlands	Reid†	Anderson	Rudge	Daws	Brady	Edwards	McKenna	Wiggins	Hughes	14
Wealands	**Lee**	**Densmore**	**Rowlands**	**Reid†**	**Anderson**	**Shaw**	**Daws**	**Brady**	**McKenna**	**Lewis**	**Wiggins**	**Hughes**	15
Wealands	Edwards	Densmore	Lee	Lewis	Anderson	Shaw	Daws	Brady†	McKenna	Rudge•	Rowlands	Hughes	16
Wealands	Edwards	Densmore	Rowlands	Lewis	Anderson	Shaw	Daws	Brady	McKenna	Lee	Hughes	Rudge	17
Berryman	Edwards	Densmore	Rowlands	Lewis•	Anderson	Shaw	Daws	Brady	McKenna	Lee	Hughes	Rudge	18
Berryman	Edwards	Densmore	Rowlands	Lewis	Anderson	Shaw•	Daws	Brady	McKenna	Lee	Rudge†	Hayde	19
Berryman	Edwards•	Densmore	Rowlands	Reid	Anderson	Wiggins	Daws	Hayde	McKenna	Lee	McDonald	Hughes	20
Berryman	Edwards•	Densmore	Rowlands	Reid	Anderson	Wiggins	Daws	Hayde†	McKenna	Lee	McDonald	Hughes	21
Berryman	**Edwards**	**Densmore**	**Rowlands**	**Reid**	**Anderson**	**Wiggins**	**Daws•**	**Hayde**	**McKenna**	**Lee**	**McDonald**	**Hughes**	22
Berryman	Edwards	Densmore	Rowlands	Reid	Anderson	Wiggins	Daws†	Hayde•	McKenna	Lee	Shaw	Brady	23
Berryman	Edwards	Densmore	Wiggins	Reid	Anderson	Shaw	Daws	Hayde•	Hughes	Lee	Brady	Lewis	24
Berryman	**Edwards•**	**Densmore**	**Wiggins**	**Reid**	**Lewis**	**Shaw**	**Daws†**	**Brady**	**Hughes**	**Lee**	**McDonald**	**Hayde**	25
Berryman	Edwards	Densmore	Wiggins	Reid	Anderson	Shaw	Lewis	Hughes	McKenna	Lee†	Brady	Daws	26
Berryman	Edwards•	Densmore	Rowlands	Reid	Anderson	Shaw	Wiggins	Hughes	McKenna	Lee	Brady	Daws	27
Berryman	Edwards•	Densmore	Rowlands	Reid	Anderson	Shaw	Wiggins	Hughes	McKenna	Lee	Brady	Daws	28
Berryman	Edwards	Densmore	Rowlands	Wiggins	Anderson•	Shaw	Daws	Brady	McKenna	Lee	Hughes	McDonald	29
Berryman	Edwards	Densmore	Wiggins	Lewis	Anderson	Shaw	Daws	Hughes	McKenna	Lee	McDonald	Hayde	30
Wealands	**Edwards**	**Densmore**	**Wiggins**	**Lewis**	**Anderson**	**Shaw**	**Daws**	**Hughes•**	**McKenna**	**Lee**	**Rudge**	**Hayde**	31
Wealands	Edwards	Densmore	Wiggins	Lewis	Anderson	Shaw	Daws	McDonald•	McKenna	Lee	Rudge	Hayde	32
Wealands	**Edwards**	**Densmore**	**Wiggins**	**Lewis**	**Anderson**	**Shaw**	**Daws**	**McDonald**	**McKenna**	**Lee**	**Rudge**	**Hayde**	33
Wealands	**Chilton**	**Densmore**	**Reid**	**Lewis**	**Anderson**	**Shaw**	**Daws**	**McDonald•**	**McKenna**	**Lee†**	**Rudge**	**Edwards**	34
Wealands	Chilton•	Densmore	Reid	Lewis	Anderson	Shaw	Daws	McDonald	McKenna	Edwards	Rudge	Wiggins	35
Wealands	**Chilton**	**Densmore**	**Wiggins**	**Lewis**	**Anderson•**	**Shaw**	**Daws**	**McDonald**	**McKenna**	**Lee**	**Rudge**	**Edwards**	36
Wealands	Worrall	Densmore†	Wiggins	Lewis	Rudge	Shaw	Daws	McDonald	McKenna	Lee	Chilton	Edwards	37
Wealands	**Worrall**	**Densmore**	**Wiggins**	**Lewis**	**Rudge**	**Shaw**	**Daws**	**McDonald**	**McKenna**	**Lee**	**Chilton**	**Edwards**	38
Wealands	Edwards•	Chilton	Wiggins	Reid	Rudge	Shaw	Daws	McDonald†	McKenna	Lee	Worrall	Kilshaw	39
Davies	Edwards	Chilton•	Wiggins	Reid	Rudge	Kilshaw	Daws	McDonald†	McKenna	Lee	Shaw	Burns	40
Davies	Edwards	Wiggins	Burns	Reid	Rudge	Shaw	Daws	Kilshaw•	McKenna	Lee	McDonald	Chilton	41
Davies	Edwards	Chilton•	Wiggins	Reid	Rudge	Shaw	Daws	McDonald	Burns	Lee	Kilshaw	Lewis	42
Davies	Lewis	Densmore	Lee	Reid	Anderson	Shaw	Daws	McDonald•	Burns	Kilshaw	Hayde	Wiggins	43
Wealands	Lewis	Densmore	Lee	Reid	Anderson	Shaw	Daws	McDonald	Burns	Rudge•	Kilshaw	Wiggins	44
Shaw	Lewis	Densmore	Lee	Reid	Anderson	Edwards	Daws	McDonald	Burns	Rudge•	Hayde	Wiggins	45
Roberts	Edwards	Densmore	Lee	Reid	Anderson	Shaw	Daws	McDonald•	Burns	McKenna	Kilshaw	Wiggins	46
Roberts	Edwards	Densmore	Lee	Reid	Anderson	Wiggins	Daws	Lewis	Hayde	McKenna†	Kilshaw	Burns	47
Roberts	Edwards	Densmore	Lee	Reid	Anderson	Wiggins	Daws	Lewis	Hayde	McKenna•	Shaw	Burns	48
Roberts	Edwards•	Densmore	Lee	Reid	Anderson	Wiggins	Daws	Lewis	McKenna†	Hayde	Shaw	Burns	49
Roberts	Lewis	Densmore	Lee	Reid	Anderson	Wiggins	Daws	Shaw	Burns	Hayde•	Gresty	McDonald	50
Wealands	Lewis•	Densmore	Lee	Reid	Anderson	Wiggins	Daws	Shaw	Burns	Hayde•	Rudge	McDonald	51

• substituted by No. 12. † substituted by No. 14.

League Appearances: Daws 51; Densmore, McKenna 48; Edwards 44; Anderson 43; Lee 42; Shaw 41; Reid 40; Lewis 36; Wiggins 33; Wealands 31; Rowlands 25; Rudge 22; Brady 20; McDonald 19; Berryman 13; Chilton, Hughes 11; Hayde 10; Burns 8; Davies 4; Kilshaw 3; Carter, Roberts, Worrall 2; Miller 1.

Altrincham

GERRY QUINN

Gerry was appointed as manager of Altrincham in June 1992. He had previously been in charge at HFS Loans League Premier Division club Emley where he enjoyed a huge amount of success. A former player with the Yorkshire side, he took over as manager in 1984 and immediately set about winning honours for the club. They were Northern Counties East League runners-up in 1985/86, won that league in 1987/88 when they also reached the FA Vase Final at Wembley. However, they came up against the fast-rising Colne Dynamoes side and lost the final 1-0. The previous season saw Emley reach the semi-final of the same competition but they lost on aggregate to St Helens Town despite winning the first leg in Lancashire.

After gaining promotion to the HFS Loans League, Gerry, who had been player-manager, hung up his boots for good and, following a seasons consolidating, they won promotion to the Premier Division in 1991. That 1990/91 season also saw the club reach the quarter-finals of the FA Trophy. To reach that stage, Gerry's team had beaten Southport, Ferryhill Athletic, Morecambe, Hyde United and two Conference club, Telford United and Kettering Town.

Gerry has brought a number of former Emley players with him to Moss Lane and Altrincham are certain to be a hard side to beat this coming season.

Altrincham put Kettering Town under pressure during a Vauxhall Conference match at Moss Lane.
Photo: Colin Stevens

Programme details:
    32 pages for 80p
    Editor - Mark Harris and
        Terry Surridge
Any other club publications:

Local Newspapers:
    Sale And Altrincham Messenger
    Sale and Altrincham Express
    Manchester Evening News
    Manchester Metro News
Local Radio Stations:
    GMR (BBC)
    Piccadilly Radio
    Signal Radio

ALTRINCHAM - PLAYING SQUAD 1992-93

Player	Honours	Birthplace and date	Transfer Fees	Previous Clubs
GOALKEEPERS				
Steve Roberts		Altrincham 10/2/66		None
DEFENDERS				
Tony Edwards		Ormskirk 6/9/62		Marine, Runcorn
Peter Densmore	ESP, FAT CSC	Liverpool 16/3/60		Ford Motors, Altrincham, Runcorn
Tony Chilton	FAT, HFS FA XI	Maryport 7/9/65	Player Exchange	Sunderland, Burnley, Hartlepool, Workington, Gretna, Barrow
Mick Farrar				Rochdale, Bradley Rangers, Emley
Russell Green				Barnsley, Emley
Carl Hodgert				Salford, Atherton Coll, Altrincham, Hyde Utd, Runcorn, Hyde Utd
Martin Lewis		Birkenhead 19/9/68		Christleton, Newtown, Cammell Laird, Newtown
MIDFIELD				
Nicky Daws		Manchester 15/3/70		Flixton
Andy Reid	CSC	Davyhulme 4/7/62		Everton, Witton Alb, Southport, Runcorn
Gary Anderson	FAT, CSC	Liverpool 5/1/60		Altrincham, Sth Liverpool, Altrincham, Runcorn
Charlie Bradshaw				Ossett Town, Accrington Stanley, Emley
Mick Hayde		20/6/71		Liverpool, Chester City, St Helens
FORWARDS				
Simon Woodhead		Dewsbury 26/12/62		Mansfield, Crewe, Shepshed, Scunthorpe, Frickley
Simon Rudge		Warrington 30/12/64		Bolton W, Hyde Utd, Runcorn
Paul Burns		1/10/67		Caernarfon
Brian Kilshaw		10/9/68		Skelmersdale Utd
Andy Bondswell				Leeds Utd, Thackley, Guiseley, Harrogate Town, Accrington Stanley

Departures during season:
Mark Hughes (Witton Alb), John Brady & Paul Rowlands (Barrow), Steve Berryman (Northwich), Ken McKenna (Barrow), Nigel Shaw (Runcorn), Tommy Miller (Morecambe), Neil Kelly (Barrow), Andy Lee (Telford).

Players who joined on loan during season:
Steve Berryman (Barnet).

Moss Lane, Altrincham

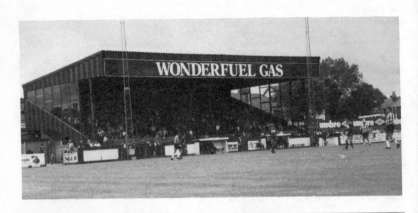

Address and telephone number: Moss Lane, Altrincham, Cheshire, WA15 8AP. Tel: 061 928 1045
Information line: 0898 888678   **Official capacity:** 6,000
Simple ground directions: Leave M6 motorway at junction 19 and follow A556 and A56 towards Altrincham. At first traffic lights past M56 motorway junction turn right onto B5161 into Altrincham centre and right at second traffic lights into Moss Lane.
Seats: 1,000   **Covered accommodation:** 5,000
Cost of seats: £5.00   **Cost of standing:** £4.00
Official opening of floodlights: 4th April 1966: Altrincham 4 Witton Albion 3, Cheshire County League (attendance 4,323)
Record attendance: 10,275: Altrincham Boys v Sunderland Boys, English Schools Shield 3rd round, 28th February 1925
Social facilities: Four snack bars with hot pies, drinks, crisps, chocolate etc. Bar open to public on match days.
Car parking: Official car park on two sides of ground.

Sponsored by: Maunders   **ALTRINCHAM F.C.**   **Nickname:** The Robins

Previous leagues: Manchester; Lancashire Combination; Cheshire County; Northern Premier
Club colours: Red and white striped shirts; black shorts; white socks   **Change colours:** All sky blue
Midweek home matches: Tuesday   **Club Metal Badges:** Yes
Record transfer fee paid: To Telford United for Ken McKenna
Record transfer fee received: From Crewe Alexandra for Paul Edwards
Record appearances for club: John Davison; 671 + 6 subs, 1971-86
Record aggregate goalscorer: Jack Swindells, 252, 1965-71
Record scorer in season: Jack Swindells, 84 in 1965-66
Past players who have progressed to the Football League: Graham Barrow (Wigan Athletic, 1981); Frank Carrodus (Manchester City, 1969); Peter Conning (Rochdale, 1986); Robert Dale (Bury, 1951); Paul Edwards (Crewe Alexandra, 1988); Eddie Bishop (Tranmere Rovers, 1988); Brian Green (Exeter City, 1962); John Hughes (Stockport County, 1976); Steve Johnson (Bury, 1977); Joe Kennedy (West Bromwich Albion, 1948); Andy Kilner (Stockport County, 1990); Stan March (Port Vale, 1959); Charlie Mitten (Halifax Town, 1965); Brian Phillips (Middlesbrough, 1954); Eric Robinson (West Bromwich Albion, 1957); John Rogers (Wigan Athletic, 1982); Nelson Stiffle (Chesterfield, 1954); Jeff Street (Barrow, 1969).
Club Honours: Alliance Premier League champions 1980, 1981; FA Trophy winners 1978, 1986; Bob Lord Trophy winners 1981; Northern Premier League Cup winners 1970; Northern Premier League Shield winners 1980; Cheshire County League champions 1966, 1967; Cheshire County League Cup winners 1953, 1951, 1964; Cheshire Senior Cup winners 1905, 1934, 1967, 1982; Manchester League champions 1905; Cheshire Amateur Cup winners 1904.
Managers since 1935: T. J. Moran; A. Steward; T. C. Lockhead; F. H. Williams; M. Swinnerton; J. Morris; P. Fagan; C. Mitten; F. Pye; M. Woods; F. Pye; L. Brown; R. rees; A. Sanders; J. King; J. Williams; T. Docherty; J. Johnson; J. King; S. Allan.

BATH CITY

Formed: 1889

President:
F. A. Entwistle

Chairman:
R. C. Stock

Vice Chairman:
K. Foster

Directors:
T. J. Quincey LLB
P. Britton
R. Boyd
S. Bryant
R. Chester

Life Vice Presidents:
D. H. Counsell FRICS
A. Hawkins
B. J. Head
A. F. Walshaw
A. C. Walshaw
S. E. Woodman
F. A. Entwistle
M. Russell

Secretary:
Paul Britton

Manager:
Tony Ricketts

Commercial Manager:
Bob Brimson

Fine season for City

After the previous season's miraculous escape from relegation in the final third of the season, City performed better than many fans expected to finish in a creditable 9th position, their highest since 1984/85. After a fine win at Northwich on the first day of the season (the last time City won their opening game of the season was 10 years ago!) City struggled for the next month, especially at home. Despite an excellent win at Runcorn it was early October before they registered their first Conference home win of the campaign. It was at home where City tended to give some lacklustre performances, especially in the first half of the season, whilst away from Twerton Park they picked up points with regularity. It was at home, in an FA Cup tie, that they reached their lowest point of the season when they lost 1-2 to Worcester City, who were bottom of the Beazer Homes Premier Division at the time. For the second season running City failed to reach the First Round Proper of the FA Cup, a feat that had been achieved for 6 seasons on the trot just recently.

The FA Trophy brought some success. After wins at Sutton United and at home to Dorking, City drew 1-1 with Wycombe in front of 2,899 people at Twerton Park before going out 0-2 in the replay. The Bob Lord Trophy saw City's usual early exit, this time at the hands of Slough, and the Somerset Premier Cup saw an embarrasing defeat at Western League Radstock Town.

Highlights of the season were two excellent games against Wycombe at Twerton Park, both ending in 1-1 draws, fine home victories against local rivals Cheltenham and Yeovil, plus excellent away wins at Northwich, Runcorn, Telford, Welling and Farnborough.

City's defence performed admirably with player of the season, Ian Hedges, in fine form, ably supported by the ever consistent Chris Banks. Up front City again relied on the evergreen goalscoring skills of Paul Randall, who notched 26 goals, reaching his 100 goals for the club in 166 appearances in the fine 5-0 win at Welling.

Bath City F.C. 1991-92. Back Row (L-R): Dean Radford, Paul Hirons, Ian Hedges, Dave Singleton, Jim Preston, Graham Withey, Alan Churchward, Richard Crowley, Paul Randall, Adi Mings. Centre (L-R): Bob Westlake (reserve team trainer), Dave Monks (physio), Martin Boyle, Dave Payne, Rob Cousins, Keith Brown, Gary Smart, Chris Townsend (now Chesham), Peter Aitken (now left), Paul Morris (reserve team manager). Front (L-R): Ian Weston,

Bath City

Match No.	Date	Competition	Venue H/A	Opponents	Result	League H/T	Pos.	Goalscorers (Times if known)	Attendance
1	Aug 17	GMVC	A	Northwich Victoria	W 3-1	2-1		Banks 4; Randall 17,75	707
2	Aug 24	GMVC	H	Stafford Rangers	L 0-1	0-0			862
3	Aug 26	GMVC	A	Merthyr Tydfil	D 1-1	1-1	8	Withey 36	917
4	Aug 31	GMVC	A	Colchester Utd	L 0-5	0-3	15		2416
5	Sep 3	BLT 1-1	H	Slough	W 2-1	1-0		Randall 25 (pen), 88 (Pen)	404
6	Sep 7	GMVC	A	Barrow	L 0-2	0-0	21		1440
7	Sep 10	GMVC	H	Welling Utd	L 0-3	0-1	21		626
8	Sep 14	FAC 1Q	A	Stroud	W 3-1	2-1		Withey 8; Randall 19 (pen); Brown 63	274
9	Sep 21	GMVC	A	Runcorn	W 2-0	0-0	17	Randall 60,80	531
10	Sep 24	BLT 1-2	A	Slough	L 0-2	0-1			584
11	Sep 28	FAC 2Q	H	Maesteg Park	W 5-2	2-1		Randall 14 (pen), 27; Boyle 50; Ricketts 62; Gill 81	422
12	Oct 1	GMVC	H	Cheltenham	W 5-1	2-0	13	Boyle 12,89; Mings 34; Randall 81 (pen), 85	657
13	Oct 5	GMVC	A	Telford Utd	W 2-0	0-0	11	Boyle 71; Randall 89	1092
14	Oct 8	GMVC	H	Farnborough	L 1-2	1-2	14	Crowley 11	759
15	Oct 12	FAC 3Q	H	Worcester City	L 1-2	1-0		Ricketts 9	813
16	Oct 15	GMVC	H	Slough	W 2-1	2-0	8	Randall 33; Boyle 39	600
17	Oct 19	GMVC	A	Witton Albion	D 2-2	2-1	7	Randall 32; Boyle 38	742
18	Oct 26	GMVC	H	Macclesfield	D 1-1	1-1	9	Randall 38 (pen)	523
19	Nov 3	GMVC	A	Kettering	D 2-2	2-1	8	Brown 15; Randall 44	2379
20	Nov 9	GMVC	H	Gateshead	L 0-1	0-1	13		632
21	Nov 11	SPC	A	Clevedon	W 2-1	1-0		Randall; Withey	238
22	Nov 16	GMVC	A	Gateshead	W 1-0	1-0	11	Brown 20	355
23	Nov 23	GMVC	A	Altrincham	L 0-4	0-1	12		771
24	Nov 26	GMVC	A	Redbridge Forest	W 3-1	1-2	13	Gill 44	475
25	Nov 30	GMVC	H	Kidderminster H	L 0-1	0-0	14		544
26	Dec 7	GMVC	A	Cheltenham	W 2-1	1-0	13	Mings 37; Boyle 87	800
27	Dec 21	GMVC	A	Slough	D 2-2	2-2	13	Randall 26; Weston 41	608
28	Dec 26	GMVC	H	Yeovil Town	W 3-1	1-1	12	Withey 22,89; Kean 89	1504
29	Jan 1	GMVC	A	Yeovil Town	D 1-1	0-1	13	Boyle 59	3340
30	Jan 4	GMVC	H	Wycombe Wanderers	D 1-1	0-0	13	Singleton 89	1386
31	Jan 11	FAT 1	A	Sutton Utd	W 2-1	1-0		Randall 38; Withey 67	757
32	Jan 18	GMVC	H	Redbridge Forest	D 0-0	0-0	14		614
33	Feb 1	FAT 2	H	Dorking	W 2-0	0-0		Withey 54; Mings 79	601
34	Feb 8	GMVC	A	Macclesfield	D 0-0	0-0	15		578
35	Feb 11	GMVC	H	Merthyr Tydfil	D 0-0	0-0	13		629
36	Feb 15	GMVC	H	Altrincham	W 3-2	3-1	10	o.g. 17; Withey 34; Boyle 43	590
37	Feb 18	SPC	A	Radstock	L 0-1	0-0			110
38	Feb 23	FAT 3	H	Wycombe Wanderers	D 1-1	0-1		Hedges 62	2899
39	Feb 25	FAT 3R	A	Wycombe Wanderers	L 0-2	0-1			3542
40	Feb 29	GMVC	H	Runcorn	W 3-1	1-1	9	Withey 12; Hedges 52; Boyle 86	575
41	Mar 7	GMVC	A	Boston Utd	L 0-1	0-1	13		1008
42	Mar 9	GMVC	A	Kidderminster H	W 1-0	1-0	10	Withey 2	928
43	Mar 17	GMVC	H	Telford Utd	L 1-2	0-1	10	Cousins 50	524
44	Mar 21	GMVC	A	Welling Utd	W 5-0	2-0	8	Banks 13; Randall 26,81; Hedges 84; Cousins 86	806
45	Mar 24	GMVC	H	Colchester	D 0-00	0-0	9		1101
46	Mar 28	GMVC	H	Witton Albion	L 0-2	0-1	11		550
47	Mar 31	GMVC	A	Farnborough	W 2-1	0-0	9	Randall 69,78	680
48	Apr 4	GMVC	H	Barrow	W 2-1	0-0	8	Randall 73,75	485
49	Apr 14	GMVC	H	Boston Utd	W 2-0	1-0	9	Hedges 9; Withey 87	401
50	Apr 18	GMVC	H	Kettering Town	D 1-1	1-0	9	Cousins 28	699
51	Apr 20	GMVC	A	Wycombe Wanderers	L 0-1	0-0	9		4263
52	Apr 25	GMVC	H	Northwich Victoria	W 2-0	2-0	8	Randall 3; Boyle 13	510
53	May 2	GMVC	A	Stafford Rangers	L 0-2	0-1	9		895

Best Home League Attendance: 1504 v Yeovil 26.12.91   Smallest: 401 v Boston Utd 14.4.92   Average Home Attendance: 698 Compared with 90/91: 883

Goalscorers League: Randall 105; Singleton 91; Withey 80; Smart 41; Brown 39; Palmer 23; Ricketts 22; Boyle 11; Cousins 10; Mings 7; Crowley 6; Banks 5; Hedges 4; Weston 1.

Bath City

1	2	3	4	5	6	7	8	9	10	11	12	14	Match No.
Churchward	Hedges	Lundon	Ricketts	Crowley	Radford	Banks	Brown	Withey	Randall	Mings	Boyle	Singleton	1
Churchward	Hedges	Lundon	Singleton	Crowley	Radford	Banks	Brown	Withey	Randall	Boyle	Hirons	Ricketts	2
Churchward	Hedges	Lundon	Singleton	Crowley	Radford	Banks	Brown	Withey	Randall•	Boyle	Hirons	Ricketts	3
Churchward	Hedges	Payne	Singleton	Crowley†	Radford	Banks	Brown	Withey	Randall•	Boyle	Painter	Ricketts	4
Preston	**Hedges**	**Singleton**	**Ricketts**	**Crowley**	**Payne•**	**Banks**	**Brown**	**Withey†**	**Randall**	**Boyle**	**Mings**	**Radford**	**5**
Churchward	Hedges•	Singleton	Ricketts	Crowley	Boyle	Banks	Brown	Withey†	Randall	Mings	Lundon	Payne	6
Churchward	Hedges	Singleton	Ricketts	Crowley	Lundon	Banks	Brown	Withey	Randall	Mings	Boyle	Radford	7
Churchward	**Hedges**	**Singleton**	**Ricketts**	**Crowley**	**Lundon**	**Banks**	**Brown**	**Withey**	**Randall•**	**Mings**	**Boyle**	**Radford**	**8**
Churchward	Hedges	Lundon	Singleton	Crowley	Gill	Banks	Weston	Withey	Randall	Mings	Boyle	Ricketts	9
Churchward	**Hedges**	**Lundon**	**Singleton**	**Crowley**	**Gill**	**Banks**	**Weston**	**Withey†**	**Randall•**	**Mings**	**Boyle**	**Ricketts**	**10**
Churchward	**Hedges**	**Lundon**	**Ricketts†**	**Singleton**	**Gill**	**Banks**	**Weston**	**Boyle**	**Randall**	**Mings**	**Withey**	**Radford**	**11**
Preston	Hedges	Brown†	Ricketts	Singleton•	Gill	Banks	Weston	Boyle	Randall	Mings	Withey	Lundon	12
Preston	Hedges	Lundon	Ricketts	Gill	Weston•	Banks	Brown	Boyle	Randall	Mings	Crowley	Withey	13
Preston	Hedges	Lundon	Ricketts	Gill	Crowley•	Banks	Brown	Boyle	Randall	Mings	Singleton	Withey	14
Preston	**Hedges**	**Lundon**	**Ricketts**	**Gill†**	**Weston**	**Banks**	**Brown**	**Boyle**	**Randall**	**Mings**	**Singleton**	**Withey**	**15**
Preston	Hedges	Cousins	Ricketts	Withey	Weston	Banks	Brown	Boyle	Randall	Mings•	Lundon	Gill	16
Churchward	Hedges•	Cousins	Ricketts	Weston	Mings	Banks	Brown	Withey	Randall	Boyle	Lundon	Gill	17
Churchward	Singleton•	Cousins	Ricketts	Weston	Mings	Banks	Brown	Withey	Randall	Boyle	Lundon	Gill	18
Churchward	Hedges	Lundon•	Ricketts	Cousins	Brown	Banks	Weston	Boyle	Randall	Withey	Mings	Singleton	19
Churchward	Hedges	Lundon	Ricketts	Cousins	Brown	Banks	Weston†	Boyle	Randall	Withey	Gill	Singleton	20
Churchward	Hedges	Lundon	Crowley	Gill	Kean	Banks	Cousins	Boyle	Randall•	Withey†	Singleton	Brown	21
Churchward	Hedges	Lundon	Singleton	Cousins•	Brown	Banks	Weston	Boyle	Randall	Withey†	Crowley	Gill	22
Churchward	Hedges	Lundon	Crowley	Singleton	Cousins	Banks	Brown	Boyle†	Randall	Withey	Kean	Gill	23
Churchward	Hedges	Lundon	Ricketts	Singleton	Cousins	Banks	Gill	Boyle•	Randall	Kean	Withey	Crowley	24
Churchward	Hedges	Singleton	Ricketts	Crowley	Cousins	Banks	Gill•	Withey	Randall	Kean†	Mings	Boyle	25
Churchward	Hedges	Kean	Ricketts	Crowley	Cousins	Banks	Weston	Withey	Boyle	Mings†	Singleton	Randall	26
Churchward	Hedges	Dicks	Ricketts	Cousins	Boyle	Banks	Weston	Withey	Randall	Kean	Singleton	Crowley	27
Churchward	Hedges	Kean	Ricketts	Dicks	Cousins†	Banks	Weston	Withey	Randall	Boyle	Crowley	Singleton	28
Churchward	Hedges	Dicks	Cousins	Crowley	Weston	Banks	Kean	Withey	Randall	Boyle	Singleton	Brown	29
Churchward	Hedges	Dicks	Cousins	Crowley	Weston•	Banks	Kean†	Withey	Randall	Boyle	Singleton	Brown	30
Churchward	Hedges	Dicks	Cousins	Crowley	Weston	Banks	Kean†	Withey	Randall	Boyle•	Singleton	Brown	31
Churchward	Hedges	Dicks	Cousins	Crowley	Weston	Banks	Kean†	Withey	Randall	Boyle	Singleton	Brown	32
Churchward	**Hedges**	**Dicks**	**Cousins**	**Crowley**	**Weston**	**Banks**	**Kean†**	**Withey**	**Randall•**	**Boyle**	**Singleton**	**Mings**	**33**
Churchward	Hedges	Dicks	Cousins	Crowley	Weston	Banks	Kean	Withey	Randall•	Boyle	Mings	Ricketts	34
Churchward	Hedges	Dicks	Cousins	Crowley	Weston	Banks	Brown	Withey	Boyle•	Mings†	Singleton	Randall	35
Churchward	Hedges	Dicks	Cousins	Crowley	Weston	Banks	Brown	Withey	Boyle	Mings	Singleton	Randall	36
Churchward	**Bailey**	**Dicks**	**Ricketts**	**Radford**	**Singleton**	**Gill**	**Brown**	**Mings**	**Randall**	**Theobald**	**Boyle**	**Cousins**	**37**
Churchward	**Hedges**	**Dicks**	**Cousins**	**Crowley**	**Brown**	**Banks**	**Randall**	**Withey**	**Boyle•**	**Mings**	**Singleton**	**Gill**	**38**
Churchward	**Hedges**	**Dicks**	**Cousins•**	**Crowley**	**Brown**	**Banks**	**Randall**	**Withey**	**Boyle**	**Mings**	**Singleton**	**Ricketts**	**39**
Churchward	Hedges	Dicks	Cousins	Crowley	Brown	Banks	Weston	Withey	Randall	Mings†	Singleton	Boyle	40
Churchward	Hedges	Dicks•	Crowley	Brown	Cousins	Banks	Weston†	Withey	Randall	Boyle	Gill	Singleton	41
Churchward	Hedges	Dicks	Cousins	Singleton	Crowley	Banks	Brown	Withey	Randall	Boyle	Gill	Ricketts	42
Churchward	Hedges	Dicks	Cousins	Crowley	Brown	Singleton	Randall•	Withey	Boyle	Weston	Mings	Gill	43
Churchward	Hedges	Dicks	Crowley	Singleton	Cousins	Banks	Weston	Withey	Randall	Boyle	Mings	Brown	44
Churchward	Hedges	Dicks	Crowley	Singleton	Cousins	Banks	Weston	Withey	Randall	Boyle•	Gill	Brown	45
Churchward†	Hedges	Dicks	Crowley	Singleton	Cousins	Banks	Weston•	Withey	Randall	Mings	Gill	Ricketts	46
Preston	Hedges	Dicks	Ricketts	Cousins	Crowley	Banks	Brown	Gill	Randall	Mings	Theobald	Bailey	47
Preston	Gill	Dicks	Ricketts	Crowley	Cousins	Banks	Brown	Withey•	Randall	Mings	Boyle	Singleton	48
Preston	Hedges•	Dicks	Ricketts†	Crowley	Cousins	Banks	Brown	Withey	Randall	Gill	Boyle	Singleton	49
Preston	Hedges	Dicks	Ricketts†	Crowley	Cousins	Banks	Brown•	Withey	Randall	Gill	Boyle	Singleton	50
Preston	Hedges	Dicks	Cousins	Crowley	Weston	Banks	Boyle†	Withey•	Randall	Mings	Ricketts	Singleton	51
Preston	Hedges	Dicks	Ricketts•	Crowley	Cousins	Banks	Weston	Boyle†	Randall	Mings	Singleton	Theobald	52
Preston	Hedges	Dicks	Ricketts	Crowley•	Weston†	Banks	Cousins	Boyle	Randall	Mings	Withey	Radford	53

• substituted by No. 12.   † substituted by No. 14.

GMVC Appearances: Banks 41; Hedges 40; Randall 39(3); Withey 34(4); Boyle 32(7); Cousins 32; Crowley 31(3); Churchward 31; Weston 27; Brown 26(2); Ricketts 22(3); Dicks 22; Mings 21(4); Singleton 17(12); Lundon 12(5); Preston 11; Gill 10(8); Kean 9(1); Radford 4(1); Payne 1(1); Hirons (2); Painter (1). **FA Cup:** Randall 11; Banks 10; Hedges 10; Churchward 9; Boyle 8(4); Crowley 8; Withey 8(1); Mings 8(2); Brown 6(2); Cousins 5(1); Dicks 5; Gill 5; Lundon 5; Ricketts 5; Singleton 5(6); Weston 5; Kean 3; Preston 2; Bailey 1; Payne 1; Radford 1(4); Theobald 1;

Bath City

TONY RICKETTS

Tony Ricketts' first full season in charge at Twerton Park can be counted as a great success, leading the side to a fine finishing position of 9th.

Tony took over as player-manager midway through the 1990/91 season, following the departure of George Rooney. His determined attitude on the field inspired his colleagues and he is a well respected Conference player with Bath and Yeovil Town, where he won the Vauxhall League and Cup double.

Tony started his playing days at nearby Clandown so is a local man who has Bath City FC very much at heart.

Graham Withey challenges Wycombe Wanderers' keeper Paul Hyde in the Vauxhall FA Trophy tie at Twerton Park.
Photo: Alan Marshall

Programme details:
    32 pages for 80p
    Editor - Bob Chester

Any other club publications:

Local Newspapers:
    Evening Chronicle
    Evening Post
    Western Daily Press

Local Radio Stations:
    Radio Bristol
    GWR

BATH CITY - PLAYING SQUAD 1992-93

Player	Honours	Birthplace and date	Transfer Fees	Previous Clubs
GOALKEEPERS				
Alan Churchward		Swindon 19/8/68		Swindon, Cheltenham
DEFENDERS				
Richard Crowley		Bristol 28/12/59	Nominal	Forest Green R, Bath, Frome Cheltenham
Tony Ricketts	VOLC	Bristol 21/6/59	£12,500	Clandown, Bath, Yeovil
Ian Hedges		Bristol		Bristol Manor Farm, Newport Co, Gloucester, Bournemouth
Grantley Dicks		Bristol		Paulton Rovers
Dave Singleton	Beazer Homes Runner up	Bournemouth 20/11/56	£4,500	Taunton, Weymouth
MIDFIELD				
Rob Cousins	Beazer Homes Runner up	Bristol 9/1/71		Bristol City
Keith Brown	Beazer Homes Runner up	Bristol 25/9/59	Nominal	Bristol Rovers, Bath Cheltenham
Ian Weston	Leyland Daf R/U 88/89	Bristol 6/5/68		Bristol Rovers, Torquay
Jeremy Gill		Bristol 8/9/70		Trowbridge, Leyton Orient, Weston-S-Mare
Chris Banks	Beazer Homes Runner up	Stone, Staffs 12/11/65		Port Vale, Exeter
FORWARDS				
Paul Randall	VOLC, Beazer Homes R/U	Liverpool 10/12/56	£1,000	Bristol Rovers, Stoke Yeovil
Martyn Boyle		Bristol		Bristol Rovers, Trowbridge Mangotsfield
Graham Withey		Bristol 11/6/60		Bath, Bristol Rovers, Coventry, Cardiff, Bristol C, Exeter, Gloucester
Adie Mings		Chippenham 17/10/68	£2,000	Melksham, Chippenham

Departures during season:
Paul Stevens (Retired), David Payne (Weymouth), Phil Underhill (Gloucester), Phil Flattery (Scoland), Chris Townsend (Dorchester), Sean Lundon (Runcorn). Jim Preston & David Palmer (Released).

Twerton Park, Bath City

Ground address and Tel. No.: Twerton Park, Twerton, Bath, Avon BA2 1DB. Tel: 0225 423087 or 313247 - Supporters Lounge 0225 429227

Simple ground directions: Just off the A36/A4 Lower Bristol Road. Approx. 2 miles from Bath Spa Railway Station.

Official capacity: 9,800	**Seating:** 800	**Covered accommodation:** 4,200
Cost of seats: £5.00		**Cost of standing:** £4.00

Official opening of floodlights:

Record attendance: 18,020 v Brighton and Hove Albion, FA Cup

Social facilities available (Bars, hot & cold food etc.): Full bar facilities with extensive menu available - function rooms catering for all types of parties from 1 to 300 people. Also available for business meetings and conferences

Car parking:

Sponsored by: Card Care	**BATH CITY**	**Nickname:** 'City'

Previous ground: Lambridge

Previous leagues: Western League, Southern League

Club colours: Black & white stripes/black/black & white   **Change colours:** All yellow

Midweek home matches: Tuesday   **Club metal badges:** Yes   **Club shop:** Yes

Record transfer fee paid: £10,000 to Yeovil for Tony Ricketts

Record Transfer fee received: £37,000 from Southampton for Jason Dodd

Record appearances for club:

Record goalscorer for club:

Record goalscorer in a season: Paul Randall, 51, 1989-90

Best Performance in F.A. Cup: 3rd Round 1931-32. Lost 2-1 to Brentford

Past players who have progressed to the Football League: A. Skirton (Arsenal), T. Book (Plymouth Argyle, Manchester City), K. Allen (Bournemouth, Swindon Town), P. Rogers, M. Rogers (Exeter City), R. Bourne (Torquay), D. Wilfil (Manchester City), S. Mortensen (Blackpool), B. Wade (Swindon Town), J. Meacham (Bristol Rovers), M. Hirst (Bristol City), P. Bodin (Swindon), G. Withey (Coventry), J. Dodd (Southampton)

Club Honours: Southern League (2); League Cup, Somerset Premier Cup (12); Anglo-Italian Cup finalists

BOSTON UNITED

Formed: 1934

Chairman:
P Malkinson

Vice Chairman:
S Burgess

Directors:
S Malkinson
L Shaw
S Bateman

Financial Executive:
B R James FCA

Secretary:
John Blackwell

Manager:
Peter Morris

Assistant Manager:
Ernie Moss

Physiotherapist:
Ted Goddard

Club Doctor:
Dr L D Taffinder

Club Chaplain:
Rev J Moore

All change now at York Street

After finishing the 1990/91 season just above the relegation places, Boston United's 1991/92 campaign must go down as a success. Manager Dave Cusack lost the services of prolific scorer Paul Cavell and influential midfielder Paul Richardson half-way through the season when they both departed to Redbridge Forest. However, certainly Cavell's loss was cushioned by the form shown by former Kettering Town striker Gary Jones. York Street seemed to suit Jones, who never really settled at Kettering. His 27 goals were a real bonus for Cusack.

Boston's cup performances were, again disappointing. Beazer Homes Midland Division side Tamworth knocked the Pilgrims out of the FA Cup and there was also early exits in both the Vauxhall FA Trophy and Bob Lord Trophy.

Despite the good league season, Cusack was surprisingly sacked at the end of the season. The club have now turned to former Kettering Town boss Peter Morris. His track record suggests that Boston United will be a force to be reckoned with this season.

Boston United F.C. 1991-92. Back Row (L-R): Glenn Maddison (kit assistant), Gary Jones, Andy Moore, Mark Cook, Steve Raffell, John McKenna, John McGinley, Paul Richardson, Steve Collins, Tony Deane, Alan Smith. Front (L-R): Paul Casey, Steve Adams, Paul Cavell, Mike Nesbitt, Steve Buckley, Mr Pat Malkinson (Chairman), Dave Cusack, Martin Hardy, Steve Stoutt, Richard Toone, Paul Shirtliff.

Boston United

Match No.	Date	Competition	Venue H/A	Opponents	Result	League H/T	Pos.	Goalscorers (Times if known)	Attendance
1	Aug 3	LSC	H	Scunthorpe Utd	W 2-1	1-1		Cav ell; Stoutt	654
2	Aug 17	GMVC	H	Merthyr Tydfil	W 2-0	1-0		Toone 1; Cavell 82	1312
3	Aug 24	GMVC	A	Runcorn	D 2-2	0-2	7	Stoutt	72,81
4	Aug 31	GMVC	H	Kidderminster	L 1-2	1-1	12	Adams 10	1319
5	Sep 3	BLT	A	Redbridge Forest	L 0-2	0-0			202
6	Sep 7	GMVC	H	Cheltenham	D 3-3	1-2	15	Cavell 36; Jones 65,74	1164
7	Sep 11	GMVC	H	Witton Albion	W 3-2	1-1	8	Jones 41; Cavell 66; McGinley 73	1187
8	Sep 14	FAC 1Q	A	Blakenall	W 2-1	1-1		Cavell 14; Jones 81	502
9	Sep 18	BLT	H	Redbridge Forest	W 4-0	2-0		Casey 4; Cavell 36; Shirtliff 49; Jones 66	746
10	Sep 21	GMVC	A	Northwich Victoria	D 1-1	1-1	9	Cavell 23	654
11	Sep 25	GMVC	A	Welling Utd	W 3-1	0-1	8	Cavell 48; Jones 70,90	726
12	Sep 28	FAC 2Q	H	Tamworth	D 1-1	1-1		Jones 15	1375
13	Oct 1	FAC 2QR	A	Tamworth	L 0-1	0-0			1215
14	Oct 5	GMVC	H	Farnborough	L 0-1	0-1	8		1134
15	Oct 8	BLT	A	Northwich Victoria	L 2-3	0-2		Nesbitt 58,77	474
16	Oct 12	GMVC	A	Macclesfield	W 1-0	0-0	8	Nesbitt 63	869
17	Oct 16	LSC	H	Grimsby Town	L 1-6	0-3		Cavell	926
18	Oct 19	GMVC	H	Wycombe Wanderers	D 2-2	0-1	8	Moore 61; Nesbitt 79	1706
19	Oct 26	GMVC	H	Redbridge Forest	W 2-1	1-1	6	Cavell 16,73	1058
20	Nov 2	GMVC	A	Barrow	D 2-2	1-1	6	Jones 18; McGinley 75	1018
21	Nov 9	GMVC	A	Altrincham	W 4-2	0-1	5	Jones 22,61,75; Fletcher 80	908
22	Nov 16	GMVC	H	Northwich Victoria	L 0-2	0-0	7		1218
23	Nov 23	GMVC	H	Yeovil Town	L 1-3	1-0	11	Jones 31	1240
24	Nov 26	GMVC	A	Stafford Rangers	W 1-0	0-0	7	Stoutt 57	681
25	Nov 30	FAT 3Q	A	Moor Green	W 3-1	2-0		Howarth 30; McGinley 32; Jones 61	408
26	Dec 7	GMVC	A	Gateshead	L 1-2	1-0	8	McGinley 10	271
27	Dec 19	GMVC	H	Welling Utd	W 5-1	2-1	7	Jones 16,29,78; Casey 53; Nuttell 64	755
28	Dec 26	GMVC	H	Kettering Town	D 1-1	0-1	8	Toone 53	2919
29	Jan 1	GMVC	A	Kettering Town	W 3-1	1-0	8	Stoutt 23; Nuttell 58; McGinley 63	3207
30	Jan 4	GMVC	A	Witton Albion	L 0-1	0-1	8		749
31	Jan 11	FAT 1	A	Macclesfield	D 0-0	0-0			833
32	Jan 15	FAT 1R	H	Macclesfield	L 0-2	0-1			947
33	Jan 18	GMVC	H	Macclesfield	L 1-5	1-0	10	Hardy 15	951
34	Jan 31	GMVC	A	Slough	L 1-3	0-1	12	McGinley 83	732
35	Feb 11	GMVC	A	Colchester	L 0-1	0-0	12		3229
36	Feb 15	GMVC	H	Slough	W 3-1	1-0	11	Nuttell 33 (pen), 55; Jones 74	721
37	Feb 19	GMVC	A	Gateshead	W 4-0	2-0	7	Jones 22,32,80; Nuttell 72 (pen)	639
38	Feb 29	GMVC	A	Telford Utd	W 2-0	1-0	7	Nesbitt 30; Jones 89	841
39	Mar 7	GMVC	H	Bath City	W 1-0	1-0	6	Jones 21	1008
40	Mar 10	GMVC	A	Wycombe Wanderers	L 1-2	1-1	6	Jones 78	2580
41	Mar 14	GMVC	A	Farnborough	L 0-5	0-1	7		724
42	Mar 21	GMVC	H	Barrow	W 4-1	0-1	7	Hardy 55; Stoutt 67; Jones 79; North 81	775
43	Mar 28	GMVC	A	Cheltenham	D 1-1	1-1	7	Stoutt 24	894
44	Mar 30	GMVC	H	Kidderminster H	W 3-1	1-1	7	Jones 45,88; Nuttell 57	1009
45	Apr 4	GMVC	H	Altrincham	W 2-1	1-0	6	Swailes 14; Jones 48	891
46	Apr 8	GMVC	H	Telford Utd	L 1-2	0-0	8	Hardy 3	901
47	Apr 11	GMVC	A	Stafford Rangers	D 2-2	1-0	8	Jones 25; o.g. 89	839
48	Apr 14	GMVC	H	Bath City	L 0-2	0-1	8		401
49	Apr 18	GMVC	A	Yeovil Town	D 1-1	1-0	8	Jones 31	1823
50	Apr 22	GMVC	H	Colchester	L 0-4	0-1	10		2035
51	Apr 25	GMVC	A	Merthyr Tydfil	L 0-2	0-2	10		589
52	Apr 28	GMVC	A	Redbridge Forest	W 4-1	3-0	8	Stoutt 10; Hardy 12; Jones 27; Nuttell 71	472
53	May 2	GMVC	H	Runcorn	W 2-1	0-1	8	Nuttell 68,71	864

Best Home League Attendance: 2919 v Kettering 26.12.91   Smallest: 639 v Gateshead 19.2.92   Average Home Attendance: 1173
Compared to 1990/91: 1372

Goalscorers GMVC: Jones 27; Nuttell 9; Cavell 7; Stoutt 6; McGinley 5; Hardy 4; Casey, Nesbitt, Toone 2; Adams, Fletcher, Moore, North, Swailes 1.
FA Cup: Jones 4; Cavell 3; Nesbitt 2; Casey, Hardy, Howarth, McGinley Shirtliff 1.

Boston United

1	2	3	4	5	6	7	8	9	10	11	12	14	Match No.
McKenna	Shirtliff	Toone	Richardson	Hardy	Moore	Nesbitt	Stoutt	Cavell	McGinley	Adams	Raffell	Jones	1
McKenna	Shirtliff	Collins	Richardson	Hardy	Swailes	Toone•	Stoutt	Cavell	Jones	Adams	Beech	Moore	2
McKenna	Shirtliff	Collins	Richardson	Hardy	Swailes	Toone•	Stoutt	Cavell	Jones†	Adams	Moore	McGinley	3
McKenna	Shirtliff	Collins	Richardson	Hardy	Swailes	Nesbitt•	Stoutt	Cavell	Jones†	Adams	Moore	McGinley	4
Lamont	Shirtliff	Collins	Richardson	Hardy	Swailes	Nesbitt	Stoutt	Cavell	Jones	Adams	Moore	McGinley	5
Lamont	Shirtliff	Collins	Toone	Hardy	Swailes	Casey	Stoutt	Cavell	Jones	Adams	Moore	McGinley	6
McKenna	Shirtliff	Collins	Richardson	Hardy•	Swailes	Casey†	Stoutt	Cavell	Jones	Adams	Moore	McGinley	7
McKenna	Shirtliff	Collins	Richardson	Hardy	Swailes	Casey	Stoutt	Cavell	Jones	Adams	Moore	McGinley	8
McKenna	Shirtliff	Collins	Richardson	Moore	Swailes	Casey	Stoutt	Cavell	Jones	Adams	Toone	McGinley	9
McKenna	Shirtliff	Collins	Richardson•	Moore	Swailes	Casey	Stoutt	Cavell	Jones†	Adams	Toone	McGinley	10
McKenna	Shirtliff†	Collins	Richardson•	Moore	Swailes	Casey	Stoutt	Cavell	Jones	Adams	Raffell	McGinley	11
McKenna	Shirtliff	Collins	Richardson	Moore	Swailes	Casey	Stoutt	Cavell	Jones	Adams	Raffell	McGinley	12
McKenna	Shirtliff	Collins	Toone	Moore	Swailes	Casey	Stoutt	Cavell	Jones	Adams	Raffell	McGinley	13
McKenna	Shirtliff	Collins	Richardson	Moore	Raffell	Casey	Stoutt•	Cavell†	Jones	Adams	Nesbitt	McGinley	14
McKenna	Shirtliff	Collins	Richardson	Moore	Raffell	Casey	Stoutt	Cavell	Jones	Adams	Nesbitt	McGinley	15
McKenna	Shirtliff	Collins	Richardson•	Moore	Raffell	Adams	Nesbitt	Cavell	McGinley†	Casey	Stoutt	Jones	16
McKenna	Shirtliff	Collins	Stoutt	Moore	Raffell	Adams	Toone	Cavell	McGinley	Casey	Jones	Nesbitt	17
McKenna	Shirtliff	Collins	Stoutt•	Moore	Hardy	Adams	Nesbitt	Cavell	Jones	Casey	Toone	McGinley	18
McKenna	Shirtliff	Collins	Richardson	Moore	Hardy	Adams	Nesbitt	Cavell	Jones	Casey	Swailes	Stoutt	19
McKenna	Shirtliff	Collins	Stoutt	Moore	Hardy	Adams	Nesbitt	Jones	McGinley†	Casey	Swailes	Toone	20
McKenna	Shirtliff	Collins	Stoutt	Moore	Howarth	Adams†	Nesbitt•	Jones	McGinley	Casey	Toone	Fletcher	21
McKenna	Shirtliff	Collins	Stoutt	Moore	Howarth	Adams	Nesbitt•	Jones	McGinley	Casey	Toone	Hardy	22
McKenna	Shirtliff•	Myles	Stoutt	Moore	Howarth	Casey	Toone	Jones	Nuttell†	McGinley	Swailes	Evans	23
McKenna	Raffell•	Myles	Stoutt	Moore	Howarth	Casey	Toone	Jones	Nuttell	McGinley	Hardy	Swailes	24
McKenna	Shirtliff	Myles	Stoutt	Swailes	Howarth	Casey	Toone	Jones	Nuttell	McGinley	Hardy	Evans	25
McKenna	Hardy	Myles	Stoutt	Swailes	Howarth	Casey	Toone	Jones	Nuttell	McGinley	Evans	Reddin	26
McKenna	Shirtliff	Collins•	Hardy	Swailes	Howarth	Casey	Toone	Jones	Nuttell†	McGinley	Myles	Reddin	27
McKenna	Shirtliff	Collins	Hardy	Swailes	Howarth	Casey	Toone	Jones	Nuttell•	McGinley	Moore	Adams	28
McKenna	Shirtliff	Collins	Hardy	Swailes	Howarth	Casey	Stoutt	Jones†	Nuttell	McGinley	Moore	Adams	29
McKenna	Shirtliff	Collins	Hardy	Swailes	Howarth	Casey	Stoutt	Jones	Nuttell	McGinley†	Moore	Adams	30
McKenna	Shirtliff	Collins	Hardy	Swailes	Howarth	Casey	Stoutt	Jones	Nuttell	Adams	Moore	McGinley	31
McKenna	Shirtliff	Collins	Hardy	Swailes	Howarth	Casey†	Stoutt	Jones	Nuttell	Adams	Moore	McGinley	32
McKenna	Shirtliff	Collins	Hardy	Swailes	Howarth	Casey	Stoutt	Jones	Nuttell	Adams	Moore	McGinley	33
McKenna	Shirtliff	Collins	Hardy	Swailes	Moore•	Adams	Stoutt	Jones†	Nuttell	McGinley	Raffell	Nesbitt	34
McKenna	Shirtliff	Raffell	Hardy	Swailes	Moore•	Nesbitt	Stoutt	Jones	Nuttell	Adams†	Retallick	Collins	35
McKenna	Shirtliff	Collins	Hardy	Swailes	Raffell	Retallick	Stoutt	Nuttell	Jones	Adams	Casey	Nesbitt	36
McKenna	Shirtliff	Collins	Hardy	Swailes	Raffell	Retallick	Stoutt	Nuttell	Jones	Adams	Casey	Nesbitt	37
McKenna	Shirtliff	Collins	Hardy	Swailes	Raffell	Retallick†	Casey	Nesbitt	Jones	Adams	Moore	Toone•	38
McKenna	Shirtliff	Collins	Hardy	Swailes	Raffell•	Retallick†	Casey	Nesbitt	Jones	Adams	Moore	Stoutt	39
McKenna	Shirtliff	Collins	Hardy	Swailes	Raffell	Retallick	Casey	Nesbitt	Jones	Adams	Moore	Stoutt	40
McKenna	Shirtliff	Collins	Hardy	Swailes	Raffell	Retallick†	Casey	Nesbitt•	Jones	Adams	Moore	Stoutt	41
McKenna	Moore	Collins	Hardy	Swailes	Raffell	Casey†	Stoutt	North	Jones	Adams†	Toone	Retallick	42
McKenna	Shirtliff	Collins	Hardy	Swailes	Raffell	Casey	Stoutt	Nuttell	Jones	Adams†	Moore	Retallick	43
McKenna	Shirtliff	Collins	Hardy	Swailes	Raffell	Casey	Stoutt	Nuttell	Jones	Adams	Moore	Toone	44
McKenna	Shirtliff	Collins†	Hardy	Swailes•	Raffell	Casey	Stoutt	Nuttell	Jones	Adams	Moore	Retallick	45
McKenna	Shirtliff	Collins	Hardy†	Moore	Raffell	Casey	Stoutt	Nuttell	Jones	Adams	Toone	Retallick	46
McKenna	Shirtliff	Collins	Hardy	Moore	Raffell	Casey	Stoutt	Nuttell	Jones	Adams	Swailes	Retallick	47
McKenna	Raffell	Collins	Hardy	Swailes	Moore	Casey	Stoutt	Nuttell	Jones	Adams	Toone	Retallick	48
McKenna	Shirtliff	Collins	Hardy	Moore	Raffell	Casey	Stoutt	Nuttell	Jones	Adams†	Toone	Retallick	49
McKenna	Shirtliff	Collins	Hardy	Moore	Raffell	Casey†	Stoutt	Nuttell	Jones	Adams	Toone	Retallick	50
McKenna	Shirtliff	Collins	Hardy	Moore†	Raffell	Retallick•	Stoutt	Nuttell	Jones	Adams	Toone	Swailes	51
McKenna	Shirtliff	Collins•	Hardy	Swailes	Raffell	Casey	Stoutt	Nuttell	Jones	Adams†	Toone	Smith	52
McKenna	Shirtliff	Collins	Hardy	Swailes	Raffell	Casey	Stoutt•	Nuttell	Jones	Adams	Toone	Retallick	53

• substituted by No. 12.   † substituted by No. 14.

GMVC Appearances (max 42): Jones, McKenna 41; Collins 38; Shirtliff 37; Adams 35; Hardy 34; Stoutt, Casey 33; Swailes 28; Raffell 22; Moore 20; Nuttell 18; McGinley 12; Cavell 11; Howarth, Richardson 9; Nesbitt, Toone 8; Retallick 7; Myles 3; Lamont, North 1; Fletcher (1).

Cup Appearances (max 11): Shirtliff, Stoutt 11; Adams, McKenna 10; Casey, Collins, Jones, Swailes 9; Cavell 8; Moore, Richardson 6; Hardy, Toone 5; Howarth, Nuttell 3; McGinley, Nesbitt, Raffell 2; Lamont, Myles 1.

Boston United

PETER MORRIS

Born in Mansfield, Peter made his debut for his local club at 16, captaining the side when only 18. After over 200 games for Mansfield, Bill McGarry took him to Ipswich where he played 300 times before moving on to Norwich at the age of 31.

Appropriately, he started in management at Mansfield, taking them into the Second Division, and has since had spells with Peterborough, Crewe, Southend, Nuneaton Borough, in Saudi Arabia and as assistant manager at Leicester City. He then took over as manager of Kettering Town in June 1988 and enjoyed a highly successful four years at Rockingham Road. Although the club didn't win any major honours, Peter led the club to FA Cup success, reaching the Fourth Round in 1989 and the Third Round last season, and guided the Poppies to finish in the top five of the Conference in each of his campaigns in charge.

He left the club in June and was quickly snapped up by Boston United where he has already begun to strengthen the York Street squad. The Boston faithfull can expect an interesting season ahead.

Boston United defend in numbers at relegated Barrow's Holker Street ground. However, they couldn't prevent Paul Slater from netting for the home side.   Photo: Ged Rule.

Programme details:
    36 pages for £1.00
    Editor - Nick Thompson

Any other club publications:
    From Behind Your Fences (Fanzine)

Local Newspapers:
    Lincolnshire Standard
    Boston Target
    Lincolnshire Echo

Local Radio Stations:
    BBC Radio Lincs
    Hereward Radio

BOSTON UNITED - PLAYING SQUAD 1992-93

Player	Honours	Birthplace and date	Transfer Fees	Previous Clubs
GOALKEEPERS				
DEFENDERS				
Martin Hardy	LSC	Worksop 12/12/62	£10,000	Notts Co, Worksop
Stephen Raffell		Blyth 27/4/70		Doncaster Rovers
Andy Moore	GMVC	Grimsby 14/11/65		Grimsby, Lincoln, Western Suburbs(Aust)
Darren Bloodworth	Lincs FA	Mkt Deeping 10/2/67		Bourne, Kettering
Drew Coverdale		Middlesbrough 20/6/69		Middlesbrough, Darlington
MIDFIELD				
Richard Toone		Lincoln 31/3/69	£15,000	Leicester City, Lincoln Utd
Paul Casey	GMVC FAT R/U	Rintein 6/10/61	£5,500	Sheff Utd, Boston Utd, Lincoln
Steve Stoutt		Halifax 5/4/64		Wolves, Grimsby, Lincoln
Graham Retallick				Histon
Neil Grayson		York 1/1/64		Rowntree Mackintosh, Doncaster, York City, Chesterfield
Steve Chambers		Worksop 20/7/68		Sheffield Wednesday, Mansfield
FORWARDS				
Darren Smith		Nottingham 29/4/70		Burton Albion, Wolves
Darren Munton				Bourne Town
Gary Jones		Huddersfield 6/4/69	£3,000	Rossington Main, Doncaster, Grantham, Kettering
Mark Hallam		Leicester		Leicester United
Mike Nesbitt		Doncaster 8/1/69	£2,000	Armthorpe Welfare, Doncaster

Departures during season:
Winston Campbell & Tony Deane (Frickley), Glenn Beech (Stamford), Lee Lamont (Armthorpe Welfare), Steve Myles (Released), Dave Reddin (Shepshed Alb), Paul Richardson & Paul Cavell (Redbridge F). Chris Swailes & Mick Nuttell (Kettering), Steve Adams & John McGinley (Released), Steve Collins (Corby), Paul Shirtliff & John McKenna (Dagenham & Redbridge).

Players who joined on loan during season:
Gary Evans (Chesterfield), Marc North (Shepshed Alb).

York Street, Boston

Ground address and Tel. No. : York Street Ground, York Street, Boston. Tel: 0205 65524/25. Fax No. 0205 354063

Clubcall Line: 0898 121539

Simple ground directions: Two minutes walk from Town Centre.

Official capacity: 14,000   **Seating:** 2,000   **Covered accommodation:** All four sides

Cost of seats: £5.00   **Cost of standing:** £4.00

Official opening of floodlights: v Corby Town, 1955

Record attendance: 10,086 v Corby Town

Social facilities available (Bars, hot & cold food etc): Open every day except Tuesday 7-11 pm, Friday & Saturday 11-3 pm, Sunday 12-2, live entertainment Saturday & Sunday. Darts, pool, dominoes.

Car parking: For 400 cars in front of ground

Sponsored by: Batemans   **BOSTON UNITED**   **Nickname:** Pilgrims

---

Previous names: Boston Town, Boston Swifts

Previous leagues: Central Alliance, Midland Counties, United Counties, West Midlands League, Northern Premier

Club colours: Old Gold/ black   **Change colours:** Sky blue

Midweek home matches: Tuesday   **Club shop:** Club Offices, 14-16 Spain Place, Boston

Record transfer fee paid: £12,500 to Frickley Athletic for Paul Shirtlitt, June 1988

Record transfer fee received: £15,000 Brendon Phillips (Mansfield Town), Steve Thompson (Lincoln City), Gordon Simmonite (Blackpool), Paul Casey (Lincoln City), 20,000 Greg Fee (Sheffield Wed), Undisclosed for Paul Carell & Paul Richardson (Redbridge F)

Record appearances for club: Billy Howells, over 500

Record goalscorer in a season: Jimmy Rainer, 55, 1966-67

Past players who have progressed to the Football League: Jim Smith (Colchester Utd), Steve Thompson (Lincoln City), Brendon Phillips (Mansfield Town), Gordon Simmonite (Blackpool), Simon Garner (Blackburn Rovers), John Froggatt - Bobby Svarc (Colchester Utd), David Gilbert (Northampton Town), Tim Dalton (Bradford City)

Club Honours: United Counties League Champions; West Midlands League Champions (2); NPL Champions (4); NPL Cup (2); NPL Shield Winners (3); NPL Vase Champions (2); Lincs County Cup winners 1987-88.

Past clubmanagers: Dave Cusack, George Kerr, Mick Walker, Gordon Bolland/ Frud Taylor (caretaker), Ray O'Brien, Albert Phelan, Jim Smith, Arthur Mann, Howard Wilkinson, Don Donoavan, John Froggatt, Keith Josling.

BROMSGROVE ROVERS

Formed: 1885

President:
Charles W Poole

Chairman:
Chris Lloyd

Vice Chairman:
Keith MacMaster

Directors:
Jack Sharkey
Jack Stewart
Peter Slater
Brian Evans
George Perry
John Teece

Treasurer:
Mike Davies

Secretary:
Barry Hewings

Manager:
Bobby Hope

Assistant-Manager:
Doug Griffiths

Commercial Manager:
Miss R O'Neill

Physiotherapist:
Leigh Talton

Trainer:
Stewart Pinfield

Record Breakers

The long season finished on a high note as Bromsgrove Rovers added the Worcestershire Senior Cup to the Beazer Homes League title, a season that will be recorded as the best in the clubs history.

The season started off with an amazing match at Dartford, both the keepers were sent-off, three penalties of which only two were scored from. The Rovers did not have the best of starts, by the time VS Rugby won at the Victoria Ground on November 2nd they were the leaders of the division, we had lost 3 times at home and were 22 points behind them. However, our cup exploits were a bonus as we progressed through to the first round of the FA Cup where we enjoyed an away day at AFC Bournemouth and our 1-3 defeat was the springboard for our players who felt hard done by as the Cherries' last 2 goals came from penalty kicks. The following Tuesday, November 19th, was the last time Rovers dropped any home points, 15 matches to the end of the season all won. This is both a club record and a Beazer Homes League record.

Individuals who warrant a mention are Shaun O'Meara - who in his Testimonial Year at the age of 35, had the best season of his career in which he has played over 690 matches. Jimmy Skelding - was ever-present and ever reliable. Scott Cooksey - for his 100% committment and outstanding goalkeeping. Chris Hanks - who once again top scored with 30 plus goals and has broken the club's goalscoring record passing the previous record of 227, not bad considering he'd only scored 4 goals by January 17th! Tommy Daly - in his first season. an old fashioned winger with 12 goals. Stewart Brighton - who came so close to selection for an England Semi-Professional cap. Kevin Richardson - the captain who led by example. Mark Crisp - who's play is so unselfish and yet he scored 22 goals. Martyn O'Connor - his artistry in midfield is a joy to watch and it has earned him a transfer to Crystal Palace. Steve Stott - arrived in September back in England and added strength to our open style of play. Paul Webb - who probably made more goals than anyone else, although he scored some important goals himself including the 88th minute equaliser at Dover before a record Beazer Homes crowd of 4,035. In addition to the above players, who all played in at least 50 matches, a special thanks to our back-up squad.

Finally to our manager Bobby Hope and his management team, the Directors and Staff who have worked together with the players who have made this both an historical and successful season for Bromsgrove Rovers.

Brian Perry

Bromsgrove Rovers F.C. 1991-92. Back Row (L-R): J Hanks, S Pinfield, L Talton, S Cooper, C Hanks, M Crisp, P Wardle, S Cooksey, R Moran, P Masefield, S Stott, P Sunners, D Griffiths, B Hewings. Front: T Daly, M O'Connor, P Webb, S Brighton, K Richardson, B Hope, S Burgher, J Skelding, S O'Meara, M

Bromsgrove Rovers

Beazer Homes League: 1st.   **FA Cup: 1st Round.**   **FA Trophy: 1st Round.**

Match No.	Date	Competition	Venue H/A	Opponents	Result	League H/T Pos.	Goalscorers (Times if known)	Attendance
1	Aug 17	BHL	A	Dartford	D 1-1		Webb (p)	601
2	Aug 20	BHL	H	Atherstone	W 2-0		Cunningham; O'Meara (p)	639
3	Aug 24	BHL	H	Cambridge	L 0-2			603
4	Aug 26	BHL	A	Burton Albion	L 1-3		O'Connor (p)	692
5	Aug 31	BHL	A	Waterlooville	W 1-0		Hanks	252
6	Sep 3	BHL	H	Gloucester City	L 0-2			550
7	Sep 7	BHL	H	Dover athletic	D 0-0			552
8	Sep 14	FAC Q1	A	Bedworth	W 2-0		O'Meara; Hanks	264
9	Sep 21	FAT	H	Bedworth	D 1-1		Stott	480
10	Sep 24	FAT Q1 R	A	Bedworth	W 2-0		Crisp; Stott	350
11	Sep 28	FAC Q2	H	Rushden	W 1-0		Richardson	472
12	Oct 5	BHL	A	Crawley Town	W 3-0		Durkin 2; Rolfe	466
13	Oct 8	SL Cup	H	Worcester City	W 3-5		O'Meara (p); Wardle; Webb	597
14	Oct 12	FAC Q3	H	Redditch Utd	W 2-0		Crisp; Cooper	1050
15	Oct 19	FAT Q2	H	Hednesford	W 1-0		Daly	648
16	Oct 26	FAC Q4	A	Tamworth	W 1-0		Crisp	1546
17	Nov 2	BHL	H	V.S. Rugby	L 1-2		Daly	545
18	Nov 4	SL Cup	H	Worcester City	W 4-1		Cooper; Stott; Daly	640
19	Nov 9	BHL	A	Fisher Athletic	W 3-1		O'Meara (p); Stott; Daly	195
20	Nov 12	WS Cup	H	Redditch Utd	W 3-0		Daly; Stott; Rose	428
21	Nov 16	FAC R1	A	Bournemouth	L 1-3		O'Meara (p)	4301
22	Nov 19	BHL	H	Burton Albion	D 1-1		Crisp	445
23	Nov 23	BHL	A	Moor Green	D 1-1		Stott	486
24	Nov 26	BCS Cup	A	Moor Green	D 0-0			334
25	Nov 30	FAT Q3	A	Fisher Athletic	D 1-1		O.G.	121
26	Dec 3	FAT Q3R	H	Fisher Athletic	W 2-0		Crisp; Daly	625
27	Dec 7	BHL	H	Corby Town	W 3-0		Daly; Stott; Hacks (p)	550
28	Dec 21	BHL	A	Chelmsford City	D 1-1		Crisp	550
29	Dec 26	BHL	A	Worcester City	W 2-0		Crisp 2	1279
30	Dec 28	BHL	H	Waterlooville	W 1-0		Crisp	668
31	Jan 1	BHL	A	Halesowen Town	D 1-1		Hanks	1330
32	Jan 4	BHL	H	Dartford	W 1-0		Daly	806
33	Jan 7	BCS Cup	H	Moor Green	W 5-0		O'Connor 2; Crisp 2; O'Meara	647
34	Jan 11	FAT 1R	A	Redbridge Forest	D 1-1		O.G.	624
35	Jan 14	FAT 1Rr	H	Redbridge Forest	L 0-1			995
26	Jan 18	BHL	A	Fisher Athletic	W 7-0		Crisp; O'Meara; Hanks; Stott; Daly 2; Webb	558
37	Jan 21	BCS Cup	H	Hednesford	D 1-1		Hanks	603
38	Jan 25	BHL	A	Dorchester	W 2-1		Crisp 2	622
39	Feb 1	BHL	H	Gravesend	W 1-0		Hanks	625
40	Feb 3	BCS Cup	A	Hednesford	W 1-0		O'Connor *	598
41	Feb 8	BHL	A	Cambridge	L 0-1			351
42	Feb 11	BCS Cup	H	Burton Albion	W 6-0		Hanks 3 (1p); Crisp 2; Stott	395
43	Feb 15	BHL	A	Wealdstone	W 3-1		Hanks 3	422
44	Feb 17	WS Cup	A	Kidderminster Har.	W 2-0		Stott; O'Connor	1051
45	Feb 22	BHL	H	Chelmsford	W 2-1		Stott 2	717
46	Feb 25	BCS Cup	H	Burton Albion	W 3-0		Webb; Crisp; Hanks	600
47	Feb 29	BHL	H	Crawley Town	W 5-1		Hanks 2; Stott; O'Meara; O'Connor	650
48	Mar 3	BHL	A	Trowbridge	W 2-0		Crisp; Stott	540
49	Mar 7	BHL	A	V.S. Rugby	D 1-1		Hanks	880
50	Mar 10	BCS Cup SF1	A	Dorchester	L 1-4		Hanks	359
51	Mar 14	BHL	H	Moor Green	W 5-3		Hanks 2; O'Meara 2; Webb	867
52	Mar 17	BHL	A	Atherton	L 0-2			570
53	Mar 21	BHL	A	Gravesend	W 1-0		Hanks	423
54	Mar 24	BCS Cup	H	Dorchester	W 2-1		Hanks 2	689
55	Mar 28	BHL	H	Wealdstone	W 1-0		Hanks	768
56	Mar 31	BHL	H	Trowbridge	W 3-1		Daly 3	797
57	Apr 2	BHL	A	Bashley	W 1-0		O'Connor	320
58	Apr 4	BHL	A	Corby Town	W 3-1		O'Connor; Hanks; Whitehouse	360
59	Apr 7	BHL	A	Dorchester Town	W 5-1		Hanks 2; Masefield; Whitehouse; Brighton	1224
60	Apr 11	BHL	H	Poole Town	W 3-1		Crisp; O'Meara; Hanks	1117
61	Apr 16	BHL	A	Dover Athletic	D 2-2		Hanks; Webb	4045
62	Apr 18	BHL	H	Halesowen Town	W 1-0		Hanks	1765
63	Apr 20	BHL	A	Worcester City	D 1-1		Stott	2558
64	Apr 23	BHL	A	Poole Town	W 1-0		O'Meara	242
65	Apr 25	BHL	H	Bashley	W 3-0		Crisp; O'Meara; Hanks	1658
66	May 2	BHL	A	Cloucester City	W 2-1		O'Connor; Whitehouse	875
67	May 4	WSC Final	A	Sutton Coldfield	D 1-1		Crisp	490
68	May 7	WSC Final	H	Sutton Coldfield	W 3-0		Crisp; Stott; Burgher	1246

Best Home League Attendance: 1765 v Halesowen 18.4.92   **Smallest: 484 v Burton Albion 19.11.91**   **Average Home Attendance: 839**

Goalscorers League (78): Hanks 22; Crisp11; Stott 9; Daly 8; O'Connor 6; Webb 4; Whitehouse 3; Durkin 2; Brighton, Cunningham, Masefield, Rolfe 1. **F.A.C. (7):** O'Meara, Crisp 2; Richardson, Hanks, Cooper 1. **F.A.T. (8):** Stott, Daly, Crisp, Own goals 2. **Barclays C.SS.LC (26):** Hanks 8; Crisp 5; O'Connor 3; Webb, Stott, Cooper, O'Meara 2; Wardle, Daly 1. **Worcs SNR C (9):** Sottt, Crisp 2; Hanks, Brighton, Burgher, Ross, Daly 1.

Bromsgrove Rovers

1	2	3	4	5	6	7	8	9	10	11	12	14	Match No.
Cooksey	Skelding	Brighton	Richardson	Wardle	Webb	O'Connor	O'Meara	Hanks	Crisp	Cunningham	James	Durkin	1
Cooksey	Skelding	Brighton	Richardson	Wardle	Webb	O'Connor	O'Meara	Hanks	Crisp•	Cunningham	James	Durkin	2
Cooksey	Skelding	Brighton	Richardson	Wardle	Webb	O'Connor†	O'Meara	Hanks•	Crisp	Cunningham	James	Durkin	3
Cooksey	Skelding	Webb	Richardson	Wardle	O'Connor	Cooper	James†	Cunningham	Crisp	Brighton	Hanks	Durkin	4
Moran	Webb	Skelding	Richardson	Wardle	O'Connor	Cooper	O'Meara	Hanks	Brighton	Cunningham	James	Guest	5
Cooksey	Webb	Brighton	Richardson	Wardle	Skelding	Cooper	O'Meara•	Hanks	Crisp	O'Connor	Durkin	Stott	6
Cooksey	Webb	Brighton	Richardson	Wardle	Skelding	O'Connor•	Stott†	Hanks	Crisp	Durkin	O'Meara	James	7
Cooksey	Skelding	O'Meara	Webb	Wardle	Richardson	O'Connor	Brighton	Hanks†	Crisp	Cunningham•	James	Cooper	8
Cooksey	Skelding	O'Meara	Richardson	Wardle	Webb	O'Connor	Stott	Hanks•	Crisp	Brighton	James	Cooper	9
Cooksey	Skelding	O'Meara	Richardson	Wardle	Webb	O'Connor	Stott•	Cunningham	Crisp	Brighton	Hanks	James	10
Cooksey	Skelding	Brighton	Richardson	Wardle	Webb	O'Connor	James	O'Meara	Crisp	Cunningham•	Hanks	Cooper	11
Cooksey	Skelding	O'Meara	Richardson	Wardle	Webb	O'Connor	James†	Durkin	Crisp•	Brighton	Daly	Rolfe	12
Cooksey	Skelding	O'Meara	O'Connor•	Wardle	Webb	Daly	James†	Durkin	Crisp	Brighton	Hanks	Cooper	13
Cooksey	Skelding	O'Meara	O'Connor	Wardle	Webb†	Daly•	Stott	Durkin	Crisp	Brighton	Cooper	James	14
Cooksey	Durkin	O'Meara	O'Connor	Wardle	Skelding	Daly	Stott	James•	Crisp	Brighton	Hanks	Cooper	15
Cooksey	Skelding	O'Meara	Richardson	Durkin	O'Connor	Daly	Stott	Cunningham	Crisp	Brighton	Hanks	Cooper	16
Cooksey	Skelding	O'Meara	Richardson	Durkin	O'Connor	Daly	Stott	Cunningham	Crisp	Brighton	Hanks	Cooper	17
Cooksey	O'Meara	Brighton	O'Connor	Durkin	Skelding	Daly	Stott	Hanks	Burgher	Cooper•	Crisp	Cunningham	18
Cooksey	O'Meara	Brighton	O'Connor	Durkin	Skelding	Daly	Stott	Hanks	Crisp	Cooper•	Ross	Cunningham	19
Cooksey	Skelding	O'Meara	Richardson	Durkin†	Burgher	Daly	Stott	Hanks	Cooper	Henry•	Sweeney	Pugh	20
Cooksey	Skelding	Brighton	Richardson	O'Meara	O'Connor	Daly	Stott	Hanks•	Crisp	Cooper	Cunningham	Webb	21
Cooksey	Skelding	Brighton	Richardson	O'Meara	Burgher	Daly	Stott†	O'Connor	Crisp	Cooper•	Cunningham	Rolfe	22
Cooksey	Skelding	Brighton	Richardson	O'Meara	O'Connor	Daly	Stott	Hanks	Crisp	Cooper•	Cunningham	Rolfe	23
Cooksey	Skelding	Brighton	Richardson	O'Meara	O'Connor	Daly	Burgher	Hanks†	Crisp	Cooper	Webb	Rolfe	24
Cooksey	Skelding	Brighton	Richardson	Webb	O'Connor	Daly	Hanks	Stott	Crisp•	Cooper†	Cunningham	Volrath	25
Cooksey	Skelding	Brighton	Richardson	Webb	Burgher	Daly	Hanks	O'Connor	Crisp	Cooper	Durkin	Volrath	26
Cooksey	Skelding	Brighton	Richardson	Webb	O'Connor	Daly	Stott	Hanks	Crisp	Cooper	Volrath	Rolfe	27
Cooksey	Skelding	Brighton	Richardson	O'Meara	Webb	Daly	O'Connor	Hanks	Crisp	Cooper	Rolfe	Cunningham	28
Cooksey	Skelding	Brighton	Richardson	O'Meara•	Webb	Daly†	Stott	Hanks	Crisp	Cooper	Cunningham	O'Connor	29
Cooksey	Skelding	Brighton	Richardson	O'Meara	Webb	O'Connor	Burgher	Hanks	Crisp	Cunningham	Volrath	Wardle	30
Cooksey	Skelding	Brighton	Richardson	O'Meara	Webb	O'Connor	Stott	Hanks•	Crisp	Cunningham	Durkin	Daly	31
Cooksey	Skelding	Brighton	Richardson	O'Meara	Webb	Daly	Stott	Rolfe	Crisp	O'Connor•	Hanks	Durkin	32
Cooksey	Skelding	Brighton	Richardson	O'Meara	Webb	Daly	Stott	Rolfe	Crisp	O'Connor•	Durkin	Ross	33
Cooksey	Skelding	Brighton	Richardson	O'Meara	Webb	Daly•	Burgher	Rolfe†	Crisp	O'Connor•	Hanks	Durkin	34
Cooksey	Skelding	Brighton	Richardson	O'Meara	Webb	Daly†	Stott	Rolfe	Crisp	Burgher	Hanks	Pugh	35
Cooksey	Skelding	Brighton	Richardson	O'Meara	Webb	Daly	Stott	Burgher	Crisp	O'Connor	Hanks	Pugh	36
Cooksey	Skelding	Brighton	Richardson	O'Meara	Webb	Daly	Stott	Hanks	Crisp	O'Connor	Wardle	Rolfe	37
Cooksey	Skelding	Brighton	Richardson	O'Meara	Webb	Daly	Stott	Hanks	Crisp	O'Connor	Burgher	Rolfe	38
Cooksey	Skelding	Brighton	Richardson	O'Meara	Webb	Daly•	Stott	Hanks	Crisp	O'Connor	Rolfe	Wardle	39
Cooksey	Skelding	O'Meara	Richardson	Wardle	Webb	Daly	Stott	Hanks	Crisp	O'Connor	Rolfe	Volrath	40
Cooksey	Skelding	Burgher	Richardson	O'Meara	Webb	Mead	Volrath	Hanks	Crisp	O'Connor	Wardle	Rolfe	41
Cooksey	Skelding	O'Meara	Richardson	Wardle	Webb	Daly	Stott	Hanks•	Crisp	O'Connor	Durkin	Volrath	42
Cooksey	Skelding	Brighton	Richardson	O'Meara	Webb	Daly•	Stott	Burgher	Crisp	O'Connor	Wardle	Hanks	43
Cooksey	Skelding	O'Meara	Richardson	Wardle	Webb	Daly	Stott	Hanks	Brighton	O'Connor	Durkin	Rolfe	44
Cooksey	Skelding	Brighton	Richardson	O'Meara	Webb	Daly	Stott•	Hanks	Burgher	O'Connor	Durkin	Honeyfield	45
Cooksey	Skelding	Brighton	Richardson	O'Meara	Webb	Daly	Stott	Hanks	Crisp	O'Connor	Wardle	Durkin	46
Cooksey	Skelding	Brighton	Richardson	O'Meara	Webb	Daly•	Burgher†	Hanks	Crisp	O'Connor	Wardle	Honeyfield	47
Cooksey	Skelding	Brighton	Richardson	O'Meara	Webb	Daly†	Stott	Hanks	Crisp	O'Connor	Durkin	Rolfe	48
Cooksey	Skelding	Brighton	Burgher	O'Meara	Webb	Daly	Stott	Hanks	Crisp	O'Connor	Wardle	Durkin	49
Cooksey	Skelding	Righton	Daly†	Durkin	Webb	Whitehouse	Stott	Hanks	Crisp	O'Connor	Volrath	Sweeney	50
Cooksey	Skelding	Brighton	Richardson	Durkin•	Webb	Whitehouse	Stott	Hanks	Crisp	Burgher	Dal;y	Sweeney	51
Gandy	Skelding	Brighton	Richardson	O'Meara	Webb	Whitehouse	Stott	Hanks	Crisp	Daly	Durkin	Hussey	52
Gandy	Skelding	Brighton	Richardson	O'Meara	Webb	Burgher	Stott	Hanks	Crisp•	O'Connor	Whitehouse	Daly	53
Moran	Skelding	Brighton	Richardson	O'Meara	Webb	Daly†	Stott	Hanks	Whitehouse	O'Connor	Wardle	Crisp	54
Moran	Skelding	Brighton	Richardson	O'Meara•	Webb	Daly†	Stott	Hanks	Crisp	O'Connor	Whitehouse	Burgher	55
Cooksey	Skelding•	Brighton	Richardson	O'Meara	Webb	Daly	Stott	Hanks	Crisp	O'Connor	Whitehouse	Wardle	56
Cooksey	Skelding	Brighton	Richardson	O'Meara	Webb	Daly•	Stott	Hanks	Crisp	Whitehouse	Cooper	Masefield	57
Cooksey	Skelding	Brighton	Richardson	O'Meara	Webb	Daly	Burgher	Hanks†	Crisp	O'Connor•	Cooper	Masefield	58
Cooksey	Skelding	Brighton	Richardson	O'Meara	Webb	Daly•	Stott	Hanks	Crisp	O'Connor•	Whitehouse	Masefield	59
Cooksey	Skelding	Brighton	Richardson	O'Meara	Masefield	Daly•	Stott	Hanks	Crisp	Burgher	Whitehouse	Wardle	60
Moran	Skelding	Brighton	Richardson	O'Meara	Webb†	Daly	Stott	Hanks•	Crisp	O'Connor	Whitehouse	Masefield	61
Cooksey	Skelding	Brighton	Richardson	O'Meara	Webb	Daly†	Stott	Hanks	Crisp	O'Connor	Burgher	Whitehouse	62
Cooksey	Skelding	Brighton	Richardson	O'Meara	Webb	Daly†	Stott	Hanks	Crisp	O'Connor•	Whitehouse	Masefield	63
Cooksey	Skelding	Brighton	Richardson	O'Meara	Webb	Daly†	Stott	Hanks•	Crisp	Burgher	Whitehouse	Cooper	64
Cooksey	Skelding	Brighton	Richardson	O'Meara	Webb	Daly†	Stott	Hanks•	Crisp	Burgher	Whitehouse	Cooper	65
Cooksey	Skelding	Brighton	Richardson	O'Meara†	Webb	Daly•	Stott	Hanks	Crisp	O'Connor	Whitehouse	Masefield	66
Cooksey	Skelding	Brighton	Richardson	Masefield	Webb	Daly†	Stott	Hanks•	Crisp	O'Connor	Whitehouse	Cooper	67
Cooksey	Skelding	Brighton	Richardson	Masefield	Webb	Burgher	Stott	Whitehouse	Crisp	O'Connor	Hanks	Wardle	68
Cooksey	Skelding	Brighton	Richardson	Masefield	Webb	Burgher	Stott	Hanks	Crisp•	O'Connor	Whitehouse	Cooper	69

• substituted by No. 12.   † substituted by No. 14.

League Appearances (max 42): Skelding 42; Crisp 40; Brighton 40; Richardson 39; O'Meara 38; Webb 38; Hanks 38; Cooksey 37; O'Connor 36; Stott 35; Daly 28; Whitehouse 15; Cooper 12; Wardle 11; Durkin 10; Cunningham 10; Masefield 8; Burgher 6; James 5; Rolfe 4; Moran 3; Gandy 2; Sweendy 1.

Cup Appearances (max 26): Skelding 26; Crisp 25; Cooksey 25; O'Connor 24; Brighton 24; Daly 23; Richardson 22; O'Meara 21; Webb 20; Hanks 20; Stott 18; Burgher 15; Cooper 9; Wardle 9; Durkin 9; James 6; Whitehouse 4; Cunningham 4; Rolfe 4; Masefield 2; Pugh 2; Meade 2; Moran 1; Sweeney 1; Ross 1; Henry 1; Honeyfield 1; Watson 1.

Bromsgrove Rovers

BOBBY HOPE

Bobby Hope was born in Bridge of Allan, Scotland. He began his playing career with West Bromwich Albion whom he joined in 1959 as a junior. He went on to make over 330 appearances at The Hawthorns before moving on to Birmingham City and Sheffield Wednesday. Bobby represented Scotland at Schoolboy, Under-23 and twice at Full International level.

He is now in his second spell in charge of Bromsgrove Rovers after leaving for a brief period with Burton Albion. His excellent leadership qualities have shown through to lead the club into the GM Vauxhall Conference for the first time.

Bromsgrove Rovers top-scorer Chris Hanks in action against Dartford. Photo - Reed Midland Newspapers.

Programme details:
    32 pages for 50p
    Editor - Geoff Key

Any other club publications:

Local Newspapers:
    Bromsgrove Advertiser
    Bromsgrove Messenger

Local Radio Stations:

BROMSGROVE ROVERS - PLAYING SQUAD 1992-93

Player	Honours	Birthplace and date	Transfer Fees	Previous Clubs
GOALKEEPERS				
Scott Cooksey	BHL	Birmingham 24/6/72		Derby County, Shrewsbury Town
Richard Moran		Bromsgrove 7/3/63		Malvern Town
DEFENDERS				
Paul Masefield		Lichfield 21/10/70		Birmingham City, Exeter City
Jimmy Skelding	BHL	Bilston 30/5/64		Bilston, Wolves, Bromsgrove Rvrs, Burton Albion, Worcester City
Steve Cooper	BHL	Worcester 29/5/70		Malvern Town, Archdales
Stewart Brighton	BHL FA XI	Bromsgrove 3/10/66		Crewe Alexandra
Paul Wardle	BHL	Burton-on-Trent 1/2/70		Belper Town, Denaby United
Shaun O'Meara	BHL, WSC	Bromsgrove 24/4/56		Bromsgrove Rvrs, Stourbridge, Alvechurch, Bromsgrove Rvrs, Worcester City
Nigel Larkins		Burton-on-Trent 6/4/72		Birmingham City
Chris Hodges				Walsall, Rushall Olympic
David Rolfe				Youth
MIDFIELD				
Paul Webb	BHL	Wolverhampton 30/11/67		Bilston, Shrewsbury Town
Mark Crisp	BHL			Smethwick, Redditch Utd, Bromsgrove Rvrs, Alvechurch
Kevin Richardson	BHL	Walsall 22/11/62		Pelsall V, Sutton C, Stafford R, Worcester, Sutton C, Alvechurch, Hednesford Town
Paul Honeyfield				King's Heath
Matthew Pugh		Bromsgrove 13/5/71		Worcester City
Ian Gandy		Droitwich		Youth
FORWARDS				
Chris Hanks	BHL	Alvechurch 29/4/63		Studley Sporting
Steve Stott	BHL	Leeds 3/2/65		Bromsgrove Rvrs, Alvechurch
Tommy Daly	BHL	Birmingham 24/10/63		Coleshill Town
Mark Whitehouse	FAXI	Birmingham 27/9/61		Moor Green, Oldbury, Tamworth, Redditch, Worcester, Burton Alb, Kidderminster
Jason Ross				Youth

Departures during season:
Martyn O'Connor (Crystal Palace), Sylvester Cunningham (Nuneaton), Steve Mead (Moor Green).

Bromsgrove Rovers

Ground address and Tel. No.: Victoria Ground, Birmingham Road, Bromsgrove, Worcs. (0527 78260 / 76949)
Simple ground directions: Situated north of town centre on the Birmingham road, opposite petrol station
Official capacity: 9,600   **Seating:** 375   **Covered accommodation:** 5,700
Cost of seats: **Cost of standing:**
Floodlights: Yes   **Shop:** Yes
Record attendance: 7,563 v Worcester City, Birmingham Senior Cup 1957-58
Social facilities available: Clubhouse: Open every night. Television and pool table   **Steward:** Mr & Mrs Slater
Car parking:

Sponsored by: Clarks Motors   **GROMSGROVE ROVERS**   Nickname:

Previous leagues: Birmingham Combination 1896-1953 / West Mids. 53-72
Club colours: Red/black/red   **Change colours:** Green/white/green
Midweek home matches: Tuesday   **Club metal badges:** Yes
Club programme: 28 pages   **Editor:** Geoff Key
Local Newspapers: Bromsgrove Messenger. 91/92 Bromsgrove Advertiser
Record transfer fee paid:
Record transfer fee received: Undisclosed for Martyn O'Connor from C. Palace
Record appearances for club:
Record goalscorer for club:
Top goalscorer: Chris Hanks   **92-93 Captain:** Kevin Richardson   **91-92 P.o.Y.** Martyn O'Connor
Best FA Cup season: 1st Rd 47-48, 49-50, 50-51, 56-57, 86-87, 88-89, 89-90
Past players who have progressed to the Football League: Mike McKenna (Northampton 1946), Ray Hartle (Bolton 1952), Angus McLean (Bury 1953), Alan Smith (A. Villa 1954), Mike Deakin (C. Palace 1954), Brian Puster (Leicester 1958), Tom Smith (Sheff. Utd 1978), Malcolm Goodman (Halifax 1979), Steve Smith (Walsall 1980), Gary Hackett (Shrewsbury 1983), Bill McGarry, Martyn O'Connor (C. Palace 1992)
Club honours: Southern Lg R-up 86-87, Southern Lg Midland Div 85-86, Bill Dellow Cup 85-86 (R-up 73-74), Worcs Senior Cup 46-47, 47-48, 59-60, 86-87, Birmingham Senior Cup 46-47, Westgate Insurance Cup R-up 87-88, West Mids Lg 60-61 (R-up 56-57, 60-61, 69-70), Birmingham Comb. 46-47 (R-up 04-05, 49-50)
Past club managers:

DAGENHAM & REDBRIDGE

Formed: 1992

President:
Barry East BSC

Joint Chairmen:
Dave Andrews
Norman Sparrow

Directors:
D Almond
K Mizen
P Ryan
S Thompson
G Hanning
J Sherman

Secretary:
Ken Mizen

Manager:
John Still

Assistant Manager:
George Dudley

Coach:
John Kane

Physiotherapist:
Jim Payne

New Beginnings

The club in its first season in the Conference had an indifferent start, John Still keeping faith with the promotion side of the previous season, it became apparent after a long losing run put the club firmly on the bottom of the table that changes had to be made. New signings were quickly brought in, Paul Cavell and Paul Richardson from Boston United, Mario Walsh from Colchester, Gary Blackford from Barnet and later on Ian Bennett and Marcus Ebdon on loan from Peterborough. The side was quickly transformed and the scoring power of Paul Cavell in particular proved decisive and an unbeaten run soon saw a rise in the table reaching third place with notable wins over Colchester and Farnborough, the club's final placing was a creditable 7th.

A best ever run in the FA Trophy came to a halt with the 1-0 defeat by Marine in an emotional quarter-final replay at Victoria Road having previously defeated Bromsgrove, Enfield and Farnborough in earlier rounds.

The name of Redbridge Forest went on the Essex Senior Cup for the first time when Chelmsford were beaten 3-0 in the final.

The merger of Dagenham and Redbridge Forest was confirmed at the end of the season and the joining of resources under one banner will add stability and push the club further towards its ambitions. It now means that a reserve team and a new youth policy can be implemented and it is hoped inbred talent will emerge. The basis of last season's team will start the new campaign with John Warner and Steve Porter from Dagenham being introduced and the capture of England pair John McKenna and Paul Shirtliff from Boston and Gary Butterworth from Peterborough further strengthen the squad.

Redbridge Forest FC. 1991-92. Back Row (L-R): Jim Payne (Physio), K Davidson (left), R Garvey (left), K Foster, T Pamphlett, M Cawston (left), K Barrett, S Conner, A Daffom (left). Front (L-R): M Gurney (left), T Williams (left), L Fulling (left), T Sullivan, D Jacques, J Simmonds, M Stewart (left), J Broom, P Watts.

Redbridge Forest

Match No.	Date	Competition	Venue H/A	Opponents	Result	League H/T	Pos.	Goalscorers (Times if known)	Attendance
1	Aug 17	GMVC	A	Telford Utd	D 3-3	2-2		Sowerby 30; Conner 37; Hessenthaler 55	835
2	Aug 24	GMVC	H	Kettering	W 4-0	1-0	6	Mayes 6; Garvey 77; Pamphlett 82; Watts 85	726
3	Aug 31	GMVC	H	Macclesfield	D 0-0	0-0	9		472
4	**Sep 3**	**BLT 1-1**	**H**	**Boston Utd**	**W 2-0**	**0-0**		**Conner 50; Sowerby 87**	**202**
5	**Sep 14**	**FAC 1Q**	**H**	**Haringey Borough**	**W 5-0**	**1-0**		**Mayes 32; Sowerby 53; Broom 56; Garvey 61; Davidson 67**	**244**
6	**Sep 18**	**BLT 1-2**	**A**	**Boston Utd**	**L 0-4**	**0-2**			**746**
7	Sep 21	GMVC	H	Altrincham	L 0-1	0-0	21		514
8	Sep 24	GMVC	A	Farnborough	L 0-1	0-0	21		721
9	**Sep 28**	**FAC 2Q**	**A**	**Grays Athletic**	**L 1-3**	**0-0**		**o.g. 51**	**274**
10	Oct 5	GMVC	H	Cheltenham	L 1-2	0-0	21	Garvey 85	360
11	Oct 7	GMVC	A	Kidderminster	L 1-5	1-4	21	Mayes 27	1045
12	Oct 12	GMVC	A	Witton Albion	L 0-2	0-0	21		851
13	Oct 19	GMVC	H	Barrow	D 2-2	2-1	22	Cherry 11; Watts 19	332
14	Oct 22	GMVC	A	Slough	L 0-4	0-3	22		910
15	Oct 26	GMVC	A	Boston Utd	L 1-2	1-1	22	o.g. 3	1058
16	Nov 2	GMVC	A	Wycombe	L 0-1	0-0	21		2285
17	Nov 5	GMVC	A	Welling Utd	D 2-2	0-2	21	Mayes 48; Conner 85	615
18	Nov 9	GMVC	H	Kidderminster	W 5-0	1-0	20	Walsh 9; Conner 54; Mayes 67; Ebdon 68,79	479
19	Nov 16	GMVC	H	Stafford Rangers	W 4-3	2-1	18	Walsh 24,34; Mayes 83; Hayrettin 90	452
20	Nov 23	GMVC	A	Northwich Victoria	W 2-0	0-0	17	Cavell 88; Richardson 89	823
21	Nov 26	GMVC	H	Bath City	W 3-1	2-1	15	Cavell 17,81; Walsh 26	475
22	Nov 30	GMVC	A	Gateshead	W 1-0	1-0	13	Walsh 19	286
23	Dec 4	GMVC	A	Yeovil	W 1-0	0-0		Ebdon 68	1832
24	Dec 7	GMVC	H	Welling Utd	W 2-0	1-0		Cavell 45,75	763
25	Dec 14	GMVC	A	Runcorn	L 0-1	0-0			446
26	Dec 21	GMVC	H	Barrow	W 1-0	0-0		Cavell 25	1049
27	Dec 26	GMVC	H	Colchester	W 2-1	1-1		Pamphlett 21; Walsh 82	2327
28	Jan 1	GMVC	A	Colchester	L 0-1	0-1			4773
29	Jan 4	GMVC	H	Slough	W 4-0	2-0		Cavell 17,65,83; Walsh 21	673
30	**Jan 11**	**FAT 1**	**H**	**Bromsgrove**	**D 1-1**	**1-1**		**Garvey 29**	**623**
31	**Jan 14**	**FAT 1R**	**A**	**Bromsgrove**	**W 1-0**	**0-0**		**Walsh 76 (pen)**	**995**
32	Jan 18	GMVC	A	Bath City	D 0-0	0-0			614
33	**Feb 1**	**FAT 2**	**H**	**Enfield**	**W 2-0**	**0-0**		**Broom 49,64**	**843**
34	Feb 8	GMVC	A	Merthyr Tydfil	D 2-2	1-1		Cavell 18,46	702
35	Feb 15	GMVC	H	Gateshead	W 2-1	1-0		Richardson 2; Cavell 49	428
36	**Feb 22**	**FAT 3**	**H**	**Farnborough**	**W 3-2**	**3-0**		**Walsh 20; Pamphlett 31; Cavell 37**	**1353**
37	Feb 29	GMVC	A	Cheltenham	W 7-0	5-0		Cavell 11,18,24,89; Pamphlett 15; Blackford 43; Ebdon 82	909
38	Mar 7	GMVC	H	Northwich Victoria	W 4-3	2-2		Walsh 9; Cavell 33; Ebdon 63 (pen), 74	623
39	**Mar 14**	**FAT 4**	**A**	**Marine**	**D 1-1**	**0-0**		**Cavell 84**	**1150**
40	**Mar 17**	**FAT 4R**	**H**	**Marine**	**L 0-1**	**0-0**			**1239**
41	Mar 21	GMVC	A	Altrincham	W 3-0	1-0		Ebdon 1; Cavell 82; Blackford 83	497
42	Mar 24	GMVC	H	Yeovil	D 0-0	0-0			503
43	Mar 28	GMVC	H	Farnborough	W 2-0	1-0		Riley 4,90	743
44	Mar 31	GMVC	A	Stafford Rangers	L 1-2	0-0		o.g. 14	709
45	Apr 4	GMVC	H	Merthyr Tydfil	D 1-1	0-0		Pamphlett 53	502
46	Apr 14	GMVC	H	Runcorn	L 1-2	0-1		Richardson 50	435
47	Apr 16	GMVC	H	Witton Albion	W 3-1	1-0	5	Broom 32,86; Walsh 49	437
48	Apr 18	GMVC	A	Macclesfield	D 0-0	0-0	6		460
49	Apr 25	GMVC	H	Telford Utd	W 1-0	1-0	6	Cavell 33	509
50	Apr 28	GMVC	H	Boston Utd	L 1-4	0-3	6	Cavell 75	472
51	Apr 30	GMVC	H	Wycombe	L 0-5	0-3	7		2891
52	May 2	GMVC	A	Kettering	L 2-3	1-2	7	Cavell 19; Grice 57	1304

Redbridge Forest

1	2	3	4	5	6	7	8	9	10	11	12	14	Match No.
Cawston	Jackman	Watts	Pamphlett	Conner	Barrett	Garvey	Hessenthaler	Broom	Sowerby	Mayes	Davidson	Daley	1
Cawston	Jackman	Watts	Pamphlett	Conner	Barrett	Garvey	Hessenthaler	Broom	Sowerby	Mayes	Davidson	Williams	2
Foster	Jackman	Watts	Pamphlett	Conner	Barrett	Garvey	Hessenthaler	Broom	Sowerby•	Mayes	Davidson	Jacques	3
Foster	**Jackman**	**Watts**	**Pamphlett**	**Conner**	**Barrett**	**Garvey**	**Hessenthaler**	**Broom**	**Sowerby**	**Mayes**	**Davidson**	**Jacques**	**4**
Foster	Jackman	Watts	Pamphlett	Conner	Jacques	Garvey	Davidson	Broom	Sowerby	Mayes	Docker	Cherry	5
Foster	**Jackman•**	**Watts**	**Pamphlett**	**Conner**	**Jacques**	**Garvey**	**Davidson**	**Broom**	**Sowerby**	**Mayes**	**Docker**	**Cherry**	**6**
Foster	Jackman•	Watts	Pamphlett	Conner	Jacques	Garvey	Docker	Broom	Sowerby†	Davidson	Barrett	Cherry	7
Foster	Jacques	Watts	Pamphlett	Conner	Davidson	Garvey	Docker	Cherry	Sowerby	Broom	Barrett	Fulling	8
Foster	**Jacques**	**Watts**	**Pamphlett**	**Conner**	**Davidson**	**Garvey**	**Docker**	**Cherry**	**Sowerby**	**Broom**	**Barrett**	**Fulling**	**9**
Foster	Jackman	Watts	Jacques	Conner	Barrett	Garvey	Docker	Cherry	Ashford	Mayes	Sowerby	Cole	10
Foster	Jackman	Broom	Jacques	Conner	Barrett	Garvey	Docker•	Cherry†	Ashford	Mayes	Sowerby	Cole	11
Scott	Jackman	Broom	Pamphlett	Conner	Ashford	Garvey	Cole	Cherry	Sowerby	Mayes	Davidson	Docker	12
Scott	Jackman†	Watts	Pamphlett	Conner	Barrett	Garvey	Docker	Cherry•	Ashford	Sowerby	Davidson	Cole	13
Scott	Davidson	Watts	Pamphlett	Conner	Barrett	Garvey	Docker	Cherry	Sowerby†	Fulling	Sullivan	Cole	14
Hucker	Blackford	Watts	Pamphlett	Conner	Barrett	Garvey	Davidson	Hayrettin	Walsh	Mayes•	Docker	Cherry	15
Hucker	Blackford	Watts	Pamphlett	Conner	Ebdon	Hayrettin	Richardson	Davidson•	Walsh	Mayes†	Jacques	Cherry	16
Hucker	Blackford	Watts	Pamphlett	Conner	Ebdon	Hayrettin•	Richardson	Davidson†	Walsh	Mayes	Taylor	Cherry	17
Hucker	Jacques	Watts	Pamphlett	Conner	Ebdon	Hayrettin†	Richardson	Blackford	Walsh	Mayes	Davidson	Garvey	18
Hucker	Jacques	Watts	Pamphlett	Conner	Hayrettin	Blackford	Richardson	Cavell	Walsh	Mayes	Davidson	Garvey	19
Hucker	Jacques	Watts	Pamphlett	Conner	Ebdon	Blackford	Richardson	Cavell	Walsh	Mayes	Davidson	Ashford	20
Bennett	Jacques	Watts	Pamphlett	Conner	Ebdon	Blackford	Richardson	Cavell	Walsh	Mayes†	Davidson	Ashford	21
Bennett	Jacques	Watts	Pamphlett	Conner	Ebdon	Ashford	Richardson	Cavell	Walsh	Mayes	Davidson	Owers	22
Bennett	Jacques	Watts	Pamphlett	Conner	Ebdon	Ashford	Richardson	Cavell	Walsh	Mayes	Davidson	Owers	23
Bennett	Jacques	Watts	Pamphlett	Conner	Ebdon	Ashford†	Richardson	Cavell	Walsh	Mayes	Davidson	Owers	24
Bennett	Jacques†	Watts	Pamphlett	Conner	Ebdon	Owers	Richardson	Cavell	Walsh•	Blackford	Davidson	Mayes	25
Bennett	Jacques	Watts	Pamphlett	Conner	Ebdon	Owers†	Richardson	Cavell	Walsh	Blackford	Davidson	Mayes	26
Bennett	Jacques	Watts	Pamphlett	Conner	Ebdon	Mayes	Richardson†	Cavell	Walsh	Blackford	Davidson	Broom	27
Bennett	Jacques	Watts	Barrett†	Conner	Broom	Mayes	Richardson	Cavell	Walsh	Blackford	Sowerby	Garvey	28
Bennett	Jacques	Watts	Pamphlett	Conner	Ebdon	Mayes•	Richardson	Cavell	Walsh	Blackford	Broom	Garvey	29
Bennett	**Jacques**	**Watts**	**Pamphlett**	**Conner**	**Garvey**	**Mayes**	**Richardson**	**Cavell**	**Walsh**	**Broom**	**Davidson**	**Jackman**	**30**
Bennett	**Jacques**	**Watts**	**Pamphlett**	**Conner**	**Garvey**	**Mayes**	**Richardson**	**Cavell**	**Walsh**	**Broom**	**Davidson**	**Jackman**	**31**
Bennett	Jacques	Watts	Pamphlett	Conner	Broom	Mayes	Richardson	Cavell	Walsh	Davidson•	Garvey	Jackman	32
Bennett	**Jacques**	**Watts**	**Pamphlett**	**Conner**	**Broom**	**Mayes**	**Richardson**	**Cavell**	**Walsh**	**Davidson**	**Garvey**	**Jackman**	**33**
Bennett	Jacques	Watts	Pamphlett	Conner	Ebdon	Broom	Riley•	Cavell	Walsh	Blackford	Mayes	Ashford	34
Bennett	Jacques	Watts	Pamphlett	Conner	Ebdon	Broom†	Richardson	Cavell	Riley	Blackford	Mayes	Ashford	35
Bennett	**Jacques**	**Watts**	**Pamphlett**	**Conner**	**Owers**	**Broom**	**Richardson**	**Cavell**	**Mayes**	**Blackford**	**Barrett**	**Ashford**	**36**
Bennett	Jacques	Watts	Pamphlett	Conner	Ebdon	Mayes	Owers	Cavell	Walsh	Blackford	Richardson	Broom	37
Bennett	Jacques	Watts	Pamphlett	Conner	Ebdon	Mayes	Richardson	Cavell†	Walsh	Blackford•	Owers	Broom	38
Bennett	**Jacques**	**Watts**	**Pamphlett**	**Conner**	**Ebdon**	**Mayes**	**Richardson†**	**Cavell**	**Walsh**	**Blackford•**	**Owers**	**Broom**	**39**
Bennett	**Jacques**	**Watts**	**Pamphlett**	**Conner**	**Ebdon**	**Mayes**	**Richardson†**	**Cavell**	**Walsh**	**Blackford•**	**Owers**	**Broom**	**40**
Bennett	Jacques	Watts	Pamphlett	Conner	Ebdon	Mayes•	Richardson	Cavell	Owers	Blackford	Walsh	Broom	41
Hopping	Jacques	Watts	Pamphlett	Conner	Ebdon	Owers	Richardson	Cavell	Walsh	Blackford•	Mayes	Broom	42
Bennett	Jacques	Watts	Pamphlett	Conner	Ebdon	Owers†	Broom	Cavell	Riley	Mayes	Walsh	Docker	43
Bennett	Jacques	Watts	Pamphlett	Conner	Ebdon	Broom	Grice•	Cavell	Riley	Mayes	Walsh	Docker	44
Bennett	Jacques	Watts	Pamphlett	Conner	Ebdon	Grice†	Richardson	Cavell	Riley	Mayes•	Walsh	Broom	45
Shoemake	Jacques	Watts	Pamphlett	Conner	Ebdon†	Mayes•	Richardson	Cavell	Walsh	Owers	Ashford	Broom	46
Shoemake	Jacques	Watts	Pamphlett	Conner	Ebdon	Mayes	Richardson	Cavell	Walsh	Owers	Ashford	Broom	47
Foster	Jacques	Watts	Pamphlett	Conner	Ashford	Blackford	Richardson	Cavell	Broom	Mayes	Grice	Walsh	48
Foster	Jacques	Watts	Pamphlett	Conner	Broom	Mayes†	Richardson	Cavell	Walsh	Grice	Docker	Sullivan	49
Foster	Jacques	Watts	Pamphlett	Conner	Broom	Riley	Richardson	Cavell	Walsh†	Barrett•	Docker	Blackford	50
Foster	Jacques	Watts	Pamphlett	Conner	Broom	Riley	Richardson	Cavell	Walsh	Grice	Docker	Blackford	51
Shoemake	Jacques	Watts	Pamphlett	Conner	Broom	Grice	Richardson	Cavell	Walsh	Blackford†	Docker	Sullivan	52

• substituted by No. 12. † substituted by No. 14.

Dagenham & Redbridge

JOHN STILL

John Still's playing career ended through injury prematurely but he had played for the winning Bishop's Stortford side in the last FA Amateur Cup Final and was a well respected centre half with Leyton Orient (as an apprentice), Ilford, Dagenham and Bishop's Stortford.

His amazing success as a manager is based on his excellent knowledge of players and he has guided his clubs to triumphs in the Beazer Homes, Vauxhall and Conference (Maidstone United) competitions. His clubs, all of whom won honours, are Leytonstone and Ilford, Maidstone United and Redbridge Forest.

John now has the task of guiding the newly merged Dagenham and Redbridge club. The way in which he transformed a struggling side last season into one which reached the quarter finals of the FA Trophy and to 7th position in the Conference has to be admired.

Skipper and joint player of the year Tony Pamphlett clears under pressure from the Colchester attack during the home league match against the Conference champions.

Programme details:
    24 pages for 80p
    Editor - Len Llewellyn

Any other club publications:

Local Newspapers:
    Dagenham Post
    Waltham Forest Guardian
    Ilford Recorder

Local Radio Stations:
    Breeze AM
    BBC Radio Essex
    Capital Radio

UNFORTUNATELY

THE NEW CLUB

PROGRAMME COVER

NOT AVAILABLE

GOING TO PRESS

DAGENHAM & REDBRIDGE - PLAYING SQUAD 1992-93

Player	Honours	Birthplace and date	Transfer Fees	Previous Clubs
GOALKEEPERS				
Kevin Foster	Vaux Lge	Essex 22/12/60		Chelmsford City, Wealdstone
John McKenna	ESP, LSC	Liverpool 21/3/61		Everton, Leeds, Morecambe, Mamelodi(SA), Nuneaton Borough
DEFENDERS				
David Jacques	Vaux Lge GMVC, Beazer	London 7/10/58	Player exchange	L/Ilford, Enfield, Maidstone, Dartford
Paul Watts	ESP Vaux. Lge	London 20/9/62	£3,500	Barking
Tony Pamphlett	GMVC, Beazer Vaux Lge	London 13/4/60		Dartford, Maidstone Utd
Paul Shirtliff	ESP LSC	Barnsley 3/11/62		Sheff Wed, Northampton, Frickley, Boston Utd
Steve Conner	ESP Vaux Lge	Essex 14/7/64	Player exchange	Dartford, Tilbury, E. Thurrock, Purfleet
MIDFIELD				
Paul Richardson	GMVC GMVC R/U	Nottingham 7/11/62	Undisc	Eastwood, Nuneaton, Derby, Kettering, Barnet, Boston Utd
Jason Broom	Vaux Lge	Essex 15/10/69	£3,000	Billericay
Steve Porter				Leyton Orient, Watford, Hornchurch, Collier Row, Aveley, Harlow, Dagenham
Gary Butterworth		Peterborough 8/9/69		Peterborough Utd
Bobby Mayes				West Ham, FC Boon(Bel), Ipswich, Bury T, Kettering, Wivenhoe
Gary Blackford			£12,000	Fisher Ath, Barnet
Adrian Owers		Chelmsford 26/2/65		Southend, Chelmsford, Brighton, Maidstone
FORWARDS				
Paul Cavell	ESP	Worksop 13/5/63	Undisc	Notts F, Worksop, Goole, Stafford, Boston Utd
Mario Walsh		London 28/1/69	£10,000	Portsmouth, Torquay, Colchester, Southend, Colchester
Ian Docker		Norwich 4/9/69		Gillingham
John Warner				Burnham Ramblers, Colchester, Heybridge Swifts, Braintree, Dagenham

Departures during season:
Malcolm Stewart (Harlow), Dave Cooper (Crawley), Andy Hessenthaler (Watford), Peter Daley (Southport), Tommy Williams (Grays), Lee Fulling (Billericay), Lloyd Scott (Aveley), Richard Cherry (Kingstonian), Mervyn Cawston (Southend Manor), Kurt Davidson, Colin Sowerby & Rob Garvey (Hendon). Kevin Shoemake (Kettering).

Players who joined on loan during season:
Mick Cole (Fulham), Peter Hucker (Aldershot), Gary Blackford & Hakan Hayrettin (Barnet), Marcus Ebdon, David Riley, Ian McInerney & Ian Bennett (Peterborough).

Victoria Road, Dagenham and Redbridge

Ground address and Tel. No.: Victoria Road, Dagenham RM10 7XL. Tel: (081 592 7194)
Simple ground directions: On A112 between A12 & A13, 500 yards from Dagenham East station; turn left and Victoria Road is 5th turning right. Buses No. 103 & 174
Official capacity: 4,750   **Seating:** 550   **Covered accommodation:** 2,350
Floodlights: Yes   **Shop:** Yes   **Metal Badges:** £2.25
Social facilities available: Clubhouse: Four bars and two halls. Open daily

---

Sponsored by: Dagenham Post   **DAGENHAM & REDBRIDGE**   **Nickname:** The Reds

---

Previous leagues: None. (Predecessors) Ilford FC (1881-1979) - Southern 1894-96/London 96-98/South Essex 98-1904; Leytonstone FC (1886-1979) - South Essex: Walthamstow Avenue (1900-88) - Athenian/Spartan
Club colours: Red shirts/blue trim   **Change colours:** All yellow
Midweek home matches: Tuesday
Record transfer fee paid: £20,000 for Noel Ashford (Maidstone)
Record transfer fee received: £60,000 for Andy Hessenthaler (Watfor
Record appearances for club: Micky Dingwall
Record goalscorer for club: Micky Dingwall   **Players of the year:** David Jacques & Tony Pamphlett
Top scorer: Paul Cavell (29)   **91-92 Captain:** Tony Pamphlett
Best FA Cup season: 1st Rd 79-80, 81-82 (Ilford: 2nd Rd 74-75, L'stone 2nd Rd 48-49; Walt. Av. 5th Rd rep. 1953)
Past players who have progressed to the Football League: Terry Hurlock (Brentford 1980), Trevor Morgan (B'mouth 1980), Liburd Henry (Watford 1987), Paul Roverts (Exeter 1988), Warren Barton (M'stone), Lawrence Osbourne (M'stone 1990), Andy Hessenthaler (Watford 1991)
Club honours: As Leytonstone-Ilford (prior to 1989) Isthmian Lg (IL) 81-82, 88-89 (R-up 82-83, Lg Cup 81-82, Div 1 79-80, 86-87, Charity Shield 81-82, 89-90, London Senior Cup (LSC) 79-80, 81-82, Essex Senior Cup (ESC) 81-82, Essex Int Cup 80-81, Fred Budden Trophy 86-87, FA Trophy 3rd Rd rep 89-90. Ilford: FA Amat Cup (FAC) 28-29, 29-30 (R-up 35-36, 57-58, 73-74), IL (3) 06-07, 20-22 (R-up (5) 11-12, 26-27, 31-32, 37-39), ESC (13) 1887-90, 91-92, 1903-04, 07-08, 12-13, 23-24, 26-29, 52-54, Essex T'side Trophy (ETT) 49-50, 54-55, 59-60, 70-71, LSC 00-01, 04-05, 13-14, 21-22, 28-29, 29-30, 53-54, London Charity Cup (LCC) 21-22, 29-30, 37-38, 54-55, 62-63 (jt) 65-66. L'stone FA Cup (3) 46-48, 67-68, IL (8) 37-39, 46-48, 49-52, 65-66 (R-up 08-09, 10-11, 12-13, 32-33, 61-62), ESC (7) 04-05, 13-14, 47-49, 64-67, ETT 45-47, 48-49, 50-51, 52-53, 65-66, 67-68, 72-73, LSC 19-20, 47-48, 65-66, LCC 09-10, 52-53. Walt. Av.: FAC 51-52, 60-61, IL 45-46, 52-53, 54-55, (R-up 48-49, 50-51, 53-54, 60-61, 66-67, 79-80), ESC (12) 32-33, 35-36, 38-39, 55-56, 57-60, 68-69, 71-72, 73-74, 76-77, 84-85, ETT (5) 53-54, 61-62, 71-72, 76-78, LSC (9) 35-37, 39-40, 41-42, 43-44, 52-53 (jt) 54-55, 77-78, 85-86, LCC 33-34, 38-39, 48-49, 50-51, 55-56. Redbridge Forest 1989-90 Vauxhall Lge Charity Shield winners; 1990-91 Vauxhall Lge Champions

FARNBOROUGH TOWN

Formed: 1967

President:
Maurice O'Brien

Vice President:
Richard Molden

Chairman:
Alan Churchill

Directors:
Terry Parr
Russell Chapman
(Financial)
Alan Gillespie
Charles Mortimore
Mrs Janet Parr

Secretary/Press Officer:
Terry Parr

Manager:
Ted Pearce

Coach:
Alan Taylor

Physiotherapist:
Alan Morris LCSP

Club Doctor:
Alan Gillespie
FRCS FRCOG

Farnborough Town manager Ted Pearce's twenty second year in charge at Cherrywood Road was without doubt his most successful. Although silverware was not won in abundance, like in some of his previous season's, 'Boro's 1991/92 campaign brought them to the fore in the GM Vauxhall Conference and made them a formidable side.

Obviously, Farnborough's exploits in the FA Cup brought them national headlines and quite rightly so. Their games against West Ham United, which could easily have gone either way in the end, gave players such as Andy Bye, Simon Read and John Power a platform to show off their skills on the national stage.

The club in general learnt a great deal about life at the top of the Pyramid when they were members in 1989. They were somewhat unfortunate to suffer relegation then, but they bounced back stronger and much wiser. Ted Pearce has now been able to sign experienced ex-professionals like Dean Coney, David Leworthy, Alan Comfort, Peter Hucker and Steve Baker which has added great depth and strength to the squad.

Although the cup run was marvellous for all connected with the club it probably took away any chance Farnborough had of lifting the Conference title. They topped the table by overtaking Wycombe Wanderers but some indifferent league performances around Christmas and New Year took away their championship challenge. However, if they can maintain the improvement shown during last season there is no reason why they cannot sustain a serious challenge this time around. If success does come their way, it couldn't happen to a more friendly club.

Farnborough Town F.C. 1991-92.

Farnborough Town

Match No.	Date	Competition	Venue H/A	Opponents	Result	League H/T	Pos.	Goalscorers (Times if known)	Attendance
1	Aug 17	GMVC	A	Stafford Rangers	W 1-0	1-0		Doherty 10	1052
2	Aug 24	GMVC	H	Northwich Victoria	L 2-4	0-1		Holmes 50; Comfort 55	796
3	Aug 26	BHLC	H	Chelmsford	W 6-1			Hurton (3); Doherty (2); Comfort	459
4	Aug 31	GMVC	A	Telford	W 2-1	1-0	7	Read 15,53	1017
5	Sep 3	BLT 1	H	Yeovil	W 3-2	2-1		Coombes 9 pen; Read 16,74	461
6	Sep 7	GMVC	A	Gateshead	W 2-0	1-0	5	Coomes 34; Bye 60	415
7	Sep 10	GMVC	A	Colchester	W 3-2	2-1	2	Doherty 8; Read 33,57	2954
8	Sep 14	GMVC	H	Runcorn	L 0-2	0-1	5		932
9	Sep 17	BLT 1	A	Yeovil	L 0-3	0-1			1473
10	Sep 21	GMVC	A	Barrow	W 1-0	1-0	4	Doherty 20	1384
11	Sep 24	GMVC	H	Redbridge Forest	W 1-0	0-0	2	Read 66	721
12	Sep 28	GMVC	H	Witton	D 1-1	1-0	3	Coombes 5	560
13	Oct 5	GMVC	A	Boston	W 1-0	1-0	2	Bye 10	1134
14	Oct 8	GMVC	A	Bath City	W 2-1	2-1	1	Cooper 4; Bye 10	759
15	Oct 12	GMVC	H	Altrincham	W 3-0	0-0	1	Read 46; Broome 77; Horton 81	1113
16	Oct 19	GMVC	H	Macclesfield	W 2-1	2-0	1	Doherty 15; Read 22	752
17	Oct 26	FAC 4Q	A	Salisbury	W 7-1	3-0		Doherty 6; Read 31,45,64,82; Horton 48,89	808
18	Nov 2	GMVC	H	Yeovil	D 0-0	0-0	1		685
19	Nov 9	GMVC	H	Colchester	L 0-2	0-0	3		3069
20	Nov 16	FAC 1	A	Halesowen	D 2-2	2-2		Hobson 5; Broome 41	1866
21	Nov 23	GMVC	A	Kidderminster	D 1-1	1-0	3	Coombes 14	1175
22	Nov 26	FAC 1R	H	Halesowen	W 4-0	2-0		Read 32,36,64; Coombes 84 pen	1673
23	Nov 30	GMVC	H	Kettering	L 1-3	1-1	3	Read 39	1086
24	Dec 2	HSC 1	H	Havant	L 1-4			Coles	121
25	Dec 7	FAC 2	A	Torquay	D 1-1	1-0		Read 30	2725
26	Dec 17	FAC 2R	H	Torquay	W 4-3	2-0		Coney 35; Read 41; Doherty 65; Broome 68	2285
27	Dec 21	GMVC	A	Yeovil	D 2-2	1-1	3	Holmes 44; Broome 51	1959
28	Dec 26	GMVC	A	Welling	L 0-1	0-0	4		1164
29	Dec 28	GMVC	H	Barrow	W 5-0	2-0	3	Holmes 3,34; Doherty 49,90; Read81	982
30	Jan 1	GMVC	H	Welling	D 1-1	1-0	3	Broome 40	975
31	Jan 4	FAC 3	H*	West Ham	D 1-1	0-0		Coney 82 pen	23449
32	Jan 11	FAT 1	A	Sutton Coldfield	W 3-0	0-0		Road 59; Doherty 77 pen; Horton 86	646
33	Jan 14	FAC 3R	A	West Ham	L 0-1	0-0			23869
34	Jan 18	GMVC	A	Altrincham	D 1-1	0-0	3	Coney 76	694
35	Feb 1	FAT 2	H	Southport	W 5-0	3-0		Coney 2; Read 16,89; Bye 23; Horton 73	1021
36	Feb 8	GMVC	A	Runcorn	D 1-1	0-1	3	Read 73	595
37	Feb 11	GMVC	H	Telford	D 2-2	1-1	3	Broome 33; Read 64	786
38	Feb 15	GMVC	H	Kidderminster	W 2-1	0-0	3	Wigmore 82; Leworthy 85	822
39	Feb 22	FAT 3	H	Redbridge Forest	L 2-3	0-3		Leworthy 66; Coney 73	1353
40	Feb 29	GMVC	A	Witton	L 1-4	0-2	4	Coney 48	838
41	Mar 6	GMVC	A	Kettering	W 2-1	1-0	4	Keast o.g.13; Coney 76	1993
42	Mar 10	GMVC	H	Macclesfield	W 4-2	2-1	3	Leworthy 3,6,59,81	615
43	Mar 14	GMVC	H	Boston	W 5-0	1-0	3	Leworthy 6,80; Read 52,77,90	724
44	Mar 18	GMVC	A	Wycombe	L 1-2	0-2	3	Horton 82	2275
45	Mar 21	GMVC	H	Cheltenham	D 1-1	0-0	3	Horton 74	773
46	Mar 24	GMVC	A	Merthyr Tydfil	L 0-1	0-0	3		517
47	Mar 28	GMVC	A	Redbridge Forest	L 0-2	0-1	5		743
48	Mar 31	GMVC	A	Bath City	L 1-2	0-0	5	Read 56	680
49	Apr 4	GMVC	H	Wycombe	L 1-3	1-2	7	Read 19	2236
50	Apr 7	GMVC	H	Slough	W 2-1	1-0	5	Coney 30; Read 71	762
51	Apr 11	GMVC	A	Cheltenham	L 3-4	1-2	5	Coney 11; Read 47; Leworthy 51 pen	846
52	Apr 18	GMVC	H	Gateshead	W 3-1	1-0	6	Coney 37; Leworthy 77; Read 90	675
53	Apr 20	GMVC	A	Slough	W 5-0	3-0	4	Read 25,32; Leworthy 38; Cockram 65; Rogers 71	784
54	Apr 23	GMVC	H	Merthyr Tydfil	D 0-0	0-0	4		682
55	Apr 25	GMVC	A	Stafford	D 1-1	0-1	4	Leworthy 68	811
56	May 2	GMVC	A	Nantwich	D 1-1	1-0	5	Broome 6	543

* Played at Upton Park

Farnborough Town

1	2	3	4	5	6	7	8	9	10	11	12	14	Match No.
Power	Lovell	K.Baker	Holmes	Bye	Wigmore	Rogers	Doherty	Horton	Read•	Confort†	Stevens	Broome	1
Power	Lovell	K.Baker	Holmes	Bye	Wigmore	Rogers	Doherty	Horton	Read	Confort	Stevens	Broome	2
Thompson	Lovell	Stevens	Broome	Bye	Wigmore	Rogers	Doherty	Horton	Read	Comfort	K.Baker	Holmes	3
Power	Lovell†	Stevens	Broome	Bye	Wigmore	Rogers	Holmes	Horton	Read•	Confort†	K.Baker	Doherty	4
Power	Holmes	Stevens†	Broome•	Bye	Wigmore	Rogers	Doherty	Coombs	Read	Horton	Lovell	K.Baker	5
Power	Holmes	K.Baker	Broome	Bye	Wigmore	Rogers	Doherty	Coombs•	Read•	Horton	Lovell	Stevens	6
Power	Holmes•	K.Baker	Broome	Bye	Wigmore	Rogers	Doherty	Coombs•	Read•	Horton	Lovell	Stevens	7
Thompson	Lovell	K.Baker	Broome	Bye	Wigmore	Rogers	Doherty	Coombs	Read•	Horton	Lovell	Stevens	8
Power	Stemp	K.Baker	Broome	Bye	Wigmore	Rogers	Holmes	Coombs•	Read	Horton	Coles	Stevens	9
Power	Stemp	K.Baker	Broome	Bye	Wigmore	Rogers	Doherty	Horton•	Read•	Holmes	Lovell	Stevens	10
Power	Stemp	K.Baker	Broome	Bye	Wigmore	Rogers•	Horton	Coombs	Read•	Holmes	Lovell	Stevens	11
Power	Stemp	K.Baker	Broome	Bye	Wigmore	Rogers•	Horton	Coombs	Doherty	Comfort†	Stevens	Doherty	12
Power	Stemp	K.Baker	Broome	Bye	Wigmore	Rogers	Holmes	Coombs	Horton•	Comfort†	Stevens	Doherty	13
Power	Stemp	K.Baker	Broome	Bye	Wigmore	Rogers	Holmes	Coombs†	Doherty	Cooper•	Stevens	Horton	14
Power	Stemp	K.Baker	Broome	Bye	Wigmore	Rogers	Doherty	Holmes	Read†	Cooper•	Horton	Coombs	15
Power	Stemp	Stevens	Broome	Bye	Wigmore	Rogers†	Doherty	Holmes	Read	Cooper	Horton	Hanchard	16
Power	Stemp	Stevens	Broome	Bye	Wigmore	Rogers†	Doherty	Holmes	Read	Cooper	Lovell	Hanchard	17
Thompson	Stemp	K.Baker	Broome†	Bye	Wigmore•	Hobson	Doherty	Horton	Read	Holmes	Fleming	Rogers	18
Power	Stemp	K.Baker	Broome	Bye	Wigmore	Holmes	Doherty†	Hobson	Read	Rogers•	Fleming	Horton	19
Power	Stemp	K.Baker	Broome	Fleming	Wigmore	Holmes†	Hobson	Coombs	Read	Horton	Stevens	Doherty	20
Power	Stemp	K.Baker	Broome	Fleming	Wigmore	Rogers	Hobson•	Coombs	Read†	Horton	Stevens	Doherty	21
Power	Stemp•	K.Baker	Broome	Fleming	Wigmore	Rogers	Hobson•	Coombs	Read†	Horton	Stevens	Doherty	22
Power	Stemp	K.Baker	Broome	Bye	Wigmore	Rogers	Hobson	Coney	Read	Horton†	Holmes	Coombs	23
Thompson	Thorpe	Stevens	Wagstaff	Bye	Coles	Allen	Bell	Coombs	Johnston†	O'Neill•	Cheesman	Newberry	24
Power	Stemp	K.Baker	Broome	Bye	Wigmore	Rogers	Fleming	Coney	Read	Horton	Holmes	Coombs	25
Power	Stemp	K.Baker	Broome	Bye	Wigmore	Doherty	Holmes	Coney	Read•	Horton•	Fleming	Coombs	26
Power	Stemp	K.Baker	Broome•	Bye	Wigmore	Doherty	Holmes	Coney	Read	Fleming	Horton	Coombs	27
Power	Stemp	K.Baker	Broome	Bye	Wigmore	Doherty	Holmes	Coney	Read†	Fleming	Horton	Coombs•	28
Power	Stemp	K.Baker	Broome	Bye	Wigmore	Doherty	Holmes	Horton	Read	Fleming•	Rogers	Coombs	29
Power	Stemp	K.Baker	Broome	Bye	Wigmore	Doherty	Holmes	Coney	Read†	Fleming	Rogers	Horton	30
Power	Stemp	K.Baker†	Broome	Bye	Wigmore	Doherty	Holmes	Coney	Read	Fleming	Rogers	Horton	31
Power	Stemp	K.Baker†	Broome	Bye	Wigmore	Doherty	Holmes	Coney	Read	Fleming	Rogers	Horton	32
Power	Stemp	K.Baker•	Broome	Bye	Wigmore	Doherty	Holmes	Coney	Read	Fleming	Rogers	Horton	33
Power	Stemp	K.Baker†	Broome	Bye	Wigmore	Doherty	Holmes	Coney	Read	Fleming	Stevens	Horton	34
Lapointe	Stemp	Fleming	Broome•	Bye	Wigmore	Doherty†	Holmes	Coney	Read	Horton	K.Baker	Rogers	35
Hucker	Stemp†	Fleming	Broome	Bye	Wigmore	S.Baker	Holmes	Coney	Leworthy	Horton	K.Baker	Read	36
Hucker	S.Baker†	K.Baker	Broome	Bye	Wigmore	Leworthy	Holmes	Coney	Read•	Horton	Fleming	Turkington	37
Hucker	Turkington	Fleming	Broome	Bye	Wigmore	Leworthy	Holmes	Coney	Read	Horton	K.Baker	Coles	38
Hucker	Turkington	K.Baker	Broome	Bye	Wigmore	Leworthy	Holmes•	Coney	Fleming†	Horton	Coles	Comfort	39
Hucker	S.Baker	K.Baker	Broome	Bye	Batey	Leworthy	Holmes†	Coney	Read	Horton	Turkington	Comfort	40
Hucker	S.Baker	K.Baker	Broome•	Bye	Wigmore	Leworthy	Holmes	Coney	Turkington	Comfort•	Fleming	Read	41
Hucker	S.Baker	K.Baker	Broome	Bye	Wigmore	Leworthy	Holmes	Read	Turkington	Comfort	Horton	Read	42
Hucker	S.Baker	K.Baker	Broome	Bye	Wigmore•	Leworthy	Holmes	Read	Turkington	Horton	Rogers	Cockram	43
Hucker	S.Baker	K.Baker	Broome	Batey	Fleming	Leworthy	Holmes	Read	Turkington	Horton†	Wigmore	Coles	44
Hucker	S.Baker	K.Baker	Broome	Batey	Batey	Leworthy	Holmes	Fleming•	Read	Horton†	Wigmore	Coles	45
Hucker	Turkington	Coleman	Coles†	Bye	Batey	Leworthy	Holmes	Coney	Read	Cockram	Coleman	Read	46
Dalton	Turkington	Coleman	Coles†	Bye	Batey	Leworthy	Holmes	Coney	Read	Cockram	Coleman	Read	47
Dalton	Fleming	Coleman	Coleman	Bye	K.Baker	Leworthy	Holmes	Coney	Read	Horton	Wigmore	Fleming	48
Dalton	Fleming	Coleman	Batey	Bye	K.Baker•	Leworthy	Holmes	Coney	Read	Horton	Wigmore	Turkington	49
Dalton	Fleming	Coleman•	Broome	Bye	Wigmore	Holmes	Broome	Coney	Read	Horton	K.Baker	Holmes	50
Dalton	S.Baker	Coleman	Batey	Bye	Wigmore	Leworthy	S.Baker	Coney†	Read	Horton	K.Baker	Holmes	51
Dalton	S.Baker	Coleman	Batey	Bye	Wigmore	Leworthy	Broome†	Coney	Read	Holmes•	Fleming	Horton	52
Dalton	S.Baker	Coleman	Batey	Bye	Wigmore	Leworthy	Cockram	Horton†	Read	Fleming†	K.Baker	Rogers	53
Dalton	S.Baker	Coleman	K.Baker	Bye	Wigmore	Leworthy	cockram	Coney	Read•	Fleming	Rogers	Holmes	54
Dalton	S.Baker	Coleman	K.Baker	Batey	Wigmore	Leworthy	Holmes	Coney	Horton†	Rogers	Broome	Fleming	55
Dalton	S.Baker	Coleman	K.Baker	Batey•	Wigmore	Leworthy	Broome	Coney†	Read	Rogers	Holmes	Horton	56

• substituted by No. 12.   † substituted by No. 14.

Farnborough Town

TED PEARCE

Ted Pearce has now completed twenty two years as Farnborough Town's team manager having taken charge of over 1,150 competative matches in that time. He has been in charge at Cherrywood Road fo all but two seasons of the club's existence and has been a key factor in the clubs amazing rise from the Surrey Senior League to the top level of non-league football - an example to every club wishing to progress in the Pyramid structure.

During his playing days, Ted appeared in Woking's Isthmian League team in the mid-60s and has also played for Thorneycroft in the Hampshire League. He took over as player-manager at Farnborough in 1970, but after just half a season, decided to hang up his boots to concentrate on management. He has since guided the team to eight league championships and numerous other triumphs. Relegation from the Conference three seasons ago remains the only failure in Ted's remarkable managerial career, but last season's successes will, no doubt have wiped that memory away.

Farnborough Town attack in numbers against Yeovil Town at Cherrywood Road.   Photo: Eric Marsh.

Programme details:
>   36 pages for 80p
>   Editor - Terry Parr & Paul
>   Johnstone

Any other club publications:
>   Simon's Haircut (Fanzine)

Local Newspapers:
>   Farnborough News
>   Reading Evening Post

>   **Local Radio Stations:**
>   County Sound Radio
>   Radio 210

FARNBOROUGH TOWN - PLAYING SQUAD 1992-93

Player	Honours	Birthplace and date	Transfer Fees	Previous Clubs
GOALKEEPERS				
John Power	BHL, HSC FA XI	London 10/12/59		Limerick Utd, Limerick C, Brentford, Kingstonian
Tim Dalton		Waterford 14/10/65		Coventry City, Notts Co, Boston Utd, Bradford City, Derry City
DEFENDERS:				
Andy Bye	BHL HSC, FA XI	Winchester 5/6/63	£4,000	Gosport, Fareham, Basingstoke
Jim Wigmore	BHL HSC	Feltham 20/1/63		Malden Vale, Feltham Hampton
Steve Baker		Newcastle 2/12/61		Southampton, Leyton Orient, Aldershot
Peter Batey				Army
MIDFIELD				
Brian Broome	BHL, HSC FA XI	Reading 14/4/60		Camberley, Farnborough, Wokingham
Jamie Horton	BHL, HSC FA XI	Aldershot 20/4/62		Godalming Ash Utd
Danny Holmes				AFC Bournemouth
Andy Rogers	BHL, HSC SSC	Ely 1/12/56		Chatteris, Peterboro, Kettering, Hampton, S'Hampton, Plymouth, Reading,
Alan Comfort		Aldershot 8/12/64		QPR, Camb Utd, Leyton Orient, Middlesbrough
FORWARDS				
Simon Read	BHL, HSC FA XI, HC	Surrey 4/4/61		Staines Wycombe W
Dean Coney		Dagenham 18/9/63		Fulham, QPR, Norwich, Ernest Borel(HK)
David Leworthy		Portsmouth 22/10/62		Portsmouth, Fareham, Spurs, Oxford Utd, Reading
Martin Hanchard	NPL, BLT FA XI	Germany 23/9/62		Stoke, Stafford R, Altrincham, Telford, Northwich V

Departures during season:
Gordon Hobson (Salisbury), Mick Doherty (Macclesfield), Mark Fleming (Woking), Keith Baker (Aldershot Town), Peter Hucker (Enfield), Allan Cockram (Woking).

Players on loan during season:
Wayne Stemp (Brighton), Geoff Cooper (Barnet), David Coleman (Bournemouth).

John Roberts Ground, Farnborough

Ground address and Tel. No. : Cherrywood Road, Farnborough, Hants, GU14 8UD. 0252 541469 (Football), 0252 545553 (Social Club)

Simple ground directions: From M3 (Junction 4) along A325 towards Farnborough. Turn right into Prospect Avenue, second right into Cherrywood Road. 20-30 minutes walk from Farnborough (Main), Farnborough North and Frimley stations. "Whippet" mini bus Route 19 passes ground.

Official capacity: 4,900   **Seating:** 500   **Covered accommodation:** 1,000

Cost of seats: £5.00   **Cost of standing:** £4.00

Record attendance: 3,069 v Colchester

Cost of Advertising boards: Negotiable

Social facilities available: Menbers club and Vice Presidents lounge. Snack bars in ground serving hot and cold food and drinks.

Car parking: Large car park plus limited parking available in nearby roads.

Sponsored by: To be announced   **FARNBOROUGH TOWN**   **Nickname:** The "Boro"

Previous ground: Queens Road, Farnborough (1968-1976)

Previous leagues: Beazer Homes League, GM Vauxhall Conference, Vauxhall-Opel League (Isthmain League), Athenian League, London Spartan League, Surry Senior League.

Club colours: All yellow with blue trim

Change colours: White shirts and shorts with red trim, red socks

Midweek home matches: Tuesday   **Reserve team's league:** Suburban league

Club programme: 36 pages, 60p   **Editor:** Nigel Long   **Club shop:** Yes two

Record transfer fee paid: £6,000 to Runcorn for Mick Doherty

Record transfer fee received: £10,000 (+£7,000) from Crystal Palace for Dennis Bailey

Record appearances for club: Brian Broome

Record goalscorer (career): Simon Read.   **Record goalscorer (season):** SimonRead, 53 1988/89.

Top goalscorer: Simon Read (20), Paul Coombs (20)

Past players who have progressed to the Football League: Dennis Baily (Crystal Palace, Birmingham City); Paul Mortimer (Charlton Athletic); Tommy Jones (Aberdeen, Swindon Town); Allan Cockram (Brentford).

Best F.A. Cup performance: !st Round - 1980/81, 83/84, 84/85, 85/86, 87/88, 89/90and 90/91.

Best F.A. Trophy performance: 3rd round - 1989/90

Club Honours: Beazer Homes League Champions 1990-91; Vauxhall-Opel League Premier Division Runners-up 1988/89; Isthmian League Division One Champions 1984-85; Isthmian League Division Two Champions 1978-79; Athenian League Division Two Champions 1976-77; London Spartan League Champions 1975-76; Spartan League Champions 1972-73, 1973-74 and 1974075; Hampshire Senior League Cup Winners 1974-75, 1981-82, 1983-84, 1985-85 and 1990-91; London Spartan League Cup Winners 1975-76; Spartan League Cup Winners 1974-75

Past club managers: Arther Mylett 1968-69; Tom Richardson 1969- 70; Ted Pearce 1970-to date

GATESHEAD

Formed: 1977

President:
J. C. Thomas

Chairman:
J. Gibson

Directors:
P. Robinson
J. Foxcroft
J. Bayne

Secretary:
Claire Tierney

Manager:
Tommy Cassidy

Coach:
Billy Horner

Physiotherapist:
Terry Ainsley

Press Officer:
Jeff Bowron

Improving Gateshead

Gateshead achieved their highest placing in 5 seasons of Conference football despite suffering their second managerial casualty inside a year. In a carbon copy of the previous season, the Tynesiders found themselves only one place off the foot of the table by mid-November when Tony Lee was replaced by former Northern Ireland midfielder Tommy Cassidy. The new managers brief was to maintain the clubs Conference status and a final placing of 14th was testimony to the improvements made both on and off the field at the International Stadium.

There had also been changes behind the scenes where Alex Cuscani, the only Italian chairman in English football, left the club shortly after Lee's departure. The early season upheavals were a sharp contrast to the pre-season euphoria that had greeted the news that Gateshead had clinched a record sponsorship deal with Cameron Hall Developments, the driving force behind the towns prestigious Metro Centre. A 3 year deal worth £150,000 fuelled speculation on Tyneside that better times were ahead for a club that had lost its Football League status so unjustly back in 1960.

The clubs fortunes in the FA Cup were in the National spotlight when BBC TV featured the club's 2nd, 3rd and 4th qualifying round ties as part of their annual 'Road to Wembley' series. However, a single goal defeat at Runcorn deprived Gateshead of what would have been only a second appearance in the 1st Round Proper. Victories over neighbours Blyth Spartans and Barrow in the FA Trophy saw a rejuvenated Gateshead equal their best ever run in non-leagues premier cup. But another single goal reverse, this time by Telford, ended hopes of a place in the quarter-finals.

An eight match unbeaten run in the league during March and April proved to be the determining factor in preserving the clubs Conference future. In Alan Lamb Gateshead unearthed a striker of quality. The locally-born marksman registered 14 goals in 26 matches and proved to be Cassidy's most astute signing.

With the continued backing of Cameron Hall, manager Tommy Cassidy is confident the club can become a force in the league. One of the most experienced squads in the clubs history has been assembled during the close season and there is belief in the North-East that another significant step can now be taken towards reclaiming that coveted place in the Football League.

Gateshead F.C. 1991-92. Back Row (L-R): Gerry Forrest, Steve Chambers, Kevin Dixon, Bruce Halliday, Nigel Saddington. Middle Row: John Gibson (vice chairman), Billy Horner (coach), Jimmy Robertson, Charlie Butler, David Corner, Simon Smith, Phil Linacre, Neal Granycome, Peter Robinson (director), Terry Ainsley (physio), Jeff Bowron (press officer). Front Row: Michael Farrey, Tony Lowery, Tommy Cassidy (manager), Alex Cuscani, Derek Bell, Craig Veart, Alan Lamb.

Gateshead

Match No.	Date	Competition	Venue H/A	Opponents	Result	H/T	League Pos.	Goalscorers (Times if known)	Attendance
1	Aug 17	GMVC	A	Wycombe	L 1-2	1-1		Forrest 42	2603
2	Aug 24	GMVC	A	Kidderminster	L 3-5	2-2	22	Corner 4; Dixon 45; Linacre 53 (pen)	1051
3	Aug 26	GMVC	H	Runcorn	D 1-1	1-1	21	Butler 10	530
4	Aug 31	GMVC	A	Yeovil	L 0-1	0-0	22		2222
5	Sep 4	BLT 1-1	H	Witton Albion	W 3-0	2-0		Bell 20; Corner 24 (pen); Butler 53	260
6	Sep 7	GMVC	H	Farnborough	L 0-2	0-1	22		415
7	Sep 14	FAC 1Q	A	Workington	W 1-0	1-0		O'Brien 25	205
8	Sep 17	BLT 1-2	A	Witton Albion	L 0-5	0-2			501
9	Sep 21	GMVC	H	Merthyr Tydfil	L 0-1	0-0	22		328
10	Sep 24	GMVC	A	Altrincham	D 1-1	1-1	22	Franycome 43	842
11	Sep 28	FAC 2Q	H	Alnwick Town	W 6-0	2-0		Bell 6,52; Butler 30,64,80; Emson 65	232
12	Oct 5	GMVC	A	Welling Utd	D 2-2	1-1		Corner 28; Guthrie 61	748
13	Oct 12	FAC 3Q	H	Netherfield					
14	Oct 15	FAC 3QR	A	Netherfield	W 3-0	0-0		Saddington 48; Leishman 67,69	847
15	Oct 19	GMVC	A	Stafford Rangers	W 3-1	2-0	21	Chambers 2, 12; Emson 84	707
16	Oct 22	GMVC	A	Northwich Victoria	D 1-1	1-1	21	Veart 28	540
17	Oct 26	FAC 4Q	A	Runcorn	L 0-1	0-0			734
18	Nov 2	GMVC	H	Telford Utd	L 0-2	0-1	21		264
19	Nov 9	GMVC	A	Bath City	W 1-0	1-0	21	Linacre 12	632
20	Nov 16	GMVC	H	Bath City	L 0-1	0-1	21		355
21	Nov 23	GMVC	H	Witton Albion	W 2-1	0-1	20	Halliday 60; Butler 65	273
22	Nov 30	GMVC	H	Redbridge Forest	L 0-1	0-1	20		286
23	Dec 7	GMVC	H	Boston Utd	W 2-1	0-1	20	Butler 81; Dixon 87	271
24	Dec 14	GMVC	H	Colchester	L 0-2	0-2	21		530
25	Dec 21	GMVC	A	Telford Utd	D 1-1	0-0	20	Linacre 62	717
26	Dec 26	GMVC	A	Barrow	D 1-1	0-0	20	Dixon 68	1521
27	Dec 28	GMVC	A	Altrincham	W 4-0	1-0	18	Dixon 26; Lamb 73,80,89	386
28	Jan 1	GMVC	H	Barrow	D 1-1	0-0	18	Linacre 74	747
29	Jan 4	GMVC	H	Northwich Victoria	W 2-0	1-0	16	Lamb 31,51	346
30	Jan 11	FAT 1	A	Blyth Spartans	D 0-0	0-0			1480
31	Jan 14	FAT 1R	H	Blyth Spartans	W 3-0			Dixon 101; Lowery 115; Veart 119	920
32	Jan 18	GMVC	A	Slough	L 0-2	0-1	17		730
33	Jan 25	GMVC	A	Cheltenham	L 2-3	1-0	19	Bell 3; Lamb 69	701
34	Feb 1	FAT 2	H	Barrow	W 1-0	1-0		Lowery 26	1129
35	Feb 8	GMVC	H	Cheltenham	W 2-1	1-1	17	Lamb 42; Corner 89 (pen)	343
36	Feb 15	GMVC	A	Redbridge Forest	L 1-2	0-1	17	Gourlay 54	428
37	Feb 19	GMVC	A	Boston Utd	L 0-4	0-2	18		639
38	Feb 22	FAT 3	A	Telford Utd	D 0-0	0-0			1027
39	Feb 26	FAT 3R	H *	Telford Utd	L 0-1	0-1			535
40	Feb 29	GMVC	A	Merthyr Tydfil	W 4-1	3-1	17	Corner 15; Lamb 22; Grayson 45; Cuthbert 66	575
41	Mar 7	GMVC	A	Colchester	L 0-2	0-1	19		2897
42	Mar 14	GMVC	H	Welling Utd	D 1-1	0-1	18	Lamb 57	307
43	Mar 21	GMVC	H	Kettering	D 0-0	0-0	19		420
44	Mar 28	GMVC	H	Macclesfield	W 2-0	0-0	18	Lamb 61; Butler 90	375
45	Apr 4	GMVC	A	Kettering	D 1-1	1-1	17	Healey 37	1497
46	Apr 7	GMVC	A	Witton Albion	W 3-0	2-0	16	Healey 6; Cuthbert 38; Lamb 87	593
47	Apr 11	GMVC	H	Yeovil	W 1-0	0-0	15	Grayson 48	344
48	Apr 15	GMVC	A	Stafford Rangers	D 0-0	0-0	14		202
49	Apr 18	GMVC	A	Farnborough	L 1-3	0-1	14	Lamb 55	675
50	Apr 20	GMVC	A	Runcorn	D 1-1	0-0	13	Grayson 88	489
51	Apr 25	GMVC	H	Wycombe	L 2-3	1-1	13	Lamb 30,68	912
52	Apr 28	GMVC	A	Macclesfield	L 0-1	0-0	14		369
53	May 2	GMVC	H	Kidderminster	L 0-3	0-2	14		505

• Game played at Blyth Spartans.

Gateshead

1	2	3	4	5	6	7	8	9	10	11	12	14	Match No.
Smith	Farrey	O'Brien	Forrest	Halliday•	Corner	A.Dixon†	Bell	Linacre	Butler	Veart	Johnson	K.Dixon	1
Smith	Farrey	O'Brien	Forrest	Johnson	Corner	A.Dixon†	Bell	Linacre	Butler	Veart	Granycome	K.Dixon	2
Smith	Farrey	O'Brien	Forrest	Johnson†	Corner	A.Dixon†	Bell	Linacre•	Butler	Granycome	Johnson	K.Dixon	3
Smith	Davies	O'Brien	Forrest†	Corner	Halliday	A.Dixon	Bell	McInerney•	Butler	Granycome	K.Dixon	Brabin	4
Smith	**Davies**	**Veart**	**Forrest†**	**Corner**	**Halliday**	**A.Dixon**	**Bell**	**McInerney•**	**Butler**	**Granycome**	**K.Dixon**	**Brabin**	**5**
Smith	Davies	Veart	Forrest	Corner	Halliday	A.Dixon	Bell	McInerney•	Butler	Granycome†	K.Dixon	Brabin	6
Smith	**Farrey**	**O'Brien**	**Saddington•**	**Corner**	**Halliday**	**Forrest**	**Bell**	**Linacre†**	**Butler**	**Granycome**	**A.Dixon**	**K.Dixon**	**7**
Smith	**Farrey**	**O'Brien**	**Saddington•**	**Halliday**	**Forrest**	**A.Dixon†**	**Granycome**	**Guthrie**	**Butler**	**Linacre**	**Davies**	**Bell**	**8**
Smith	Farrey	O'Brien	Bell	Forrest	Halliday	Leishman	Granycome	Guthrie	Butler	Emson	Davies	Veart	9
Smith	Farrey	O'Brien	Bell	Forrest	Halliday	Leishman	Granycome	Guthrie	Butler	Emson	Davies	A.Dixon	10
Smith	**Farrey**	**O'Brien**	**Bell**	**Forrest**	**Halliday**	**Leishman**	**Granycome•**	**Veart†**	**Butler**	**Emson**	**Davies**	**Veart**	**11**
Smith	Chambers	O'Brien	Forrest	Corner	Halliday	Leishman•	Bell	Guthrie	Granycome	Butler	Farrey	Emson	12
Smith	**Farrey**	**O'Brien**	**Forrest**	**Corner**	**Halliday**	**Bell**	**Granycome**	**Guthrie**	**Emson•**	**Butler†**	**Veart**	**Leishman**	**13**
Smith	**Farrey**	**Saddington•**	**Forrest**	**Corner**	**Halliday**	**Bell**	**Granycome**	**Guthrie†**	**Leishman**	**Butler**	**Veart**	**Emson**	**14**
Smith	Farrey	Saddington	Forrest	Halliday	Corner	Bell•	Butler	Chambers	Leishman†	Granycome	Emson	Linacre	15
Smith	Chambers	O'Brien	Forrest	Corner	Halliday	Leishman†	Bell	Guthrie	Butler	Veart	Emson	Linacre	16
Smith	**Farrey**	**Saddington**	**Forrest**	**Corner**	**Halliday**	**Bell•**	**Veart**	**Guthrie**	**Leishman**	**Butler**	**Emson**	**Davies**	**17**
Smith	Farrey	Saddington	Corner	Halliday	Chambers	Bell†	Veart•	Butler	Linacre	Forrest	Emson	K.Dixon	18
Smith	Johnson	Saddington	Forrest	Corner	Halliday	Chambers•	Bell	Linacre	Peverell†	Veart	Butler	O'Brien	19
Smith	Johnson	Saddington	Forrest†	Corner	Halliday	Peverell	Bell	Linacre	Butler	Veart	Chambers	O'Brien	20
Smith	Johnson	Saddington	Forrest	Corner	Halliday	Chambers	Bell	Linacre†	Veart	O'Brien	Peverell	Butler•	21
Smith	Johnson	Saddington	Forrest	Corner	Halliday	Chambers	Bell	Farrey	Veart†	O'Brien•	Peverell	Butler•	22
Smith	Johnson	Saddington	Forrest	Corner	Halliday	Chambers	Bell	Farrey†	Butler	O'Brien	Veart	K.Dixon	23
Smith	Forrest	Saddington	Lowery	Corner	Halliday	Chambers	Bell	Farrey	Lamb	Veart•	Dixon	Johnson	24
Smith	Farrey	Saddington	Forrest	Corner	Lowery	Chambers†	Lamb	Bell	Linacre•	Butler	Dixon	Veart	25
Smith	Farrey	Saddington	Forrest	Lowery	Halliday	Dixon	Bell	Linacre	Butler•	Lamb	Veart	Robertson	26
Smith	Farrey	Saddington	Forrest	Corner	Askew	Lowery	Bell	Butler•	Dixon	Lamb	Veart	Linacre	27
Smith	Farrey	Saddington	Forrest	Corner	Askew	Dixon	Bell†	Lamb	Butler•	Lowery	Veart	Linacre	28
Smith	Farrey	Saddington	Butler•	Corner	Halliday	Lowery	Bell	Linacre	Dixon	Lamb	Veart	Forrest	29
Smith	**Farrey**	**Saddington**	**Askew**	**Corner†**	**Halliday**	**Lowery**	**Bell**	**Linacre•**	**Dixon**	**Butler**	**Veart**	**Forrest**	**30**
Smith	**Farrey**	**Saddington**	**Askew**	**Forrest**	**Halliday**	**Lowery**	**Bell**	**Linacre•**	**Dixon**	**Butler**	**Veart**	**O'Brien**	**31**
Smith	Farrey	Saddington	Askew	Veart	Halliday	Lowery	Bell	Butler•	Dixon	Lamb	Linacre	Chambers	32
Smith	Farrey	Saddington	Askew•	Corner	Halliday	Lowery	Bell	Wharton	Dixon†	Lamb	Veart	Linacre	33
Smith	**Farrey**	**Saddington**	**Gourlay**	**Corner**	**Halliday**	**Lowery•**	**Bell**	**Linacre**	**Dixon**	**Butler**	**Veart**	**Granycome**	**34**
Smith	Farrey	Saddington	Gourlay	Corner	Halliday	Butler†	Bell	Linacre	Dixon•	Lamb	Veart	Granycome	35
Smith	Farrey	Saddington•	Gourlay†	Veart	Halliday	Granycome	Bell	Scope	Dixon	Lamb	Forrest	Butler	36
Smith	Farrey	Veart	Healey	Forrest†	Halliday	Granycome	Bell	Scope•	Dixon	Lamb	Cuthbert	Butler	37
Smith	**Farrey**	**Veart**	**Granycome**	**Corner**	**Halliday**	**Scope**	**Bell**	**Linacre**	**Dixon**	**Butler**	**Forrest**	**/**	**38**
Smith	**Farrey**	**Veart**	**Granycome**	**Corner**	**Halliday**	**Gourlay**	**Forrest**	**Linacre**	**Dixon•**	**Butler**	**Scope**	**Bell**	**39**
Smith	Farrey	Veart•	Granycome	Corner	Halliday	Healey	Forrest	Cuthbert	Grayson	Lamb	Butler	Scope	40
Smith	Farrey	Veart†	Granycome	Corner	Halliday	Healey	Forrest	Cuthbert•	Grayson	Lamb	Bell	Butler	41
Smith	Higgins	Veart	Forrest	Corner	Bell	Granycome†	Healey	Veart	Grayson	Lamb	Farrey	Wheatley	42
Smith	Higgins	Farrey	Wheatley	Corner	Halliday	Healey	Bell	Veart	Grayson	Lamb	Granycome	Cuthbert	43
Smith	Higgins	Veart	Wheatley†	Corner	Halliday	Healey	Bell	Granycome	Grayson	Lamb	Cuthbert	Butler	44
Smith	Higgins	Veart	Granycome	Corner	Halliday•	Healey	Bell	Cuthbert†	Grayson	Lamb	Butler	Linacre	45
Smith	Higgins	Veart	Granycome	Corner	Farrey	Healey	Bell	Cuthbert•	Grayson	Lamb	Wheatley	Hopkinson	46
Smith	Higgins	Veart	Granycome	Corner	Farrey	Healey	Bell	Cuthbert•	Grayson	Lamb	Butler	Wheatley	47
Smith	Higgins	Veart	Farrey	Corner	Halliday†	Healey	Bell	Cuthbert	Butler•	Lamb	Wheatley	Forrest	48
Smith	Higgins	Veart	Granycome	Corner	Forrest	Healey•	Bell	Cuthbert†	Grayson	Lamb	Farrey	Wheatley	49
Smith	Higgins	Veart•	Granycome	Corner	Forrest†	Farrey	Bell	Wheatley	Grayson	Lamb	Cuthbert	Butler	50
Smith	Higgins	Veart	Granycome†	Corner	Forrest	Farrey	Bell	Cuthbert•	Grayson	Lamb	Butler	Wheatley	51
Smith	Higgins	Veart	Granycome	Corner	Forrest	Farrey	Bell	Healey	Grayson	Lamb	Butler	Saddington	52
Smith	Higgins	Veart	Granycome	Cuthbert	Forrest	Farrey	Bell	Healey	Grayson	Lamb	Butler	Lowery	53
Smith•	Higgins	Veart	Granycome	Corner	Forrest	Farrey	Bell	Healey†	Grayson	Lamb	Hopkinson	Lowery	54

Gateshead

TOMMY CASSIDY

Replaced Tony Lee as Gateshead manager in November 1991 after previously spending 8 months at the International Stadium as Commercial Manager. A former Northern Ireland International who represented his country on 24 occasions, including the 1982 World Cup Finals, during a 10 year association with Newcastle United he made 212 appearances. He played in the 1974 FA Cup Final and 1976 League Cup Final before transferring to Burnley in 1980.

His first experience of management came with Cypriot club Apoel Nicosia where he spent 4 successful seasons.

After taking over at Gateshead he guided tham to their highest league placing and is confident of making further progress in the 1992/93 season.

Gateshead's vastly experienced midfield duo Tony Lowery and Billy Askew seen here in action during the Tynesiders' comprehensive 4-0 victory over Altrincham at the International Stadium.

Programme details:
    22 pages for 60p
    Editor - John Gibson

Any other club publications:
    Supporters Club Broadsheet

Local Newspapers:
    Gateshead Post
    Newcastle Chronicle & Journal

Local Radio Stations:
    BBC Radio Newcastle
    Metro Radio

GATESHEAD - PLAYING SQUAD 1992-93

Player	Honours	Birthplace and date	Transfer Fees	Previous Clubs
GOALKEEPERS				
Simon Smith	FA XI, NPL NL	Newton Aycliffe 16/9/62		Newcastle Utd, Whitley Bay, Blyth Spartans
Mark Hopkinson	ES	Sunderland 18/9/71		Shildon, Bishop Auckland
DEFENDERS				
Michael Farrey	WL	Gateshead 17/8/65		Chester-Le-Street, Whickham
David Corner	EY, GMVC Div 4, LC	Sunderland 15/5/66		Sunderland, Leyton Orient, Darlington
Chris O'Donnell		Newcastle 26/5/68		Ipswich Town, Leeds Utd, Exeter City
Steve Higgins	FAT, NPL, FAXI	Gateshead 6/10/60		Gateshead, Barrow, Newcastle Blue Star, Barrow
Bruce Halliday	Div 4(P)	Sunderland 3/1/61		Newcastle Utd, Bury, Bristol C, Hereford, Bath City, Apia(Aust)
MIDFIELD				
Billy Askew	Div 3(P) Div 4(P)	Lumley 2/10/59		Middlesbrough, Hull City, Newcastle United
Craig Veart		Hartlepool 18/11/70		Middlesbrough, Ferryhill Ath
Mark Telford	MYC	Jarrow 27/12/71		Nottingham Forest, Notts County, Marchienne(Belg)
Derek Bell	FA XI NPL	Newcastle 19/12/63		Newcastle Utd, North Shields
Tony Lowery	FRT Div 4(P)	Wallsend 6/7/61		Ashington, WBA, Walsall, Mansfield, Carlisle Utd
FORWARDS				
Tony Fyfe		Carlisle 23/2/62		Carlisle United, Halifax Town, Carlisle United
John Cooke	EY, Div 2	Salford 25/4/62		Sunderland, Sheffield Wed, Carlisle Utd, Stockport, Chesterfield
Alan Lamb		Gateshead 30/10/70		Nottingham Forest, Hartlepool Utd, Brandon United

Departures during last season:
Sean O'Brien (Billingham Syn), Ian Johnson (Whitley Bay), Nigel Saddington (Blyth), Gary Brabin (Runcorn), Ian McInerney (Morecambe), Ken Davies (Stockport), Paul Emson (Whitby), Brian Healey (Spennymoor), Steve Cuthbert (Spennymoor). Gerry Forrest, Danny Wheatley, Neal Granycome, Charlie Butler, Phil Linacre, Steve Chamber (Boston Utd), Kevin Dixon, Andy Dixon, Graham Leishman (Gainsborough Trin).

Players who joined on loan during the season:
Simon Guthrie (Sunderland), Billy Askew (Newcastle Utd), Archie Gourlay (Newcastle Utd), Nick Peverell (Middlesbrough), Neil Grayson (Chesterfield), Dave Scope (Northampton)

International Stadium, Gateshead

Ground address and Tel. No. : Neilson Road, Gateshead, Tyne & Wear, NE10 0EF. Tel: 091 4100070
Simple ground directions: A6127 to Town Centre. A6115 (South Shields/Sunderland) for 1 mile, Stadium on left. By Public Transport: Metro train to Gateshead Stadium Station. Turn rightout of station and then right at main road (Felling By Pass).
Official capacity: 12,000   **Seating:** 12,000   **Covered accommodation:** 3,300
Cost of seats: £%.00   **O.A.P.:** £1.00   **Cost of standing:** £4.00
Record attendance: 5,012 v. Newcastle United, Testimonial 20.8.84. 20,752 v Lincoln City, 1937 as Gateshead A.F.C.
Social facilities available: Stadium Bar, The Stadium Public House - adjacent to ground.
Car parking: Stadium Car Park.

Sponsored by: Cameron Hall Dev.   **GATESHEAD F.C.**   **Nickname:** Tynesiders

Previous names: Gateshead A.F.C. 1930-1973, Gateshead United 1973-1976, Gateshead F.C. 1977
Previous leagues: Northern Premier 1977-83, Alliance Premier 1983-85, 1986-87, Northern Premier 1985-86, 1987-90, Vauxhall Conference 1990-91
Club colours: White/black/black   **Change colours:** Yellow/yellow/yellow
Midweek home matches: Wednesday   **Clubmetal badges:** Yes
Record transfer fee paid: £1,000 to Sunderland for John McGinley
Record transfer fee received: £3,000 from Sunderland for John McGinley
Record appearances for club: Simon Smith
Record goalscorer for club: Bob Topping
Record goalscorer in a season: Jim Pearson (31) 1982-83
Best performance in F.A. Cup: 1st round Proper 1980-81 v Lincoln City
Best performance in F.A. Trophy: £rd round 1983-84 v Bangor City
Past players who have progressed to the Football League: Osher Williams (Southampton, Stockport, Port Vale, Preston; John McGinley (Sunderland, Lincoln); Billy Askew (Hull City, Newcastle United); Lawrie Pearson (Hull City, Port Vale); Ian Johnson (Northampton Town); Ken Davies (Stockport).
Club Honours: Northern Premier League Champions 1982-83, 1985-86, Runners-up 1989-90; Northern Premier League Cup Finalists 1989-90
Past club managers: Ray Wilkie (1977-86); Terry Hibbitt (1986-87), Dave Parnaby (1987-90), Tony Lee (1990-91)
General Motor Dealer: Priory Garage, St. James Square, Gateshead, Tyne & Wear.

KETTERING TOWN

Formed: 1880

President:
T. G. Bradley

Chairman:
M. Gill-Anderson

Managing Director:
M. English

Directors:
Mrs T English
T Dartford
G Ellitson (Non-Exec)

Company Secretary:
George Ellitson

Manager:
Dave Cusack

Assistant Manager:
Steve Buckley

Club Doctor:
Dr John Smith

Another 'nearly' season for the Poppies

Kettering Town created a new Vauxhall Conference record by finishing in the top five for the fifth consecutive season. Although a final placing of third behind Colchester United and Wycombe Wanderers is comendable, the Poppies were never really in with a realistic chance of winning the title this time around.

As usual at Rockingham Road under the managership of Peter Morris, players came and went regularly without upsetting league form. However, Morris has now departed to Boston United and their previous manager, Dave Cusack, has taken over.

Once again, off the field activities have overshadowed activities on it. Former England midfielder Brian Talbot's reign as Managing Director ended after only a few months and Mark English has now taken over that role. Financial difficulties still cause problems, although the situation has improved slightly. This season the club begin with their fifth chairman in just over a year, so stability is needed to ensure that the Poppies can maintain a challenge at the top of the Conference.

Support at Rockingham Road fell last season, although the away support remains tremendous. They will be hoping that Dave Cusack and his assistant, Steve Buckley, the former Derby and Luton player, will be able to settle down and produce a team worthy of their support.

Kettering Town F.C. 1991-92. Back Row (L-R): Paul Jones, Gareth Price, Steve Appleby, Richard Huxford, Paul Emson. Middle: Richie Norman (physio), Trevor Christie, Perry Cotton, Paul Bastock, Darren Bloodworth, Jon Graham, Ernie Moss (coach). Front Row: Phil Brown, Paul Bancroft, Peter Morris (manager), Doug Keast, Richard Hill. Photo: Mick Cheney.

Kettering Town

GM Vauxhall Conference: 3rd.   **FA Cup: 3rd Round.**   **FA Trophy: 3rd Round.**

Match No.	Date	Competition	Venue H/A	Opponents	Result	League H/T	Pos.	Goalscorers (Times if known)	Attendance
1	Aug 17	FMVC	A	Altrincham	D 1-1	1-1		Christie 23	1293
2	Aug 24	GMVC	A	Redbridge Forest	L 0-4	0-1			726
3	Aug 26	GMVC	H	Welling Utd	D 1-1	1-1	20	Emson 26	1962
4	Aug 31	GMVC	H	Witton Albin	D 1-1	0-0	20	Walker 56	1508
5	Sep 7	GMVC	A	Runcorn	D 0-0	0-0	20		637
6	Sep 14	FAC 1Q	A	**Wisbech**	**W 3-0**	**2-0**		**Brown 21,54; Christie 25**	1017
7	Sep 21	GMVC	H	Kidderminster H	W 2-1	0-1	15	Brown 70; Graham 76	1532
8	Sep 25	GMVC	A	Cheltenham	W 3-0	3-0	11	Graham 37; Brown 38; Hill 44	1006
9	Sep 28	FAC 2Q	H	**Braintree**	**W 3-1**	**2-1**		**Graham 11; Jones 16; Hill 73**	1609
10	Oct 5	GMVC	H	Stafford Rangers	W 2-1	0-0	10	Graham 63; Hill 79 (pen)	1318
11	Oct 8	BLT	A	**Colchester Utd**	**L 0-4**	**0-2**			1296
12	Oct 12	FAC 3Q	H	**Heybridge**	**W 3-0**	**2-0**		o.g. 4; Graham 27; Brown 80	1587
13	Oct 15	GMVC	H	Telford Utd	W 3-0	1-0	5	Hill 19 (pen); Brown 53,84	1664
14	Oct 19	GMVC	A	Yeovil Town	W 1-0	1-0	5	Graham 45	1929
15	Oct 26	FAC 4Q	H	**Stafford Rangers**	**D 0-0**	**0-0**			1785
16	Oct 29	FAC 4QR	A	**Stafford Rangers**	**W 2-0**	**0-0**		**Christie 71; Jones 87**	1070
17	Nov 3	GMVC	H	Bath City	W 2-2	1-2	7	Christie 26; Keast 46	2379
18	Nov 9	GMVC	A	Macclesfield	W 2-0	0-0	6	Christie 70; Brown 79	940
19	Nov 16	FAC 1	H	**Wycombe Wanderers**	**D 1-1**	**0-0**		**Christie 71**	3317
20	Nov 23	GMVC	H	Slough	L 2-3	1-2	9	Christie 9; Graham 73	1830
21	Nov 27	FAC 1R	A	**Wycombe Wanderers**	**W 2-0**	**0-0**		**Brown 83**	5299
22	Nov 30	GMVC	A	Farnborough	W 3-1	1-1	6	Brown 45; Graham 46; Hill 76	1086
23	Dec 7	FAC 2	A	**Maidstone Utd**	**W 2-1**	**1-1**		**Brown 44; o.g. 58**	2750
24	Dec 21	GMVC	H	Merthyr Tydfil	W 3-1	1-0	9	Nicol 5; Hill 57,63 (pen)	1616
25	Dec 26	GMVC	A	Boston Utd	W 1-1	1-0	6	Nicol 10	2919
26	Dec 28	GMVC	A	Stafford Rangers	W 2-1	0-1	6	Brown 58; Christie 62	1089
27	Jan 1	GMVC	H	Boston Utd	L 1-3	0-1	6	Slack 71	3207
28	Jan 4	FAC 3	A	**Blackburn Rovers**	**L 1-4**	**0-1**		**Brown 77**	13821
29	Jan 11	FAT 1	A	**V.S. Rugby**	**W 1-0**	**0-0**		**Hill 52**	1790
30	Jan 18	GMVC	A	Barrow	D 0-0	0-0	8		1384
31	Jan 24	GMVC	H	Colchester Utd	D 2-2	2-2	6	Hill 15,31 (pen)	4100
32	Feb 1	FAT 2	A	**Bashley**	**W 3-2**	**1-0**		**Culpin 36; Brown 70; Hill 79**	1065
33	Feb 8	GMVC	H	Barrow	W 3-2	1-1	7	Graham 29; o.g. 63; Brown 64	1750
34	Feb 11	GMVC	A	Witton Albion	L 0-1	0-0	7		887
35	Feb 15	GMVC	H	Runcorn	W 3-0	1-0	6	Hill 9,62 (2 pens); Brown 80	1519
36	Feb 18	GMVC	A	Merthyr Tydfil	L 1-4	1-0	6	Hill 28	570
37	Feb 22	FAT 3	A	**Marine**	**L 1-2**	**1-0**		**Keast 44**	1111
38	Feb 29	GMVC	A	Northwich Victoria	L 3-4	3-0	8	Bancroft 7; Hill 20; Graham 21	665
39	Mar 6	GMVC	H	Farnborough	L 1-2	0-1	9	Bancroft 68 (pen)	1993
40	Mar 11	GMVC	A	Welling Utd	W 3-2	2-2	6	Gavin 27; Graham 35; Hill 50 (pen)	636
41	Mar 14	GMVC	A	Slough	W 2-0	1-0	4	Graham 25,82	698
42	Mar 17	GMVC	H	Northwich Victoria	W 1-0	0-0	4	Bancroft 66	1513
43	Mar 21	GMVC	A	Gateshead	D 0-0	0-0	5		420
44	Mar 24	GMVC	H	Macclesfield	W 2-0	0-0	4	Brown 59,60	1367
45	Mar 28	GMVC	A	Wycombe Wanderers	L 0-1	0-0	4		4069
46	Mar 31	GMVC	H	Cheltenham	W 3-0	0-0	3	North 57,89; Huxford 75	1336
47	Apr 4	GMVC	H	Gateshead	D 1-1	1-1	3	North 26	1497
48	Apr 7	GMVC	H	Yeovil Town	W 2-0	0-0	3	Hill 67 (pen); Graham 76	1257
49	Apr 11	GMVC	A	Telford Utd	D 1-1	1-0	3	Butterworth 7	890
50	Apr 13	GMVC	A	Kidderminster H	W 3-2	1-1	3	Graham 19,75; Gavin 53	1243
51	Apr 18	GMVC	A	Bath City	D 1-1	0-1	3	o.g. 57	699
52	Apr 22	GMVC	H	Wycombe Wanderers	D 1-1	1-0	3	Gavin 45	2918
53	Apr 25	GMVC	H	Altrincham	W 5-0	0-0	3	North 47; Graham 55,69; Hill 65,70	1347
54	Apr 28	GMVC	A	Colchester	L 1-3	0-1	3	North 90	6303
55	May 2	GMVC	H	Redbridge Forest	W 3-2	2-1	3	Brown 26; North 44; Graham 70	1304

Best Home League Attendance: 4100 v Colchester 24.1.92   **Smallest: 1267 v Yeovil 7.4.92**   **Average Home Attendance: 1857 Compared with 90/91: 2563**

Goalscorers League: Graham 21; Brown 19; Hill 19; Christie 8; North 7; Bancroft 3; Gavin 3; Jones 2; Keast 2; Nicol 2; Butterworth 1; Slack 1.

Kettering Town

1	2	3	4	5	6	7	8	9	10	11	12	14	Match No.
Shoemake	Huxford	Keast	Nicol	Slack	Price	Cotton	Jones	Christie	Bancroft	Hill	Brown	Emson	1
Shoemake	Huxford	Price	Nicol	Slack	Bloodworth	Cotton	Jones•	Christie	Bancrroft	Hill†	Brown•	Emson†	2
Shoemake	Huxford	Price	Nicol	Slack	Bloodworth	Emson	Bancroft	Christie	Cotton	Hill	Brown	Appleby	3
Shoemake	Huxford	Price	Nicol	Walker	Bloodworth	Emson•	Cotton	Christie	Bancroft	Hill†	Brown•	Keast†	4
Shoemake	Huxford	Jones	Nicol	Slack	Walker	Graham	Brown	Christie	Bancroft	Hill	Keast	Appleby	5
Shoemake	**Huxford**	**Keast**	**Nicol**	**Slack**	**Jones•**	**Graham**	**Brown**	**Christie**	**Bancroft**	**Hill†**	**Cotton•**	**Price†**	**6**
Shoemake	Huxford	Keast	Nicol	Slack	Walker	Walsh	Brown	Christie	Bancroft•	Hill	Graham•	Jones	7
Shoemake	Huxford	Keast	Nicol	Slack	Walker	Brown	Graham	Walsh	Jones	Hill	Christie	Price	8
Shoemake	**Huxford**	**Keast†**	**Nicol**	**Slack**	**Price**	**Graham**	**Brown**	**Christie**	**Jones**	**Hill**	**Cotton**	**Appleby†**	**9**
Shoemake	Huxford	Jones	Nicol	Slack	Walker†	Graham	Brown	Walsh	Bancroft	Hill	Cotton	Appleby†	10
Bastock	**Price**	**Jones**	**Nicol**	**Slack•**	**Bloodworth**	**Graham**	**Brown**	**Cotton**	**Bancroft**	**Appleby**	**Christie•**	**Reddin**	**11**
Shoemake	**Huxford**	**Keast**	**Nicol**	**Price**	**Bloodworth**	**Graham**	**Brown**	**Christie**	**Bancroft**	**Hill•**	**Jones•**	**Appleby**	**12**
Shoemake	Huxford	Keast	Nicol	Price	Bloodworth	Graham	Brown	Walsh	Bancroft	Hill	Slack	Christie	13
Shoemake	Huxford	Keast	Nicol	Price	Bloodworth•	Graham	Brown	Walsh	Bancroft	Hill	Slack•	Christie	14
Bastock	**Huxford•**	**Keast**	**Nicol**	**Price**	**Slack**	**Graham**	**Brown**	**Christie**	**Bancroft**	**Hill**	**Jones•**	**Bloodworth**	**15**
Bastock	**Huxford**	**Keast**	**Nicol**	**Price**	**Slack**	**Graham**	**Brown**	**Christie•**	**Bancroft**	**Hill**	**Jones•**	**Bloodworth**	**16**
Bastock	Huxford	Keast	Nicol	Price	Slack	Graham	Brown	Christie•	Bancroft†	Hill	Jones•	Bloodworth†	17
Shoemake	Huxford	Keast	Nicol	Price	Slack	Graham	Brown	Christie	Jones	Hill•	Bloodworth	Appleby	18
Shoemake	**Huxford**	**Jones**	**Nicol**	**Price**	**Slack**	**Graham**	**Brown**	**Christie**	**Bancroft•**	**Hill**	**Cotton•**	**Appleby**	**19**
Shoemake	Huxford	Jones	Nicol	Price	Slack	Graham	Brown	Christie	Bancroft•	Hill	Cotton•	Bloodworth	20
Bastock	**Huxford**	**Jones**	**Nicol**	**Price**	**Slack**	**Graham**	**Brown**	**Christie**	**Bancroft**	**Hill**	**Cotton•**	**Appleby**	**21**
Bastock	Huxford	Jones	Nicol	Price	Slack	Graham	Brown	Christie	Bancroft	Hill	Keast	Cotton	22
Bastock	**Huxford**	**Jones**	**Nicol**	**Price**	**Slack**	**Graham**	**Brown**	**Christie**	**Bancroft**	**Hill**	**Keast**	**Cotton**	**23**
Bastock	Huxford	Jones	Nicol	Price	Slack	Graham•	Brown	Christie	Bancroft	Hill	Keast•	Cotton	24
Bastock	Huxford•	Jones	Nicol	Price	Slack	Graham†	Brown	Christie	Bancroft	Hill	Keast•	Waller†	25
Bastock	Huxford	Jones	Nicol	Price•	Slack	Graham	Brown	Christie	Bancroft	Hill	Keast•	Waller	26
Bastock	Huxford	Jones	Nicol	Price•	Slack	Graham†	Brown	Christie	Bancroft	Hill	Keast•	Waller†	27
Bastock	**Huxford•**	**Jones**	**Nicol**	**Price**	**Slack**	**Keast**	**Brown**	**Christie**	**Bancroft†**	**Hill**	**Graham•**	**Waller†**	**28**
Shoemake	**Huxford**	**Jones•**	**Nicol**	**Price**	**Slack**	**Keast**	**Brown**	**Christie**	**Bancroft**	**Hill**	**Graham•**	**Waller**	**29**
Shoemake	Huxford	Jones	Nicol	Price	Slack	Waller•	Brown	Christie	Keast	Hill	Graham•	Bloodworth	30
Shoemake	Huxford•	Jones	Nicol	Price†	Slack	Keast	Brown	Christie	Culpin•	Hill	Graham	Bancroft	31
Shoemake	**Huxford**	**Jones†**	**Nicol**	**Price**	**Slack**	**Keast**	**Brown**	**Christie•**	**Culpin**	**Hill**	**Graham**	**Bloodworth**	**32**
Shoemake	Huxford	Bancroft	Nicol	Bloodworth	Slack	Graham	Brown	Culpin	Keast	Hill	Jones	Price	33
Shoemake	Huxford	Bancroft	Nicol	Bloodworth†	Slack	Graham	Brown	Culpin†	Keast	Hill	Jones	Waller	34
Shoemake	Huxford	Curtis	Nicol	Slack	Price	Keast	Brown	Waller	Culpin•	Hill	Graham	Bancroft	35
Shoemake	Huxford	Curtis•	Bloodworth	Slack	Price	Graham	Brown	Christie†	Keast	Hill	Bancroft	Waller	36
Shoemake	**Huxford**	**Keast**	**Nicol**	**Slack**	**Price**	**Waller†**	**Brown**	**Bancroft**	**Culpin•**	**Hill**	**Christie**	**Graham**	**37**
Bastock	Huxford	Keast	Nicol	Slack	Bloodworth	Graham	Brown	Christie	Bancroft	Hill	Waller	Jones	38
Bastock	Huxford	Keast	Nicol	Slack	Curtis	Jones	Brown	Christie	Bancroft	Hill•	Graham	Bloodworth	39
Bastock	Huxford	Bancroft	Nicol	Slack	Curtis	Graham	Brown	Gavin	Butterworth	Hill	Keast	Bloodworth	40
Bastock	Huxford•	Curtis	Nicol	Slack	Howarth	Graham	Brown	Gavin	Bancroft	Hill	Keast	Jones	41
Bastock	Huxford	Bancroft†	Nicol	Slack	Curtis	Graham	Brown	Gavin	Cox•	Hill	Keast	Jones	42
Bastock	Huxford	Curtis†	Nicol	Slack	Howarth	Graham	Brown	Gavin	Bancroft	Hill	Keast	Jones	43
Bastock	Huxford	Curtis•	Nicol	Slack	Howarth	Graham†	Brown	Gavin	Bancroft	Hill	Keast	Christie	44
Bastock	Huxford	Keast	Nicol	Slack	Howarth	Graham†	Brown	Gavin	Butterworth	Hill	Bancroft	Curtis	45
Bastock	Huxford	Keast	Nicol	Slack†	Howarth	Graham•	Brown	Gavin	Butterworth	Hill	North	Bancroft	46
Bastock	Huxford	Keast	Nicol	Butterworth	Curtis	North	Brown	Gavin	Bancroft	Hill	Graham	Price	47
Bastock	Huxford	Keast	Nicol	Curtis•	Howarth	North	Brown	Gavin	Butterworth	Hill	Graham	Bancroft	48
Bastock	Huxford	Keast	Nicol	Slack	Curtis	Graham	Brown	Gavin	Butterworth	Hill	North	Bancroft	49
Bastock	Huxford	Keast	Nicol	Slack•	Curtis	Graham	Brown	Gavin	Butterworth	Bancroft	Hill	Price	50
Bastock	Huxford	Keast	Nicol	Barker	Curtis	Graham	Brown	Gavin	Bancroft•	North	Hill	Price	51
Bastock	Huxford	Keast	Nicol	Slack	Curtis†	Brown	Graham	Gavin•	Butterworth	Hill	North	Bancroft	52
Bastock	Huxford	Keast	Nicol	Slack	Curtis	Graham•	Brown	North	Barker	Hill	Price	Bancroft	53
Bastock	Huxford	Keast	Nicol†	Slack	Curtis	Graham•	Brown	Gavin	Barker	Hill	North	Price	54
Bastock	Huxford	Keast	Nicol	Slack	Curtis	North	Brown	Gavin	Barker•	Hill	Graham	Bancroft	55

• substituted by No. 12.   † substituted by No. 14.

League & Cup Appearances: Bastock 30; Bancroft 35; Bloodworth 12; Butterworth 8; Barker 2; Brown 51; Christie 30; Cotton 5; Culpin ; Curtis 17; Cox 1; Emson 2; Graham 39; Gavin 14; Huxford 54; Hill 52; Howarth 5; Keast 35; Nicol 53; North 5; Price 29; Slack 48; Shoemake 25; Walsh 5; Waller 3; Walker 4; Jones 24; Appleby 1.

Kettering Town

DAVE CUSACK

Born in Rotherham, Dave joined Sheffield Wednesday as an apprentice in October 1975 and went on to make almost 100 appearances for the Owls. In 1978 he moved to Southend where a further 186 first team appearances were made. Millwall was Dave's next stop before tasting management for the first time at both Rotherham and Doncaster Rovers where he was player-boss.

He joined Boston United originally as a player before taking over as caretaker-manager after the departure of George Kerr in 1990. He helped United stave off the threat of relegation and was offered the job on a permanent basis.

Last season, his first full season in charge, he guided the Pilgrims to a fine 8th position. Unfortunately, he wasn't happy with the budget offered to him for the new campaign and departed from York Street. However, he was quickly appointed as the man to take over from Peter Morris at Kettering and has ambitions to take the Poppies into the Football League.

One of Kettering Town's most consistent performers, England Semi-Professional defender Paul Nicol, clears this Wycombe attack at Adams Park. Photo: Mick Cheney.

Programme details:
    32 pages for £1.00
    By Keyprint

Any other club publications:
    Poppies at the Gates of Dawn (Fanzine)

Local Newspapers:
    Evening Telegraph
    Chronicle & Echo
    Herald & Post
    Citizen

Local Radio Stations:
    Radio Northampton
    Northants 96
    KCBC

KETTERING TOWN -PLAYING SQUAD 1992-93

Player	Honours	Birthplace and date	Transfer Fees	Previous Clubs
GOALKEEPERS				
Paul Bastock		Redditch 19/5/70		Cambridge Utd, Coventry
Kevin Shoemake		Wickford 28/1/65		Leyton Orient, Harlow, Chelmsford, Welling, Peterborough, Kettering, Redbridge
DEFENDERS				
Richard Huxford				Scunthorpe, Burton Alb, Matlock, Gainsborough Trin
Paul Nicol	ESP	Scunthorpe 31/10/67		Scunthorpe
Irvin Gernon	EY Eu21	Birmingham 30/12/62		Ipswich, Gillingham, Reading, Northampton
Trevor Slack	EY	Peterborough 26/9/62		Peterboro, Rotherham, Grimsby, Northampton, Chesterfld
Gareth Price		Swindon 21/2/70		Mansfield Town, Bury
Chris Swailes		Gateshead 19/10/70	£5,000	Ipswich Town, Peterborough Utd, Boston Utd
MIDFIELD				
Paul Bancroft	ESP	Derby 10/9/64	£12,000	Derby, Northampton, Nuneaton, Burton Alb, Kidderminster
Steve Adams	GMVC	Sheffield 7/5/59		Rotherham Utd, Worksop Town, Scarborough, Doncaster, Boston Utd
Richard Hill		Hinckley 20/9/63		Leicester C, Nuneaton, Northampton, Watford, Oxford Utd
FORWARDS				
Jon Graham		Leicester		Local football
Phil Brown		Sheffield 16/1/66		Chesterfield, Stockport, Lincoln C
Marc North		Ware 29/5/66		Luton, Grimsby, Leicester, Luton, Shepshed Albion
Mick Nuttell		Boston 22/11/68	£11,000	Peterborough, Cheltenham, Wycombe, Boston Utd
David Riley		Northampton 8/12/60		Keyworth Utd, Notts Forest, Port Vale, Peterborough Utd
Andrew Curtis		Doncaster 2/12/72		York City

Departures during season:
Paul Emson (Gateshead), Dave Reddin (Boston Utd), Steve Appleby (Bourne), Perry Cotton (New Zealand), Kevin Shoemake (Redbridge), Paul Jones (Stafford), Trevor Christie (VS Rugby). Darren Bloodworth (Boston Utd), Dean Barker (Sudbury), Dougie Keast (Corby).

Players on loan during season:
Richard Walker (Notts Co), Mario Walsh (Colchester), Hamish Curtis, Pat Gavin, Gary Butterworth, Lee Howarth, Paul Culpin (all Peterborough), Paul Cox (Notts Co).

Rockingham Road, Kettering Town

Name of ground: Rockingham Road
Ground address and Tel. No.: Rockingham Road, Kettering, Northants NN16 9AW. Tel: (0536) 83028 (Office)
Simple ground directions: On the A6003 Kettering to Oakham road
Official capacity: 6,500   **Seating:** 1,250   **Covered accommodation:** 5,250
Cost of seats: £5.00   **Cost of standing:** £4.00
Record attendance: 11,536 Kettering v Peterborough (pre-Taylor report)
Social facilities available (Bars, hot & cold food etc.): Social Club (Poppies), Vice-Presidents Bar
Car parking: Club car-park and surrounding roads

Sponsored by: P H S   **KETTERING TOWN**   **Nickname:** Poppies

---

Previous leagues: Southern League, Northants League, Midland League, Birmingham League, Central Alliance, United Counties League
Club colours: All red   **Change colours:** All blue
Midweek home matches: Tuesday   **Club metal badges:** Yes
Club programme: 32 pages £1.00   **Editor:** Gerry Knowles
Record transfer fee paid: £17,500 to Grantham for Gary Jones
Record transfer fee received: £150,000 from Newcastle United for Andy Hunt
Record appearances for club: R. Ashby
Record goalscorer for club: A. Woolhead
Record goalscorer in a season: Roy Clayton
Past players who have progressed to the Football League: Kellock (Peterborough), G. Wood (Notts Co.), Longhurst (Nott'm Forest), S. Endersby (Ipswich), S. Fallon (Cambridge Utd), J. Sellers (Manchester Utd), A. Rogers (Plymouth), M. Forster (Northampton), J. Brown (Chesterfield), Cohen Griffith (Cardiff City), Andy Hunt (Newcastle)
Club honours: GMAC Cup Winners; FA Trophy finalists and semi-finalists; Alliance Premier League runners-up; Alliance Premier League Cup runners-up; Southern League Winners; County Cup Winners; Deventry Charity Cup Winners; Hillier Senior Cup Winners; Daventry Charity Cup Winners; Maunsell Cup Winners
91-92 P.O.Y.: Richard Huxford

KIDDERMINSTER HARRIERS

Formed: 1886

Chairman:
David Reynolds

Vice Chairman
Richard Painter

Directors:
Brian Bayliss
Graham Lane
Ray Mercer
Roger Smith
Colin Youngjohns

Secretary:
Ray Mercer

Manager:
Graham Allner

**Asst Manager/
Physiotherapist:**
Jimmy Conway

Commercial Manager:
Phil Wright

The 1991/92 season so very nearly ended disastrously for Kidderminster Harriers. Only a battling 3-0 win at Gateshead on the last Saturday of the season secured their Conference position, although in the end results elsewhere also aided them.

Manager Graham Allner remained faithful to his young side, although he did turn to coach Graham Mackenzie to lend his experience on the field towards the end of the season. Mackenzie has now left Aggborough after it was decided to disband the club's YT programme. Harriers have some very talented young players, many of whom came through their YT scheme. But the Conference is a very tough league and it was questionable whether so many youngsters in one team can survive in the competition for long. Allner has experienced players at his disposal such as striker Paul Davies and England midfielder Antone Joseph, but he needs a few more if Harriers are to progress.

The usually prolific Davies managed only three league goals last season and Allner will need a better return from the England striker next season and also add extra firepower to the front line. Yet another Harriers' youngster has joined the ranks of the full-time game with Steve Lilwall's move to West Bromwich Albion. He follows goalkeeper Paul Jones and defender Dave Barnett who both moved into the League during last season.

Kidderminster Harriers F.C. 1991-92. Back Row (L-R): S Lilwall (now WBA), J Lowe, D Hadley, A Attwood, D Benton, A Kurila, B Wilcox, R Forsyth. Middle: M Brown (Med. Asst), M Weir, D Steadman, D Barnett (now Barnet), J McGrath, P Jones (now Wolves), P Davies, J Conway (Asst Man). Front: G Allner (Manager), C Burton, M Carroll, A Joseph, D Humphreys, P Howell, G Mackenzie.

GM Vauxhall Conference: 19th.　　　　**FA Cup: 1st Round.**　　　　**FA Trophy: 3rd Round.**

Match No.	Date	Competition	Venue H/A	Opponents	Result	League H/T	Pos.	Goalscorers (Times if known)	Attendance
1	Aug 17	GMVC	A	Slough	L 1-3	0-1		Forsyth 76 (pen)	823
2	Aug 24	GMVC	H	Gateshead	W 5-3	2-2		Barnett 3,29; Humphreys 50; Johnson og,64; Wilcox 83	1051
3	Aug 26	GMVC	A	Northwich Victoria	L 1-3	0-1		Lilwall 80	1015
4	Aug 31	GMVC	A	Boston Utd	W 2-1	1-1		Whitehouse 7,90	1319
5	Sep 4	BLT 1	A	Cheltenham	L 2-4	0-1		Davies 46; Humphreys 57	675
6	Sep 7	WC 1	H	Rhayader T.	W 5-1	4-1		Davies 10,35,60; Lilwall 25; Joseph 30	705
7	Sep 10	GMVC	A	Telford Utd	L 1-3	1-2		Kurila 14	1430
8	Sep 14	GMVC	H	Welling Utd	L 1-3	1-1		Whitehouse 31	1168
9	Sep 21	GMVC	A	Kettering	L 1-2	1-0		Howell 1	1532
10	Sep 23	GMVC	H	Macclesfield	D 1-1	1-1		Weir 3	1326
11	Sep 28	GMVC	H	Northwich Victoria	W 1-0	1-0		Howell 43	929
12	Oct 1	GMVC	A	Witton Albion	L 1-2	1-0		Howell 14	792
13	Oct 5	WC 2	H	Morda Utd	W 7-1	3-0		Humphreys; Wilcox (2); Whitehouse (2); Davies; Howell	586
14	Oct 7	GMVC	H	Redbridge Forest	W 5-1	4-1		Humphreys 10;Lilwall 25;Whitehouse 31,47pens;Wilcox 44	1045
15	Oct 12	GMVC	A	Yeovil	D 1-1	1-1		Whitehouse 22 pen	1305
16	Oct 14	BLT 1	H	Cheltenham	W 3-1	2-0		Howell 10; Davies 28; Whitehouse 60	733
17	Oct 19	GMVC	A	Runcorn	L 1-4	0-1		Howell 76	544
18	Oct 26	GMVC	H	Wycombe Wanderers	W 1-0	1-0		Whitehouse 8	2037
19	Oct 28	WC 3	H	Llansantffraid	W 4-1	2-0		Joseph 7; Whitehouse 20,50; Davies 55	754
20	Nov 2	GMVC	A	Merthyr Tydfil	L 1-2	0-1		Whitehouse 81	422
21	Nov 4	GMVC	H	Altrincham	W 1-0	1-0		Whitehouse 29	1128
22	Nov 9	GMVC	A	Redbridge Forest	L 0-5	0-1			479
23	Nov 16	FAC 1	H	Aylesbury Utd	L 0-1	0-0			1773
24	Nov 23	GMVC	H	Farnborough	D 1-1	0-1		Lilwall 55	1175
25	Nov 30	GMVC	A	Bath City	W 1-0	0-0		Howell 51 pen	544
26	Dec 3	WSC 2	A	Moor Green	W 4-0			Hadley (2); Davies (2)	356
27	Dec 7	GMVC	A	Macclesfield	D 0-0	0-0			851
28	Dec 17	BLT 2	A	Slough	W 1-0	0-0		Howell 77	405
29	Dec 21	GMVC	A	Cheltenham	W 2-1	0-0		Wilcox 43; Howell 58	872
30	Dec 26	GMVC	H	Telford Utd	L 1-2	1-2		Wilcox 24	1922
31	Jan 1	GMVC	A	Altrincham	D 1-1	1-0		Howell 44	842
32	Jan 4	GMVC	H	Barrow	L 1-2	1-1		Whitehouse 4	1256
33	Jan 6	WC 4	H	Swansea City	L 1-3	0-2		Howell 75	1815
34	Jan 11	FAT 1	A	Walton & Hersham	W 2-0	2-0		Howell 16,32	426
35	Jan 13	GMVC	H	Stafford Rangers	W 2-1	1-1		Weir 44; Forsyth 58 pen	1136
36	Jan 17	GMVC	A	Wycombe Wanderers	L 0-2	0-1			3913
37	Jan 20	BLT 3	H	Yeovil	L 1-2	1-0		Howell 38	681
38	Jan 25	GMVC	A	Yeovil	D 1-1	0-1		Forsyth 57	2111
39	Feb 1	FAT 2	A	Runcorn	D 1-1	0-1		Davies 85	681
40	Feb 3	FAT 2R	H	Runcorn	W 5-2			Davies 23,72; Howell 91; Benton 105; Wolsey 119	1189
41	Feb 7	GMVC	H	Colchester Utd	D 2-2	2-0		Davies 15; Humphreys 24	1828
42	Feb 15	GMVC	A	Farnborough	L 1-2	0-0		Weir 47	822
43	Feb 17	WSC SF	H	Bromsgrove	L 0-2				1051
44	Feb 22	FAT 3	H	Yeovil	L 1-3	0-2		Forsyth 67	2679
45	Feb 29	GMVC	A	Welling Utd	L 2-3	2-2		Hadley 35; Joseph 44	815
46	Mar 7	GMVC	H	Witton Albion	L 0-1	0-0			1074
47	Mar 9	GMVC	H	Bath City	L 0-1	0-1			928
48	Mar 21	GMVC	A	Merthyr Tydfil	D 2-2	1-0		Benton 24; Humphreys 73	1014
49	Mar 28	GMVC	A	Colchester Utd	L 0-3	0-2			3073
50	Mar 30	GMVC	H	Boston Utd	L 1-3	1-1		Davies 43	1009
51	Apr 4	GMVC	A	Stafford Rangers	L 0-2	0-0			1102
52	Apr 11	GMVC	H	Runcorn	W 2-1	1-1		Grainger 35,71	1078
53	Apr 13	GMVC	H	Kettering	L 2-3	1-1		Weir 29; Davies 62	1243
54	Apr 18	GMVC	A	Barrow	L 1-5	0-3		Wilcox 50	1109
55	Apr 21	GMVC	H	Cheltenham	W 2-1	1-1		Howell 30; Davies 65	2158
56	Apr 25	GMVC	H	Slough	D 3-3	0-2		Howell 61; Grainger 70,78	1541
57	May 2	GMVC	A	Gateshead	W 3-0	2-0		Humphreys 1,9,48	505

Kidderminster Harriers

1	2	3	4	5	6	7	8	9	10	11	12	14	Match No.
Green	Mulholland	McGrath	Benton	Kurila	Forsyth	Joseph	Whitehouse	Hadley†	Wilcox	Humphreys	Bradley	Lilwall	1
Green	Mulholland	McGrath	Benton	Barnett•	Forsyth	Wilcox	Whitehouse	Davies	Lilwall	Humphreys	Joseph	Bradley	2
Green	Mulholland	McGrath	Benton	Kurila	Forsyth•	Wilcox	Whitehouse	Davies†	Lilwall	Humphreys	Joseph	Bradley	3
Green	Hulholland	McGrath	Benton	Kurila	Wilcox•	Joseph	Whitehouse	Davies	Lilwall	Humphreys	Gillett	Bradley	4
Green	**Mulholland**	**McGrath**	**Benton†**	**Kurila**	**Wolsey**	**Joseph**	**Whitehouse**	**Davies**	**Lilwall**	**Humphreys**	**Brdley**	**Gillett**	**5**
Green	Mulholland	McGrath•	Benton	Gillett	Wolsey	Joseph	Bradley	Davies	Lilwall	Humphreys†	Kurila	Taylor	6
Green	Mulholland	McGrath	Benton	Kurila	Wilcox•	Joseph	Whitehouse	Davies	Lilwall	Humphreys	Wolsey	Gillett	7
Steadman	Benton	McGrath	Weir	Barnett	Wilcox•	Joseph	Whitehouse	Davies†	Carroll	Humphreys	Lilwall	Howell	8
Green	Benton	McGrath	Weir	Barnett	Wilcox†	Joseph	Howell	Whitehouse	Lilwall	Humphreys	Davies	Czarroll	9
Green	Benton	McGrath	Weir	Barnett	Wilcox	Joseph	Howell	Whitehouse	Lilwall	Humphreys	Carroll	Davies	10
Green	Benton	McGrath	Weir	Barnett	Wilcox	Joseph	Howell	Whitehouse	Lilwall	Humphreys	Davies	Dodd	11
Green	Benton	McGrath	Weir	Barnett	Wilcox	Joseph	Howell	Whitehouse	Lilwall	Humphreys	Davies	Dodd	12
Green	**Benton**	**McGrath**	**Weir**	**Barnett**	**Wilcox**	**Joseph**	**Howell**	**Whitehouse•**	**Lilwall**	**Humphreys†**	**Davies**	**Hadley**	**13**
Green	Benton	McGrath	Weir	Barnett	Wilcox	Joseph	Howell	Whitehouse	Lilwall	Humphreys	Davies	Carroll	14
Green	Benton	McGrath	Weir	Barnett	Wilcox	Joseph	Howell	Whitehouse•	Lilwall†	Humphreys	Davies	Carroll	15
Green	**Benton**	**McGrath•**	**Weir**	**Barnett**	**Wilcox**	**Joseph**	**Howell**	**Whitehouse**	**Davies**	**Humphreys**	**Gillett**	**Taylor**	**16**
Green	Benton	Gillett	Weir	Barnett	Wilcox	Joseph	Howell	Whitehouse	Davies†	Humphreys	Taylor	Wolsey	17
Green	Benton	McGrath	Weir	Barnett	Wilcox†	Joseph	Howell	Whitehouse	Wolsey	Humphreys	Davies	Kurila	18
Green	**Dodd**	**McGrath**	**Benton•**	**Barnett**	**Wolsey**	**Joseph**	**Howell†**	**Whitehouse**	**Davies**	**Humphreys**	**Kurila**	**Carroll**	**19**
Green	Benton	McGrth	Weir	Barnett	Wolsey•	Joseph	Howell	Whitehouse	Lilwall	Humphreys	Davies	Carroll	20
Green	Benton	McGrth	Weir	Barnett†	Lilwall	Joseph	Howell	Whitehouse	Davies	Humphreys	Wolsey	Carroll	21
Green	Kurila	Lilwall	Weir	Barnett	Wolsey	Joseph	Howell	Whitehouse	Davies	Humphreys	Gillett	Carroll	22
Green	**Benton**	**McGrath**	**Weir**	**Barnett**	**Wolsey**	**Joseph**	**Howell•**	**Whitehouse**	**Lilwall**	**Humphreys**	**Davies**	**Carroll**	**23**
Green	Benton	McGrath	Weir	Barnett	Lilwall	Joseph	Howell	Hadley	Davies	Humphreys	Wolsey	Whitehouse	24
Green	Benton	McGrath†	Weir	Barnett	Lilwall	Joseph	Howell	Hadley	Davies	Humphreys•	Wilcox	Coogan	25
Steadman	**Benton**	**Lilwall**	**Weir**	**Gillett**	**Wilcox**	**Carroll•**	**Taylor**	**Hadley**	**Davies**	**Coogan†**	**Dodd**	**Howell**	**26**
Green	Benton	McGrath	Weir	Barnett	Wilcox	Joseph	Howell	Hadley	Dazvies	Lilwall	Gillett	Carroll	27
Green	**Benton**	**McGrath**	**Weir**	**Barnett**	**Forsyth**	**Wilcox**	**Howell**	**Hadley**	**Davies**	**Lilwall**	**Whitehouse**	**Gillett**	**28**
Green	Benton	McGrath	Weir	Barnett	Forsyth†	Wilcox	Howell•	Hadley	Davies	Lilwall	Humphreys	Joseph	29
Green	Benton	McGrath	Weir	Barnett	Forsyth	Wilcox	Howell	Hadley•	Davies	Lilwall†	Humphreys	Joseph	30
Green	Benton	McGrath	Weir	Barnett	Forsyth	Wilcox	Howell	Hadley•	Davies	Lilwall	Whitehouse	Joseph	31
Green	Benton	McGrath	Weir .	Joseph	Forsyth	Wilcox	Humphreys	Whitehouse	Davies	Lilwall	Hadley	Howell	32
Green	**Benton**	**McGrath**	**Weir**	**Joseph**	**Forsyth**	**Wilcox**	**Humphreys•**	**Whitehouse†**	**Davies**	**Lilwall**	**Hadley**	**Howell**	**33**
Green	**Benton**	**McGrath**	**Weir**	**Joseph**	**Forsyth†**	**Wilcox**	**Howell**	**Whitehouse**	**Davies**	**Humphreys**	**Hadley**	**Lilwall**	**34**
Green	Benton	McGrath	Weir	Joseph	Forsyth	Wilcox	Howell	Whitehouse	Davies	Humphreys	Hadley	Wolsey	35
Green	Benton	McGrath†	Weir	Barnett	Forsyth	Wilcox	Howell	Hadley•	Wilcox	Humphreys	Davies	Joseph	36
Green	**Benton**	**McGrath**	**Weir**	**Wilcox**	**Forsyth**	**Humphreys†**	**Howell**	**Taylor**	**Davies**	**Lilwall•**	**Whitehouse**	**Gillett**	**37**
Green	Benton	McGrath	Weir	Gillett	Forsyth	Wilcox	Howell•	Taylor	Davies	Humphreys	Hadley	Joseph	38
Green	Benton	McGrath†	Weir	Gillett	Forsyth	Wilcox	Howell	Taylor•	Davies	Humphreys	Hadley	Joseph	39
Green	**Benton**	**Joseph**	**Weir**	**Gillett**	**Forsyth**	**Wilcox†**	**Howell**	**Taylor•**	**Davies**	**Humphreys**	**Hadley**	**Wolsey**	**40**
Green	Benton	Joseph	Weir	Gillett	Forsyth	Lilwall•	Howell	Hadley	Davies	Humphreys	Hadley	Taylor	41
Green	Benton	Joseph	Weir	Gillett	Forsyth	Lilwall†	Howell	Hadley	Davies	Cazrroll	Taylor	Davis	42
Green	**Benton**	**Davis**	**Weir**	**Gillett**	**Forsyth**	**Wolsey**	**Howell**	**Hadley**	**Davies**	**Carroll•**	**Taylor**	**Blacklock**	**43**
Green	**Benton**	**McGrath**	**Weir**	**Gillett**	**Forsyth**	**Joseph**	**Howell**	**Hadley**	**Davies**	**Wolsey**	**Taylor**	**Carroll**	**44**
Green	Benton	McGrath	Weir	Davis	MacKenzie	Joseph	Howell	Hadley	Davies	Humphreys	Gillett	Wolsey	45
Green	Benton	McGrath	Weir	Davis	Forsyth	Joseph	MacKenzie	Hadley•	Davies	Hackett	Carroll	Gillett	46
Green	Benton	McGrath	Weir	Davis†	Forsyth	Joseph	MacKenzie	Hadley•	Davies	Hackett	Howell	Gillett	47
Green	Benton	McGrath	Weir	Joseph	Wilcox	Humphreys	MacKenzie†	Hanson	Davies	Hackett	Lillwall	Forsyth	48
Green	Benton	McGrath	Weir	Joseph	Wilcox†	MacKenzie•	Grainger	Hanson	Davies	Humphreys	Howell	Lilwall	49
Green	Benton	McGrath	Weir	Joseph	Wilcox	Humphreys	Grainger	Hanson	Davies	Hackett•	Howell	MacKenzie	50
Steadman	Benton	McGrath	Weir	Wilcox	MacKenzie	Humphreys	Grainger	Howell•	Davies	Lilwall	Hanson	Gillett	51
Green	Benton	McGrath	Weir	Gillett	MacKenzie	Joseph	Grainger	Hadley	Davies	Humphreys	Howell	Wilcox	52
Green	Benton	Lilwall	Weir	Gillett	MacKenzie	Joseph†	Grainger	Hadley	Davies	Humphreys	Howell	Wilcox	53
Green	Benton	McGrath	Weir	Gillett	MacKenzie	Joseph	Wilcox	Hadley•	Davies	Humphreys	Hanson	Wolsey	54
Green	Wilcox	Joseph	Weir	Gillett•	MacKenzie	Wolsey	Grainger	Howell	Davies†	Humphreys	Benton	Hadley	55
Green	Wilcox	Joseph	Weir	Gillett•	MacKenzie	Wolsey	Grainger	Howell	Hadley	Humphreys	Benton	Hanson	56
Green	Wilcox	McGrath	Weir	Gillett	Joseph	Wolsey	Grainger	Howell	Hadley	Humphreys	Benton	Hanson	57

• substituted by No. 12.   † substituted by No. 14.

Kidderminster Harriers

GRAHAM ALLNER

Graham Allner joined Kidderminster Harriers as manager in October 1983. Formerly assistant manager at Cheltenham Town, he had won the Southern League championship when manager of the now defunct AP Leamington.

Graham's playing days began at Walsall where he gained England Youth honours. He then moved into non-league football where he played at Worcester City, Stafford Rangers and Alvechurch.

During his time at Aggborough, Graham has encouraged youth through their YT programme and many of his young players have come through to the first team. Last season was a difficult one for both him and the club and he will be hoping that Harriers can once again be a force to be reckoned with in the GM Vauxhall Conference.

Kidderminster Harriers' defend in numbers to prevent Barrow from scoring during last season's Conference clash at Holker Street. Photo: Ged Rule.

Programme details:
    40 pages for 80p
    Editor - Roger Barlow

Any other club publications:
    The Soup (Fanzine)

Local Newspapers:
    Kidderminster Shuttle/Times
    Kidderminster Chronicle
    Evening Mail
    Express & Star
    Worcester Evening News
Local Radio Stations:
    BBC Hereford & Worcester
    Radio Wyvern

KIDDERMINSTER HARRIERS - PLAYING SQUAD 1992-93

Player	Honours	Birthplace and date	Transfer Fees	Previous Clubs
GOALKEEPERS				
Ron Green		Birmingham 3/10/56		Alvechurch, Walsall, Shrewsbury, Bristol R, Scunthorpe, Walsall
Darren Steadman	ES	Kidderminster 26/1/70		None
DEFENDERS				
John McGrath	FA XI	Dumbarton 20/12/63		Shrewsbury, Worcester
Martin Weir	FA XI Middx Wand	Birmingham 4/7/68		Birmingham City
David Benton		West Bromwich 8/1/71		Birmingham City
Craig Gillett		Birmingham 17/10/72		Ex-YTS
Brett Wilcox		Sutton Coldfield 27/12/68	£1,000	Bridgnorth Town
MIDFIELD				
Paul Grainger		Walsall 28/1/68	£10,000	Aston Villa, Mile Oak R, Wolves, Telford Utd
Antone Joseph	ESP FAT(2)	Manchester 30/9/59	£17,500	WBA, Cardiff, Weymouth, Telford Utd
Richard Forsyth		Dudley 3/10/70		Stourbridge
Mark Wolsey		27/12/73		Ex-YTS
FORWARDS				
David Hadley		Birmingham 7/12/64	£10,000	Moor Green, Mile Oak R, Tamworth
Peter Howell		Birmingham 5/6/67		Aston Villa
Paul Davies	ESP, FAT FA XI	Kidderminster 9/10/60		Cardiff City, SC Herecles(Hol), Trowbridge Town
Les Palmer		Quinton 5/9/71		West Bromwich Albion
Jon Hanson		Birmingham		West Bromwich Albion
Delwyn Humphreys	ESP	Shrewsbury 13/2/65	£10,000	Bridgnorth Town

Departures during season:
Denis Mulholland (Chelmsley), Martin Dean (Dudley), Alan Kurila (Burton Alb), Dave Barnett (Barnet), Marc Coogan (Barry), Mark Whitehouse (Bromsgrove), Lee Horrocks (Redditch), Graham Mackenzie (America), Matthew Carroll (Sutton Coldfield), Justin Taylor (Tamworth), Glyn Jones & Russell Dodd (Sandwell Boro), Craig Langford (Hereford Utd), Carl Smith (Alcester), Max Woodward (Pershore), Steve Lilwall (West Brom).
Players who joined on loan during season:
Jon Hanson (WBA), Brendan Hackett (Telford).

Aggborough, Kidderminster Harriers

Name of ground: Aggborough.
Ground address and Tel. No.: Hoo Road, Kidderminster DY10 1NB. Tel: 0562 823931/747404
Simple ground directions: Follow Town Centre signs approaching Kidderminster, join ring road and turn into Comberton Hill. Hoo Road is the first on the right and ground is 1/4 mile on left
Official capacity: 10,000   **Seating:** 400   **Covered accommodation:** 6,000
Record attendance: 9,155 v Hereford United
Social facilities available (Bars, hot & cold food etc.): Vice Presidents Lounge/bar & Social Club (3 bars - hot and cold food)
Car parking: 2 large car parks adjacent to ground

Sponsored by: Ansells   **KIDDERMINSTER HARRIERS**   **Nickname:** The Harriers

---

Previous leagues: Birmingham League, Birmingham Combination, West Midland League, Southern League
Club colours: Red & white halves/white/white   **Change colours:** Yellow & blue/blue/blue
Midweek home matches: Monday   **Club metal badges:** Yes
Club shop: Open daily 9am to 5pm (Monday to Friday) and Match days (1st XI)
Record transfer fee paid: £17,000 to Telford United for Antone Joseph, December 1989
Record transfer fee received: £40,000 from WBA for Steve Lilwall, June 1992
Record appearances for club: Brendan Wassall 686 (1972-74)
Record goalscorer for club: Peter Wassall, 432 (1963-74)
Past players who have progressed to the Football League: Albert Christmas (Arsenal), John Baird (Aston Villa), Sam Nicholls (W.B.A.), Frank Danbee (Arsenal), Fred Brown (Stoke), Jack Raybould (Wolves), Sam Broome (Bury), Jim Thorpe (Stoke), Tommy Homer (Man. Utd), Bert Parsons (Aston Villa), Gil Brookes (Stoke), Arthur Filton (W.B.A.), Bill Blake (Crystal Palace), Billy Kingdon (Aston Villa), Stan Fazackerley (Derby County), Jim Russell (Port Vale), Fred Lawrence (West Ham Utd), Eric Jones (Wolves), George Mountford (Stoke City), Keith Jones (Aston Villa), Jack Edwards (Notts County), Bob Raine (Aldershot), Gerry Hitchens (Cardiff City), Kevin Keelan (Wrexham), Bill Tucker (Hereford), Paul McGee (QPR), Tony Cunningham (Lincoln, Barnsley, Man. City, Newcastle), Paul Jones (Wolves), Dave Barnett (Barnet), Steve Lilwall (W.B.A.)
Club honours: FA Trophy Winners 1987; Welsh FA Cup finalists 1986, 1989; Southern League Cup (1); Worcs. Senior Cup (19); Birmingham Senior Cup (7); Staffs Senior Cup (4); West Midland League Champions (6); Runners-up (3); Southern Premier Runners-up (1); West Mid. League Cup Winners (7); Keys Cup Winners (7); Border Counties Floodlit League Champions (3); Camkin Floodlit Cup Winners (3); Bass County Vase Winners (1); FA Trophy Finalists 1991
Club Captain: Antone Joseph   **Player of the Year:** Martin Weir

MACCLESFIELD TOWN

Formed: 1874

Chairman:
A Brocklehurst

Vice Chairman
A Masheder

Directors:
A Cash
N Bardsley
J Chesworth
R Higginbotham
R Curran
P Campbell
J R Mattin

Secretary:
B Lingard

Manager:
Peter Wragg

Asst Manager:
Mickey Roberts

Physiotherapist:
Eric Campbell

Club Doctor:
Dr M Whiteside

Commercial Manager:
R Price

The Silkmen are renowned as one of the hardest teams to beat in the Conference. But they are also one of the most inconsistent. On their day Peter Wragg's team can compete with the best. However, as in their FA Cup Second Quaifying Round exit at the hands of little Central Midlands League side Borrowash Victoria suggests, they can also be an enigma.

Defensively, Macclesfield have always been sound but the 1991/92 campaign saw them concede slightly more goals than they would have liked and also found goals hard to come by at the other end. The signing of much-travelled striker Mick Doherty helped and Wragg will be hoping for better things this coming season from £7,000 signing from Belgian club Binche, former South Liverpool striker Andy Green. The recent capture of highly-rated winger Stuart Leicester from Conference newcomers Stalybridge Celtic will improve Macclesfield's supply of crosses which should provide plenty of amunition for the likes of Doherty, Green and Colin Lambert.

The Silkmen's consolation last season came in both the FA Trophy and Cheshire Senior Cup competitions. They reached the semi-finals of the Trophy after victories over Boston United, Bangor City, Northwich Victoria and Yeovil Town but eventually found Colchester United too much for them over two legs, the tie effectively being over after United had gained a 3-0 lead from their home leg at Layer Road. However, they did manage to lift the Cheshire Senior Cup for the 17th time, but for the first time since 1983, by beating neighbours Witton Albion at Tranmere Rovers' Prenton Park ground by two goals to nil.

Macclesfield Town F.C. 1991-92. Back Row (L-R): M Farrelly, P Clayton, D Heesom (now Witton), P Kendall, G Shepherd, R Ellis, J Askey. Middle: E Campbell (Physio), J Dawson, S Bimson, W Thompson, S Farrelly, A Zelem, C Lambert, J Timmons, M Roberts (Asst-Man). Front: G Tobin, M Dempsey, E Edwards, P Wragg (Manager), S Hanlon, J Imrie (now Mossley), P Johnson. Photo: John Rooney.

Macclesfield Town

Match No.	Date	Competition	Venue H/A	Opponents	Result	League H/T	League Pos.	Goalscorers (Times if known)	Attendance
1	Aug 17	GMVC	A	Colchester	L 0-2	0-2			2333
2	Aug 24	GMVC	H	Slough	L 0-1	0-0	22		879
3	Aug 26	GMVC	H	Cheltenham	D 3-3	0-1	22	Lambert 62,70; Dempsey 81 (pen)	834
4	Aug 31	GMVC	A	Redbridge Forest	D 0-0	0-0	21		472
5	Sep 3	GMVC	H	Telford Utd	W 2-1	0-0	15	Timmons 68,78	838
6	Sep 7	GMVC	H	Yeovil	W 1-0	1-0	6	Lambert 17	2110
7	Sep 14	FAC 1Q	A	Skelmersdale	W 4-0	3-0		Shepherd 7; Heesom 14; Dawson 37; Askey 52	417
8	Sep 17	GMVC	H	Runcorn	W 3-0	1-0	6	Edwards 5,63; Heesom 90	1065
9	Sep 21	GMVC	H	Wycombe	W 1-0	0-0	6	Timmons 68	3821
10	Sep 23	GMVC	A	Kidderminster	D 1-1	1-1	5	Lambert 29	1326
11	Sep 28	FAC 2Q	H	Borrowash Victoria	L 1-2	1-2		Timmons 35	871
12	Oct 1	GMVC	A	Northwich Victoria	D 0-0	0-0	5		905
13	Oct 8	BLT 2	A	Telford Utd	W 2-1	1-1		Timmons 14; Dawson 94	597
14	Oct 12	GMVC	H	Boston Utd	L 0-1	0-0	6		869
15	Oct 19	GMVC	H	Farnborough	L 1-2	0-2	10	Dawson 78	752
16	Oct 26	GMVC	A	Bath City	D 1-1	1-1	11	Askey 5	523
17	Nov 2	GMVC	A	Welling Utd	L 1-2	1-2	14	o.g. 17	505
18	Nov 5	GMVC	H	Stafford Rangers	W 1-0	1-0	10	Green 45	522
19	Nov 9	GMVC	H	Kettering	W 2-0	0-0	10		940
20	Nov 16	GMVC	A	Cheltenham	W 3-2	1-1	9	Green 31,72; Ellis 51	783
21	Nov 23	GMVC	A	Telford Utd	W 1-0	0-0	4	Lambert 51	1199
22	Nov 26	GMVC	A	Barrow	L 0-2	0-1	4		1158
23	Nov 30	GMVC	H	Witton Albion	W 1-0	0-0	4	Farrelly 74 (pen)	1015
24	Dec 7	GMVC	H	Kidderminster	D 0-0	0-0	4		851
25	Dec 17	BLT 3	H	Altrincham	D 1-1	0-0		Green 60	447
26	Dec 26	GMVC	H	Altrincham	D 1-1	0-0	6	Askey 62	1301
27	Jan 1	GMVC	A	Stafford Rangers	D 1-1	1-1	9	Green 18	994
28	Jan 11	FAT 1	H	Boston Utd	D 0-0	0-0			833
29	Jan 15	FAT 1R	A	Boston Utd	W 2-0	0-0		Edwards 22; Lambert 76	947
30	Jan 18	GMVC	A	Boston Utd	W 5-1	0-1	6	Askey 47,75; Green 60; Timmons 63; Clayton 89	951
31	Feb 4	FAT 2	H	Bangor City	W 1-0	0-0		Hanlon 75	631
32	Feb 6	BLT 3R	A	Altrincham	L 1-3	0-3		Askey 85	524
33	Feb 8	GMVC	H	Bath City	D 0-0	0-0	8		578
34	Feb 10	CSC	H	Hyde Utd	W 3-2	1-2			256
35	Feb 15	GMVC	H	Merthyr Tydfil	W 3-0	1-0	7	Askey 20; o.g. 75; Hanlon 82	568
36	Feb 22	FAT 3	A	Northwich Victoria	W 1-0	0-0		Hanlon 65	1537
37	Feb 29	GMVC	H	Yeovil	L 1-2	0-1	10	Doherty 82	701
38	Mar 2	GMVC	A	Northwich Victoria	L 1-2	0-1		Doherty 10 (pen)	802
39	Mar 4	CSC	A	Winsford Utd	W 3-1	2-0			355
40	Mar 7	GMVC	A	Runcorn	D 0-0	0-0	12		661
41	Mar 10	GMVC	A	Farnborough	L 2-4	1-2	14	Hopley 23; o.g. 67	615
42	Mar 14	FAT 4	A	Yeovil	W 2-1	0-1		Green 61; Askey 85	4269
43	Mar 17	GMVC	H	Barrow	L 0-1	0-1	14		502
44	Mar 20	GMVC	A	Witton Albion	D 1-1	0-0	14	Green 52	1308
45	Mar 24	GMVC	A	Kettering	L 0-2	0-0	14		1367
46	Mar 28	GMVC	A	Gateshead	L 0-2	0-0	14		375
47	Mar 30	CSC	H	Winsford Utd	W 3-1	1-1			278
48	Apr 4	FAT S/F1	A	Colchester	L 0-3	0-2			5443
49	Apr 10	FAT S/F2	H	Colchester	D 1-1	1-1		Timmons 20	1650
50	Apr 14	GMVC	H	Wycombe	W 3-1	1-1	14	Johnson 9 (pen); Green 51; Lambert 62	693
51	Apr 18	GMVC	H	Redbridge Forest	D 0-0	0-0	14		460
52	Apr 20	GMVC	A	Altrincham	L 1-3	0-2	14	Green 89	767
53	Apr 22	GMVC	H	Welling Utd	L 1-2	1-1	14	Ellis 42	338
54	Apr 25	GMVC	H	Colchester	D 4-4	1-2	14	Lambert 27,62; Doherty 48; Edwards 52	886
55	Apr 28	GMVC	H	Gateshead	W 1-0	0-0	13	Hopley 49	369
56	May 2	GMVC	A	Slough	W 3-0	1-0	13	Bimson 9,71; Doherty 79	588

Best Home Attendance: 1301 v Altrincham 26.12.91   Lowest: 338 v Welling 22.4.92

Average Home Attendance: 754
Compared to 1990/91: 994

Macclesfield Town

1	2	3	4	5	6	7	8	9	10	11	12	14	Match No.
S.Farrelly	Shepherd	Johnson†	Edwards	Tobin	Hanlon	Askey	Lambert	Dempsey	Clayton	Imrie•	Dawson	M.Farrelly	1
S.Farrelly	Shepherd•	Johnson†	Edwards	Tobin	Hanlon	Askey	Dempsey	Lambert	Clayton	Dawson†	M.Farrelly	Timmons	2
S.Farrelly	M.Farrelly	Johnson	Edwards	Tobin	Hanlon	Askey	Dempsey	Lambert	Clayton•	Dawson	Timmons	Imrie	3
S.Farrelly	Shepherd	Heesom†	Edwards	Tobin	Hanlon	Askey	M.Farrelly	Lambert	Dempsey	Dawson•	Timmons	Ellis	4
S.Farrelly	Shepherd	Heesom	Edwards	Tobin	Hanlon	Askey	M.Farrelly	Lambert	Dempsey	Dawson•	Timmons	Ellis	5
S.Farrelly	Shepherd	Heesom	Edwards	Kendal	Hanlon	Askey	Dempsey	Lambert•	Timmons†	M.Farrelly	Clayton	Ellis	6
S.Farrelly	**Shepherd**	**Heesom**	**Edwards**	**Kendal†**	**Hanlon**	**Askey•**	**Dawson**	**Lambert**	**Dempsey**	**M.Farrelly**	**Clayton**	**Ellis**	**7**
S.Farrelly	Shepherd	Bimson	Edwards	Kendal	Hanlon	Askey	Timmons	Lambert	Dempsey	M.Farrelly	Dawson	Ellis	8
S.Farrelly	Shepherd	Johnson	Edwards	Kendal	Hanlon	Askey•	Timmons†	Lambert	Dempsey	M.Farrelly	Dawson	Ellis	9
S.Farrelly	Shepherd	Johnson	Edwards	Kendal	Hanlon	Askey	Timmons†	Lambert	Dempsey	Heesom	Dawson	Ellis	10
S.Farrelly	**Shepherd**	**Bimson**	**Edwards**	**Johnson**	**Hanlon**	**Askey**	**Timmons**	**Lambert**	**Dempsey**	**Ellis•**	**Dawson**	**Clayton**	**11**
S.Farrelly	Shepherd	Heesom	Edwards	Johnson	Hanlon	Askey	Timmons	Lambert	Dempsey	M.Farrelly•	Ellis	Clayton	12
S.Farrelly	**Shepherd**	**Heesom**	**Edwards**	**Johnson**	**Hanlon**	**Dawson**	**Timmons**	**Lambert**	**Clayton•**	**Ellis**	**Miller**	**Bimson**	**13**
S.Farrelly	Shepherd†	Bimson	Edwards	Johnson	Hanlon	Dawson	Ellis	Lambert	Timmons	Heesom•	Clayton	Kendal	14
S.Farrelly	M.Farrelly	Bimson	Edwazrds	Rutter	Hanlon	Askey•	Timmons†	Lambert	Ellis	Johnson	Clayton	Dawson	15
S.Farrelly	M.Farrelly	Heesom	Edwards	Johnson	Hanlon	Askey	Dempsey	Lambert	Timmons	Ellis•	Dawson	Clayton	16
S.Farrelly	M.Farrelly	Heesom	Edwards	Johnson	Hanlon	Askey	Green	Lambert	Timmons†	Dempsey	Ellis	Dawson	17
S.Farrelly	M.Farrelly	Heesom	Edwards	Johnson	Hanlon	Askey•	Green	Lambert	Timmons†	Dempsey	Ellis	Dawson	18
S.Farrelly	Shepherd†	Johnson	Edwards	M.Farrelly	Hanlon	Ellis	Dempsey	Green	Lambert	Timmons	Dawson		19
S.Farrelly	Shepherd	Heesom	Edwards	Johnson	Hanlon	Dempsey	Green	Lambert	Clayton	M.Farrelly	Ellis	Timmons	20
S.Farrelly	Shepherd	Johnson	Edwards	M.Farrelly	Hanlon	Ellis†	Green	Timmons	Lambert	Dempsey	Clayton	Bimson	21
S.Farrelly	Shepherd	Johnson	Edwards	M.Farrelly	Hanlon	Askey	Green	Lambert	Timmons	Dempsey	Clayton	Bimson	22
S.Farrelly	Shepherd	Bimson	Edwards	M.Farrelly	Hanlon	Askey	Green	Lambert	Timmons	Dempsey	Clayton	Johnson	23
S.Farrelly	Shepherd	Heesom	Edwards	Johnson	Hanlon	Askey	Green	Lambert•	Timmons†	Dempsey	Dawson	Clayton	24
S.Farrelly	**Shepherd**	**Johnson**	**Edwards**	**M.Farrelly**	**Hanlon**	**Askey**	**Green•**	**Dawson†**	**Timmons**	**Dempsey**	**Clayton**	**Heesom**	**25**
S.Farrelly	Shepherd	Bimson	Edwards	Johnson	Hanlon	Askey	Green†	Lambert	Timmons	Dempsey	Dawson	Clayton	26
S.Farrelly	Shepherd	Bimson	Edwards	Johnson	Hanlon	Askey	Green	Lambert††	Timmons•	Dempsey	Dawson	Clayton	27
S.Farrelly	**Shepherd**	**Bimson**	**Edwards**	**Johnson**	**Hanlon**	**M.Farrelly**	**Green•**	**Lambert**	**Askey**	**Dempsey**	**Timmons**	**Clayton**	**28**
S.Farrelly	**Shepherd**	**Bimson**	**Edwards**	**Johnson**	**Hanlon**	**Askey**	**M.Farrelly**	**Lambert**	**Green**	**Dempsey**	**Timmons**	**Clayton**	**29**
S.Farrelly	M.Farrelly	Johnson	Edwards	Clayton	Hanlon	Askey	Green	Lambert	Timmons	Dempsey	Shepherd	Dawson	30
S.Farrelly	**Shepherd**	**Johnson**	**Edwards**	**M.Farrelly**	**Hanlon**	**Timmons†**	**Green**	**Lambert**	**Dawson•**	**Dempsey**	**Ellis**	**Clayton**	**31**
S.Farrelly	**Shepherd†**	**Johnson**	**Edwards**	**M.Farrelly**	**Hanlon**	**Askey**	**Green**	**Lambert**	**Clayton**	**Dempsey**	**Timmons**	**Ellis**	**32**
S.Farrelly	Lambert	Johnson	Edwards	M.Farrelly	Hanlon	Askey	Green	Ellis•	Timmons	Dempsey	Hopley	Dawson	33
S.Farrelly	**Shepherd**	**Johnson**	**Edwards**	**M.Farrelly**	**Hanlon**	**Askey**	**Green**	**Lambert**	**Timmons**	**Dempsey**	**Dawson**	**Ellis**	**34**
S.Farrelly	Shepherd	Johnson	Edwards	M.Farrelly	Hanlon	Askey	Green	Lambert	Timmons	Dempsey	Ellis	Doherty	35
S.Farrelly	**Shepherd**	**Johnson**	**Edwards**	**M.Farrelly**	**Hanlon**	**Askey**	**Lambert**	**Green**	**Timmons**	**Dempsey**	**Ellis**	**Clayton**	**36**
S.Farrelly	Shepherd	Clayton	Edwards	Johnson	Hanlon	Askey	Doherty	Lambert	Timmons	Dempsey	Ellis	Hopley	37
S.Farrelly	Shepherd	Johnson	Tobin	Lambert	Hanlon	Askey	Doherty	Ellis	Timmons	Dempsey	Clayton	Green	38
S.Farrelly	**Shepherd**	**Johnson**	**Edwards**	**Lambert**	**Hanlon**	**Askey**	**Doherty**	**Green**	**Timmons**	**Dempsey**	**Ellis**	**Clayton**	**39**
S.Farrelly	Shepherd	Johnson	Edwards	Lambert	Hanlon	Askey	Doherty	Green	Timmons	Dempsey	Ellis	Clayton	40
Zelem	Lambert	Timmons	Kendall	Tobin	Hanlon	Hopley	Green	Clayton	Doherty	Ellis	Edwards	Dempsey	41
S.Farrelly	**Shepherd**	**Johnson**	**Edwards**	**M.Farrelly**	**Hanlon**	**Askey**	**Lambert**	**Green**	**Timmons**	**Dempsey**	**Clayton**	**Kendal**	**42**
S.Farrelly	Shepherd	Johnson	Edwards	Kendal	Hanlon	Askey•	Lambert	Green	Timmons	Doherty	Hopley	Clayton	43
S.Farrelly	**Lambert**	**Johnson**	**Edwards**	**M.Farrelly**	**Hanlon**	**Askey†**	**Doherty**	**Green•**	**Timmons**	**Dempsey**	**Hopley**	**Clayton**	**44**
S.Farrelly	Shepherd	Johnson	Edwards	M.Farrelly	Hanlon	Askey	Doherty	Green•	Timmons	Dempsey	Clayton	Kendal	45
S.Farrelly	Shepherd	Johnson	Edwards	M.Farrelly†	Hanlon	Askey	Timmons	Lambert•	Doherty	Dempsey	Clayton	Boughey	46
Zelem	**Shepherd**	**Johnson**	**Kendal**	**Tobin**	**Hanlon**	**Timmons•**	**Doherty**	**Green†**	**Clayton**	**Dempsey**	**Ellis**	**Hopley**	**47**
S.Farrelly	**Shepherd**	**Johnson**	**Edwards**	**M.Farrelly**	**Hanlon**	**Askey**	**Green**	**Lambert**	**Timmons**	**Dempsey**	**Clayton**	**Kendal**	**48**
S.Farrelly	**Shepherd**	**Johnson**	**Edwards**	**M.Farrelly**	**Hanlon**	**Askey**	**Green**	**Lambert**	**Timmons**	**Dempsey**	**Clayton**	**Boughey**	**49**
Zelem	Shepherd	Johnson	Edwards	M.Farrelly	Hanlon	Askey	Green	Lambert	Timmons	Dempsey	Doherty	Boughey	50

• substituted by No. 12.   † substituted by No.14.

Macclesfield Town

PETER WRAGG

Peter played for Leek Town, winning the Cheshire League. He became manager when injury ended his career and the club came 4th and 2nd during his two years in charge. He then had spells with Stalybridge Celtic, Chorley and Hyde United, taking the latter to the First Round of the FA Cup for the first time in 20 years.

In early 1986 he joined Macclesfield Town and took them to an unprecedented treble of Northern Premier League, League Cup and Presidents Cup and promotion to the Conference. After consolidating he has seen his side go from strength to strength, including reaching Wembley in the 1989 FA Trophy Final - his proudest moment to date.

Macclesfield's consistent midfielder Steve Hanlon challenges Telford keeper Darren Acton during the Silkmen's 2-1 victory. Photo: Coli Stevens.

Programme details:
   28 pages for 70p
   Editor - Tony Masheder

Any other club publications:
   Silk Yarns (Fanzine)

Local Newspapers:
   Macclesfield Express
   Manchester Evening News
   Manchester Evening News Pink
   Local Radio Stations:
   GMR (BBC)
   BBC Radio Stoke
   Piccadilly Radio
   Signal Radio

MACCLESFIELD TOWN - PLAYING SQUAD 1992-93

Player	Honours	Birthplace and date	Transfer Fees	Previous Clubs
GOALKEEPERS				
Steve Farrelly	CSC	Manchester		Chester, Knowsley Utd
DEFENDERS				
Elfyn Edwards	WSP, APL NPL, CSC	Aberystwyth 4/5/60		Tranmere, Wrexham, Bangor, Runcorn, Altrincham
George Shepherd	CSC		£6,000	Man City, Bolton, Preston, Hyde Utd
Paul Johnson		Stoke 25/5/59		Stoke, Shrewsbury, York
Mick Farrelly	ESP, ES FAT	Manchester 1/11/62		Preston, Altrincham
Stuart Bimson			£10,000	Prescot, Ellesmere Pt, Southport
MIDFIELD				
Paul Kendall	GMVC	Halifax 19/10/64		Halifax, Scarborough
Steve Hanlon	ESP, NPL CSC	Chester 18/7/63		Crewe, Nantwich, Ekenas(Fin), Oswestry
Ronnie Ellis	FAT, CSC	Liverpool 15/3/58		Burscough, Winsford Runcorn, Altrincham
Mark Dempsey	Div 4 89	Manchester 14/1/64		Manchester Utd, Sheffield Utd, Rotherham
John Timmons	CSC	Manchester 1/7/60		Maine Road, Hyde Utd Altrincham
FORWARDS				
John Askey	ESP, NPL CSC	Stoke 4/11/64		Port Vale, Milton Utd
Colin Lambert	CSC		£2,000	Winsford Utd
Andrew Green			£7,000	Bootle, South Liverpool, Binche(Bel)
Mick Doherty	ESP, BHL VOL	Liverpool 8/3/61		Reading, Basingstoke, Weymouth, Maidstone, Yeovil, Runcorn, Farnboro

Departures during season:
John Imrie (Runcorn), Mark Rutter (Barrow), Jason Dawson (Stafford), Alan Zelem (Witton Alb).

Players who joined on loan during season:
Matthew Beeby (Port Vale), Darren Boughey (Stoke).

Moss Rose, Macclesfield Town

Name of ground: Moss Road
Ground address and Tel. No.: London Road, Macclesfield, Cheshire SK11 7SP. Tel. 0625 511545 (Office), 0625 511113 (Social Club). Fax. 0625 619021
Clubcall Line: 0898 121546
Simple ground directions: Approx. 1 mile south of Town Centre on the A523 (Leek Rd). British Rail Macclesfield approx 1.5 miles, regular bus service on match days
Official capacity: 6,000   **Seating:** 600   **Covered accommodation:** 2,500
Cost of seats: £5.00   **Cost of standing:** £4.00
Record attendance: 10,041 (Semi-Final CSC Winsford v Northwich, April 1948)
Social facilities available (Bars, hot & cold food etc.): The Blues Club - open match days and functions
Car parking: Ample unrestricted around ground

Sponsored by: **MACCLESFIELD TOWN**   **Nickname:** The Silkmen

---

Previous leagues: Manchester, Cheshire, Northern Premier (Multipart)
Club colours: Blue/white/blue   **Change colours:** White/black/red
Midweek home matches: Tuesday   **Club metal badges:** Yes
Record transfer fee paid: £7,000 to Binche for Andy Green 1991
Record transfer fee received: £40,000 for Mike Lake (Sheffield United) 1988
Record appearances for club:
Record goalscorer for club: Albert Valentine, 84, 1933-34
Record goalscorer in a season:
Past players who have progressed to the Football League: Numerous
Club honours: FA Trophy 1970, Finalists 1989, 1970, 1986; NPL Challenge Cup 1986; Presidents Cup 1986; Cheshire Cup 1890, 1891, 1894, 1896, 1911, 1930, 1935, 1951, 1952, 1954, 1960, 1964, 1969, 1971, 1973, 1983; Cheshire County League 1932, 1933, 1953, 1961, 1964, 1968
Past club managers: Peter Robinson 1958-59, Frank Bowyer 1960-61, Albert Leake 1963-64, Keith Goalen 1967-68, Frank Beaumont 1968-69, Billy Haydock 1971-72, Eddie Brown 1973-74, Willie Stevenson 1974-75, John Collins 1974-75, John Barnes 1975-76, Dave Connor 1976-77, Derek Partridge 1977-78, Phil Staley 1978-79, Jimmy Williams 1980-81, Brian Booth 1980-81, Neil Griffiths 1985-86, Peter Wragg 1985-86, (Date quoted is season appointed)

MERTHYR TYDFIL

Formed: 1945

Joint Presidents:
The Archbishop of Cardiff
His Grace John A Ward
The Lord Bishop of Llandaff
The Right Rev.Roy Davies

**Chairman/
Managing Director:**
John Reddy

Directors:
Wayne Hodgkins
Phil Dauncey

Secretary:
Phil Dauncey

Manager:
Wynford Hopkins

Asst Manager:
Tommy Hutchison

Coach:
George Wood

Trainer:
Frank Hegarty

Commercial Manager:
Mrs Jackie Darby

No Silverware - But Promotion Won?

Season 1991/92 may not have brought any silverware to the Pennydarren Park trophy cabinet but in reality this was a promotion year for the Martyrs!

Once permission to play in the English Pyramid from next season onwards had been revoked by the Welsh FA in November Merthyr had in effect been relegated three divisions!! It became doubly clear that the football field was not the only platform the Martyrs would need to use in order to preserve Conference status.

It was to the great credit of Merthyr chairman John Reddy and his Board of Directors that the club eventually won their appeal against the Welsh FA's decision and February 7th is now in the Martyr's record books as the day when Merthyr once again won promotion - unconditionally!

With that sort of threat hanging over the team it was no wonder that they made an auspicious start to the campaign to say the least. The first ten league games produced only two victories and once the Martyrs had been knocked out of both the Welsh Cup (by Swansea City) and the FA Cup (by Windsor and Eton) in the space of 6 days, things looked bleak. However, as the campaign progressed, some of the younger players in the side started consistently producing good performances and that, coupled with the outstanding form of Tommy Hutchison brought a Christmas and New Year double over doomed Cheltenham and a fine victory over eventual champions Colchester.

The latter months of the season saw the mercurial David Webley produce the form he is known for and this contributed to creditable victories over the likes of Farnborough, Kettering and Welling, whilst the team were also desperately unlucky to go out of the FA Trophy at the hands of eventual winners Colchester in a replay.

The final day of the season even lived up to the Martyrs' late form as they notched a grand 2-1 win at Telford to help them to a final finishing position of 4th in the table. This was a fantastic achievement by all at the club, especially manager Wynford Hopkins and assistant Tommy Hutchison who often had to motivate players when there was so much off-the-field activity ging on.

The only disappointment at the end of the campaign was the level of attendances at Pennydarren Park which hit new lows.

Anthony Hughes

Merthyr Tydfil F.C. 1991-92. Back Row (L-R): S Hookings, G Wager, I Thompson, G Wood, E Chiverton, D Webley. Middle: F Hegarty (Trainer), R James, C Hemming (now Stafford), R Lewis (left), C Summers, T Hutchison, M Williams, C Williams, W Hopkins (Manager). Front: P Evans, M Pengelly, C Thomas, K Rogers, A Beattie, J Morgan (left), D Burrows. Photo: Les Williams.

217

Merthyr Tydfil

Match No.	Date	Competition	Venue H/A	Opponents	Result	H/T	League Pos.	Goalscorers (Times if known)	Attendance
1	Aug 17	GMVC	A	Boston Utd	L 0-2	0-1			1312
2	Aug 24	GMVC	H	Telford Utd	D 2-2	2-0	19	Webley 3; Thompson 30	886
3	Aug 26	GMVC	H	Bath City	D 1-1	1-1	19	C. Williams 15	917
4	Aug 31	GMVC	A	Stafford Rangers	D 0-0	0-0	18		945
5	Sep 7	GMVC	H	Northwich Victoria	W 2-1	1-1	12	Rogers 39; C. Williams 69	587
6	Sep 14	GMVC	A	Witton Albion	L 2-3	0-0	15	C. Williams 68,85	885
7	Sep 17	GMVC	H	Wycombe Wanderers	L 1-2	0-1	15	Boyle 66	1088
8	Sep 21	GMVC	A	Gateshead	W 1-0	0-0	11	C. Williams 88	328
9	Sep 28	GMVC	H	Yeovil	D 2-2	1-1	12	Webley 11; C. Williams 80	618
10	Oct 5	ABWC 1	A	Porthcawl T.	W 4-1	1-1		Beattie 28; Webley 46; Rogers 67; C. Williams 72	310
11	Oct 12	GMVC	A	Barrow	D 2-2	1-1	15	C. Williams 34; Rogers 53	1268
12	Oct 15	BLT	H	Wycombe Wanderers	L 1-3	0-2		C. Williams 70	526
13	Oct 19	GMVC	A	Welling Utd	W 2-1	0-0	14	D'Auria 61; C. Williams 80	426
14	Oct 26	FAC 4Q	H	Windsor & Eton	D 1-1	1-1		C. Williams 10	521
15	Oct 29	ABWC 2	H	Swansea City	L 0-2	0-2			1089
16	Nov 2	GMVC	A	Kidderminster	W 2-1	1-0	13	C. Williams 35; Webley 85	422
17	Nov 4	FAC 4QR	A	Windsor & Eton	L 0-1	0-0			736
18	Nov 9	GMVC	A	Wycombe Wanderers	L 0-4	0-2	16		3339
19	Nov 23	GMVC	H	Runcorn	W 2-0	1-0	14	Tucker 30,88	603
20	Nov 30	GMVC	A	Altrincham	D 1-1	0-0	15	C. Williams 46	896
21	Dec 7	GMVC	H	Stafford Rangers	W 1-0	1-0	15	Webley 5	586
22	Dec 14	GMVC	H	Slough	L 1-2	1-0	15	Webley 28	592
23	Dec 21	GMVC	A	Kettering	L 1-3	0-1	15	Rogers 67 (pen)	1616
24	Dec 26	GMVC	A	Cheltenham	W 2-1	0-0	12	D'Auria 65; Rogers 89	1080
25	Jan 1	GMVC	H	Cheltenham	W 3-1	2-1	10	Rogers 26; C. Williams 30; Hutchison 48	835
26	Jan 4	GMVC	H	Colchester	W 2-0	0-0	8	Coates 54; D'Auria 82	1032
27	Jan 11	FAT 1	H	Dartford	D 1-1	0-0		D'Auria 87	750
28	Jan 14	FAT 1R	A	Dartford	W 2-1	1-0		C. Williams 25; Coates 70	520
29	Jan 18	GMVC	A	Northwich Victoria	L 1-4	0-0	11	Webley 83	689
30	Feb 2	FAT 2	H	Colchester	D 0-0	0-0			1211
31	Feb 4	FAT 2R	A	Colchester	L 0-1	0-0			2746
32	Feb 8	GMVC	H	Redbridge Forest	D 2-2	1-1	12	D'Auria 28; C. Williams 82 (pen)	702
33	Feb 11	GMVC	A	Bath City	D 0-0	0-0	12		629
34	Feb 15	GMVC	H	Macclesfield	L 0-3	0-1	13		568
35	Feb 18	GMVC	H	Kettering	W 4-1	1-1	11	Webley 42,58,88; Tucker 47	570
36	Feb 29	GMVC	H	Gateshead	L 1-4	1-3	13	C. Williams 43	575
37	Mar 7	GMVC	H	Altrincham	W 3-1	1-1	10	Webley 5,62,86	517
38	Mar 14	GMVC	A	Runcorn	D 1-1	0-0	11	D'Auria 61	404
39	Mar 21	GMVC	A	Kidderminster	D 2-2	0-1	12	Webley 59; Tucker 78	1014
40	Mar 24	GMVC	A	Farnborough	W 1-0	0-0	10	Hutchison 77	517
41	Mar 28	GMVC	H	Barrow	W 2-1	1-1	8	Webley 9; Davey 90	576
42	Mar 31	GMVC	A	Slough	D 0-0	0-0	9		521
43	Apr 4	GMVC	A	Redbridge Forest	D 1-1	0-0	10	Webley 86	502
44	Apr 7	GMVC	H	Macclesfield	W 3-2	0-2	8	Webley 62,85; C. Williams 88	588
45	Apr 11	GMVC	A	Welling Utd	W 2-1	0-1	8	Boyle 50; Webley 60	759
46	Apr 18	GMVC	H	Witton Albion	W 1-0	0-0	7	C. Williams 60	632
47	Apr 20	GMVC	A	Colchester	L 0-2	0-1	7		4148
48	Apr 23	GMVC	A	Farnborough	D 0-0	0-0	7		682
49	Apr 25	GMVC	H	Boston Utd	W 2-0	2-0	5	Webley 10; C. Williams 41	589
50	Apr 28	GMVC	A	Yeovil	D 1-1	0-1	5	Webley 85	1587
51	May 2	GMVC	A	Telford Utd	W 2-1	1-0	4	C. Williams 20; Chiverton 74	1303

Best Home Attendance: 1088 v Wycombe Wanderers 17.9.91   Lowest: 517 v Altrincham 7.3.92   Average Home Attendance: 647

Merthyr Tydfil

1	2	3	4	5	6	7	8	9	10	11	12	14	Match No.
Wood	James	Evans	Boyle	Hemming	Rogers	Tucker	Webley	Thompson	Beattie	C.Williams	Pengelly	Hutchison	1
Wood	M.Williams	Evans	Boyle	Hemming	Rogers	Tucker•	Webley†	Thompson	Beattie	C.Williams	Morgan	Hutchison	2
Wood	M.Williams	Evans	Boyle	Hemming	Rogers	Tucker†	Morgan•	Thompson	Beattie	C.Williams	Chiverton	Hutchison	3
Wood	M.Williams	Hemming	Boyle	Lewis	Rogers†	Tucker	Webley	Thompson	Beattie	C.Williams	D'Auria	Hutchison	4
Wood	Hemming•	Evans	Boyle	Lewis	Rogers	Tucker	Webley	Thompson	Beattie	C.Williams	D'Auria	Hutchison	5
Wood	Tucker	Hemming	Boyle	Lewis	Rogers	D'Auria	Webley	Thompson†	James	C.Williams	Evans	Hutchison	6
Wood	M.Williams	Evans	Boyle	Lewis	Rogers	D'Auria	Webley	Tucker	Beattie•	C.Williams	Thompson	Hutchison	7
Wood	M.Williams	James	Boyle	Lewis	Rogers	D'Auria	Withers	Tucker	C.Williams	Hemming	Hutchison	Evans	8
Wood	M.Williams	James	Boyle	Lewis	Rogers	D'Auria	Webley	Tucker†	Beattie	C.Williams	Hutchison	Withers	9
													10
Wager	M.Williams	James	Boyle	Lewis	Rogers	D'Auria•	Webley	Hemming	Beattie	C.Williams	Tucker	Withers	11
													12
Wager	Tucker	James	Boyle	Lewis	Rogers	D'Auria	Webley	Hemming	Beattie	C.Williams	M.Williams	Withers	13
Wager	Tucker	James	Boyle	Lewis	Rogers	D'Auria	Webley	Hemming	Beattie	C.Williams	M.Williams	Withers	14
													15
Wager	Tucker	James	Boyle	Lewis	Rogers	D'Auria	Webley	Hemming	Beattie	C.Williams	M.Williams	Hutchison	16
Wager	Tucker	James	Boyle	Lewis	Rogers	D'Auria	Webley	Hemming	Beattie	C.Williams	M.Williams	Hutchison	17
Wager	M.Williams	James	Boyle	Lewis	Rogers	D'Auria	Webley	Evans	Beattie•	Withers†	Tucker	Hutchison	18
Wager	M.Williams	James	Boyle	Lewis	Rogers	Beattie	Webley	Tucker	Hutchison	C.Williams	Chiverton	Morgan	19
Wager	M.Williams	James	Boyle	Lewis	Rogers	Beattie	Webley†	Tucker	Hutchison	C.Williams	D'Auria	Withers	20
Wager	M.Williams	James	Boyle	Lewis	Rogers	Beattie	Webley	Tucker•	Hutchison	C.Williams	D'Auria	Withers	21
Wager	M.Williams	James	Boyle	Lewis	Rogers	Beattie	Webley	D'Auria	Hutchison	C.Williams•	Coates	Evans	22
Wager	M.Williams	James	Boyle	Lewis	Rogers	Beattie	Webley	D'Auria	Hutchison	C.Williams•	Coates	Evans	23
Wager	M.Williams	James	Boyle	Lewis	Rogers	Beattie	Coates	D'Auria	Hutchison†	C.Williams	Withers	Webley	24
Wager	M.Williams	James	Boyle	Lewis	Rogers	Beattie	Coates	D'Auria	Hutchison	C.Williams	Withers	Webley	25
Wager	M.Williams	James	Boyle•	Lewis	Rogers	Beattie	Coates	D'Auria	Hutchison	C.Williams	Tucker	Webley	26
													27
													28
Wager	M.Williams	Evans	James	Tucker	Webley	Beattie	Coates	D'Auria	Hutchison	C.Williams•	Chiverton	Thomas	29
													30
													31
Wager	M.Williams	James	Boyle	Lewis	Rogers	Beattie•	Coates	D'Auria†	Hutchison	C.Williams	Webley	Tucker	32
Wager	M.Williams	James	Boyle	Lewis	Rogers•	Webley†	Coates	D'Auria	Hutchison	C.Williams	Beattie	Tucker	33
Wager	M.Williams	James	Boyle	Lewis	Rogers	Beattie	Coates	D'Auria	Hutchison	Webley	Chiverton	Tucker	34
Wager	M.Williams	James	Boyle	Lewis	Webley	Beattie	Tucker	D'Auria	Hutchison	C.Williams	Coates	Rogers	35
Wood	M.Williams	Evans	Boyle	Lewis•	Webley	Beattie†	Tucker	D'Auria	Hutchison	C.Williams	Rogers	Chiverton	36
Wood	M.Williams	James	Boyle	Sherwood	Webley	Beattie	Tucker	D'Auria	Hutchison•	C.Williams	Rogers	Chiverton	37
Wager	M.Williams	James	Boyle	Sherwood	Webley	Beattie	Tucker	D'Auria	Hutchison•	C.Williams	Rogers	Chiverton	38
Wager	M.Williams	James	Boyle	Sherwood	Webley	Beattie•	Tucker	D'Auria	Hutchison	C.Williams†	Rogers	Chiverton	39
Wager	M.Williams	James	Boyle	Abraham	Webley	Beattie	Tucker	D'Auria	Hutchison	Chiverton	Lewis	Rogers	40
Wager	M.Williams	James	Boyle	Abraham	Webley	Beattie	Tucker†	D'Auria	Hutchison	Chiverton•	C.Williams	Davey	41
Wager	M.Williams	James	Boyle	Abraham	Webley	Beattie	Tucker	D'Auria	Hutchison†	C.Williams	Chiverton	Davey	42
Wager	M.Williams†	James	Boyle	Abraham	Webley	Davey	Tucker	D'Auria	Hutchison•	C.Williams	Beattie	Sherwood	43
Wager	M.Williams	James	Boyle	Abraham†	Webley	Davey	Tucker	D'Auria	Hutchison	C.Williams	Beattie	Sherwood	44
Wager	M.Williams	James	Boyle	Abraham	Webley	Davey	Tucker	D'Auria	Hutchison•	C.Williams	Beattie	Sherwood	45
Wager	M.Williams	James	Boyle	Abraham	Webley	Davey	Tucker	D'Auria	Hutchison•	C.Williams	Beattie	Sherwood	46
Wager	M.Williams	James	Boyle	Abraham	Webley	Davey	Tucker	D'Auria	Hutchison•	C.Williams	Beattie	Sherwood	47
Wager	Tucker	James	Boyle	Sherwood	Webley	Davey	Beattie	D'Auria†	Hutchison•	C.Williams	Rogers	Chiverton	48
Wager	M.Williams	James	Boyle	Sherwood	Webley	Tucker	Beattie	Rogers	Hutchison	Chiverton	C.Williams	D'Auria	49
Wager	M.Williams	James	Boyle	Sherwood	Webley	Tucker	Beattie	Rogers	Hutchison	C.Williams†	Chiverton	D'Auria	50
Wager	M.Williams	James	Boyle	Sherwood	Webley•	Tucker	Beattie	Rogers	Hutchison	C.Williams	Chiverton	D'Auria	51

219

Merthyr Tydfil

WYNFORD HOPKINS

Wynford Hopkins was born in Mountain Ash, Mid Glamorgan on the 18th July 1953. His first contact with Merthyr Tydfil came in the mid-seventies as a player in their Southern League days, and his playing career took him to Newport County, Gloucester City, Ton Pentre and Pontllanfraith in the Welsh League. It was at Pontllanfraith where Wynford first experienced management, enjoying a highly successful spell with the Gwent Valley club. From there he answered an S.O.S. from Merthyr manager Lyn Jones to bolster the midfield once again, shortly afterwards taking over as Jones' number two. As a partnership they enjoyed unparalleled success and therefore it seemed the natural progression for the club to make Wynford caretaker manager when Lyn Jones resigned in March 1991. After only 4 games, a 100% record and Conference survival almost assured, the offer of a permanent post came and, shortly after the end of the 1990/91 campaign, a new management team was formed with the appointment of Tommy Hutchison, the former Scottish International, as assistant manager.

Last season, despite the off-the-field uncertainties brought about by the League of Wales affair, Hopkins and Hutchison steered Merthyr to a marvellous finishing position of 4th in the Conference.

Merthyr Tydfil's Cerri Williams, seen here taking on England's Paul Shirtliff, had a fine goalscoring season in tandem with David Webley. Photo: Mike Floate

Programme details:
    44 pages for £1.00
    Editor - Anthony Hughes (0685 359921 H)
       (0685 874221 B)
Any other club publications:
    Dial 'M' for Merthyr (Fanzine)
    The Junior Martyr - For Junior Members
Local Newspapers:
    Merthyr Express
    Merthyr Herald and Post
    South Wales Echo
    Western Mail
Wales on Sunday
Local Radio Stations:
    Radio Wales
    Red Dragon Radio

MERTHYR TYDFIL - PLAYING SQUAD 1992-93

Player	Honours	Birthplace and date	Transfer Fees	Previous Clubs
GOALKEEPERS				
Gary Wager	WSP, BHL	Bridgend 21/5/62		Bridgend Town
DEFENDERS				
Terry Boyle	Welsh Int & U21 WSP	Ammanford 29/10/58		Tottenham, Newport Co, C Palace, Cardiff C, Swansea C
Mark Williams	WSP, Welsh Y Welsh Sch	Merthyr Tydfil 11/8/70		Aston Villa
Ryan James		Blackwood 3/12/71		Blackpool
Phil Evans		Swansea 1/3/71		Swansea City
Gareth Abrahams		Merthyr Tydfil 13/2/69		Cardiff City
MIDFIELD				
Tommy Hutchison	Scottish Int Scottish U23	Cardenden 22/9/47		Alloa, Blackpool, Coventry, Man City, Burnley, Swansea City
Andrew Beattie	WSP, BHL SWSC	Newport 26/9/58		Newport Co, Bridgend, Mangotsfield
Mark Tucker	WSP, Welsh Y Welsh Sch, SWSC	Pontypool 10/2/63		Abergavenny Thursdays
Kevin Rogers	WSP, BHL SWSC	Merthyr Tydfil 23/9/63		Aston Villa, Birmingham, Wrexham, Rhyl
David D'Auria		Swansea 26/3/70		Swansea City
FORWARDS				
David Webley	WSP, BHL SWSC	Ebbw Vale 25/2/64		Pontllanfraith, Abertillery Town
Cerri Williams	WSP, BHL Welsh Y, SWSC	Tonyrefail 16/10/65		Blaenrhondda, Newport Co
Eston Chiverton		Cardiff		Cardiff Civil Service
Simon Davey		Swansea 1/10/70		Swansea City

Departures during season:
Paul Sanderson (Newport AFC), Jon Morgan (Gloucester), Ian Thompson (Work committments), Chris Hemming (Stafford), David Withers (Newport AFC), Russell Lewis (Rushden & Diamonds).
Players who joined on loan during season:
Marc Coates (Swansea), Adrian Needs (Swansea).

Penydarren Park, Merthyr Tydfil

Name of ground: Penydarren Park
Ground address and Tel. No.: Penydarren Park, Merthyr Tydfil, Mid Glamorgan CF47 8RF. Tel. 0685 4102 (office), 0685 71395 (social club), 0898 884533 (24 hour Club Information line) 888669
Simple ground directions: From North & Midlands - M5, M50, A40, A465 & A4054 into Merthyr Tydfil. 1st lights after 4th roundabout on A4054 fork right, then take 1st right and take 1st right again and again for a 3rd time which leads to club. FromSouth & East - M4 junction 32 for A470 - on leaving A470 expressway take 1st left off 3rd roundabout and then right hand exit off next mini roundabout, then take 3rd left, 1st right and 1st right into ground straight ahead

Official capacity: 10,000 **Seating:** 1,500 **Covered accommodation:** 5,000
Cost of seats: £5.00 **Cost of standing:** £4.00
Record attendance: 21,000 v Reading F.A. Cup 2nd round, 1949
Social facilities available: 'Strikers' club available for functions as well as luxurious lounge facilities. Bar facilities 7 days a week with hot meals and snacks available at certain times. Main grandstand incorporates a players lounge as well as 'The Leo Calaghan Suite' for season ticket holders and Vice-Presidents on matchdays. Also available for functions and conferences on non-match days. Seperate sponsors lounge available.
Car parking: Limited within ground, although plenty of off-street parking around the ground. Large free car parks available in town centre - 5 to 10 minutes walk away.

Sponsored by: Hoover **MERTHYR TYDFIL** **Nickname:** The Martyrs

---

Previous leagues: Welsh League, Football League, Southern (Beazer Homes) League
Club colours: White shirts/black shorts/black socks **Change colours:** Red shirts/red shorts/red socks
Club Shop: Open on matchdays **Proprietor:** Mel Jenkins, Tel: 0443-692336
Midweek home matches: Tuesday
Programme Editor: Anthony Hughes, Tel: 0685-874221(B); 0685 359921(H)
Record transfer fee received: £12,000 for Ray Pratt from Exeter City, 1980
Past players who have progressed to the Football League: (since 1945) Syd Howarth (Aston Villa), Cyril Beech, Gilbert Beech, Bill Hullett, Ken Tucker (Cardiff City), Nick Deacy (Hereford Utd), Gordon Davies (Fulham), Ray Pratt (Exeter City), Peter Jones, Paul Giles (Newport County)
Best FA Cup performance: 2nd round proper on 4 occasions
Best FA Trophy performance: 1977-78, quarter-final (replay) v Runcorn L 2-3
Club honours: Winners Welsh FA Cup: 1948-49, 1950-51, 1986-87. Winners Southern League Championship: 1947-48, 1949-50, 1950-51, 1951-52, 1953-54, 1988-89. Runners-up 1952-53. Winners Southern League 1st Division: 1987-88, Runners-up 1970-71, 1978-79. Winners Southern League Cup: 1947-48, 1950-51. Winners Welsh Football League: 1948-49, 1950-51, 1961-62. Runners-up 1946-47. Welsh Representatives in European Cup Winners Cup 1987-88 lost to Atalanta of Italy 2-3 on aggregate.
Club Captain: 1991-92 Kevin Rogers **Player of the Year:** 1990-91 Ryan James

NORTHWICH VICTORIA

Formed: 1873

President:
Ken Edwards

Chairman:
Dave Stone

Vice Chairman
Derek Nuttall

Directors:
Ernie Fryer
Jim Rafferty
Ian Smith

Company Secretary:
Phil Sheridan

Team Secretary:
Derek Nuttall

Manager:
Sammy McIlroy

Asst Manager:
Gilly Prescott

Physiotherapist:
Andy Jones

Club Doctor:
Dr Robert Chapman

**Commercial Manager/
Press Officer:**
Dave Thomas

Have Vic's finally turned the corner?

At first glance it seems as if Northwich Victoria made little or no progress during the 1991/92 campaign, as not only did they finish in a roughly similar position to that achieved a year ago, but again no major silverware was to grace the Drill Field Boardroom. This assumption, however, is far from the case. Whereas the 1990/91 season had seen the Greens occupy a position in and around the danger zone until very late on in the season, this time around the spectre of relegation was never seen at the Drill Field. Indeed, apart from the week following the opening day reverse against Bath City, the club never dropped below 14th spot and generally they hovered around mid-table throughout. To some this would seem unremarkable, but to a club that has been fighting a rearguard action against the drop since the mid-eighties with limited resources, this was a welcome relief.

The majority of the credit for Vic's revival can be given to manager Sammy McIlroy, who produced a position, attacking side that played some superb football at times. Given that the former Northern Ireland International came into the job 'cold', having never before witnessed a Conference game, he did extremely well. As he himself says, the side has taken some very progressive steps towards being a side to be reckoned with and he feels that with a few additions to the squad, Vic's can make a concerted challenge for top honours next season.

If there was one criticism that could be levelled at the team is was one of lack of consistency. This was ably shown by the fact that they didn't string together consecutive wins, draws or defeats in all competitions between late August and mid-January!

Obviously there were disappointments. The shock FA Cup exit at Eastwood being an example, but on the whole there were more positive aspects than negative. The excellent form shown by newcomers such as Stuart Locke and Brian Butler and existing players Malcolm O'Connor and the exciting, if enigmatic Tony Hemmings. The 3-0 win over deadly rivals Witton Albion on Boxind Day, a match which was the first Northwich league derby since April 1968, attracted the Vic's biggest ever GMVC attendance of 2,809.

Having entered into an agreement to sell their famous old Drill Field ground to a property developer in 1986, Vics were faced with the prospect of being evicted from their home of 118 years in May 1992 the developer wanted to take up his option to buy the stadium. Thankfully this situation was averted at the eleventh hour and once again the Drill Field is back in the ownership of the club. The story doe not end there though, as in order to finance the re-purchasing of the world's oldest ground, the directors were given no option but to take out a loan which now has to be repaid, along with the clubs existing debts. With this in mind the supporters have launched a trust fund with the intention of paying off the loan in order to save the historic stadium. Over £20,000 has been raised already by Vic's fans.

The majority of supporters are of the opinion that the worst years have now passed and after a decade of struggle Vics have finally turned the corner.

James Wood

Northwich Victoria F.C. 1991-92. Back Row (L-R): Vaughan, Locke, Graham, Ball, O'Connor, Blundell, Jones, Wrench. Front Row: McCarrick, Butler, Hemmings, Blain, Holland.   Photo: Garry Clarke.

Northwich Victoria

GM Vauxhall Conference: 11th.   **FA Cup: 1st Qualifying Round.**   **FA Trophy: 3rd Round.**

Match No.	Date	Competition	Venue H/A	Opponents	Result	League H/T	Pos.	Goalscorers (Times if known)	Attendance
1	Aug 17	GMVC	H	Bath City	L 1-3	1-2		Graham 22	707
2	Aug 24	GMVC	A	Farnborough Town	W 4-2	1-0	3	O'Connor 8,48p,61; Graham 67	796
3	Aug 26	GMVC	H	Kidderminster Harriers	W 3-1	1-0	3	O'Connor 22p; Blain 70; Holland 90	1015
4	Aug 31	GMVC	H	Welling Utd	L 1-2	1-1	4	Graham 8	729
5	Sep 3	BLT 1-1	H	**Stafford Rangers**	W 2-0	2-0	8	O'Connor 12,34	501
6	Sep 7	GMVC	A	Merthyr Tydfil	L 1-2	1-1	9	O'Connor 14p	587
7	Sep 14	FAC 1Q	A	**Eastwood Hanley**	L 1-2	0-1		Buxton 73	321
8	Sep 17	BLT 1-2	H	**Stafford Rangers**	D 1-1	0-0		Vaughan 73	540
9	Sep 21	GMVC	H	Boston Utd	D 1-1	1-1	13	Stringer 18	654
10	Sep 24	GMVC	H	Barrow	W 6-1	2-0	13	Butler 11; O'Connor 34,57; Blain 59; Hemmings 80; Blundell 82	615
11	Sep 28	GMVC	A	Kidderminster Harriers	L 0-1	0-1	9		929
12	Oct 1	GMVC	A	Macclesfield Town	D 0-0	0-0	9		905
13	Oct 5	GMVC	H	Yeovil Town	W 1-0	1-0	8	O'Connor 13	654
14	Oct 8	BLT 2	H	**Boston Utd**	W 3-2	2-0		Graham 5,20; Butler 89	474
15	Oct 19	GMVC	A	Cheltenham Town	L 0-1	0-0	13		518
16	Oct 22	GMVC	H	Gateshead	D 1-1	1-1	9	Stringer 32	540
17	Oct 26	GMVC	H	Cheltenham Town	W 3-1	1-0	8	Stringer 12; Ainsworth 57; O'Connor 72	484
18	Nov 2	GMVC	H	Altrincham	L 1-2	1-1	11	Hemmings 11	747
19	Nov 4	GMVC	A	Runcorn	W 3-0	1-0	9	O'Connor 37; Easter 73; Butler 78p	812
20	Nov 9	GMVC	A	Stafford Rangers	L 1-2	1-0	9	Blain 20	733
21	Nov 16	GMVC	A	Boston Utd	W 2-0	0-0	4	o.g. 56; Ainsworth 61	1218
22	Nov 23	GMVC	H	Redbridge Forest	L 0-2	0-0	7		823
23	Nov 26	CBSSC 2	H	**Stalybridge Celtic**	W 2-1	1-1		Butler; Easter	380
24	Nov 30	GMVC	H	Colchester Utd	D 1-1	1-0	10	Butler 44p	1042
25	Dec 17	BLT 3	A	**Runcorn**	L 1-2	0-0		Graham 61	558
26	Dec 26	GMVC	H	Witton Albion	W 3-0	2-0	9	O'Connor 18; Blain 43; Ainsworth 63	2809
27	Dec 28	GMVC	A	Yeovil Town	L 1-2	0-0	10	Hemmings 56	1992
28	Jan 1	GMVC	A	Telford Utd	W 4-1	2-1	10	Ainsworth 7; O'Connor 42,64; Stringer 51	1738
29	Jan 4	GMVC	A	Gateshead	L 0-2	0-0	10		346
30	Jan 14	FAT 1	H	**Hyde Utd**	W 1-0	1-0		Hemmings 43p	644
31	Jan 18	GMVC	H	Merthyr Tydfil	W 4-1	0-0	7	Holland 60; Hemmings 70p,74; Feeley 81	689
32	Jan 25	GMVC	A	Runcorn	L 1-3	1-3	9	o.g. 20	733
33	Feb 1	FAT 2	H	**Cheltenham Town**	W 4-2	2-1		O'Connor 1; Blain 17,68; Blundell 72	701
34	Feb 4	CBSSC 3	A	**Witton Albion**	L 1-3	1-1		Hemmings	1152
35	Feb 15	GMVC	H	Wycombe Wanderers	L 0-1	0-0	14	Casey 67	1043
36	Feb 22	FAT 3	A	**Macclesfield**	L 0-1	0-0			1537
37	Feb 26	GMVC	A	Welling Utd	L 1-6	0-2	16	Stringer 89	548
38	Feb 29	GMVC	H	Kettering	W 4-3	0-3	14	O'Connor 46,61,80; Green 89	665
39	Mar 2	GMVC	H	Macclesfield	W 2-1	0-1	11	Hemmings 72 (pen); O'Connor 83	802
40	Mar 7	GMVC	A	Redbridge Forest	L 3-4	2-3	11	Hemmings 3,58; Carter 38	623
41	Mar 13	GMVC	A	Altrincham	W 1-0	1-0	9	Hemmings 43	693
42	Mar 17	GMVC	A	Kettering	L 0-1	0-0	10		1513
43	Mar 21	GMVC	A	Colchester	L 0-1	0-0	11		3218
44	Mar 24	GMVC	A	Wycombe Wanderers	L 0-2	0-1	12		2750
45	Mar 27	GMVC	H	Telford Utd	D 1-1	0-1	12		604
46	Apr 4	GMVC	A	Slough	W 1-0	0-0	12	Hemmings 59	528
47	Apr 11	GMVC	A	Barrow	W 2-0	0-0	12	Stringer 48; Edwardson 90	1217
48	Apr 18	GMVC	H	Stafford Rangers	L 1-2	1-0	12	Hemmings 22 (pen)	745
49	Apr 20	GMVC	A	Witton Albion	D 1-1	1-1	12	O'Gorman 45	1902
50	Apr 25	GMVC	A	Bath City	L 0-2	0-2	12		510
51	Apr 28	GMVC	H	Slough	W 3-0	0-0	11	O'Connor 52,81; O'Gorman 65	444
52	May 2	GMVC	H	Farnborough	D 1-1	0-1	11	Hemmings 67 (pen)	543

Best Home League Attendance: 2809 v Witton Albion 26.12.91   **Smallest: 444 v Slough 28.4.92**   **Average Home Attendance: 791 Compared to 1990/91: 748**

Goalscorers: GMVC (63): M O'Connor 19 (2 pens); T Hemmings 12 (4 pens); J Stringer 6; G Ainsworth 4; C Blain 4; B Butler 3 (2 pens); G Easter 3; A Graham 3; S Holland 2; D O'Gorman 2; C Blundell 1; B Edwardson 1; A Feeley, Goals !. **FA Cup (1):** S Buxton 1. **FA Trophy (5):** C Blain 2; C Blundell 1; T Hemmings 1 (1 pen); M'Connor 1. **Bob Lord Trophy (7):** A Graham 3; M O'Connor 2; B Butler 1; G Vaughan 1. **Cheshire Senior Cup (3):** B Butler 1 (1 pen); G Easter 1; t Hemmings 1. **Mid-Cheshire Senior Cup (3):** D O'Gorman 1; M Hancock 1; M O'Connor 1.

Northwich Victoria

1	2	3	4	5	6	7	8	9	10	11	12	14	Match No.
Ball	McCarrick	Blundell	Holland	Locke	Jones	Blain	Butler	Graham	O'Connor	Hemmings	Wrench	Vaughan	1
Ball	McCarrick	Blundell	Jones	Locke	Holland	Blain	Butler†	Graham	O'Connor	Hemmings	Wrench	Vaughan	2
Ball	McCarrick	Blundell	Jones	Locke	Holland	Blain	Vaughan	Graham	O'Connor	Hemmings	Stringer	Wrench	3
Ball	McCarrick	Blundell	Jones	Locke	Holland•	Blain	Butler	Graham	O'Connor	Hemmings	Vaughan	Buxton	4
Bullock	**McCarrick**	**Blundell**	**Jones**	**Locke**	**Vaughan**	**Blain•**	**Butler**	**Graham**	**O'Connor**	**Hemmings†**	**Wrench**	**Buxton**	**5**
Bullock	McCarrick	Blundell•	Jones	Locke	Vaughan	Blain	Butler	Graham†	O'Connor	Hemmings	Wrench	Buxton	6
Bullock	**McCarrick**	**Wrench**	**Jones•**	**Locke**	**Vaughan**	**Blain**	**Butler**	**Buxton**	**O'Connor**	**Hemmings**	**Holland**	**Stringer**	**7**
Bullock	**Locke**	**Blundell**	**Jones**	**M.Hancock**	**Vaughan**	**Buxton**	**Butler**	**Graham•**	**O'Connor**	**Stringer**	**Hemmings**	**Wrench**	**8**
Bullock	Locke	Blundell	Jones	M.Hancock	Vaughan	Blain	Butler	Hemmings	O'Connor	Stringer	Graham	Holland	9
Bullock	Locke	Blundell	Jones	M.Hancock	Vaughan	Blain	Butler	Hemmings	O'Connor	Stringer†	Graham	Holland	10
Bullock	Locke	Blundell	Jones	M.Hancock	Vaughan	Blain	Butler	Hemmings	O'Connor	Holland•	Graham	Wrench	11
Bullock	Locke	Blundell	Jones	M.Hancock	Vaughan	Blain	Butler	Hemmings	O'Connor	Hemmings	Holland	Wrench	12
Bullock	Locke	Blundell	Jones	M.Hancock	Vaughan	Ainsworth•	Butler	T.Hancock	O'Connor	Hemmings	Blain	Graham	13
Bullock	**Locke**	**Blundell**	**Jones**	**M.Hancock**	**Vaughan**	**Ainsworth•**	**Butler**	**Graham**	**O'Connor**	**Hemmings**	**Blain**	**Holland**	**14**
Bullock	Locke	Wrench	Jones	M.Hancock	Vaughan	Ainsworth	Butler	Graham	O'Connor	Hemmings	Blain	T.Hancock	15
Bullock	Locke	Blundell	Jones	M.Hancock	Stringer	Ainsworth	Butler	T.Hancock†	O'Connor	Hemmings	Blain	Graham	16
Bullock	Locke	Blundell	Jones	M.Hancock	Stringer	Ainsworth	Vaughan	Graham	O'Connor	Hemmings	Blain	T.Hancock	17
Bullock	Locke	Blundell	Jones	M.Hancock	Stringer	Ainsworth	Vaughan	Graham†	O'Connor	Hemmings	Blain	Easter	18
Bullock	Locke	Blundell	Jones	M.Hancock	Stringer	Ainsworth•	Vaughan	Easter	O'Connor	Blain†	Graham	Butler	19
Bullock	Locke	Blundell	Jones	M.Hancock	Stringer	Ainsworth•	Vaughan	Easter	O'Connor	Blain	Hemmings	Holland	20
Bullock	Locke	Blundell	Jones	M.Hancock	Stringer	Ainsworth•	Butler	Easter	O'Connor	Blain	Hemmings	Holland	21
Bullock	Locke	Blundell	Jones	M.Hancock	Hemmings	Ainsworth	Butler	Easter	O'Connor	Blain	Hemmings	Graham	22
Bullock	**Locke**	**Butler†**	**Jones**	**M.Hancock**	**Stringer**	**Ainsworth**	**Blain**	**Easter**	**O'Connor**	**Hemmings**	**Graham**	**Holland**	**23**
Bullock	Locke	Butler	Jones	M.Hancock	Stringer	Ainsworth	Feeley	Easter	O'Connor†	Blain	Hemmings	Graham	24
Bullock	**Locke**	**Blundell**	**Jones**	**M.Hancock**	**Stringer**	**Ainsworth•**	**Butler**	**Graham**	**O'Connor**	**Blain**	**Hemmings**	**Holland**	**25**
Bullock	Locke	Blundell	Jones	M.Hancock	Stringer	Ainsworth	Butler	Graham	O'Connor	Blain	Feeley	Hemmings	26
Bullock	Locke	Blundell	Jones	M.Hancock†	Feeley	Ainsworth	Butler	Graham	O'Connor	Blain	Holland	Hemmings	27
Ball	Locke	Blundell	Jones	M.Hancock†	Feeley	Ainsworth	Blain	Stringer	O'Connor	Hemmings	Graham	Holland	28
Ball	Locke	Blundell	Jones	M.Hancock	Feeley	Ainsworth	Blain	Stringer	O'Connor	Hemmings•	Graham	Holland	29
Ball	**Locke**	**Blundell**	**Jones**	**M.Hancock†**		**Blain•**	**Butler**	**Easter**	**Stringer**	**Hemmings**	**Holland**	**Graham**	**30**
Ball	Butler	Blundell	Jones	Locke	Feeley	Holland	Vaughan	Easter	Graham•	Hemmings	Gresty	Stringer	31
Ball	Butler	Blundell	Jones•	Locke	Feeley	Holland†	Vaughan	Easter	Graham•	Hemmings	Gresty	Stringer	32
Bullock	**Locke**	**Blundell**	**Jones**	**M.Hancock**	**Feeley**	**Blain†**	**Butler**	**Easter**	**O'Connor**	**Hemmings**	**Graham**	**Stringer**	**33**
Bullock	**Locke**	**Blundell**	**Jones**	**M.Hancock**	**Feeley**	**Blain**	**Butler**	**Easter**	**O'Connor**	**Hemmings•**	**Graham**	**Stringer**	**34**
Bullock	Locke	Blundell	Jones	M.Hancock	Feeley	Blain	Butler	Easter	O'Connor	Hemmings•	Gresty	Vaughan	35
Bullock	**Locke**	**Butler**	**Jones**	**M.Hancock**	**Stringer**	**Blain**	**Feeley•**	**Easter**	**O'Connor**	**Hemmings**	**Graham**	**Lenton**	**36**
Bullock	Locke	Stringer	Jones	M.Hancock	Vaughan	Easter	Butler	Lenton	O'Connor	Hemmings	Holland	Graham	37
Bullock	Locke	Blundell	Jones	M.Hancock	Vaughan	Easter	Butler	Lenton•	O'Connor	McIlroy	Hemmings	Graham	38
Bullock	Locke	Blundell	Jones	M.Hancock	Stringer•	Easter	Butler	Hemmings	O'Connor	McIlroy	Vaughan	Graham	39
Bullock	Locke	Blundell	Jones	M.Hancock	Vaughan	Easter	Butler	Hemmings	O'Connor	McIlroy	Holland	Graham	40
Berryman	Locke	Blundell	Jones	M.Hancock	Vaughan	Edwardson	Butler	Hemmings	O'Connor	Easter†	Holland	Graham	41
Berryman	Locke	Blundell	Jones	M.Hancock	Vaughan	Edwardson	Butler	Hemmings	O'Connor•	O'Corman	Holland	Lenton	42
Berryman	Locke	Blundell	Jones	M.Hancock	Vaughan	McIlroy	Butler	Hemmings	O'Connor	O'Corman	Blain	Lenton	43
Berryman	Locke	Blundell	Jones	M.Hancock	Vaughan	Easter†	Butler	Hemmings	O'Connor	O'Corman	Blain	Edwardson	44
Berryman	Locke	Blundell	Jones	M.Hancock	Donnelly	Blain	Butler	Hemmings	O'Connor	Hackett•	Lenton	Edwardson	45
Berryman	Locke	Blundell	Jones	M.Hancock†	Donnelly	McIlroy	Butler	Stringer	O'Connor	Hemmings	Lenton	Edwardson	46
Berryman	Blain	B lundell	Feeley	Locke	Donnelly	McIlroy	Vaughan	Hemmings	O'Connor	Edwardson	Lenton	Holland	47
Berryman	Locke	Blundell	Jones	Feeley	Donnelly†	Stringer	Butler	McIlroy	O'Connor	Hemmings	Edwardson	O'Gorman	48
Berryman	Locke	Butler	Jones	M.Hancock	Feeley	Edwardson•	Stringer	O'Gorman	O'Connor	Hemmings	Blain	Donnelly	49
Berryman	Locke	Blundell†	Jones	M.Hancock	Feeley	Butler	Stringer	O'Gorman•	O'Connor	Hemmings	Vaughan	Donnelly	50
Berryman	Vaughan	Butler	Jones	Locke	Feeley	Blain•	Donnelly	O'Gorman	O'Connor	Hemmings	Holland	Lenton	51
Berryman	Locke	Butler	Jones	M.Hancock	Feeley	Blain	Donnelly	O'Gorman	O'Connor	Hemmings	Vaughan	Lenton	52

• substituted by No. 12.   † substituted by No. 14.

League Appearances (max no. 42): S Locke 42; M Jones 41; M O'Connor 40; T Hemmings 34+5; c Blundell 36; B Butler 34+1; M Hancock 32; C Blain 24+1; G Vaughan 22+3; T Bullock 22; J Stringer 19+1; A Graham 13+7; G Easter 14+1; G Ainsworth 14; A Feeley 13; s Berryman 12; S Holland 7+3; T Ball 8; P O'Gorman 7+1; s McIlroy 7; P Donnelly 6+1; M McCarrick 5; B Edwardson 4+1; D Lenton 2+2; S Gresty 0+3; T Hancock 2; L Hackett 1; M Wrench 1; S Buxton 0+1.

Cup Appearances (max no. 12): M Jones 12; S Locke 12; B Butler 11; M O'Connor 11; J Stringer 10+1; C Blain 9+2; T Hemmings 9+2; T Bullock 9; M Hancock 9; a Graham 4+3; A Feeley 6; c Blundell 5; G Easter 5; G Vauchan 4+1; S Holland 1+3; G Ainsworth 3; S Buxton 2+1; S Berryman 2; M McCarrick 2; D O'Gorman 1+1; M Wrench 1+1; T Ball 1; P. Donnelly 1; B Edwardson 1; D Lenton 1.

Northwich Victoria

SAMMY McILROY

The last of the 'Busby Babes', Sammy followed in the footsteps of the legendary George Best when ho moved from his native Belfast to join Manchester United as a raw teenager in the late sixties. He became an established member of the highly successful and exciting United side built by Tommy Docherty. In all he made 418 appearances for United, the highlight being the 1978 FA Cup Final success over Liverpool.

In 1982 he moved to Stoke City where he played 144 times before heading back to Manchester to join United's deadly rivals, City. His time at Maine Road was curtailed when he accepted an offer to join Bury, then managed by Martin Dobson, whom he was to succeed at the Drill Field. He then took up a post as player-coach with Preston, but a severe knee injury virtually ended his playing days.

In July 1991, he was appointed as manager at the Drill Field. Coming into the job cold with virtually no experience of the non-league scene, everyone at the club was delighted with his own, and his team's, performance. Happily his own injuries recovered sufficiently for him to make a welcome, and most effective comeback as a player with the Vics towards the end of thre season. The experience of playing in a green shirt again no doubt brought back memories of his 78 appearances in an emerald shirt for his country, Northern Ireland.

Having now assembled a young squad, he personally feels that with one or two additions Vics could well be challenging for the top honours this coming season.

Welling United defenders under pressure from the Northwich Victoria attack at the Drill Field. Photo: Garry Clarke

Programme details:
    24 pages for 80p
    Editor - James Wood (0606 75964)

Any other club publications:
    'Resign Roberts Re-Sign'
    Fanzine, published quarterly

Local Newspapers:
    Northwich Guardian
    Northwich Chronicle
    Manchester Evening News
    Manchester Evening News Pink

Local Radio Stations:
    GMR (BBC)
    Piccadilly Radio
    Signal Radio

NORTHWICH VICTORIA - PLAYING SQUAD 1992-93

Player	Honours	Birthplace and date	Transfer Fees	Previous Clubs
GOALKEEPERS				
Steve Berryman	MCSC	Blackburn 26/12/66		Barnet, Altrincham
Tony Bullock	SSC			Barnton
DEFENDERS				
Mark Jones	MCSC, SSC FA XI	Liverpool 16/9/60		Runcorn, Preston NE, Southport
Mark Hancock	FAT, SSC ShSC, MCSC, FAC	Ellesmere Port 30/9/60	£3,000	Van Leer, Telford Utd
Chris Blundell	MCSC	Billinge 7/12/69		Oldham Ath, Rochdale
Stuart Locke	MCSC			Manchester City, Crewe Alexandra
Jeff Parker		Liverpool 23/1/69		Everton, Crewe Alexandra
MIDFIELD				
Colin Blain	MCSC, SSC	Manchester 7/3/70		Halifax Town
Brian Butler		Salford 4/7/66		Blackpool, Stockport Co, Halifax Town
Paul Donnelly		Liverpool 23/12/71		Halifax Town
Andy Feeley		Hereford 30/9/61		Hereford, Trowbridge, Leicester City, Brentford, Bury
John Stringer	FAT, SSC ShSc, MCSC	Birkenhead 15/6/64		Barnton, Runcorn, Telford Utd
Sammy McIlroy	N Ire, FAC	Belfast 2/8/54		Manchester Utd, Stoke, Manchester City, Bury, Preston NE
FORWARDS				
Graham Easter		Epsom 26/9/69		West Bromwich Albion, Crewe, Preston NE
Malcolm O'Connor	MCSC, SSC NPLC, FAXI	Ashton-U-Lyne 25/4/65	£10,000	Curzon Ashton, Notts Forest, Rochdale, Curzon Ashton, Hyde Utd
Tony Hemmings	MCSC		£8,000	Burton Albion, Rocester
Darren Lenton	MCSC			Chester City
Dave O'Gorman	MCSC	Chester 20/6/72		Wrexham, Hyde Utd

Departures during season:
Trevor Ball (Colwyn Bay), Neil Salathiel (Newtown), Steve Buxton (Newtown), Andy Graham (Hyde), Mark Wrench (Hyde), Ian Callaghan (Hyde), Simon Gresty (Christleton), Mark McCarrick (Retired), Tony Hancock (Prescot). Steve Holland (Hyde), Gary Vaughan (Hyde).

Players on loan during season:
Gareth Ainsworth (Preston), Barry Edwardson (Wigan), Lee Hackett (Wigan), Lawrence Greenhalgh (Bury).

The Drill Field, Northwich Victoria

Name of ground: The Drill Field, (it has been proved that the Drill Field is the oldest ground on which Senior Football has been played continuously in the United Kingdom and therefore, the World
Ground address and Tel. No.: The Drill Field, Drill Field Rd, Northwich, Cheshire. Tel: 0606 41450. Fax: 0606 330577
Simple ground directions: Leave M6 at Junc. 19 and follow A556 towards Chester. At second roundabout (approx. 6 miles) turn right onto A533. Ground on right 1.5 miles behind Volunteer Public House
Official capacity: 14,000 (currently limited to 3,500)   **Seating:** 660   **Covered accommodation:** 2,000
Cost of seats: £5.00   **Cost of standing:** £4.00
Clubcall No. 'The Vics Call' 0898 664813
Cost of Advertising Boards - Varies. Please contact Commercial Manager Dave Thomas
Record attendance: 11,290 v Witton Albion, Cheshire League, Good Friday 1949
Social facilities available: Large Social Club with members lounge and seperate function room - both available for hire, Tel: 0606 43120. Food available on matchdays with prior notice. Bass beers, Pool, Darts, TV
Disabled supporters: Most welcome, but prior notice welcome, limited accommodation however
Car parking: Parking in Drill Field Road **not** advised. Ample parking behind magistrates court off Brockhurst St.

Sponsored by: Sandbury Construction   **NORTHWICH VICTORIA**   **Nickname:** The Vics

---

Previous leagues: The Combination (1890) (Founder members), Football League Division Two (1892) (Founder members), Manchester League (1894), Lancashire Combination (1912), Cheshire County League (1919) (Founder members), Northern Premier League (1968) (Founder members), Football Conference (1979) (Founder members)
Club colours: Green shirts/white shorts/green socks   **Change colours:** Claret shirts/sky blue shorts/claret socks
Midweek home matches: Tuesday   **Club metal badges:** Two designs - £2.50 plus p&p
Club programme: 'The Drill Fielder'   **Editor:** James Wood Tel: 0606-75964
Club Shop: Located inside ground. Open matchdays only   **Manager:** Andy Dakin
Record transfer fee paid: £10,000 to Hyde United for Malcolm O'Connor August 1988
Record transfer fee received: £50,000 from chester City for Neil Morton, October 1990
Record appearances for club: 970 by Ken Jones 1969-1985
Record goalscorer for club: Peter Burn 160, 1955-1965
Record goalscorer in a season: Len Barber 1956/57, 60 (from 47 games)
Best FA Cup performance: Quarter-Finals1883/84 v Blackburn Olympic 1-9(A), Fourth rnd1976/77 v Oldham Athletic 1-3(N)
Best FA Trophy performance: Winners 1983/84, Runners-up 1982/83
Past players who have progressed to the Football League: (Currently playing League football) Graham Abel, Eddie Bishop, Neil Morton (all Chester City), Roger Eli (Burnley), Dave McKeaney (Crewe Alex), Don Page (Wigan Athletic), Shaun Teale (Bournemouth), Chris Malkin (Tranmere Rovers)
Former League players: Jim Walker (Derby Co.), Alf Ringstead (Sheffield Utd & Eire), Steve Craven (Tranmere), Phil Power (Crewe Alex), Frank Corrigan (Wigan Ath), Billy Meredith (Manchester City, Manchester Utd & Wales)
Club honours: Welsh Cup Runners-up 1881/82, 1888/89; FA Trophy Winners 1983/84, Runners-up 1982/83; GM Vauxhall Conference Cup (Bob Lord Trophy) Winners 1979/80; Northern Premier League Runners-up 1976/77; Northern Premier League Cup Winners 1972/73, Runners-up 1978/79; Cheshire County League Champions 1956/57, Runners-up 1924/25, 1924/25, 1947/48; Cheshire County League Cup Winners 1925/26, 1934/35; Manchester League Champions 1902/03; The Combination Runners-up 1890/91; Cheshire Senior Cup Winners 1880/81, 1881/82, 1882/83, 1883/84, 1884/85, 1885/86, 1928/29, 1936/37, 1949/50, 1954/55, 1971/72, 1976/77, 1978/79, 1983/84, Runners-up 1891/92, 1896/97, 1905/06, 1908/09, 1947/48, 1950/51, 1963/64, 1965/66, 1969, 1970/71, 1977/78, 1985/86; Staffordshire Senior Cup Winners 1978/79, 1979/80, 1989/90, Runners-up 1986/87, 1990/91; Cheshire Amateur Cup Winners 1898/99; Northwich Senior Cup Winners 1948/49, 1958/59, 1959/60, 1963/64, 1964/65, 1965/66, 1967/68, 1968/69, 1969/70, 1971/72, 1974/75 Runners-up 1953/54, 1954/55, 1955/56, 1957/58, 1960/61, 1961/62, 1972/73; Mid Cheshire Senior Cup Winners 1984/85, 1985/86, 1987/88, 1989/90, Runners-up 1982/83, 1983/84, 1990/91; North-West Floodlit League Winners 1966/67, 1975/76; Cheshire League Lancashire Combination Inter-League Cup Winners 1961/62; Guardian Charity Shield Winners 1985/86, 1986/87, 1987/88
Past club managers: (Post War) (longest serving first) Cliff Roberts, Jack Bonnell, Harry Ware, John King, Jack Boothway, Billy Wooton, Roy Clarke, Felix Reilly, Paul Ogden, Ray Williams, Terry Murphy, Terry Bradbury, Stan Storton, Tommy Spratt, Don Moore, Tom Manley, George Heslop, Bob Murphy, Sandy McNab, Billy Russell, Norman Kirkham, Noel Kelly, Stuart Pearson, Brian Taylor, Arthur Woodruft, Ian McNeil, Jackie Mudie, Lammie Robertson, John Green, Martin Dobson

RUNCORN

Formed: 1918-19

President:
H Braveman

Chairman:
D Robinson

Vice Chairman:
G H Worrall

Director:
B McCunnell

Secretary:
D Bignall

Manager:
John Carroll

Asst Manager:
John Owens

Physiotherapist:
J Graham

Runcorn began the 1991/92 campaign in search of their third manager in only just over a year following Peter O'Brien's decision to move to Witton Albion to take over from Stan Allan. Highly respected centre half, John Carroll was put in temporary charge and was giventhe job on a permanent basis shortly after the start of the season.

With very little money to spend on players, Carroll had to search the local leagues and free transfer market for new players and did remarkably well in the circumstances. Although league form was generally poor, their final finishing position of 16th was the former champions' lowest since joining the competition, they did manage to reach the final of the Bob Lord Trophy. Unfortunately they came up against a very determined Wycombe Wanderers side in the final itself and they had to be content with a losers medal.

Support at Canal Street fell to an average of 629 and Carroll will have to find more players of the calibre of Steve Shaughnessy, Jamie Bates and Darryl McCarty from lower down the Pyramid if they are to survive this season.

Runcorn F.C. 1991-92. Back Row (L-R): P O'Brien (left), J Graham (Physio), S Shaughnessy, I Brady, I Harold, G Hill, J Pacey, A Williams, J Carroll (Manager), R Sang, T King, T Bratt (Kit man), K Keelan (Left). Front: G Wilson, P Hughes, T Edwards (now Altrincham), C Hawtin, M Henshaw, S Byrne, G Dooner, P Withers, S Saunders, S Rudge.

Runcorn

GM Vauxhall Conference: 16th. FA Cup: 1st Round. FA Trophy: 2nd Round. Bob Lord Trophy: Finalist (Runner-Up).

Match No.	Date	Competition	Venue H/A	Opponents	Result	H/T	League Pos.	Goalscorers (Times if known)	Attendance
1	Aug 17	GMVC	H	Welling Utd	D 2-2	0-0		Shaughnessy 55; Brady 65	577
2	Aug 24	GMVC	H	Boston Utd	D 2-2	2-0	11	Shaughnessy 35,45	575
3	Aug 26	GMVC	A	Gateshead	D 1-1	1-1	11	Hanchard 26	530
4	Aug 31	GMVC	A	Slough	L 0-1	0-0	16		799
5	Sep 7	GMVC	H	Kettering	D 0-0	0-0	19		637
6	Sep 14	GMVC	A	Farnborough	W 2-0	1-0	11	Carroll 4; Saunders 57	932
7	Sep 17	GMVC	A	Macclesfield	L 0-3	0-1	15		1065
8	Sep 21	GMVC	H	Bath City	L 0-2	0-0	16		531
9	Sep 28	GMVC	A	Altrincham	D 2-2	1-1	16	Saunders 44; Withers 50 (pen)	1049
10	Oct 5	GMVC	H	Wycombe Wanderers	L 1-2	0-1	18	Hill 56	951
11	Oct 12	GMVC	A	Colchester Utd	L 1-2	0-0	19	Redmond 68	2617
12	Oct 15	BLT 2	H	Witton Albion	D 2-2	1-0		Redmond 20; Hawtin 120	850
13	Oct 19	GMVC	H	Kidderminster Harriers	W 4-1	1-0	18	Withers 5; Brabin 51; Shaughnessy 62; Saunders 72	544
14	Oct 26	FAC 4Q	H	Gateshead	W 1-0	0-0		Shaughnessy 49	734
15	Nov 2	GMVC	A	Cheltenham	L 1-4	1-2	18	Redmond 17	450
16	Nov 4	GMVC	A	Northwich Victoria	L 0-3	0-1	18		812
17	Nov 9	GMVC	H	Barrow	D 2-2	1-0	19	Withers 35; Saunders 48	629
18	Nov 16	FAC 1	H	Tranmere Rovers	L 0-3	0-1			6563
19	Nov 23	GMVC	A	Merthyr Tydfil	L 0-2	0-1	22		603
20	Nov 26	CSC	H	Warrington Town	W 2-1	1-0		Carroll; Shaughnessy	-
21	Nov 29	GMVC	H	Telford Utd	L 0-2	0-1	22		686
22	Dec 7	GMVC	A	Barrow	W 3-2	1-1	21	Saunders 29; Shaughnessy 48; McCarty 54	1087
23	Dec 10	BLT 2R	A	Witton Albion	W 2-0	0-0		Withers 56; McCarty 65	503
24	Dec 14	GMVC	H	Redbridge Forest	W 1-0	0-0	19	Shaughnessy 73	446
25	Dec 17	BLT 3	H	Northwich Victoria	W 2-1	0-0		Withers 59; McCarty 65	558
26	Dec 21	GMVC	A	Wycombe Wanderers	L 0-1	0-0	19		2688
27	Dec 26	GMVC	A	Stafford Rangers	D 0-0	0-0	19		688
28	Dec 28	GMVC	H	Colchester Utd	L 1-3	1-1	20	Saunders 7	883
29	Jan 1	GMVC	A	Witton Albion	W 3-1	0-1	19	Brabin 70; Shaughnessy 87; McCarty 88	978
30	Jan 4	GMVC	H	Altrincham	D 2-2	1-1	19	Saunders 45; McCarty 88	907
31	Jan 11	FAT 1	A	Leek Town	D 3-3	1-0		Shaughnessy 44, o.g.57; McCarty 74	789
32	Jan 13	FAT 1R	H	Leek Town	W 3-1	1-1		McCarty 20,49,87	713
34	Jan 17	GMVC	A	Telford Utd	L 0-1	0-1	20		913
34	Jan 25	GMVC	H	Northwich Victoria	W 3-1	3-1	17	McCarty 23,24; Shaughnessy 35	733
35	Feb 1	FAT 2	H	Kidderminster	D 1-1	1-0		Shaughnessy 41	681
36	Feb 3	FAT 2R	A	Kidderminster	L 2-5	2-1		Saunders 42,44	1189
37	Feb 8	GMVC	H	Farnborough	D 1-1	1-0	18	McCarty 46	595
38	Feb 11	BLT S/F 1	H	Altrincham	W 2-1	0-1		Hill 72; McCarty 75	532
39	Feb 15	GMVC	A	Kettering	L 0-3	0-1	21		1519
40	Feb 18	BLT S/F 2	A	Altrincham	W 3-1	0-1		Disley 2,16; Richards 24	605
41	Feb 22	GMVC	A	Cheltenham	W 2-1	0-1	17	Hill 67; McCarty 79	438
42	Feb 29	GMVC	A	Bath City	L 1-3	1-1	20	Disley 36	575
43	Mar 7	GMVC	H	Macclesfield	D 0-0	0-0	20		661
44	Mar 14	GMVC	H	Merthyr Tydfil	D 1-1	0-0	19	McCarty 65	404
45	Mar 17	GMVC	H	Witton Albion	L 0-1	0-0	19		838
46	Mar 21	GMVC	A	Yeovil	W 4-1	2-1	17	McCarty 15; Saunders 36,65; Lundon 69	1821
47	Mar 28	GMVC	A	Stafford Rangers	L 0-1	0-1	19		762
48	Mar 31	BLT F 1	H	Wycombe Wanderers	W 1-0	1-0		Saunders 21	853
49	Apr 4	GMVC	H	Yeovil	D 2-2	1-2	19	Shaughnessy 36; Lundon 77	474
50	Apr 7	BLT F 2	A	Wycombe Wanderers	L 0-2	0-2			2519
51	Apr 11	GMVC	A	Kidderminster	W 1-2	1-1	19	Saunders 9 (pen)	1078
52	Apr 14	GMVC	A	Redbridge Forest	W 2-1	1-0	17	Brabin 7; Wall 73	435
53	Apr 18	GMVC	H	Slough	W 1-0	0-0	17	Wellings 68	533
54	Apr 20	GMVC	H	Gateshead	D 1-1	0-0	17	Saunders 86	489
55	Apr 25	GMVC	A	Welling Utd	W 2-1	1-0	15	Shaughnessy 10; Saunders 72 (pen)	712
56	May 2	GMVC	A	Boston Utd	L 1-2	1-0	16	Shaughnessy 37	864

Best Home League Attendance: 951 v Wycombe 5.10.91   Smallest: 404 v Merthyr Tydfil 14.3.92

Average Home Attendance: 629
Compared to 1990/91: 729

Runcorn

1	2	3	4	5	6	7	8	9	10	11	12	14	Match No.
Pallidino	Bates	Harold	Hill	Carroll	Byrne	Brady	Mullen	Shaughnessy	Hanchard	Withers	Henshaw	Diggle	1
Pallidino	Bates•	Mullen	Carroll	Hill	Byrne	Brady†	Harold	Shaughnessy	Hanchard	Withers	Henshaw	Varden	2
Pallidino	Henshaw	Mullen	Carroll	Hill	Hawtin	Byrne†	Harold	Shaughnessy	Hanchard	Withers•	Diggle	Varden	3
Pallidino	Byrne	Mullen	Carroll	Hill	Diggle•	Henshaw	Harold	Shaughnessy	Hanchard†	Withers	Hawtin	Varden	4
Pallidino	Henshaw	Mullen	Carroll	Hill	Hawtin	Byrce	Harold	Shaughnessy	Hanchard†	Withers	Redman	Varden	5
Pallidino	Byrne	Mullen	Carroll	Hill	Hawtin	Henshaw	Harold	Shaughnessy•	Saunders	Withers	Redman	Varden	6
Pallidino	Byrne	Mullen•	Carroll	Hill	Hawtin	Henshaw†	Harold	Shaughnessy	Saunders	Withers	Redman	Varden	7
Pallidino	Byrne	Mullen	Carroll•	Hill	Imrie	Brabin	Harold	Shaughnessy	Saunders	Withers	Redman	Henshaw	8
Pallidino	Byrne	Redman	Carroll	Hill	Imrie	Brabin	Harold	Shaughnessy	Saunders	Withers†	Abrahams	Hagan	9
Pallidino	Hughes	Redman	Carroll	Hill	Hagan•	Brabin	Harold	Shaughnessy	Saunders	Withers	Hawtin	Abrahams	10
Pallidino	Byrne	Redman	Carroll	Hill	Hagan†	Hughes•	Harold	Shaughnessy	Saunders	Withers	Hawtin	Abrahams	11
Pallidino	**Byrne**	**Redman**	**Carroll**	**Hill**	**Hagan†**	**Hughes•**	**Harold**	**Shaughnessy**	**Saunders**	**Withers**	**Hawtin**	**Abrahams**	**12**
Pallidino	Byrne	Mullen	Carroll	Hill	Imrie†	Brabin	Harold†	Shaughnessy	Saunders	Withers	Redman	Hawtin	13
Pallidino	**Byrne**	**Mullen**	**Carroll**	**Hill**	**Redman**	**Brabin**	**Harold†**	**Shaughnessy**	**Saunders**	**Withers**	**Hawtin**	**Hagan**	**14**
Williams	Byrne•	Mullen	Redman	Hill	Hawtin†	Brabin	Harold	Shaughnessy	Saunders	Withers†	Hawtin	Abrahams	15
Pallidino	Byrne	Mullen	Redman	Hill	Hawtin	Brabin	Harold•	Shaughnessy	Saunders	Withers	Abrahams	Rigby	16
Pallidino	Byrne	Mullen	Carroll	Hill	Redman•	Brabin	Harold•	Shaughnessy†	Saunders	Withers	Rigby	Waring	17
Pallidino	**Byrne**	**Mullen**	**Carroll**	**Hill**	**Redman•**	**Brabin**	**Harold**	**Shaughnessy**	**Saunders**	**Withers†**	**Hawtin**	**Imrie**	**18**
Pallidino	Bates	Mullen	Hill	Carroll	Redman	Brabin•	Hawtin	Shaughnessy	Saunders	Withers	Abrahams	Waring	19
Pallidino	**Bates**	**Mullen**	**Carroll**	**Hill**	**Highdale**	**Brabin**	**Wellings**	**Shaughnessy**	**Saunders**	**Withers†**	**Redman**	**Hawtin**	**20**
Pallidino	Bates	Mullen	Carroll	Hill	Byrne	Brabin	Carter	Shaughnessy•	Saunders	McCarty†	Hawtin	Withers	21
Williams	Bates	Mullen	Redman	Hill	Byrne	Brabin	Wellings	Shaughnessy†	Saunders	McCarty	Richards	Withers	22
Williams	**Bates**	**Mullen**	**Redman**	**Withers**	**Byrne•**	**Richards**	**Wellings**	**Shaughnessy**	**Saunders†**	**McCarty**	**Harold**	**Waring**	**23**
Williams	Bates	Mullen	Redman	Hill	Byrne•	Brabin	Wellings	Shaughnessy	Richards	McCarty	Withers	Imrie	24
Williams	**Bates**	**Mullen**	**Redman**	**Hill**	**Withers**	**Imrie**	**Wellings**	**Shaughnessy**	**Richards**	**McCarty**	**Varden**	**Waring**	**25**
Williams	Baters	Mullen	Redman	Hill	Richards	Brabin•	Wellings	Shaughnessy	Saunders	McCarty	Withers	Imrie	26
Williams	Bates	Mullen	Redman	Hill	Byrne•	Brabin	Richards	Shaughnessy†	Saunders	McCarty	Withers	Waring	27
Williams	Bates	Mullen	Redman	Hill	Hughes•	Brabin	Withers	Shaughnessy	Saunders	McCarty	Richards	Waring	28
Williams	Bates	Mullen†	Redman	Hill	Richards	Brabin	Withers	Shaughnessy	Saunders	McCarty	Waring	King	29
Williams	Bates	Lundon	Redman	Hill	Richards†	Brabin	Withers	Shaughnessy	Saunders	McCarty	Waring	Henshaw	30
Williams	**Bates**	**Mullen**	**Redman**	**Hill**	**Lundon**	**Brabin**	**Wellings**	**Shaughnessy**	**Saunders**	**McCarty**	**Withers**	**Henshaw**	**31**
Williams	**Bates**	**Mullen**	**Redman**	**Hill**	**Lundon**	**Brabin**	**Wellings**	**Shaughnessy**	**Saunders**	**McCarty**	**Withers**	**Henshaw**	**32**
Williams	Bates†	Mullen	Redman	Hill	Lundon•	Brabin	Withers	Shaughnessy	Saunders	McCarty	Wellings	Henshaw	33
Williams	Bates	Mullen	Redman	Harold	Lundon	Richards	Henshaw•	Shaughnessy	Saunders	McCarty	Withers	Brady	34
Williams	**Bates**	**Mullen**	**Redman**	**Hill**	**Lundon**	**Brabin**	**Withers**	**Shaughnessy**	**Saunders**	**McCarty**	**Harold**	**Brady**	**35**
Williams	**Bates**	**Mullen**	**Redman**	**Hill**	**Lundon**	**Brabin**	**Withers**	**Shaughnessy**	**Saunders**	**McCarty**	**Harold**	**Brady**	**36**
Williams	Bates	Mullen	Byrne•	Hill	Lundon	Harold	Withers	Shaughnessy	Saunders	McCarty	Redman	Richards	37
Williams	**Bates**	**Mullen**	**Byrne**	**Hill**	**Lundon**	**Harold**	**Withers**	**Shaughnessy**	**Saunders**	**McCarty**	**Redman**	**Richards**	**38**
Williams	Bates	Mullen•	Redman	Hill	Lundon	Richards	Harold	Shaughnessy	Saunders	Brabin	Withers	Wellings	39
Williams	**Bates**	**Mullen**	**Redman**	**Hill**	**Lundon**	**Harold**	**Withers**	**Shaughnessy**	**Saunders**	**McCarty**	**Richards**	**Wellings**	**40**
Routledge	Bates	Mullen	Redman	Hill	Wellings†	Brabin	Harold	Disley	Saunders•	McCarty	Withers	Richards	41
Routledge	Bates	Mullen	Redman	Hill	Lundon	Brabin	Harold•	Shaughnessy	Disley†	McCarty	Withers	Richards	42
Williams	Bates	Mullen	Henshaw†	Hill	Brabin	Wellings	Harold	Shaughnessy•	Saunders	McCarty	Withers	Lundon	43
Williams	Bates	Mullen	Wall	Hill	Brabin	Wellings†	Harold	Shaughnessy•	Saunders	McCarty	Withers	Lundon	44
Williams	Wall	Mullen	Harold	Hill•	Brabin	Wellings†	Withers	Shaughnessy	Saunders†	McCarty	Withers	Lundon	45
Williams	Bates	Mullen	Harold•	Hill	Brabin	Wellings†	Withers	Shaughnessy	Saunders	McCarty	Richards	Lundon	46
Williams	Bates	Mullen	Harold•	Hill	Brabin	Wellings†	Withers	Shaughnessy	Saunders	McCarty	Richards	Lundon	47
Williams	**Bates**	**Mullen**	**Harold**	**Hill**	**Brabin**	**Wellings**	**Withers**	**Shaughnessy**	**Saunders**	**McCarty**	**Richards**	**Lundon**	**48**
Williams	Bates•	Mullen	Harold	Hill	Wall	Lundon	Richards	Shaughnessy	Saunders	McCarty	Withers	Brady	49
Williams	**Bates**	**Mullen**	**Harold**	**Hill**	**Brabin**	**Lundon**	**Withers**	**Shaughnessy**	**Saunders**	**McCarty**	**Richards**	**Brady**	**50**
Williams	Bates	Mullen	Carroll	Harold	Brabin†	Lundon	Richards	Saunders	Withers	McCarty	Shaughnessy	Brady	51
Williams	Bates	Mullen†	Carroll	Harold	Wall	Brabin	Richards	Saunders	Brady†	McCarty	Shaughnessy	Wellings	52
Williams	Bates	Mullen†	Carroll	Harold	Wall	Brabin	Richards	Saunders	Brady	McCarty•	Shaughnessy	Wellings	53
Williams	Bates	Lundon	Carroll	Harold	Wall	Brabin•	Ric hards	Saunders	Brady†	McCarty	Shaughnessy	Wellings	54
Williams	Bates	Lundon	Carroll	Harold	Wall	Brady	Richards†	Shaughnessy•	Saunders	Brady	Withers	Wellings	55
Williams	Bates	Lundon	Carroll	Harold	Wall	Brady	Richards†	Shaughnessy	Saunders	McCarty	Byrne	Wellings	56

• Substituted by No. 12   † Substituted by No. 14

Runcorn

JOHN CARROLL

John Carroll became Runcorn's third manager in a year when he was appointed to take over permanently at Canal Street after a short period as caretaker-manager. Peter O'Brien had filled the vacancy left by Barry Whitbread but left prior to the start of last season to take over at Witton Albion.

Carroll, aged 33, played for South Liverpool and Weymouth and has now made over 200 appearances for the Linnets and is regarded as one of the best centre backs in the Vauxhall Conference.

Runcorn's Darryl McCarty, signed during the season from Horwich RMI, shoots past Colchester's Scott Barrett only to be denied by the post. Photo: Rob Ruddock

Programme details:
32 pages for 80p

Any other club publications:
The Jolly Green Giant (Fanzine)

Local Newspapers:
Runcorn Weekly News
Liverpool Echo
Runcorn World

Local Radio Stations:
Radio Merseyside
Radio Ciy

RUNCORN - PLAYING SQUAD 1992-93

Player	Honours	Birthplace and date	Transfer Fees	Previous Clubs
GOALKEEPERS				
Arthur Williams		Widnes 14/7/64		Chester City, General Chemicals
DEFENDERS				
Jamie Bates		Manchester		Maine Road
Graham Hill		Manchester		Curzon Ashton
Sean Lundon	7/3/69	Liverpool		Everton, Chester City, Bath City
John Carroll	CSC 6/8/59	Liverpool		Sth Liverpool, Weymouth
Paul Mullen		Liverpool		Heswall, Sth Liverpool, Caernarfon, Sth Liverpool
Ian Harold		Liverpool 16/1/69		Newton
MIDFIELD				
Craig Hawtin		Crewe		Burnley, Chester City
Ian Brady		Liverpool		Bootle, Heswall
Steve Byrne		Huyton 11/11/62		Vauxhall GM
Barry Wellings		Liverpool 10.6.58		Everton, York, Rochdale, Tranmere, Northwich, Tranmere, Swansea, Southport
Nigel Shaw	NPL, NPLC	Stoke 13/2/63		Stoke, Nantwich, Congleton, Macclesfield, Altrincham
Tommy King		Liverpool 3/4/69		Local football
FORWARDS				
Steve Shaughnessy		Manchester		Maine Road
Steve Saunders		Warrington		Bolton W, Grimsby, Scarborough
Paul Varden		Manchester		Maine Road
Darryl McCarty				Chorley, Horwich, Bolton, Marine, Morecambe, Horwich
Alan Richards		Preston 1/10/71		Luton Town

Departures during season:
Tony Edwards (Altrincham), Richard Harris (Hyde), Andy Diggle (Released), Graham Parsons (Released), Mark Henshaw (Chorley), John Imrie (Mossley), Peter Withers (Southport), Gary Henshaw (Hyde), Ian Redman (Witton Alb).

Players who joined on loan during season:
Martin Hanchard (Farnborough), Steve Carter (Scarborough), Martin Disley (Crewe), Justin Wall (Crewe).

Canal Street, Runcorn

Ground address and Tel. No.: Canal Street, Runcorn. Tel: 09285 60076
Simple ground directions: M56 junction 12 follow signs for Runcorn Old Town
Official capacity: 9,700   **Seating:** 200   **Covered accommodation:** 3,500
Cost of seats: £5.00   **Cost of standing:** £4.00
Official openion of floodlights:
Record attendance: 10,011
Social facilities available (Bars, hot & cold food etc.): Annual membership - Mid Day catering - 2 bars, VP
lounge. Open matchdays and special events
Car parking: Main car park adjacent to ground and Social Club

---

Sponsored by: **RUNCORN**   **Nickname:** Linnets

Previous leagues: Cheshire County, Northern Premier (Multipart)
Club colours: Yellow/green/green   **Change colours:** Red & white/red/red
Midweek home matches: Tuesday   **Club metal badges:** Yes
Club programme: 32 pages 60p   **Editor:** D. Bignall
Record transfer fee paid:
Record transfer fee received:
Record appearances for club:
Record goalscorer for club:
Record goalscorer in a season:
Past players who have progressed to the Football League: Mark McCarrik, Eddie Bishop, Jimmy Cumbes,
Graham Abel, Barry Knowles, Mark Jones, Don Page, David Pugh, Ian Woan
Club honours: Cheshire League 1936-37, 1938-39, 1962-63; Cheshire Bowl 1937-38; Cheshire Senior Cup
1924-25, 1935-36, 1961-62, 1964-65, 1973-74, 1974-75, 1984-85, 1985-86, 1986-87, 1988-89; Northern Premier
League 1975-76, 1980-81; Northern Premier Shield 1980-81; Alliance Premier League 1981-82; Alliance Premier
JV Thompson Shield 1982-83, 1984-85; Bob Lord Trophy 1982-83, 1984-85; FA Trophy Finalists 1985-86

SLOUGH TOWN

Formed: 1890

Chairman:
Alan Thorne

Managing Director:
Bob Pearson

Financial Director:
Byron Thorne
Directors:
Trevor Gorman
Ray Head

Life Vice President:
Alan Turvey

Secretary:
Vic McCulloch

Manager:
David Kemp

Club Doctor:
Dr David Small

Press Officer:
Richard Hayward

Physiotherapist:
Kevin McGoldrick

Groundsman:
Terry Powell

Slough - On The Up

In the Rebels second season in the Conference, the start and first half was bright and encouraging. From an opening home win over Kidderminster Harriers, with a great solo goal from Steve Thompson, who was later in the season transferred to Wycombe after 4 years with Slough, his last game away at Boston in February from which he scored Slough's consolation goal.

From 3rd position to 5th/6th, and a superb 7-3 away win at Altrincham, which was the highest aggregate win in Conference action last season, an excellent 3-2 win at Kettering in which the football played was a credit to all concerned, Slough slumped to the lower reaches and poor results including only three draws out of the last 14 games. The away win at Barrow was the last win in early March. Relegation fears loomed, and the final position of 20th being a narrwo escape from an exit from the Conference.

FA Cup action was interesting as progression from he qualifying rounds was stuttering to start with. Eventually wins over Croydon, Yeading, Berkhamsted and Kingstonian brought a First Round tie at home to Reading. A crowd of 3,990 saw Slough take a 1-0 lead, drop to 3-1 down then equalise with goals in the 88th and 89th minutes. The replay at Elm Park in front of over 6,000 saw the Rebels exit 1-2.

Both Bob Lord and FA Trophy runs were brief. After beating Bath, Kidderminster won a second round Bob Lord match whilst Enfield progressed in the FA Trophy after beating Slough 4-0 at Southbury Road.

During this season Slough went into receivership and after negotiations the club was finally purchased by a consortium led by Managing Director Bob Pearson and Father and Son Alan and Byron Thorne. They had previously been connected at Millwall and between them have a wealth of football experience to offer Slough. Since their takover in February many changes have occured, including playing and management staff and numerous off the field activities. The long term aim is to encourage youth soccer, community spirit and interests centering on Wexham Park

Richard 'Ollie' Hayward

Slough Town F.C. 1991-92. Back Row (L-R): P Stacey, T Knight, T Bunting, S Scott, T Roffey (now Wycombe), M Mallinson, E O'Connor, T Langley (now Basingstoke). Middle: G Cox, M Walsh, D Anderson, M Putnam, S Thompson (now Wycombe), B Rake (now Chesham), M Turkington, N Bashir, T Houston, S Hickey, A Pluckrose, M Hill, P McKinnon, N Stanley, J Watt, B Burke. Front: A Davies, T Gorman, R Furey, T Dean, T Abbott, R Franks.

Slough Town

Match No.	Date	Competition	Venue H/A	Opponents	Result	League H/T	Pos.	Goalscorers (Times if known)	Attendance
1	Aug 17	GMVC	H	Kidderminster	W 3-1	1-0		O'Connor 30 (pen); Thompson 53,59	823
2	Aug 24	GMVC	A	Macclesfield	W 1-0	0-0	4	Thompson 79	879
3	Aug 26	GMVC	H	Colchester	L 2-4	2-4	4	O'Connor 5; Thompson 12	2226
4	Aug 31	GMVC	H	Runcorn	W 1-0	0-0	3	McKinnon 55	799
5	Sep 3	BLT 1-1	A	Bath City	L 1-2	0-1		Hll 82	404
6	Sep 7	GMVC	H	Telford Utd	L 0-3	0-2	4		877
7	Sep 11	GMVC	A	Cheltenham	L 0-1	0-0	7		821
8	Sep 14	FAC 1Q	H	Croydon	D 2-2	1-1		Pluckrose 25; O'Connor 70	524
9	Sep 16	FAC 1QR	H	Croydon	W 3-0	0-0		Anderson 60; Stanley 73; McKinnon 85	246
10	Sep 21	GMVC	A	Stafford Rangers	D 1-1	0-0	8	O'Connor 59 (pen)	690
11	Sep 24	BLT 1-2	H	Bath City	W 2-0	1-0		Knight 45; Joseph 76	584
12	Sep 28	FAC 2Q	H	Yeading	D 0-0	0-0			351
13	Oct 1	FAC 2QR	H	Yeading	W 1-0	0-0		Anderson 89	722
14	Oct 5	GMVC	H	Barrow	W 1-0	1-0	12	Turkington 31	611
15	Oct 12	FAC 3Q	A	Berkhamsted	W 4-1	1-1		Anderson 47; McKinnon 51,63; Donnellan 88	502
16	Oct 15	GMVC	A	Bath City	L 1-2	0-2	12	Stacey 75	600
17	Oct 19	GMVC	A	Altrincham	W 7-3	3-2	9	Pluckrose 5,60; Thompson 7,15,84; McKinnon 55,58	884
18	Oct 22	GMVC	H	Redbridge Forest	W 4-0	3-0	5	McKinnon 21,24,40; Mallinson 77	910
19	Oct 26	FAC 4Q	H	Kingstonian	W 2-1	1-0		o.g. 34; Mallinson 67	990
20	Nov 2	GMVC	H	Witton Albion	W 2-1	0-1	5	Anderson 67 (pen); McKinnon 70	610
21	Nov 9	GMVC	H	Welling Utd	L 0-3	0-2	8		907
22	Nov 16	FAC 1	H	Reading	D 3-3	1-0		Pluckrose 19; Fielder 88; McKinnon 90	3990
23	Nov 23	GMVC	A	Kettering	L 3-2	2-1	5	Joseph 1,55; Thompson 3	1830
24	Nov 27	FAC 1R	A	Reading	L 1-2	0-2		Joseph 87	6363
25	Nov 30	FAT 3Q	H	Margate	D 0-0	0-0			663
26	Dec 3	FAT 3QR	A	Margate	W 2-1	0-0		Pluckrose 52; Scott 54	482
27	Dec 14	GMVC	A	Merthyr Tydfil	W 2-1	0-1	6	Anderson 60; scott 65	592
28	Dec 17	BLT 2	H	Kidderminster	L 0-1	0-0			408
29	Dec 21	GMVC	H	Bath City	D 2-2	2-2	9	Pluckrose 5; Anderson 32	608
30	Dec 26	GMVC	H	Wycombe Wanderers	L 0-1	0-0	12		3703
31	Jan 1	GMVC	A	Wycombe Wanderers	L 0-3	0-1	14		5162
32	Jan 4	GMVC	A	Redbridge Forest	L 0-4	0-2	14		673
33	Jan 11	FAT 1	A	Enfield	L 0-4	0-2			670
34	Jan 18	GMVC	H	Gateshead	W 2-0	1-0	12	Anderson 15; Donnellan 89	730
35	Jan 25	GMVC	A	Witton Albion	L 1-2	0-0	14	Thompson 49	814
36	Jan 31	GMVC	H	Boston Utd	W 3-1	1-0	8	Anderson 27 (pen); McKinnon 75,84	732
37	Feb 8	GMVC	H	Altrincham	L 2-3	0-1	9	Donnellan 58; Pluckrose 83	860
38	Feb 15	GMVC	A	Boston Utd	L 1-3	0-1	12	Thompson 78	721
39	Feb 21	GMVC	A	Welling Utd	W 2-0	0-0	10	McKinnon 49; o.g. 90	866
40	Feb 25	GMVC	H	Cheltenham	L 1-3	0-1	11	Anderson 47	659
41	Feb 29	GMVC	H	Stafford Rangers	D 2-2	1-1	11	Pluckrose 39; Donnellan 46	658
42	Mar 7	GMVC	A	Barrow	W 4-3	4-1	8	McKinnon 1,19; Pluckrose 44; Stanley 12	1035
43	Mar 10	GMVC	H	Yeovil	L 1-4	0-0	10	Donnellan 46	584
44	Mar 14	GMVC	H	Kettering	L 0-2	0-1	12		698
45	Mar 21	GMVC	A	Telford Utd	D 2-2	2-0	13	McKinnon 8; Anderson 12 (pen)	691
46	Mar 28	GMVC	A	Yeovil	L 0-1	0-1	13		1763
47	Mar 31	GMVC	H	Merthyr Tydfil	D 0-0	0-0	13		521
48	Apr 4	GMVC	H	Northwich Victoria	L 0-1	0-0	13		528
49	Apr 7	GMVC	A	Farnborough	L 1-2	0-1	15	Anderson 85 (pen)	762
50	Apr 12	GMVC	A	Gateshead	L 1-2	0-1	15	Scott 87	292
51	Apr 14	GMVC	A	Colchester	L 0-4	0-0	16		3197
52	Apr 18	GMVC	A	Runcorn	L 0-1	0-0	16		533
53	Apr 20	GMVC	H	Farnborough	L 0-5	0-3	16		784
54	Apr 25	GMVC	A	Kidderminster	D 3-3	2-0	17	Stanley 18; McKinnon 22,62	1541
55	Apr 28	GMVC	A	Northwich Victoria	L 0-3	0-0	19		444
56	May 2	GMVC	H	Macclesfield	L 0-3	0-1	20		588

Best Home League Attendance: 3,703 v Wycombe W. 26.12.91.2　　　Lowest: 521 v Merthyr Tydfil 31.3.92.　　　Average Home Attendance: 885
Compared with 1990/91:

Slough Town

1	2	3	4	5	6	7	8	9	10	11	12	14	Match No.
Bunting	Stacey	Pluckrose	Hill	Putnam	Turkington	Fielder	McKinnon•	Donnellan	Thompson	O'Connor	Stanley	Anderson	1
Bunting	Stacey	Pluckrose	Hill	Putnam	Turkington	Fielder	McKinnon	Donnellan	Thompson	O'Connor	Stanley	Anderson	2
Bunting	Stacey	Pluckrose	Hill	Putnam	Turkington	Fielder	McKinnon	Donnellan	Thompson	O'Connor	Stanley	Anderson	3
Bunting	Knight	Pluckrose	Hill	Putnam	Turkington	Fielder	McKinnon	Donnellan	Thompson	O'Connor	Stanley	Scott	4
Bunting	**Knight**	**Pluckrose**	**Hill**	**Anderson**	**Turkington**	**Fielder**	**McKinnon**	**Donnellan**	**Thompson**	**Mallinson**	**Stanley**	**O'Connor**	**5**
Burns	Stacey	Pluckrose	Hill•	Putnam†	Rake	Fielder	McKinnon	Donnellan	Thompson	O'Connor	Stanley	Anderson	6
Burns	Stacey	Pluckrose	Hill	Putnam†	Anderson	Fielder	McKinnon	Stanley	Thompson	O'Connor	Turkington	Rake	7
Burns	**Stacey**	**Pluckrose**	**Hill**	**Putnam**	**Anderson**	**Fielder**	**McKinnon**	**Stanley**	**Thompson**	**O'Connor**	**Turkington**	**Rake**	**8**
Burns	**Stacey**	**Pluckrose**	**Hill**	**Anderson**	**Turkington**	**Fielder**	**McKinnon**	**Stanley**	**Thompson**	**O'Connor**	**Mallinson**	**Rake**	**9**
Burns	Stacey	Pluckrose	Hill	Anderson	Turkington	Fielder	McKinnon	Joseph	Thompson	O'Connor	Stanley	Knight	10
Burns	**Stacey**	**Pluckrose**	**Knight**	**Anderson**	**Turkington**	**Fielder**	**McKinnon**	**Joseph**	**Thompson**	**O'Connor**	**Stanley**	**Hickey**	**11**
Burns	**Stacey**	**Pluckrose**	**Knight**	**Anderson**	**Turkington**	**Fielder**	**McKinnon**	**Stanley**	**Thompson**	**O'Connor**	**Hill**	**Rake**	**12**
Bunting	**Stacey**	**Mallinson**	**Knight**	**Anderson**	**Turkington**	**Fielder**	**McKinnon**	**Rake**	**Thompson**	**O'Connor**	**Stanley**	**Hickey**	**13**
Bunting	Stacey	Pluckrose	Knight	Anderson	Turkington	Fielder	McKinnon	Donnellan	Stanley	Mallinson	Whitby	Hill	14
Burns	**Stacey**	**Pluckrose**	**Knight**	**Anderson**	**Turkington**	**Fielder**	**McKinnon**	**Donnellan**	**Thompson**	**Mallinson**	**Whitby**	**Stanley**	**15**
Bunting	Stacey	Pluckrose	Knight	Anderson	Turkington	Fielder	McKinnon	Donnellan	Thompson†	Mallinson	Whitby	Stanley	16
Bunting	Stacey	Pluckrose	Hill	Anderson	Turkington	Fielder	McKinnon	Whitby	Thompson	Mallinson	Stanley	Dell	17
Bunting	Stacey	Pluckrose	Hill	Anderson	Turkington	Fielder	McKinnon	Donnellan	Thompson	Mallinson	Dell	Joseph	18
Bunting	**Stacey**	**Pluckrose**	**Hill**	**Anderson**	**Turkington**	**Fielder**	**McKinnon**	**Whitby**	**Thompson**	**Mallinson**	**Dell**	**Joseph**	**19**
Bunting	Stacey	Pluckrose	Hill	Anderson	Dell	Fielder	McKinnon	Whitby•	Thompson	Mallinson	Joseph	Stanley	20
Bunting	Stacey	Pluckrose	Hill	Anderson	Turkington	Fielder	McKinnon	Whitby	Thompson	Mallinson•	Joseph	Dell	21
Bunting	**Stacey**	**Pluckrose**	**Hill**	**Anderson**	**Donnellan**	**Fielder**	**McKinnon**	**Turkington**	**Thompson**	**Mallinson**	**Whitby**	**Dell**	**22**
Bunting	Stacey	Pluckrose	Knight	Anderson	Donnellan	Fielder	McKinnon	Joseph	Thompson	Mallinson•	Whitby	Dell	23
Bunting	**Whitby**	**Pluckrose**	**Hill**	**Anderson**	**Donnellan•**	**Fielder**	**Dell**	**Joseph**	**Thompson**	**Mallinson**	**Stanley**	**Knight**	**24**
Bunting	**Stacey**	**Pluckrose**	**Hill**	**Anderson**	**Donnellan•**	**Fielder**	**McKinnon**	**Joseph**	**Thompson**	**Mallinson**	**Stanley**	**Whitby**	**25**
Bunting	**Stacey**	**Pluckrose**	**Hill**	**Anderson**	**Donnellan•**	**Fielder**	**McKinnon**	**Joseph**	**Thompson**	**Mallinson**	**Stanley**	**Whitby**	**26**
Bunting	Whitby	Mallinson	Hill	Anderson	Pluckrose	Dell	McKinnon•	Joseph	Thompson	Scott	Stanley	Knight	27
Bunting	**Whitby**	**Mallinson**	**Hill**	**Anderson**	**Pluckrose**	**Dell**	**McKinnon•**	**Joseph**	**Thompson**	**Scott**	**Stanley**	**Knight**	**28**
Bunting	Whitby	Pluckrose	Hill	Anderson	Fielder	Scott	Stanley	Joseph•	Thompson	Pluckrose	O'Connor	Knight	29
Bunting	Whitby•	Pluckrose	Hill	Anderson	Scott•	Fielder	Stanley	Lynch	Thompson	Mallinson	O'Connor	Dell	30
Bunting	Whitby•	Pluckrose	Knight	Anderson	Dell†	Fielder	Stanley	O'Connor	Thompson	Stacey	Scott	Mallinson	31
Bunting	Whitby	Stacey	Knight	Anderson•	Dell	Fielder	Stanley	Scott†	Thompson	O'Connor	Putnam	Brown	32
Bunting	**Stacey**	**Mallinson**	**Knight**	**Anderson**	**O'Connor**	**Fielder**	**McKinnon**	**Donnellan**	**Thompson**	**Pluckrose**	**Scott**	**Whitby**	**33**
Bunting	Stacey	Mallinson	Hill	Anderson	O'Connor	Fielder	McKinnon	Donnellan	Thompson	Pluckrose	Whitby	Brown	34
Bunting	Stacey	Mallinson	Hill	Anderson	O'Connor	Fielder	McKinnon	Donnellan	Thompson	Pluckrose	Brown	Scott	35
Bunting	Stacey	Mallinson	Hill	Anderson	O'Connor•	Fielder	McKinnon	Donnellan	Thompson	Pluckrose	Brown	Scott	36
Watkiss	Stacey	Hill•	Hemsley	Anderson	Whitby	Fielder	McKinnon	Donnellan	Thompson	Pluckrose	Stanley	Mallinson	37
Bunting	Knight	Hill•	Hemsley	Anderson	Whitby	Fielder	McKinnon	Donnellan	Thompson	Pluckrose	Stanley	Scott	38
Bunting	Knight	Mallinson•	Hemsley	Anderson	Whitby†	Fielder	McKinnon	Donnellan	Stanley	Pluckrose	O'Connor	Scott	39
Moussaddik	Knight•	Mallinson	Hemsley	Anderson	Whitby	Fielder	McKinnon	Donnellan	Stanley	Pluckrose	O'Connor	Scott	40
Moussaddik	Stacey	Mallinson•	Hemsley	Knight	Whitby	Anderson	McKinnon	Donnellan	Stanley	Pluckrose	O'Connor	Stacey	41
Moussaddik	Stacey	Mallinson•	Hemsley	Anderson	Knight	Whitby	McKinnon	Donnellan	Stanley	Pluckrose	O'Connor	Scott	42
Bunting	Stacey	Hill†	Knight	Hemsley	Booker•	Fielder	McKinnon	Donnellan	Stanley	Pluckrose	O'Connor	Hickey	43
Bunting	Stacey	Mallinson	Hill	Anderson	Hemsley†	Fielder	McKinnon	Donnellan	Booker	Pluckrose	Stanley	Knight	44
Bunting	Stacey	Mallinson	Hill	Anderson	Whitey	Fielder	McKinnon	Donnellan	Booker•	Pluckrose	Stanley	Knight	45
Bunting	Stacey	Hill	Sitton	Anderson	Knight	Fielder	McKinnon	Donnellan•	Stanley	Mallinson	Whitby	Scott	46
Bunting	Stacey	Mallinson	Sitton	Anderson	Knight	Fielder	McKinnon•	Donnellan•	Stanley†	Pluckrose	Whitby	Hill	47
Bunting	Stacey	Hill	Sitton	Anderson	Knight	Fielder	McKinnon	Donnellan	Stanley	Mallinson	Whitby	Scott	48
Watkiss	Stacey	Hill	Knight	Anderson	Mallinson	Fielder†	McKinnon	Donnellan•	Whitby	Pluckrose	Scott	Putnam	49
Watkiss	Stacey	Hill	Knight	Anderson	Mallinson	Scott	McKinnon	Whitby	Stanley†	Pluckrose	Fielder	Hickey	50
Watkiss	Knight	Pluckrose	Stacey	Anderson	Mallinson	Fielder	McKinnon	Scott	Donnellan	Hickey	Whitby	Hemsley	51
Watkiss	Knight	Mallinson	Sitton	Anderson	Hill	Fielder	McKinnon•	Donnellan†	Scott	Pluckrose	Hickey	Hemsley	52
Watkiss	Knight	Mallinson	Sitton	Anderson	Hill	Fielder	Booker	Whitby	Hemsley	Scott•	Hickey	Stacey	53
Watkiss	Knight	Stacey	Hemsley	Anderson	Whitby	Fielder	McKinnon•	Scott	Stnaley	Hill	Hickey	Sitton	54
Watkiss	Stacey	Hill	Hemsley	Anderson•	Knight	Fielder	Mallinson	Stanley	Scott	Whitby	Hickey	Booker	55
Watkiss	Stacey	Hill	Pluckrose	Anderson	Knight	Fielder	Mallinson	Stanley	Scott	Hickey	O'Connor	Sitton	56

• substituted by No. 12. † substitued by No. 14.

Slough Town

DAVID KEMP

David Kemp was appointed full-time manager of Slough Town on 23 July 1992. This has brought Dave's career in a full cycle. Having been a prolific goalscorer with the 'Rebels' for two years, 1973 - 1974, in which was the early playing days in the Isthmian League and at the then new Wexham Park. Coincidentally, Managing Director Bob Pearson, who was a scout for Brentford in those days, spotted Dave's scoring ability and recommended that his talents would be beneficial to the professional game.

This recommendation proved correct, as Dave joined Crystal Palace. Spells at Portsmouth, Carlisle United and Plymouth Argyle followed and in all cases he became the leading goalscorer. The United States beckoned, and on returning to the UK Dave started his managerial career at Wimbledon, firstly with the youth team and then as assistant manager. This was followed by two years as manager of Plymouth Argyle until the end of February 1992.

Dave's immediate aim is to ensure that Slough gain a more professional attitude with all playing staff and form a team capable of winning honours.

Programme details:
   28 pages for 80p
   Editor - Eddie Marr

Any other club publications:
   Rebels Without a Clue
   (Fanzine)
Local Newspapers:
   Slough Observer
   Slough Express

Local Radio Stations:
   Berkshire Radio
   Radio 210

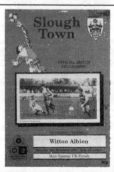

SLOUGH TOWN - PLAYING SQUAD 1992-93

Player	Honours	Birthplace and date	Transfer Fees	Previous Clubs
GOALKEEPERS				
Trevor Bunting		Chalfont St Giles 22/5/68		Burnham, Wycombe W, Marlow
DEFENDERS				
Mark Hill		Perivale 21/1/61		Maidstone Utd, Wycombe W, Brentford
Darren Anderson	EY	Wimbledon 6/9/66		Aldershot
Phil Stacey	Clubcall C	Chingford 10/9/61		Leyt & Ilf, Camb Utd, Walthamstow A, B Stortford, Epping, Enfield, Dagenham,
Stuart Hemsley	SSC, FAXI	Carshalton 18/11/64		Croydon, Sutton United
MIDFIELD				
Steve Whitby		Edgware 27/8/70	£8,000	Berkhamsted, Wycombe W
Mark Mallinson	RAF, Combined Services	Blackburn 26/9/63		Oxford City, Hungerford
Colin Fielder	BHL, HSC	Winchester 5/1/64	£18,000	Aldershot, Farnborough
Alan Pluckrose	RAF, Combined Services	Southwater 3/7/63		Falmouth, Torquay Utd, SV Viktoria Goch(Ger), Aylesbury
Steve Scott		Chiswick 8/5/67		QPR, Friska Viljor(Swe), Farnborough, Harrow Borough, Hibernians(Malta)
Eammon O'Connor		Wembley 4/9/63		Wembley, Harrow Borough, Kingsbury, Harrow Borough
FORWARDS				
Paul McKinnon	VOL,SSC	Camberley 1/8/58		Chelsea, Camberley, Woking, Sutton Utd, Malmo, Blackburn, Sutton Utd
Steve Hickey		Slough 1/9/74		Youth
Neal Stanley		Banbury 30/5/61		Wycombe W, Wokingham

Departures during last season:
Phil Burns (Airdrie), Tony Dell (Chesham), Barry Rake (Chesham), Steve Thompson (Wycombe), Mark Turkington (Farnborough), Gary Donnellan (Hendon). Francis Joseph, Mike Putnam, Trevor Booker, Richard Watkiss.

Players on loan during season:
Tony Lynch (Barnet), Chuck Moussaddik (Wycombe)

Wrexham Park Stadium, Slough Town

Name of ground: Wrexham Park Stadium
Ground address and Tel. No.: Wrexham Road, Slough SL2 5QR. Tel: 0753 523358/526738 & 57170
Information line: 0891 446 885
Simple ground directions: Turn North at Co-op Superstore on A4 just East of Town Centre, A412. Go over two bridges, turn left at next set of traffic lights and then at T-junction turn right. Ground 0-5 mile down on left
Official capacity: 5,000   **Seating:** 390   **Covered accommodation:** 2,000
Cost of seats: £5.00   **Cost of standing:** £4.00
Record attendance: 8,000 Slough Schools U-15 Final v Liverpool Schools 1976, 5,000 v Millwall FA Cup 1982
Social facilities available (Bars, hot & cold food etc.): Lounge, games and TV bar. Main hall (licensed for 300 for disco type functions). Open daily
Local newspapers: Slough Observer, Slough Express
Car parking: 400 cars

Sponsored by: **KETTERING TOWN**   **Nickname:** The Rebels

Previous leagues: S. Alliance, Berks & Bucks, S W Suburban, Spartan, Herts & Middx, Corinthian, Athenian, Isthmian
Year formed: 1890   **Club shop:** Yes
Club colours: Amber/navy/navy   **Change colours:** Green/white
Midweek home matches: Tuesday   **Club metal badges:** Yes £2.00
Club programme: **Editor:** Eddie Marr
Record transfer fee paid: £18,000 to Farnborough Town for Colin Fielder
Record transfer fee received: £20,000 from Brighton & H.A. for Eric Young & Airdrie for Phil Burns
Record appearances for club: (present player) Tony Knight (302)
Record goalscorer for club: (present player) Neil Stanley (77)
Record goalscorer in a season: (present player) Steve Thompson
Past players who have progressed to the Football League: Paul Barron, David Kemp, Roy Davies, Mickey Droy, Eric Young (Wimbledon), Alan Paris (Leicester City), Tony Dennis (Cambridge Utd)
Best performance in the FA Cup: 2nd Round Proper: 1970-71 v Barnet 0-1; 1978-79 Yeovil 0-1; 1982-83 Bishop Stortford 1-4; 1985-86 Orient 2-2, 2-3; 1986-87 Swansea 0-3

STAFFORD RANGERS

Formed: 1876

Chairman:
R J Horton

Vice Chairman:
L H Douglas

Directors:
F Dellicompagni
M T Hughes
W E Hodgson
R E Tonge
C S Went

Secretary:
Mrs Angela Meddings

Manager:
Dennis Booth

Coach:
Mal Meddings

Trainer:
Robert Walters

Commercial Manager:
George Berry

Physiotherapist:
Len Cox

Club Doctor:
Dr Merriott

Mixed Fortunes

Once again Rangers have struggled in the league and have languished near the bottom of the table for most of the campaign, although an unbeaten run of 9 games at the end lifted them to a final position of 17th. For the third time in 4 years, Rangers entered the last game requiring points to be certain of retaining their Conference status.

Manager Chris Wright struggled from the opening game to find the right blend despite encouraging pre-season performances, and, although hit by injuries, used over 40 players before he was dismissed in January 1st 1992 after a disappointing run in which Rangers had only won 4 games out of 25. In addition, Rangers had been dumped out of the Bob Lord Trophy and the FA Cup at the first hurdles by fellow Conference sides Northwich Victoria and Kettering Town.

The club were dealt further blows by falling gates and the closure of the Town End of the ground due to an unsafe perimeter wall. Financial difficulties were not helped by the failure to secure a lucrative first round FA Cup tie against League opposition for the first time in 4 years.

Following the departure of Wright, the managers position was taken by former Aston Villa man Dennis Booth who had joined Rangers as coach in October 1991. Booth had the difficult task of lifting a demoralised and depleted squad to maintain Conference status with only 17 games to play. After the disappointment of losing at home to Marine in the FA Trophy and a 6-0 thrashing at Witton Albion, Booth gradually built a squad of experienced players including the likes of Nigel Callaghan, Ian Miller and Keith Edwards who together with ex-Aldershot, Stoke and Wolves stalwart George Berry brought the stability and consistency that was previously missing and culminated in the unbeaten run which secured Conference safety.

Highlights of the season included the sale in February of promising youngster Paul Devlin (who had loan spells with Liverpool and Leeds) to Notts County, and success in reaching the final of the Staffs Senior Cup.

The club will be hoping for early success on the field in 92/93 which together with the programme of ground improvements planned for completion by August, will bring the crowds back to Marston Road and Rangers challenging for a place in the Football League.

M. T. Hughes

Stafford Rangers F.C. 1991-92. Back Row (L-R): L Cox (Physio), M Bradshaw, I Miller, D Newman, S Essex, R Price, C Heggs, C Hemming, D Lyons, K Edwards. Front (L-R): L Boyle, S Berks, P Devlin (now Notts Co), D Harle, D Booth (Manager), M Meddings (Coach), W Simpson, I Brown, D Hope. Photo: Courtesy of Staffordshire Newsletter.

Stafford Rangers

FA Cup: 4th Qualifying Round.

FA Trophy: 1st Round.

Match No.	Date	Competition	Venue H/A	Opponents	Result	League H/T	Pos.	Goalscorers (Times if known)	Attendance
1	Aug 17	GMVC	H	Farnborough	L 0-1	0-1			1052
2	Aug 24	GMVC	A	Bath City	W 1-0	0-0		Devlin 65	862
3	Aug 26	GMVC	A	Barrow	D 0-0	0-0	10		1547
4	Aug 31	GMVC	H	Merthyr Tydfil	D 0-0	0-0	11		945
5	Sep 3	BLT	A	Northwich Victoria	W 2-0	2-0			501
6	Sep 7	GMVC	H	Wycombe Wanderers	L 0-2	0-2	17		1381
7	Sep 14	GMVC	A	Altrincham	W 3-0	2-0	19		1201
8	Sep 17	BLT	H	Northwich Victoria	D 1-1	0-0		Pearson 61	540
9	Sep 21	GMVC	H	Slough	D 1-1	0-0	18	Hodkinson 46 (pen)	690
10	Sep 27	GMVC	A	Telford Utd	L 1-4	1-3	20	Wighe 42	1179
11	Oct 5	GMVC	A	Kettering	L 1-2	0-0	20	Devlin 74	1318
12	Oct 8	GMVC	H	Witton Albion	W 3-2	2-0	18	Tuohy 24; Palgrave 31; Simpson 65 (pen)	817
13	Oct 12	GMVC	H	Welling Utd	D 1-1	0-0	18	Devlin 53	822
14	Oct 19	GMVC	H	Gateshead	L 1-3	0-2	19	Booth 65	707
15	Oct 22	SSC 1	H	Boldmere St. M.	W 3-0	1-0		Tuohy (2); Wood	312
16	Oct 26	FAC 4Q	A	Kettering	D 0-0	0-0			1785
17	Nov 2	GMVC	A	Colchester	L 0-2	0-2	19		2139
18	Nov 5	GMVC	A	Macclesfield	L 0-1	0-0	19		522
19	Nov 9	GMVC	A	Northwich Victoria	W 2-1	0-1	18	Palgrave 75; Tuohy 79	733
20	Nov 12	SSC 2	H	Stoke City	W 2-1	1-1		Simpson; Hope	295
21	Nov 16	GMVC	A	Redbridge Forest	L 3-4	1-2	19	Simpson 26; P. Berks 51; Hope 54	452
22	Nov 23	GMVC	A	Cheltenham	D 0-0	0-0	19		808
23	Nov 26	GMVC	A	Boston Utd	L 0-1	0-0	19		681
24	Nov 30	GMVC	A	Yeovil	W 1-0	0-0	19	Wolverson 86	2339
25	Dec 3	GMVC	H	Colchester	D 3-3	0-1	19	Wolverson 89; Simpson 67 (pen); Bradshaw 84	961
26	Dec 7	GMVC	A	Merthyr Tydfil	L 0-1	0-1	18		586
27	Dec 21	GMVC	H	Altrincham	L 1-2	1-0	19	Wood 38	680
28	Dec 26	GMVC	A	Runcorn	D 0-0	0-0	19		688
29	Dec 28	GMVC	H	Kettering	L 1-2	1-0	20	Wood 15	1089
30	Jan 1	GMVC	A	Macclesfield	D 1-1	1-1	20	Wells 1	994
31	Jan 4	GMVC	H	Telford Utd	W 3-2	0-1	20	o.g. 63; Edwards 76; Simpson 86 (pen)	943
32	Jan 11	FAT 1	H	Marine	L 0-1	0-1			778
33	Jan 13	GMVC	A	Kidderminster	L 1-2	1-1	20	Edwards 45	1136
34	Jan 18	GMVC	H	Welling Utd	D 0-0	0-0	18		637
35	Feb 8	GMVC	A	Witton Albion	L 0-6	0-4	22		912
36	Feb 14	GMVC	H	Yeovil	D 0-0	0-0	22		758
37	Feb 25	SSC 3	H	Oldbury Utd	W 1-0	0-0		P. Berks	254
38	Feb 29	GMVC	A	Slough	D 2-2	1-1	22	Heggs 6; Edwards 77	658
39	Mar 7	GMVC	H	Cheltenham	D 2-2	1-2	22	Simpson 25 (pen); Wood 60	667
40	Mar 21	GMVC	A	Wycombe	L 0-3	0-1	22		3202
41	Mar 28	GMVC	H	Runcorn	W 1-0	1-0	22	Miller 27	762
42	Mar 31	GMVC	H	Redbridge Forest	W 2-1	1-0	21	o.g. 42; Simpson 51 (pen)	709
43	Apr 4	GMVC	H	Kidderminster	W 2-0	0-0	20	Foreman 59,82	1102
44	Apr 11	GMVC	A	Boston Utd	D 2-2	0-1	20	Dawson 71; Foreman 83	839
45	Apr 15	GMVC	A	Gateshead	D 0-0	0-0	20		202
46	Apr 18	GMVC	A	Northwich Victoria	W 2-1	0-1	19	Foreman 62,66	745
47	Apr 20	GMVC	H	Barrow	D 0-0	0-0	19		1139
48	Apr 25	GMVC	A	Farnborough	D 1-1	1-0	19	Essex 30	811
49	May 2	GMVC	H	Bath City	W 2-0	1-0	17	Foreman 15; Berry 89 (pen)	895

Best Home Attendance: 1381 v Wycombe 7.9.91   Lowest: 637 v Welling 18.1.92   Average Home Attendance: 874
Compared to 1990/91: 1172

Goalscorers League: Simpson 6; Foreman 5; Devlin 3; Edwards 3; Wood 3; Own goal 3; Bradshaw 2; Palgrave 2; Wolverson 2; Berks 1; Berry 1; Booth 1; Dawson 1; Essex 1; Heggs 1; Hodkinson 1; Hope 1; Miller 1; Withe 1. **FA Cup:** Berks 1; Essex 1; Hope 1; Miller 1; Pearson 1; Simpson 1; Tuohy 1; Wood 1; Own goal 1.

Stafford Rangers

1	2	3	4	5	6	7	8	9	10	11	12	14	Match No.
Price	Pearson	Bradshaw	Simpson	Essex	Booth	Butterworth	Wood•	Tuohy	Straw	Devlin	Rooney	Palgrave	1
Price	Pearson	Bradshaw	Simpson	Essex	Rooney	Bremner	Palgrave	Tuohy	Booth	Devlin	Straw	Wareing	2
Price	Pearson	Bradshaw	Simpson	Essex	Rooney	Bremner	Palgrave†	Tuohy	Booth•	Devlin	Straw	Wood	3
Price	Pearson	Bradshaw	Simpson	Essex	Rooney†	Bremner	Wood	Tuohy•	Hollier	Devlin	Wareing	Straw	4
Price	**Pearson**	**Bradshaw†**	**Simpson**	**Essex**	**Rooney**	**Bremner**	**Wood**	**Tuohy**	**Hollier•**	**Wareing**	**Anastasi**	**Berks**	**5**
Price	Pearson	Wood	Simpson	Essex	Hodkinson	Bremner	Rooney†	Tuohy•	Anastasi	Devlin	P.Berks	Lyndsey	6
Price	**Lyndsey**	**Whitehouse**	**Simpson**	Essex	**Hodkinson**	Bremner	Rooney†	Wood•	Anastasi	Devlin	Wareing	P.Berks	7
Price	Lyndsey	Whitehouse	Wood	Essex	**Hodkinson**	**Pearson**	**Hollier**	**Anastasi**	**Straw**	**Devlin**	**P.Berks**	**Bremner**	**8**
Price	Pearson	Bradshaw	Simpson	Essex	Hodkinson	Bremner	Pearson	Anastasi	P.Berks	Devlin	Wareing	Newman	9
Price	Pearson	Booth•	Simpson	Essex	Wood	Bremner•	Berks†	Anastasi	Withe	Devlin	Lyndsey	Whitehouse	10
Price	Pearson	Bradshaw	Simpson	Essex†	Wilson	Palgrave	Wood	Tuohy	Booth	Devlin	Anastasi	Lyndsey	11
Price	Pearson	Bradshaw	Simpson	Mower	Wilson	Palgrave	Wood	Tuohy	Booth	Devlin	P.Berks	Lyndsey	12
Price	Lyndsey	Bradshaw	Simpson	Mower	Booth	Pearson	Wood	Tuohy	Booth	Devlin	P.Berks	Lyndsey	13
Price	**Pearson•**	**Bradshaw**	**Simpson**	**Mower**	**Booth**	**Wilson**	**Wood**	**Tuohy**	**Withe**	Palgrave	P.Berks	Newman	14
Price	**Pearson•**	**Bradshaw**	**Simpson**	**Mower**	**Booth†**	**Wilson**	**Wood**	**Tuohy**	**Withe**	**Palgrave**	**Lyndsey**	**Newman**	**15**
Price	Lyndsey	Palgrave	Simpson	Wood	P.Berks	Wilson	Hope	Tuohy	Newman	Devlin	Essex	Bradshaw	17
Price	Pearson	Bradshaw	Simpson	Essex	Wood	Wilson	Lyndsey†	Tuohy	Palgrave	Devlin	P.Berks	Newman	18
Price	Pearson	Bradshaw	Simpson	Essex	Lyndsey†	Wood	Palgrave	Tuohy	Newman	Devlin	P.Berks	Hope	19
Price	**Pearson**	**Bradshaw**	**Lyndsey**	**Essex**	**P.Berks**	**Simpson**	**Byrne†**	**Tuohy•**	**Newman**	**Palgrave**	**Hope**	**Lyons**	**20**
Price	Pearson	Bradshaw	Simpson	Essex	P.Berks	Wolverson	Lyndsey	Palgrave•	Newman	Devlin	Hope	Pountney	21
Price	Lyndsey	Bradshaw	Simpson	Essex	Wood	Hope	Wolverson	Palgrave	P.Berks	Devlin	Newman	Pountney	22
Price	Pearson	Bradshaw	Simpson	Essex	Wood	Hope	Wolverson•	Palgrave	P.Berks	Devlin	Newman	Pountney	23
Price	Pearson	Bradshaw	Simpson	Essex	Wood	Wolverson•	Hemming	Hope	P.Berks	Devlin	Baker	Newman	24
Price	Pearson	Bradshaw	Simpson	Essex	Wood	Wolverson	Hemming	Hope	P.Berks	Devlin	Baker	Newman	25
Price	Pearson	Bradshaw	Simpson	Essex	Wood	Wolverson	Hemming•	Roberts†	P.Berks	Devlin	Baker	Hope	26
Price	Pearson	Bradshaw	Simpson	Essex	Wells•	Harmon	Hemming	Wood	P.Berks	Brown	Hope	Newman	27
Price	Pearson	Bradshaw	Simpson	Hemming	Essex	Harmon	Wells	Brough	Wood	Brown	Hope	Newman	28
Price	Pearson	Bradshaw	Simpson	Hemming	Essex	Harmon•	Wood	Brough	Brown†	Devlin	Hope	Wells	29
Price	Pearson	Bradshaw	Wood	Hemming	Essex	Harmon•	Wells	Brough	P.Berks	Devlin	Newman	Lyndsey	30
Price	Pearson	Bradshaw	Simpson	Hemming	Essex	Wood	Wells	Brough	Edwards	Devlin	P.Berks	Newman	31
Price	**Pearson•**	**Bradshaw**	**Simpson**	**Hemming**	**P.Berks**	**Wood**	**Wells**	**Brough**	**Edwards**	**Devlin**	**Hope**	**Newman**	**32**
Price	Wood	Bradshaw	Simpson	Hemming	Essex	Miller•	Wells	Brough†	Edwards	Devlin	P.Berks	Hope	33
Price	Hemming	Bradshaw•	Simpson	Harle	Essex	Miller	Wells	Wood	Edwards	Devlin	Brown	Brough	34
Price	Hemming	Bradshaw	Simpson	Harle	Essex	Brown†	Boyle	Heggs	Edwards	Devlin	Miller	P.Berks	35
Price	Boyle	Bradshaw	Simpson	Hemming	Harle	Miller	Wood	Heggs	Edwards	Brown	Hope	P.Berks	36
Price	**Boyle•**	**Bradshaw**	**Simpson**	**Hemming**	**Harle**	**Miller**	**Wood**	**Heggs**	**Edwards**	**P.Berks•**	**Hope**	**Pearson**	**37**
Price	Boyle•	Bradshaw	Simpson	Essex	Harle•	Miller	Wood	Heggs	Edwards	J.Berks†	Pearson	Hope	38
Price	Pearson	Hemming	Simpson	Essex	J.Berks	Miller	Hemming	Heggs	Edwards†	Wood	J.Berks	Hope	39
Price	Pearson	Hemming	Simpson	Essex	Wood	Miller	Wood	Dawson	Hope†	Foreman	Brown	Booth	40
Price	Simpson	Hemming†	Wood	Essex	Berry	Miller	Jones	Foreman	Dawson	Callaghan	Bradshaw	J.Berks	41
Price	Simpson	Hemming†	Wood	Essex	Berry	Miller	Jones	Foreman	Dawson	Callaghan	Pearson	Bradshaw	42
Price	Simpson	Bradshaw	Wood	Essex	Berry	Miller	Jones	Foreman	Dawson	Callaghan	Pearson	Bradshaw	43
Price	Simpson	Bradshaw	Hemming	Essex	Wood	Miller	Jones	Foreman	Dawson†	Callaghan•	Pearson	Hope	44
Price	Simpson	Bradshaw	Wood	Essex	Berry	Miller	Jones	Foreman	Dawson	Hope	Pearson	J.Berks	45
Price	Wood	Bradshaw	Palgrave•	Essex	Berry	Hemming	Jones	Foreman	Dawson	Hope	J.Berks	Palgrave	46
Price	Simpson	Bradshaw	Wood•	Essex	Berry	Hemming	Jones	Foreman	Dawson†	Callaghan	Miller	Hope	47
Price	Pearson	Bradshaw	Simpson	Essex	Jones	Miller	Palgrave	Dawson	Callaghan	Hope	Lyons	Pountney	49
Price	Simpson•	Bradshaw	Wood	Essex	Berry	Miller	Jones	Foreman	Palgrave	Callaghan	Pearson	Dawson	50

• substituted by No. 12. † substituted by No. 14.

League Appearances: Price 42; Simpson 39; Wood 38(1); Essex 37; Bradshaw 34(3); Pearson 27(4); Devlin 26; Hemming 22; Palgrave 15(2); Tuohy 12; Miller 12(1); P. Berks 11(5); Foreman 10; Jones 9; Hope 8(10); Lindsey 8(3); Dawson 8(1); Booth 7(1); Berry 7; Bremner 7; Callaghan 7; Edwards 7; Wells 6(1); Wolverson 6; Rooney 5(1); Brown 5(1); Brough 5; Harle 5; Wilson 5; Anastasi 4(1); Harmon 4; Heggs 4; Newman 3(3); Boyle 3; Hodkinson 3; J. Berks 2(1); Mower 2; Withe 2; Straw 1(3); Whitehouse 1(1); Butterworth 1; Hollier 1; Roberts 1; Wareing (3); Baker (2).

FA Cups: Price 8; Simpson 8; Pearson 7; Bradshaw 6; Wood 6; Tuohy 5; Essex 4; Palgrave 4; P. Berks 3(2); Devlin 3; Mower 3; Wilson 3; Lindsey 2(2); Newman 2(1); Withe 2(1); Booth 2; Edwards 2; Hemming 2; Hollier 2; Anastasi 1(1); Boyle 1; Bremner 1; Brough 1; Byrne 1; Harle 1; Heggs 1; Hodkinson 1; Miller 1; Rooney 1; Straw 1; Wareing 1; Wells 1; Whitehouse 1; Hope (3).

Appearances as substitutes shown in brackets.

Stafford Rangers

DENNIS BOOTH

Dennis was born in Ilkeston, Derbyshire on the 9th of April 1949. He took over as manager of Stafford Rangers at the beginning of January 1992 after the departure of Chris Wright. Dennis had been assistant manager at Marston Road since November 1991. Prior to moving to Stafford he had been at Aston Villa for three years as first team coach, working with both Graham Taylor and Jozef Venglos.

Dennis started his playing career with Charlton Athletic before moving to Blackpool, Southend United, Lincoln City, Watford and, finally, Hull City. In all, Dennis made over 500 Football League appearances. He had a spell as caretaker manager at Boothferry Park prior to becoming assistant to Eddie Gray.

Stafford Rangers' highly-rated goalkeeper Ryan Price saves brilliantly in this match against Slough Town. Photo: Roger Cain.

Programme details:
    40 pages for £1.00
    Editor - C & W Bedford

Any other club publications:

Local Newspapers:
    Staffordshire Newsletter
    Express & Star
    Evening Sentinel

Local Radio Stations:
    Radio Stoke
    Beacon Radio
    Signal Radio

STAFFORD RANGERS - PLAYING SQUAD 1992-93

Player	Honours	Birthplace and date	Transfer Fees	Previous Clubs
GOALKEEPERS				
Ryan Price	FA XI	Coven 13/3/70		Bolton W
DEFENDERS				
Jon Pearson	FA XI, FAT WSC	Birmingham 12/10/66	£5,000	Leicester C, Kidderminster, Burton Albion
Wayne Simpson	FA XI	Newcastle 19/9/68		Port Vale
Steve Essex	FA XI, BLT BSC	Walsall 2/10/60	£8,000	Darlaston, Gresley R, Burton Albion, Aylesbury
George Berry	Welsh Int. Lge Cup	Rostrup(Ger) 19/11/57		Wolves, Stoke, Peterborough, Aldershot
Mark Bradshaw		Ashton 7/6/69		Blackpool
MIDFIELD				
Chris Hemming		Newcastle 13/4/66		Stoke, Hereford, Merthyr Tydfil
Fraser Wood	FAT, NPL BLT, SSC	Wednesfield 18/12/58	£1,500	Tipton, Stafford, Kidderminster
Paul Jones		Walsall 6/9/65		Walsall, Wolves, Kettering
Brian Palgrave	WSC	Birmingham 12/7/66	£500	Walsall, Port Vale, Nuneaton, Bromsgrove
Nigel Callaghan	EU-21 & B Div 2	Singapore 12/9/62		Watford, Derby, Aston Villa
FORWARDS				
Jason Dawson		Burslem 99/2/71		Port Vale, Rochdale, Macclesfield
Darren Foreman	ES	Southampton 12/2/68		Barnsley, Crewe, Scarborough

Departures during season:
Richard Straw (Nuneaton), Des Bremner (Retired), Savvas Anastasi (Leek), Jason Withe (Telford), Phil Wilson (Witton Alb), Kenny Mower (Released), Mick Tuohy (Solihull), Darren Roberts (Armitage), Scott Lyndsey (Burton Alb), Paul Devlin (Notts Co), Keith Edwards (Released).

Players who joined on loan during season:
Jason Wolverson (Worcester), Jon Brough, Darren Harmon, Mark Wells (All Notts Co), Dave Harle (Doncaster), Carl Heggs (WBA), Lee Boyle (Doncaster), John Berks (Stoke).

Marston Road, Stafford Rangers

Name of ground: Marston Road
Ground address and Tel. No.: Marston Road, Stafford ST16 3BX. Tel: 0785 42750
Simple ground directions: M6 junction 14 on to next roundabout, take 2nd exit, slip to A34 roundabout straight across, 3rd right and the ground is 1/4 mile down
Official capacity: 6,328   **Seating:** 426   **Covered accommodation:** 3,000
Cost of seats: £5.00   **Cost of standing:** £4.00
Record attendance: 8,536 v Rotherham United, FA Cup Third Round, 4.1.1975
Social facilities available (Bars, hot & cold food etc.): Social club open 11am onwards. Sat 7pm-11pm, Evenings. 3 Canteens on ground serving hot & cold drinks and hot & cold food
Car parking: Club car park at ground, limited street parking

Sponsored by: **STAFFORD RANGERS**   **Nickname:** Boro

Previous grounds: Lammascotes, Stone Road, Newton Doxey
Previous leagues: Birm. & District, Shropshire, North Shropshire, Birmingham Comb., Cheshire, Northern Prem.
Club colours: Black & white/white/white   **Change colours:** All yellow with red trim
Midweek home matches: Tuesday   **Club metal badges:** Yes
Programme: £1   **Editor:** Mrs A. Meddings
Record transfer fee paid: For Trevor Dance from Port Vale in 1980
Record transfer fee received: £100,000 from Crystal Palace for Stanley Collymore 1990
Record appearances for club: Jim Sargeant
Record goalscorer for club: M. Cullerton, 176   **In a season:** Ray Williams, 47, 1971-72
Best FA Cup performance: 4th Round, 1974-75
Best FA Trophy performance: Winners 1971-72 and 1978-79
Past players who have progressed to the Football League: M. Alcksie (Plymouth, Luton, Spurs), J. Arnold (Blackburn, Everton, Port Vale), R. Williams, M. Cullerton, T. Bailey (all Port Vale), K. Barnes (Man. City), A. Lee (Tranmere Rov.), E. Cameron (Exeter), W. Blunt (Wolves), G. Bullock (Barnsley), K. Mottershead (Doncaster), McIlvenny (WBA), S. Collymore.
Club honours: Birmingham Comb. Champions 1912-13; Birmingham League Champions 1925-26; Northern Premier League Champions 1971-72, 1984; FA Trophy Winners 1971-72, 1978-79, Runners-up 1975-76; Bob Lord Trophy 1985-86; Wednesbury Charity Cup Winners 1920-21; Midland Floodlight Cup Winners 1970-71; NPL Championship Shield Winners 1984-85; Jim Thompson Shield Winners 1986-87; Staff Senior Cup Winners 1954-55, 1956-57, 1962-63, 1971-72, 1977-78, 1986-87
Past club managers: George Austin Feb 1947-May 1947; Jack Dowen Aug 1947-May 1948; Billy Frith Aug 1948-May 1950; Charlie Evans Aug 1950-May 1951; Eric Hampson Aug 1952-Nov 1953; Frank Brown Feb 1945-Nov 1955; George Antonio Sep 1957-May 1958; Len Millard Aug 1958-May 1959; Bert Mitchell Aug 1959-Sep 1960; Graham Cordell Jan 1961-Oct 1963; Ken Griffiths Feb 1964-May 1964; Stan Smith (caretaker Aug 1964-May 1965;); Colin Hutchinson Aug 1965-May 1969; Ray Chapman Aug 1969-Sep 1975; Ken Jones Sep 1975; Colin Meldrum Sep 1975-May 1976; Bob Heath/Bob Ritchie/Barrie Whittaker (caretakers Jun 1976); Paul Ogden May 1980-Oct 1981; Alan Fogarty (caretaker Oct 1981); Bobby Thomson Oct 1981-Jan 1983; Colin Clarke Jan-Sep 1983; Mal Meddings/Bob Walters/Barrie Whittaker (caretakers Sep 1983); Ron Reid Sep 1983-May 1988; Bryan Chambers Jun 1988-Feb 1989; Ron Reid Feb 1989-Nov 1989; John Williams Dec 1989-May 1990; C. Wright Jun 1990-Jan 1992; D. Booth Jan 1992

STALYBRIDGE CELTIC

Formed: 1911

President:
Joe Knott

Chairman:
Peter Barnes

Vice Chairman:
Derek Wolstenholme

Directors:
David Norton
Jack Hammersley
Alex Murdoch
Ray Connor
Mrs Dorothy Norton

Vice President:
Louis McDonald
Tommy Williams

Secretary & Press Officer:
Martyn Torr

Manager:
Phil Wilson

Assistant Manager:
David Stewart

Coach:
Dave Stevens

Commercial Manager:
Brian Carruthers

Momentous campaign at Bower Fold

Season 1991/92 was momentous for Stalybridge Celtic. After only five years in the HFS Loans League (one of which was spent in the First Division) they clinched the title and promotion to the Vauxhall Conference.

The season started with Celtic everyone's favourites for the title, having finished runners up to Witton Albion the previous year. But there were question marks about the team's ability to score goals. In finishing runners up they scored only 44 goals in 42 league matches, while conceding only 25. Manager Phil Wilson addressed this problem by signing the prolific Chris Camden from Cheltenham Town on a free transfer, and paying a club record fee of £1,250 for one-time Altrincham and Witton striker Paul Higginbotham from Glossop. With wingers chris Sharratt and Stuart Leicester also in competition for places the omens were good.

After two draws, the team got a win at Fleetwood and they were on their way. Goals began to flow from Camden and even the loss of Sharratt to Wigan Athletic did not halt their momentum. Leicester took his chance of regular football with such elanthat Sharratt was not missed at all. The loss of Higginbotham with cruciate ligament damage in a 3-1 win at Matlock was a massive blow, and he has not played since. However, the club spent £750 on Eric Priest, top scorer at neighbours Curzon Ashton, to partner Camden, who was now the league's leading scorer by some way. Defeat was avoided until the 21st game of the season at Gainsborough, then bottom of the table and, after half-time, with only ten men. Celtic shrugged off this defeat and did not lose again in the league until the final home game of the campaign when they lost to Hyde United in front of 1,400 fans, ironically the day they clinched the title. The final league game was drawn at Emley and so Celtic had gone 42 league games in a season with only two defeats, equalling the record of Wigan in 1970.

Manager Phil Wilson collected three Mail on Sunday Manager of the Month awards and defender John Aspinall won the Mail on Sunday Player of the Season award. Camden, after his 45 goals in all competitions, received an award from the Mail on Sunday as the Premier Division's leading scorer. His goal against Horwich gave him a post-war record, beating the 39 goals scored by Colin Skillen in 1979/80.

Martyn Torr

Stalybridge Celtic F.C. 1991-92. Back Row (L-R): Mark Edwards, Eric Priest, Ricky Blackman, Russ Hughes, Martin Filson, Stuart Leicester (now Macclesfield), John Brown. Centre (L-R): Dave Stevens (Physio), Dave Stewart (Assistant-Manager), Paul Higginbotham, Kevin O'Connell, Neil Edmonds. Front (L-R): Mark Burrell, Alan Woan, Paul Bennett, Phil Wilson (Manager), John Aspinall, Kevin Booth, Chris Camden (now Marine).

Stalybridge Celtic

Match No.	Date	Competition	Venue H/A	Opponents	Result	League H/T Pos.	Goalscorers (Times if known)	Attendance
1	Aug 24	HFS P	H	B. Auckland	D 0-0			405
2	Aug 26	HFS P	A	Droylsden	D 2-2		Higginbottom; Camden	580
3	Aug 31	HFS P	A	Fleetwood	W 2-0		Camden (2)	251
4	Sep 3	HFS P	H	Marine	W 3-1		Aspinall; Higginbottom; Camden	411
5	Sep 7	HFS P	A	Goole	D 1-1		Camden	325
6	Sep 10	HFS P	H	Emley	W 1-0		Smith	679
7	**Sep 14**	**FA Cup 1Q**	**H**	**Worksop**	**W 4-0**		**K. Booth; Brown; Camden (2)**	**403**
8	Sep 21	HFS P	A	Leek	W 3-2		Camden (2); Leicester	675
9	Sep 24	HFS P	A	Southport	W 1-0		Camden	523
10	**Sep 28**	**FAC 2Q**	**A**	**Southport**	**W 2-1**		**Bennett; Smith**	**417**
11	Oct 5	HFS P	H	Frickley	D 2-2		Smith (2)	544
12	Oct 8	HFS P	A	Chorley	W 3-2		Burrell; Leicester; Camden	329
13	**Oct 12**	**FAC 3Q**	**A**	**Eastwood Hanley**	**W 2-1**		**Aspinall; Smith**	**382**
14	Oct 15	HFS P	H	Bangor City	D 1-1		Camden	471
15	Oct 19	HFS P	A	Mossley	W 1-0		Camden	605
16	Oct 23	HFS P	H	B. Auckland	W 4-1		Camden (2); Higginbottom; Aspinall	225
17	**Oct 26**	**FAC 4Q**	**A**	**Gretna**	**L 2-3**		**Camden; Brown**	**449**
18	Oct 29	HFS P	H	Whitley Bay	W 3-1		Camden (2); Sharratt	364
19	Nov 2	HFS P	H	Accrington S.	W 3-0		Camden (2); Higginbottom	329
20	Nov 5	HFS P	A	Horwich	D 0-0			243
21	Nov 9	HFS P	H	Shepshed Albion	W 2-1		Camden (2)	631
22	Nov 12	HFS P	H	Morecambe	W 1-0		Brown	403
23	Nov 16	HFS P	A	Matlock	W 3-0		Camden; Bauress; Brown	524
24	Nov 23	HFS LC2	H	Leek	W 4-1		Camden (2); Leicester; Aspinall	640
25	**Nov 26**	**CSC 1**	**A**	**Northwich Victoria**	**L 1-2**		**Camden**	**380**
26	Nov 30	HFS P	H	Leek	W 1-0		Brown	629
27	Dec 7	HFS P	A	Gainsborough	L 1-3		O'Connell	369
28	Dec 14	HFS P	H	Buxton	D 2-2		Aspinall; Bauress	587
29	**Dec 17**	**Pres. Cup 2**		**Eastwood Town**	**W 2-0**		**Camden (2)**	**114**
30	Dec 20	HFS P	H	Matlock	W 4-0		Camden; Bennett; Brown; Priest	303
31	Dec 26	HFS P	A	Hyde Utd	W 2-1		Camden; Bauress	1117
32	Dec 28	HFS P	H	Accrington Stanley	W 2-1		Brown; Priest	687
33	Jan 1	HFS P	H	Droylsden	W 2-0		Dixon; Priest	726
34	Jan 4	HFS LC3	H	Fleetwood	W 5-0		Camden (3); Brown; Woan	418
35	**Jan 11**	**FAT 1**	**A**	**Altrincham**	**W 2-1**		**Priest; Leicester**	**1256**
36	Jan 18	HFS P	H	Mossley	W 5-0		Camden (3); Brown; Bauress	739
37	Jan 21	HFS P	A	Bangor City	W 1-0		Brown	211
38	**Feb 1**	**FAT 2**	**A**	**Harrow Boro**	**W 3-1**		**Camden; Bauress; Leicester**	**701**
39	Feb 4	HFS P	A	Southport	D 0-0			389
40	Feb 8	HFS P	H	Chorley	D 3-3		Camden (2); Priest	717
41	Feb 15	HFS P	H	Morecambe	D 0-0			660
42	Feb 18	HFS P	H	Goole	W 7-0		Camden (4); Priest; Bauress; Leicester	338
43	**Feb 22**	**FAT 3**	**A**	**Witton Albion**	**L 0-1**			**1755**
44	Feb 25	HFS LC4	H	Frickley	L 0-2			456
45	Feb 29	HFS P	H	Frickley	D 1-1		Priest	374
46	Mar 3	HFS P	A	Buxton	W 2-1		Camden; Aspinall	735
47	**Mar 10**	**Pres. Cup SF1**	**H**	**B. Auckland**	**W 3-2**		**Aspinall; Brown; Edwards**	**329**
48	Mar 14	HFS P	A	Gainsborough	W 3-0		Bennett (2); Edwards	577
49	Mar 21	HFS P	A	Accrington S.	W 3-0		Edwards (2); Leicester	632
50	Mar 28	HFS P	H	Fleetwood	W 2-0		Edwards; Brown	606
51	Apr 4	HFS P	A	Whitley Bay	W 2-0		Edwards; Blackman	333
52	**Apr 8**	**Pres. Cup SF2**	**A**	**B. Auckland**	**W 1-0**		**Brown**	**290**
53	Apr 11	HFS P	H	Horwich	W 2-0		Camden; Aspinall	628
54	**Apr 14**	**Pres. Cup F1**	**A**	**Morecambe**	**W 2-1**		**Edwards; Brown**	**511**
55	Apr 18	HFS P	A	Shedshed Albion	D 3-3		Camden; Aspinall; o.g.	288
56	Apr 20	HFS P	H	Hyde Utd	L 1-2		Leicester	1225
57	Apr 23	HFS P	A	Marine	D 0-0			428
58	**Apr 28**	**Pres. Cup SF2**	**H**	**Morecambe**	**L 0-2**			**713**
59	May 1	HFS P	A	Emley	D 2-2		Camden (2)	501

Best Home League Attendance: **Lowest:**   **Average Home Attendance:**

Goalscorers League: Camden 47; Brown 14; Aspinall 9; Edwards, Leicester, Priest 7; Bauress 6; Bennett, Higginbottom 4; Blackman, Booth, Burrell, Dixon, O'Connell, Woan 1.

Stalybridge Celtic

1	2	3	4	5	6	7	8	9	10	11	12	14	Match No.
Hughes	Bennett	K.Booth	Dixon	Aspinall	Blackman	O'Shea	H'bottom	Camden	Smith	Sharratt•	Leicester	C.Booth	1
Hughes	Bennett	K.Booth	Dixon	Aspinall	Blackman	O'Shea	H'bottom	Camden	Smith†	Sharratt•	Leicester	C.Booth	2
Hughes	Bennett	K.Booth	Dixon	Aspinall	O'Shea	Brown	H'bottom	Camden	Smith	Sharratt	Leicester	Burrell	3
Hughes	Bennett	K.Booth	Dixon	Aspinall	O'Shea	Brown	H'bottom	Camden	Smith	Sharratt•	Leicester	Burrell	4
Hughes	Bennett	K.Booth	Dixon	Aspinall	Burrell	Brown	H'bottom•	Camden	Smith†	Sharratt	Leicester	O'Shea	5
Hughes	Bennett	K.Booth	Dixon	Aspinall	Burrell	Brown	H'bottom	Camden	Smith	Sharratt•	Leicester	O'Shea	6
Hughes	**Bennett**	**K.Booth**	**Dixon**	**Aspinall**	**Burrell**	**Brown**	**H'bottom**	**Camden**	**Smith**	**Sharratt•**	**Leicester**	**O'Shea**	**7**
Hughes	Bennett	K.Booth	Dixon	Aspinall	Burrell	Brown	H'bottom	Camden	Smith	Leicester	Sharratt	O'Shea	8
Coyne	Bennett	K.Booth	Dixon	Aspinall	Burrell	Brown	Sharratt	Camden	Smith•	Leicester	O'Shea	O'Connell	9
Hughes	**Bennett**	**K.Booth**	**Dixon**	**Aspinall**	**Burrell†**	**Blackman•**	**Leicester**	**Camden**	**O'Shea**	**Sharratt**	**Smith**	**O'Connell**	**10**
Hughes	Bennett	K.Booth	Dixon	Aspinall	Burrell	O'Shea	Leicester	Camden†	Smith	Sharratt	Blackman	O'Connell	11
Hughes	Bennett	K.Booth•	Dixon	Aspinall	Burrell	Brown	Leicester	Camden	Smith	Sharratt	Blackman	O'Connell	12
Hughes	**Bennett**	**Blackman**	**Dixon**	**Aspinall**	**Burrell**	**Brown**	**Leicester**	**Camden**	**Smith**	**Sharratt†**	**K.Booth**	**O'Connell**	**13**
Hughes	Bennett	Blackman	Dixon	Aspinall	Burrell	Brown	Leicester	Camden	Smith	O'Connell•	Sharratt	K.Booth	14
Hughes	Bennett	Blackman	Dixon•	Aspinall	Bauress	Brown	H'bottom	Camden	Smith	Sharratt	K.Booth	O'Connell	15
Hughes	Bennett	Blackman	Dixon	Aspinall	Bauress	Brown	H'bottom	Camden	Smith	Sharratt	K.Booth	O'Connell	16
Hughes	**Bennett**	**Blackman**	**Dixon**	**Aspinall**	**K.Booth•**	**Brown**	**H'bottom†**	**Camden**	**Smith**	**Sharratt**	**Bauress**	**O'Connell**	**17**
Hughes	Bennett	Blackman	Dixon	Aspinall	Bauress	Brown	H'bottom	Camden	Smith•	Sharratt	Burrell	O'Connell	18
Hughes	Bennett	Blackman	Dixon	Aspinall	Bauress	Brown	H'bottom	Camden	Burrell•	Sharratt	Leicester	K.Booth	19
Hughes	Bennett	Blackman	Dixon	Aspinall	Bauress	Brown	H'bottom•	Camden	Burrell	Sharratt	Leicester	K.Booth	20
Hughes	Bennett	Blackman	Dixon	Aspinall	Bauress	Brown•	H'bottom	Camden	K.Booth	Leicester	Sharratt	O'Connell	21
Hughes	Bennett	Blackman	Dixon	Aspinall	Bauress	Brown	H'bottom	Camden	K.Booth	Leicester•	Sharratt	O'Connell	22
Hughes	Bennett	Blackman	Dixon	Aspinall	Bauress	Brown	H'bottom•	Camden	K.Booth	Leicester	Sharratt	Burrell	23
Hughes	Bennett	Blackman	Dixon	Aspinall	Bauress	Brown	Sharratt	Camden	K.Booth	Leicester	O'Connell	Woan	24
Hughes	**Bennett**	**Blackman**	**Dixon**	**Aspinall**	**Bauress**	**Brown**	**Sharratt**	**Camden**	**K.Booth**	**Leicester•**	**O'Connell**	**Burrell**	**25**
Hughes	Bennett	Blackman	Dixon	Aspinall	Bauress	Brown	Sharratt	Camden	K.Booth	Leicester	O'Connell	Burrell	26
Hughes	Burrell†	Blackman	Dixon	Aspinall	Bauress	Brown	Sharratt	Camden	K.Booth	O'Connell	Henshaw	Woan	27
Hughes	Bennett	Blackman	Dixon	Aspinall	Bauress	Brown	Priest	Camden	K.Booth	Leicester	Woan	Burrell	28
Hughes	**Bennett**	**Blackman**	**Dixon**	**Woan**	**Bauress**	**Brown†**	**Priest•**	**Camden**	**K.Booth**	**Leicester**	**O'Connell**	**Burrell**	**29**
Hughes	Bennett	Blackman	Dixon	Aspinall	Bauress	Brown	Priest	Camden	K.Booth	Leicester	Burrell	Woan	30
Hughes	Bennett	Blackman	Dixon	Aspinall	Bauress	Brown	O'Connell†	Camden	K.Booth	Leicester	Burrell	Woan	31
Hughes	Bennett	Blackman	Dixon	Aspinall	Bauress	Brown	Priest	Camden	K.Booth	Leicester	Burrell	Woan	32
Hughes	Bennett	Blackman	Dixon	Aspinall	Bauress	Brown	Priest	Camden	K.Booth	Leicester	Burrell	Woan	33
Hughes	Bennett	Blackman	Dixon	Aspinall	Bauress	Brown	Woan	Camden	K.Booth•	Leicester	Burrell	Stewart	34
Hughes	**Bennett**	**Blackman**	**Dixon**	**Aspinall**	**Bauress**	**Brown**	**Priest**	**Camden**	**K.Booth**	**Leicester**	**Burrell**	**Woan**	**35**
Hughes	Bennett	Blackman	Dixon•	Aspinall	Bauress	Brown	Priest†	Camden	K.Booth	Leicester	Burrell	Woan	36
Hughes	Bennett	Blackman	Dixon	Aspinall	Bauress	Brown	Priest	Camden	K.Booth	Leicester	Burrell	Woan	37
Hughes	**Bennett**	**Blackman**	**Burrell**	**Aspinall**	**Bauress**	**Brown•**	**Priest**	**Camden†**	**K.Booth**	**Leicester**	**Filson**	**Woan**	**38**
Hughes	Bennett	Blackman	Burrell	Aspinall	Bauress	Brown	Priest	Camden	K.Booth	Leicester	Filson	Woan	39
Hughes	Bennett	Blackman	Burrell	Aspinall	Bauress•	Brown	Priest	Camden	K.Booth	Leicester	Dixon	Woan	40
Hughes	Bennett	Blackman	Dixon	Aspinall	Bauress	Brown	Priest	Camden	K.Booth	Leicester	Burrell	Woan	41
Hughes	Bennett†	Blackman	Dixon	Aspinall•	Bauress	Brown	Priest	Camden	K.Booth	Leicester	Edmonds	Filson	42
Hughes	**Bennett**	**Blackman**	**Dixon**	**Edmonds**	**Bauress**	**Brown**	**Priest•**	**Camden**	**K.Booth†**	**Leicester**	**Woan**	**Filson**	**43**
Hughes	Bennett	Blackman	Dixon	Edmonds†	Bauress	Brown	Woan•	Camden	Burrell	Leicester	Cronin	O'Connell	44
Hughes	Bennett•	Blackman	Dixon	Aspinall	Bauress	Brown	Priest	Camden	Burrell	Leicester†	Edmonds	Edwards	45
Hughes	Bennett	Blackman	Dixon	Aspinall	Bauress	Brown	Priest†	Camden	Burrell•	Leicester	Edmonds	Edwards	46
Hughes	**Bennett**	**Blackman**	**Dixon**	**Aspinall**	**Bauress**	**Brown**	**Edwards**	**Camden**	**Edmonds**	**Leicester**	**Filson**	**Priest**	**47**
Hughes	Bennett	Blackman	Dixon	Aspinall	Bauress	Brown	Edwards	Camden	Edmonds	Leicester†	Filson	Priest	48
Hughes	Bennett	Blackman	Dixon	Aspinall	Bauress	Brown	Edwards	Camden†	Edmonds	Leicester	Edmonds	Priest	49
Hughes	Bennett	Blackman	Dixon	Aspinall	Bauress	Brown	Edwards	Camden†	K.Booth	Leicester	Edmonds	Priest	50
Hughes	Bennett	Blackman	Dixon	Aspinall	Bauress	Brown	Edwards†	Camden	K.Booth	Leicester	Edmonds	Priest	51
Hughes	**Bennett**	**Blackman**	**Dixon**	**Aspinall**	**Bauress**	**Brown•**	**Edwards**	**Camden**	**K.Booth**	**Leicester**	**Edmonds**	**Priest**	**52**
Hughes	Bennett	Blackman	Dixon	Aspinall	Bauress	Brown	Edwards†	Camden	K.Booth	Leicester	Edmonds	Priest	53
Hughes	**Bennett**	**Blackman**	**Dixon**	**Aspinall**	**Bauress**	**Brown**	**Edwards†**	**Camden**	**K.Booth**	**Edmonds•**	**Edmonds**	**Priest**	**54**
Hughes	Bennett	Blackman	Dixon	Aspinall	Bauress	Brown	Priest	Camden	K.Booth	Edmonds	Woan	Filson	55
Hughes	Bennett	Blackman	Dixon	Aspinall	Bauress	Brown	Edwards†	Camden†	K.Booth	Leicester	Edmonds	Priest	56
Hughes	Bennett	Edmonds	Dixon	Aspinall	Bauress	Brown	Edwards	Camden†	K.Booth	Leicester	Blackman	Priest	57
Hughes	**Bennett**	**Edmonds**	**Dixon**	**Aspinall**	**Bauress**	**Brown**	**Edwards**	**Camden**	**K.Booth**	**Leicester**	**Burrell**	**Priest**	**58**
Hughes	Bennett	Edmonds	Dixon	Aspinall	Bauress	Brown	Edwards	Camden	K.Booth	O'Connell	Burrell	Woan	59

• substituted by No. 12. † substituted by No. 14.

League Appearances (max 59): Camden 59; Bennett, Hughes 58; Dixon 57; Aspinall 56; Brown 55; Booth, Leicester 52; Blackman 50; Bauress 45; Burrell 36; Priest 27; O'Connell 20; Woan 19; Edmonds 18; Higginbottom 17; Edwards 14; O'Shea 11; Filson 8; coyne, Cronin, Stewart 1.

Stalybridge Celtic

PHIL WILSON

Phil Wilson joined Stalybridge Celtic in November 1989 on the dismissal of Kevan Keelan. Celtic survived being relegated by the skin of their teeth and in his first full season finished runners up, before taking the title last season.

Wilson, 40, played as a 17-year-old for New Brighton and had an illustrious non-league career with Runcorn, Mossley, Altrincham and Northwich Victoria, winning NPL championships with Runcorn and Mossley and a Conference medal with Altrincham. He appeared in seven FA Trophy semi-finals and reached three finals at Wembley, finally getting a winners' medal with Northwich, who beat Bangor City in a replay at the Victoria Ground, Stoke. He captained Caernarfon Town to the third round proper of the FA Cup and managed the Welsh side for a season.

A fully qualified FA Coach, he is director of the Tranmere Rovers' Centre of Excellence on the Wirral.

Stalybridge Celtic's John Brown powers in a header from Paul Bennett's corner in this HFS Loans League match against Leek Town. Photo: Calvin Palmer

Programme details:
  40 pages for 80p
  Editor - Nick Shaw

Any other club publications:

Local Newspapers:
  Manchester Evening News
  Manchester Evening News Pink
  Local Radio Stations:
  GMR (BBC)
  Piccadilly Radio

STALYBRIDGE CELTIC - PLAYING SQUAD 1992-93

Player	Honours	Birthplace and date	Transfer Fees	Previous Clubs
GOALKEEPERS				
Russ Hughes	HFS			Tranmere Rovers, Sth Liverpool, Caernarfon Town
DEFENDERS				
Ricky Blackman	HFS			Chadderton
John Aspinall	HFS	Birkenhead 15/3/59		Cammell Laird, Tranmere R, Altrincham, Bangor City, Tranmere, Bangor C, Northwich V, Chorley
Paul Dixon	HFS			Chadderton
Mark Burrell	HFSLC HFS	18/6/63		Retford, Gainsborough Trin, Goole, Witton Alb
Gary Bauress	HFS	Liverpool 19/1/71		Tranmere Rovers
Martin Filson	HFS			Wrexham, Rhyl
Kevin Booth	HFS			Stalybridge Celtic, Bacup Borough, Stalybridge Celtic, Curzon Ashton
Mark Williams	HFS			Oswestry, Rhyl, Caernarfon Winsford Utd
MIDFIELD				
Paul Bennett	HFS	Liverpool 30/1/61		Everton, Port Vale, Northwich V, Telford Utd, Northwich V, Buxton
Steve Wood		23/6/63		Chadderton, Mossley, Droylsden
John Brown	HFS	Liverpool 6/12/67		Liverpool, Winsford Utd, Witton Alb
Peter King		Liverpool 5/7/64		Liverpool, Crewe, Southport, Marine, Stafford R, Chorley, Barrow, Marine
Alan Woan	HFS	Wirrall		Newtown
Shaun O'Shea				Flixton
FORWARDS				
Mark Edwards	NPL, HFS	Wigan 6/12/61		Wigan Ath, Marine, Horwich RMI, St Helens, Chorley, Witton Alb, Horwich RMI
Neil Edmonds		Accrington 18/10/68		Oldham Ath, Rochdale, Chorley, India
Phil Power	GMAC	Salford 25/7/66		Northwich V, Witton Alb, Crewe, Horwich, Chorley, Barrow
Eric Priest	HFS			Curzon Ashton
Kevin O'Connell	HFS			Barnton
Dennis Cronin		Manchester 30/10/67		Man Utd, Stockport, Crewe, Colne Dynamoes, Droylsden

Departures during season:
John Smith (Bangor City), Chris Sharratt (Wigan), Chris Camden (Marine), Stuart Leicester (Macclesfield), Mark Henshaw (Chorley).

Stalybridge Celtic

Ground address and Tel. No.: Bower Ford, Mottram Road, Stalybridge, Cheshire (061 338 2828)
Simple ground directions: On A6108 Ashton to Glossop road. 1 mile from Stalybridge (BR). Buses 236, 216 and 237 pass ground
Official capacity: 3,500   **Seating:** 409   **Covered accommodation:** 1,200
Floodlights: Yes
Social facilities available: Clubhouse: Bower Fold Social Club   **Steward:** Alan Slack

---

Sponsored by: Manro Products Ltd   **STALYBRIDGE CELTIC**   **Nickname:**

Previous leagues: Lancs Combination 1911-12 / Central Lg 12-21 / The Football Lg 21-23 / Cheshire County 23-82 / North West Counties 82-87, HFS Loans 87-92
Club colours: All royal blue
Midweek home matches: Tuesday
Club programme: 40 pages 80p
Record transfer fee paid: £1,250 for Paul Higginbotham from Glossop 1991
Record transfer fee received: £4,000
Record attendance: 9,753 v WBA, FA Cup 1st Rd replay 22-23
Top scorer 1991-92: Chris Camden 45   **Captain 91-92:** Paul Bennett   **P.o.Y. 91-92:** Chris Camden
Best FA Cup season: 2nd Rd 35-36. Competition Proper also 22-23, 32-33, 34-35, 36-37, 38-39, 45-46, 47-48, 84-85
Change colours: All red
Club metal badges: Yes
Editor: Nick Shaw
Past players who have progressed to the Football League: Cyril Crawshaw (Hull 1946), Alf Clarke (Crewe 1948), Fred Pye & Dennis Winterbottom (Acc Stan 1948 & 51), Eric Kerfoot (Leeds 1949), Frank Tomlinson & Cyril Coyne (Halifax 1950 & 51), Charles Young (Sheff. U. 1951), Albert McPherson (W'sall 1954), John Brocklehurst (B'ford PA 1954), Alvin Williams (Bury 1954), anthony Bartley (Bolton 1956), William Rudd (B'ham C. 1959), Gary France (B'ley 1966), Eamon O'Keefe (Plymouth 1974), John Anderson (Everton), Paul Jones (R'dale 1984). Chris Sharratt (Wigan 1991)
Club honours: HFS Loans League Premier Deivision Champions 91-92, NPL R-up 90-91 (Div 1 R-up 87-88), Ches. County Lg 79-80 (R-up 77-78), Lg Cp 21-22 (R-up 46-47, 81-82), Chal. Shield 77-78 (R-up 79-80), (Res. Div. R-up 81-82), NW Counties Lg 83-84, 86-87 (Lg Cp R-up 83-84), Champions v Cup Winners Trophy 83-84, (Res. Div. R-up 82-83), Lancs Comb. Div. 2 11-12, Cheshire Senior Cup 52-53 (R-up 54-55, 80-81), Manchester Cup 22-23 (I'mediate Cup 57-58, 68-69 (R-up 56-57, 67-68, 69-70), Chal. Shield 54-55, (Junior Cup 62-63), Lancs. Floodlit Cup 88-89 (R-up 89-90), Reporter Cup R-up 74-75, Edward Case Cup 77-78, FA Trophy 2nd Rd 73-74, 79-80, 82-83.

TELFORD UNITED

Formed: 1876

Chairman:
Tony Esp

Directors:
Bernard G Bagnall
Brian Taylor
Terry Anderson
David Kirkland
Robert Cave

Secretary:
Mike Ferriday

Manager:
Gerry Daly

Trainer:
Lenny Lloyd

Club Doctor:
Dr Paul Spencer

Commercial Manager:
D Harris

A final league placing of sixth seems, on the face of it, to have been quite a successful season for Telford United. However, despite that respectable position, neither manager Gerry Daly or the Bucks Head faithfull were very happy with performances in general. There were some high spots of course, most notably the FA Cup tie with Stoke City which saw a marvellous 2-1 victory, and league performances against Wycombe Wanderers and Stafford Rangers. But, by and large, United did not do themselves justice, despite the final league placing.

The FA Trophy, a competition that always seems to bring out the best in Telford United, again produced some useful results. Tricky-looking home ties against Guisborough Town and Northallerton Town were overcome then Gateshead were beaten in a replay in the North East. However, eventual winners Colchester United knocked United out in the quarter-final with a resounding 4-0 Layer Road victory.

Gerry Daly has some very talented young players at his disposal. But in the tough world of the Conference these players need time to come through. He has managed to acquire some useful additions to his squad for the new campaign and the Telford fans will be hoping that 1992/93 will be the season when the club break their forty year duck and win a major league title, namely the GM Vauxhall Conference.

Telford United F.C. 1991-92. Back Row (L-R): G Gatward, D Jones, J Bagby, M Baker, D McGregor, A Cooke, G Amos, D Beddoes, A Garratt. Middle: C McBride (Physio), D Hall, K Thompson, C Brindley, M Sutton, D Acton, S Nelson, P Dyson (now Solihull), J Bagby, L Lloyd (Trainer), D Pritchard. Front: P Grainger (now Kidderminster), T Langford, P Whitehouse (left), I Brown, G Daly (Manager), T Whittington (left), M Myers, S Clarke, S Worrall (left).

253

Telford United

GM Vauxhall Conference: 6th. **FA Cup: 2nd Round.** **FA Trophy: 4th Round.**

Match No.	Date	Competition	Venue H/A	Opponents	Result	League H/T	Pos.	Goalscorers (Times if known)	Attendance
1	Aug 13	SS Cup F	A	Shrewsbury Town	W 1-0	0-0		Whittington	1151
2	Aug 17	GMVC	H	Redbridge Forest	D 3-3	2-2		Dyson 28; Myers 43; Langford 50	835
3	Aug 24	GMVC	A	Merthyr Tydfil	D 2-2	0-2	8	Brown 65; Dyson 87	886
4	Aug 26	GMVC	H	Altrincham	W 2-1	1-0	5	Langford 16,69	1235
5	Aug 31	GMVC	H	Farnborough Town	L 1-2	0-1	10	Clarke 79	1017
6	Sep 3	GMVC	A	Macclesfield Town	L 1-2	0-0	9	Benbow 65 (pen)	838
7	Sep 7	GMVC	A	Slough Town	W 3-0	2-0	5	Langford 2; Clarke 7; Williamson 83	877
8	Sep 10	GMVC	H	Kidderminster Harriers	W 3-1	2-1	4	Langford 15; Brindley 40; Dyson 49	1430
9	Sep 14	GMVC	H	Barrow	W 4-2	1-1	3	Langford 44; Benbow 64; Culpin 68,82	1034
10	Sep 21	GMVC	A	Yeovil Town	W 2-0	1-0	2	Whittington 16; Langford 61	2116
11	Sep 27	GMVC	H	Stafford Rangers	W 4-1	3-1	2	Langford 1; Benbow 5; Whittington 38; Brindley 70	1179
12	Oct 5	GMVC	H	Bath City	L 0-2	0-0	3		1092
13	Oct 8	BLT 2	H	Macclesfield	L 1-2	1-1		Brindley 17	597
14	Oct 12	GMVC	A	Wycombe Wanderers	L 1-6	1-1	4	Ross 34	4283
15	Oct 15	GMVC	A	Kettering Town	L 0-3	1-0	4		1664
16	Oct 18	GMVC	A	Colchester Utd	L 0-3	0-3	4		1109
17	Oct 26	FAC 4Q	H	Knowsley Utd	W 1-0	0-0		Langford 63	743
18	Nov 2	GMVC	A	Gateshead	W 2-0	1-0	4	Whittington 36; Benbow 62	264
19	Nov 9	GMVC	A	Whitton Albion	D 1-1	0-1	4	Myers 80	875
20	Nov 16	FAC 1	A	Stoke City	D 0-0	0-0			9984
21	Nov 23	GMVC	H	Macclesfield	L 0-1	0-0	8		1199
22	Nov 26	FAC 1R	H	Stoke City	W 2-1	1-0		Benbow 29,33	4052
23	Nov 29	GMVC	A	Runcorn	W 2-0	1-0	5	Langford 19; Brindley 69	686
24	Dec 7	FAC 2	A	Wrexham	L 0-1	0-0			3897
25	Dec 21	GMVC	H	Gateshead	D 1-1	0-0	8	Myers 46	717
26	Dec 26	GMVC	A	Kidderminster Harriers	W 2-1	2-1	7	Brindley 6; Langford 13	1992
27	Jan 1	GMVC	H	Northwich Victoria	L 1-4	1-2	10	Myers 9	1738
28	Jan 4	GMVC	A	Stafford Rangers	L 2-3	1-0	11	Clarke 27; Benbow 90	943
29	Jan 11	FAT 1	H	Guisborough Town	W 2-0	0-0		Langford 70,88	795
30	Jan 17	GMVC	H	Runcorn	W 1-0	1-0	9	Benbow 35	913
31	Jan 25	GMVC	A	Welling Utd	L 1-3	0-2	10	Benbow 68 (pen)	848
32	Feb 1	FAT 2	H	Northallerton Town	W 3-0	0-0		Langford 58; Benbow 80,90	757
33	Feb 4	GMVC	H	Yeovil Town	W 1-0	0-0	7	Dyson 75	766
34	Feb 8	GMVC	H	Wycombe Wanderers	W 1-0	0-0	5	Langford 70	1520
35	Feb 11	GMVC	A	Farnborough	D 2-2	1-1	5	Langford 30; Benbow 53	786
36	Feb 15	GMVC	H	Witton Albion	W 2-1	1-1	4	Dyson 31; Parrish 61	935
37	Feb 22	FAT 3	H	Gateshead	D 0-0	0-0			1027
38	Feb 26	FAT 3R	A	Gateshead	W 1-0	1-0		Humphreys 30	535
39	Feb 29	GMVC	H	Boston Utd	L 0-2	0-1	6		841
40	Mar 7	GMVC	H	Welling Utd	W 2-1	0-1	5	Myers 65; Fergusson 85 (pen)	698
41	Mar 14	GMVC	A	Colchester	L 0-4	0-1	6		3894
42	Mar 17	GMVC	A	Bath City	W 2-1	1-0	6	Myers 6,80	524
43	Mar 21	GMVC	H	Slough	D 2-2	0-2	6	Brindley 68; Cook 89	691
44	Mar 24	GMVC	A	Cheltenham	L 1-2	0-0	6	Myers 53	736
45	Mar 27	GMVC	A	Northwich Victoria	D 1-1	1-0	6	Myers 32	604
46	Apr 4	GMVC	H	Cheltenham	W 2-1	1-1	4	Benbow 17,57	684
47	Apr 8	GMVC	A	Boston Utd	W 2-1	0-1	4	Benbow 85; Brindley 87	901
48	Apr 11	GMVC	H	Kettering Town	D 1-1	0-1	5	Fergusson 61 (pen)	890
49	Apr 18	GMVC	A	Colchester	L 0-2	0-0	5		3964
50	Apr 22	GMVC	A	Barrow	L 0-3	0-1	6		1113
51	Apr 25	GMVC	A	Redbridge Forest	L 0-1	0-1	7		509
52	Apr 28	GMVC	A	Altrincham	W 3-2	1-2	6	Benbow 9; Fergusson 75; Alleyne 81	507
53	May 2	GMVC	H	Merthyr Tydfil	L 1-2	0-1	6	Myers 51	1303

Best Home League Attendance: 1738 v Northwich 1.1.92   **Smallest: 684 v Cheltenham 4.4.92**   **Average Home Attendance: 1048**
Compared to 1990/91: 1186

Goalscorers GMVC (max 62): Benbow 12; Langford 12; Myers 10; Brindley 6; Dyson 5; Whittington 4; Clarke 3; Fergusson 3; Culan 2; Alleyne, Brown, Cooke, Parrish
Ross 1. **FA Cup (Max 3):** Benbow 2; Langford 1. **FA Trophy (max 6):** Langford 3; Benbow 2; Humphreys 1. **Bob Lord Trophy:** Brindley 1. **Shrop. Sen.:** Benbow 2;
Langofrd, Whittington 1.

Telford United

1	2	3	4	5	6	7	8	9	10	11	12	14	Match No.
Hughes	Humphreys	Whitehouse	Dyson	Brindley	Whittington	Myers	Grainger	Benbow	Langford	Worrall	Clarke	Brown	1
Hughes	Nelson	Whitehouse	Dyson	Brindley	Clarke	Myers	Grainger	Benbow	Langford†	Worrall•	Humphries†	Brown•	2
Acton	Nelson†	Whitehouse	Dyson	Brindley	Worrall	Myers	Grainger	Benbow	Langford	Brown	Humphries†	Clarke	3
Acton	Humphreys	Whitehouse	Dyson	Brindley	Whittington	Myers	Grainger	Benbow	Langford	Brown	Worrall	Clarke	4
Acton	Nelson	Whitehouse†	Dyson	Brindley	Whittington	Myers	Grainger•	Benbow	Langford	Brown	Worrall†	Clarke•	5
Acton	Nelson	Downes	Dyson	Brindley	Whittington	Myers	Clarke†	Benbow	Langford	Brown	Worrall†	Whitehouse	6
Acton	Humphreys	Nelson	Dyson	Brindley	Whittington	Myers	Clarke	Benbow	Langford	Brown	Worrall	Thompson	7
Acton	Humphreys	Nelson	Brindley	Dyson	Whittington•	Myers	Grainger	Benbow	Langford	Brown	Clarke†	Worrall	8
Acton	Humphreys	Nelson	Dyson	Brindley	Whittington†	Myers	Grainger	Benbow	Langford	Culpin	Clarke†	Brown	9
Acton	Humphreys	Nelson	Dyson	Brindley	Whittington	Myers	Grainger	Benbow	Langford	Carr	Clarke	Brown	10
Acton	Humphreys	Nelson	Dyson	Brindley	Whittington	Myers	Grainger	Benbow	Langford	Ross	Carr	Brown	11
Acton	Humphreys	Nelson	Dyson•	Brindley	Whittington	Myers	Grainger	Benbow	Langford	Ross	Worrall	Brown•	12
Acton	Humphreys	Nelson	Dyson	Brindley	Whittington	Myers	Grainger	Benbow	Langford	Ross†	Worrall•	Brown†	13
Acton	Humphreys	Nelson†	Dyson	Brindley•	Whittington	Myers	Grainger	Benbow	Langford	Ross	Worrall†	Duffy•	14
Acton	Humphreys	Amos†	Dyson	Duffy	Parrish	Myers	Grainger	Benbow	Langford	Ryan•	Brown•	Worrall†	15
Acton	Humphreys	Nelson	Dyson	Brindley•	Whittington	Myers	Grainger•	Benbow	Langford	Parrish	Worrall•	Brown	16
Acton	Humphreys	Parrish	Dyson	Nelson	Whittington	Myers	Grainger	Benbow	Langford	Worrall	Cooke	Brown	17
Acton	Humphreys	Parrish	Dyson	Nelson	Whittington	Myers	Grainger	Benbow	Langford•	Worrall	Brindley	Brown•	18
Acton	Humphreys	Parrish	Dyson	Nelson	Whittington	Myers	Benbow•	Benbow	Langford	Worrall†	Brindley†	Ferguson•	19
Acton	Humphreys	Brindley	Dyson	Nelson	Whittington	Myers	Grainger	Benbow	Langford	Parrish	Clarke	Cooke	20
Acton	Humphreys•	Brindley	Dyson	Nelson	Whittington	Myers	Grainger	Withe	Langford	Hackett	Clarke	Parrish•	21
Acton	Humphreys	Brindley	Dyson	Nelson	Whittington	Myers	Grainger	Benbow	Langford	Parrish	Clarke	Cooke	22
Acton	Fergusson	Brindley	Clarke	Nelson	Whittington	Myers	Grainger	Benbow	Langford	Parrish	Cooke	Hackett	23
Acton	Humphreys	Brindley	Dyson	Nelson	Whittington	Myers	Grainger	Benbow	Langford	Parrish	Clarke	Cooke	24
Acton	Brindley	Parrish	Dyson	Nelson	Whittington	Myers	Grainger†	Fergusson•	Langford	Hackett	Clarke†	Withe•	25
Acton	Brindley	Clarke	Dyson	Nelson	Whittington†	Myers	Grainger	Fergusson	Langford	Hackett	Humphreys†	Benbow	26
Acton	Brindley†	Parrish	Dyson	Nelson	Clarke	Myers	Grainger	Fergusson	Langford	Hackett	Benbow	Humphreys†	27
Acton	Brindley	Parrish	Dyson	Nelson	Clarke	Myers	Grainger	Fergusson†	Langford	Hackett	Benbow†	Humphreys	28
Acton	Humphreys	Nelson	Dyson•	Brindley	Whittington	Myers	Grainger	Benbow	Langford	Parrish	Fergusson•	Hackett	29
Acton	Humphreys	Nelson	Fergusson	Brindley	Whittington	Myers	Grainger	Benbow†	Langford•	Parrish	Hackett•	Cooke†	30
Acton	Humphreys	Parrish	Nelson	Brindley	Whittington	Myers	Grainger	Benbow	Langford	Hackett†	Withe†	Clarke	31
Acton	Humphreys	Nelson	Dyson	Brindley	Whittington	Myers†	Parrish	Benbow	Langford	Hackett	Withe	Clarke	32
Acton	Humphreys	Nelson	Dyson	Brindley	Whittington	Clarke†	Parrish	Benbow	Langford	Hackett	Withe†	Cooke	33
Acton	Humphreys	Nelson	Dyson	Brindley	Whittington	Myers	Fergusson	Benbow	Langford	Parrish	Hackett	Cooke	34
Acton	Humphreys	Nelson†	Dyson	Brindley	Whittington	Myers	Fergusson	Benbow•	Langford	Parrish	Hackett•	Cooke	35
Acton	Humphreys	Nelson	Dyson	Brindley	Whittington	Myers	Fergusson	Benbow†	Langford	Parrish	Hackett	Cooke†	36
Acton	Humphreys	Nelson	Dyson	Brindley	Whittington	Myers	Fergusson	Benbow†	Langford	Parrish	Hackett†	Cooke	37
Acton	Humphreys	Parrish	Dyson	Brindley	Whittington	Myers	Fergusson	Benbow	Langford	Grainger	Hackett	Cooke	38
Acton	Humphreys	Parrish	Dyson	Brindley	Whittington•	Myers	Fergusson	Benbow†	Langford	Grainger	Hackett	Cooke†	39
Charlton	Humphreys	Whittington	Dyson	Brindley	Clarke	Myers	Fergusson	Cooke	Langford	Grainger	Benbow	Nelson	40
Acton	Humphreys	Nelson	Dyson	Brindley	Whittington†	Myers	Fergusson	Benbow	Grainger	Clarke•	Withe•	Cooke†	41
Acton	Humphreys	Nelson	Dyson	Brindley	Clarke	Myers	Fergusson	Benbow•	Langford	Grainger	Withe	Fitzpatrick•	42
Acton	Humphreys	Nelson	Dyson	Brindley	Clarke	Perks•	Fergusson	Cooke	Langford	Grainger†	Garrett•	Withe†	43
Burke	Robinson	Nelson	Dyson	Brindley	Fitzpatrick	Myers	Fergusson	Benbow†	Gilman	Grainger	Cooke†	Humphreys	44
Acton	Humphreys	Nelson	Dyson	Brindley	Forsyth	Myers	Fergusson	Gilman	Alleyne	Clarke	Withe	Garrett	45
Acton	Humphreys	Nelson•	Dyson	Brindley	Forsythe	Myers	Fergusson	Benbow	Gilman	Clarke	Garrett•	Cooke	46
Burke	Humphreys	Clarke	Dyson	Brindley	Forsyth	Myers	Fergusson	Benbow	Alleyne	Gilman•	Langford•	Garrett	47
Acton	Withe	Clarke	Dyson	Brindley	Forsyth	Garrett	Fergusson	Benbow	Gilman•	Alleyne	Cooke•	Amos	48
Acton	Humphreys	Clarke	Dyson	Brindley	Forsyth	Garrett	Fergusson	Benbow	Gilman•	Alleyne†	Cooke•	Withe†	49
Acton	Humphreys	Clarke	Withe	Brindley	Forsyth	Myers	Fergusson	Benbow	Alleyne	Garrett•	Amos•	Cooke	50
Acton	Humphreys	Clarke	Withe•	Brindley	Forsyth	Myers	Fergusson	Benbow	Langford	Alleyne†	Garrett††	Cooke•	51
Acton	Garrett	Clarke	Gilman	Brindley•	Forsyth	Myers	Fergusson	Benbow	Langford	Cooke	Alleyne•	Amos	52
Acton	Humphreys	Clarke	Withe•	Brindley	Forsyth	Myers	Fergusson	Benbow	Langford	Garrett	Gilman•	Alleyne†	53

* substituted by No. 12.   † substituted by No. 14.

GMVC Appearances: Acton 38; Alleyne 6+2; Amos 1+1; Benbow 34+1; Brindley; 39+1; Brown 6+4; Burke 2; Carr, Charlton 1; Clarke 20+4; Cooke 3+8; Culan, Downes 1; Duffy 1+1; Dyson 35; Fergusson 23+1; Fitzpatrick 1+1; Forsyth 9; Garratt 5+3; Gilman 7+1; Grainger 27; Hackett 7+3; Hughes 1; Humphreys 30+4; Langford 35+1; Myers 38; Nelson 31; Parrish 15+1; Perks, Robertson 1; Ross 3; Ryan 1; Whitehouse 4; Whittington 25; Withe 5+4; Worrall 4+6. **FA Cup:** Acton 4; Benbow 4; Brindley 3; Dyson 4; Grainger 4; Humphreys 4; Langford 4; Myers 4; Nelson 4; Parrish 4; Whittington 4; Worrall 1. **FA Trophy:** Acton 5; Benbow 5; Brindley 5; Clarke 1+1; Dyson 5; Fergusson 3+1; Grainger 3; Hackett 1+1; Humphreys 5; Langford 4; Myers 5; Nelson 4; Parrish 4; Whittington 5; Withe 0+1. **Bob Lord Trophy:** Benbow 1; Brindley 1; Dyson 1; Grainger 1; Humphreys 1; Langford 1; Myers 1; Nelson 1; Ross 1; Whittington 1. **Shrop Senior:** Acton 1; Benbow 2; Clarke 0+1; Dyson 2; Grainger 2; Hughes 1; Humphreys 1; Langford 2; McGinty 1; Myers 2; Thompson 1; Whitehouse 2; Whittington 2; Worrall 2.

Telford United

GERRY DALY

Gerry was born in Dublin and joined Manchester United from Irish side Bohemians in April 1973. During a distinguished playing career, Gerry made over 400 League appearances with United, Derby County, Coventry City, Birmingham City, Shrewsbury and Stoke City as well as gaining international honours for the Republic of Ireland, including 46 full caps.

He arrived at the Bucks Head from Doncaster Rovers in December 1989 as assistant player-coach to Derek Mann, who had just replaced the long-serving Stan Storton. Gerry then took over as player-manager in the summer of 1990 and in his two seasons in charge has guided the club to sixth position on both occasions.

Telford United's midfielder Martin Myers in action against Macclesfield Town during last season. Photo: Colin Stevens.

Programme details:
   28 pages for 80p
   Editor - Bernard G Bagnall

Any other club publications:

Local Newspapers:
   Shropshire Star
   Telford Journal

   Local Radio Stations:
   BBC Radio Shropshire
   Beacon Radio

TELFORD UNITED - PLAYING SQUAD 1992-93

Player	Honours	Birthplace and date	Transfer Fees	Previous Clubs
GOALKEEPERS				
Darren Acton				Ex-YTS
Damian Grange				Aston Villa(T)
DEFENDERS				
Chris Brindley	FAT	Stoke 5/7/69		Hednesford, Wolves
Stuart Leeding		Wolverhampton 6/1/72		Wolves
Stuart Clarke				Ex-YTS
John Humphreys		Nottingham 23/2/65		Spalding, Grantham
Andy Lee	ESP, FAT HFS	Liverpool 4/7/62		Liverpool, Wrexham, Bangor, Stafford, Tranmere, Camb Utd, Runcorn, Altrincham, Telford, Colne D, Witton Alb, Altrincham
Dave Pritchard		Wolverhampton 27/5/72		West Bromwich Albion
Steve Nelson	FAT	Stoke 6/12/60		Macclesfield, Leek, Northwich V
MIDFIELD				
Martin Myers		Birmingham 10/1/66		Shrewsbury, Tamworth
Steve Fergusson				Redditch, Bromsgrove, Moor Green, Alvechurch, Worcester, Gloucester
Loy Stobart		Birmingham 6/4/72		Wolves, Cheltenham Town,
Sean Parrish		Wrexham 14/3/72		Shrewsbury Town
Anthony Garrett				Ex-YTS
Andrew Cooke				Ex-YTS
FORWARDS				
Ian Benbow		Hereford 9/1/69		Hereford Utd
Sean Francis		Birmingham 1/8/72		Birmingham City
Tim Langford		Kingswinford 12/9/65		Stourbridge, Dudley, Tividale, Dudley, Halesowen Town
Shaun Gilman				Bicester, Army, Windsor & Eton, Bridgnorth
Gary Amos				Ex-YTS

Departures during season:
Phil Whitehouse (Stafford), John McGinty (Hednesford), Ian Brown (Stafford), Steve Worrall (Altrincham), Kevin Thompson (Halesowen Harriers), Trevor Whittington (Evesham), Paul Grainger (Kidderminster).

Players who joined on loan during season:
Paul Culpin (Peterborough), Brian Ross (Chorley), Darryl Duffy (Aston Villa), Shaun Parrish & Darren Ryan (Shrewsbury), Richard Forsyth (Kidderminster).

Bucks Head, Telford United

Ground address and Tel. No.: Watling Street, Wellington, Telford, Shropshire TF1 2NJ. Tel: 0952 223838 (Office), 0952 255662 (Social Club)
Simple ground directions: M54 Junction 6 onto B5061 (Watling St.)
Official capacity: 10,000   **Seating:** 1,200   **Covered accommodation:** 3,000
Cost of seats: £5.00   **Cost of standing:** £4.00
Official opening of floodlights: 1963 v Leeds Utd
Record attendance: 13,000 v Shrewsbury Town
Social facilities available (Bars, hot & cold food etc.): Social Club open match days and selected other hours
Car parking: Ample at ground and surrounding area

Sponsored by: Blockleys plc   **TELFORD UNITED**   **Nickname:** The Lilywhites

---

Previous leagues: Birmingham, Cheshire, Southern
Club colours: White/blue/white   **Change colours:** Yellow/red/red
Midweek home matches: Tuesday   **Club metal badges:**
Club programme: 40 poages 80p   **Editor:** B. G. Bagnall
Record transfer fee paid: £10,000 to Northwich Victoria for Paul Mayman
Record transfer fee received: £50,000 from Scarborough for Stephen Norris
Record appearances for club:
Record goalscorer for club:
Record goalscorer in a season:
Past players who have progressed to the Football League: A. Walker (Lincoln City), G. French (Luton Town), K. McKenna (Tranmere Rovers), S. Norris (Scarborough)
Club honours: Brimingham League 1920-21, 1934-35, 1935-36; Cheshire League 1945-46, 1946-47, 1951-52; Edward Case Cup 1952-53, 1954-55; Welsh Cup 1901-02, 1905-06, 1939-40; Birmingham Senior Cup 1946-47; Walsall Senior Cup 1946-47; Birmingham League Challenge Cup 1946-47; Shropshire Senior Cup (30); Southern League Cup 1970-71; Midland Floodlit Cup 1970-71, 1982-83, 1988-89, Runners-up 1969-70, 1987-88
Past club managers: Gordon Banks, Ian Cooper, Geoff Hurst, Fred Badham, Alan Spavin, Basil Hayward, Ron Flowers (Coach), Ron Lewin, Grenville Hair, Jack White, Johnny Hancocks, Neil Franklin, George Antonie, Dick Groves, Stan Storton, Derek Mann

WELLING UNITED

Formed: 1963

President:
E Brackstone

Chairman:
P Websdale

Vice Chairman:
K Nicholls

General Manager:
Graham Hobbins

Secretary:
Barrie Hobbins

Team Manager:
Nicky Brigden

Assistant Manager:
Ray Burgess

Medical Officer:
Dr Baruah

Press Officer:
Paul Carter

Physiotherapist:
Bill Gallagher

Mixed bag for Welling

The 1991/92 season will go down as one of the most successful for strikers Terry Robbins and Gary Abbott, but not one of the most spectacular for the club as a whole.

Unusually for Welling, a leaky defence, which shipped in 79 goals, cost them dear and probably was the difference between finishing in 12th position and one higher.

Garry Abbott and Terry Robbins contributed an amazing 48 out of 69 league goals between them. They, along with the now departed Mark Golley, also made it into the England Semi-Professional squad.

This year Welling will have the benefit of running a YTS programme at Park View Road. The club have been successful in producing their own talent in the past, such as Andy Townsend, Tony Agana and Paul Barron, so they will be hoping that with the benefit of full-time training new stars will come along before too long.

Welling United F.C. 1991-92. Back Row (L-R): Nicky Brigden, Gary Abbott, Steve Robinson, Lennie Dennis, Paul Barron, Mark Hone, Mark Golley, Wayne Brown, John Glover, Nigel Ransom. Front (L-R): Ray Burgess, Joe Francis, Trevor Booker, Tony Reynolds, Paul Websdale (Chairman), Ollie McGuiness (Sponsor), Terry Robbins, Neil Clemmence, Stuart White, Peter Green. Photo: Keith Gillard.

Welling United

Match No.	Date	Competition	Venue H/A	Opponents	Result	League H/T	Pos.	Goalscorers (Times if known)	Attendance
1	Aug 17	GMVC	A	Runcorn	D 2-2	0-0		o.g. 50; Robbins 58	577
2	Aug 24	GMVC	H	Cheltenham	D 1-1	0-1		Robbins 84	759
3	Aug 26	GMVC	A	Kettering	D 1-1	1-1	12	Abbott 29	1962
4	Aug 31	GMVC	A	Northwich Victoria	W 2-1	1-1	5	Francis 24; Robbins 75	729
5	Sep 4	GMVC	H	Wycombe Wanderers	L 1-3	0-1	8	Abbott 89	1337
6	Sep 7	GMVC	H	Altrincham	D 2-2	2-1	8	Ransom 34; Hone 44	777
7	Sep 10	GMVC	A	Bath City	W 3-0	1-0	4	o.g. 9; Abbott 55,77	626
8	Sep 14	GMVC	A	Kidderminster Harriers	W 3-1	1-1	4	Abbott 37,47; Brown 88	1168
9	Sep 21	GMVC	H	Witton Albion	D 1-1	1-1	5	Robbins 8	914
10	Sep 25	GMVC	H	Boston Utd	L 1-3	1-0	7	Abbott 15	726
11	Sep 28	GMVC	A	Barrow	L 1-6	1-1	7	Robbins 13	1129
12	Oct 5	GMVC	H	Gateshead	D 2-2	1-1	7	Robbins 4; Golley 55	748
13	Oct 12	GMVC	A	Stafford Rangers	D 1-1	0-0	7	Robbins 79	822
14	Oct 19	GMVC	A	Merthyr Tydfil	L 1-2	0-0	11	Abbott 89	426
15	**Oct 22**	**BLT 1**	**A**	**Yeovil Town**	**L 0-2**	**0-2**			**1340**
16	Oct 26	FAC 4Q	H	Alvechurch	W 5-1	2-0		Abbott 19,41,49,66,90	704
17	Nov 2	GMVC	A	Macclesfield	W 2-1	2-1	9	Robbins 29; Ransom 31	505
18	Nov 5	GMVC	H	Redbridge Forest	D 2-2	2-0	8	Robbins 14; Abbott 20	615
19	Nov 9	GMVC	A	Slough	W 3-0	2-0	7	Robbins 26,35; Abbott 48	907
20	**Nov 11**	**KSC**	**H**	**Fisher Athletic**	**L 1-2**	**0-1**		**Abbott**	**504**
21	**Nov 16**	**FAC 1**	**A**	**Leyton Orient**	**L 1-2**	**1-0**		**Berry 6**	**4695**
22	Nov 23	GMVC	A	Colchester	L 1-3	0-0	11	Reynolds 62	2933
23	Nov 30	GMVC	H	Barrow	W 5-3	4-1	8	Brown 3; Abbott 22,40,89; Robbins 31	763
24	Dec 7	GMVC	A	Redbridge Forest	L 0-2	0-1	10		763
25	Dec 19	GMVC	A	Boston Utd	L 1-5	1-2	11	Robbins 25	755
26	Dec 26	GMVC	H	Farnborough	W 1-0	0-0	10	Glover 56	1164
27	Dec 28	GMVC	A	Witton Albion	D 2-2	1-1	11	Robbins 41,53	712
28	Jan 1	GMVC	A	Farnborough	D 1-1	0-1	12	o.g. 90	975
29	**Jan 11**	**FAT 1**	**H**	**Dover Athletic**	**W 3-2**	**3-0**		**Brown 10; Abbott 19; Robbins 21**	**1606**
30	**Jan 14**	**LCC**	**A**	**Hoddesdon**	**W 1-0**	**1-0**		**Golley**	**100**
31	Jan 18	GMVC	A	Stafford Rangers	D 0-0	0-0	13		637
32	Jan 25	GMVC	H	Telford Utd	W 3-1	2-0	8	Abbott 24; Robbins 30; White 57	848
33	**Feb 4**	**FAT 2**	**A**	**Morecambe**	**L 1-2**	**0-2**		**Reymonld 50**	**810**
34	Feb 8	GMVC	A	Yeovil Town	L 0-3	0-2	10		2127
35	Feb 15	GMVC	H	Colchester	W 4-1	2-1	9	Robbins 5,74; Ransom 24; White 89	1837
36	**Feb 19**	**LCC**	**H**	**Hampton**	**L 2-1**	**1-0**		**Robbins; Abbott**	**204**
37	Feb 21	GMVC	H	Slough	L 0-2	0-0	12		866
38	Feb 26	GMVC	H	Northwich Victoria	W 6-1	2-0	7	Francis 2; Robbins 33,47,65,66; Reynolds 75	548
39	Feb 29	GMVC	H	Kidderminster Harriers	W 3-2	2-2	5	White 28; Brown 45; Clemmence 84	815
40	Mar 7	GMVC	A	Telford Utd	L 1-2	1-0	7	Abbott 5	698
41	Mar 11	GMVC	H	Kettering Town	L 2-3	2-2	8	Abbott 2; Robbins 28	636
42	Mar 14	GMVC	A	Gateshead	D 1-1	1-0	8	Robbins 45	307
43	**Mar 17**	**LCC**	**H**	**Walthamstow P.**	**W 5-1**	**3-0**		**Abbott (3); Robbins (2)**	**306**
44	Mar 21	GMVC	H	Bath City	L 0-5	0-2	10		806
45	Mar 28	GMVC	H	Altrincham	W 2-1	1-1	10	Robbins 39 (pen); Howell 50	537
46	Aopr 11	GMVC	H	Merthyr Tydfil	L 1-2	1-0	11	Robbins 45	759
47	**Apr 15**	**LCC F**	**N**	**Dulwich Hamlet**	**W 2-0**	**0-0**		**Ransom; Abbott**	
48	Apr 18	GMVC	A	Wycombe Wanderers	L 0-4	0-1	11		3910
49	Apr 20	GMVC	H	Yeovil Town	W 1-0	0-0	11	Robbins 59	704
50	Apr 22	GMVC	A	Macclesfield	W 2-1	1-1	10	Abbott 36,63	338
51	Apr 25	GMVC	H	Runcorn	L 1-2	0-1	11	Golley 69	712
52	May 2	GMVC	A	Cheltenham	L 2-3	1-1	12	White 26; Robbins 88	1197\

Best Home League Attendance: 1837 v Colchester 15.2.91   Smallest: 505 v Macclesfield 2.11.92   Average Home Attendance: 844
Compared to 1990/91: 985

Goalscorers GMVC: Robbins 29; Abbott 19; White 5; Brown 3; Golley, Ransom 2; Clemmence, Francis, Glover, Hone, Howell 1.

Welling United

1	2	3	4	5	6	7	8	9	10	11	12	14	Match No.
Stapley	Hone	Golley	Glover	Ransom	Berry	White	Francis	Abbott	Robbins	Reynolds	Clemence	Robinson	1
Barron	Hone	Robinson	Glover	Ransom	Golley	White	Francis	Abbott•	Robbins	Reynolds	Brown	Clemmence	2
Barron	Hone	Robinson	Glover•	Ransom	Golley•	White	Francis	Abbott	Robbins	Reynolds	Brown	Clemmence	3
Barron	Hone	Robinson	Brown	Ransom	Golley•	White	Francis	Abbott•	Robbins	Reynolds	Burgess	Clemmence	4
Barron	Hone	Robinson	Golley	Ransom	Berry	Golley	Francis	Abbott	Robbins	Reynolds	Brown	White	5
Barron	Hone	Robinson	Clemmence	Ransom	Berry	White	Francis	Abbott	Robbins	Reynolds	Brown	Clemmence	6
Barron	Hone	Robinson	Clemmence	Ransom	Berry	White	Francis•	Abbott•	Robbins	Reynolds	Brown	Burgess	7
Parsons	Hone	Brown	Clemmence	Ransom	Berry	White	Burgess	Abbott•	Robbins•	Reynolds	Booker	Burgess	8
Barron	Hone	Brown	Clemmence	Ransom	Berry	White	Burgess•	Abbott•	Robbins	Reynolds	Booker	Glover	9
Barron	Hone	Glover	Clemmence	Ransom	Berry	White	Burgess•	Abbott•	Robbins	Reynolds	Booker	Glover	10
Barron	Hone	Robinson	Clemmence	Ransom	Berry	White	Golley	Brown	Robbins	Reynolds	Booker	Robinson	11
Barron	Hone	Robinson	Clemmence	Ransom	Berry	White	Golley	Abbott	Robbins	Reynolds	Glover	Brown	12
Barron	Hone	Robinson	Clemmence	Ransom	Glover	White	Golley	Abbott	Robbins	Francis•	Brown	Booker	13
Barron	Hone•	Berry	Clemmence	Ransom	Glover	White	Golley	Abbott	Robbins	Booker	Reynolds	Robinson	14
Barron	**Golley•**	**Robinson**	**Clemmence**	**Brown**	**Berry**	**White**	**Burgess•**	**Abbott•**	**Robbins**	**Reynolds**	**Booker**	**Ransom**	**15**
Barron	**Clemmence•**	**Robinson**	**Brown•**	**Ransom**	**Berry**	**White**	**Burgess**	**Abbott**	**Robbins**	**Reynolds**	**Glover**	**Hone**	**16**
Barron	Clemmence	Robinson	Brown	Ransom	Berry	White	Burgess	Abbott	Robbins	Reynolds	Hone	Glover	17
Barron	Clemmence•	Robinson	Brown	Ransom	Berry	White	Burgess	Abbott	Robbins	Reynolds	Hone	Glover	18
Barron	Hone	Clemmence	Brown	Ransom	Berry	White	Francis	Abbott	Robbins	Reynolds	Glover	Robinson	19
Stapley	**Hone**	**Robinson**	**Burgess**	**Glover**	**Berry**	**White**	**Francis**	**Abbott**	**Robbins**	**Reynolds**			**20**
Barron	**Hone**	**Clemmence**	**Brown**	**Ransom**	**Berry**	**White**	**Francis**	**Abbott**	**Robbins**	**Reynolds**	**Robinson**	**Glover**	**21**
Barron	Hone	Clemmence	Brown	Ransom	Berry	White	Francis	Abbott	Robbins	Reynolds•	Robinson	Burgess	22
Barron	Hone	Clemmence	Brown	Ransom	Berry	White	Francis	Abbott	Robbins	Reynolds	Robinson	Burgess	23
Stapley	Hone	Clemmence	Brown	Ransom	Berry	White	Francis	Abbott	Robbins	Reynolds	Robinson	Burgess	24
Barron	Hone	Robinson	Brown	Ransom	Berry	White	Francis	Abbott	Robbins	Reynolds	Clemmence	Burgess	25
Barron	Glover	Robinson	Brown	Ransom	Clemmence	White	Francis	Abbott	Robbins	Hone	Reynolds	Golley	26
Barron	Glover	Robinson	Brown	Ransom	Clemmence	White	Francis•	Abbott	Robbins	Hone	Reynolds	Golley	27
Barron	Glover	Robinson	Brown•	Ransom	Clemmence	White•	Francis	Abbott	Robbins	Hone•	Reynolds	Golley	28
Barron	**Glover**	**Robinson**	**Brown**	**Ransom•**	**Clemmence**	**White•**	**Francis**	**Abbott**	**Robinson**	**Hone**	**Reynolds**	**Golley**	**29**
Stapley	**Burgess**	**Golley**	**Glover**	**Hone**	**Berry**	**White**	**Francis**	**Abbott**	**Montice**	**Reynolds**	**Ransom**	**Clemmence**	**30**
Barron	Glover	Robinson	Brown	Ransom	Clemmence	White	Francis•	Abbott	Robbins	Hone	Burgess	Golley	31
Barron	Glover	Robinson•	Golley	Ransom	Clemmence	White	Francis	Abbott	Robbins	Reynolds	Burgess	Brown	32
Barron	**Glover**	**Robinson**	**Berry**	**Ransom**	**Clemmence**	**Hone**	**Francis**	**Golley**	**Robbins**	**Reynolds**	**Burgess**	**Slater**	**33**
Barron	Hone	Robinson	Glover	Ransom	Clemmence	White	Francis	Golley	Robbins	Reynolds	Berry	Burgess	34
Harrison	Golley	Robinson	Glover	Ransom	Berry	White	Francis	Hone	Robbins	Reynolds	Clemmence	Burgess	35
Harrison	**Burgess**	**Berry**	**Glover**	**Brown**	**Clemmence**	**White**	**Golley**	**Abbott**	**Robbins**	**Reynolds**	**Robinson**	**Montice**	**36**
Harrison	Golley	Robinson	Glover	Ransom	Berry	White	Francis	Hone	Robbins	Reynolds	Clemmence	Abbott	37
Harrison	Hone	Robinson	Glover	Ransom	Golley	White	Francis	Abbott	Robbins	Reynolds	Clemmence	Berry	38
Harrison	Golley	Robinson	Clemmence	Ransom	Berry	White	Brown	Abbott	Robbins	Reynolds	Burgess	Hone	39
Harrison	Abboh	Robinson	Clemmence	Ransom	Berry	Burgess	Brown	Abbott	Robbins•	Golley	Hone	Glover	40
Harrison	Golley	Robinson	Glover•	Ransom	Berry	White	Brown	Abbott	Robbins	Clemmence	Hone	Abboh	41
Harrison	Golley	Robinson	Clemmence	Ransom	Berry	White	Brown	Abbott	Robbins	Reynolds	Hone	Burgess	42
Harrison	**Golley**	**Robinson**	**Brown**	**Ransom•**	**Berry**	**White**	**Burgess**	**Abbott**	**Robbins**	**Reynolds**	**Clemmence**	**Montice**	**43**
Harrison	Golley	Robinson	Glover	Golley	Berry•	White	Burgess	Abbott	Robbins	Reynolds	Montice	Abboh	44
Sullivan	Burgess	Robinson	Brown	Ransom	Berry	Clemmence	Howell	Abbott	Robbins	Golley	Abboh	Montice	45
Sullivan	Golley	Robinson	Brown•	Ransom	Berry	White	Howell•	Abbott	Robbins	Reynolds	Hone	Clemmence	46
Sullivan	**Golley**	**Robinson**	**Brown**	**Ransom**	**Berry**	**White**	**Burgess**	**Abbott**	**Robbins**	**Reynolds**	**Hone**	**Clemmence**	**47**
Sullivan	Hone	Robinson	Glover	Ransom	Golley	White	Howell•	Abbott	Robbins	Reynolds•	Brown	Clemmence	48
Sullivan	Brown	Golley	Clemmence	Ransom	Berry	White	Howell	Abbott	Robbins	Reynolds	Robinson	Glover	49
Sullivan	Clemmence	Robinson	Glover	Golley	Berry	White	Howell	Abbott	Robbins	Hone•	Ransom	Brown	50
Sullivan	Clemmence	Robinson	Golley	Ransom	Berry	White	Howell	Abbott	Robbins	Hone	Brown	Reynolds	51
Sullivan	Clemmence	Robinson	Golley	Glover	Brown	White	Howell	Hone	Robbins	Reynolds	Ransom	Burgess	52

• Player substituted

League Appearances (42): Robbins 42; Ransom 40; White 39; Abbott 37; Robinson 33; Hone 32; Reynolds 31; Berry 30; Clemmence 29; Golley 28; Barron 25; Brown 24; Francis 22; Harrison 8; Burgess, Howell, Sullivan 7; Stapley 2; Abboh, Parsons 1.

Welling United

NICKY BRIGDEN

Now in his 11th season with the club, Nicky coached and played at local level and was, perhaps, a somewhat surprising choice to become the club's assistant manager whilst still in his twenties. He was promoted to Team Manager five years ago at a time when Welling were fighting to establish themselves as a worthy Conference club.

In his five years in charge Nicky has, on a part-time basis, taken the club to the Third Round of the FA Cup, the last eight of the FA Trophy and, equally important, has ensured that the Wings have become a recognised and respected Conference side.

The prolific Terry Robbins scores Welling United's first goal in the 2-1 win at Kidderminster. Photo: Keith Gillard

Programme details:
    32 pages for 90p
    Editor - Paul Carter

Any other club publications:
    Wings Review

Local Newspapers:
    Kentish Times
    Bexleyheath & Welling Mercury
    Local Radio Stations:
    Radio Kent
    Radio Invicta

WELLING UNITED - PLAYING SQUAD 1992-93

Player	Honours	Birthplace and date	Transfer Fees	Previous Clubs
GOALKEEPERS				
Nicky Sullivan	EY	Forest Gate 4/1/61		Arsenal, Tooting, Bromley, Dulwich, Sutton Utd
DEFENDERS				
Nigel Ransom	LSC, KSC SLP, MW	London 12/3/59		None
Paul Collins	SLP	Southwark 1963		Millwall, Fisher Athletic
Andy Salako		Nigeria 8/11/72		Charlton Athleic
John Glover	ESP, LSC	Bedford 13/9/56	£2,000	Bedford, Nuneaton, Dulwich, Maidstone Utd
Wayne Brown		London 12/5/70		None
Mark Hone	ESP, LSC	Croydon 21/8/69		Crystal Palace
Steve Robinson				Arsenal, Dartford, Leyt & Ilf, Dartford
MIDFIELD				
Stuart White	LSC, KSC	Ashford 30/11/63		Charlton, Gillingham, Brighton
Neil Clemmence	LSC	Gravesend 29/7/64		Dartford
Joe Francis	LSC	Sidcup	£2,000	Charlton, Erith & Belvedere
Tony Reynolds	LSC	Ashford 24/4/63		Ashford, Folkestone, Maidstone Utd
Ray Burgess	SLP, LSC KSC	London 14/10/56		None
FORWARDS				
Terry Robbins	ESP, LSC MW	London 18/7/65	£8,000	Spurs, Gillingham, Maidstone Utd, Crawley
Gary Abbott	ESP, KSC	Catford 7/11/64	£30,000	Welling, Enfield, Barnet

Departures during season:
Trevor Booker (Fisher), Paul Barron (Birmingham), Mark Golley (Sutton Utd).

Players who joined on loan during season:
Jonathan Hunt & Hakan Hayrettin (Barnet), Lee Harrison (Charlton), Greg Howell (Tottenham).

Park View Road, Welling United

Name of ground: Park View Road
Ground address and Tel. No.: Park View Road, Welling, Kent. Tel: 081 301 1196
Simple ground directions: By Train: from London to Welling Station, ground 3/4 mile through High Street. By Road: M25, then A2 towards London, taking Welling turn off
Official capacity: 5,500   **Seating:** 500   **Covered accommodation:** 1,000
Cost of seats: £5.00   **Cost of standing:** £4.00
Record attendance: 4,o2o v Gillingham (FA Cup, 1989/90)
Social facilities available (Bars, hot & cold food etc.): Clubroom with Tea Bar adjoining
Car parking: Officials only inside ground. Supporters parking in surrounding roads

---

Sponsored by: Welling Building Services Ltd   **WELLING UNITED**   **Nickname:** The Wings

Previous leagues: Athenian, London Spartan, Southern
Club colours: Red/white/red   **Change colours:** All white
Midweek home matches: Wednesday   **Club metal badges:** Yes
Record transfer fee paid: £30,000 to Enfield for Gary Abbott
Record transfer fee received: £22,000 from Barnet for Duncan Horton
Record goalscorer in a career: John Bartley 533   **In a season:** John Bartley 58
Past players who have progressed to the Football League: Paul Barron (Plymouth, Arsenal, Stoke, WBA, C. Palace, Q.P.R.); Andy Townsend (Southampton, Norwich, Chelsea); Ian Thompson (Bournemouth); John Bartley (Millwall); Dave Smith (Gillingham, Bristol City); Murray Jones (C. Palace, Bristol City, Exeter); Kevin Shoemaker (Peterborough); Tony Agana (Watford, Sheff. Utd); Duncan Horton (Barnet)
Club honours: Southern League Premier Division, Kent Senior Cup, London Senior Cup, F.A. Cup 3rd Round, F.A. Trophy 4th Round

WITTON ALBION

Formed: 1890

President:
Mr T Selfox

Chairman:
D Shirley

Vice Chairman
D Lloyd

Directors:
S Kirk
V Conneely
L Gatley
B Gittings
J Metcalf
I Dobson
G Knop
P Mather
E Phillips

Company Secretary:
D Lloyd

Team Secretary:
D M Leather

Manager:
Peter O'Brien

Coach:
Kevan Keelan

Physiotherapist:
Keith Higgins

Marvellous first season for Albion

If ever a season typified the ups and downs of this great game of football, then Witton Albion's first season in the Conference stands as a prime example.

It all started off reasonably enough and the new status didn't appear to hold any terrors, having met up with the two top contenders in the early games. Whitley Bay away looked a tough task in the FA Cup Fourth Qualifying Round, but despite playing with ten men from the 8th minute, Albion ran out convincing 4-1 winners. Halifax Town at home in Round One promised further progress but Witton needed to go to the Shay for a replay to get a deserved win. In between some league reverses, Albion went to Preston for the Second Round and although it was a 5-1 defeat, most people thought that they deserved better.

December represented the lowest episode of Albion's season and the club did not register a win and salvaged but one point. Manager Peter O'Brien was struck with a serious illness in January and the players rallied round and started to win once more. The FA Trophy seemed to have been the catalyst. After the extra time win at Billingham in a replay, two home draws, both won by a single goal, brought a quarter-final tie against Wycombe Wanderers at Adams Park. With 600 or so Albion fans cheering them on, they gained an excellent 2-1 win and a place in the semi-finals for the second year running.

February and March saw Albion surge up the Conference table, performances which culminated in Peter O'Brien winning the March Manager of the Month award. With relegation fears banished, Witton faced Marine at home in the 1st leg of the Trophy semi-final. An indifferent display saw Marine claw back a two goal deficit. But it was a different story at Rossett Park as Albion powered their way to Wembley with a 4-1 victory.

The final few league results were mixed but they were good enough for a very creditable finishing position of 10th - which would have probably satisfied most Albion fans prior to the start of the campaign.

The FA Trophy Final at Wembley was hugely disappointing, although obviously enjoyable as a day out. Colchester United duly clinched the 'double' and we didn't play to our potential on the day. However, no-one can take away the marvellous first season enjoyed by all at Wincham Park.

Vic Conneely

Witton Albion F.C. 1991-92. Back Row (L-R): K Keelan (Coach), D Heesom, L Coathup, Joe Connor, M Lutkevitch, K Mason, Jim Connor, J McCluskie, C Alford, M Hughes, K Higgins (Physio). Front Row: B Robb (Kit man), G Stewart, S McNeilis, A Grimshaw, P O'Brien (Manager), S Anderson, K Thomas, M Halliday, W Dodd (Chief Scout).

Witton Albion

GM Vauxhall Conference: 10th. **FA Cup: 2nd Round.** **FA Trophy: Finalists.**

Match No.	Date	Competition	Venue H/A	Opponents	Result	League H/T	Pos.	Goalscorers (Times if known)	Attendance
1	Aug 17	GMVC	A	Cheltenham	W 1-0	1-0		Thomas 28	1059
2	Aug 24	GMVC	H	Wycombe Wanderers	L 1-2	0-1	13	Thomas 47 (pen)	1242
3	Aug 26	HFS Shield	H	Southport	W 2-1	1-1		Ellis; Edwards	547
4	Aug 31	GMVC	A	Kettering	D 1-1	0-0	13	McCluskie 81	1508
5	Sep 4	BLT 1-1	A	Gateshead	L 0-3	0-2			260
6	Sep 7	GMVC	H	Colchester	D 2-2	1-1	16	Thomas 19; Ellis 60	1045
7	Sep 11	GMVC	A	Boston Utd	L 2-3	1-1	16	Lutkevitch 41; Thomas 62	1187
8	Sep 14	GMVC	H	Merthyr Tydfil	W 3-2	0-0	9	McCluskie 49; Grimshaw 77,90	885
9	Sep 17	BLT 1-2	H	Gateshead	W 5-0	2-0		Thomas 3; Hill 44; Lutkevitch 62; McCluskie 104,113	501
10	Sep 21	GMVC	A	Welling Utd	D 1-1	1-1	10	Stewart 11	914
11	Sep 28	GMVC	A	Farnborough	D 1-1	0-1	10	Stewart 81 (pen)	560
12	Oct 1	GMVC	H	Kidderminster	W 2-1	0-1	9	Anderson 78 ,82	792
13	Oct 8	GMVC	A	Stafford Rangers	L 2-3	0-2	9	McCluskie 47; Anderson 90	817
14	Oct 12	GMVC	H	Redbridge Forest	W 2-0	2-0	5	Thomas 35; Stewart 40	851
15	Oct 15	BLT 2	A	Runcorn	D 2-2	0-1		McCluskie 65; 107	850
16	Oct 19	GMVC	H	Bath City	D 2-2	1-2	6	McNeilis 10; Connor 61	742
17	Oct 26	FAC 4Q	A	Whitley Bay	W 4-1	1-1		McNeilis 34; Connor 65,85; Stewart 89 (pen)	443
18	Oct 29	GMVC	A	Altrincham	D 2-2	0-1	10	Stewart 52, Anderson 74	1059
19	Nov 2	GMVC	A	Slough	L 1-2	1-0	12	o.g. 20	610
20	Nov 9	GMVC	H	Telford Utd	D 1-1	1-0	12	Thomas 31	875
21	Nov 16	FAC 1	H	Halifax Town	D 1-1	1-0		Thomas 31	2002
22	Nov 23	GMVC	A	Gateshead	L 1-2	1-0	15	Grimshaw 31	273
23	Nov 27	FAC 1R	A	Halifax Town	W 2-1	0-0		Thomas 96; Grimshaw 112	2172
24	Nov 30	GMVC	A	Macclesfield	L 0-1	0-0	17		1015
25	Dec 7	FAC 2	A	Preston N.E.	L 1-5	0-3		Thomas 64	6736
26	Dec 11	BLT 3	H	Runcorn	L 0-2	0-0			503
27	Dec 14	GMVC	H	Barrow	L 0-1	0-0	18		690
28	Dec 21	GMVC	A	Colchester	L 2-3	1-2	18	Thomas 41,86	2842
29	Dec 26	GMVC	A	Northwich Victoria	L 0-3	0-2	18		2809
30	Dec 28	GMVC	H	Welling Utd	D 2-2	1-1	18	Thomas 12,78 (pen)	712
31	Jan 1	GMVC	H	Runcorn	L 1-3	1-0	18	Thomas 9	978
32	Jan 4	GMVC	H	Boston Utd	W 1-0	1-0	18	Hill 45	749
33	Jan 11	FAT 1	H	Billingham Syn.	D 2-2	1-1		Thomas 14; Connor 57	725
34	Jan 18	GMVC	A	Yeovil	L 1-2	0-1	19	Thomas 87	1659
35	Jan 20	FAT 1R	H	Billingham Syn.	W 2-1	1-0		Heesom 40; McCluskie 108	245
36	Jan 25	GMVC	H	Slough	W 2-1	0-0	18	Thomas 82; McCluskie 87	814
37	Feb 1	FAT 2	H	Aylesbury	W 1-0	0-0		Thomas 47	852
38	Feb 4	CSC	H	Northwich Victoria	W 3-1	0-0		Thomas (2); Alford	1152
39	Feb 8	GMVC	H	Stafford Rangers	W 6-0	4-0	16	Alford 7; Connor 14,19,88; Thomas 32(pen); Lutkevitch 80	912
40	Feb 11	GMVC	H	Kettering	W 1-0	0-0	16	Thomas 58	887
41	Feb 15	GMVC	A	Telford Utd	L 1-2	1-1	16	Hughes 34	935
42	Feb 22	FAT 3	H	Stalybridge C.	W 1-0	0-0		Heesom 66	1755
43	Feb 29	GMVC	H	Farnborough	W 4-1	2-0	15	Alford 16,67; McNeilis 40; Thomas 89	838
44	Mar 3	CSC	A	Altrincham	W 4-1	2-0		Hughes (2); Lutkevitch; Grimshaw	730
45	Mar 7	GMVC	A	Kidderminster	W 1-0	0-0	15	Thomas 65	874
46	Mar 10	GMVC	A	Barrow	W 1-0	0-0	13	Stewart 53	1026
47	Mar 14	FAT 4	A	Wycombe Wanderers	W 2-1	0-0		Lutkevitch 50; Thomas 89	4636
48	Mar 17	GMVC	A	Runcorn	W 1-0	0-0	9	McCluskie 87	838
49	Mar 20	GMVC	H	Macclesfield	W 1-1	0-0	9	Thomas 76	1308
50	Mar 28	GMVC	A	Bath City	W 2-0	1-0	9	Thomas 6; Connor 90	550
51	Mar 31	GMVC	H	Yeovil	W 3-1	0-0	9	McCluskie 66,88; Connor 89	783
52	Apr 4	FAT S/F 1	H	Marine	D 2-2	2-1		Alford 25,31	2030
53	Apr 7	GMVC	A	Gateshead	L 0-3	0-0	10		593
54	Apr 11	FAT S/F 2	A	Marine	W 4-1	1-0		Thomas 5; McCluskie 81; Halliday 89; Lutkevitch 90	2212
55	Apr 14	GMVC	H	Altrincham	W 2-0	0-0	9	Lutkevitch 51; Rose 63	825
56	Apr 16	GMVC	A	Redbridge Forest	L 1-3	0-1	10	McCluskie 90	437
57	Apr 18	GMVC	A	Merthyr Tydfil	W 1-0	0-0	10		632
58	Apr 20	GMVC	H	Northwich Victoria	D 1-1	1-1	1-	Connor 29	1902
59	Apr 25	GMVC	H	Cheltenham	W 4-2	2-1	9	Thomas 13,89; Alford 15; McCluskie 76	759
60	May 2	GMVC	A	Wycombe Wanderers	L 0-4	0-2	10		6035
61	May 10	FAT Final	N	Colchester	L 1-3	0-2		Lutkevitch 57	27806

Best Home League Attendance: 1902 v Northwich 20.4.92 **Smallest: 593 v Gateshead 7.4.92** **Average Home Attendance: 890**

Goalscorers: GMVC: Thomas 10; McCluskie 7; Connor 6; Stewart 5; Alford, Anderson 4; Grimshaw, Lutkevitch 3; McNeilis 2; Ellis, Hill, Hughes, Rose 1. **F.A. Cups:** Thomas 10; McCluskie 7; Lutkevitch 6; Alford 4; Joe Connor 3; Grimshaw, Heesom, Hughes 2; Edwards, Ellis, Halliday, Hill, McNeilis, Stewart 1.

Witton Albion

1	2	3	4	5	6	7	8	9	10	11	12	14	Match No.
Mason	Connor	Fuller	McNeilis	Morgan	Ellis	Grimshaw	McDonald	Thomas	McCluskie	Connor	Edwards	Cuddy	1
Mason	Connor	Fuller	McNeilis	Morgan	Ellis	Grimshaw	McDonald•	Thomas	Edwards	Connor	Stewart	Cuddy	2
Mason	**Connor**	**Fuller**	**McNeilis**	**Ellis**	**Stewart**	**Grimshaw**	**Anderson**	**Connor**	**McCluskie•**	**Edwards**	**McDonald**	**Cuddy**	**3**
Mason	Connor	Fuller	McNeilis	Ellis†	Anderson	Grimshaw•	Lodge	Thomas	McCluskie	Connor	Edwards	Stewart	4
Mason	**Connor**	**Coathup**	**McNeilis**	**Cuddy**	**Anderson**	**Grimshaw†**	**Lodge**	**Thomas**	**McCluskie•**	**Connor**	**Lutkevitch**	**Edwards**	**5**
Mason	Stewart	Coathup	McNeilis	Ellis•	Cuddy	Anderson	Lodge	Thomas†	Lutkevitch	Connor	McCluskie	Edwards	6
Mason	Stewart	Coathup	McNeilis	Cuddy	Grimshaw	Lodge	McDonald	Thomas	Lutkevitch•	Connor	McCluskie	Edwards	7
Mason	Stewart	Coathup	McNeilis†	Cuddy	Grimshaw	Lodge	Anderson	Thomas	Lutkevitch*	McCluskie	Ellis	Connor	8
Mason	**Stewart**	**Coathup**	**Connor**	**Ellis**	**Grishaw**	**Anderson**	**Hill**	**Lutkevitch**	**Thomas**	**McCluskie**	**Connor**	**Lodge**	**9**
Mason	Stewart•	McNeilis	Connor	Cuddy	Grimshaw	Anderson	Hill	Thomas	Lutkevitch	McCluskie†	Connor	Jarvis	10
Newall	Stewart	Coathup	Connor	McNeilis	Anderson	Hill•	McCluskie	Lutkevitch	Grimshaw	Connor	Edwards	Cuddy	11
Mason	Stewart	Coathup	Connor	McNeilis	Anderson	Hill†	McCluskie	Lutkevitch•	Grimshaw	Connor	Thomas	Edwards	12
Mason	Stewart	Coathup	Connor	McNeilis	Anderson	Hill†	Thomas	Lutkevitch	Grimshaw•	Connor	McCluskie	Cuddy	13
Mason	Stewart	Coathup	McNeilis	Cuddy	Anderson	Connor	Thomas†	McCluskie	Grimshaw	Edwards•	Connor	Lutkevitch	14
Mason	**Stewart**	**Coathup**	**NcNeilis**	**Connor**	**Cuddy**	**Anderson**	**Thomas•**	**McCluskie**	**Grimshaw**	**Connor**	**Lutkevitch**	**Edwards**	**15**
Mason	Stewart	Coathup	McNeilis	Connor	Cuddy•	Anderson	Thomas†	McCluskie	Grimshaw	Connor	Lutkevitch	Edwards	16
Mason	**Connor**	**Coathup**	**McNeilis**	**Cuddy**	**Stewart**	**Anderson**	**Lutkevitch•**	**McCluskie**	**Grimshaw**	**Connor**	**Dyson**	**Edwards**	**17**
Mason	Connor	Coathp	McNeilis	Cuddy	Anderson	Stewart	Lutkevitch	McCluskie•	Grimshaw	Connor	Dyson	Edwards	18
Mason	Connor	Coathup•	McNeilis	Cuddy	Anderson	Stewart	Lutkevitch	Dyson†	Grimshaw	Connor	Hooton	Edwards	19
Zelem	Stewart	Coathup	NcNeilis	Connor	Anderson	Thomas†	Hooton	Lutkevitch•	Grimshaw	Connor	Dyson	Alford	20
Zelem	**Stewart**	**Coathup**	**McNeilis**	**Connor**	**Anderson**	**Thomas**	**Hooton**	**Lutkevitch•**	**Grimshaw**	**Connor**	**Dyson**	**Alford**	**21**
Zelem	Connor	Coathup	McNeilis	Morgan	Anderson	Thomas	Wilson	Alford•	Grimshaw	Connor†	Hooton	Dyson	22
Zelem	**Connor**	**Coathup**	**McNeilis**	**Cuddy**	**Anderson•**	**Thomas**	**Hooton**	**Lutkevitch•**	**Grimshaw**	**Connor**	**Hill**	**Alford**	**23**
Zelem	Connor	Coathup	McNeilis	Cuddy	Hill•	Thomas†	Hooton	Lutkevitch	Grimshaw	Connor	Wilson	Alford	24
Mason	**Coathup•**	**Hooton**	**McNeilis**	**Connor**	**Anderson**	**Thomas**	**Cuddy†**	**Lutkevitch**	**Grimshaw**	**Connor**	**Stewart**	**McCluskie**	**25**
Mason	**Connor**	**Hooton**	**McCluskie**	**Morgan**	**Anderson**	**Thomas**	**Wilson**	**Lutkevitch**	**Grimshaw**	**Connor**	**McNeilis**	**Coathup**	**26**
Mason	Stewart	Hooton	McNeilis	Morgan	Cuddy	Thomas	Wilson	McCluskie	Grimshaw	Connor	Coathup	Alford	27
Mason	Coathup	Cuddy	McNeilis	Morgan	Anderson	Thomas	Stewart†	McCluskie	Wilson•	Connor	Alford	Connor	28
Mason	Coathup	Hooton•	McNeilis	Cuddy	Anderson	Thomas	Stewart	McCluskie†	Hill	Connor	Lutkevitch	Alford	29
Mason	Hill	Hooton	McNeilis	Morgan	Anderson	Thomas	Wilson	McCluskie	Grimshaw	Connor	Lutkevitch	Coathup	30
Mason	Stewart	Hooton	McNeilis	Morgan	Hill	Thomas	Wilson	McCluskie•	Grimshaw	Connor	Alford	Heesom	31
Mason	Anderson	Hooton	McNeilis	Connor	Stewart•	Thomas	Heesom†	Hill	Grimshaw	Connor	McCluskie	Wilson	32
Mason	**Anderson**	**Hooton**	**McNeilis**	**Connor**	**Stewart**	**Thomas**	**Hill**	**Heesom•**	**Grimshaw**	**Conor**	**Lutkevitch**	**Wilson**	**33**
Mason	Coathup	Hooton†	McNeilis	Connor	Anderson	Thomas	Stewart	Heesom	Grimshaw	Connor	Lutkevitch	Wilson	34
Mason	**Stewart**	**Heesom**	**McNeilis**	**Connor**	**Anderson•**	**Thomas**	**Wilson**	**Lutkevitch†**	**Grimshaw**	**Connor**	**McCluskie**	**Hooton**	**35**
Mason	Halliday	Heesom	McNeilis	Connor	Anderson	Thomas	Rose•	Hughes	Grimshaw	Connor†	Stewart	McCluskie	36
Mason	**Halliday**	**Heesom**	**McNeilis**	**Connor**	**Anderson**	**Thomas**	**Rose**	**McCluskie•**	**Grimshaw**	**Connor**	**Stewart**	**Lutkevitch**	**37**
Mason	**Coathup**	**Heesom**	**Alford**	**Connor**	**Anderson†**	**Thomas**	**Stewart**	**McCluskie•**	**Grimshaw**	**Connor**	**Lutkevitch**	**Hooton**	**38**
Mason	Halliday	Heesom	McNeilis•	Connor	Alford†	Thomas	Rose	Hughes	Grimshaw	Connor	Stewart	Lutkevitch	39
Mason	Halliday	Heesom†	Jackson	Connor	Stewart	Thomas	Rose	Hughes•	Grimshaw	Connor	Lutkevitch	Coathup	40
Mason	Halliday	Heesom	McNeilis	Hughes	Stewart†	Thomas	Rose	Hughes•	Grimshaw	Connor	Lutkevitch	Coathup	41
Mason	**Halliday**	**Heesom**	**McNeilis**	**Connor**	**Anderson**	**Thomas**	**Rose**	**Lutkevitch•**	**Grimshaw**	**Connor**	**Alford**	**McCluskie**	**42**
Mason	Halliday	Heesom	McNeilis	Connor	Anderson	Thomas	Alford•	Hughes	Grimshaw	Lutkevitch†	Connor	Coathup	43
Mason	**Halliday**	**Heesom**	**McNeilis**	**Connor**	**Anderson†**	**Thomas**	**Lutkevitch•**	**Hughes**	**Grimshaw**	**Connor**	**McCluskie**	**Coathup**	**44**
Mason	Halliday	Heesom	McNeilis	Connor	Anderson	Thomas	Lutkevitch•	Hughes	Grimshaw	Connor†	McCluskie	Coathup	45
Paladino	Halliday	Coathup	McNeilis	Alford	McCluskie	Stewart	Rose	Hughes•	Grimshaw	Lutkevitch†	Connor	Heesom	46
Mason	**Halliday**	**Heesom**	**McNeilis**	**Connor**	**Anderson**	**Thomas**	**Rose**	**Alford**	**Grimshaw**	**Lutkevitch•**	**Stewart**	**Connor**	**47**
Mason	Halliday	Coathup	McNeilis	Connor	Anderson	Stewart•	Alford	Hughes†	Grimshaw	McCluskie	Connor	Lutkevitch	48
Mason	Halliday	Heesom	McNeilis	Connor	Stewart†	Thomas	Alford	McCluskie	Hughes•	Connor	Lutkevitch	Anderson	49
Mason	Halliday	Coathup	McCluskie	Connor•	Alford	Stewart	Lutkevitch	Hughes	Grimshaw	Connor	Heesom	Anderson	50
Mason	Halliday	Coathup	McNeilis	Connor	Anderson	Thomas•	Lutkevitch†	Alford	Grimshaw	Rose	McCluskie	Connor	51
Paladino	**Halliday**	**Heesom**	**Stewart**	**Connor**	**Anderson**	**Burndred**	**Alford**	**McCluskie**	**Hughes•**	**Connor**	**Lutkevitch**	**Rose**	**52**
Mason	Halliday	Heesom	Stewart	Connor	Anderson	Thomas	Rose	Alford	Lutkevitch•	Connor	McCluskie	C oathup	53
Paladino	**Halliday**	**Coathup**	**Stewart**	**Burndred•**	**Anderson**	**Thomas**	**Rose**	**Alford**	**Grimshaw**	**Lutkevitch**	**McCluskie**	**Heesom**	**54**
Mason	Halliday	Coathup	McNeilis	Connor	Anderson	Thomas•	Stewart†	Alford	Grimshaw	Lutkevitch	McCluskie	Rose	55
Mason	Halliday	Coathup	McNeilis	Connor•	Anderson	Rose	McCluskie†	Alford	Grimshaw	Lutkevitch	Stewart	Connor	56
Mason	Halliday	Coathup	McNeilis	Burndred†	Anderson•	Thomas	Rose	Alford	Heesom	Lutkevitch	McCluskie	Connor	57
Mason	Halliday	Coathup	McNeilis	Stewart	Anderson	Thomas	Alford	Lutkevitch•	Rose	Connor	Hughes	Heesom	58
Mason	Halliday	Coathup	McNeilis	Connor	Rose	Thomas	Stewart†	Alford	McCluskie	Grimshaw	Lutkevitch•	McCluskie	59
Mason	Halliday	Coathup	McNeilis	Stewart	Anderson•	Thomas†	Alford	McCluskie	Grimshaw	Rose	Heesom	Connor	60
Mason	**Halliday**	**Coathup**	**McNeilis**	**Connor**	**Anderson**	**Thomas**	**Rose**	**Alford**	**Grimshaw†**	**Lutkevitch•**	**McCluskie**	**Connor**	**61**

• substituted by No. 12. † substituted by No. 14.

GMVC Appearances: McNeilis 39 (2); Mason 35; Grimshaw 34 (3); Thomas 34 (1); Joe Connor 31 (8); Anderson 30 (1); Stewart 29 (5); Coathup 26 (4); Jim Connor 26 (2); McCluskie 20 (9); Lutkevitch 20 (11); Halliday 17; Alford 15 (5); Rose 13 (1); Cuddy 12 (1); Heesom 12; Hughes 11 (1); Hill 9 (1); Hooton 8 (1); Morgan 7; Wilson 5; Ellis, Lodge 4; Burndred, Fuller, McDonald, Paladino, Zelem 3; Edwards 2 (6); Dyson 1 (3); Hughes T., Jackson, Newell 1; Jarvis (1).
Cup Appearances (max 20): Jim Connor 20; Anderson, Grimshaw 19; Mason 18; Thomas 17; Joe Connor 16; McNeilis 15; Lutkevitch 14; Coathup, Stewart 11; McCluskie 9; Halliday 7; Alford 6; Hooton, Rose 5; Cuddy 4; Ellis, Hill, Hughes, Wilson, Zelem 2; Dyson, Edwards, Fuller, Lodge, Morgan 1; McDonald (1).

Witton Albion

PETER O'BRIEN

Peter came to the club less than two weeks before the start of the 1991/92 season from Runcorn who he had joined in November 1990. During that period he had steered the Linnets to a respectable 6th position after they were struggling in the lower reaches of the league in the early months of the season.

As a player, Peter spent most of his time with Hyde United where he was a forward with a prodigious strike rate. He started his managerial career with some success at Stalybridge Celtic and then had several successful seasons with Hyde United before taking the Runcorn post.

Peter, along with assistant Kevan Keelan, another former Stalybridge Celtic boss, enjoyed a fine first season with Witton, guiding them to 10th in the table and to the FA Trophy and Cheshire Senior Cup Finals. With some useful additions already made to the Wincham Park squad during the summer, Albion will be looking to mount a serious challenge for the Conference title this season.

Witton Albion's Jim Connor scores his side's second goal in the 2-2 draw with Bath City at Wincham Park.   Photo: Mark Brooker.

Programme details:
   24 pages for 60p
   Editor - Vic Conneely

Any other club publications:

Local Newspapers:
   Northwich Chronicle
   Northwich Guardian
   Manchester Evening News

Local Radio Stations:
   BBC Radio Manchester
   Piccadilly Radio
   Signal Radio

WITTON ALBION -PLAYING SQUAD 1992/93

Player	Honours	Birthplace and date	Transfer Fees	Previous Clubs
GOALKEEPERS				
Keith Mason	HFS, FAV	Leicester 19/7/58		Lutterworth, Wigston Fields, Leicester C, Huddersfield, Colne Dynamoes
DEFENDERS				
Steve McNeilis	HFS, MCSC FAXI	Liverpool		Formby, Burscough, Northwich V, Colne Dynamoes
Mike Halliday				Man City, Stockport, Mossley, Witton Alb, Buxton, Stalybridge, Chorley, Leek
Jim Connor	CSC	Stockport 31/1/59		Stockport, Northwich V, Napier City(NZ), Stalybridge, Mossley, Macclesfield
Darren Heesom	CSC	Warrington 8/5/68		Burnley, Altrincham, Macclesfield
Lee Coathup				Everton, Newtown, Vauxhall GM, Stalybridge Celtic
MIDFIELD				
Stewart Anderson	HFS, FAV ATS, NWCL	20/11/59		Chadderton, Colne Dynamoes
Andy Grimshaw	HFS	Manchester		Colne Dynamoes, Rossendale Utd, Colne Dynamoes
Paul Kelly		Urmston 6/3/71		Manchester City, Crewe Alexandra
Ian Redman				Ashton United, Curzon Ashton, New Zealand, Runcorn
Gary Stewart	HFS	Manchester 7/10/61		Irlam, Mossley, Northwich V, Altrincham
Joe Connor	HFS	Stockport	£10,000	Stockport, Hyde Utd, Mossley, Hyde Utd
Colin Rose		Winsford 22/1/72		Crewe Alexandra
John Burndred				Knypersley Victoria
FORWARDS				
Karl Thomas	HFS		£10,000	Ellesmere Port, South Liverpool, Colne Dynamoes
Jim McCluskie	HFS	Rossendale 29/9/66	£10,000	Rochdale, Mossley, Hyde Utd
Mark Lillis		Manchester 17/1/60		Huddersfield, Manchester City, Derby, Aston Villa, Scunthorpe, Stockport
Mike Lutkevitch	HFSLC CCS	15/4/62		Curzon Ashton, Stalybridge Celtic, Hyde Utd
Brendan Burke		Manchester 13/10/70		Manchester Utd, Oldham Town, Mossley
Karl Alford				Burnley
Mark Hughes		Liverpool 30/6/69	£5,000	Irlam, Altrincham

Departures during season:
Dave Fuller (Southport), Alan McDonald (Accrington Stanley), Tony Jarvis (Southport), Dave Morgan (Guiseley), Paul Lodge (Morecambe), Steve Ellis (Retired), Mark Edwards (Horwich), Alan Zelem (Macclesfield), Phil Wilson (Guiseley), Jon Hill (Horwich).

Players who joined on loan during season:
Andy Newell (AQccrington Stanley), Colin Rose, Mike Jackson & Tony Hughes (Crewe)

Witton Albion

Ground address and Tel. No.: Wincham Park, Chapel St., Wincham, Northwich, Cheshire CW9 6DA. Tel: 0606 43008
Information line:
Simple ground directions: M6 junction 19, follow A556 toward Northwich, after 3 miles turn on to A559, follow Warrington signs, turn left opposite Black Greyhound Inn, ground on left.
Official capacity: 4,500   **Seating:** 650   **Covered accommodation:** 1,650
Cost of seats: £5.00   **Cost of standing:** £4.00
Official opening of floodlights: Not yet "officially" opened
Record attendance: 3,940 v Kidderminster H., FA Trophy S.Final 1991
Social facilities available: Bars & V.P. Lounge
Car parking: 1,250

Sponsored by: Boddingtons   **WITTON ALBION**   **Nickname:** Albion

---

Previous leagues: Cheshire County League (now NW Counties League), Lancashire Combination
Club colours: Red & white striped shirts, black shorts, red socks   **Change colours:** All blue
Midweek home matches: Tuesday   **Club metal badges:** Yes
Record transfer fee paid: £10,000 twice, 1 to Colne Dynamoes for Karl Thomas and 2 to Hyde United for Jim McCluskie
Record transfer fee received: £11,500 from Chester City for P. Henderson, £35,000 from Leeds United for Mike Whitlow & Neil Parsley
Record appearances for club: J. Goryl - 652
Record aggregate goalscorer: Frank Fidler 122
Record goalscorer in a season: Frank Fidler 64
Past players who have progressed to the Football League: P. Henderson (Chester City), Chris Nicholl (ex Southampton manager), Phil Powell (Crewe), Neil Parsley & Mike Whitlow (Leeds)
Club honours: H.F.S. Loans Premier Division Champions 1990-91; Cheshire County League Winners - 1948-49, 1949-50, 1953-54; Cheshire County League Runner-up - 1950-51; Cheshire County League Cup - 1953-54, 1975-76; Cheshire County FA Senior Cup (5 times)
Past club managers since 1935: Mark Radcliffe, Mike Pickup, Norman Law, Ken Barnes, Brian Booth, L. Sutton, John Rogers, T. Murphy, S. Allan, P. O'Brien

WOKING

Woking's Best Ever

It is difficult to imagine that just 5 years ago Woking were languishing in the Isthmian League Second Division, but last season saw Geoff Chapple lead the club to its third promotion in six seasons and bring their first ever Isthmian League title after 89 years of membership.

In truth, the title was won with consumate ease, with The Cards leading by 26 points at one stage and eventually finishing 18 points ahead of their nearest challengers Enfield. The title was won with 4 weeks and 7 games remaining, with the 5-0 thrashing of the North London clun in November in front of 3,125 spectators at Kingfield being pivotal to the eventual outcome.

Many people felt that it was only Woking's magnificent cup run the previous season which prevented them from gaining Conference status, but again the club reached the Third Round of the FA Cup, only being robbed of a glamorous meeting twith Nottingham Forest by an extra time replay defeat at Hereford United. It is now five years since Woking have been beaten by a non-league team in the competition. However, with the exception of a Charity Shield victory over the previous years champions, Redbridge Forest, the cups eluded the club, with defeat in the Loctite Cup Final against Surrey neighbours Sutton United being particularly disappointing. The 1-0 defeat at holders Wycombe Wanderers in the 2nd round of the FA Trophy was by no means a disgrace.

The clubs success on the field has been matched by the level of support, with the clubs average league gate now almost 2,000 and the army of travelling support will surely be most welcome in the Conference next season.

Geoff Chapple's shrewd signing of former League players Laurence Batty and George Friel proved highly significant with goalkeeper Batty's tremendous displays earning him a call-up to the England Semi-Professional side as well as being voted the clubs Player of the Year.

One thing is certain, Woking FC will continue with their exciting brand of attacking football and will have no fears in taking on the best non-league sides in the country.

Mike Deavin

Woking with the Diadora League championship. Back Row (L/R): Stuart Mitchell, Barry Kimber (Physio), Adie Cowler, Laurence Batty, Trevor Baron, Francis Vines, Nick Collier, Colin Lippiatt (Asst Manager), Shane Wye, Geoff Chapple, Dereck Brown. Front: Andy Parr, Mark Biggins, George Friel, Steve Milton, Mascot, Lloyd Wye, Bradley Pratt. Photo - Eric Marsh.

Woking

Diadora League: 1st. **FA Cup: 3rd Round.** **FA Trophy: 2nd Round.**

Match No.	Date	Competition	Venue H/A	Opponents	Result	League H/T Pos.	Goalscorers (Times if known)	Attendance
1	Aug 17	DL	H	Carshalton	W 3-0		Biggins; Friel (2)	1402
2	Aug 20	DL	A	Kingstonian	W 2-1		Walkes; Friel	2071
3	Aug 24	DL	A	Chesham Utd	D 0-0			1299
4	Aug 31	DL	H	Dagenham	W 3-1		Russell; Friel; L.Wye	1374
5	Sep 3	DL	H	Bromley	L 1-2		Friel	1521
6	Sep 7	DL	A	Wokingham	W 3-0		Friel; Milton; Parr (pen)	1080
7	Sep 10	LC 1	A	**Barton Rovers**	W 3-1		Friel; Baron; Parr (pen)	404
8	Sep 14	DL	H	Hayes	W 4-1		Friel (2); Baron; Biggins	1434
9	Sep 21	DL	A	Wivenhoe	W 7-1		Friel (4); Milton (2); Batty	393
10	Sep 28	DL	A	Carshalton	W 2-0		Friel; o.g.	893
11	Oct 5	DL	H	Grays Athletic	W 1-0		Milton	1689
12	Oct 12	DL	A	Dagenham	D 0-0			883
13	Oct 15	DL	H	Basingstoke	W 5-0		Milton (3); Friel (2)	1701
14	Oct 19	DL	H	Harrow Boro	W 2-0		Friel; Perry	1451
15	Oct 26	DL	A	St. Albans	D 1-1		L. Wye	828
16	Oct 29	DL	A	Marlow	W 3-0		Biggins (2); Friel	1020
17	Nov 2	DL	H	Staines	D 2-2		Baron; Pratt	1209
18	Nov 5	DL	H	Sutton Utd	W 1-0		S. Wye	2327
19	Nov 9	DL	A	Bishop's Stortford	W 2-1		Baron; Parr (pen)	723
20	Nov 19	LC 2	H	**Rainham**	W 4-1		Smith (2); White; Milton	944
21	Nov 23	DL	A	Hendon	W 5-0		Biggins (2); Baron; Brown; Friel	751
22	Nov 26	FAC 1	A	**Windsor & Eton**	W 4-2		Mitchell; Biggins; Milton; Friel	2537
23	Nov 30	DL	A	Enfield	W 5-0		Friel (2); Pratt; Milton; o.g.	3125
24	Dec 7	FAC 2	H	**Yeovil**	W 3-0		Friel (3)	4250
25	Dec 18	LC 3	A	**Chesham Utd**	W 2-1		Friel; Mitchell	574
26	Dec 21	DL	A	Staines	W 2-0		Baron; Milton	1410
27	Dec 28	DL	A	Aylesbury Utd	W 4-0		Pratt; Milton; Collier; Batty (pen)	2165
28	Jan 4	FAC 3	H	**Hereford Utd**	D 0-0			4753
29	Jan 7	SSC 1	H	**Walton & Hersham**	W 6-1		Milton (3); Baron; Biggins; S. Wye	1455
30	Jan 11	FAT	H	**Wembley**	W 4-2		Pratt; Milton; Friel (pen); o.g.	2087
31	Jan 14	FAC 2R	A	**Hereford Utd**	L 1-2		Pratt	8679
32	Jan 18	DL	H	Chesham Utd	W 2-1		Milton; Friel	2305
33	Jan 20	LOC 1	H	**Walton & Herhsam**	W 2-1		L. Wye; o.g.	1274
34	Jan 25	DL	A	Bromley	W 2-0		Milton; Friel	1545
35	Jan 28	SSC 2	A	**Kingstonian**	W 3-2		Friel; Batty (pen); o.g.	1352
36	Feb 1	FAT	A	**Wycombe Wanderers**	L 0-1			5801
37	Feb 8	DL	H	Hayes	D 2-2		Friel (2)	1148
38	Feb 11	LC 4	H	**Enfield**	L 0-2			1578
39	Feb 15	DL	A	Basingstoke	W 3-0		Pratt; Collier; Parr (pen)	1578
40	Feb 18	DL	H	Wokingham	L 0-1			1871
41	Feb 22	DL	H	Wivenhoe	W 2-0		Milton (2)	1953
42	Feb 26	LOC 2	A	**Chesham Utd**	W 5-2		Milton (2); Devine; Biggins; Brown	793
43	Feb 29	DL	A	Grays Athletic	W 2-0		S. Wye; Brown	1012
44	Mar 3	SSC 3	H	**Carshalton**	L 0-2			1629
45	Mar 7	DL	H	Bognor Regis	W 3-1		Brown; Devine; Parr (pen)	1608
46	Mar 10	LOC 3	H	**Yeading**	W 1-0		Friel	1063
47	Mar 14	DL	A	St. Albans	W 4-1		Friel; Brown; Batty (pen); Parr (pen)	1912
48	Mar 17	DL	H	Windsor & Eton	W 2-0		S. Wye; L. Wye	1952
49	Mar 21	DL	A	Harrow Boro	W 3-1		S. Wye; Friel; Baron	1139
50	Mar 28	DL	H	Aylesbury Utd	W 2-1		Vines; Milton	2294
51	Mar 31	LOC S/F	A	**Harrow Boro**	W 2-0		Mitchell (2)	780
52	Apr 4	DL	A	Windsor & Eton	W 3-0		Vines; Friel; Milton	1184
53	Apr 7	DL	H	Kingstonian	W 3-1		Friel (2); Parr	3073
54	Apr 11	DL	H	Bishop's Stortford	W 3-0		Parr (2); Pratt	2396
55	Apr 14	DL	A	Bognor Regis	D 1-1		Biggins	580
56	Apr 18	DL	A	Sutton Utd	L 0-2			1658
57	Apr 25	DL	H	Hendon	D 1-1		Vines	1629
58	Apr 28	DL	H	Marlow	L 0-1			1283
59	May 2	DL	A	Enfield	L 0-1			1182
60	May 5	LOC F	A	**Sutton Utd**	L 0-2			1935

Woking

1	2	3	4	5	6	7	8	9	10	11	12	14	Match No.
Batty	Mitchell	Cowler	Russell	Baron	Parr	Brown	Biggins•	Walkes	Friel†	L.Wye	Mulvaney	Barrowcliff	1
Batty	Mitchell	Cowler	Russell	Baron	Parr	Brown	Biggins•	Walkes	Friel†	L.Wye	Mulvaney	Barrowcliff	2
Batty	Mitchell	Cowler	Russell	Baron	Parr	Brown	Biggins	Walkes	Friel•	L.Wye	Perry	Barrowcliff	3
Batty	Mitchell	Cowler	Russell	Baron	Parr	Brown	Biggins•	Mulvaney	Friel	L.Wye	Perry	Barrowcliff	4
Batty	Mitchell	Cowler	Russell	Baron	Parr	Brown	Biggins	Perry•	Friel	L.Wye	Mulvaney	Barrowcliff	5
Batty	Mitchell	Cowler†	Russell	Baron	Parr	Brown	Biggins	Milton	Friel	L.Wye•	Perry	Pratt	6
Batty	**Mitchell**	**Cowler**	**Russell**	**Baron**	**Parr**	**Brown•**	**Biggins**	**Milton**	**Friel**	**L.Wye**	**Perry**	**Pratt**	**7**
Batty	Mitchell	Cowler	Russell	Baron	Parr	Hunt	Biggins	Milton•	Friel†	L.Wye•	Perry	Walkes	8
Batty	Mitchell	L.Wye	Russell	Baron	Parr	Cockram	Biggins	Milton	Friel†	Hunt•	Perry	Walkes	9
Batty	Mitchell	Pratt	Russell	Baron	Parr	Cockram	Biggins	Milton	Friel	L.Wye	Perry	Walkes	10
Batty	Mitchell	Cowler	Russell	Baron	Parr	Pratt•	Biggins	Milton	Friel	L.Wye	Perry	Walkes	11
Batty	Parr	Cowler	Pratt	Baron	S.Wye	Brown	Biggins†	Milton	Friel	L.Wye	Mitchell	Mulvaney	12
Batty	Mitchell	Cowler	Pratt	Baron	S.Wye	Parr	Biggins•	Milton	Friel†	L.Wye	Perry	Mulvaney	13
Batty	Parker•	Cowler	Pratt	Baron	S.Wye	Parr	Biggins	Milton	Friel	L.Wye	Perry	Mulvaney	14
Batty	S.Wye	Cowler	Pratt	Baron	Parr	Brown	Biggins	Milton	Friel†	L.Wye	Mitchell	Perry	15
Batty	Mitchell	Cowler	Pratt	Baron	S.Wye	Brown	Biggins	Milton	Friel	L.Wye	Parr	Perry	16
Batty	Parr	Cowler	Pratt	Baron	S.Wye	Brown	Biggins	Milton	Friel	L.Wye	Perry	Parker	17
Batty	Mitchell	Cowler	Pratt	Baron	S.Wye	Brown	Biggins	Milton†	Friel	L.Wye	Perry	Smith	18
Batty	Mitchell	Cowler	Pratt	Baron	S.Wye•	Parr	Biggins	Milton†	Friel	L.Wye	Smith	White	19
Batty	**Parr**	**Cowler**	**Pratt**	**Baron**	**S.Wye†**	**Brown**	**Biggins**	**Smith•**	**White**	**Collier**	**Friel**	**Milton**	**20**
Batty	Mitchell†	Cowler	Pratt	Baron	S.Wye	Brown	Biggins	Milton	Friel•	Collier	Smith	Parr	21
Batty	**Mitchell**	**Cowler**	**Pratt**	**Baron**	**S.Wye**	**Brown**	**Biggins**	**Milton**	**Friel**	**Collier**	**Parr**	**Mulvaney**	**22**
Batty	Mitchell•	Cowler	Pratt	Baron	S.Wye	Brown	Parr	Milton	Friel†	Collier	L.Wye	Smith	23
Batty	**Mitchell**	**Cowler**	**Pratt**	**Baron**	**S.Wye**	**Brown**	**Parr**	**Milton**	**Friel**	**Collier**	**L.Wye**	**Mulvaney**	**24**
Batty	**Mitchell**	**Cowler•**	**Pratt**	**Baron**	**S.Wye**	**Brown†**	**Parr**	**Milton**	**Friel**	**Collier**	**L.Wye**	**Smith**	**25**
Batty	Mitchell	L.Wye	Pratt	Baron	S.Wye	Brown	Biggins	Milton	Friel	Collier	Parr	Smith	26
Batty	Mitchell•	Cowler	Pratt	Baron	S.Wye	Brown	Biggins	Milton	Friel	Collier†	L.Wye	Parr	27
Batty	**Mitchell**	**Cowler**	**Pratt**	**Baron**	**S.Wye**	**Brown**	**Biggins**	**Milton**	**Friel**	**Collier**	**Parr**	**L.Wye**	**28**
Batty	**Parker**	**Cowler**	**Pratt**	**Baron**	**S.Wye**	**Parr**	**Biggins**	**Milton**	**Friel•**	**L.Wye**	**Brown**	**Smith**	**29**
Batty	**Mitchell**	**Cowler**	**Pratt**	**Baron**	**S.Wye†**	**Brown**	**Biggins**	**Milton**	**Friel**	**Collier**	**L.Wye**	**Parr**	**30**
Batty	**Mitchell**	**Cowler**	**Pratt**	**Baron**	**S.Wye**	**Brown**	**Biggins**	**Milton**	**Friel**	**Collier**	**L.Wye**	**Parr**	**31**
Batty	Mitchell	Cowler	Pratt	Baron	S.Wye	Brown	Biggins	Milton	Friel	Collier	L.Wye	Parr	32
Read	Parr•	Russell	Pratt	Baron	S.Wye	Brown	Biggins	Smith†	Friel	L.Wye	Collier	Milton	33
Batty	Mitchell	Cowler	Pratt	Baron	L.Wye	Brown	Biggins	Milton	Friel•	Lynch	Parr	Collier	34
Batty	**Mitchell**	**Cowler**	**Russell**	**Baron**	**S.Wye**	**Brown**	**Biggins**	**Milton**	**Friel**	**L.Wye**	**Collier**	**Parr**	**35**
Batty	**Mitchell**	**Cowler**	**Russell**	**Baron**	**S.Wye**	**Brown**	**Biggins**	**Milton**	**Friel**	**L.Wye•**	**Collier**	**Parr**	**36**
Batty	Mitchell	Cowler	Pratt	Baron	S.Wye	Brown	Biggins•	Lynch	Friel	Collier	Milton	L.Wye	37
Batty	**Mitchell**	**Cowler**	**Pratt**	**Baron**	**S.Wye**	**Brown**	**L.Wye•**	**Milton**	**Friel**	**Lynch**	**Collier**	**Parr**	**38**
Batty	Mitchell	Cowler	Pratt	Baron	S.Wye	Brown	Parr	Milton•	Friel†	Collier	Lynch	McPherson	39
Batty	Mitchell•	Cowler	Pratt	Baron	S.Wye	Brown	Parr	Milton	Friel	Collier†	Lynch	McPherson	40
Batty	Parr	Cowler	Pratt	Baron	S.Wye	Brown	Biggins	Milton	Devine	L.Wye	Friel	McPherson	41
Batty	**Parr**	**Cowler**	**Pratt**	**Baron**	**S.Wye**	**Brown**	**Biggins**	**Milton**	**Devine**	**L.Wye**	**Collier**	**Friel**	**42**
Batty	Parr	Cowler†	Pratt	Baron	S.Wye	Brown	Biggins	Milton	Friel	Collier	Mitchell	Russell	43
Batty	**Parr**	**L.Wye**	**Pratt**	**Baron**	**S.Wye**	**Brown**	**Biggins**	**Milton**	**Friel**	**Collier•**	**Russell**	**Mitchell**	**44**
Batty	Mitchell	Cowler	Pratt	Baron	S.Wye	Brown	Parr	Milton	Devine	L.Wye	Friel	Biggins	45
Batty	**Russell**	**L.Wye**	**Pratt**	**Baron**	**S.Wye**	**Brown**	**Biggins•**	**Devine†**	**Friel**	**Parr**	**Mitchell**	**Milton**	**46**
Batty	Mitchell	Cowler	Pratt	Baron	S.Wye	Brown†	Parr	Milton	Friel	L.Wye	Devine	Biggins	47
Batty	Mitchell	Cowler	Pratt	Baron	S.Wye	Parr	Biggins	Vines	Friel•	L.Wye	Milton	Devine	48
Batty	Mitchell	Cowler	Pratt	Baron	S.Wye	Parr	Biggins†	Vines•	Friel	L.Wye	Milton	Brown	49
Batty	Mitchell	Cowler	Pratt	Baron	S.Wye	Parr	Biggins†	Vines	Friel	L.Wye•	Milton	Collier	50
Batty	**Mitchell**	**Cowler**	**Pratt**	**Baron**	**S.Wye**	**Brown**	**Parr**	**Milton**	**Friel•**	**L.Wye**	**Biggins**	**Collier**	**51**
Batty	Mitchell	Cowler	Pratt	Baron	S.Wye	Brown	Parr†	Vines	Friel•	L.Wye	Milton	Biggins	52
Batty	Mitchell	Cowler	Pratt	Baron	S.Wye	Brown	Parr	Vines	Friel	L.Wye	Milton	Biggins	53
Batty	Mitchell	Cowler	Pratt	Baron	Parr	Brown	Biggins	Vines	Friel•	L.Wye†	Milton	Collier	54
Batty	Mitchell	Cowler	Pratt	Baron	Parr	Brown†	Biggins	Vines	Friel	L.Wye	Milton	Collier	55
Batty	Mitchell	Cowler	Pratt	Baron	Parr	Brown	Biggins†	Vines•	Milton	L.Wye	Friel	Paris	56
Batty	Mitchell	Cowler	Pratt	Baron	S.Wye	Parr	Brown•	Milton†	Friel	L.Wye	Biggins	Vines	57
Batty	Mitchell	Cowler	Pratt	Baron	S.Wye	Parr•	Biggins†	Vines	Friel	L.Wye	Brown	Milton	58
Batty	Parker	Mitchell	Russell	Baron	S.Wye	Brown	Parr	Biggins	Cockram•	Milton†	Vines	Friel	59
Batty	**Mitchell†**	**L.Wye**	**Russell**	**Baron**	**S.Wye**	**Brown**	**Parr**	**Biggins**	**Friel**	**Cockram•**	**Milton**	**Parker**	**60**

Woking

GEOFF CHAPPLE

The 87 supporters who witnessed Woking's 1-0 victory over Clapton on 29th September 1984 probably had little idea that the game would become a landmark in the history of the club. Not because it was the first game of the season that didn't end in defeat, but because it was the first match fir the new manager Geoff Chapple.

Chapple joined Aldershot from school but did not play first team football. He played for Woking in the 1970's and also had a spell with Guildford City. He broke a leg whilst playing for Windsor & Eton in 1980 and then became manager of that club before moving to Kingfield in 1984. The game referred to above was in Division One of the Isthmian League and ended a run of seven consecutive defeats since the first game of the season. Even Chapple was unable to prevent relegation that season and for the first time in their history Woking played Division Two football.

Chapple, however, used the time to build a firm foundation which was to produce arguably one of the best ever Isthmian League sides. Promotion to Division One did not come until the 86/87 season when the club won the title scoring 110 goals in the process. The Cards eventually re-claimed their place in the Premier Division in 1990 and just two seasons later the club takes it's place in the top level of non-league football.

Geoff Chapple's 8 year reign as manager has now been rewarded with a full time contract as he prepares for the clubs hardest challenge. That September day in 1984 saw the start of the Chapple revolution, who is to say where it will end?

Woking players leave the Kingfield pitch after clinching the Diadora title. Photo - Eric Marsh.

Programme details:
    28 pages for 70p
    Editors - Mike Deavin &
        Paul Tuckey
Any other club publications:

Local Newspapers:
    Woking News/Mail
    Surrey Advertiser
    Woking Herald

Local Radio Stations:
    County Sound

WOKING - PLAYING SQUAD 1992-93

Player	Honours	Birthplace and date	Transfer Fees	Previous Clubs
GOALKEEPERS				
Laurence Batty	Diadora Lge	London 15/2/64		Maidenhead Utd, Farense(Port), Fulham, Brentford
DEFENDERS				
Lloyd Wye	Diadora Lge			Southampton(Sch)
Andy Clement	WY	Cardiff 12/11/67		Wimbledon, Woking, Plymouth Argyle
Denis Parker			£10,000	Rainham, Redbridge F, Barking, Bishop's Stortford
Wayne Stemp		Epsom 9/9/70		Brighton
Bradley Pratt	Diadora Lge			Camberley, Wycombe, Bracknell, Egham, Farnborough, North Shore(NZ), Farnborough
Kevan Brown		Andover 2/1/66		Southampton, Brighton, Aldershot, Portsmouth
Richard Nugent	GMVC	Birmingham 20/3/64		Hitchin, Vauxhall M, Stevenage, Barnet, Royston, St Albans, Barnet
Mark Fleming		Hammersmith 11/8/69		Queens Park Rangers, Brentford, Farnborough
Trevor Baron	Diadora Lge			Marlow, Burnham, Chertsey, Windsor & Eton, Slough, Windsor & Eton
MIDFIELD				
Shane Wye	Diadora Lge			Woking, Chertsey, Hayes, Chertsey
Derek Brown	Diadora Lge			Wembley, Crystal Palace, Hendon, Wembley, Hendon
Mark Biggins	Diadora Lge			Hampton, Hanwell, Feltham, Maidenhead, St Albans City, Windsor & Eton
Spencer Paris				Maidstone Utd
FORWARDS				
George Friel	Diadora Lge	Reading 11/10/70		Reading
Steve Milton	Diadora Lge	London 13/4/63	£15,000	West Ham, Croydon, Whyteleafe, Fulham
Tim Buzaglo				Weysiders
Robbie Carroll		Perivale 15/2/68		Southampton, Gosport Borough, Brentford, Fareham, Yeovil
Trevor Senior	Div 3	Dorchester 28/11/61		Dorchester, Portsmouth, Reading, Watford, Middlesbrough, Reading

Departures during season:
Ricky Walkes (Carshalton), Mark Smith (Hitchin), Paul Mulvaney (Cove), Lance Pedlar (Harrow Boro), Paul Barrowcliff (Kingstonian), Andy Parr (Sutton Utd), Adie Cowler & Andy Russell (Kingstonian), Tim Read (Aldershot T-Loan), Nicky Collier, Stewart Mitchell & Andy Perry (Released).

Players who joined on loan during season:
Gavin McPherson, Jonathan Hunt & Tony Lynch (Barnet), Sean Devine (Millwall), Christian White (Southampton), Allan Cockram (Reading).

Woking

Ground address and Tel. No.: Kingfield Stadium, Woking GU22 9AA (0483 772470/722208)
Simple ground directions: M25 exit 10 or 11 and follow signs for Woking, then Kingfield. 1.5 miles from Woking (BR)
Official capacity: 6,000   **Seating:** 650   **Covered accommodation:** 1,500
Floodlights: Yes
Record attendance: 6,000 v Swansea City, FA Cup 2nd Rd replay 78-79
Social facilities available: Clubhouse: Members bar & separate function hall   **Steward:** Clive Norman

---

Sponsored by: **TELFORD UNITED**   **Nickname:**

Previous leagues: West Surrey 1895-97, Isthmian
Club colours: Red/white/white   **Change colours:** All yellow (blue trim)
Midweek home matches: Tuesday   **Club metal badges:** Yes
Club programme: 28 pages 70p   **Editor:** Mike Deavin
Local Newspapers: Woking News-Mail, Surrey Advertiser, Woking Herald   **Local Radio Station:** County Sound
Record transfer fee paid: £15,000 for Steve Milton (Fulham)
Record transfer fee received: £2,500 for Tony Field (Dulwich)
Best F.A. Cup seson: 4th Rd 90-91 (lost 0-1 at Everton), 2nd Rd 1978-79, 89-90, 3rd Rd 1991-92, 1st Rd on 8 other occasions; 07-08, 26-27, 28-29, 58-59, 68-69, 78-79, 86-87, 88-89
League clubs defeated in F.A. Cup: West Bromwich Albion 90-91
Top scorer 91-92: George Friel 37   **Captain 91-92:** Adie Cowler   **P.o.Y. 91-92:** Laurence Batty
Past players who have progressed to the Football League: Ray Elliott (M'wall 1946), Charlie Mortimore (A'shot 1949), Robert Edwards (C'sea 1951), Ron Newman (Portsmouth 1955), Mervyn Gill (Southampton 1956), John Mortimore (C'sea 1957), Reg Stratton (Fulham 1959), George Harris (N'port 1961), Norman Cashmore (A'shot 1963), Alan Morton (c. Palace 1967), William Holmes (M'wall 1970), Richard Forbes (Exeter 1979)
Club honours: FA Amateur Cup 57-58, Isthmian Lg R-up 56-57 (Lg (AC Delco) Cup 90-91, Div. 1 R-up 89-90, Div. 2 South 86-87, Reserve Secion (2)), West Surrey Lg (4), London Senior Cup R-up 82-83, Surrey Cup 12-13, 26-27, 55-56, 56-57, 71-72, 90-91, Surrey Senior Shield (9), Surrey Premier Cup (2), Surrey Invitation Cup 66-67, Surrey Intermediate Cup (2), Channel Islands Victory Cup (2), Suburban Lg (2) (Lg Cup (2)), Diadora Premier Div. 91-92, Isthmian Charity Shield 91-92.

WYCOMBE WANDERERS

Formed: 1884

Patron:
J Adams

Chairman:
I L Beeks

President:
M E Seymour

Directors:
G Coc, A Parry,
G F Peart, G Richards,
A Thibault

Secretary:
John Goldsworthy

Manager:
Martin O'Neill

Asst Manager:
John Reardon

Physiotherapist:
David Jones

Management Committee:
W Cleere, R Hart,
R Holt, D Sutton,
A King, R Saunders,
R Schofield, Mrs T
Schofield

So Close - Yet So Far

A marvellous second season at the impressive Adams Park but one which ended in extreme disappointment at losing out on the Championship (and the coveted place in the Football League) on goal difference to the full-timers of Colchester United. The club's 94 points tally and 30 victories were both Vauxhall Conference records, but any chance of a 'backdoor' entry into the new Third Division was dashed by the League's refusal to consider a replacement for Aldershot.

The team justified their close season favourites tag by winning the first seven league outings in style. During that run the Championship Shield was acquired by defeating Barnet at Adams Park.

The defence, built around skipper Glyn Creaser and new recruits Paul Hyde and Jason Cousins, was generally sound, conceding only 35 goals. Up front, last season's hero Mark West was sadly out of touch, and all but 3 of top scorer Keith Scott's 18 league goals came in the last 9 weeks of the season. Goalscoring options were greatly increased by the new year signings of prolific marksman Kim Casey, the long sought after Steve Thompson and Dennis Greene, who finished with 10 goals from 11 starts including four at Altrincham on April 11th. After the 1-0 defeat at Yeovil on March 7th, the team trailed Colchester by 11 points, but 12 victories and 1 draw in the last 14 fixtures ensured the nail-biting climax to the season.

Although Kettering inflicted an early exit from the FA Cup and Witton Albion dashed hopes of repeating the FA Trophy success of 1991, further cup glory was found in the Bob Lord Trophy, won on aggregate over Runcorn.

The Buckinghamshire public turned out in force to support their heroes - the average home Conference attendance was 3,606 with a ground record of 6,035 set on the last day of the season. Those fans will be optimistic that in 1992/93 the Chairboys will go one better and claim their deserved place in the Football League.

Adrian Wood

Wycombe Wanderers 1991/92. Back Row (L-R): Jason Cousins, Dave Carroll, Paul Hyde, Keith Scott, Trevor Roffey, Simon Stapleton. Middle: Dave Jones (physio), Geoff Cooper, Keith Ryan, Matt Crossley, Andy Kerr, Simon Hutchinson, Steve Thompson, Steve Guppy, Paul Franklin (coach). Front: John Reardon (asst. manager), Kim Casey, Mark West, Gary Smith, Glyn Creaser, Martin O'Neill (manager), Dennis Greene, Ty Gooden, Gavin Covington, John Deakin.

Wycombe Wanderers

GM Vauxhall Conference: 2nd. **FA Cup: 4th Qualifying Round.** **FA Trophy: Quarter Final.**

Match No.	Date	Competition	Venue H/A	Opponents	Result	H/T	Pos.	Goalscorers (Times if known)	Attendance
1	Aug 17	GMVC	H	Gateshead	W 2-1	1-0	1	West 11; Carroll 58	2603
2	Aug 24	GMVC	A	Witton Albion	W 2-1	1-0	1	Guppy 31; Nuttell 80	1242
3	Aug 26	GMVC	H	Yeovil	W 1-0	0-0	1	Nuttell 49	3360
4	Aug 31	GMVC	H	Altrincham	W 4-2	2-1	1	Nuttell 5,48,88; West 45	3245
5	Sep 4	GMVC	A	Welling Utd	W 3-1	1-0	1	Guppy 23; West 55,63	1337
6	Sep 7	GMVC	A	Stafford Rangers	W 2-0	2-0	1	West 44 (pen), 48	1381
7	**Sep 10**	**Champ. Shield**	**H**	**Barnet**	**W 1-0**	**0-0**		**West 57 (pen)**	**3461**
8	Sep 17	GMVC	A	Merthyr Tydfil	W 2-1	1-0	1	Ryan 40; Nuttell 84	1088
9	Sep 21	GMVC	H	Macclesfield	L 0-1	0-0	1		3821
10	Sep 28	GMVC	H	Colchester	L 1-2	0-0	1	Guppy 56	5184
11	Oct 5	GMVC	A	Runcorn	W 2-1	1-0	1	Scott 35; Guppy 47	951
12	Oct 12	GMVC	H	Telford Utd	W 6-1	1-2	2	Guppy 36; Smith 47; West 49(p),90; Kerr 56; Hutchinson 75	4283
13	**Oct 15**	**BLT 2**	**A**	**Merthyr Tydfil**	**W 3-1**	**2-0**		**Crossley 15; Hutchinson 23; Gooden 73**	**526**
14	Oct 19	GMVC	A	Boston Utd	D 2-2	1-0	2	Stapleton 31, 64	1706
15	Oct 26	GMVC	A	Kidderminster	L 0-1	0-1	2		2037
16	Nov 2	GMVC	H	Redbridge Forest	W 1-0	1-0	3	Cousins 20	2285
17	Nov 9	GMVC	H	Merthyr Tydfil	W 4-0	2-0	2	Carroll 9; Smith 31; Kerr 62; Hutchinson 65	3339
18	**Nov 16**	**FAC 1**	**A**	**Kettering**	**D 1-1**	**0-0**		**Carroll 63**	**3317**
19	Nov 23	GMVC	A	Barrow	W 1-0	1-0	2	Scott 6	1438
20	**Nov 27**	**FAC 1R**	**H**	**Kettering**	**L 0-2**	**0-0**			**5299**
21	Nov 30	GMVC	H	Cheltenham	D 2-2	1-1	2	Scott 38; Hutchinson 60	3060
22	Dec 7	GMVC	A	Colchester	L 0-3	0-1	2		5083
23	**Dec 16**	**BLT 3**	**A**	**Colchester**	**W 6-2**	**1-1**		**West 28,89; Scott 51; Hutchinson 62,66; Creaser 76**	**919**
24	Dec 21	GMVC	H	Runcorn	W 1-0	0-0	2	Hutchinson 62	2688
25	Dec 26	GMVC	H	Slough	W 1-0	0-0	2	Guppy 58	3703
26	Jan 1	GMVC	H	Slough	W 3-0	1-0	2	Crossley 9; West 51 (pen); Guppy 53	5162
27	Jan 4	GMVC	A	Bath City	D 1-1	0-0	2	Carroll 58	1386
28	**Jan 11**	**FAT 1**	**H**	**Salisbury**	**W 2-0**	**1-0**		**Carroll 40; Scott 61**	**2917**
29	**Jan 15**	**B&B**	**H**	**Reading**	**L 1-2**	**1-0**		**o.g.**	**461**
30	Jan 17	GMVC	A	Kidderminster	W 2-0	1-0	2	Creaser 11; o.g. 86	3913
31	**Feb 1**	**FAT 2**	**H**	**Woking**	**W 1-0**	**1-0**		**Casey 28**	**5801**
32	Feb 4	GMVC	A	Cheltenham	L 1-2	1-1	2	Stapleton 6	1320
33	Feb 8	GMVC	A	Telford Utd	L 0-1	0-0	2		1520
34	**Feb 11**	**BLT SF1**	**A**	**Yeovil**	**D 0-0**	**0-0**			**1816**
35	Feb 15	GMVC	A	Northwich Victoria	W 1-0	0-0	2	Casey 67	1043
36	**Feb 18**	**BLT SF2**	**H**	**Yeovil**	**W 2-0**	**0-0**		**Creaser 69; Greene 89**	**1883**
37	**Feb 23**	**FAT 3**	**A**	**Bath City**	**D 1-1**	**1-0**		**Carroll 18**	**2899**
38	**Feb 25**	**FAT 3R**	**H**	**Bath City**	**W 2-0**	**1-0**		**Carroll 35; Casey 68**	**3542**
39	Feb 29	GMVC	H	Barrow	W 3-2	1-1	2	Scott 14,74; Creaser 65	3699
40	Mar 7	GMVC	A	Yeovil	L 0-1	0-1	2		2901
41	Mar 10	GMVC	H	Boston Utd	W 2-1	1-1	2	Greene 5,54	2580
42	**Mar 14**	**FAT 4**	**H**	**Witton Albion**	**L 1-2**	**0-0**		**West 90 (pen)**	**4636**
43	Mar 18	GMVC	H	Farnborough	W 2-1	2-0	2	Creaser 29; Scott 41	2275
44	Mar 21	GMVC	A	Stafford Rangers	W 3-0	1-0	2	Scott 33,89 (2 pens); Thompson 56	3202
45	Mar 24	GMVC	A	Northwich Victoria	W 2-0	1-0	2	Greene 31; Kerr 75	2750
46	Mar 28	GMVC	A	Kettering	W 1-0	0-0	2	o.g. 72	4069
47	**Mar 31**	**BLT F1**	**A**	**Runcorn**	**L 0-1**	**0-1**			**853**
48	Apr 4	GMVC	A	Farnborough	W 3-1	2-1	2	Greene 2; Scott 3; Stapleton 68	2236
49	**Apr 7**	**BLT F2**	**H**	**Runcorn**	**W 2-0**	**1-0**		**Guppy 16; Carroll 74**	**2519**
50	Apr 11	GMVC	A	Altrincham	W 4-0	3-0	2	Greene 3,20,43,73	1166
51	Apr 14	GMVC	H	Macclesfield	L 1-3	1-1	2	Scott 39	693
52	Apr 18	GMVC	H	Welling Utd	W 4-0	1-0	2	Scott 15,90; Greene 69; Kerr 88	3910
53	Apr 20	GMVC	H	Bath City	W 1-0	0-0	2	Scott 72	4263
54	Apr 22	GMVC	A	Kettering	D 1-1	0-1	2	Casey 46	2918
55	Apr 25	GMVC	A	Gateshead	W 3-2	1-1	2	Scott 39 (pen), 88; Creaser 56	912
56	Apr 30	GMVC	H	Redbridge Forest	W 5-0	3-0	2	Scott 16,(pen),39; Casey 42,47; Carroll 46	2891
57	May 2	GMVC	H	Witton Albion	W 4-0	2-0	2	Casey 13; Stapleton 44; Scott 48; Greene 83	6035

Best Home League Attendance: 6035 v Witton Albion 2.5.92. **Lowest: 2275 v Farnborough 18.3.92** **Average Home Attendance: 3606**
Compared with 1990/91 + 806 + 29%

Goalscorers League (84): Scott 18; Greene 10; West 9; Guppy 7; Nuttell 6; Casey, Stapleton 5; Carrol, Creaser, Hutchinson, Kerr 4; Smith 2; Cousins, Crossley, Ryan, Thompson 1; Oppentents 2. **FA Trophy (7):** Carroll 3; Casey 2; Scott, West 1. **FA Cup (1):** Carroll 1. **Bob Lord Trophy (13):** Hutchinson 3; Creaser, Sest 2; Crossley, Gooden, Greene, Guppy, Scott 1; Opponents 1. **County Cup (1):** Opponents 1. **Championship Shield (1):** West 1.

Wycombe Wanderers

1	2	3	4	5	6	7	8	9	10	11	12	14	Match No.
Hyde	Cousins	Walford	Kerr	Creaser	Smith	Carroll	Stapleton	West	Nuttell	Guppy†	Hutchinson	Gooden	1
Hyde	Cousins	Walford	Kerr	Creaser	Smith	Carroll•	Stapleton	West	Nuttell	Guppy	Hutchinson	Gooden	2
Hyde	Cousins	Walford	Kerr	Creaser	Smith	Carroll	Stapleton	West	Nuttell	Guppy	Hutchinson	Gooden	3
Hyde	Cousins	Walford	Kerr	Creaser	Smith•	Carroll	Stapleton	West	Nuttell	Guppy	Hutchinson	Gooden	4
Hyde	Cousins	Walford	Kerr	Creaser	Smith	Carroll•	Stapleton†	West	Nuttell	Guppy†	Hutchinson	Gooden	5
Hyde	Cousins	Walford	Kerr	Creaser	Smith	Carroll	Ryan	West	Nuttell	Guppy	Hutchinson	Gooden	6
Hyde	**Cousins**	**Walford†**	**Kerr**	**Creaser**	**Smith**	**Carroll•**	**Ryan**	**West**	**Nuttell**	**Guppy**	**Hutchinson**	**Gooden**	**7**
Hyde	Cousins	Covington•	Kerr	Creaser	Smith	Carroll	Ryan	West	Nuttell	Guppy	Crossley	Gooden	8
Hyde	Cousins	Crossley†	Kerr	Creaser	Smith•	Carroll	Ryan	West	Nuttell	Guppy	Hutchinson	Gooden	9
Hyde	Cousins	Crossley†	Kerr	Creaser	Smith	Carroll	Stapleton•	West†	Nuttell	Guppy	Hutchinson	Scott	10
Hyde	Crossley	Covington•	Kerr	Creaser	Smith	Carroll	Stapleton	West	Scott	Guppy	Hutchinson	Gooden	11
Hyde	Cousins†	Crossley	Kerr	Creaser	Smith	Carroll	Stapleton•	West	Scott	Guppy	Hutchinson	Gooden	12
Hyde	**Crossley**	**Covington**	**Kerr**	**Creaser**	**Deakin**	**Hutchinson**	**Stapleton**	**West**	**Scott**	**Gooden**	**Carroll**	**Smith**	**13**
Hyde	Cousins	Crossley•	Kerr	Creaser	Smith	Carroll	Stapleton	West	Scott	Guppy	Hutchinson	Gooden	14
Hyde	Cousins	Crossley•	Kerr	Creaser	Smith	Carroll†	Stapleton	West	Scott	Guppy	Hutchinson	Gooden	15
Hyde	Cousins	Stapleton	Kerr	Creaser	Smith	Hutchinson	Deakin	West	Scott	Gooden	Guppy	Nuttell	16
Hyde	Cousins	Stapleton	Kerr†	Creaser	Smith	Hutchinson	Deakin	Carroll	Scott•	Guppy	Nuttell	Gooden	17
Hyde	**Cousins**	**Stapleton**	**Crossley**	**Creaser**	**Smith**	**Hutchinson**	**Deakin**	**Carroll**	**Scott**	**Guppy**	**Nuttell**	**West**	**18**
Hyde	Cousins	Stapleton	Crossley	Creaser	Smith	Hutchinson•	Deakin	Carroll	Scott•	Guppy	West	Gooden	19
Hyde	**Cousins**	**Stapleton**	**Crossley**	**Creaser**	**Smith•**	**Carroll**	**Deakin**	**West**	**Scott**	**Guppy**	**Hutchinson**	**Gooden**	**20**
Hyde	Cousins	Cooper	Crossley	Creaser	Stapleton	Hutchinson	Deakin•	Carroll	Scott	Guppy	Smith	West	21
Hyde	Cousins•	Stapleton	Crossley	Creaser	Smith	Hutchinson	Carroll	West	Scott†	Guppy	Cooper	Deakin	22
Hyde	**Cousins†**	**Stapleton**	**Crossley**	**Creaser**	**Smith**	**Hutchinson**	**Carroll**	**West**	**Scott•**	**Guppy**	**Deakin**	**Cooper**	**23**
Hyde	Cousins	Stapleton	Crossley	Creaser	Smith	Hutchinson	Carroll	West	Scott	Guppy	Deakin	Cooper	24
Hyde	Cousins	Stapleton	Crossley	Creaser	Smith	Hutchinson	Carroll	West	Scott	Guppy	Deakin	Cooper	25
Hyde	Cousins	Stapleton	Crossley	Creaser	Smith†	Hutchinson	Carroll•	West	Scott	Guppy	Deakin	Cooper	26
Hyde	Cousins	Stapleton	Crossley	Creaser	Smith†	Hutchinson	Carroll	West	Scott	Guppy	Ryan	Deakin	27
Hyde	**Cousins**	**Covington**	**Crossley**	**Creaser**	**Smith†**	**Hutchinson**	**Stapleton**	**Carroll•**	**Scott**	**Guppy**	**Deakin**	**Cooper**	**28**
Roffey	Spalding	Sciaraffa†	Kerr	Tilly	Myatt	Chalwin•	Ryan	Norman	Deakin	Gooden	Pool	Kelloway	29
Hyde	Cousins	Covington	Crossley	Creaser	Carroll•	Hutchinson	Casey	Stapleton	Scott	Guppy	Ryan†	Deakin	30
Hyde	**Cousins**	**Crossley**	**Kerr**	**Creaser**	**Carroll**	**Hutchinson•**	**Casey**	**Stapleton**	**Scott**	**Guppy**	**Ryan**	**Deakin**	**31**
Hyde	Cousins	Crossley	Kerr	Creaser	Carroll†	Hutchinson	Casey	Stapleton	Scott•	Guppy	Ryan	Deakin	32
Hyde	Cousins	Crossley†	Kerr	Creaser	Carroll•	Hutchinson	Casey	Stapleton	Ryan	Guppy	West	Cooper	33
Hyde	**Stapleton**	**Cooper**	**Kerr**	**Creaser**	**Blackler†**	**Guppy**	**Deakin**	**West**	**Scott**	**Gooden•**	**Hutchinson**	**Ryal**	**34**
Hyde	Stapleton	Cooper	Kerr	Creaser	Smith	Deakin	Casey	West	Scott	Guppy	Hutchinson	Muttock	35
Hyde	**Stapleton**	**Cooper**	**Kerr**	**Creaser**	**Muttock†**	**Ryal**	**Deakin**	**West**	**Scott**	**Gooden•**	**Guppy**	**Greene**	**36**
Hyde	**Stapleton**	**Cooper**	**Cousins**	**Creaser**	**Smith**	**Deakin**	**Casey**	**Carroll•**	**Scott**	**Guppy**	**Ryan**	**Norman**	**37**
Hyde	**Stapleton**	**Cooper**	**Cousins**	**Creaser**	**Smith**	**Deakin**	**Casey**	**Carroll•**	**Scott**	**Guppy**	**Ryan**	**Norman**	**38**
Hyde	Cousins	Cooper	Kerr	Creaser	Thompson	Deakin•	Casey	Stapleton	Scott	Guppy	Greene	West	39
Hyde	Cousins	Cooper	Kerr	Creaser	Carroll•	Thompson	Stapleton	Green†	Scott	Guppy	West	Deakin	40
Hyde	Cousins	Johnson	Kerr	Creaser	Carroll	Deakin	Stapleton	Greene	Scott	Guppy	West	Smith	41
Hyde	**Cousins**	**Johnson**	**Kerr**	**Creaser**	**Smith**	**Stapleton**	**Casey**	**Carroll**	**Scott**	**Guppy•**	**West**	**Ryan**	**42**
Hyde	Cousins	Johnson	Kerr	Creaser	Thompson	Stapleton	Ryan	Greene	Scott	Carroll	Casey	Guppy	43
Hyde	Cousins	Johnson	Kerr	Creaser	Thompson	Stapleton	Ryan	Greene	Scott	Carroll	Casey	Guppy	44
Hyde	Cousins	Johnson	Kerr	Creaser	Carroll	Stapleton	Ryan	Greene	Scott	Guppy	Casey	Smith	45
Hyde	Cousins	Johnson	Kerr	Creaser	Thompson	Stapleton	Carroll	Greene•	Scott	Ryan†	Casey	Guppy	46
Hyde	**Cousins**	**Johnson**	**Kerr**	**Creaser**	**Carroll**	**Stapleton**	**Ryan**	**Greene**	**Scott**	**Guppy**	**West**	**Smith**	**47**
Hyde	Cousins	Johnson	Kerr	Creaser	Thompson	Carroll	Stapleton	Greene	Scott	Guppy	Casey	Ryan	48
Hyde	**Cousins**	**Johnson**	**Kerr**	**Creaser**	**Carroll**	**Stapleton**	**Ryan**	**Greene**	**Scott**	**Guppy**	**West**	**Smith**	**49**
Hyde	Cousins	Johnson	Kerr	Creaser	Thompson†	Carroll	Stapleton	Greene	Scott•	Guppy	Casey	Smith	50
Hyde	Cousins	Crossley	Kerr	Creaser	Thompson	Carroll	Stapleton•	Greene	Scott•	Guppy	Casey	Smith	51
Hyde	Cousins	Crossley	Kerr	Creaser	Thompson	Carroll	Stapleton	Greene•	Scott•	Guppy	Casey	Ryan	52
Hyde	Cousins	Crossley	Kerr	Creaser	Thompson	Carroll	Stapleton	Greene•	Scott•	Guppy	Casey	Ryan	53
Hyde	Cousins	Crossley	Kerr	Creaser	Thompson†	Carroll	Stapleton	Casey•	Scott	Guppy	Greene	Ryan	54
Hyde	Cousins	Crossley	Kerr	Creaser	Deakin†	Carroll	Stapleton	Casey	Scott•	Guppy•	Greene	Hutchinson	55
Hyde	Cousins	Crossley	Kerr	Creaser†	Ryan	Carroll	Stapleton	Casey	Scott•	Guppy•	Greene	Hutchinson	56
Hyde	Cousins	Crossley•	Kerr	Creaser	Ryan†	Carroll	Stapleton	Casey	Scott•	Guppy	Greene	Hutchinson	57

• substituted by No. 12. † substituted by No. 14.

League Appearances (max 42): Creaser 42; Hyde 41; Cousins 40; Stapleton 39; Guppy 38+1; Carroll 37; Kerr 34; Scott 32+1; Smith 24+3; Crossley 22+1; West 20+3; Hutchinson 12+12; Greene 11+5; Thompson 11; Ryan 10+3; Casey 9+5; Nuttell 9+1; Deakin 8+5; Johnson 8; Walford 6; Cooper 4+3; Covington 3; Gooden 1+6.
Cup Appearances (max 15): Creaser, Hyde 13; Guppy 12+1; Scott, Stapleton 12; Cousins 11; Smith 10; Carroll, Kerr 9; Deakin 8+2; Crossley 8; West 7+1; Hutchinson 6+3; Ryan 5+5; Cooper 4+1; Gooden 4+1; Casey 4; Greene 2+1; Covington, Johnson, roffey 2; Blackler, Chalwin, Muttock, Myatt, Norman, Nuttell, Sciaraffa, Spalding, Tilly, Walford 1; Kelloway 0+1; Poole 0+1.

Wycombe Wanderers

MARTIN O'NEILL

Born in Kilrea, Northern Ireland, Martin started his career with Derry City before signing for Nottingham Forest in 1971. He enjoyed a fabulous ten years at the City Ground, winning League Championship, European Cup and League Cup winners medals. After leaving Forest, Martin played for Norwich City (two spells), Manchester City and Notts County. He won 64 caps for Northern Ireland, captaining them in the 1982 World Cup in Spain when, against all the odds, they reached the second round.

Martin then turned to management, joining Grantham Town in the Beazer Homes Midland Division and finishing third behind Merthyr Tydfil. After a spell with Shepshed Charterhouse, business committments forced him to quit the game but he returned to become the Wycombe manager in February 1990, leading them to fifth position in his first season in charge and then to second place last season.

Dennis Greene, Wycombe's signing from Chelmsford City, celebrates after scoring one of his four goals against Altrincham at Moss Lane.   Photo: Colin Stevens.

Programme details:
    40 pages for £1.20
    Editor - Adrian Wood

Any other club publications:
    The Adams Family (Fanzine)

Local Newspapers:
    Bucks Free Press
    Wycombe Star
    Bucks Midweek
    Bucks Advertiser

Local Radio Stations:
    Radio 210 (Reading)
    Chiltern Radio

WYCOMBE WANDERERS - PLAYING SQUAD 1992-93

Player	Honours	Birthplace and date	Transfer Fees	Previous Clubs
GOALKEEPERS				
Chuck Moussaddik	Moroccan U-21	Morocco 23/2/70		Spurs, Wimbledon
Paul Hyde	Isthmian Lge BLT, FAXI	Hayes 7/4/63	£10,000	Hillingdon Borough, Hayes
Trevor Roffey		Sutton 22/7/65		Sutton Utd, Tooting & Mitcham, Camberley, Sutton Utd, Slough
DEFENDERS				
Glyn Creaser	FAT, FAX1, CTOY 90-91, BLT	London 1/9/59	£15,000	Wolverton, Northampton T., Kettering, Barnet
Matt Crossley	FAT, BBSC BLT	Basingstoke 18/3/68		Aldershot, Basingstoke, Newbury, Overton Utd
Andy Kerr	FAT, FAXI, BBSC, BLT	West Brom 7/4/66	£3,000	Shrewsbury, Cardiff, Telford
Jason Cousins	BLT FAXI	Hillingdon 4/10/70		Brentford
Peter Johnson		Harrogate 5/10/58		Middlesboro', Newcastle, Doncaster, Darlinton, Crewe, Southend, Gill'ham, P'boro
Steve Walford	EY, FAC	Highgate 5/1/58		Spurs, Arsenal, Norwich, West Ham, Hudderfld, Gillingham, WBA,
MIDFIELD				
Dave Carroll	EY, FAT FAXI, BLT	Paisley 20/9/66	£6,000	Fulham, Wembley, Ruislip Manor
Simon Stapleton	FAT, BBSC, BLT	Oxford 10/12/68		Portsmouth, Bristol Rovers
Steve Thompson	RAF, Comb Serv FAXI	Plymouth 12/1/63		Bristol C, Torquay, Saltash Utd, Slough
Steve Guppy	FAT, BBSC, BLT	Winchester 29/3/69		Southampton
Simon Hutchinson	FAT, ES, BLT	Sheffield 24/9/69	£7,000	Manchester Utd, Eastwood Town
Keith Ryan	FAT BLT	Northampton 25/6/70		Berkhamsted
FORWARDS				
Keith Scott	FAT, BLT	London 10/6/67	£10,000	Hinckley A, Leicester Utd Lincoln
Mark West	ES, ESP VOL, FAT, BLT	Wycombe 12/2/66		West Ham, Reading
Dennis Greene	BLT	Stoke Newington 14/4/65	£15,000	B Stortford, Basildon, Harlow Sawbridgeworth, Ware, Chelmsford
Kim Casey	ES, ESP FAT, FAXI	Birmingham 3/3/61	£9,000	AP Leamington, Gloucester Kidderminster, Cheltenham
Ty Gooden		Canvey Island 23/10/72		Arsenal

Departures during season:
Martin Blackler (Wealdstone), Mick Nuttel (Boston), Steve Whitby (Slough). Gavin Covington (Released), John Deakin (Released), Gary Smith (Released).

Players who joined on loan during season:
Geoff Cooper (Barnet), Jon Muttock (Oxford Utd).

Adams Park, Wycombe Wanderers

Ground address and Tel. No.: Hillbottom Road, Sands, High Wycombe, Bucks HP12 4HJ. Tel: 0494 472100. Ringing the Blues Newsline 0898 446855. Fax No. 0494 27633

Simple ground directions: Ground situated 2½ miles west of town. Leave M40 at Junc. 4 and take Aylesbury road (A4010). Pass over 3 mini-roundabouts and after going down steep hill, turn sharp left at next mini-roundabout into Lane End Road. Turn right at next mini-roundabout into Hillbottom Road. Ground situated at end of Sands Ind. Est. From town centre take A40 west. After 1½ miles turn left into Chapel Lane (after traffic lights). Turn right then right again at double mini-roundabouts into Lane End Road, then as above.

Official capacity: 6,000   **Seating:** 1,267   **Covered accommodation:** 6,000

Cost of seats: £5.00   **Cost of standing:** £4.00   **Family stand:** Block 'A', main stand

Segragation: Yes, away supporters in Woodland Terrace, entrance 3

Record attendance: 15,678 v St Albans 1950 (Loakes Park), 5,695 v Peterborough Utd 1991 (Adams Park)

Social facilities available (Bars, hot & cold food etc.): 'Centre Spot' P.H. (Open 11-3.30, 5-11 every day for public, 2 hrs before and 1 hr after game for members, including visiting supporters holding their own club membership card). 6 Tea Bars, Hot & Cold Food (also open during game). Banqueting/Conference facilities for 8-240 (Vere banquet suite, 240 seated, stage, dance floor, V.P. Lounge, 100 seated)

Car parking: 320

Sponsored by: VERCO   **WYCOMBE WANDERERS**   **Nickname:** Chairboys

---

Previous leagues: Southern, Berks & Bucks Contiguous, Berks & Bucks Senior, Gt Western Suburban, Spartan, Isthmian/V-O-L

Club colours: Camb. & Oxf. blue quarters/Oxf. blue/Camb. & Oxf. blue   **Change colours:** All red

Midweek home matches: Tuesday   **Club metal badges:** Yes

Club programme: 40 pages £1.10

Record transfer fee paid: £28,000 to Barnet for Nicky Evans (January 1991)

Record transfer fee received: £25,000 from Barnet for Nicky Evans (January 1991)

Past players who have progressed to the Football League: K. Abis, S. Hyde, R. Rafferty, G. Truett, J. Tratt, D. Edwards, L. Worley, P. Fuschillo, A. Gane, M. Mellows, P. Suddaby, V. Busby, J. Delaney, K. Swain, S. Perrin, I. Pearson, G. Bressington, M. Carmichael

Club honours: Isthmian League Champions (x7); F.A. Amateur Cup - Winners, Runners-up; Berks & Bucks Senior Cup (x23); FA Cup 3rd Round (x2); FA Trophy Winners; V.O.L. Premier Div Champions; Capital League President's Cup; GMVC Runners-up, Bob Lord Trophy Winners.

YEOVIL TOWN

Formed: 1895

President:
N Burfield MBE

Chairman:
Bryan Moore

Vice Chairman:
J A Houghton

Directors:
M P Spearpoint
A K Williams
G R Smith
J E Clements
C Robinson

Gen. Manager/Secretary:
Roger Brinsford

Commercial Manager:
Alan Skirton

Player-Manager:
Steve Rutter

Coach:
Paul Rodgers

Physiotherapist:
Tony Farmer

Groundsman:
Gordon Prosser

Twenty-one Cup ties enjoyed

Much has been written about the desperate financial situation at Yeovil, but whatever the mistakes of the past have been, the club is now battling positively to survive with some style.

Steve Rutter inherited a squad that he could not strengthen for financial reasons. In this light he deserves the greatest respect for the club finally finishing in a safe Vauxhall Conference position and for a really good cup season where twenty one ties were contested.

The quarter final of the FA Trophy, the Third Round, and Walsall's scalp, in the FA Cup, a Somerset Senior Cup Final against Bristol Rovers and a two-legged semi-final in the Bob Lord Trophy against Wycombe Wanderers all kept the season interesting and financially rewarding.

Mickey Spencer scored thirty goals and along with Mark Shail, new goalkeeper David Coles, Steve Harrower and the player-manager, enjoyed impressive seasons.

The clubs' fund raising and the loyal local support has never been better and while still accepting there is a long way to go before the club can put in a challenge fror the serious honours that the ground and support deserves, everyone at Yeovil Town will be looking for another season with the spirit as good as it was last year, both on and off the field.

Tony Williams

Yeovil Town F.C. 1991-92. Back Row (L-R): Steve Harrower, Peter Conning, Nigel Stevenson, Mark Hervin, Mark Shail, David Fry, Matt Carr, Nathan Bush (YTS), Mark Boulton, Howard Pritchard, Richard Cooper. Middle (L-R): John Flatters (youth physio), Mickey Spencer, Brian McDermott, Robbie Carroll, Chris Whalley (Comm Dev Officer), Steve Rutter (Manager), Paul Wilson, Paul Batty, Mike McEvoy, Andy Wallace, Tony Farmer (physio). Front (L-R): (all YTS) D. Birrell, M. McPherson, S. Sivell, A. Clothers, T. Oades, P. Dowding, N. Flory. Photo: Tilzey Studios.

Yeovil Town

GM Vauxhall Conference: 15th.   FA Cup: 2nd Round.   FA Trophy: 4th Round.

Match No.	Date	Competition	Venue H/A	Opponents	Result	League H/T	Pos.	Goalscorers (Times if known)	Attendance
1	Aug 17	GMVC	H	Barrow	W 2-0	0-0		Spencer 47; Carroll 78	2573
2	Aug 24	GMVC	A	Altrincham	L 1-2	1-0	10	Carroll 24	937
3	Aug 26	GMVC	A	Wycombe	L 0-1	0-0	13		3360
4	Aug 31	GMVC	H	Gateshead	W 1-0	0-0	6	Pritchard 76	2222
5	Sep 3	BLT 1 (1)	A	Farnsborough	L 2-3	1-2		Spencer 41,89	461
6	Sep 7	GMVC	H	Macclesfield	L 0-1	0-1	11		2110
7	Sep 13	GMVC	A	Colchester	L 0-4	0-1	16		2979
8	Sep 17	BLT 1 (2)	H	Farnborough	W 3-0	2-0		Carroll 3,67; Boulton 85	1473
9	Sep 21	GMVC	A	Telford Utd	L 0-2	0-1	20		2116
10	Sep 28	GMVC	A	Merthyr Tydfil	D 2-2	1-1	18	Carroll 39,67	618
11	Oct 5	GMVC	A	Northwich Victoria	L 0-1	0-1	19		654
12	Oct 12	GMVC	A	Kidderminster	D 1-1	1-1	20	Spencer 15	1305
13	Oct 19	GMVC	H	Kettering	L 0-1	0-1	20		1929
14	Oct 22	BLT 2	H	Welling Utd	W 2-0	2-0		Batty 24 (pen); Spencer 45	1340
15	Oct 26	FAC 4Q	A	Tonbridge	W 2-1	2-1		Spencer 3; Shail 11	1300
16	Oct 30	GMVC	A	Colchester	L 0-1	0-0	20		2385
17	Nov 2	GMVC	A	Farnborough	D 0-0	0-0	20		685
18	Nov 9	GMVC	A	Cheltenham	D 1-1	0-1	22	Rutter 69	1963
19	Nov 16	FAC 1	H	Walsall	D 1-1	0-0		Wilson 59	4635
20	Nov 23	GMVC	A	Boston Utd	W 3-1	0-1	20	Rowlands 84; McDermott 88; Carroll 90	1240
21	Nov 27	FAC 1R	A	Walsall	W 1-0	0-0		Cooper 95	3869
22	Nov 30	GMVC	H	Stafford Rangers	L 0-1	0-0	21		2339
23	Dec 4	GMVC	H	Redbridge Forest	L 0-1	0-0	22		1832
24	Dec 7	FAC 2	A	Woking	L 0-3	0-1			4500
25	Dec 21	GMVC	H	Farnborough	D 2-2	1-1	22	Pritchard 43; Spencer 47	1959
26	Dec 26	GMVC	A	Bath City	L 1-3	1-1	22	Spencer 39	1504
27	Dec 28	GMVC	H	Northwich Victoria	W 2-1	0-0	22	McDermott 61 (pen); Spencer 71	1992
28	Jan 1	GMVC	H	Bath City	D 1-1	1-0	22	Spencer 8	3340
29	Jan 4	GMVC	A	Cheltenham	D 1-1	1-0	22	Wallace 11	912
30	Jan 11	FAT 1	H	Chesham Utd	W 3-1	2-0		Spencer 17,39; McDermott 87 (pen)	1733
31	Jan 18	GMVC	H	Witton Albion	W 2-1	1-0	21	Wallace 10,47	1659
32	Jan 20	BLT 3	A	Kidderminster	W 2-1	0-1		Shail 88; Carroll 110	681
33	Jan 25	GMVC	H	Kidderminster	D 1-1	1-0	22	Spencer 12	2111
34	Feb 1	FAT 2	A	Bromley	W 3-1	2-0		Carroll 10; Spencer 21,90	665
35	Feb 4	GMVC	A	Telford Utd	L 0-1	0-0	22		766
36	Feb 8	GMVC	H	Welling Utd	W 3-0	2-0	20	Spencer 7; McDermott 24,84	2127
37	Feb 11	BLT S/F1	H	Wycombe	D 0-0	0-0			1816
38	Feb 14	GMVC	A	Stafford Rangers	D 0-0	0-0	19		758
39	Feb 18	BLT S/F2	A	Wycombe	W 2-0	0-0			1883
40	Feb 22	FAT 3	H	Kidderminster	W 3-1	2-0		Robinson 14; Carroll 44; McDermott 47 (pen)	2679
41	Feb 29	GMVC	A	Macclesfield	W 2-1	1-0	19	Robinson 6; Spencer 65	701
42	Mar 7	GMVC	H	Wycombe	W 1-0	1-0	17	Spencer 22	2901
43	Mar 10	GMVC	A	Slough	W 4-1	0-0	16	Boulton 47,58; Robinson 85; Spencer 89	584
44	Mar 14	FAT 4	H	Macclesfield	L 1-2	1-0		Wallace 19	4269
45	Mar 21	GMVC	H	Runcorn	L 1-4	1-2	16	Spencer 45	1821
46	Mar 24	GMVC	A	Redbridge Forest	D 0-0	0-0	15		503
47	Mar 28	GMVC	H	Slough	W 1-0	1-0	15	Spencer 22	1763
48	Mar 31	GMVC	A	Witton Albion	L 1-3	0-0	15	Conning 71	783
49	Apr 4	GMVC	A	Runcorn	D 2-2	2-1	15	Carroll 1; Robinson 12	474
50	Apr 7	GMVC	A	Kettering	W 2-0	0-0	18		1257
51	Apr 11	GMVC	A	Gateshead	L 0-1	0-0	18		344
52	Apr 18	GMVC	H	Boston Utd	D 1-1	0-1	18	Wilson 52	1823
53	Apr 20	GMVC	H	Welling Utd	L 0-1	0-0	18		704
54	Apr 25	GMVC	A	Barrow	D 0-0	0-0	18		1281
55	Apr 28	GMVC	H	Merthyr Tydfi	D 1-1	1-0	18	Spencer 44	1587
56	May 2	GMVC	H	Altrincham	W 2-1	1-1	15	Spencer 4,58	1919

Best Home League Attendance: 3340 v Bath City   Lowest: 1587 v Merthyr Tydfil   Best Home Cup Attendance: 4653 v Walsall

Goalscorers League (40): Spencer 16; Carroll 6; McDermott 4; Robinson 3; Wallace 3; Boulton 2; Pritchard 2; Conning 1; Rutter 1; Shail 1; Wilson 1. FA Cup (39): Spencer 14; Carroll 8; McDermott 4; Conning 3; Cooper 2; Wallace 2; Batty, Boulton, Robinson, Shail, Wilson, Opponents 1.

1	2	3	4	5	6	7	8	9	10	11	12	14	Match No.
Fry	Harrower	Ferns	Shail	Rutter	Conning	McDermott	Cooper	Wilson	Spencer	Carroll	Batty	Pritchard	1
Fry	Harrower	Ferns	Shail	Rutter	Conning	McDermott	Cooper	Pritchard•	Spencer	Carroll†	Batty	Boulton	2
Fry	Harrower	Ferns	Shail	Rutter	Batty	McDermott	Cooper	Wilson	Spencer	Conning•	Pritchard	McEvoy	3
Fry	Horrower•	Ferns	Shail	Rutter	Conning	McDermott	Cooper	Wilson	Spencer	Batty	Boulton	Pritchard	4
Fry	**McEvoy•**	**Ferns**	**Shail**	**Harrower**	**Cooper**	**McDermott**	**Batty**	**Wilson**	**Spencer**	**Conning**	**Pritchard**	**Boulton**	5
Fry	Harrower†	Ferns	Shail	Pritchard•	Cooper	McDermott	Batty	Carroll	Spencer	Conning	McEvoy	Boulton	6
Fry	Harrower•	Ferns	Shail	Rutter	Cooper	Carroll	Batty	Pritchard†	Spencer	Conning	McDermott	McEvoy	7
Fry	**Harrower**	**Ferns**	**Shail†**	**Rutter**	**Cooper**	**McEvoy•**	**Conning**	**Pritchard**	**Spencer**	**Carroll**	**Batty**	**Boulton**	8
Fry	Harrower	Ferns	Wallace	Rutter	Cooper†	McEvoy	Conning	Pritchard•	Spencer	Carroll	Batty	Boulton	9
Fry	Harrower•	Ferns	Batty	Rutter	Conning	Cooper	Wallace	Wilson	Spencer	Carroll	McEvoy	Pritchard	10
Fry	Harrower•	Ferns	Shail	Rutter	Cooper	Carroll	Wallace	Wilson	Spencer	Conning†	Batty	Dixon	11
Fry	Harrower	Batty	Shail	Rutter	Cooper	Carroll•	Wallace	Wilson†	Spencer	Conning	McDermott	Dixon	12
Fry	Harrower	Rowbotham	Shail	Rutter	Cooper	Carroll	Batty	McDermott•	Spencer	Conning	Dixon	Boulton	13
Hervin	**Harrower**	**Rowbotham**	**Shail**	**Rutter**	**Cooper**	**Carroll**	**Batty**	**Boulton•**	**Spencer**	**Conning**	**McDermott**	**Dixon**	14
Fry	**Harrower**	**Rowbotham**	**Shail**	**Rutter**	**Cooper**	**McDermott**	**Carroll**	**Wilson**	**Spencer**	**Conning**	**Dixon**	**Boulton**	15
Fry	Harrower	Rowbotham	Shail	Batty	Cooper	Carroll	Wallace	Rowland	Spencer	Conning	McDermott	Wilson	16
Hervin	Harrower	Rowbotham	Shail	Rutter	Batty	Carroll	Wallace	Wilson•	Rowland	Conning	Spencer	McDermott	17
Hervin	Harrower	Rowbotham	Shail	Rutter	Batty	Spencer	Wallace	Wilson	Rowland	Conning•	McDermott	Cooper	18
Hervin	**Harrower**	**Rowbotham**	**Shail**	**Rutter•**	**Batty**	**McDermott**	**Wallace**	**Wilson**	**Spencer**	**Conning**	**Cooper**	**Pritchard**	19
Hervin	Harrower	Rowbotham•	Shail	Rutter	Batty	Spencer	Wallace	Wilson	Rowland†	Conning	McDermott	Carroll	20
Fry	Harrower	Cooper	Shail	Rutter•	Batty	McDermott	Wallace	Wilson	Spencer	Conning	Henderson	McEvoy	21
Hervin	Harrower	Batty	Shail	Rutter	Spencer	McDermott	Wallace	Wilson•	Henderson†	Conning	Cooper	Pritchard	22
Hervin	**Harrower**	**Batty**	**Shail**	**Rutter**	**Carroll•**	**McDermott**	**Wallace**	**Wilson**	**Spencer**	**Conning†**	**Pritchard**	**Henderson**	24
Hervin	Harrower	McEvoy	Shail	Rutter	Pritchard•	McDermott	Wallace	Henderson	Spencer	Conning	Carroll	Sivell	25
Hervin	Harrower	Batty	Shail	Rutter	Cooper	McDermott†	Wallace	Wilson•	Spencer	Conning	Carroll	Henderson	26
Coles	McEvoy	Harrower	Shail	Rutter	Cooper	McDermott	Wallace	Wilson	Spencer	Carroll	Henderson	Batty	27
Coles	McEvoy•	Harrower	Shail	Rutter	Cooper	McDermott	Wallace	Wilson	Spencer	Carroll	Conning	Batty	28
Coles	McEvoy†	Harrower	Shail	Rutter	Cooper•	McDermott	Wallace	Wilson	Spencer	Conning	Batty	Ferns	29
Coles	**Harrower**	**Ferns**	**Shail**	**Rutter**	**Cooper•**	**McDermott**	**Wallace**	**Wilson**	**Spencer**	**Batty**	**Conning**	**McEvoy**	30
Coles	Harrower	Ferns	Shail	Rutter•	Cooper	McDermott	Wallace	Wilson	Spencer	Batty	Conning	Carroll	31
Coles	**Harrower**	**Batty**	**Shail**	**Ferns**	**Cooper•**	**McDermott•**	**Conning**	**Wilson**	**Spencer**	**McEvoy**	**Boulton**	**Carroll**	32
Coles	Harrower	Batty	McEvoy	Rutter	Cooper	McDermott•	Wallace	Wilson	Spencer	Carroll	Conning	Boulton	33
Coles	**Batty**	**Ferns**	**Harrower**	**Rutter**	**Cooper**	**Carroll**	**Wallace**	**Wilson**	**Spencer**	**McDermott**	**Conning**	**Boulton**	34
Coles	Batty	Flory	Shail	Rutter	Conning	Carroll	Wallace	Pritchard•	Spencer	McDermott	Boulton	Crothers	35
Coles	Harrower	Ferns	Shail	Rutter	Conning	Carroll†	Wallace	Robinson	Spencer	McDermott	Batty	Cooper	36
Coles	**Harrower**	**Ferns**	**Shail**	**Rutter**	**Conning**	**Carroll**	**Wallace**	**Robinson•**	**Spencer**	**McDermott**	**Batty**	**Cooper**	37
Coles	Harrower	Ferns	Shail	Rutter	Cooper	Carroll	Wallace	Robinson•	Spencer	McDermott	Batty	Boulton	38
Coles	**Harrower**	**Ferns**	**Shail**	**Rutter**	**Cooper•**	**Carroll**	**Wallace**	**Robinson**	**Spencer**	**McDermott**	**Conning**	**Batty**	39
Coles	**Harrower†**	**Ferns**	**Shail**	**Rutter**	**Conning**	**Carroll**	**Wallace**	**Robinson**	**Spencer**	**McDermott**	**Cooper**	**Batty**	40
Coles	Harrower	Ferns	Shail	Rutter•	Conning	Carroll	Wallace	Robinson	Spencer	McDermott	Batty†	Cooper	41
Coles	Harrower	Ferns	Shail	Batty	Conning	McDermott	Wallace	Robinson	Spencer	Pritchard†	Rutter	McEvoy	42
Coles	Harrower	Ferns	Shail	Batty	Conning	McDermott	Wallace	Robinson	Spencer	Boulton•	Rutter	McEvoy	43
Coles	**Harrower**	**Ferns**	**Shail**	**Batty†**	**Conning**	**McDermott**	**Wallace**	**Robinson•**	**Spencer**	**Carroll**	**Rutter**	**Cooper**	44
Coles	Harrower	Ferns	Shail	Batty	Conning	McDermott	Wallace	Robinson•	Spencer	Carroll	Wilson	McEvoy	45
Coles	Batty	Ferns	Shail	Rutter	Conning	Carroll	Wallace	Wilson	Spencer	Robinson	McEvoy	Boulton	46
Coles	Batty	Harrower	Shail	Rutter	Conning	Carroll	Wallace•	Wilson	Spencer	Robinson	McEvoy	Boulton	47
Coles	McEvoy	Ferns	Shail	Rutter	Conning	Carroll	Batty	Harrower	Spencer	Robinson•	Boulton	Sivell	48
Coles	McEvoy•	Ferns	Shail	Rutter	Conning	Batty	Wallace	Carroll	Spencer	Robinson†	McDermott	Boulton	49
Coles	Harrower•	Ferns	Shail	Sivell	Batty	McDermott	Conning	Boulton†	Carroll	Robinson	Pritchard	Cooper	50
Coles	Harrower	Ferns	Shail	Rutter	Conning	Carroll	Batty•	Wilson	Spencer	McDermott	Cooper	Sivell	51
Coles	Batty	Ferns	Shail	Rutter	Conning	Cooper	Wallace	Wilson•	Spencer	McDermott	Pritchard	McEvoy	52
Coles	Sivell	Ferns	Shail	Rutter	Conning	Batty	Wallace	Pritchard†	Cooper•	McDermott	McEvoy	Carroll	53
Coles	Harrower	Ferns	Shail	Rutter	Conning†	Robinson	Wallace	Carroll•	Spencer	McDermott	Batty	Cooper	54
Coles	Harrower	Ferns	Shail	Rutter	Conning	Robinson	Wallace	Carroll	Spencer	McDermott	Batty	Cooper	55
Coles	Batty	Ferns	Shail	Rutter	Conning	Carroll	Wallace	Robinson	Spencer	McDermott	McEvoy	Cooper	56

• substituted by No. 12. † substituted by No. 14.

GMVC Appearances (max 42):

FA Cup Appearances (max 21):

Yeovil Town

STEVE RUTTER

Steve took over as player-manager during the 1990/91 campaign, following the departure of Clive Whitehead. He led the club to safety then and did the same again last season, his first full season in charge, despite crippling financial constraints which earned him the respect of officials, players and supporters of Yeovil Town.

An uncompromising defender with strong leadership qualities, he joined the club from the Police Force, having played for Rushden Town, Northampton Town, Kettering Town, Wellingborough Town and Wealdstone.

Although the financial state of the club will still not allow him to go out and spend a fortune in the transfer market, the character of the man will lift the players at his disposal and continue the excellent team spirit he has fostered.

Leading scorer Mickey Spencer in action for Yeovil Town last season.

Programme details:
48 pages for £1.00
Editor - Roger Brinsford

Any other club publications:

Local Newspapers:
Western Gazette
Western Daily Press, Somerset Star,
Sunday Independant, Yeovil Express

Local Radio Stations:
Radio Bristol
Radio Camelot (Hospital)
Orchard FM, Somerset Sound

YEOVIL TOWN - PLAYING SQUAD 1992-93

Player	Honours	Birthplace and date	Transfer Fees	Previous Clubs
GOALKEEPERS				
David Coles		Wandsworth 15/6/64		Birmingham, Mansfield, Aldershot, Brighton, Aldershot, Fulham
DEFENDERS				
Phil Ferns	Vaux Lge AC Delco	Liverpool 12/9/61		Bournemouth, Charlton, Blackpool
Steve Harrower	Div 4	Exeter 9/10/61		Dawlish, Exeter
Steve Rutter	Vaux Lge AC Delco, BLT	Northampton 14/10/62		Rushden T, Kettering T, Wellingborough, Wealdstone
Mark Shail	BLT	Sandvikon(Swe) 15/10/66	£5,000	Worcester City
Mike McEvoy		Wigan 5/7/73		Ex-YTS
MIDFIELD				
Paul Batty	Div 4	Edington 9/1/64		Swindon, Chesterfield, Exeter
Richard Cooper		London 7/6/65		Sheff Utd, Lincoln, Exeter, Weymouth
Andy Wallace	Vaux Lge, BLT AC Delco	London 30/6/62		Met Police, Kingstonian, Wealdstone
Neil Coates				Watford, Bournemouth, Yeovil, Dorchester
FORWARDS				
Micky Spencer	British Army Comb Services	Manchester 27/11/62		Wokingham
Paul Wilson	ESP	Doncaster 16/11/60	£13,000	Frickley, Boston Utd

Departures during season:
David Fry (Released). Peter Conning (Bashley), Mark Boulton (Released), Howard Pritchard (Released), Robbie Carroll (Woking), Brian McDermott (Hong Kong).

Players on loan during season:
Jason Rowbotham (Plymouth), Andy Rowland (Torquay), Damian Henderson (Leeds Utd), David Robinson (Cambridge Utd).

Huish Park, Yeovil

Ground address and Tel. No.: Huish Park, Lufton Way, Yeovil, Somerset BA22 8YF. Tel: 0935 23662 (Office). Fax: 0935 73956

Information line: 0891-333092

Simple ground directions: Leave A303 at Cartgate Roundabout and take A3088 to Yeovil. Take first exit at next roundabout and first exit again at next roundabout into Lufton Way

Official capacity: 8,800　　　　　**Seating:** 4,800　　　　　**Covered accommodation:** 4,800

Cost of seats: £4.80　　　　　**Cost of standing:** £4.00

Official opening of floodlights: v Newcastle United

Record attendance: 6,153 England v Wales U18 Youth International

Social facilities available: Tea Bars around the ground, VP & sponsors lounges, Executive Restaurant and Social Club

Car parking: 800 cars

Sponsored by: Bass　　　　　**YEOVIL TOWN**　　　　　**Nickname:** The Glovers

Previous leagues: Southern, London Combination (1 season), Vauxhall-Opel.

Club colours: White & green stripes, white shorts, green socks　　　**Change colours:** Sky blue

Midweek home matches: Tuesday　　　　　**Club metal badges:** Yes

Record transfer fee paid: £15,000 to Worcester City for Joe Jackson

Record transfer fee received: £20,000 from Enfield for Gary Donnellan

Record appearances for club: L. Harris 1959-69

Record aggregate goalscorer: Dave Taylor, 285, 1960-69

Record goalscorer in a season: Dave Taylor, 59, 1960-61

Past players who have progressed to the Football League: Over 40 players + 18 managers including since 1985: Nigel Jarvis (Torquay); Ian Davies (Bristol R.); Alan Pardew (Crystal Pal.); Paul Miller (Wimbledon); John McGinlay (Shrewsbury); Guy Whittingham (Portsmouth)

Club honours: Southern League: Champions 1954-55, 1964-65 & 1970-71; Runner-up 1923-24, 1931-32, 1934-35, 1969-70, 1972-73. Southern League Cup: Winners 1948-49, 1954-55, 1960-61, 1965-66. Vauxhall-Opel (Isthmian) League: Champions 1987-88; Runners-up 1985-86 & 86-87. A.C. Delco (Isthmian) League Cup: Winners 1987-88. Bob Lord Trophy (Conference League Cup): Winners 1989-90. Western League: Champions 1921-22; Runners-up 1930-31. Somerset Premier Cup: Winners 13 times.

Managers since 1922: Jack Gregory, Tommy Lawes, Dave Pratt, Louis Page, Dave Halliday, Billy Kingdon, Alec Stock, George Patterson, Harry Lowe, Ike Carter, Norman Dodgin, Jimmy Baldwin, Basil Hayward, Glyn Davis, Joe McDonald, Ron Saunders, Mike Hughes, Cecil Irwin, Stan Harland, Barry Lloyd, Malcolm Allison, Jimmy Giles, Trevor Finnigan, Ian McFarlane, Gerry Gow, Brian Hall, Clive Whitehead, Steve Rutter.

DIADORA LEAGUE

Chairman: A C F Turvey, MCIM.
Hon. Secretary: N R Robinson,
226 Rye Lane, Peckham, London SE15 4NL.

WOKING'S WONDERFUL YEAR

It seemed almost inevitable that Woking would win the Premier Division title. Sometimes, being such strong favourites to win a competition can work against you. However, Woking have proved that they are, without any doubt, streets ahead of other team in the division.

Manager Geoff Chapple kept faith with the majority of players that did so well for him in the 1990/91 F.A. Cup competition. Many of those players, such as Trevor Baron, Adie Cowler, Mark Biggins, the Wye twins and Tim Buzaglo had been with the club since their Division One days but had proved that they were good enough for the higher level. Chapple knew that he would have to do without Buzaglo for most, if not all of the campaign. That appeared to be a major blow to Woking's hopes. However, Chapple obtained the services of 21 year-old George Friel on a free transfer from Reading and bought Steve Milton from Fulham. Their partnership, which has been worth over 50 goals, has meant that Buzaglo's absence has been more than adequately covered. Milton had been around the Isthmian League scene before, as prior to joining Fulham, he had spells at Whyteleafe, Kingstonian, Croydon and Epsom and Ewell after being released by West Ham as a youngster. Another very important signing by Chapple was goalkeeper Lawrence Batty. Although Woking's other keeper, Tim Read, had done well the previous season, when Batty became available after being released by Brentford, his experience was seen as vital to Woking's promotion charge. Batty, formerly with Fulham and Portugese club Farence, had plenty of other offers to choose from, including more than one from Vauxhall Conference clubs, but decided that Woking's offer was too good to turn down as well as being not far from home.

Promotion rivals like Enfield and Sutton United must have hoped that Woking might have suffered from a drop in league form whilst they were engaged in F.A. Cup and Trophy action. But, although they did well again in those competitions, the lead they had built up before the Trophy and Cup started ensured that the pursuing clubs had little chance of catching them. Also, Woking's form remained good during those cup runs. The pressure finally told on Enfield especially, and manager Graham Pearce paid the price with his job.

Woking's attendances have been remarkable. All 21 matches held at Kingfield have attracted gates of over 1,000 with over 3,000 watching the top of the table clash against Enfield. Their away support too has ensured that all but five clubs had gates in excess of a thousand when Woking were the visitors. A great deal of the money generated from the club's F.A. Cup run of last season has gone into improving their Kingfield stadium in readiness for Vauxhall Conference football. Their support will be a welcome boost to the Conference.

I suppose Enfield must feel agrieved that they should again end up as runners-up to an outstanding side. Last season, Enfield found Redbridge Forest too good to catch and perhaps thought that this would be their year. However, the loss of highly respected player and manager Peter Taylor, who moved to Watford as assistant to Steve Perryman, before the season began, surely affected their chances. His replacement, Graham Pearce, battled on manfully and Enfield could always be relied on to play attractive football, but Woking were just too good for them. Now, Enfield once again have Eddie McCluskey at the helm, and they must be hoping that success will again come to Southbury Road under his guidance. *(continued on page 290)*...

Woking FC - presented with the Championship at their home fixture with Bishop's Stortford. Photo - Eric Marsh.

Stevenage Borough's achievement of winning the Division Two (North) and Division One titles in successive seasons is nothing short of magnificent. This friendly and well-run club will not be caught out by obtaining promotion to the Premier Division too quickly. Manager Paul Fairclough, who arrived from Hertford Town in 1990, and coach Paul Peterson, deserve immense credit for guiding Borough to two titles in two years. Fairclough relies heavily on a very experienced defence, a solid and aggressive midfield and the scoring prowess of Martin Gittings and Andy Walker. In defence, Borough have Paul Bowgett, who has seen it all before during a long career which included leading Wealdstone to the non-league double in 1985. He has Noel Blackwell, Ian Whitehead and Miguel Luque partnering him. They are all good, honest players and, together, they form a very solid back four. In midfield, Shaun Debnam, Micky Nunn, Shaun Marshall, the experienced ex-Brentford player Gary Roberts, and Dave Brown are all very useful performers. The partnership of Gittings and Walker up front will worry more than a few Premier Division defences next season. Support at Broadhall Way is excellent. Borough regularly attract gates of around 700 and, if they do well next season, support of nearer a thousand is expected.

Yeading's promotion was probably not as unexpected as Stevenage Borough's. Last season, Yeading finished in third spot which would, ironically, have seen them promoted this term. However, Yeading's progress over the last two or three years has seen them win the F.A. Vase and Division Two (South) title in 1989/90 and, this season, obtain a place in the Premier Division. Manager Gordon Bartlett has been in charge at Beaconsfield Road during the successful run and has steadily built a strong squad of players. Survivers of Yeading's 'double' winning side include goalkeeper Stuart Mackenzie, defenders Steve Croad and Jon Denton, midfielders Paddy McCarthy and Steve Cordery, and strikers Hector Welsh and Lee Charles. Bartlett has made important additions to his squad, such as defenders Phil Dicker and Robbie Johnson and striker Lee Holman, who has formed a successful partnership in attack with Welsh and another new signing, Kevin Quinn.

Formed as recently as 1967, Yeading's progress in the Premier Division will be followed with interest. They can certainly be pointed to as an example of how well the Pyramid system can work.

Dulwich Hamlet are one of the best known names in non-league football. Four time winners of the Amateur Cup, Dulwich found themselves relegated from the Premier Division at the end of the 1989/90 season. Following that, the former Crystal Palace stalwart, Jim Cannon, was appointed as player-manager and after a season of re-adjustment, when they finished mid-table, Dulwich have now made it back to the Premier Division. Dulwich have benefitted from both the merger of Dagenham and Redbridge Forest and the fact that the Diadora League will receive no relegated Conference club, thereby going up by way of finishing third behind Stevenage and Yeading. However, Cannon's achievement of obtaining promotion is especially notable as Dulwich have had to play away from their Champion Hill ground whilst it is being re-developed. They should be back at the re-vamped Champion Hill Stadium in time for next season's kick-off.

Boreham Wood just missed out on a promotion place in the end, which must have been extremely disappointing for manager Trevor Harvey. He signed a whole host of "star" non-league players like Micky Dingwall, Nicky Ironton, Joe Simmonds and David Flint, but in the end, Dulwich Hamlet's 6-1 thrashing of Croydon on April 27th, denied them the third promotion spot.

Life is certainly not dull at Purfleet. They won the Essex League title in 1988, were runners-up in the Vauxhall-Opel League Division Two (North) in 1989, moved to the re-constituted Second Division in 1990 and have now won the title. Just to top the season off nicely, Purfleet also added the Loctite Trophy to their collection. Manager Gary Calder has the attitude of attack being the best form of defence as his side notched 97 league goals but also conceded 48. Calder brought a number of Aveley players with him when he made the short journey from Mill Road to Ship Lane. However, former Crawley and Dartford striker, Jeff Wood, has been the goalscoring hero, notching 26, with Chris Blakeborough and Alan Brett helping to overcome the loss of last season's leading marksman, Dave Matthews, who had scored 11 goals this term, when he decided to move to Billericay.

Lewes' success in winning promotion back to Division One at the first attempt has perhaps surprised the club somewhat as it has been achieved with a very young team. Manager Brian Donnelly, has mixed experienced players such as Grant Horscroft, Herbie Smith, Glen Geard, Micky Russell and Kevin Crooks with highly promising youngsters like Marc Rice, Syd Harman and Steve Richardson and the mix obviously worked. Lewes completed a highly successful season when their youth team captured the Loctite Youth Cup with a 3-1 win over Clapton. The foundations have now been laid for a very promising future at the Dripping Pan. (continued on page 291).

Dulwich Hamlet fans at Hitchin celebrate their heroes' promotion to the Premier Division. Photo - Paul Dennis.

(Continued from page 290)

Billericay Town are on their way back to Division One, after four years of re-grouping themselves in Division Two. Manager John Kendall has built a very strong squad at New Lodge, although he may have to fight to keep one or two of his promising youngsters at the club. Already, 32-goal striker Steve Jones looks likely to be heading for West Ham United for a fee reputedly to be around £25,000. To supplement the younger players, Kendall has used the services of two vastly experienced forwards. Former Charlton and Crystal Palace star, Mike Flanagan and the much travelled ex-Chelsea, Coventry and Q.P.R. player, Tommy Langley, who have both helped enormously during the crucial run-in.

Edgware Town and Chertsey Town, promoted along with Tilbury, have both enjoyed marvellous seasons. Edgware, members of the Isthmian League only since 1990, clinched the championship on the last Saturday of the season when they beat Feltham & Hounslow 2-0 whilst Chertsey surprisingly lost at home 3-4 to improving Horsham. Both clubs enjoyed superb runs in the F.A. Vase. Edgware went out to eventual finalists Guiseley in the Fifth Round and Chertsey's valiant effort to reach Wembley stumbled at the Quarter-final stage where they were beaten by Bamber Bridge.

Edgware, the club that launched the careers of Chelsea's Dave Beasant and Luton's Brian Stein amongst others, are managed by Brian Rider, who joined the club initially as reserve boss in 1985. Last season, their first in the Diadora League, Edgware finished in 14th spot as the club settled down into the higher grade. However, Rider made some important signings during the close season, such as leading scorer Steve Newing, signed from St.Albans City, and the much-travelled Gursel Gulfer, who arrived from Wembley later in the season, and his experience has served Town well. Egdware's White Lion Ground compares favourably with any in the Diadora League and once housed over 8,000 for an F.A. Cup match against neighbours Wealdstone.

Chertsey Town's promotion has been led by manager Jimmy Kelman, one of the most experienced bosses in the league. Kelman, who was in charge of Vauxhall Conference club Wycombe Wanderers only two years ago, took over at Alwyns Lane during last season. However, he arrived too late to do much about their 1990/91 campaign in which, curiously, like Edgware they finished in 14th spot in Division Two South. This season, with a much-changed squad, Chertsey have had a great campaign. Quite a few of Kelman's signings came out of local football, but his more experienced players like striker Carlton Walcott, defender Peter Skerrett (ex-Slough) and Paul Sweales, who played in the 1986 Vase Final for Southall and the 1990 final with Yeading, have been vital to Chertey's promotion push. One rather surprising fact is that, although between them, Chertsey and Edgware blasted 221 league goals, neither club had a player featuring amongst the top scorers.

The third promotion place in Division Three went to Tilbury, who managed to hold off the challenge of Hampton. Again, like Edgware and Chertsey, the Dockland club had a poor 1990/91 season but have managed to find life in the Third Division much more to their liking. Tilbury are jointly managed by Ian Bodley and Nicky Phillips, with midfielder Jimmy Hallybone, the ex-Leyton Orient player, performing an equally important role as coach. Phillips, who made five appearances for Coventry City in 1979, still plays and dictates the pattern on the pitch, whilst Bodley watches from the bench.

Tilbury have two good strikers in Mark Phillips and Dean Henry. Between them, they have scored over 50 goals this season. Important contributions have also been made by the experienced duo of goalkeeper Dave Annetts and centre-half Geoff Nicholson, midfielders Kevin Broderick and Jon Camp, and ex-Dagenham winger Spencer Fletcher.

Steve Whitney

Edgware Town completed a fantastic campaign, winning the Third Division title in only their second season in the Isthmian League. Here they are pictured after their 3-1 home victory over Welton Rovers in the Fourth Round of the FA Vase. Photo - Eric Marsh.

DIADORA LEAGUE CUP 1991-92

Preliminary Round	Res	Att
Abingdon Town v Hemel Hempstead	2-0	307
Barton Rovers v Clapton	3-2	113
Billericay Town v Petersfield Utd	4-1	258
Bracknell Town v Harefield United	0-1	69
Chertsey Town v Tring Town	1-0	101
Collier Row v Ruislip Manor	1-4	110
Eastbourne Utd v Southwick *(aet)*	2-2	101
Southwick v Eastbourne United	6-0	78
Edgware Town v Ware *(aet)*	0-1	150
Hertford Town v Purfleet	2-1	82
Horsham v Feltham & Hounslow Bor.	4-1	116
Hungerford Town v Berkhamsted Town	2-4	115
Leatherhead v Banstead Athletic	1-2	93
Lewes v Hornchurch *(aet)*	0-0	160
Hornchurch v Lewes	2-3	65
Maidenhead Utd v Kingsbury *(aet)*	2-3	138
Malden Vale W/O Vauxhall Motors		
Rainham v Epsom & Ewell *(at Epsom)*	4-2	78
Saffron Walden Town v Newbury *(aet)*	2-2	109
Newbury Town v Saffron Walden Town	0-2	82
Southall v Metropolitan Police	3-1	40
Stevenage Borough v Cove	3-0	314
Thame United v Camberley Town	1-2	92
Tilbury v Hampton	1-0	87
Witham Town v Flackwell Heath *(aet)*	1-2	63
Worthing v Egham Town *(aet)*	1-1	186
Egham Town v Worthing	4-2	86

First Round	Res	Att
Abingdon Town v Harefield United	2-0	305
Aveley v Hayes	1-3	175
Barking v Southwick	4-3	121
Banstead Athletic v Grays Athletic	1-2	62
Barton Rovers v Woking	1-3	404
Basingstoke Town v Dagenham	1-0	301
Bishop's Stortford v Hertford *(aet)*	1-2	326
Carshalton Athletic v Croydon	3-2	277
Chalfont St Peter v Hendon *(aet)*	4-6	182
Chertsey Town v Tooting & Mitcham	2-0	195
Chesham Utd v Tooting & Mitcham *(aet)*	2-2	428
Tooting & Mitcham Utd v Chesham Utd	2-3	173
Dorking v Malden Vale	2-1	172
Egham Town v Boreham Wood	2-0	109
Harrow Borough v Walton & Hersham	2-1	275
Heybridge Swifts v Kingstonian	1-0	197
Hitchin Town v Billericay Town *(aet)*	1-2	281
Lewes v Camberley Town	3-0	92
Leyton-Wingate v Bromley	1-2	224
Marlow v Wokingham Town	2-1	270
Molesey v Kingsbury Town	1-0	67
Rainham Town v Bognor Regis Town	1-0	61
Royston Town v Berkhamsted Town	0-2	53
Ruislip Manor v St Albans City	2-3	278
Saffron Walden Town v Enfield	0-2	255

	Res	Att
Southall v Tilbury	1-3	59
Staines Town v Flackwell Heath	2-0	200
Sutton United v Stevenage Borough	2-1	465
Uxbridge v Harlow Town	0-3	115
Ware v Horsham *(aet)*	2-2	159
Horsham v Ware	1-2	178
Whyteleafe v Wivenhoe Town	2-1	103
Windsor & Eton v Wembley	4-1	186
Yeading v Dulwich Hamlet *(aet)*	2-1	157

Second Round	Res	Att
Abingdon Town v Lewes	2-0	182
Barking v Heybridge Swifts	2-1	96
Berkhamsted Town v Carshalton Athletic	1-6	108
Chertsey Town v Enfield	0-4	122
Dorking v Molesey *(aet)*	3-3	180
Molesey v Dorking	0-2	81
Egham Town v Billericay Town	0-1	122
(Billericay removed from competition)		
Harlow Town v Grays Athletic	0-4	122
Harrow Borough v Basingstoke Town	1-0	151
Hayes v Yeading	1-0	390
Hertford Town v Sutton United	0-5	171
Marlow v Windsor & Eton *(aet)*	3-4	235
St Albans City v Bromley	4-1	155
Staines Town v Chesham United	0-1	305
Tilbury v Hendon	3-0	57
Ware v Whyteleafe	2-1	82
Woking v Rainham Town	4-1	944

Third Round	Res	Att
Abingdon Town v Sutton United	1-2	445
Chesham United v Woking	1-2	574
Dorking v Grays Athletic	3-4	138
Enfield v Hayes	3-0	249
Harrow Borough v Carshalton Athletic	0-1	162
St Albans City v Tilbury	5-0	255
Ware v Barking	2-0	139
Windsor & Eton v Egham Town *(aet)*	0-0	163
Egham Town v Windsor & Eton *(aet)*	0-0	187
Egham Town v Windsor & Eton	3-1	147

Quarter Finals	Res	Att
Carshalton Athletic v Ware *(aet)*	2-2	298
Ware v Carshalton Athletic	1-0	253
Egham Town v Grays Athletic	1-4	141
Sutton United v St Albans City *(aet)*	2-3	277
Woking v Enfield	0-2	1578

Semi Finals	Res	Att
St Albans City v Grays Athletic	2-2	351
Grays Athletic v St Albans City	1-0*	336
(Grays win 3-2 on aggregate)		
Ware v Enfield	1-2	664
Enfield v Ware	0-0	445
(Enfield win 2-1 on aggregate)		

FINAL: AT DAGENHAM FC, 4th MAY 1992

GRAYS ATHLETIC (1)3 *(Keen 44(og),Wittingham 52,Campbell 57))*, **ENFIELD** (0)1 *(Kane 66)*
Att: 1,264.
Grays: B Delf, S Ward, D Crumpton, A Alexander, I Brown, J Deadman, B Fox, P Sammons, J Campbell, W Whittingham (H Nelson 79), N Crown. Unused sub: A French. *Enfield:* M McCutcheon, E Smart, P Brush, M Keen, G Heald, M Kane, T Mason (M Salmon 79), P Turner, D Wells, C Richards (C Warmington 65), G Westley.

DIADORA LEAGUE CUP ATTENDANCES 1991-92

Round	Matches (1990-91 figures in brackets)	Total	Average	% Change compared with 1990-91
Preliminary	26 (25)	3193 (2887)	123 (115)	+ 6.9
First	34 (36)	6905 (8475)	203 (235)	- 15.7
Second	17 (18)	3693 (4333)	217 (241)	- 11.0
Third	10 (8)	2459 (1619)	246 (202)	+ 21.7
Fourth	5 (4)	2547 (1541)	509 (385)	+ 32.2
Semi Final	4 (4)	1836 (2660)	459 (665)	- 44.8
Final	1 (1)	1264 (2292)		- 81.3
Total	**97 (96)**	**21897 (23807)**	**226 (248)**	**- 9.7**

Grays Athletic celebrate their League Cup victory. Back (L/R): Phil Sammons, Barry Fox (Captain), Barrie Delf, Dean Crompton, Ian Brown, Nicky Crown. Front: John Campbell, Horace Nelson, John Deadman, Adam French, Winston Whittingham, Andy Alexander, Steve Ward.

Grays captain Barrie Fox tries to shake off Enfield's Carl Richards during the League Cup Final. Photo - Paul Dennis.

A.D.T. HEALTHQUEST CHARITY SHIELD 1991-92

(Annual Challenge between League Champions and League Cup Winners)

(Played at Woking FC, Monday 26th August 1991)

WOKING (0)(1)3 *(Baron 53 95,Biggins 100)*, **REDBRIDGE FOREST** (1)(1)1 *(Davidson 42) (AET)* Att: 1,397.
Woking: L Batty, S Mitchell, A Cowler, A Russell, T Baron, A Parr, D Brown, M Biggins, A Perry, G Friel (P Mulvaney 82), L Wye. Unused sub: P Barrowcliff. *Redbridge:* K Foster, P Daly (R Mayes 57), P Watts, T Pamphlett, D Jacques, K Barrett, R Garvey, A Hessenthaler, J Broom, T Williams (C Sowerby 68), K Davidson.

LOCTITE CUP 1991-92

First Round	Res	Att
Aveley v St Albans City	1-6	115
Aylesbury United v Barking	1-3	337
Basingstoke Town v Croydon	1-0	237
Harrow B. v Heybridge *(aet, 5-4 pens)*	2-2	143
Hendon v Chalfont St Peter	3-1	75
Hitchin Town v Abingdon Town	0-3	221
Tooting & Mitcham v Stevenage *(aet)*	1-2	105
Wembley v Uxbridge	0-1	62
Windsor & Eton v Harlow Town	2-3	128
Wokingham Town v Bishop's Stortford	2-0	100
Yeading v Kingstonian *(aet)*	3-2	125

Second Round	Res	Att
Barking v Dagenham	1-5	203
Boreham Wood v Yeading *(aet)*	1-2	113
Bromley v Bognor Regis Town	0-1	223
Dorking v Harrow Borough	3-4	149
Enfield v Molesey *(aet, 2-4 pens)*	2-2	157
Harlow Town v Hayes	2-4	70
Hendon v Abingdon Town	1-2	116
Leyton-Wingate v Chesham United	0-4	69
Maidenhead v B'stoke *(aet, 2-3 pens)*	2-2	170
Marlow v Carshalton Athletic	1-2	140
St Albans City v Wokingham Town	1-3	258

	Res	Att
Staines Town v Dulwich Hamlet	0-3	153
Sutton United v Whyteleafe	4-0	277
Uxbridge v Grays Athletic *(aet)*	4-2	111
Wivenhoe Town v Stevenage Borough	0-4	116
Woking v Walton & Hersham	2-1	1274

Third Round	Res	Att
Carshalton Athletic v Abingdon Town	2-1	328
Chesham United v Woking	2-5	738
Dagenham v Yeading	0-2	205
Dulwich H. v Bognor *(aet, 5-4 pens)*	0-0	53
Harrow Borough v Wokingham Town	2-0	179
Hayes v Uxbridge *(AET)*	1-3	142
Molesey v Stevenage *(aet, 3-0 pens)*	4-4	96
Sutton United v Basingstoke Town	3-2	313

Quarter Finals	Res	Att
Dulwich v Sutton Utd *(aet, 4-5 pens)*	0-0	303
Harrow v Carshalton *(aet, 3-1 pens)*	2-2	220
Molesey v Uxbridge *(aet)*	1-0	100
Woking v Yeading	1-0	1063

Semi Finals	Res	Att
Harrow Borough v Woking	0-2	734
Sutton United v Molesey	4-1	444

FINAL: AT HAYES FC, 5th MAY 1992

SUTTON UNITED (1)2 *(A Scott 18,Browne 58)*, **WOKING** (0)0
Sutton: R Fearon, P Gates, S Smart, S Priddle, M Costello, M Underdown, S Browne, M Jenkins (M Ford 88), D Feltham, Z Newman (R Scott 82), A Scott. *Woking:* L Batty, S Mitchell (P Parker 88), L Wye, A Russell, T Baron, S Wye, D Brown, A Parr, M Biggins, G Friel, A Cockram (S Milton 72).

LOCTITE CUP ATTENDANCES 1991-92

Round	Matches (1990-91 figures in brackets)	Total	Average	% Change compared with 1990-91
First	11 (12)	1648 (1899)	150 (158)	- 5.3
Second	16 (19)	3599 (3074)	225 (162)	+ 38.8
Third	8 (8)	2054 (1684)	257 (211)	+ 21.8
Fourth	4 (4)	1686 (1385)	422 (346)	+ 21.9
Semi Final	2 (4)	1178 (1911)	589 (478)	+ 23.2

REPRESENTATIVE MATCHES 1991-92

At Aylesbury United FC, 21st January 1992

DIADORA LEAGUE X1 (0)1 *(Hobson 71)*, **F.A. X1** (3)7 *(Abbott 21 42 43 50 60,Fielder 83,Reid 87)*
Attendance: 331.
Diadora League: D Root (Hendon), E Smart (Enfield - sub, D Lay (Marlow) 45 mins), A Dear (Kingstonian), T Baron (Woking), S Bateman (Chesham), D Brown (Woking), M Watkins (Marlow - sub, P Hobson (St Albans) 45 mins), M Biggins (Woking), C Hercules (Aylesbury - sub, M O'Shea (Harrow)), D Collins (Aylesbury - sub, R Braithwaite (Kingstonian) 45 mins), P Ryan (Chesham - sub, P Gordon (Bromley)).

At Aldershot Military Stadium, 4th February 1992

COMBINED SERVICES (1)3 *(Maynard 34,Thompson 52,Gill 82)*, **DIADORA LEAGUE X1** (1)1 *(Deer 12)*
Attendance: 230.
Diadora League: L Batty (Woking), A Dear (Kingstonian), S Norman (Chesham - sub, D Lay (Marlow) 61 mins), T Baron (Woking), S Bateman (Chesham), P Ryan (Harrow), G Friel (Woking - sub, P Davidson (Sutton) 61 mins), G Britnell (Enfield - sub, D Collins (Aylesbury) 45 mins), C Hercules (Aylesbury - sub, S Massey (Sutton) 45 mins), D Brown (Woking), P Hobson (St Albans).

RESULTS SERVICES 1991-92

Division	Played	Home Wins	Away Wins	Draws	Goals Total
Premier	462 (100%)	183 (39.6%)	163 (35.3%)	116 (25.1%)	1355 (2.93/game)
First	420 (100%)	174 (41.4%)	157 (37.4%)	89 (21.2%)	1192 (2.84/game)
Second	464 (100%)	203 (43.9%)	159 (34.4%)	100 (21.6%)	1375 (2.98/game)
Third	420 (100%)	203 (48.3%)	140 (33.3%)	77 (18.3%)	1359 (3.24/game)
Total	**1764 (100%)**	**763 (43.2%)**	**619 (35.1%)**	**382 (21.6%)**	**5281 (2.99/game)**

LOCTITE TROPHY 1991-92

First Round	Res	Att
Banstead Athletic v Eastbourne Utd	7-1	22
Barton Rovers v Horsham *(aet)*	3-2	68
Collier Row v Lewes	4-3	45
Cove v Berkhamsted Town	4-0	30
Epsom & Ewell v Hertford Town	3-1	48
Hampton v Hornchurch	2-1	119
Hemel Hempstead v Harefield United	0-2	33
Leatherhead v Ware	1-3	96
Ruislip Manor v Witham Town	1-0	100
Tilbury v Purfleet	0-2	82
Tring Town v Camberley Town	1-2	27

Second Round	Res	Att
Banstead Athletic v Southall	0-1	32
Barton Rovers v Southwick	10-2	67
Bracknell v Newbury *(aet, 2-4 pens)*	1-1	60
Chertsey Town v Kingsbury Town	1-3	76
Clapton v Ruislip Manor	1-3	60
Collier Row v Saffron Walden Town	2-4	124
Cove v Hampton	2-1	80
Epsom & Ewell v Royston Town	4-1	62
Flackwell Heath v Egham Town	0-1	70
Harefield United v Camberley Town	2-1	68
Hungerford Town v Malden Vale	0-1	71

	Res	Att
Metropolitan Police v Feltham & H'low	1-2	81
Petersfield United v Rainham Town	2-1	50
Purfleet v Edgware Town	2-0	50
Thame United v Billericay Town	1-0	178
Ware v Worthing	2-3	139

Third Round	Res	Att
Egham Town v Harefield United	3-0	78
Epsom & Ewell v Cove	0-1	78
Feltham & Hounslow v Ruislip Mnr *(aet)*	1-3	80
Kingsbury Town v Barton Rovers	0-2	54
Newbury Town v Purfleet	0-5	83
Petersfield United v Thame United	1-2	50
Saffron Walden Town v Southall	4-1	100
Worthing v Malden Vale	0-3	173

Quarter Finals	Res	Att
Cove v Saffron Walden Town	0-2	93
Egham Town v Thame United	2-0	73
Malden Vale v Barton Rovers	6-0	129
Purfleet v Ruislip Manor	3-0	125

Semi Finals	Res	Att
Malden Vale v Egham Town *(aet)*	2-2	241
Egham Town v Malden Vale	4-3	68
Saffron Walden Town v Purfleet	0-2	180

FINAL: AT SUTTON UNITED FC, 14th APRIL 1992

PURFLEET (1)3 *(Brett 36,Jeyes 47,J Wood 53)*, **EGHAM TOWN** (2)2 *(Butler 6,B Smith 34)*
Attendance: 241
Purfleet: M Desborough, L Matthews, G Daly, G Wood, J McFarlane, C Blakeborough, J Spiteri, J Rees, J Wood, A Brett, N Jeyes (M Tarling 89). Unused sub: T Macklin. *Egham:* P Allies, J Exer, B Roper, S Bennett, P Lucas, J O'Shea, M Duffy (L Maynard 7), N Horton, B Smith, M Butler, M Green. Unused sub: P Holt.

Purfleet FC pictured after winning the Loctite Trophy. They did particulary well because at one stage in the final they were trailing Egham Town by two goals before rallying to win by the odd goal in five. Back Row: T Macklin, G Wood, A Brett, J McFarlane, J Wood, J Rees. Front Row: N Jeyes, L Matthews, C Blakeborough, J Spiteri, M Tarling, M Desborough. Photo - Dave West.

LOCTITE TROPHY ATTENDANCES 1991-92

Round	Matches (1990-91 figures in brackets)	Total	Average	% Change compared with 1990-91
First	11 (15)	670 (1314)	61 (88)	- 44.2
Second	16 (16)	1268 (1561)	79 (98)	- 24.0
Third	8 (10)	596 (1045)	75 (105)	- 40.0
Fourth	4 (4)	420 (468)	105 (117)	- 11.4
Semi Final	3 (4)	489 (1060)	163 (265)	- 62.5
Final	1 (1)	241 (507)		- 110.3
Totals	**43 (50)**	**3684 (5955)**	**86 (119)**	**- 38.3**

LOCTITE YOUTH CUP 1991-92

First Round	Res	Att
Chalfont St Peter v Kingsbury Town	0-1	40
Feltham & Hounslow v Egham Town	5-6	42
Flackwell Heath v Marlow	3-1	21
Harrow Borough v Clapton	1-4	51
Hitchin Town v Boreham Wood	0-3	25
Kingstonian v Croydon	4-1	
Lewes v Horsham	5-4	21
Maidenhead United v Bracknell Town	4-2	
Malden Vale v Hampton	4-0	45
Ruislip Manor v Uxbridge	3-1	
Saffron Walden Town v Wivenhoe Town	5-3	20
Southall v Yeading *(aet, 6-7 pens)*	2-2	
Southwick v Carshalton Athletic	1-5	
Stevenage Borough v St Albans City	0-18	20
Sutton United v Leatherhead	3-0	83
Tring v Wokingham *(aet, 3-4 pens)*	1-1	22

Second Round	Res	Att
Billericay v Leyton-W *(aet, 3-4 pens)*	3-3	36
Carshalton Ath v Basingstoke Town *(aet)*	2-1	
Egham Town v Ruislip Manor	2-4	43
Epsom & Ewell v Bromley	0-1	44
Harefield United v Clapton	0-2	22
Hendon v St Albans City	1-4	26
Hertford Town v Boreham Wood	1-2	22
Replayed: Hertford v Boreham Wood	0-2	
Maidenhead v Flackwell *(aet, 5-3 pens)*	2-2	
Molesey v Kingstonian	3-5	45

	Res	Att
Petersfield United v Whyteleafe	3-2	20
Saffron Walden Town v Witham Town	13-0	14
Staines Town v Yeading	1-2	61
Sutton United v Lewes	2-3	65
Walton & Hersham v Malden Vale	2-0	12
Wembley v Kingsbury Town	5-3	12
Wokingham Town v Newbury Town	1-0	19

Third Round	Res	Att
Boreham Wd v St Albans *(aet, 8-7 pens)*	3-3	50
Carshalton Athletic v Bromley *(aet)*	4-3	
Clapton v Wembley *(aet)*	3-1	24
Kingstonian v Petersfield United	2-1	61
(Kingstonian removed from competition)		
Maidenhead United v Wokingham Town	0-3	
Lewes v Walton & Hersham	2-0	45
Saffron Walden Town v Leyton Wingate	5-3	30
Yeading v Ruislip Manor	5-0	20

Quarter Finals	Res	Att
Lewes v Boreham Wood	3-1	
Saffron Walden Town v Clapton	0-4	30
Wokingham Town v Carshalton *(aet)*	2-3	45
Yeading v Petersfield United	1-2	

Semi Finals	Res	Att
Carshalton Athletic v Clapton *(aet)*	1-1	
Clapton v Carshalton Athletic	4-1	
Lewes v Petersfield United	3-2	68

FINAL: AT BROMLEY FC, 28th APRIL 1992

LEWES (0)3 *(Hughes 46,Harman 84,Freeman 86)*, **CLAPTON** (0)1 *(Dolan 89)*   *Attendance:* 196
Lewes: S Hughes, D Freeman (J Shrubb 90), C Troak, P Laycock, P Berry, A Handley, M Piper, P Read (P Paine 88), R Hughes, S Harman, M Sayers. *Clapton:* A Marsh, S Heron, D Fallows (D O'Leary 71), B Bailey, D Bailey, J Morling, C Sweeney, R Hazle, T Dolan, M Hunt, D Carter (Moss 77).
COMPETITION LEADING SCORERS: Robbie Williams (Carshalton) 8 goals, Neal Docking (Saffron Walden) 7.

ATTENDANCE ANALYSIS 1991-92

PREMIER DIVISION

Top Gates (each club)

3125	Woking v Enfield (30/11/91)
2165	Aylesbury v Woking (28/12/91)
2071	Kingstonian v Woking (20/8/91)
1658	Sutton Utd v Woking (18/4/92)
1578	Basingstoke v Woking (15/2/92)
1545	Bromley v Woking (25/1/92)
1502	St Albans v Enfield (1/1/92)
1410	Staines v Woking (21/12/91)
1398	Carshalton v Sutton (1/9/92)
1299	Chesham v Woking (24/8/91)
1184	Windsor v Woking (4/4/92)
1182	Enfield v Woking (2/5/92)
1148	Hayes v Woking (8/2/92)
1139	Harrow v Woking (21/3/92)
1081	Wokingham v Woking (7/9/91)
1020	Marlow v Woking (24/1/91)
1012	Grays v Woking (29/2/92)
883	Dagenham v Woking (12/10/91)
751	Hendon v Woking (23/11/91)
723	Bishop's Stortford v Woking (9/11/91)
580	Bognor Regis v Woking (14/4/92)
393	Wivenhoe v Woking (21/9/91)

Total Attendances (90-91 figures in brackets)

	Total		Games		Ave.		% change
Aug	26395	(20680)	49	(43)	539	(481)	+12.0
Sep	19978	(21319)	35	(46)	571	(463)	+23.3
Oct	23503	(25733)	47	(50)	500	(515)	-3.0
Nov	29449	(20335)	56	(47)	525	(433)	+21.2
Dec	15548	(22149)	32	(53)	486	(417)	+16.5
Jan	26446	(16612)	48	(37)	551	(449)	+22.7
Feb	30984	(13010)	64	(24)	484	(542)	-11.9
Mar	28702	(29289)	61	(75)	471	(391)	+20.4
Apr	29316	(26400)	59	(73)	497	(449)	+10.6
May	4493	(5168)	11	(14)	408	(401)	+1.7
Tot	234814	(182434)	462	(462)	508	(469)	+8.3

Best gate achieved in August: 2 clubs
Best gate achieved in September: 2 clubs
Best gate achieved in October: 2 clubs
Best gate achieved in November: 3 clubs
Best gate achieved in December: 2 clubs
Best gate achieved in January: 2 clubs
Best gate achieved in February: 3 clubs
Best gate achieved in March: 1 club
Best gate achieved in April: 3 clubs
Best gate achieved in May: 1 club

DIVISION ONE

Top Gates (each club)

1551	Stevenage v Hitchin (7/10/91)
889	Hitchin v Stevenage (7/12/91)
478	Abingdon v Maidenhead (1/1/92)
341	Maidenhead v Stevenage (4/4/92)
337	Croydon v Whyteleafe (19/8/91)
304	Tooting v Dulwich (20/8/91)
288	Yeading v Uxbridge (20/8/91)
286	Walton & H v Stevenage (4/1/92)
282	Uxbridge v Yeading (1/1/92)
270	Boreham v Stevenage (20/8/91)
258	Dorking v Stevenage (18/1/92)

Total Attendances (90-91 figures in brackets)

	Total		Games		Ave.		% change
Aug	7201	(7393)	38	(35)	190	(205)	-7.8
Sep	5040	(6730)	33	(33)	153	(204)	-33.3
Oct	9766	(9112)	49	(47)	199	(194)	+2.5
Nov	7108	(11377)	47	(59)	151	(193)	-27.8
Dec	5132	(8969)	33	(51)	156	(176)	-12.8
Jan	8999	(6179)	44	(34)	205	(182)	+12.6
Feb	9630	(5220)	62	(29)	155	(180)	-16.1
Mar	9486	(14806)	58	(81)	164	(183)	-11.5
Apr	8127	(14550)	47	(79)	173	(184)	-6.3
May	1286	(2165)	9	(12)	143	(180)	-32.8
Tot	71775	(86500)	420	(462)	171	(187)	-9.3

256	Chalfont SP v Stevenage (9/11/91)	Best gate achieved in August: 7 clubs
255	Heybridge v Stevenage (7/3/92)	Best gate achieved in September: 0 clubs
245	Harlow v Stevenage (23/11/91)	Best gate achieved in October: 2 clubs
243	Dulwich v Tooting (24/3/92)	Best gate achieved in November: 3 clubs
206	Molesey v Walton & H (21/8/91)	Best gate achieved in December: 1 club
206	Wembley v Stevenage (1/2/92)	Best gate achieved in January: 4 clubs
190	Whyteleafe v Tootng (24/8/91)	Best gate achieved in February: 1 club
186	Barking v Aveley (20/8/91)	Best gate achieved in March: 2 clubs
175	Aveley v Stevenage (1/10/91)	Best gate achieved in April: 1 club
161	Leyton-Wingate v Dulwich (23/11/91)	Best gate achieved in May: 0 clubs

DIVISION TWO

Top Gates (each club)

363	Billericay v Malden V. (18/4/92)
307	Ruislip Mnr v Met Police (16/3/92)
298	Witham v Billericay (1/1/92)
276	Worthing v Lewes (18/2/92)
276	Lewes v Harefield (18/4/92)
257	Southwick v Worthing (1/1/92)
242	Berkhamsted v Hemel H. (1/1/92)
223	Purfleet v Witham (1/5/92)
211	Leatherhead v Met Police (16/11/91)
195	Met Police v Billericay (19/11/91)
185	Hemel H v Billericay (15/10/91)
185	Ware v Billericay (17/3/92)
184	Barton Rvrs v Egham (28/12/91)
181	Harefield v Barton Rvrs (1/1/92)
178	Newbury v Hungerford (21/8/91)
175	Egham v Billericay (16/4/92)
172	Rainham v Billericay (28/3/92)
171	Saffrom Walden v Purfleet (29/2/92)
163	Malden Vale v Leatherhead (11/1/92)
153	Hungerford v Newbury (1/1/92)
127	Southall v Ruislip Mnr (20/8/91)
97	Banstead v Leatherhead (29/2/92)

Total Attendances

	Total	Games	Ave.
Aug	4258	35	122
Sep	4926	45	109
Oct	6212	60	104
Nov	5780	54	107
Dec	3548	32	111
Jan	6468	49	132
Feb	6696	62	108
Mar	6229	56	111
Apr	6944	58	120
May	1487	11	135
Tot	**52492**	**462**	**114**

Best gate achieved in August: 2 clubs
Best gate achieved in September: 0 clubs
Best gate achieved in October: 1 club
Best gate achieved in November: 2 clubs
Best gate achieved in December: 1 club
Best gate achieved in January: 6 clubs
Best gate achieved in February: 3 clubs
Best gate achieved in March: 3 clubs
Best gate achieved in April: 3 clubs
Best gate achieved in May: 1 club

DIVISION THREE

Top Gates (each club)

389	Chertsey v Horsham (2/5/92)
270	Royston v Hertford (1/1/92)
269	Kingsbury v Edgware (1/1/92)
261	Tilbury v Hampton (20/4/92)
250	Horsham v Chertsey (3/3/92)
221	Hampton v Chertsey (7/3/92)
220	Edgware v Kingsbury (21/8/91)
180	Tring v Thame Utd (21/8/91)
167	Cove v Chertsey Town (18/2/92)
159	Thame Utd v Edgware (3/3/92)
156	Camberley v Chertsey (25/4/92)
139	Collier Row v Hornchurch (21/8/91)
120	Hornchurch v Chertsey (11/4/92)
119	Hertford v Chertsey (25/2/92)
117	Eastbourne Utd v Horsham (21/8/91)
110	Petersfield v Horsham (9/11/92)
109	Epsom & Ewell v Horsham (5/11/91)
105	Bracknell Town v Chertsey (21/3/92)
100	Flackwell Hth v Edgware (11/1/92)
90	Feltham & H. v Hampton (1/1/92)
65	Clapton v Tilbury (1/1/92)

Total Attendances

	Total	Games	Ave.
Aug	3097	31	100
Sep	3382	40	85
Oct	4007	46	87
Nov	3264	42	78
Dec	2590	31	84
Jan	4853	46	106
Feb	5418	60	90
Mar	6037	64	94
Apr	4497	50	90
May	1327	10	133
Tot	**38472**	**420**	**92**

Best gate achieved in August: 4 clubs
Best gate achieved in September: 0 clubs
Best gate achieved in October: 0 club
Best gate achieved in November: 2 clubs
Best gate achieved in December: 0 clubs
Best gate achieved in January: 5 clubs
Best gate achieved in February: 2 clubs
Best gate achieved in March: 4 clubs
Best gate achieved in April: 3 clubs
Best gate achieved in May: 1 club

Premier Division

	P	W	D	L	F	A	Pts
Woking	42	30	7	5	96	25	97
Enfield	42	23	10	9	59	45	79
Sutton United	42	19	13	10	88	51	70
Chesham United	42	20	10	12	67	48	70
Wokingham Town	42	10	10	13	73	58	67
Marlow	42	20	7	15	56	50	67
Aylesbury United	42	16	17	9	69	46	65
Carshalton Athletic	42	18	8	16	64	67	62
Dagenham	42	15	16	11	70	59	61
Kingstonian	42	17	8	17	71	65	59
Windsor & Eton	42	15	11	16	56	56	56
Bromley	42	14	12	16	51	57	54
St Albans City	42	14	11	17	66	70	53
Basingstoke Town	42	14	11	17	56	65	53
Grays Athletic	42	14	11	17	53	68	53
Wivenhoe Town	42	16	4	22	56	81	52
Hendon	42	13	9	20	59	73	48
Harrow Borough	42	11	11	13	58	78	46
Hayes	42	10	14	18	52	63	44
Staines Town	42	11	10	21	43	73	43
Bognor Regis Town	42	9	11	22	51	89	38
Bishop's Stortford	42	7	12	23	41	68	33

Leading Scorers (League Matches Only)

George Friel (Woking)	28
Jim Bolton (Carshalton)	22
John Warner (Dagenham)	19
Dave Thompson (Wokingham)	19
Graham Westley (Enfield)	19

THE DIADORA LEAGUE PREMIER DIVISION RESULT CHART 1991-92

HOME TEAM	1	2	3	4	5	6	7	8	9	10	11	12	13	14	15	16	17	18	19	20	21	22
1. Aylesbury Utd	*	2-1	0-0	1-1	1-2	0-0	1-2	1-1	1-1	3-1	7-1	0-0	4-1	0-1	1-0	2-0	0-1	4-4	4-0	1-1	0-4	4-0
2. Basingstoke	0-0	*	1-1	1-1	1-1	1-2	2-2	2-2	1-2	1-2	0-1	4-2	0-1	1-0	2-0	1-1	2-0	0-2	0-2	5-1	0-3	3-3
3. B Stortford	1-0	0-1	*	1-2	2-3	1-0	0-0	0-4	0-1	3-0	2-0	1-1	3-2	1-3	0-2	1-1	1-2	0-2	1-1	1-2	1-2	1-5
4. Bognor RT	2-2	1-2	1-1	*	0-0	1-0	0-6	1-0	0-1	2-2	2-2	3-4	1-4	2-2	0-1	2-4	2-2	0-0	0-1	3-0	1-1	1-3
5. Bromley	0-0	2-0	1-0	1-4	*	3-1	0-1	0-0	0-1	2-3	0-2	0-0	1-1	0-2	0-0	2-0	1-1	2-0	1-1	2-0	0-0	2-0
6. Carshalton	1-0	2-1	2-2	4-0	5-1	*	3-0	0-3	1-1	2-1	1-0	3-1	5-4	4-4	2-1	1-2	1-3	2-1	0-0	0-2	0-2	3-2
7. Chesham	0-2	2-1	2-1	1-3	1-0	4-0	*	0-1	0-2	2-2	1-0	2-2	0-0	3-2	3-0	3-1	4-0	1-0	0-0	2-1	0-0	4-0
8. Dagenham	2-4	2-2	3-0	4-1	1-1	1-1	3-0	*	2-1	2-0	5-2	3-3	0-1	1-2	4-1	0-0	1-0	0-0	2-2	2-2	0-0	0-1
9. Enfield	2-2	0-2	1-0	3-1	0-1	2-1	3-2	3-5	*	2-2	3-0	2-0	1-0	4-0	0-2	3-1	0-0	3-1	0-0	1-0	1-0	3-2
10. Grays	3-3	1-0	3-1	1-2	5-1	2-1	1-3	2-1	0-4	*	0-0	0-0	0-0	1-2	1-2	0-0	1-1	0-2	0-0	4-1	0-2	1-1
11. Harrow B.	0-4	5-1	3-2	4-1	2-1	1-2	1-1	2-2	1-2	0-2	*	2-4	1-1	1-1	2-1	2-2	6-1	1-1	3-1	1-0	1-3	1-2
12. Hayes	0-0	0-1	1-0	4-1	1-3	3-2	0-0	4-0	2-0	4-0	1-1	*	3-0	0-0	1-3	0-1	0-1	0-2	0-2	0-2	2-2	0-3
13. Hendon	1-2	0-2	0-1	3-1	4-1	1-1	2-3	0-1	1-0	1-2	2-2	1-0	*	4-1	1-2	0-1	5-0	0-6	1-1	2-0	0-5	2-1
14. Kingstonian	0-1	0-1	2-3	3-1	0-2	1-2	3-1	2-2	3-0	4-1	3-1	2-1	5-0	*	4-1	3-5	0-2	0-0	2-0	3-0	1-2	1-2
15. Marlow	0-0	2-4	1-0	2-1	0-4	4-1	3-0	2-0	0-1	1-0	1-0	1-1	4-0	2-1	*	0-0	4-0	1-0	1-1	1-2	0-3	1-1
16. St Albans	3-3	1-1	3-2	2-3	4-2	2-0	1-2	1-2	1-2	1-2	6-0	0-0	1-1	2-2	2-0	*	1-2	1-2	1-2	1-2	1-1	0-3
17. Staines T.	0-0	4-1	2-2	0-1	0-1	1-2	1-5	2-2	0-1	0-1	0-0	0-0	1-3	1-2	1-0	1-2	*	1-3	0-3	3-0	0-2	1-3
18. Sutton Utd	2-2	1-2	2-2	5-0	1-1	2-0	1-1	5-3	0-1	5-0	1-1	3-2	4-2	2-2	3-2	2-3	1-2	*	4-0	4-2	2-0	5-0
19. Windsor	2-3	1-3	2-2	1-0	2-1	1-2	1-2	0-1	2-3	1-2	4-0	1-2	1-4	3-0	0-0	2-3	3-1	2-2	*	4-1	0-3	1-0
20. Wivenhoe	0-3	4-1	1-0	4-0	3-2	2-4	1-0	4-0	1-1	1-1	1-1	1-4	2-0	2-1	2-0	1-3	1-2	3-0	0-1	*	1-7	2-0
21. Woking	2-1	5-0	3-0	3-1	1-2	3-0	2-1	3-1	5-0	1-0	2-0	4-1	1-1	3-1	0-1	4-1	2-2	1-0	2-0	2-0	*	0-1
22. Wokingham	4-0	1-1	0-0	3-1	1-4	0-0	1-0	1-1	2-0	3-1	1-1	5-2	2-1	0-1	2-3	4-1	1-3	3-3	0-1	6-0	0-3	*

THE DIADORA LEAGUE PREMIER DIVISION ATTENDANCE CHART 1991-92

HOME TEAM	1	2	3	4	5	6	7	8	9	10	11	12	13	14	15	16	17	18	19	20	21	22
1. Aylesbury Utd	*	473	464	546	536	411	1318	702	902	459	490	802	687	742	819	602	567	509	603	758	2165	573
2. Basingstoke	416	*	359	685	498	514	614	381	482	324	381	367	502	533	251	341	341	594	460	451	1578	631
3. B Stortford	303	301	*	231	298	235	318	367	474	328	320	334	394	367	244	295	285	388	276	304	723	311
4. Bognor RT	243	345	214	*	352	215	240	185	290	175	240	208	202	240	230	270	260	408	260	212	580	215
5. Bromley	431	482	505	340	*	429	439	433	518	568	324	463	413	557	384	489	532	783	335	422	1545	451
6. Carshalton	300	389	274	266	441	*	383	263	396	366	335	300	369	686	385	308	214	1398	285	357	893	368
7. Chesham	960	550	569	478	400	409	*	613	662	445	421	374	674	591	764	460	395	304	505	491	1299	525
8. Dagenham	441	451	462	449	609	421	370	*	527	381	435	287	426	625	379	319	328	435	393	307	883	372
9. Enfield	735	462	520	512	816	720	451	581	*	570	484	372	522	399	312	717	649	708	570	599	1182	406
10. Grays	292	357	234	275	452	304	465	494	393	*	309	333	364	435	397	339	206	341	303	339	1012	295
11. Harrow B.	243	217	267	295	302	203	389	232	501	289	*	401	411	401	284	292	288	324	297	252	1139	241
12. Hayes	275	218	242	207	254	190	329	171	352	311	337	*	242	241	238	309	291	392	266	329	1148	233
13. Hendon	363	199	240	175	306	236	327	244	363	205	372	266	*	329	241	271	265	388	233	183	751	243
14. Kingstonian	550	375	489	505	625	515	429	503	875	662	555	357	551	*	650	636	488	1491	676	549	1905	757
15. Marlow	581	245	240	181	275	212	640	260	430	227	240	305	340	404	*	510	272	444	302	255	1025	385
16. St Albans	436	421	485	546	388	418	578	328	1502	331	394	536	510	341	303	*	298	366	308	638	826	481
17. Staines T.	336	324	295	283	415	274	446	252	571	191	406	321	299	525	403	291	*	492	352	254	1410	324
18. Sutton Utd	530	629	418	706	790	1146	767	634	890	517	558	479	667	865	655	734	617	*	551	611	1658	823
19. Windsor	282	304	168	259	254	322	307	232	246	243	303	317	273	405	225	256	225	342	*	201	1184	258
20. Wivenhoe	296	283	184	207	309	283	195	193	328	247	203	265	234	242	343	253	242	343	154	*	393	194
21. Woking	2218	1701	2369	1608	1521	1402	2305	1374	3125	1689	1451	1484	1629	3073	1299	1912	1209	2327	1962	1953	*	1867
22. Wokingham	462	452	230	324	325	282	475	345	280	272	450	306	282	432	407	348	299	347	464	217	1081	*

Diadora League Premier Division Ten Year Record

	82/3	83/4	84/5	85/6	86/7	87/8	88/9	89/90	90/1	91/2
Aylesbury United	-	-	-	-	-	-	-	3	3	7
Barking	14	16	19	18	8	19	10	20	21	-
Basingstoke Town	-	-	-	-	-	22	-	8	18	14
Billericay Town	10	15	18	21	-	-	-	-	-	-
Bishop's Stortford	13	11	16	7	10	13	7	9	13	22
Bognor Regis Town	8	13	6	15	5	16	9	19	17	21
Bromley	15	22	-	-	11	2	14	21	-	12
Carshalton Athletic	16	20	15	20	15	9	4	10	9	8
Chesham United	-	-	-	-	-	-	-	-	-	4
Croydon	11	17	12	4	7	18	22	-	-	-
Dagenham	-	-	-	-	-	-	18	6	14	9
Dulwich Hamlet	6	10	7	9	18	20	16	22	-	-
Enfield	-	-	-	-	-	-	-	-	2	2
Epsom & Ewell	-	-	13	22	-	-	-	-	-	-
Farnborough Town	-	-	-	3	9	8	2	-	-	-
Grays Athletic	-	-	-	-	-	-	5	5	6	15
Harlow Town	-	12	22	-	-	-	-	-	-	-
Harrow Borough	3	1	8	5	6	12	19	18	20	18
Hayes	4	5	9	16	16	6	8	14	8	19
Hendon	12	9	17	19	4	10	12	12	15	17
Hitchin Town	20	6	20	17	20	21	-	-	-	-
Kingstonian	-	-	-	8	12	14	6	4	5	10
Leatherhead	22	-	-	-	-	-	-	-	-	-
Leytonstone-Ilford					(See Redbridge Forest)					
Leyton-Wingate	-	-	-	-	-	17	15	7	22	-
Marlow	-	-	-	-	-	-	20	17	7	6
Redbridge Forest	2	19	21	-	-	4	1	11	1	-
St Albans City	-	-	-	-	14	15	17	15	16	13
Slough Town	7	3	14	6	3	3	3	1	-	-
Staines Town	19	14	-	-	-	-	-	16	19	20
Sutton United	5	4	1	1	-	-	-	-	-	3
Tooting & Mitcham United	9	21	10	12	19	11	21	-	-	-
Walthamstow Avenue	18	18	11	13	22	-	-	-	-	-
Windsor & Eton	-	-	5	11	13	7	13	13	12	11
Wivenhoe Town	-	-	-	-	-	-	-	-	10	16
Woking	21	-	-	-	-	-	-	-	4	1
Wokingham Town	17	8	4	10	17	5	11	2	11	5
Worthing	-	2	2	14	21	-	-	-	-	-
Wycombe Wanderers	1	7	3	-	1	-	-	-	-	-
Yeovil Town	-	-	-	2	2	1	-	-	-	-
No. of clubs competing	22	22	22	22	22	22	22	22	22	22

Formed: 1897 # AYLESBURY UNITED

The Ducks

Back: John Williams, Kevin Davies, Tim Garner, Simon Gregory, Darren Collins, Cliff Hercules, Pat Smith (physio). Centre: Chris Scott (team asst), Paul Benning, Francis Cassidy, Andy Wright, Kevin Day, Nick Ashby, Ron Schmidt (team asst). Front: Simon Mason, Peter Hutter, Trevor Gould (manager), Steve Lambert, Andy Robinson. Photo - Brian Turvey.

Chairman: F W N Stonell **President:** J Durban **Vice Chairman:** K T Arnold.
Secretary/Press Officer: Tony Graham c/o the club. (0296 88178 H / 436350 or 436525 B)
Team Manager: Trevor Gould **Coach:** David Sansom **Physio:** Pat Smith
Ground: The Stadium, Buckingham Road, Aylesbury HP19 3QL (0296 436350/436525).
Directions: On A413 to Buckingham, just off ring road opposite Horse & Jockey PH.
Capacity: 4,035 (900 Covered) **Seats:** 400 **Floodlights:** Y **Shop:** Y **Metal Badges:** Y
Colours: Green & white hoops/green/green **Change colours:** All red
Newsline: 0898 446 839 **Sponsors:** Pura Foods
Previous Leagues: Bucks Contiguous 1897-1903/ South Eastern 03-07/ Spartan 07-51/ Delphian 51-63/ Athenian 63-76/ Southern 76-88/ GMV Conference 88-89.
Previous Grounds: Printing Works Ground 1897-1935/ Turnfurlong Lane 35-85.
Previous Name: Night School, Printing Works (merged in 1897).
Midweek home matchday: Tuesday
Record Attendance: 6,000 v England 1988 *(at old ground: 7,500 v Watford, FA Cup 1st Rd 1951).*
Best F.A. Cup season: 2nd Rd 88-89 89-90 91-92 (1st Rd 51-52 85-86 86-87 87-88 90-91).
League clubs defeated in F.A. Cup: Southend Utd 89-90.
Record Fees - Paid: £15,000 for Glenville Donegal (Northampton, 1989)
Received: £35,000 for Glenville Donegal (Maidstone Utd, 1991).
Players progressing to Football League: Ray Mabbutt (Bristol Rovers), Phil Barber (Crystal Palace 1986)
Clubhouse: Members bar open daily except during matches. Function room available for hire.(0296 436891).
Steward: Alan Davies. **Club Record Scorer:** Cliff Hercules 212 **Record Apps:** Cliff Hercules 417.
91-92 Captain: Peter Hutter **91-92 P.o.Y.:** Nick Ashby **91-92 Top scorer:** Cliff Hercules.
Local Newspapers (+Tel.Nos.): Bucks Herald, Bucks Advertiser, Herald & Post.
Local Radio Stations: BBC Radio Beds, Chiltern Radio, Fox FM.
Honours: Southern Lg 87-88 (Mids Div R-up 84-85, Sth Div R-up 79-80), Ath'n Lg Div 2 R-up 67-68, Delp'n Lg 53-54 (R-up 52-53, Lg Cup 59-60), Spartan Lg 08-09 (R-up 52-53, West Div 28-29 (R-up 45-46), Div 1 38-39 (R-up 34-35)), Berks & Bucks Snr Cup 13-14 85-86), FA Tphy 4th Rd rep. 80-81.

GOALKEEPERS:
Tim Garner (Corby, Northampton, Kidderminster, AP Leamington, Nuneaton B), **Simon Gregory** (Tring, Aylesbury, Hazells Club, Tring)
DEFENDERS: Simon Mason (Leicester Utd, Shepshed, Enderby, Leicester C), **Nick Ashby** (Rushden, Notts Forest(T)), **Peter Benning** (Chesham, Hungerford, Hayes, Peterborough, Gosnells City(Aust), Hayes), **Kevin Day** (Wycombe, Worsbrough Bridge, Carnegie Coll), **Mike Tomlinson** (British Univ)
MIDFIELD: Andy Wright (Kettering, Rothwell, Desborough, Kettering), **Andy Robinson** (Wycombe, Carlisle, Bury, Man Utd), **Steve Lambert** (Doncaster(Aust), Buckingham, Aylesbury, Arsenal(A)), **Dave Pert** (Irthlingboro, Rushden, Wolverton, Buckingham), **Phil Heath** (Aldershot, Cardiff, Oxford Utd, Stoke), **Steve Grenfell** (Dagenham, Bromley, Colchester, Spurs)
FORWARDS: Cliff Hercules (Oving), **Darren Collins** (Northampton, Petersfield), **Kevin Davies** (Marlow, Chesham, Tring, Kingstonian, Aylesbury, Luton(J)), **Dave Sansom** (Fisher, Aylesbury, Chesham, Barnet, Fisher, Tooting, C Palace), **Owen Wright** (Shepshed, Leicester Utd, Bedworth, Worcester)

PROGRAMME DETAILS:
Pages: 44 **Price:** 60p
Editor: D Gamage
WMPCC Rating: 33

BASINGSTOKE TOWN

Basingstoke's Player-of-the-Year, Jason Chewins, in action against Hayes. Photo - Roger Doswell.

Chairman: Gordon A Hill **President:** Charles Foyle, Esq
Secretary (Add & Tel): David Knight, 1 The Vale, Oakley, Basingstoke RG23 7LB (0256 781422)
Team Manager: Fred Callaghan **Asst Mgr:** Alan Humphries **Coach:** Fred Callaghan
Press Officer: David Knight **Physio:** Derek Browning **General Mgr:** Alan Humphries.
Ground Address & Tel: Camrose Road, Western Way, Basingstoke RG24 6HW (0256 781422).
Directions: Exit 6 off M3 and follow A30 west, ground off Winchester Road. Two miles from bus and rail stations.
Capacity: 6,000 (1,500 Covered) **Seats:** 840 **Floodlights:** Y **Shop:** Y **Metal Badges:** Y
Colours: All blue (gold trim) **Change colours:** All gold **Sponsors:** Basingstoke Press.
Previous Leagues: Hants 1900-40 45-71/ Southern 71-87.
Previous Ground: Castle Field 1896-1947.
Midweek home matchday: Tuesday **Reserve Team's League:** Suburban.
Record Attendance: 4,091 v Northampton, FA Cup 1st Rd 1971.
Best F.A. Cup season: 2nd Rd 89-90 (lost 2-3 at home to Torquay). Also 1st Rd 71-72.
League clubs defeated in F.A. Cup: None.
Record Fees - Paid: £4,750 for Steve Ingham (Gosport) **Received:** £6,750 for Steve Ingham (Bashley)
Players progressing to Football League: Tony Godfrey (Southampton 1958), John Neale (Exeter 1972), Mike Doherty (Reading 1982), Micky Cheetham (Ipswich 1988), Matt Carmichael (Lincoln), Tony Franklin (Exeter), Steve Welsh (Peterborough 1990).
Clubhouse: Open every day (including lunchtime)(0256 464353) **Steward:** Colin Wood
Club Record Goalscorer: **Club Record Apps:** Billy Coombs
91-92 Captain: Paul Chambers **91-92 P.o.Y.:** Jason Chewins **91-92 Top scorer:** Paul Combs.
Local Newspapers (+Tel.Nos.): Basingstoke Gazette (461131).
Local Radio Stations: Radio 210 (0734 413131)
Honours: Southern Lg Southern Div 85-86, Isthmian Lg Div 1 R-up 88-89, Hants Lg 67-68 69-70 70-71 (R-up 65-66 66-67 68-69, North Div 11-12 19-20), Hants Senior Cup 70-71 89-90

GOALKEEPERS:
Dean Beale (Andover, Pirelli General, Sunderland, Southampton(A))

DEFENDERS:
Sandy Brown (Chesham, Bashley, Basingstoke, Dorking, Carshalton, Hungerford, Ballymena Utd), **Steve Riley** (Fareham, Royal Navy), **Barry Cranmer** (Salisbury, Andover), **Jason Chewins** (Local football), **Dave Hawtin** (Farnborough, Alton), **Micky Butt** (Local football), **Barry Blankley** (Bashley, Basingstoke, Farnborough, Woking, Aldershot)

MIDFIELD:
Paul Worsfold (Bournemouth), **Peter Terry** (Aldershot), **Paul Holohan** (Local football), **Brian Mundee** (Salisbury, Weymouth, Maidstone, Camb Utd, Northampton, Bournemouth, Hungerford)

FORWARDS:
Chris Lawrence (Youth), **Lee Cormack** (Bognor Regis, Brighton, Southampton(T)), **Paul Coombs** (Farnborough, Aldershot), **Dean Callaghan** (Local football), **Dave Maskell** (Andover, Bashley, Andover, Bashley, RS Southampton, Waterlooville, Sholing Sports, Brockenhurst, Winchester)

PROGRAMME DETAILS:
Pages: 32 Price: 50p
Editor: David Knight
WMPCC Rating: 29

1883 # BOGNOR REGIS TOWN The Rocks

Bognor's Kevin Maddock screws a shot just wide of the Bishop's Stortford goal during a relegation battle in the Premier Division. Photo - Dennis Nicholson.

Chairman: Mr J Pearce   **President:** Mr S Rowlands
Secretary (Add & Tel): Ted Brice, c/o The Club. (0243 864228(H)).
Manager: Mick Pullen   **Gen. Manager:** Jack Pearce   **Coach:** Neil Hider
Press Officer: Martin Denyer   **Physio:** Steve Robinson   **Comm Manager:** Maurice Warner
Ground Address & Tel: Nyewood Lane, Bognor Regis PO21 2TY (0243 822325).
Directions: West along seafront from pier, past Aidwick shopping centre, and right into Nyewood Lane.
Capacity: 6,000 (3,800 Covered)   **Seats:** 243   **Floodlights:** Y   **Shop:** Y **Metal Badges:** Y
Colours: White (green trim)/white/green   **Change colours:** All yellow (red trim)
Previous Leagues: West Sussex/ Sussex County 28-72/ Southern 72-81
Midweek home matchday: Monday   **Reserve Team's League:** Unijet Sussex Reserve section.
Record Attendance: 3,642 v Swansea FA Cup 1st Rd replay, 1984.   **Sponsors:** Hall Signs & Blinds.
Best F.A. Cup season: 2nd Rd 84-85 (lost 2-6 at Reading), 85-86 (1-6 at Gillingham), 88-89 (lost 0-1 at home to Cambridge). 1st Rd 72-73 86-87 87-88.   **League clubs beaten in FA Cup:** Swansea 84-85, Exeter 88-89.
Record Fees - Paid: None   **Received:** £10,500 for John Crumplin & Geoff Cooper (Brighton.)
Players progressing to Football League: Ernie Randall (Chelsea 1950), John Standing (Brighton 1961), Andy Woon (Brentford 1972), John Crumplin & Geoff Cooper (Brighton 1987), Simon Rodger (Crystal Palace 1989).
Clubhouse: Members bar with normal opening hours. Available for private hire. **Steward:** Gordon Marshall
Club Record Goalscorer: Kevin Clements   **Club Record Appearances:** Mick Pullen, 831.
91-92 Captain: Mick Pullen   **91-92 P.o.Y.:** Mick Pullen   **91-92 Top scorer:** Kevin Maddock 9.
Local Newspapers (+Tel.Nos.): Bognor Regis Joural & Guardian (865421), Bognor Observer (864267), Brighton Argus (606799), Portsmouth News (64488).
Local Radio Stations: Radio Sussex, Ocean Sound, Radio Solent, Southern Sound.
Hons: Isthmian Lg Div 1 R-up 81-82, (Lg Cup 86-87), Southern Lg R-up 80-81 (Lg Cup R-up 80-81, Merit Cup 80-81), S'sex Lg 48-49 71-72 (R-up 38-39 51-52, Div 2 70-71, Invitation Cup 40-41 49-50 62-63 71-72), Brighton R-up 26-27, 1st Rd 72-73 86-87 87-88. S'sex Lg(5) 20-25 (R-up 1896-97, 25-26), W S'sex Jnr Lg 10-11 13-14, Southern Co's Comb 78-79, S'sex Snr Cup(8) 54-56 79-84 86-87 (R-up 51-52 58-59 84-85), S'sex Prof. Cup 73-74, S'sex RUR Cup 71-72, S'sex I'mediate Cup 52-53, Littlehampton Hosp. Cup 29-30 33-34, Bognor Charity Cup(8) 28-29 30-31 32-33 37-38 47-48 58-59 71-73, Gosport War Mem. Cup(2) 81-83 (R-up 86-87), Snr Midweek F'lit Cup R-up 74-75, FA Amtr Cup 1st Rd 71-72, FA Tphy 1st Rd 80-81 90-91.

GOALKEEPERS:
Andy Woodman (Carshalton, C Palace)

DEFENDERS:
Chris Rustell (Pagham), Mick Pullen (Youth), Mark Bird (Pagham), Rob O'Shaunessy (YTS), Graham Marriner (Gravesend, Portsmouth), Darren Burnett (Gosport, Bognor, Southampton(T), Bognor)

MIDFIELD:
Paul Pullen (Youth), Garry Stanley (Waterlooville, Bristol C, Wichita Wings(USA), Portsmouth, Swansea, Everton, Chelsea), David Poole (Southampton(A), Wick), Nick Torpey (Charlton), Gary Young (Worthing, Wick), David Cleeve (Aldershot(T), Portsmouth(Sch)), Billy Bone (Aldershot, Sunderland(T))

FORWARDS:
Gary Biddle (Local football), Chris Stanley(Portsmouth(T)), Peter Kearvell (Chichester), Gary Mansbridge (YTS), Kevin Maddock (Fareham, Willem II(Holl), RS Southampton, Waterlooville, Fareham, Portsmouth)

BROMLEY

Bromley celebrate their 2-0 victory over Erith & Belvedere in the final of the North East Kent Charity Shield. Photo - Dave West.

Chairman: G C Beverley **President:** G T Ransom, AM Inst BE, MHTTA
Secretary (Add & Tel): J M Cooper, 185 Burnt Ash Lane, Bromley, Kent BR1 5DJ (081 857 3961).
Team Manager: George Wakeling **Asst Manager:** Lee Holmes
Press Officer: Brian Traer (0689 820457) **Physio:** Geoff Brittan
Commercial Manager: Ian Pettyfer.
Ground Address & Tel: Hayes Lane, Bromley, Kent BR2 9EF (081 460 5291).
Directions: 1 mile from Bromley South (BR). Buses 146 and 119 pass ground. Junction 4 off M25, then A21.
Capacity: 8,500 (4,000 Covered) **Seats:** 2,000 **Floodlights:** Y **Shop:** Y **Metal Badges:** Y
Colours: White/black/white **Change colours:** All red **Sponsors:** O'Keefe Construction.
Previous Leagues: South London -1894/ Southern 94-96/ London 96-98 99-1901/ Kent 1898-99/ Spartan 07-08/ Isthmian 08-11/ Athenian 19-52.
Previous Grounds: White Hart Field Cricket Ground, Widmore Road. Plaistow Cricket Field 1904-37.
Midweek home matchday: Tuesday **Reserve Team's League:** Suburban
Record Attendance: 12,000 v Nigeria, 1950. **Newsline:** 0898 122 904.
Best F.A. Cup season: 2nd Rd replay v Scarborough 37-38, Lincoln 38-39, Watford 45-46.
Record Fees - Paid: Undisclosed **Received:** £50,000 for Jon Goodman (from Millwall).
Players progressing to Football League: Roy Merryfield (C'sea), Stan Charlton (Arsenal 1952), Roy Heckman (Orient 1955), John Gregory (W Ham 1951), Bill Lloyd (M'wall 1956), Brian Kinsey (Charlton 1956), Harold Hobbs (Charlton & England), Matt Carmichael (L'coln 1990), Leslie Locke (QPR 1956), Jon Goodman (M'wall).
Clubhouse: Open matchdays and for private functions. **Steward:** Frank Ferrett.
Club Record Goalscorer: George Brown 570 (1938-61) **Club Record Apps:** George Brown
91-92 Captain: Frank Coles **91-92 P.o.Y.:** Curtis Hayes **91-92 Top scorer:** Paul McMenemy, 17.
Local Newspapers (+Tel.Nos.): Bromley Times (081 309 1234), Bromley Advertiser (081 668 4811).
Local Radio Stations: Radio Kent, Bromley Hospital Radio, Bromley Local Radio.
Honours: FA Amtr Cup 10-11 37-38 48-49, Isthmian Lg(4) 08-10 53-54 60-61 (R-up 52-53 55-56 87-88, Div 1 R-up 79-80 85-86 90-91, Prince Phillip 5-a-side Cup 1979), Athenian Lg 22-23 48-49 50-51 (R-up 35-36), London Lg Div 2 1896-97, Spartan Lg 07-08, London Snr Cup 09-10 45-46 50-51, Kent Senior Cup 49-50 76-77 91-92, Kent Amtr Cup(12) 07-08 31-32 35-37 38-39 46-47 48-49 50-51 52-53 53-55 59-60, FA Tphy 2nd Rd 91-92.

GOALKEEPERS:
Curtis Hayes (Metrogas), Peter Dale (Abingdon, Molesey)
DEFENDERS: Paul Coates (New Studio), John O'Hehir (Leyton-Wingate, C Palace, Millwall), Ian Rawlings (Leyton-Wingate, Leyton Orient), Olu Adedeji (Finchley), Mark Denton (Leytonstone & Ilford, Croydon, Dulwich, Chelsea(A)), Kenton Campbell (Leyton-Wingate), Martin Morgan (Tooting, Hendon, Tooting, Gravesend, Dulwich, Carshalton, Dulwich), Steve Hamberger (Leyton-Wingate, Maidstone, Portsmouth, Leyton Orient, Walthamstow Ave, Barking, Millwall), John Raffington (Carshalton, Sutton Utd, Hendon, Carshalton, Epsom & Ewell, Carshalton, Croydon)
MIDFIELD: Martin Coates (Leytonstone Ilford, Barking, Hendon, Dartford, Dulwich), **Phil Lovell** (Leyton-Wingate, Hounslow, Leyton-Wingate, Wycombe, Leyton-Wingate, Brighton), **Gary Campbell** (Leyton Orient, Leyton-Wingate, Boreham Wood, Finchley), **Lloyd Moncur** (Leyton Orient), **Paul Taylor** (Leyton-Wingate, Leytonstone & Ilford, Dagenham, Enfield, Barking, Leyton Orient, Arsenal), **Frank Coles** (Enfield, Leyton-Wingate, Leytonstone & Ilford, Dagenham, Leytonstone & Ilford, Charlton)
FORWARDS: Paul McMenemy (Margate, Bromley, West Ham), **Mark Fitzgerald** (Whyteleafe), **Micky Brown** (Wealdstone, Tooting, Dulwich, Croydon), **Pat Gordon** (Leyton-Wingate, Millwall(J)), **Russell Green** (Brighton(T)), **Craig Orriss** (Wimbledon(T))

BROMLEY FOOTBALL CLUB
SEASON 1991/92
Centenary Year 1892-1992
60p
BROMLEY F.C. NEWSLINE 0898 122904

Pages: 44 **Price:** 60p
Editor: John Self
WMPCC Rating: 19

Back Row (L/R): Steve Tomlin, David Stevens, Gary Richards, Les Cleevely, Ricky Walkes, Andy Riley, Kevin Fitzgerald, Tony Carter. Front: Eddie Martin, Phil Dawson, Jimmy Bolton, Robin Beste, Gary Wilgoss. Photo - V J Robertson.

Chairman: T Cripps   **Vice Chairman:** W Stephenson   **President:** W Cooper
Secretary (Add & Tel): Ron McLean, 27 White Lodge, Upper Norwood SE19 3HR (081 764 6233).
Team Manager: Billy Smith   **Asst Manager:** Ron King   **Coach:** Colin Turner
Press Officer: Secretary   **Physio:** Ken Jones   **Comm Manager:** Roger Fear.
Ground Address & Tel: War Memorial Sports Ground, Colston Av, Carshalton SM5 2EX (081 6428658).
Directions: Turn right out of Carshalton Station, and Colston Avenue is first left. Entrance 150 yards on right. London Transport bus 157 to Wrythe Green.
Capacity: 8,000 (3,000 Covered)   **Seats:** 220   **Floodlights:** Y   **Shop:** Y   **Metal Badges:** Y
Colours: Maroon (white trim)/white/maroon   **Change colours:** White (maroon trim)/maroon/white.
Previous Leagues: Surrey Senior 22-23/ London 23-46/ Corinthian 46-56/ Athenian 56-73.
Midweek home matchday: Monday   **Reserve Team's League:** Suburban.   **Sponsors:** T C Cleaning.
Record Attendance: 7,800 v Wimbledon, London Senior Cup.
Best F.A. Cup season: 2nd Rd 82-83, lost 1-4 at Torquay. (1st Rd 69-70 87-88).
League clubs defeated in F.A. Cup: None.   **Newsline:** 0898 446849.
Record Fees - Paid: £2,000 for Jimmy Bolton   **Received:** £15,000 for Curtis Warmington (Enfield).
Players progressing to Football League: Ernie Taylor (Newcastle, B'pool, Man Utd), Billy Barragon (QPR), John McDonald (Notts Co 1948), Frank George (Orient 1954), Thomas Williams (Colchester 1956), Alan Eagles (Orient 1957), Derek Razzell (QPR), Terry Stacey (Plymouth 1959), Roy Lunnes (C Palace 1960), Les Burns (Charlton 1967), Ron Walker (W'ford), Nobby Warren (E'ter), Gus Caesar (Arsenal).
Clubhouse: Open every evening and weekend lunches. Licenced bar, food on matchdays, pool, darts, machines, live music on Sat & Sun. (081 642 8425).
Steward: Brenda
Club Record Goalscorer: G Allen   **Club Record Apps:** J Raffington 423
91-92 Captain: **91-92 P.o.Y.:**   **91-92 Top scorer:**
Local Newspapers (+Tel.Nos.): Wallington & Carshalton Advertiser (668411), Carshalton Herald (6612221).
Local Radio Stations: Capital.
Hons.: Isthmian Lg Div 2 R-up 76-77, Corinthian Lg 52-53 53-54, Surrey Snr Lg R-up 22-23, Surrey Snr Cup(2) 88-90, Surrey Snr Shield (R-up(2)), FA Tphy 3rd Rd 80-81 (lost 0-3 at home to Mossley (eventual R-up)).

GOALKEEPERS:
Les Cleevely (Epsom & Ewell, Farnborough, Wealdstone, C Palace, Southampton),
DEFENDERS: Bobby Green (Hampton, Corinthian Cas, Dulwich, Sutton Utd, Tooting), **Kevin Fitzgerald** (Dorking, Epsom & Ewell, Dorking), **Mensah Offei** (Local football), **Tony Powell** (Leyton-Wingate), **Andy Riley** (Leatherhead, Whyteleafe, Malden V), **Stuart Lawson** (Youth), **Dave Stevens** (C Palace), **Tony Carter** (Wokingham, Basingstoke, Farnborough)
MIDFIELD: Gary Bowyer (Bromley, Whyteleafe, Carshalton, C POalace(A)), **Steve Tomlin** (Croydon, Carshalton, Leatherhead, Dulwich, Bromley), **Paul Weekes** (Youth), **Gary Richards** (Leatherhead, Crawley), **Phil Dawson** (Sutton Utd, Chipstead), **Gary Wilgoss** (Whyteleafe), **Eddie Martin** (Dagenham, B Stortford, Dagenham, Carshalton, Gravesend, Dulwich, Spurs), **Cliff Cant** (Horsham, Crawley, Welling, Crawley, Carshalton, Fulham, Arsenal)
FORWARDS: Robin Beste (Warlingham, Dulwich, Chelsea(A)), **Conrad Kane** (Dulwich, Bromley, Dulwich, Merstham), **Jon Warden** (Tooting, Croydon), **Jimmy Bolton** (Harrow B, Farnborough, Kiruna(Swe), Farnborough, Tooting, Farnborough, Wimbledon, Hillingdon, Spurs), **David Cooper** (Crawley, Redbridge F, Plymouth, Wimbledon), **Eddie Akuomoah** (Youth)

Pages: 32 **Price:** 50p
Editor: Roger Fear
WMPCC Rating: 23

Formed: 1886

CHESHAM UNITED

The Generals

Chesham United beat Beazer Midland Division club Tamworth for a second consecutive season in the FA Trophy. Here Gary Attrell (left) makes a clearance under pressure from Steve Cartwright. Photo - Francis Short.

Chairman: Tony Aplin   **Directors:** A Aplin, R Old, J Conrad, P Gibbons.
Secretary: David Stanley, 17 Old Vicarage Gdns, Markyate, St Albans, Herts AL3 9PW (0582 840707).
Team Manager: Gerald Aplin   **Asst Mgr:** Alan Randall   **Coach:** Micky Gilchrist
Fitness Coach: Keith Power   **Physio:** Ann Wheeler   **Commercial Manager:** Jim Halley.
Ground Address & Tel: Meadow Park, Amy Lane, Amersham Road, Chesham HP5 1NE (0494 783964 - ground clubhouse. 0494 791608 - fax. 0898 884580 - match information service).
Directions: M25 junction 18, A404 to Amersham, A416 to Chesham - go down to r-about at foot of Amersham Hill, then sharp left. 10 mins walk from Chesham station (Metropolitan Line).
Capacity: 5,000 (2 sides covered)   **Seats:** 224   **Floodlights:** Y   **Shop:** Y   **Metal Badges:** Y
Colours: Claret & blue   **Change colours:** Yellow & black.   **Sponsors:** M.F.I.
Previous Leagues: Spartan 17-47/ Corinthian 47-63/ Athenian 63-73.
Midweek home matchday: Wednesday   **Reserve Team's League:** N/A.
Record Attendance: 5,000 v Cambridge Utd, FA 3rd Rd 5/12/79.
Best F.A. Cup season: 3rd Rd as above (lost 0-2). Also 1st Rd 66-67 68-69 76-77 82-83.
Record Fees - Paid: Undisclosed (club policy).   **Received:** Undisclosed (club policy).
Players progressing to Football League: William Shipwright & Jimmy Strain (Charlton 1953 & 55), Stewart Scullion (Charlton 1965), John Pyatt (L'pool 1967), Brian Carter (Brentford 1968), Kerry Dixon (Spurs 1978), Tony Curie (T'quay 1984).
Clubhouse: Open every evening. Bar snacks. Available for hire (business training meetings, weddings etc).
Steward: Mr Charles Dunkerton.
Club Record Goalscorer: Arthur Howlett, John Willis (50 in 1963)
Club Record Apps: Martin Baguley (600+).
91-92 Captain: Steve Bateman   **91-92 P.O.Y.:** Paul Benning   **91-92 Top scorer:**
Local Newspapers (+Tel.Nos.): Bucks Examiner (0494 792616), Bucks Advertiser (0895 632000), Bucks Free Press (0494 21212).
Local Radio Stations: Radio Chiltern (0582 666001).
Honours: FA Amtr Cup R-up 67-68, Isthmian Lg Div 1 90-91 (Div 2 Nth 86-87, Loctite Cup R-up 90-91), Athenian Lg Div 1 Cup 63-64 68-69, Corinthian Lg R-up(2) 60-62 (Lg Cup 60-61), Spartan Lg(4) 21-23 24-25 32-33 (R-up 26-27 29-30 33-34), Berks & Bucks Snr Cup 21-22 25-26 28-29 33-34 47-48 50-51 64-65 66-67 75-76.

GOALKEEPERS:
Andy Lomas (Barnet, Baldock), **Stuart Walton** (Harrow B, Staines, Flackwell Heath, Harrow B, Wycombe, Maidenhead, Woking, Slough, QPR)
DEFENDERS:
Billy Goldstone (Chelmsford, Barking, East Ham, Woodford, Barking), **Steve Bateman** (Harrow B, Everton, Hemel Hempstead), **Andrew Yorke** (Merthyr Tydfil, Ebbw Vale, Exeter), **Sean Norman** (Wealdstone, Wycombe, Colchester, Lowestoft), **Mick Barnes** (Barnet, Windsor, Maidenhead, Basingstoke, Northampton, Reading), **Paul Vowles** (Briton Ferry, Swansea, QPR(T))
MIDFIELD: Lloyd Davies (Ebbw Vale, BOA Caerphilly, Swansea), **Mark Dawber** (Staines, Wycombe, Woking, Virginia Water), **Lee Costa** (Man Utd), **John Richardson** (Papatoetoe(NZ), Chalfont, Chesham), **Ady Adebowale** (Bishop's Stortford, Hertford, Balls Park), **Mark Lawrenson** (Corby, Peterborough, Tampa Bay Rowdies(USA), Barnet, Oxford Utd, Liverpool, Brighton, Preston)
FORWARDS:
Micky Banton (Barnet, Windsor, Hellenic(SA), **Gary Attrell** (Marlow, Burnham, Windsor, Farnborough, Windsor, Maidenhead, Slough, Britwell Hawks), **Ian Mitchell** (Hereford, Merthyr Tydfil, Newport Co), **Chris Townsend** (Gloucester, Bath, Dorchester, Gloucester, Cheltenham, Forest

Pages: 28 Price: 80p
Editor: John Ashworth
WMPCC Rating: 25

DULWICH HAMLET

Back Row (L/R): Dermott Hennessey (Physio), Clive Gartel, Willie Lillington, Ali Reeve, Pat Brown, Julian Gray, Dave Coppin, Dave Newman, John Egan, Dixon Gill (Asst Manager). Front: Billy Allerdyce, Bobby Armitt, John Mahoney, Jim Cannon, Ronnie Murrock, Gary Hewitt, Paul Rogers, Lee Akers. Photo - Dave West.

Chairman: Steve Dye **President:** Tommy Jover
Secretary (Add & Tel): Terry Stephens, 27 Christchurch Close, Colliers Wood SW19 2NZ (081 542 8905).
Team Manager: Jim Cannon **General Manager:** John Langford
Press Officer: John Lawrence (071 733 6385) **Physio:** John Harris
Commercial Manager: John Langford (081 699 6771). **Coach:** Dixon Gill.
Ground: Champion Hill Stadium, Dog Kennel Hill, East Dulwich, London SE22 8BD (071 274 5187).
Directions: East Dulwich Station, 200yds. Denmark Hill, 10 mins walk. Herne Hill then bus 37 stops near ground. Also buses 184 from Elephant & Castle, 185 from Victoria.
Capacity: 3,000 (1,000 covered) **Seats:** 500 **Club Shop:** Yes (Colin Campbell 071 639 6355).
Previous Grounds: Woodwarde Road, College Farm, Sunray Ave, Champion Hill (til 1991), Sandy Lane 91-92.
Colours: Pink & blue stripes/blue/blue **Change colours:** All yellow **Sponsors:**
Previous Leagues: Camberwell 1894-97/ Southern Suburban 1897-1900 01-07/ Dulwich 00-01.
Midweek home matchday: Tuesday **Former Name:** Camberwell
Reserve Team's League: Suburrban.
Record Attendance: 20,744, Kingstonian v Stockton, FA Amateur Cup Final 1933.
Best F.A. Cup season: 1st Rd replay 30-31 33-34. 1st Rd on 13 occasions; 25-31 32-38 48-49.
Record Fees - Paid: T Eames, G Allen **Received:** E Nwajiobi (Luton).
Players progressing to Football League: W Bellamy (Spurs), A Solly (Arsenal), J Moseley & E Tozer (M'wall), G Pearce (Plymouth), Gordon Jago (Charlton 1951), Ron Crisp (W'ford 1961), James Ryan (Charlton 1963), Emeka Nwajiobi (Luton 1983), Andy Gray (C Pal 1984), C Richards (B'mouth), Phil Coleman (M'wall 1986), Andy Perry (P'smouth 1986).
Clubhouse: Open matchdays and training nights. Separate function hall available for hire.
Steward: Bill Andrews
Club Record Goalscorer: Edgar Kail 427 (1919-33) **Club Record Apps:** Reg Merritt 571 (50-66).
91-92 Capt: Lee Akers/Andy Fisher **91-92 P.o.Y.:** Paul Rogers **91-92 Top scorer:** Willie Lillington 15
Local Newspapers (+Tel.Nos.): S L'don Press (081 769 4444), SE L'don & Kentish Mercury (081 692 1122).
Honours: FA Amtr Cp 19-20 31-32 33-34 36-37, Isth. Lg 19-20 25-26 32-33 48-49 (R-up(7) 21-22 23-24 29-31 33-34 46-47 58-59, Div 1 77-78), L'don Snr Cp 24-25 38-39 49-50 83-84 (R-up 05-06 07-08 20-21 27-28), S'rey Snr Cp(16) 04-06 08-10 19-20 22-23 24-25 27-28 33-34 36-37 46-47 49-50 57-59 73-75 (R-up(6) 11-12 31-33 37-38 50-51 67-68), L'don Chal. Cup R-up 91-92, L'don Charity Cp(12) 10-11(jt) 19-21 22-23 23-24(jt) 25-26 27-29 30-31 (jt) 47-48 56-58, S'rey Snr Shield 72-73, S'rey Centen. Shld 77-78, Sth of the Thames Cp(4) 56-60, Southern Comb Cp 73-74, FA Tphy QF 79-80.

GOALKEEPERS:
Julian Gray (Whyteleafe, Farnboro, Croydon, Whyteleafe, Hampton, Croydon, C Palace), Dave Morgan (Dagenham, Dulwich, Erith, Barking, Dulwich, Leatherhead, Dulwich, Merstham, Whyteleafe, Croydon)
DEFENDERS:
Wayne Kerrins (Kingstonian, Dulwich, Farnboro, Fulham), Jim Cannon (Bromley, Redbridge, Dartford, Croydon, C Palace), Dave Coppin (Molesey, Whyteleafe, Carshalton), Micky Gillam (Whyteleafe, Croydon, Banstead, Molesey, Leatherhead, Whyteleafe, Croydon), Paul Rogers (Leatherhead, Alma S, Bromley, Welling, Maidstone, Fulham)
MIDFIELD:
Neil Missen (Croydon, Cray W, Croydon, Bromley, Greenwich B, Bromley, Millwall, Arsenal), Andy Fisher (Dorking, Molesey, Leatherhead, Carshalton), Jim Mahoney (Farleigh R, Whyteleafe), Lee Akers (Malden V, Croydon, Bromley, Greenwich B, Bromley, Dulwich, Carshalton), Bob Armitt (Harlow, Kingstonian, Carshalton, Bromley, Dulwich, Corinthian C, Sutton Utd, Tooting), Jon Daly (Whyteleafe, Croydon, Tooting, Croydon, C Palace), Gary Hewitt (Erith, Bromley, Margate, Bromley, Gravesend, Hendon, Dulwich, Erith, Gateway)
FORWARDS:
Willie Lillington (Molesey, Wimbledon), John Egan (Molesey, Dulwich, Dorking, Molesey, Whyteleafe), Matt Norris (Croydon, Cray W, Dulwich).

PROGRAMME DETAILS:
Pages: 32 **Price:** 60p
Editor: John Lawrence
WMPCC Rating: 21

ENFIELD

Enfield FC, April '92. Back Row (L/R): F Donnelly (asst mgr), M Banks (physio), Curtis Warmington, Dean Wells, Nick Francis, Carl Richards, Stuart Horne, Mark McCutcheon, Dave Flemming, Paul Turner, Paul Brush (capt), Martin Robinson, Mark Keen, Dave Jones (trainer), Eddy McCluskie (manager). Front: Gary Britnell, Tony Vance, Marc Salmon, Graham Westley, Erskine Smart, Tommy Mason, Terry Harris, Mark Quamina, Alan Hull, Mark Kane.

Chairman: A Lazarou   **President:** T F Unwin.
Secretary (Add & Tel): Alan Diment, 30 Apple Grove, Enfield, Middx EN1 3DD (081 363 6317).
Team Manager: E McCluskie   **Asst Manager:** F Donnelly   **Coach:**
Press Officer: Lee Harding   **Physio:** M Banks   **Comm Manager:** J Jefferson
Ground: The Stadium, Southbury Road, Enfield EN1 1YQ (081 363 2858).
Directions: At junction of A10 & A110. 800 yards from Southbury Road station. Buses from town centre.
Capacity: 8,500 (3,500 Covered)   **Seats:** 820   **Floodlights:** Y   **Shop:** Y **Metal Badges:** Y
Colours: All white (blue trim)   **Change colours:** All yellow   **Sponsors:** Cable London Plc.
Previous Leagues: Tottenham & Dist 1894-95/Nth Middx 96-1903/ London 03-13 20-21/Middx 08-12 19-20/ Athenian 12-14 21-39 45-63/Herts & Middx Comb 39-42/ Isthmian 63-81/ GMV Conference 81-90.
Previous Name: Enfield Spartans   **Previous Ground:** Cherry Orchard Lane 1894-1914 1919-36.
Midweek matchday: Tuesday   **Reserve Team's League:** Essex & Herts Border Comb. (Western Div)
Record Attendance: 10,000 (10/10/62) v Spurs, floodlight opener.
Best F.A. Cup season: 4th Rd replay 80-81 (lost 0-3 to Barnsley at Spurs (Att 35,244) after 1-1 draw).
League clubs beaten in F.A. Cup: Wimbledon, Northampton 77-78, Hereford, Port Vale 80-81, Wimbledon 81-82, Exeter 84-85, Orient 88-89, Aldershot 91-92.
Record Fees - Paid: For Gary Abbott (Barnet)   **Received:** For Paul Furlong (Coventry City)
Players progressing to Football League: John Hollowbread & Peter Baker (Spurs 1952), Terry McQuade (Millwall 1961), Roger Day (Watford 1961), Jeff Harris (Orient 1964), Peter Feely (Chelsea 1970), Carl Richards (B'mouth 1980), Paul Furlong (Coventry 1991), Andy Pape (Barnet 1991).
Clubhouse: Bar open every lunch & evening, snacks available. Starlight nightclub, cabaret, dinner & dance (081 363 3127 or 2858).
Club Record Goalscorer: Tommy Lawrence   **Club Record Appearances:** Steve King 617
91-92 Captain: Paul Brush   **91-92 P.o.Y.:** Graham Westley   **91-92 Top scorer:** Graham Westley, 33
Local Press: Enfield Gazette (081 367 2345), Enfield Advertiser, Enfield Independent.
Hons: FA Tphy 81-82 87-88, FA Amtr Cup R-up 66-67 69-70 (R-up 63-64 71-72), GMV Conference 82-83 85-86 (R-up 81-82, Lg Cup R-up 81-82), Isthmian Lg(7) 67-70 75-78 79-80 (R-up(6) 64-65 71-72 74-75 80-81 90-92, Lg Cup(2) 78-80 (R-up 91-92)), Athenian Lg(2) 61-63 (R-up 34-35), London Lg Div 1 11-12 (R-up 04-05 06-07, Middx Snr Cup(13) 13-14 46-47 61-62 65-66 68-71 77-81 88-89 90-91 (R-up(12) 10-11 20-21 47-48 51-52 57-60 62-63 66-67 72-73 75-76 84-85), London Snr Cup(6) 34-35 60-61 66-67 71-73 75-76 (R-up 63-64 67-68 70-71), Middx Lg (West) 09-10 (R-up 10-11), European Amtr Cup Winners Cup 69-70.

GOALKEEPERS:
Mark McCutcheon (Dartford, Billericay, Leyton-Wingate)
DEFENDERS:
Erskine Smart (Hendon, Kingsbury, Watford(A), Arsenal(J), **Tommy Mason** (Farnborough, North Shore(NZ), Dulwich, Brighton, Fulham), **Paul Brush** (Southend, C Palace, West Ham), **Curtis Warmington** (Carshalton, Yeovil, Dulwich, Tahmes Poly, West Ham(J))
MIDFIELD:
Dean Wells (Gravesend, Purfleet, Chelmsford, Dartford, Basildon, Southend, West Ham), **Terry Harris** (Sheff Utd, Norseman, Enfield), **Gary Britnell** (Dartford, Chelmsford, Canvey Is), **Mark Keen** (Dartford, Witham), **Paul Hobson** (St Albans, Burnley), **Mark Kane** (Chelmsford, Barking, Tampa Bay(USA), Barking, Woodford, Walthamstow Ave, Woodford, Leyton O), **Paul Turner** (Farnborough, Camb utd, Arsenal(T)), **Greg Heald** (Local football)
FORWARDS:
Lincoln Manderson (Bishop's Stortford, Redbridge F, Dagenham, Leyton County), **Martin Robinson** (Camb Utd, Southend, Gillingham, Charlton, Spurs), **Graham Westley** (Harlow, Kingstonian, Wycombe, Barnet, Gillingham, QPR), **Carl Richards** (Blackpool, Peterborough, Birmingham, Bournemouth, Enfield, Dulwich), **Tony Vance** (Guernsey), **Marc Salmon** (Local football), **Pat Staunton** (Dagenham, Tonbridge, Basildon, B Stortford, Leyt & Ilf, B Stortford, Clapton)

Saturday, 2nd May 1992
Enfield Winning
Diadora League Premier Division
Official Programme £1

Pages: 24 **Price:** £1
Editor: Lee Harding
WMPCC Rating: 30

GRAYS ATHLETIC

The Blues

Grays striker Ricky Walkes in the thick of the action at Windsor & Eton. Here he is bravely denied by home 'keeper Nigel Winscombe, and the match, on 11/4/92, ended goalless. Photo - Paul Dennis.

Chairman: F W Harris.   **Patron:** R J Billings.
Secretary (Add & Tel): J G Saxton, 216 Thundersley Park Road, South Benfleet SS7 1HP (0268 756964).
Team Manager: Fred & Jeff Saxton   **Physio:** Dave Lawson   **Coach:** P Carey
Press Officer: Gordon Norman (04024 51733)   **Comm Mgr:** Premier Promotion/ Lee Windsor (lottery).
Ground Address & Tel: Recreation Ground, Bridge Road, Grays RM17 6BZ (0375 391649).
Directions: Seven minutes walk from Grays station - turn right round one way system, right into Clarence Road, and at end into Bridge Road. Bus No. 370.
Capacity: 5,500 (2,250 Covered)   **Seats:** 350   **Floodlights:** Y   **Shop:** Y   **Metal Badges:** £1.00
Colours: Royal/white/royal   **Change colours:** All yellow.   **Newsline:** 0898 884 421.
Sponsors: Cory Environmental, London Advertising Centre Ltd, Harris Group.
Previous Leagues: Athenian 12-14 58-83/ London 14-24 26-39/ Kent 24-26/ Corinthian 45-58.
Midweek home matchday: Tuesday   **Reserve Team's League:** Essex & Herts Border Comb.
Record Attendance: 9,500 v Chelmsford, FA Cup 1959.   **Best F.A. Cup season:** 1st Rd 51-52 88-89.
Record Fees - Paid: Tony Macklin (Tilbury 1991)   **Rec'd:** Undisclosed for D Marshall (Plymouth 1991).
Players progressing to Football League: John Jordan (Spurs 1947), Ray Kemp (Reading 1949), Barry Silkman & Tony Banfield (Orient), Gary O'Reilly (Spurs), Wayne Entwhistle (Bury 1983), Michael Welch (Wimbledon 1984), Tony Witter (C Palace 1990), Dwight Marshall (Plymouth 1991).
Clubhouse: Bar, pool, indoor sports hall, en-tout-cas surface 70' x 120' (377753).   **Steward:** Peter Levett.
Club Record Goalscorer: Harry Brand 269 (1944-52)   **Club Record Apps:** Phil Sammons 405.
91-92 Captain: Barry Fox   **91-92 P.o.Y.:** Barrie Delf   **91-92 Top scorer:** Winston Whittingham
Local Newspapers (+Tel.Nos.): Thurrock Gazette (0375 372293)**Local Radio:** BBC Essex, Radio Essex.
Hons: Isth'n Div 1 R-up 87-88 (Div 2 Sth 84-85, Lg Cup 91-92), Ath'n Lg R-up 82-83 (Res Sect R-up 58-59 (Cp R-up 59-60)), Corinth. Lg 45-46 (R-up 51-52 54-55 56-57, Lg Cp(2) 45-47, Mem Shield(4) 45-47 77-78 79-80), L'don Lg 21-22 26-27 29-30 (R-up(4) 20-21 27-29 30-31, Lg Cp 36-37), Essex Snr Cp 14-15 20-21 22-23 44-45 56-57 87-88 (R-up(9) 19-20 23-24 25-26 52-55 57-58 65-66 88-89), East Anglian Cp 44-45 (R-up 43-44 54-55), Essex T'side Tphy(6) 47-48 78-79 80-81 87-89 90-91 (R-up(6) 45-46 58-59 61-62 68-69 84-86), Essex Elizabeth 76-77 (R-up 65-66), Claridge Tphy 87-88 88-89, Mithras Cp 79-80, Essex Int Cp(3) 56-57 58-60 (Junior Cp 19-20 (R-up 58-59)), Essex & Herts Border Comb East 87-88 (Ancillary Cp 78-79, Comb Cp 82-83), Fred Budden Tphy 86-87, Hornchurch Charity Cp 78-79 86-87, Neale Tphy 50-51, Ford Rate Tphy 83-84 85-86 87-88 (R-up 84-85 86-87).

GOALKEEPERS:
Barrie Delf (Dartford, Trinity FC, Southend, Aston Villa(A))

DEFENDERS:
Andy Alexander (Brimsdown R), **Barry Fox** (Millwall), **Ian Brown** (Dartford, Grays, Ards), **Paul Timson** (Aveley), **John Deadman** (Youth), **Dean Crumpton** (Billericay, Grays, Basildon, Dagenham, West Ham(A)), **Steve Ward** (Local football)

MIDFIELD:
Phil Sammons (Hornchurch, Walthamstow Ave, Tilbury, Dagenham), **Ian McIntyre** (Youth), **Dave Stittle** (Brentwood), **John Campbell** (Dagenham, Barking, Dagenham, East Ham), **Martin King** (Barking, Basildon)

FORWARDS:
Karl Tuohy (Colchester(T)), **Winston Wittingham** (Barkingside), **Tony Smith** (Tilbury, West Ham), **Nicky Crown** (Leyt & Ilf, Dartford, Barking, Epping, Grays), **Ricky Walkes** (Carshalton, Woking, Hampton, Apop(Cyp), Hampton, Merstham), **Tommy Williams** (Redbridge F, Leyton-Wingate, Finchley, Leyton-Wingate, Walthamstow Ave, Leyton Orient)

GRAYS ATHLETIC
FOOTBALL
CLUB

SPONSORED BY
CORY ENVIRONMENTAL
THE LONDON ADVERTISING
CENTRE LTD.
HARRIS GROUP OF
COMPANIES

The Diadora Football League
SEASON 1991 - 1992

BISHOPS STORTFORD
DIADORA LEAGUE PREMIER DIVISION
SATURDAY 20th APRIL, 1992
KICK OFF 3.00pm

OFFICIAL PROGRAMME 50p

Pages: 44 **Price:** 50p
Editor: Jeremy Mason
WMPCC Rating: 21

1933

HARROW BOROUGH

The Boro

Harrow Borough v Stalybridge Celtic; FA Trophy Second Round Proper 1/2/92. Harrow defender Steve Shea hurtles in to challenge Stalybridge's ace goalscorer Chris Camden. Photo - Rob Ruddock.

Chairman: Martin Murphy   **President:** Jim Rogers
Secretary: Peter Rogers, 21 Ludlow Close, South Harrow HA2 8SR (081 422 8606).
Team Manager: George Borg   **Asst Manager:** John Morris.
Press Officer: TBA   **Physio:** Phil Sheddon
Ground: Earlsmead, Carlyon Avenue, South Harrow HA2 8SS (081 422 5989/5221).
Directions: Underground to Northolt (Central Line) then 140 or 282 bus, or to South Harrow (Piccadilly Line) then 114 or H10. By road leave A40 at Target PH towards Northolt station, left at lights, right at next island, ground 5th turning on right.
Capacity: 3,070 (1,000 Covered)   **Seats:** 200   **Floodlights:** Y   **Shop:** Y   **Metal Badges:** Y
Colours: Red   **Change colours:** Sky blue   **Sponsors:** TBA.
Previous Leagues: Harrow & Dist 33-34/ Spartan 34-58/ Delphian 58-63/ Athenian 63-75.
Previous Names: Roxonian 1933-34/ Harrow Town 36-66.   **Previous Ground:** Northolt Road 33-34.
Midweek home matchday: Tuesday   **Reserve Team's League:** N/A.
Record Attendance: 3,000 v Wealdstone FA Cup 1946.
Best F.A. Cup season: 2nd Rd 83-84, lost 1-2 at home to Newport County.
League clubs defeated in F.A. Cup: None.
Record Fees - Paid: To Dagenham for George Duck & Steve Jones
Received: £15,000 for Chris Hutchings (Chelsea)
Players progressing to Football League: Richard Shaw (Torquay 1947), Tom Carpenter (Watford 1950), Mike Bottoms (QPR 1960), Chris Hutchings (Chelsea 1980), Robert Holland (Crewe 1985), John Kerr (Portsmouth 1987).
Clubhouse: Open every day with normal licensing hours. Four bars, games room, varied entertainment venue for major sporting and social events.
Steward: Mike Cox
Club Record Scorer: Dave Pearce 153
Club Record Apps: Steve Emmanuel 478 (1st team only), Les Cunell 582, Colin Payne 538.
91-92 Captain: Mick O'Shea   **91-92 P.o.Y.:** Steve Crompton   **91-92 Top scorer:** Paul Ripley 22.
Local Papers (+Tel.Nos.): Harrow Observer (081 427 4404).   **Local Radio:** None.
Honours: Isthmian Lg 83-84 (R-up 78-79), Athenian Lg Div 2 R-up 63-64, Spartan Lg R-up 57-58, Spartan Lg R-up 57-58 (Div 2 West 38-39 (R-up 37-38)), Middx Senior Cup 82-83, Middx Charity Cup 79-80, FA Trophy SF 82-83, FA Amateur Cup 2nd Rd 63-64.

GOALKEEPERS:
Steve Crompton (Hounslow, Harrow B, Wycombe, Stockport, Carlisle)
DEFENDERS: Peter Byrne (Chesham, Altrincham, Runcorn, Liverpool, Everton), Mark Barnard (Sandridge R, Chesham, Hitchin, St Albans), Colin Payne (Youth), Steve Shea (St Albans, Hitchin, Hendon, Chesham, Stevenage B, St Albans, Edlesborough, Bedford), Mark Harrison (Wealdstone, Maidstone, Hayes), Craig Johnstone (St Albans, Harrow B, Staines, Wealdstone, Ruislip Park, Bradford C(J)), Lloyd Powell (Hounslow, Belmont)
MIDFIELD: Warren May (Chesham, Chelmsford, Barking, Chelmsford, Dartford, Maidstone, Southend), Micky Engwell (Chesham, Chelmsford, Barking, Chelmsford, Southend), Mick O'Shea (Chehsma, St Albans, Finchley, Boreham Wood), Steve Frazer (Met Police, Hendon, Southall, Harrow B), Neil Henry (Yeading, Hendon, St Albans, Hendon, Watford(J)), Mark Pye (Nth Greenford, West Ham(J)), Pat Ryan (Chesham, B Stortford, Takeley, B Stortford, Wrexham, Newcastle), Keith Cooper (Wimbledon(T))
FORWARDS: Steve Conroy (Kingstonian, Hitchin, Chesham, St Albans, Hemel Hempstead, Colchester(J)), Paul Ripley (Finchley, Ruislip Manor, Harrow B), Steven Ford (Kingsbury), Mark Kelly (Belfont), David Gipp (Chesham, Wealdstone, Barnet, Brighton), Jeremy Arnull (Yeading, St Albans), Rob Thorpe (Wycombe, Bracknell, Swindon(J)), Rob Smale (St Albans, Hayes, St Albans, Hayes, St Albans)

PROGRAMME DETAILS:
Pages: 24 **Price:** 70p
Editor: Jim Rogers
WMPCC Rating: 22

309

HAYES

Hayes players display understandable delight at Craven Cottage. John Stephen (No.10, third left) has just scored the second goal that clinched a 2-0 success against Third Division Fulham in the FA Cup First Round on 15th November 1991. Photo - Dave West.

Chairman: Derek Goodall   **Vice Chairman:** Alan Golby   **President:** L R Lovering
Secretary: John Price, 18 Ickenham Court, West Ruislip, Middx HA4 7DJ (0895 631933).
Team Manager: Clive Griffiths   **Asst Manager:** TBA   **Coach:** TBA
Press Officer: Emile Van Leer (081 573 2001)   **Physio:** TBA
Commercial Manager: Dave Kennedy.   **Sponsors:** L Goodall & Sons
Ground: Townfield House, Church Road, Hayes, Middx UB3 2LE (081 573 4598).
Directions: Close to M4 & A4020 (Uxbridge Rd). 1 mile from Hayes & Harlington (BR). Buses 90, H98 & 195.
Capacity: 9,000 (2,450 Covered)   **Seats:** 450   **Floodlights:** Y   **Shop:** Y   **Metal Badges:** Y
Colours: Red & white stripes/black/black   **Change colours:** Blue & white halves/blue/blue
Previous Leagues: Great Western Suburban 19-22/ London 22-24/ Spartan 24-30/ Athenian 30-71.
Previous Names: Botwell Mission 1909-24.   **Previous Ground:** Botwell Common.
Midweek home matchday: Tuesday   **Reserve Team's League:** Suburban (North).
Record Attendance: 15,370 v Bromley, FA Amateur Cup, February 1951.
Best F.A. Cup season: 2nd Rd replay 72-73. 1st Rd 13 times 27-28 31-32 33-34 38-39 46-47 64-65 72-74 87-92.
League clubs defeated in F.A. Cup: Bristol Rovers 72-73, Cardiff 90-91, Fulham 91-92.
Record Fees - Paid: £6,000 for Gary Keen (Hendon).   **Received:** £30,000 for Les Ferdinand (QPR).
Players progressing to Football League: Cyril Bacon (Orient 1946), Phil Nolan (Watford 1947), Dave Groombridge (Orient 1951), Jimmy Bloomfield (Brentford 1952), Derek Neale & Les Champelover (Brighton 1956 & 57), Gordon Phillips (Brentford 1963), Robin Friday (Reading 1974), Les Smith (A Villa & England), Cyrille Regis (WBA 1977), Les Ferdinand (QPR 1987).
Clubhouse: (081 573 0933). Open evening, all day Saturdays and Sunday lunchtimes. Snacks, dancehall.
Steward: Fred Heritage   **Club Record Scorer:**   **Club Record Apps:** Johnny Reay, 700 +
91-92 Captain: Reg Leather   **91-92 P.o.Y.:** Paul O'Reilly   **91-92 Top scorer:** John Lawford 13.
Local Newspapers (+Tel.Nos.): Hayes Gazette (0895 37161).   **Local Radio Stations:** Capital.
Honours: FA Amtr R-up 30-31 (SF 56-57), Isthmian Lg Cup R-up 78-79 80-81 87-88, Athenian Lg 56-57 (R-up 31-32 49-50), Spartan Lg 27-28 (R-up 25-26), Gt Western Suburban Lg(4) 20-24 (R-up 19-20), London Snr Cup 31-32 80-81 (R-up 36-37), London Snr Cup(8) 19-21 25-26 30-31 35-36 39-40 49-50 81-82, Middx Charity Cup (16 times), London Charity Cup 60-61, London Challenge Cup R-up 73-74, Middx Mnr Cup 11-12, FA Tphy 4th Rd 78-79.

GOALKEEPERS:
Paul O'Reilly (St Albans, London Colney, Dunstable)
DEFENDERS: Reg Leather (Southall, Hayes, Woking, Hillingdon, Hayes), Simon Asprey (Local football), Micky Bennett (Burnham, Hounslow, Burnham, Harrow B), Jason Court (Boreham Wood, Chalfont, St Albans), Warren Kelly (St Albans, Hemel Hempstead), Alan Myers (Kingstonian, Wycombe, Feltham), Andy Cox (St Albans, Berkhamsted, Tring, Chipperfield), Gary Churchouse (Takapuna(NZ), Hayes, Uxbridge, Southall, Maidenhead, Wealdstone, Charlton, Windsor)
MIDFIELD: Roy Marshall (Uxbridge, Hillingdon), Glenn Hayward (Hounslow, Brentford), Nicky Ryder (Brentford(T)), Darren Seabrook (Kelmscott(Aust)), Terry Benning (St Albans, Chesham, Hendon, St Albans, Tring, Northwood, Brentford, Watford(Sch)), Francis Cassidy (Aylesbury, Chesham, Harrow B, B Stortford, Peterborough, Watford), Colin Day (Thorn EMI), Alan Galloway (Local football)
FORWARDS: John Lawford (B Stortford, Luton), Steve Pope (Woking, Uxbridge), Chris Dixon (Uxbridge, Hillingdon), John Stephen (Local football), Chris Walton (Hanwell, Feltham, Kingstonian), Neal Stevens (Local football), Phil Wingfield (Walton & Hersham, Kingstonian, Walton & Hersham), Gary Eaton (QPR(T)), Phil Okoro (Local football), Darren Brown (Local football), Lance Pedlar (Leatherhead, Harrow B, Woking, St Albans, Chelmsford, Wealdstone, Hounslow, Wembley, Ruislip Manor)

Pages: 20 **Price:** 60p
Editor: Mark Owen
WMPCC Rating: 24

HENDON

Back Row (L/R): Alan Campbell, Victor Green (Chairman), Ronnie Duke (Coach), Paul Shirt, Andy Beattie, Kurt Davidson, Robbie Garvey, Dave Root, Adam King, Nigel Keen, Jude Monteath (Physio), Malcolm Stewart, Michael Cox (Secretary), Gwyn Walters (Manager). Front: Uche Egbe, Gary Keen, Roy Parkyn, Colin Sowerby, Marc Das, Tony Hopkins, Mark Xavier, Simon Clark.

Chairman: Victor Green   **Presidents:** Monty Hyams and Bobbie Butlin
Secretary: Michael Cox, 1 Myrtle Avenue, Eastcote, Ruislip, Middx HA4 8SA (081 866 8016).
Team Manager: Gwyn Walters   **Asst Manager:** Ronnie Duke   **Coach:** Ronnie Duke
Press Officer: Secretary   **Physio:** Jude Monteath
Ground: Claremont Road, Cricklewood, London NW2 1AE (081 201 9494).
Directions: Golders Green station, then bus 226. Brent Cross station then from east take first left after 'fly-over on North Circular.
Capacity: 8,000 (5,500 Covered)   **Seats:** 500   **Floodlights:** Y   **Shop:** Y   **Metal Badges:** Y
Colours: Green/white/green   **Change colours:** All yellow   **Sponsors:**
Previous Leagues: Finchley/ Middx 10-11/ London 11-14/ Athenian 19-63.
Previous Names: Hampstead Town 08-33/ Golders Green 33-46.
Previous Grounds: Kensal Rise 08-12/ Cricklewood Lane 12-26.   **Midweek matchday:** Tuesday
Reserve Team's League: Suburban Lg.   **Record Gate:** 9,000 v Northampton, FA Cup 1952.
Best F.A. Cup season: 3rd Rd replay 73-74 (lost 1-4 to Newcastle at Watford after 1-1 draw away). 1st Rd (15) 34-35 52-53 55-56 60-61 64-67 69-71 72-74 75-76 77-78 81-82 88-89.
League clubs defeated in F.A. Cup: Reading 75-76.
Record Fees - Paid: £4,500 for Martin Duffield (Enfield).   **Received:** £30,000 for Iain Dowie (Luton).
Players progressing to Football League: Arnold Siegel (Orient 1946), William Dare (Brentford 1948), Roy Stroud (West Ham 1952), Miles Spector (Chelsea 1950), Jeff Darey (Brighton), Doug Orr (QPR 1957), Peter Shearing (West Ham 1960), Iain Dowie (Luton 1988), Peter Anderson (Luton), Jeff Harris (Orient), Phil Gridelet (Barnsley 1990), Gerry Soloman (Leyton Orient 1991).
Clubhouse: (081 455 9185). Two bars open during normal licensing hours. Entertainment on Friday and Saturday evenings. **Social Managers:** Aiden & Eileen Maher.
Club Record Goalscorer: Freddie Evans 176 (1929-35)   **Club Record Apps:** Bill Fisher 787 (1940-62).
91-92 Captain: M Duffield   **91-92 P.o.Y.:** D Root   **91-92 Top scorer:** M Xavier.
Local Newspapers (+Tel.Nos.): Hendon Times (081 203 0411).   **Local Radio Stations:** Capital.
Hons: FA Amtr Cup 59-60 64-65 71-72 (R-up 54-55 65-66), European Amtr Champions 72-73, Isthmian Lg 64-65 72-73 (R-up 63-64 65-66 73-74, Lg Cup 76-77 (R-up 86-87)), Prem. Inter Lg Cup R-up 86-87, Athenian Lg 52-53 55-56 60-61 (R-up 28-29 32-33 47-48 48-49 51-52), London Lg Div 1 R-up 12-13 (Amtr Div 13-14), London Snr Cup 63-64 68-69 (R-up 35-36 50-51 54-55 58-59 71-72, Middx Snr Cup(11) 33-34 38-39 55-56 57-58 59-60 64-65 66-67 71-74 85-86 (R-up 83-84), Middx Charity Cup(14) 21-22 26-27 35-36 44-48 53-54 56-57 75-77 78-79 84-85 87-88, FA Tphy 3rd Rd replay 76-77 77-78.

GOALKEEPERS:
Dave Root (Eton M, Hendon, Walthamstow Ave, Barking, Launceston), **Simon Brading** (Youth)
DEFENDERS: Tony Hopkins (Aldershot, Bristol C, Newport Co), **Roy Parkyn** (Gravesend, Enfield), **Alan Campbell** (St Albans, Dagenham, Enfield, Dagenham, Leyt & Ilf, Hendon, Dagenham, Barnet, Hendon, Finchley), **Paul Shirt** (Barking, Hendon), **Kevin Fowler** (Arsenal(T)), **Simon Clark** (King's Lynn, Holbeach, Boston FC, Lincoln(J)), **Trevor Keen** (Army), **Andy Beattie** (Camb C, Barnet, Maidstone, Barnet, Camb Utd), **Robbie Garvey** (Redbridge F, Dartford, Grays, Billericay, Purfleet), **Paul Webb** (Brentford(T))
MIDFIELD: Gary Keen (Hayes, Hendon, St Albans, Hendon, St Albans, Chesham), **Marc Das** (Hertford, Grays, Harlow), **Malcolm Stewart** (B Stortford, Harlow, Redbridge F, Maidstone, Dartford, Maidstone, Dagenham, Hoddesdon), **Nigel Keen** (Enfield, Preston, Barrow, Arcadia(SA), Hendon), **Chris Harwood** (West Ham), **Leo Donnellan** (Wealdstone, Fulham, Chelsea), **Gary Donnellan** (Slough, Yeovil, Wealdstone, Reading, Watford, Chelsea)
FORWARDS: Uche Egbe (Watford(J)), **Mark Xavier** (Youth), **Troy Birch** (Kingsbury, Uxbridge), **Kurt Davidson** (Redbridge F, Dartford, Billericay, Leyt & Ilf, Hornchurch, Barking, Ford Utd), **Colin Sowerby** (Redbridge F, Dartford, Rainham, Leyton O, Southend, Hendon, Aveley, Tilbury), **Adam King** (Plymouth, West Ham), **Barry Blackman** (Dulwich, Gloucester, Wealdstone, Yeovil, Tooting, Edsbro(Swe), Croydon, Uppsala(Swe), Charlton(T))

Pages: 28 **Price:** 80p
Editor: Michael Cox
WMPCC Rating: 22

KINGSTONIAN

Back Row (L/R): Chris Kelly (manager), Keith Barratt, Francis Vines, Dave Pearce, Richard Cherry, Robert Franklin, Soloman Eriemo, Matthew Pearson, Micky Cook (asst manager). Front: Lee Davidson, Andy Dear, David Kempton, David Harlow, Roddy Braithwaite, Graham Pearce. Photo - V J Robertson.

Chairman: T D Weir   **President:** Ted Croker, CBE
Secretary (Add & Tel): W R McNully, 71 Largewood Av, Tolworth, Surbiton KT6 7NX (081 391 4522).
Team Manager: Chris Kelly   **Asst Manager:** Micky Cook   **Coach:** Fred Callaghan
Press Officer: Brendan Frawley (081 5415250)   **Physio:** Gary Scott
Ground Address & Tel: Kingsmeadow Stadium, Kingston Road, Kingston-on-Thames KT1 3PB (081 547 3335).
Directions: On A2043 Kingston to Malden road. 1 mile from Kingston (BR), bus 65 passes the ground.
Capacity: 6,500 (1,500 Covered)   **Seats:** 1,200   **Floodlights:** Y   **Shop:** Y   **Metal Badges:** Y
Colours: Red & white hoops/black/black   **Change colours:** All white   **Sponsors:** Hunting Gate 444.
Previous Leagues: Kingston & Dist/ West Surrey/ Southern Suburban/ Athenian 1919-29.
Previous Names: Kingston & Surbiton YMCA 1885-87/ Saxons 87-90/ Kingston Wanderers 1893-1904/ Old Kingstonians 08-19.
Previous Ground: Richmond Road until 1989.   **Newsline:** 0898 884 441.
Midweek home matchday: Tuesday   **Reserve Team's League:** Suburban Lg.
Record Attendance: 2,507 v Woking, November 1990. 11,000 at previous ground (Richmond Road) v Bishop Auckland, FA Amateur Cup 5/2/55.
Best F.A. Cup season: 1st Rd replay 1932 (after 2-2 draw at Luton lost 2-3 at home). 1st Rd on three other occasions; 1926 (0-1 at Nunhead), 1930 (0-3 at Tunbridge Wells), 1933 (1-7 at home to Bristol City).
League clubs defeated in F.A. Cup: None.
Record Fees - Paid: For Jimmy Brown (Slough)   **Received:** For Giles Still (Brighton)
Players progressing to Football League: Carlo Nastri (C Palace), Hugh Lindsay (Southampton 1965), Giles Still (Brighton 1979), David Byrne (Gillingham 1985), John Power (Brentford 1987).
Clubhouse: (081 547 3336). Open every lunchtime and evening. Three separate functions rooms with conference and banqueting facilities for all social and business events. **Steward:** Alan Dawkins
Club Record Goalscorer: Johnny Wing 295   **Club Record Apps:** Micky Preston 557.
91-92 Captain: **91-92 P.o.Y.:**   **91-92 Top scorer:**
Local Newspapers (+Tel.Nos.): Surrey Comet (081 546 2261).   **Local Radio Stations:** County Sound.
Hons: FA Amtr Cup 32-33 (R-up 59-60), Isthmian Lg 33-34 36-37 (R-up 47-48 62-63, Div 1 R-up 84-85), Athenian Lg 23-24 25-26 (R-up 26-27), London Snr Cup 62-63 64-65 86-87 (R-up 23-24 25-26 30-31 46-47 83-84), Surrey Snr Cup(9) 25-26 30-32 34-35 38-39 51-52 62-64 66-67.

GOALKEEPERS:
Adrian Blake (Walton & Hersham, Yeading, Feltham, Walton & Hersham)
DEFENDERS: Graham Pearce (Enfield, Maidstone, Brentford, Gillingham, Brighton, Barnet, Hillingdon), **Andy Dear** (Walton & Hersham, Epsom & Ewell, Leatherhead, Ronnskars IF(Fin), Wimbledon(J)), **Solomon Eriemo** (Wealdstone, Leyton-Wingate, Walthamstow Ave, Leyt & Ilf), **David Kempton** (Ditton, Molesey, Walton & Hersham, Kiwi Utd(NZ), Napier City(NZ), Wimbledon), **Geoff Thomas** (Dorking, Charlton), **Martin Nelmes** (Hounslow, Fulham(Sch)), **Jim Hicks** (Oxford Utd, Fulham), **Paul Underwood** (Youth)
MIDFIELD: Steve Galliers (Maidstone, Bristol C, Wimbledon, C Palace, Wimbledon, Chorley), **Paul Gbogidi** (Wealdstone, Dulwich, Croydon), **David Harlow** (Farnborough, Fulham), **Lee Davidson** (Woking), **Peter Woods** (Epsom & Ewell)
FORWARDS: David Pearce (Wokingham, Dagenham, Barnet, Harrow B, Wealdstone, Millwall), **Robin Lewis** (Enfield, Kingstonian, Tooting, Epsom & Ewell, Hampton, Leatherhead, Epsom & Ewell. Wimbledon(J)), **Richard Smart** (Woking, Whyteleafe, Leatherhead, Old Wilsonians), **Richard Cherry** (Redbridge F, Grays, Barking, Woodford, Colchester, Gillingham), **Roddy Braithwaite** (Farnborough, Fulham), **Francis Vines** (Molesey, Thames Poly, Carshalton)

PROGRAMME DETAILS:
Pages: 24 **Price:** 70p
Editor: William McNully
WMPCC Rating: 23

MARLOW

Marlow's biggest game this century; the line in the FA Cup First Round tie at West Bromwich Albion. Back Row (L/R): Phil George, Micky Poole, Steve Ellis, Kevin Stone, John Franks, Mark Watkins, Al-James Hannigan. Front: John Caesar, Dean Hooper, John Regan, David Lay, Paul West, Billy Hubbick. Photo - Rudi Gnoyke (Maidenhead Advertiser).

Chairman: Michael Eagleton   **President:** Mr L Goodway.
Secretary (Add & Tel): Paul Burdell, 69 Wycombe Road, Marlow, Bucks SL7 3HZ (0628 483722).
Team Manager: Dave Russell   **Asst Manager:** Laurie Craker   **Coach:**
Press Officer: Terry Staines   **Physio:** Brian Lay
Commercial Manager: Michael Eagleton.
Ground Address & Tel: Alfred Davis Memorial Ground, Oaktree Road, Marlow SL7 3ED (0628 483970).
Directions: A404 to Marlow (from M4 or M40), then A4135 towards town centre. Turn right into Maple Rise (by ESSO garage), ground in road opposite. 1 mile from Marlow (BR). Beeline bus to Chapel Street.
Capacity: 5,000 (300 Covered)   **Seats:** 260   **Floodlights:** Y   **Shop:** Y   **Metal Badges:** Y
Colours: Royal blue (white trim)   **Change colours:** Gold and black   **Sponsors:** Platts of Marlow.
Previous Leagues: Spartan 1908-10 28-65/ Great Western Suburban/ Athenian 65-84.
Previous Name: Great Marlow.
Previous Grounds: Crown Ground (prior to 1919)/ Star Meadow 19-24.
Midweek home matchday: Tuesday   **Reserve Team's League:** Suburban.
Record Attendance: 8,000 Slough v Wycombe, Berks & Bucks Final 1973.
Best F.A. Cup season: Semi Finals 1882. 1st Rd 18 times 1871-85 86-88 92-93 1991-92.
Players progressing to Football League: Leo Markham (Watford 1972), Naseem Bashir (Reading).
Clubhouse: Open most nights and Sunday lunchtimes.   **Steward:** Committee
Club Record Goalscorer: Kevin Stone 31   **Club Record Apps:** Mick McKeown 500+.
91-92 Captain: Kevin Stone   **91-92 P.o.Y.:** Al-James Hannigan   **91-92 Top scorer:** David Lay
Local Newspapers (+Tel.Nos.): Marlow Free Press (0494 21212), Maidenhead Advertiser (0628 771155), Evening Post (0734 575833).
Local Radio Stations: Radio 210
Honours: Isthmian Lg Div 1 87-88 (Div 2 South R-up 86-87), Spartan Lg Div 1 37-38 (Div 2 West 29-30), Berks & Bucks Senior Cup 1880-81 82-83 84-85 85-86 87-88 88-89 89-90 93-94 96-97 98-99 99-1900 90-91, FA Trophy 1st Rd 1987-88 91-92, FA Vase 5th Rd replay 74-75.

GOALKEEPERS:
Steve Ellis (Youth), **Gary Lester** (Chalfont, Slough, Wycombe, Chalfont)
DEFENDERS: Andy Harman (Wycombe), **Elvis Jack** (Staines, Flackwell, Maidenhead Utd, Chesham, Burnham, Reading(A)), **Tony White** (Flackwell, Marlow, Flackwell), **Al-James Hannigan** (Harlow, Harwich, Barnet, Arsenal(T)), **Richard Mikurenda** (Wycombe), **Kevin Tilley** (Leatherhead, Maidenhead Utd, Southall, Chalfont, Basingstoke, Slough, Hayes, Wycombe, Hayes, Aylesbury, Maidstone, Wimbledon, QPR)
MIDFIELD: Tony Dell (Chesham, Slough, Wycombe, Marlow), **Kevin Stone** (Beaconsfield, Maidenhead T, Wycombe), **Billy Hubbick** (Wycombe, Maidenhead Utd, Walton & Hersham, Marlow), **Paul West** (Hillingdon, Wycombe, Flackwell), **Neil Catlin** (Flackwell, Maidenhead Utd), **Phil George** (Hayes, Worthing, Walton & Hersham, Leatherhead, Kingstonian, Feltham, Staines, Hasselt(Belg), Addlestone), **Kenny Glasgow** (Flackwell, Chalfont, Marlow, Flackwell, Marlow, Flackwell), **Geoff Charles** (Wokingham, Marlow, Flackwell)
FORWARDS: John Regan (Hounslow, Wycombe, Chalfont, Hayes, Southall, Kingstonian, Burnham), **Martin Stone** (Chalfont, Uxbridge), **David Lay** (Dunstable, Chesham, Reading(A)), **Ray Jack** (Flackwell, Southall, Maidenhead Utd), **Mark Watkins** (Tring, Harrow B, Tring, St Albans, Aylesbury, Winslow), **Dean Hooper** (Youth), **John Caesar** (Flackwell, Oakridge)

Pages: 28 **Price:** 50p
Editor: Paul Burdell
WMPCC Rating: 22

ST ALBANS CITY

The Saints

Back Row (L/R): John Mitchell (manager), Trevor Wilkinson, Paul Price, Kevin Mudd, Steve Clark, Andy Hopping, John Lacy, Michael Danzey, Robert Dowie, Steve Storey. Ricky Cornish. Front: David Ross, Tony Joyce, Paul Hobson, Steve Scott, Craig Johnstone, Steve Ketteridge (capt, asst mgr), Ian Scott, John Colfer, Jimmy King, Gary Brooke, Bradley Anderson. Photo - John Sherwood.

Chairman: Bernard Tominey
Vice Chairman: John Mitchell
Secretary (Add & Tel): S R Trulock, 42 Heath Road, St Albans AL1 4DP (0727 834920).
Team Manager: John Mitchell
Press Officer: Dave Taverner (0582 64296)
Ground: Clarence Park, St Albans, Herts AL1 4QW (0727 866819).
Directions: 200 yards from station.
Patron: The Mayor of St Albans.
President: Malcolm McMillan.
Asst Manager: Steve Ketteridge.
Commercial Mgr: None at present.
Capacity: 7,000 (1,500 Covered)   **Seats:** 1,000   **Floodlights:** Y   **Shop:** Y   **Metal Badges:** Y
Colours: Yellow/blue/yellow   **Change colours:** Blue/yellow/blue   **Sponsors:** Interfax Plc.
Newsline: 0898 664 354.   **Previous Leagues:** Spartan 08-20/ Athenian 20-23.
Midweek home matchday: Tuesday   **Reserve Team's League:** Suburban.
Record Attendance: 9,757 v Ferryhill Athletic, FA Amateur Cup 27/2/26.
Best F.A. Cup season: 2nd Rd replay 68-69 (lost 1-3 at Walsall after 1-1 draw), 80-81 (lost 1-4 at Torquay after 1-1 draw). Also 1st Rd 25-26 26-27.
League clubs defeated in F.A. Cup: Brentford 24-25.
Record Fees - Paid: £5,000 for Martin Duffield (Sutton)
   Received: £40,000 for Tony Kelly (Stoke City).
Players progressing to Football League: Ronnie Burke (Man Utd), John Meadows (W'ford 1951), Mike Rose (Charlton 1963), Lee Kinear (Spurs 1965), John Mitchell (Fulham 1972), Allan Cockram (Brentford 1988), Dean Austin (Southend 1990), Tony Kelly (Stoke 1990), Robert Peters (Brentford).
Clubhouse: (0727 64296). Bar & boardroom open matchdays only.   **Steward:** Ray McCord
Club Record Goalscorer: W H (Billy) Minter 349 (1920-32)   **Club Record Apps:** Phil Wood 1,017 (62-84)
90-91 Captain: Steve Ketteridge   **90-91 P.o.Y.:** Paul Hobson   **90-91 Top scorer:** Steve Clark 29
Local Newspapers (+Tel.Nos.): Herts Advertiser, St Albans Review, St Albans Herald, St Albans Observer.
Local Radio Stations: BBC Radio Beds, Chiltern Radio.
Honours: Isthmian Lg 23-24 26-27 27-28 (R-up 54-55, Div 1 85-86, Div 2 R-up 83-84, Lg Cup R-up 89-90), Athenian Lg 20-21 21-22 (R-up 22-23), Spartan Lg 11-12 (R-up 09-10 12-13), Herts County Lg 09-10, London Senior Cup 70-71 (R-up 69-70), Herts Senior Cup 24-25 28-29 34-35 43-44 46-47 50-51 54-55 55-56 56-57 65-66 67-68 68-69 (R-up 10 times), Herts Senior Trophy 86-87, Herts Charity Cup (24 times) (R-up 17 times), AFA Senior Cup 33-34 (R-up 30-31 32-33 34-35), FA Amateur Cup SF 22-23 24-25 25-26 69-70, FA Trophy 2nd Rd 81-82.

GOALKEEPERS:
Lee Bozier (Baldock, Stevenage, St Albans), Simon Bartley (Youth), Gary Westwood (Wokingham, Reading, Ipswich)
DEFENDERS: Kevin Mudd (Harrow B, Finchley, Enfield, Mount Grace), **Steve Scott** (Dagenham, Hendon, Enfield, Dagenham, Leytonstone & Ilford, Cheshunt), **Paul Price** (Wivenhoe, Chelmsford, Peterborough, Saltash Utd, Swansea, Minnesota Kicks(USA), Spurs, Luton), **John Lacy** (Wivenhoe, St Albans, Barnet, Stanungsund(Swe), C Palace, Spurs, Fulham, Kingstonian), **Roy Edwards** (Dagenham, Leyton-Wingate)
MIDFIELD: Steve Ketteridge (Aylesbury, Leyton Orient, C Palace, Wimbledon, Derby), **Bob Dowie** (Hendon, St Albans, Hertford, Cheshunt, Hatfield T, Bishop's Stortford), **John Colfer** (Hitchin, London Colney), **Garry Brooke** (Wivenhoe, Reading, Brentford, Wimbledon, Norwich, Groningen(Holl), Spurs), **Martin Duffield** (Sutton Utd, Hendon, Enfield, QPR), **David Ross** (Wealdstone), **Marti Gurney** (Wokingham, Redbridge, Harrow B, St Albans)
FORWARDS: Steve Clark (Wivenhoe, Saffron Walden, Stansted), **Michael Danzey** (Peterborough, Notts Forest), **Bradley Anderson** (Boreham Wood, Watford(J)), **Jimmy King** (Wivenhoe, Harwich, Ipswich), **Trevor Wilkinson** (Hendon, Enfield, Bogndai(Nor), Enfield, Spurs), **Paul Halbert** (Aldershot, St Albans), **Dean Williams** (Wokingham, Hemel Hempstead, Chesham, Hemel Hempstead, St Albans, Camb Utd)

PROGRAMME DETAILS:
Pages: 44 **Price:** 75p
Editor: Mike Nelnyk
WMPCC Rating: 31

Formed: 1892   # STAINES TOWN   The Swans

Staines Town FC, who are enjoying their centenary in 1992, pictured before their FA Trophy confrontation with Heybridge Swifts. Photo - Eric Marsh.

Chairman: Alan Boon   **President:** Nigel Iggulsden
Secretary (Add & Tel): Len Gregory, 70 Convent Road, Ashford, Middx TW15 2EL (0784 255993).
Manager: Wayne Wanklyn   **Asst Mgr/Coach:** Micky Noades   **Physio:** Peter Judd
Press Officer: Steven Parsons (0784 450420)   **Sponsors:** McVittie
Ground: Wheatsheaf Park, Wheatsheaf Lane, Staines TW18 2PD (0784 455988).
Directions: From Staines (BR) turn right along Gresham Rd to 'T' junction, left into Laleham Rd and Wheatsheaf Lane is on right (ground 100 yards down on left). Buses 218, 518 and 767 pass Wheatsheaf Lane.
Capacity: 2,500 (850 Covered)   **Seats:** 250   **Floodlights:** Y   **Shop:** N   **Metal Badges:** £2.50
Colours: Old gold/blue/blue   **Change colours:** Sky blue & white halves/black/white
Previous Leagues: West London Alliance/ West Middx/ Gt Western Suburban 05-14 20-24/ Hounslow & District 18-20/ Spartan 24-35 58-71/ Middx Senior/ Parthenon 52-53/ Hellenic 53-58/ Athenian 71-73.
Previous Names: Staines Albany and St Peters Institute (merged) in 1905/Staines 05-18/Staines Lagonda 18-25/Staines Vale (pre-2nd World War).
Previous Grounds: Hammonds Farm, Linoleum Sports Grounds, Staines Moor, The Anglers Rest, Gorings Meadow, Shepperton Road (Raleham), Mill Mead.
Record Gate: 2,750 v Banco de Roma (Barassi Cup) 1975 *(70,000 saw 1st leg in Rome).*
Best F.A. Cup season: 1st Rd 84-85 (lost 0-2 at Burton Alb).   **Midweek home matchday:** Tuesday
Record Fees - Paid: Undisclosed for Richard Teale (Slough)
    Received: Undisclosed for Mark Dawber (Chesham).
Players progressing to Football League: Robert Bennett (Southend 1972), John Love (C Palace 1975), Peter Shaw (Charlton 1977), Eric Young (Brighton, W'don), Gordon Hill (M'wall, Man Utd, Derby, Wayne Stemp (Brighton), Martin Ferney (Fulham).
Clubhouse: Fully furnished clubhouse & function hall, open 7-11 pm.   **Steward:** Simon Fry
Club Record Goalscorer: Alan Gregory 122   **Club Record Appearances:** Dickie Watmore 840
91-92 Captain: John Crouch   **91-92 P.O.Y.:** John Crouch   **91-92 Top scorer:** Gary Crawshaw 10
Local Newspapers (+Tel.Nos.): Staines & Ashford News, Middx Chronicle.
Local Radio Stations: County Sound, LBC, GLR, Capital.
Hons: Isth. Lg Div 1 88-89 (Div 2 74-75), Ath'n Lg Div 1 R-up 72-73 (Div 2 71-72), Spartan Lg 59-60 (R-up 71-72, Lg Cup 68-69 (R-up 70-71)), Hel'c Lg R-up 55-56 (Lg Cup R-up 53-54 55-56), Gt West. Suburban Lg R-up(3) 11-12 22-24, W L'don Alliance Div 1 1899-1900, W L'don Lg Div 1 08-09, Middx Lg Div 2 20-21, L'don Snr Cup R-up 76-77 80-81, Middx Snr Cup(5) 74-77 87-88 89-90, Middx Jnr Cup 01-02 03-04, Barassi Cup 1976, Southern Amtr Comb Cup 64-65 66-67 68-69 (R-up 67-68), W Middx Cup 23-24, Staines Cottage Hosp Cup 24-25, FA Tphy 2nd Rd 2nd rep 76-77.

GOALKEEPERS:
Trent Phillips (Camberley, Staines, Wimbledon(J)), **Peter Lara** (Chelsea(A), QPR(Sch))
DEFENDERS:
John Crouch (Godalming), **Kevin Fidler** (Ashford(Middx)), **Steve Livey** (Leatherhead, Egham, Kingstonian, Staines, Addlestone, Walton & Hersham, Wimbledon), **Paul Cox** (Peppard, Newbury, Worthing, Brentford), **Steve Collins** (Camberley, Staines), **Martyn Latham** (Youth), **Micky Noad** (Wokingham, Farnborough, Wokingham, Addlestone, Hounslow, Walton & Hersham, Hounslow), **Alan Williams** (Wokingham, Thatcham, Newbury, Leatherhead)
MIDFIELD:
Simon Pentland (Farnborough, Wycombe, Hungerford, Wokingham), **Jon Price** (Wycombe, Watford), **Gerry Crawford** (Wokingham, Staines, Chertsey, Southall, Yeading, Woking, Wokingham, Reading(J)), **Nicky Jones** (Chalfont, Staines), **Gary Dodd** (Kingstonian, Slough, Kingstonian, Farnborough, Westfields), **Eurshall Fearon** (Thatcham, Woking, Wokingham, Burnham, Wokingham)
FORWARDS:
Gary Crawshaw (Luton), **Wayne Hancock** (Youth), **Steve Beeks** (Sutton Utd, Aldershot, Egham), **Brian Inch** (Fetcham, Staines, Virginia Water), **Stefan McGarrell** (Hillingdon, Northwood, Chalfont, Uxbridge, Southall, Yeading, Hayes, Staines, Watford(J), Arsenal(J)), **Neil Proctor** (Local football)

STAINES TOWN F.C. OFFICIAL PROGRAMME

SEASON 1984-85   THE SWANS   PRICE 25p

Pages: 40 **Price:** 70p
Editor: Steve Parsons & Stuart Moore
WMPCC Rating: 21

315

Stevenage Borough - Diadora League Division One champions 1991-92. Back Row (L/R): Paul Fairclough (Manager), Ray Lainchbury (Physiotherapist), Nigel Hann, Shaun Debnam, Gary Roberts, Miguel Luque, Richard Wilmot, Ian Fergusson, Ian Whitehead, Steve Cox, Paul Peterson (Assistant Manager). Front: Noel Blackwell, Shaun Marshall, Duncan Hardy, Ian Lindsay, Martin Gittings, Paul Bowgett, Dave Brown, Micky Nunn, Tony Ward, John Gibbs. Photo - D Rees.

Chairman: Ken Vale   **Vice Chairmen:** Keith Berners, John Jackson   **President:** Rod Resker
Secretary: John Jackson, 36 Kessingland Avenue, Stevenage, Herts SG1 2JR (0438 362045).
Team Manager: Paul Fariclough   **Asst Mgr:** Paul Peterson   **Coach:** Paul Peterson.
Press Officer: Martin Rosenburg (0438 743482)   **Physio:** Ray Lainchbury.
Commercial Manager: Mike Kitchener   **Treasurer:** Ken Solley.
Promotions Manager: Peter Taylor
Ground: Stevenage Stadium, Broadhall Way, Stevenage SG2 8RH (0438 367059).
Directions: Stevenage South exit off A1(M). Ground on right at second roundabout. One mile from Stevenage (BR). Buses SB4 and SB5.
Capacity: 6,000 (700 Covered)   **Seats:** 500   **Floodlights:** Y   **Shop:** Y   **Metal Badges:** Y
Colours: Red & white stripes/red/red   **Change colours:** All yellow (red trim)
Newsline: 0898 884487.   **Sponsors:** Several
Previous Leagues: Cliltern Youth/ United Counties/ Wallspan Southern Combination.
Midweek home matchday: Monday   **Reserves' League:** Essex & Herts Border Comb.
Record Gate: 3,000 v All Stars XI, May 1980. *(For league match: 1,551 v Hitchin, October 1991).*
Best F.A. Cup season: Third Qualifying Rd 86-87, lost 1-3 at home to Halesowen Town.
League clubs defeated in F.A. Cup: None.
Record Fees - Paid: **Received:** .
Players progressing to Football League: None.
Clubhouse: Open daily (lunch & evening). Dancehall, darts, pool.   **Steward:** Dave Wraight.
Club Record Goalscorer: Martin Gittings   **Club Record Apps:** Denny Tyler
91-92 Captain: Paul Bowgett   **91-92 P.o.Y.:** Richard Wilmot   **91-92 Top Scorer:** Martin Gittings
Local Newspapers (+Tel.Nos.): Stevenage Gazette, Comet, Herald & Post.
Local Radio Stations: Chiltern Radio, BBC Radio Bedfordshire.
Honours: Isthmian Lg Div 1 91-92 (Div 2 (North) 85-86 90-91), Utd Counties Lg Div 1 80-81 (Div 1 Cup 80-81), Herts Snr Cup R-up 85-86, Herts Charity Shield R-up 83-84, Televised Sports Snr Floodlit Cup 89-90.

GOALKEEPERS:
Richard Wilmott (Hitchin, Pirton)
DEFENDERS: Noel Blackwell (Vauxhall M, Tring, Chesham, Dunstable, Barton R, Barnet), **Nigel Hann** (Boreham Wood, Hitchin, St Albans, Boreham W), **Ian Whitehead** (Hitchin, Dunstable, Wembley, St Albans, Boreham W, St Albans, Camb Utd(J)), **Paul Bowgett** (Hitchin, Baldock, Wealdstone, Wimbledon, Spurs, Letchworth), **Steve Cox** (St Albans, Aylesbury, Barnet, Dagenham, Enfield, Spurs), **Miguel Luque** (Hertford, Harlow, B Stortford, Harlow), **Colin Hull** (Baldock, B Stortford, Watford)
MIDFIELD: Shaun Debnam (Hertford), **Micky Nunn** (Baldock, B Stortford, Hitchin, Hoddesdon, Camb Utd), **Shaun Marshall** (Youth), **Duncan Hardy** (Harrow B, Hendon, B Stortford, Barnet, Cheshunt, Hendon, Cheshunt, Finchley, St Albans), **David Brown** (Hitchin, Stevenage, Royston, Baldock, Hertford, Stevenage, Vauxhall M, Harlow), **Steve Graham** (Wembley, Basildon), **Steve Cook** (Stotfold), **Terry Milbourne** (B Stortford, Harlow, B Stortford, Camb City, Harlow, Southampton(A))
FORWARDS: Martin Gittings (Wivenhoe, Baldock, Wivenhoe, Harlow, Stevenage, Harlow, Letchworth, Hertford, Barnet, Stevenage, Hitchin, Stevenage), **Andy Walker** (Harlow, Boreham W, Grays, Harlow, San Diego Sockers(USA), Harlow), **Rob McComb** (Hertford), **Steve Flain** (Youth), **Ian Lindsay** (Hitchin, Rushden, Wellingboro, Kempston R, Bedford), **Mark Smith** (Hitchin, Woking, Hitchin, Letchworth, Hitchin)

Pages: 36 **Price:** 50p
Editor: Simon Mortimer
WMPCC Rating: 24

SUTTON UNITED

Sutton United before their FA Cup tie at Maidstone. Back Row (L/R): Alan Gane (Manager), Richard Parkin (Coach), Gwymme Berry, Sean Priddle, Steve Griffiths, Gary McCann, Paul Gates, Nigel Golley, Dominic Feltham, Stuart Massey, Frank Dotson (Asst Manager), Bill Webb. Front: Andy Scott, Mark Smith, Stewart Hemsley, Paul Rogers, Steve Beeks, Phil Dawson, Jimmy Dack. Photo - V J Robertson.

Chairman: David G Hermitage   **President:** Andrew W Letts.
Secretary (Add & Tel): Brian Williams c/o Sutton United.
Team Manager: Alan Gane   **Asst Manager:** Frank Dotson.
Press Officer: Tony Dolbear   **Coach:** Richard Parkin.
Ground: Borough Spts Ground, Gander Green Lane, Sutton, Surrey (081 644 5120/4440 Fax: 081 6445120).
Directions: Gander Green Lane runs between A232 (turn by Sutton Cricket Club) and A217 (turn at 'Gander' PH lights). Ground opposite 'The Plough' adjacent to West Sutton (BR).
Capacity: 8,000 (1,500 Covered)   **Seats:** 1,000   **Floodlights:** Y   **Shop:** Y   **Metal Badges:** Y
Colours: Amber (chocolate trim)   **Change colours:** White (chocolate trim).   **Sponsors:** Securicor.
Previous Leagues: Sutton Junior/ Southern Suburban 10-21/ Athenian 21-63/ Isthmian 63-86/ GMVC 86-91.
Previous Names: Sutton Association, Sutton Guild Rovers (merged in 1898).
Midweek home matchday: Tuesday   **Reserve Team's Lge:** Suburban. (Midweek: Capital).
Record Attendance: 14,000 v Leeds United, FA Cup 4th Rd 24/1/70.
Best F.A. Cup season: 4th Rd 69-70 88-89. Also 3rd Rd 87-88, 2nd Rd 81-82.
League clubs defeated in F.A. Cup: Aldershot, Peterborough 87-88/ Coventry City 88-89.
Record Fees - Paid: To Malmo FF for Paul McKinnon
               Received: For Efan Ekoku (Bournemouth)/ Andy Barnes (Crystal Palace)
Players progressing to Football League: M Robinson (C Pal), Charles Vaughan (Charlton 1947), Roy Hancox & Len Coules & Ray Colfar & Steven Galloway (C Pal 1950 & 51 & 58 & 84), T Barton (Fulham), Phil Woosnam (Orient 1955), Derek Gamblin (P'smouth 1965), Mike Pentecost (Fulham 1966), John Faulkner (Leeds 1970), Mike Mellows (Reading 1970), Mick Fillery (C'sea & QPR), Frank Cowley (Derby 1977), Paul McKinnon (B'burn 1986), Ron Fearon (I'wich 1987), Paul Harding (Notts Co via Barnet), Efan Ekoku (B'mouth 1991), Mark Golley (M'stone), Andy Barnes (C Palace 1991), Paul Rogers (Sheff Utd 1992), Stuart Massey (C Palace 1992).
Clubhouse: 3 bars open lunchtime & evenings. Halls and meeting rooms for hire.
Club Record Scorer: Paul McKinnon   **Club Record Appearances:** Larry Pritchard 781 (1965-84)
91-92 Captain: Nigel Golley   **91-92 P.o.Y.:** Nigel Golley **91-92 Top scorer:** Domenic Feltham
Local Newspapers (+Tel.Nos.): Sutton Herald, Croydon Advertiser, Sutton Guardian.
Hons: FA Tphy R-up 80-81, FA Amtr Cup R-up 62-63 68-69 (SF 28-29 36-37 67-68), Isth. Lg(3) 66-67 84-86 (R-up 67-68 70-71 81-82, Lg Cup(3) 82-84 85-86 (R-up 79-80), Loctite Cup 91-92), Ath'n Lg 27-28 45-46 57-58 (R-up 46-47), Anglo Italian Cup 78-79 (R-up 79-80 81-82), L'don Snr Cup 57-58 82-83, L'don Charity Cup 69-70 (R-up(3) 67-69 72-73), Surrey Snr Cup(11) 45-46 64-65 67-68 69-70 79-80 82-88 (R-up(8) 44-45 54-55 61-64 65-66 75-76 81-82), Surrey Prem. Cup 82-83 (R-up 85-86 88-89), Surrey Interm. Cup 66-67 71-72 78-79 81-82, Surrey Jnr Cup R-up 09-10, Surrey Snr Charity Shield(3) 33-34 36-38 (R-up 49-50 51-52 59-60 61-62 64-65 74-75, Surrey Interm. Charity Cup 31-32 (R-up 34-35 38-39).

GOALKEEPERS:
Gary McCann (Fulham), **Ron Fearon** (Ipswich, Sutton Utd, Reading, QPR)
DEFENDERS:
Steve Smart (Wealdstone, Barnet), **Neil Hopkins** (Youth), **Nigel Golley** (Whyteleafe), **Gary Elliott** (Youth), **Phil Davison** (Kingstonian), **Sean Priddle** (St Albans, Southall, Harrow B, St Albans, Brentford, Exeter, Crewe, Wimbledon), **Mark Costello** (Youth), **Gwynne Berry** (Whyteleafe, Banstead Ath, Whyteleafe), **Stuart Hemsley** (Croydon)
MIDFIELD:
Peter Evans (Croydon, Charlton), **Paul Gates** (Chipstead, Whyteleafe), **Stuart Massey** (Walton & Hersham, Carshalton, Sutton Utd, Chipstead), **Mark Underdown** (Staines, QPR(J)), **Jimmy Dack** (Epsom & Ewell), **Mark Golley** (Welling, Maidstone, Sutton Utd, C Palace), **Andy Parr** (Woking, Chertsey, Woking, Marlow, Farnborough, West Ham(A))
FORWARDS:
Dominic Feltham (Baltimore Blasts(USA), Chelsea(J)), **Mark Jenkins** (Youth), **Mark Smith** (Kingstonian, Wimbledon(T)), **Steve Browne** (Wealdstone, Barking, Wealdstone, Newmont Travel, Grays, Dartford, Maidstone, Fulham, Charlton), **Robin Seagroatt**(Redhill), **Andy Scott** (Youth), **Paul Tye** (Youth)

Formed: 1892

WINDSOR & ETON

The Royalists

Windsor & Eton's Derek Walters hares down the wing as team-mate Mark Woods (No.6) tangles with Grays Athletic striker Winston Whittingham. This Premier Division match, at Grays on April 11th 1992, finished scoreless. Photo - Paul Dennis.

Chairman: Michael Broadley   **President:** Sir David Hill-Wood, Bt
Secretary: Cynthia Cherry, 5 Clare Road, Taplow, Maidenhead, Berks SL6 0LH (0628 664533).
Team Managers: Brian Caterer   **Asst Manager:** Keith White   **Coach:** Jerry Williams.
Press Officer: Ian Lucas   **Physio:** Janet Howarth.
Ground: Stag Meadow, St Leonards Road, Windsor SL4 3DR (0753 860656).
Directions: A332 from M4 junct 6. Left at lights (B3173), ground 500 yards on right on B3022 opposite Stag & Hounds PH. 1 mile from town centre.
Capacity: 4,500 (650 Covered)   **Seats:** 320   **Floodlights:** Y   **Shop:** Y   **Metal Badges:** Y
Colours: Red (green piping)/red/white   **Change colours:** White/red/black   **Sponsors:** Rational Kitchens
Previous Leagues: Southern 1895-96/ West Berks/ Great Western Suburban 1907-22/ Athenian 22-29 63-81/ Spartan 29-32/ Great Western Comb/ Corinthian 45-50/ Metropolitan 50-60/ Delphian 60-63.
Previous Ground: Ballon Meadow 1892-1912.
Midweek home matchday: Tuesday   **Reserve Team's League:** Suburban
Record Attendance: 8,500 (Charity match).   **League clubs defeated in F.A. Cup:** None.
Best F.A. Cup season: 2nd Rd replay 83-84. 1st Rd on seven occasions; 25-26 80-81 82-86 91-92.
Record Fees - Paid: £9,000   **Received:** £10,000
Players progressing to Football League: Reg Dare (Southampton 1949), Steve Adams (Charlton 1979), Dave Barnett (Colchester 1988), Vic Woodley (Chelsea & England), Billy Coward (QPR, Walsall), Ken Groves (Preston), Dave Regis (Notts County).
Clubhouse: (0753 860656). Open six days a week 7.30-11 pm and Sunday lunchtimes. Darts & Pool.
Steward: Roy Underwood.
91-92 Captain: Mark Woods   **91-92 P.o.Y.:** Mark Woods   **91-92 Top scorer:** Richard Evans, 25
Local Newspapers (+Tel.Nos.): Windsor & Eton Express, Windsor & East Berks Observer, Evening Post.
Local Radio Stations: Radio 210
Hons: Isth. Lg Div 1 83-84 (Div 2 R-up 82-83), Ath'n Lg 79-80 80-81 (Lg Cup 79-80 (R-up 78-79 80-81), Div 2 Cup 63-64 (R-up 68-69)), Spart. Lg R-up 36-37 37-38 (Div 1 30-31), Metr'tan Lg R-up 53-54 (Lg Amtr Cup 51-52 52-53, Lg Cup 52-53 (R-up 53-54 54-55)), Gt West. Suburban Lg R-up 21-22, Berks & Bucks Snr Cup(11) 10-11 36-38 40-45 61-62 87-89 (R-up 07-08 24-25 26-27 38-39 46-47 62-63), Berks & Bucks Benev. Cup 35-36 37-38 46-47 62-63 (R-up 38-39 47-48 49-50), FA Amtr Cup 4th Rd 21-22, FA Vase SF 80-81 (QF 79-80), FA Tphy 3rd Rd 88-89.

GOALKEEPERS:
Kevin Mitchell (Slough, Leatherhead, Woking, Windsor, Egham, Reading),
Paul Frame (Youth), **Nigel Wiscombe** (Basingstoke, Hungerford, Bognor Regis, Andover, Basingstoke, Army)

DEFENDERS:
Derek Walters (Egham, Staines), **Robert Gold** (Slough, Hampton, Slough, Windsor), **Kevin Brown** (Wycombe, Weymouth), **Ian Richards** (Youth), **Mark Woods** (Walton & Hersham, Tooting, Windsor, Addlestone, QPR(J))

MIDFIELD:
Terry Merriman (Camb Utd, Coventry(T)), **Mark Mahoney** (Army, King's Lynn, Aston Villa), **Brian Connor** (Marlow, Chesham, Yeading, Slough, QPR(T)), **Steve Bates** (Army, Chalfont, Billingham Town), **Keith White** (Slough, Burnham, Chelsea(J)), **Jerry Williams** (Aldershot, Gillingham, Reading), **Steve Playle** (Slough)

FORWARDS:
Richard McDowell (Local football), **Stuart Walsh**(Youth), **Mark Franks** (Woking, Windsor, Maidenhead, Woking, Windsor), **Rowan Dodds** (Burnham, Windsor, Aylesbury, Windsor, Wycombe, Windsor, Slough), **Leroy Messitt** (Staines, Uxbridge, Staines, Slough, Staines, Wycombe, Brentford, Reading)

PROGRAMME DETAILS:
Pages: 24 **Price:** 60p
Editor: Steve Rowland
WMPCC Rating: 30

Formed: 1927   # WIVENHOE TOWN   The Dragons

Wivenhoe Town defender Lee Hunter (left) tangles with Roy McDonough, who had just been appointed as Colchester United's new manager, during a pre-season friendly at Broad Lane between the two very near neighbours. Photo - John Robinson.

Chairman: David Whymark   **President:** Harry Welsh
Secretary: R Adler, 794 Halling Hill, Harlow, Essex CM20 3JN (0279 436750).
Team Manager: Mick Loughton   **Asst Mgr:** Alan Springett   **Coach:**
Press Officer: John Robinson (0206 330382)   **Physio:** Martin Toole
Ground: Broad Lane Ground, Elmstead Road, Wivenhoe CO7 7HA (0206 823416).
Directions: Coming out of Colchester towards Clacton take first turning to Wivenhoe. Ground clearly visible on left turning left towards Clacton (B1027). 1 mile from Wivenhoe (BR).
Capacity: 4,000 (3,000 Covered)   **Seats:** 500   **Floodlights:** Y   **Shop:** Y   **Metal Badges:** Y
Colours: Royal blue/white/white   **Change colours:** All white   **Newsline:** 0898 884 458.
Previous Leagues: Brighlingsea & Dist/ Colchester & East Essex/ Essex & Suffolk/ Essex Senior 79-86.
Midweek home matchday: Tuesday   **Reserve Team's League:** Essex & Herts Border Comb.
Record Attendance: 1,912 v Runcorn, FA Trophy 1st Rd, Feb 1990.
Best F.A. Cup season: 4th Qual Rd 89-90 (lost 2-3 at Halesowen Town).
Record Fees - Paid: N/A   **Received:** Bobby Mayes (Redbridge Forest), Steve Clark (St Albans City).
Players progressing to Football League: None.
Clubhouse: (0206 825380). Open 12-2.30, 6.30-11pm daily (except Sunday), 4.30-11pm Saturdays.
Steward: Rob Proops.
Club Record Goalscorer: Paul Harrison   **Club Record Apps:** Keith Bain.
91-92 Captain: Steve Wright   **91-92 P.O.Y.:** Wayne Hannigan   **91-92 Top scorer:** Steve Restarick.
Local Newspapers (+Tel.Nos.): East Anglian Daily Times, Colchester Evening Gazette.
Local Radio Stations: BBC Radio Essex, Radio Orwell, BBC TV (Norwich).
Hons: FA Tphy 2nd Rd replay 89-90, FA Vase 5th Rd 82-83, Isth. Lg Div 1 89-90 (Div 2 Nth 87-88), Ess. Snr Lg R-up 79-80 81-82 85-86 (Harry Fisher Tphy 83-84 85-86), Ess. & Suff. Border Lg 78-79 (Div 1 72-73, Div 2 71-72, Lg Cup R-up(2) 75-77), Colch. & E Essex Lg 52-53 55-56 (R-up 70-71, Div 1 59-60 69-70, Lg Cup 52-53), Brighlingsea & Dist Lg Div 1 35-36 36-37 (R-up 37-38, Section A 47-48, Lg Knock-out & Challenge Cups 36-37), Ess Snr Tphy 87-88, Ess. Jnr Cp R-up 55-56 78-79 (Group Finalists(3) 52-53 70-72), Amos Charity Cp(7) 36-38 51-56 (R-up 72-73), Stokes Cup(3) 48-49 52-54, Wivenhoe Charity Cp 52-53 68-69 73-74 (R-up 69-70 72-73), Cristal Monopole Cp 68-69 (R-up 65-66 67-68), Sidney James Mem Tphy 69-70 (R-up 72-73), Tolleshunt D'Arcy Mem Cp(3) 71-74 (R-up 70-71 77-78), Walton & Dist Charity Cp 73-74 78-79, Coggeshall Brotherhood Cp 80-81, Worthington Evans Cup 81-82 (R-up 80-81 85-86), Harwich Snr Cp R-up 84-85, Woodbridge Chal. Cup 91-92.

GOALKEEPERS:
Gerry Warner (ex-Wivenhoe, out of retirement)

DEFENDERS:
Steve Dowman (Brightlingsea, Camb Utd, Newport Co, Charlton, Wrexham, Colchester), **Steve Wright** (Chelmsford, Rhyl, Crewe, Torquay, Wrexham, HJK Helsinki(Fin), Colchester), **Steve Howe** (Brightlingsea, Clacton), **Jonathon March** (Brightlingsea), **Phil Coleman** (Colchester, Millwall, Dulwich, Aldershot, Exeter, Chelmsford, Colchester, Millwall), **Lee Hunter** (Wigan, Colchester)

MIDFIELD:
Sean Duffett (Gas Recreation, Colchester(T)), **Gary Harvey** (Harwich, Bury T, Braintree, Clacton, Harwich, Wivenhoe, Clacton), **Shaun Bailey** (Brightlingsea), **Wayne Hannigan** (Colchester)

FORWARDS:
Mitchell Springett (Baldock, Bury T, Chelmsford, Witham, Braintree, Wivenhoe, Heybridge, Harlow, Colchester, Camb Utd), **Sven Alexis** (Youth), **Jeff Welsh** (Gas Recreation)

Pages: 52 **Price:** 50p
Editor: Mike Boyle
(0206 870879)
WMPCC Rating: 28

WOKINGHAM TOWN

Wokingham Town line up for the camera before their FA Trophy Third Qualifying Round home tie against Salisbury. Photo - Eric Marsh.

Chairman: G Gale   **President:** A McKinley.
Secretary: John Aulsberry, 24 Shefford Crescent, Wokingham RG11 1YP (0734 790441).
Manager: Roy Merryweather   **Asst Manager:** Terry Brown   **Coach:** Terry Brown
Press Officer: John Ansell (0734 787699)   **Physio:** D Lane
Comm Manager: Roy Merryweather (0734 780253).
Ground: Finchampstead Road, Wokingham, Berks RG11 2NR (0734 780253).
Directions: Half mile from town centre - turn down Denmark Street (A321 towards Camberley & Sandhurst. After 2 r'bouts ground entrance on right immediateley after railway bridge. Half mile from Wokingham (BR).
Capacity: 4,500 (1,500 Covered)   **Seats:** 250   **Floodlights:** Y   **Shop:** Y   **Metal Badges:** Y
Colours: Amber/black/black   **Change colours:** Red/white/red.   **Sponsors:** Glentworth.
Previous Leagues: Reading & Dist, Great Western Comb 07-54/ Metropolitan 54-57/ Delphian 57-59/ Corinthian 59-63/ Athenian 63-73.
Previous Grounds: Oxford Road, Wellington Road, Langborough Road.
Midweek home matchday: Tuesday   **Reserve Team's League:** Suburban, Capital.
Record Attendance: 3,473 v Norton Woodseats, FA Amateur Cup 57-58.
Best F.A. Cup season: 1st Rd replay 82-83 (lost 0-3 at Cardiff after 1-1 draw).
League clubs defeated in F.A. Cup: None.
Record Fees - Paid: £5,000 for Fred Hyatt (Burnham)   **Received:** £25,000 for Mark Harris (C Palace).
Players progressing to Football League: Ian Kirkwood (Reading 1953), John Harley (Hartlepool 1976), Kirk Corbin (Cambridge 1978), Phil Alexander (N'wich 1981), Doug Hatcher (A'shot 1983), Steven Butler & George Torrance (Brentford 1984), Mark Harris (C Palace 1988), Gary Smart (Oxford 1988), Darren Barnard (Chelsea 1990), Paul Holsgrove (Luton Town 1991).
Clubhouse: Open for lunches. Whippet racing May to October.   **Steward:** K Merryweather.
Club Record Goalscorer: Dave Pearce 79.   **Club Record Apps:** Dave Cox 533.
91-92 Captain: Dean Murphy   **91-92 P.o.Y.:** Darron Wilkinson   **91-92 Top scorer:** Dave Thompson 21
Local Newspapers (+Tel.Nos.): Wokingham Times (782000), Wokingham News (Bracknell 20363), Reading Evening Post (55875).
Local Radio Stations: Radio 210.
Honours: Isthmian Lg R-up 89-90 (Div 1 81-82), Berks & Bucks Snr Cup 68-69 82-83 84-85, Berks & Bucks Intermediate Cup 52-53, FA Tphy SF 87-88, FA Amtr Cup 4th Rd 57-58.

GOALKEEPERS:
Steve Aldham (Chertsey, Wokingham, Maidenhead Utd)

DEFENDERS:
Chris Hodge (Basingstoke, Farnborough, Kingstonian, Farnborough, Southampton), Bobby Purser (Youth), Jimmy Devereux (Basingstoke, Aldershot), Dean Murphy (Barnet, Harpenden), Martin Malins (Reading(T)), Colin Smith (Aldershot, Cardiff, See Bee(HK), Norwich, Notts Forest)

MIDFIELD:
Darron Wilkinson (Youth), Freddie Hyatt (Burnham, Ruislip), Kevin Merryweather (Youth), Gary Woolf (Hemel Hempstead, St Albans, Hemel Hempstead, Camb Utd), Ian McGrath (Youth), James Bradley (Staines), Andy McKenzie (Local football), Gary Woolf (Hemel Hempstead, St Albans, Hemel Hempstead, Camb Utd)

FORWARDS:
Elliott Pearce (Youth), Danny Allsop (Southampton(T)

V. ENFIELD
A.C. DELCO CUP 1st. ROUND
Wednesday, 12th September, 1990
Programme 60p

PROGRAMME DETAILS:
Pages: 20 **Price:** 60p
Editor: Ann Gale
WMPCC Rating: 16

YEADING

With a helping hand from Croydon's Dave Boyton, Yeading's Alan Aroren is able to climb high enough to make a clearing header. Yeading won this First Division fixture 3-0 at the Sports Arena as they continued their unassailable march up the Pyramid. Photo - Alan Coomes.

Chairman: Phillip Spurden   **President:** Mr R Carter
Secretary (Add & Tel): Peter Bickers, 67 Syke-ings, Richins Park, Iver Bucks SL0 9ES (0753 653103).
Team Manager: Gordon Barrett   **Asst Manager:** Leo Morris   **Coach:** W Wordsworth.
Press Officer: Simon Cox (0895 30744)   **Physio:** Edward Cole
Commercial Manager:
Ground Address & Tel: The Warren, Beaconsfield Road, Hayes, Middx (081 848 7362).
Directions: Two miles from Hayes (BR) - take Uxbridge Road and turn right towards Southall, right into Springfield Road and then left into Beaconsfield Road. Bus 207 stops half mile from ground.
Capacity: 3,000 (300 Covered).   **Seats:** 100   **Floodlights:** Y   **Shop:** N   **Metal Badges:** Y
Colours: Red & black stripes/black/black   **Change colours:** Yellow
Sponsors: Wings Coaches.
Previous Leagues: Hayes & District Yth/ Uxbridge/ S W Middx 1967-74/ Middx 74-84/ Spartan 1984-87.
Midweek home matchday: Tuesday   **Reserve Team's League:** Suburban Lg (North).
Record Attendance: 3,000 v Hythe Town, FA Vase SF 1990.
Best F.A. Cup season: 4th Qualifying Rd.
League clubs defeated in F.A. Cup: None.
Record Fees - Paid: **Received:**
Players progressing to Football League:
Clubhouse: Open normal pub hours.   **Steward:** Jim Pilkington (081 848 7362).
Club Record Goalscorer: D Burt 327   **Club Record Apps:** Norman Frape.
91-92 Captain: S Croad   **91-92 P.O.Y.:**   **91-92 Top scorer:**
Local Newspapers (+Tel.Nos.): Hayes Gazette.   **Local Radio Stations:**
Honours: FA Vase 89-90, FA Tphy 3rd Qual. Rd 90-91, Isth. Lg Div 2 Sth 89-90 (Div 1 R-up 91-92), Spartan Lg 86-87 (R-up 85-86, Senior Div R-up 84-85, Lg Cup 85-86 86-87), Middx Snr Lg(6) 71-73 74-76 81-82 83-84 (R-up 73-74 74-75 78-79, Lg Cup(6) 72-73 75-76 79-83), South West Middx Lg(2) 69-71, Middx Snr Cup 89-90 91-92, Middx Prem. Cup 80-81, Middx I'mediate Cup(5) 70-72 74-76 77-78, Middx Jnr Cup(4) 68-69 70-72 74-75, Uxbridge Lg 66-67, Middx Border Lg Cup 86-87 (AJA Cup 86-87), Suburban Lg Nth 87-88, Allied Counties Yth Lg 89-90 (Lg Cup 89-90).

GOALKEEPERS:
Stuart Mackenzie (Harrow B, Hounslow, Southall, Hounslow), **Matthew Fox** (Local football)
DEFENDERS: Jason Tucker (Aldershot), **Alan Ardren** (Hayes, Yeading, Southall, Ruislip, Yeading), **Iain Williams** (Borough Rd Coll, Bristol C, Plymouth), **Steve Croad** (Farnborough, Carshalton, Southall, Hounslow, Addlestone), **Phil Dicker** (St Albans, Southall, Harrow B, Hanwell, Brentford(J)), **Robbie Johnson** (Slough, Enfield, Harrow B, Hayes, Brentford, Arsenal)
MIDFIELD: Steve Cordery (Chesham, Uxbridge, Windsor, Maidenhead, Egham, Hampton, Maidenhead, Feltham, Hayes), **Jon Denton** (Hounslow, Harefield, Hillingdon), **Paddy McCarthy** (Chesham, Farnborough, Yeovil, Weymouth, Wealdstone, Chelsea), **Fergus Moore** (Brentford(T)), **Mark Harmsworth** (Hayes, Fisher, Hampton, Kingstonian, Hampton, Epsom & Ewell), **Roger Moses** (Northwood, Yeading), **Charlie Oatway** (Youth)
FORWARDS: Hector Welsh (Hive), **Stokeley Sawyers** (Harrow B, Finchley, Harrow B, Dulwich, Walton & Hersham, Sollestea(Swe), Chelsea), **Roy Lee** (Kingstonian), **Lee Charles** (Youth), **Lee Holman** (Walton & Hersham, Croydon, Hampton), **Jerry Murphy** (Wealdstone), **Kevin Quinn** (Hendon, Ruislip Manor, Walthamstow Ave), **Vinnie Murphy** (Kingsbury, Yeading)

YeadingFC 40p

SPONSORED BY
WINGS LUXURY TRAVEL LTD.

1990/91 SEASON
PROGRAMME & FIXTURES
THE ANDREW'S LEAGUE DIVISION ONE

PROGRAMME DETAILS:
Pages: 36 **Price:** 50p
Editor: Les Pratt
WMPCC Rating: 24

First Division

	P	W	D	L	F	A	Pts
Stevenage Borough	40	24	10	6	83	34	82
Dulwich Hamlet	40	22	9	9	71	40	75
Boreham Wood	40	22	7	11	65	40	73
Wembley	40	21	6	13	54	43	69
Abingdon Town	40	19	8	13	60	47	65
Worcester City	40	19	8	13	60	47	65
Tooting & Mitcham United	40	16	13	11	57	45	61
Hitchin Town	40	17	10	13	55	45	61
Walton & Hersham	40	15	13	12	62	50	58
Molesey	40	16	9	15	55	61	57
Dorking	40	16	7	17	68	65	55
Barking	40	14	11	15	51	54	53
Chalfont St Peter	40	15	6	19	62	70	51
Leyton-Wingate	40	13	11	16	53	56	50
Uxbridge	40	13	8	19	47	62	47
Maidenhead United	40	13	7	20	52	61	46
Harlow Town	40	11	9	20	50	70	42
Croydon	40	11	6	23	44	68	39
Heybridge Swifts	40	8	9	23	33	71	33
Whyteleafe	40	7	10	23	42	78	31
Aveley	40	8	3	29	33	95	27

Leading Scorers (League Only)

Martin Gittings (Stevenage Borough)	29
Phil Grainger (Dorking)	22
Steve Portway (Barking)	21
Steve Kuhne (Uxbridge)	19
John Collins (Tooting)	19

THE DIADORA LEAGUE FIRST DIVISION RESULT CHART 1991-92

HOME TEAM	1	2	3	4	5	6	7	8	9	10	11	12	13	14	15	16	17	18	19	20	21
1. Abingdon T	*	3-0	2-2	1-2	1-0	1-0	2-0	2-1	2-1	7-1	2-2	0-0	1-2	3-2	4-0	1-1	1-2	1-0	1-0	0-3	1-3
2. Aveley	0-1	*	2-1	1-2	2-0	0-4	2-0	2-5	0-4	0-0	1-0	1-5	1-0	1-1	0-4	0-2	0-4	1-0	0-2	0-1	0-2
3. Barking	1-0	5-1	*	2-0	1-0	3-3	2-1	2-0	0-1	1-0	0-2	2-2	2-0	1-1	1-3	0-3	0-1	0-1	1-1	2-1	1-1
4. Boreham W.	2-0	4-0	1-1	*	4-2	3-0	3-3	1-1	0-1	0-0	3-0	3-1	1-0	2-1	0-3	4-0	3-0	2-3	1-2	2-2	0-1
5. Chalfont SP	1-3	1-2	1-2	1-1	*	1-1	3-2	1-2	2-0	4-1	1-1	1-2	0-1	2-0	0-0	2-0	2-1	1-1	1-2	2-1	2-4
6. Croydon	0-0	1-0	1-3	0-1	4-3	*	3-2	0-4	0-0	1-0	2-0	2-0	1-0	0-1	1-1	1-2	0-3	0-1	2-3	0-3	0-3
7. Dorking	3-0	3-1	2-2	0-1	2-3	1-0	*	3-1	0-3	1-2	4-0	3-3	0-2	0-2	3-1	1-3	0-3	3-0	2-1	0-2	1-1
8. Dulwich H.	1-1	2-0	3-0	1-0	2-3	6-1	3-4	*	1-0	3-0	3-1	1-0	2-1	0-1	0-1	1-1	2-1	2-2	1-0	1-1	0-0
9. Harlow T	1-3	2-3	0-2	0-1	1-3	2-1	0-2	2-0	*	0-1	2-1	2-1	2-2	0-1	0-2	2-2	1-5	2-3	2-5	1-1	1-3
10. Heybridge	0-1	2-1	1-1	2-3	2-4	2-0	1-3	0-2	1-1	*	0-0	1-3	0-3	0-2	0-3	2-3	2-0	0-0	1-3	3-1	0-2
11. Hitchin T.	1-1	5-2	1-0	2-1	1-3	1-1	1-2	0-1	1-0	1-0	*	3-1	2-0	1-1	1-1	0-1	2-0	0-0	4-0	2-0	1-0
12. L-Wingate	1-0	4-2	0-3	0-3	0-2	1-0	1-2	1-1	0-0	2-0	1-3	*	1-2	0-0	2-2	2-1	4-0	1-3	2-1	3-0	1-0
13. Maidenhead	1-2	3-2	4-0	0-2	3-1	0-1	1-3	0-1	3-3	1-1	1-3	3-2	*	1-2	0-3	0-3	2-1	1-2	0-0	1-2	0-2
14. Molesey	0-2	2-1	4-0	0-1	2-1	2-4	0-3	0-4	1-1	3-1	2-4	0-0	1-3	*	1-1	2-1	4-1	0-3	1-2	2-1	2-4
15. Stevenage	4-1	5-0	2-0	2-0	5-1	4-2	2-1	1-1	7-1	3-1	2-0	4-1	2-0	3-2	*	2-0	2-0	3-2	2-0	4-0	2-2
16. Tooting	2-1	3-0	1-1	0-1	1-3	3-2	2-2	2-2	2-3	2-0	0-0	1-0	2-1	0-0	3-1	*	2-0	0-0	0-1	3-1	0-1
17. Uxbridge	1-2	1-0	0-0	2-3	2-0	1-0	1-1	1-2	1-3	1-1	1-1	0-2	2-2	2-3	1-3	1-1	*	2-1	0-0	2-0	0-3
18. Walton & H	1-1	4-2	3-2	2-1	1-2	2-0	2-2	0-1	2-2	0-0	2-1	1-1	2-2	0-1	2-3	1-1	4-0	*	0-1	4-1	2-2
19. Wembley	2-1	3-1	2-1	1-0	2-2	1-0	2-0	3-2	1-0	0-1	3-2	2-1	1-2	0-2	0-1	1-0	1-1	0-3	*	1-1	0-0
20. W'leafe	1-3	1-1	1-3	2-2	2-0	2-3	0-1	1-4	1-3	1-3	0-2	1-1	0-2	1-1	0-1	1-0	1-1	0-3	1-3	*	1-1
21. Yeading	2-1	3-0	1-0	0-1	5-0	4-2	3-2	0-1	3-0	4-0	0-2	0-0	2-2	6-2	4-0	1-1	1-2	2-0	2-1	5-2	*

THE DIADORA LEAGUE FIRST DIVISION ATTENDANCE CHART 1991-92

HOME TEAM	1	2	3	4	5	6	7	8	9	10	11	12	13	14	15	16	17	18	19	20	21
1. Abingdon T	*	180	234	227	177	211	224	405	210	216	225	201	478	142	324	220	310	341	291	144	202
2. Aveley	85	*	165	85	120	85	75	105	65	110	135	95	95	55	175	105	65	105	75	80	90
3. Barking	102	186	*	102	104	155	91	137	86	87	102	104	102	55	127	137	116	81	93	52	124
4. Boreham Wd	146	109	110	*	110	101	130	142	130	120	252	109	121	113	270	110	229	135	124	102	182
5. Chalfont SP	85	78	110	108	*	60	165	65	131	128	150	65	118	108	256	150	195	147	101	87	206
6. Croydon	75	72	66	175	127	*	85	126	86	121	48	70	105	63	140	88	68	110	90	337	65
7. Dorking	175	166	152	168	126	186	*	140	178	147	196	133	187	163	258	179	129	186	257	152	152
8. Dulwich H.	158	185	131	145	116	175	153	*	122	102	144	125	130	123	231	243	128	171	128	152	110
9. Harlow Town	108	85	95	78	84	79	67	99	*	114	117	70	112	94	245	85	30	80	51	109	108
10. Heybridge	168	142	126	142	123	157	147	172	214	*	172	129	136	146	255	136	147	177	146	156	156
11. Hitchin T.	329	350	306	190	288	251	236	366	409	410	*	313	326	260	889	422	235	277	205	239	278
12. L-Wingate	121	90	127	105	129	106	108	161	129	145	71	*	111	108	158	141	126	108	110	74	84
13. Maidenhead	309	191	162	208	204	189	219	241	192	261	218	234	*	204	341	208	155	242	142	221	194
14. Molesey	89	41	65	98	51	80	110	125	76	75	108	105	120	*	119	101	86	206	79	79	145
15. Stevenage	718	561	591	702	938	542	521	417	601	527	1551	329	585	554	*	525	678	546	465	771	737
16. Tooting & M.	122	144	151	143	154	135	147	304	134	150	146	177	123	126	185	*	137	132	129	137	97
17. Uxbridge	78	139	95	99	103	72	121	111	114	106	88	110	127	94	209	105	*	92	127	72	282
18. Walton & H.	126	102	112	86	83	127	194	214	106	108	152	157	282	263	266	102	137	*	146	170	122
19. Wembley	110	119	106	191	114	87	110	151	91	89	75	109	160	130	206	72	90	84	*	113	176
20. Whyteleafe	87	101	105	72	113	145	168	85	77	137	59	136	68	138	190	74	113	69	*		109
21. Yeading	107	92	117	115	134	120	145	110	140	157	173	110	159	108	208	151	268	209	115	124	*

NB. Walton v Heybridge, Tooting & Boreham Wood played at Staines. Harlow v Wembley at Stevenage, v Aveley at Bishop S'ford, v Uxbridge at Aveley. All Dulwich home games played at Tooting.

Div. One 10-year record

	82/3	83/4	84/5	85/6	86/7	87/8	88/9	89/90	90/1	91/2
Abingdon Town	-	-	-	-	-	-	-	-	-	6
Aveley	11	12	13	22	-	-	-	-	4	21
Barking	-	-	-	-	-	-	-	-	-	12
Basildon United	-	-	16	18	12	7	21	-	-	-
Basingstoke Town	-	-	-	-	-	-	2	-	-	-
Billericay Town	-	-	-	-	13	20	-	-	-	-
Boreham Wood	6	5	17	9	8	4	11	7	14	4
Bracknell Town	-	-	-	-	3	19	20	-	-	-
Bromley	-	-	8	2	-	-	-	-	2	-
Chalfont St Peter	-	-	-	-	-	-	16	11	11	13
Chesham United	15	9	4	20	-	18	14	10	1	-
Cheshunt	18	21	-	-	-	-	-	-	-	-
Clapton	-	20	21	-	-	-	-	-	-	-
Collier Row	-	-	-	-	-	-	19	-	-	-
Croydon	-	-	-	-	-	-	-	17	17	18
Dorking	-	-	-	-	-	-	-	6	10	11
Dulwich Hamlet	-	-	-	-	-	-	-	-	12	3
Epsom & Ewell	16	2	-	-	20	-	-	-	-	-
Farnborough Town	3	6	1	-	-	-	-	-	-	-
Feltham	14	22	-	-	-	-	-	-	-	-
Finchley	-	-	-	13	22	-	-	-	-	-
Grays Athletic	-	-	-	14	6	2	-	-	-	-
Hampton	9	7	9	5	11	9	17	19	-	-
Harlow Town	2	-	-	21	-	-	-	8	13	17
Hertford Town	4	14	22	-	-	-	-	-	-	-
Heybridge Swifts	-	-	-	-	-	-	-	-	18	19
Hitchin Town	-	-	-	-	-	-	4	4	5	8
Hornchurch	19	18	18	19	-	-	-	-	-	-
Kingsbury Town	-	-	-	-	7	14	8	22	-	-
Kingstonian	12	19	2	-	-	-	-	-	-	-
Leatherhead	-	11	3	15	10	10	12	20	-	-
Lewes	17	16	15	11	15	16	6	15	20	-
Leytonstone-Ilford	-	-	-	12	1	-	-	-	-	-
Leyton-Wingate	-	-	-	6	2	-	-	-	-	14
Maidenhead United	20	4	11	17	21	-	-	-	-	16
Marlow	-	-	-	-	-	1	-	-	-	-
Metropolitan Police	7	8	20	-	-	-	13	9	21	-
Molesey	-	-	-	-	-	-	-	-	8	10
Oxford City	5	15	14	4	17	12	-	-	-	-
Purfleet	-	-	-	-	-	-	-	21	-	-
St Albans City	21	-	6	1	-	-	-	-	-	-
Southwick	-	-	-	-	4	11	15	3	19	-
Staines Town	-	-	10	8	14	5	1	-	-	-
Stevenage Borough	-	-	-	-	16	21	-	-	-	1
Tilbury	13	10	7	16	19	-	-	-	-	-
Tooting & Mitcham United	-	-	-	-	-	-	-	12	6	7
Uxbridge	-	-	-	7	9	17	9	18	16	15
Walthamstow Avenue	-	-	-	-	-	15	-	-	-	-
Walton & Hersham	8	17	12	10	18	8	7	5	7	9
Wembley	10	3	5	3	5	6	10	16	15	5
Whyteleafe	-	-	-	-	-	-	-	14	9	20
Windsor & Eton	-	1	-	-	-	-	-	-	-	-
Wivenhoe Town	-	-	-	-	-	-	5	1	-	-
Woking	-	13	19	-	-	-	3	3	2	-
Wolverton Town	-	-	-	-	-	-	22	-	-	-
Worthing	1	-	-	-	-	-	13	18	13	22
Yeading	-	-	-	-	-	-	-	-	3	2
No. of clubs competing	21	22	22	22	22	22	21	22	22	21

ABINGDON TOWN

Abingdon Town, before their excellent 4-0 win over Stevenage Borough on 19/10/91. Back Row (L/R): David Cook, Andy Martin, Darren Hickey, John Harvey-Lynch, Paul Bradbury, Colin Fleet, Peter Rhodes-Brown. Front: Brian House, Kelvin Alexis, Keith Appleton, Kenny Campbell, Liam Herbert. Photo - Steve Daniels.

Chairman: Trevor Gladwell   **Vice Chairman:** Kevin Rowlands   **President:** Reg Lee.
Secretary (Add & Tel): Dave Sharp, 35 Fir Tree Avenue, Wallingford, Oxon OX10 0PD (0491 36796).
Team Manager: Trevor Butler   **Asst Manager:** Richard Nicholls   **Physio:** Ian Cummings.
Commercial Manager: Peter Edwards   **Press Officer:** Nick Quail (0235 832499)
Ground Address & Tel: Culham Road, Abingdon OX14 3BT (0235 555566-boardroom & press box).
Directions: On A415 half a mile south of town centre. Radley (BR) 3 miles - frequent buses to Abingdon. Didcot Parkway and Oxford (BR), 6 and 8 miles respectively with two hourly bus services.
Capacity: 4,000 (800 Covered)   **Seats:** 280   **Floodlights:** Y   **Shop:** Y   **Metal Badges:** £2
Colours: Yellow/green/yellow   **Change colours:** All blue.   **Sponsors:** Courage.
Previous Name: Abingdon FC (amalgamated with St Michaels in 1899).
Previous Leagues: Oxford & District/ West Berks/ Reading Temperance/ North Berks/ Reading & District 1927-50/ Spartan 50-53/ Hellenic 53-88/ London Spartan 88-89.
Midweek home matchday: Tuesday   **Reserve Team's League:** Suburban.
Record Attendance: 1,400 v Oxford City, FA Cup September 1960. (Crowds of over 5,000 in 20s and 30s).
Best F.A. Cup season: 4th Qualifying Rd 60-61 (lost 0-2 v Hitchin), 89-90 (0-3 at home to Slough).
Record Fees - Paid: **Received:**
Players progressing to Football League: Maurice Owen (Swindon), George Buck (Stockport & Reading), Sammy Chung (Reading, Norwich, Watford & Wolves).
Clubhouse: (0235 521684). 7.30-11pm. 6pm matchdays. 12.30-2.30, 4-11 on Saturdays. Hot food on matchdays. Pool, darts, jukebox, canteen. **Steward:** John Hamlet.
91-92 Captain: **91-92 P.O.Y.:** Darren Hickey   **91-92 Top scorer:**
Local Newspapers (+Tel.Nos.): Oxford Mail, Oxford Times, Abingdon Herald, South Oxon Guardian.
Local Radio Stations:
Hons: FA Vase 5th Rd rep 89-90, Berks & Bucks Snr Cup 58-59 (R-up 88-89), Isthmian Lg Div 2 (Sth) 90-91 (Loctite Tphy R-up 90-91), L'don Spartan Lg 88-89 (Lg Cup SF 88-89), Hellenic Lg(4) 56-57 58-60 86-87 (R-up(3) 70-72 87-88, Lg Cup 57-58 70-71 81-82 (R-up 83-84 86-87), Div 1 75-76, Div 1 Cup 75-76, Res. Div(3) 69-71 86-87, Res. Div Cup 70-71 85-86, Res. Div Suppl. Cup 74-75), Oxford & Dist Lg(3) 1898-1901, Reading & Dist Lg 47-48, Berks & Bucks Jnr Cup 06-07, Abingdon Centen. Cup 58-59, Joan Lee Mem. Cup 69-70 70-71 86-87, Oxford I'mediate Lg (Reserves) 47-48.

GOALKEEPERS:
Colin Fleet (Chesham, Bicester, Oxford C, Preseed Steel, Oxford Utd)
DEFENDERS:
Brian House (Oxford C), John Harvey-Lynch (Abingdon Utd, Oxford Utd), Kurt Douglas (Thame, Abingdon T, Bicester), Kelvin Alexis (Thame, Bicester, Oxford Utd), Darren Hickey (Clifton Hampden), Kenny Campbell (Queen's Park)
MIDFIELD:
Keith Appleton (Bicester, Witney, Oxford Utd(J)), Andy Martin (Bicester), Ian Barrett (Abingdon Utd, Wallingford), Roger Charles (Oxford Utd(J)), Dave Cook (Witney), Kevin Connolly (Burnham, Flackwell Heath, Wycombe, Harwell), Gary Tyrrell (Maidenhead Utd, Abingdon Utd), Jamie Ferguson (Thatcham, Wealdstone, Chertsey, Maidenhead Utd, Marlow)
FORWARDS:
Liam Herbert (Bicester, Banbury, Bicester, Abingdon T, Thame), Paul Bradbury (Abingdon Utd, Oxford C, Didcot, Pressed Steel, Oxford Utd), Mike Durkin (Youth), Steve Aries (Oxford C, Wokingham, IFK Nornan(Swe), Oxford Utd), Peter Rhodes-Brown (Oxford Utd, Chelsea)

OVER THE BRIDGE
Abingdon Town Football Club
SEASON 1991/92

The Diadora Football League
DIVISION ONE
V

OFFICIAL PROGRAMME
Pages: 28 **Price:** 30p
Editor: Andy Molden
WMPCC Rating: 21

Formed: 1927

AVELEY

The Millers

Aveley FC 91-92.

Chairman: A J Wallace   **President:** K J Clay
Secretary: Ken Sutliff, 9 Westlyn Close, Rainham, Essex RM13 9JP (0708 555271).
Team Manager: Tom Lee   **Asst Mgr:** Ray Jarman   **Coach:** Ray Jarman
Comm Manager: Peter Little   **Physio:** Phil Hunter
Ground Address & Tel: Mill Road, Aveley, Essex RM15 4TR (0708 865940).
Directions: London - Southend A13, turn into Sandy Lane at Aveley. Rainham or Purfleet (BR), Bus No. 375.
Capacity: 8,000 (2,000 Covered)   **Seats:** 350   **Floodlights:** Y   **Shop:** Y   **Metal Badges:** Y
Colours: Royal blue/white/royal blue   **Change colours:** All yellow.
Previous Leagues: Thurrock Combination 46-49/ London 49-57/ Delphian 57-63/ Athenian 63-73.
Midweek home matchday: Tuesday   **Reserve Team's League:** Essex & Herts Border Comb
Record Attendance: 2,623 v Wycombe, FA Cup 1978.
Best F.A. Cup season: 1st Rd 70-71 (lost 0-1 to Yeovil).
League clubs defeated in F.A. Cup: None.
Record Fees - Paid: **Received:** .
Players progressing to Football League: David Case & Alan Hull (Orient), Alan Parkinson (Orient 1967), Yilmaz Orhan (W Ham 1972), Keith Day (Colchester 1984), Paul Williams (Charlton & Sheff Wed).
Clubhouse: 12-3, 7-11pm. Darts, keep fit, pool, dances, bingo.   **Steward:** Jean Veeles.
Club Record Goalscorer: Jotty Wilks 55   **Club Record Apps:** Ken Riley.
91-92 Captain: Glen Dyson   **91-92 P.O.Y.:** Glen Dyson   **91-92 Top scorer:** Stewart Harvey 19
Local Newspapers (+Tel.Nos.): Thurrock Gazette (0375 372293).
Local Radio Stations: Radio Essex, Essex Radio.
Honours: Isthmian Lg Div 2 (North) R-up 89-90 (Lg (AC Delco) Cup 89-90), London Lg 51-52 54-55 (R-up 55-56, Lg Cup 53-54), Delphian Lg R-up 57-58 (Lg Cup 61-62), Athenian Lg 70-71 (Div 2 R-up 68-69), Essex Junior Cup 47-48 48-49, Essex Thameside Trophy 79-80, Hornchurch Charity Cup 81-82 (R-up 83-84), East Anglian Cup 88-89, FA Amateur Cup QF 70-71, FA Tphy 3rd Qualifying Rd replay 74-75, FA Vase 3rd Rd 89-90.

GOALKEEPERS:
Brian Balkwill (Clapton), **Paul Mulchinock** (Local football)

DEFENDERS:
Charlie Catchpole (Eton Manor), **Jimmy Cooper** (Hornchurch, Barking, Dagenham, Leyt & Ilf, Barking), **Tony Randell** (Dagenham, Eton Manor), **Marc King** (Local football), **Alan Day** (Dagenham, Tampa Bay Rowdies(USA), Dagenham, Billericay, Enfield, Dagenham, Billericay, Heybridge, Billericay, East Thurrock)

MIDFIELD:
Phil Harvey (Eton Manor), **Russell Cox** (Hornchurch), **Paul Franklin** (Grays, Aveley, Grays), **Glen Hardwick** (Dagenham, B Stortford, Aveley, Dartford, Dagenham, Spurs(J)), **Mark Keune** (Billericay, Gravesend, B Stortford, Witham, Billericay), **Mark Embery** (Local football)

FORWARDS:
John Gilliland (Local football), **Stewart Harvey** (Eton Manor), **Darren Harris** (Eton Manor), **Andy Woolley** (Billericay, Basildon, Heybridge, Bowers Uts, Basildon)

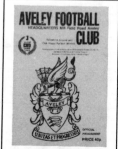

PROGRAMME DETAILS:
Pages: 28 **Price:** 40p
Editor: Peter Kemsley
WMPCC Rating: 19

BARKING

Barking FC.

Chairman: Alan R Wetherall **Managing Director:** Mr John Knight.
Secretary (Add & Tel): Mike Roberts, 168 Dawlish Drive, Sevenkings Ilford IG3 9EG (081 599 2384).
Team Manager: Dave Patient **Asst Manager:** N/A **Coach:** Henry Houghton.
Press Officer: Mike Roberts **Physio:** TBA **Comm Manager:** John Knight
Ground: Mayesbrook Park, Lodge Avenue, Dagenham RM8 2JR (081 595 6511).
Directions: Come off A13 on A1153 (Lodge Avenue), and ground 1 mile on left. Bus 162 from Barking station.
Nearest tube station is Becontree.
Capacity: 4,200 (600 Covered) **Seats:** 200 **Floodlights:** Y **Shop:** N **Metal Badges:** N
Colours: All blue **Change colours:** All white (blue trim)
Previous Leagues: London 1896-98 1909-26/ South Essex/ Athenian 23-52.
Sponsors: Dagenham Motors Lt.
Previous Names: Barking Rovers, Barking Institute, Barking Woodville, Barking Town.
Previous Grounds: Eastbury Field, Vicage Field (until 1973). **Midweek home matchday:** Tuesday
Record Attendance: (At Mayesbrook) 1,972 v Aldershot FA Cup 2nd Rd 1978.
Best F.A. Cup season: 2nd Rd replay 81-82 (lost 1-3 at Gillingham after 1-1 draw). Also 2nd Rd 78-79 79-80 83-84,
and 1st Rd 26-27 28-29 78-80.
League clubs defeated in F.A. Cup: Oxford Utd 79-80.
Record Fees - Paid: None over £1,000 **Received:** £6,500 for Alan Hull (Orient).
Players progressing to Football League: Don Colombo (P'smouth 1953), Wally Bellet (Chelsea 1954), John
Smith (Millwall 1956), Peter Carey (Orient 1957), Lawrie Abrahams (Charlton 1977), Kevin Hitchcock (Nottm Forest
1983), Dennis Bailey (F'ham 1986), Alan Hull (Orient 1987).
Clubhouse: Two large bars, open 11am - 11pm (Sundays Noon-10.30pm) **Steward:**
Club Record Goalscorer: Micky Guyton 135 (1924-30) **Club Record Apps:** Bob Makin 566
91-92 Captain: Perry Coney **91-92 P.o.Y.:** Danny Benstock **91-92 Top scorer:** Steve Portway 34.
Local Newspapers (+Tel.Nos.): Dagenham & Barking, Barking & Dagenham Post.
Local Radio Stations: BBC Radio Essex.
Honours: FA Amateur Cup R-up 26-27, Isthmian Lg 78-79 (Lg Cup R-up 76-77), Athenian Lg 34-35 (R-up 24-25),
London Lg 20-21 (Div 1 (A) 09-10), South Essex Lg Div 1 1898-99 (R-up 08-09, Div 2 1900-01 01-02 04-05 05-06),
London Senior Cup 11-12 20-21 26-27 78-79 (R-up 19-20 75-76 79-80), Essex Senior Cup 1893-94 95-96 1919-20
45-46 62-63 69-70 89-90, Dylon Shield 79-80, Eastern Floodlit R-up 85-86, London Intermediate Cup 85-86.

GOALKEEPERS:
Broderick Tucker (Dartford, Crockenhill), **Steve Wallduck** (St Albans,
Harlow, Walthamstow Ave, Boreham Wood, Cheshunt, Hoddesdon)

DEFENDERS:
Neal Simmonds (Barkingside, Basildon), **Henry Hughton** (Enfield,
Trollhatten(Swe), Leyton Orient, Brentford, C Palace, Leyton Orient), **John
Ray** (Wycombe, Colchester), **Terry Beck** (Basildon, Dagenham), **Stuart
Gibbons** (Dulwich), **Gary Crampton** (Dover, Leyt & Ilf, Hendon, Leyt & Ilf, St
Albans, Dover, Dagenham)

MIDFIELD:
Perry Coney (East Thurrock, Rainham), **Craig Coney** (Basildon), **David
Jarvis** (Redbridge F), **Chris Harvey** (Basildon, B Stortford, Dagenham,
Spurs), **Lou Mason** (Local football), **James Murphy** (Aldershot, Leyton
Orient)

FORWARDS:
Danny Benstock (Enfield, Gillingham(J)), **Jamie Hoy** (Finchley, J & M
Sports, Enfield), **John Evans** (Ford Utd), **Derek Charles** (Redbridge F)

PROGRAMME DETAILS:
Pages: 20 **Price:** 60p
Editor:
WMPCC Rating: 14

Formed:

BILLERICAY TOWN

The Town

Back Row (L/R): John Kendall (Manager), Steve Jones, Mark Jenkins, Robbie Quinnell, Dave Cass, Dave Roser, Darren Southgate, Robbie Savage, Peter Brabrook (Coach). Front: Andy Jones, Andy Howard, Mark Entwistle, Mark Keune, Steve Munday, Andy McDonald, Peter Williams (Trainer). Photo - Southend Evening Echo.

Chairman: Brian Cornes **Vice C'man:** Derek Hanks **President:**
Secretary: Len Dewson, 14 Graham Close, Billericay, Essex CM12 0QW (0277 622375).
Manager: John Kendall **Coach:** Peter Brabrook **Asst Manager:**
Press Officer: Phil Heady (652226) **Commercial Manager:** **Physio:** Ken Howell
Ground: New Lodge, Blunts Wall Road, Billericay CM12 0QW (0277 655177).
Directions: From Shenfield (A129) turn right at 1st lights then 1st right. From Basildon (A129) proceed over 1st lights in town, then left at next lights and 1st right. Half mile from Billericay (BR), 5 mins from buses 151 & 251.
Capacity: 3,000 **Seats:** 250 **Cover:** 1,000 **Floodlights:** Yes **Founded:** 1880
Colours: Royal/white/royal **Change colours:** Yellow/black/black
Club Shop: Yes **Metal Badges:** Yes
Previous Ground: Archer Hall, Laindon (pre-1971) **Midweek Matches:** Tuesday.
Previous Leagues: Romford & Dist./ Mid Ess./ Ess. Olympian/Ess. Snr 71-77/ Athenian 77-79.
Reserve Team's League: **Best FA Trophy year:**
Best FA Cup year: 4th Qual Rd 77-78 **Best FA Vase year:** Winners
Record Gate: 3,641 v West Ham, F'light opener 1977 **Sponsors:**
Record Fees - Paid: **Received:**
Players progressing to Football League: Danny Westwood (QPR & Gillingham), Alan Hull, Danny Carter & Dave Cass (Orient).
Clubhouse: (0277 652188) Open every night (bar Monday) and weekend lunchtimes. Discos, live entertainment, alcoves on ground floor and glass fronted viewing gallery on second. Steward - Ron Firmin.
Club Record Goalscorer: Fred Clayden 338 **Club Record Apps:** John Pullen 490.
91-92 Captain: Mark Entwistle **91-92 P.O.Y.:** Dave Roser **91-92 Top scorer:** Steve Jones 46
Local Press: Evening Echo (0268 522792), Billericay Gazette 0245 262421).
Local Radio Stations: BBC Radio Essex (0268 522792), Essex Radio (0702 33311).
Hons: FA Vase (3 - a record) 75-77 78-79, Ess. Snr Lg(3) 72-73 74-75 75-76 (R-up 71-72 73-74, Lg Cup(4) 71-74 76-77 (R-up 74-75)), Isthmian Lg Div 1 R-up 80-81, Athenian Lg(2) 77-79 (Lg Cup 77-78), E Anglian Cup 79-80 84-85, Ess. Snr Cup 75-76 (R-up 85-86), Ess. Snr Tphy 77-78 79-80, Ess. Thameside Tphy 86-87 (R-up 90-91), Ess. F'lit Tphy 77-78, Phillips F'lit Tphy 76-77.

GOALKEEPERS:
Dave Cass (Leyton Orient, Billericay, Aveley)
DEFENDERS: Rob Quinnell (Chelmsford, Collier R, Enfield, Leyton Orient, Collier R), **Mark Entwistle** (St Albans, Basildon, Dartford, Chelmsford, Spurs), **Paul Taylor** (Hornchurch, Chelmsford, Hornchurch), **Darren Southgate** (Collier R), **Robbie Savage** (Southend Manor), **Ian Templeton** (Chelmsford, Heybridge S, B Stortford, Billericay, Chelmsford, Billericay, Colchester, Ipswich)
MIDFIELD: Mark Jenkins (Southend Manor, Basildon, Southend Manor, Southend Utd(J)), **Dave Roser** (Hornchurch), **Andy McDonald** (Heybridge S, Billericay, Heybridge S, Hornchurch, Aveley, Enfield), **Matt Howard** (Youth), **Stewart Winchester** (Aveley, Grays), **Kevin Rendell** (Grays)
FORWARDS:
Steve Munday (Collier R, Basildon, Billericay, Tilbury, Ford Utd), **Andy Jones** (Rainham, Billericay, Purfleet, Basildon), **Mike Flanagan** (Margate, Charlton, QPR, C Palace, Charlton, Spurs), **Adrian West** (Witham, Southend Utd(T)), **Stuart Jukes** (Rainham, Aveley, Billericay, Hornchurch, Basildon, Aveley, Fulham(A)), **Dominic Ludden** (Youth), **Tommy Langley** (Basingstoke, St Albans, Staines, Aylesbury, Slough, Tampa Bay Rowdies(USA), Exeter, South China, Aldershot, Wolves, Coventry, AEK Athens(Greece), C Palace, QPR, Chelsea), **Andy Howard** (Basildon)

Pages: 20 **Price:** 30p
Editor: Phil Heady
(0277 652226)

327

BISHOP'S STORTFORD

Bishop's Stortford 1, Woking 2: Premier Division 9/11/91. Bishop's Stortford goalkeeper Martin Taylor flicks the ball away from a corner. The home side, bottom of the table, nearly produced a major surprise in this game having led at half-time, but the leaders eventually overhauled them. Photo - Robbie Pragnell.

Chairman: Gordon Lawrence **President:** B W A Bayford
Secretary (Add & Tel): Jim Reynolds, 182 Fold Croft, Harlow CM20 1SN (0279 639821).
Team Manager: John Radford **Assistant Manager:** Ray Wickenden.
Coach: **Physio:** Andy Taylor.
Press Officer: Gareth Stephens (0279 505157) **Comm Manager:** John Radford
Ground Address & Tel: George Wilson Stadium, Rhodes Avenue, B S'ford CM23 3JN (0279 654140/656538)
Directions: 800 yards from station. From town centre take South Street, then South Road. Rhodes Avenue 600 yards on right.
Capacity: 6,000 (1,500 Covered) **Seats:** 228 **Floodlights:** Y **Shop:** Y **Metal Badges:** Y
Colours: White & blue stripes/blue/blue **Change colours:** Red/blue/red **Sponsors:** Brooks
Previous Leagues: Stansted & Dist/ Herts County/ Spartan 29-51/ Delphian 51-63 Athenian 63-71
Previous Grounds: Silver Leys, Plow Hatch, The Laundry Field, Dunmow Road, Travers Lane.
Midweek home matchday: Tuesday **Reserve Team's League:** Essex & Herts Border Comb.
Record Attendance: 6,000 v Middlesbrough FA Cup 3rd Rd replay (lost 1-2 after 2-2 draw).
Best F.A. Cup season: 3rd Rd replay (see above). 1st Rd 70-71 72-73 74-76 81-83 84-87.
League clubs beaten in FA Cup: Reading 82-83. **Newsline:** 0898 333 097.
Record Fees - Paid: **Received:** £10,000 for Carl Hoddle (Orient)
Players progressing to Football League: Bryan Atkinson (Watford 1954), Mick Hallow (Orient 1962), Peter Phillips (Luton 1969), Tom English (Colchester), Carl Hoddle (Orient).
Clubhouse: Two bars, three tea bars, Members Club and executive boxes. Open matchdays, training nights and for private functions. **Steward:** Colin Wood
Club Record Scorer: (Since 1964) Dave Worrall 103 (78-83).
Club Record Apps: Gordon Atkinson 596 (56-69).
91-92 Captain: **91-92 P.o.Y.:** **91-92 Top scorer:**
Local Newspapers (+Tel.Nos.): Bishop's Stortford Gazette, Herts & Essex Observer, Herald & Post.
Local Radio Stations: BBC Essex, Essex Radio, Breeze AM.
Honours: FA Trophy 80-81, FA Amateur Cup 73-74, Isthmian Lg Div 1 80-81 (Lg Cup 88-89), Premier Inter Lg Cup 89-90, Athenian Lg 69-70 (R-up 66-67, Div 1 65-66, Div 2 R-up 64-65), Delphian Lg 54-55, Spartan Lg Div 2 (East) 31-32, London Senior Cup 73-74, Herts Senior Cup 32-33 58-59 59-60 63-64 70-71 72-73 73-74 75-76, East Anglian Cup 81-82, Herts Charity Cup 62-63 65-66 73-74 81-82 82-83 84-85, Courage Eastern Floodlit Cup.

GOALKEEPERS:
Martin Taylor (Epping, Woodford, Hendon, Charlton, Arsenal), **Dave Mallett** (Harlow, Redbridge F, Dartford, Enfield, Leyt & Ilf, Leyton Orient)
DEFENDERS: Billy Harrigan (Chesham, Leytonstone & Ilford, Walthamstow Ave, B Stortford, Camb Utd), **Ian Smith** (Youth), **Steve Sailsman** (Wembley, Finchley, Kingsbury, Wembley, Hayes), **Phil Hopkins** (Walthamstow Ave, Chelmsford, Colchester(A)), **Phil Boyce** (Harlow, B Stortford, Sawbridgeworth, Billericay, Dagenham, Leytonstone & Ilford, Clapton, West Ham), **Dave Forey** (Harlow, Boreham Wood, Finchley, B Stortford, Walthamstow Ave), **Dick Empson** (Purfleet, Harlow, Hertford, Tooting, Haringey B, Cheshunt, Leytonstone & Ilford, Walthamstow Ave), **Martin Sedgewick** (Local football)
MIDFIELD: Darren Went (Chelmsford, Leyton Orient), **Andy Edmonds** (Enfield, Dagenham, Hendon, Enfield, Spurs), **Giles Parnwell** (Camb Utd(T)), **Rob Fearey** (Boreham Wood, B Stortford), **Nicky White** (Youth), **Julian Bedford** (Cuffley)
FORWARDS: Peter Petrou (Kingsbury, B Stortford, Kingsbury), **Paul Chinnery** (B Stortford Swifts), **Tommy English** (Wivenhoe, Crawley, Colchester, B Stortford, Colchester, Plymouth, Rochdale, Leicester C, Coventry, Colchester), **Devon Gayle** (Harlow, B Stortford, Woodford, Dagenham, Walthamstow Ave, Hendon, Cheshunt, Dagenham, Hendon), **Les Pritchard** (B Stortford Swifts)

Pages: 28 **Price:** 60p
Editor: Roy Kemp
WMPCC Rating: 26

Formed: 1948

BOREHAM WOOD

The Wood

Boreham Wood FC 1991-92.

Chairman: Phil Wallace   **President:** W F O'Neill.
Secretary (Add & Tel): A H F Perkins, 48 Saltash Road, Hainault IG6 2NL (081 500 3902).
Team Manager: Trevor Harvey   **Asst Manager:**   **Coach:** Phil Wallace.
Press Officer: John Gill (081 998 6446)   **Physio:** Dave Dickens
Ground Address & Tel: Meadow Park, Broughinge Road, Boreham Wood WD6 5AL (081 953 5097).
Directions: Elstree & Boreham Wood station (Thameslink), then bus 292 or 107 to Red Lion (5 minutes walk).
Capacity: 3,500 (1,500 Covered)   **Seats:** 350   **Floodlights:** Y   **Shop:** Y   **Metal Badges:** Y
Colours: White/black/red   **Change colours:** Red/red/black
Previous Leagues: Mid Herts 48-52/ Parthenon 52-57/ Spartan 56-66/ Athenian 66-74.
Previous Ground: Eldon Avenue 1948-63
Previous Names: Boreham Wood Rovers and Royal Retournez, amalgamated in 1948 to form the current club.
Midweek home matchday: Tuesday   **Reserve Team's League:** Essex & Herts Border Comb
Record Attendance: 2,500 v St Albans, FA Amateur Cup 70-71.
Best F.A. Cup season: 1st Rd replay (v Swindon) 77-78. Also 1st Rd (v Southend) 73-74.
Record Fees - Paid: **Received:**
Players progressing to Football League: Colin Franks (Watford & Sheff Utd), Charles Ntamark (Walsall).
Clubhouse: (081 953 5097). Holds 250, open every night. Hall available for hire.   **Steward:** R C Taylor.
Club Record Goalscorer: Micky Jackson 208   **Club Record Apps:** Steve Waller 575
91-92 Captain: **91-92 P.O.Y.:**   **91-92 Top scorer:**
Local Newspapers (+Tel.Nos.): Boreham Wood Times, Watford Observer, Herts Advertiser.
Local Radio Stations: Chiltern Radio.
Honours: FA Amateur Cup 3rd Rd replay 70-71, FA Tphy 1st Rd replay 86-87, Isthmian Lg Div 2 76-77 (Yth Cup R-up 80-81), Athenian Lg 73-74 (Div 2 68-69, Div 1 R-up 69-70), Spartan Lg R-up 65-66, Herts Senior Cup 71-72 (R-up 66-67 74-75 79-80 87-88), Herts Junior Cup 51-52, Parthenon Lg 55-56 (R-up(2) 53-55 56-57), Herts Charity Shield 64-65, Herts Intermediate Cup 69-70, Herts Charity Cup(5) 80-81 83-84 85-86 88-90 (R-up 71-72 84-85 86-87 90-91), London Senior Cup R-up 89-90, London Intermediate Cup 70-71, Neale Trophy 69-70, Essex & Herts Border Comb 72-73 (Lg Cup 72-73), Western Div R-up 82-83 89-90), Mithras Cup 76-77, Middx Border Lg 81-82 (Lg Cup 79-80), Wallspan Floodlit 86-87.

GOALKEEPERS:
Jeremy Parsons (Barnet, Welling)
DEFENDERS: Jon Corbett (Wycombe, Hitchin, Dunstable, Aylesbury), Matt Howard (St Albans, Brentford, B Wood), Martin Gardener (Yeovil, Watford), Dave Hatchett (Enfield), Peter Sim (B Stortford, Brentford), Keith Hayzelden (Purfleet, Dartford, Enfield, Redbridge, Dartford, Enfield, Leyt & Ilf)
MIDFIELD: Gary Seymour (Dagenham, Walthamstow A, Woodford, Barking, Clapton, Dagenham, Chelmsford, Woodford, Barking, Leyt & Ilf, Leyton O), Lee Faulkner (Chelsea(T)), Joe Simmonds (Redbridge, Barking, B Stortford, Dartford, B Stortford, Bigog(Den), Spurs), Nicky Ironton (Gravesend, Leyt-Win, Enfield, Barnet, Enfield, Barking, QPR), Matt Potter (Dorchester, Watford), Steve Smith (Chalfont, Wembley, Hounslow, Harrow B, Hendon, Harrow B), Paul Bhatia (Wembley, Kingsbury, Wembley, Hendon)
FORWARDS: Micky Dingwall (Redbridge F, Dartford, Maidstone, Leyt & Ilf, Barking), Dave Flint (Gravesend, Wealdstone, Redbridge F, Tooting, Enfield, Leyton Co), Colin Cardines (Enfield, Stevenage B, Hendon, Baldock, Hitchin, B Stortford, Letchworth), Jimmy Hughes (Hitchin, Stevenage B, B Wood, Letchworth, Hertford, Stevenage B), Lawrence Holmes (Hendon, Redbridge F, Harrow B, Harlow, Edgware), Lee Fulling (Billericay, Redbridge F, Spurs(J))

Boreham Wood
FOOTBALL CLUB

PROGRAMME DETAILS:
Pages: 32 Price: 60p
Editor: John Gill
WMPCC Rating: 18

CHALFONT ST PETER

The Saints

Chalfont St Peter 2, Harlow Town 0 - 24/8/91. As Gary Lester climbs high to see off an early Harlow attack, he is challenged by Devon Gayle. Photo - Gavin Ellis.

Chairman: Mr David Pembroke   **President:**
Secretary: Mr Peter Court, 8 Lovel End, Chalfont St Peter, Bucks SL9 9NZ.
Team Manager: Tony O'Driscoll.   **Asst Manager:**   **Coach:**
Press Officer: John Smith (02407 5488).   **Physio:**
Commercial Manager:
Ground: The Playing Fields, Amersham Road, Chalfont St Peter SL9 7BQ (0753 885797).
Directions: A413 from Uxbridge (London) to Chalfont. Turn left 100 yds after 2nd major roundabout (between Ambulance station and Community Centre. Two miles from Gerrards Cross (BR), regular buses from Slough.
Capacity: 4,500 (220 Covered)   **Seats:** 220   **Floodlights:** Y   **Shop:** Y   **Metal Badges:** Y
Colours: Red & green/white/white   **Change colours:** Yellow/blue/blue
Previous Leagues: Great Western Combination 1948-58/ Parthenon 58-59/ London 60-62/ Spartan 62-75/ London Spartan 75-76/ Athenian 76-84.
Midweek home matchday: Tuesday   **Reserve Team's League:** Suburban
Record Attendance: 2,500 v Watford, benefit match 1985.
Best F.A. Cup season: 3rd Qualifying Rd 85-86 (wins over Banbury, King's Lynn and Barking).
League clubs defeated in F.A. Cup: None.
Record Fees - Paid: £750 to Chertsey (Steve Church, March 1989)   **Received:** .
Players progressing to Football League:
Clubhouse: Open every evening, Saturday afternoons and Sunday lunchtimes.   **Steward:** Joe Eakins.
Club Record Goalscorer: **Club Record Apps:** Colin Davies.
91-92 Captain: Tony Thompson   **91-92 P.o.Y.:** Kevin Cadmore
91-92 Top scorer: Ansill Bushay 13, Steve Darlington 13.
Local Newspapers (+Tel.Nos.): Bucks Advertiser (0753 888333), Bucks Examiner, Bucks Free Press, Wycombe Midweek.
Local Radio Stations: Chilton Radio.
Honours: Isthmian Lg Div 2 87-88, Athenian Lg R-up 83-84 (Lg Cup 76-77 82-83), London Spartan Lg Div 2 75-76, Berks & Bucks Intermediate Cup 52-53, FA Tphy 3rd Qualifying Rd 89-90 91-92, FA Vase 4th Rd 87-88, Berks & Bucks Benevolent Cup 64-65.

GOALKEEPERS:
Kevin Ward (Uxbridge, Harrow B, Chalfont, Uxbridge, Chalfont, Windsor, Ruislip Manor, Uxbridge)

DEFENDERS:
Steve Toll (Marlow, Wycombe, Flackwell, Wycombe, Chalfont), **Mark Bishop** (Harefield), **Paul Fitzgerald** (Wembley, Chalfont, Kingsbury, Wembley, Southall, Harrow B, Willesden), **Steve Lucas** (Kingsbury, Wembley, Sudbury Ct), **Kevin Cadmore** (Harlow, Uxbridge, Chalfont, Mill End), **Guy McLachlan** (Hayes)

MIDFIELD:
Naseem Bashir (Slough, Reading), **Gibril Kamara** (Harefield), **Tony Thompson** (Chesham, Uxbridge, Chalfont, Chesham, Dunstable, Chesham, Aylesbury), **Mark Wingate** (Local football), **John Grout** (Harrow B)

FORWARDS:
Ansil Bushay (Beaconsfield, Flackwell), **Steve Darlington** (Hounslow), **Lance Cadogan** (Uxbridge, Wembley, Chalfont, Wembley, Maidenhead Utd, Stop Out Wellington(NZ), Maidenhead Utd, Wembley, Leatherhead, Woking, Windsor, Sutton Utd), **Brian Cronk** (Local football)

SEASON 90/91 OFFICIAL PROGRAMME
Chalfont St. Peter
Football Club
20p

PROGRAMME DETAILS:
Pages: 16 Price: 60p
Editor: John Smith
WMPCC Rating: 19

CROYDON

Croydon FC. Back Row (L/R): Peter Gaydon, Matt Norris, Dave Clark, Gary Molesey, Mark Gilham, Jason Peters, Kevin Langford. Front: Trevor Franklin, Simon Ullathorne, Dave Boyton, Micky Paye, Chris Lambert, John Roles. Photo - Dave West.

Chairman: Frank Armstrong **President:** T W Fogarty.
Secretary (Add & Tel): Geoff Beeson, 13 Impact Court, Stembridge Road, Anerley SE20 7UP (081 778 7163).
Team Manager: Dave Boyton **Asst Manager:** Tony Booth **Coach:** Bill Fogarty.
Press Officer: John Sanford (081 654 9835). **Physio:** John Knapp.
Ground Address & Tel: Croydon Sports Arena, Albert Road, South Norwood SE25 4QL (081 654 3462).
Directions: Train to East Croydon or Norwood Junction, then bus 12 to either Belmont or Dundee Road. Walk down either - ground at bottom. 5 mins walk from Woodside (BR).
Capacity: 8,000 (450 Covered) **Seats:** 450 **Floodlights:** Y **Shop:** Y **Metal Badges:** £2.50
Colours: Sky blue/blue **Change colours:** All red **Sponsors:**
Previous Leagues: Surrey Senior 53-63/ Spartan 63-64/ Athenian 64-74.
Midweek home matchday: Monday **Previous Name:** Croydon Amateurs 1953-74.
Record Attendance: 1,450 v Wycombe, FA Cup 4th Qualifying Rd 1975.
Best F.A. Cup season: 2nd Rd replay 79-80 (lost 2-3 to Millwall after 1-1 draw).
Record Fees - Paid: Steve Brown **Received:** Peter Evans (to Sutton Utd).
Players progressing to Football League: Alan Barnett (P'mouth 1955), Peter Bonetti (Chelsea), Leroy Ambrose (Charlton 1979), Steve Milton (Fulham - via Whyteleafe), Murray Jones (Crystal & Exeter - via Carshalton).
Clubhouse: (081 654 8555). Open every evening and lunchtime, holds 250, snacks available. Dancing, discos, bingo. Lounge bar available for private hire.
Steward: Enda Moran.
Club Record Apps: Alec Jackson (400+)
91-92 Captain: Gary Mitchell **91-92 P.O.Y.:** Gary Mitchell **91-92 Top scorer:** Matt Norris
Local Newspapers (+Tel.Nos.): Croydon Advertiser (081 668 4111), Croydon Midweek Post, Croydon Times, Croydon Guardian.
Honours: FA Amateur Cp 3rd Rd 71-72, FA Tphy 2nd Rd(2) 81-83, Isthmian Lg Div 2 R-up 75-76, Surrey Snr Cp 81-82 (R-up 76-77), Surrey Prem Cp 86-87, Spartan Lg 63-64, Athenian Lg R-up 71-72 (Div 2 65-66 (R-up 70-71)), Surrey Snr Lg R-up 56-57 60-61 62-63 (Lg Cp 60-61, Charity Cp 53-54 62-63, Res Section 57-58), London Snr Cp R-up 78-79, Suburban Lg South 86-87 (Lg Cp(2)), Southern Yth Lg 85-86 (Lg Cp 85-86 87-88), Berger Yth Cp 78-79.

GOALKEEPERS:
Darren Mace (Rainham)
DEFENDERS:
Chris Lambert (Bromley, Croydon, Horley, Croydon, Cornish), **Jon Bryant** (Cray W, Dulwich, Croydon, Tooting, Bromley), **Louis Robinson** (Cray W, Erith, Danson, Sheppey, Welling, Millwall), **Mark Gillham** (Cray W, Tonbridge, Tunbridge Wells), **Kevin Langford** (Cray W, Dulwich), **Gary Mitchell** (Carshalton), **John Roles** (Margate, Fisher, Bromley, Sutton Utd, Portsmouth), **Micky Paye** (Cray W, Croydon, Charlton), **Jason Peters** (Southampton(T)), **John Latigo** (Fisher, Uganda).
MIDFIELD:
Dave Boyton (Cray W, Gravesend, Tonbridge, Bromley, Brighton), **Jason Brown** (Carshalton), **Michael Morgan** (Carshalton), **Dave Clark** (Local football), **Rob Ratcliffe** (Cray W), **Billy Allardyce** (Dulwich, Molesey, Croydon, Molesey, Hampton, Tooting, Corinthian Cas)
FORWARDS:
Glen Leaburn (Dorking, Croydon, Catford W), **Dave Collymore** (Maiden V, Croydon, Tooting, Barking, Tooting, Fulham(T)), **Paul Murray** (Deal, Croydon, Deal, Gravesend, Erith, Dover, Charlton), **Carl Wilmot** (Local football)

PROGRAMME DETAILS:
Pages: 16 **Price:** 40p
Editor: John Sanford
WMPCC Rating: 20

Formed: 1880

DORKING

The Chicks

Back Row (L/R): S Barbury, M Norman, V Flynn, T Welch, P Grainger, L Richardson, M Hanlan, F Sheridan, T Rains. Front (L/R): S Rose, K Wedderburn, S Lunn, D Wyatt (Mascot), R Yorke (Captain), L Collis (Mascot), C Lewington, S White, S Tutt. Missing from photo - N Robson, L Orkney, C Anderson, M Gill, D Bird, S Rogers.

Chairman: Tom Howes   **President:** Ingram Whittingham
Vice Chairman: Dave Manning   **Financial Director:** Martin Collins.
Secretary: Mr Derek Plumridge, 20 Alexander Rd, South Park, Reigate, Surrey RH2 8EA (0737 241536).
Team Manager: John Rains   **Asst Manager:** Tony Rains
Press Officer: Chris Collis (0293 821380)   **Coach:** Tony Rains
General Manager: John Rains   **Physio:** Carloine Brouwer/Ian Miller
Ground: Meadowbank, Mill Lane, Dorking, Surrey RH4 1DX (0306 884112).
Directions: Mill Lane is off Dorking high street opposite the White Horse. Fork right in Mill Lane past the Malthouse. Half mile from Dorking (BR).
Capacity: 6,500 (200 Covered)   **Seats:** 200   **Floodlights:** Y   **Shop:** N   **Metal Badges:** Y
Colours: Green & white/white/white   **Change colours:** All blue
Sponsors: **Previous Ground:** Prixham Lane (until 1953).
Previous Leagues: Surrey Senior 22-56 77-78/ Corinthian 56-63/ Athenian 63-74 78-80/ Southern 74-77.
Previous Names: Guildford & Dorking United (when club merged with Guildford in 1974)/Dorking Town 77-82.
Midweek home matchday: Tuesday   **Reserve Team's League:** Suburban
Best F.A. Cup season: 4th Qualifying Rd 90-91 (lost 2-3 at home to Cheltenham).
League clubs defeated in F.A. Cup: None.   **Record Attendance:** 4,500 v Folkestone 54-55.
Record Fees - Paid: **Received:**
Players progressing to Football League: Steve Scrivens & John Finch (Fulham), Andy Ansah (Brentford 1989).
Clubhouse: Open matchdays and Sunday lunchtimes   **Steward:**
Club Record Goalscorer: Andy Bushnell, 230 goals in 325 games.
Club Record Apps: Rob Dilger, 329.
91-92 Captain: Richard Yorke   **91-92 P.o.Y.:** Tony Welch   **91-92 Top scorer:** Phil Grainger.
Local Newspapers (+Tel.Nos.): Dorking Advertiser, Surrey Mirror.
Local Radio Stations: County Sound, Radio Surrey, Radio Mercury.
Honours: Isth. Lg Div 2 Sth 88-89, Surrey Snr Cup R-up 1885-86 1989-90, Surrey Snr Shield(2) 58-60 (R-up 07-08 10-11 60-61), Surrey Snr Lg(4) 28-30 54-56 (R-up 51-52 53-54, Lg Cup 48-49 50-51 53-54, Lg Charity Cup(4) 48-49 53-54(jt), 54-56 (R-up(5) 28-30 46-47 50-51 77-78)), Gilbert Rice F'lit Cup 87-88 (R-up 89-90), Surrey I'mediate Cup 56-57 (R-up 54-55), FA Tphy 2nd Rd 91-92, FA Vase 3rd Rd(3) 83-84 86-88.

GOALKEEPERS:
Lee Orkney (Walton & Hersham, Hampton), **Richard Short** (Molesey)
DEFENDERS: Daren Bird (Leatherhead, Kingstonian, Wimbledon(J), Cranleigh), **Mark Phillips** (Youth), **Tony Rains** (Sutton Utd, Fulham), **Kevin Wedderburn** (Leatherhead, Kingstonian, Wimbledon), **Vernon Pratt** (Slough, Sutton Utd, Egham, Camberley), **Robin Dobinson** (Raynes Pk, Sutton Utd), **Lee Richardson** (Whyteleafe, Banstead, Epsom & Ewell, Hampton, Dulwich, Whyteleafe), **Steve Rogers** (Walton & Hersham, Hampton, Sutton Utd, Dulwich, Chelsea), **Victor Flynn** (Woking)
MIDFIELD: Martyn Gill (Chertsey, Sutton Utd, Stafford R, Worcester, Stafford R, Boston Utd, Stafford R, Mossley, Frickley, Bridlington Trin, Worsbrough Bridge MW), **Steve Lunn** (Walton & Hersham, Dorking, Leatherhead, C Palace), **Richard Yorke** (Banstead), **Neil Robson** (Sutton Utd, Epsom & Ewell, Sutton Utd), **Steve White** (Molesey, Banstead, Carshalton, Whyteleafe, Banstead, Dulwich, Sutton Utd, C Palace), **Mark Norman** (Leatherhead, Molesey, Epsom & Ewell, Leatherhead),
FORWARDS: Carey Anderson (Leatherhead, Sutton Utd, Dulwich, Leatherhead), **Matthew Hanlan** (Wycombe, Sutton Utd), **Phil Grainger** (Hull City, Goole), **Steve Tutt** (Kingstonian, Sutton Utd, Chelsea, QPR, Fulham(J)), **Tony Welch** (Tooting, Leatherhead, Staines, Millwall(J)), **Simon Rose** (Walton & Hersham)

PROGRAMME DETAILS:
Pages: 28 Price: 50p
Editor: Chris Collis
WMPCC Rating: 23

HARLOW TOWN

The Owls

Harlow Town striker Martin St Hilaire scores his side's first goal in their home match against Croydon. Photo - Tim Pike.

Chairman: Alan Howick   **President:**
Secretary: Mr G Auger, 19 Abbott Crescent, Highams Park, London E4 9SA (081 527 7470).
Team Manager: Dave Edwards   **Asst Manager:** Arthur Wenborn/Dave Hoddle   **Coach:** Roger Redmond
Press Officer: Colin Barrat (0279 482342)   **Physio:** Micky Stevens
Ground: Harlow Sports Centre, Hammarskjold Road, Harlow (0279 421927/635100). *Soon Harlow will be moving to; Harlow Football Stadium, Roydon Road, The Pinnacles, Harlow CM19 5DU (0279 444182). However, in the interim period the club will be using alternative home venues, so spectators are strongly advised to check before travelling.*
Directions: Near Town centre. 10 mins walk from Harlow Town (BR).
Capacity: 10,000 (450 covered)   **Seats:** 450   **Floodlights:** Y   **Shop:** N   **Metal Badges:** Y
Colours: All red   **Change colours:** Blue   **Sponsors:** Bowman Webber.
Previous Leagues: Spartan 32-39 46-54/ London 54-61/ Delphian 61-63/ Athenian 63-73.
Previous Grounds: Marigolds 1879-1930/ Green Man Field 30-60.   **Newsline:** 0898 122 936.
Midweek home matchday: Monday   **Reserve Team's League:** Essex & Herts Border Combination.
Record Attendance: 9,723 v Leicester, FA Cup 3rd Rd replay 8/1/80.
Best F.A. Cup season: 4th Rd 79-80 (lost 3-4 at Watford). Also 1st Rd 80-81 81-82.
League clubs defeated in F.A. Cup: Southend, Leicester 79-80.   **Record Fees:** Undisclosed.
Players progressing to Football League: Jeff Wood (Charlton 1975), Neil Prosser (B'mouth 1980)
Clubhouse: Darts, pool etc. Usual hours, at Sportscentre and Roydon Road.   **Steward:** Ken Shrubb.
Club Record Goalscorer: Jeff Wood (44 in 88-89)   **Club Record Apps:** Norman Gladwin
91-92 Captain: **91-92 P.o.Y.:**   **91-92 Top scorer:**
Local Press (+Tel.): Harlow Citizen (451698), Harlow Star (420333), Harlow Herald & Post (0279 655225).
Local Radio Stations: Essex Radio, BBC Essex.
Honours: FA Amtr Cup 2nd Rd 72-73, FA Tphy 2nd Rd(2) 80-82, FA Vase 3rd Rd 88-89, Isthmian Lg Div 1 78-79 (R-up 82-83, Div 2 Nth 88-89, Yth Cup 77-78), Ath'n Lg Div 1 71-72, E Angl. Cup 89-90, Knight F'lit Cup R-up 87-88, Essex Snr Cup 78-79, Essex F'lit Competition R-up 71-72, London Lg Chal. Cup 59-60, Spartan Lg Cup 52-53, Epping Hosp. Cup(3) 46-49, Essex & Herts Border Comb Cup 75-76, Fred Budden Tphy 88-89 89-90, Chelmsford Yth Lg 86-87 (Lg Cup 86-87 87-88).

GOALKEEPERS:
Mark Irish (Local football)
DEFENDERS: Micky Hall (Heybridge, East Thurrock, Canvey Is), Richard Head (Basildon, Leyt & Ilf, Dagenham, Harlow), Rory Gleeson (Harrow B, Finchley, St Albans, Hitchin, Dunstable), Brian Cottington (Kingstonian, Enfield, Fulham), Danny Gibson (Walthamstow Pennant), Doug McClure (Baldock, Hendon, St Albans, Fisher, Enfield, Wealdstone, Wimbledon, Crewe, Peterborough, Wimbledon, Torquay, Exeter, QPR).
MIDFIELD: Gary Armstrong (Hornchurch, Heybridge, Haringey B, Heybridge, Barnet, Kemi(Fin), Crewe, Gillingham, TPS Turun(Fin), Wimbledon, Gillingham), Lee Burns (Stevenage B, B Stortford, Stevenage B, Hertford, Harlow, Sawbridgeworth), John Margerrison (St Albans, Wealdstone, Barnet, Wealdstone, Boreham Wood, Kansas(USA), Leyton Orient, Fulham, Spurs), Steve Emmanuel (Chesham, Hayes, Harrow B, Staines, Harrow B, Watford, Wolves), Martin St Hilaire (Chesham, Aveley), Terry Burns (Stevenage B, Harlow, Ware, Cossor Sports)
FORWARDS: Paul Battram (Gravesend, Welling, Gravesend, Hornchurch, Aveley, Barking), Dave Dobson (B Stortford, Witham, B Stortford, Grays, Leyton Orient), Jason Reed (Hitchin, Kempston R), Paul Neufville (Stevenage B, Hitchin, Langford, Vauxhall M, 61FC)

Pages: 20 **Price:** 50p
Editor: Phil Tuson
WMPCC Rating: 22

HEYBRIDGE SWIFTS

Heybridge Swifts had a long hard struggle in the First Division during 1991-92. Here they face the camera before the FA Cup Second Qualifying Round tie away to Staines Town. Photo - Eric Marsh.

Chairman: Michael Gibson   **President:** John Knight
Secretary (Add & Tel): Dennis Fenn, 31 Saxon Way, Maldon, Essex CM9 7JN (0621 854798).
Team Manager: Gary Hill   **Asst Manager:** Pat Ferry   **Coach:** Pat Ferry
Press Officer: Chris Daines (0621 850915).   **Physio:** Barry Anthony
Comm Manager:
Ground Address & Tel: Scraley Road, Heybridge, Maldon, Essex (0621 852978).
Directions: Leave Maldon on main road to Colchester, pass through Heybridge then turn right at sign to Tolleshunt Major (Scraley Road). Ground on right. Six miles from nearest station (Witham). By bus via Chelmsford and Maldon.
Capacity: 5,000 (200 Covered).   **Seats:** 200   **Floodlights:** Y **Shop:** N **Metal Badges:** N
Colours: Black & white stripes/black/black & white **Change colours:** Orange/white/orange
Sponsors: Knight Contractors Ltd
Previous Leagues: North Essex/ South Essex/ Essex & Suffolk Border/ Essex Senior 1971-84.
Midweek home matchday: Tuesday   **Reserve Team's League:** Essex & Herts Border Comb.
Record Attendance: 572 v Dartford, FA Cup 3rd Qualifying Rd 89-90.
Best F.A. Cup season: 4th Qualifying Rd 90-91 (lost 1-3 at Barnet).
League clubs defeated in F.A. Cup: None.
Record Fees - Paid: None   **Received:** £12,000.
Players progressing to Football League: Simon Royce.
Clubhouse: Two bars open every night. Games room, boardroom, kitchen (on matchdays).
Club Record Goalscorer: J Lamb 115   **Club Record Apps:** H Askew 500+.
91-92 Captain: Kevin Lee   **91-92 P.O.Y.:** Kevin Lee
91-92 Top scorer: Wayne Adcock, Robbie Nihill, Phil Thrift (all seven).
Local Newspapers (+Tel.Nos.): Maldon & Burnham Standard (0621 8522233).
Local Radio Stations: BBC Essex, Essex Radio.
Honours: Isthmian Lg Div 2 North 89-90, Essex Senior Trophy 81-82, Essex Senior Lg 81-82 82-83 83-84 (Lg Cup 82-83), JT Clarke Cup 82-83, Thorn EMI National Floodlit Competition R-up 82-83, Essex & Herts Border Combination R-up 88-89 90-91.

GOALKEEPERS:
Alby Bridge (Local football)

DEFENDERS:
Robbie Sach (Maldon, Chelmsford), **Ian Hastings** (Maldon), **Richard Sach** (Local football), **John Stoker** (Local football), **Dave Groom** (Chelmsford, Billericay, Heybridge, Farnborough, Chelmsford, Heybridge, Billericay, Basildon, Heybridge, Tilbury, Southend, Millwall)

MIDFIELD:
Kevin Lee (Basildon, Chelmsford, Heybridge), **Wayne Pannell** (Halstead, Tiptree), **Paul Bardo** (Maldon), **Colin Rogers** (Local football), **Mark Bewers** (Maldon St Marys), **Kenny Kerr** (local football)

FORWARDS:
John Pollard (Bury T, Colchester), **Wayne Adcock** (Maldon), **Dave Atkinson** (Local football), **Gary Barden** (Chelmsford), **Phil Thrift** (Chelmsford, Stambridge, Heybridge, Chelmsford, Heybridge, Dagenham, Chelmsford, Writtle), **Robbie Nihill** (Local football), **Mark Shanley** (Spurs(T))

Scraley Road, Heybridge, Essex
Telephone (0621) 852978   30p

PROGRAMME DETAILS:
Pages: 32 **Price:** 30p
Editor: Chris Daines
WMPCC Rating: 22

Formed: 1865

HITCHIN TOWN

The Canaries

Hitchin Town FC. Photo - Alan J Miller.

Chairman: Terry Barratt   **President:** J Dawson
Secretary (Add & Tel): Alan Sexton, 66 Ninespring Way, Hitchin, Herts SG4 9NU (0462 456003).
Team Manager: Andy Melvin   **Asst Manager:**   **Coach:** Robin Wainwright
Press Officer: Alan Sexton (as above).   **Physio:** Ray Ashcroft/Colin Bell.
Newsline: 0898 122 934   **Commercial Manager:** Jack Russell
Ground Address & Tel: Top Field, Fishponds Road, Hitchin SG5 1NU (0462 459028).
Directions: On A505 near town centre opposite large green. 1 mile from Hitchin (BR).
Capacity: 4,000 (1,000 Covered).   **Seats:** 400   **Floodlights:** Y   **Shop:** Y   **Metal Badges:** Y
Colours: Yellow/emerald/yellow   **Change colours:** All red   **Sponsors:** Hallmark Luxury Travel.
Previous Leagues: South Eastern 01-08/ Spartan 09-11 28-39/ Athenian 45-63.
Midweek home matchday: Tuesday   **Reserve Team's League:** Essex & Herts Border Comb.
Record Attendance: 7,878 v Wycombe, FA Amateur Cup 3rd Rd 18/2/56.
Best F.A. Cup season: QF 1871-72. Also 2nd Rd replay (v Swindon) 1976-77, 2nd Rd (v Boston Utd) 73-74.
Record Fees - Paid: £2,000 for Ray Seeking (Potton 1989)   **Rec:** £6,000 for Steve Conroy (K'nian 1990).
Players progressing to Football League: Reg Smith (M'wall & England skipper), Len Garwood (Spurs 1946), C J Walker, W Odell, S Foss, R Stevens, T Clarke, G Goodyear, L Harwood, P Burridge, Ray Kitchener (C'sea 1954), D Bumstead, M Dixon, David Pacey (Luton 1956), Mike Dixon & Brian Whitby (Luton 1957), Keith Abiss (Brighton 1957), D Hille, G Ley, R Morton, L Payne (N'castle & Reading), Micky Small (Brighton), Richard Nugent (Barnet).
Clubhouse: (0462 434483). Members' bar, kitchen and function hall (hireable). Open every day. Ample parking, new Ashe Boardroom (1985). Charrington's beer.
Steward: Eileen Wilson.
Club Record Goalscorer: Eddie Armitage 84 (1932)   **Club Record Apps:** Paul Giggle 950+ 67-88.
91-92 Captain: **91-92 P.o.Y.:**   **91-92 Top scorer:**
Local Papers (+Tel.Nos.): Hitchin Gazette & Express (59651), Hitchin Comet (31666), Hitchin Herald & Post.
Local Radio Stations: Radio Chiltern (0582 666766), BBC Radio Beds (0582 455555).
Hons: FA Amtr Cp SF 60-61 62-63, Isth. Lg R-up 68-69, Spart. Lg 34-35, AFA Snr Cp 30-31, Herts Snr Cp(18-record) 1894-96 97-98 89-1900 02-03 04-05 09-10 30-32 33-34 37-39 40-41 42-43 61-62 69-70 74-77, L'don Snr Cp 69-70 (R-up 72-73), E Angl. Cp 72-73, Herts Charity Cp(16) 01-03 04-05 39-40 43-44 54-55 60-61 67-68 75-80, Herts I'mediate Cp(8) 39-40 46-47 48-49 56-57 60-62 67-69, Woolwich Tphy 82-83, Televised Sport Int Cup 88-89 90-91, Sthern Comb. Snr F'lit Cup 90-91, FA Tphy 3rd Rd rep. 76-77. Only Surviving FA founder member (1867).

GOALKEEPERS:
Bradley Gillham (Stotfold, Letchworth GC)
DEFENDERS:
Mark Burke (Luton, QPR(A)), Darren Thompson (Luton), Mark Campbell (Youth), Colin McGill (Stevenage), Matthew Hill (Staines, Wycombe, Hemel Hempstead, Hitchin), Steve Miller (Vauxhall M, Stevenage, St Albans, Hitchin), Frank Mingo (Vauxhall M)
MIDFIELD:
Terry Nightingale (Berkhamsted, Hitchin, Hertford, St Albans, Hitchin), Rob Johnson (Barnet, Leicester C, Luton), Jon Friend (Berkhamsted, Hitchin, Barton R, Chesham, Hitchin, Stevenage, St Albans, Hitchin, Barton R), David Taylor (Barton R), Richard Fisher (Stevenage, Arlesey), Mark McGonagle (Luton), Stuart Brown (Tring, Slough, Luton), Jon Bone (Baldock, Hitchin, Luton(J))
FORWARDS: Gordon Guile (Pirton), Paul Quarman (Caddington, Luton(J)), Aaron Tighe (Luton), Paul Olney (Youth), Alan Cosby (Chesham, St Albans, Barnet, Hitchin, Hendon, Hitchin), Graham Coles (Staines, Hemel Hempstead, Hitchin, Staines, St Albans, Berkhamsted, Tring, Hemel Hempstead, St Albans, Dunstable, Spurs(A)), Ian Scott (St Albans, Aylesbury, Luton)

Pages: 28 **Price:** 50p
Editor: Barry Swain
WMPCC Rating: 20

LEWES

Lewes 3, Hailsham Town 1: Sussex Senior Cup Quarter Final, 15/2/92. Pandemonium reigns in the Hailsham box as Micky Russell of Lewes heads for goal. With a young team, the Rooks raised a few eyebrows by earning promotion back to Division One at the first attempt. Photo - Colin Stevens.

Chairman: P Brook   **President:** W D Carr, Esq
Secretary: Mr P Rea, 8 St Michaels Terrace, Lewes, East Sussex (0273 477969).
Team Manager: B Donnelly   **Asst Manager:** T Graves   **Coach:**
Press Officer: **Commercial Manager:**   **Physio:** B Winterborn.
Ground: The Dripping Pan, Mountfield Road, Lewes BN7 1XN (0273 472574).
Directions: Two minute walk from Lewes (BR) - turn left out of station and left into Mountfield Road. Ground 100 yards on right.
Capacity: 5,000 (400 Covered).   **Seats:** 400   **Floodlights:** Y   **Shop:** Y   **Metal Badges:** Y
Colours: Black & red hoops/black/red   **Change colours:** Yellow/blue
Sponsors: Nico Construction Ltd
Previous Leagues: Mid Sussex 1886-1920/ Sussex County 20-65/ Athenian 65-77.
Midweek home matchday: Tuesday   **Reserve Team's League:** Sussex Co. reserve section.
Record Attendance: 2,500 v Newhaven, Sussex County Lg 26/12/47.
Best F.A. Cup season: 4th Qualifying Rd (lost to Harwich & Parkeston)
League clubs defeated in F.A. Cup: None.
Record Fees - Paid: **Received:** £2,500 for Grant Horscroft (Brighton)
Players progressing to Football League: *(to Brighton unless stated)* Don Bates (1950), Peter Knight (1964), Terry Stanley (1969), Colin Woffuden (1970), G Elphick & Steve Ford (Stoke 1981), Glen Geard, Grant Hrscroft (1987), J Hammond (Fulham), S Funnell, L Allen (Wimbledon), M Rice (Watford).
Clubhouse: (0273 472100). Bar, tea bar, pool, table tennis.   **Steward:** P Brook.
Club Record Goalscorer: Pip Parris 332   **Club Record Apps:** Terry Parris 641
91-92 Captain: **91-92 P.o.Y.:**   **91-92 Top scorer:**
Local Newspapers (+Tel.Nos.): Evening Argus, Sussex Express.
Local Radio Stations: BBC Radio Sussex, Southern Sound.
Honours: Isth. Lg Div 2 R-up 79-80 91-92, Ath'n Lg Div 1 69-70 (Div 2 67-68), Sussex Co. Lg 64-65 (R-up 24-25 33-34 58-59 63-64, Lg Cup 39-40), Mid Sussex Lg 10-11 13-14, Sussex Snr Cup 64-65 70-71 84-85 (R-up 79-80 82-83 87-88), Sussex Royal Ulster Rifles Charity Cup(3) 61-63 64-65, Gilbert Rice F'lit Cup 82-83 88-89, Neale Tphy 68-69, Sussex F'lit Cup 76-77 (SF 83-84), Southern Counties Comb Div 1 80-81, FA Tphy 1st Rd 82-83, FA Amtr Cup 2nd Rd 67-68, FA Vase 1st Rd 79-80.

GOALKEEPERS:
Keith Cheal (Bognor, Southwick, Worthing, Southwick, Horsham, Southwick, Steyning), **Graham Bannantyne** (Seaford)
DEFENDERS:
Grant Horscroft (Brighton, Lewes, Ringmer), **Mark Horscroft** (Ringmer), **Mark Risley** (Local football), **Shaun Manley** (Youth), **Mick Russell** (Southwick, Horsham, Eastbourne Utd), **Colin Pateman** (Local football)
MIDFIELD:
Glen Geard (Whitehawk, Southwick, Shoreham, Southwick, Eastbourne Utd, Whitehawk, Horsham, Lewes, Brighton), **Spencer Mintram** (Brighton(T)), **Rob MacMillan** (Youth), **Syd Harman** (Brighton(J)), **Paul Stokes** (Youth), **Lee Cox** (Southwick, Peacehaven, Horsham, Shoreham), **Neil Ryan** (Eastbourne Utd, Littlehampton), **Darren Freeman** (Youth)
FORWARDS:
Steve Richardson (Whitehawk), **Kevin Crooks** (Whitehawk, Southwick, Worthing, Southwick, Crawley, Southwick, Whitehawk, Southwick), **Paul Laycock** (Youth), **Herbie Smith** (Alma S, Fisher, Dunstable, Aylesbury, Barnet, Fisher, Southwick, Littlehampton, Tooting, Luton, Tooting), **Gavin Spooner** (Eastbourne Utd)

PROGRAMME DETAILS:
Pages: 32 **Price:** 50p
Editor: M J Webster
WMPCC Rating: N/A

LEYTON

Leyton's ground at Lea Bridge Road. Photo - Dave West.

Chairman: George Gross   **President:** Laurie Aldridge
Secretary (Add & Tel): Alan Hunter, Flat E 86-88 Finsbury Park, London N4 2HW (081 809 5057).
Team Manager: Kevin Moran   **Asst Mgr:** Martin Busson   **Coach:** Alec Welsh
Press Officer: George Gross (081 850 9082)   **Physio:** Brian Morris
Ground: Wingate-Leyton Stadium, 282 Lea Bridge Road, Leyton E10 7LD (081 539 6861).
Directions: Leyton (Central Line), Clapton (BR), Blackhorse Road (Victoria Line), thence buses 48, 55, 58 or 230.
Capacity: 1,500 (600 Covered)   **Seats:** 202   **Floodlights:** Y   **Shop:** Y   **Metal Badges:** Y
Colours: White/navy/white   **Change colours:** Navy/white/navy   **Sponsors:** OTV
Previous Names: Wingate FC (founded 1946) and Leyton FC (prev. Matlock Swifts, founded 1895) merged in 1975. Leyton-Wingate 1975-92.
Previous Leagues: Athenian 1975-82. *(Predecessors, Leyton(1): London, Southern, S Essex).*
Midweek home matchday: Tuesday   **Reserve Team League:** Essex & Herts Border Comb.
Record Attendance: 500 v Whickham, FA Vase 6th Rd 83-84.
Best F.A. Cup season: 1st Rd 85-86. *(Leyton(1) reached 3rd Rd in 09-10, and 1st Rd on 14 other occasions).*
League clubs defeated in F.A. Cup: None. *(Leyton(1) beat Stockport (09-10) and Merthyr Town (29-30).*
Record Fees - Paid: **Received:** £4,000 for Frank Coles (Enfield).
Players progressing to Football League: None. *(From predecessors - Ken Facey (Orient 1952), Mortimer Costello (Aldershot 1956), David Clark (Orient 1961)).*
Clubhouse: (081 539 5405). Hot food, pool, darts, music.   **Steward:** S Goodwin
Club Record Goalscorer: Steve Lane 118   **Club Record Apps:** Steve Hamberger 387.
91-92 Captain: Mark Mennell   **91-92 P.o.Y.:** Mark Mennel **91-92 Top scorer:**
Local Press (+Tel.Nos.): Waltham Forest Guardian, Hackney Gazette   **Local Radio Stations:** LBC.
Honours: Isthmian Lg Div 1 R-up 86-87 (Div 2 North 84-85), Athenian Lg 81-82 (R-up 77-78, Div 1 76-77), Essex Snr Tphy 84-85, Essex Thameside Trophy 81-82, Thorn EMI National F'light Cup, FA Trophy 3rd Rd 87-88, FA Vase 6th Rd 83-84. *As Leyton(1); FA Amateur Cup 26-27 27-28 (R-up 28-29 33-34 36-37 51-52), London Senior Cup 03-04 (R-up 33-34 45-46), London Charity Cup 34-35 36-37, London Lg 23-24 24-25 25-26 (R-up 26-27, Lg Cup 56-57), Athenian Lg 28-29 65-66 66-67 (R-up 45-46, Div 2 Cup R-up 69-70), London Challenge Cup R-up 26-27, Essex Senior Cup 1896-97 97-98 99-1900 00-01 02-03 29-30 30-31 34-35, Essex Thameside Trophy 64-65 66-67, Parthenon Lg 51-52.*

GOALKEEPERS:
Alex Welsh
(Stevenage B, Boreham Wood, Hertford, Hounslow, Wealdstone, Hertford, B Stortford, Dunstable, Milton Keynes, Enfield, Luton, Lincoln, Middlesbrough)

DEFENDERS:
Steve O'Neil (Southgate Ath, Finchley, Boreham Wood, St Albans, Barnet), **Chris Swash** (Local football), **Darren Woodhurst** (Enfield, QPR(J)), **Andy Groom** (Finchley, Hendon, Barking), **Paul Frain** (Collier R, Redbridge F, Walthamstow Ave), **Steve Newman** (Dagenham, East Ham)

MIDFIELD:
Barry Popplewell (Southgate Ath, Luton(A)), **Mark Mennell** (Southgate Ath), **Kevin Morley** (Local football, Walthamstow Ave, Crown & Anchor), **Steve Bradshaw** (Runcorn), **Paul Salmon** (Youth)

FORWARDS:
Dave Steppings (Enfield, Stockport, Spurs(J)), **Tony Kennedy** (Southgate Ath, Walthamstow Pennant), **Colin John** (Local football, Grays, c Palace), **Gary Stanton** (Southgate Ath, Maiden Vale), **Mike Fredericks** (Boreham Wood, Hertford, Welwyn GC)

Pages: 24 **Price:** 60p
Editor: G Gross
WMPCC Rating: 23

MAIDENHEAD UNITED

Magpies

Abingdon United goalkeeper Richardson punches clear under pressure from the Maidenhead attack during a Berks & Bucks Senior Cup Second Qualifying Round tie. The match finished goalless. Photo - Maurice Cann.

Chairman: Jim Parsons   **Joint Presidents:** Messrs C & R West.
Secretary (Add & Tel): Stan Payne, 14 Brookside, Honeycroft Hill, Uxbridge UB10 9NH (0895 236709).
Team Manager: John Clements   **Asst Manager:** Derek Sweetman **Coach:** Various.
Press Officer: John Swan (0628 473411)   **Physio:** Jim Barrs.
Commercial Manager: Brian Knights.   **Newsline:** 0898 122 903.
Ground: York Road, Maidenhead, Berks SL6 1SQ (0628 24739).
Directions: In town centre, 400 yds from station and two minutes from town centre car parks.
Capacity: 1,500 (500 Covered)   **Seats:** 150   **Floodlights:** Y   **Shop:** Y   **Metal Badges:** Y
Colours: White/black/red   **Change colours:** All blue, or red/red/white
Sponsors: Maidenhead Advertiser.
Previous Name: Maidenhead/ Maidenhead Norfolkians.
Previous Leagues: Great Western Combination/ Spartan/ Corinthian/ Athenian/ Southern.
Midweek home matchday: Tuesday   **Reserve Team's League:** Suburban.
Record Attendance: 7,920 v Southall, FA Amateur Cup 1936.
Best F.A. Cup season: Quarter Finals 1873-74 74-75 75-76.
Record Fees - Paid: **Received:**
Players progressing to Football League: Alan Cordice, Paul Priddy, David Kemp, Laurie Sanchez, Eddie Kelsey, Jackie Palethorpe, Benny Laryea, Roy Davies.
Clubhouse: Open every evening. Hot and cold food, dancehall, darts, pool.
Club Record Goalscorer: George Copas   **Club Record Apps:** B Randall.
91-92 Capt: Stuart Muir/ Peter Rackley   **91-92 P.o.Y.:** Paul Holder **91-92 Top scorer:** Benny Laryea 21.
Local Newspapers (+Tel.Nos.): Maidenhead Advertiser, Reading Evening Post.
Local Radio Stations: Radio 210, Capital.
Hons: FA Amtr Cup SF 35-36, isth. Lg Div 2 Sth R-up 90-91 (Yth Cup R-up 77-78), Spart. Lg(3) 26-27 32-34, Corinth. Lg 57-58 60-61 (R-up 59-60, Shield 56-57 (R-up(3) 50-51 59-61), Neale Cup 48-49 57-58 60-61, Res. Div 50-51 62-63), Gt Western Lg 19-20, Gt Western Comb. 48-49, Berks & Bucks Snr Cup(16) 1894-96 1906-07 11-12 27-28 29-32 38-39 45-46 55-57 60-61 62-63 65-66 69-70 (R-up(14) 1881-82 92-94 97-98 1913-14 19-20 22-23 26-27 28-29 35-38 57-58 59-61), Mithras Cup 62-63 66-67 (R-up 79-80), Reading Snr Cup 55-56 58-59, Berks & Bucks Benev. Cup(6) 30-31 36-37 39-40 58-61 (R-up 48-49 50-51), Berks & Bucks I'mediate Cup 57-58 65-66, Southern Comb. Cup R-up 82-83, Berks & Bucks Yth Cup 83-84 90-91.

GOALKEEPERS:
Peter Rackley (Hungerford, Maidenhead Utd, Newbury, Slough, Reading)
DEFENDERS:
Paul Holder (Feltham, Leatherhead, Carshalton, Leatherhead, Woking, Slough, Dulwich, Epsom & Ewell, Crawley, Three Bridges), **Dean Bailey** (Hungerford, Newbury, Thatcham), **Andy Cullum** (Leatherhead, Carshalton, Dorking, Arsenal), **Deane Foster** (Farnborough, Reading), **Kenny Alleyne** (Appollo), **Alvin Whittaker** (Youth)
MIDFIELD:
Stuart Muir (Windsor, Maidenhead Utd, Waterlooville), **Simon Chandler** (Finchley, Chelsea(J)), **Steve Croxford** (Youth), **Elliott Payne** (Youth), **Glen Wickham** (Enfield), **Micky Floyd** (Local football)
FORWARDS:
Gary Hall (Woking, Chalfont, Yeading, Woking), **Cliff Alleyne** (Appollo), **Benny Laryea** (Yeading, Wealdstone, Windsor, Torquay, Dundalk, Maidenhead Utd, Watford), **Graig Gill** (Hungerford, Yeovil, Bashley, Hungerford, Merthyr, Morriston, Dunvants, Killay), **Paul Reeve** (Youth), **Paul Dadson** (Wokingham, Coventry C), **Paul Mulvaney** (Cove, Woking, Bracknell, Cheltenham, Wycombe, Bracknell)

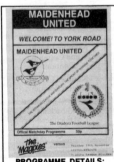

PROGRAMME DETAILS:
Pages: 28 **Price:** 50p
Editor: John Swan
WMPCC Rating: 22

MOLESEY

Molesey FC.

Chairman: Gary Mayne   **President:** Fred Maynard
Secretary: TBA
Team Manager: Tony Dunne   **Asst Manager:**   **Coach:** Richard Higgs.
Press Officer: Peter Bowers (0420 89085).   **Physio:** Alan Brilliant
Football Club Manager: Martin Eede   **Sponsors:** Ivy Express.
Ground: 412 Walton Road, West Molesey, Surrey KT8 0JG (081 979 4823).
Directions: A3 from London to Hook, then A309 to Marquis of Granby pub, right to Hampton Court station, ground one mile through Molesey, on left.
Capacity: 4,800 (650 Covered).   **Seats:** 400   **Floodlights:** Y   **Shop:** Y   **Metal Badges:** Y
Colours: White/black/black   **Change colours:** Yellow/blue/yellow
Previous Leagues: Surrey Intermediate/ Surrey Senior 53-59/ Spartan 59-73/ Athenian 73-77.
Previous Name: Molesey St Pauls
Midweek home matchday: Wednesday   **Reserve Team's League:** Suburban.
Record Attendance: 1,255 v Sutton United, Surrey Senior SF 1966.
Best F.A. Cup season: 3rd Qualifying Rd 76-77.
League clubs defeated in F.A. Cup: None.
Record Fees - Paid: £500 for Chris Vidal (Leatherhead)   **Received:** £5,000 for Chris Vidal (Hythe Town).
Players progressing to Football League: John Finch (Fulham), Cyrille Regis (WBA, Coventry & England).
Clubhouse: Open every evening, two bars, discos, live artists, darts, bingo, pool.
Steward: John Chambers
Club Record Goalscorer: Michael Rose 38   **Club Record Appearances:** Frank Hanley 453
91-92 Captain: Clive Gartell.
91-92 P.O.Y.: Clive Gartell (Fans' choice: Roger Worrall).
91-92 Top Scorer: Chris Vidal.
Local Newspapers (+Tel.Nos.): Surrey Comet, Surrey Herald, Molesey News.
Local Radio Stations: County Sound, Capital.
Honours: Isthmian Lg Div 2 South R-up 89-90, Surrey Senior Lg 57-58, Surrey Senior Lg Charity Cup, Spartan Lg R-up 59-60 (Lg Cup 61-62), Surrey Senior Shield R-up, Southern Combination Cup 90-91, FA Vase 6th Rd 81-82, FA Tphy 1st Rd replay 90-91.

GOALKEEPERS:
Dave Brace (Walton Cas, Fulham(J))

DEFENDERS:
Mark Dodman (Whyteleafe, Carshalton, Leatherhead, Pretoria(SA), C Palace(A)), **Simon White** (Malden V, Banstead), **David Pope** (Youth), **Roger Worrall** (Horley), **Dean Smith** (Banstead, Leatherhead)

MIDFIELD:
Clive Gartell (Dulwich, Molesey, Leatherhead, Epsom & Ewell), **Paul Harris** (Epsom & Ewell, Tooting, Whyteleafe), **David Shepherd** (Dulwich, Bromley, Whyteleafe, Sutton Utd, Croydon), **Dave Rattue** (Whyteleafe, Hampton, Leatherhead, Kingstonian, Molesey)

FORWARDS:
Micky Rose (Carshalton, Leatherhead, Crawley, Dulwich), **Russell Cobley** (Youth), **Chris Vidal** (Hythe, Molesey, Leatherhead), **Shaun Rice** (Hampton, Ditton)

PROGRAMME DETAILS:
Pages: 24 **Price:** 50p
Editor: Peter Bowers
WMPCC Rating: 26

PURFLEET

Purfleet FC, Diadora League Division Two Champions 1991-92. Back Row (L/R): Gary Calder (manager), Chris King (asst mgr), Denis Moore (coach), Jeff Wood, Graham Wood, Jimmy McFarlane, Mickey Desborough, Lee Matthews, John Rees, Daren Houlding, Denis Pollock (asst coach), Bob Johnson (physio). Front: Nigel Jeys, Alan Brett, Chris Blakeborough, Mickey Tarling, Tony Machlin, Jason Spiteri.

Chairman: Harry South.   **Vice Chairman:** K Worrall.
Secretary: Norman Posner, 1 Chase House Gardens, Hornchurch, Essex RM11 2PJ (0708 458301).
Team Manager: Gary Calder   **Asst Manager:** Chris King   **Coach:** Denis Moore
Press Officer: Bob Andrews (0376 376602)   **Physio:** Bob Johnson.
Commercial Manager: Bob Andrews (as above).
Ground: Thurrock Hotel, Ship Lane, Grays, Essex (0708 868901).
Directions: M25 or A13 to Dartford tunnel r'bout. Ground is fifty yards on right down Ship Lane.
Capacity: 2,500 (800 Covered)   **Seats:** 300   **Floodlights:** Y   **Shop:** N   **Metal Badges:** N
Colours: Yellow/green/yellow   **Change colours:** Blue & white stripes/white/blue.
Sponsors: **Previous Names:** None.
Previous Leagues: Essex Senior.
Midweek home matchday: Monday   **Reserve Team's League:** Suburban.
Record Attendance: 950 v West Ham United, 1989.
Best F.A. Cup season: Second Qualifying Rd 1991-92 (lost 2-4 v King's Lynn).
Record Fees - Paid: **Received:**
Players progressing to Football League: Paul Cobb (Leyton Orient).
Clubhouse: 10am-10pm every day. Snooker, squash, weights room, aerobics, a-la carte restaurant, steam room.
Steward: Tom South.
Club Record Goalscorer: **Club Record Apps:**
91-92 Captain: Jimmy McFarlane   **91-92 P.o.Y.:** Jimmy McFarlane   **91-92 Top scorer:** Jeff Wood 32.
Local Newspapers (+Tel.Nos.): Thurrock Recorder, Thurrock Gazette.
Local Radio Stations: Essex Radio, BBC Radio Essexx.
Hons: Isthmian Lg Div 2 91-92 (Div 2 Nth R-up 88-89, Loctite Tphy 91-92), Essex Snr Lg 87-88 (Lg Cup(2) 86-88), Stanford Charity Cup 87-88 (R-up 85-86).

GOALKEEPERS:
Micky Desborough (Aveley, Hornchurch, Clapton), **Jimmy Chapman** (Ford Utd, Rainham)

DEFENDERS:
Darren Houlding (Aveley, Clapton, Millwall W), **Graham Daley** (Aveley, Walthamstow Ave, Woodford), **Tony Pizzey** (Heybridge S, Purfleet, East Thurrock), **Jim McFarlane** (Clapton, Millwall W), **Ian Ward** (Aveley), **John Shippey** (Local football)

MIDFIELD:
Tony Macklin (Grays, Tilbury, West Ham), **Jason Spiteri** (Aveley, Redbridge F, Clapton), **Lee Matthews** (Southend(T)), **John Rees** (Aveley), **Mike Tarling** (Beckton Utd), **Rob Gammons** (Aveley, Barking, Chesham, Chelmsford, Barking, Arsenal(J))

FORWARDS:
Chris Blakeborough (Aveley, Redbridge F, Clapton, Hornchurch, Clapton, Hornchurch), **Jeff Wood** (Harlow, B Stortford, Dartford, Crawley, Greenwich B, West Ham(J)), **Nigel Jeyes** (Aveley, Basildon, Billericay, Tilbury, Barking, Dartford), **Alan Brett** (Aveley, Hornchurch)

PROGRAMME DETAILS:
Pages: 28 **Price:** 50p
Editor: Bob Andrews
WMPCC Rating: N/A

Back Row (L/R): Danny Wood, Peter Mills, David Gabriel, Sam Shosanya, Ralph Cowan, Dave Taylor, Kevin Duffell.
Front Row: Bobby Dennington, Paul Loughlin, David Powell, Robin Welch, Micky Stephens, Mark Irwin.

Chairman: J Payne   **President:** L Walters
Secretary: Chris Jackson, 1 Abercorn Close, Selsdon Ridge, S Croydon CR2 8TG (081 651 2568).
Manager: Trevor Ford   **Asst Manager:** Micky Sorensen **Coach:** Peter Shaw
Press Officer: Frank Janaway (081 648 7240)   **Physio:** Danny Keenan
Ground: Sandy Lane, Mitcham, Surrey CR4 2HD (081 648 3248).
Directions: Tooting (BR) quarter mile. Sandy Lane is off Streatham Road near Swan Hotel.
Capacity: 8,000 (1,990 Covered).   **Seats:** 1,990   **Floodlights:** Y   **Shop:** Y   **Metal Badges:** Y
Colours: White/black/red   **Change colours:**   **Sponsors:**
Previous Leagues: London 32-37/ Athenian 37-56.
Midweek home matchday: Tuesday   **Reserve Team's League:** Suburban.
Record Attendance: 17,500 v QPR, FA Cup 2nd Rd 56-57.
Best F.A. Cup season: 4th Rd 75-76 (lost 1-3 at Bradford City). Also 3rd Rd 58-59, 2nd Rd 56-57 76-77, 1st Rd 48-49 50-51 63-64 74-75 77-78.
League clubs defeated in F.A. Cup: Bournemouth & Boscombe Ath, Northampton 58-59, Swindon 75-76.
Record Fees - Paid: £9,000 for Dave Flint (Enfield)   **Received:** £10,000 for H Smith (Luton).
Players progressing to Football League: Trevor Owen (Orient 1958), Dave Bumpstead (M'wall 1958), Paddy Hasty (Aldersot 1958), Walter Pearson (A'shot 1961), Richie Ward & Alex Stepney (M'wall 1962 & 63), Vic Akers (W'ford 1975), Paul Priddy (W'don 1978), Carlton Fairweather & Brian Gayle (W'don 1984).
Clubhouse: Open Mon-Fri 6.30-11pm, Sat 12.30-2.45, 4.45-11pm, Sun 12-2, 7-10.30 pm. Hot meals and wide selection of snacks.
Steward: C Mills.
Club Record Goalscorer: Alan Ives 92 (1972-78)   **Club Record Apps:** Danny Godwin 470.
91-92 Captain: Micky Stephens   **91-92 P.o.Y.:** Ralph Cowan   **91-92 Top scorer:** John Collins 21
Local Newspapers (+Tel.Nos.): Mitcham News (081 672 1077), South London Press (081 769 4444), South London Guardian (081 644 4300).
Local Radio Stations: Capital.
Honours: Isthmian Lg 57-58 59-60, Athenian Lg 49-50 54-55, London Challenge Cup R-up 59-60, Surrey Senior Cup 37-38 43-44 44-45 52-53 59-60 75-76 76-77 77-78, London Senior Cup 42-43 48-49 58-59 59-60 (R-up 43-44 44-45), South Thames Cup 69-70, Surrey Senior Shield 51-52 60-61 61-62 65-66, FA Tphy 2nd Qual Rd Replay 71-72 81-82, FA Amateur Cup 1st Rd replay 22-23.

GOALKEEPERS:
Peter Mills (Leyton-Wingate, Bromley, Sittingbourne, Croydon, Reading, Tilbury, Welling), **Adrian McManus** (Old Prestonians)
DEFENDERS:
David Taylor (Croydon, Dulwich, Hayes, Epsom & Ewell), **Ralph Cowan** (Lewes, Oxford C, Witney), **Dave Gabriel** (Corinthian Cas), **Dave Stephenson** (Dorking, Croydon, London Boys), **Sam Shosanya** (Local football), **Simon Ward** (Molesey, Epsom & Ewell, Molesey, Cobham), **Tony Scott** (Dulwich, Tooting), **Kevin Duffell** (Epsom & Ewell, Leatherhead, Epsom & Ewell), **Jeremy Jones** (Chelsea(T))
MIDFIELD:
Paul Loughlin (Bromley), **Micky Stephens** (Sutton Utd), **Derek Allman** (Corinthian Cas), **Peter Kingston** (Dulwich, Croydon, Dulwich, Tooting, Dulwich, Carshalton, Fisher), **John Myatt** (Wycombe, Crewe, Watford, C Palace(J)), **Noel Costelloe** (Molesey, Leatherhead, Molesey, Hampton, Tooting)
FORWARDS:
John Collins (Wealdstone, Dulwich, Cuffley), **Bobby Dennington** (Bromley, Leyton-Wingate), **Robin Welch** (Dulwich, Malden Vale, Whyteleafe), **Luke Harding** (Molesey, Epsom & Ewell), **Wade Falana** (Leytonstone & Ilford, Millwall(T), Chelsea(Sch)), **Mark Irwin** (Folkestone)

PROGRAMME DETAILS:
Pages: 20 Price: 50p
Editor: Ian Bullock
WMPCC Rating: 15

UXBRIDGE

Uxbridge defend desperately during their fixture away to Tooting & Mitcham United on 7th January 1992.

Chairman: A Holloway   **Presidents:** Alan Odell/ Tom Barnard.
Secretary: G Hiseman, 98 New Peachey Lane, Cowley, Uxbridge, Middx UB8 3SY (0895 237195).
Team Manager: M Harvey   **Asst Manager:** G Talbot   **Coach:**
Press Officer: A Peart   **Physio:** E Kempster
Ground: Honeycroft, Horton Road, West Drayton, Middx UB7 8HX (0895 445830 - 24 hr information line).
Directions: From West Drayton (BR) turn right then 1st left (Horton Road). Ground 1 mile on left.
Capacity: 5,000 (480 Covered).   **Seats:** 201   **Floodlights:** Y   **Shop:** Y   **Metal Badges:** £1.65
Colours: Red/white/red   **Change colours:** All sky blue.
Previous Leagues: Southern 1894-99/ Gt Western Suburban 1906-19 20-23/ Athenian 1919-20 24-37 63-82/
Spartan 37-38/ London 38-46/ Gt Western Comb. 39-45/ Corinthian 46-63.
Previous Name: Uxbridge Town (1923-45). **Previous Grounds:** RAF Stadium 23-48/ Cleveland Road 48-76.
Midweek home matchday: Tuesday   **Reserve Team's League:** Suburban (North Division).
Record Attendance: 1,000 v Arsenal, floodlight opening 1981.
Best F.A. Cup season: 2nd Rd 1873-74. 1st Rd on three other occasions 1883-84 84-85 85-86.
League clubs defeated in F.A. Cup:
Record Fees - Paid: **Received:**
Players progressing to Football League: William Hill (QPR 1951), Lee Stapleton (Fulham 1952), Gary
Churchouse.
Clubhouse: (0895 443557). Large clubhouse with bar and dance hall. Open every evening and lunchtime.
Steward: Mrs A Hinde.
Club Record Goalscorer: Danny Needham, 125   **Club Record Apps:** Roger Nicholls, 1054.
91-92 Captain: Mark Gill   **91-92 P.o.Y.:** Winston White   **91-92 Top scorer:** Steve Kuhne 24.
Local Newspapers (+Tel.Nos.): Middx Gazette (0895 58290).
Local Radio Stations: Capital, Greater London Radio.
Honours: FA Amateur Cup R-up 1897-98, FA Tphy 1st Rd replay 88-89, FA Vase 4th Rd 83-84, Isthmian Lg Div 2
South R-up 84-85 (Lg Cup R-up 85-86), Athenian Lg Cup R-up 81-82 (Div 2 Cup R-up 70-71), Corinthian Lg 59-60
(R-up 49-50, Lg Memorial Shield 50-51 52-53), London Lg Western Div R-up 45-46, Middx Senior Cup 1893-94 95-
96 1950-51, Middx Senior Charity Cup 07-08 12-13 35-36 81-82 (R-up 69-70 82-83 85-86), Allied Counties Yth Lg
Cup 86-87 (Lg Shield 88-89).

GOALKEEPERS:
Sean Dawson (Hanwell)
DEFENDERS: Troy McAuliffe (Yeading, Aveley, Uxbridge, Edgware,
Hendon), **Andy Taylor** (Hayes, Uxbridge), **Howard Williams** (Harefield,
Yeading), **Steve Toms** (Harefield, Chalfont, Uxbridge, Yeading, Southall), **Gary Bray** (Hayes, Ruislip Manor, Kingsbury,
Haringey B, Ruislip Manor, Harrow B, Ruislip Manor), **Leroy La Croix**
(Yeading, Uxbridge, Yeading), **Darren Colwill** (Slough, Wegberg(Ger),
Northwood, Rayners Lane), **Roy Davies** (Hendon, Chelsea)
MIDFIELD: Nick Regan (Harefield, Chalfont, Harefield, Ruislip, Southall,
Kingstonian, Harefield, Hounslow, Burnham), **Fergus Rushe** (Spalding,
Newry, Hendon, Brighton, Newry), **Steve Matthews** (Molesey, Yeading, St
Albans, Yeading, Hounslow), **Mark Gill** (Hampton, Feltham, Hendon,
Feltham, Brentford), **Nick Harman** (Harefield, Uxbridge, Yeading, Uxbridge,
Chesham, Uxbridge), **Adam Wickens** (Yeading, Hounslow), **Jeff Hamlet**
(Southall, Uxbridge, Dulwich, Crawley, Tooting, Wimbledon), **Tony Pleasant**
(Ruislip Manor)
FORWARDS: Sylvester Williams (Chalfont, Wembley, Hendon), **Vic
Schwartz** (Yeading, Hounslow, Yeading, Northwood), **Steve Kuhne**
(Yeading, Hampton, Hayes, Arlesey, St Neots), **Raoul Sam** (Harefield,
Uxbridge, Yeading), **Stuart Ashton** (Yeading, Rochdale, Galway R, Burnley)

PROGRAMME DETAILS:
Pages: 32 Price: 50p
Editor: M Bodman
WMPCC Rating: 21

WALTON & HERSHAM

Walton & Hersham 0, Kidderminster Harriers 2: FA Trophy 1st Round Proper, 11/1/92. Harriers' goalkeeper is forced into action by the Walton & Hersham attack. Photo - Eric Marsh.

Chairman: N F Swindley
President: Sir Stanley Matthews
Secretary (Add & Tel): Gerry Place, 24 Stratton Road, Sunbury, Middx TW16 6PQ (0932 782414).
Manager: C Wainwright
Asst Manager/Coach: Keith Bristow
Press Officer: B Freeman (0932 560738)
Physio: Frankie Kempster
Commercial Manager:
Ground Address & Tel: Sports Ground, Stompond Lane, Walton-on-Thames (0932 245263).
Directions: Ten minutes walk fron Walton-on-Thames (BR). Bus 218 passes ground.
Capacity: 6,500 (2,500 Covered).   **Seats:** 500   **Floodlights:** Y   **Shop:** Y   **Metal Badges:** Y
Colours: Red & white/white/red   **Change colours:** Blue & black stripes/black/back.
Previous Leagues: Surrey Senior/ Corinthian 45-50/ Athenian 50-71.
Midweek home matchday: Tuesday
Reserve Team's League: Suburban.
Sponsors: General Data.
Record Gate: 6,500 v Brighton, FA Cup 73-74.
Best F.A. Cup season: 2nd Rd 72-73 (v Margate), 73-74 (v Hereford).
League clubs defeated in F.A. Cup: Exeter 72-73, Brighton 73-74.
Players progressing to Football League: Denis Pacey (Orient 1951), John Whitear (A Villa 1953), Andy McCulloch (QPR 1970), Mick Heath (Brentford 1971), Paul Priddy (Brentford 1972), Richard Teale (QPR 1973), Steve Parsons (W'don 1977).
Clubhouse: (0932 245263). Open most nights. Bar, TV, darts, pool, refreshments on matchdays.
Steward: G Rush.
Club Record Scorer:
Club Record Appearances:
91-92 Captain: Mark Wilson   **91-92 P.o.Y.** Ross Davidson   **91-92 Top Scorer:** Justin Mitchell
Local Newspapers (+Tel.Nos.): Surrey Herald.   **Local Radio Stations:** County Sound.
Honours: FA Amateur Cup R-up 72-73 (SF 51-52 52-53), Isthmian Lg R-up 72-73, Barassi Cup 73-74, Athenian Lg 68-69 (R-up 50-51 69-70 70-71, Lg Cup 69-70), Corinthian Lg(3) 46-49 (R-up 49-50), Premier Midweek F'lit Lg(3) 67-69 70-71 (R-up 71-72), Surrey Snr Cup 47-48 50-51 60-61 61-62 70-71 72-73 (R-up 46-47 51-52 59-60 69-70 71-72 73-74), London Snr Cup R-up 73-74, Southern Comb Cup 82-83 88-89, Surrey Comb Cup 49-50.

GOALKEEPERS:
Ken Addai (Dulwich, Sutton Utd), Mike Erlebach (Dorking)

DEFENDERS:
Ross Davidson (Youth), Dougie Hughes (Farnborough, Walton & Hersham, Wimbledon(J)), Gary Cambridge (Hampton, New Moon), Jimmy Gasson (Youth), Mark Fabian (Egham, Ashford(Middx), Staines)

MIDFIELD:
Gary Powell (Staines), Mark Wilson (Farnborough, Feltham, Hampton, Harrow B, Feltham), David Jones (Epsom & Ewell, Kingstonian, Epsom & Ewell, Wimbledon(Sch)), Darren Smith (Egham, Farnborough, Brighton), Richard Burnell (Egham, Ruislip Manor, Brentford(J), Ruislip Manor)

FORWARDS:
Ashley Styles (Merstham), Steve Griffiths (Sutton Utd, Kingstonian), Justin Mitchell (Youth), Paul Thornton (Carshalton, Sutton Utd), Ian Kilpatrick (Leatherhead, Walton & Hersham)

PROGRAMME DETAILS:
Pages: 20 **Price:** 50p
Editor: Brian Freeman
WMPCC Rating: 18

WEMBLEY

Wembley FC. Back Row (L/R): Roy Calmels (match secretary), Rod Romain, Micky Devane, Kenny Page, Paul Shields, Tony Headlam, Steve Lawrence, Mark Witter, Jeff Fanner, Bob Hutchinson, Andy O'Brien, Charlie Turlunch, Adrian Smith, Paul Reynolds, Robert Hollingdale, Andy Smith, Eric Stringer (Vice Chairman). Front Row: Paul Bhatia, Ray Bennett, Tony Simpson (reserve team manager), Alan Dafforn (first team manager), Brian Gumm (Chairman), Fred Smart (asst Manager), Glen Charles (reserve team asst manager), Jim Bryan (President), Charlie Flaherty, Guiliano Grazioli, Henry Clark. Photo - V J Robertson.

Chairman: Brian Gumm **President:** Jim Bryan, BEM
Secretary (Add & Tel): R V Calmels, The Poplars, Mill Street, Gamlingay, Nr Sandy, Beds SG19 3JS. (0767 51539).
Team Manager: Alan Dafforn **Asst Manager:** Fred Smart
Press Officer: R Markiewicz (081 902 0541) **Physio:** Lee Arthur

Ground Address & Tel: Vale Farm, Watford Road, Sudbury, Wembley HA0 4UR (081 908 8169).
Directions: Sudbury (BR) 400 yds, or ten minutes walk from North Wembley tube.
Capacity: 3,000 (1,000 Covered). **Seats:** 250 **Floodlights:** Y **Shop:** N **Metal Badges:** £2
Colours: Red & white quarters **Change colours:** Royal blue or white.
Sponsors: G & B Builders.
Previous Leagues: Middx 46-49/ Spartan 49-51/ Delphian 51-56/ Corinthian 56-63/ Athenian 63-75.
Midweek home matchday: Tuesday **Reserve Team's League:** Suburban.
Record Attendance: 2,654 v Wealdstone 52-53.
Best season in F.A. Cup: 1st Round Proper 1980-81.
League clubs defeated in F.A. Cup: None.
Record Fees - Paid: **Received:** £10,000 for G Roberts (Brentford).
Players progressing to Football League: Ken Coote (Brentford 1949), Keith Cassells (W'ford 1977), Mike O'Donague (Southampton 1979), A McGonigle (Olympiakos), Gary Roberts (Brentford 1980), Richard Cadette (Orient 1984).
Clubhouse: (081 904 8169). Open nightly, large bar, usual club facilities.
Record Win: 11-1 v Hermes, Lon. Snr Cup 1963 **Record Defeat:** 0-16 v Chelsea, Lon Chal Cup 59-60
Club Record Goalscorer: Bill Handrahan 105 (1946-52) **Club Record Apps:** Spud Murphy 505 (78-88).
91-92 Captain: Paul Shields **91-92 P.o.Y.:** Andy O'Brien **91-92 Top Scorer:** Ken Page.
Local Newspapers (+Tel.Nos.): Wembley & Harrow Observer.
Honours: FA Amateur Cup 2nd Rd 66-67 68-69, FA Tphy 1st Rd Proper 91-92, Middx Senior Cup 83-84 86-87 (R-up 55-56 68-69 78-79 87-88 91-92), Middx Lg 47-48 (Lg Cup 46-47), Middx Charity Cup 67-68(joint) 80-81(joint) 82-83 86-87 (R-up 83-84 87-88), Middx Invitation Cup 56-57, Athenian Lg R-up 74-75 (Div 1 R-up 67-68), Corinthian Lg Memorial Shield R-up 58-59, Delphian Lg R-up 55-56, Spartan Lg Div 1 West 50-51 (Dunkel Trophy 50-51(joint)), London Senior Cup R-up 55-56, Hitachi Cup SF 83-84, Suburban Lg North 85-86 (Lg Cup 84-85 (R-up 83-84)).

GOALKEEPERS:
Jeff Fanner (Hounslow, Hillingdon, Harrow B)
DEFENDERS:
Paul Shields (Kingsbury, Leyt & Ilf, Kingsbury, Hendon, Wembley, Hendon, Slough, Kingsbury, Edgware, Willesden), **Tony Headlam** (Southall, Hayes, Ruislip Manor), **Andy O'Brien** (Hendon, Kingsbury, Hendon), **Charlie Turlunch** (Ruislip Manor, Hendon, Ruislip Manor, Wembley), **Rodney Romain** (Local football), **Charlie Flaherty** (Chalfont, Wembley, Burnham, Slough, Harrow B)
MIDFIELD:
Bobby Hutchinson (Egham, Kingsbury, Yeading, Edgware, Wembley, Spurs), **Ray Bennett** (Haringey B), **Mark Witter** (Local football), **Frank Omere** (Local football)
FORWARDS:
Steve Lawrence (Ruislip Manor, Ruislip T), **Andy Smith** (Hendon, Finchley, Hendon), **Kenny Page** (Stevenage B, Finchley, Harrow B, Hendon, Kingsbury), **Adrian Smith** (Chalfont, Northwood, Kingsbury, Wembley, Hendon, Harrow B), **Henry Clark** (Boreham Wood, Kingsbury, Walthamstow Ave, Barking, Woodford, Walthamstow Ave, Dartford, Leyt & Ilf), **Paul Reynolds** (Harrow B, Windsor, Yeading, Staines, Wycombe, Watford(T)), **Marcus Veiga** (Ruislip Manor)

WEMBLEY
FOOTBALL CLUB
OFFICIAL MATCH PROGRAMME

WELCOME TO VALE FARM

PROGRAMME DETAILS:
Pages: 32 **Price:** 50p
Editor: Richard Markiewicz & Roy Calmels
WMPCC Rating: 27

Whyteleafe FC. Back Row (L/R): Paul Hinshelwood, Micky Gillam, Barry Stone, Steve Dungey, Frank Sheridan, David Fry, Dave Rattue. Front: Matt Kember, David Dutton, Russell Harmsworth, Jon Daly, Ian Cox, Tony Boorman. Photo - Dave West.

Chairman: A F Lidbury   **President:** F E Ovenden
Secretary (Add & Tel): Syd Maddex, 20 Goidel Close, Wallington, Surrey (081 669 1672).
Team Manager: Steve Kember.   **Asst Manager/Coach:** Mick Stratford
Press Officer: **Physio:** S Glass, R Pakeman
Ground Address & Tel: 15 Church Road, Whyteleafe, Surrey CR3 0AR (081 660 5491).
Directions: Five minutes walk from Whyteleafe (BR) - turn right from station, and left into Church Road.
Capacity: 5,000 (200 Covered).   **Seats:** 200   **Floodlights:** Y   **Shop:** N   **Metal Badges:** Y
Colours: Green & white/green/white   **Change colours:** Yellow/black/black
Sponsors: Dale Express
Previous Leagues: Caterham & Edenbridge/ Croydon/ Thronton Heath & Dist/ Surrey Intermediate (East) 54-58/ Surrey Senior 58-75/ Spartan 75-81/ Athenian 81-84.
Midweek home matchday: Tuesday   **Reserve Team's League:** Suburban.
Record Attendance: 533.
Best F.A. Cup season:
League clubs defeated in F.A. Cup: None.
Record Fees - Paid: £1,000 for Gary Bowyer (Carshalton)   **Received:** £25,000 for Steve Milton.
Players progressing to Football League: Steve Milton (Fulham).
Clubhouse: Open every lunchtime and evening. Hot and cold food, pool, darts, gaming machines.
Steward:
91-92 Captain: **91-92 P.o.Y.:**   **91-92 Top scorer:**
Local Press (+Tel.Nos.): Croydon Advertiser.   **Local Radio Stations:**
Honours: FA Vase 5th Rd 80-81 85-86, FA Tphy 3rd Qualifying Rd 89-90, Isthmian Lg Div 2 South R-up 88-89, Surrey Senior Lg 68-69 (Lg Cup R-up 68-69, Lg Charity Cup 71-72, Reserve Section 62-63 (Challenge Cup 62-63 (R-up 59-60), Surrey Senior Cup 68-69 (R-up 87-88), Surrey Premier Cup R-up 84-85, East Surrey Charity Cup 79-80 (R-up 76-77 77-78), Thornton Heath & Dist Lg 51-52 (Lg Cup 51-52, Div 4 R-up 51-52), Edenbridge Charity Cup 51-52, Caterham & Purley Hospital Cup 51-52, Surrey County Intermediate Lg East Section 1 55-56 Surrey Junior Cup R-up 51-52, Caterham & Edenbridge Lg Div 3 51-52, Borough of Croydon Charity Cup 56-57, Southern Yth Lg 89-90 (R-up 88-89, Lg Cup 88-89 89-90).

GOALKEEPERS:
Lee Harmsworth (Barking, Fisher, Dulwich, Charlton), **Steve Dungey** (Croydon, Farleigh R)
DEFENDERS: Barry Stone (Dulwich, Whyteleafe, Molesey, Croydon, Molesey, Chipstead), **Russell Harmsworth** (Croydon, Epsom & Ewell, Croydon, Redhill, Wimbledon(J)), **Darren Tidy** (Youth), **Nick Lloyd** (Dulwich, Bromley, Whyteleafe, Sutton Utd), **Micky Stratford** (Leatherhead, Grays, Croydon, Epsom & Ewell, Sutton Utd, Epsom & Ewell, Kingstonian, Woking, Slough), **Dave Kenny** (Three Bridges), **Dean Howland** (Youth)
MIDFIELD: Matthew Kember (Youth), **Steve Shaw** (Tooting), **Paul Hinshelwood** (Chelmsford, Dartford, Basildon, Southend, Colchester, Millwall, Oxford Utd, C Palace), **Bobby Clement** (Youth), **Tony Boorman** (Bromley, Leatherhead, Whyteleafe, Grays, Croydon, Epsom & Ewell, Crockenhill), **Jamie Fascione** (Youth), **Paul Kember** (Youth)
FORWARDS: Ian Cox (Youth), **Errol Vassell** (Tooting), **Dave Dutton** (Croydon, Molesey, Banstead, Croydon, West Ham(A)), **John Fowler** (Three Bridges), **Mark Watkins** (Youth), **Adrian Grant** (Banstead, Hampton, Whyteleafe), **Malcolm Smart** (Local football), **Trevor Franklin** (Cray W, Dulwich, Croydon, Gravesend, Canterbury, Enfield, Bromley, Chatham, Welling, Maidstone), **Graeme Lane** (Barking, Dulwich, Bromley, Enfield, Camb City, Bristol C)

Whyteleafe
Football Club

DALE
EXPRESS

50p

PROGRAMME DETAILS:
Pages: 24 **Price:** 50p
Editor: Tony Lidbury
WMPCC Rating: 16

Second Division 1991-92

	P	W	D	L	F	A	Pts
Purfleet	42	27	8	7	97	48	89
Lewes	42	23	14	5	74	36	83
Billericay Town	42	24	8	10	75	44	80
Leatherhead	42	23	6	13	68	40	75
Ruislip Manor	42	20	9	13	74	51	69
Egham Town	19	19	12	11	81	62	69
Metropolitan Police	42	20	9	13	76	58	69
Saffron Walden Town	42	19	11	12	86	67	68
Hemel Hempstead	42	18	10	14	63	50	64
Hungerford Town	42	18	7	17	53	58	61
Barton Rovers	42	17	8	17	61	64	59
Worthing	42	17	8	17	67	72	59
Witham Town	42	16	11	15	56	61	59
Banstead Athletic	42	16	10	16	69	58	58
Malden Vale	42	15	12	15	63	48	57
Rainham Town	42	14	13	15	53	48	55
Ware	42	14	9	19	58	62	51
Berkhamsted Town	42	13	11	18	56	57	50
Harefield United	42	11	7	24	47	66	40
Southall	42	8	7	27	39	93	31
Southwick	42	6	2	34	29	115	20
Newbury Town	42	4	8	30	30	117	20

Leading Scorers (League Matches Only)

Mark Butler (Egham Town)	31
Steve Jones (Billericay)	29
Richard Camp (Barton Rovers)	25
Jeff Wood (Purfleet)	26

THE DIADORA LEAGUE SECOND DIVISION RESULT CHART 1991-92

HOME TEAM	1	2	3	4	5	6	7	8	9	10	11	12	13	14	15	16	17	18	19	20	21	22
1. Banstead Ath.	*	1-1	2-2	1-0	0-0	2-1	1-1	0-1	2-1	2-3	3-1	0-1	7-1	3-3	0-0	3-4	1-2	4-1	2-0	1-1	0-1	0-2
2. Barton Rvrs	0-2	*	2-1	0-0	0-1	2-0	0-3	2-1	0-3	0-1	2-1	2-1	1-1	1-2	1-1	1-1	2-3	5-1	3-0	3-0	1-1	3-0
3. Berkhamsted	3-1	4-1	*	2-3	1-2	1-3	1-2	2-3	1-0	0-0	0-3	3-0	1-0	1-1	0-1	2-5	1-4	2-0	5-1	4-0	2-0	3-0
4. Billericay	2-0	4-0	2-0	*	2-2	1-1	0-0	4-1	0-3	1-1	3-0	3-2	7-0	0-2	1-1	4-3	2-1	1-0	4-0	1-0	4-1	3-1
5. Egham T.	3-1	2-1	1-1	1-4	*	1-1	3-1	1-3	0-1	3-1	2-1	4-2	1-1	3-4	1-1	3-2	1-1	5-0	5-4	1-1	5-1	1-3
6. Harefield	1-2	0-2	1-1	0-3	0-3	*	4-0	0-1	2-3	0-1	0-0	2-1	2-0	2-4	2-3	0-0	0-1	1-1	5-2	1-2	1-0	0-1
7. Hemel H.	4-1	0-1	1-0	0-1	1-2	2-0	*	1-3	2-1	1-1	3-1	1-1	6-1	1-1	1-0	2-0	0-1	4-0	0-2	6-3	0-1	2-2
8. Hungerford	0-0	1-1	2-1	2-0	1-3	2-1	2-2	*	0-0	0-0	2-0	1-0	1-1	1-2	2-0	2-1	1-1	1-2	2-1	0-2	0-1	4-1
9. Leatherhead	0-1	1-0	0-2	1-0	0-3	1-0	4-0	1-0	*	1-1	1-0	0-1	4-0	3-1	1-0	0-3	0-0	4-0	2-1	1-2	2-0	3-0
10. Lewes	2-2	1-0	3-2	2-1	0-0	1-0	2-0	2-1	0-1	*	1-1	2-2	5-0	1-3	0-0	0-2	4-0	3-0	0-0	2-1	1-0	9-1
11. Malden Vale	1-0	1-2	1-0	3-0	4-1	4-0	2-0	2-0	1-2	2-3	*	1-1	3-0	0-2	1-1	1-1	4-1	1-1	2-0	3-1	1-2	2-1
12. Met. Police	3-2	0-0	3-0	1-2	3-3	4-1	1-0	3-2	2-1	0-3	2-2	*	0-0	1-2	2-0	1-0	2-2	6-1	4-1	3-0	5-1	1-0
13. Newbury	1-3	3-5	1-1	1-1	2-1	0-1	1-2	0-2	2-2	0-3	0-4	0-1	*	0-6	1-3	1-2	1-7	1-0	0-3	1-3	2-4	1-2
14. Purfleet	2-0	5-0	3-1	0-1	4-3	2-2	1-1	1-2	1-1	2-3	1-0	1-3	4-1	*	2-1	2-0	1-2	2-0	4-0	1-1	1-1	2-1
15. Rainham	2-1	2-1	0-0	0-1	0-1	5-1	0-1	0-1	2-1	1-1	1-1	1-1	3-0	1-2	*	2-3	3-2	3-0	0-1	2-1	1-2	3-2
16. Ruislip M.	1-0	1-3	0-1	0-1	2-0	1-0	2-2	3-0	3-0	0-1	2-1	3-1	3-0	1-4	1-1	*	1-1	3-0	1-0	4-1	2-0	2-1
17. Saffron W.	1-1	1-2	2-0	1-0	1-1	1-0	0-1	4-0	2-4	2-4	4-2	3-2	1-2	1-2	2-2	3-3	*	2-2	5-0	0-4	3-3	3-1
18. Southall	1-2	2-1	1-1	0-1	1-2	1-3	0-3	2-4	0-4	0-1	0-0	0-4	4-0	0-4	0-0	1-0	2-3	*	7-1	1-0	2-3	2-0
19. Southwick	1-6	0-3	0-1	0-2	2-5	2-1	1-3	1-0	0-6	0-2	0-3	1-2	1-2	1-2	0-2	0-4	0-2	0-2	*	1-0	0-2	0-4
20. Ware	1-3	4-1	1-1	1-1	1-0	0-2	1-0	2-0	3-1	0-0	1-1	2-0	3-0	1-4	0-2	2-2	1-2	0-0	9-1	*	1-2	1-0
21. Witham	1-2	2-4	0-0	4-0	1-0	1-3	0-2	2-0	1-1	0-1	1-1	2-3	0-0	2-0	4-2	1-1	1-6	4-0	0-0	2-0	*	1-1
22. Worthing	1-4	5-1	1-1	5-4	1-1	1-0	1-1	5-1	1-2	2-2	0-0	3-0	4-1	0-4	2-0	2-1	3-2	4-1	1-0	0-1	0-0	*

HOME TEAM	1	2	3	4	5	6	7	8	9	10	11	12	13	14	15	16	17	18	19	20	21	22
1. Banstead	*	41	36	62	56	27	30	58	97	48	53	46	46	31	38	31	32	33	47	38	32	56
2. Barton Rvrs	105	*	97	154	184	135	131	107	127	111	104	103	117	113	92	122	92	139	97	94	95	94
3. Berkhamsted	69	82	*	70	87	76	242	64	139	80	90	133	88	83	54	105	77	87	76	53	62	73
4. Billericay	241	230	218	*	267	294	264	241	252	189	363	234	178	282	326	208	246	251	193	256	321	264
5. Egham	63	195	66	175	*	135	125	65	83	84	95	63	98	104	87	123	78	131	88	63	115	87
6. Harefield	57	181	90	175	79	*	118	131	141	107	72	93	88	62	107	163	102	121	77	105	102	109
7. Hemel H.	85	98	180	185	102	80	*	80	128	116	110	110	123	130	116	92	108	167	103	83	105	106
8. Hungerford	98	104	110	89	86	95	111	*	82	106	101	101	153	120	104	116	104	108	114	110	104	126
9. Leatherhead	75	112	75	170	150	94	153	92	*	180	84	211	160	126	119	75	165	110	55	118	100	132
10. Lewes	171	157	111	198	184	276	194	175	206	*	160	169	185	193	168	138	153	162	173	194	195	225
11. Malden V.	107	94	88	147	94	81	88	105	163	118	*	116	87	151	61	102	116	74	78	74	138	128
12. M. Police	95	49	80	195	108	80	140	96	150	95	105	*	102	96	80	89	89	92	95	56	90	101
13. Newbury	63	130	91	118	61	62	89	178	89	63	41	101	*	74	76	112	95	81	64	57	76	70
14. Purfleet	73	85	57	217	87	35	53	58	138	114	92	54	117	*	79	68	78	59	59	89	223	102
15. Rainham	55	52	50	172	39	46	70	66	62	52	41	66	48	110	*	54	50	44	53	41	46	95
16. Ruislip M.	115	130	205	208	180	135	125	125	282	173	108	307	125	180	218	*	150	181	120	110	115	125
17. Saffron W.	129	104	116	154	117	130	89	135	143	93	97	97	101	171	111	144	*	110	113	123	114	120
18. Southall	32	48	40	115	47	36	45	42	49	76	38	27	50	42	49	127	40	*	42	47	49	56
19. Southwick	57	50	62	125	47	77	63	-68	65	158	36	75	57	64	37	47	55	40	*	55	27	257
20. Ware	87	168	108	185	144	152	146	109	151	143	98	115	129	95	102	123	163	137	132	*	156	124
21. Witham	107	79	74	298	125	63	98	85	92	70	125	140	76	116	89	103	75	74	96	102	*	139
22. Worthing	83	216	249	219	169	197	201	142	198	276	179	197	186	175	103	175	197	239	254	150	95	*

NB. **Rainham** v Hungerford at Deri Park, Rainham but all other home games at Rainham FC. **Southall** v Harefield, Saffron Walden & Worthing at Maidenhead Utd, v Lewes at Yeading, v Malden Vale at Chalfont SP, v Rainham at Hampton, v Southwick at Hayes, v Leatherhead at Harefield, v Witham at Uxbridge.

Diadora League Division Two Ten Year Record
(See Page 370 for clubs who only played in Div. 3 or Regionalised Div. 2)
(N - Denoted Division Two (North),   S - Denotes Division Two (South))

	82/3	83/4	84/5	85/6	86/7	87/8	88/9	89/90	90/1	91/2
Banstead Athletic	-	-	9S	11S	17S	21S	16S	11S	11S	14
Barton Rovers	3	14	15N	17N	7N	15N	8N	5N	10N	11
Basildon United	5	1	-	-	-	-	-	7N	18N	-
Berkhamsted Town	-	-	9N	10N	16N	4N	15N	17N	5N	18
Billericay Town	-	-	-	-	-	-	6N	15N	3N	3
Clapton	1	-	-	19N	19N	13N	7N	12N	20N	-
Corinthian-Casuals	8	5	-	-	-	-	-	-	-	-
Dorking Town	14	9	12S	9S	3S	3S	1S	-	-	-
Eastbourne United	17	20	16S	15S	11S	12S	11S	16S	20S	-
Egham Town	9	11	6S	17S	14S	14S	10S	10S	3S	6
Epping Town	18	12	-	-	-	-	-	-	-	-
Finchley	20	19	2N	-	-	12N	3S	18N	21N	-
Grays Athletic	-	8	1S	-	-	-	-	-	-	-
Hampton	-	-	-	-	-	-	-	-	12S	-
Harefield United	-	-	18N	18N	10S	13S	5S	12S	7S	19
Harwich & Parkeston	22	-	-	-	-	-	-	-	-	-
Hemel Hempstead	15	17	14N	14N	20N	19N	12N	14N	9N	9
Horsham	21	22	10S	18S	13S	15S	20S	21S	15S	-
Hungerford Town	7	6	4S	13S	9S	8S	6S	9S	9S	10
Leatherhead	-	-	-	-	-	-	-	-	10S	4
Letchworth Garden City	11	15	10N	12N	6N	11N	21N	22N	-	-
Lewes	-	-	-	-	-	-	-	-	-	2
Leyton-Wingate	4	3	1N	-	-	-	-	-	-	-
Malden Vale	-	-	-	-	-	-	-	15S	4S	15
Metropolitan Police	-	-	-	7S	7S	2S	-	-	-	7
Molesey	13	13	3S	6S	19S	17S	4S	2S	-	-
Newbury Town	-	16	18S	4S	20S	18S	19S	7S	8S	22
Purfleet	-	-	-	-	-	-	2N	-	7N	1
Rainham Town	16	18	13S	13N	18N	16N	19N	21N	8N	16
Ruislip Manor	-	-	11S	19S	5S	9S	7S	4S	5S	5
Saffron Walden Town	-	-	5N	9N	11N	18N	20N	10N	11N	8
St Albans City	-	2	-	-	-	-	-	-	-	-
Southall	12	10	7S	8S	21S	16S	18S	6S	6S	20
Southwick	-	-	-	1S	-	-	-	-	-	21
Tring Town	10	4	6N	7N	8N	10N	3N	19N	22N	-
Uxbridge	6	7	2S	-	-	-	-	-	-	-
Ware	19	21	20N	15N	10N	6N	11N	13N	4N	17
Windsor & Eton	2	-	-	-	-	-	-	-	-	-
Witham Town	-	-	-	-	-	7N	13N	20N	6N	13
Worthing	-	-	-	-	-	-	-	-	-	12
No. of clubs competing	22	22	20N	20N	22N	22N	22N	22N	22N	22
			19S	20S	21S	22S	21S	21S	22S	

BANSTEAD ATHLETIC

Chairman: Terry Molloy   **President:**
Secretary: Gordon Taylor, 116 Kingston Avenue, North Cheam, Surrey SM3 9UF (081 641 2957).
Manager: Bobby Knock   **Asst Manager:**   **Coach:** Ken Simmons
Press Officer: F Fuller   **Commercial Manager:** A McIlvenna   **Physio:**
Ground: Merland Rise, Tadworth, Surrey KT20 5JG (0737 350982).
Directions: Follow signs to Tattenham Corner (Epsom racecourse), then to Banstead Sports Centre. Ground adjacent to swimming pool. Half a mile from Tattenham Corner (BR). Bus 420 from Sutton stops outside ground. Also buses E1, 406, 727 from Epsom.
Capacity: 3,000   **Seats:** 250   **Cover:** 400   **Floodlights:** Yes   **Founded:** 1944
Colours: Amber/black/black   **Change colours:** Red & white   **Club Shop:** No
Programme: 36 pages,40p   **Editor:** A Salmon   **Metal Badges:** No
Previous Ground: Tattenham Way Rec.   **Midweek Matchday:** Tuesday
Previous Leagues: Surrey Int./Surrey Snr 49-65/ Spartan 65-75/ London Spartan 75-79/ Athenian 79-84.
Reserve Team's League: Suburban   **Nickname:** A's
Record Gate: 1,400 v Leytonstone, FA Amateur 1953.   **Sponsors:** PDM Marketing
Best FA Cup year: 3rd Qual.Rd. 86-87   **Best FA Vase year:**
Record Fees - Paid: **Received:**
Players progressing to Football League: W Chesney & B Robinson (C Palace).
Clubhouse: Normal licensing hours, food available, 2 bars, real ale.   **Steward:**
Club Record Goalscorer: Harry Clark   **Club Record Apps:** Dennis Wall.
91-92 Captain: Mark Cleaver   **91-92 P.o.Y.:** Gary Grabban   **91-92 Top scorer:** Gary Grabban 28
Local Press: Banstead Herald.   **Local Radio Stations:.**
Hons: Surrey Snr Lg(6) 50-54 56-57 64-65 (R-up(5) 49-50 54-56 57-59, Lg Cup 56-57, Charity Cup 52-53 58-59), London Spartan Lg R-up 77-78 (Lg Cup(2) 65-67), Surrey Snr Shield 55-56, Gilbert Rice F'lit Cup 81-82 86-87 (R-up(4) 82-86), Athenian Lg Cup(2) 80-82 (R-up 82-83 (SF 79-80)), Surrey Int. Lg(2) 47-49, Surrey Int. Cup 46-47 54-55, E. Surrey Charity Cup(4) 59-60 66-67 76-78 (R-up 79-80), Southern Comb. Cup 69-70.

GOALKEEPERS:
Tony Webb (Local football)
DEFENDERS: Keith Thomas (Molesey, Banstead, Molesey, Whyteleafe), **Dave Hyner** (Chipstead, Whyteleafe, Leatherhead, Croydon), **Mark Cleaver** (Whyteleafe, Carshalton, Banstead, Tooting, Dulwich, Corinthian Cas, Molesey, Fulham), **Roy Botterill** (Molesey, Banstead, Dulwich, Bromley, Croydon, Dulwich, Crawley, Leatherhead, C Palace, Millwall(J)), **Sean Allen** (Local football)
MIDFIELD: Dave Bygraves (Croydon Ath, Banstead), **Paul Osbourn** (Local football), **Peter Mann** (Chipstead), **Paul Bentley** (Malden V, Molesey, Banstead, Molesey), **Mark Doherty** (Chipstead, Farleigh R, Bromley, C Palace), **Dave Bell** (Local football)
FORWARDS: Keith Ward (Tooting, Dulwich), **Nick Ferguson** (Youth), **Gary Grabban** (Whyteleafe, Crawley, C Palace), **Scott Thomas** (Local football), **Darren Salmon** (Sutton Utd), **Andy Blades** (Local football)

BARTON ROVERS

Chairman: R E Roberts   **President:** Pat Howarth.
Secretary: Owen Clark, 108 Manor Road, Barton-le-Clay, Bedford MK45 4NS (0582 882398).
Manager: Brian Williams   **Gen. Manager:** Mick Huckle   **Coach:** TBA.
Press Officer: N Rhodes (0462 834980)   **Comm. Manager:** Sec.   **Physio:** Roy Cullis
Ground: Sharpenhoe Road, Barton-le-Cley, Bedford MK45 4SD (0582 882607).
Directions: M1 Jct 12, from London exit turn right, take 2nd righ through Harlington and Sharpenhoe. Ground on right entering village. Four and a half miles from Harlington (BR), 6 miles from Luton (BR), good hourly bus service from Luton.
Capacity: 4,000   **Seats:** 110   **Cover:** 1,100   **Floodlights:** Yes   **Founded:** 1898
Colours: White/navy/white   **Change colours:** Blue/white/white   **Club Shop:** Yes
Programme: 32/36 pages,50p   **Editor:** Nick Rhodes/Owen Clark   **Metal Badges:** Yes
Previous Ground: Barton Rec.   **Midweek Matchday:** Tuesday
Previous Leagues: Luton & Dist./Sth Mids 54-79.
Reserve Team's League: Campri Sth Mids.   **Nickname:** Rovers
Record Gate: 1,900 v Nuneaton, FA Cup 4th Qual. Rd 1976.   **Sponsors:**
Best FA Cup year: 1st Rd. 80-81   **Best FA Vase year:** Finalists 77-78.
Record Fees - Paid: **Received:**
Players progressing to Football League: Kevin Blackwell (Notts County, Scarborough).
Clubhouse: Noon-3pm weekends, 7-11pm weekdays, all afternoon Saturday matchdays. Real ale, snacks.
Steward: Sid Williams
Club Record Goalscorer: **Club Record Apps:**
91-92 Captain: **91-92 P.o.Y.:** Nick Chilvers   **91-92 Top scorer:** Richard Camp 31.
Local Press: Luton News, Herald.   **Local Radio:** Radio Chiltern, Radio Beds.
Hons: Sth Mids Lg(8) 70-73 74-79 (R-up 67-68, Div 1 64-65 (R-up 55-56), Div 2 54-55, Lg Shield 57-58 60-61 68-69, Chal. Tphy 71-72 74-75 77-78 78-79), Beds Snr Cup(5).

GOALKEEPERS:
Paul Marshall (Dunstable, Leighton T)
DEFENDERS: Danny Driscoll (Vauxhall M, Hitchin, Barton R, Sandviken IF(Swe), Luton), **Nicky Chilvers** (Vauxhall M, Stevenage B, Bournemouth(T)), **Bill Goodyear** (61FC, Arlesey, Barton R, Hendon), **Kelvin King** (Gt Wyrley, Bloxwich, Pelsall V), **Kevin Wright** (Youth), **Leroy Corbin** (Dunstable, Clapton, Vauxhall M), **Michael Thomas** (Dunstable, Barton R, Vauxhall M, Hitchin, Vauxhall M, Barton R)
MIDFIELD: Dennis Foster (Finchley, Hillingdon, Southall, Barnet), **Trevor Dasilva** (Vauxhall M, Barton R, Wealdstone, Barton R), **Brian Lalor** (Local football), **Carl Wilson** (Local football), **Bobby Smith** (Vauxhall M, Wolverton)
FORWARDS: Richard Camp (Shillington, Vauxhall M), **Paul Young** (St Albans, Barton R, Caddington, Luton OB), **Frank Geddes** (Vauxhall M), **Gerry Harvey** (Stirling Alb)

Banstead Athletic. Back Row (L/R): Bobby Knock (Manager), Dave Hyner, Dave Bell, Paul Meredith, Tony Webb, Gary Grabban, Nick Ferguson, David Bygraves. Front: Paul Osborn, Scott Thomas, Peter Mann, Mark Cleaver, David Fahey, Keith Ward. Photo - Dave West.

Leatherhead's James Hoyte scores his side's 4th goal against Hemel Hempstead on March 28th. Photo - Eric Marsh.

Saffron Walden's Bobby Simpson puts over a cross against Metropolitan Police. Photo - Craig Pickering.

BERKHAMSTED TOWN

Chairman: Bob Sear   **President:** George Kite   **Vice C'man:**
Secretary/Comm. Mgr: Alan Dumpleton, 44 Woodlands Av., Berkhamsted, Herts HP4 2JQ (0442 863929).
Manager: Roy Butler   **Asst Manager:**   **Coach:**
Press Officer: Graham Hastle   **Physio:**
Ground: Broadwater, Lower Kings Road, Berkhamsted, Herts HP4 2AA (0442 862815).
Directions: Adjacent to Berkhamsted station (Euston-Birmingham line). A41 to Berkhamsted town centre traffic lights, left into Lower Kings Road.
Capacity: 2,000   **Seats:** 120   **Cover:** 200   **Floodlights:** Yes   **Founded:** 1895
Colours: White/black/black   **Change colours:** All sky blue   **Club Shop:** Yes
Programme: 28 pages,40p   **Editor:** Bob Sear   **Metal Badges:** No
Previous Ground: Sunnyside Enclosure 1895-1919/ Sports Ground 1919-83.
Previous Leagues: W Herts & Herts Co. 95-22/ Spartan 22-51 66-75/ Delphian 51-63/ Athenian 63-66 83-84/ London Spartan 75-83.
Midweek Matchday: Tuesday   **Sponsors:** Kite (Glass) Ltd   **Nickname:**
Reserve Team's League: **Record Gate:** 1,163 v Barnet, FA Cup 3rd Qual. Rd 1987.
Best FA Cup year: 3rd Qual Rd 87-88   **Best FA Vase year:**
Record Fees - Paid: **Received:**
Players progressing to Football League: Frank Broome, Maurice Cook.
Clubhouse: Open 7 days a week. Pool & darts. Steward - Daphne Gregory.
91-92 Top scorer: Ian Ranger 12.   **Local Press:** Berkhamsted Herald, Berkhamsted Gazette.
Local Radio Stations: Chiltern Radio, Radio Beds.
Hons: Herts Snr Cup 52-53, London Spartan Lg 79-80 (Div 2 26-27), Herts Char. Shld 73-74 79-80 84-85 90-91 50-51(jt), Aubrey Cup 52-53, St Marys Cup(12), Apsley Snr Char. Cup(9), Wallspan Sthn Com. 84-85 (F'lit Cup 84-85).

GOALKEEPERS:
Scott Ashcroft (Local football)
DEFENDERS: Lee Herdman (Youth), John O'Donnell (Local football), Ray Jeffrey (Hemel Hempstead, Tring, Chesham), Peter Brown (St Albans, Hemel Hempstead, Chesham, Barnet, Tring, Aylesbury, Napier City(NZ), Wimbledon, Chelsea), Sean Hancock (Stevenage B, Hemel Hempstead, Berkhamsted, Tring, Hemel Hempstead, Berkhamsted)
MIDFIELD: Gavin Smith (Shillington, Tring, Berkhamsted, Hemel Hempstead, Tring, Hemel Hempstead, Watford), Keith Conroy (Hemel Hempstead, Berkhamsted, Chelsea(A)), Paul Hobbs (Tring, Hemel Hempstead, Berkhamsted, Hemel Hempstead), Richard Moriarty (Tring, Berkhamsted, Hemel Hempstead, Harrow B, Hemel Hempstead), Simon Illman (Hemel Hempstead), Shaun Walker (Thame), Paul Roache (Local football), Mick Garrini (Tring, Berkhamsted, Hemel Hempstead, Harrow B, Boreham Wood, Aylesbury, Hendon, Tring)
FORWARDS: Gary Winks (Hemel Hempstead), Ian Ranger (Youth), Mark Osborne (Youth), Gary Harthill (Boreham Wood, Tring, Aylesbury, Tring, Aylesbury, Hitchin, Tring, Chalfont, Chesham, Berkhamsted), Mark Lincoln (Chalfont, Boreham Wood, Southall, Chesham, Dunstable, Stevenage B, Dunstable, Chesham, Boreham Wood, Hertford, Hitchin)

CHERTSEY TOWN

Chairman: David Rayner   **Vice Chairman:** Chris Mason   **President:** Chris Norman
Secretary: Chris Gay, 23 Richmond Close, Frimley, Camberley, Surrey GU16 5NR (0276 20745).
Manager: Jim Kelman   **Asst Manager:**   **Coach:** Andy Ritchie
Press Officer: Secretary   **Comm. Manager:**   **Physio:**
Ground: Alwyns Lane, Chertsey, Surrey KT16 9DW (0932 561774).
Directions: Off Windsor Street at north end of shopping centre. 10 mins walk from Chertsey (BR). London Country bus.
Capacity: 3,000   **Seats:** 200   **Cover:** 400   **Floodlights:** Yes   **Founded:** 1890
Colours: Blue & white stripes/white/blue   **Change colours:** All yellow
Club Shop: Yes (manager - Martin Gay)   **Sponsors:**
Programme: 28 pages,50p   **Editor:** Chris Gay   **Metal Badges:** Yes
Previous Ground: **Midweek Matchday:** Tuesday
Previous Leagues: Surrey Jnr/ Surrey Intermediate/ Surrey Snr 46-63/ Metropolitan 63-66/ Gtr London 66-67/ Spartan 67-75/ London Spartan 76-76/ Athenian 76-84/ Isthmian 84-85/ Combined Counties 85-86.
Previous Names: None   **Previous Grounds:** None.
Reserve Team's League: **Nickname:** Curfews
Record Gate: 1,480 v Walton & Hersham, FA Amtr Cup 1962.
Best FA Cup year: 2nd Qualifying Rd.
Record Fees - Paid: **Received:** £5,000.
Players progressing to Football League: Rachid Harkouk (Notts County).
Clubhouse: Open most evenings. Dancehall, pool, darts.   **Steward:** Fred Nordstrom.
Club Record Goalscorer: **Club Record Apps:**
91-92 Captain: Carlton Walcott   **91-92 P.o.Y.:** Peter Skerritt   **91-92 Top scorer:** Peter Skerritt.
Local Press: Surrey Herald.   **Local Radio:**
Hons: FA Vase QF 87-88 91-92, Isthmian Lg Div 3 R-up 91-92, Surrey Snr Lg 59-60 61-36 62-63 (Lg Cup 59-60 61-62), Combined Co's Lg R-up 85-86 (Concours Tphy 85-86), Surrey Snr Cup R-up 85-86, Spartan Lg & Lg Cup R-up 74-75.

GOALKEEPERS:
Alan Henly (Bracknell)
DEFENDERS: Paul Hutchins (Bracknell, Camberley, Wokingham, C Palace), Peter Skerritt (Slough), Kevin Hill (Windsor), Andy Pearson (West Ham(T)), Darren Britnell (Chalfont, Chesham, Harrow B, Marlow, Wycombe, Oxford Utd)
MIDFIELD: Colin Davis (Youth), Keith Dearling (Camberley), Rodney Richards (Wealdstone), Nick Hopkins (Youth), Marco Ellerker (Local football)
FORWARDS: Carlton Walcott (Epsom & Ewell, Cobham), Paul Sweales (Uxbridge, Yeading, Harefield, Hounslow, Uxbridge, Burnham, Southall, Egham, Southall), Rob Dilger (Leatherhead, Dorking, Carshalton, Dorking, Epsom & Ewell, Leatherhead), Andy Ritchie (Yeading, Newbury, Wokingham, Maidenhead Utd, Dulwich, Woking, Newbury)

Berkhamsted Town. Back Row (L/R): C Humphreys, S Walker, S Ashcroft, M Garrini, P Hobbs, P Roach, R Jeffrey, G Winks, K Wishart (Physio). Front: G Harthill, P Brown, L Herdman, I Ranger, G Kite (President), R Butler (Manager), M Knight, G Smith. Photo - Bob Sear.

Chertsey Towrn. Back Row (L/R): C Walcott, R Dilger, P Skerritt, A Henly, A Ritchie, D Britnell, P Richards, P Sweales. Front: M Ellerker, K Dearling, C Davis, N Hopkins, K Hill. Photo - V Hardwick.

Diadora League Chairman, Mr Alan Turvey, presents a centenary plaque to Chertsey Town Chairman, Dave Rayner, and Vice Chairman C Mason. Photo - V Hardwick.

EDGWARE TOWN

Chairman: Vince Deritis **President:** Ken Batten **Patron:** Russell Grant.
Secretary: Thomas Higgins, 34 Francis Rd, Harrow, Middx HA1 2QX (081 863 4022).
Manager: Brian Rider **Coach:** J McGleish **Assistant Manager:**
Press Officer: **Treasurer:** J Burgess **Physio:** J Tyler MCSP
Ground: White Lion Ground, High Street, Edgware HA8 5AQ (081 952 6799).
Directions: Edgware station, turn left, left again, ground on right. Buses 186 and 142.
Capacity: 6,000 **Seats:** 220 **Cover:** 1,200 **Floodlights:** Yes **Founded:** 1939
Colours: All green **Change colours:**
Club Shop: **Metal Badges:** **Sponsors:**
Programme: 6 pages with admission **Editor:** Manager/Secretary
Midweek Matchday: Wednesday **Previous Leagues:** Corinthian 46-63/ Athenian 64-84/ London
Spartan 84-90.
Previous Names: Edgware FC **Previous Grounds:** None.
Reserve Team's League: Suburban **Nickname:**
Record Gate: 8,500 v Wealdstone, FA Cup 1948.
Clubhouse: Open nightly and weekend lunchtimes. Dancehall, three bars, pool, darts, juke box.
Steward: J Connell.
Players progressing to Football League:
Club Record Goalscorer: **Club Record Apps:**
91-92 Captain: **91-92 P.o.Y.:** Gerry Brennan 91-92 **Top scorer:** Steve Newing
Local Newspapers: **Local Radio:**
Hons: FA Vase 5th Rd 91-92, Isthmian Lg Div 3 91-92, London Spartan Lg 87-88 89-90 (Lg Cup 87-88), Corinthian Lg R-up 53-54 (Memorial Shield 52-53 61-62), Athenian Lg R-up 81-82, Middx Snr Lg 40-41 41-42 42-43 43-44 44-45, Middx Snr Cup 47-48 (R-up 73-74), London Snr Cup R-up 47-48, Middx Border Lg Cup 79-80, Suburban Lg Div R-up 89-90.

GOALKEEPERS:
Kevin Beckles (Watford(T)), **Sean Griffiths** (Wembley, Harrow B, Finchley, Wokingham, Watford(A))
DEFENDERS: Seamus Finnerty (Yeading, Edgware, Watford(J), Brentford(J)), **Vince Deritis** (Boreham Wood, Edgware, Boreham Wood, Brentford(A), Watford(J)), **John Mangan** (Local football), **Gerry Brennan** (Kingsbury, Arsenal(Sch), **Darren Coleman** (Finchley, Forest Utd), **Joe Sheridan** (Hounslow, Finchley, Watford(J)), **Steve Evans** (Kingsbury)
MIDFIELD: John Coleman (Kingsbury, Man Utd(J)), **Lawrence Murphy** (Wembley, Harrow B, Edgware, Yeading, Edgware, C Palace), **Les Thompson** (Wembley, Hounslow, Yeading), **Eugene Flynn** (Wembley, Edgware, Corinthian Cas), **Darin Solomon** (Kingsbury)
FORWARDS: Gursel Gulfer (Wembley, Harlow, Kingsbury, Haringey B, Kingsbury, Wembley, Boreham Wood, Walton & Hersham, Charlton), **Colin Chance** (Finchley), **Martyn Kidd** (Harrow B, Spurs(J)), **Lee Rider** (Brentford(J, C Palace(J)), **Steve Newing** (St Albans, Yeading, Finchley, Ruislip Manor, Dunstable, Hendon, QPR(Sch))

EGHAM TOWN

Chairman: Pat Bennett **President:** D Harmston **Vice C'man:**
Secretary: Colin Simpson, 'Huntspill', Stanwell New Rd, Staines TW18 4HY (0784 463910).
Manager: Bobby Roper **Coach:** Richard Burnell **Asst Mgr:** Keith Bristow
Press Off.: Mark Ferguson (0932 783333) **General Manager:** Eric Howard **Physio:**
Ground: Tempest Road, Egham, Surrey TW20 9DW (0784 436466).
Directions: Off M25 at Staines exit, Victoria r'bout left at Police station, over railway crossing, left at next junction, past Prince Alfred PH, first left. Bus 441 to Pooley Green, 200yds.
Capacity: 3,000 **Seats:** 220 **Cover:** 450 **Floodlights:** Yes **Founded:** 1963
Colours: White (blue & gold trim) **Change colours:** Blue & gold **Club Shop:** No
Programme: 28 pages,40p **Editor:** Mark Ferguson (0932 783333) **Metal Badges:** £1.70
Club Sponsors: Paton of Walton **Midweek Matches:** Tuesday.
Previous Leagues: Surrey Snr 65-67/ Spartan 67-74/Athenian 74-77.
Reserve Team's League: Suburban **Nickname:** Town
Best FA Cup year: 4th Qual Rd 90-91 **Best FA Vase year:**
Record Gate: 1,400 v Wycombe, FA Cup 2nd Qual Rd 1972.
Record Fees - Paid: **Received:** £4,200 from Wycombe for Mark Butler
Players progressing to Football League:
Clubhouse: (0784 435226) 7-11pm and weekend lunchtimes. Members bar, function hall and pool room. Steward
- Dave & Bet Jones.
Club Record Goalscorer: **Club Record Apps:** Dave Jones
91-92 Captain: **91-92 P.o.Y.:** **91-92 Top scorer:** Mark Butler 36.
Local Press: Herald & News (0932 561111). **Local Radio:** County Sound.
Hons: Spartan Lg 71-72 (Lg Cup R-up), Athenian Lg R-up 75-76 (Div 2 74-75).

GOALKEEPERS:
Dave Camis (Youth)
DEFENDERS: Bobby Roper (Chalfont, Uxbridge, Harefield), **Chris Wheatley** (Slough, Staines), **John Exer** (Chalfont, Maidenhead, Hounslow, Staines, Brentford, Southall, Hounslow, Hampton), **Stephen Bennett** (Youth), **Phil Holt** (Wimbledon(J))
MIDFIELD: Paul Lucas (Hampton, Feltham), **Nick Shepherd** (Woking, Wokingham), **Nicky Horton** (Dorking, Bracknell, Chertsey, Woking), **Joe O'Shea** (Feltham, Hounslow, Staines), **Mark Green** (Walton & Hersham)
FORWARDS: Brett Smith (Youth), **Martin Duffy** (Farnham, Ash Utd, Camberley, Farnborough), **Alan Gregory** (Ruislip Manor, Staines, Gillingham(J)), **Danny Collyer** (Youth), **Derek Traylen** (Ash Utd), **Lee Maynard** (Youth)

Steve Newing fires in a cross during Edgware's emphatic 4-0 win over Clapton. Photo - Colin Goulding.

Worthing's ex-Plymouth 'keeper Gary Penhaligan makes a fine save from Southall's Finch Holes. Photo - Mike Floate.

Billericay attack strongly in their table-topping fixture at Lewes on January 11th. Photo - Roger Turner.

HAMPTON

Chairman: Robert Hayes
President: Alan Simpson
Secretary: Adrian Mann, 30 Burniston Ct, Manor Rd, Wallington, Surrey SM6 0AD (081 773 0858).
Manager: Mark Fewings
Assistant Manager:
Coach:
Press Officer: Ray Franks (0932 227303)
Physio:
Ground: Beveree, Beaver Close, off Station Rd, Hampton TW12 2BX (081 979 2456-clubhouse, 941 4936-boardroom).
Directions: 5 mins walk along Station Rd from Hampton (BR). Buses 11 and 267. By road; M3 jct 1, A308 to High Street, Hampton. Or from Hampton Court A308 to Hampton High Street.
Capacity: 4,000 **Seats:** 200 **Cover:** 2,000 **Floodlights:** Yes **Founded:** 1920
Colours: Red & blue/white/blue **Change colours:** White/tangerine/white **Nickname:** Beavers.
Club Shop: Yes **Metal Badges:** Yes **Sponsors:** Saft-Nife Ltd.
Programme: 32 pages, 50p **Editor:** Secretary
Midweek Matchday: Tuesday
Previous Leagues: Kingston & Dist./ SW Middx/ Surrey Snr 59-64/ Spartan 64-71/ Athenian 71-73.
Previous Names: None **Reserve Team's League:** Suburban
Best FA Cup year: 4th Qualifying Round 77-78 (lost 1-2 v Barnet).
Record Fees - Paid: £400 for Peter Shodiende (Hendon)
  Received: £2,500 from APOP (Cyprus) for Ricky Walkes (June 1989).
Clubhouse: (081 979 2456). Two bars, hall for hire. **Steward:** S Penny.
Players progressing to Football League: Andy Rogers (Southampton, Plymouth, Reading), Dwight Marshall (Plymouth), Paul Rogers (Sheffield Utd).
Club Record Goalscorer: **Club Record Apps:**
91-92 Captain: Malcolm Dickenson **91-92 P.O.Y.:** David Hook **91-92 Top scorer:** Gary Ewings 30.
Local Newspapers: Middx Chronicle, Surrey Comet, Richmond & Twickemham Times, The Informer.
Hons: London Snr Cup(2) 86-88, Spartan Lg(4) 64-67 69-70 (Lg Cup(4) 64-68), Middx Charity Cup 69-70 (R-up 68-69 71-72 90-91), Middx Snr Cup R-up 71-72 76-77, Southern Comb. Cup 68-69 71-72 76-77 81-82 83-84 85-86 (R-up 77-78 79-80).

GOALKEEPERS:
David Hook (Feltham), **Paul Wilson** (Feltham & Hounslow)
DEFENDERS: Malcolm Dickenson (Feltham, Malden V, Feltham), **Tim Hollands** (Walton & Hersham, Hampton), **Roland Terry** (Local football), **Simon Edwards** (Walton & Hersham, Hampton, Addlestone, Birmingham(J), Chelsea(J)), **Brian Bere** (Feltham & Hounslow, Hampton, Staines, Hounslow, Staines), **Martin Heath** (Youth), **Chris O'Neill** (Youth)
MIDFIELD: Steve Cheshire (Molesey, Hampton), **Steve Bates** (Feltham), **Gary Cope** (Youth), **Freddie Amissah** (Fulham(T), Hampton), **Paul Reed** (Walton & Hersham), **Robin Watt** (Southall), **Peter Sansom** (Alma S, Yeading, Chesham)
FORWARDS: Matthew Downs (Feltham, Walton & Hersham), **Micky Beadle** (Molesey, Hampton), **John Twyford** (Feltham, Hounslow), **Gary Ewing** (Walton & Hersham, Hampton, Feltham), **Gary Jenkins** (Maidenhead Utd, Hayes, Walton & Hersham, Hampton, Hounslow, Feltham), **Paul Clarke** (Hayes, Feltham)

HAREFIELD UNITED

Chairman: Mr Ken Rutland
President: Mr Ivor Mitchell
Secretary: Terry Devereux, 132 Organ Hall Rd, Boreham Wood WD6 4TL (081 207 0324).
Manager: Peter Holmes
Assistant Manager: David Holt **Coach:**
Press Officer: Peter Holmes
Physio: Alan Carpenter, John Godfrey.
Ground: Preston Park, Breakespeare Rd, North Harefield, Middx UB9 6DG (0895 827522).
Directions: M25 jct 17, follow signs to Swakely corner then to Harefield A40. Denham (BR). Bus 347 from Watford.
Capacity: 2,000 **Seats:** 150 **Cover:** Yes **Floodlights:** Yes **Founded:** 1868
Colours: Red & white/black/red **Change colours:** Sky & navy.
Club Shop: No **Metal Badges:** Yes **Sponsors:**
Programme: 12-40 pages, 30p **Editor:** Secretary
Midweek Matchday: Tuesday **Previous Leagues:** Uxbridge & Dist./ Gt Western Comb. 46-64/ Parthenon 64-68/ Middx 68-75/ Athenian 75-84.
Previous Names: None **Previous Grounds:**
  Nickname: Hares.
Reserve Team's League: Suburban
Record Gate: 430 v Bashley, FA Vase.
Best FA Cup year: Never past Qualifying Rounds.
Record Fees - Paid: **Received:**
Clubhouse: (0895 823474). Lunchtimes and evenings. Two bars, cold snacks (hot on matchdays).
Steward: J Connell.
Players progressing to Football League:
Club Record Goalscorer: **Club Record Apps:**
91-92 Captain: **91-92 P.O.Y.:** **91-92 Top scorer:** Pedro Herbert 9.
Local Newspapers: Watford Observer, Harefield Gazette, Sports Weekly.
Local Radio: Hillingdon Hospital, Chiltern.
Hons: Middx Premier Cup 85-86, Athenian Lg R-up 83-84, Parthenon Lg 64-65 (Div 1 Cup 65-66), Middx Lg 66-67 68-69 69-70 70-71 (Lg Cup 66-67 68-69).

GOALKEEPERS:
Neil Deamer (Hemel Hempstead, Berkhamsted, Ruislip Manor, Harrow B, Everton(A))
DEFENDERS: Tony Forrest (Hemel Hempstead), **Roger Jashek** (Hemel Hempstead), **Ian Waugh** (Chalfont, Wealdstone), **Jim Carson** (Hemel Hempstead, St Albans, Hemel Hempstead), **Darren Sparrowhawk** (Local football), **Peter Holmes** (Chalfont, Harefield, Berkhamsted, Chesham, Boreham Wood, Chesham), **Dave Holt** (Hemel Hempstead, Chesham, Hampton, Oxford C), **Mark Hesk** (Uxbridge, Yeading, Burnham, Shepshed, Rushden, Corby, Grantham, Shepshed, Leicester Utd, Sth Liverpool, Chesterfield, Coventry, Liverpool)
MIDFIELD: Steve Storey (St Albans, California State Univ, St Albans), **Martin Keane** (Local football), **Doug Taylor** (Chalfont, Harefield, Hayes), **Gary Ferguson** (Local football), **Matt Bowen** (St Albans), **Terry Hall** (Local football)
FORWARDS: Steve Harris (Local football), **Paul Masters** (Local football), **Greg White** (St Albans), **Steve Morran** (Local football), **Nick Lines** (Local football)

Hampton. Back Row (L/R): David Hook, Steve Bates, Malcolm Dickenson (Capt), Brian Dere, Matt Downs, Tim Hollands, Paul Reed, Mark Fewings (Manager). Front: Gary Cope, Martin Heath, Peter Sansom, Fred Amissah, Gary Ewing, Steve Cheshire. Photo - V J Robertson.

Gary Ewing (partly hidden) scores the first of his hat-trick as Hampton thrash bottom club Eastbourne United 5-0. Photo - Dennis Nicholson.

Harefield United before their 1-2 defeat against Dulwich at Tooting in the FA Cup. Photo - Dave West.

355

HEMEL HEMPSTEAD

Chairman: Roy Howells   **President:**
Secretary: William McGrae, 209 Fletcher Way, Hemel Hempstead HP2 5SA (0442 251503).
Manager: Gordon Taylor   **Assistant Manager:** Bob Peck   **Coach:** Bob Peck
Press Officer: Secretary   **Physio:** Ken McParland   **Comm. Mgr:** D Evans
Ground: Vauxhall Ground, Adeyfield Rd, Hemel Hempstead HP2 4HW (0442 242081-club, 259777-boardroom).
Directions: Euston to Hemel Hempstead Station. H2 or H3 bus to Windmill Rd, Longlands.
Capacity: 3,000   **Seats:** 100   **Cover:** Yes   **Floodlights:** Yes   **Founded:** 1885
Colours: All red   **Change colours:** All blue
Club Shop: Yes   **Metal Badges:** No   **Sponsors:**
Programme: 24 pages, 30p   **Editor:** Gordon Field
Midweek Matchday: Tuesday   **Previous Leagues:** Spartan 22-52/ Delphian 52-63/ Athenian 63-77.
Previous Names: Apsley 1885-1947)/ Hemel H'stead Town (merged with Hemel H'stead Utd in 1947).
Previous Grounds: Crabtree Lane (til '71).
Reserve Team's League: **Nickname:**
Record Gate: 2,000 v Watford 1985 (at Crabtree Lane: 3,000 v Tooting, 1963).
Best FA Cup year: Never past Qualifying Rounds.
Record Fees - Paid: **Received:**
Clubhouse: (0442 259777). 7-11pm weekends, noon-11pm weekends and Bank Holidays. Pool and darts.
Steward: Robert Alexander.
Players progressing to Football League: Colin and Ernie Bateman (Watford).
Club Record Goalscorer: Dai Price   **Club Record Apps:** John Wallace, 1012.
91-92 Captain: Neal Bartlett   **91-92 P.o.Y.:** Neal Bartlett   **91-92 Top scorer:** Andy Linsell.
Local Press: Hemel Gazette, Herald.   **Local Radio:** Beds Radio.
Hons: Herts Snr Cup, Herts Charity Shield 76-77 83-84 (R-up 90-91), West Herts St Mary Cup 89-90, Athenian Lg Div 1 R-up 64-65.

GOALKEEPERS:
Trevor England (St Albans, Walden R, Dunstable), **Mark Pearson** (Pitstone, St Albans, Dunstable, St Albans, Oxford C, Hampton, St Albans, Tring)
DEFENDERS: Micky Cooke (Dunstable), **Paul Lowe** (St Albans, Chesham, St Albans), **David Walters** (Hitchin, St Albans, Dunstable, Watford(J)), **Tony McNally** (Barton R, Kingsbury, Vauxhall M), **John Pedder** (Local football), **Neal Bartlett** (Chesham, Dunstable, Chesham, Barnet, Hendon, Wealdstone)
MIDFIELD: Paul Rumble (Maidstone, Watford), **Tony Flanagan** (St Albans, Farnborough, Norwich), **Steve Hoar** (Tring, Berkhamsted, Tring, Chesham, Hemel Hempstead, Dunstable, Berkhamsted), **Graham Coles** (Hitchin, Staines, St Albans, Berkhamsted, Tring, Hemel Hempstead, St Albans, Dunstable, Spurs(A))
FORWARDS: Matt Loddy (Harrow B, Chesham, Windsor, Harrow B, Dunstable, Chesham), **Andy Linsell** (Berkhamsted, Harrow B), **Lee Pattison** (Shillington), **David Henstock** (St Albans)

HUNGERFORD TOWN

Chairman: R A Tarry   **President:** Sir Seton Wills.
Secretary: Eric Richardson, 3 Windermere Way, Thatcham, Berks RG13 4UL (0536 68674).
Manager: Wilf Tranter   **Assistant Manager:** John Cowan   **Coach:**
Press Officer: Michael Hall (0488 685241)   **Physio:** Cyril Dumelow
Ground: Town Ground, Bulpit Lane, Hungerford RG17 0AY (0488 682939-club, 684597-boardroom).
Directions: Through town centre on A338, left into Priory Rd, second left into Bulpit Rd, over crossroads, ground on left.
Capacity: 5,000   **Seats:** 130   **Cover:** 1,000   **Floodlights:** Yes   **Founded:** 1886
Colours: White/navy/white   **Change colours:** All red.
Club Shop: Yes   **Metal Badges:** Yes
Programme: 8 pages, 30p   **Editor:** Mike Hall.
Midweek Matchday: Tuesday
Previous Leagues: Newbury & Dist./ Swindon & Dist./ Hellenic 58-78.
Previous Names: None   **Previous Grounds:** None.
Reserve Team's League: **Nickname:** Crusaders.
Record Gate: 1,684 v Sudbury Town, FA Vase SF 1st leg 88-89 (20,000 v Modena in Italy 1981).
Best FA Cup year: 1st Rd 79-80 (lost 1-3 at Slough Town).
Record Fees - Paid: **Received:**
Clubhouse: (0488 682939). Mon-Sat 7-11pm, weekend lunchtimes. Darts, pool, hot & cold snacks. Two bars.
Stewards: Bob & Sandra Ponsford.
Players progressing to Football League: Steve Hetzke (Reading, Blackpool, Sunderland), Bruce Walker (Swindon, Blackpool), Des McMahon (Reading), Brian Mundee (B'mouth, Northampton, Darren Anderson.
Club Record Goalscorer: Ian Farr (over 200)   **Club Record Apps:** Dean Bailey (approx 400)
91-92 Captain: Andy Henry   **91-92 P.o.Y.:** Mark Payne   **91-92 Top scorer:** Tim Brooks 12
Local Press: Newbury Weekly News, Newbury Evening Post   **Local Radio:** Brunel Radio, Radio 210.
Hons: FA Vase SF 77-78 79-80 88-89, Berks & Bucks Snr Cup 81-82 (R-up 75-76 76-77), Hellenic Lg Div 1 70-71 (Prem Div Cup 77-78, Div 1 Cup 70-71, Benevolent Cup 60-61).

GOALKEEPERS:
Micky Cummins (Thatcham, Hungerford, Reading)
DEFENDERS: Kevin Bailey (Chippenham, Devizes, Illogan), **John Potter** (Local football), **George Martin** (Calne, Swindon T), **Tony Dyer** (Local football), **Gary Kingston** (Uxbridge, Chesham, Hungerford, Maidenhead Utd, Reading, Swansea), **Alan Firmin** (Swindon T)
MIDFIELD: Simon Notton (Chippenham, Norwich), **Shaun Tull** (AFC Aldermaston, Newbury, Basingstoke), **Len Brayshaw** (Witney, Hungerford, Lancaster City), **Micky Parker** (Wokingham), **John Stanfield** (RAF, Vitoria Straeton(Ger), Lancaster Univ, Linfield), **Richard Christopher** (Devizes), **Andy Henry** (Carterton, Hungerford), **Mark Payne** (Newbury, Hungerford, Trowbridge, Gloucester, Ledbury, Swindon T)
FORWARDS: Tim Brooks (Camberley, Wokingham), **Steve Tucker** (Gloucester), **Mark Jell** (Calne), **Dave Ward** (Abingdon T, Abingdon Utd, Abingdon T), **Paul Corry** (Local football)

Hemel Hempstead pictured at Leatherhead on March 28th. Photo - Eric Marsh.

Hungerford's John Potter is involved in a crunch tackle with Noel McMenamin of West Mids Police. Hungerford were beaten 0-3 and thus failed to reach a record fourth FA Vase Semi Final. Photo - Dave West.

Hungerford Town. Back Row (L/R): Alan Firmin, Ian Howells, Micky Cummins, George Martin, John Potter, Lenny Brayshaw, Mark Jell, Mark Payne, Simon Norton. Front: Tim Brooks, Sean Till, Kevin Bailey, Andy Henry (Capt), Micky Parker, Steve Tucker. Photo - Dave West.

LEATHERHEAD

Chairman: G Darby   **President:** A Eldridge
Secretary: M Cole, C/O The Club (see below).
Manager/Coach: Mickey Byrne   **Assistant Manager:**
Press Officer: Keith Oram (0306 882746)   **Physio:** Ted Richards.
Ground: Fetcham Grove, Leatherhead, Surrey KT22 9AS (0372 377636-boardroom, 372634-clubhouse).
Directions: M25 jct 9 to Leatherhead; follow signs to Leisure Centre, ground adjacent. Half mile from Leatherhead (BR). London Country Buses 479 and 408.
Capacity: 4,000   **Seats:** 280   **Cover:** 1,100   **Floodlights:** Yes   **Founded:** 1946
Colours: Green/green/green   **Change colours:** White/black/black   **Nickname:** Tanners
Programme: 20 pages, 40p   **Editor:** Neil Grant (0372 386628)   **Club Shop:** No
Midweek Matchday: Wednesday   **Sponsors:** Clarkes New Press   **Metal Badges:** No
Previous Leagues: Surrey Snr 46-50/ Metropolitan 50-51/ Delphian 51-58/ Corinthian 58-63/ Athenian 63-72.
Previous Name: None   **Previous Grounds:** None.
Reserve Team's League: Suburban   **Record Gate:** 5,500 v Wimbledon, 1976.
Best FA Cup year: Fourth Round 74-75 (lost 2-3 at Leicester City).
League Clubs defeated in FA Cup: Colchester, Brighton 74-75/ Cambridge Utd 75-76/ Northampton 76-77.
Players progressing to Football League: Chris Kelly (Millwall), B Friend (Fulham), L Harwood (Port Vale), John Humphrey (Millwall).
Record Fees - Paid: £1,500 to Croydon (B Salkeld)   **Rec'd:** £1,500 from Croydon (B Salkeld)
Clubhouse: Open matchdays.   **91-92 Top scorer:** Cliff Soares 11 (inc 6 for Newbury)
Club Record Scorers: **Club Record Appearances:**
91-92 Captain: Paul Wooler   **91-92 P.o.Y.:** Roland Pierre
Local Press: Leatherhead Advertiser, Surrey Advertiser   **Local Radio:** County Sound.
Hons: Isthmian Lg Cup 77-78, Corinthian Lg 62-63, Athenian Ld Div 1 63-64, Surrey Snr Cup 68-69 (R-up 64-65 66-67 74-75 78-79), Surrey Snr Lg 46-47 47-48 48-49 49-50 (Lg Cup 49-50, Charity Cup 46-47 49-50), East Surrey Charity Cup 58-59 63-64, FA Amtr Cup SF 70-71 73-74 (QF 65-66 66-67 71-72), FA Tphy R-up 77-78, London Snr Cup R-up 74-75 77-78, Surrey Intermediate Cup, Southern Combination Cup 89-90.

GOALKEEPERS:
Colin Caulfield (Woking, Wokingham, Addlestone, Wimbledon, Addlestone), **Paul Martin** (Wembley)
DEFENDERS: Bryan Stannard (Carshalton), **Mike Dalton** (Hampton), **Dave Fahey** (Banstead, Molesey), **Paul Wooler** (Woking), **Darren Munden** (Youth)
MIDFIELD: Andy Taylor (Dorking, Walton & Hersham), **Mark Joyner** (Hampton, Leatherhead, Molesey), **John Lawler** (Local football), **Jerry Alleyne** (Yeading, Southall, Burnham), **Steve Lammiman** (Molesey)
FORWARDS: Ray Arnett (Dorking), Steve Russell (Walton & Hersham, Carshalton, Walton & Hersham, Dorking, Walton & Hersham, Hampton, Malden Vale, Malden T), **Roland Pierre** (Local football), **Earl Whiskey** (Yeading, Hayes, Kingstonian), **Clifton Soares** (Newbury, Mt Roskill(NZ), Newbury), **Clevere Forde** (Southall, Fisher, Southall, Dunstable, Barnet, Hayes, Wycombe, Hayes, Harrow B, Tooting, Harrow B, Wealdstone, Plymouth, Hounslow)

MALDEN VALE

Chairman: S A Pearce   **President:** M I Webb.
Secretary: Andrew Pearce, 31 Ancaster Cres., New Malden, Surrey KT3 6BD (081 949 1475).
Manager/Coach: Michael Browne   **Assistant Manager:** Ged Murphy
Press Officer: S A Pearce (081 337 4302)   **Physio:** Leslie Williams.
Ground: Grand Drive, Raynes Park, London SW20 (081 542 2193).
Directions: 500 yards from Raynes Park (BR). Buses 77a and 77c.
Capacity: 3,500   **Seats:** 185   **Cover:** 200   **Floodlights:** Yes   **Founded:** 1967
Colours: Royal/royal/red   **Change colours:** Red/green/white.
Club Shop: Yes   **Metal Badges:** Yes
Programme: 12 pages, 40p   **Editor:** Len Langham.
Midweek Matchday: Monday   **Nickname:** The Vale.
Previous Leagues: Surrey Snr 77-78/ London Spartan 78-84/ Combined Counties 84-89.
Previous Name: None   **Previous Grounds:** None.
Sponsors: Fullers of Malden (Ford Main Dealers) 081 949 3331.
Reserve Team's League: Suburban   **Record Gate:** 1,500 v Eastenders, Charity Match.
Best FA Cup year: Second Qualifying Rd 89-90 (lost 0-2 at Whyteleafe).
Record Fees - Paid: **Received:**
Clubhouse: Most evenings, Sat+Sun. Hall for hire (birthdays + weddings etc). Two bars, hot food.
Players progressing to Football League:
Club Record Scorers: David Stroud, Martin Caller
Club Record Appearances: David Stroud 1040, Trevor Pearce 940.
91-92 Captain: Rob Jones   **91-92 P.o.Y.:** Rob Jones   **91-92 Top scorer:** Michael Browne 21
Local Press: Surrey Comet, Morden Guardian, Wimbledon News.
Local Radio: County Sounds.
Hons: London Spartan Lg 80-81 (R-up 83-84, Lg Cup 83-84 (R-up 81-82 82-83)), Combined Co's Lg 84-85 (R-up 88-89, Concours Tphy 84-85 (R-up 85-86)), Surrey Snr Lg 77-78, Southern Combination Cup 78-79, Loctite Tphy QF 90-91.

GOALKEEPERS:
Barry Gartell (Kingstonian, Epsom & Ewell, Molesey, Brentford(J))
DEFENDERS: Micky Browne (Croydon, Hertford, Tooting, Cheshunt, Banstead, St Mary's Coll, Wolves), **Gerry Harvey** (Local football), **Joe Connolly** (Carshalton, Banstead), **Bryn Evans** (St Mary's Coll), **Paul Paxton** (Leatherhead), **Alasdair McKenzie** (Local football)
MIDFIELD: Tony Mathias (Croydon, Dulwich), **Rob Jones** (Local football), **Gavin Mayoss** (Leatherhead, Carshalton, Tooting), **Tommy Gibson** (Merstham, Banstead, Merstham), **Ian Anto** (Carshalton), **Carlo Corbin** (Dartford, Carshalton), **Rob Green** (Dorking)
FORWARDS: Barry Ferdinand (Stevenage B), **Martyn Jones** (Carshalton), **Phil Gallagher** (Local football), **John Wood** (Vikings FC), **David Burke** (Maidenhead Utd), **Rob Wadey** (Molesey, Malden V, Leatherhead, Corinthian Cas, Merstham, Banstead), **Stan Blair** (Croydon, Banstead, Carshalton, Banstead, Corinthian Cas), **Jerry Rossati** (Whyteleafe, Dulwich, Dorking, Croydon, Welling, Charlton, Middlesbrough)

Leatherhead. Back Row (L/R): Mickey Byrne (Manager), Paul Steffe, Bryan Stannard, Carey Anderson, Colin Caulfield, Heath Dickenson, Roland Pierre, Paul Wooler, Kevin Wedderburn, Steve Russell, Ted Richards (Physio). Front: John Lawler, Mark Joyner, Glen Brophy, Andy Taylor, Scott Singleton, Kevin Tilley.

Leatherhead's Mickey Byrne receives the Division Two 'Manager of the Month' award for November from Andrew Probert of William Hill at Fetcham Grove. Photo - Tim Edwards.

Worthing's ex-Northern Ireland international Gerry Armstrong jumps for the ball during the fixture at Malden Vale on 28th March. Photo - Graham Cotterill.

METROPOLITAN POLICE

Chairman: J A Smith **President:** Sir Peter Imbert.
Secretary: Derek Aldridge MBE, Woodbeck, 3 Elmshorn, Epsom Downs, Surrey KT17 3PE (0737 50525).
Manager: Colin Rose **Assistant Manager:** **Coach:**
Press Officer: Len Parry (081 541 1212) **Physio:**
Ground: Police Sports Ground, Imber Court, East Molesey (081 398 7358).
Directions: A3 then A309 to Scilly Isles r'bout, right into Hampton Court Way, left at r'bout into Imber Court. Half mile from either Thames Ditton or Esher BR stations.
Capacity: 4,000 **Seats:** 500 **Cover:** 2,000 **Floodlights:** Yes **Founded:** 1919
Colours: All blue **Change colours:** All red.
Club Shop: No **Metal Badges:** No
Programme: 18 pages, free **Editor:** Len Parry.
Midweek Matchday: Tuesday **Nickname:**
Previous Leagues: Spartan 28-60/ Metropolitan 60-71/ Southern 71-77.
Previous Name: None **Previous Grounds:** None.
Reserve Team's League: Suburban **Record Gate:** 4,500 v Kingstonian, FA Cup 1938.
Best FA Cup year: 1st Rd 32-33 (v Northampton) 84-85 (v Dartford).
Clubhouse: (081 398 1267). Four bars, dancehall, cafeteria.
Players progressing to Football League:
Club Record Scorers: Philip Cowper **Club Record Appearances:** Pat Robert.
91-92 Captain: Graham Taylor 91-92 P.o.Y.: **91-92 Top scorer:** John Nicholson 14
Local Press: Surrey Comet, Surrey Herald. **Local Radio:** County Sounds.
Hons: Isthmian Lg Div 2 R-up 77-78 87-88, Spartan Lg 28-29 29-30 36-37 38-39 45-46 53-54 54-55 (R-up 47-48, Lg Cup 59-60 (R-up 57-58)), Middx Snr Cup 27-28, Surrey Snr Cup 32-33, Surrey Charity Shield 38-39, Metropolitan Lg Cup 68-69 (Amtr Cup 68-69 69-70), London Snr Cup R-up 34-35 40-41, Herts & Middx Comb. 39-40.

GOALKEEPERS:
Ian Stillwell (Woking, Epsom & Ewell, Walton & Hersham)
DEFENDERS: Graham Taylor (Hampton), Dave Dubberley (Shrewsbury), Les Bateman (Harefield, Harrow B), Duncan McKelvie (Croydon), Paul Carruth (Queen's Park, St Mirren), Paul Richardson (Cove, Farnborough, Southampton(A)), Brian Taylor (Watford)
MIDFIELD: Ian Pendry (Hassocks), Billy Mochan (Local football), Laurie Bays (Walthamstow Ave, B Stortford), Mark Adams (Slough, New York Arrows(USA), Harrow B, Hendon, Hayes, Chesham, Kingstonian, Hendon, Wealdstone), Steve Lynch (Leyton Orient(J)), Mick Tynan (Met Police(Hayes)), John Nicholson (Boreham Wood, Met Police, Wisbech, March T, Huntingdon), Ken McKenzie (Carlisle Utd, FC Emmendingen(Ger), Carlisle Utd, Carlisle C)
FORWARDS: Mark Reed (Rainham, Beckton Utd, Barkingside), Mario Russo (None), Joe Taylor (None), Jason Peacock (C Palace(J)), Chris Holding (Hampton, Molesey, Epsom & Ewell, Met Police), Steve Bogidi (Dulwich, Croydon)

NEWBURY TOWN

Chairman: Brian Barnes **Vice Chairman:** Ron Meagrow
Secretary: Wally Dent, 66 Volunteer Rd, Theale, Reading, Berks RG7 5DN (0734 323570).
Manager: John Griffith **Assistant Manager:** **Coach:**
Press Officer: Wally Dent **Physio:** 'Manny' Preston
Commercial Manager: Roy Harrington
Ground: Faraday Road, Newbury RG13 2AD (0635 40048-club, 36601-office).
Directions: A34 Robin Hood r'bout then A4 towards Reading, right at lights after 100 yards into Faraday Road. Ground at end.
Capacity: 2,500 **Seats:** 100 **Cover:** 200 **Floodlights:** Yes **Founded:** 1887
Colours: Amber/black/black **Change colours:** Red & white.
Club Shop: Yes (contact Mrs Lovelock) **Metal Badges:** Yes
Programme: 12-16 pages, 30p **Editor:** Neville Whiting.
Midweek Matchday: Tuesday **Sponsors:** Newbury Instant Motors.
Previous Leagues: Gt Western Suburban 04-27/ Hants 27-28/ Reading & Dist. 28-52/ Metropolitan 52-59/ Hellenic 59-82/ Athenian 82-83.
Previous Names: None **Previous Grounds:**
Reserve Team's League: **Record Gate:** 2,300 Reading v Southampton, Hants Lg.
Best FA Cup year: Third Qualifying Round 80-81 (lost 1-4 to Farnborough).
Record Fees - Paid: £300 **Received:** £2,500 **Nickname:** Town.
Clubhouse: (0635 36601). Every night, Thurs-Sun lunchtimes. Two bars, function room, kitchen.
Players progressing to Football League: D McCartney (WBA), Darren Angell (P'smouth), Brett Angell (Southend), M Berry (Southampton), Ian Maidment (Reading).
Club Record Scorer: **Club Record Appearances:**
91-92 Captain: **91-92 P.o.Y.:** Dave Turner **91-92 Top scorer:** Jimmy Rowland.
Local Press: Newbury Weekly News, Newbury Evening Post.
Local Radio: Radio 210, Reading.
Hons: FA Vase 5th Rd 79-80, Athenian Lg 82-83, Berks & Bucks Snr Cup 1898, Hellenic Lg 78-79 80-81 (Lg Cup 59-60 Lg Cup 68-69), Metropolitan Lg Amtr Cup(6) 54-60, Newbury (Graystone Cup), Reading & District Lg(5), Hungerford Cup 88-89 89-90 90-91.

GOALKEEPERS:
Robert Acteson (Local football)
DEFENDERS: Mark Sands (Local football), Jason Tillen (Local football), Mark Taylor (Local football), Nevada Phillips (Hungerford, Maidenhead Utd, Newbury), Leon Tyson (Local football)
MIDFIELD: Dave Turner (Local football), Steve Mabbutt (Leatherhead), Mark Emery (Local football), Robin Jones (Local football), Jimmy Rowland (Local football)
FORWARDS: Keith Bowen (Staines, Wokingham), Steve Fuller (Local football), Paul Steffe (Leatherhead), Matt Swadling (Local football)

RAINHAM TOWN

Chairman: Tony Brooking　　　**President:** G W Burrell
Secretary: Terry King, 5 Syracuse Ave., Rainham, Essex RM13 9SR (0708 557596).
Manager: Mick Acland　　　**Assistant Manager:** Tony Brooking　　**Coach:**
Press Officer: Secretary　　　**Physio:** Roy Davison.
Ground & Directions: As for Purfleet FC (see page 340).　　**Nickname:** Reds.
Colours: Red & white stripes/red/red　　**Change colours:** All blue.　　**Founded:** 1945
Club Shop: No　　　　　　　　　　**Metal Badges:** Yes
Programme: 22 pages, 50p　　　**Editor:** T King, S Acland.
Midweek Matchday: Wednesday　　**Sponsors:** Byrne Brothers.
Previous Leagues: South Essex/ Romford/ London 47-51/ Delphian 51-61/ Metropolitan 61-64/ Athenian 64-77.
Previous Grounds: Rainham Working Mens Ground 1945-48/ Deri Park, Wennington Rd 1948-91.
Record Gate: 1,760 v Finchley, FA Cup 1952 (at Deri Park).
Best FA Cup year: Never past Qualifying Rounds.
Record Fees - Paid:　　　　　**Received:**
Clubhouse: As Purfleet FC.
Players progressing to Football League: Liburd Henry (Watford), Richard Iles (Bristol Rovers).
Club Record Scorer: Steve Kirby, 135　　**Club Record Appearances:** Steve Kirby, 348.
91-92 Captain: Billy Partridge　**91-92 P.o.Y.:** Brian Smart　　**91-92 Top scorer:** Steve Kirby 16.
Local Press: Romford Recorder (0708 766044)　　**Local Radio:** BBC Essex, Essex Radio.
Hons: Essex Snr Tphy R-up 87-88, Athenian Lg Div 2 R-up 73-74, Delphian Lg R-up 56-57, Essex Thamesside Tphy SF 82-83, Essex Snr Cup SF 81-82, Sth Essex Lg Cup 47-48 (R-up 45-46 46-47), Grays County Cup 46-47, Essex Elizabethan Tphy 58-59 (R-up 75-76 77-78 78-79), Hornchurch Charity Cup 47-48 83-84, Romford Charity Cup 84-85.

GOALKEEPERS:
Brian Smart (Brechin City)
DEFENDERS: Billy Partridge (Aveley, Rainham, Aveley, Billericay, Clapton, Dartford), Jimmy Asplin (Tilbury, Slade Green), Darren Ivory (Youth), Nicky Lane (Aveley, Barking), Barry Mouyia (Tiptree Utd, Aveley, Grays), Tony Fleming (Local football), Andy Thompson (Woodford), Sean O'Dea (Collier Row, Hornchurch)
MIDFIELD: Paul Tousent (Aveley, Billericay, Basildon), Micky Heselden (Leyton-Wingate, Hampton, Erith & Belvedere, Swanley T), Micky Linnell (Hornchurch, Rainham), Kevin Alexander (Gravesend, Dartford, Hastings T, Erith & Belvedere, Gillingham(J), Erith & Belvedere), Dave Gordon (Youth), Elliott Taylor (Erith & Belvedere, Croydon), Dave Walker (Beckton Utd), Peter McKey (Erith & Belvedere)
FORWARDS: Steve Kirby (Beckenham, Rainham, Greenwich B, Gravesend, Rainham, Hendon), Dave Allen (Hornchurch, Basildon), Micky Waite (Beckton Utd), Steve Emery (Sheppey Utd), Tony Read (Woodford)

RUISLIP MANOR

Chairman: Jim Klarfield　　　**President:** J Barnett
Secretary: TBA (Match Secretary: 5 Brickwall Lane, Ruislip, Middx HA4 8JS (0895 633474)).
Manager: Michael Schools　　**Assistant Manager:**　　　　**Coach:**
Press Officer: Chris Pacey (081 459 9337)　　　　　　　**Physio:**
Ground: Grosvenor Vale, off West End Road, Ruislip, Middx (0895 637487-office, 676168-boardroom).
Directions: Ruislip Manor station, left, then first right into Shenley Avenue, third left Cranley Drive to ground. E2 bus (200 yards).
Capacity: 6,000　　**Seats:** 160　　**Cover:** 175　　**Floodlights:** Yes　　**Founded:** 1938
Colours: White/black/black　　**Change colours:** All yellow.
Club Shop: Yes　　　　　　　　**Metal Badges:** Yes
Programme: Yes　　　　　　　　**Editor:** Keith Harris.
Midweek Matchday: Monday　　**Sponsors:** Light Years.
Previous Leagues: Middx Snr/ London 46-58/ Spartan 58-65/ Athenian 65-84.
Previous Grounds: None　　　**Previous Names:** None.
Record Gate: 2,000 v Tooting & Mitcham, FA Cup 1962.
Best FA Cup year: Never past Qualifying Rounds.
Record Fees - Paid:　　　　　**Received:**
Clubhouse: Every lunchtime & evening. Hot and cold food. Three bars.　　**Steward:** Tom Rolfe.
Players progressing to Football League:
Club Record Scorer:　　　　**Club Record Appearances:**
91-92 Captain:　　　　**91-92 P.o.Y.:**　　　　**91-92 Top scorer:** Gary Farrant.
Local Press: Ruislip Northwood Gazette, All Sport Weekly　　**Local Radio:**
Hons: Middx Snr Cup SF(6), Middx Charity Cup R-up 90-91.

GOALKEEPERS:
Micky Simmons (Dulwich, Ruislip Manor)
DEFENDERS: Martin Rowen (Wembley), Lee Parker (Youth), Peter Wilkins (Wembley), Jon Pettifer (Harefield), Gary Collinson (Youth), Fred Cummings (Wembley, Chalfont, Uxbridge, Hillingdon), Spud Murphy (Kingsbury, Wembley, Walton & Hersham, Ruislip Manor, Hounslow, Brentford), Tim Atkins (Uxbridge), Warren Price (Southall), Gary Downes (Uxbridge, Harefield, Ruislip, Hounslow)
MIDFIELD: Paul Barrowcliff (Kingstonian, Woking, St Albans, Harrow B, Hayes, Ruislip Manor, Finchley, Hendon, Brentford(J)), Andy Skyers (Youth), Pedro Herbert (Harefield, Hanwell, Kingstonian, Hounslow, Hillingdon), Gary Farrant (Local football), Chris Balls (Chalfont, Ruislip Manor, Northwood, Wembley)
FORWARDS: Isaac Gumbs (Southall, Bracknell), Jon Zneimer (Local football), Paul Lomas (Youth), Tony Waugh (Sutton C, Ruislip Manor, Wembley, Boreham Wood, Wembley, Staines, Egham)

SAFFRON WALDEN TOWN

Chairman: Harold Claydon   **President:**
Secretary: P Harris, 51 Victoria Avenue, Saffron Walden, Essex CB11 3AD (0799 242203).
Manager: B Dodd/T Mercer   **Assistant Manager:**   **Coach:**
Press Officer: Secretary   **Physio:** Peter White
Ground: Catons Lane, Saffron Walden, Essex CB10 2DU (0799 22789).
Directions: M11 jct 9, 3rd exit on r'bout marked B184. To town, left at Museum Str., left again down Catons Lane.
Capacity: 4,000   **Seats:** 300   **Cover:** 500   **Floodlights:** Yes   **Founded:** 1872
Colours: Red & white (black trim)   **Change colours:** All yellow.
Club Shop: Yes   **Metal Badges:** No
Programme: 12 pages, 25p   **Editor:** R Kitchener
Midweek Matchday: Tuesday   **Sponsors:**
Previous Leagues: Haverhill & Dist./ Stansted & Dist./ Cambridgeshire/ Nth Essex/ Herts Co./ Spartan 33-49 50-54/ Parthenon 49-50/ Essex Snr 71-74/ Eastern Co's 74-84.
Previous Grounds: None   **Previous Names:** None.
Record Gate: 6,000 v Rainham Ath., Essex Junior Cup Final 1926 (played at Crittals, Braintree).
Best FA Cup year: Second Qualifying Round.
Clubhouse: Open matchdays and Sunday lunchtimes. Available for functions. Vice Presidents Bar in seperate room. Steward: Paul Diggons.
Club Record Scorer: Alec Ramsey   **Club Record Appearances:** Les Page.
91-92 Captain: T Cuelch   **91-92 P.o.Y.:** S Atkinson   **91-92 Top scorer:** T Welch.
Local Press: Saffron Walden Weekly News, Herald & Post.   **Local Radio:** Essex Radio, Radio Essex.
Hons: Essex Snr Lg 73-74, Eastern Co's Lg 82-83, Spartan Lg Eastern Div 2 36-37, Essex Snr Tphy 82-83 83-84 84-85, Knight F'lit Cup R-up 88-89, Essex Jnr Cup 1896-97 (R-up 25-26), Cambs Lg R-up 22-23, Essex & Herts Border Lg R-up 25-26.

GOALKEEPERS:
Rhys Jones (Purfleet, Dagenham, Wealdstone)
DEFENDERS: Karl Shuttlewood (Stansted, Saffron Walden), **Kevin Hawkes** (Bury T, Camb City), **Martin Hodges** (Local football), **Colin Croft** (Rainham, Saffron Walden, Stansted), **John Simmonds** (Leyton-Wingate, Barking, Woodford, Walthamstow Ave, Hendon, Woodford, B Stortford, Leytonstone & Ilf, Dartford, Walthamstow Ave, B Stortford), **Kevin Austin** (Leyton-Wingate)
MIDFIELD: Micky Leslie (Walthamstow Pennant, Saffron Walden, Chelmsford, Redbridge F, Haringey B, Woodford, Sutton Utd, Kingstonian, Finchley), **Tony Sanderson** (Local football), **Stuart Atkinson** (Stansted), **Micky Laws** (Local football), **Wayne Mitchell** (Hornchurch), **Ryan Sparrow** (Local football)
FORWARDS: Tony Mercer (Purfleet, Saffron Walden, Dagenham, Leytonstone & Ilf, Basildon, Leytonstone m& Ilf, Woodford, Leytonstone & Ilf, Clapton, B Stortford, Clapton, Leyton Orient, C Palace, Coventry(A)), **Mark Simpson** (Dagenham, Basildon, Dagenham, Chelmsford, Crawley, Maidstone, Charlton), **John Neal** (B Stortford, Barking, Dagenham, Harlow, Basildon, Walthamstow Ave, Barnet, Millwall), **Tony Welch** (Harwich, Woodford, West Ham), **Lenny Clarke** (Leyton-Wingate, Saffron Walden, Woodford, Leytonstone & Ilf)

SOUTHALL

Chairman: J J Loftus   **President:** R E Fowler
Secretary: M Smith, 22 Barchester Rd, Harrow Weald, Middx HA3 5HH (081 863 6888).
Manager: George Richardson   **Assistant Manager:**   **Coach:**
Press Officer: Secretary   **Physio:** George Richardson
Ground: Western Road, Southall, Middx UB2 5HX (081 574 1084). *Important Note: Western Road is being redeveloped, and Southall are playing home matches at Harefield United (see page 354). This arrangement is likely to last throughout the 1992-93, so one is urged to check before travelling).*
Directions: 10 mins walk from Southall station; turn left, then 3rd right into Western Road. Buses 105, 195, 232 to ground from station. Exit 3 on M4.
Capacity: 10,000   **Seats:** 200   **Cover:** 500   **Floodlights:** Yes   **Founded:** 1871
Colours: Red & white stripes/white/white   **Change colours:** Grey & white
Club Shop: No   **Metal Badges:** No
Programme Editor: Steve James   **Reserve Team's League:** Middx County.
Midweek Matchday: Tuesday   **Sponsors:**
Previous Leagues: Southern 1896-1905/ Gt Western Suburban/ Herts & Middx/ Athenian 19-73.
Previous Grounds: None   **Previous Names:** Southall & Ealing Borough (1970s)
Record Gate: 17,000 v Watford.   **Nickname:** Fowlers.
Best FA Cup year: 3rd Round 35-36 (lost 1-4 at home to Watford)
League clubs defeated in FA Cup: Swindon Town 35-36.
Record Fees - Paid: **Received:** £5,000 for Alan Devonshire.
Players progressing to Football League: Alan Devonshire (West Ham), Gordon Hill (Millwall, Manchester Utd, Derby), Chris Hutchings (Chelsea, Brighton), Roger Joseph (Brentford), Les Ferdinand (QPR).
Clubhouse: Noon-11pm. Bar and function hall.
Club Record Scorer: **Club Record Appearances:**
91-92 Captain: **91-92 P.o.Y.:**   **91-92 Top scorer:** Lee Budd 10.
Local Press: Ealing Gazette, Allsports Weekly.   **Local Radio:** Capital.
Hons: FA Amtr Cup R-up 24-25, FA Vase R-up 85-86, Gt Western Suburban Lg 12-13, Athenian Lg 26-27 (R-up 54-55), Middx Snr Cup(12) 07-08 10-11 11-12 12-13 22-23 23-24 24-25 26-27 36-37 44-45 53-54 54-55, Middx Charity Cup 10-11 11-12 13-14 22-23(jt with Botwell Mission) 23-24(jt with Botwell Mission) 27-28 36-37 51-52 68-69 83-84.

GOALKEEPERS:
Lee Woodbridge (Maidenhead Utd), **Mark Stuart** (Youth)
DEFENDERS: Colin O'Shea (Uxbridge, Hounslow, Feltham, Hounslow, Staines, Feltham), **Keith Bedwell** (Harefield, Yeading), **Rod Shearer** (Local football), **Rob Andrews** (Bracknell, Southall), **Ian Bates** (Youth), **Bernie Cronin** (Harefield, Dunstable, Wealdstone, Ruislip, Hillingdon), **Neil Martin** (Local football)
MIDFIELD: Robert Haynes (Harrow B), **Lee Howell** (Youth), **Damian Gillespie** (Youth), **Chris Yeardley** (Youth), **Steve Hawkins** (Harrow B), **Paul Thomas** (Youth)
FORWARDS: John Donaghy (Maidenhead Utd), **Mark Kellier** (Youth), **Finch Holas** (Local football), **Lee Budd** (Youth)

Rainham Town. Back Row (L/R): Mick Acland (Manager), Micky Waite, Barry Mouyia, Brian Smart, Stuart Jukes, Sean O'Dea, Steve Kirby, Tony Brooking (Coach), Roy Davidson (Physio). Front: Dave Allen, Nicky Lane, Dave Gordon, Steve Emery, Peter McKey, Allan Roots. Not in picture: Billy Partridge. Photo - Dave West.

Metropolitan Police defenders Les Bateman (2) and Graham Taylor are troubled by Leatherhead's (left to right) Paul Marshall, Roland Pierre, Justin Fashenu and Paul Wooler. Photo - Tim Edwards.

Southall Reserves, who compete in the Middlesex County League. Back Row (L/R): Paul Cook, Steve Rabbett, John Nolan, Richard Davidson, Anthony Parker, Mark Jessop, Keith Loader, Gerry Collins, Jason Hawkes. Front Row: Keith Chamberlain (Manager), Martin Grey, Neil Nolan, Orlando Ames-Lewis, John Ruggins, Ian Bates, Chris Yeardley, David Gerrish, Ian Hern (Asst Mgr).

TILBURY

Chairman: J B Wilson **President:** None.
Secretary: L P Brown, 52 Lionel Oxley House, New Rd, Grays, Essex RM17 6PP (0375 377427).
Manager: Ian Bodley/Nicky Phillips **Asst Mgr:** Nicky Phillips
Physio: Ian Bodley **Coach:** Jimmy Hallybone.
Commercial Manager: R Nash. **Press Officer:** J B Wilson
Ground: Chadfields, St Chads Rd, Tilbury, Essex RM18 8NL (0375 23093).
Directions: BR from Fenchurch Street to Tilbury Town then 15 mins walk. By road; M25 - A13 Tilbury Docks turn off, Chadwell St Mary turn off - ground visible on right. Bus 378.
Capacity: 3,500 **Seats:** 200 **Cover:** 1,000 **Floodlights:** Yes **Founded:** 1900
Colours: Black & white/black/white **Change colours:** All red. **Club Shop:** No
Programme: Min 20 pages, 30p **Programme Editor:** Lloyd Brown. **Metal Badges:** No
Midweek Matchday: Tuesday **Reserve Team's League:** Essex & Herts Border Comb.
Previous Leagues: Grays & Dist. + Sth Essex (simultaneously)/ Kent 27-31/ London 31-39 46-50 57-62/ Sth Essex Comb. (war-time)/ Corinthian 50-57/ Delphian 62-63/ Athenian 63-73.
Previous Names: None **Previous Grounds:** Newmarket Rd, Baldock Rd, Mackeral Hall.
Record Gate: 5,500 v Gorleston, FA Cup 4th Qual. Rd 48-49 (won 2-0). **Sponsors:**
Best FA Cup year: Third Round Proper 77-78 (lost 0-4 at Stoke City). **Nickname:** Dockers.
Record Fees - Paid: Nil **Rec'd:** £2,000 for Steve Conner (Dartford)
Clubhouse: Every evening and weekend lunchtimes. Pool, darts, TV, Function Hall. Live music and discos at weekends. **Steward:** R Nash.
Players progressing to Football League: I Le May, T Scannell, T Oakley, J Evans.
Club Record Scorer: Ross Livermore 305 (in 252 games, 1958-66).
Club Record Appearances: Nicky Smith 424 (1975-85).
91-92 Captain: Nicky Phillips **91-92 P.o.Y.:** Mark Phillips **91-92 Top scorer:** Mark Phillips 30.
Local Press: Thurrock Gazette, Thurrock Recorder. **Local Radio:** Essex Radio, BBC Essex.
Hons: FA Amtr Cup QF, Isthmian Lg Div 2 75-76, London Lg 58-59 59-60 60-61 61-62 (Lg Cup(3)(R-up(3))), Delphian Lg 67-68 (Div 2 62-63), Essex Snr Cup 60-61, Essex Jnr Cup 08-09 24-25 (R-up 03-04), Grays & Dist. Lg(numerous).

GOALKEEPERS:
Dave Annetts (Aveley, Basildon, Billericay, Tilbury, Witham, Barry)
DEFENDERS: Marti Dale (Purfleet), **Geoff Nicholson** (Purfleet, Woodford, Oxford C, Kingstonian), **Andy Swann** (Local football), **Matthew Fursedonne** (Purfleet), **Darren Webber** (Aveley, Tilbury, Aveley, Tilbury, Billericay, Aveley), **Jon Camp** (Purfleet, Tilbury)
MIDFIELD: Kevin Broderick (Aveley), **Jimmy Hallybone** (Basildon, Grays, Tilbury, Billericay, East Thurrock, Barking, Dagenham, Halifax, Dagenham, Leyton Orient), **Paul Joynes** (Hornchurch), **Nicky Phillips** (Billericay, Barking, East Thurrock, Barking, Coventry), **Craig Whitehill** (Local football), **Jason Morris** (Chelsea(T)), **Colin Hart** (Local football)
FORWARDS: Mark Phillips (East Ham, Birmingham, Norwich), **Lee Antoniou** (Local football), **Dean Henry** (Local football), **Spencer Fletcher** (Purfleet, Dagenham, Arsenal), **Colin Moriarty** (Purfleet)

WARE

Chairman: C T Hudson **President:**
Secretary: M L Rose, 12 The Green, Ware, Herts SG12 0QN (0920 464448).
Manager: Stuart Todd **Asst Mgr:**
Physio: Frank Roberts **Coach:**
Commercial Manager: **Press Officer:** C T Hudson (0992 581862)
Ground: Buryfield, Park Road, Ware, Herts SG12 0AJ (0920 463247).
Directions: A10 off at junction A602 & B1001 signposted behind Rank Cintel factory. 1 mile from Ware (BR).
Capacity: 4,500 **Seats:** 250 **Cover:** 500 **Floodlights:** Yes **Founded:** 1892
Colours: Blue & white stripes/blue/red **Change colours:** Amber/black
Club Shop: No **Metal Badges:** No
Programme: 12 pages, 20p **Editor:** C T Hudson.
Midweek Matchday: Tuesday **Sponsors:** Charvill Bros Ltd.
Prev. Lges: East Herts/ Middx 07-08/ Herts County 08-25/ Spartan 25-55/ Delphian 55-63/ Athenian 63-75.
Previous Names: None **Previous Grounds:**
Reserve Team's League: Essex & Herts Border Comb.
Record Gate: 2,500 v Arsenal 1974-75.
Best FA Cup year: First Round Proper 68-69 (lost 1-6 to Luton Town). **Nickname:** Blues.
Record Fees - Paid: **Rec'd:**
Clubhouse: Fully licensed. Open most evenings, two bars.
Players progressing to Football League: Derek Saunders (Chelsea), Ken Humphrey (QPR).
Club Record Scorer: M Hibbert 229 **Club Record Appearances:** A W Cliss 411.
91-92 Captain: John Lambert **91-92 P.o.Y.:** Steve Ratcliff **91-92 Top scorer:** Sean Brett 25.
Local Press: Herts Mercury, Herts Star (0920 554611), Herald & Post (0279 655225).
Hons: Herts Snr Cup 1898-99 03-04 06-07 21-22 53-54, Herts Charity Shield 26-27 52-53 56-57 62-63 85-86, Spartan Lg 52-53 (Div 1 Sect.B 51-52), Athenian Lg Div 2 Cup 65-66 72-73 (Div 2 Reserve Sect. 66-67 70-71), East Anglian Cup 73-74, Herts Co. Lg 08-09 21-22, East Herts Lg 04-05 06-07 (Lg Cup 06-07), Perry Cup 26-27 28-29 37-38 51-52 52-53 53-54 55-56, Dunkels Cup 52-53, Rolleston Cup 39-40 51-52.

GOALKEEPERS:
Steve Ratcliff (Stevenage B, Ware, Derby(J))
DEFENDERS: Jon Bridge (Hoddesdon, Cheshunt, Ware), **Russell Sanderson** (Clacton, Hertford), **Lee Patmore** (Boreham Wood, Ware, B Stortford, Ware), **Steve Turner** (Stansted), **Steve Wansell** (Hoddesdon, Hertford), **Gary Smith** (Royston, Hertford)
MIDFIELD: Stuart Todd (Epping, B Stortford, Stansted, Ware), **Dave Farenden** (Hoddesdon, Cheshunt), **Glen Alzapeidi** (Harlow, Ware, Woodford, Southend Utd, Birmingham(A)), **Keith Isaac** (Local football), **Mark Smith** (Local football)
FORWARDS: Jon Spring (Cheshunt, Leyton-Wingate, Epping), **Gary Riddle** (Harlow, Ware, Hertford, Cheshunt, Stansted, Harlow), **Shaun Brett** (Youth), **Dave Barker** (Hitchin, Hertford, Ware, Epping), **Spencer Pugh** (Local football), **Damon Miles** (B Stortford, Ware, Saffron Walden, Ware, Stansted)

Tilbury. Back Row (L/R): Spencer Fletcher, Geoff Nicholson, Nicky Phillips (Player-Manager), Dave Annetts, Colin Moriaty, Alan Merrigan, John Camp, Ian Bodley. Front: Andy Swann, Lee Antoniou, Mark Phillips, Martin Dale, Kevin Broderick, Jason Morris. Photo - V J Robertson.

Tilbury's Spencer Fletcher shapes up for a shot as the Dockers win 4-0 at Clapton. Photo - Gavin Ellis.

Ware FC 1991-92.

WITHAM TOWN

Chairman: Mrs J Wright   **Vice Chairman:**   **President:**
Secretary: Reg Wright, 28 Mersey Rd, Witham, Essex CM8 1LJ (0376 512990).
Manager: Craig Johnson   **Asst Mgr:** Gary Smith-Herzberg   **Coach:**
Physio: Tony McCulloch   **Commercial Manager:** Premier Promotions (0376 518283).
Press Officer: Matthew Wright (0376 512990)
Ground: Spa Road, Witham, Essex CM8 1UN (0376 511198-lounge, 500146-reception).
Directions: From Witham BR; through pub car park and follow road to Faulkbourne, at main r'bout turn left and ground is on the right. By road; left at 1st lights (Spinks Lane), right at end of road, ground on left 50yds from railway bridge.
Capacity: 2,000   **Seats:** 150   **Cover:** 150   **Floodlights:** Yes   **Founded:** 1947
Colours: Red & black stripes/black/black   **Change colours:** Green & yellow
Club Shop: No   **Metal Badges:** No
Programme: 24 pages,40p   **Editor:** Matthew Wright.
Midweek Matchday: Tuesday   **Sponsors:**   **Reserve Team's League:**
Previous Leagues: Mid Essex/ Essex & Suffolk/ Essex Senior 71-87.
Previous Names: None   **Previous Ground:** None.
Record Gate: 800 v Billericay Town, Essex Senior League, May 1976.
Best FA Cup year: 2nd Qualifying Rounds 89-90, lost 1-3 to Dartford   **Nickname:** Town
Clubhouse: Three bars and large function room. Open every night and weekend lunchtimes. Darts, pool, table tennis teams. **Steward:** R Nash.
Players progressing to Football League: Steve Tilson (Southend).
Club Record Scorer: Steve Tilson   **Club Record Appearances:** Keith Dent (16 years)
91-92 Captain: Alan Vincent   **91-92 P.O.Y.:** Kingsley Banks   **91-92 Top scorer:** Micky White.
Local Press: Witham & Braintree Times, Essex Chronicle, East Anglian Daily Times.
Local Radio: BBC Essex, Essex Radio.
Hons: Essex Snr Lg 70-71 85-86 (R-up 84-85 86-87), Essex Snr Tphy 85-86 (R-up 88-89), FA Vase 5th Rd 85-86, Loctite Tphy SF 90-91.

GOALKEEPERS:
Kingsley Banks (Barking, Enfield, Basildon, Dartford, Gillingham, Spurs)
DEFENDERS: Craig Johnson (Tilbury, Aveley, Hornchurch, Grays, Dagenham), **Chris Simms** (Local football), **Denis Allen** (Springfield), **Mark Culleton** (Little Waltham), **Marc Gammon** (Local football), **Andy Dunsmuir** (Youth), **Ian Collins** (Ongar), **Ian Haydon** (Billericay, Tilbury, East Thurrock, Billericay, Tilbury, Purfleet, Grays, Corinthian)
MIDFIELD: Stuart Gooch (Chelmsford), **Darren Russell** (Local football), **Jamie Woodyard** (Heybridge S, Maldon T, Burnham R, Witham, Tiptree), **Sean Gill** (Local football), **Lee McLean** (Tilbury), **Jason Thompson** (Purfleet), **Gary Smith** (Youth), **Steve Wells** (Youth)
FORWARDS: Alan Vincent (Braintree, Bramston CML, Witham), **Damon Sunshine** (B Stortford, Witham, Saffron Walden, Stansted, Leyton Orient, Saffron Walden), **Latvia McBean** (Local football), **Darren Stevens** (Local football), **Tony Elliott** (Local football)

WORTHING

Chairman: Beau Reynolds   **President:** Monty Hollis
Secretary: Barry Lindfield, 69 Amberley Drive, Hangleton, Hove (0273 770921).
Manager: Gerry Armstrong   **Asst Mgr:** Ivan Cocker
Physio: John Robson   **Commercial Manager/Press Officer:** Secretary.   **Coach:** John Robson
Ground: Woodside Road, Worthing, West Sussex BN14 7HQ (0903 239575).   **Nickname:** Rebels.
Directions: Half a mile from Worthing (BR).   **Midweek Matches:** Tuesday.
Capacity: 4,500   **Seats:** 430   **Cover:** 600   **Floodlights:** Yes   **Founded:** 1886
Colours: All red   **Change colours:** All white   **Reserves' League:** Unijet Sussex Res. Section.
Club Shop: Yes   **Metal Badges:** No   **Programme:** 28 pages,40p **Editor:** Barry Lindfield
Previous Leagues: West Sussex/ Sussex County 20-48/ Corinthian 48-63/ Athenian 63-77.
Record Gate: 4,500 v Depot Battalion Royal Engineers, FA Amtr Cup 07-08.
Best FA Cup year: 2nd Rd 82-83, lost 0-4 to Oxford Utd. Also 1st Rd 36-37.
Record Fees - Paid: £1,500   **Received:**
Clubhouse: Two bars open daily to members (including lunchtimes).   **Steward:** Dave O'Rourke.
Players progressing to Football League: Ken Suttle (C'sea 1948), Alan Arnell & Fred Perry (L'pool '54).
Club Record Scorer: Mick Edmunds 482 **Club Record Appearances:** Paul Lelliot 542.
91-92 Top scorer: Paul Boxall   **91-92 P.O.Y.:** Gary Penhaligon/ Darren Robson
Local Press: Evening Argus, Worthing Gazette & Herald.   **Local Radio:** Radio Sussex.
Hons: FA Vase 5th Rd 78-79, FA Amtr Cup QF Rep. 07-08, FA Tphy 3rd Rd Rep. 84-85, Isthmian Lg R-up(2) 83-85 (Div 1 82-83, Div 2 81-82), Ath'n Lg Div 1 R-up 63-64 (Div 2 R-up 71-72, Lg Cup R-up 72-73, Mem. Shield 63-64), Sussex Snr Cup(19) 1892-93 1903-04 07-08 13-14 19-20 22-23 26-27 28-29 34-35 39-40 44-45 46-47 51-52 56-57 58-59 60-61 74-75 76-78, Sussex RUR Char. Cup(14) 03-04 06-08 09-10 13-14 19-20 22-23 26-27 33-34(jt) 41-42 44-45 48-49(jt) 52-54, Sussex Co. Lg(8) 20-22 26-27 28-29 30-31 33-34 38-40, W Sussex Lg(7) 1898-99 1903-04 06-08 09-10 12-14, Brighton Char. Cup(9) 29-31 34-35 62-63 69-71 73-74(jt) 80-82, Worthing Char. Cup(10) 11-12 25-27 30-31 32-35 37-39 64-65, AFA Invit. Cup 63-64 68-69 73-74 75-76 (Snr Cup R-up 36-37 46-47 48-49), Corinth. Lg Mem. Shield R-up 49-50 (Neale Tphy 58-59), Roy Hayden Mem. Tphy 1975(jt), 1977 1978, Don Morecraft Tphy 1972 1973 1976 1981 1982, Sussex F'lit Cup(2) 88-90, Sussex I'mediate Cup 34-35 64-65, Brighton Chal. Shield 29-30 31-32.

GOALKEEPERS:
Garry Penhaligon (Bognor Regis, Newquay, Plymouth, Newquay)
DEFENDERS: Darren Brown (Southwick, Gosport B, ,Worthing, Fareham, Portsmouth(J)), **Mick Montague** (Southwick, Gosport B, Newport IOW, Petersfield Utd, Aldershot(A)), **Mark Nye** (Southwick, Worthing, Southwick, Horsham, Worthing, Wigmore Ath, Brighton, Worthing), **Cameron Johnson** (Youth), **Matt Ball** (Bexhill)
MIDFIELD: Michael Brooks (Youth), **Ryan Gaylor** (Lewes, Shoreham, Southwick), **Darren Robson** (Southwick, Gosport B, Basingstoke, Waterlooville, Andover, Petersfield Utd), **Mark Gumpright** (Brighton), **Francis Haytor** (Youth)
FORWARDS: Gerry Armstrong (Southwick, Crawley, Brighton, Chesterfield, WBA, Real Mallorca(Spa), Watford, Spurs, Bangor), **Richard Tiltman** (Crawley, Brighton, Maidstone, Worthing, Littlehampton), **Mark Sherriff** (Youth), **Paul Boxhall** (Brighton)

DIADORA LEAGUE AVERAGE ATTENDANCES 1991-92

Club	Total 91-92	Ave. 91-92	Ave. 90-91	% Change
PREMIER DIVISION				
Aylesbury United	15,128	720	946	-31.3
Basingstoke Town	10,753	512	371	+38.0
Bishop's Stortford	7,096	338	320	+5.6
Bognor Regis Town	5,608	267	225	+18.6
Bromley	10,843	516	507	+1.7
Carshalton Athletic	8,964	427	328	+30.1
Chesham United	11,889	566	436	+29.8
Dagenham	9,300	443	426	+3.9
Enfield	12,206	581	732	-25.9
Grays Athletic	7,820	372	459	-23.3
Harrow Borough	7,273	346	299	+15.7
Hayes	6,369	303	309	-1.9
Hendon	6,200	295	322	-9.1
Kingstonian	14,451	688	853	-23.9
Marlow	7,474	356	322	+10.5
St Albans City	10,438	497	439	+13.2
Staines Town	8,464	403	343	+17.4
Sutton United	15,285	728	874	-20
Windsor & Eton	6,626	316	286	+10.4
Wivenhoe Town	5,109	243	381	-56.7
Woking	39,488	1,880	1,471	+27.8
Wokingham Town	8,034	383	321	+19.3
DIVISION ONE				
Abingdon Town	4,962	248	281	-13.3
Aveley	1,970	99	145	-46.4
Barking	2,143	107	195	-82.2
Boreham Wood	2,845	142	144	-1.4
Chalfont St Peter	2,509	125	188	-50.4
Croydon	2,117	106	122	-15
Dorking	3,430	172	216	-25.5
Dulwich Hamlet	2,970	149	195	-30.8
Harlow Town	1,910	96	114	-18.7
Heybridge Swifts	3,147	157	170	-8.2
Hitchin Town	6,599	330	377	-14.2
Leyton-Wingate	2,310	116	198	-70.6
Maidenhead United	4,335	217	246	-13.3
Molesey	1,958	98	101	-3
Stevenage B.	12,859	643	485	+32.5
Tooting & Mitcham	2,973	149	169	-13.4
Uxbridge	2,344	117	126	-7.6
Walton & Hersham	2,975	149	197	-32.2
Wembley	2,383	119	99	+20.2
Whyteleafe	2,153	108	138	-27.7
Yeading	2,883	144	129	+11.6

Club	Total 91-92	Ave. 91-92	Ave. 90-91	% Change
DIVISION TWO				
Banstead Athletic	939	45	44	+2.2
Barton Rovers	2,413	115	142	-23.4
Berkhamsted	1,890	90	97	-7.7
Billericay Town	5,318	253	242	+4.5
Egham Town	2,033	97	113	-16.4
Harefield United	2,280	109	100	+9
Hemel Hempstead	2,407	115	105	+9.5
Hungerford Town	2,240	107	107	
Leatherhead	2,688	128	111	+15.3
Lewes	3,787	180	163	+10.4
Malden Vale	2,210	105	106	-0.9
Metropolitan Police	2,005	95	112	-17.8
Newbury Town	1,791	85	113	-32.9
Purfleet	1,937	92	93	-1
Rainham Town	1,312	62	69	-4.8
Ruislip Manor	3,417	163	200	-22.6
Saffron Walden	2,511	120	136	-13.3
Southall	1,096	52	84	-61.5
Southwick	1,522	72	127	-76.3
Ware	2,767	132	147	-11.3
Witham Town	2,226	106	108	-1.8
Worthing	3,703	176	145	+21.3
DIVISION THREE				
Bracknell Town	1,298	65	85	-30.7
Camberley Town	1,651	83	58	+43.1
Chertsey Town	2,773	139	112	+24.1
Clapton	871	44	70	-59
Collier Row	1,666	83	109	-31.3
Cove	1,739	87	72	+20.8
Eastbourne United	1,282	64	75	-17.1
Edgware Town	3,100	155	143	+8.3
Epsom & Ewell	1,422	71	92	-29.5
Feltham & Hounslow	919	46	92	-100
Flackwell Heath	813	41	64	-56
Hampton	3,215	161	144	+11.8
Hertford Town	1,664	83	109	-31.3
Hornchurch	1,331	67	78	-16.4
Horsham	3,516	176	105	+67.6
Kingsbury Town	1,474	74	70	+5.7
Petersfield United	1,320	66	76	-15.1
Royston Town	2,410	121	179	-47.9
Thame United	2,012	101		
Tilbury	2,775	139	87	+59.7
Tring Town	1,221	61	90	-47.5

Premier Division action: Gary Attrell, Chesham winger (right) being chased by Kingstonian midfielder David Kempton (left). Chesham won this fixture on 2nd February 3-2 at home. Photo - Neville Sankey.

DIADORA SPONSORSHIP AWARDS 1991-92

Club	Champs	Four-goal	Loc-tite	Total(£)
PREMIER DIVISION				
Aylesbury *	950	527.41		1620.27
Basingstoke Town		105.49	250	355.49
Bishop's Stortford				
Bognor Regis Town			250	250
Bromley *		105.49		248.34
Carshalton Athletic	700	210.98	800	1710.98
Chesham United	1750	527.41	250	2527.45
Dagenham	500	105.49	250	855.49
Enfield *	3000	210.98		3353.84
Grays Athletic		105.49		105.49
Harrow Borough *		210.98	800	1153.84
Hayes		210.98	250	460.98
Hendon		105.49		105.49
Kingstonian	350	105.49		455.49
Marlow	1250	210.98		1460.98
St Albans City		105.49		105.49
Staines Town				
Sutton United	2000	316.47	2000	4316.47
Windsor & Eton		105.49		105.49
Wivenhoe Town *		210.98		353.84
Woking * +	3750	527.40	1400	6820.26
Wokingham Town	1500	316.47	350	2166.47
DIVISION ONE				
Abingdon Town	950	235.70	250	1435.70
Aveley				
Barking		117.85		117.85
Boreham Wood	1500	235.70	100	1836.70
Chalfont St Peter				
Croydon		117.85		117.85
Dorking *		117.85		260.70
Dulwich Hamlet	1750	355.55	500	2603.55
Harlow Town		117.85		117.85
Heybridge Swifts				
Hitchin Town	500	117.85		617.85
Leyton-Wingate		235.70		235.70
Maidenhead United		117.85		117.85
Molesey	270	117.85	800	1187.85
Stevenage B.	3000	589.45	250	3839.45
Tooting & Mitcham	700			700
Uxbridge		235.70	500	737.70
Walton & Hersham	350	117.85		467.85
Wembley	1250			1250
Whyteleafe				
Yeading	2000	471.40	600	3071.40

Club	Champs	Four-goal	Loc-tite	Total(£)
DIVISION TWO				
Banstead Athletic		96.72		96.72
Barton Rovers		48.37	425	473.37
Berkhamsted		96.74		96.74
Billericay Town	1500	145.11		1645.11
Egham Town	700	96.74	1000	1796.74
Harefield United		48.37	200	248.37
Hemel Hempstead	270	96.74		366.74
Hungerford Town	170			170
Leatherhead	1250	241.85		1491.85
Lewes	1750	145.11		1895.11
Malden Vale		96.74	725	821.74
Metropolitan Police	500	145.11		645.11
Newbury Town			200	200
Purfleet	2000	241.85	1500	3741.85
Rainham Town		48.37		48.37
Ruislip Manor	950	48.37	425	1423.37
Saffron Walden	350	198.48	825	1368.48
Southall		96.74	200	296.74
Southwick				
Ware		96.97		96.97
Witham Town		96.74		96.74
Worthing		145.11	200	345.11
DIVISION THREE				
Bracknell Town		39.82		39.82
Camberley Town		39.82		39.82
Chertsey T. $ x	1500	278.67	750	2778.67
Clapton		119.46	400	519.46
Collier Row	100	119.46		219.46
Cove	500	76.64	425	1004.64
Eastbourne United				
Edgware Town	1750	318.68		2068.68
Epsom & Ewell	170		200	370
Feltham & Hounslow		39.82	200	239.82
Flackwell Heath	350	119.46		469.46
Hampton	950	238.92		1188.92
Hertford Town		39.82		39.82
Hornchurch				
Horsham	700	199.05		899.05
Kingsbury Town		119.46	200	319.46
Petersfield United		39.82	500	539.82
Royston Town		39.82		39.82
Thame United	270	199.05	425	894.05
Tilbury	1250	119.43		894.43
Tring Town				

* - 142.85 for FA Trophy run
+ 1,000.00 for FA Cup run

$ - 750 for FA Vase run
x - 250 for first to 100 goals

Steve Scott (6) scores the only goal for St Albans City in their win at Hayes. Photo - John Sherwood.

Third Division

	P	W	D	L	F	A	Pts
Edgware Town	40	30	3	7	106	44	93
Chertsey Town	40	29	4	7	115	44	91
Tilbury	40	26	9	5	84	40	87
Hampton	40	26	5	9	93	35	83
Horsham	40	23	8	9	92	51	77
Cove	40	21	9	10	74	49	72
Flackwell Heath	40	19	12	9	78	50	69
Thame United	40	19	7	14	73	46	64
Epsom & Ewell	40	17	11	12	55	50	62
Collier Row	40	17	9	14	67	59	60
Royston Town	40	17	7	16	59	58	58
Kingsbury Town	40	12	10	18	54	61	46
Hertford Town	40	12	10	18	55	73	46
Petersfield United	40	12	9	19	45	67	45
Camberley Town	40	11	8	21	52	69	41
Feltham & Hounslow Borough	40	11	7	22	53	78	40
Bracknell Town	40	10	7	23	48	90	37
Hornchurch	40	8	7	25	40	87	31
Tring Town	40	9	4	27	35	94	31
Clapton	40	9	3	28	47	93	30
Eastbourne United	40	5	5	30	34	121	20

Leading Scorers (League Only)

Nigel Thompson (Cove)	28
Tony Wood (Flackwell Heath)	27
Gary Ewing (Hampton)	27
David Whitehead (Hertford)	27

THE DIADORA LEAGUE FIRST DIVISION RESULT CHART 1991-92

HOME TEAM	1	2	3	4	5	6	7	8	9	10	11	12	13	14	15	16	17	18	19	20	21
1. Bracknell	*	4-2	0-4	1-0	1-1	2-0	4-3	1-5	1-1	1-2	1-3	0-5	0-1	5-1	1-4	2-1	1-1	1-1	1-2	2-2	3-0
2. Camberley	2-3	*	0-2	2-0	0-3	0-1	4-1	2-3	3-1	3-2	2-3	0-1	0-0	2-2	3-1	0-2	1-2	1-2	0-2	0-0	3-0
3. Chertsey	2-0	4-0	*	10-1	1-2	2-1	5-1	4-2	0-1	4-1	4-0	4-3	2-0	4-2	3-4	3-1	1-1	3-0	1-0	4-2	5-0
4. Clapton	1-0	0-1	0-3	*	3-1	0-3	5-1	0-5	0-1	0-1	2-4	1-3	4-0	0-1	2-2	0-0	1-2	2-0	0-1	0-4	6-0
5. Collier Row	5-0	1-1	2-3	2-0	*	3-3	3-0	2-2	4-0	1-0	2-1	2-1	6-2	2-0	0-2	4-1	1-1	0-3	3-3	0-0	1-0
6. Cove	4-0	3-0	4-2	2-0	4-1	*	2-0	1-2	1-3	1-1	4-3	2-1	3-1	2-0	3-0	2-3	0-0	2-0	1-1	2-1	5-0
7. E'bourne U.	2-1	1-4	0-3	0-1	3-0	1-2	*	1-1	0-1	1-1	1-5	0-6	1-3	2-1	0-1	0-8	2-3	1-3	0-3	0-6	0-3
8. Edgware T.	2-1	2-1	3-1	4-0	2-2	3-1	9-1	*	2-0	2-0	3-4	2-1	5-0	3-2	2-4	2-0	4-0	2-0	2-3	1-2	5-0
9. Epsom & E.	1-1	1-1	2-3	3-1	1-1	1-1	2-0	0-1	*	3-1	2-2	1-1	3-1	2-0	0-1	2-0	3-1	1-0	1-0	0-0	2-0
10. Feltham & H.	1-4	2-2	1-3	3-2	2-3	2-2	1-1	0-1	2-0	*	4-3	0-3	1-2	0-1	2-0	1-0	0-1	0-4	1-6	1-2	4-0
11. Flackwell H.	3-0	0-1	0-0	4-0	1-0	1-1	1-2	1-2	2-2	3-1	*	2-1	0-0	6-0	3-1	2-0	2-1	2-2	3-1	1-2	2-1
12. Hampton	4-0	0-0	2-1	3-2	0-3	5-0	5-0	0-1	3-0	2-1	1-2	*	4-2	6-0	0-0	4-1	3-0	2-0	2-0	3-2	1-2
13. Hertford T.	2-1	6-2	0-3	5-3	4-1	0-0	0-2	0-1	2-2	2-4	0-0	0-3	*	4-1	2-2	2-0	3-0	0-0	0-3	3-0	1-1
14. Hornchurch	1-1	3-0	1-3	0-1	2-1	0-3	3-0	1-4	1-3	3-4	1-1	1-3	2-0	*	1-1	1-1	0-0	1-0	1-1	0-2	0-1
15. Horsham	7-0	0-0	1-2	4-1	5-1	1-2	3-0	4-0	5-1	4-2	1-1	1-2	2-1	5-1	*	2-1	3-1	4-2	3-0	2-4	2-0
16. Kingsbury	2-1	0-2	1-1	0-1	1-0	4-1	4-0	0-3	1-1	2-0	1-1	0-0	1-1	1-2	1-0	*	1-1	1-1	2-2	1-2	1-0
17. Petersfield	0-1	1-0	2-0	2-0	0-1	1-0	2-2	0-2	0-1	2-2	0-3	2-1	2-0	3-2	1-1	1-5	*	0-3	0-3	2-3	6-1
18. Royston T.	1-0	2-1	1-3	4-1	3-0	1-2	2-0	0-4	2-1	0-1	1-1	0-2	3-3	1-0	2-4	4-2	3-2	*	0-4	2-2	3-0
19. Thame Utd	6-1	2-1	0-3	4-2	0-1	2-3	4-0	1-2	1-0	1-1	0-1	1-1	2-0	3-0	0-1	5-1	2-0	1-2	*	1-3	2-0
20. Tilbury	2-0	6-1	2-2	4-1	1-0	1-0	3-3	2-1	3-2	2-0	1-1	0-2	3-0	2-0	1-1	3-0	1-0	1-0	2-0	*	3-0
21. Tring T.	3-1	0-4	0-7	3-3	2-1	0-0	3-1	1-4	1-3	1-0	0-1	0-2	0-2	4-1	2-3	1-2	4-1	0-1	0-0	1-2	*

HOME TEAM	1	2	3	4	5	6	7	8	9	10	11	12	13	14	15	16	17	18	19	20	21
1. Bracknell T	*	73	105	56	63	60	37	80	64	59	66	58	69	85	78	55	49	47	58	86	50
2. Camberley	98	*	156	83	84	147	68	106	72	67	51	124	88	62	67	74	66	66	52	62	58
3. Chertsey	97	86	*	89	87	215	162	191	108	84	111	184	88	108	389	113	137	152	143	132	97
4. Clapton	25	60	47	*	49	20	43	62	30	64	41	49	48	43	48	43	30	34	30	65	56
5. Collier Row	67	72	130	81	*	69	42	97	89	62	96	117	87	139	76	79	82	76	72	97	78
6. Cove	82	147	167	78	95	*	67	87	85	92	78	73	93	82	107	70	85	52	87	60	55
7. E'bourne U.	53	37	55	79	89	57	*	71	57	53	55	51	73	59	117	49	59	71	81	67	49
8. Edgware	115	180	122	156	208	128	120	*	155	208	106	205	177	122	126	220	158	211	169	128	86
9. Epsom	64	58	74	86	64	71	80	73	*	79	63	94	63	92	109	48	65	52	57	67	63
10. Feltham & H.	50	15	85	35	28	28	20	57	45	*	28	90	69	45	50	54	32	26	69	23	20
11. F'well Hth	42	32	36	33	52	25	30	100	43	30	*	45	31	42	30	50	35	30	55	30	42
12. Hampton	179	180	221	111	147	183	154	129	171	143	149	*	163	151	157	150	205	167	169	175	108
13. Hertford	70	106	119	94	66	78	68	92	95	66	95	100	*	68	96	64	78	68	102	69	70
14. Hornchurch	48	65	120	90	94	82	70	78	54	40	48	90	75	*	40	48	30	56	60	76	73
15. Horsham	151	170	250	157	166	165	225	124	160	240	156	125	148	205	*	173	178	212	156	180	175
16. Kingsbury	73	46	81	42	58	56	90	269	54	54	57	83	76	68	74	*	73	44	62	64	50
17. Petersfield	85	80	75	50	50	80	35	35	50	60	60	100	90	50	110	50	*	60	60	80	60
18. Royston	108	156	48	76	74	129	91	161	168	86	96	108	270	120	68	128	96	*	132	206	91
19. Thame Utd	73	90	152	63	83	80	76	159	123	108	103	90	136	70	84	83	112	69	*	118	140
20. Tilbury	141	114	142	147	162	117	160	170	141	163	78	261	137	97	143	84	87	97	243	*	91
21. Tring T.	62	22	80	31	62	63	58	66	74	62	51	58	36	46	57	58	61	42	180	52	*

Diadora League Division Two Three Year Record

(N - Denoted Division Two (North), S - Denotes Division Two (South))

	82/3	83/4	84/5	85/6	86/7	87/8	88/9	89/90	90/1	91/2
Abingdon Town	N/A	N/A	-	-	-	-	-	3S	1S	-
Aveley	N/A	N/A	-	-	5N	21N	9N	2N	-	-
Bracknell Town	N/A	N/A	8S	2S	-	-	-	19S	17S	17
Camberley Town	N/A	N/A	15S	16S	15S	19S	14S	17S	22S	15
Chalfont St Peter	N/A	N/A	7N	6N	8S	1S	-	-	-	-
Chertsey Town	N/A	N/A	19S	-N	6S	6S	12S	13S	14S	2
Chesham United	N/A	N/A	-	-	1N	-	-	-	-	-
Cheshunt	N/A	N/A	12N	4N	22N	-	-	-	-	-
Clapton	N/A	N/A	(see page 347 for Div.2 record)							20
Collier Row	N/A	N/A	-	-	9N	2N	-	8N	12N	10
Cove	N/A	N/A	-	-	-	-	-	-	-	6
Eastbourne United	N/A	N/A	(see page 347 for Div.2 record)							21
Edgware Town	N/A	N/A	-	-	-	-	-	-	14N	1
Epsom & Ewell	N/A	N/A	-	-	-	5S	9S	14S	13S	9
Feltham (* - F. & Hounslow)	N/A	N/A	14S	10S	4S	4S	8S	18S	18S	16
Flackwell Heath	N/A	N/A	8N	14S	16S	20S	13S	8S	16S	7
Hampton	N/A	N/A	-	-	-	-	-	-	12S	4
Haringey Borough	N/A	N/A	19N	11N	3N	20N	-	-	-	-
Harlow Town	N/A	N/A	-	-	17N	5N	1N	-	-	-
Hertford Town	N/A	N/A	-	5N	15N	22N	10N	3N	15N	13
Heybridge Swifts	N/A	N/A	3N	3N	4N	9N	5N	1N	-	-
Hornchurch	N/A	N/A	-	-	14N	14N	16N	16N	19N	18
Horsham	N/A	N/A	(see page 347 for Div.2 record)							5
Kingsbury Town	N/A	N/A	17N	2N	-	-	-	-	13N	12
Maidenhead United	N/A	N/A	-	-	-	11S	17S	5S	2S	-
Marlow	N/A	N/A	13N	20S	2S	-	-	-	-	-
Petersfield United	N/A	N/A	17S	12S	18S	22S	21S	20S	21S	14
Royston Town	N/A	N/A	11N	8N	21N	17N	18N	9N	16N	11
Stevenage Borough	N/A	N/A	4N	1N	-	-	4N	4N	1N	-
Thame United	N/A	N/A	-	-	-	-	-	-	-	8
Tilbury	N/A	N/A	-	-	-	3N	17N	6N	17N	3
Tring Town	N/A	N/A	(see page 347 for Div.2 record)							19
Vauxhall Motors	N/A	N/A	-	16N	13N	8N	14N	11N	2N	-
Whyteleafe	N/A	N/A	5S	5S	12S	7S	2S	-	-	-
Wivenhoe Town	N/A	N/A	-	12N	1N	-	-	-	-	-
Woking	N/A	N/A	-	3S	1S	-	-	-	-	-
Wolverton Town	N/A	N/A	16N	20N	2N	-	22N	-	-	-
Yeading	N/A	N/A	-	-	-	10S	15S	1S	-	-
No. of clubs competing	N/A	N/A	20N	20N	22N	22N	22N	22N	22N	21
			19S	20S	21S	22S	21S	21S	22S	

ALDERSHOT TOWN (1992)

Chairman: Terry Owens   **President:** Arthur English   **Vice President:** Bill Warren
Directors: Karl Prentice, Peter Bloomfield, David Hunt, Graham Brookland, John McGinty, Malcolm Grant.
Secretary: Peter Bridgeman, 4 Shortheath Rd, Farnham, Surrey GU9 8SR (0252 725437. Fax:0252 733659).
Team Manager: Steve Wignall   **Asst Manager:** TBA   **Physio:** 'Ginger' McAllister
Commercial Manager: TBA   **Press Officer:** TBA
Youth Development Officer: Paul Beves   **Youth Coach:** Andy Meyer.
Hon. Club Doctor: Dr Alan Gillespoe, FRCS.
Ground: Recreation Ground, High Street, Aldershot, Hants GU11 1TW.
Directions: From M3 (jct 4) take A325 to Aldershot. After five miles at r'bout take 1st exit marked town centre (A323) into Wellington Ave. At Burger King r'bout take 2nd exit into High Street - ground on left. 5 mins walk from Aldershot (BR).
Capacity: 5,000 (4,500 Covered)   **Seats:** 1,800   **Floodlights:** Y   **Metal Badges:** Y
Colours: Red/white/blue   **Change colours:** White/blue/red.   **Club Shop:** Two
Sponsors: TBA   **Founded:** 1992.
Previous Leagues: None.   **Previous Name:** None.   **Nickname:** Shots
Midweek home matchday: Tuesday   **Reserve Team's League:** TBA
Record Attendance: 19,138 Aldershot FC v Carlisle United, FA Cup 4th Rd replay 28/1/70.
Best F.A. Cup season: N/A
Record Fees - Paid: **Received:**
Players progressing to Football League: N/A.
Clubhouse: Yes   **Steward:** Supporters Club.
Supporters Club Secretary: Nick Fryer, 23 Barnwood Close, Guildford, Surrey GU2 6GG.
91-92 Captain: N/A   **91-92 P.o.Y.:** N/A   **91-92 Top scorer:** N/A
Local Newspapers (+Tel.Nos.): Aldershot News (0252 28221), Farnham Herald (0252 725224).
Local Radio: County Sound (203m m/w, 1476 khz), BBC Radio Surrey (104.6 fm), Radio 210 (210m m/w).
Hons: None to date; first season in existence.

GOALKEEPERS:
Tim Read (Loan from Woking)
DEFENDERS: Kevin Parkins (Windsor, Army), **Keith Baker** (Farnborough, Chesham, Egham, Farnborough, Staines, Southall)
MIDFIELD: Dave Osgood (Maidenhead, Burnham, Newbury, Basingstoke, Windsor, Maidenhead, Wimdsor), **Steve Wignall** (Brentford, Colchester, Doncaster, Liverpool), **Koo Dumbaya** (Bracknell, Chertsey, Basingstoke, Wokingham, Aldershot)
FORWARDS: Brian Lucas (Basingstoke, Wokingham, Basingstoke, Farnborough, Aldershot), **Mark Butler** (Egham, Chesham, Wycombe, Egham, Ash Utd, Tongham), **Chris Tomlinson** (Canterbury, Aldershot)

BRACKNELL TOWN

Chairman: TBA   **President:** TBA
Secretary: Mr Gill McFadden, 15 Goodways Drive, Bracknell, Berks RG12 3AU (0344 52803).
Manager: Martin Benford   **Asst Manager:** TBA   **Coach:**
Press Officer: Mr R Scully   **Commercial Manager:**   **Physio:**
Ground: Larges Lane, Bracknell RG12 3AN (0344 412305).
Directions: Turn off A329 just before Met Office r'bout by Bracknell College, ground 200 yards. From Bracknell (BR) turn right over bridge, left down track keeping railway track on your left, 100 yards along follow curve over footbridge. Turn right and follow lane to end, then turn left and the ground is on left after bend.
Capacity: 3,000   **Seats:** 200   **Cover:** 200   **Floodlights:** Yes   **Founded:** 1896
Colours: All red   **Change colours:** All sky   **Club Shop:** No
Programme: 24 pages,40p   **Editor:** Mr Robert Scully (0344 423749)   **Metal Badges:** Yes
Previous Ground: **Midweek Matchday:** Tuesday
Previous Leagues: Surrey Snr 63-70/ London Spartan 70-75.
Reserve Team's League: Suburban   **Nickname:** Robins
Record Gate: 2,500 v Newquay, FA Amateur Cup 1972.   **Sponsors:**
Best F.A. Cup season: 4th Qualifying Rd 1988 (lost 1-2 v Cheltenham Town).
Record Fees - Paid: **Received:**
Players progressing to Football League: Willie Graham (Brentford).
Clubhouse: 7-11pm weekdays, 12-11pm Saturdays.   **Steward:**
Club Record Goalscorer: Roger Cleverley   **Club Record Apps:** James Woodcock.
91-92 P.o.Y: Mark Hyde   **91-92 Player's P.o.Y.:** Jason Day   **91-92 Top scorer:** Justin Day
Local Press: **Local Radio Stations:.**
Hons: Isthmian Lg Div 2 Sth R-up, Berks & Bucks Snr Cup R-up, Spartan Lg(1) (R-up(2)).

GOALKEEPERS:
Mark Hyde (Hillingdon, Hayes, Hillingdon)
DEFENDERS: Jason Day (Youth), **Andy Mihell** (Youth), **Rory Todd** (Youth), **Moran Dodds** (Burnham, Flackwell Heath, Chertsey, Burnham, Windsor, Slough, Maple FC, Slough), **Declan Ford** (Youth), **Michael Lambourn** (Local football), **Steve Hibbins** (Newbury, Frimley Green, Bracknell, Camberley)
MIDFIELD: Jeff Mathews (Youth), **Alan Shields** (Youth), **Gary Freer** (Australia, Bracknell), **Adam Markwell** (Flackwell Heath), **Chris Warren** (Local football), **Mark West** (Local football), **Martin Benford** (Local football), **Ken Chin-Yue** (Local football), **Richard Burton** (Local football)
FORWARDS: Justin Day (Youth), **Mark Murphy** (Camberley), **John Smith** (Local football), **Steve Rapley** (Youth), **Anthony Jones** (Local football), **Andy Leader** (Egham, Newbury, Windsor, Bracknell, Newbury), **Louis Barratt** (Local football)

CAMBERLEY TOWN

Chairman: Ian Waldren   **Vice Chairman:** Gordon Foss   **President:** TBA
Secretary: Ron Trindles, 26 Mathon Court, Cross Lane, Guildford GU1 1TD (0483 60829).
Manager: Paul Devis   **Asst Manager:** Phil Caulfield   **Coach:**
Press Officer: Andy Vaughan   **Comm. Manager:** Chris Richardson   **Physio:**
Ground: Krooner Park, Krooner Road, off Frimley Rd, Camberley, Surrey GU15 2QP (0276 65392).
Directions: M3 Jct 4, follow signs to Frimley, follow B3411 to shops, ground on left.
Capacity: 3,000   **Seats:** 196   **Cover:** 196   **Floodlights:** Yes   **Founded:** 1896
Colours: All red   **Change colours:** All yellow   **Club Shop:** Yes (contact Barry Funnell)
Programme: 28 pages,50p   **Editor:** Andy Vaughan   **Badges:** New 92-93
Previous Ground: **Midweek Matchday:** Tuesday
Previous Leagues: Ascot & Dist./West Surrey/ Surrey Snr 22-73/ Spartan 73-75/ Athenian 75-77 82-84/ Isthmian 77-82.
Previous Names: Camberley FC, Yorktown (merged in 1969)
Reserve Team's League: Suburban   **Nickname:** Krooners
Record Gate: 3,500 v Crystal Palace, floodlight opening, December 1973.   **Sponsors:**
Best FA Cup year: 3rd Qualifying Rd. 78-79
Record Fees - Paid: **Received:**
Players progressing to Football League:
Clubhouse: Evenings (except Mondays). Dancehall, pool, darts.   **Steward:** TBA.
Club Record Goalscorer: **Club Record Apps:**
91-92 Captain: **91-92 P.o.Y.:**   **91-92 Top scorer:** Keith Hoad 11.
Local Press: Camberley News (0276 64444).   **Local Radio:**
Hons: FA Vase QF 85-86 89-90, Isthmian Lg Div 2 R-up 78-79, Surrey Snr Lg 30-31 31-32 32-33 (R-up 46-47 61-62, Lg Charity Cup 37-38 51-52 (R-up 31-32 36-37 54-55)), Surrey Snr Cup 78-79 (R-up 35-36), W Surrey Lg 13-14 (R-up 12-13), Ascot & Dist Lg 03-04, Surrey Jnr Charity Cup R-up 08-09, Surrey Jnr Cup 1897-98 1909-10 (R-up 07-08).

GOALKEEPERS:
Mark Watson (Newbury, Plymouth, Reading, Southampton)
DEFENDERS: Simon Bates (Ditton), **Dave Jordan** (Staines), **Paul Screawn** (Local football), **Steve Garrood** (Egham, Staines, Fulham(J)), **Dave Veale** (Fleet, Bracknell), **Richard Packman** (Egham, Virginia Water, Staines), **Derek Neave** (Bracknell), **John Miller** (Hounslow), **Troy Tomsett** (Youth), **Lee White** (Local football)
MIDFIELD: Mick Watmore (Egham, Ashford(Middx), Chertsey, Walton & Hersham, Staines, Chelsea(Sch), **Craig Windmill** (Staines), **Jason Bell** (Youth), **Paul Xibberas** (Cove, Ashford(Middx), Staines, Abbey R, Woking, Old Hamptonians), **Mark Gibbons** (Youth)
FORWARDS: Steve Lynch (Chelsea(Sch), **Lewis Jones** (Staines, Hanworth, Staines), **Steve Lloyd** (Bagshot), **Keith Hoad** (Hounslow, Ruislip, Kingsbury, Worthing, Brighton(J)), **Kevin James** (Exeter(J))

CLAPTON

Chairman: Mike Fogg   **Vice Chairman:**   **President:** G M Gliksten
Secretary: Roger Chilvers, 50 Harrow Rd, Barking, Essex IG11 7RA (081 591 5313).
Manager: Micky Connolly   **Asst Manager:**   **Coach:**
Press Officer: Secretary   **Comm. Manager:**   **Physio:**
Ground: The Old Spotted Dog, Upton Lane, Forest Gate, London E7 9NP (081 472 0822).
Directions: BR to Forest Gate, tube to Plaistow (District Line), or bus 278 passes ground. Officials entrance in Upton Lane, spectator's in Disraeli Rd.
Capacity: 2,500   **Seats:** 150   **Cover:** 2 stands   **Floodlights:** Yes   **Founded:** 1878
Colours: Red & white stripes/black/black   **Change colours:** All jade
Club Shop: No   **Sponsors:**
Programme: 10 pages,50p   **Editor:** Peter Pendle (081 519 1084).   **Metal Badges:** Yes
Previous Ground: **Midweek Matchday:** Tuesday
Previous Leagues: Southern 1894-96 (founder members)/ London 1896-97.
Previous Names: None   **Previous Grounds:** None.
Reserve Team's League: **Nickname:** Tons
Record Gate: 12,000 v Spurs, 1898-99.
Best FA Cup year: 3rd Rd Proper 25-26 (lost 2-3 to Swindon at Upton Park.
League clubs defeated in FA Cup: Norwich City 1925-26.
Record Fees - Paid: **Received:**
Clubhouse: Open all hours.   **Players progressing to Football League:**
Club Record Goalscorer: **Club Record Apps:**
91-92 Captain: **91-92 P.o.Y.:**   **91-92 Top scorer:** Peter Mason 14.
Local Newspapers: **Local Radio:**
Hons: FA Amtr Cup 06-07 08-09 14-15 23-24 24-25 (R-up 04-05), London Snr Cup, London Charity Cup, Essex Snr Cup. First English team to play on the continent.

GOALKEEPERS:
Johnny Briggs (Local football)
DEFENDERS: Kenny Deacon (Finchley, Dulwich, Wembley, Tooting, Dulwich, Carshalton), **Paul French** (Youth), **Bill Bailey** (Youth), **Micky Porter** (Local football), **Leon Pickering** (Youth)
MIDFIELD: Alan Bowers (West Ham, Norwich), **Dean Pitts** (Youth), **Joe Richards** (Collier Row), **Danny Hazle** (Local football), **Dave Fahy** (Local football), **Dave Flynn** (Hornchurch, Rainham, Hornchurch, Billericay, Clapton, Rainham, Beckton Utd)
FORWARDS: Peter Mason (Wealdstone), **Eddie Selwyn** (Local football), **Darren Carter** (Youth), **Mark Smith** (Barking), **Trevor Christian** (Local football)

Camberley Town. Back Row (L/R): Phil Caulfield (Player-Coach), David Melham, Lee White, Gary Woods, Steve Garrood, John Miller, Troy Tornsett, Tony Phasey (Trainer), Paul Devis (Manager). Front: Paul Xiberras, Kevin Metcalfe, Paul Screawn, Mark Watson, Steve Lloyd, Lee Innes. Photo - V J Robertson.

Clapton's Robert Ramsey (8) is challenged by Tilbury's Geoff Nicholson (8). Tilbury easily won this New Year's Day derby at the Spotted Dog by four goals without reply. Photo - Gavin Ellis.

Horsham pictured at their FA Cup local derby with Crawley Town. Photo - Eric Marsh.

COLLIER ROW

Chairman: Alan Punter **Vice Chairman:** **President:** Ron Walker
Secretary: Phil Sammons, 41 Riversdale Rd, Collier Row, Romford, Essex RM5 2NP (0708 768845).
Manager: Reg Wells **Coach:** Micky Cleaver **Assistant Manager:**
Press Officer: Secretary **General Manager:** Colin Rufus **Physio:**
Ground: 'Sungate', Collier Row Rd, Collier Row, Romford, Essex (0708 722766).
Directions: A12 from London, left at Moby Dick (PH) traffic lights, right at next r'bout, ground entrance signposted 200 yards on right.
Capacity: 2,000 **Seats:** 110 **Cover:** Yes **Floodlights:** Yes **Founded:** 1929
Colours: Red/black/black **Change colours:** White/red/red
Club Shop: Yes **Metal Badges:** Yes **Sponsors:**
Programme: 32 pages,30p **Editor:** Phil Sammons.
Midweek Matchday: Wednesday **Previous Leagues:** London Spartan 81-86.
Previous Names: None **Previous Grounds:** None.
Reserve Team's League: Essex Business Houses. **Nickname:** The Row
Record Gate: 1,095 v Garforth Town, FA Vase 6th Rd 1987.
Best FA Cup year: 1st Qualifying Rd 89-90, lost 1-2 to Dulwich Hamlet.
Record Fees - Paid: **Received:**
Clubhouse: Three bars, two halls. Open every day. **Steward:** Mick Bragger.
Players progressing to Football League:
Club Record Goalscorer: Steve Thompson 158 **Club Record Apps:** Graham Cole 278.
91-92 Captain: Gary Foire **91-92 P.o.Y.:** Gary Nisbet **91-92 Top scorer:** Tony Samuels 24
Local Newspapers: Havering Recorder **Local Radio:** Essex Radio, BBC Essex.
Hons: FA Vase SF 86-87, London Spartan Lg 83-84 (R-up 84-85).

GOALKEEPERS:
Dean Mann (Leyton-Wingate, Corinthian, Grays, Bristol R(J), Millwall(J)), **Nigel Lynn** (Local football)
DEFENDERS: Gary Nisbet (Local football), **Dave Bushell** (Leyton-Wingate, Spurs(J)), **Gary Edwards** (Leyton-Wingate), **Billy Clarke** (Leyton-Wingate, Leyton Orient(T)), **Rod Vitalis** (Leyton-Wingate, Arsenal(J)), **Mark Abbott** (Leyton-Wingate, Woodford, C Palace(J), Arsenal(J)), **Gary Fiore** (Barking, Bromley, Erith & Belvedere, Leyton-Wingate, Dulwich, Wimbledon), **Paul Attridge** (Local football), **Andy Orr** (Local football)
MIDFIELD: Ian Punter (Local football), **Tony Marsh** (Barkingside, Collier Row), **Tony Samuels** (Bromley, Leyton-Wingate, Leyt & Ilf), **Darren Bush** (Clapton, Leyton Orient(J)), **Ian Jenkins** (Leyton-Wingate, Man Utd(J)), **Ian Whiteley** (Clapton, Leyton-Wingate), **Leon Braithwaite** (Leyton-Wingate), **Leroy Houston** (Leyton-Wingate, Boreham Wood, Finchley, Wolverton, Enfield), **Sean Adamson** (Local football)
FORWARDS: Rob Mansfield (West Ham(J)), **Ian Little** (Leyton-Wingate), **Godfrey Obabo** (Leyton-Wingate, Leyton Orient), **Richard Chick** (Leyton-Wingate, Camb Utd, Millwall(J)), **Graham Minton** (Leyton-Wingate, West Ham(J), Spurs(J)), **Mark Salmon** (Leyton-Wingate)

COVE

Chairman: Dave Tyler **President:** R Brown **Treasurer:** R Clark
Secretary: Dave Graham, 149 Aldershot Rd, Crookham, Hants GU14 0JS (0252 623021).
Manager: Chick Botley **Asst Manager:** **Coach:**
Press Officer: Chick Botley (0252 518587)**Commercial Mgr:** R Stacey **Physio:**
Ground: Oak Farm, off Romayne Close, Cove, Farnborough, Hants GU14 8LB (0252 543615).
Directions: Farnborough (BR) 2 miles; right into Union Street, right at lights into Prospect Rd, left into West Heath Rd, right into Romayne close and follow signs to Cove FC. Or, M3 jct 4, follow A325 towards Farnborough, right into Prospect Avenue (signposted Cove FC and Farnborough Town FC), then as above.
Capacity: 3,500 **Seats:** 86 **Cover:** 500 **Floodlights:** Yes **Club Shop:** No
Colours: Amber/amber (black stripe)/amber **Change colours:** **Metal Badges:** No
Programme: 24 pages,50p **Editor:** Bob Sear
Previous Grounds: Cove Green/ Southwood Rd.
Previous Leagues: Aldershot Jnr/ Aldershot Intermediate 45-48/ Surrey Intermediate 48-71/ Surrey Snr 71-73/ Hants 74-81/ Combined Counties 81-90.
Midweek Matchday: Tuesday **Sponsors:** Murata Electronics/ Barry Ward Builders
Record Gate: 210 v Windsor & Eton, FA Cup 1st Qual. Rd 90-91. **Nickname:**
Reserve Team's League: Suburban **Best FA Cup year:** Never past Qualifying Rounds
Players progressing to Football League: Frank Broome, Maurice Cook.
Clubhouse: Open evenings, matchdays and Sunday lunchtimes. Snacks, juke box, pool, darts.
Club Record Goalscorer: **Club Record Apps:**
91-92 Captain: **91-92 P.o.Y.:** Paul Riley/ Paul Shrubb **91-92 Top scorer:** Nigel Thompson
Hons: Surrey I'mediate Lg, Surrey Prem. Lg 49-50 52-53 53-54 63-64 67-68 (R-up 48-49 61-62 64-65, Lg Cup 59-60 60-61 69-70), Combined Co's Lg Cup 81-82, Hants Lg Div 3 76-77 (Div 4 73-74, Div 2 R-up 77-78), Aldershot Snr Cup 71-72 77-78 79-80 90-91 91-92 (R-up 72-73), Aldershot Snr Shield 37-38 38-39 46-47 71-72, Aldershot Snr Cup + Cup.

GOALKEEPERS:
Paul Riley (Leatherhead, Tooting, Farnborough, Walton & Hersham, Epsom & Ewell, Molesey, Hampton, Chertsey), **Andy Pagden** (Fleet)
DEFENDERS: Paul Shrubb (Dorking, Leatherhead, Dorking, Woking, Aldershot, Brentford, Hellenic(SA), Fulham), **Neil Banks** (Farnborough, Notts Co(T), Derby(Sch)), **Ricky Jones** (Petersfield, Farnborough), **Dave Menzies** (Lancing), **Craig Jeffery** (Farnborough), **Peter Hughes** (Ash Utd, Farnborough)
MIDFIELD: Justin Horner (Walton & Hersham, Dorking, Sutton Utd, Woking, Virginia Water, Westfields), **Darren Broad** (Farnborough, RAF), **Dave Newbery** (Egham), **Jeremy Lynch** (Camberley, Yateley), **Wayne Fulford** (Farnham, Petersfield), **Mick Harding** (Leatherhead, Westfields, Bracknell, Chobham, Woking), **Steve Kerbey** (Farnborough, Camberley, Ash Utd, Woking), **Andy Lawrence** (Woking), **John Cassidy** (Molesey, Leatherhead, Worthing, Leatherhead, Woking, Addlestone, Woking, Addlestone, Woking), **Des Vertannes** (Farnborough, Aldershot, Fulham)
FORWARDS: Nigel Thompson (Alton), **Mark Simmonds** (Mytchett Ath), **Lee Ryan** (Fleet Spurs, Farnborough), **Lee Warwick** (Farnham, Ash Utd), **Ken McMillan** (Leatherhead, Cove, Fleet), **Andy Rawlinson** (Farnham)

EAST THURROCK UNITED

Chairman: B Grover   **Vice Chairman:** Ian Firman   **President:** Len Firman
Secretary: M Harris, 14 Colne Valley, Upminster, Essex RM14 1QA (07082 28812).
Manager: Roger Bond   **Coach:** Andy McDermid
Press Officer: M Harris   **Commercial Manager:**   **Physio:** Ron Potts
Ground: Rookery Hill, Corringham, Essex (0375 644166-club, 641009-boardroom).
Directions: A13 London-Southend, take 1014 at Stanford le Hope for two and a half miles - ground on left. Three quarters of a mile from Stanford le Hope and Basildon BR stations.
Seats: 160   **Cover:** Yes   **Capacity:** 3,000   **Floodlights:** Yes   **Founded:** 1969.
Colours: Amber & black   **Change colours:** Blue   **Nickname:** Rocks
Prog: 20 pages, 30p **Editor:** Terry Keating (0375) 644166   **Club Shop:** Yes
Record Attendance: 947 v Trevor Brooking XI, May 1987.   **Metal Badges:** Yes
Sponsors: Partridge's Dairies.
Previous Name: Corringham Social (pre-1969 Sunday side).
Previous Leagues: South Essex Combination/ Gtr London/ Metropolitan 72-75/ London Spartan 75-79/ Essex Snr 79-82.
Previous Grounds: Billet 70-73 74-76/ Grays Ath 73-74/ Tilbury FC 77-82/ New Thames Club 82-84.
Record Fees - Paid: **Received:** £2,000 from Orient for Greg Berry.
Players progressing to Football League: Greg Berry (Leyton Orient).
Clubhouse: Open normal licensing hours. Hot and cold snacks. Darts, pool, indoor bowls.
Club Record Goalscorer: Graham Stewart 102   **Club Record Apps:** Glen Case 550.
91-92 Captain: Paul Driscoll   **91-92 P.o.Y.:** Steve Wiseman **91-92 Top Scorer:** Danny Wallace 17.
Local Press: Thurrock Gazette/ Thurrock Recorder   **Local Radio:** BBC Essex.
Honours: Metropolitan Lg Div 2 (72-73), Essex Snr Lg Cup 88-89 91-92 (Sportsmanship Award 81-82 86-87 89-89), Essex & Herts Border Lg 89-90 (Lg Cup 89-90).

GOALKEEPERS:
Glen Case (Southend(J)), **Gary Piggott** (Billericay)
DEFENDERS: John Chick (Ford Utd, Tilbury), **Mark Beisser** (Basildon, Purfleet), **Ian Fleming** (Met Police, East Thurrock, Harlow), **Steve Wiseman** (Purfleet, Basildon, Purfleet, Dagenham, Purfleet, Basildon, East Thurrock, Herongate Ath), **Andy Innell** (Stambridge, Hullbridge Sports)
MIDFIELD: Paul Driscoll (Ford Utd), **Jason Apps** (Clapton, Hornchurch, Woodford), **Graham Haley** (Ford Utd, Averley, Tilbury), **Laurie Ashworth** (East Ham), **Paul Ross** (Youth), **Danny Smith** (Youth)
FORWARDS: Danny Wallace (Rainham, Hornchurch), **Kurt Davies** (Stambridge, Basildon, Billericay), **Dave Matthews** (Billericay, Purfleet, Dagenham, Southend, Walsall, Basildon, Aveley, West Ham(A))

EPSOM & EWELL

Chairman: Peter Atkins   **President:**   **Vice C'man:**
Secretary: David Wilson, 33 Delaporte Rd, Epsom KT17 4AF (0372 729817).
Manager: Adrian Hill   **Asst Mgr:**   **Coach:** John Wood
Press Off.: Stella Lamont (0737 356245) **General Manager:**   **Physio:**
Ground: West Street, Ewell, Surrey KT17 1XU (081 393 7077).
Directions: West Street is in Ewell village off A24 Epsom Road. Ewell West (BR) 400yds, buses 293, 406, 408.
Capacity: 4,250   **Seats:** 250   **Cover:** 250   **Floodlights:** Yes   **Founded:** 1917
Colours: Royal & white hoops/blue/blue   **Change colours:**
Club Shop: No   **Metal Badges:** No
Programme: 20/24 pages,35p   **Editor:** Stella Lamont.**Club Sponsors:**
Midweek Matches: Tuesday.
Previous Leagues: Surrey Snr 24-27/ London 27-49/ Corinthian 45-46 49-63/ Athenian 63-73 75-77.
Previous Names: Epsom FC, Epsom Town (til 1960)   **Previous Ground:** Horton Lane (til '20s).
Reserve Team's League: Suburban   **Nickname:** E's.
Best FA Cup year: 1st Rd Proper 33-34, lost 2-4 at Clapton Orient.
Best FA Vase year: Finalists 74-75   **Best FA Trophy year:** 2nd Rd Proper 81-82.
Record Gate: 1,800 v Chelsea, Tommy Tuite testimonial, 10/3/87.
Players progressing to Football League: Matt Elliott (Torquay), Chris Powell (Southend), Paul Harding (Notts County), Murray Jones (Grimsby), Alan Pardew (Charlton), Mick Leonard (Chesterfield).
Clubhouse: Mon-Fri 5-11pm, Sat 12-11pm, Sun 12-2.30pm. Pool, darts, dancehall.
Club Record Goalscorer: **Club Record Apps:**
91-92 Captain: **91-92 P.o.Y.:** Alan Webster (1st team), Darren Webb (Res), Mark Connelly (Yth).
91-92 Top Scorers: Epsom FC, Epsom Town (til 1960) Andy Webster 26, Andy Skeet 13, Mark Pepper 9.
Hons: London Lg 27-28 (R-up 31-32 32-33 34-35 36-37 37-38), Corinthian Lg Memorial Shield 59-60, Athenian Lg Div 2 R-up 75-76.

GOALKEEPERS:
Dave Hyatt (Leatherhead, Horsham), **Julian Viggars** (Local football)
DEFENDERS: Micky Clark (Sutton Utd), **Ian Estall** (Chipstead), **Darren Webb** (Youth), **Matt Varndell** (Sutton Utd), **Paul Keeley** (Local football), **Scott Hayworth** (Dorking), **Mark Connolly** (Youth), **Richard Strong** (Leatherhead, Epsom & Ewell, Worthing, Harrow B, Croydon, Epsom & Ewell, Carshalton, Flackwell Heath, Staines, Slough, Wycombe, Ashlea), **Ray Purvis** (Dulwich, Epsom & Ewell, Whyteleafe, Croydon, Redhill, Dorking, Barnet, Arsenal(A))
MIDFIELD: Simon Alldridge (Whyteleafe, Leatherhead, Epsom & Ewell, Cobham, Kingstonian), **Nigel Bennett** (Youth), **Dave Bruty** (Local football), **Tony Hoy** (Whyteleafe, Croydon, Dulwich, Leatherhead), **Maurice Laverty** (Youth), **Dean Meyer** (Youth), **Graham Morris** (Sutton Utd, Maiden V), **Craig Swift** (Corinthian Cas), **Martin Taylor** (Sutton Utd), **Joe Turner** (Leatherhead), **Tim Tweedy** (Maiden V, Epsom & Ewell)
FORWARDS: Ricky Dymond (Youth), **Mark Nicholls** (Local football), **Mark Pepper** (C Palace(T)), **Sean Robinson** (Local football), **Richard Sell** (Chelsea(T)), **Andy Skeet** (Croydon, Charlton(T)), **Adrian Stovell** (Youth), **Andy Webster** (Local football)

FARNHAM TOWN WITHDRAWN

Chairman: J Butters   **President:** D Russell   **Treasurer:**
Secretary: Mr G Southgate, 42 Merrow Lane, Guildford, Surrey (0252 715305).
Manager: **Asst Manager:**   **Coach:**
Press Officer: **Commercial Mgr:**   **Physio:**
Ground: Aldershot Town FC (See page 371). *Farnham will be groundsharing at Aldershot whilst their own ground, at Babbs Mead off West Street in Farnham, is brought up to Diadora League standard.*
Directions: As for Aldershot Town (page 371).
Capacity Etc: (As Aldershot Town)   **Founded:** 1921
Colours: Claret & sky stripes/sky/claret   **Change colours:** Yellow & black   **Club Shop:** No
Programme: Yes   **Editor:**   **Metal Badges:**
Previous Name: Farnham Star   **Previous Grounds:** Farnham Park.
Previous Leagues: Surrey Intermediate/ Surrey Snr 47-71/ Spartan 71-75/ London Spartan 75-80/ Combined Counties 80-92.
Midweek Matchday: **Sponsors:** Frazer Freight.
Record Gate: 500 v Kingstonian, Surrey Snr Cup 1960.   **Nickname:**
Reserve Team's League: **Best FA Cup year:** Never past Qualifying Rounds
Record Fees - Paid: **Received:**
Players progressing to Football League:
Clubhouse:
Club Record Goalscorer: **Club Record Apps:**
91-92 Captain: **91-92 P.o.Y.:**   **91-92 Top scorer:** S Stairs 28.
Local Press: **Local Radio Stations:**
Hons: Dan-Air (Combined Counties) Lg 90-91 91-92 (Challenge Tphy 91-92 (R-up 89-90).

FELTHAM & HOUNSLOW BOROUGH

Chairman: W F P Seuke & S Das   **President:** E J Pauling MBE, JP.
Secretary: Mrs Ann Wilson, 2 Farrier Close, Sunbury-on-Thames, Middx TW16 6NJ (0932 789492).
Manager: Bruce Butler   **Physio:** Sarah Whitworth   **Coach:** Bruce Butler
Ground: Feltham Arena, Shakespeare Avenue, Feltham, Middx TW14 9HY (081 890 6241-club, 6905/6119-ground). *Nb- the club have an artificial pitch.*
Directions: BR to Feltham then 5 mins walk through Glebelands Park. Buses 90, 285, 117, 237, H24 or H25 to Feltham station, or 116 to top of Shakespeare Avenue. By car; M3, M4, A312 Staines road towards Bedfont, second left is Shakespeare Avenue.
Capacity: 10,000   **Seats:** 750   **Cover:** 1,500   **Floodlights:** Yes   **Founded:** 1991
Colours: Royal blue & red stripes/red/blue   **Change colours:** Blue & white/blue/white.
Club Shop: No (old progs from Robert Healy, C/O the club)   **Metal Badges:** No
Programme: 20 pages, 30p   **Editor:**   **Nickname:** Borough.
Midweek Matchday: Wednesday   **Reserve Team's League:** Suburban.   **Sponsors:**
Previous Names: 1991 merger of Feltham FC and Hounslow FC. Feltham previously Tudor Park, Hounslow previously Hounslow Town.
Previous Grounds: Feltham: Rectory Fields, Glebelands, Hounslow: Denbigh Road.
Previous Leagues: Feltham: West Middx Sunday/ Staines & Dist./ Hounslow & Dist./ Surrey Snr 63-68/ Spartan 68-73/ Athenian 74-77. Hounslow: West London/ West Middx/ London 1898-99 1927-29/ Gt Western Suburban/ Spartan 29-46/ Corinthian 46-55/ Athenian 55-76/ Southern 76-83 86-90/ Hellenic 83-86 90-91.
Record Gate: 1,938 v Hampton, Middx Snr Cup 1968 (Hounslow; 8,546 v Wycombe, FA Amtr Cup 53-54).
Best FA Cup year: 3rd Qual Rd 77-78 (lost 1-4 to Tilbury) 82-83 (0-1 v Chesham. Hounslow: 1st Rd Proper 55-56 (lost to Hastings United).
Record Fees - Paid: Martin Tyler (Kingstonian)   **Rec'd:** Richid Harkouk (C Palace).
Clubhouse: Sun, Mon, Wed-Sat. 2 bars, dancehall available for hire. Pool, darts. **Steward:** P Bennett.
Players progressing to Football League: Rachid Harkouk (Crystal Palace, QPR, Notts Co), Andy Pape (QPR), Pat Gavin (Gillingham, Leicester), Bobby Wilson (Brentford), Tony Witter (Crystal Palace).
Club Record Scorer: Paul Clarke 130   **Club Record Appearances:** Paul Clarke 326.
91-92 Captain: Tony Nicholson   **91-92 P.o.Y.:**   **91-92 Top scorer:**
Local Press: Middx Chronicle, Hounslow Feltham & Hanworth Times, Hounslow Borough Recorder.
Local Radio: Capital, Capital Gold, County Sounds.
Hons: Surrey Snr Lg R-up 65-66 (Lg Cup 65-66, Charity Cup 63-64 65-66), Southern Comb. Cup(2)(R-up(2)), Middx Summer Cup, Ashford Cup R-up. Hounslow: FA Amtr Cup R-up 61-62 (SF 53-54), Hellenic Lg R-up 85-86 (Lg Cup 85-86), Gt Western Suburban Lg 24-25, Spartan Lg 45-46, West London Lg 1895-96, FA Vase 5th Rd 87-88.

GOALKEEPERS:
Tont Tsoukkas (Local football)
DEFENDERS: Duncan Ford (Hounslow, Ruislip, Hounslow), **Darren Girvan** (Local, Feltham), **Paul Harris** (Hounslow), **Simon Cundle** (Youth)
MIDFIELD: Tony Nicholson (Egham, Appleby Frodingham, Scunthorpe), **Mark Griffiths** (Hampton, Epsom & Ewell, Hampton), **Phil Greenwood** (Local football), **Tess Laquda** (Local football), **Tim Moody** (Local football)
FORWARDS: Obinni Ulassi (Youth), **Jason Baigent** (Local football), **Lee Channell** (Local football)

Farnham Town. Back Row (L/R): Steve Stairs, Steve Harris, Paul Cann, Andy Metcalfe, Ben Deighan, Shaun May, Peter Browning, Steve Buckingham. Front: Roy Atkin, Paul Warner, Andy Rawlinson, Terry Dale, Paul Bonner, Ben Russle (Mascot). Photo - Eric Marsh.

A taste of things to come; Dan-Air champions-to-be Farnham take on Isthmian opposition in the form of Leatherhead in a pre-season friendly, and force their 'keeper, Colin Caulfield, into action. Photo - Tim Edwards.

Kingsbury Town. Back Row (L/): Niall O'Rourke, Dino Pashias, Chris Simpson, Martin Latham, Jason Dale, Keith Williams, Mark Gower, Simon O'Shea, Fran Brien (Manager). Front: Omed Ghandali, Neil Hide, Steve Surridge, Bobby Cook, Mark Ivers. Photo - V J Robertson.

FLACKWELL HEATH

Chairman: Tony Cheshire **President:** Ken Crook **Vice C'man:**
Secretary: Cyril Robinson, 5 Chapman Lane, Flackwell Heath, High Wycombe, Bucks HP10 9AZ (0628 526204).
Manager: Dave Crook **Asst Mgr:** **Coach:**
Press Off.: TBA **General Manager:** **Physio:**
Ground: Wilks Park, Heath End Rd, Flackwell Heath, High Wycombe, Bucks HP10 9EA (0628 523892).
Directions: M40 jct 3, follow signs to Flackwell Heath, ground at rear of Magpie (PH), Heath End.
Capacity: 3,000 **Seats:** 150 **Cover:** 200 **Floodlights:** Yes **Founded:** 1907
Colours: Red/white/red **Change colours:** Yellow & black.
Club Shop: No **Metal Badges:** No
Programme: 12 pages,30p **Editor:** TBA **Club Sponsors:**
Midweek Matches: Tuesday.
Previous Leagues: Wycombe & District/ Gt Western Comb./ Hellenic 76-82/ Athenian 82-84.
Previous Names: None **Previous Ground:**
Reserve Team's League: **Nickname:**
Best FA Cup year:
Record Gate: 4,500 v Oxford United, charity match 1986.
Record Fees - Paid: **Received:**
Players progressing to Football League:
Clubhouse: Every night 6.30-11pm, before and after matches, and Sunday lunchtimes. Hot & cold snacks.
Club Record Goalscorer: **Club Record Apps:**
91-92 Captain: **91-92 P.o.Y.:** Ben Richards. **91-92 Top Scorers:** Tony Wood.
Local Newspapers: **Local Radio:**
Hons: Gt Western Combination 57-58 62-63, Hellenic Lg Div 1 R-up 76-77, Berks & Bucks Snr Cup SF 85-86.

GOALKEEPERS:
Matt Timberlake (Youth)
DEFENDERS: Dave Crook (Local football), **Paul Bates** (Burnham), **Clive Sharp** (Local football), **Simon Walker** (Hungerford, Flackwell, Beaconsfield, Marlow, Wycombe), **Kenny Charles** (Marlow), **Dave Mitchell** (Local football)
MIDFIELD: Ben Richards (Local football), **Greg Dover** (Youth), **Richard Price** (Bracknell), **Tony Baker** (Local football), **Martin Flint** (Local football), **Neil Ludgate** (Local football)
FORWARDS: Steve Wallace (Boreham Wood, St Albans, Hendon, Chesham, Boreham Wood, St Albans, Boreham Wood, Watford), **Rob Swallow** (Youth), **Tony Wood** (Burnham), **Andy Pierre** (Burnham, Dunstable, Southall, Burnham, Ruislip Manor, Burnham, Ruislip, Kingsbury, Hillingdon, Ruislip Manor)

HERTFORD TOWN

Chairman: Bernard Molloy **President:** Jock Gillam **Vice Chairman:**
Secretary: Stephen Hedley, 28 Cherry Tree Green, Hertford SG14 2HP (0992 587011).
Manager: Paul Janaway **Asst Mgr:** Ernie Ford **Coach:**
Press Officer: Graham Wood **General Manager:** **Physio:** Ray Price
Ground: Hertingfordbury Park, West Street, Hertford (0992 5837011).
Directions: By train to Hertford North (from Moorgate) or Hertford East (from Liverpool Street; both stations 15 mins walk. Green Line bus to town centre then 10 mins walk. By road; off bypass heasing east, turn off at Trimoco garage.
Capacity: 6,500 **Seats:** 200 **Cover:** 1,500 **Floodlights:** Yes **Founded:** 1908
Colours: All navy blue **Change colours:** All red **Club Shop:** No.
Programme: 24 pages,20p **Editor:** Graham Wood **Metal Badges:** No
Midweek Matches: Tuesday. **Nickname:** Blues
Previous Leagues: Herts Co./ Spartan 21-47 48-59/ Delphian 59-63/ Athenian 63-72/ Eastern Co's 72-73.
Previous Names: None **Previous Ground:**
Reserve Team's League: Essex & Herts Border Comb.
Best FA Cup year: Never past Qualifying Rounds.
Record Gate: 5,000 v Kingstonian, FA Amtr Cup 2nd Rd 55-56.
Record Fees - Paid: **Received:**
Players progressing to Football League: G Mazzon (Aldershot)
Clubhouse: Every night and weekend lunctimes. Members bar, function hall. Steward - Barry Smith.
Club Record Goalscorer: **Club Record Apps:**
91-92 Captain: **91-92 P.o.Y.:** **91-92 Top Scorer:** David Whitehead 27.
Local Newspapers: Hertfordshire Mercury **Local Radio:**
Hons: Herts Charity Cup 72-73, Herts Snr Cup 66-67, Hertford Charity Shield 19-20 20-21 35-36 49-50 55-56 59-60, Eastern Co's Lg Cup 72-73, East Anglian Cup 62-63 69-70, Mithras Cup SF 85-86.

GOALKEEPERS:
Terry Henderson (Local football)
DEFENDERS: Paul McCluskey (Edgware, St Albans, Yeading), **Kevin Allen** (Local football), **John Walsh** (Wembley, Edgware), **John Downey** (Local football), **Henry Rios** (St Albans), **Steve Franklin** (Saffron Walden), **Alex Paget** (Local football), **Neil Hayes** (Local football)
MIDFIELD: Fergal O'Hagan (Finchley, Wembley, Ruislip Manor, Wembley), **Graham Golds** (Sandridge R, St Albans), **John Meakes** (Welwyn GC), **Gary Barnett** (Saffron Walden, Witham, Saffron Walden, St Margaretsbury, Kingsbury, Stansted, Brimsdown R, Hoddesdon, Hertford), **Stuart Palfrey** (Boreham Wood, Hertford, Wembley), **Sean Glynn** (Local football)
FORWARDS: Durk Reyner (Welwyn GC, London Colney, B Stortford, Mowlems), **Dave Whitehead** (Colney Heath), **Marvin Bates** (Stevenage B, St Albans), **Micky Johns** (Ware, Wormley R), **Don Campionello** (St Albans), **Lee Allsop** (Local football)

Flackwell Heath. Back Row (L/R): Gary Anderson (Coach), Tony Wood, Dave Crook (Manager), Ken Crook (President), Robert Swallow, Matt Timberlake, Richard Price, Andy Pierre, Bill Smith (Physio), Cyril Robinson (Secretary), Malc Hazel (Committee). Front: Dave Mitchell, Simon Walker, Kenny Charles, Clive Sharp, Ben Richards, Greg Dover, Steve Wallace, Neil Ludgate, Bill Tapping (Committee). Photo - V J Robertson.

Hertford Town's Marvin Bates runs at the Kingsbury Town defence. Photo - V J Robertson.

Hertford Town. Back Row (L/R): Ray Price (Physio), Henry Pacquette, Paul Janaway (Manager), Darren Croucher, John Meakes, Brian Peggs, Sean Glynn. Front: John Downey, Ian Hart, Durk Reyner, Paul McCluskey, David Whitehead, Marvin Bates, Henry Rios. Mascot: Jamie Lancaster. Photo - V J Robertson.

HORNCHURCH

Chairman: James Bradshaw   **President:**
Secretary: Edward Harris, 13 Claremont Gdns, Upminster, Essex RM14 1DW (0402 227891).
Manager: K Newman   **Assistant Manager:**   **Coach:**
Press Officer: Robert Monger (0702 460539)   **Comm. Mgr:**
Ground: The Stadium, Bridge Avenue, Upminster, Essex RM14 2LX (0402 220080).
Directions: Fenchurch Street to Upminster (BR) then 10 mins walk. Or tube to Upminster Bridge (LT), turn right outside station, second right into Bridge Avenue and ground 150yds on right. Bus 248 Romford-Upminster. Also buses 246 & 370.
Capacity: 3,500   **Seats:** 500   **Cover:** 750   **Floodlights:** Yes   **Founded:** 1923
Colours: White (red trim)/white/white   **Change colours:** All blue
Club Shop: Yes (Manager Ron Quantock)   **Metal Badges:** No
Programme: 12 pages, 30p   **Editor:** Brian Davie
Midweek Matchday: Tuesday
Previous Leagues: Romford/ Spartan 38-39 46-50/ Delphian 52-59/ Athenian 59-75.
Previous Names: Upminster/ H'church & Upminster   **Previous Grounds:** Upminster.
Reserve Team's League: **Nickname:** Urchins.
Record Gate: 3,000 v Chelmsford City, FA Cup.
Best FA Cup year:
Record Fees - Paid: **Received:**
Clubhouse: Open every evening and weekend lunchtimes. Hot & cold snacks. **Steward:** Mrs Sheila Davie.
Players progressing to Football League: D Armstrong (Millwall), R Lee (Charlton), Nicky Bissett (Brighton).
Club Record Goalscorer: **Club Record Apps:**
91-92 Captain: **91-92 P.o.Y.:** Andy Tickner   **91-92 Top scorer:** Brian Weekes.
Local Press: Romford Recorder (0708 766044)   **Local Radio:** Beds Radio.
Hons: Romford Lg(2), Essex Jnr Cup, Thamesside Tphy, Isthmian Yth Cup.

GOALKEEPERS:
Steve Ridgley ((Local football))
DEFENDERS: Geoff Davis (Tilbury), **Kevin Cooper** (Barking, Met Police, Barking, Dagenham, Coventry), **Colin Moriarty** (Local football), **Brian Weekes** (Collier Row, Dagenham), **Chris Bulgea** (Local football), **Mick Lowe** (Aveley)
MIDFIELD: Andy Tickner (Hertford), **Lee O'Connor** (Dagenham, East Ham, Grays), **Steve Farrugia** (Aveley), **Darren Hudson** (Tilbury), **Lee Murcott** (Walthamstow Pennant, Maidstone, Barking), **Danny Wickes** (Local football)
FORWARDS: John Berry (Basildon, Leyt & Ilf), **Dave Allen** (Basildon), **Tony Flynn** (Barking, Basildon, East Thurrock, B Stortford, Dagenham, Chelmsford, Aveley, Clapton), **Mark Sexton** (Local football)

HORSHAM

Chairman: Mick Browning   **President:** G G Hotorn
Secretary: Frank King, 51 Laughton Rd, Horsham, West Sussex RH21 4EJ (0403 64647).
Manager: P Evans   **Assistant Manager:**   **Coach:** Rod Tapp
Press Officer: **Comm. Mgr:**
Ground: Queen Street, Horsham RH13 5AD (0403 65787).
Directions: From Horsham (BR) along North Street past Arts Centre, fork left, left at lights, ground opposite Queens Head (PH).
Capacity: 3,000   **Seats:** 300   **Cover:** 3 sides   **Floodlights:** Yes   **Founded:** 1885
Colours: Lincoln green & amber stripes/green/amber   **Change colours:** All white.
Club Shop: **Metal Badges:**   **Nickname:** Hornets
Programme: 20 pages, 30p   **Editor:** Mrs Maureen Smith.
Midweek Matchday: Wednesday   **Previous Leagues:** W Sussex/ Sussex County 26-51/ Metropolitan 51-57/ Corinthian 57-63/ Athenian 63-73.
Previous Names: **Reserve Team's League:** Suburban
Record Gate: 8,000 v Swindon Town, FA Cup, November 1966.
Best FA Cup year: 1st Rd 47-48 (lost 1-9 at Notts County), 66-67 (lost 0-3 v Swindon).
Record Fees - Paid: **Received:**
Clubhouse: Normal licensing hours. Hot and cold snacks, dancehall, darts.
Players progressing to Football League:
Club Record Goalscorer: **Club Record Apps:**
91-92 Captain: **91-92 P.o.Y.:** David Clark   **91-92 Top scorer:** Mark Dunk 24.
Local Press: West Sussex County Times: Market Square, Horsham (0403 53371).
Local Radio: Beds Radio.
Hons: Sussex Snr Cup 33-34 38-39 49-50 53-54 71-72 73-74 75-76, Sussex RUR Charity Cup 1899-1900 30-31 31-32 33-34(jt with Worthing) 34-35 35-36 36-37 37-38(jt with Southwick) 45-46 48-49(jt with Worthing) 50-51 51-52 56-57, Sussex County Lg 31-32 32-33 34-35 35-36 36-37 37-38 46-47 (R-up 29-30 30-31 47-48 48-49, Lg Cup 45-46 46-47), Metropolitan Lg 51-52, Athenian Lg Div 2 72-73.

GOALKEEPERS:
Duncan Green (Steyning, Lancing, Worthing), **Gary Pike** (Local football)
DEFENDERS: Mark Stepney (Horsham YMCA, Brighton(J)), **David Clark** (Bognor, Wick), **Wayne Wren** (Worthing), **Terry Botting** (Leatherhead), **Mark Chaplin** (Storrington), **Steve Breach** (Three Bridges, Crawley, Dover, Margate, Brighton, Arsenal), **Andy Heryet** (Worthing, Steyning, Southwick)
MIDFIELD: Phil Somers (Worthing, Whitehawk, Worthing, Whitehawk), **Russell Gunn** (Whitehawk), **Mark Dunk** (Worthing, Southwick, Whitehawk, Southwick, Whitehawk), **Marcus Cooke** (Three Bridges, Horsham, Eastbourne Utd, Horsham, Crawley, Horsham), **Darren Hinton** (Whyteleafe, Bognor, Brighton, Chelsea(T))
FORWARDS: Paul Crimmen (Local football, Horsham, Oakwood, Southwick, Horsham, Oakwood, MEL), **Moray Forrest** (Youth), **John Bailey** (Littlehampton, Lancing), **Duane Reed** (Youth), **John Walters** (Southwick)

KINGSBURY TOWN

Chairman: Euric Patel   **President:**
Secretary: Peter Green, 57 Wembley Park Drive, Wembley, Middx HA9 8HE (081 902 1561).
Manager: Frank O'Brien   **Assistant Manager:** Peter Blain   **Coach:** F O'Brien
Press Officer/Commercial Mgr: Alan Davies (0895 443761)   **Physio:**
Ground: Silver Jubilee Park, Townsend Lane, Kingsbury, London NW9 0DE (081 205 1645-club, 5204-boardroom).
Directions: Underground to Kingsbury, cross road and take bus 183 to Townsend Lane.
Capacity: 4,000   **Seats:** 200   **Cover:** 300   **Floodlights:** Yes   **Founded:** 1927
Colours: Blue/white/blue   **Change colours:** Yellow/navy/yellow.
Club Shop: No   **Metal Badges:** No
Programme: 28 pages, 50p   **Editor:** Alan Davies.
Midweek Matchday: Tuesday
Previous Leagues: Willesden & District 30-43/ Middx Snr 44-47/ Parthenon 47-59/ Spartan 59-76 78-81/ Athenian 76-78 81-84.
Previous Name: Davis Sports   **Previous Grounds:** None.
Reserve Team's League: Suburban   **Sponsors:** VPA Entertainment Technology.
Record Gate: 1,112 v Spurs, 1981.   **Nickname:**
Best FA Cup year:
Record Fees - Paid: £500   **Received:** £600.
Clubhouse: (081 205 1645). Mon-Fri 7-11pm, Sat 12-2.30pm. Pool, darts, dancehall, food on matchdays.
Players progressing to Football League: Billy Dare, John Meadows, Dave Underwood, Dwight Marshall (Plymouth).
Club Record Goalscorer: **Club Record Apps:**
91-92 Captain: Bobby Cook   **91-92 P.o.Y.:** Neil Hide   **91-92 Top scorer:** Mark Ivers 15
Local Press: Harrow Observer, Hendon Times, Willesden Chronicle, Allsport Weekly, Edgware & Finchley Times.
Local Radio:
Hons: FA Vase 4th Rd 74-75, Isthmian Lg Div 2 Nth R-up 85-86, Spartan Lg Cup R-up 59-60 64-65, Parthenon Lg 51-52 (Prem Charity Cup 52-53 53-54), Snr Charity Cup 53-54), Middx Lg Charity Cup(3) 44-47, Willesden & Dist. Lg R-up 30-31 (Div 2 34-35).

GOALKEEPERS:
John Cheesewright (Southend), **Mark Gower** (Local football)
DEFENDERS: Chris Simpson (Chalfont, Kingsbury, Hendon), **Bobby Cook** (Local football), **Ray Mangan** (Edgware), **Keith Williams** (Malden Vale, Banstead, Dorking, Leatherhead, Banstead, Sutton Utd), **Damian Donald** (Local football)
MIDFIELD: Mark Ivers (Hendon), **Dino Pashias** (Local football), **Neil Hide** (Tring, Leighton), **Steve Surridge** (Hendon, Old Aloysians), **Vic Hardwicke** (Hendon)
FORWARDS: Gerry Mulhern (Hendon), **Niall O'Rourke** (Local football), **Martin Latham** (Local football), **Jason Dale** (yeading), **Ricky Ghandali** (Local football)

LEIGHTON TOWN

Chairman: Bruce Warner   **Vice Chairman:** G Cook   **President:** M Hide
Secretary: Mr R McClelland, 193 Grasmere Way, Leighton Buzzard, Beds LU7 7QB (0462 670471).
Manager: William Harrison   **Assistant Manager:**   **Coach:** P Mead
Press Officer: **Physio:** G Lathwell/ S Lathwell.
Commercial Manager:
Ground: Bell Close, Lake Street, Leighton Buzzard, Beds (0525 373311).
Directions: Off A5 at Stanbridge for Leighton Buzzard. Ground behind Camden Motors just before town centre. Half mile from Leighton Buzzard (BR). Buses 70 and 71 from Luton.
Capacity: 2,000   **Seats:** Yes   **Cover:** Yes   **Floodlights:** Yes   **Founded:** 1885
Colours: All red   **Change colours:** All blue   **Club Shop:**
Programme: 24 pages   **Editor:** Paul Smith (0525 852461).   **Metal Badges:**
Midweek Matchday:
Previous Leagues: Leighton & District/ South Midlands 22-24 26-29 46-54 55-56 76-92/ Spartan 22-53 67-74/ United Counties 74-76.
Previous Name: Leighton United   **Previous Grounds:**
Reserve Team's League: Campri Sth Mids Reserve Division.   **Sponsors:**
Record Gate: 1,614 v MK Borough, South Mids Lg 28/4/92   **Nickname:**
Best FA Cup year: Never past Qualifying Rounds.
Record Fees - Paid: **Received:**
Clubhouse: Open Mon-Fri 7-11pm, hot food on matchdays.
Players progressing to Football League:
Club Record Goalscorer: **Club Record Apps:**
91-92 Captain: **91-92 P.o.Y.:**   **91-92 Top scorer:**
Local Press: **Local Radio:**
Hons: Sth Midlands Lg 66-67 91-92 (Lg Cup 90-91, O'Brien Tphy 90-91, Reserve Div 1 87-88 (Div 2 76-77)), Beds Snr Cup 26-27 66-67 67-68 68-69, Spartan Lg Div 2 23-24 27-28, Leighton & District Lg, Beds Intermediate Cup 90-91.

GOALKEEPERS:
Mark Townson (Stanbridge, Linslade R)
DEFENDERS: Shaun Cavanagh (Youth), **Paul Firth** (Wolverton, Leighton), **Neil Edwards** (Thame), **Mark Southon** (Pitstone, Tring, Man City(A)), **Enzo Miceli** (Youth), **Jim McCarthy** (Shillington, Dunstable, Amersham, Wycombe, Chesham, Hitchin, Hemel Hempstead)
MIDFIELD: Steve Kirkby (Kingsbury, Finchley, Hendon, Haringey B), **Sean Downey** (Wolverton, Leighton, Vauxhall M, British Univ), **Gary Wray** (Local football), **Martin Brown** (Pitstone), **Rob Larkin** (Thame)
FORWARDS: Steve Norman (Youth), **Shaun Bryant** (Berkhamsted, Hemel Hempstead, St Albans, Hemel Hempstead, Dunstable, Watford(J), Leyton Oreint(J)), **Gary Sealey** (Local football), **Tony McGuiness** (Buckingham, Chesham, Aylesbury), **Keith Walker** (Aylesbury, Leighton, Aylesbury)

NORTHWOOD

Chairman: A Johnson   **President:** H P G Pamenter
Secretary: Steve Williams, 35 Evelyn Drive, Hatch End, Pinner, Middx (081 428 1533 - home + fax).
Manager: Alan Merison   **Asst Mgr:** Marcel Pinto   **Coach:** John Toogood.
Press Officer: M Russell (0923 827690)   **Commercial Manager:** A Evans (081 566 2880)
Ground: Chestnut Avenue, Northwood (0923 827148).
Directions: A404 (Pinner-Rickmansworth) - Chestnut Avenue is on left by large grey iron railway bridge and Shell petrol station. Third of a mile from Northwood Hills station (Metropolitan Line). Buses 282 and H11 to Northwood Hills.
Capacity: 1,750   **Seats:** 120   **Cover:** 200   **Floodlights:** Yes   **Founded:** 1907.
Colours: All red   **Change colours:** All blue.   **Midweek Matches:** Tuesday
Programme: 24 pages, 50p   **Editor:** Alan Evans   **Metal Badges:** No
Reserve Team's League: Suburban   **Sponsors:** IFS Freight Services Ltd.   **Club Shop:** No
Previous Leagues: Harrow & Wembley/ Middx/ Hellenic 78-84.
Previous Names: Northwood Town   **Previous Grounds:** None.
Record Gate: 794 v Chelsea 28/12/91, Middx Snr Charity Cup.
Best FA Cup year: Preliminary Round 89-90 90-91 91-92   **Best FA Vase year:** 4th Rd 91-92.
Record Fees - Paid: None   **Received:** None
Clubhouse: Evenings and matchdays, hot and cold food. Pool, darts, juke-box.
Players progressing to Football League: Gavin McGuire (Portsmouth).
Club Record Scorer: Garfield Blackman 89   **Club Record Appearances:** Peter Lammin
91-92 Captain: Robert Holland **91-92 P.o.Y.:** Ken Lawrence   **91-92 Top scorer:** Garfield Blackman
Local Newspapers: Ruislip & Northwood Gazette, Allsport Weekly   **Local Radio:** None.
Hons: London Spartan Lg 91-92 (R-up 89-90, Lg Cup 89-90 91-92), Hellenic Lg Div 1 78-79 (Prem Div Cup 81-82, Div 1 78-79), Middx Lg 77-78 (R-up 72-73 76-77, Div 1 R-up 71-72, Challenge Cup 74-75 76-77 77-78).

GOALKEEPERS:
Ken Lavender (Kingsbury, Ruislip, Woking, Harrow B, Chesham, Harefield, QPR, Southall, Wealdstone), **Ricky Murphy** (Hounslow), **Matthew Ward** (Local football)
DEFENDERS: Scott Singleton (Harrow B, Leatherhead), **Paul Curran** (Finchley, Hendon, Kingsbury), **Peter Augustine** (Edgware, Kingsbury, Burnham, Ruislip, Chesham, Hounslow, Wycombe), **Ronnie John** (Wembley), **Rob Holland** (Chalfont, Harrow B, Wokingham, Staines, Hounslow, Ruislip M, Dulwich, Southall, Crewe, Wimbledon, Slough, Hendon, Harrow B), **Peter Lammin** (Amersham), **Steve Gee** (Heinz), **Karl Griggs** (Rayners Lane)
MIDFIELD: Dave Nolan (Local football), **Paul Rogan** (Cheshunt, Boreham Wood, Enfield, QPR(J), Spurs(J)), **Jeremy Billins** (Local football), **Tim Vincent** (Chalfont, Uxbridge, Chalfont, Ruislip M, Uxbridge, Maidenhead Utd, Harrow B, Southall, Ruislip M), **Greg Phillips** (Wembley), **Andy Edey** (Local football), **Steve Baynes** (Windsor, Maidenhead Utd), **Martin Randall** (Local football)
FORWARDS: Warren Patmore (Harefield), **Garfield Blackman** (Local football), **Mick Devane** (Wembley, Chalfont, Ruislip M, Chalfont, Ruislip M, Wembley), **John McCormack** (Ruislip M, Southall), **Rod Findlay** (Burnham, Wealdstone, Burnham, Chesham, Burnham, Dunstable, Ruislip, Hillingdon, Harrow B, Leyton Orient(J), Watford(J))

PETERSFIELD UNITED

Chairman: Dave Burnett   **President:**
Secretary: John Stimpson, 'Moraira', Love Lane, Petersfield, Hants GU31 4BW (0730 60715).
Manager: Chris Eade   **Asst Mgr:**   **Coach:**
Press Officer: Secretary   **Commercial Manager:** Simon Hawkins   **Physio:** Kevin Evans
Ground: Love Lane, Petersfield, Hants (0730 662177).
Directions: 10 mins walk from Petersfield station heading towards London. On A3 circulatory system.
Capacity: 4,000   **Seats:** 135   **Cover:** 385   **Floodlights:** Yes   **Founded:** 1889.
Colours: Red & black/white/red   **Change colours:** Blue/white/red or black
Midweek Matches: Tuesday
Club Shop: No   **Metal Badges:** No
Programme: 20 pages, 30p   **Programme Editor:** Mark Nicoll
Reserve Team's League: Jewson Wessex Comb.   **Sponsors:**
Previous Leagues: Portsmouth/ Hants.   **Nickname:** 'United' or 'Reds'.
Previous Names: None   **Previous Grounds:** Love Lane 1889-1910/ Princes Rd 11-48.
Record Gate: 1,300 v Portsmouth, Friendly 1985.
Best FA Cup year: Never past Qualifying Rounds
Record Fees - Paid: **Received:**
Clubhouse: Hot food on matchdays. Pool & darts. Clubroom open daily except Sunday evenings.
Players progressing to Football League: Darren Collins (Northampton).
Club Record Scorer: **Club Record Appearances:**
91-92 Captain: **91-92 P.o.Y.:**   **91-92 Top scorer:** Philip Vaughan 9.
Local Newspapers: East Hants Post, The News (Portsmouth)
Local Radio: Radio 210.
Hons: Hants Lg Div 2 81-82 (Div 77-78), Aldershot Snr Cup Cup 81-82 82-83, Portsmouth Snr Cup 77-78.

Northwood FC. Back Row (L/R): George Price (Physio), Derek Carpenter (Res. Coach), Scott Singleton, Greg Phillips, John McCormack, Rod Findlay, Ken Lavender, John Toogood (Coach), Alan Merison (Manager), Rick Murphy, Peter Lammin, Robert Holland, Paul Curran, Steve Baynes, Vic Harris (Res. Mgr), Marcel Pinto (Coach). Centre: Garfield Blackman, Tim Vincent, Jim Bardsley (Committee), Geoff Foster (Vice C'man), Andy Johnson (Chairman), Steve Williams (Football Secretary), Mick Russell (Committee), Jeremy Billins, Michael Devane. Front: Andy Edey, Peter Augustine, David Nolan, Paul Rogan.

Northwood's record scorer, Garfield Blackman, in Spartan League action at Eltham last season. Photo - Mike Floate.

Petersfield United. Back Row (L/R): S Barton, T Chinyou, G Wood, K Brown, N Yates, P Vaughan, D Head. Front: P Tindal (Capt), A North, S Parvin, R Thorn (now Bass Alton), G Ashton, S North. Photo - Eric Marsh.

ROYSTON TOWN

Chairman: Bill Cosgrove   **President:** F Bradley
Secretary: Trevor Glasscock, 14 Goodwood Rd, Royston, Herts SG8 9TF (0763 244580).
Manager: John Halliwell   **Assistant Manager:** John Smith   **Coach:**
Press Officer: Secretary   **Physio:** Brian O'Flanaghan
Commercial Manager: Fred Bradley.
Ground: Garden Walk, Royston, Herts SG8 7HP (0763 241204).
Directions: From Baldock, A605 to Royston Town Hall then A10 towards Cambridge. Second turn on left is Garden Walk; ground 100 yds on left. Ten mins walk from Royston (BR).
Capacity: 4,000 **Seats:** 300   **Cover:** 300   **Floodlights:** Yes   **Founded:** 1875
Colours: White/black   **Change colours:** Red/black.
Club Shop: No   **Metal Badges:** Yes   **Nickname:** Crows.
Programme: 16 pages, 30p   **Editor:** Bernard Brown (0763 243969).
Midweek Matchday: Wednesday   **Sponsors:**
Previous Leagues: Buntingford & Dist. 18-28/ Cambs 28-50s/ Herts Co. 50s-59 62-77/ Sth Mids 59-62 77-84.
Previous Names: None   **Previous Grounds:** Newmarket Rd, Baldock Rd, Mackeral Hall.
Reserve Team's League: Essex & Herts Border Comb.   **Record Gate:** 800 v Cambridge U., Oct '80.
Best FA Cup year: Second Qualifying Round 59-60 (lost 0-9 at Barnet), 89-90 (lost 0-3 at Bromley).
Clubhouse: Mon-Fri 7-11pm, lunchtimes Fri, Sat, Sun (11.30-2.30), matchdays 4-11pm. Large hall. Darts, pool, discos and live bands. **Steward:** Mr & Mrs Nesbitt.
Players progressing to Football League: John Smith (Spurs).
Club Record Scorer: Trevor Glasscock 289 (1968-82)   **Club Record Appearances:** Fred Bradley 713.
91-92 Captain: Denny Tyler   **91-92 P.O.Y.:** Ian Rogers, Nigel Plummer
91-92 Top scorer: Duncan Easley **Local Radio:** Radio Cambridgeshire, Radio Bedfordshire, Chiltern Radio.
Local Press: Royston Crow (0763 245142), Cambridge Evening News (0223 358877).
Hons: Herts Co. Lg 76-77 (Div 1 69-70 76-77), Sth Mids Lg 77-78 (R-up 79-80, Res Div 1 79-80 (Div 2 78-79), Res Section Tphy 82-83), Herts Charity Shield 81-82 89-90 (R-up 79-79 88-89), Creake Shield 20-21, Cambs Lg Div 2 29-30, Herts Intermediate Cup 88-89 (R-up 89-90).

GOALKEEPERS:
Simon Dobson (Youth), **Mick Adamson** (Stevenage B, Harlow, Hitchin, Watford(A))
DEFENDERS: Stuart Brown (Youth), **Derwyn Hardwick** (B Stortford), **David Cooper** (Saffron Walden, Stevenage B, Royston, Arsenal(J)), **John Moulding** (Youth), **Ian Rogers** (Youth), **Danny Silver** (Youth)
MIDFIELD: Paddy Butcher (Ware, Brentwood, Stevenage B, Ware, Letchworth GC), **Nigel Plummer** (Potton Utd, Baldock, Langford, Royston, Stevenage B), **Matt McQueen** (Potton Utd, Stotfold, Royston, Stevenage B, Letchworth GC, Royston, Hitchin), **Grant McRae** (Potton Utd, Stotfold, Royston, Stevenage B, Letchworth GC, Royston, Hitchin), **Ricky Marshall** (Local football), **Doug Bailey** (Histon, Saffron Walden, B Stortford)
FORWARDS: Kevin Lowe (Letchworth GC, Stevenage B, Pirton, Knebworth), **Duncan Easley** (Youth), **Lee Jacobs** (Letchworth GC, Royston, Stevenage B, Hitchin), **Paul Palma** (Vauxhall Motors, Arlesey, Stevenage B, Royston, Letchworth GC, Royston, Letchworth GC, St Albans), **Geoff Mills** (Local football), **Alan Saunders** (Local football)

THAME UNITED

Chairman: Mr O J Tite   **President:** Mr M Dowling.
Vice Chairman: Mr Paul Smith.
Secretary: Dave Blake, 4 Sun Crescent, Oakley, Aylesbury, Bucks HP18 9RF (0844 237573).
Manager: Bob Pratley   **Asst Manager:** Malcolm McIntosh   **Coach:**
Commercial Mgr: TBA   **Press Officer:** Paul Smith (0844 213482) **Physio:** TBA.
Ground: Windmill Road, Thame, Oxon OX9 2DR (0844 213017).
Directions: Into Nelson Street from Market Square. Two and a half miles from Haddenham & Thame Parkway (BR).
Capacity: 2,000 **Seats:** 250   **Cover:** 350   **Floodlights:** Yes   **Founded:** 1883
Colours: Red & black   **Change colours:** All white.
Club Shop: **Metal Badges:**
Programme: 24 pages   **Editor:** Paul Smith
Midweek Matchday: Tuesday   **Sponsors:** Dayla Soft Drinks.
Previous Leagues: Oxon Snr/ Hellenic 59-86/ Sth Midlands 86-91.
Previous Grounds: None   **Previous Name:** Thame FC
Record Gate: 2,000.   **Newsline:** 0898 122907   **Nickname:** U's.
Best FA Cup year: Third Qualifying Round 91-92 (lost 0-4 to Salisbury).
Record Fees - Paid: **Received:**
Clubhouse: Open every evening, normal licensing hours. Banquetting facilities for 200.
Players progressing to Football League:
Club Record Scorer: **Club Record Appearances:**
91-92 Captain: Julian Dark   **91-92 P.O.Y.:** Matt Hayward   **91-92 Top scorer:** Paul Rayson.
Local Press: Oxford Mail, Thame Gazette, Bucks Free Press.
Local Radio: BBC Radio Oxford, Fox FM.
Hons: Hellenic Lg 61-62 69-70, Sth Mids 90-91, Oxon Snr Cup 1894-95 05-06 08-09 09-10 75-76 80-81, Oxon I'mediate Cup(3), Oxon Charity Cup.

GOALKEEPERS:
Steve Mayhew (Abingdon Utd)
DEFENDERS: Julian Dark (Banbury, Abingdon T, Oxford C), **Richard Gregory** (Local football), **Darren Stone** (Flackwell Heath, Marlow, Flackwell Heath), **Mick Faulkner** (Local football), **Matt Hayward** (Pitstone)
MIDFIELD: Paul Lewis (Witney, Headington Am, Witney, Banbury, Aylesbury), **Andy Thomas** (Abingdon Utd), **Dave Watson** (Witney, Buckingham, Witney, Bicester, Oxford Utd(J)), **Darren Lord** (Flackwell Heath), **Gary Wanless** (Local football), **Mark O'Hara** (Banbury, Witney, Kidlington, Banbury, Oxford Utd), **Tony Cobb** (Marlow, Buckingham, Thame, Aylesbury, Winslow Utd, Aylesbury)
FORWARDS: Paul Rayson (Banbury, Brackley, Witney), **Dave Winwood** (Local football), **Julio Baressi** (Witney), **Kelly Lonergan** (Buckingham, Aylesbury), **Dennis Gascoyne** (Local football)

Royston Town. Back Row (L/R): Frank Cornwell (Manager, no longer with club), Brian O'Flanagan, Paddy Butcher, Duncan Easley, Mick Adamson, John Moulding, Kevin Lowe, Trevor Glasscock (Secretary). Front: Ronnie Lawson (no longer with club), Derwyn Hardwick, Matt McQueen, Nigel Plummer, Graham Cox (no longer with club), Denny Tyler (Captain), Ian Rogers. Photo - Eric Marsh.

Thame United. Back Row (L/R): Malcom McIntosh (Asst Mgr), Mark Gee, Brett Chowns, Michael Faulkner, Joel Arnett, Neil Edwards, David Bird, Steve Mayhew, Gary Wanless, Matt Howard, Dean Hill, Kerry Lonergan, Bob Pratley (Manager). Front: Andy Thomas, Paul Rayson, Dennis Gascoyne, Ronnie Russell, Dave Winwood, Dave Watson, Daren Stone, Richard Gregory. Photo - Steve Daniels.

Geoff Chapple of Woking receives one of his three Premier Division 'Manager of the Month' awards. A full list of all the awards appears on page 386. Photo - Eric Marsh.

TRING TOWN

Chairman: **Chief Executive:** Roger Payne   **President:** G Smith
Secretary: David Bradding, 71 Mortimer Hill, Tring, Herts HP23 5JA (0442 824118).
Manager: John Wortley   **Asst Mgr:**
Physio: **Coach:**
Commercial Manager: **Press Officer:** Alan Lee
Ground: Pendley Sports Centre, Cow Lane, Tring, Herts HP23 5NS (0442 23075).
Directions: One mile from Tring centre on A41. One and a half miles from Tring (BR).
Capacity: 2,000   **Seats:** 200   **Cover:** 230   **Floodlights:** Yes   **Founded:** 1904
Colours: All red   **Change colours:** All blue.
Club Shop: No   **Metal Badges:** No
Programme: 40p   **Editor:** Alan Lee.
Midweek Matchday: Wednesday   **Sponsors:**
Previous Leagues: Gt Western Combination/ Spartan 53-75/ Athenian 75-77.
Previous Names: None   **Previous Ground:** The Cricket Ground.
Reserve Team's League:
Record Gate: 2,000; Aylesbury United v Slough Town, FA Cup 1986.
Best FA Cup year: Never past Qualifying Rounds   **Nickname:**
Record Fees - Paid: **Rec'd:**
Clubhouse: Dancehall, pool, darts, kitchen.   **Steward:** R Nash.
Players progressing to Football League: Peter Gibbs (Watford).
Club Record Scorer: **Club Record Appearances:**
91-92 Captain: **91-92 P.o.Y.:** None   **91-92 Top scorer:** Mark Dewick.
Local Press: Bucks Herald, Tring Gazette, Watford Observer.
Local Radio: Chiltern, BBC Radio Bedford.
Hons: Spartan Lg 66-67, Herts Charity Shield (Numerous times).

GOALKEEPERS:
Andy Macardy
DEFENDERS: Mick Freeman, Steve Bell, Colin Howe, Martin Mills, Kevin Archer, Glen Bunce, Steve Last:
MIDFIELD: Simon Green, Chris Sheedy, Carl Fraser, Jamie Osborne
FORWARDS: Brendan Low, Steve Horsfall, Mark Dewick, Dave Percy:

WILLIAM HILL MANAGER OF THE MONTH AWARDS

SEPTEMBER	PREMIER DIVISION	GEOFF CHAPPLE	WOKING
	DIVISION ONE	KEITH HULL	HEYBRIDGE
	DIVISION TWO	STUART TODD	WARE
	DIVISION THREE	PETER EVANS	HORSHAM
OCTOBER	PREMIER DIVISION	GEORGE WAKELING	BROMLEY
	DIVISION ONE	JIM CANNON	DULWICH
	DIVISION TWO	BOBBY KNOCK	BANSTEAD
	DIVISION THREE	BRIAN RIDER	EDGWARE
NOVEMBER	PREMIER DIVISION	GEOFF CHAPPLE	WOKING
	DIVISION ONE	TREVOR FORD	TOOTING
	DIVISION TWO	MICKY BYRNE	LEATHERHEAD
	DIVISION THREE	JIM KELMAN	CHERTSEY
DECEMBER	PREMIER DIVISION	JOHN MITCHELL	ST ALBANS
	DIVISION ONE	DEREK PARSONS	WALTON & HERSHAM
	DIVISION TWO	DAVID EVANS	HEMEL HEMPSTEAD
	DIVISION THREE	CHICK BOTLEY	COVE
JANUARY	PREMIER DIVISION	EDDIE McCLUSKEY	ENFIELD
	DIVISION ONE	GORDON BARTLETT	YEADING
	DIVISION TWO	GARY CALDER	PURFLEET
	DIVISION THREE	MARK FEWINGS	HAMPTON
FEBRUARY	PREMIER DIVISION	ROY MERRYWEATHER	WOKINGHAM
	DIVISION ONE	PAUL FAIRCLOUGH	STEVENAGE
	DIVISION TWO	WILF TRANTER	HUNGERFORD
	DIVISION THREE	JIM KELMAN	CHERTSEY
MARCH	PREMIER DIVISION	GEOFF CHAPPLE	WOKING
	DIVISION ONE	TREVOR BUTLER	ABINGDON TOWN
	DIVISION TWO	JOHN KENDALL	BILLERICAY
	DIVISION THREE	NICKY PHILLIPS	TILBURY
APRIL	PREMIER DIVISION	GERALD APLIN	CHESHAM UNITED
	DIVISION ONE	JIM CANNON	DULWICH
	DIVISION TWO	JOHN KENDALL	BILLERICAY
	DIVISION THREE	MARK FEWINGS	HAMPTON
MANGER OF THE SEASON	PREMIER DIVISION	GEOFF CHAPPLE	WOKING
	DIVISION ONE	PAUL FAIRCLOUGH	STEVENAGE
	DIVISION TWO	GARY CALDER	PURFLEET
	DIVISION THREE	BRIAN RIDER	EDGWARE

SPARTAN FOOTBALL LEAGUE

President: K G Aston, JP/
Chairman: B Stallard, Esq.
Hon. Secretary: Dennis Cordell,
44 Greenleas, Waltham Abbey, Essex EN9 1SZ (0992 712428).

NORTHWOOD DESERVEDLY WIN FIRST TITLE

At the beginning of the season there were a number of clubs who over the past few years have had their eye on the top spot in the League in order to progress up the Pyramid to the Diadora (Isthmian) League. Of last season's top seven it was Northwood and Brimsdown Rovers who came through best.

Brimsdown were favourites at one time. They had a great start to their season with a good run in the FA Challenge Cup. Defeats were few and far between, and towards the end of the campaign they looked likely winners having games in hand. But as it turned out it was a case of too many drawn matches, and Northwood came through to win by six points.

Last year's champions and runners-up, Walthamstow Pennant and Barkingside, only managed fifth and sixth places this season, whilst Cheshunt (fourth last season) and Corinthian-Casuals (fifth last time) came eigth and ninth. Clubs who improved were Brook House (twelfth to fourth) and Croydon Athletic (fifteenth to tenth). Newcomers Cockfosters finished twelfth after a slow start.

In the League Cup, Corinthian Casuals met Northwood who were looking to complete the double and follow up their 1990 cup win. With only one goal separating them in each of the two League games, Casuals were hoping to turn the tables on Northwood. The match was keenly contested and resulted in Northwood winning by the odd goal, yet again.

In outside cup matches there were many successes by Spartan League clubs. Once again the League fielded both London Senior Cup finalists. Hanwell Town beat Croydon Athletic after extra-time, this after the initial match had ended in a draw after extra-time.

Not to be outdone by the seniors, Walthamstow Trojans beat holders Tower Hamlets in the London Intermediate Cup Final, and so the Spartan League provided both clubs in this Final for the second season running.

In Division One of the League, Willesden, Tower Hamlets and Elms changed places weekly at the top. Willesden were eventual winners by three points with goal difference separating the other two. The next three clubs all finished up with the same number of points and they too had to be separated by goal difference.

The near perfect football weather during the season, together with the fact that the majority of clubs in the Premier Division have lights, enabled the League programme to be completed on time. The general improvement in facilities at clubs is pleasing to note, as is the standard of programmes.

Northwood, after their miss last season, graduate to the Diadora (Isthmian) League. In Division One, Royal George have disbanded, and Pheonix Sports, after struggling for a few years, have together with Penhill Standard reverted to local football.

Basil Stallard, League Chairman.

Northwood with the Championship Shield and League Cup. Back Row (L/R): George Price (Physio), Derek Carpenter (Res. Coach), Scott Singleton, Peter Augustine, Greg Phillips, John McCormack, Ken Lavender, John Toogood (Coach), Rick Murphy, Peter Lammin, Jeremy Billins, Andy Edey, Steve Baynes, Vic Harris (Res. Mgr), Marcel Pinto (Coach). Front: Garfield Blackman, Paul Curran, Tim Vincent, Robert Holland, Alan Merison (Manager), Paul Rogan, David Nolan, Rod Findley, Michael Devane.

SPARTAN LEAGUE TABLES 1991-92

Premier Division	P	W	D	L	F	A	Pts
Northwood	36	26	4	6	97	38	82
Brimsdown R.	36	23	7	6	76	28	76
Haringey B.	36	21	8	7	74	57	71
Brook House	36	21	6	9	68	51	69
W'stow Pennant	36	20	8	8	92	35	68
Barkingside	36	19	8	9	56	41	65
Hanwell Town	36	18	7	11	41	47	61
Cheshunt	36	16	12	8	52	31	60
C-Casuals	36	17	3	16	75	44	54
Croydon Ath.	36	16	5	15	66	63	53
Waltham Abbey	36	14	8	14	49	52	50
Cockfosters	36	12	10	14	47	52	46
Hillingdon B.	36	13	6	17	52	65	45
Beaconsfield Utd	36	11	8	17	43	69	41
Southgate Ath.	36	11	5	20	41	61	38
Amersham Town	36	7	6	23	33	69	27
N. Greenford U.	36	5	10	21	36	81	25
Beckton Utd	36	4	8	24	33	100	20
Eltham Town	36	2	3	31	25	115	9

Division One	P	W	D	L	F	A	Pts
Willesden (H'eye)	26	21	3	2	75	28	63*
Tower H'lets (Tip.)	26	19	3	4	69	15	60
Elms	26	19	3	4	86	36	60
Craven	26	12	6	8	68	51	42
Metrogas	26	12	6	8	55	45	42
W'stow Trojans	26	11	9	6	55	48	42
Leyton County	26	12	4	10	52	44	40
Cray Valley	26	10	2	12	48	60	34
Metpol (Chigwell)	26	9	4	13	52	72	31
Royal George	26	8	4	14	46	50	28
Old Roan	26	6	6	14	39	69	24
Swanley Town	26	5	5	16	37	77	20
Pheonix Sports	26	4	4	18	31	73	16
Catford Wdrs	26	2	3	21	19	64	9

* - 3 points deducted - ineligible player.

Division Two	P	W	D	L	F	A	Pts
Clapton Villa	20	16	3	1	75	20	51
A.F.C. Eltham	20	15	2	3	72	24	47
Chingford Wdrs	20	13	4	3	39	16	43
Crescent '89	20	9	3	8	62	49	30
Bridon Sports	20	7	5	8	43	40	26
Singh Sabha	20	8	1	11	37	37	25
S.E. Olympic	20	7	4	9	30	37	25
Garfields	20	7	2	11	32	48	23
Woolwich Town	20	7	1	12	32	56	22
Villacourt Rvrs	20	6	2	12	46	68	20
Penhill Standard	20	1	1	18	16	83	4

Reserve Division	P	W	D	L	F	A	Pts
Willesden (H) Rs	18	16	1	1	56	14	49
W'stow Troj. Rs	18	13	3	2	51	16	42
Leyton County Rs	18	8	6	4	39	22	30
Elms Rs	18	8	4	6	39	33	28
Eltham T. Rs	18	7	3	8	31	35	24
Catford Wdrs Rs	18	6	4	8	29	27	22
Beckton Utd Rs	18	6	1	11	26	49	19
Southgate A. Rs	18	5	3	10	36	45	18
Woolwich T. Rs	18	5	3	10	39	59	18
Metpol (Chig.) Rs	18	0	4	14	14	60	4

PREMIER DIVISION RESULT CHART 1991/92

HOME TEAM

	1	2	3	4	5	6	7	8	9	10	11	12	13	14	15	16	17	18	19
1. Amersham Town	*	1-1	2-3	2-2	1-2	0-7	1-2	0-1	1-2	2-0	3-1	0-3	1-2	2-1	3-1	0-3	1-4	1-0	0-1
2. Barkingside	3-2	*	1-0	1-1	2-1	2-3	1-1	0-1	2-1	2-1	2-0	1-0	3-3	1-0	1-0	1-0	6-1	2-3	0-2
3. Beaconsfield United	0-3	1-1	*	0-2	0-3	2-2	1-2	2-1	1-0	3-4	4-1	0-3	1-6	1-4	2-2	1-4	2-2	1-1	0-2
4. Beckton United	1-1	0-3	3-0	*	1-3	2-2	0-4	2-2	0-1	3-5	0-1	1-7	1-2	2-3	0-1	0-4	2-4	2-1	0-4
5. Brimsdown Rovers	6-0	2-0	5-0	1-1	*	1-2	2-1	1-0	2-1	2-1	5-0	4-0	1-2	0-0	4-1	3-0	1-0	1-1	2-2
6. Brook House	0-0	1-1	0-1	3-1	0-0	*	0-1	1-0	1-0	4-0	2-1	2-0	1-3	5-3	3-2	4-0	1-1	2-0	1-1
7. Cheshunt	0-0	4-1	1-2	0-1	1-3	2-0	1-4	*	0-2	2-1	4-1	1-0	1-1	2-1	1-1	0-1	3-1	0-1	0-0
8. Cockfosters	2-0	0-1	2-3	2-0	0-3	0-1	1-1	5-1	*	1-2	4-0	2-1	6-1	3-1	7-0	2-1	2-1	7-0	3-4
9. Corinthian Casuals	3-0	2-1	0-0	2-1	1-1	3-0	2-1	2-1	2-1	*	4-1	1-0	0-3	0-1	2-2	1-4	4-0	0-2	3-3
10. Croydon Athletic	1-1	0-1	0-2	2-2	1-3	1-2	0-2	1-1	0-5	0-3	*	0-7	3-4	0-4	2-0	0-5	0-2	0-2	2-9
11. Eltham Town	1-0	0-3	1-3	8-0	1-1	0-1	0-1	2-2	2-2	3-1	3-0	*	2-1	3-1	3-2	1-0	2-0	4-2	
12. Hanwell Town	1-0	2-2	1-1	3-0	1-0	2-3	0-2	1-0	6-3	1-0	3-3	*	2-1	3-1	3-2	1-0	2-0	4-2	
13. Haringey Borough	0-2	2-1	4-2	1-1	1-2	2-2	2-1	1-0	1-4	2-1	2-1	1-6	0-2	*	2-0	0-1	2-1	1-1	0-5
14. Hillingdon Borough	3-0	1-1	0-1	1-0	1-2	2-4	1-1	3-3	2-2	2-5	5-2	1-1	1-1	1-2	*	1-2	0-2	0-0	2-1
15. North Greenford United	3-0	1-1	0-1	1-0	1-2	2-4	1-1	3-3	2-2	2-5	5-2	1-1	1-1	1-2	*	1-2	0-2	0-0	2-1
16. Northwood	2-1	3-1	2-1	12-1	2-1	4-1	0-1	1-1	3-2	5-2	4-1	1-1	3-1	3-1	5-0	*	4-0	1-2	3-3
17. Southgate Athletic	2-1	0-1	1-1	2-0	0-1	0-2	1-4	2-3	0-2	3-1	3-0	0-2	0-1	3-0	1-2	0-3	*	1-0	1-1
18. Waltham Abbey	2-1	0-1	2-0	4-0	0-4	1-2	4-0	2-1	1-0	1-1	6-3	1-2	1-3	2-2	4-0	0-1	2-0	*	0-2
19. Walthamstow Pennant	5-0	2-3	0-1	4-0	2-0	3-0	0-0	3-0	2-0	1-2	4-0	2-3	1-1	1-0	5-0	1-3	5-0	6-0	*

SPARTAN LEAGUE CUP 1991-92

First Round

Waltham Abbey v Corinthian Casuals	1-2
Willesden (Hawkeye) v Brimsdown Rovers	1-4
Cheshunt W/O Eltham Town	
Cockfosters v Walthamstow Pennant	1-2
Pheonix Sports v Southgate Athletic	2-2,0-5
Barkingside v Beckton United	2-1
Amersham Town v Catford Wanderers	2-0

Second Round

Beaconsfield United v Corinthian Casuals	0-1
Southgate Athletic v Swanley Town	3-2
North Greenford United v Barkingside	1-1,0-4
Hanwell Town v Amersham Town	2-0
Brook House v Croydon Athletic	1-0
Hillingdon Borough v Brimsdown Rovers	2-3
Haringey Borough v Eltham Town	6-2
Northwood v Walthamstow Pennant	4-0

Third Round

Corinthian Casuals v Brook House (AET)	3-2
Barkingside v Haringey Borough	3-0
Southgate Athletic v Brimsdown Rovers	0-0,1-2
Hanwell Town v Northwood	1-2

Semi-Finals

Corinthian Casuals v Brimsdown Rovers (AET)	2-1
Barkingside v Northwood	1-2

Final (at Hanwell Town FC, 8-5-92)

Northwood v Corinthian Casuals	3-0

Spartan Football League Premier Division Ten Year Record

	82/3	83/4	84/5	85/6	86/7	87/8	88/9	89/0	90/9	91/2
Abingdon Town							1			
Ambrose Fleming	13	15								
Amersham Town	10	11	11	15	10	15	13	19	10	16
Barkingside					12	9	5	8	2	6
Beaconsfield Utd		6	9	6	16	11	18	17	13	14
Beckton United	5	7	15	13	13	13	19	10	14	18
Berkhamstead Town	8									
Bracknell Town	1	4								
Brimsdown Rovers		3	3	5	3	5	7	14	7	2
B R O B Barnet	9	12	17							
Bromley Athletic (see Eltham Town)										
Brook House								11	12	4
Burnham			1							
Cheshunt						4	6	4	4	8
Chingford	12	14								
Cocfosters										12
Collier Row		1	2	1						
Corinthian Casuals			16		14	17	16	5	5	9
Crown & Manor				11	9	16	20			
Croydon Athletic						10	2	13	15	10
Danson (Bexley Borough)			12	12	15					
Edgware Town			14	7	4	1	4	1		
Eltham Town							17	18	18	19
Greenwich Borough	3	8								
Hanwell Town			5	9	11	6	11	12	8	7
Haringey Boro								6	6	3
Highfield	7	13								
Hillingdon Boro									16	13
Malden Vale	4	2								
Merstham	6	10								
North Greenford United							14	15	17	17
Northwood			6	8	7	12	3	2	3	1
Pennant (see Walthamstow Pennant)										
Redhill			7	3	2	7				
Southgate Athletic					5	2	8	3	11	15
Southwark Borough					3	9				
Swanley Town	2	9	13	16						
Thamesmead Town							15	16	19	
Thatcham Town			4	4						
Ulysses					17					
Waltham Abbey	11	5	8	10	6	14	12	9	9	11
Walthamstow Pennant			10	14	8	8	10	7	1	5
Wandsworth & Norwood (see Croydon Athletic)										
Yeading				2	1					
No. of Clubs competing	13	15	17	16	17	17	20	19	19	19

Barkingside FC. Back Row (L/R): M Stevens (Physio), G Barnard (Manager), L Parnell, A Victor, R Parnell, P Cooke, C Hutton, R Noble, S Harvey, A White. Front: N Simmonds, J Harris, C Edwards, R Saunders (Captain), T Boyce, M Carter, J Pyne.

PREMIER DIVISION CLUBS 1992-93

AMERSHAM TOWN

Secretary: R McKeen, 3 Hazel Park, Amersham, Bucks (0494 728426).   **Manager:** Tony Bennett.
Ground: Spratley's Meadow, School Lane, Amersham (0494 727428).
Directions: A413 to Broadway, right into Church St, first left into School Lane. Ground on left 200yds past school. One mile from Amersham Station - Underground Metropolitan Line).
Seats: 150   **Cover:** 150   **Capacity:** 2,500   **Floodlights:** Yes   **Founded:** 1890
Previous Leagues: Gt Western Suburban 20-23/ Spartan 23-53 61-62/ Hellenic 53-61 62-72.
Record Gate: 2,000 v Aston Villa, centenary match 1990 (played at Chesham United FC).
Colours: Black & white stripes/Black/Hose   **Change colours:** Tan/Black
Clubhouse: Clubroom, players Lounge, bar, kitchen, boardroom **Previous Grnd:** Barn Meadow (pre-1923).
Hons: Hellenic Lg 63-64 (R-up 62-63), London Spartan Lg R-up 79-80, St Marys Cup 89-90 (R-up 90-91).

BARKINGSIDE

Secretary: N A Ingram, 45 Cheneys Rd, Leytonstone, London E11 3LL (081 4551447).
Ground: Oakside, Station Road, Barkingside, Ilford, Essex (081 550 3611).
Directions: From London A12 to Green Gate, left into Hurnes Road, Barkingside, right into Craven Gardens, right again Carlton Drive leading to Station Road. Adjacent to Barkingside station (Central Line), 3 miles from Ilford station (BR). Bus 169 to Craven Gardens.
Seats: 60   **Cover:** 60   **Capacity:** 1,000   **Floodlights:** Yes   **Founded:** 1898.
Previous Leagues: Ilford & Dist./ London 50-64/ Gtr London 64-71/ Metropolitan-London 71-75.
Previous Grounds: Fulwell Cross PF 1898-1921/ Clayhall Rec 21-29/ Hainault PF 29-33/ Barkingside Rec 33-57.
Colours: Blue & white hoops/white/blue   **Change colours:** All Red
Programme: 12 pages, with admission   **Record Gate:** 957 v Arsenal Reserves, London Lg 1957.
Clubhouse: Open evenings and matchdays. Food on matchdays, pool, darts.

BEACONSFIELD UNITED

President: T Keylock   **Chairman:** J McDaid.
Secretary: Cliff Sparkes, 'Rumah Kita', Blackpool Lane, Farnham Royal, Bucks SL2 3EA (0753 642490).
Manager: Ian Feaver   **Programme Editor:** Cliff Sparkes   **Coach:** Martyn Busby
Ground: Holloways Park, Slough Road, Beaconsfield, Bucks (0494 676868).
Directions: M40 (Jct 2), 1st exit to A355. Club 100yds on right. One and a miles from Beaconsfield (BR). Bus 441 Slough/ High Wycombe.
Seats: None   **Cover:** 60   **Capacity:** 1,000   **Floodlights:** Yes   **Founded:** 1921.
Previous Leagues: Wycombe & District/ Maidenhead   **Best FA Vase season:** 1st Rd 83-84 85-86 87-88.
Record Gate: 300 v Chesham United, Berks & Bucks Snr Cup 1985.
Cols: Blue & black stripes/black/black   **Change colours:** Red & black stripes/black/black
Local Newspapers: Bucks Advertiser, Bucks Free Press, Slough Observer.
Clubhouse: Open evenings and matchdays. Bar, Committee Room, Hall, Kitchen, Changing Room

BECKTON UNITED

Secretary: W Stockley, 6 Cheltenham Road, East Ham, London (081 471 3055).
Ground: East Ham, Manor Way, London E6, near Industrial Park (071) 476 4857
Directions: A13 from City or Essex, Nth Circular Rd from Middlesex. By rail, East Ham (Underground). Buses from East Ham or North Woolwich.
Seats: None   **Cover:** 150   **Capacity:** 1,000   **Floodlights:** No   **Founded:** 1966.
Previous Name: Ceevor FC   **Previous Grounds:** None.
Colours: Green & white stripes/black/green   **Change colours:** Yellow/red/red
Clubhouse: None; adjacent pub used   **Best FA Vase season:** 3rd Rd 85-86.

BRIMSDOWN ROVERS

Secretary: B Martin, 13 Bonnington House, Ayley Croft, Enfield EN1 1XT (081 3668523).
Ground: Goldsdown Road, Enfield, Middlesex (081 804 5491).
Directions: BR from Liverpool Street to Brimsdown (half mile away), by road off Green Street (A1010), itself off Hertford Road (A10). Buses 191 or 307.
Seats: None   **Cover:** 50   **Capacity:** 1,000   **Floodlights:** Yes   **Founded:** 1948.
Previous Leagues: Northern Suburban   **Previous Name:** Durham Rovers/ Brimsdown FC
Colours: Black & white stripes/black/black   **Change colours:** All yellow
Best FA Vase season: 2nd Rd rep. 84-85 **Best FA Cup season:** 3rd Qual. replay 91-92
Record Gate: 412 v Chesham Utd, FA Cup 3rd Qual. Rd 12/10/91.
Clubhouse: Large lounge & clubroom, games room & stage. 3 bars (300 capacity)

BROOK HOUSE

Secretary: G Bundy, 43 Heatherwood Drive, Hayes, Middlesex UB4 8TN (081 845 7355).
Ground: Farm Park, Kingshill Avenue, Hayes, Middlesex (081 845 0110).
Directions: From London or North Circular Road: A40 Western Avenue to Target roundabout, turn left towards Hayes, turn right at traffic lights in to Kingshill Avenue.
Seats: None   **Cover:** Yes   **Capacity:**   **Floodlights:** Yes   **Founded:**
Colours: Blue & white stripes/blue/blue   **Change colours:** Green & white/green/green
Best FA Vase season: Preliminary Rd 90-91 91-92.

CHESHUNT

Secretary: Fred Beer, 12 Railway Rd, Waltham Cross, EN8 7TA (0992 761138).
Ground: The Stadium, Theobalds Lane, Cheshunt, Herts (0992 26752).
Directions: M25 to junction 25, A10 to Hertford past ground on right, turn back towards London at first traffic lights to enter. 400yds from Theobalds Grove BR station. Buses 352, 242 and 310 to Theobalds Grove station.
Seats: 150   **Cover:** 500   **Capacity:** 1,000   **Floodlights:** Yes   **Founded:** 1946.
Colours: Yellow/blue/blue   **Change colours:** Blue/yellow/yellow
Programme: 30 pages, 40p   **Previous Ground:** Broomfield Lane 52-56.
Previous Leagues: Athenian 19-20 21-31 64-77/ London 20-21 24-25 46-51 55-59/ Delphian 51-55/ Aetolian 59-62/ Spartan 62-64/ Isthmian 77-87.
Best FA Vase season: Qtr Final 81-82   **Best FA Cup season:** 4th Qual. Rd(4)
Hons: Ath'n Lg 75-76 (R-up 73-74, Div 1 67-68, Div 2 R-up 65-66, Lg Cup 74-75 75-76, Spart. Lg 62-63, L'don Lg 49-50 (R-up 56-57, Div 1 47-48 48-49 (R-up 46-47), Park Royal Cup 46-47), L'don Spart. Lg Cup R-up 89-90.

Beaconsfield United. Back Row (L/R): Martyn Busby (Coach), Steve Killick, Moran Dodds, Nick Dean, Scott Sidley (Captain), James Skerritt, Simon Franks, Jamie Daw, Ian Feaver (Manager). Front: Mascot, Phillip Nelson, Jason Weston, Domenico Di Ciocco, Sean Whitcombe, David Patience, Andy Humphrey.

Eltham Town. Back Row (L/R): Sid Hare (Coach), Keith Wenham (Manager), Peter Stanley, Terry Nelson, Paul Turner, Dave Lacey, Dean Dennis, Clayton Walters, Peter Lawson (Gen. Sec.). Front: Terry Quick (Asst Mgr), Dave Kemp, Stuart Bell, Jim Hare, Paul Connell, Andy Sparksman, Sean Clifford, Alfie Hines. Photo - Roger Judges.

Cheshunt FC. Photo - Gavin Ellis.

COCKFOSTERS

Secretary: G Bint, 15 Chigwell Park, Chigwell, Essex IG7 5BE (081 500 7369).
Ground: Cockfosters Sports Ground, Chalk Lane, Cockfosters, Barnet (081 449 5833).
Directions: Ground on A111. M25 Jct 24 (Potters Bar), take the A111 to Cockfosters - Ground on right. Adjacent to Cockfosters underground station (Picadilly Line). Bus 298 to Cockfosters station.
Seats: None **Cover:** 40 **Capacity:** 1,000 **Floodlights:** No **Founded:** 1927.
Previous League: Herts Co. (pre-1991) **Record Gate:** 408 v Saffron Walden, Herts Lg 68-69.
Colours: All Red **Change colours:** All White
Previous Name: Cockfosters Athletic **Previous Grounds:** None
Best FA Vase season: 2nd Rd 91-92 **Programme:** 12 pages, with £1 admission
Clubhouse: Tues & Thurs nights, Sunday lunchtimes & matchdays. Hot and cold snacks, darts, pool.

CORINTHIAN CASUALS

Manager: Steve Bangs **Secretary:** K Nicholls, C/O the club.
Ground: King George's Field, Hook Rise, South Tolworth, Surrey KT6 7NA (081 397 3368).
Directions: A3 to Tolworth (The Toby Jug). Hook Rise is slip road behind the Toby Jug, 2nd left under railway bridge - ground immediately on right. Half mile from Tolworth (BR); turn left, continue to Toby Jug, then as above. K2 Hoppa bus from Kingston passes ground.
Seats: 30 **Cover:** 150 **Capacity:** 1,700 **Floodlights:** Yes **Founded:** 1939.
Previous Leagues: Isthmian 39-84
Previous Names: Casuals (founded 1883), Corinthians (founded 1882) merged in 1939.
Previous Grounds: Many, including The Oval, Wimbledon Park Stadium, Tooting & Mitcham United FC.
Colours: White/navy/navy **Change colours:** Chocolate & Pink/Navy/Navy
Programme: 24-48 pages, 50p **Best FA Cup season:** 1st Rd replay 85-86.
Clubhouse: Evenings, matchdays, Sunday lunchtimes. Darts, pool, hot & cold snacks on matchdays.
Hons: FA Amtr Cup R-up 55-56 (SF 56-57), London Spartan Lg Cup R-up 91-92, London Snr Cup R-up 91-92.

CROYDON ATHLETIC

Chairman: Keith Tuckey **Vice Chairman:** Ken Fisher.
Secretary: A Peck, 60 Cheviot Road, West Norwood, London SE27 0LG (081 684 4951).
Manager: Ken Fisher **Asst Manager:** Tony Peck.
Press Officer: Trevor Finch **Coach:** Derek Fitzpatrick.
Ground: N.F.C. Sports off Mayfield Road, Thornton Heath (081 684 4951).
Directions: From Norbury follow London Rd towards Croydon, turn right into Headcorn Rd, left into Silverleigh Rd, right into Mayfield Crescent, right into Mayfield Rd, left at end and follow road to ground. One mile from Norbury (BR). Buses 109, 154.
Seats: Yes **Cover:** Yes **Capacity:** 1,200 **Floodlights:** Yes **Founded:** 1986.
Colours: Maroon & white stipes/maroon/maroon **Change colours:** All Yellow
Previous Names: Wandsworth FC, Norwood FC (merged 1986)/ Wandsworth & Norwood 86-90.
Previous Grounds: Norwood FC - Lloyds Park 1948-82/ Wandsworth FC - Wisley RHS 78-83.
Best FA Vase season: 2nd Rd 89-90 **Best FA Cup season:** 1st Qual. Rd Rep. 89-90
Record Gate: 400 **Reserve Team's League:** Suburban.
Hons: London Spartan Lg R-up 88-89 (Reserve Div R-up 88-89, Reserve Cup 88-89).

ELTHAM TOWN

Secretary: P Lawson, 13 Brome Road, Eltham, London SE9 1LD (081 859 6070)
Ground: Footscray Road, Eltham, London SE9 (081 850 0695).
Directions: From London: end of Eltham High Street, turn right into Footscray Road, ground three quarters of a mile on the right, corner of Green Lane.
Seats: **Cover:** Yes **Capacity:** **Floodlights:** No **Founded:**
Colours: Yellow/green/gellow **Change colours:** All white

HANWELL TOWN

Secretary: P Player, 3 Oakington Avenue, North Harrow, Middlesex HA2 7JQ (081 8662507).
Ground: Reynolds Field, Perivale Lane, Perivale, Greenford, Middx (081 9981701).
Directions: On South side of Western Ave, (A20) past Hoover Factory. Third of a mile from Perivale tube station.
Seats: None **Cover:** 200 **Capacity:** 2,000 **Floodlights:** Yes **Founded:** 1948
Previous Leagues: Middx/ Middx County **Previous Grounds:** Local parks.
Colours: Black & white stripes/black/red **Change colours:** White/white/red
Record Gate: 600 v Spurs, Floodlight opening November 1989.
Clubhouse: Yes **Hons:** London Senior Cup 91-92

HARINGEY BOROUGH

Secretary: S O'Connell, 64a Station Road, Wood Green, London N22 4SY (081 881 7631).
Ground: Coles Park, White Hart Lane, Wood Green, N22 (081 8819184).
Directions: Wood Green (Picadilly Line). BR (Eastern Region) to White Hart Lane, W3 bus passes ground A105 or A10 from Nth. Circular to Wood Green.
Seats: 280 **Cover:** Yes **Capacity:** 2,500 **Floodlights:** Yes **Founded:**
Previous Leagues: London 19-52 Isthmian 19-52 84-88/ Spartan 52-54/ Delphian 54-63/ Athenian 63-84.
Previous Names: Edmonton/ Tufnell Park/ Tufnell Park Edmonton/ Edmonton & Haringey.
Colours: All green **Change colours:** All white **Clubhouse:** Open 7 days a week

HILLINGDON BOROUGH

Secretary: Jack Whitehead, 43 Frays Waye, Uxbridge, Middlesex UB8 2QU (0895 31012).
Ground: Breakspear Road, Ruislip, Middx (0895 639544).
Directions: From A40 take B467 (signposted Ickenham), at 2nd r'bout turn left into Breakspear Road South, after 1 mile turn right by the Breakspear Public House - ground half a mile on the left.
Seats: 200 **Cover:** **Capacity:** 2,000 **Floodlights:** Yes **Founded:** 1990
Midweek Matches: Tuesday
Colours: White/blue/white **Change colours:** Tangerine/white/wangerine
Programme: 20 pages, 30p **Programme Editor:** Jack Whitehead
Clubhouse: Open every evening plus Saturday & Sunday lunchtimes.

Corinthian Casuals FC, Finalists in both the Spartan League Cup and the London Senior Cup in 1992-93. Photo - Dave West.

Hanwell Town. Back Row (L/R): Arthur Rowlands, Andy Paul, Nigel Coil, Dick Barker, Graham Maudsley, Paul Riordan, Peter Sargeant, Jason Delicata, Chris Boothe, Roy Nairn (Manager), Roy Tyler (Physio). Front: Craig Girling, Ian Lancaster, Phil Player (Captain), Ray Duffy, Steve Leonard, Dave Curry. Photo - Dave West.

Haringey Borough. Back Row (L/R): Kotey, Watson (Manager), Flanagan, Doley, Milton, Buckland, Roberts, Brown. Front: Johnston, C Campbell, Burke, Rhodes, Hamlet, S Campbell. Photo - Francis Short.

NORTH GREENFORD UNITED

Secretary: R Johnson, 63 Berkeley Avenue, Greenford, Middlesex UB6 0NY. (081 864 2645).
Ground: Berkeley Fields, Berkeley Avenue, Greenford, Middlesex (081 422 8923).
Directions: A406 or A40 from London to Hanger Lane, then A40 westwards approx 2 miles to junction with A4127. Right into Greenford Rd at r'bout, through lights, next right is Berkeley Avenue.
Seats: **Cover:** Yes   **Capacity:**   **Floodlights:** No   **Founded:**
Colours: Blue & white/blue/blue   **Change colours:** Yellow/black/yellow.

ST ANDREWS

Secretary: C Hammond (081 222 6481).   **Ground:** Bellingham Sports Ground, Randlesdown Road, Catford.
Seats: **Cover:**   **Capacity:**   **Floodlights:**   **Founded:**
Previous Leagues: Surrey Premier (until 1992)
Club colours: **Change colours:**
Clubhouse: Yes   **Hons:** Surrey Premier Lg 91-92.

ST MARGARETSBURY

Secretary: Alan B Green, 133 Caxton Rd, Hoddesdon, Herts EN11 9NX (0992 464682).
Ground: Recreation Ground, Stanstead, St Margaretsbury, Herts (0920 870473).
Directions: A414 to Amwell r'bout, B181 to Stanstead Abbotts - ground quarter mile on right.
Seats: Yes   **Capacity:** Yes   **Programme:** Yes   **Floodlights:** No   **Founded:** 1894
Previous Leagues: East Herts/ Waltham & District/ Herts Co. (until 1992)   **Nickname:** The Bury
Club colours: Red/black/black (red & white tops)   **Change colours:** Green/white/white.
Hons: Herts County Lg Div 2 48-49 (Aubrey Cup 48-49 71-72)

SOUTHGATE ATHLETIC

Secretary: K P Cullen, 39 Hillrise, Potters Bar, Herts EN6 2RX (0707 56136).
Ground: Tottenhall Road Sports, Tottenhall Road, Palmers Green, London N13 (081 8881542).
Directions: From west; To Green Lanes on to North Circular Road, turn right and second left (Tottenhall Road), ground on right. From east; under underpass on A406, turn off left at Wolves Lane to r'bout, left in to Tottenhall Road. One mile from Wood Green (BR). Bus No. 34.
Seats: None   **Cover:** 50   **Capacity:** 500   **Floodlights:** No   **Founded:** 1939.
Colours: Amber/black/black   **Change colours:** All blue
Record Gate: 290 v Northampton Spencer, FA Vase November 1987.   **Previous Names:** None
Previous Grounds: None.   **Clubhouse:** Open normal hours. Hot & cold snacks.

TOWER HAMLETS (TIPPLES)

Secretary: J Westwood, 69 Chadbourn Street, Poplar, London E14 (071 515 9830).
Ground & Directions: Mile End Stadium, Rhodeswell Road (081 980 1885). From Blackwall tunnel left into East India Dock Road to Commercial Road, right into Burdett Road, ground on left. Mile End tube.
Colours: Blue & white   **Change Colours:** Yellow or white

WALTHAM ABBEY

Chairman: T Hodges   **Sec.:** D Brittain, C/O The Broadway, Woodford Green, Essex (0992 716747).
Ground: Capershotts, Sewardstone Road, Waltham Abbey, Essex (0992 711287).
Directions: A112 from Chingford. Waltham Cross (BR Eastern Region) station three miles distant. 242 Bus.
Seats: None   **Covered:** 200   **Capacity:** 3,000   **Floodlights:** Yes   **Founded:** 1920s.
Colours: Green & white/green   **Change colours:** Red/blue
Previous Leagues: Northen Suburban   **Midweek matchday:** Wednesday
Record Gate: 1,800 v Spurs, charity game   **Previous Names:** W. Abbey Utd/ W. Abbey Beechfield
Programme: 16 pages, £1.50 inc. admission.   **Editor:** J Stacey.
Best FA Cup season: Prel. Rd 90-91   **Best FA Vase season:** Prel. Rd 87-88 88-89 89-90
Clubhouse: Evenings & weekend lunchtimes. Cold snacks, pool, darts.

WALTHAMSTOW PENNANT

Secretary: T Bellotti, 37 Carnanton Road, Walthamstow, London E17 4DB (081 527 1441).
Ground: Wadham Lodge, Brookscroft Road, Walthamstow (081 527 2444).
Directions: North Cirular Road to Crooked Billet, turn into Chingford Road, Brookscroft Road first turning on left. Walthamstow Central tube (Victoria Line) one mile away, then buses W21 or 256.
Seats: 100   **Cover:** 100   **Capacity:** 5,000   **Floodlights:** Yes   **Founded:** 1966
Colours: White/Blue/Blue   **Change colours:** Blue/White/White
Previous Name: Pennant FC   **Previous Grounds:** None.
Record Gate: 860 v Leyton Orient, Floodlight opening 1989.
Best FA Vase season: 5th Rd 90-91   **Best FA Cup season:** 1st Qual. Rd 89-90 90-91
Clubhouse: Evenings & weekend lunchtimes. Hot & cold snacks, pool, darts.
Hons: London Spartan Lg 90-91 (Lg Cup 90-91).

WILLESDEN (HAWKEYE)

Secretary: C Jackson, Flat 1, Vale Farm House, Watford Rd, Sudbury, Middx HA0 3HG (081 908 2664).
Ground & Directions: West London, Stadium, Artillery Lane, Dun Cane Road, Shepherds Bush, London W12 (081 749 5502). Ffive minutes walk from Queens Park Rangers FC.
Colours: Red & white/red/red   **Change Colours:** Blue/black/black
Previous Ground: Willesden Sports Centre, Donnington Rd (until 1992).
Previous Name: Hawkeye (Willesden)   **Hons:** Spartan Lg Div 1 91-92.

North Greenford United FC. Photo - Dave West.

Newcomers to the Spartan League are Surrey Premier League champions St Andrews. Here their midfielder Steve Charge (right) is felled during a 2-1 at Frinton Rovers. Photo - Dave West.

O'Brien scores Beckton's second in a 2-0 away win despite the efforts of Beaconsfield keeper Steve Killick. Photo - Gavin Ellis.

SPARTAN LEAGUE DIVISION ONE CLUBS 1992-93

A.F.C. ELTHAM
Secretary: R Williams, 90 Earlshore Rd, Eltham, London SE9 1PR (081 859 1422).
Ground & Directions: Whitehorse Sports Club, Footscray Road, New Eltham. A20 from London to Fiveways junction, left into Southwood Road, rights at lights, ground 200 yds on left. New Eltham (BR).
Colours: Red & black stripes/black   **Change Colours:** Blue & white

CATFORD WANDERERS
Secretary: J Freeman, 84 Allington Drive, Strood, Near Rochester, Kent (0634 715812).
Ground & Directions: Beckenham Hill Road, Catford SE6 (081 698 1259). From Bromley Road, left into Sainsbury Homebase and left into car park. Beckenham Hill (BR).
Colours: Black & white/black   **Change Colours:** Red/white

CHINGFORD TOWN WANDERERS
Secretary: R Cheek, 50a Richmond Crescent, Highams Park, London E4 9RU (081 527 4958).
Ground & Directions: Chingdale Road, Friday Hill, Chingford (081 529 0485). North Circular to Woodford New Road, into Chingford Lane, into Chingdale Road at r'bout. Chingford bus to Friday Hill.
Colours: Red/white/red   **Change Colours:** Sky/white or black

CLAPTON VILLA
Secretary: G Kendrick, 51 Lakeside Crescent, East Barnet, Herts EN4 8QH (081 440 1938).
Ground & Directions: Douglas Eyre Sports Centre, Coppermill Lane, Walthamstow (081 520 4918). 5 mins walk from Blackhorse Road (Victoria Line). By road; Forest Road from Woodford, Lea Bridge Road and Blackhorse Road from south of Thames.
Colours: All sky   **Change Colours:** White (black trim)/black

CRAVEN
Secretary: T Day, 23 Chudleigh Crescent, Ilford, Essex IG3 9AT (081 590 4471).
Ground & Directions: Jenkins Lane, Barking (081 594 8442). 200 yds east from junction of A406 (North Circular) and A13 (Newham Way) on A13. Barking (BR).
Colours: Sky/royal/royal.   **Change Colours:** All green.

CRAY VALLEY
Secretary: R A Manger, 45 Queens Wood Road, Sidcup, Kent DA15 8QP (081 850 7839).
Ground & Directions: S.T.C. Ivor Grove, New Eltham (081 850 2057). A20 from London to Fiveways junction, left into Southwood Road, left at lights, Ivor Grove on left. New Eltham (BR).
Colours: Black & white/black/black   **Change Colours:** Blue & sky blue stripes

LEWISHAM (ELMS)
Secretary: C Rhule, 6 Waldon Close, Croydon CR0 4JP (081 680 6893).
Ground & Directions: Elm Lane, Catford Hill, London SE6 (081 311 3123). One minute from South Circular. Catford Bridge (BR).
Colours: Red & white stripes/navy   **Change:** Red & black/black/blue
Previous Name: Elms FC (pre-1992).

LEYTON COUNTY
Secretary: K Kirwan, 120 Malvern Road, Leytonstone E11 3DL (081 539 9210).
Ground & Directions: Crawley Road, Leyton E10 (081 539 1924). Approx one and a half miles from Leyton station, in direction of Walthamstow.
Colours: All white   **Change Colours:** Yellow/blue/yellow

METPOL CHIGWELL
Secretary: B Hunt, 134 Stanley Avenue, Gidea Park, Romford RM2 5DA (0708 743533).
Ground & Directions: Met Police Sports Ground, Chigwell (081 500 2735 or 500 1017). A113 Chigwell Road off North Circular, left at mini r-about for just over a mile. Club on left after junction with Chigwell Rise. Chigwell (tube - Central Line).
Colours: White (red & black trim)   **Change:** All blue or black & red

METROGAS
Secretary: D Kidd, 23 Tudor Close, Dartford, Kent DA1 3HU (0322 71685).
Ground & Directions: Forty Footway, Eltham (081 859 1579 or 081 859 4534). A20 from London to Fiveways junction, left into Southwood Road, on to Averyhill Road, ground on left in Forty Footway. New Eltham (BR).
Colours: Royal/white/blue   **Change Colours:** All green

OLD ROAN
Secretary: Ian Stuart Daniels, 24 Waldeck Road, Dartford, Kent DA1 1UA (0322 220165).
Ground & Directions: Roan School Playing Fields, Kidbrooke Park Road, London SE12 (081 856 1915). At start of A20. Kidbrooke (BR) or buses 21 and 22.
Colours: Blue/black/black   **Change Colours:** All red

SOUTH EAST OLYMPIC
Secretary: D Wilson, 74 Shrofford Road, Bromley BR1 5PF (081 698 1192).
Ground & Directions: Elliott Sports, Manor Way, Blackheath SE3 (081 852 3602). Lee Green into Lee Road - Manor Way 2nd right. Blackheath (BR).
Colours: All blue   **Change Colours:** White/silver/black

SWANLEY TOWN
Secretary: P Matthews, 4 Moultain Hill, Swanley, Kent BR8 8BS (0322 66939).
Ground & Directions: St Marys Road, Swanley, Kent (0322 60371). A2, M20 or M25 - turn off before Swanley bypass. Swanley (BR).
Colours: Red, blue & white/blue/blue   **Change Colours:** White/black/black

WALTHAMSTOW TROJANS
Secretary: E Webb, 34 Bidwell Gardens, Bounds Green N11 2AU (081 881 0538).
Ground & Directions: Ive Farm Arena, Villiers Close, Leyton E10 (081 539 6352). From Lea Bridge Road turn into Church Road, then after half a mile right into Villiers Close. Leyton (tube - Central Line).
Colours: All sky   **Change Colours:** All amber

Clapton Villa celebrate their Spartan League Benevolent Cup win over Bridon Ropes. Photo - Dave West.

Cockfosters 2 Hillingdon Borough 1, Premier Division 29/2/92. Steve Robinson of Cockfosters is pursued by Gary Thompson for the opposition. Photo - Richard Brock.

Eltham Town attack strongly in the second half of their pre-season friendly 2-1 home win against Catford Wanderers on Thursday 1st August. Photo - Gavin Ellis.

(Continued from page 396)

WOOLWICH TOWN

Secretary: J Gustins, Gustins, 102 Edington Rd, Abbey Wood, London SE2 9GT (081 310 2178).
Ground & Directions: Flamingo Park, Sidcup by-pass (A20)(081 300 6754). Blackwall Tunnel to A20, past Crossways to St Marys r'bout, past Beaver Wood Club, next left. New Eltham (BR).
Colours: Yellow & black/black/black   **Change Colours:** All red & black

DIVISION TWO CLUBS 1992-93

BRIDON ROPES

Secretary: R Clements, 3 Fenwick Close, Woolwich SE18 4DD (081 854 9844).
Ground & Directions: Meridian Sports Club, Charlton Park Lane, Charlton SE7 (081 856 1923). Central London exit from Blackwall Tunnel, left at island, 6th right, ground on left. Woolwich Arsenal (BR).
Colours: All red   **Change Colours:** Green/white

GARFIELDS

Secretary: B Siani, 13 Grantolk Road, Walthamstow, London E17 (081 927 9839).
Ground & Directions: Walthamstow Pennant FC (see Premier Division).
Colours: Blue & red stripes/blue   **Change Colours:** All white

LEWISHAM TOWN

Secretary: Mike Cheeseman, 142 Old Bromley Rd, Downham, Bromley, Kent (081 290 5558).
Ground & Directions: TBA.
Colours: TBA   **Change Colours:** TBA
Previos Leagues: Chigwell & District (pre'91)/ South East London 91-92.

LOUGHTON

Secretary: K Campen (081 508 4757).
Ground: London Polytechnic Sports Ground, Luxborough Lane, Chigwell.
Colours: Red/black/black   **Change Colours:** Green/black/green.
Previous Lge: Essex I'mediate (pre'92)   **Hons:** Essex I'mediate Lg Snr Div 3 91-92.
Previous Ground: Roding Valley Playing Fields, Roding Road, Loughton (pre'92).

MARSHALLS

Secretary: Ian Marshall, 21 Liphook Crescent, London (081 699 6080).
Ground: Cold Harbour Sports, Chapel Farm Road, Eltham.
Colours: All White   **Change:** All blue.

OLLERTON

Secretary: Mr B Marrion, 55 Ollerton Green, Jodwell Rd, London Bow (081 980 6685).
Ground: Drapers, Gorton Road, Leyton.
Colours: Green/green/black   **Change Colours:** Claret & blue/claret/white.

SINGH SABHA

Secretary: J Singh, 28 Abbotsford Road, Goodmayes, Ilford IG3 9SL (081 599 5044).
Ground & Directions: Barking FC (see page 322).
Colours: White/black/white   **Change Colours:** All red

VILLACOURT ROVERS

Secretary: B Bayfield, 64 Manor Way, Blackheath SE3 (081 852 0064).
Ground & Directions: Manor Way, Blackheath SE3 (081 852 0064). See South East Olympic FC above.
Colours: Yellow & blue/blue/blue   **Change Colours:** All red

This Division also contains the reserve sides of; Beckton United, Catford Wanderers, Lewisham (Elms), Leyton County, Metpol (Chigwell), Walthamstow Trojans and Woolwich Town).

Waltham Abbey FC. Photo - Dave West.

HERTS SENIOR COUNTY LEAGUE

President: Mr W J R Veneear, **Chairman:** Mr C T Hudson.
Secretary: Mr E H Dear, 48 Wilshere Road, Welwyn, Herts.

HATFIELD'S HAT-TRICK

The departure of champions Mount Grace (now Potters Bar Town), with Leverstock Green and Cockfosters, to pastures new, coupled with the demise of Rolls Royce Engines, left the Premier Division depleted to fifteen clubs for the 1991-92 season despite the promotion of Hatfield Town, Kings Langley, St Margaretsbury and Cuffley from Division One. Nevertheless, competition was as keen as ever with the championship race developing, for the most part of the season, into a contest between three main contenders; Hatfield Town, Kings Langley and Sun Sports. In the final stages Hatfield pulled away to clinch the title by a comfortable margin. This gave them a unique hat-trick of championships as they had won the Division One and Two titles in the previous two seasons. A late rally by London Colney saw them finish third.

At the bottom it was a long season of struggle for J & M Sports whose impending closure due to the loss of their ground did not help morale. Oxhey Jets had another tough season finishing in fourteenth place for the second year running.

In Division One Wellcome, from Berkhamsted, clinched top spot with a 5-0 home win in their final game, against third placed Bovingdon. Runners-up Wormley Rovers might have claimed the championship but for faltering form in the final weeks of the seaso. Bottom three places were decided very early with I.C.L. Letchworth, Welwyn and Sarratt falling behind the rest, the latter claiming the unwanted last place.

In Division Two, once again, newcomers did well. Hertford Youth ran away with the title, only surrendering their unbeaten status in their final match of the season, going down 1-2 at home against Harpenden Rovers. Other new boys, Metropolitan Police (Bushey) were third with Evergreen seperating the two.

In the Aubrey Cup, Sun Sports beat Hatfield Town 1-0 in the final played at London Colney FC on May Day Bank Holiday in front of a large crowd, and the Reserve Cup was won by London Colney Reserves who overwhelmed Knebworth Reserves 4-0 in the final at Cuffley FC.

The League's representative side, drawn from Division One and Two clubs, once again reached the final of the Herts Inter-League Cup but were, surprisingly, beaten 2-0 by the McMullen Hertford & District League at Ware FC.

Division One club Walkern competed in the final of the Herts Intermediate Cup, losing out 0-2 after extra-time against Boreham Wood Reserves at Hertford Town FC.

In the Wirral Non-League Programme Survey, Division One Dynamics were the top club in the League and achieved eighth place nationally thus making them tops in Hertfordshire for the second successive season.

Four new clubs are joining for the 1992-93 season. Valmar LR and St Peters are coming from the Mid-Herts League, Somersett Ambury V & E have arrived from the Hertford & District League, whilst Stevenage CIU join from the North Herts League. On the way out are J & M Sports (who have lost their ground), Hatfield Town (moving to the Campri South Midlands League Premier Division), London Colney (to the Campri Division One), and St Margaretsbury (to the London Spartan League).

Conscious of the fact that at present the membership is declining, the Management Committee decided to reconstitute the league into two divisions in both Senior and Reserve sections. This has given rise to a Premier Division of 20 clubs and a Division One of 19. For the first time in a number of years the league are operating reserve sides in the Reserve Section. The reconstitution was welcomed by clubs as they now have a fuller programme.

Kevin Folds (League Management Committee)

AUBREY (LEAGUE) CUP 1991-92

First Round

Bovingdon v Welwyn	4-0	Croxley Guild v Harpenden Rovers		2-1
Dynamics v BAC Stevenage	0-4	Met. Police (Bushey) v ICL Letchworth		2-1
North Mymms v De Havilland Hatfield	3-2	Sarratt v Evergreen		0-2
Walkern v Kimpton Rovers	2-0	Whitwell Athletic v Standon & Puckeridge		2-3

Second Round

Allensburys Sports v Hertford Youth	2-3	Bedmond Social v Knebworth		2-0
Bushey Rangers v J & M Sports	1-0	Croxley Guild v Oxhey Jets		2-0
Cuffley v Evergreen	4-0	Hatfield Town v BAC Stevenage		2-1
Kings Langley v Chipperfield Cor.	1-1,1-0	Kodak Hemel Hempstead v Met. Police (Bushey)		1-0
Little Gaddesden v Park Street	1-4	London Colney v Colney Heath		3-0
North Mymms v Elliott Star	2-3	Sandridge Rovers v Wellcome		3-0
Standon v Lucas Spts	0-5 *(Lucas expelled)*	Sun Sports v St Ippolyts		4-0
Walkern v Bovingdon	1-0	Wormley Rovers v St Margaretsbury		3-2

Third Round

Park Street v Walkern	0-2	Sun Sports v Standon & Puckeridge	7-2
Kings Langley v Hertford Youth	2-0	Croxley Guild v Cuffley	0-2
London Colney v Hatfield Town	1-2	Wormley Rovers v Bedmond Social	0-1
Bushey Rangers v Elliott Star	1-0	Sandridge Rovers v Kodak Hemel Hempstead	5-2

Quarter Finals

Walkern v Sun Sports	1-2	K Langley v Cuffley	2-0 *(K Langley expelled)*
Hatfield Town v Bedmond Social	6-1	Bushey v Sandridge	1-3 *(S'ridge expelled)*

Semi Finals

Sun Sports v Cuffley	2-0	Hatfield Town v Bushey Rangers	3-1

Final (at London Colney FC): Sun Sports v Hatfield Town 1-0

PREM. DIVISION	P	W	D	L	F	A	PTS
Hatfield Town	28	21	4	3	85	30	67
Kings Langley	28	16	6	6	65	35	54
London Colney	28	15	5	8	57	53	50
Elliott Star	28	14	5	9	62	47	47
Sun Sports	28	14	5	9	47	43	47
Bushey Rangers	28	12	6	10	60	48	42
St Margaretsbury	28	12	4	12	58	51	40
Chipperfield C.	28	9	12	7	53	45	39
Bedmond Social	28	11	6	11	47	43	39
Sandridge Rovers	28	11	6	11	45	48	39
Cuffley	28	10	4	14	35	46	34
Park Street	28	9	5	14	29	55	32
Colney Heath	28	8	5	15	47	61	29
Oxhey Jets	28	4	5	19	28	59	17
J & M Sports	28	4	2	22	27	81	14

DIVISION ONE	P	W	D	L	F	A	PTS
Wellcome	26	19	2	5	81	35	59
Wormley Rovers	26	17	6	3	63	27	57
Bovingdon	26	16	5	5	56	38	53
BAC Stevenage	26	15	5	6	63	35	50
Lucas Sports	26	14	6	6	49	26	48
Allenburys Sports	26	12	5	9	50	40	41
Walkern	26	11	4	11	58	37	37
Croxley Guild	26	9	6	11	41	52	33
Kodak Hemel H.	26	7	10	9	41	47	31
Knebworth	26	7	9	10	39	46	30
Dynamics Stev.	26	7	8	11	41	47	29
ICL Letchworth	26	3	7	16	27	68	16
Welwyn	26	4	3	19	38	83	15
Sarratt	26	2	2	22	17	83	8

DIVISION TWO	P	W	D	L	F	A	PTS
Hertford Youth	20	16	3	1	77	16	51
Evergreen	20	14	3	3	56	19	45
Met.Pol. (Bushey)	20	11	3	6	52	33	36
North Mymms	20	11	2	7	50	40	35
Standon/Puckeridge	20	10	1	9	39	46	31
Whitwell Ath.	20	9	3	8	49	46	30
Harpenden Rvrs	20	7	2	11	25	38	23
St Ippolyts	20	6	3	11	32	53	21
Little Gaddesden	20	4	5	11	32	67	17
Kimpton Rovers	20	3	5	12	34	47	14
De Havilland	20	3	2	15	20	61	11

RESERVE DIV. 1	P	W	D	L	F	A	PTS
London Colney	26	23	1	2	97	18	70
Hatfield Town	26	17	4	5	75	32	55
Elliott Star	26	16	4	6	51	33	52
Wormley Rovers	26	15	4	7	55	34	49
Oxhey Jets	26	15	3	8	63	44	48
Sun Sports	26	9	8	9	49	45	35
Colney Heath	26	11	1	14	49	59	34
Kings Langley	26	9	5	12	36	54	32
St Margaretsbury	26	9	5	12	32	56	32
Chipperfield C.	26	7	5	14	38	47	26
Walkern*	26	8	2	16	38	54	26
Bedmond Social**	26	6	6	14	31	62	24
Bushey Rangers	26	5	4	17	39	67	19
Park Street	26	5	2	19	28	76	17

RESERVE DIV. 2	P	W	D	L	F	A	PTS
Bovingdon	24	18	3	3	66	24	57
Knebworth	24	15	4	5	50	34	49
Welwyn	24	12	6	6	45	35	42
BAC Stevenage	24	11	7	6	53	42	40
Croxley Guild	24	12	4	8	59	54	40
Dynamics Stev.	24	11	4	9	49	44	37
Lucas Sports	24	9	7	8	46	48	34
Sandridge Rovers	24	9	3	12	53	50	30
De Havilland	24	8	3	13	44	65	27
Wellcome	24	6	7	11	38	45	25
ICL Letchworth	24	7	3	14	39	55	24
Cuffley	24	6	2	16	31	48	20
Evergreen	24	5	1	18	32	61	16

RESERVE DIV. 3	P	W	D	L	F	A	PTS
Kodak Hemel H.	20	14	2	4	61	28	44
Hertford Yth***	20	13	2	5	51	21	41
Sarratt	20	12	2	6	57	29	38
J & M Sports	20	11	3	6	37	24	36
Allenburys Spts	20	10	3	7	41	35	33
North Mymms	20	8	6	6	33	34	30
Harpenden Rvrs	20	9	2	9	40	32	29
Kimpton Rovers	20	4	7	9	27	42	19
Standon/Puck****	20	4	5	11	24	52	17
Little Gaddesden	20	4	3	13	34	62	15
St Ippolyts	20	3	1	16	14	60	10

* - Points awarded (match abandoned)
** - Points deducted (match abandoned)
*** - Points deducted (ineligible player)
**** - Points awarded (ineligible player)

PREMIER DIVISION RESULT CHART 1991/92

HOME TEAM	1	2	3	4	5	6	7	8	9	10	11	12	13	14	15
1. Bedmont Social	*	2-5	3-0	1-0	3-2	0-2	1-2	1-1	1-3	2-0	1-1	2-2	7-1	0-1	
2. Bushey Rangers	4-2	*	1-1	5-3	1-0	1-5	1-3	6-0	1-2	0-0	3-2	0-1	6-0	1-1	0-1
3. Chipperfield Corinthians	1-1	1-2	*	3-0	3-4	2-2	1-2	4-1	0-0	1-1	1-2	4-2	3-1	3-2	3-3
4. Colney Heath	0-1	1-1	1-1	*	4-1	3-2	0-4	6-3	0-5	0-3	1-0	2-3	0-1	2-2	1-3
5. Cuffley	1-0	0-2	0-0	1-3	*	0-2	0-2	3-0	1-2	4-1	2-2	1-1	0-2	5-4	1-0
6. Elliott Star	5-1	2-1	3-3	2-2	0-3	*	2-5	3-0	1-3	2-3	2-0	2-0	2-0	3-0	3-0
7. Hatfield Town Athletic	2-1	6-2	3-1	3-1	2-0	2-2	*	5-0	2-0	6-0	6-0	4-0	4-2	2-2	1-1
8. J & M Sports	0-1	0-3	1-2	2-0	0-1	2-1	0-3	*	1-0	2-2	3-1	1-2	1-2	1-4	0-1
9. Kings Langley	2-2	1-1	1-1	4-3	5-1	3-1	1-1	6-2	*	0-2	1-0	4-0	4-2	3-1	0-0
10. London Colney	2-1	1-6	1-3	0-0	2-0	2-4	6-4	6-4	4-3	*	4-1	0-1	1-3	3-1	2-0
11. Oxhey Jets	0-2	1-1	1-1	1-6	0-1	1-2	2-1	6-2	1-3	3-0	*	0-1	0-0	1-3	1-4
12. Park Street	1-4	2-1	1-2	1-4	1-1	1-2	0-3	2-0	0-4	1-1	3-1	*	1-2	0-1	1-0
13. Sandridge Rovers	0-0	5-3	2-5	1-2	2-0	4-1	1-3	4-0	2-1	1-3	0-0	0-0	*	3-1	1-2
14. St Margaretsbury	1-3	1-2	2-1	3-1	1-0	2-1	1-3	4-0	3-1	0-1	3-0	6-1	1-1	*	6-0
15. Sun Sports	1-3	4-0	2-2	4-1	1-2	3-3	2-1	2-0	1-4	1-3	2-1	4-1	2-1	2-1	*

TOP SCORERS 1992-93 (League, Aubrey, Reserve & Supplementary Cups)

Premier Division: E Rogers (Hatfield) 30, J McGuire (Sun) 26, S Wibberley (K Langley) 21, N Frazer (Bushey) 17, M Fenton (Elliott) 16, S Reid (K Langley) 15, L Talbot (Elliott) 15, P Reid (K Langley) 14, P Rastrick (Chipperfield) 13, C Johnson (Margaretsbury) 12, S Cotterill (Cuffley) 12, M Hymes (Sandridge) 12, G Eames & T Bond (Colney Hth) 11, P Smith (Margaretsbury) 11, A Agomber (Sandridge) 10, G Day (Elliott) 10.

First Division: S Mahoney (Walkern) 21, P Clifford (Wellcome) 20, K Headley (Wormley) 18, R Mellor (Croxley) 16, L Sinclair (BAC) 16, A Walker (Wellcome) 15, G Matthews (Allensburys) 15, R Day (Wellcome) 15, I Poupart (Bovingdon) 14, L Clement (Dynamics) 13, M Phillips (Knebworth) 12, P Copson (Lucas) 12, C Swann (Bovingdon) 12, L Gregory (Kodak) 11, D Wilson (Lucas) 11, N Johnson (BAC) 11, R Binns (Allensburys) 11, G Ferguson (Wormley) 10, P Gregory (Bovingdon) 10, M Livermore (Walkern) 10.

Second Division: R Grant (MP Bushey) 26, A McShannon (Evergreen) 22, K Minnis (Whitwell) 21, S Humphries & S Juniper (H'ford Yth) 20 & 19, P Jay (N Mymms) 18, D Boston (Whitwell) 17, A Miles (MP Bushey) 12, G Gardner (Standon) 11, D Barnes (Whitwell) 11, D Hutchins (H'ford Yth) 11, I Wicks (Evergreen) 11, P Barr (H'den Rvrs) 10, P McComb (H'ford Yth) 10, P Waller (Little Gad.) 10.

Res. Div. 1: B McCarthy (L Colney) 33, A Parker (Hatfield) 23, S Smith (L Colney) 20, N Layton (Wormley) 17, A Mead (K Langley) 16, G Hipgrave (Hatfield) 15, E O'Connor (Oxhey) 14, S Fowles (Colney Hth) 14, M Cole (Walkern) 12, I Pepper & J Harrison (Sun) 12 & 11, B Yates (L Colney) 11, M Lafayette (Wormley) 11.

Res. Div. 2: P Kitchen & A Jones (Bovingdon) 16 & 15, B Austin (De Hav.) 13, R Cripps (BAC) 13, M Collins (K'worth) 12, A Thayne & D Ewington (Sandridge) 11 & 10, M Vooght & K Jones (BAC) 10, L Tiernan (Dynamics) 10, M White (ICL) 10.

Res. Div. 3: N Hillyard (A'burys) 21, A Kemp (Sarratt) 19, R Jones (Little G.) 16, N Morrison (Kodak) 15, P Coyle (H'ford Yth) 13, B Messer (J & M), C Reid (H'den Rvrs), M Gray (J & M) 11, M Proctor (A'burys) 11.

DIVISION ONE RESULT CHART 1991/92

HOME TEAM	1	2	3	4	5	6	7	8	9	10	11	12	13	14
1. Allensbury Sports	*	2-1	1-2	3-1	4-2	4-2	4-4	4-0	1-3	5-0	1-0	1-3	5-0	0-4
2. BAC Stevenage	1-2	*	2-3	2-0	1-1	3-1	4-1	2-0	1-2	2-1	1-1	4-3	8-1	1-1
3. Bovingdon	3-0	0-3	*	3-1	2-0	0-0	1-1	2-0	2-1	3-0	2-1	1-7	2-1	3-3
4. Croxley Guild	1-1	3-3	1-2	*	1-0	2-2	2-2	1-1	1-0	3-0	2-2	1-8	3-5	1-3
5. Dynamics Stevenage	0-1	2-1	2-1	1-1	*	1-1	4-2	3-3	0-1	2-1	0-1	2-3	1-1	3-3
6. ICL Letchworth	3-3	0-4	0-5	1-3	0-2	*	0-0	1-5	1-4	2-0	4-0	0-3	2-1	0-2
7. Knebworth	0-1	0-5	0-1	1-2	5-2	4-0	*	2-2	2-1	3-0	1-1	1-2	2-2	0-2
8. Kodak Hemel Hempstead	1-0	2-2	2-2	1-2	1-3	2-2	1-1	*	0-0	2-2	3-2	0-3	5-0	1-2
9. Lucas Sports	4-2	0-1	2-0	1-0	2-2	2-2	3-0	1-1	*	3-1	0-0	0-0	5-0	1-0
10. Sarratt	1-0	0-1	0-4	0-1	1-4	3-1	0-2	1-3	1-4	*	0-4	1-1	2-5	1-8
11. Walkern	0-0	1-3	1-3	3-0	4-1	5-1	0-1	4-1	1-3	6-0	*	3-4	3-2	1-2
12. Wellcome	0-3	5-2	5-0	2-1	3-1	3-1	5-2	4-1	2-1	5-0	1-4	*	3-0	2-3
13. Welwyn	4-2	2-3	0-5	3-6	1-1	2-4	1-2	1-2	1-4	2-1	1-5	0-3	*	2-3
14. Wormley Rovers	0-0	1-2	4-4	2-0	2-1	1-0	0-0	0-1	4-1	7-0	3-1	2-1	1-0	*

DIVISION TWO RESULT CHART 1991/92

HOME TEAM	1	2	3	4	5	6	7	8	9	10	11
1. De Havilland Hatfield	*	2-3	1-3	0-5	1-1	1-2	0-4	2-2	2-1	1-2	1-4
2. Evergreen	6-0	*	2-1	0-0	1-0	6-1	2-2	2-0	4-0	1-0	3-0
3. Harpenden Rovers	2-0	0-7	*	1-1	2-1	1-2	1-1	0-2	3-0	2-1	1-3
4. Hertford Youth	10-0	3-0	1-2	*	3-1	9-1	3-1	3-1	2-0	4-2	6-0
5. Kimpton Rovers	3-1	1-3	0-1	1-2	*	3-3	2-2	0-3	3-3	2-5	1-4
6. Little Gaddesden	3-0	1-5	1-2	1-9	1-1	*	2-1	2-3	2-2	2-2	3-5
7. Metropolitan Police Bushey	1-2	0-2	3-2	2-4	2-1	6-2	*	5-1	4-0	3-0	5-2
8. North Mymms	3-2	3-1	4-0	0-2	4-3	4-1	5-1	*	2-2	1-4	2-1
9. St Ippolyts	2-1	4-2	2-0	1-5	1-4	4-1	1-3	1-5	*	4-2	3-2
10. Standon & Puckeridge	3-0	0-5	4-3	0-3	4-2	2-0	0-2	2-1	3-1	*	0-5
11. Whitwell Athletic	1-3	1-1	1-0	2-2	1-4	1-1	1-4	6-4	3-0	6-2	*

RESERVE DIVISION ONE RESULT CHART 1991/92

HOME TEAM	1	2	3	4	5	6	7	8	9	10	11	12	13	14
1. Bedmond Social Res	*	1-1	1-1	2-3	1-1	3-0	0-5	2-5	5-1	0-4	1-5	1-1	1-0	
2. Bushey Rangers Res	5-1	*	3-0	1-4	0-1	1-5	2-3	1-4	3-0	3-1	1-1	3-5	0-2	1-3
3. Chipperfield Corries Res	7-1	2-1	*	5-0	0-1	4-2	0-1	0-6	0-1	4-1	0-1	1-4	1-1	0-0
4. Colney Heath Res	2-3	2-0	0-2	*	3-1	0-6	3-0	1-3	1-2	4-1	0-2	2-1	5-3	0-3
5. Elliott Star Res	3-0	4-2	1-1	2-1	*	3-1	4-0	0-5	3-1	3-0	6-0	1-0	4-3	0-3
6. Hatfield Town Res	+	2-3	1-1	4-0	2-2	*	1-3	2-1	4-2	4-0	6-0	2-0	4-1	4-0
7. Kings Langley Res	1-2	2-0	1-0	3-0	0-2	1-5	*	0-3	2-2	2-2	4-0	1-1	2-1	1-1
8. London Colney Res	4-1	1-0	5-0	5-1	4-1	2-1	6-1	*	6-0	5-0	3-1	2-0	3-2	0-1
9. Oxhey Jets Res	3-0	6-0	3-1	5-1	1-1	1-2	2-1	0-7	*	1-0	6-0	3-3	5-1	3-0
10. Park Street Res	2-3	2-2	3-2	2-8	0-3	1-6	2-1	0-3	2-1	*	2-1	2-0	1-2	3-4
11. St Margaretsbury Res	0-0	7-1	2-0	1-3	2-1	0-2	2-2	0-4	0-4	can	*	4-1	2-0	1-1
12. Sun Sports Res	3-1	1-1	3-2	1-3	0-0	3-3	5-1	3-3	0-3	2-0	0-0	*	5-2	1-3
13. Walkern Res	$	3-2	1-4	0-4	2-0	1-2	0-1	3-2	3-2	4-0	0-4	0-1	*	4-0
14. Wormley Rovers Res	4-0	4-2	3-0	2-0	0-1	1-3	5-2	2-4	3-1	4-0	5-1	1-1	2-0	*

+ - Non-fulfillment by Bedmond, points awarded to Hatfield. $ - Abandoned at 2-1 due to actions of a Bedmond player. 0-0 score recorded, points awarded to Walkern

RESERVE DIVISION TWO RESULT CHART 1991/92

HOME TEAM	1	2	3	4	5	6	7	8	9	10	11	12	13
1. BAC Stevenage Res	*	1-1	3-3	2-1	2-1	1-3	3-1	2-2	5-1	1-2	3-1	4-3	4-1
2. Bovingdon Res	3-0	*	2-1	4-1	3-0	6-0	1-0	5-0	2-1	3-2	4-2	3-0	5-1
3. Croxley Guild Res	2-0	3-2	*	2-2	0-5	1-4	6-1	1-3	2-2	5-4	2-2	2-4	3-1
4. Cuffley Res	0-2	1-2	2-3	*	1-0	0-3	2-1	3-0	0-2	2-1	0-1	1-2	
5. De Havilland Res	2-2	3-5	0-6	1-5	*	1-1	2-1	2-7	2-1	1-2	3-5	2-0	0-5
6. Dynamics Stevenage Res	4-5	1-4	1-0	2-2	3-2	*	3-1	3-1	2-3	4-1	0-2	3-0	2-4
7. Evergreen Res	2-3	0-2	2-3	2-1	3-5	1-0	*	0-2	1-3	3-4	2-2	1-0	1-2
8. ILL Letchworth Res	0-4	3-2	0-3	5-2	1-2	1-2	1-3	*	0-1	0-0	2-4	2-0	1-3
9. Knebworth Res	2-1	2-1	2-0	2-0	5-2	2-1	2-1	1-1	*	1-1	5-1	2-1	2-3
10. Lucas Sports Res	1-1	1-1	1-5	3-0	1-3	1-4	5-1	4-2	3-2	*	1-0	1-1	1-1
11. Sandridge Rovers Res	3-1	0-3	9-0	3-1	2-0	1-1	2-3	2-3	1-2	3-2	*	6-2	0-2
12. Wellcome Res	2-2	1-1	1-2	1-2	2-2	3-1	5-1	2-1	2-3	2-2	3-0	*	1-1
13. Welwyn Res	1-1	0-1	1-4	1-0	2-3	1-1	2-0	4-1	1-1	2-0	3-1	1-1	*

RESERVE DIVISION THREE RESULT CHART 1991/92

HOME TEAM	1	2	3	4	5	6	7	8	9	10	11
1. Allensburys Spts Res	*	2-1	0-2	3-1	2-2	2-3	1-0	2-0	1-0	0-3	4-1
2. Harpenden Rovers Res	1-0	*	0-3	0-3	0-1	0-1	2-0	1-2	7-0	2-1	2-2
3. Hertford Youth Res	2-1	5-1	*	2-2	2-0	3-1	2-5	0-1	3-0	0-2	+
4. J & M Sports Res	1-0	4-2	3-1	*	2-0	3-1	2-0	1-2	2-0	0-2	1-0
5. Kimpton Rovers Res	2-2	2-2	1-6	1-1	*	1-2	4-2	2-2	2-1	0-3	3-0
6. Kodak Hemel H'stead Res	4-5	1-0	1-5	2-1	4-0	*	5-1	2-2	2-1	3-2	8-0
7. Little Gaddesden Res	6-3	1-4	1-4	1-2	3-2	1-1	*	3-3	6-0	0-14	1-1
8. North Mymms Res	3-3	2-3	0-1	0-3	2-0	0-6	4-0	*	1-2	2-2	2-1
9. St Ippolyts Res	1-2	0-7	0-3	2-1	2-2	0-6	1-0	0-2	*	1-5	0-1
10. Sarratt Res	1-3	1-2	1-1	1-0	3-1	0-6	4-2	1-2	4-2	*	3-0
11. Standon & Puckeridge Res	1-5	1-3	1-4	4-4	1-1	1-2	3-1	1-1	3-1	2-4	*

+ - 14/9/91, Hertford won 2-0, but fielded ineligible player; points to Standon & Puckeridge

PREMIER DIVISION CLUBS 1992-93

B.A.C. STEVENAGE

Secretary: Raymond C Poulter, 292 Jessop Rd, Stevenage, Herts SG1 5NA (0438 358078).
Ground: Bragbury End, Stevenage (0438 812985).
Directions: A1(M) to Stevenage Sth (jct 7), A602 Hertford/Ware signs to Bragbury End, ground on left at just past golf course.

Seats: None	**Cover:** Yes	**Programme:** Yes	**Nickname:**	**Founded:** 1953
Colours: Blue/white/red		**Change colours:** Amber/black/amber.
Previous League: Nth Herts/Sth Mids		**Hons:** Aubrey Cup 87-88.

BEDMOND SOCIAL

Secretary: W E (Bill) Smith, 71 Bedmond Green, Bedmond Green, Abbots Langley, Herts WD5 0QZ (0923 270298).
Ground: The Pavillion, Toms Lane, Bedmond (0923 267991).
Directions: M1 jct 8, then A4147 to 2nd r'bout, left on St Albans route (A414), bear right to Bedmond at church (Bedmond Rd), right in village into Toms Lane at mini r'bout, ground 300yds on left.
Seats: None   **Cover:** Yes   **Programme:** Yes   **Nickname:** Mons   **Founded:** pre-1913
Cols: White (red pin stripes)/green/red   **Change colours:** Green & red quarters/green/red
Previous Leagues: West Herts/ Watford & District
Hons: Herts Lg 84-85 85-86 (Aubrey Cup 80-81)

BOVINGDON

Secretary: Ronald Carter, 21 Yew Tree Drive, Chipperfield Rd, Bovingdon, Hemel Hempstead HP3 0TA (0442 834414).
Ground: Green Lane, Bovingdon (0442 832628).
Directions: From Hemel Hempstead to Bovingdon, left by Halfway House then right into Green Lane. Ground on left at top of hill.
Seats: Yes   **Cover:** Yes   **Programme:** No   **Nickname:** None
Colours: Green & white stripes/green/green   **Change colours:** Tangerine/black/tangerine.
Previous League: West Herts   **Hons:** Herts Lg Div 1 55-56 80-81 83-84 (Div 2 69-70).

BUSHEY RANGERS

Secretary: Rowland Marshall, 45 Blackwell Drive, Watford, Herts WD1 4HP (0923 816856).
Ground: Moatfield, Bournehall Lane, Bushey (081 950 1875).
Directions: A41 to Hartspring Lane, into Aldenham Rd, left at r'bout into the Avenue, right at top into Herkomer Rd, take 4th left.
Seats: None   **Cover:** Yes   **Programme:** No   **Nickname:** Rangers
Colours: Blue (white sleeves)/blue/white   **Change colours:** White/black/black.

CHIPPERFIELD CORINTHIANS

Secretary: Stephen J Hall, 3 Rowley Close, Oxhey, Watford, Herts WD1 4DT (0923 253803).
Ground: Queen Street, Chipperfield.
Directions: To Chipperfield via Kings Langley. Take 1st left, over crossroads, ground 400yds on right.
Seats: None   **Cover:** Yes   **Programme:** Yes   **Nickname:** None   **Founded:** 1987
Colours: Red & black stripes/red/red   **Change colours:** Blue/black/black.
Previous Leagues: None   **Hons:** Herts Lg Div 1 87-88, Herts Interm. Cup 87-88.

COLNEY HEATH

Secretary: Martin Marlborough, 16 Meadway, Colney Heath, St Albans AL4 0PT (0727 824820).
Ground: The Pavillion Recreation Ground, High Street, Colney Heath (0727 826188).
Directions: Turn off A414 in Colney Heath village, ground behind school on left.
Seats: None   **Cover:** Yes   **Programme:** Yes   **Nickname:** Magpies   **Founded:** 1907
Colours: White & black stripes/black/black & white   **Change colours:** Yellow (blue trim)/yellow/yellow.
Previous Leagues: Nth Mymms & District/Mid Herts.
Hons: Herts Lg 58-59 (Div 1 55-56 88-89, Div 2 53-54, Aubrey Cup 53-54 59-60), Herts I'mediate Cup 59-60).

CROXLEY GUILD

Secretary: Dave Rickman, 18 Tudor Walk, Watford, Herts WD2 4PA (0923 231543).
Ground: Croxley Guild of Sport, The Green, Croxley Green (0923 770534).
Directions: M25 to Chorleywood (jct 18), left off slip road (A404) to r'bout (2 miles), 1st exit to next r'bout, follow Watford sign (A412) to next r'bout, 1st exit, ground 300 yds on right opposite Artichoke pub.
Seats: None   **Cover:** No   **Programme:** No   **Nickname:** Dicko's   **Founded:** 1920
Previous Leagues: West Herts/Middx County.   **Reformed:** 1983
Colours: White & black stripes/black/black   **Change colours:** Yellow & black stripes/black/black.

CUFFLEY

Secretary: David C Chapman, 51 Woodlands Rd, Hertford, Herts SG13 7JF (0992 582358).
Ground: King Georges Playing Fields, Northaw Rd East, Cuffley (0707 875395).
Directions: A121 from Potters Bar or Cheshunt, 5 miles from either Jct 25 or 26 on M25.
Seats: None   **Cover:** Yes   **Programme:** No   **Nickname:** Zeplins   **Founded:** 1958
Colours: Maroon & sky/maroon/maroon & sky   **Change colours:** White & blue stripes/blue/blue.
Previous Leagues: Barnet/ Nth London Combination.   **Hons:** Herts Lg Div 2 77-78.

ELLIOTT STAR

Secretary: Ray Capper, 28 Alban Crescent, Boreham Wood, Herts WD6 5JF (081 207 3940).
Ground: GEC Sports Centre, Rowley Lane, Boreham Wood (081 953 5087).
Directions: A1 to Elstree Moat House, turn left (flyover) into town and turn into Elstree Way. Ground on right behind Clarenden Garage. One mile from Elstree & Boreham Wood (BR).
Seats: None   **Cover:** None   **Programme:** No   **Nickname:** None   **Founded:** 1957
Colours: Black & red stripes/black/black   **Change colours:** White/black/black.
Previous League: London Commercial   **Hons:** FA Vase 2nd Rd 91-92.

KINGS LANGLEY

Secretary: Brian Aldersley, 12 Elm Grove, Watford, Herts WD2 6QE (0923 251130).
Ground: Leavesden Hospital Ground, Woodside Rd, Abbots Langley.
Directions: A405 to Garston traffic lights. From Watford turn left (from St Albans, right) into Horseshoe Lane. Woodside Rd is one mile on right, ground quarter mile on left.
Seats: Yes   **Cover:** Yes   **Programme:** No   **Nickname:** None   **Founded:** 1886
Colours: Blue/black/black   **Change colours:** Black & white stripes/black/black.
Previous League: West Herts.
Hons: Herts Lg 47-48 49-50 51-52 65-66 66-67 (Div 1 75-76, Aubrey Cup 67-68).

KNEBWORTH

Secretary: John Stevens, 12 Olden Mead, Letchworth, Herts SG6 2SP (0462 673735).
Ground: Old Knebworth Lane, Stevenage (0438 313320).
Directions: A1(M) to Stevenage South, A602 towards Hertford, 3rd exit at 2nd r'bout (B197). Follow to Roebuck Inn and turn right opposite pub into Old Knebworth Lane. Ground 200yds on left.
Seats: Yes   **Cover:** Yes   **Programme:** Yes   **Nickname:** None   **Founded:** 1901
Colours: Tangerine/black/black   **Change colours:** Sky/blue/white
Previous Leagues: Nth Herts/Sth Mids.   **Hons:** Herts Lg 73-74 (Div 1 76-77, Aubrey Cup 76-77).

KODAK HEMEL HEMPSTEAD

Secretary: Brian Pollard, 33 Curtis Rd, Leverstock Green, Hemel Hempstead HP3 8LE (0442 256720).
Ground: Kodak Sports Ground, Wood End Lane, off Maylands Avenue, Hemel Hempstead (0442 242597).
Directions: M1 jct 8, right at 2nd r'bout (A4147) to lights, then right into Wood End Lane. Ground quarter mile on right.
Seats: None   **Cover:** No   **Programme:** No   **Nickname:**   **Founded:** 1960
Colours: Green & black stripes/black/black   **Change colours:** Yellow (red pin stripes)/black/black.
Previous League: West Herts/Sth Mids   **Hons:** Herts Lg Div 2 87-88.

LUCAS SPORTS

Secretary: Mark Revell, 223 Bennetts End Rd, Hemel Hempstead HP3 8DZ (0442 62717).
Ground: Lucas Sports Ground, Maylands Avenue, Hemel Hempstead (0442 66749).
Directions: M1 jct 8, right at 2nd r'bout (A4147). 1st factory on right is Lucas Aerospace; ground accessed through factory.
Seats: None   **Cover:** No   **Programme:** Yes   **Nickname:** None   **Founded:** 1953
Colours: Green & white hoops/green/green   **Change colours:** All red.
Hons: Herts Lg Div 2 85-86.

OXHEY JETS

Secretary: David G Fuller, 18 Woodhurst Ave., Garston, Watford, Herts WD2 6RQ (0923 679494).
Ground: Chilwell Gardens, South Oxhey (081 421 4965).
Directions: Follow Bushey signs from Watford centre, at Bushey Arches turn right into Eastbury Rd, left into Brookdene Avenue, continue along Prestwick Rd past station, right into Northwick Rd and left into Chilwell Gdns.
Seats: None   **Cover:**   **Programme:** No   **Nickname:** Jets   **Founded:** 1972
Colours: All blue   **Change colours:** All yellow.
Previous Leagues: Watford & District/West Herts.

PARK STREET

Secretary: John Mayhew, 6 Hunters Ride, Bricket Wood, St Albans, Herts AL2 3LX (0923 677996).
Ground: Recreation Ground, Park Street Lane, Park Street (0727 975302).
Directions: From Park Street (M10), proceed to A5183 towards Radlett, in Park Street village Park Street Lane is just past the Falcon pub on right hand side.
Seats: None   **Cover:** Yes   **Programme:** Yes   **Nickname:** Street
Colours: Maroon/sky/maroon   **Change colours:** Yellow/sky/blue.
Previous Leagues: Mid Herts   **Hons:** Herts Div 2 82-83.

SANDRIDGE ROVERS

Secretary: Graham C Hardwick, 21 Woodcock Hill, Sandridge, St Albans AL4 9EF (0727 55334).
Ground: Spencer Recreation Ground, Sandridge (0727 55159).
Directions: B651 from St Albans or Wheathampstead to High Street. Ground at rear of public car park.
Seats: None   **Cover:** Yes   **Programme:** Yes   **Nickname:** Rovers   **Founded:** 1896
Colours: Black & white stripes/black/red   **Change colours:** Green & white stripes/white/green.
Previous League: Mid Herts
Hons: Herts Lg 81-82 82-83 87-88 (Div 1 68-69), Herts Intermediate Cup 81-82.

SUN SPORTS

Secretary: Dave Price, 62 The Ridgeway, Watford, Herts WD1 3TL (0923 31347).
Ground: Bellmont Wood Avenue, Watford (0703 254364).
Directions: From Kings Langley to Watford on Hempstead road, turn right at Langley lights, right at r'bout then 1st left. Entrance 50yds on right.
Seats: None　　**Cover:** Yes　　**Programme:** Yes　　**Nickname:**　　**Founded:**
Colours: Yellow/blue/blue　　**Change colours:** All red.
Previous Leagues: Watford & District/West Herts.
Hons: Aubrey Cup 88-89, Herts Intermediate Cup 75-76.

WALKERN

Secretary: Ann Huggins, 3 Spinney Close, Hitchin, Herts SG4 9PD (0462 456477).
Ground: High Street, Walkern (0432 861615).
Directions: Leave A1(M) for Stevenage South, over 1st r'bout (A602), left at 2nd r'bout (Burger King), over next and right at swimming pool. Follow signs to Walkern (B1037) and in village turn right at junction. Ground 200yds on left.
Seats: None　　**Cover:** No　　**Programme:** No　　**Nickname:** None　　**Founded:** 1899
Colours: All blue　　**Change colours:** White/navy/navy.
Previous League: North Herts.

WELLCOME

Secretary: Stephen Sells, 1 Robin Hill, Berkhamsted, Herts HP4 2HX (0442 864649).
Ground: Kitcheners Field, Castle Hill, Berkhamsted (0442 74937).
Directions: A41 into Berkhamsted. At main lights turn into Lower Kings Rd, at railway station turn left under bridge, then 2nd right. Entrance on next corner.
Seats: None　　**Cover:** None　　**Programme:** No　　**Nickname:** None　　**Founded:** 1967
Colours: All blue　　**Change colours:** Green/white/green.
Previous League: West Herts Sunday　　**Hons:** Herts Lg Div 1 82-83 91-92 (Div 2 81-82).

WORMLEY ROVERS

Secretary: David M Smith, 19 Nursery Gardens, Enfield, Middx EN3 5NG (081 804 3608).
Ground: Sports Club, Church Lane, Wormley (0992 460650).
Directions: From A10 take A1170 turning for Broxbourne and Turnford. Left at New River Arms, left again into Church Lane. Ground quarter mile on right.
Seats: None　　**Cover:** No　　**Programme:** No　　**Nickname:** Robins　　**Founded:** Unknown
Colours: Red & black hoops/black/black　　**Change colours:** All blue.
Previous Leagues: Ware & District/Hertford & District/Northern Suburban.
Hons: Herts Lg Div 1 86-87 (Div 3 76-77).

DIVISION ONE CLUBS 1992-93

ALLENSBURYS SPORTS

Secretary: Paul C Connolly, 64 Vicarage Rd, Ware, Herts SG12 7BE (0920 469337).
Ground: Harris Lane, Ware (0920 462742).
Directions: From A10, take B1001 to Ware. 3rd right into Fanshawe Crescent, over crossroads into Harris Lane, ground on right.
Seats: None　　**Cover:** No　　**Programme:** No　　**Nickname:** None
Colours: Blue/blue/yellow　　**Change colours:** Yellow/blue/blue
Previous League: Hertford & District　　**Hons:** Herts Lg Div 2 90-91

DYNAMICS (STEVENAGE)

Secretary: Kevin Folds, 6 Lanthony Ct, High Street, Arlesey, Beds SG15 6TU (0462 834084).
Ground: Fairview Road, Stevenage, Herts (0438 747708).
Directions: A1(M) to Stevenage South (A602). Exit towards industrial area then turn left at next r'bout into Gunnelswood Rd. Take underpass and at following r'bout turn right into Fairlands Way. 1st left into Fairview Rd, ground 150yds on right.
Seats: None　　**Cover:** Yes　　**Programme:** Yes　　**Nickname:** None　　**Founded:** 1955
Colours: White/black/white　　**Change colours:** Claret/sky/claret.
Previous League: North Herts

EVERGREEN

Secretary: Dennis McCrystal, 76 Woodmere Ave., Watford, Herts WD2 4LW (0923 235663).
Ground: Southway, Abbots Langley (0927 767812).
Directions: A41 or A405 to r'bout junction and head for Leavesden. Right at next r'bout towards Abbots Langley, pass Rolls Royce works, then first left into Southway. Clubhouse entrance in Essex Lane at end of Southway.
Seats: None　　**Cover:** No　　**Programme:** No　　**Nickname:** None　　**Founded:** 1957
Cols: Green & white hoops/white/red　　**Change colours:** Black & blue stripes/black/black.
Previous Leagues: West Herts Youth.　　**Hons:** Herts Lg 64-65 67-88 68-69 69-70 70-71 71-72 79-80 (Aubrey Cup 64-65 66-67 69-70 70-71), Herts Intermediate Cup 79-80.

HARPENDEN ROVERS

Secretary: Fred Day, 69 Tassell Hall, Redbourn, St Albans, Herts AL3 7JD (0582 792408).
Ground: Acres Corner, Harpenden Common, Cravells Rd, Harpenden.
Directions: Cravells Rd is on A1081 (formerly A6) between Harpenden and St Albans at end of golf course.
Seats: None　　**Cover:** No　　**Programme:** No　　**Nickname:**　　**Founded:** 1928
Colours: Red/white/red　　**Change colours:** Blue/white/blue.
Previous League: Mid Herts　　**Hons:** Herts Lg Div 3 66-67.

HERTFORD YOUTH

Secretary: Dennis Head, 11 Crouchfield, Bengeo, Hertford, Herts SG14 3LP (0992 584258).
Ground: Crouchfields, Wadesmill Rd, Chapmore End, Nr Ware.
Directions: Head for Bengeo from Hertford and take B158 through Bengeo forking right at small r'bout into Wadesmill Rd. Ground about one mile on right.
Seats: None   **Cover:** None   **Programme:** No   **Nickname:**   **Founded:** 1980
Colours: Gold & red stripes/black/yellow   **Change colours:** Maroon & blue stripes/blue/blue
Previous League: Hertford & District   **Hons:** Herts Lg Div 2 91-92.

I.C.L. LETCHWORTH

Secretary: Geoff Holbrook, 43 Lawrence Ave., Letchworth, Herts SG6 2EY (0462 674493).
Ground: Whitehorn Lane, Letchworth (0462 673789).
Directions: A1 to Letchworth Gate, at elongated r'bout take 2nd left, then 2nd right into Whitehorn Lane. Ground 200yds on left.
Seats: None   **Cover:** No   **Programme:** No   **Nickname:** None   **Founded:** 1925
Colours: Gold/black/black   **Change colours:** Black & white stripes/black/black
Previous League: Mid Herts   **Hons:** Herts Lg Div 1 58-59 65-66 (Div 2 54-55).

KIMPTON ROVERS

Secretary: Neil Matthews, 30 Commons Lane, Kimpton, Herts SG4 8QG (0438 832625).
Ground: Recreation Ground, High Street, Kimpton.
Directions: Kimpton is between Stevenage, Luton & Welwyn on insection of B651 and B652. Ground is set back on hill off the High Street.
Seats: None   **Cover:** No   **Programme:** No   **Nickname:** Rovers   **Founded:** 1910
Colours: White/blue/white   **Change colours:** Dark yellow/blue/white.
Previous Leagues: Nth Herts/Mid Herts

LITTLE GADDESDEN

Secretary: Michael Fensome, 34 Old Farm, Pitstone, Leighton Buzzard, Beds LU7 9RD (0296 661612).
Ground: Church Road, Little Gaddesden, Berkhamsted.
Directions: From Hemel Hempstead follow Leighton Buzzard road. Take 2nd left after Red Lion in Waterend and follow signs to Little Gaddesden. Church Rd is 2nd right in village.
Seats: None   **Cover:** None   **Programme:** No   **Nickname:** None   **Founded:** 1936
Colours: Gold/black/black   **Change colours:** Red & black stripes/black/black.
Previous Leagues: West Herts   **Hons:**

METROPOLITAN POLICE (BUSHEY)

Secretary: Brian Southern, c/o Met Police Spts Club, Aldenham Rd, Bushey, Herts WD2 3TR (0923 243947).
Ground: Aldenham Road, Bushey (0923 243947).
Directions: M1 jct 5, A41 for Harrow/South Watford, at 1st r'bout right into Hartspring Lane which runs into Aldenham (A4008). Ground quarter mile on left opposite Caledonian School.
Seats: None   **Cover:** No   **Programme:** No   **Nickname:** None
Colours: Yellow/red/red   **Change colours:** Green/black/green.

NORTH MYMMS

Secretary: Mick Fitt, 61 Holloways Lane, North Mymms, Hatfield, Herts AL9 7NU (0707 269790).
Ground: Recreation Ground, Dellsome Lane, Welham Green (07072 66972/60338).
Directions: Welham Green is 2 miles south of Hatfield. At village crossroads turn north into Dellsome Lane. Ground on left.
Seats: None   **Cover:** None   **Programme:** No   **Nickname:** None   **Founded:** 1968
Colours: Sky/navy/sky   **Change colours:** Red/red/red.

ST IPPOLYTS

Secretary: Andre Edmonds, 35 Crabtree Dell, Letchworth, Herts SG6 2TJ (0462 679753).
Ground: Recreation Ground, Orchard Close, off Mill Road, St Ippolyts (0462 456748).
Directions: B656 from Welwyn. Left at St Ippolyts crossroads, right into The Crescent, left into Mill Rd. Orchard Close is a turning off this road.
Seats: None   **Cover:** No   **Programme:** No   **Nickname:** Saints   **Founded:** 1908
Colours: Black & red stripes/black/black   **Change colours:** Blue/black/black.
Previous League: North Herts.

ST PETERS (ST ALBANS)

Secretary: Peter Gordon, 63 Lodies Grove, St Albans, Herts AL3 5TZ (0727 55286).
Ground: Toulmin Drive, St Albans, Herts.
Directions: St Albans ring-road towards Betchwood Golf Club. 20 yds from north entrance turn into Green Lane. At top of hill turn left into Toulmin Drive.
Seats: Yes   **Cover:** Yes   **Programme:** No   **Nickname:** Saints   **Founded:** pre-1904
Colours: Red/black/red   **Change colours:** Blue/black/black.
Previous League: Mid Herts

SARRATT

Secretary: Mick Warner, 'Colinwood', 45 Church Lane, Sarratt, Herts WD3 6HN (0923 264618).
Ground: King George V Playing Fields, King George Avenue, Sarratt.
Directions: To Kings Langley, and then via Chipperfield.
Seats: None   **Cover:** No   **Programme:** No   **Nickname:**   **Founded:** Unknown
Colours: Black & amber/black/black   **Change colours:** Red & black stripes/black/red.
Previous League: West Herts   **Hons:** Herts Lg Div 2 79-80.

SOMERSETT AMBURY V & E

Secretary: Ian Whittle, 21 Kilwardby Street, Ashby-de-la-Zouch, Leics LE65 2FR (0530 41347).
Ground: V & E Youth Club, Goffs Lane, Cheshunt (0992 24281).
Directions: M25 jct 25, A10 north, left at 1st r'bout onto Flamstead End relief road to r'bout with Goffs Lane. Right into Goffs Lane, clubhouse immediately on right.
Seats: None   **Cover:** No   **Programme:** No   **Nickname:**   **Founded:** 1960
Colours: White/blue/blue   **Change colours:** Red/black/black.
Previous Leagues: Enfield Alliance, Hertford & District.

STANDON & PUCKERIDGE

Secretary: David North, 66 Batchelors, Puckeridge, Nr Ware, Herts SG11 1TJ (0920 821838).
Ground: Recreation Ground, Station Rd, Standon, Nr Ware (0920 822489).
Directions: A10 6 miles north of Ware or 4 miles south from Buntingford. Take A120 from A10 Bishop's Stortford r'bout. Over Standon Hill and into Station Rd (3rd left after r'bout), ground quarter mile on left.
Seats: None   **Cover:** No   **Programme:** No   **Nickname:** None   **Founded:** 1931
Colours: Blue & white/white/blue   **Change colours:** White/green/green.
Previous League: Hertford & District/Norhern Suburban Intermediate.

STEVENAGE CLUB & INSTITUTE

Secretary: David Cook, 42 Carters Close, Stevenage, Herts SG2 9QA (0438 729900).
Ground: Meadway Recreation Ground, Redcar Road, Stevenage.
Directions: A1(M) to Stevenage South (A602), exit towards Industrial area then turn into Gunnelswood Road. Over next two r'bouts, left at next towards Meadway Industrial area. Recreation ground signposted in Redcar Road.
Seats: None   **Cover:** No   **Programme:** No   **Nickname:** None
Colours: Sky & white stripes/sky/sky   **Change colours:** All green.
Previous League: North Herts

VALMAR L.R.

Secretary: John Walsh, 44 Western Avenue, St Albans, Herts AL3 5HP (0727 233511).
Ground: Lemsford Village Hall, Brocket Road, Lemsford (0707 335548).
Directions: Welwyn Garden City exit from A1(M), left to Stanborough 'Ball' r'bout, 2nd exit towards Wheathipstead, Lemsford three quarters of a mile on the right.
Seats: None   **Cover:** No   **Programme:** No   **Nickname:** None
Colours: Red & black hoops/black/black   **Change colours:** Sky/navy/navy
Previous League: Mid Herts

WELWYN

Secretary: Michael Pestle, 4 Marsden Close, Welwyn Garden City, Herts AL8 6YE (0707 335503).
Ground: Welwyn Playing Field, Ottway Walk, London Rd, Welwyn (0438 714183).
Directions: From A1(M) take A1000 turning 1st left off r'bout, then 1st right at Nodeway filling station into London Rd. Ground quarter mile on left opposite Steamer pub.
Seats: None   **Cover:** No   **Programme:** Yes   **Nickname:** None   **Founded:** 1893
Colours: All blue   **Change colours:** All red.
Previous Leagues: North Herts/Mid Herts   **Hons:** Herts Lg Div 1 79-80.

WHITWELL ATHLETIC

Secretary: Michael Atkinson, 17 Dalton Way, Whitwell, Nr Hitchin, Herts SG4 8BG (0438 871250).
Ground: King Georges Recreation Ground, Bradway, off Horn Hill, Whitwell.
Directions: B651 from St Albans. From A1 via Welwyn and Codicote.
Seats: None   **Cover:** Yes   **Programme:** No   **Nickname:** None   **Reformed:** 1991
Colours: Blue/white/blue   **Change colours:** Red & white/red/red.

RESERVE SECTION CONSTITUTIONS 1992-93

Division One
1. BAC Stevenage Reserves
2. Bedmond Sports & Social Reserves
3. Bovingdon Reserves
4. Bushey Rangers Reserves
5. Chipperfield Corinthian Res.
6. Colney Heath Reserves
7. Croxley Guild Reserves
8. Dynamics Stevenage Reserves
9. Elliott Star Reserves
10. Kings Langley Reserves
11. Knebworth Reserves
12. Lucas Sports Reserves
13. Oxhey Jets Reserves
14. Park Street Reserves
15. Sandridge Rovers Reserves
16. Sun Sports Reserves
17. Walkern Reserves
18. Welwyn Reserves
19. Wormley Rovers Reserves

Division Two
1. Allensbury Sports Reserves
2. Cuffley Reserves
3. Evergreen Reserves
4. Harpenden Rovers
5. Hertford Youth Reserves
6. ICL Letchworth Reserves
7. Kimpton Rovers Reserves
8. Kodak Hemel Hempstead Reserves
9. Little Gaddesden Reserves
10. Met. Police (Bushey) Reserves
11. North Mymms Reserves
12. St Ippolyts Reserves
13. St Peters Reserves
14. Sarratt Reserves
15. Standon & Puckeridge Reserves
16. Stevenage Club & Institute Reserves
17. Somersett Ambury V & E Reserves
18. Valmar L.R. Reserves
19. Wellcome Reserves
20. Whitwell Athletic Reserves

MIDDLESEX COUNTY LEAGUE

Patron: Russell Grant,
President: Peter Rogers,
Chairman: Fred Griggs,
Hon. Secretary: Keith Chamberlin,
4 Shelley Ave., Greenford, Middx UB6 8RU.

TITLE RACE GOES TO FINAL GAME

1991-92 proved to be another exciting season for the Middlesex County Football League. For the third year in succession the League provided the winners of the Middlesex County Premier Cup, and for the first time both finalists were members of the County League. Osterley defeated Northfield Rangers in a thrilling match in front of a large crowd at Edgware Town FC. Broadwater United also came close to tasting County Cup success as they were beaten finalists in the London Junior Cup.

The League championship was decided on the very last day when the top two teams, Shamrock and Northfield Rangers, met in the final fixture. Northfield took all three points and therefore made sure of their first County League championship, having finished as runners-up the previous season.

The Division One title was won by Broadwater United, at the first attempt, with Pitshanger runners-up after heading the table for most of the campaign. Division Two champions, Bridge Park, were also newcomers to the League. They won their division on goal difference from Heathrow Club.

The League's senior cup competition, the Alec Smith Cup, was played for by those clubs in membership of the top two divisions. Pitshanger, from Division One, won a pulsating final against New Hanford at Hayes FC to add to their promotion back to the top flight. Osterley Reserves won the Division Two Cup with New Hanford, in the form of their reserves, once again providing the beaten opposition.

The League representative team performed creditably in their debut season in the South Eastern Intermediate Inter-League Competition. They finished third, when a win in their final fixture would have seen them champions.

Unprecedented interest from prospective member clubs has enabled the League to expand for the 1992-93 season into three larger divisions.

John Taylor, Hon. Secretary 1991-92.

LEAGUE TABLES 1991-92

Premier Division	P	W	D	L	F	A	PTS
Northfield Rangers	22	14	6	2	46	22	48
Shamrock	22	13	6	3	61	27	*44
New Hanford	22	10	7	5	39	25	37
Technicolor Sports	22	10	4	8	38	39	34
W'den (Constantine)	22	8	8	6	29	26	32
Maple Cross	22	9	4	9	47	38	31
Osterley	22	7	7	8	26	32	28
Brook House Res	22	8	4	10	30	35	*27
CAV Northolt	22	7	4	11	39	36	25
Simba All Stars	22	7	4	11	29	39	25
Southall Reserves	22	4	6	12	23	47	18
Flackwell Hth Res	22	3	4	15	31	72	13

* - Denotes one point deducted

Division One	P	W	D	L	F	A	PTS
Broadwater Utd	22	16	3	3	76	40	51
Pitshanger	22	13	6	3	52	27	45
Hanworth Villa	22	13	3	6	62	38	42
Rayners Lane Res	22	12	3	7	45	32	39
St Clarets (Hayes)	22	11	3	8	61	47	36
Cockfosters Res	22	10	5	7	51	35	35
Neasden	22	9	5	8	53	49	*31
Harrow St Mary's	22	6	3	13	31	64	21
Beaconfield Utd Res	22	5	5	12	33	52	20
Northfield Rgrs Res	22	5	5	12	34	60	20
Amersham Res	22	4	5	13	30	55	17
Nth Greenford Res	22	3	4	15	27	56	13

* - denotes 1 point deducted

Division Two	P	W	D	L	F	A	PTS
Bridge Park	18	11	4	3	54	25	37
Heathrow Club	18	11	4	3	45	25	37
Technicolor Res	18	11	1	6	55	42	34
Osterley Reserves	18	10	1	7	50	36	31
CAV Northolt Res	18	8	4	6	40	39	28
New Hanford Res	18	7	3	8	35	33	24
Hanwell Town 'A'	18	7	3	8	35	36	24
Utd Biscuits (H'den)	18	6	3	9	38	52	21
Pitshanger Res	18	3	4	11	24	43	13
Nth Hayes Academ.	18	1	3	14	22	67	6

PREMIER DIVISION RESULTS 1991/92

HOME TEAM	1	2	3	4	5	6	7	8	9	10	11	12
1. Brook House Reserves	*	1-2	2-0	5-1	1-4	0-1	2-1	0-3	0-1	2-2	4-1	2-1
2. CAV Northolt	1-1	*	1-2	2-2	0-1	0-3	0-0	2-3	3-0	4-5	0-1	2-1
3. Flackwell Hth Res	2-3	1-6	*	1-4	1-1	0-4	1-2	2-2	1-5	6-1	1-4	1-4
4. Maple Cross CSSC	4-1	1-2	11-0	*	2-4	3-1	1-2	0-2	1-2	1-0	2-1	2-0
5. New Hanford	0-0	2-0	1-2	1-1	*	2-2	2-1	2-2	3-1	1-3	4-0	4-0
6. Northfield Rangers	1-0	3-2	3-3	4-3	1-1	*	2-0	2-1	3-0	1-0	1-0	0-0
7. Osterley	2-0	1-0	1-1	1-1	1-2	1-1	*	2-2	2-1	3-1	1-0	1-2
8. Shamrock	1-1	2-2	5-2	5-0	0-1	3-2	5-2	*	5-1	7-1	2-2	0-1
9. Simba All Stars	1-3	1-2	3-1	2-0	2-0	1-3	1-1	1-3	*	1-1	1-3	1-0
10. Southall Reserves	0-1	0-5	4-1	0-2	2-1	1-4	0-0	0-3	0-0	*	1-1	0-1
11. Technicolor Sports	2-1	3-2	2-1	1-4	2-1	0-3	4-0	1-2	4-3	2-1	*	3-3
12. Willesden (Constantine)	4-0	2-1	3-1	1-1	1-1	1-1	3-1	0-3	0-0	0-0	1-1	*

ALEC SMITH (MIDDLESEX COUNTY LEAGUE) CUP 1991-92

Group One	P	W	D	L	F	A	PTS
Pitshanger	5	5	0	0	13	4	15
CAV Northolt	5	3	1	1	10	7	10
Southall Reserves	5	2	2	1	12	6	8
Rayners Lane Res	5	1	1	3	12	10	4
Amersham T. Res	5	1	0	4	8	17	3
Flackwell Hth Res	5	1	0	4	8	19	3

Group Three	P	W	D	L	F	A	PTS
Shamrock	5	5	0	0	24	2	15
Cockfosters Res	5	3	0	2	6	8	9
Maple Cross	5	2	0	3	10	7	6
Nth Greenford Res	5	1	2	2	5	10	5
Simba All Stars	5	1	2	2	7	9	5
Northfield R. Res	5	0	2	3	4	20	2

Group Two	P	W	D	L	F	A	PTS
Northfield Rgrs	5	5	0	0	24	2	15
Neasden	5	3	1	1	10	8	10
Broadwater United	5	3	0	2	20	8	9
Osterley	5	1	2	2	4	7	5
Beaconsfield Res	5	0	2	3	5	28	2
Brook House Res	5	0	1	4	3	13	1

Group Four	P	W	D	L	F	A	PTS
New Hanford	5	5	0	0	14	4	15
Technicolor Sports	5	4	0	1	24	8	12
Hanworth Villa	5	3	0	2	8	8	9
Harrow St Mary's	5	1	1	3	4	15	4
St Clarets (Hayes)	5	1	0	4	9	14	3
W'den (Constantine)	5	0	1	4	4	14	1

Quarters Finals

Northfield Rangers v CAV Northolt	6-1	New Hanford v Cockfosters Res	4-3(aet)
Pitshanger v Neasden	2-0	Shamrock v Technicolor Sports	1-2(aet)

Semi Finals

Pitshanger v Technicolor Spts (4//4/92)2-1   Northfield Rgrs v New Hanford (11/4/92)   0-1

Final (at Hayes FC, 2/5/92): Pitshanger 4, New Hanford 2

PREMIER DIVISION CLUBS 1992-93

BROADWATER UNITED
Secretary: Godfrey Lowe, 53 Rochford Road, Tottenham N17 6HX (081 801 7616).
Ground: Lordship Lane Recreation Ground, Lordship Lane, Tottenham, London N17.
Colours: All blue   **Change colours:** Red/white/red.

C.A.V. NORTHOLT
Ground: Armenian Community Centre, West End Road, Northolt, Middx (081 845 1796).
Secretary: Pauline Jones, 6 Siverst Close, Northolt, Middx (081 845 5416).
Colours: Blue/navy/navy   **Change colours:** Red/white/red.

HANWORTH VILLA
Secretary: David Brown, 93 Tudor Drive, Kingston KT2 5NP (081 546 5979).
Ground: Twickenham Park Golf Club, Staines Road, Twickenham TW2 5JD (081 783 1748).
Colours: White/sky/sky   **Change colours:** Red/sky/sky.

MAPLE CROSS C.S.S.C.
Ground: Maple Cross Playing Fields, Maple Cross, Rickmansworth, Herts.
Secretary: Frank Bailey, 43 Longcroft Road, Maple Cross, Rickmansworth, Herts WD3 2TS (0923 775964).
Colours: Red & black/black/red & black   **Change colours:** Green/black/black.

NEASDEN
Secretary: Everton King, 109 Village Way, Neasden NW10 0LN (081 450 9747).
Ground: Chalkhill Youth Community Centre, Poplar Grove, Wembley, Middx (081 904 1974).
Colours: Blue & red checks/white/blue.

NEW HANFORD
Secretary: Jerry Scanlon, 70 Bridge Avenue, Hanwell W7 3DJ (081 575 0113).
Ground: Birkbeck College Playing Fields, Birkbeck Avenue, Greenford, Middx.
Colours: All sky   **Change Colours:** Amber/black/black.

NORTHFIELD RANGERS
Secretary: Bob Webster, 82 Rushdene Cres, Northolt UB5 6NQ (081 845 0031).
Ground: Yeading FC (see page 321).
Colours: Yellow/black/yellow   **Change Colours:** White/black/black.

OSTERLEY
Secretary: Avice Horne, 49 Evelyn Close, Whitton, Twickenham, Middx TW2 7BL (081 898 3581).
Ground: The White Lodge Club, Syon Lane, Osterley, Middx (081 758 1191).
Colours: Blue & white stripes/white/blue **Change Colours:** Red & white stripes/red/red.

PITSHANGER
Secretary: Dave Grundy, 19 Mulgrave Road, Ealing W5 1LF (081 998 6553).
Ground: Scotch Common, Ealing, London W13 (081 991 9826).
Colours: White/white/tangerine.   **Club Colours:** Tangerine/black/black.

SHAMROCK
Secretary: Richard Gallagher, 32 Beamont Avenue, Wembley HA0 3BZ (081 902 3591).
Ground: Shamrock Club House, Horn Lane, Acton (081 993 1270). **Colours:** Green & white green/green.

SIMBA ALL STARS
Secretary: Lewis John, 64b Southerton Road, Hammersmith, London W6 (081 748 0389).
Ground: West London Stadium, Artillery Lane, Du Cane Road, London W12 (081 749 5502).
Colours: All red   **Change Colours:** All white.

SPELTHORNE SPORTS
Secretary: Ron Ford, 35 Walton Gardens, Feltham, Middx TW13 4QY (081 890 8346).
Ground: Spelthorne Spts Ground, 296 Staines Rd West, Ashford Common, Middx (0932 783625).
Colours: Sky & navy/navy/navy   **Club Colours:** Yellow/blue/blue

TECHNICOLOR SPORTS
Secretary: Roy Shields, 26 Shorediche Road, Ickenham, Uxbridge UB10 8EB (0895 679031).
Ground: Technicolor Sports Ground, Springfield Road, Hayes, Middx (081 573 1203).
Cols: Claret & blue/white/claret & blue **Change Cols:** Black & white stripes/black/black.

WILLESDEN (CONSTANTINE)

Secretary: Dwight John, 29 Tangmere Gardens, Northolt UB5 6LS (081 845 9887).
Ground: Roe Green Park, Bacon Lane, Kingsbury, London NW9 (081 204 3541).
Colours: All blue   **Club Colours:** Red & white stripes/white/red.

DIVISION ONE CLUBS 1992-93

BEACONSFIELD UNITED RESERVES *(See page 390 for full details)*

BRIDGE PARK

Secretary: Brian Wilson, 19 Severn Way, Neasden NW10 2UU (081 459 4545).
Ground: Bridge Park, Brentfield, Harrow Road, London NW10 0RG (081 961 5353).
Colours: Red & black stripes/black/red   **Change colours:** Blue & white stripes/blue/blue

BRIMSDOWN ROVERS RESERVES & BROOK HOUSE RESERVES (see page 390), COCKFOSTERS RES. *(see page 392)*, FLACKWELL HEATH RES. *(see page 378)*

HARROW ST MARY'S

Secretary: David Campbell, 11 Walford Road, Uxbridge UB8 2NF (0895 272473).
Ground: Harrow Recreation Ground, Roxborough Road, Harrow (081 427 0661).
Colours: White/black/red   **Change colours:** Yellow/black/green.

HEATHROW CLUB

Ground: Heathrow Club Sports Ground, Syon Lane, Osterley, Middx (081 758 0659).
Secretary: Les Cordery, 26 Jellicoe Close, Windsor Meadows, Cippenham, Bucks SL1 9HN (0753 516015).
Colours: Emerald green/green/green   **Change colours:** Royal blue & scarlet/royal/royal

HOUNSLOW TOWN '91

Secretary: Catherine Horne, 49 Evelyn Close, Whitton, Twickenham TW2 7BL (081 898 3581).
Ground: Inwood Park, Inwood Road, Hounslow, Middx.
Colours: White/tangerine/tangerine   **Change colours:** Red & black stripes/red/red.

NORTHOLT SAINTS

Secretary: Robert Bevis, 118 Costons Lane, Greenford, Middx UB6 8RP (081 578 8504).
Ground: Lord Halsbury Playing Fields, Eastcote Lane, Northolt, Middx (081 841 1249).
Colours: Yellow/blue/blue   **Change colours:** Red/black/black.

RAYNERS LANE RESERVES *(See Hellenic League section for full detailts)*

ST CLARETS (HAYES)

Secretary: Michael Burke, 7 Gledwood Drive, Hayes, Middx UB4 0AG (081 573 4517).
Ground: Cranford Community School, High Street, Cranford, Hounslow, Middx (081 897 6609).
Colours: Yellow/green/green   **Change colours:** Red & white/white/white.

SOUTHALL RESERVES (see page 362), SOUTHGATE ATHLETIC RESERVES (see page 394)

DIVISION TWO CLUBS 1992-93

AMERSHAM TOWN RES., BRIMSDOWN ROVERS 'A' *(see page 390)*, **C.A.V. NORTHOLT RES.** *(see page 408)*, **HANWELL TOWN 'A'** *(see page 392)*, **NEW HANFORD RES., NORTHFIELD RANGERS RES.** *(see page 408)*, **NORTH GREENFORD UNITED RES.** *(see page 394)*

NORTHOLT DYNAMO

Secretary: Martin Copeland, 19 Ribblesdale Avenue, Northolt, Middx UB5 4NF (081 423 1019).
Ground: As Osterley FC (page 408).   **Colours:** Yellow/blue/red

OSTERLEY RESERVES, PITSHANGER RESERVES (see page 408)

SCOLAR

Secretary: Errol Williams, 102 Roundwood Rd, Harlesden, London NW10 9UN (081 451 5807).
Ground: As Bridge Park FC (above).
Colours: Silver grey/red/black   **Change colours:** Red/red/grey.

SPELTHORNE SPORTS RESERVES, TECHNICOLOR SPORTS (see page 408)

UNITED BISCUITS (HARLESDEN)

Secretary: Mick O'Connell, 19 Kenmore Avenue, Harrow HA3 8PA (081 909 3690).
Ground: TBA
Colours: Blue/white/white & blue   **Change Colours:** Yellow/blue/yellow & blue.

MISCELLANEOUS LEAGUES

WINDSOR, SLOUGH & DISTRICT LEAGUE

PREM. DIVISION	P	W	D	L	F	A	PTS
Slough Heating	18	14	1	3	45	27	29
Slough Irish Soc.	18	11	4	3	59	20	26
Orchard Sports	18	10	0	8	45	31	20
Iver	18	7	4	7	40	26	18
Chalvey Sports	18	6	5	7	41	41	17
Singh Sabha Slough	18	6	4	8	38	34	16
I.C.I. (Slough)	18	0	0	18	13	102	0

DIVISION ONE	P	W	D	L	F	A	PTS
John Crane (UK)	24	20	2	2	102	29	43
Jolly Londoner	24	17	3	4	87	40	37
Iver Heath Rovers	24	15	3	6	63	46	34
Slough Laurencians	24	13	3	8	58	55	29
Forum	24	10	6	8	66	39	26
Slough Heating Res	24	7	4	13	46	73	18
Iver Reserves	24	5	3	16	27	66	13
Old Paludians	24	3	4	17	29	73	10
Eton Town	24	2	4	18	29	86	8

DIVISION TWO	P	W	D	L	F	A	PTS
ICI Slough Res	18	14	2	2	62	24	30
Sl. Laurenc. Res	18	13	1	4	70	30	27
Chalvey Spts Res	18	10	3	5	35	28	23
Crane Sports	18	9	2	7	40	39	20
Iver Hth Rvrs Res	18	6	3	9	41	46	15
Mercian United	18	4	1	13	27	62	9
Cargo	18	1	0	17	26	72	2

Senior Cup Final (at Beaconsfield Utd)
Slough Irish Society 4, Iver 0

Junior Cup Final (at Burnham FC)
Slough Laurencians Res 3, Slough Heating Res 2 *(aet)*

BASINGSTOKE LEAGUE

PREM. DIVISION	P	W	D	L	F	A	PTS
Burghlere	20	13	5	2	57	28	44
Hook	20	13	4	3	65	23	43
Sherborne	20	14	1	5	72	32	43
Wootton	20	12	2	6	52	33	38
Bramley United	20	11	3	6	55	36	36
Tadley	20	10	2	8	57	42	32
R & J Transport	20	6	4	10	46	53	22
Skewers Select	20	6	4	10	42	54	22
Hare & Hounds	20	5	0	10	27	70	15
Basing Rovers	20	3	2	15	35	94	11
FHS Sherfield	20	2	3	15	35	78	9

DIVISION ONE	P	W	D	L	F	A	PTS
Winkle	22	16	2	4	88	32	50
Hannington Utd	22	16	0	6	66	32	48
Oakley Athletic	22	15	2	5	66	35	47
Kingsclere	22	15	0	7	63	37	45
Wootton Res	22	13	2	7	54	38	41
FC Winklebury	22	12	3	7	64	44	39
Hook Res	22	12	2	8	61	32	38
Tadley Res	22	10	3	9	52	39	33
Basingstoke L.C.	22	6	2	14	43	96	20
Headley	22	3	3	17	34	87	9
Unipath	22	2	2	18	25	77	8
Mercantile	22	2	1	19	26	93	7

NORTH HAMPSHIRE LEAGUE

	P	W	D	L	F	A	PTS
Whitchurch Utd Res	22	18	2	2	56	14	56
Charlton Royal	22	15	3	4	69	25	48
Aldermaston Res	22	14	2	6	50	37	44
Winchester City Res	22	13	4	5	46	28	43
Overton Utd Res	22	10	3	9	37	38	33
Camrose Social	22	10	2	10	37	34	32
RAPV Worthy Down	22	9	4	9	61	47	31
Alresford T. Res	22	7	5	10	37	45	26
Malshanger Res	22	7	1	14	27	62	22
Worthies Sports	22	6	3	13	34	59	21
Kings Somborne	22	3	3	16	34	73	12
Winch. Castle Res	22	3	2	17	31	57	11

'CEILING SYSTEM SUPPLIES' READING LEAGUE

SEN. DIVISION	P	W	D	L	F	A	PTS
Reading Exiles	20	14	3	3	67	32	45
Broadmoor	20	13	3	4	66	23	42
West Reading	20	11	4	5	44	29	37
Forest Old Boys	20	9	9	2	49	28	36
Cookham Dean	20	9	6	5	32	29	33
Mortimer	20	8	5	7	43	32	29
South Reading	20	7	5	8	37	39	26
R.E.M.E.	20	7	1	12	34	50	22
Marlow	20	6	1	13	36	53	19
Old Prestonians	20	3	5	12	22	55	14
Cotswold	20	1	2	17	22	81	5

DIVISION ONE	P	W	D	L	F	A	PTS
Woodley Arms	20	15	3	2	75	20	48
Newton Henley	20	15	2	3	62	22	47
Tilehurst	20	11	5	4	63	35	38
Berks Civil Service	20	10	6	4	62	27	33
Reading Old Boys	20	10	0	10	46	46	30
Thames Vale	20	9	2	9	39	40	29
Earlbourne	20	6	5	9	37	55	23
Reading University	20	6	3	11	37	43	21
Sonning	20	4	4	12	30	54	16
Nettlebed	20	3	4	13	27	81	13
Bucklebury	20	2	4	14	23	78	10

ALDERSHOT LEAGUE

SEN. DIVISION	P	W	D	L	F	A	PTS
Yateley	18	12	1	5	38	26	37
Frimley Town	18	10	4	4	59	29	34
Four Marks	18	10	2	6	37	36	32
Tongham	18	10	1	7	53	38	31
Old Salesians	18	8	3	7	40	26	27
Bordon	18	6	2	10	27	38	20
Yateley Green	18	5	5	8	23	26	20
Alton T. Bass Res	18	5	2	11	16	46	17
Liphook	18	4	3	11	21	41	15

DIVISION ONE	P	W	D	L	F	A	PTS
Covies Res	20	16	2	2	62	18	50
Spennys	20	16	2	2	59	29	50
Frimley Town Res	20	13	6	1	60	23	45
Ashley Park	20	10	4	6	55	37	34
Yateley Green Res	20	10	3	7	35	37	33
Fleet Spurs Res	20	9	4	7	48	31	31
Admel	20	6	4	10	46	53	22
Lindford Ryl Ex.	20	5	3	12	35	65	18
Yateley Res	20	4	5	11	24	51	17
Tongham Res	20	1	3	16	28	66	6
Liphook Res	20	1	2	17	21	63	5

MID-ESSEX LEAGUE

PREM. DIVISION	P	W	D	L	F	A	PTS
Danbury Trafford	24	19	4	1	87	25	61
United Glass Spts	24	19	3	2	72	27	60
Boreham	24	13	4	7	63	57	43
Weir House	24	12	7	5	51	34	43
Southminster	24	11	5	8	50	45	38
Braintree United	24	10	6	8	69	62	36
Outwood Common	24	10	5	9	66	41	35
Heybridge Sports	24	7	6	11	42	55	27
Writtle Victoria	24	7	6	11	49	65	27
Burnham Rblrs 'A'	24	6	5	13	36	69	23
Roxwell	24	6	3	15	45	73	21
St Margarets	24	6	0	18	41	69	18
Terling Villa	24	2	4	18	20	68	18

HUNTINGDONSHIRE LEAGUE

DIVISION ONE	P	W	D	L	F	A	PTS
St Neots Town	18	14	3	1	49	20	45
Clarksteel Yax. Res	18	13	2	3	52	21	41
Offord	18	11	0	7	56	40	33
Brampton	18	9	2	7	37	26	29
Hemingford	18	8	2	8	47	33	26
Huntingdon Utd Res	18	8	1	9	45	32	25
Buckden	18	7	2	9	36	46	23
Needingworth	18	7	0	11	29	52	21
Fenstanton	18	5	2	11	37	58	17
West Huntingdon	18	1	0	17	15	75	3

ESSEX SENIOR FOOTBALL LEAGUE

Chairman: Allan Montgomery.

Treasurer: Margaret Errington.

Hon. Secretary: Denis Metson,
79 Larkswood Road, Corringham, Stanford-le-Hope SS17 9DD (0375 67099).

A CLOSE SHAVE

Ford United rekindled their glory days of the fifties as Briggs Sports with a championship that finished as the closest in the history of the League and probably that of British football. Three clubs (Ford, Brentwood and East Thurrock) all finished on 66 points with Sawbridgeworth just one point behind, so it was goal difference that decided the placings. In addition to this, the 'Motormen' retained the Essex Senior Trophy in the process, and fought out a thrilling tussle with Billericay to be just pipped for the Essex Thameside Trophy.

East Thurrock gained the coveted league placing required for promotion to the Diadora League, and won the League Cup with a 2-0 win over Basildon United.

Although leading the table for most of the season, Brentwood had to accept second spot for the second year running. The joyous news from this camp for all the folk who love this friendly club is that, despite losing their Larkins ground as it does not come up to senior standard, Brentwood will groundshare at East Thurrock and thus keep their place in the League. Sadly, we lose Stambridge who drop down to Intermediate Football, but we warmly welcome the Intermediate team of the year, Great Wakering Rovers, to the fold along with the reformed Romford who will, initially, groundshare at Hornchurch.

Bowers United won the Harry Fisher Memorial Trophy beating last season's treble winners, Southend Manor, 1-0. The Reserve Section was a runaway success for Sawbridgeworth Reserves with the Cup going to Eton Manor's second string, and the Shield to Canvey Island.

In only their second season in the League, Hullbridge Sports deservedly won the Sportsmanship Award, and in their first season, Concord Rangers performance on and off the field was most pleasing.

Saddest retirement of the season was that of Lester Metcalf of Southend Manor after 27 years at the helm, whilst Keith Farrow of Canvey Island was responsible for their Programme Award in the Wirral Survey keeping up the excellent tradition of journalist art from the island. Sawbridgeworth won double honours for goalscoring with Tony Liddle the leading Senior Section marksman and Nicky Camp for the Reserves.

Robert A Errington, League Vice Chairman

Ford United, Essex Senior League champions 1991-92. Back Row (L/R): M Taylor, T St Pier, P Evans, D Spittle, P Jeffery, M Baker, P Mitchell. Front: D McGovern, I Sutton, M Chester, G Hudspeth, R Duley, C Wood, J Evans. Photo - Dave West.

411

LEAGUE TABLES 1991-92

Senior Division	P	W	D	L	F	A	PTS
Ford United	32	20	6	6	64	18	66
Brentwood	32	20	6	6	77	37	66
East Thurrock Utd	32	19	9	4	62	24	66
Sawbridgeworth T.	32	19	8	5	67	43	65
Canvey Island	32	19	6	7	49	24	63
Basildon United	32	17	5	10	65	39	56
Bowers United	32	15	9	8	49	31	54
Southend United	32	14	6	12	62	40	48
Stambridge	32	12	8	12	63	49	44
Woodford Town	32	12	7	13	46	44	43
Concord Rangers	32	10	10	12	39	52	40
Stansted	32	11	6	15	40	50	39
Burnham Ramblers	32	10	4	18	48	71	34
Hullbridge Sports	32	7	7	18	25	63	38
East Ham United	32	7	5	20	35	72	26
Eton Manor	32	5	3	24	24	71	18
Maldon Town	32	1	3	28	20	104	6

Reserve Division	P	W	D	L	F	A	PTS
Sawbridgeworth Res	28	21	6	1	69	14	69
Woodford T. Res	28	19	5	4	79	34	*59
Concord Rgrs Res	28	14	4	10	50	46	46
Brentwood Res	28	12	7	9	47	37	43
Brightlingsea Res	28	12	6	10	58	44	42
Bowers Utd Res	28	12	5	11	58	55	41
Stambridge Res	28	11	5	12	56	46	38
Eton Manor Res	28	11	5	12	49	38	38
Stansted Res	28	12	2	14	49	59	38
Burnham Rblrs Res	28	10	7	11	51	50	37
Canvey Island Res	28	10	7	11	39	48	37
Basildon Utd Res	28	8	4	16	35	66	28
Maldon Town Res	28	8	3	17	38	70	27
Southend Mnr Res	28	6	6	16	38	64	24
Hullbridge Res	28	6	4	18	36	67	22

* - 3 pts deducted; ineligible players

SENIOR SECTION RESULTS 1991/92

HOME TEAM	1	2	3	4	5	6	7	8	9	10	11	12	13	14	15	16	17
1. Basildon Utd	*	3-0	0-1	1-2	0-2	2-0	5-0	3-1	4-1	1-1	3-0	4-1	3-2	2-1	4-0	5-1	3-2
2. Bowers United	2-1	*	2-2	2-0	0-0	0-0	1-1	0-3	2-0	1-1	6-1	4-0	3-0	2-1	1-0	0-0	0-1
3. Brentwood	4-0	0-1	*	6-1	2-4	4-1	2-0	2-1	2-0	0-2	2-0	5-1	5-5	2-0	2-2	3-1	0-0
4. Burnham Ramblers	0-1	1-2	0-1	*	2-0	1-3	2-4	3-3	1-1	0-3	3-0	3-1	1-2	1-7	2-1	0-2	1-2
5. Canvey Island	1-0	0-3	1-1	4-0	*	1-2	0-1	0-0	1-0	1-0	2-0	3-0	2-2	2-1	0-0	1-0	1-0
6. Concord Rangers	1-2	3-2	0-5	2-3	1-1	*	1-0	0-0	2-1	1-2	4-1	3-1	3-3	0-0	1-5	0-0	2-2
7. East Ham United	1-1	0-3	2-6	2-5	0-1	0-1	*	0-4	1-0	0-3	1-1	3-0	4-2	1-3	0-2	1-2	0-1
8. East Thurrock United	0-2	1-1	1-1	5-1	2-1	1-0	6-1	*	3-1	1-0	2-0	5-1	0-0	1-1	0-0	3-0	3-2
9. Eton Manor	0-2	1-0	0-1	0-3	1-5	2-0	3-1	0-1	*	0-4	0-1	1-1	0-2	1-4	1-1	2-0	0-3
10. Ford United	2-0	2-0	3-0	4-0	0-1	0-0	3-0	1-2	3-0	*	2-0	4-0	3-4	2-0	2-1	1-1	2-0
11. Hullbridge Sports	1-1	0-1	1-1	1-3	0-3	3-1	1-2	1-1	1-4	0-2	*	1-0	1-3	1-1	2-1	0-0	3-3
12. Maldon Town	0-4	2-2	1-2	1-1	0-4	0-3	1-3	0-2	1-1	1-6	0-1	*	0-3	1-4	0-4	2-3	0-7
13. Sawbridgeworth T.	3-2	2-1	2-1	2-1	1-0	1-1	2-3	0-3	2-1	0-0	2-0	2-0	*	3-2	1-1	0-0	2-1
14. Southend Manor	3-3	0-1	0-4	2-0	2-5	0-2	0-4	4-0	0-6	0-3	1-0	0-2	*	3-0	0-0	1-0	1-2
15. Stambridge	1-1	3-3	3-5	2-1	0-2	2-3	4-2	1-1	7-0	1-2	2-0	4-1	1-5	2-1	*	2-1	3-0
16. Stansted	3-1	1-3	0-2	1-4	1-2	2-0	4-2	0-1	6-1	2-1	1-2	4-1	0-5	1-3	1-0	*	0-1
17. Woodford Town	2-1	1-0	1-3	3-1	3-2	0-0	0-0	3-1	0-3	0-0	5-0	0-2	2-3	1-4	1-2	*	

RESERVE DIVISION RESULTS 1991/92

HOME TEAM	1	2	3	4	5	6	7	8	9	10	11	12	13	14	15
1. Basilton U. Res	*	1-6	0-1	0-2	1-5	2-1	4-2	1-0	3-0	1-1	0-4	1-3	2-2	2-0	0-2
2. Bowers Utd Res	1-1	*	1-2	0-4	4-1	3-1	1-2	0-3	5-2	2-3	1-1	3-0	2-3	2-1	1-3
3. Brentwood Res	4-0	1-1	*	2-1	3-5	0-1	1-2	1-0	2-0	5-1	0-1	2-1	1-4	0-1	2-2
4. Brightlingsea Res	5-0	2-4	1-1	*	4-0	6-2	0-3	1-1	1-0	3-0	0-0	7-1	0-2	3-1	0-3
5. Burnham Rblrs Res	5-1	1-2	0-0	1-0	*	1-1	1-1	1-2	2-0	5-0	0-4	1-1	0-0	3-0	2-3
6. Canvey Island Res	1-1	0-0	1-0	0-2	2-2	*	2-0	2-0	3-0	4-0	1-1	0-0	1-0	4-1	2-0
7. Concord Rgrs Res	3-1	1-4	3-1	1-0	1-0	4-2	*	0-0	3-1	3-2	1-5	0-2	1-1	4-1	1-1
8. Eton Manor Res	3-4	3-1	2-3	3-3	4-1	1-2	1-0	*	2-2	2-1	5-2	2-1	0-2	1-2	1-3
9. Hullbridge Spts Res	1-2	1-0	3-5	1-1	2-5	4-1	2-1	2-2	*	3-2	0-1	5-1	1-4	1-2	1-4
10. Maldon Town Res	3-5	0-3	0-4	3-3	0-1	1-0	3-2	0-1	3-1	*	0-2	6-4	2-0	0-1	0-4
11. Sawbridgeworth Res	2-0	6-1	1-0	3-1	2-0	4-0	4-0	3-1	6-0	3-0	*	1-1	5-1	2-0	2-0
12. Southend Manor Res	2-1	2-3	0-1	2-3	2-1	0-0	3-1	4-2	1-2	2-2	1-1	*	0-6	0-1	0-3
13. Stambridge Res	2-0	7-1	1-1	0-1	2-2	2-1	3-5	3-4	2-0	2-3	0-2	2-1	*	0-1	3-4
14. Stansted Res	2-1	0-3	2-2	5-3	4-5	5-3	0-3	2-3	1-1	0-1	0-1	6-3	2-1	*	5-2
15. Woodford Town Res	3-0	3-3	2-2	5-1	4-0	8-1	0-3	2-0	4-0	0-0	1-0	3-1	5-3	*	

LEAGUE CUP 1991-92

Preliminary Round
Canvey Island v Concord Rangers   4-0,1-0

First Round

East Thurrock v Hullbridge Sports 4-0,2-1	Bowers United v Burnham Ramblers 1-1,2-3
Southend Manor v Sawbridgeworth Town 1-4,2-3	East Ham United v Canvey Island 1-4,1-2
Eton Manor v Maldon Town 1-1,1-4	Ford United v Brentwood 1-0,3-1
Woodford Town v Stambridge 3-1,2-1	Stansted v Basildon United 3-3,0-4

Quarter-Finals

East Thurrock Utd v Burnham Ramblers 2-2,3-1	Sawbridgeworth Town v Canvey Island 2-1,3-1
Maldon Town v Ford United 1-0,0-3	Woodford Town v Basildon United 2-2,1-2

Semi-Finals

East Thurrock Utd v Sawbridgeworth T. 0-0,2-1	Ford United v Basildon United 0-2,4-3(aet)

Final (at Bowers United FC, Saturday 25th April. Attendance: 304):
East Thurrock United 2 (Ross 75, Matthews 88), **Basildon United 0**
East Thurrock: Case, Driscoll, Chick, Fleming, Innell, Ross, Haley, Ashworth, Wiseman, Matthews, Wallace.
Basildon: Caskey, Fowler, King, Girling, E Maddocks, Bellamy, Ablitt, Lynch, K Maddocks, Stewart, Moorcraft.
Subs: Watson, Slatford.

SENIOR SECTION TOP-SCORERS:
27 - Anthony Liddle (Sawbridgeworth), 26 - Paul Flack (Southend Manor) Chris Payne (Brentwood), 24 - Jimmy Prue (Stambridge), 22 - Len Cook (Brentwood), 20 - Graham Stewart (Basildon) Paul Wren (Bowers), 17 - Danny Wallace (East Thurrock), 14 - Andy Mollison (Sawbridgeworth), 13 - Dorado (Southend Manor) Reid (Woodford) Moorcraft (East Thurrock), 12 - Gordon (Bowers) Powell (East Ham), 11 - Corfield (Burnham), 11 - Ablitt (Basildon) Swan (Stansted), 10 - Ayaoge (East Ham) Dance (Stansted) Farthing & Mahoney (Canvey) Toogood (Concord), Harding (Burnham). **Other Senior Clubs Leading Scorers:** Eton Manor: F Sollof 6, Maldon: D Brough 5, Hullbridge: G Weeks 4.

HARRY FISHER MEMORIAL TROPHY 1991-92

Preliminary Round
Stansted v Concord Rangers	1-5,2-4

Quarter-Finals
Bowers United v Eton Manor	2-0,3-0	Stambridge v Brentwood	2-1,1-2,2-1
Hullbridge Sports v East Ham United	0-4,0-1	Concord Rangers v Southend Manor	0-4,2-3

Semi-Finals
Bowers United v Stambridge	1-1,2-1	East Ham United v Southend Manor	2-1,0-2

Final *(at East Ham United FC, Monday 4th May, Attendance: 138)*:
Bowers United 1 *(Wren 119)*, **Southend Manor 0** *(After Extra-time)*
Bowers: Mead, Doyle, Wagner, Short, Barnett, Eyre, Woolley, Hollingsworth, Wren, Rainbird, Gordon, Johnson. Sub: Purser. *Manor:* Cawston, Heffer, Downey, Wiggins, Ikin, D Saggers, Dixon, Lawrence, Flack, Dorado, Brown.

RESERVE SECTION TOP-SCORERS:
22 - Nick Kemp (Sawbridgeworth Res), 18 - Bobby Hope (Stambridge Res), 17 Peter Duley (Brightligsea Res), 15 - Everson (Woodford Res), 14 - Ardley (Stansted Res) Daley (Woodford Res) Robertson (Brentwood Res), 13 - Nixon (Sawbridgeworth Res), 11 - Cherrie (Burnham Res) Buckingham (Canvey Res) Lee (Eton Manor Res) Hammond (Bowers Res), Foley (Concord Res) Reid (Woodford Res) Simpson & Purser (Bowers Res) Swanborough (Burnham Res).

RESERVE DIVISION CUP 1991-92

First Round
Brentwood Res v Hullbridge Spts Res	2-0,1-2	Southend Manor Res v Woodford Town Res	1-1,2-3
Canvey Island Res v Stambridge Res	2-4,2-1	Sawbridgeworth Res v Stansted Res	3-0,2-0
Burnham Rblrs Res v Bowers United Res	1-1,1-5	Maldon Town Res v Basildon Utd Res	4-2,1-4
Concord Rgrs Res v Brightlingsea Utd Res	0-1,0-6	Eton Manor Reserves	Bye

Quarter-Finals
Brentwood Res v Woodford Town Res	3-2,3-0	Stambridge Res v Sawbridgeworth Res	1-0,1-1
Bowers Utd Res v Basildon Utd Res	2-2,0-2	Brightlingsea Utd Res v Eton Manor Res	1-3,0-1

Semi-Finals
Brentwood Res v Stambridge Res	5-0,2-0	Basildon United Res v Eton Manor Res	3-3,0-2

Final *(at East Thurrock United FC, Saturday 18th April, Attendance: 82)*:
Eton Manor Reserves 2 *(Lee 36(pen) 41)*, **Brentwood Reserves 1** *(Dackcome 57(pen))*

RESERVE DIVISION SHIELD 1991-92

First Round
Hullbridge Spts Res v Concord Rangers	3-0,1-1	Burnham Res v Stansted Res	3-0,1-3
Maldon Town Res v Canvey Island Res	1-1,2-5		

Semi-Finals
Hullbridge Spts Res v Burnham Res	1-1,3-0	Southend Manor Res v Canvey Island Res	2-2,2-4

Final *(at Basildon United FC, Tuesday 5th May, Attendance: 202)*:
Canvey Island Reserves 2 *(Heale 13, Dulieu 71, Buckingham 87(pen))*, **Hullbridge Reserves 1** *(Petrie 73(pen))*

Another goal for the Essex Senior League's top-scorer; Sawbridgeworth Town's Tony Liddle. This was his second in a 2-0 win at Eton Manor on Saturday 21st March. Photo - Dave West.

BASILDON UNITED

Chairman: John Oakes **Manager:** Kevin Maddocks
Secretary: Trevor Thomas, Littlecroft, South Woodham Ferrers, Essex CM3 5GQ (0245 323645).
Ground: Gardiners Close, Gardiners Lane, Basildon, Essex SS14 3AW (0268 520268).
Directions: A176 off Southend arterial (A127), left into Cranes Farm Road, proceed to end of duel carriageway, Gardiners Close on left at lights. Two and a half miles from Basildon BR station.
Seats: 400 **Cover:** Yes **Capacity:** 2,000 **Floodlights:** Yes **Founded:** 1967.
Colours: Amber & black **Change colours:** Red **Previous Name:** Armada Sports
Previous Leagues: Grays & Thurrock/ Gtr London 68-70/ Essex Snr 70-80/ Athenian 80-81/ Isthmian 81-91.
Record Gate: 4,000 v West Ham, ground opening 11/8/70 **Programme Editor:** Frank Ford.
Previous Ground: Grosvenor Park **Clubhouse:** Lunchtimes & evening **Nickname:** Bees.
Players progressing to Football League: Jeff Hull (Colchester), David Matthews (Southend).
Hons: Isthmian Lg Div 2 83-83, Essex Snr Lg(4) 76-80 (Lg Cup 77-78). **Midweek Matches:** Tuesday

BOWERS UNITED

Chairman: P Felham **Manager:** Steve Wheeler
Secretary: E D Brown, 92 Quilters Straight, Fryerns, Basildon, Essex SS14 2SJ (0268 521201).
Ground: Crown Avenue, off Kenneth Rd, Pitsea, Basildon (0268 555583).
Directions: Turn into Rectory Rd from Old London Rd (B1464) at Pitsea Broadway into Kenneth Rd, right at top into Crown Avenue. One and a quarter miles from Pitsea (BR). Bus 523 to Rectory Rd, Bowers Guild.
Seats: 200 **Stand:** Yes **Capacity:** 2,000 **Floodlights:** No **Founded:** 1946.
Colours: Red & black **Change colours:** All white **Previous Ground:** Gun Meadow, Pitsea.
Previous Leagues: Thurrock & Thameside Comb./Olympian. **Clubhouse:** Open every night.
Players progressing to Football League: Steve Tilson (Southend Utd).
Record Gate: 1,800 v Billericay Town, FA Vase. **Midweek Matches:**
Hons: Thurrock & Thameside Comb. 58-59/ Essex Snr Lg 80-81 (Div 1 Cup 90-91, Harry Fisher Mem. Tphy 91-92).

BRENTWOOD

Chairman: K J O'Neale **Manager:** Derek Stittle
Secretary: C Harris, 56 Viking Way, Brentwood, Essex CM15 9HY (0277 219564).
Ground & Directions: As East Thurrock United FC (see page 375). **Founded:** 1955.
Colours: Sky & navy **Change colours:** All yellow **Programme:** Free with admission
Previous Names: Manor Ath. 55-70/ Brentwood Ath. 70-72. **Midweek Matches:**
Previous Grounds: King George, Hartswood/ 'Larkins', Ongar (pre-1992) **Nickname:** Blues
Previous Leagues: Romford & District/ Sth Essex Combination/ London & Essex Border/ Olympian.
Hons: Olympian Lg Cup 67-68, Essex Intermediate Cup 76-77, Essex Lg Cup 75-76 78-79 90-91.

BURNHAM RAMBLERS

Chairman: Gordon Brasted **President:** R J Cole, Esq.
Secretary: Gordon Brasted, 4 Riverside Rd, Burnham-on-Crouch, Essex CM0 8JY (0621 782785).
Manager: Dennis Tyrell **Assistant Manager:** Doug Aitken.
Ground: 'Leslie Field', Springfield Rd, Burnham-on-Crouch CM0 8TE (0621 784383).
Directions: On B1010 from South Woodham Ferrers, turn right half mile before town. 15 mins from Burnham (BR).
Seats: 300 **Stand:** Yes **Capacity:** 5,000 **Floodlights:** Yes **Founded:** 1900
Colours: Royal blue **Change colours:** Red **Nickname:** Ramblers
Previous Lges: N Essex/ Mid-Essex/Olympian/ SE Essex **Midweek matches:** Tuesday.
Previous Grounds: Wick Rd, Millfields 27-87/ Saltcourts (orig.) **Record Gate:** 1,500.
Hons: Olympian Lg 65-66, Essex I'mediate Cup R-up 81-82 **Clubhouse:** Evenings & weekends
Programme: 36 pages **Editor:** Ron Bush (0621 783706).

CANVEY ISLAND

Chairman: W Overall **Manager:** Jeff King.
Secretary: Mrs Francis Roche, 56 Harvest Way, Canvey Island SS8 9RP (0268 698586).
Ground: Park Lane, Canvey Island (0268 682991).
Directions: A130 from A13 or A127 at Sadlers Farm r'bout, 1 mile right through town centre, first on right past old bus garage. Bus 3 or 151 from Benfleet (PH) to stop after Admiral Jellicoe (PH).
Seats: None **Cover:** 250 **Capacity:** 2,500 **Floodlights:** Yes **Founded:** 1926.
Colours: Yellow **Change cols:** Red **Record Gate:** 800 v Spurs 1964, v Billericay 1980
Programme Editor: Keith Farrow **Nickname:** Gulls.
Previous Lges: Southend & Dist./ Thurrock & Thameside Comb./ Parthenon/ Metropolitan/ Gtr London 64-71.
Hons: Essex Snr Lg 86-87 (Lg Cup & Sportsmanship Award 83-84, Reserve Shield 91-92), Gtr London Lg(2) 67-69 (Lg Cup 68-69).

CONCORD RANGERS

Chairman: Albert Lant **Manager:** Eddie Crace.
Secretary: Robert Fletcher, 76 Eastwood Rd, Rayleigh, Essex (0268 770885).
Ground: Thames Road, Canvey Island (0268 691780). **Midweek Matches:** Wednesday.
Seats: No **Capacity:** 1,500 **Cover:** Yes **Floodlights:** No **Founded:** 1967.
Colours: Yellow/blue **Change colours:** Blue **Club Sponsor:** Aspect Contracts.
Previous Lges: Southend & Dist Alliance/ Essex I'mediate (pre-1991) **Programme:** Yes
Record Gate: 1,500 v Lee Chapel North, FA Sunday Cup 89-90 **Previous Ground:** Waterside.
Hons: Essex I'mediate Lg Div 2 & Lg Cup, Southend Alliance. **Clubhouse:** Evenings & weekends.

EAST HAM UNITED

Chairman: E H Whatmough **Manager:** Reuben Gane.
Secretary: Rueben Gane, 108 Beccles Drive, Barking IG11 9HZ (081 594 7861).
Ground: Ferndale Spts Grnd, Pennyroyal Ave, off East Ham Manorway, Beckton E6 4NG (071 476 5514).
Seats: 150 **Capacity:** 2,500 **Nickname:** Hammers **Floodlights:** Yes **Founded:** 1933.
Colours: Green, white & gold **Change colours:** Claret & sky **Programme:** Yes.
Record Gate: 4,250 - East Ham (inc George Best) v West Ham, friendly 15/2/76 at Terrance McMillan Stadium. 2,400 v Sutton United, FA Amateur Cup 14/11/53.
Previous Lges: Spartan, Metropolitan **Previous Name:** Storey Athletic 1933-53
Previous Ground: Tilletts Farm (previous East Ham Utd, formed 1880 and played in Sth Essex Lge).
Hons: Metropolitan Lg, FA Vase QF, Essex Snr Tphy 76-77, Gtr London Lg Cup 69-70, London Jnr Cup 46-47.
Clubhouse: Evenings & weekends. **Midweek Matchday:** Tuesday

Eton Manor. Back Row (L/R): Richard Derrick, Barry Goldman, Mick Pantelli, Tony Maskell, Felipe Sollof, Jeff Webb, Mark Downes. Front: Kylie Rankin, Adam Cliss, Tim Passey, Chris Lovelace, Lee Leather, Steve Kent. Photo - Dave West.

East Ham United FC 1991-92. Photo - Gavin Ellis.

Sawbridgeworth Town. Back Row (L/R): Don Watters (Manager), Jason Lawes, Ally Mollison, Tony Liddle, Ray Godfrey, Shaun Vinton, John Scott, Dave Fawcett, Dave Townsend (Physio). Front: Tony Jelliman, Dave Lawrence, Andy Lewis, J Merritt, P Mutimer, Stuart Martin. Photo - Dave West.

ETON MANOR

Chairman: Reg Curtis   **Manager:** Barry Goldman
Secretary: George E Whiting, 69 John Walsh Tower, Montague Rd., Leytonstone E11 3ET (081 550 9618).
Ground: Roding Lane, Buckhurst Hill (081 504 9937).   **Floodlights:** Opened Jan 89 v Orient (0-5).
Directions: East of Buckhurst Hill (Central Line), Three quarters of a mile west of Chigwell High Str (A113).
Seats: None   **Cover:** No   **Capacity:** 3,000   **Nickname:** Manor   **Founded:** 1901.
Programme Editor: Secretary   **Record Gate:** 12,000 v Romford, Essex Snr Cup Final 1938.
Colours: Sky   **Change colours:** White   **Midweek Matches:** Tuesday.
Previous Grounds: Temple Mills/ Walthamstow Avenue/ GUS/ Norwegian Ground, Barking.
Previous Name: Wilderness Leyton.   **Hons:** Essex Snr Cup R-up 37-38, London Lg 37-38 52-53 53-54 55-56, Essex Snr Lg Sportsmanship Award 75-76 (Div 1 Cup 90-91, Reserve Div Cup 91-92).
Clubhouse: Evenings (except Mondays).   **Previous Leagues:** London Metropolitan, Aetolian.

FORD UNITED

Chairman: L H R Constable   **President:** Stuart J Harmer
Vice Chairman: J Rowe   **Manager:** Donal McGovern
Secretary: K D Dobson, 16 Tenby Court, Tenby Road, Walthamstow E17 7AT (071 521 9285).
Ground: Ford Sports & Social Club, Rush Green Rd., Romford (0708 45678).
Directions: On the A124 (Rush Green road) on left going towards Hornchurch. 2 miles from Romford (BR). Buses 173, 175 87, 106, 23.
Seats: 800   **Cover:** Yes   **Capacity:** 2,500   **Floodlights:** Yes   **Founded:** 1958
Colours: All royal   **Change colours:** All red   **Prog. Ed.:** Colin Mynott (0268 281002).
Previous Names: Briggs Sports (founded 1934) & Fords Sports (founded 1934) merged in 1958.
Previous Ground: Victoria Rd (now Dagenham FC)   **Nickname:** Motormen
Previous Leagues: Spartan, Aetolian, Metropolitan
Players progressing to Football League: Les Allen (Spurs), Mick Flanagan (QPR, Charlton, Crystal Palace), Jim Stannard (Fulham, Southend, Millwall), Nicky Hammond (Arsenal, Swindon), Laurie Abrahams (Charlton), Doug Barton (Reading, Newport).
Record Gate: 58,000 Briggs Sports v Bishop Auckland, at St James Park, Newcastle, FA Amateur Cup.
Hons: FA Amateur Cup SF 53-54, London Snr Cup 55-56 56-57, Essex Snr Trophy 90-91 91-92, Essex Snr Cup 39-40 49-50 50-51 51-52, Spartan Lg 49-50 50-51 55-56 56-57 57-58, London Lg 36-37 38-39, Essex Elizabethan 59-60 60-61 70-71, Gtr London Lg 70-71, Essex Snr Lg 91-92 (Lg Cup 85-86, Sportsmanship Award 77-78 79-80 80-81).
Clubhouse: 4 bars, 2 dance halls, tea bar, snooker room.

GREAT WAKERING ROVERS

Chairman: Trevor Lovell   **Manager:** Ben Embery.
Secretary: Roger Simpson, 37 Lee Lotts, Gt Wakering, Southend-on-Sea, Essex SS3 0HA (0702 218794).
Ground: Burroughs Pk, Little Wakering Hall Lane, Gt Wakering, Southend-on-Sea SS3 0HQ (0702 217812).
Directions: 4a bus from Shoeburyness (BR), 4a or 4b from Southend. A127 past Southend signposted Gt Wakering, at Parsons Corner - Poynford Lane then into Star Lane, right to High Street, Little Wakering Hall Lane is half mile on left, ground 250 yds on left.
Seats: None   **Stand:** Due   **Capacity:** 1,500   **Floodlights:** No   **Founded:** 1919
Cols: Green & white stripes/white/green   **Change cols:** Red & yellow/white/white   **Nickname:** Rovers
Programme: Yes   **Editor:** N Johnson   **Midweek Matchday:** Tuesday
Previous Ground: Gt Wakering Rec.   **Record Gate:** 350.   **Sponsors:** TBA.
Previous Leagues: Southend & District/ Southend Alliance/ Essex Intermediate (pre-1992).
Clubhouse: Self built, completed August 1989. Bar (capacity 150), boardroom, changing rooms.
Hons: Essex I'mediate Cup 91-92, Essex I'mediate Lg Div 2 91-92 (Div 3 90-91, Lg Cup 91-92).

HULLBRIDGE SPORTS

Chairman: Brian Hughes   **Manager:** Mark Lloyd
Secretary: Mrs Lynne Ward, 'Riverview', The Avenue, Hullbridge, Essex SS5 6LF.
Ground: Lower Road, Hullbridge, Essex SS5 6BJ (0702 230420).
Directions: Turn into Rawreth Lane from A130 (left if arriving from Chelmsford), down to mini-r'bout, left, across next mini-r'bout, up hill, ground signed on right just past garage.
Seats: No   **Cover:** Yes   **Capacity:**   **Floodlights:** No   **Founded:** 1945
Colours: Royal blue & white stripes/blue/blue   **Change colours:** Yellow
Programme: Yes   **Programme Editor:** Secretary   **Sponsor:** Thermo Shield
Previous Leagues: Southend & District/ Alliance/ Essex Intermediate.
Previous Grounds: Pooles Lane Recreation Ground.   **Midweek matches:** Tues/Thursday.
Honours: Essex Intermediate Snr Cup 87-88, Southend & District Lg Div 1 65-66 (Div 2 51-52, Div 3 56-57), French Cup 51-52, Essex Snr Lg Sportsmanship Award 91-92.
Clubhouse details: Lounge bar, function hall with bar & changing rooms - set in 16 acre land.

MALDON TOWN

Chairman: Trevor Thompson   **Manager:** Keith Hull.
Secretary: Ms Toni Morrant, 12 Blackwater Close, Heybridge Basin, Maldon CM9 7SB (0621 858041).
Ground: Fambridge Road, Maldon (0621 853762).
Directions: Half mile south of town on west side of Fambridge Road. Bus 92 from Chelmsford (BR).
Seats: 400   **Cover:** Yes   **Capacity:** 2,500   **Floodlights:** No   **Founded:** 1946.
Colours: Blue & white hoops   **Change colours:** Red & white hoops   **Programme:** Yes
Previous Lges: Eastern Counties, Essex & Suffolk Border.   **Hons:** Essex Snr Lg 84-85 (Sportsmanship 88-89), Essex & Suffolk Border Lg 55-56 (Cup 64-65), Essex Intermediate Cup 51-52.

ROMFORD

Chairman: Dave Howie   **Manager:** Lyndon Lynch.   **Press Officer:** Ian Levene (0708 755824).
Secretary: Paul Krisman, 64 Cantley Gdns, Gants Hill, Ilford, Essex IG2 6QB (081 518 2290).
Ground & Directions: As Hornchurch FC (see page 380)   **Founded:** 1929   **Reformed:** 1992.
Colours: Gold/blue/gold   **Change colours:** Blue/gold/blue   **Nickname:** The Boro
Programme: 24 pages, 50p   **Editor:** Ian Howitt   **Club Shop:** Yes
Previous Grounds: Brooklands Sports Ground, Romford.   **Midweek Matchday:** Thursday.
Record Gate: 2,005 v Arsenal Celebrity XI, 28/5/92.   **Sponsors:** Romford Recorder
Previous Leagues: None *(Original club: London 29-31/ Athenian 31-39/ Isthmian 45-59/ Southern 59-78)*
Local Newspapers: Romford Recorder, Post, Yellow Advertiser, Observer.   **Clubhouse:** Yes
Hons: None *(Original club: FA Amtr Cup R-up 48-49, Southern Lg 66-67 (Div 1 R-up 59-60), Athenian Lg 35-36 36-37 (R-up 38-39), Essex Snr Cup 31-32 33-34 37-38 46-47, Essex Thameside Tphy 51-52 55-56 57-58).*

SAWBRIDGEWORTH TOWN

Chairman: Alan Townsend **Manager:** Don Watters
Secretary: Mr H T Annis, 15 Tunmeade, Harlow, Essex CM20 3HS (0279 425865).
Ground: Crofters End, West Road, Sawbridgeworth (0279 722039). **Floodlights:** No
Directions: Three quarters of a mile from station; up Station Road then West Road.
Seats: No **Capacity:** 1,500 **Cover:** 250 **Nickname:** Robins **Founded:** 1890.
Colours: Red & black **Change colours:** Blue
Programme Editor: Ron Alder (0279 722360) **Previous Leagues:** Essex Olympian, Spartan 36-53.
Previous Grounds: Hyde Hall/ Pishiobury/ Hand & Crown. **Record Gate:** 250 v Stansted
Hons: Essex Olympian Lg 71-72, Essex Snr Lg Harry Fisher Mem. Cup 87-88 (Reserve Div 91-92), Herts Snr Tphy 90-91.

SOUTHEND MANOR

Chairman: Simon Dibley **Manager:** John Seaden/ Paul Saggers.
Secretary: Dave Kittle, 15 Seymour Rd, Hadleigh, Benfleet, Essex SS7 2HB (0702 559581)
Ground: Southchurch Park Arena, Lifstan Way, Southend-on-Sea. (0702 615577)
Directions: A127 then A1159 for 1 mile turn right at second r-about at Rusty Bucket PH, due south for 1 mile – ground on right near sea front.
Seats: 500 **Cover:** Yes **Capacity:** 2,000 **Floodlights:** Yes **Founded:** 1955
Colours: Yellow, red & black **Change colours:** Blue & white **Nickname:** The Manor
Programme: Yes **Sponsors:** Brooks Sports Ltd **Midweek Matchday:** Wednesday
Record Attendance: 1,521 v Southend Utd, 22.7.91 (Floodlight inauguration).
Previous Leagues: Southend Borough Combination, Southend Alliance
Previous Grounds: Victory Spts/ Oakwood Rec. **Clubhouse:** Weekends
Hons: Essex Intermediate Cup 78-79; Essex Snr Lg Div 1 90-91 (Lg Cup 87-88, ESL Challenge Cup 89-90, Harry Fisher Mem. Tphy 90-91 (R-up 91-92)).

STANSTED

Chairman: Terry Shoebridge **Manager:** Phil Gilham
Secretary: R A G Heale, 28 Mountfitchet Rd, Stanstead CM24 8NW. (0279 812897)
Ground: Hargrave Sports Ground, Cambridge Rd, Stansted. (0279 812897)
Directions: B1383 north of Bishops Stortford on west side of Cambridge Rd. Stansted (BR) – 1/2 mile
Seats: 200 **Cover:** Yes **Capacity:** 2,000 **Floodlights:** Yes **Founded:** 1902
Colours: Blue/white/blue **Change colours:** White & black **Programme:** Yes **Midweek:** Tue/Wed
Record attendance: 828 v Whickham (FA Vase 83-84), 12,000 v Stamford (FA Vase Final at Wembley 83-84)
Previous Ground: Greens Meadow/Chapel Hill **Previous Leagues:** Spartan, London, Herts Co.
Honours: FA Vase winners 83-84; Essex Snr Lg 83-84; Essex Snr Lg Cup 83-84; East Anglian Cup 83-84; Courage Eastern Floodlight Comp 83-84; Harry Fisher Cup 82-83 84-85

WOODFORD TOWN

Chairman: TBA **Manager:** TBA **Secretary:** TBA
Ground: 265 Snakes Lane, Woodford Green IG8 7JJ. (081-504 0831)
Directions: Woodford (LT) Close to M11
Seats: 600 **Cover:** Yes **Capacity:** 4,000 **Floodlights:** Yes **Founded:** 1937
Colours: White/black/black **Change colours:** Yellow/blue **Midweek:** Wednesday
Programme: Yes **Nickname:** The Town **Sponsor:** Thermo Shield
Previous Leagues: Sth Essex 37-39/ London 47-51/ Delphian 51-61/ Metropolitan 61-63 70-71/ junior football 63-70/ Southern 71-72 82-87/ Essex Snr 76-79/ Athenian 79-82.
Record Attendance: 6,000 v Colchester United, FA Cup 1952 (1-7)
Hons: FA Cup 1st Rd Proper 86-87 (lost 0-1 at home to Orient), Essex Snr Lg Div 1 75-76 84-85 85-86 89-90 (Lg Cup 75-76 85-86, Harry Fisher Mem. Tphy R-up 87-88), Stepney Charity Cup 85-86.

ESSEX SENIOR LEAGUE TEN YEAR RECORD

	82/3	83/4	84/5	85/6	86/7	87/8	88/9	89/90	90/1	91/2
Basildon United	–	–	–	–	–	–	–	–	–	6
Bowers United	4	2	9	8	4	14	15	11	5	7
Brentwood	11	6	5	6	10	2	9	7	2	2
Brighlingsea Utd	14	16	12	11	17	11	1	1	–	–
Burnham Ramblers	–	–	–	12	6	13	4	8	3	13
Canvey Island	5	8	7	9	1	10	6	4	9	5
Chelmsford Reserves	8	5	6	7	9	12	13	14	–	–
Coggeshall Town	9	17	16	17	–	17	14	–	–	–
Concord Rangers	–	–	–	–	–	–	–	–	–	11
East Ham United	15	14	15	16	16	15	16	16	14	15
East Thurrock United	17	12	13	5	5	5	2	3	8	3
Eton Manor	16	11	10	10	13	9	8	12	11	16
Ford United	12	10	8	3	12	6	3	9	7	1
Halstead United	3	15	11	15	11	3	–	–	–	–
Heybridge Swifts	1	1	–	–	–	–	–	–	–	–
Hullbridge Sports	–	–	–	–	–	–	–	–	12	14
Maldon Town	10	13	1	4	15	16	17	15	13	17
Purfleet	–	–	–	–	3	1	–	–	–	–
Sawbridgeworth Town	13	7	14	14	8	8	11	5	4	4
Southend Manor	–	–	–	–	–	–	7	10	1	8
Stambridge	–	–	–	–	–	–	12	6	6	9
Stansted	2	4	3	13	14	7	5	13	10	12
Witham Town	6	3	2	1	2	–	–	–	–	–
Wivenhoe Town	7	9	4	2	–	–	–	–	–	–
Woodford Town	–	–	–	–	–	4	10	2	15	10
Woodford Town Reserves	–	–	–	–	7	–	–	–	–	–
No. of Clubs	**17**	**17**	**16**	**17**	**17**	**17**	**17**	**16**	**15**	**17**

ESSEX INTERMEDIATE LEAGUE

President: P K Byford, Esq.
Hon. Secretary: R F Hurrell,
102 Falmouth Road, Springfield, Chelmsford CM1 5JA (0245 256922).

STANDARD WIN THEIR FIRST TITLE

After coming close on a number of occasions, Standard thoroughly deserve their first Senior Division One championship. They have been very consistent and their strength also showed when they reached the Semi-Final of the Essex Intermediate Cup where they lost out to Kelvedon Hatch, a club who found themselves not only runners-up to Great Wakering in that competition but also to the same club in the Senior Divisions Cup and to Standard in the league. All conquering Great Wakering Rovers leave us with the Senior Division Two championship and the Senior Divisions Cup. Essex Police picked themselves up after being relegated last season and finished runners-up in Senior Division Two to earn promotion along with third placed Rayleigh Town. Loughton leave us to join the Spartan League with some success as Senior Division Three champions, while newcomers Doddinghurst Olympic had a good season finishing as runners-up and gaining promotion at the first attempt. All conquering Standard retained the Reserve Division One title for the fourth consecutive year, a remarkable performance, and completed the double when winning the Cup after a replay against Great Wakering. Writtle improved a place on last season and finished as runners-up in Reserve Division One, and Shell Club continued to climb from Third Division champions last season to Reserve Division champions with some impressive performances. They also produced the leading scorer; Andrew Kirby. G.B.R.E. moved up two places and finished runners-up to Shell. From a mid-table position last year, Maldon St Mary's consolidated and came out on top as Reserve Division Three champions, and Doddinghurst Ollympic matched their seniors by being runners-up.

Other competition successes for our clubs have been; Standard winners of the West Essex Border Cup, Runwell the Burnham Charity Cup, Maldon St Mary's Reserves the Tiptree Charity Cup, Barnston the Braintree Cup Senior Section, White Notley Reserves the Braintree Cup Reserve Section and Standard Reserves the Ongar & District Cup. Well done to all these clubs.

Senior Div. One	P	W	D	L	F	A	PTS
Standard (Harlow)	22	15	2	5	48	23	32
Kelvedon Hatch	22	14	2	6	47	22	30
Rayleigh Athletic	22	13	2	7	37	21	28
Harold Wood Ath.	22	11	2	9	47	30	24
Gt Baddow R.E.	22	10	4	8	37	39	24
Writtle	22	9	5	8	34	31	23
Old Chelmsfordians	22	8	6	8	31	37	22
Runwell Hospital	22	9	3	10	32	30	21
Herongate Athletic	22	7	6	9	25	27	20
Benfleet	22	7	3	12	20	31	17
Caribbean Int. Spts	22	6	3	13	29	46	15
Takeley	22	3	2	17	18	68	8

Top Scorers: B Lawrence (Standard) 31, S Field (Harold Wd) 20, M McCarthy (Rayleigh) 17, W Alderton (O Chelm.) 16, P Warner (Rayleigh) 14.

Senior Div. Two	P	W	D	L	F	A	PTS
Gt Wakering Rvrs	24	15	6	3	73	27	36
Essex Police	24	14	6	4	43	30	34
Rayleigh Town	24	14	3	7	64	28	31
B Stortford Swifts	24	11	9	4	38	23	31
Shell Club	24	13	4	7	48	34	30
S. Woodham Ferrers	24	10	7	7	40	27	27
Ekco Sports	24	10	6	8	46	60	26
S.C. Henderson	24	10	5	9	49	40	25
White Notley	24	6	5	13	28	58	17
Upminster	24	6	4	14	34	60	16
Mountnessing	24	6	3	15	25	41	15
Hambros Bank	24	4	6	14	29	59	14
Great Baddow	24	3	4	17	28	58	10

Top Scorers: H Mackler (Gt Wakering) 24, N Ramsey (Gt Wakering) 23, S Rush (Gt Wakering 19), T Long (Rayleigh) 16, D Seaby (Ekco) 15, J Doyle (Henderson) 15.

Kelvedon Hatch FC, Runners-Up in the Essex Intermediate League, the Essex Intermediate League Cup and the Essex Intermediate Cup in 1991-92. Back Row (L/R): Ron Bluck (Manager), Brian Powell, Jon Grant, John Dalton, James McCayna, John McCayna, Richard Harley, Dave Hughes. Front: Jason Lee, Ray De Keyzer, Wayne Collard, Stuart Murray, Mark Norman, Steve Orrin, Dave Ridley. Photo - Dave West.

Senior Division 3	P	W	D	L	F	A	PTS
Loughton	24	18	3	3	79	22	39
Doddinghurst Olym.	24	16	4	4	47	18	36
Barnston	24	12	5	7	44	37	29
Basildon Town	24	11	6	7	44	35	28
Ramsden	24	11	4	9	48	33	26
Coopersale	24	11	4	9	29	36	26
Ongar Town	24	10	5	9	49	47	25
Springfield	24	9	5	10	35	44	23
AFC Notley	24	7	6	11	38	40	20
Hutton	24	4	9	11	27	35	17
Broomfield	24	6	4	14	28	51	16
Maldon St Marys	24	6	4	14	29	55	16
Galleywood	24	4	3	17	21	65	11

Top Scorers: M Keeble (Ongar) 21, N Cook (Loughton) 20, P Perry & B Capps (both Doddinghurst) 18, L Stevenson (Basildon) 15.

Res. Division 1	P	W	D	L	F	A	PTS
Standard Res	22	13	7	2	67	29	33
Writtle Res	22	15	2	5	73	39	32
Old Chelmsf. Res	22	11	7	4	48	28	29
Runwell Hosp Res	22	13	2	7	53	27	28
Kelvedon Hatch Res	22	12	2	8	53	26	26
Benfleet Res	22	10	4	8	30	36	24
Gt Wakering Res	22	8	4	10	31	44	20
Herongate A. Res	22	8	2	12	33	38	18
Harold Wd A. Res	22	7	4	11	25	46	18
Rayleigh Town Res	22	6	3	13	28	46	15
Takeley Res	22	3	5	14	20	72	11
Upminster Res	22	4	2	16	25	55	10

Top Scorers: C Rees (Standard) 31, C Delphin (Writtle) 20, C Cleminson (Kelvedon Hatch) 15, R Mays (Standard) 14, T Mould (Writtle) 14.

Reserve Division 2	P	W	D	L	F	A	PTS
Shell Club Res	26	21	2	1	89	19	44
Gt Baddow RE Res	24	19	2	3	77	24	40
Ekco Sports Res	24	13	5	6	53	41	31
B S'ford Swifts Res	24	13	1	10	55	43	27
S Woodham F. Res	24	10	5	9	52	49	25
Essex Police Res	24	11	2	11	44	43	24
SC Henderson Res	24	10	4	10	43	53	24
Hambros Bank Res	24	10	3	11	56	56	23
Springfield Res	24	9	2	13	37	55	20
Caribbean S. Res	24	8	3	13	46	53	19
Mountnessing Res	24	7	2	15	42	62	16
Ongar Town Res	24	4	3	17	33	94	11
Gt Naddow Res	24	4	0	20	22	57	8

Top Scorers: A Kirby (Shell) 46, K Green (Hambros) 34, P McKean (Shell) 21, S Constantine (Ekco) 18, C Lodge (GBRE) 17.

Reserve Div. 3	P	W	D	L	F	A	PTS
Maldon St M. Res	24	16	7	1	65	23	39
Doddinghurst Res	24	12	5	7	48	34	29
Ramsden Res	24	13	3	8	55	43	29
Coopersale Res	24	10	9	5	38	30	29
Basildon T. Res	24	13	3	8	41	36	29
Hutton Res	24	12	4	8	40	33	28
Loughton Res	24	12	3	9	64	38	27
Barnston Res	24	12	3	9	56	48	27
White Notley Res	24	8	6	10	45	49	22
Broomfield Res	24	5	5	14	33	52	15
Galleywood Res	24	7	1	16	34	59	15
Rayleigh A. Res	24	5	4	15	31	59	14
AFC Notley Soc.	24	4	1	19	28	74	9

Top Scorers: C Sage (Maldon SM) 26, S Thickboom (Ramsden) 15, J Lempierre (Maldon SM) 14, M Newman (Loughton) 13, C Lear 13.

CUP COMPETITIONS

Senior Divisions Cup Final *(at Chelmsford City, Wed. 22nd April)*:
Great Wakering Rovers 2, Kelvedon Hatch 0

Reserve Divisions Cup Final *(at Heybridge Swifts, Wed. 29th April)*:
Great Wakering Rovers Reserves 0, Standard (Harlow) Reserves 0 *(after extra-time)*.
Replay *(at Maldon FC, Saturday 16th May)*:
Standard (Harlow) Reserves 2, Great Wakering Rovers Reserves 1 *(after extra-time)*.

Bill Sturgeon Cup Final *(at Heybridge Swifts, Fri. 1st May)*:
Old Chelmsfordians 3, Herongate Athletic 2

Southend Charity Shield Final *(at Southend United, Fri. 15th May)*:
Great Wakering Rovers 4, Rayleigh Athletic 3

Burnham Charity Shield Final *(Mon. 11th May)*: Runwell Hospital 1, Burnham Ramblers 0

West Essex Border Cup Final *(Mon. 4th May)*: Coopersale 1, Standard (Harlow) 6

Tiptree Charity Cup Final *(Sat. 2nd May)*: Maldon St Mary's 3, Beacon Hill Rovers 0

Braintree Cup Senior Section Final *(Mon. 4th May)*: Barnston 2, A.F.C. Notley 1

Braintree Cup Reserve Section Final *(Thurs. 28th April)*: White Notley Reserves 4, Earls Colne Reserves 0

Dave Glimsby of Great Baddow Royals gets in a shot despite the attentions of Takeley's Ellie Ballance. Visiting Great Baddow won this Senior Division One fixture 5-1 on 9th December. Photo - Richard Brock.

Caribbean Sports International, pictured before their Essex Intermediate League Senior Division One fixture at Kelvedon Hatch on 23rd May. Back Row (L/R): James Thomas Jnr (Secretary), Michael Smart, John Fortune, Junior Crawford, Winston Henry, James Thomas Snr (Chairman). Front: Henry Baptiste, Ivan Thomas, Michael McFoy, Howard Cyprien. Photo - Dave West.

Southend Manor, who by their standards had a disappointing season in the Senior League. Photo - Eric Marsh.

The Essex Senior League flag, that will reside at Ford United for a year. Photo - Robert Errington.

PARASOL (COMBINED COUNTIES) LEAGUE

Chairman: J O Esau.

Hon. Secretary: Mr J J Whitefoot,
8 Compton Road, Church Crookham, Hampshire.

FANTASTIC FARNHAM

The Combined Counties League, that has been known as the 'Dan-Air League' for several seasons, has new sponsors for 1992-93, and will be henceforth the 'Parasol League'. The 1991-92 season saw Farnham Town not only retain their title with great ease, but also win the two main cup competitions to achieve a fabulous treble. A black cloud has hung over the club for a while due to the inadequacy of their facilities, but thankfully this has now been resolved; Farnham will groundshare at Aldershot for a couple of years while their own ground is upgraded, and this move allows them to take up their deserved place in the Diadora League under the Pyramid system.

While Farnham move out, two clubs arrive for 1992-93; DCA Basingstoke from the Hampshire League, and Peppard, promoted within the Pyramid as Charrington Chiltonian League champions.

Farnham Town, Dan-Air League champions 1991-92. Back Row (L/R): David Lindsay, Steven Harris (capt), Shaun May, Andy Metcalfe, Paul Cann, Gary Millard, Stephen Flanagan, Peter Browning, Marc Hogg. Front: Ben Deighan, Paul Warner, Stephen Stairs, Terry Daly, Gary Iddenten, Stephen Buckingham. Photo - Gavin Ellis

Another, unique, picture of Farnham Town, who on the final day of the season played a double header against Farleigh Rovers. As the first team came off, and the reserves came on, photographer Dave West captured them in one picture.

LEAGUE TABLES 1991-92

Premier Division	P	W	D	L	F	A	PTS
Farnham Town	36	26	7	3	89	28	85
Malden Town	36	21	7	8	72	39	70
Chipstead	36	19	7	10	68	46	64
Cobham	36	17	10	9	81	56	61
Ditton	36	16	11	9	61	44	59
Ashford T. (Middx)	36	17	7	12	57	41	58
Cranleigh	36	18	3	15	68	62	57
Bedfont	36	16	8	12	56	40	56
Ash United	36	14	13	9	63	52	55
Steyning Town	36	16	6	14	67	65	54
Farleigh Rovers	36	14	9	13	53	59	51
Viking Sports	36	13	10	13	59	49	49
Frimley Green	36	13	9	14	64	61	48
Merstham	36	12	6	18	49	68	42
Hartley Wintney	36	12	5	19	50	70	41
Westfield	36	8	10	18	43	60	34
Godalming Town	36	6	8	22	35	76	26
Horley Town	36	5	8	23	39	83	23
Sandhurst Town	36	6	2	28	34	109	20

Reserve Section	P	W	D	L	F	A	PTS
Cobham Res	34	23	9	2	92	19	78
Frimley Green Res	34	20	8	6	86	45	68
Ashford (Mx) Res	34	16	12	6	60	44	60
Malden Town Res	34	17	7	10	73	50	58
Viking Sports Res	34	17	7	10	64	43	58
Ditton Res	34	19	1	14	72	63	58
Westfield Res	34	15	7	12	55	49	52
Farnham Town Res	34	15	6	13	60	59	51
Ash United Res	34	13	9	12	53	63	48
Hartley Wintney Res	34	13	6	15	69	70	45
Chipstead Res	34	13	4	17	50	66	43
Bedfont Res	34	12	4	18	47	49	40
Merstham Res	34	12	4	18	53	70	40
Godalming T. Res	34	10	10	14	41	64	40
Cranleigh Res	34	9	8	17	55	90	35
Horley Town Res	34	7	10	17	49	61	31
Farleigh Rvrs Res	34	9	4	21	42	66	31
Sandhurst T. Res	34	4	8	22	24	74	20

PREMIER DIVISION RESULT CHART 1991-92

HOME TEAM	1	2	3	4	5	6	7	8	9	10	11	12	13	14	15	16	17	18	19
1. Ash United	*	2-2	1-1	4-1	1-1	0-1	1-0	5-1	0-1	5-0	1-1	2-1	4-1	0-1	2-2	2-1	1-2	3-0	2-2
2. Ashford (Mx)	2-2	*	1-0	0-1	1-5	2-0	0-0	1-2	2-0	3-1	4-1	4-1	0-2	3-0	2-2	6-1	0-0	2-0	
3. Bedfont	0-0	0-0	*	0-1	0-1	4-0	3-1	1-3	0-1	0-1	2-1	2-0	4-3	0-0	0-2	5-1	3-0	3-0	0-1
4. Chipstead	4-1	3-0	1-4	*	6-0	0-3	1-1	2-1	0-4	3-0	2-2	7-0	0-0	2-0	2-1	6-0	1-1	3-0	1-1
5. Cobham	0-1	2-0	1-2	1-1	*	2-0	0-1	1-0	2-4	3-2	3-1	2-2	2-3	1-1	5-1	2-0	2-2	3-1	0-0
6. Cranleigh	3-4	0-2	2-1	4-0	1-0	*	3-3	1-1	0-6	2-1	4-0	3-2	4-2	1-2	1-2	3-1	2-3	1-0	3-1
7. Ditton	0-2	0-1	3-3	1-1	2-2	3-0	*	0-0	0-4	0-0	3-1	2-1	3-0	2-1	1-0	1-0	1-4	1-1	2-0
8. Farleigh	1-1	0-5	0-1	2-3	3-5	2-1	0-3	*	1-1	0-2	2-0	0-0	1-1	2-1	1-0	5-1	1-0	1-1	1-1
9. Farnham	4-0	1-1	5-1	3-1	2-0	4-1	2-2	2-2	*	2-0	3-0	0-1	1-1	3-1	2-0	4-0	3-1	3-0	1-0
10. Frimley G.	3-4	3-1	0-2	4-5	2-2	2-2	1-4	7-0	2-0	*	4-0	1-1	3-2	3-2	2-2	3-0	3-1	2-2	0-1
11. Godalming	1-2	0-2	1-1	0-2	3-2	1-3	0-5	1-0	1-3	0-2	*	2-3	1-0	0-4	1-1	4-1	3-0	1-3	2-2
12. Hartley W.	4-2	1-0	0-3	1-0	3-4	0-1	3-3	3-2	1-4	2-0	1-2	*	2-1	2-3	0-1	4-1	1-3	1-3	0-1
13. Horley T.	1-1	0-3	0-1	1-3	1-3	1-7	0-2	1-3	1-1	3-3	1-1	1-1	*	0-2	0-3	2-1	0-1	1-3	3-1
14. Malden T.	1-1	3-0	2-0	1-0	4-4	2-0	1-0	0-1	1-2	4-0	0-0	2-3	3-2	*	3-2	6-0	1-1	4-2	3-1
15. Merstham	0-0	1-0	2-1	2-1	3-7	0-3	1-2	4-2	0-1	1-1	3-0	0-1	0-1	2-3	*	1-2	1-4	0-3	2-1
16. Sandhurst	1-3	1-2	1-3	0-1	0-8	1-5	0-5	0-2	2-5	0-4	2-1	1-0	4-0	1-4	2-3	*	1-2	0-2	1-1
17. Steyning T.	2-0	2-0	3-3	1-2	2-2	4-0	4-2	0-4	2-3	2-3	2-0	0-2	2-1	1-4	6-1	0-1	*	1-0	5-2
18. Viking Spts	2-2	4-2	1-1	2-0	0-1	2-3	2-0	0-1	1-1	1-0	1-1	4-1	4-1	1-1	2-2	7-1	3-0	*	1-2
19. Westfield	4-1	0-1	0-1	0-1	0-2	1-1	2-2	3-5	0-3	0-0	3-1	5-2	1-2	0-1	2-3	1-3	2-1	1-0	*

RESERVE SECTION RESULTS 1991/92

HOME TEAM	1	2	3	4	5	6	7	8	9	10	11	12	13	14	15	16	17	18
1. Ash United Res	*	9-0	3-1	2-1	1-4	5-1	1-1	3-2	1-2	1-2	5-0	1-3	2-0	3-3	5-1	3-1	1-8	1-1
2. Ashford Town (Mx) Res	0-0	*	2-1	3-1	1-1	3-2	4-1	0-2	1-1	4-2	0-0	5-0	1-0	2-1	4-1	4-0	3-2	1-2
3. Bedfont Res	0-0	0-3	*	3-1	1-0	2-2	2-0	4-0	1-0	0-2	3-0	0-1	1-0	1-3	2-1	1-0	2-3	2-3
4. Chipstead	0-2	0-3	1-0	*	0-2	0-2	6-0	3-2	2-1	4-4	7-2	2-1	2-1	1-6	2-0	1-0	0-3	2-3
5. Cobham Res	5-1	2-2	3-0	3-0	*	3-0	5-2	2-0	2-0	0-0	2-3	5-0	1-1	2-1	6-0	7-0	2-0	0-0
6. Cranleigh Res	6-0	2-2	2-9	0-2	1-2	*	4-2	0-2	3-1	3-3	2-2	1-4	1-7	3-3	3-2	3-1	1-1	0-2
7. Ditton Res	4-0	1-0	2-1	3-0	1-6	4-1	*	4-1	3-2	1-3	4-0	3-2	2-1	3-0	2-1	6-1	4-1	1-4
8. Farleigh Rvrs Res	2-1	0-0	2-1	2-2	0-4	1-2	2-3	*	5-1	2-0	0-2	1-2	2-2	0-1	3-0	0-1	1-3	1-3
9. Farnham Town Res	4-2	2-1	2-3	3-2	0-3	3-1	2-0	1-2	*	1-2	1-1	3-2	3-2	2-4	2-1	2-2	1-3	4-1
10. Frimley Green Res	3-3	3-0	1-1	0-1	2-2	9-0	3-2	2-0	4-1	*	3-0	2-1	3-0	1-3	2-1	6-2	3-2	1-1
11. Godalming Town Res	2-0	0-0	2-0	4-0	0-0	2-1	3-2	0-0	0-2	2-3	*	2-3	3-2	3-2	2-1	0-0	1-2	0-0
12. Hartley Wintney Res	3-2	2-2	1-0	1-3	0-5	2-4	1-0	5-2	2-2	2-1	1-1	*	3-2	2-1	0-0	0-0	2-0	
13. Horley Town Res	2-1	1-1	0-1	2-1	0-0	1-1	0-2	2-1	1-3	1-2	6-1	2-2	*	1-1	2-4	0-0	1-2	1-6
14. Malden Town Res	1-0	0-1	2-1	2-2	1-1	4-1	0-1	3-0	0-1	0-5	4-0	4-0	2-1	*	1-3	3-0	0-3	4-3
15. Merstham Res	5-1	2-2	2-1	0-0	3-4	4-1	2-4	4-1	1-1	0-2	3-1	4-1	1-1	1-4	*	2-1	1-0	0-5
16. Sandhurst T. Res	2-4	0-1	1-1	0-1	0-3	0-0	2-4	0-1	0-4	0-5	1-1	0-1	2-4	1-1	1-0	*	0-1	0-1
17. Viking Spts Res	0-1	2-1	4-2	3-0	0-1	2-0	1-0	2-0	1-1	3-1	2-0	2-2	1-1	1-4	2-1	2-3	*	0-0
18. Westfield Res	0-4	1-2	0-1	3-0	1-5	0-1	1-0	3-2	2-1	1-1	2-1	0-1	0-0	2-3	0-2	0-2	1-2	*

Youth Division	P	W	D	L	F	A	PTS
Farnham Town Yth	12	7	1	4	43	22	*22
Westfield Yth	12	7	1	4	41	21	22
Godalming T. Yth	12	7	1	4	28	16	22
Cranleigh Yth	12	7	1	4	19	35	=61
Malden Town Yth	12	6	1	5	27	18	19
Frimley Green Yth	12	5	1	6	23	25	16
Sandhurst T. Yth	12	0	0	12	10	64	0

Malden Town withdrawn
* - 3 pts awarded
= - 6 pts awarded

TOP SCORERS

Premier Division: D Hooker (Ash) 31, N Kay (Cobham) 30, S Stairs (Farnham) 28, C Lamboll (Cranleigh) 27, G Salter (Steyning) 27, W Patterson (Chipstead) 24, Y Lavetive (Merstham) 19, J Haines (Farleigh) 19, M Collins (Hartley Wintney) 19.

Reserve Division: M Clarke (Frimley) 24, B Greene (Westfield) 18, N Morwood (Ashford) 16, N Davies (Malden) 14, G Ward (Westfield) 13, S Poole & P Waller (both Frimley) 11.

Youth Division: S Mitchell (Farnham) 39, A Clark (Farnham) 31, C Terry (Malden) 18.

REPRESENTATIVE MATCH 1991-92

Royal Electrical & Mechanical Engineers (UK) 0, Dan-Air Football League 0

DAN-AIR LEAGUE CUP COMPETITIONS 1991-92

LEAGUE CHALLENGE CUP

First Round

Cranleigh v Horley Town	2-0	Merstham v Hartley Wintney	4-3(aet)
Sandhurst Town v Ditton F & SC	0-2		

Second Round

Ash United v Malden Town	1-3	Bedfont v Cobham	1-2
Farleigh Rovers v Westfield	2-1	Farnham Town v Ashford Town (Middx)	1-0
Godalming Town v Chipstead	0-1	Ditton F & SC v Merstham	1-0
Steyning Town v Cranleigh	2-0	Viking Sports v Frimley Green	3-0

Quarter-Finals

Farleigh Rovers v Steyning Town	1-0	Chipstead v Cobham	2-0
Farnham Town v Malden Town	2-1	Ditton F & SC v Viking Sports	0-1

Semi-Finals

Farleigh Rovers v Viking Sports	2-1	Farnham Town v Chipstead	2-1

Final *(at Woking FC, Wednesday 22nd April)*: Farnham Town 1, Farleigh Rovers 0

DAN-AIR CLASS ELITE CUP

First Round

Cobham v Viking Sports	2-0	Farnham Town v Malden Town	2-1
Merstham v Steyning Town	2-1		

Second Round

Ash United v Ditton F & SC	3-7(aet)	Chipstead v Westfield	2-0
Cobham v Farleigh Rovers	0-1	Farleigh Rovers v Bedfont	2-3
Godalming Town v Ashford Town (Middx)	0-4	Hartley Wintney v Frimley Green	1-1(aet),0-3
Merstham v Horley Town	2-2(aet),4-1	Sandhurst Town v Cranleigh	1-4

Quarter-Finals

Bedfont v Frimley Green	0-1	Cranleigh v Merstham	9-1
Ditton F & SC v Ashford Town (Middx)	1-2	Farnham Town v Chipstead	1-0

Semi-Finals

Ashford Town (Middx) v Frimley Green	2-1	Farnham Town v Cranleigh	2-1

Final *(at Woking FC)*: Farnham Town 3, Ashford Town (Middx) 0

RESERVE SECTION CHALLENGE CUP

First Round

Farnham Town Res v Bedfont Res	2-0	Viking Sports Res v Westfield Res	2-0

Second Round

Ash United Res v Farnham Town Res	1-0	Ashford (Middx) Res v Chipstead Res	3-3(aet),0-2
Ditton Res v Godalming Town Res	2-4(aet)	Hartley Wintney Res v Cobham Res	1-2
Malden Town Res v Frimley Green Res	0-1	Merstham Res v Farleigh Rovers Res	4-2
Sandhurst Town Res v Cranleigh Res	2-0	Viking Sports Res v Horley Town Res	2-0

Quarter-Finals

Ash United Res v Godalming Town Res	0-2	Cobham Res v Chipstead Res	0-0(aet),2-1(aet)
Frimley Green Res v Viking Sports Res	0-1	Sandhurst Town Res v Merstham Res	2-1

Semi-Finals

Sandhurst Town Res v Cobham Res	2-1(aet)	Viking Sports Res v Godalming Town Res	1-2

Final *(at Cove FC)*: Godalming Town Reserves 4, Sandhurst Town Reserves 0

GRANT-McCLELLAN YOUTH CUP

First Round

Chipstead Yth v Sandhurst Town Yth	4-0,3-0	Godalming Town Yth v Cranleigh Yth	2-1,2-1
Steyning Town Yth v Frimley Green Yth	1-2,5-0		

Quarter-Finals

Bedfont Yth v Steyning Town Yth	2-0,2-0	Chipstead Yth W/O Horley Town Yth	
Farnham Town Yth v Malden Town Yth	0-2,1-4	Godalming Town Yth v Westfield Yth	2-0,2-2

Semi-Finals

Malden Town Yth *(withdrawn)* Bedfont Yth	W/O	Godalming Town Yth v Chipstead Yth	0-0,0-2

Final *(at Cobham FC)*: Bedfont Youth 4, Chipstead Youth 0

YOUTH CHALLENGE SHIELD

Group One

Godalming Town Yth v Frimley Green Yth	1-1
Frimley Green Yth v Godalming Town Res	2-5
Malden Town Yth *(withdrew from competition)*	

Group Two

Sandhurst Town Yth v Cranleigh Yth	0-1
Sandhurst Town Yth v Farnham Town Yth	2-6
Westfield Yth v Cranleigh Yth	5-0
Westfield Yth v Farnham Town Yth	2-1
Westfield Yth v Sandhurst Town Yth	17-0
Cranleigh Yth v Farnham Town Yth	0-6
Cranleigh Yth v Sandhurst Town Yth	4-1
Cranleigh Yth v Westfield Yth	3-6
Farham Town Yth v Cranleigh Yth	5-1
Farnham Town Yth v Sandhurst Town Yth	16-1
Farnham Town Yth v Westfield Yth	3-2

	P	W	D	L	F	A	Pts
Godalming T. Yth	2	1	1	0	6	3	4
Frimley Green Yth	2	0	1	1	3	6	1
Malden Yth withdrew - record expunged							

	P	W	D	L	F	A	Pts
Westfield Yth	6	5	0	1	40	7	15
Farnham Town Yth	6	5	0	1	37	8	15
Cranleigh Yth	6	2	0	4	9	23	6
Sandhurst Town Yth	6	0	0	6	4	52	0

Final *(at Sandhurst Town FC)*: Westfield Youth 1, Godalming Town Youth 0

ASHFORD TOWN (MIDDX)

President: Mr E Britzman   **Chairman:** R Parker   **Vice Chairman:** S Clark
Secretary: A B J Constable, 30 Marlborough Rd, Ashford, Middx TW15 3QA (0784 244515).
Manager: M Snowden   **Commercial Manager:** Mr R Osborn
Physio: D Hanks   **Press Secretary:** Mr D Baker
Ground: Short Lane, Stanwell, Staines, Middx (0784 245908).
Directions: A30 towards London, third left after Ashford Hospital crossroads - ground signposted after quarter of a mile on right down Short Lane. Two miles from Ashford (BR).
Seats: None   **Cover:** 60   **Capacity:**   **Floodlights:** No   **Year Formed:** 1964
Colours: Tangerine & white stripes/white/tangerine   **Change colours:** Blue & black/blue/blue
Programme: 24 pages   **Programme Editor:** Secretary
Previous Leagues: Hounslow & Dist. 64-67/ Surrey Intermediate 67-82/ Surrey Premier 82-90.
Hons: Dan-Air Elite Class Cup R-up 91-92, Surrey I'mediate Lg   **Previous Ground:** Clockhouse Lane Rec.

ASH UNITED

President: Mrs B Williams   **Chairman:** R T Atkins
Secretary: A Haberle, 30 Longfield Rd, Ash, Nr Aldershot (0252 310092).
Ground: Youngs Drive, off Shawfield Rd, Ash, Nr Aldershot (0252 20385).
Directions: A323 towards Ash, left into Shawfield Rd, right into Ash Church Rd, right at crossroads into Shawfield Rd. 1 mile from both Ash and Ash Vale BR stations.
Seats: None   **Cover:** None   **Capacity:** 1,500   **Floodlights:** No   **Founded:** 1911
Colours: Green/red/red   **Change colours:** All blue   **Programme:** Sometimes.
Midweek Matchday: Tuesday   **Previous Ground:** Ash Common Rec. 70-71
Previous Leagues: Surrey Snr, Aldershot Snr

BEDFONT

Chairman: D Marshall   **Sec:** R D Cooper, 148 Hamilton Rd, Feltham, Middx TW13 4PX (081 751 4070).
Ground: The Orchard, Hatton Rd, Middx (081 890 7264).   **Clubhouse details:** Large.
Directions: Turn down Faggs Rd opposite Hatton Cross (Picadilly Line) station on Great South Western Rd (A30), then sharp right into Hatton Rd. Ground opposite Duke of Wellington pub.
Seats: None   **Cover:** 50   **Capacity:**   **Floodlights:** Yes   **Programme:** Yes
Colours: Gold/blue/blue   **Change colours:** Blue/yellow/yellow.
Hons: Grant McClennan Yth Cup 91-92.

CHIPSTEAD

President: B Nicholls   **Chairman:** Keith Rivers
Secretary: K Allsopp, 51 Lakers Rise, Woodsterne, Banstead, Surrey SM7 3JX (0737 359989).
Manager: John Sears   **Coach:** Paul Duffield.
Ground: High Road, Chipstead, Surrey (0737 553250).
Directions: Brighton Road northbound, left into Church Lane, left into Hogcross Lane, right into High Road. One and a half miles from Chipstead (BR).
Seats: 30   **Cover:** 30   **Capacity:** 2,000   **Floodlights:** Due   **Founded:** 1906
Cols: Green & white stripes/green/black   **Change cols:** Yellow & white   **Programme:** 44 pages
Previous Leagues: Surrey Intermediate 62-82/ Surrey Premier 82-86   **Nickname:** Chips
Hons: Surrey Premier Lg R-up 82-83 83-84 85-86 (Lg Cup 82-83 84-85 85-86), Combined Co's Lg 89-90 (R-up 90-91, Lg Cup 86-87 90-91, Elite Class Cup R-up 89-90).

COBHAM

Chairman: E Strange   **Sec:** A O'Dea, 53 Cotwood Gdns, Collier Wood, London SW19 2DS (081 542 8860).
Ground: Leg O'Mutton Field, Downside Bridge Rd, Cobham, Surrey (0932 65959).
Directions: A307 (Portsmouth Road) towards Leatherhead, right into Between Streets, right into Downside Rd then right opposite car park. Two miles from Cobham & Stoke D'Abernon (BR).
Seats: None   **Cover:** No   **Capacity:** 2,000   **Floodlights:** No   **Founded:** 1892
Colours: Red/white/red   **Change colours:** All yellow.
Previous League: Surrey Senior.   **Previous Grounds:** Cobham Rec.
Programme: FA Vase matches only   **Record Gate:** 2,000 v Showbiz team, charity match 1975.

CRANLEIGH

Chairman: P Slater   **President:** J S Wiskar.
Secretary: Mr S Inwood, 22 Long Poles Rd, Cranleigh, Surrey (0483 277058).
Ground: Snoxall Fields, Knowle Lane, Cranleigh (0483 275295).
Directions: A281 from Guildford towards Horsham, B2128 to Cranleigh High Street - turn off into Knowle Lane, 200 yds turn left into Snoxall Playing Fields.
Seats: None   **Cover:** No   **Capacity:** 750   **Floodlights:** No   **Programme:** Yes
Colours: Blue/yellow/blue   **Change colours:** Grey/black/black.   **Founded:** 1893.
Record Gate: 450 v C Palace, friendly 1989   **Clubhouse:** Open Tues/Thurs/weekend evenings.

D.C.A. BASINGSTOKE

Secretary: D Brand (0256 57309).   **Previous League:** Hampshire (Pre-1992).
Ground: Whiteditch Playing Fields, Sherbourne Road, Basingstoke, Hants (0256 844866).

DITTON F. & S.C.

Secretary: R Clune (081 399 7537).
Ground: Ditton Recreation Ground, Windmill Lane, Long Ditton, Surbiton, Surrey (081 398 7428).
Directions: At A307/A309 'Scilly Isles' r'bout east of Esher, take A307 towards Surbiton. Windmill Lane is one and a half miles on right. One and a half miles from Surbiton (BR); turn left into Victoria Rd, right at crossroads, left into Balaclava, right into Effingham Rd and right into Windmill Lane.
Seats: None   **Cover:** No   **Capacity:**   **Floodlights:** No   **Founded:** 1912
Colours: Yellow/green   **Change colours:** White/black/white   **Programme:** Yes.
Previous Leagues: Kingston & Dist./ Surrey Snr/ Surrey I'mediate/ Surrey Comb. 72-85/ Surrey Premier.
Previous Name: Ditton Old Boys (pre-1972).
Hons: Surrey Premier Lg 85-86, Surrey Co. Premier Cup R-up 85-86, Surrey I'mediate Cup R-up 53-54 81-82 83-84, Surrey Comb. 84-85, Surrey Jnr Charity Cup 22-23 (R-up 21-22 44-45), Surrey Lower Jnr Cup 81-82, War Emergency Cup 46-47.

Cobham FC pictured before their 0-2 defeat at Ditton in December. Photo - Gavin Ellis.

Cranleigh FC who will celebrate their centenary during 1992-92. Photo - Eric Marsh.

Ditton, whose final placing of 5th represents a satisfactory debut in the Combined Co's League. Photo - Gavin Ellis.

FARLEIGH ROVERS

President: C D Scott   **Chairman:** TBA   **Secretary:** TBA.
Ground: Parsonage Field, Harrow Road, Warlingham, Surrey (0883 626483).
Directions: Limpsfield Road (B269) south eastwards, left into Farleigh Rd, left at T-junction, right into Harrow Rd, right into Green Lane. Three miles from Upper Warlingham (BR); left into Chelsham Rd 1 mile left into Harrow Rd. Bus 403 to Harrow Rd.
Seats: None   **Cover:** No   **Capacity:** 2,000   **Floodlights:** No   **Founded:** 1922
Colours: Red/black/black   **Change colours:** Blue & black/blue/blue   **Programme:** Yes
Previous Name: Farleigh & Chelsham Utd (pre-1929)   **Previous Ground:** Farleigh Common (pre-1925).
Previous League: Surrey Premier   **Record Gate:** 130 v Chipstead, League 28/12/87.
Hons: Combined Co's Cup R-up 91-92.

FRIMLEY GREEN

President: B Potter   **Chairman:** T Brown
Secretary: M Ridge, 55 Larch Way, Southwood, Farnborough (0252 373626).
Ground: Recreation Ground, Frimley Green Road, Frimley Green (0252 835089).
Directions: A325 (Portsmouth road) south westwards into town centre, left into Grove Cross and straight over into Frimley Green Rd. From Frimley (BR); right into Frimley High Str., fork right into Church Rd and right into Frimley Green Rd.
Seats: None   **Cover:** 100   **Programme:** No   **Floodlights:** No   **Founded:** 1919
Colours: White/blue/blue   **Change cols:** Sky & navy   **Previous Lge:** (London) Spartan 74-81

GODALMING & GUILDFORD

President: W Kyte   **Chairman:** M Palmer   **Manager:** Tim Daly
Secretary: Mrs J Phillips, 135 Manor Rd, Stoughton, Guildford, Surrey GU2 6NR (0483 571372).
Ground: Weycourt, Meadrow, Godalming, Surrey (0483 417520).
Directions: A3100 from Guildford to Godalming, road becomes Meadrow after Godalming High Street, turn left into Weycourt after bridge over River Wey. Three quarters of a mile from Farncombe (BR).
Seats: Yes   **Cover:** 200   **Capacity:** 1,500   **Floodlights:** No   **Programme:** Yes
Colours: Green & white/white   **Change colours:** All yellow.   **Founded:** 1971
Previous Lge: Surrey County Snr   **Previous Ground:** Broadwater Pk, Farncombe 71-73
Previous Names: Godalming & Farncombe 71-80/ Godalming Town 80-92.
Record Gate: 600+ - Ex-Guildford City XI v Ex-Football Lg XI, Tony Burge benefit, 1991.
Hons: Combined Co's Reserve Challenge Cup 91-92.

HARTLEY WINTNEY

President: D Gorsky   **Chairman:** W Mitchell
Secretary: S Pratt, 'Grafton', 29 Queens Rd, Fleet, Hants GU13 9LA (0252 6239561).
Ground: Memorial Playing Fields, Green Lane, Hartley Wintney, Hants (0251 263586).
Directions: A30 west through Camberley, left at parade of shops at beginning of village then sharp right - ground on right. Two miles from Winchfield (BR).
Seats: 2 benches   **Cover:** No   **Capacity:** 2,000   **Floodlights:** No   **Founded:** 1897
Colours: Tangerine/black/tangerine   **Change colours:** White/blue/blue   **Programme:** Yes
Previous Leagues: Basingstoke/ Aldershot   **Nickname:** The Row

HORLEY TOWN

President: B T Sired   **Chairman:** J H J Dignum
Secretary: P Freeman, Long Acre, 140 Balcombe Rd, Horley, Surrey RH6 9DS (0293 784368).
Ground: The Defence, Smallfield Rd, Horley, Surrey (0293 786075).
Directions: From Horley (BR) cross road, down Station Approach, left into The Grove, into Station Rd, across Balcombe Rd B2036 crossroads - ground 1 mile on left down Smallfield Rd.
Seats: None   **Cover:** 100   **Capacity:** 2,000   **Floodlights:** No   **Founded:** 1898
Colours: Claret & blue/white/white   **Change colours:** Green & yellow.   **Programme:** Yes
Previous League: Surrey Snr 51-55 70-78/ London Spartan 78-81/ Athenian 81-84.
Previous Ground: Gasworks Ground, Balcombe Rd.
Record Gate: 1,000 v Tottenham Hotspur, pre-season friendly 1983.

MALDEN TOWN

Chairman: K Bernard   **Manager:** K Bernard.
Secretary: F Thompson, 13 Dorchester Rd, Worcester Park, Surrey (081 337 7026).
Ground: Manor Park, Malden Road, New Malden, Surrey (081 942 6521).
Directions: A3 towards London, turn off in order to take A2043 (right turn off r'bout) - ground situated down turning on left between concrete pillars. Half mile from both New Malden and Worcester Park BR stations.
Seats: Yes   **Cover:** 120   **Capacity:**   **Floodlights:** No   **Programme:** Yes
Colours: Red/white/red   **Change colours:** White/black/black.   **Founded:** 1936.
Previous League: Surrey County Senior.

MERSTHAM

President: F Fox   **Chairman:** P Dyason
General/Commercial Manager: D Parsons (0737 552682).
Secretary: F Fox, 153 Albury Rd, Merstham, Redhill, Surrey RH1 3LW (0737 643279).
Ground: Albury Road, Merstham, Redhill, Surrey (0737 43279).
Directions: Left out of Merstham (BR), down School Hill, under railway bridge, fork left then right into Albury Road, ground entrance half way down on left.
Seats: 100   **Cover:** 100   **Capacity:** 2,100   **Floodlights:** Yes (177 lux)
Colours: Amber & black   **Change colours:** Mauve/white   **Founded:** 1892.
Clubhouse: Normal licensing hours   **Programme:** 44 pages, Editor - John Stancombe.
Previous Leagues: Redhill & Dist./ Surrey Co. S.E. I'mediate/ Surrey Snr 64-78/ London Spartan 78-85.
Previous Name: Ditton Old Boys (pre-1972).
Hons: Combined Co's Lg R-up 87-88 89-90 (Elite Class Cup 89-90 (R-up 90-91)), London Spartan Lg 79-89 (Lg Cup 79-80), Surrey Snr Lg 71-72, Surrey Snr Charity Cup 79-80, East Surrey Charity Cup 80-81, Surrey I'mediate Lg 52-53.

Farleigh Rovers at Woking for the League Challenge Cup Final against Farnham Town. Photo - Eric Marsh.

Frimley Green pictured before their match againgst Godalming on 1st February. Photo - Eric Marsh.

Godalming Town, who will start afresh as Godalming & Guildford in 1992-92. Photo - Eric Marsh.

PEPPARD

Chairman: C F Clayton   **President:** V F Clayton   **Manager:** Graham Haddrell
Secretary: Nr D North, 35 Oregon Avenue, Tilehurst, Reading, Berks RG4 9TB (0734 423557).
Ground: Bishopswood Sports Centre, Horsepond Road, Sonning Common, Reading (0734 712265).
Seats: None   **Cover:** No   **Capacity:** All red   **Floodlights:** No   **Founded:** 1903
Clubhouse: Bar & function room   **Previous Lges:** Reading & Dist. 70-87/ Chiltonian 87-92.
Previous Names: Sonning Common Peppard (Peppard FC merged with Sonning Common FC in 1984 - name reverted to Peppard FC in 1990).
Prog.: 40 pages, 50p **Ed.:** Reece Pigden (0734 723445)   **Sponsors:** Greenwood Tighe Public Relations
Colours: All red   **Leading Scorers 91-92:** D Smith 26, D Jones 21, M Weller 14.
Change: All blue   **Leading Apps 91-92:** J Murray 41, D Jones 40, C Rutherford 40.
Local Newspapers: Reading Evening Post, Henley Standard   **Local Radio:** Radio 210, Radio Oxford.
Hons: Chiltonian Lg(2) 90-92 (R-up 89-90, Lg Cup(4) 87-89 90-92), Reading & Dist. Lg(7), Oxon Snr Cup 79-80 81-82 (R-up 89-90), Oxon I'mediate Cup(2) 74-76, Reading Snr Cup(6), Wycombe Snr Cup 90-91, Reading Jnr Cup 61-62 81-82(res).

SANDHURST TOWN

Chairman: M J Morgan   **Secretary:** D W Norman, 1 Elm Tree Close, Chertsey, Surrey (0932 563937).
Ground: Memorial Ground, Yorktown Rd, Sandhurst (0252 873767).
Directions: A30 westwards through Camberley, right at r-bout with traffic lights, past superstore turning right, left at next r'bout. Ground next to Town & Council offices and Community Sports Centre.
Seats: None   **Cover:** No   **Capacity:**   **Floodlights:** No   **Programme:** Yes
Colours: Red/black/black   **Change colours:** All gold   **Metal Badges:** Yes
Previous Lge: Chiltonian (pre-1990)   **Hons:** Combined Co's Reserve Chal. Cup R-up 91-92

STEYNING TOWN

President: R Head   **Chairman:** I Kennett
Secretary: I Kennett, 1 Breach Close, Steyning, West Sussex (0903 813262).
Ground: The Shooting Field, Steyning, West Sussex (0903 812228).
Directions: A27 east then A283 turn off - town centre turning at r'bout, right into Church Street, straight into Church Lane, straight into Shooting Field. Ground on left by Grammar School.
Seats: None   **Cover:** 400   **Capacity:** 1,200   **Floodlights:** Yes   **Programme:** Yes
Colours: Red/white/red   **Change colours:** Blue & white/blue/blue   **Founded:** 1900
Previous Lge: Sussex Co. 64-88   **Record Gate:** 1,100 v Halesowen Town, FA Vase QF 84-85.
Hons: FA Vase QF 84-85, Sussex Snr Cup 85-86 88-89, Sussex Co. Lg 84-85 85-86 (Lg Cup 77-78 83-84 85-86, Div 2 Invitation Cup 65-66, Reserve Section West 88-89), Sussex RUR Charity Cup 79-80, Vernon Wentworth Cup 33-34, Sussex Jnr Cup 01-02 37-38.

VIKING SPORTS

President: R Bartlett   **Chairman:** H H Mesham   **Manager:** George Goode
Secretary: J D Bennett, 6 Bridge House, Boston Manor Rd, Brentford TW8 9LH (081 568 9047).
Ground: Avenue Park, Western Avenue, Greenford, Middx (081 578 2706).
Directions: On London-bound carriageway of A40, 300 yds before Greenford flyover. Greenford BR & Central Line stations are 1 mile north east on Oldfield Lane North.
Seats: 20   **Cover:** 20   **Capacity:** 400   **Floodlights:** No   **Founded:** 1945
Colours: Tangerine/black   **Change colours:** Sky blue   **Programme:** Yes
Clubhouse: Open Mon-Sat evenings   **Record Gate:** 180 v Lambourn, Hellenic Lg 1982
Previous Lge: Middx/ Hellenic 80-91   **Previous Grounds:** Churchfield (pre-1965)
Players progressing to Football League: Gordon Bartlett (Portsmouth), Alan Devonshire (West Ham).
Nickname: Vikings   **Hons:** Hellenic Lg Div 1 85-86.

WESTFIELD

Chairman: E Strange   **Manager:** John Martin.
Secretary: Mr Philip Arthur-Worsop, 10 Martin Way, Woking, Surrey (0483 715659).
Ground: Woking Park, Kingfield, Woking, Surrey (no telephone).
Directions: Adjacent to Woking FC (see GMV Conference section).
Seats: None   **Cover:** No   **Capacity:**   **Floodlights:** No   **Programme:** No
Colours: All royal blue **Change colours:** All yellow.   **Previous League:** Surrey Co. Snr.

Westfield FC, pictured before playing in front of their bigggest home crowd of the season; some 160. The reason for this massive gate; Woking were playing Yeovil next door in the FA Cup and with Kingfield full to capacity many were locked out and had to seek a counter attraction! Photo - Eric Marsh.

Hartley Wintney FC. Photo - Eric Marsh.

Malden Town. Back Row (L/R): B Barnes (Sponsor), M Gillings, D Finn, M Bridgwater, J Richards, D Perry, J Mills, K Bernard (Manager). Front: A Hutching, N Costello, T Holtby, M Broderick, C Payne, S Whittle. Photo - Dave West.

Sandhurst Town, who finished bottom again but improved markedly on 1990-91. Photo - Eric Marsh.

PARASOL (COMBINED COUNTIES) LEAGUE TEN YEAR RECORD

	82/3	83/4	84/5	85/6	86/7	87/8	88/9	89/90	90/1	91/2
Alton Town	11	16	–	–	–	–	–	–	–	–
Ashford Town (Middx)	–	–	–	–	–	–	–	–	5	6
Ash United	2	3	5	3	1	13	10	4	8	9
B.A.e. Weybridge				(See Weybridge Town)						
Bedfont	–	–	–	–	–	11	12	16	7	8
Chertsey Town	–	–	–	2	–	–	–	–	–	–
Chessington United	6	17	–	–	–	–	–	–	–	–
Chipstead	–	–	–	–	4	7	4	1	2	3
Chobham	4	4	13	12	12	15	18	18	–	–
Cobham	9	10	17	8	11	4	11	8	10	4
Cove	5	13	18	13	13	12	17	3	–	–
Cranleigh	13	15	12	17	16	16	15	17	15	7
Ditton F. & S.C.	–	–	–	–	–	–	–	–	–	5
Farleigh Rovers	–	–	11	15	14	14	8	9	6	11
Farnham Town	15	8	10	5	2	3	5	6	1	1
Fleet Town	–	–	19	19	–	–	–	–	–	–
Frimley Green	8	12	14	18	15	17	16	13	9	13
Godalming Town	3	1	9	10	7	5	13	10	13	17
Guildford & Worplesdon	12	7	–	–	–	–	–	–	–	–
Hartley Wintney	1	5	16	11	8	10	7	11	14	15
Horley Town	–	–	15	16	9	9	9	14	16	18
Lingfield	18	–	–	–	–	–	–	–	–	–
Malden Town	10	2	6	6	10	6	14	5	3	2
Malden Vale	–	–	1	4	3	8	2	–	–	–
Merstham	–	–	3	7	6	2	3	2	4	14
Sandhurst Town	–	–	–	–	–	–	–	–	17	19
Southwick	–	–	2	–	–	–	–	–	–	–
Steyning Town	–	–	–	–	–	–	6	7	12	10
Viking Sports	–	–	–	–	–	–	–	–	–	12
Virginia Water	14	9	7	14	18	–	–	–	–	–
Westfield	16	6	8	9	17	18	19	15	11	16
Weybridge Town	7	11	4	1	5	1	1	12	–	–
Yateley Town	17	14	–	–	–	–	–	–	–	–
No. of Clubs	18	17	19	19	18	18	19	18	17	19

Viking Sports pictured before their game against Farleigh Rovers on FA Cup Final morning. Photo - Eric Marsh.

Duncan Jones, of Parasol League newcomers Peppard, beats 'keeper Simon Bird for the only goal against Penn & Tylers Green in a Chiltonian League fixture. Photo - Tony Higgs.

CHARRINGTON CHILTONIAN LEAGUE

Chairman: Mr C Anderson.
President: Mr D Newell.
Hon. Secretary: Mr R A Lipscombe,
31 Broughton Avenue, Aylesbury, Bucks (0296 394781).

SUPER PEPPARD STORM TO ANOTHER SUCCESS

A very successful season culminated with Peppard winning the title after leading for most of the season. Peppard started the season with an amazing run of eighteen straight League victories and finished the season still undefeated. Binfield finished as runners-up with Holmer Green third.

Eton Wick clinched the First Division title after a very impressive first season by winning their final game against close rivals Molins, and may provide some surprises in the Premier after some good Cup games against Premier opposition in reaching the League Cup final.

In the Reserve Divisions, clear winners of Division One were Wraysbury/Coopers followed by Peppard and Holmer Green. The champions were not decided until the final game when Wraysbury beat Peppard 2-1. The Division Two title also went to the last game, Eton Wick getting the win they needed, 7-1 against Brill. Uxbridge were second and Henley third.

The League Cup was played at the prestigious Adams Park with Peppard beating Eton Wick 3-1. The pitch was not as good as last year, but I think most people enjoyed the day. In the Reserve League Cup, Peppard met Finchampstead at Holmer Green, and after a keenly contested game, Peppard won 3-1 to retain the trophy. This season saw the introduction of a Subsidiary Cup for teams who finished their fixtures early. In the final at Penn & Tylers Green, Stokenchurch drew 3-3 with Uxbridge after extra-time before losing 2-3 on penalties.

In outside Cups the League gained notable success with Eton Wick winning the Berks & Bucks Intermediate Cup beating Lambourn Sports 2-0 in the final. In the Wycombe Senior Cup Holmer Green beat Molins 3-0, and Peppard Reserves beat Holmer Green Reserves 3-1 to win the Wycombe Junior Cup. In the Oxon Senior Cup, Peppard were unlucky to lose after extra-time to Oxford United Reserves 2-3 in the semi finals, whilst their Reserves lost 1-2 to Thame Reserves in the final of the Oxon Intermediate Cup. Brill lost to Oakley in the Oving Villages Cup final, and Stokenchurch lost 3-4 after extra-time to Wing Village in the delayed final of the Aylesbury Shield. Peppard retained the Reading Senior Cup beating Binfield 2-1, but their Reserves lost 0-1 to Tilehurst in the final of the Reading Junior Cup. Eton Wick beat local rivals Slough YCOB to win the Slough Town Cup, Stokelake beat Brill 1-0 in the Marsworth Reserve Cup final, and Binfield Reserves were triumphant in the Maidenhead Junior Cup

This season has seen the League as part of the new lower level of the Pyramid with Peppard successful in promotion to the Combined Counties League. The League is striving to increase its stature and most clubs are improving their facilities which is appreciated by the Management Committee.

R A Lipscombe, League Secretary

Peppard FC enjoyed breath-taking success again in 1991-92, maintaining a 100% record until after Christmas as they cruised to a second successive Charrington Chiltonian League championship and earned a long-awaited promotion to the Combined Counties League. Above they are pictured before the final of the 'Evening Post' Reading Senior Cup, another competition they won for a second consecutive year. Back Row (L/R): Robin Gosnell, Graham Hambridge, Dave Smith, Duncan Jones, Nigel Huddlestone, Craig Rutherford, Matt Weller, Kevin Wallace, Graham Haddrell (Manager). Front: Pat McCoy, Barry White, Kevin Watkins, Bruno Giamettei, James Murray, Kenny Cox, Steve Dale, Sid Grover. Photo - Dave West.

LEAGUE TABLES 1991-92

Premier Division	P	W	D	L	F	A	PTS
Peppard	26	22	4	0	74	15	70
Binfield	26	19	3	4	90	38	60
Holmer Green	26	15	7	4	54	32	52
Letcombe	26	13	7	6	48	37	46
Finchampstead	26	11	5	10	47	36	38
Stocklake	26	11	4	11	40	37	37
Martin Baker Spts	26	10	3	11	38	57	33
Mill End Sports	26	8	8	10	47	47	32
Wraysbury Coopers	26	9	5	12	54	55	32
Prestwood	26	7	7	12	36	58	28
Reading Town	26	8	3	15	35	65	27
Brill United	26	6	4	16	44	66	22
Chalfont Wasps	26	6	3	17	32	60	21
Penn & Tylers Gr.	26	4	3	19	25	61	15

Division One	P	W	D	L	F	A	PTS
Eton Wick	24	18	2	4	66	18	56
Molins Sports	24	17	2	5	57	32	53
Slough Y.C.O.B.	24	14	3	7	60	39	45
Broomwade Spts	24	13	5	6	46	41	44
Hazells Aylesbury	24	13	1	10	50	39	40
Stokenchurch	24	11	3	10	48	45	36
Uxbridge Town	24	11	3	10	45	33	*33
Wooburn Athletic	24	9	6	9	44	50	33
Denham United	24	7	6	11	33	49	27
Kodak Harrow	24	4	6	14	32	54	22
Henley Town	24	6	3	15	40	51	21
Wallingford Utd	24	4	5	15	24	63	17
Chinnor	24	4	3	17	27	58	15

* - 3 pts deducted

PREMIER DIVISION RESULTS 1991/92

HOME TEAM		1	2	3	4	5	6	7	8	9	10	11	12	13	14
1.	Binfield	*	5-1	6-1	5-2	5-1	5-1	7-1	2-1	2-0	1-5	2-2	8-0	7-1	4-1
2.	Brill United	1-3	*	5-4	2-3	1-2	3-5	2-1	1-1	1-2	0-4	1-1	2-2	0-4	1-2
3.	Chalfont Wasps	1-2	2-3	*	2-5	2-2	1-2	1-1	0-2	3-0	0-2	1-3	3-1	0-1	2-1
4.	Finchampstead	0-1	2-1	0-1	*	1-3	3-1	2-1	5-0	2-0	1-1	0-2	4-0	1-2	3-3
5.	Holmer Green	1-1	3-1	4-1	0-0	*	1-2	1-0	4-2	4-2	2-3	0-0	1-1	1-0	3-2
6.	Letcombe	2-1	5-1	3-0	0-0	0-0	*	5-1	1-1	3-1	1-3	0-0	5-2	W-L	1-0
7.	Martin Baker Spts	2-4	2-0	1-3	1-0	0-2	2-1	*	1-5	4-1	0-0	4-4	2-1	3-0	2-8
8.	Mill End Sports	1-3	1-3	3-1	3-3	0-1	1-1	3-0	*	7-1	0-3	1-3	1-2	1-0	2-2
9.	Penn & Tylers Green	0-3	1-3	1-1	0-2	0-3	1-0	2-1	2-2	*	1-4	0-0	2-4	0-1	0-2
10.	Peppard	3-1	1-0	5-1	1-0	2-2	5-0	2-0	2-1	1-0	*	7-1	2-0	4-1	1-0
11.	Prestwood	1-5	3-2	0-1	1-0	1-6	1-1	1-2	3-4	1-5	2-3	*	0-1	0-4	1-5
12.	Reading Town	2-3	1-4	4-0	3-6	2-1	0-0	0-2	2-3	2-1	0-5	1-0	*	0-2	2-0
13.	Stocklake	3-0	3-3	2-0	0-2	1-2	1-4	1-2	0-0	2-1	0-0	0-2	5-1	*	4-1
14.	Wraysbury Coopers	4-4	3-2	1-0	2-0	2-4	3-4	1-2	1-1	3-1	0-5	2-3	3-1	2-2	*

DIVISION ONE RESULTS 1991/92

HOME TEAM		1	2	3	4	5	6	7	8	9	10	11	12	13
1.	Broomwade Spts	*	4-0	4-4	1-0	4-1	2-1	0-0	1-2	1-3	2-0	1-6	1-1	2-1
2.	Chinnor	3-2	*	0-1	0-3	2-3	1-3	2-3	1-3	2-3	2-1	1-2	6-0	0-1
3.	Denham United	3-2	2-0	*	0-0	1-2	0-4	2-1	1-1	1-3	2-2	1-1	3-1	3-1
4.	Eton Wick	3-0	0-1	5-2	*	W-L	3-0	4-0	5-2	2-3	6-0	4-3	2-0	8-2
5.	Hazells Aylesbury	1-2	2-0	3-1	0-3	*	0-1	5-0	2-0	3-1	4-1	1-0	5-0	0-0
6.	Henley Town	2-6	1-1	1-2	0-3	2-4	*	1-1	1-2	1-2	0-1	2-4	6-2	0-4
7.	Kodak (Harrow)	2-2	5-1	1-0	0-4	4-2	0-4	*	1-2	1-2	1-2	0-2	5-0	0-0
8.	Molins Sports	0-1	2-0	5-0	0-6	6-0	2-1	3-1	*	1-0	2-1	3-1	7-1	4-0
9.	Slough Y.C.O.B.	7-2	1-1	5-2	0-1	0-5	4-2	5-0	0-2	*	6-1	2-0	0-1	4-2
10.	Stokenchurch	1-2	4-1	2-0	1-2	5-1	2-2	4-2	1-1	3-4	*	1-0	1-3	3-0
11.	Uxbridge Town	0-1	4-0	1-1	1-2	0-2	2-0	2-1	1-3	3-2	1-4	*	1-0	7-0
12.	Wallingford Utd	0-1	2-2	4-1	0-0	2-1	1-4	1-3	1-2	1-1	1-4	0-2	*	1-1
13.	Wooburn Athletic	2-2	6-0	0-2	2-0	4-3	2-1	4-1	5-2	2-2	0-3	1-1	4-1	*

LEAGUE CUP 1991-92

First Round

Uxbridge Town v Eton Wick	0-3	
Penn & Tylers Green v Finchampstead	4-2	
Slough Y.C.O.B. v Reading Town	2-1	
Broomwade v Martin Baker Sports	2-3	
Hazells (Aylesbury) v Brill United	2-1	
Wooburn v Wraysbury/Coopers	1-2	
Wallingford United v Binfield	1-2	
Letcombe v Stokenchurch	1-0	
Prestwood v Chalfont Wasps	2-0	
Kodak (Harrow) v Molins Sports	2-1	
Henley Town v Peppard	1-1,0-4	

Second Round

Chinnor v Eton Wick	0-10	
Penn & Tylers Green v Letcombe	2-1	
Prestwood v Martin Baker Sports	1-1,1-0	
Hazells (Aylesbury) v Peppard	0-3	
Binfield v Mill End Sports	2-2,4-3(aet)	
Slough Y.C.O.B. v Denham United	2-1	
Kodak (Harrow) v Stocklake	3-1(aet)	
Wraysbury/Cooper v Holmer Green	5-2	

Quarter-Finals

Eton Wick v Binfield	5-1	
Prestwood v Kodak (Harrow)	1-2(aet)	
Penn & Tylers Green v Slough Y.C.O.B.	1-3	
Peppard v Wraysbury/Coopers	1-0	

Semi-Finals

Eton Wick v Slough Y.C.O.B. (at Prestwood)	1-0	
Kodak Harrow v Peppard (at Molins Sports)	1-3	

Final (at Wycombe Wanderers FC, 4-5-92): Peppard 3, Eton Wick 1

PREMIER DIVISION CLUBS 1992-93

BINFIELD
Chairman: Paul Hammerstone **Manager:** Clive Tallentire.
Secretary: Duncan McMinn, Copperkins, Albon Rd, Binfield, Berks RG12 5HU (0344 428101).
Ground: Stubbs Lane, Binfield, Berks. **Local Press:** Bracknell News/ Times.
Seats: Yes **Cover:** Yes **Programme:** Sometimes **Founded:** 1892.
Colours: All red **Sponsors:** Churchill Financial Consultants.
Prev. League: Reading & Dist. (pre-1987). **Clubhouse:** Kitchen, bar, lounge, changing rooms, showers.
Hons: Chilt. Lg R-up 91-92 (Div 1 89-90, Lg Cup R-up 89-90), Reading Snr Cup R-up 91-92, Gt Western Comb. 46-47.

BRILL UNITED
Chairman: Mr S Shipperley **Manager:** TBA.
Secretary: Mr P J Parker, 3 Norcotts Kiln, Brill, Aylesbury, Berks HP18 9TJ (0844 237651).
Ground: Brill Recreation Ground, Church Street, Brill, Aylesbury, Bucks (0844 237388).
Directions: Church Street is immediately behind Red Lion pub in village centre.
Seats: No **Cover:** No **Programme:** No **Founded:** 1890.
Sponsors: Sun Inn, Brill **Colours:** Black & white stripes/black/black
Prev. Leagues: Oxon Snr/ Lord Jersey. **Clubhouse:** Bar, on ground.
Hons: Chilt. Lg Cup 86-87 (Div 1 R-up 90-91) **Local Press:** Oxford Mail, Bucks Herald, Thame Gazette.

ETON WICK
Chairman: J Bussey **Manager:** J Hartridge.
Secretary: Pauline Marks, 28 Colemorton Cres., Eton Wick, Windsor, Berks (0753 841886).
Ground: Haywards Mead, Eton Wick, Windsor (0753 852749). **Directions:** Windsor Rd Slough under M4
m'way to r'bout, 1st exit to lights at Eton College, turn right - club one and a half miles on left in Eton Wick.
Seats: Yes **Cover:** Yes **Programme:** Yes **Founded:** 1881.
Colours: Amber/black **Local Press:** Slough Windsor Observer/ Express
Prev. Lge: Windor Slough & Dist. (pre-'91) **Clubhouse:** Full facilities, open all sessions.
Hons: Chiltonian Lg Div 1 91-92 (Lg Cup R-up 91-92), Slough Town Cup 91-92, B & B I'mediate Cup 91-92.

FINCHAMPSTEAD
Chairman: Mr Mike Husk **Manager:** Mr Mick Shaw.
Secretary: Mr M Husk, 16 Sadlers Lane, Winnersh, Wokingham, Berks (0734 785949).
Ground: Memorial Ground, Finchampstead (0734 732890). **Directions:** From Wokingham on A321, right
onto B3016 to Greyhound pub, right onto B3348, ground 200yds on right.
Seats: No **Cover:** No **Programme:** Yes **Cols:** All blue **Founded:** 1952.
Prev. League: Reading & Dist. **Clubhouse:** Club bar, sports bar, changing facilties.
Hons: Chilt. Lg 87-88 (Lg Cup R-up 88-89)
Local Press: Wokingham Times/ Wokingham News/ Reading Ev. Post.

HOLMER GREEN
Chairman: Mr Rupert Perry **Manager:** Barry Hedley.
Secretary: Mr Bill Scholes, The Brambles, Penfold Lane, Holmer Green, Bucks HP15 6XS (0494 713867).
Ground: Holmer Green Sports Association, Watchet Lane, Holmer Green, Bucks (0494 711485).
Directions: From High Wycombe on A404 Amersham road, left at Hazlemere towards Gt Missenden, follow for one
and a half miles (ignoring sign for Holmer Green), ground on left opposite 'Mandarin Duck'.
Seats: No **Cover:** No **Sponsors:** D & E Moulds. **Founded:** 1908.
Colours: Green & white **Prev. League:** Ercol Senior. **Programme:** Yes
Local Press: Bucks Free Press. **Clubhouse:** 2 bars open daily. Function room, hot food.
Hons: Chiltonian Lg 84-85 85-86, Wycombe Snr Cup 91-92

LETCOMBE SPORTS
Chairman: Mr D Stock **Manager:** Jeremy Charles.
Secretary: Mr D Williams, 8 Larkdown, Wantage OX12 8HE (02357 4130).
Ground: Bassett Road, Letcombe Regis, Wantage, Oxon (02357 68685).
Directions: Follow road thru Letcombe Regis; ground on right on far side of village.
Seats: No **Cover:** No **Programme:** Yes **Founded:** 1960.
Colours: White/navy. **Sponsors:** W McKnight/ B Rowe.
Prev. League: North Berks. **Clubhouse:** On ground.
Hons: Chiltonian Lg Div 1 90-91 **Local Press:** Oxford Mail/ Wantage Herald.

MARTIN BAKER SPORTS & SOCIAL
Chairman: Mr B Gray **Manager:** Mr K Sibley.
Secretary: C/O Hillside Cottage, Tilehouse Lane, Denham, Bucks UB9 5DD (0895 832977).
Ground: Martin's Field, Tilehouse Lane, Denham, Bucks (0895 833077).
Directions: Tilehouse Lane is second left on A412 from A40 London-Oxford route. Travelling from Watford, entrance
is 150yds up Tilehouse Lane on right.
Seats: No **Cover:** No **Programme:** Yes **Founded:** 1961.
Colours: White/navy **Sponsors:** Martin Baker Sports & Social Club.
Prev. League: London Commercial. **Clubhouse:** Bar, with refreshments available.
Local Press: Uxbridge Gazette/ Slough Observer/ All Sport Weekly.

MOLINS SPORTS
Chairman: Mr P Dewhurst **Manager:** Mr M McCormack.
Secretary: R D Stratford, 11 Canterbury Close, Monks Risborough, Bucks (0344 4487).
Ground: Molins Sports Ground, Mill Lane, Monks Risborough, Bucks (0344 3959). **Directions:** Off A4010
Princes R'borough-Aylesbury road 1 mile out of Risborough. Turn into Mill Lane, ground 400yds on right.
Seats: No **Cover:** A little **Programme:** Yes **Founded:** 1953.
Colours: Green/black **Sponsors:** Marshalls Coaches.
Prev. League: Wycombe Senior **Clubhouse:** Seats 120s.
Hons: Chiltonian Lg Div 1 R-up 91-92 **Local Press:** Bucks Free Press/ Bucks Herald.

PENN & TYLERS GREEN
Chairman: Mr A Prowse **Manager:** Mr B Childs.
Secretary: Mr R Dalling, 28 Baring Rd, Beaconsfield, Bucks HP9 2NE (0494 671424).
Ground: French School House, Elm Road, Penn, Bucks (0494 671424).
Directions: Entrance on B474 Beaconsfield-Hazlemere road, almost opposite Horse & Groom pub.
Seats: No **Cover:** No **Programme:** Yes **Founded:** 1905.
Colours: Blue & white hoops **Local Press:** Bucks Free Press.
Prev. League: Wycombe Senior **Clubhouse:** Bar, 4 dressing rooms, 3 sets of showers.

PRESTWOOD

Chairman: M White **Manager:** C McDaid.
Secretary: N C Stansbury, 31 Colne Rd, High Wycombe, Bucks (0494 521792).
Ground: Prestwood Sports Centre, Honor End Lane, Prestwood, Great Missenden, Bucks (0240 65946).
Directions: From Chequers pub in village centre, ground half mile on left down road signed Gt Hampden.
Seats: No **Cover:** No **Programme:** Yes **Founded:** 1934.
Colours: Claret & sky. **Local Press:** Bucks Free Press/ Bucks Herald.
Clubhouse: On ground. **Prev. League:** Princes Risborough 34-36/ Wycombe 36-84.
Prev. Grnd: Prestwood Common (pre'80) **Hons:** Wycombe Lg 51-52 81-82 (Div 1 36-37).

READING TOWN

Chairman: Mr N Milne **Manager:** Mr R Ford.
Secretary: Mr D Tully, 59 Elvaston Way, Tilehurst, Reading, Berks RG3 4LX (0734 412825).
Ground: Reading Town Spts Ground, Scours Lane, Tilehurst, Reading, Berks.
Directions: West side of Reading off the Oxford road.
Seats: Yes **Cover:** Yes **Programme:** Yes **Sponsors:** None **Founded:** 1968.
Colours: All red **Previous Names:** Reading Garage/ I.T.S. Reading Town.
Prev. Leagues: Reading & District. **Prev. Ground:** Kings Meadow Rd, Reading (pre'92).
Clubhouse: Yes **Local Press:** Reading Chronicle/ Reading Evening Post.

SLOUGH YOUTH CENTRE OLD BOYS

Chairman: Mr Edward Fletcher **Manager:** Mr Ian Dare.
Secretary: Mrs J Hughes, 14 Fairfield Lane, Farnham Royal, Bucks SL2 3BX (0753 643883).
Ground: Hatmill Community Centre, 112 Burnham Lane, Slough, Berks SL1 6LZ (0628 604760).
Directions: M4 jct 7, right at r'bout onto Bath Rd (A4), left at 2nd lights, ground quarter mile on right.
Seats: No **Cover:** No **Programme:** Yes **Founded:** 1941.
Cols: Sky & white stripes/white/sky **Sponsors:** Total Football.
Clubhouse: Bar, phone, toilets, food. **Prev. Lge:** Windor Slough & Dist./ East Berks.
Hons: Slough Town Cup R-up 91-92 **Local Press:** Slough Observer, Slough Express, Maidenhead Advertiser.

STOCKLAKE SPORTS

Chairman: Mr Bob Hogg **Manager:** Mr P Harvet/ Mr J Baxter.
Secretary: Mr Tom Exton, 116 McBeth Drive, Aylesbury, Bucks (0296 415780).
Ground: Hayward Way, Aylesbury, Bucks (0296 23324).
Directions: Entering Aylesbury join A41 Bicester road, right into Jackson Way after 2 miles, 2nd left is Haywards Way.
Seats: No **Cover:** No **Programme:** Yes **Sponsors:** TBA **Founded:** 1966.
Colours: All yellow **Prev. Leagues:** Aylesbury Dist./ Wycombe Snr.
Change colours: All blue. **Clubhouse:** Bar, tea bar, games room, private bar.
Hons: Chiltonian Lg R-up 90-91 **Local Press:** Bucks Herald/ Bucks Advertiser.

WRAYSBURY

Chairman: Mr D W Hammond **Manager:** C Sherlock.
Secretary: Mr J Rice, 77 Grange Way, Iver, Bucks (0753 652780).
Ground: Memorial Ground, Wraysbury, Bucks (0784 482155).
Directions: From M4 jct 5 follow signs to Datchet, then Horton, then Wraysbury - left at George Hotel.
Seats: No **Cover:** No **Programme:** No **Founded:** 1902.
Colours: Green & white **Previous Name:** Coopers Payen.
Prev. League: Slough Windsor & Dist. **Clubhouse:** One minute walk from pitch.
Local Press: Slough Observer/ Windsor & Eton Espress.
Hons: Chiltonian Lg 86-87 88-89 89-90 (Lg Cup R-up 85-86 86-87 87-88 90-91).

DIVISION ONE CLUBS 1992-93

BROADMOOR STAFF

Chairman: Mr J W Sheppard **Manager:** Mr P Long.
Secretary: Mr M A Roberts, 14 Hone Hill, Sandhurst, Camberley, Surrey (0252 879513).
Ground: Cricket Field Grove, Broadmoor Est., Crowthorne, Berks (0344 773111). **Founded:** 1896.
Directions: Off M4 at A329(M) for Bracknell, follow signs to Crowthorne, first left Brookers Corner, ground on right at top of hill.
Seats: No **Cover:** Yes **Programme:** Yes **Colours:** Red/white/white.
Local Press: Reading Evening Post, Reading Chronicle, Crowthorne/ Wokingham News.
Prev. League: Reading Senior. **Clubhouse:** Broadmoor Staff Club.

CHALFONT WASPS

Chairman: T J Hooker **Manager:** TBA.
Secretary: M S Smith, 43 Hillside Close, Chalfont St Peter SL9 0HN (0494 873323).
Ground: Playing Fields, Bowstridge Lane, Chalfont St Giles (0494 875050).
Directions: Turn off A413 thru village, first left, top of hill, first right.
Seats: No **Cover:** Yes **Programme:** No **Clubhouse:** Yes **Founded:** 1922.
Colours: Amber & black **Sponsors:** T.D.K. Motor Company.
Prev. League: Wycombe & District **Local Press:** Bucks Free Press, Bucks Examiner.

CHINNOR

Chairman: Mr J Walker **Manager:** TBA.
Secretary: Mr F Saulsbury, 86 Station Rd, Chinnor, Oxon OX9 4HA (0844 51073).
Ground: Playing Field, Station Rd, Chinnor, Oxfordshire (0844 52579).
Seats: No **Cover:** No **Programme:** No **Cols:** All blue **Founded:** 1884.
Prev. League: Ercol Senior **Clubhouse:** Excellent bar & social fac. overlooking ground.
Local Radio: Fox F/M, Oxford Radio **Local Press:** Bucks Free Press/ Thame Gazette/ Oxford Mail.

DENHAM UNITED

Chairman: Gerry Spencer **Manager:** Gary Marks (reserves: John Osborne).
Secretary: Colin Stevens, 18 The Dene, West Molesey, Surrey KT8 2HL (081 783 0433).
Directions: Entering Uxbridge on A4020, ground is quarter mile on left after Denham roundabout.
Seats: No **Cover:** No **Programme:** Yes **Sponsors:** None **Founded:** 1905.
Colours: All blue (res: red/blue/red) **Local Press:** Berks & Bucks Advertiser, Uxbridge Gazette.
Prev. Lgs: Uxbridge & Dist./ W. Middx **Clubhouse:** Licensed bar, changing rooms and social area.

Peppard's Dave Smith is tackled by Gary Harper of Henley during a League Cup tie (1-1). Photo - Henley Standard.

Binfield, Chiltonian League Runners-up 1991-92. Back Row (L/R): John Steer (Manager), Trevor Bennett, Tony Douglas, Mark McLentire, John Forey, Graham Matthews, John Smith, Steven McClurg. Front: Gary Garner, Justin McClurg, Micky Havermans, Simon Price, Roy Harding, Russell Hyde. Photo - Dave West.

Ickleford FC, of the Campri South Midlands League (club details on page 457). Photo - Gavin Ellis.

DRAYTON WANDERERS

Chairman: Mike Ash　　　**Manager:** Roger Poulter.
Secretary: David Rock, 34 Rutters Close, West Drayton, Middx (0895 444258).
Ground: Cowley Rec., Cowley High Rd, Cowley, Nr Uxbridge.
Directions: One and a half miles south of Uxbridge opposite Grand Union - follow signs for Heathrow/ W Drayton.
Seats: No　　　**Cover:** No　　　**Programme:** Yes　　**Clubhouse:** No　　**Founded:** 1964.
Colours: Blue & white stripes/navy　　**Sponsors:** Browne's Mini-Buses.
Prev. League: West Middx.　　**Previous Name:** Uxbridge Town (mid 80s-1992).
Hons: Chilt. Lg Div 1 85-86　　**Local Press:** West Drayton & Uxbridge Gazette.

HAZELLS

Chairman: M Gaunt　　　**Ground:** Meadowcroft, Aylesbury, Bucks.
Secretary: Mr D Watkins, 21 Parker Walk, Meadowcroft, Aylesbury, Bucks HP19 3XS (0296 394721).
Directions: Ring-road to Weedon Rd, Meadowcroft 1st right in Weedon Rd, ground past houses after one mile.
Seats: No　　　**Cover:** No　　　**Programme:** No　　**Sponsors:** TBA.　　**Founded:** 1886.
Colours: Yellow/green　　　**Clubhouse:** Hazells Club, Oakfield Rd, Aylesbury.
Prev. Lges: Ercol Snr/ Hellenic 57-84　　**Local Press:** Bucks Advertiser, Bucks Herald.
Hons: Hellenic Lg 67-68 (R-up 66-67, Div 1 59-60 79-80, Prem Div Cup 80-81).

HENLEY TOWN

Chairman: Mr A R Bryan　　　**Manager:** Terry Rogers.
Secretary: Mr M J Trendall, 20 Clements Rd, Henley-on-Thames, Oxon (0491 577075).
Ground: The Triangle Ground, Mill Lane, Henley-on-Thames, Oxon (0491 576463).
Directions: Leave Henley town centre on Reading Road (A4155), Mill Lane 1 mile on left before Motor Way Tyres. 10 mins walk from BR station.
Seats: No　　　**Cover:** No　　　**Prog.:** 25p (Editor: Tony Kingston)　　**Founded:** 1871.
Colours: White/black/black　　**Sponsors:** Bear Systems　　**Clubhouse:** Bar & function room.
Prev. Lges: Reading & Dist/ Spartan 31-52/ Gt Western Comb. 52-57/ Hellenic 57-71/ Ercol Snr.
Local Radio: Radio 210, Radio Oxford　　**Local Press:** Henley Standard, Reading Evening Post.
Hons: Oxon Snr Cup 03-04 10-11 12-13 13-14 46-47 (R-up 19-20 34-35), Hellenic Lg Div 1 63-64 67-68 (Benev. Cup 62-63 (R-up 61-62)), Spartan Lg Div 1 36-37 (Div 2 33-34), Ercol Snr Lg 78-79, Chiltonian Lg Div 1 87-88, Wycombe Snr Cup 78-79, Reading Snr Cup 78-79, Oxon Charity Cup 04-05 13-14 36-37 62-63 (R-up 02-03 09-1034-35 47-48), Bradley Charity Cup 38-39, Henley Hosp. Charity Cup(15)(R-up(7)).

IVER

Chairman: Mr R Rankin　　　**Manager:** Mr M Hodges.
Secretary: Mr S Law, 59 Grange Way, Iver, Bucks SL0 9NT (0753 819780).
Ground: Lea Barton, High Street, Iver, Bucks (0753 651248).　　**Directions:** A412 from Slough or Denham to Iver Heath, Iver turning to High Street, 2nd right past school Lea Barton to club car park.
Colours: Red, white & black/black/black　　**Programme:** Yes　　**Founded:** 1946.
Prev. Lge: Windsor Slough & Dist.　　**Clubhouse:** Members bar with full facilities.
Sponsors: AK Designs, E & E Construction **Local Press:** Slough Observer/ Slough Express.

KODAK (HARROW)

Chairman: Mr C Allen　　　**Manager:** Mr C Allen.
Secretary: Mr R D Langley, 610 Whitton Av., West Greenford, Middx UB6 0EE (081 423 2189).
Ground: Headstone Lane, Harrow View, Middx (081 427 2642).　　**Directions:** Bus from Wealdstone, Nth Harrow or Rayners Lane stations to junction of Headstone drive and Harrow View. Ground 200yds on left.
Seats: No　　　**Cover:** Yes　　　**Programme:** No　　**Sponsors:** Kodak　　**Founded:** 1935.
Colours: Yellow/red/yellow　　　**Local Press:** Harrow Observer/ All Sport Weekly.
Prev. Leagues: West End AFA/ London Commercial. **Clubhouse:** Changing rooms, showers, bar and cafeteria.

MILL END SOCIAL & SPORTS

Chairman: Mr Bryn Morgan　　　**Manager:** Mr Malcolm Higgins.
Secretary: D E Shine, 12 Watford Rd, Croxley Green, Herts WD3 3BJ (0923 772596).
Ground: King George V, Shepherds Lane, Mill End, Rickmansworth, Herts (0923 776892).
Directions: M25 jct 17, left at Maple Cross r'bout onto A412, left into Grove Rd after 400yds, right after 100yds into Penn Rd, club 300yds on right.
Seats: No　　**Cover:** No　　　**Local Press:** Watford Observer.　　**Founded:** 1937.
Colours: Amber & black.　　　**Clubhouse:** Bar, social facilities (dances etc)**Programme:** Yes
Hons: Chiltonian Lg Cup 89-90　　**Prev. Leagues:** Watford & District/ Middx County.

STOKENCHURCH

Chairman: Mr D Errington　　　**Manager:** Mr R Thorne/ Mr M Dowding.
Secretary: Mrs B K Hunt, 'Deneholme', 4 Lowes Close, Stokenchurch, Bucks HP14 3TN (0494 482535).
Ground: Longburrow Park, Stokenchurch, Bucks HP14 3TQ (0494 482703).
Directions: From A40 High Wycombe/ Oxford Rd turn either just before or after Kings Arms Hotel. 100yds on behind hotel is Royal Oak pub - Park Road is down right hand side as you look at pub.
Seats: No　　　**Cover:** No　　　**Programme:** No　　　**Founded:** 1886.
Sponsors: Teal Furniture　　**Colours:** Green, black & white/black/black
Clubhouse: Fleur-de-Lys　　**Local Press:** Bucks Free Press/ Star.
Hons: Hellenic Lg R-up 56-57　　**Prev. Lges:** Wycombe Comb./ Reading & Dist./ Hellenic 53-73.

WALLINGFORD UNITED

Chairman: Mr E L Townsend　　　**Manager:** Mr D Graham.
Secretary: Mr E Gniadek, 17 Offas Close, Benson, Wallingford, Oxon OX10 6NR (0491 38540).
Ground: Bull Croft, Wallingford, Oxon (0491 37173).
Directions: Centre of Wallingford near Blackstone Upper School.
Seats: No　　　**Cover:** Yes　　　**Programme:** Yes　　**Sponsors:** Vantage　**Founded:** 1934.
Colours: Red/black/black & red　　**Local Press:** Wallingford Herald/ Reading Ev. Post.
Prev. League: Reading & Dist.　　**Clubhouse:** No (use adjacent Cross Keys pub).

WOOBURN ATHLETIC

Chairman: Mr A R Nash　　　**Manager:** Mr J Austin.
Secretary: Mr B Nash, 10 Philip Drive, Flackwell Heath, Bucks HP10 9JB (0628 523293).
Ground: Wooburn Park, Town Lane, Wooburn Green, Bucks (0628 819201/520772).
Directions: Turn off A4094 Loudwater-Maidenhead road down behind Wooburn church, left at T-junct, ground entrance straight ahead at right-hand bend in road.
Seats: No　　**Cover:** No　　　**Sponsors:** Carlsberg.　　　**Founded:** 1897.
Cols: Red/white　　**Local Press:** Bucks Free Press/ Star/ Maidenhead Advertiser　**Programme:** Yes
Prev. Lge: Wycombe Ercol Senior　　**Clubhouse:** Wooburn WMC, 16 The Green, Wooburn Green.

S.C. JOHNSON WAX
SURREY COUNTY PREMIER LEAGUE

President: L F J Smith. **Chairman:** R A Mendham. **Hon. Secretary:** D Havenhand.

Premier Division	P	W	D	L	F	A	PTS	Reserve Division	P	W	D	L	F	A	PTS
St Andrews	26	16	9	1	70	34	57	Springfield H. Res	26	17	4	5	76	38	55
Chobham	26	17	4	5	75	23	55	B.T. Res	26	16	6	4	62	30	54
Netherne	26	16	5	5	69	28	53	Chobham Res	26	14	8	4	64	29	50
Burpham	26	14	3	9	54	45	45	Surbiton T. Res	26	15	5	6	66	39	50
Croydon M.O.	26	12	5	9	45	38	41	Vandyke Res	26	15	5	6	57	34	50
British Telecom	26	9	8	9	42	42	35	Croydom M.O. Res	26	13	5	8	59	37	44
Vandyke	26	10	5	11	43	46	35	Frinton Rvrs Res	26	13	4	9	55	45	43
Surbiton Town	26	10	5	11	44	48	35	St Andrews Res	26	10	5	11	45	42	35
Frinton Rovers	26	8	7	11	46	49	31	Ashtead Res	26	9	5	12	61	68	32
Ashtead	26	8	5	13	39	53	29	Hersham RBL Res	26	9	2	15	49	69	29
Ottershaw	26	9	2	15	39	58	29	Netherne Res	26	8	3	15	43	62	27
Hersham R.B.L.	26	8	4	14	41	42	28	Ottershaw Res	26	6	7	13	40	68	25
Springfield Hosp.	26	7	7	12	36	54	28	Burpham Res	26	4	7	15	28	56	19
Kingswood Wdrs	26	2	3	21	21	104	9	Kingswood W. Res	26	0	2	24	33	121	2

Premier Challenge (Presidents) Cup:
Croydon MO 1, Chobham 0
Richard Partington Cup:
Netherne 3, St Andrews 2 *(aet)*

Reserve Chal. Cup: Chobham 2, Vandyke 1
Reserve Charity Cup: Vandyke 5, Netherne 1

With the loss of just one Saturday, this must go down as our best playing season ever, and save for a number of Cup replays, there was little disruption to the league programme. Congratulations to league champions St Andrews who now move to the Spartan League, and to all our own Cup winners. Our representative side performed extremely well, winning the Southern Counties Trophy for the first time, but surprisingly losing out to the S.E. Combination in the final of the County Inter (Saturday) League Cup. **R A Mendham, League Chairman.**

St Andrews FC, Surrey County Premier League champions 1991-92. Back Row (L/R): David Maisey, Ray Smythe, Steve Leahy, Steve Charge, Bill Taylor, Paul Anderson, Colin Staplehurst. Front: Bob Storey, Terry Gale, Terry Halcro, Gary Williscroft, Noel Hughes. Photo - Dave West.

Croydon M.O. FC, Premier Challenge Cup Winners 1991-92. Secretary Tony Osborn could not make the photo call, so he sent his dog 'Amber'. Photo - Dave West (a former player of this club).

Ashtead FC, pictured before their match away to British Telecom. Photo - Dave West.

B.T. Back Row (L/R): Dave Jackson (Club Manager), Alan Fillingham, Jamie McAneny, Mark Bushby, Adrian Weeks, Mark Stevens, Tony Cates, Dave Rand, Charlie Sinclair (1st Team Manager). Front: Andy Chegwidden, Gary Smart, Paul Tedder, Dave Gammon, Randolph Payne, Mark Thurston, Steve Ingram. Photo - Dave West.

Ottershaw FC 1991-92. Photo - Dave West.

SURREY COUNTY PREMIER LEAGUE CLUBS

ASHTEAD
Secretary: R Grange, 'Homeside', 58 Leatherhead Rd, Ashtead KT21 2SY (0372 276901).
Ground: Ashtead Rec., Barnett Wood Lane, Ashtead.
Colours: Gold/gold/amber.   **Change colours:** White/black/black.

B.T.
Secretary: Graham Moxham, 75 Shaxton Crescent, New Addington CR0 0NW (0689 843338).
Ground: LTR/ASA Spts Grnd, Plough Lane, Wallington (081 647 17117).
Colours: All royal blue   **Change colours:** All red.

BURPHAM
Secretary: Kevin Brookham, 104 Manor Rd, Guildford GU2 6NR (0483 36713).
Ground: Sutherland Playing Fields, Clay Lane, Burpham, Guildford.
Colours: Yellow/black/black   **Change colours:** Blue/black/black.

CHOBHAM
Secretary: Mrs Daisey Whalley, 8 Brook Green, Chertsey Rd, Chobham GU24 8PN   (0276 858039).
Ground: Recreation Ground, Station Road, Chobham (0276 857876)
Colours: All sky   **Change colours:** Yellow/yellow/navy.

CROYDON MUNICIPAL OFFICERS
Secretary: Tony Osborn, 15 Long Lane, Croydon CR0 7AR (081 6566120).
Ground: Russell Hill Reservoir, Pampisford Road, Purley.
Colours: Blue & white/blue/blue.

FRINTON ROVERS
Secretary: Allen Bassom, 107 Stanley Park Rd, Carshalton SM5 5JJ (071 790 3456).
Ground: Thornton Heath Sports Club, Mayfield Rd, Thornton Heath.
Directions: Adjacent to Croydon Ath. (see page 392)
Colours: Red/black/black   **Change colours:** All blue.

HERSHAM ROYAL BRITISH LEGION
Secretary: Rod Stevens, 13 Leybourne Ave., Byfleet, Surrey KT14 7HB (0932 351725).
Ground: Coronation PF, Molesey Rd, Hersham (0932 227014-club, 223037-ground).
Directions: On left hand of Molesey Rd coming from Hersham BR midway between station & Barley Row r'bout.
Colours: Sky/navy/navy

NETHERNE
Secretary: Steve Clark, 28 Lackford Rd, Chipstead, Surrey CR5 3TA (0737 552200).
Ground: Netherne Hospital Sports Field, Woodplace Lane, Coulsdon (0737 552064).
Directions: Star Lane traffic lights, Brighton Rd, Hooley - follow signs to Netherne Hospital.
Colours: Blue & black stripes/white/white.

OTTERSHAW
Secretary: Steve Caswell, 16 The Maples, Ottershaw KT16 0NU (0932 872133).
Ground: Woodham Court Sports Club, Martyrs Lane, Woodham, Woking.
Colours: All yellow.   **Previous Ground:** Abbeylands, School Lane, Addlestone.

RAYNES PARK
Secretary: Paul Armour, 6 Woodstock Rise, Sutton, Surrey SM3 3JE (081 644 2444).
Ground: Raynes Park Sports Ground, Taunton Avenue, Raynes Park SW20 (081 946 8385).
Colours: Red & black stripes/black/black.   **Change colours:** White/black.black.

SHEERWATER
Secretary: Trevor Wenden, 24 North Rd, Guildford, Surrey GU2 6PU (0483 38686).
Ground: Sheewater Recreation Ground, Blackwater Crescent, Sheerwater, Woking.
Colours: Maroon & blue/white/sky   **Change colours:**

SPRINGFIELD BATTERSEA IRONSIDES
Secretary: Les Barker, 165 Washington Rd, Worcester Park KT4 8JQ (081 337 8665).
Ground: Battersea Ironsides Sports Club, Open View, Burntwood Lane SW18 (081 874 9913).
Directions: The ground is on corner of Openview and Burntwood Lane, opposite Springfield Hospital.
Colours: Red/blue/red   **Change colours:** All white, or blue & white stripes.
Previous Names: Springfield Hospital/ Battersea Ironsides (merged 1992).

SURBITON TOWN
Secretary: Bill Jasper, 6 Paddock Close, Silverdale Rd, London SE26 4SS (081 659 0736)
Ground: Riverhill Sports Club, Worcester Park Rd, Tolworth (081 337 3866).
Directions: A3 to Tolworth, right into Kingston Rd, left at 1st lights to Worcester Pk Rd, club 400 yds on left.
Colours: Green & white/green/white   **Change colours:** White/navy/navy.

VANDYKE
Secretary: Paul Smith, 76 Court Ave., Old Coulsdon CR3 1HE (0737 552617).
Ground: West Park Hospital, Horton Lane, Epsom, Surrey (0372 727811).
Directions: Leave Epsom towards Oxshott, right after 1 mile then 1st left into hospital, follow signs for Sports Centre.
Colours: White & green/black/white   **Change colours:** Red/black/white.

VIRGINIA WATER
Secretary: John Brooks, 40 Robinsway, Hersham, Surrey (0932 242968).
Ground: 'The Timbers', Crown Rd, Virginia Water (0344 843811).
Colours: Red & green/red/red   **Change colours:** White/red/red.

WALTON CASUALS
Secretary: Stuart Roberts, 47 Foxholes, Weybridge KT13 0BN (0932 845923).
Ground: Franklyn Road Sports Ground, off Waterside Drive, Walton-on-Thames (0932 247318).
Colours: Orange & white/black/orange   **Change colours:** White/blue/white

SURREY SOUTH EASTERN COMBINATION

Presidents: L P Leech Esq, B F Scott SCFA.
Chairman: G E Ellis.
Hon. Secretary: Gordon Worsfold,
141 Livingstone Rd, Thornton Heath, Surrey CR7 8JY.

SUCCESSFUL FIRST SEASON

The League was formed in June 1991 as a result of the amalgamation of the Surrey South Eastern Intermediate League and the Surrey Combination. This first season has proved successful, if hard work, for all officers due to the increased size of the League.

All seven divisions were closely contested with two being decided by a goal difference of one and two, and three others by a single point. Although the gap in Intermediate Division One was seven points, this only appeared in the last two or three weeks when Raynes Park played Virginia Water twice and won both games. Congratulations are due to both clubs on their promotion to the Surrey Premier League. The cup finals produced some good games and were generally well supported, and thanks are due to the finalists for the entertainment and excitement provided.

Two clubs, Worcester Park and Coney Hall, had extremely successful seasons in both League and Cups. Worcester Park were runners-up in Intermediate Division Two, their Reserves reached the final of the Intermediate Invitation Shield and won a divisional sportsmanship award, and the 'A' team won the Junior Division Four and Junior Invitation Shield. Coney Hall achieved a treble of Intermediate Division Two, Senior League Cup and Senior Invitation Shield, whilst their reserves reached the final of the Junior League Cup and the semi-finals of the Intermediate Invitation Shield.

In Surrey County FA Saturday competitions the League produced a unique treble with Colliers Wood United winning the Intermediate Cup, Battersea Park Rovers Reserves the Junior Cup, and the League Representative team the Inter-League Cup.

Thanks are due to all clubs for their efforts in making the first season such a success, and it is to be hoped that the enthusiasm continues to make future seasons even better.

Gordon Worsfold, Hon. Secretary.

Int. Division 1	P	W	D	L	F	A	PTS
Raynes Park	26	17	8	1	51	20	42
Virginia Water	26	14	7	5	42	22	35
Colliers Wood Utd	26	15	4	7	69	39	34
Greenside	26	13	5	8	48	42	31
Battersea Pk Rvrs	26	11	7	8	57	37	29
N.P.L.	26	10	9	7	57	40	29
Spelthorne Spts	26	9	11	6	50	41	29
Chessington & Hk	26	10	5	11	35	37	25
Battersea Ironsides	26	6	13	7	35	37	25
RAS Knights	26	6	6	12	40	51	20
Corona	26	4	12	10	23	40	20
Monotype Spts	26	5	8	13	48	74	18
Beaufoy	26	3	11	12	30	51	17
Bletchingley	26	3	4	19	26	81	10

Int. Division 2	P	W	D	L	F	A	PTS
Coney Hall	26	20	4	2	81	31	44
Worcester Park	26	20	2	4	74	35	42
Holmesdale	26	15	6	5	60	38	36
Busheymead	26	15	5	6	69	39	35
Caius	26	14	5	7	64	42	33
Bradbank Sports	26	13	4	9	72	50	30
Halliford	26	9	7	10	55	60	25
Crescent Rovers	26	9	6	11	47	55	24
South Godstone	26	7	6	13	43	61	20
Strenue	26	8	3	15	51	58	19
Bookham	26	8	2	16	35	65	18
Oxted & District	26	3	8	15	36	83	14
Merton Risley	26	6	1	19	40	71	*12
Verdayne	26	4	3	19	34	73	=12

Int. Division 3	P	W	D	L	F	A	PTS
Sutton Athletic	22	14	4	4	73	38	32
Fetcham	22	14	4	4	59	25	32
Reigate Town	22	13	5	4	86	45	31
Woodmansterne S.	22	12	1	9	48	33	25
Hook Venturers	22	8	7	7	53	57	23
Warlingham	22	8	7	7	48	52	23
Morfax	22	10	2	10	38	41	22
Sutton High	20	9	3	10	49	46	21
Surbiton Town Utd	22	7	4	11	46	57	18
Ewell	22	4	5	13	36	61	13
Cheam Vil. Warriors	22	4	3	14	36	74	13
Croydon United	22	5	1	16	39	82	11

* - 1 pt deducted
= - 1 pt awarded
+ - 2 pts awarded
& - 2 pts deducted
^ - 4 pts deducted

Junior Div. 1	P	W	D	L	F	A	PTS
Battersea Pk R. Res	22	17	3	2	60	19	37
Beaufoy Res	22	17	3	2	64	35	37
Worcester Pk Res	22	15	5	2	64	22	35
Coney Hall Res	22	13	6	3	54	23	32
Raynes Park Res	22	10	2	10	50	44	+24
Spelthorne S. Res	22	8	4	10	35	55	&18
Crescent Rvrs Res	22	7	3	12	46	64	17
Greenside Res	22	5	6	11	37	60	16
Holmesdale Res	22	7	2	13	38	54	16
Virginia Water Res	22	6	1	15	27	47	13
Cheam V.W. Res	22	4	3	15	20	64	11
Busheymead Res	22	3	2	17	42	60	&10

Junior Div. 2	P	W	D	L	F	A	PTS
Caius Res	18	13	3	2	44	26	29
Chessington Res	18	13	2	3	52	18	28
RAS Knights Res	18	13	1	4	47	21	27
Bookham	18	11	0	7	54	41	+24
Bradbank Spts Res	18	7	4	7	39	34	^14
Sutton Ath. Res	18	6	1	11	29	48	13
Warlingham Res	18	6	0	12	39	44	12
Sutton High Res	18	4	4	10	28	44	12
St Andrews 'A'	18	4	3	11	25	46	11
Strenue Res	18	3	2	13	20	48	&10

Junior Div. 2	P	W	D	L	F	A	PTS
N.P.L. Res	22	15	3	4	54	24	=34
Monotype Res	22	14	4	4	61	29	+*33
Bletchingley Res	22	16	0	6	70	33	32
Hersham RBL 'A'	22	10	9	3	41	28	29
Verdayne Res	22	11	3	8	48	34	&23
Walton Cas. Res	22	10	3	9	32	33	23
Merton Risley Res	22	9	3	10	32	39	21
Colliers Wd Res	22	5	5	12	42	46	+17
Fetcham Res	22	7	2	13	33	59	16
Corona Res	22	7	3	12	48	70	&15
Croydon U. Res	22	6	1	15	43	77	13
Sth Godstone Res	22	3	2	17	21	53	&6

Junior Div. 4	P	W	D	L	F	A	PTS
Worcester Pk 'A'	18	12	3	3	65	24	27
Chessington 'A'	18	13	2	3	58	22	&26
Netherne 'A'	18	11	4	3	50	23	26
Vandyke 'A'	18	9	4	5	50	30	22
W'sterne Spts Res	18	7	5	6	46	28	19
B'sea Iron. Res	18	8	3	7	30	35	19
Reigate Town Res	18	7	3	8	24	39	17
Ewell Res	18	4	2	12	29	56	+12
Hook Vent. Res	18	3	1	14	27	76	7
Oxted & D. Res	18	0	5	13	25	71	5

INTERMEDIATE DIVISION ONE RESULT CHART 1991/92

HOME TEAM	1	2	3	4	5	6	7	8	9	10	11	12	13	14
1. Battersea Ironsides	*	2-1	3-2	3-0	0-1	0-1	0-0	3-3	2-1	2-2	3-2	0-0	1-1	0-0
2. Battersea Pk Rvrs	3-3	*	1-1	6-0	3-0	0-3	4-0	5-0	4-1	3-1	2-1	0-1	1-1	1-2
3. Beaufoy	0-0	2-3	*	1-0	1-1	1-3	1-1	1-0	1-1	0-1	1-1	1-3	2-2	2-2
4. Bletchingley	1-2	1-5	4-1	*	3-2	1-8	0-3	1-2	3-6	2-2	1-0	1-3	2-4	0-0
5. Chessington & Hook	4-3	1-3	3-1	5-0	*	1-2	2-2	1-2	5-2	5-3	3-1	1-2	2-1	1-3
6. Colliers Wood Utd	5-1	1-1	3-0	2-2	1-2	*	2-0	1-3	9-3	4-2	4-0	1-3	2-3	1-1
7. Corona	2-2	L-W	0-3	0-0	1-2	2-1	*	2-2	0-0	1-3	4-4	2-2	0-3	0-1
8. Greenside	1-0	4-0	5-2	2-0	2-1	1-2	3-0	*	1-1	1-5	4-1	0-0	1-5	0-4
9. Monotype Spts	2-2	3-3	2-2	4-0	1-1	1-2	2-0	2-4	*	3-1	3-3	0-3	6-1	2-4
10. N.P.L.	0-0	3-3	6-1	3-1	5-2	1-2	1-1	2-0	8-1	*	2-2	1-0	0-0	0-0
11. R.A.S. Knights	3-2	2-1	2-2	3-0	2-2	1-5	0-0	1-1	4-0	1-2	*	0-2	2-1	1-0
12. Raynes Park	1-0	0-0	3-0	4-0	3-3	3-2	0-0	2-0	5-1	2-1	1-0	*	2-2	2-1
13. Spelthorne Sports	1-1	4-3	1-1	5-1	2-0	2-2	0-1	2-5	4-0	1-1	3-2	1-1	*	0-0
14. Virginia Water	0-0	0-1	W-L	5-2	6-2	1-0	2-1	0-1	2-0	2-1	2-1	2-3	2-0	*

INTERMEDIATE DIVISION TWO RESULT CHART 1991/92

HOME TEAM	1	2	3	4	5	6	7	8	9	10	11	12	13	14
1. Bookham	*	5-1	1-5	0-1	1-4	1-2	2-0	1-2	1-2	2-2	0-0	3-2	3-2	1-2
2. Bradbank Sports	5-2	*	3-4	3-1	2-3	3-2	2-2	4-2	4-3	9-0	7-0	3-0	2-1	4-3
3. Busheymead	2-0	1-1	*	1-0	0-1	4-2	2-2	4-0	6-1	7-2	0-3	2-1	2-1	0-3
4. Caius	5-1	3-1	0-5	*	2-3	5-2	1-3	0-1	3-2	8-4	5-0	4-0	2-1	3-1
5. Coney Hall	6-0	2-1	3-3	1-1	*	2-0	2-1	4-1	5-0	1-1	3-1	3-2	4-2	0-1
6. Crescent Rovers	5-1	0-5	2-1	2-2	0-1	*	1-1	1-3	3-2	5-0	3-2	1-4	3-1	1-4
7. Halliford	5-2	2-1	3-2	2-2	2-8	3-3	*	0-5	3-1	1-1	0-1	6-4	2-4	0-2
8. Holmesdale	3-1	2-2	3-1	1-4	1-1	1-1	2-0	*	3-1	2-2	2-0	1-1	2-1	2-4
9. Merton Risley	0-1	4-2	1-4	3-4	0-4	3-2	1-2	1-4	*	0-1	0-3	4-0	V1pt	1-5
10. Oxted & District	0-1	0-2	2-2	1-2	1-8	0-2	2-2	1-7	1-4	*	2-2	0-1	4-2	1-3
11. South Godstone	2-3	2-1	1-3	1-1	1-2	2-2	5-2	0-3	1-3	3-3	*	1-6	4-1	5-2
12. Strenue	1-2	0-3	1-3	1-1	1-3	3-1	0-4	2-2	3-0	2-0	4-2	*	9-1	0-2
13. Verdayne	3-1	1-1	0-3	1-4	1-3	L-W	3-7	0-3	1-0	1-3	0-0	2-1	*	2-3
14. Worcester Park	3-0	6-0	2-2	1-0	5-4	1-1	1-0	1-2	3-1	4-2	3-1	4-2	5-0	*

INTERMEDIATE DIVISION THREE RESULT CHART 1991/92

HOME TEAM	1	2	3	4	5	6	7	8	9	10	11	12
1. Cheam Village Warriors	*	4-3	1-2	0-2	2-3	1-1	1-5	2-0	2-6	1-4	2-1	1-3
2. Croydon United	3-0	*	4-2	1-6	0-1	0-5	2-6	3-5	0-7	2-4	2-2	0-5
3. Ewell	2-1	0-4	*	0-4	2-2	0-3	1-2	3-0	2-2	1-2	2-2	1-2
4. Fetcham	8-2	1-0	4-0	*	1-1	5-1	1-1	1-3	3-3	0-3	6-1	2-1
5. Hook Venturers	6-2	7-4	5-2	3-3	*	W-L	2-6	5-1	1-3	2-2	4-1	1-2
6. Morfax	3-3	2-3	2-0	0-2	2-0	*	5-3	3-1	2-4	1-0	2-1	2-1
7. Reigate Town	8-1	7-1	4-2	2-1	6-1	8-0	*	4-4	1-5	8-1	1-1	3-1
8. Surbiton Town United	3-3	5-0	2-2	0-4	3-3	5-1	2-5	*	4-2	2-1	0-2	0-1
9. Sutton Athletic	6-2	2-5	3-3	1-2	6-1	1-0	4-1	1-0	*	2-0	3-3	0-1
10. Sutton High	1-2	5-1	3-2	1-2	3-3	1-2	3-0	4-0	3-4	*	3-6	2-3
11. Warlingham	4-2	4-0	3-6	1-0	2-2	2-1	2-2	1-6	0-4	1-1	*	2-1
12. Woodmansterne Sports	0-1	2-1	6-1	0-1	4-0	W-L	4-4	6-0	2-4	1-2	2-6	*

NB - Cambridge FC withdrawn; record expunged.

JUNIOR DIVISION ONE RESULT CHART 1991/92

HOME TEAM	1	2	3	4	5	6	7	8	9	10	11	12
1. Battersea Pk R. Res	*	1-1	2-2	3-1	2-0	4-0	3-0	3-1	2-0	5-2	4-1	2-1
2. Beaufoy Res	3-2	*	3-2	3-1	2-1	7-0	4-0	2-0	5-2	2-1	4-2	2-2
3. Busheymead Res	1-3	2-4	*	L-W	3-4	2-0	1-3	4-1	1-2	10-0	1-2	1-5
4. Cheam Village W. Res	0-2	1-8	4-1	*	0-2	1-3	2-4	1-4	0-4	W-L	W-L	3-3
5. Coney Hall Res	1-1	2-1	4-0	1-1	*	5-0	5-0	5-0	2-1	3-1	4-0	1-1
6. Crescent Rovers Res	0-2	1-2	6-6	5-0	1-3	*	3-3	3-5	3-5	0-2	4-3	0-7
7. Greenside Res	0-5	1-5	3-2	6-1	1-3	2-2	*	1-1	1-2	1-1	1-2	1-4
8. Holmesdale Res	1-6	0-1	5-1	2-1	2-2	0-3	4-2	*	+0-3	2-3	4-2	0-2
9. Raynes Park Res	1-2	0-2	5-1	6-0	3-4	2-0	2-2	1-3	*	3-3	4-2	1-6
10. Spelthorne Sports Res	0-3	3-1	*2-0	2-1	0-0	2-6	3-3	3-2	0-3	*	3-1	1-5
11. Virginia Water Res	2-3	0-1	2-1	1-1	1-0	0-4	1-2	2-0	2-0	0-2	*	0-2
12. Worcester Park Res	1-0	1-1	W-L	4-1	2-2	0-2	4-0	5-1	1-0	4-1	2-1	*

+ - 2pts to Raynes P. (Holmesdale inelig. player). * - 2pts to Busheymead (Spelthorne inelig. player)

JUNIOR DIVISION TWO RESULT CHART 1991/92

HOME TEAM	1	2	3	4	5	6	7	8	9	10
1. Bookham Res	*	2-4	2-4	0-5	5-4	4-0	2-1	2-1	2-0	4-2
2. Bradbank Sports Res	0-5	*	2-3	0-3	2-1	0-0	2-0	*4-3	1-1	5-2
3. Caius Res	4-1	3-2	*	0-0	2-3	2-2	1-0	2-0	4-2	6-4
4. Chessington & Hook Res	3-4	2-1	0-2	*	2-1	3-0	4-0	8-0	4-0	1-0
5. RAS Knights Res	4-1	3-2	2-1	0-1	*	3-1	3-0	2-1	0-0	2-0
6. St Andrews 'A'	0-9	1-2	2-3	0-3	L-W	*	3-0	2-2	2-1	4-1
7. Strenue Res	+4-3	1-1	2-2	2-5	1-5	2-3	*	2-0	2-1	1-2
8. Sutton Athletic Res	2-1	4-2	0-2	3-2	0-4	3-2	5-1	*	2-1	1-2
9. Sutton High Res	2-5	4-4	0-1	3-3	1-7	4-1	1-0	4-1	*	2-1
10. Warlingham Res	1-2	=1-3	2-3	2-3	1-3	4-2	5-1	5-1	4-0	*

+ - 2pts to Bookham, * - 2pts deducted from Bradbank but not awarded to Sutton as both clubs fielded ineligible player, = - 2pts deducted from Bradbank but not awarded to Warlingham who also fielded an ineligible player.

HOME TEAM		1	2	3	4	5	6	7	8	9	10	11	12
1.	Bletchingley Res	*	4-2	1-2	6-0	5-2	7-0	4-1	2-1	1-2	4-2	2-4	2-1
2.	Collier Wd Utd Res	1-7	*	1-0	9-0	0-2	2-4	1-1	2-5	0-0	*2-3	1-2	0-1
3.	Corona Res	0-3	3-3	*	5-0	2-1	2-2	2-3	5-1	4-5	1-1	0-2	2-7
4.	Croydon Utd Res	3-9	0-5	12-0	*	2-3	1-2	0-2	2-3	3-1	4-3	0-4	0-2
5.	Fetcham Res	0-2	4-2	3-5	1-2	*	1-1	2-1	3-3	0-7	0-3	2-1	1-2
6.	Hersham RBL 'A'	2-0	1-1	5-2	4-1	2-0	*	1-1	2-2	0-1	2-2	2-1	0-0
7.	Merton Risley Res	0-1	0-5	5-3	1-3	2-4	0-3	*	0-2	2-0	1-0	3-0	1-1
8.	Monotype Sports Res	5-0	1-0	+0-2	6-3	7-1	0-0	3-1	*	1-2	5-1	^1-1	7-0
9.	N.P.L. Res	0-2	4-1	2-1	5-2	1-0	2-2	3-2	1-2	*	1-2	6-0	3-0
10.	Sth Godstone Res	0-4	0-1	2-6	2-1	0-1	0-2	0-1	0-1	1-4	*	1-2	0-3
11.	Verdayne Res	3-1	3-3	9-0	2-3	7-2	1-0	1-2	1-3	&0-0	2-0	*	2-0
12.	Walton Casuals Res	2-3	1-0	2-1	2-2	2-0	1-4	1-2	1-2	0-1	2-0	2-0	*

* - 2pts to Colliers Wd, + - 2pts to Monotype, ^ - 1 pt from both clubs, & - 1pt to NPL; unreg./inelig. players

HOME TEAM		1	2	3	4	5	6	7	8	9	10
1.	Battersea Ironsides Res	*	2-1	3-4	3-1	4-2	4-1	2-0	2-2	1-1	1-7
2.	Chessington & Hook 'A'	3-0	*	*2-1	15-1	0-3	5-2	7-0	2-4	1-0	3-2
3.	Ewell Res	4-0	0-3	*	4-1	2-5	2-2	1-4	0-0	1-3	0-7
4.	Hook Venturers Res	0-3	0-4	5-1	*	0-5	3-3	1-2	5-7	1-2	1-6
5.	Netherne 'A'	0-0	1-1	6-2	5-1	*	5-1	2-2	2-1	5-1	2-1
6.	Oxted & District Res	1-2	3-4	0-2	0-3	1-1	*	1-2	2-11	0-8	1-8
7.	Reigate Town Res	1-0	0-2	2-1	2-1	0-3	2-2	*	4-3	1-1	2-4
8.	Vandyke 'A'	0-2	0-1	5-2	0-2	1-0	4-1	2-0	*	1-1	3-1
9.	Woodmansterne Spts Res	1-0	1-2	5-1	11-0	2-3	2-2	4-0	1-4	*	2-2
10.	Worcester Park 'A'	6-1	2-2	3-1	3-1	3-0	3-2	2-0	2-2	3-0	*

* - 2pts to Ewell (Chessington ineligible player)

CUP COMPETITIONS 1991-92

ACE AWARDS SENIOR CUP

Sutton High v Oxted & District	4-2	Bletchingley v Ewell	3-2
Battersea Pk Rvrs v Worcester Park	4-1(aet)	Corona v Verdayne	3-1
South Godstone v Greenside	3-3(aet),0-3	Virginia Water v Morfax	5-3
Warlingham v Fetcham	4-4(aet),0-2	Bradbank Sports v Raynes Park	0-2
Merton Risley v Colliers Wood United	0-3		

Second Round

Colliers Wood United v Bookham	3-2(aet)	Chessington & Hook United v Halliford	4-1(aet)
Spelthorne Sports v Sutton High	1-0	Fetcham v Greenside	0-2
Sutton Athletic v Bletchingley	1-7	Busheymead v Crescent Rovers	3-2(aet)
Hook Venturers v R.A.S. Knights	0-2	Monotype Sports v Beaufoy	1-0
Raynes Park v Woodstanterne Sports	7-1	Croydon United v Corona	1-2
Cheam Village Warriers W/O Cambridge		Strenue v Coney Hall	0-3
Virginia Water v Holmesdale	2-1	Caius v Battersea Ironsides	4-1
Reigate Town v N.P.L.	2-1(aet)	Battersea Park Rovers v Surbiton Town United	1-0

Third Round

Greenside v Cheam Village Warriors	0-2	Raynes Park v R.A.S. Knights	4-0
Reigate Town v Virginia Water	3-2	Corona v Bletchingley	1-0
Busheymead v Coney Hall	0-8	Chessington & Hook Utd v Battersea Pk Rvrs	0-1(aet)
Caius v Colliers Wood United	1-2	Spelthorne Sports v Monotype Sports	2-1

Quarter-Finals

Colliers Wood United v Raynes Park	1-2	Battersea Park Rovers v Coney Hall	1-1(aet),0-2
Corona v Reigate Town	0-2	Spelthorne Sports v Cheam Village Warriors	3-1

Semi-Finals

Raynes Park v Reigate Town	2-3	Spelthorne Sports v Coney Hall	0-3

Final: Coney Hall 1, Reigate Town 1 *(aet)*. **Replay:** Coney Hall 2, Reigate Town 1

ACE AWARDS JUNIOR CUP

Corona Res v Reigate Town Res	1-0	Woodmansterne Res v Battersea Ironsides Res	2-1
Hook Venturers Res v Oxted & Dist Res	5-2	Caius Res v Sutton Athletic Res	3-2
Holmesdale Res v Verdayne Res	0-2	Hersham R.B.L. 'A' v Monotype Spts Res	1-1,1-6
Sutton High Res v Bradbank Spts Res	5-0	Battersea Pk R. Res v Chessington & Hook Res	2-1
Morfax Res (failed to fulfill) Bletchingley Res W/O		Strenue Res v Warlingham Res	1-3
Croydon Utd Res v South Godstone Res	2-3	Virginia Water v Greeside Res	1-2(both removed)
Raynes Park Res v Worcester Park 'A'	1-0	St Andrews 'A' v Netherne 'A'	1-3

Second Round

Vandyke 'A' v South Godstone Res	2-1	Ewell Res v Fetcham Res	1-1(aet),0-4
Busheymead	Bye	Monotype Spts Res v Sutton High Res	3-1
Coney Hall Res v N.P.L. Res	5-0	Bletchingley Res v Corona Res	5-0
Raynes Park Res v Caius Res	2-1(aet)	Warlingham Res v Spelth. Res	2-1(Warl.removed)
Netherne 'A' v Cheam Village Warriors Res	3-2	B'sea Park Res v Hook Res	5-1(B'sea removed)
Verdayne Res v Chessington & Hook Utd 'A'	1-6	Beaufoy Res v Woodmansterne Sports Res	6-0
Bookham Res v Merton Res 3-0(B'ham removed)		Crescent Rovers Res v Walton Casuals Res	1-4(aet)
Surbiton Res v Knights Res	2-2(aet),RAS W/O	Worcester Park Res v Colliers Wd Utd Res	5-0

Third Round

RAS Knights Res v Hook Venturers Res	3-0	Merton Risley Res v Spelthorne Res	1-1(aet),0-2
Worcester Park Res v Coney Hall Res	1-2	Vandyke 'A' v Netherne 'A'	1-2
Raynes Park Res v Fetcham Res	4-0	Beaufoy Res v Busheymead Res	3-1
Monotype Res v Chessington & Hook 'A'	3-2	Walton Casuals Res v Bletchingley Res	3-1

Quarter-Finals

Coney Hall Res v Netherne 'A'	2-0	RAS Knights v Monotype Sports Res	3-2
Walton Casuals Res v Raynes Park Res	2-3	Spelthorne Sports Res v Beaufoy Res	3-6

Semi-Finals

Raynes Park Res v Coney Hall Res	2-3	Knights Res v Beaufoy Res	0-0(aet)(B'foy removed)

Final: R.A.S. Knights Reserves 2, Coney Hall Reserves 0

LEAGUE SENIOR SHIELD
First Round

Bradbank Sports v Strenue	4-2	Halliford v Woodmansterne Sports	5-3
Coney Hall v Morfax	3-1	Oxted & District v Merton Risley	3-4*(aet)*
Reigate Town v Ewell	3-2	Hook Venturers *W/O* Cambridge *(withdrawn)*	
Crescent Rovers v Fetcham	2-3	Sutton High v Verdayne	2-0
Warlingham v South Godstone	0-2	Croydon United v Caius	3-4
Worcester Park v Holmesdale	1-3		

Second Round

Fetcham v Holmesdale	2-3	Cheam Village Warriors v Bookham	2-3
Reigate Town v Sutton High	2-1	Surbiton Town United v Sutton Athletic	2-6
South Godstone v Bradbank Sports	1-1,1-6	Halliford v Hook Venturers	3-1
Merton Risley v Coney Hall	1-3	Caius v Busheymead	4-1

Quarter-Finals

Halliford v Caius	2-3	Reigate Town v Bookham	5-4
Coney Hall v Sutton Athletic	3-2	Bradbank Sports v Holmesdale	2-1*(aet)*

Semi-Finals

Coney Hall v Reigate Town	0-0*(aet)*,3-1	Bradbank Sports v Caius	2-3

Final: Coney Hall 3, Caius 0

INTERMEDIATE LEAGUE SHIELD
First Round

Raynes Park Res v Bradbank Sports Res	2-1	Battersea Pk Rovers Res v RAS Knights Res	2-0
Warlingham Res v Sutton High Res	4-0	Greenside Res v Worcester Park Res	0-2
Sutton Ath. *W/O* Surbiton Res *(withdrew)*		Crescent Rvrs Res v Holmesdale Res	3-2*(aet)*
Cheam Village Warriers Res v Beaufoy Res	0-2		

Second Round

Coney Hall Res v Sutton Athletic Res	2-0	Virginia Water Res v Warlingham Res	1-0
Crescent Rvrs Res v Worcester Park Res	1-6	Strenue Res v Bookham Res	0-4
Raynes Park Res v Spelthorne Spts Res	8-1	Caius Res v Beaufoy Res	0-2
St Andrews 'A' v Busheymead Res	2-2*(aet)*,3-4	Chess'ton Res v B'sea PR Res	2-0*(ab)(B'sea removed)*

Quarter-Finals

Beaufoy Res v Bookham Res	2-1	Busheymead Res v Raynes Park Res	0-2
Worcester Park Res v Chessington Res	2-0	Virginia Water Res v Coney Hall Res	0-2

Semi-Finals

Worcester Park Res v Coney Hall Res	2-1	Beaufoy Res v Raynes Park Res	3-1

Final: Beaufoy Reserves 3, Worcester Park Reserves 2

LEAGUE JUNIOR SHIELD

Oxted & District Res v South Godstone Res	6-2	B'sea Iron. Res *W/O* Morfax Res *(failed to fulfill)*	
Merton Risley Res v Verdayne Res	5-2	Hook Venturers Res v Monotype Sports Res	2-6
Chessington & Hk 'A' v Woodmansterne Res	6-0	Walton Casuals Res v Worcester Park 'A'	1-6
Colliers Wood Res v Fetcham Res	3-3*(aet)*,5-1		

Second Round

Netherne 'A' v Colliers Wood Utd Res	5-2	Merton Risley Res v Croydon United Res	3-0
Oxted & District Res v Ewell Res	4-6	Corona Res v Monotype Sports Res	2-2,0-6
Reigate Town Res v N.P.L. Res	2-6	Battersea Ironsides Res v Hersham R.B.L. 'A'	2-3
Bletchingley Res v Worcester Park 'A'	1-2	Chessington & Hook United 'A' v Vandyke 'A'	4-3

Quarter-Finals

Monotype Sports Res v N.P.L. Res	0-4	Chessington & Hook 'A' v Merton Risley Res	0-1
Worcester Park 'A' v Ewell Res	3-0	Netherne 'A' v Hersham R.B.L. 'A'	0-2

Semi-Finals

Hersham 'A' v Merton Res	3-1*(Hersham removed)*	N.P.L. Res v Worcester Park 'A'	0-2

Final: Worcester Park Reserves 'A' 4, Merton Risley Reserves 0

SURREY SOUTH EAST COMBINATION CLUBS 1992-93

BATTERSEA PARK ROVERS
Secretary: M Jones, 18 Edgecombe House, Whitelock Drive, Southfields SW19 6SL (081 788 2342).
Ground: Falcons Park, Battersea SW11 (Cabul Road). **Colours:** Gold/black/black.
Directions: Clapham Junction, 19, 45, 49, 39. Down Falcon Road to Princess Head, right at lights then first right down Cabul Road to Falcon Park.

BEAUFOY
Secretary: E Thompson, 44 Elias Place, Oval, London SW8 1NS (071 820 0958).
Ground: King George Park, Kimber Road SW18 (081 648 3239). **Colours:** All blue
Directions: Kimber Road, off Garratt Lane SW18, nearest station Earlsfield.

BLETCHINGLEY
Secretary: June Cowland, 'Aviemore', 42b Reigate Hill, Reigate, Surrey RH2 9NG (0737 242996).
Ground: Grange Meadow, Bletchingley, Surrey (0883 742844). **Colours:** Orange/red/red.
Directions: A23 to Redhill, turn onto A25 Westerham Road, approx. 5 miles Bletchingley, 'Plough' PH on left, ground opposite.

BOOKHAM
Secretary: Bob Elcome, 6 Clare Crescent, Leatherhead, Surrey (0372 378970).
Ground: Crystie Road, Recreation Grnd, Dorking Rd, Bookham (0372 459482). **Colours:** Yellow & black.
Directions: Bookham Station. Buses 408, 478, 479.

BRADBANK SPORTS
Secretary: J E Bergamin, 37 Cambridge Rd, Teddington, Middx TW11 8DT (081 977 3603).
Ground: Dundonald Recreation Ground, Avebury Road SW19 (081 542 3282). **Colours:** Blue & white.
Directions: A298 to Merton - turn left into Downhill Road (opposite Nelson Hospital), Avebury Road 2nd right. Nearest station; Wimbledon Chase.

BUSHEY MEAD
Secretary: R M Serle, 61 Limes Ave., Carshalton, Surrey SM5 2AA **(081 669 3077).**
Ground: Beverley Way, New Malden. **Colours:** Maroon/sky/sky.

CAIUS
Secretary: T Butler, 38 Hardington Belmont Str., Chalk Farm NW1 8HN (071 485 6035).
Ground: Richard Evans Memorial Playing Fields (081 228 6642). **Colours:** Sky/navy/navy.
Directions: Roehampton Vale on A3 at Robin Hoods Gate.

CHEAM VILLAGE WARRIORS
Secretary: Peter Clapton, 1 Hemingford Rd, North Cheam, Surrey SM3 8HG (081 644 6894).
Ground: Tattenham Way Recreation, The Drive, Banstead (081 337 6860). **Cols:** Yellow/blue
Directions: A217 from Sutton, right at Tattenham Way into Piguets Rise, left into The Drive, ground ahead.
Banstead BR station, buses 420 and 422 pass end of Drive.

CHESSINGTON & HOOK UNITED
Secretary: A K Warwick, 38 Hartfield Rd, Chessington, Surrey KT9 2PW (081 397 1843).
Ground: Chalky Lane, Chessington, Surrey (0372 729892). **Colours:** Blue/white/blue.
Directions: Chalky Lane off A243 opposite Chessington World of Adventure Theme Park. Chessington South (BR).

COLLIERS WOOD UNITED
Secretary: Tony Hurrell, 1 Inglewood, Pixton Way, Forestdale, Croydon CR0 9LN (081 651 3259).
Ground: Wibbandue Pavillion, Wibbandue Sports Ground, Lincoln Green, Robin Hood Way SW20 (081 942 8062).
Directions: On A3 (Robin Hood Way) between Robin Hood Gate and Raynes Park Junction.
Colours: Sky & navy/navy/navy.

CONEY HALL
Sec: B Downs, Chairmans Office, Downs & Co, Imperial House, North Str, Bromley BR1 1SD (081 464 0493).
Ground: Tiepigs Lane, Coney Hall, West Wickham, Kent (081 462 9103). **Colours:** Red/black/black.
Directions: Gravel Hill continue along Kent Gate Way, across r'bout along Addington Village Rd and Addington Rd
until next r'bout, continue ahead, 2nd left down Tiepigs, ground on left before railway bridge.

CORONA
Secretary: Kevin Howden, 1 Deeside Road, Aboyne Est., London SW17 0PH (081 947 8210).
Ground & Directions: As Bradbank Sports (page 443). **Colours:** Grey/navy/navy.

CRESCENT ROVERS
Secretary: M D Bishop, 64 Wolsey Crescent, New Addington, Surrey CR0 0PF (0689 842996).
Ground: Southern Rail Sports Club, Mollison Drive, Wallington. **Colours:** Green/black/black.
Directions: Off Stafford Rd A232 opposite Wilson School. Bus 157, 233. Waddon (BR) then bus.

CROYDON UNITED
Secretary: David Head, 14 Stambourne Way, West Wickham, Kent BR4 9NF (081 777 2755).
Ground: Croydon Post Office Ground, Warlingham (0883 624825). **Colours:** Red/black.
Directions: From Croydon proceed via Sanderstead along main Limpsfield Road (B269) until Hamsey Green, 2nd
left Trenham Drive. Regular bus from Croydon through to Chelsham bus garage.

EWELL
Secretary: Mark Osbourne, 12 Gillray House, Sutton Grove, Sutton SM1 4TQ (081 661 9540).
Ground: King George Rec., Ewell Ct, Poole Rd, West Ewell. **Cols:** Red & white quarters/red/red.
Directions: Turn down Lansdowne Rd from Ewell-Chessington road, opposite Hook Road Arena.

FETCHAM
Secretary: Howard Taylor, 53 Cock Lane, Fetcham, Surrey (0372 377557).
Ground: Cock Lane Rec., Fetcham, Surrey. **Colours:** All red.
Directions: From Leatherhead bus 462 to Fetcham, or 416 (limited time) to Cock Lane.

GREENSIDE
Secretary: E G Moon, 10 Curran Ave., Wallington SM6 7JW (081 669 7985).
Ground: Co-op Spts Ground, Balmoral Ave., off Upper Elmers End Rd, Elmers End, Beckenham, Kent.
Directions: Nearest station; Elmers End/Eden Park 194 & 54. **Colours:** All green.

HALLIFORD
Secretary: D F Waite, 46 Halliford Rd, Sunbury, Middx TW16 6DR.
Ground: Kenyngton Recreation Ground. **Colours:** White/blue/blue & white.
Directions: M3 jct 1 (Sunbury Cross), 2nd exit on left Vicarage Rd, proceed down road, 1st turning past
Beechwood Ave., into Byron Way, entrance to ground on right.

HOLMESDALE
Secretary: Tony Roberts, 78 South Norwood Hill, London SE25 6AQ (081 653 5476).
Ground: Croydon College, Cooper Rd, Waddon (081 654 3928) **Colours:** Yellow/white/white.
Directions: Cooper Rd, Croydon off Denning Ave. near Fiveways, Purley Way. Waddon (BR), buses 194/194a.

HOOK VENTURERS
Secretary: Malcolm Brenham, 11 Ellingham Rd, Chessington, Surrey KT9 2JA (081 397 3638).
Ground: King Edward Rec., Hook Way, Chessington **Colours:** All blue.
Directions: From Kingston by 72 bus (stops outside ground).

MERTON RISLEY
Secretary: F G Brockwell, 28 Wordsworth Drive, Cheam, Surrey SM3 8HF (081 644 8590).
Ground: Risley Spts Grnd, Middleton Rd, Merton. **Colours:** White & black.
Directions: Adjacent to St Helier station. Bus 93 to Central Rd, 5 mins from ground up Green Lane which runs up
to Rose Hill r'bout.

MONOTYPE SPORTS
Secretary: Stephen Hollis, 13 Avenue Gdns, Horley, Surrey RH6 9BS (0293 775184).
Ground: Monotype Spts & Social Club, Honeycrock Lane, Saltfords (0737 763250).
Directions: South on A23 Saltfords is approx. 5 miles beyond Redhill. Left into Honeycrock Lane. Ground 1st right
after railway bridge. **Colours:** Amber & black/black/black.

MORFAX
Secretary: Martin Paul, 112 St Margarets Ave., North Cheam, Surrey SM3 9TT (081 641 1506).
Ground: Morfax Spts Grnd, Carshalton Rd, Mitcham, Surrey (071 637 2345). **Colours:** All sky blue.
Directions: From Mitcham centre; A236 towards Croydon, at r'bout 50yds past railway bridge 2nd left A237 50yds
on left. Entrance by 'The Goat' PH.

N.P.L.

Secretary: Bob Carson, 8 Regency Close, Hampton, Middx TW12 8EW (081 979 4412).
Ground: Queens Rd, Teddington, Middx (081 977 6395).   **Colours:** Yellow/blue/blue.
Directions: Bushey Park, Hampton Court, Hampton Bridge - Surrey A-Z.

OXTED & DISTRICT

Secretary: Pete King, 2 The Greenways, Oxted, Surrey RH8 0JY (0883 716001).
Ground: Master Park, Oxted, Surrey (0883 712792).   **Colours:** All red.
Directions: Rail to Oxted, bus 410 to Master Park. Or, A25 from Westerham or Redhill to Church Lane, Oxted. Ground quarter mile on left.

R.A.S. KNIGHTS

Secretary: George Wilson, 69a Perry Vale, Forest Hill SE23 2NJ (081 291 3659).
Ground: Pynners Playing Fields.   **Colours:** Red & white
Directions: A205 Sth Circular to West Dulwich, ground on right 500yds past Dulwich College. BR to West Dulwich or Forest Hill.

REIGATE TOWN

Secretary: Mrs Anita Head, 82 The Crescent, Horley, Surrey RH6 7NU (0293 782084).
Ground: Reigate Heath.   **Colours:** Green/black/black.
Directions: A25 from Reigate towards Dorking, left at Black Horse into Flanchard Rd, grnd on right.

ST ANDREWS 'A'

Secretary: Lee Harris, 14 Healey House, Vassall Rd, London SW9 6NF (071 793 0853).
Ground & Directions: As Bradbank Sports (page 443)   **Colours:** Blue/white/red.

SOUTH GODSTONE

Secretary: J D Gatland, 58 Lagham Rd, South Godstone, Surrey RH9 8HB (0342 893086).
Ground: Playing Field, Lagham Rd, South Godstone, Surrey (0342 892490).   **Colours:** All red.
Directions: South from Godstone on A22 for about two and a half miles, as you enter South Godstone, 1st left into Harcourt Way, follow to end, pavillion immediately in front. 719 Green Line and 409.

SPELTHORNE SPORTS

Secretary: Ron Ford, 35 Walton Gdns, Feltham, Middx TW15 4QY (081 890 8346).
Ground: Spelthorne Sports Club (0932 783625).   **Colours:** Sky/navy/navy.
Directions: M3 jct 1 (Sunbury Cross), 1 mile on Staines by-pass on left. 296 Staines Rd West, Ashford Common.

STRENUE

Secretary: Steven Wells, 48 Kingsworthy Close, Kingston, Surrey KT1 3ER (081 546 2686).
Grnd: Lynwood Rd, Hinchley Wood (off Claygate Lane)(081 398 5374) **Cols:** Red & blue stripes/blue/blue
Directions: A3 southbound, bear left on Esher Rd directly after Aces of Spades underpass, right at r'bout into Claygate Lane - Lynwood Rd turning off Claygate Lane (signposted Strenue Association).

SURBITON TOWN UNITED (see Surbiton Town, page 439)

SUTTON ATHLETIC

Secretary: Diane Goff, 265 Malden Rd, Cheam SM3 8ET (081 641 1188).
Ground: Overton Rd Sports Ground.   **Colours:** Red/blue/blue.
Directions: From Sutton BR take turning opposite statio, Mulgrave Rd, Overton Rd 4th turning left, proceed to end of Overton Rd for ground.

SUTTON HIGH

Secretary: Ian Daggett, 178 Stanley Park Rd, Carshalton Beeches, Surrey (081 661 6323).
Ground: University of London Spts Grnd, Motspur Park (Reserves as Cheam Village page 444).
Directions: From Grand Drive left into Westway, left at end into West Barnes Lane. Over level crossing, ground on right. Motspur Park (BR).

VERDAYNE

Secretary: G Leppard, 628 Limpsfield Rd, Warlingham, Surrey CR6 9DS.
Ground: Valley (off White Knobs Way).   **Colours:** Yellow & blue/royal blue
Directions: No right turns on by-pass, do not use Caterham by-pass. Go through Caterham Valley through town - continue on Godstone Rd, White Knobs Way on right before junction with A22.

WARLINGHAM

Secretary: Stan Smith, 14a Abbey Rd, Selsdon, Surrey CR2 8NG (081 651 2439).
Ground: Church Lane, Warlingham (0883 622943)   **Colours:** Green & black.
Directions: Bus 403.

WOODMANSTERNE SPORTS

Secretary: Mrs A Woodcraft, 16 Carshalton Rd, Woodmansterne SM7 3HR (0737 354466).
Ground: The Park, Woodmansterne Str., Woodmansterne (0737 350109).   **Colours:** Gold/black/gold.
Directions: A2022 Purley-Epsom road, B278 Carshalton Rd to end, past pub, clubhouse/car park on right.

WORCESTER PARK

Secretary: Laurie Burrage, 36 Lynwood Drive, Worcester Park KT4 7AB (081 330 1289).
Ground: Skinners Field, Green Lane, Worcester Park KT4 8AJ (081 337 4995). 'A' team: Sutton Manor High School Playing Fields, Northey Avenue, East Ewell.
Directions: Off A3 at New Malden r'bout onto A2043, 1st left under 2nd railway bridge 15 Green Lane. Entrance opposite Brookside Crescent, 2nd on right down Green Lane, adjacent to Worcester Park (BR).
Colours: All blue.

B.T. 2, Ashtead 1: Surrey County Premier League, 15/2/92. Randolph Payne shows good control despite close attention from Ashtead's P Rochester. Photo - Dave West.

Netherne FC, Surrey County Premier League. Photo - Martin Wray.

Bridon Ropes FC of the Spartan League. Back Row (L/R): B White (Fixture Secretary), M Laroche, S Pettengell, L Potter, T Smith (capt), A Lucas, S Edwards, C Leys, R Clements (Manager). Front: S Reed, M Merdjan, D Ling, G Austin, L Wright, G Platt. Photo - Dave West.

446

CAMPRI LEISUREWEAR
SOUTH MIDLANDS LEAGUE

President: A G Joyce   **Chairman:** P Burns
Hon. Secretary & Treasurer: Martyn Mitchell,
26 Leighton Court, Dunstable, Beds LU6 1EW (0582 667291).

LEIGHTON WIN THRILLING TITLE RACE

In another exciting finale, Leighton clinched the Premier Division title winning their final game 1-0 at Leverstock Green. Shillington and Brache Sparta were early season pace-setters leading through to November. Leighton assumed control in December as Shillington's challenge faltered, and together with Milton Keynes Borough, who were to enjoy their best season in the top flight, they maintained a tussle for supremacy from Christmas until the exciting climax in May. When the two sides met at the end of April in what many believed would be the decider, 1,614 flocked to Bell Close to witness a thrilling 3-3 between Leighton and Borough that kept the championship on the boil.

With Borough winning their final game the following week, Leighton knew they had to win their remaining two. This was duly achieved at Leverstock Green on a cold evening on Friday 8th May, when 802, 650 of whom had made the journey from Bedfordshire, saw Leighton lift the championship for only the second time in their history. They now follow last season's champions, Thame, into the Diadora League, and take with them the best wishes of the S.M.L.

Biggleswade maintained their improved form of recent years to finish third again, and their efforts were rewarded when they went on to lift both the O'Brien Butchers Premier Division Cup defeating Brache Sparta 3-0 in the final at Shillington, and the North Beds Charity Cup where they beat local rivals Potton in the final.

Premier Division sides Leverstock Green and Potters Bar Town both enjoyed impressive debuts in their first season, but Winslow, who finished last for the second consecutive season, were relegated to Division One. Although they managed to win just two games they suffered many heavy defeats, including four by 'double-figures', amongst their 194 goals conceded. Despite this, they were rewarded at the League's A.G.M. with the S.M.L. 'Special Award Trophy' for the creditable manner which they displayed throughout despite the many setbacks. One sad note was the demise of Wolverton AFC who resigned during the season following many problems off the field which forced the club to fold after a long and distinguished history that dated back to the last century.. *(continued on page 449)*

Leighton's Steve Norman (right) heads for goal during the champions' 3-1 home win over basement club Winslow United on 25th January. Photo - Gavin Ellis.

LEAGUE TABLES 1991-92

Premier Division	P	W	D	L	F	A	PTS
Leighton Town	40	29	8	3	98	30	95
MK Borough	40	30	3	7	116	29	93
Biggleswade Town	40	26	6	8	96	38	84
Shillington	40	25	6	9	82	35	81
Wingate & Finchley	40	22	10	8	87	51	76
Hoddesdon Town	40	20	13	7	80	42	73
Brache Sparta	40	21	8	11	82	48	71
Leverstock Green	40	21	6	13	63	38	69
Oxford City	40	19	7	14	74	50	64
Langford	40	18	8	14	52	48	62
Potters Bar Town	40	17	10	13	76	64	61
Harpenden Town	40	14	11	15	70	63	53
Totternhoe	40	15	4	21	62	84	49
Letchworth G. City	40	13	6	21	58	63	45
Pitstone & Ivinghoe	40	12	8	20	63	101	44
Pirton	40	10	11	19	36	61	41
Welwyn Gdn City	40	10	10	20	62	87	40
Buckingham Ath.	40	10	6	24	60	77	36
New B'well St Peter	40	5	8	27	34	93	23
61 FC Luton	40	4	5	31	39	114	17
Winslow United	40	2	0	38	20	194	6

Division One	P	W	D	L	F	A	PTS
Ashcroft	38	30	5	3	93	30	95
Luton Old Boys	38	28	7	3	104	41	91
Bedford United	38	28	5	5	118	39	89
Bedford Town	38	26	6	6	100	32	84
Shenley & Loughton	38	20	5	13	85	42	65
Toddington Rovers	38	17	13	8	76	53	64
Delco Products	38	17	6	15	69	59	57
Risborough Rangers	38	14	11	13	61	65	53
Ampthill Town	38	14	10	14	65	57	52
Cranfield United	38	13	10	15	62	66	49
Ickleford	38	12	12	14	54	60	48
Tring Athletic	38	12	11	15	57	58	*44
Sandy Albion	38	11	8	19	61	87	41
Potters Bar Crus.	38	12	4	22	86	99	40
Walden Rangers	38	9	13	16	65	82	40
Flamstead	38	11	7	20	60	87	40
Shefford Town	38	11	7	20	41	72	40
Emberton	38	9	6	23	47	91	33
Caddington	38	4	7	27	40	103	19
Stony Stratford	38	2	7	29	41	162	13
* - 3 pts deducted							

PREMIER DIVISION RESULT CHART 1991-92

HOME TEAM	1	2	3	4	5	6	7	8	9	10	11	12	13	14	15	16	17	18	19	20	21	22
1. Biggleswade	*	1-1	5-1	3-2	1-0	0-0	0-2	2-1	0-1	0-1	5-0	4-0	0-0	3-1	5-1	1-0	9-0	3-0	1-3	1-0	4-0	*
2. Brache S.	2-3	*	2-0	1-1	0-0	0-1	1-1	0-0	1-4	3-1	0-1	3-1	4-1	0-0	1-2	1-0	1-0	3-0	5-2	0-3	3-0	2-0
3. Buck. Ath.	1-3	2-5	*	1-2	3-2	0-0	0-1	1-2	1-0	0-2	6-1	2-3	0-1	2-2	0-2	2-0	5-1	1-3	3-3	0-3	6-0	2-3
4. Harpenden	1-2	2-0	2-2	*	2-3	3-1	1-2	2-1	1-1	0-1	2-2	0-5	4-1	2-4	1-1	1-2	4-0	2-2	1-1	2-3	5-1	*
5. Hoddesdon	0-0	4-4	5-3	2-0	*	2-1	1-1	3-1	1-0	3-1	5-1	2-0	2-2	7-1	1-1	2-1	4-0	1-1	1-3	1-1	4-1	3-0
6. Langford	1-3	1-0	0-0	2-0	1-0	*	1-2	1-0	0-0	0-0	1-2	0-1	3-1	1-1	0-2	1-1	4-3	3-0	1-3	4-1	5-0	
7. Leighton	1-0	4-1	2-1	2-0	4-1	2-1	*	2-0	2-2	3-3	5-1	0-0	3-1	5-0	1-1	3-1	5-0	5-0	3-0	0-0	3-1	4-0
8. Letchworth	4-2	0-1	0-1	1-2	1-1	2-3	0-3	*	2-1	1-0	3-1	0-2	2-0	3-1	1-2	0-2	2-3	4-1	2-1	4-5	5-0	1-3
9. Leverstock	0-4	0-2	0-1	3-0	0-0	0-1	1-0	*		1-0	4-0	1-1	2-0	6-1	1-0	2-1	3-0	2-1	1-1	1-2	3-0	2-0
10. MK Borough	0-1	4-1	5-0	1-1	2-0	3-0	2-1	3-0	3-0	*	2-0	4-2	2-0	6-2	0-1	3-0	2-1	4-1	4-1	4-1	4-1	10-0
11. New Bradwell	0-3	0-4	1-5	1-2	0-1	1-1	0-2	3-1	0-2	0-4	*	0-4	1-1	1-0	0-0	0-3	1-2	1-2	1-1	0-1	3-1	1-2
12. Oxford City	1-2	4-2	1-0	1-1	0-2	0-1	0-1	3-1	1-0	0-1	2-1	*	0-0	5-1	1-0	0-2	3-2	0-2	7-1	3-3	4-0	4-0
13. Pirton	2-1	2-3	3-2	1-0	0-1	0-1	1-1	1-1	0-1	0-6	1-0	0-0	*	1-6	1-2	0-1	1-3	1-1	1-2	3-0	1-2	
14. Pitstone	2-2	1-7	0-0	1-1	0-4	3-1	0-1	1-1	1-3	0-6	2-1	1-3	3-1	*	4-2	1-3	3-0	1-3	1-1	1-1	4-0	*
15. Potters BT.	1-2	0-2	3-2	3-1	1-1	2-2	0-5	1-0	1-3	1-4	3-1	5-2	3-0	4-1	*	1-5	6-0	1-2	4-2	2-2	7-0	2-2
16. Shillington	1-1	1-1	4-0	0-1	1-0	3-1	1-0	3-3	2-2	0-1	4-0	1-0	0-0	4-0	1-0	*	6-3	3-1	5-0	3-1	7-1	*
17. The 61 FC	2-3	0-5	1-0	0-1	0-2	1-2	1-4	0-2	0-3	1-3	3-3	1-1	0-2	4-1	2-2	1-2	*	2-2	0-1	0-2	1-3	*
18. Totternhoe	1-3	0-3	1-0	1-3	0-2	0-2	2-3	1-3	4-1	1-2	3-2	0-3	2-1	1-4	3-0	0-0	4-2	*	2-0	1-2	3-1	*
19. Welwyn GC	0-3	0-6	3-1	3-3	1-1	3-2	0-6	0-0	1-3	0-4	0-0	2-1	0-0	0-1	1-3	0-1	2-0	5-1	*	1-2	6-0	1-2
20. Wingate & F.	4-0	0-1	3-2	1-3	2-2	2-0	4-0	2-1	1-0	1-1	1-1	0-1	0-0	2-2	1-4	5-2	5-1	3-1	*	9-1	1-1	
21. Winslow	0-10	1-2	0-3	0-8	0-6	1-3	0-6	1-3	1-5	0-11	0-4	0-7	0-3	3-4	0-4	0-2	2-1	0-4	0-10	0-4	*	
22. Wolverton	*	1-2	*	0-1	*	1-0	2-3	1-2	1-0	1-3	2-1	*	*	*	*	*	*	6-3	*	3-0	*	*

Wolverton AFC folded in mid-season. Playing record expunged and shown above for interest only

DIVISION ONE RESULT CHART 1991-92

HOME TEAM	1	2	3	4	5	6	7	8	9	10	11	12	13	14	15	16	17	18	19	20
1. Ampthill Town	*	0-1	0-1	5-3	2-3	0-0	1-3	4-2	1-0	4-1	1-2	2-0	2-3	1-1	2-1	0-1	7-1	4-2	1-0	1-0
2. Ashcroft	2-1	*	3-2	0-3	6-0	3-0	0-1	4-1	5-0	2-1	0-0	2-1	3-1	0-0	1-0	1-0	11-0	2-2	1-0	4-0
3. Bedford T.	1-1	2-3	*	2-0	7-0	4-1	4-1	4-0	5-0	1-2	1-0	4-1	5-0	6-2	3-1	1-0	6-0	1-5	0-0	2-0
4. Bedford Utd	2-1	1-1	1-1	*	4-1	3-1	7-1	1-0	1-0	1-2	7-3	4-0	2-2	2-0	2-3	7-0	2-0	2-0	4-1	
5. Caddington	1-1	0-4	0-9	1-2	*	3-4	1-2	2-2	2-3	1-2	1-3	1-3	0-2	1-3	0-1	0-3	4-2	1-2	0-5	2-4
6. Cranfield Utd	3-1	1-2	0-3	1-1	1-2	*	0-2	0-1	1-1	1-1	4-2	2-2	3-0	3-0	0-0	4-1	3-1	0-3	1-1	
7. Delco	3-0	0-1	2-3	1-4	2-1	3-1	*	0-0	0-1	1-1	0-2	1-2	2-0	3-1	3-2	+	6-6	2-1	1-1	5-1
8. Emberton	1-4	0-3	0-3	0-3	3-1	1-2	1-0	*	4-3	1-2	2-4	3-3	1-4	0-1	0-1	2-0	1-1	2-2	2-3	5-3
9. Flamstead	1-3	2-3	0-2	0-4	3-0	3-1	1-4	1-2	*	1-2	1-4	4-1	0-2	2-4	3-0	2-2	4-3	2-2	2-1	2-2
10. Ickleford	0-0	0-3	1-2	2-2	0-0	1-1	1-1	1-2	2-1	*	1-1	3-0	2-1	0-1	1-1	0-3	5-0	2-2	3-2	3-2
11. Luton O.B.	2-0	4-1	1-1	2-1	3-0	3-1	2-1	2-1	7-1	2-0	*	3-0	4-1	5-1	2-0	3-0	5-0	0-2	4-1	3-3
12. Potters BC	1-1	1-6	0-0	0-5	1-2	4-2	1-0	6-0	4-3	3-4	6-2	*	0-1	3-2	1-2	0-5	9-0	1-3	0-3	6-2
13. Risborough	2-2	1-2	2-0	1-2	2-2	3-2	1-0	1-1	1-1	4-1	1-4	4-1	*	3-3	2-0	1-3	5-1	2-2	0-5	1-1
14. Sandy Albion	2-4	0-3	0-4	1-3	0-0	3-4	0-2	4-0	2-0	3-3	3-4	2-2	0-2	*	4-2	2-1	3-2	1-3	0-1	2-3
15. Shefford	1-1	1-2	0-1	1-8	2-1	0-1	2-1	1-0	0-1	1-1	2-2	2-1	1-1	0-3	*	0-3	2-1	0-4	1-1	3-2
16. Shenley	5-2	0-1	3-0	2-5	1-0	0-1	6-0	5-2	6-0	4-1	0-3	1-2	1-0	0-2	7-0	*	9-2	0-0	2-1	3-2
17. Stony Strat.	1-1	1-2	1-5	0-4	4-3	2-5	3-7	0-2	0-6	1-0	0-4	0-9	0-0	2-2	0-9	1-4	*	1-1	1-1	1-4
18. Toddington	1-2	2-3	0-0	1-4	2-2	1-1	1-1	3-1	1-1	2-1	1-2	2-3	3-1	6-1	1-0	1-0	2-0	*	3-1	3-1
19. Tring Ath.	1-0	0-0	1-3	0-6	2-2	0-3	4-3	1-0	1-3	1-3	1-1	5-3	1-1	4-0	1-2	1-1	3-1	0-2	*	1-1
20. Walden Rgrs	2-2	1-2	0-1	1-3	2-0	2-2	1-4	2-0	2-2	1-0	3-3	5-3	1-2	2-0	1-1	1-1	2-1	3-3	1-4	*

+ - 3 points awarded to Delco products as Shenley & Loughton failed to fulfill fixture.

(continued from page 447)

In Division One, Ashcroft won the title for the first time in their history finishing four points clear of runners-up Luton Old Boys. Both sides occupied the top two places from October, and when Ashcroft headed the table by the end of November they were to remain there, apart from two brief weeks at the end of the season. However, only Luton Old Boys were to gain promotion, and they ended the season on a high note when they lifted the O'Brien Butchers S.M.L. Trophy for Division One clubs defeating Ashcroft in a penalty shoot-out in the replayed final.

Bedford Town, in their first season in the S.M.L. since their reformation, finished fourth and despite pressing the leaders for the majority of the season they failed to sustain a strong challenge and were eventually denied third place by local rivals Bedford United. Such was the rivalry between the two clubs that their derby on Boxing Day attracted a gate of over 1,000.

Hoddesdon lifted the League's Challenge Trophy for the third time in seven seasons by defeating Shillington 2-1 in the final at Harpenden.

In the reserve competitions, Leighton completed a championship double in Division One, while Potters Bar Town created several new club and league records with their runaway success in Division Two. The Reserve Challenge Trophy was retained by holders Barton Rovers Reserves.

S.M.L. clubs fared disappointingly in national competitions, Leighton carrying the flag as far as the Second Qualifying Round of the F.A. Cup and no club managing to go beyond the First Round of the F.A. Vase. In County Cups, Letchworth gained success in the Herts Charity Shield winning an all-S.M.L. final against Leverstock Green with a single-goal win at Hertford Town. Leverstock Green also reached the final of the Herts Centenary Trophy only to go down 1-2 to Cheshunt at Ware. In the Beds Senior Cup, Totternhoe gave a fine display in the final against Kempston losing by the only goal of the game.

The S.M.L., which is once again being sponsored by Campri Leisurewear, welcomes four new clubs for 1992-93. In the Premier Division, Arlesey Town rejoin after spending ten years in the United Counties League, whilst Hatfield Town arrive from the Herts Senior County League. Newcomers in Division One are De-Havilland and London Colney, both from Herts Senior County League.

A pleasing aspect of the past season has been the standard of matchday programmes. This has been noted and widely reported in many non-league publications, and clubs are to be congratulated. Looking forward, 1993-94 will see the Premier Division become 'all-floodlit'. With increasing membership, and many clubs continuing to make ground improvements, it has been agreed to form an additional division between the Premier and Division One starting in 1993-94. It will be known as the 'Senior Division' and will be for clubs whose facilities meet Premier Division requirements excluding floodlights.

Paul Gardner, League Historian and Statistician.

Pirton 0, Letchworth Garden City 4 - League Trophy First Round 2/11/92. Visiting 'keeper Keely Thake clears under pressure during the first half of a wind-affected tussle. Photo - Gavin Ellis.

South Midlands League Premier (top) & Division One Ten Year Records

	82/3	83/4	84/5	85/6	86/7	87/8	88/9	89/90	90/1	91/2
Ashcroft Co-Op	–	7	14	16	–	–	–	–	–	–
Baldock Town	3	–	–	–	–	–	–	–	–	–
Biggleswade Town	16	–	–	–	–	15	15	5	3	3
Brache Sparta	–	–	16	–	–	–	16	14	18	7
Buckingham Athletic	–	–	–	–	–	–	–	–	–	18
Cranfield Utd	–	–	–	14	12	16	–	–	–	–
Eaton Bray Utd	6	3	1	8	11	–	–	–	–	–
Electrolux	–	–	–	–	–	8	14	8	10	–
Hatfield Town	8	5	–	–	–	–	–	–	–	–
Harpenden Town	–	–	–	–	–	–	–	–	7	12
Hoddesdon Town	–	–	7	9	3	5	5	4	9	6
Knebworth	–	–	4	6	15	17	–	–	–	–
Langford	–	–	–	15	13	3	1	16	13	10
Leighton Town	–	–	13	3	9	6	10	3	4	1
Letchworth G C	–	–	–	–	–	–	–	–	6	14
Leverstock Green	–	–	–	–	–	–	–	–	–	8
Milton Keynes Borough	–	–	–	10	4	11	18	12	19	2
New Bradwell St Peter	–	–	12	7	14	12	11	11	17	19
Oxford City	–	–	–	–	–	–	–	–	–	9
Pirton	1	2	9	11	8	13	12	13	14	16
Pitstone & Ivinghoe	–	–	–	–	–	–	8	1	16	15
Potters Bar Town	–	–	–	–	–	–	–	–	–	11
Royston Town	7	14	–	–	–	–	–	–	–	–
Sandy Albion	15	–	–	–	–	–	–	–	–	–
Selby	9	13	10	1	1	2	3	–	–	–
Shefford Town	–	1	3	5	16	10	17	19	–	–
Shillington	5	8	6	13	2	1	4	7	5	4
61 FC (Luton)	2	6	8	4	7	7	7	15	15	20
Stotfold	4	4	–	–	–	–	–	–	–	–
Thame United	–	–	–	–	–	–	2	2	1	–
Totternhoe	–	–	–	–	6	4	9	6	11	13
Vauxhall Motors	14	12	2	–	–	–	–	–	–	–
Walden Rangers	13	15	–	–	–	–	–	–	–	–
Waterlows	12	10	15	–	–	–	–	–	–	–
Welwyn Garden City	11	11	11	2	10	9	6	10	12	17
Welwyn Garden Utd	–	–	–	–	–	–	–	18	–	–
Wingate (& Finchley)	–	–	–	–	–	–	–	–	8	5
Winslow United	10	9	5	12	5	14	13	17	20	21
Wolverton AFC	–	–	–	–	–	–	–	9	2	w/d
No. of Clubs	16	15	16	16	16	17	18	19	20	21

	82/3	83/4	84/5	85/6	86/7	87/8	88/9	89/90	90/1	91/2
Ampthill Town	–	–	–	–	–	–	–	–	–	9
Ashcroft (Co-Op)	–	–	–	–	6	8	4	5	5	1
Bedford Town	–	–	–	–	–	–	–	–	–	4
Bedford United	–	–	–	–	–	–	–	10	10	3
Biggleswade Town	–	13	10	8	2	–	–	–	–	–
Brache Sparta	3	2	–	9	9	2	–	–	–	–
Buckingham Athletic	–	–	–	1	11	9	2	4	1	–
Caddington	–	–	–	–	4	3	3	3	6	19
Cranfield Utd	4	7	6	–	–	–	7	6	14	10
Delco Products	–	–	–	–	–	12	8	13	7	7
Electrolux	14	11	7	3	1	–	–	–	–	–
Emberton	–	–	–	–	–	–	–	–	–	18
Flamstead	–	–	–	–	–	–	–	–	8	16
Harpenden Town	13	9	13	4	12	11	12	1	–	–
Henlow	–	15	–	–	–	–	–	–	–	–
Ickleford	–	–	14	11	10	13	5	14	11	11
Knebworth	–	3	–	–	–	–	–	–	–	–
Langford	9	5	3	–	–	–	–	–	–	–
Leighton Town	7	4	–	–	–	–	–	–	–	–
Luton Old Boys	–	–	–	–	–	–	–	–	–	2
Millford Villa	–	–	–	–	14	–	–	–	–	–
Milton Keynes Borough	–	–	1	–	–	–	–	–	–	–
Milton Keynes Town	–	–	–	–	–	6	–	–	–	–
M K United	–	–	8	12	7	–	–	–	–	–
Mowlem	8	5	2	–	–	–	–	–	–	–
New Bradwell St Peter	5	1	–	–	–	–	–	–	–	–
Oxford City	–	–	–	–	–	–	–	–	3	–
Pitstone & Ivinghoe	11	12	11	5	5	1	–	–	–	–
Potters Bar Crusaders	–	–	–	–	–	–	–	–	4	14
Risborough Rangers	–	–	–	–	–	–	–	15	17	8
Sandy Albion	–	10	12	10	13	10	10	16	18	13
Shefford Town	1	–	–	–	–	–	–	–	13	17
Shenley & Loughton	–	–	–	–	–	–	5	8	2	5
Stony Stratford Town	–	–	–	–	–	5	11	7	16	20
Toddington Rovers	–	–	–	–	–	–	–	12	15	6
Totternhoe	6	8	5	2	–	–	–	–	–	–
Tring Athletic	–	–	–	–	–	–	9	9	12	12
Walden Rangers	–	–	9	7	3	4	6	11	9	15
Welwyn Garden United	12	14	4	6	8	7	1	–	–	–
Wiltonians	10	–	–	–	–	–	–	–	–	–
Wingate	–	–	–	–	–	–	–	2	–	–
No. of Clubs	15	16	14	12	14	13	12	16	18	20

LEAGUE CHALLENGE TROPHY Preliminary Round

Ashcrofth v Ickleford	5-2	Bedford Town v Potters Bar Crusaders		1-0
Delco Products v Flamstead	2-4*(aet)*	Emberton v Biggleswade Town		1-3
Langford v Shenley & Loughton	0-2	Oxford City v Ampthill Town		3-0
Pirton v New Bradwell St Peter	3-0	Risborough Rangers v Harpenden Town		0-2
Toddington Rovers v Hoddesdon Town	0-3	Totternhoe v Letchworth Garden City		0-1

First Round

Bedford Town v Flamstead	4-1	Bedford United v Cranfield United		1-0
Hoddesdon Town v Sandy Albion	7-2	Biggleswade Town v Leverstock G.	2-2*(aet)*,1-0
Leighton Town v Ashcroft	2-0	Harpenden Town v Buckingham Athletic	1-2*(aet)*
Luton Old Boys v Welwyn Garden City	0-1	Oxford C. v Brache 0-0*(aet)*,2-2*(aet)*,2-0*(at Harpenden)*
Pirton v Letchworth Garden City	0-4	Shefford Town v Caddington		1-0
Shenley & Loughton v Shillington	1-3	The 61 FC v Milton Keynes Borough		0-4
Stony Stratford Town v Wingate & Finchley	2-8	Tring Athletic v Walden Rangers		1-0
Winslow United v Pitstone & Ivinghoe	0-4	Wolverton A.F.C. v Potters Bar Town		2-0

Second Round

Bedford Town v Buckingham Athletic	1-0	Bedford United v Shillington		2-3
Oxford City v Biggleswade Town	2-1	Letchworth Garden City v Wingate & Finchley		2-0
Pitstone & Ivinghoe v Tring Athletic	1-2	Shefford Town v Hoddesdon Town		0-0,0-3
Welwyn Garden City v Milton Keynes B.	2-3	Wolverton A.F.C. v Leighton Town		2-0

Quarter-Finals

Bedford Town v Letchworth Garden City	0-2	Milton Keynes Borough *W/O* Wolverton A.F.C. *Scr*
Tring Athletic v Hoddesden Town	2-4	Oxford City v Shillington	2-2*(aet)*,2-4

Semi-Finals

Hoddesdon Town v Milton Keynes B.	3-2,1-1	Shillington v Letchworth Garden City	2-0,2-1

Final *(at Harpenden Town FC, Monday 4th May)*: Hoddesdon Town 2, Shillington 1 *(aet)*

O'BRIEN BUTCHERS PREMIER DIVISION CUP Preliminary Round

Hoddesdon Town v Oxford City	4-1	New Bradwell St Peter v Brache Sparta	0-4
Pirton v Wingate & Finchley	0-2	Potters Bar Town v Winslow United	6-0
Shillington v Leighton Town	3-2	Totternhoe v Letchworth Garden City	0-1

First Round

Biggleswade Town v Harpenden Town	6-1	Brache S. v Hoddesdon 0-0*(aet)*,2-2 *(aet 5-4 pens)*
Buckingham Athletic v Milton Keynes B.	1-4	Leverstock Green *W/O* Wolverton A.F.C. *Scr.*
Shillington v Potters Bar Town	1-0	Pitstone & Ivinghoe v Letchworth Garden City	1-0
The 61 FC (Luton) v Langford	1-3	Wingate & Finchley v Welwyn Garden City	3-2

Quarter-Finals

Brache Sparta v Shillington	1-0	Biggleswade Town v Wingate & Finchley	2-1
Langford v Leverstock Green	4-0	Pitstone & Ivinghoe v Milton Keynes B.	3-2*(aet)*

Semi-Finals

Langford v Brache Sparta *(at Letchworth)*	1-2	Pitstone & Ivinghoe v Biggleswade *(at Shillington)* 0-4

Final *(at Shillington FC)*: Biggleswade Town 3, Brache Sparta 0

O'BRIEN S.M.L. TROPHY Preliminary Round

Ampthill Towns v Bedford Town	0-2	Ashcroft v Risborough Rangers	2-1
Delco Products v Bedford United	3-1	Stony Stratford Town v Shefford Town	0-2

First Round

Ashcroft v Caddington	8-0	Bedford Town v Ickleford *(at Langford)*	2-0
Emberton v Walden Rangers	2-4	Cranfield United v Sandy Albion	2-2*(aet)*,2-1
Flamstead v Tring Athletic	1-3	Luton Old Boys v Potters Bar Crusaders	4-1
Shefford Town v Delco Products	1-0	Shenley & Loughton v Toddington Rovers	2-0

Quarter-Finals

Ashcroft v Tring Athletic	2-0	Cranfield United v Shenley & Loughton	0-2
Luton Old Boys v Walden Rangers	2-0	Shefford Town v Bedford Town	0-1

Semi-Finals

Ashcroft v Bedford T. *(at Barton R.)*	3-2	Luton OB v Shenley & L. *(at Milton Keynes B.)*	3-1

Final *(at Letchworth)*: Ashcroft 1, Luton Old Boys 1 *(aet - Luton Old Boys won 5-4 on penalties).*

Ashcroft FC, Campri Leisurewear South Midlands League Division One champions 1991-92. Photo - Eric Marsh.

PREMIER DIVISION CLUBS 1992-93

ARLESEY TOWN

Chairman: John Milton   **President:** Roy Albone
Secretary: John Albon, 13 St Johns Rd, Arlesey, Beds SG15 6ST (0462 731 318).
Manager: Frank Reynolds   **Asst Manager:** Paul Stump
Ground: Lamb Meadow, Hitchin Rd, Arlesey (0462 731448).
Directions: Enter Arlesey from Hitchin, 200 yds past Biggs Wall on left.
Press Officer & Programme Editor: Tony Smith
Capacity: 4,000   **Seats:** 200   **Cover:** 300   **Floodlights:** Yes   **Founded:** 1891.
Programme: 24 pages, with admission   **Local Press:** Biggleswade Chronicle, Hitchin Gazette.
Colours: Sky & navy stripes   **Change Colours:** White & red   **Nickname:** Blues
Clubhouse: Members bar & function room. Open Lunchtime & evening.
Midweek matchday: Tuesday   **Record Gate:** 2000 v Luton Res, Beds Snr Cup 1906
Previous Ground: Bury Meadow 1919-39.
Prev. Lges: Biggleswade & Dist./ Beds Co. (S. Mids) 22-26 27-28/ Parthenon/ London 58-60/ Utd Co's 33-36 82-92.
Players to progress to Football League: Roland Legate (Luton), Pat Kruse (Brentford, Leicester)
Hons: Utd Co's Lg 84-85 (KO Cup), Sth Mids Lg 51-52 52-53 (Chal. Cup 79-80, Championship Shield 64-65, F'lit Cup),
Beds Snr Cup 65-66 78-79.

BIGGLESWADE TOWN

Chairman: M R Dorrington   **Manager:** K Davidson.
Secretary: G F Arkwright, 21 Willsheres Road, Biggleswade, Beds SG18 0BU (0767 316992).
Ground: Fairfield Road, Biggleswade (0767 312374).   **Directions:** A1 North r'bout, left immediately
after metal bridge into car park. Three Quarters of a mile from Biggleswade (BR).
Capacity: 2,500   **Seats:** 250   **Cover:** 250   **Floodlights:** Yes   **Founded:** 1874
Colours: Green/white   **Change:** Sky blue/white   **Nickname:** Waders
Previous Leagues: Utd Co's 20-39 51-55 63-74/ Bedford & District/ Eastern Co's 55-63.
Record Gate: 2,000   **Previous Name:** Biggleswade & District.
Hons: Sth Mids Lg 23-24 (Div 1 52-53, Prem. Div Tphy 91-92), Beds Snr Cup(8), Nth Beds Charity Cup 91-92, Utd Co's
Lg Cup 63-64 73-74.

BRACHE SPARTA

Chairman: Mr Roy Standring   **Manager:** Mr Kevin Millett.   **Physio:** C E Jones.
Secretary: Mr Maurice Raymond Franklin, 62 Katherine Drive, Dunstable LU5 4NU (0582 661177).
Ground: Foxdell Sports Ground, Dallow Road, Luton LU1 1UP (0582 20751).
Directions: Left off A505 to Dunstable into Chaul Lane at r'bout. Proceed across new relief road - ground entrance
adjacent to Foxdell Junior School.
Cover: 100   **Seats:**   **Capacity:** 400   **Floodlights:** No   **Founded:** 1960
Colours: All white   **Change Colours:** All blue.
Previous Lges: Luton & Dist.   **Hons:** S Mids Lg Div 1 R-up 83-84 87-88 (Prem Div Cup R-up 91-92).

BUCKINGHAM ATHLETIC

Chairman: R Ackerman   **Manager:** Andy O'Dell.
Secretary: Peter Hinson, 12 Badgers Way, Buckingham MK18 1AY (0280 6212).
Ground: Stratford Fields, Buckingham (0280 816945).
Directions: From Milton Keynes take the A422 Stony Stratford-Buckingham road – ground on left just before town
centre. From Aylesbury, turn right at 1st r-about, across 2nd r-about, left at 3rd – ground 300 yds on left.
Capacity: 1,000   **Seats:** No   **Cover:** Yes   **Floodlights:** No   **Founded:** 1933
Colours: Sky blue   **Change Colours:** Red/black.   **Nickname:** Swans
Previous League: North Bucks.   **Hons:** Sth Mids Lg Div 1 85-86 90-91 (R-up 88-89, Div 1 Cup 90-91)

HARPENDEN TOWN

Chairman: P J Eagles   **Manager:** Steve Woolfrey.
Secretary: V J Duffy, 13 Roundwood Lane, Harpenden, Herts AL5 3BW (0582 712676).
Asst Manager: Richard Hinde   **Physiotherapist:** Kim Evans.
Ground: Rothamsted Park, Amenbury Lane, Harpenden (0582 715724).
Directions: A1081 to Harpenden. Turn left/right at George Hotel into Leyton Road. Turn left into Amenbury Road, then
left again into 'Pay and Display' car park - the club entrance is signposted.
Capacity: 1,500   **Cover:** Yes   **Floodlights:** Yes   **Founded:** 1891
Colours: Yellow/blue/blue   **Change Colours:** Blue/yellow/yellow
Prev. Name: Harpenden FC 1891-1908.   **Hons:** Sth Mids Lg 61-62 64-65 (Lg Cup 70-71, Div 1 89-90, Prem Div
Tphy 89-90), Herts Snr Cup 01-02 09-10 11-12 20-21 25-26, Herts I'mediate Cup 52-53, Herts Charity Shield 07-08.

HATFIELD TOWN ATHLETIC

Chairman: Terry Edwards   **Manager:** Malcolm Doctor.
Secretary: Mrs Vivien Doctor, 1 Cloverland, Hatfield, Herts.
Ground: Gosling Stadium, Welwyn Garden City (0707 331056).
Directions: From A1 at Valley Rd, straight over r'bout, left at bottom, ground 400 yds on right.
Capacity: 3,000   **Seats:** Yes   **Floodlights:** Yes   **Programme:** No   **Founded:** 1976
Colours: Blue/white/blue   **Change Colours:** Yellow/blue/navy.
Previous Ground: Roe Hill Playing Fields, Briars Lane, Hatfield (pre-1992).
Prev. Lges: Mids Herts/ Herts Co. Snr (pre'92)   **Hons:** Herts Co. Snr Lg 91-92 (Div 1 90-91, Div 2 89-90).

HODDESDON TOWN

Chairman: Mr E Elliott   **Manager:** Mr A Greenall.
Secretary: Malcolm Owen, 1 Lower Meadow, Cheshunt, Herts EN8 0QU (0992 39793).
Ground: 'Lowfield', Park View, Hoddesdon, Herts.
Directions: A10, A1170 and follow signs to town centre until left-hand fork signposted Broxbourne. Right at 1st mini r-
about into Cock Lane and 1st right is Park View. Ground on left.
Capacity: 3,000   **Seats:** 250   **Floodlights:** Yes   **Founded:** 1879   **Nickname:** Lilywhites
Colours: White/black/white   **Change Colours:** All yellow.
Record Gate: 3,500 v West Ham, friendly 1975.
Previous Leagues: East Herts/ Herts Co./ Spartan 25-75/ London Spartan 75-77/ Athenian 77-84.
Hons: FA Vase 74-75 (1st winners), S Mids Lg Lg Cup 85-86 86-87 91-92, Spartan Lg 70-71 (R-up(3) 71-74, Div 1 35-36,
Div 2 'B' 27-28, Lg Cup(2) 70-72), Herts Snr Cup(3) 1886-88 89-90, Herts Charity Shield(4) 47-48 70-72 78-79.

LANGFORD

Chairman: Ian Chessum.   **Manager:** Gary Tilbrook.
Secretary: Frank Woodward, 8 Manor Road, Gamlingay, Sandy, Beds SG19 3EN (0767 51022).
Ground: Forde Park, Langford Road, Henlow SG16 6AF (0426 816106). *Freehold purchased Feb 1992.*
Directions: Halfway between Langford and Henlow on A6001 Hitchin to Biggleswade road.
Capacity: 4,000   **Seats:** 50   **Cover:** 150   **Floodlights:** Yes   **Founded:** 1910.
Colours: All red   **Change Colours:** All blue.   **Previous Leagues:** Bedford & Dist.
Record Gate: 450 v Q.P.R., 75th Anniversary and clubhouse opening, 22/8/85.
Honours: S Mids Lg 88-89 (Lg Cup 73-74 75-76, Prem. Div Tphy 88-89, O'Brien Div 1 Tphy 85-86), N Beds Charity Cup 69-70 74-75, Bedford Lg, Bedford I'mediate Cup, Hinchingbrooke Cup.

LETCHWORTH GARDEN CITY

Chairman: John McNeilliey   **President:** Anthony Burrows   **Manager:** Mick Clements.
Secretary: Jane Bygrave, 151 Glebe Road, Letchworth, Herts SG6 2GN (0462 670471).
Ground: Baldock Road, Letchworth, Herts SG6 2GN (0462 684691).
Directions: Jct 9 (A6141) off A1M straight over large r-about, right at next r-about, ground on right. From Luton A505 three miles after Hitchin. 2 miles from Letchworth (BR).
Capacity: 3,200   **Cover:** 550   **Seats:** 300   **Floodlights:** Yes   **Founded:** 1906
Colours: Blue/white/blue   **Change Colours:** Yellow/yellow/blue
Previous Name: Garden City/ Letchworth Ath./ Letchworth Town
Previous Leagues: Herts Co. 06-07/ Biggleswade 07-08/ Nth Herts 08-22/ S Mids 22-23 24-29/ Spartan 29-56/ Athenian 63-77/ Isthmian 77-90.
Programme: 22 pages   **Nickname:** Bluebirds.
Hons: Herts Lg 11-12, Spartan Lg 29-30 35-36 51-52/ Delphian Lg 57-58, Athenian Lg 74-75 (Mem. Shield 65-66 66-67), Herts Snr Cup 12-13 35-36 51-52, Herts Charity Shield 22-23 47-48 87-88 91-92, East Anglian Cup 76-77, Woolwich Cup 81-82, Hitchin Cup 81-82.

LEVERSTOCK GREEN

Chairman: R Saville   **Manager:** M Vipond
Secretary: S D Robinson, 11 Connaught Close, Hemel Hempstead, Herts HP2 7AB (0442 65734)
Ground: Pancake Lane, Leverstock Green, Hemel Hempstead. (0442 246280)
Ground Directions: From M1 leave at A4147 at 2nd r-about. First exit to Leverstock Green, Pancake Lane is on left 300 yrds past the 'Leather Bottle' pub.
Floodlights: No   **Founded:** 1906   **Previous League:** Herts Co. (pre-1991).
Colours: Green & white/black/green   **Change Colours:** Green & black/white/black
Hons: Herts Centenary Tphy R-up 91-92, Herts Charity Shield R-up 91-92, Frank Major Tphy 1991.

LUTON OLD BOYS

Secretary: Tim J Thomas, 10 Braceby Close, Luton, Beds LU23 2TP. (0582 579703)
Ground & Directions: As Dunstable Town FC (page 522)
Colours: Red/black/black   **Hons:** Sth Mids Lg Div 1 Tphy 91-92 (Div 2 R-up 91-92)

MILTON KEYNES BOROUGH

Chairman: Martin Russell   **Vice Chairman:** Ray Jackson.
Secretary: Brian Greenwood, 14 Maudsley Close, Shenley Lodge, Milton Keynes MK5 7BH (0908 667494).
Manager: Tom Flanagan   **Commercial Manager:** Brian Greenwood.
Ground: Manor Fields, Bletchley, Milton Keynes (0908 375256)
Directions: Old A5 to Fenny Stratford, left at r-about, straight on at next r-about. 50 yds on turn left, proceed until Canal Bridge, then into Manor Fields
Capacity: 5,000   **Seats:** Yes   **Cover:** Yes   **Floodlights:** Yes   **Founded:** 1966.
Colours: Blue/white/blue   **Change Colours:** All white
Programme: 28 pages   **Editor:** Ernie Thompson.
Clubhouse: Two bars, open every day. Function room with 8ft satellite screen for major sporting events.
Hons: Sth Mids Lg R-up 91-92 (Div 1 84-85, Premier Div Tphy 86-87.

NEW BRADWELL ST PETER

Chairman: TBA   **Manager:** TBA
Secretary: L Smith, 47 Rowle Close, Stantonbury, Milton Keynes MK14 6BJ
Ground: Recreation Ground, Bradwell Road, New Bradwell, Milton Keynes MK13 7AT (0908 315766)
Directions: From M1 Jnt 14 go towards Newport Pagnell, left at 1st r-about into H3 (A422 Monks Way). Overo 6 r-abouts, right into V6 (Grafton St.), 1st right then left at T-Junct. Ground half mile on left
Clubhouse: Yes   **Seats:** No   **Capacity:**   **Floodlights:** No   **Founded:** 1902
Colours: Maroon/blue/blue   **Change Colours:** White/black/black
Previous League: North Bucks   **Hons:** Sth Mids Lg Div 1 76-77 83-84.

OXFORD CITY

Chairman: Mr M Woodley   **Manager:** Peter Foley
Secretary: John Sheppard, 20 Howe Close, Wheatley, Oxford OX9 1SS. (08677 2181)
Ground: Pressed Steel, Roman Way, Cowley, Oxford
Directions: From A40 r-about take eastern by pass (A4142). Left at next r-about to Horspath. First right into Roman Way. Ground on left.
Capacity: 2,000   **Seats:** Yes   **Clubhouse:** Yes   **Floodlights:** No   **Founded:** 1882
Colours: Blue & white hoops/white/white   **Change Colours:** All red
Previous ground: The White Horse 1882-1988, Cuttleslowe Park 1990-91.
Previous League: Isthmian 07-88.
Hons: FA Amtr Cup R-up 02-03 12-13, Isthmian Lg R-up 34-35 45-46 (Div 1 R-up 77-78, Oxon Snr Cup(26).

PIRTON

Chairman: Mr Bob Wright   **Manager:** Mr Kenny Newton.
Secretary: Mrs Lyn Pennie, 21 Thatchers End, Hitchin, Herts SG4 0PD (0462 454961).
Ground: Pirton Recreation Ground, Walnut Tree Road. (Hitchin 0462 712531)
Directions: From M1 through Barton and Shillington to Pirton. From Hitchin first right turn off Luton Road. Four miles from Hitchin (BR).
Capacity: 1,000   **Seats:** 25   **Cover:** 100   **Floodlights:** No   **Clubhouse:** Yes
Colours: Yellow/blue/blue   **Change Colours:** All red   **Founded:** 1937.
Previous Name: Pirton Social.   **Previous League:** North Herts/ Herts Snr Co.
Hons: Sth Mids Lg 79-80 81-82 82-83 (Div 1 72-73, Lg Cup 76-77, Premier Div Tphy 84-85).

Harpenden Town. Back Row (L/R): L Edwards (Manager), S O'Loughlin, I Wedd, P Toms, J Guest, P Delderfield, K Haskins, A Blundell (Asst Mgr). Front: R McFarlane, S McClelland, M Smith, M Vidgen, L Attfield, T Caines, G Gay.

Langford FC. Photo - Gavin Ellis.

Milton Keynes Borough, Premier Division Runners-up 1991-92. Back Row (L/R): Malcolm Bendall (Physio), Ralph Burton, Dave Drewe, Zane Flanagan, Paul Warnecki, John Templeton, Steve Drewe, John McNuff, Andy Falconer (Captain). Front: Tony Shrieves, Mark Evans, Kenny Hollis, Stuart Harding, Tony Joyce, Wayne Spencer.

454

PITSTONE & IVINGHOE

Chairman: Harry Bowden   **President:** A Frazier   **Manager:** Paul Ellam
Secretary: Dave Hawkins, 26 Glebe Close, Pitstone, Leighton Buzzard, Beds LU7 9AZ (0296 661456).
Ground: Pitstone Recreation Ground, Pitstone, Bucks (0296 661271)
Directions: Tring Rd from Dunstable, turn right for Ivinghoe, and continue through to Pitstone r-about; ground left then right. From Aylesbury - left at 'Rising Sun' in Aston Clinton, keep on that road to Pitstone r'bout; ground right then right.
Cover: 250   **Seats:** No   **Capacity:** 1,000   **Floodlights:** No   **Founded:** 1958
Colours: Red & black stripes/black/red   **Change Colours:** White/black/red
Clubhouse: Matchdays & Tuesday & Friday evenings   **Programme Editor:** I Travis.
Hons: Sth Mids Lg 89-90 (Div 1 87-88, Lg Cup 88-89, Div 1 Cup 87-88, Reserve Div 2 R-up 85-86), Dunstable Alliance 73-74 75-76 76-77, Dunstable Premier Cup 74-75 76-77, Reading Jnr Cup 76-77 (R-up 75-76), Aspley Snr Cup 68-69, Aspley Jnr Cup 66-67, West Herts Chal. Cup 58-59, Marworth Cup 67-68, Roseberry Cup 67-68, Berks & Bucks Jnr Cup R-up 79-80(reserves).

POTTERS BAR TOWN

Chairman: **Manager:** Alan Bolt
Secretary: Peter Waller, 26 Queen Annes Grove, Bush Hill Park, Enfield, Middx EN1 2JR (081 360 7859).
Ground: Parkfield Centre, The Walk, Potters Bar, Herts (0707 54833).
Directions: M25 jct 24, enter Potters Bar along Southgate Rd (A111), at lights right into the High St (A1000), half mile left into The Walk, ground 200 yds on right (opp. Potters Bar Cricket Club).
Capacity: 2,000   **Clubhouse:** Yes   **Floodlights:** No   **Founded:** 1960
Colours: Red & Royal stripes/royal/royal   **Change:** White or yellow/red/red
Previous League: Barnet & Dist./ Nth London Comb. 65-68/ Herts Snr Co. 68-91.
Previous Names: Mount Grace Old Scholars/ Mount Grace (Potters Bar) until 1991.
Record Gate: 200 v Cockfosters, Herts Snr County League.
Hons: Herts Co. Lg 90-91 (Div 1 73-74 81-82, Aubrey Cup 90-91 (R-up 87-88), FA Vase 3rd Rd 90-91, Herts I'mediate Cup 73-74, Barnet & Dist. Lg R-up 64-65 (Div 1 61-62), Barnet Jnr Cup 61-62, Nth L'don Comb. 67-68 (Div 2 R-up 65-66), Barnet Charity Cup 63 64 (R-up 64-65 68-69 70-71), Potters Bar Charity Cup 76-77, Herts Charity Shield SF 74-75 75-76.

SHILLINGTON

Chairman: Stan Burgdine   **Manager:** Paul Stephens.
Secretary: Aubrey J Cole, 32 Greenfields, Shillington, Hitchin, Herts SG5 3NX. (0462 711322).
Assistant Manager/ Physiotherapist/ Programme Editor: Noel Lewis.
Ground: Playing Fields, Shillington, Hitchin (0462 711757).
Directions: From Luton, turn off A6 at Barton turn off to Higham Gobion at r-about. From Hitchin or Bedford turn off at 'Bird in Hand', Henlow Camp. Five miles from Hitchin (BR)
Capacity: 800   **Seats:** No   **Cover:** 100   **Floodlights:** Yes   **Formed:** 1946.
Colours: White/red/red   **Change Colours:** Yellow/black/yellow
Clubhouse: Refreshments availabe   **Record Gate:** 400 v Barton R., Lg Tphy early 80's.
Hons: Sth Mids Lg 87-88 (Lg Cup 82-83, Div 1 80-81, Prem Div Tphy 87-88).

THE 61 F.C. (LUTON)

Chairman: G Harker   **Manager:** R Everitt
Secretary: R Everitt, 11 Poplars Close, Luton LU2 8AE (0582 453637).
Ground: Kingsway, Beverley Road, Luton, Beds. (0582 582965)
Directions: On main A505 Luton to Dunstable Road. Entrance in Beverley Rd, approx 1.5 miles from Town Centre (watch for one-way stystem). One mile from Leagrave (BR).
Capacity: 2,000   **Cover:** 250   **Seats:** 25   **Floodlights:** No   **Formed:** 1961
Colours: Sky/royal/royal   **Change:** Red/black/red
Previous Leagues: Luton/ Hellenic 72-73.   **Record Gate:** 265 v Selby, Chal. Tphy final 1/4/88.
Hons: Beds Snr Cup 83-84.

TOTTERNHOE

Chairman: Jim Basterfield   **Manager:** Tony Ratcliffe   **Asst Mgr:** Guy Keyford.
Secretary: Jim Basterfield, 41 Park Avenue, Totternhoe, Dunstable, Beds LU6 1QF. (0582 667941)
Ground: Totternhoe Recreation Ground, Dunstable. (0582 606738)
Directions: Turn off the main Dunstable to Tring Road B489. Ground on right as you enter the Totternhoe. Five miles from Leighton Buzzard (BR), 7 miles from Luton. Bus 61 Luton-Aylesbury.
Capacity: 1,000   **Seats:** 30   **Cover:** 200   **Floodlights:** No   **Founded:** 1906
Colours: All red   **Change Colours:** Blue & white hoops/blue/blue
Record Gate: 300 v Luton Town, clubhouse opening 13/10/82
Hons: Sth Mids Lg Div 1 61-62 (R-up 68-69 85-86), Beds Snr Cup R-up 69-70 86-87 91-92, Beds I'mediate Cup 77-78, Luton & Dist. Lg 57-58.

WELWYN GARDEN CITY

Chairman: John Newman   **Manager:** Dave Lawrence
Secretary: Dick Dunning, 38 Cowper Road, Welwyn Garden City, Herts AL7 3LS (0707 334536).
Press Officer: Keith Browne.   **Physiotherapist:** Arthur Wood/ Derek Carlisle.
Ground: Herns Lane, Welwyn Garden City (0707 328470).
Directions: From A1 follow signs for industrial area. Take one-way system opposite Avdel Ltd (signed Hertford B195), take 2nd exit off one-way system. Ground 400 yards on left. One and a half miles from Welwyn GC (BR).
Capacity: 1,500   **Seats:** 40   **Cover:** 130   **Floodlights:** Yes   **Founded:** 1921
Colours: Maroon/maroon/white   **Change Colours:** Yellow & blue/blue/yellow
Midweek Matches: Tuesday   **Club Shop:** Yes   **Nickname:** Citzens.
Programme: 28 pages, 50p   **Programme Editor:** Keith Browne (0707 251854).
Clubhouse: Open every night and weekend lunchtimes. Members Bar, function Hall. Steward: Ron Baird.
Record Gate: 403 v Pitstone & Ivinghoe, Lg Challenge Trophy Final Second Leg 88-89.
Previous Leagues: Spartan/ Metropolitan/ Gtr London
Best FA Vase year: 1st Rd 86-87.   **Best FA Cup year:** Prel. Rd replay 89-90.
91-92 P.o.Y.: Andy Lawrence   **91-92 Top Scorer:** Stephen Flain (12).
Local Newspapers: Welwyn & Hatfield Times, Welwyn & Hatfield Herald & Post.
Hons: Herts Snr Centenary Tphy 84-85 (R-up 88-89), Herts Charity Shield 27-28 86-87 87-88 (R-up 48-49), Sth Mids Lg 72-73 (Div 1 69-70 81-82, Lg Cup R-up 74-75 81-82 88-89).

WINGATE & FINCHLEY

Chairman: Peter Rebak   **Manager:** Martin Burt
Secretary: Malcolm Graves, 28 Wise Lane, Mill Hill, London NW7 2RE (081 959 3825).
Ground: McMillan Stadium, Summers Lane, Finchley, London N12 (081 446 0906)
Directions: North Circular (A406) to jnt with High Road Finchley (A1000). Go north and Summers Lane is 200 yards on right.S. Tube to East Finchley Station and then 263 bus to Summers Lane.
Capacity: 2,000   **Seats:** 494   **Floodlights:** Yes   **Founded:** 1991
Colours: Blue/white/blue   **Change Colours:** White/blue/white
Previous Names: Wingate (founded 1946), Finchley (founded late 1800s) merged in 1991.
Previous Grounds: Finchley FC: Long Lane 1874-84/ Green Man 84-94/ Woodhouse Lane 94-99/ Swan & Pyramids 99-1901/ Fallow Court 01-21/ Station Meadow 21-29. Wingate: Wingate Stadium 46-75/ Brickfield Lane, Arkley 75-91.
Prev. Lges: Finchley: London 02-12 14-1523-25 30-39/ Athenian 12-14 29-30 45-73/ Isth'n 73-91. Wingate: Middx 46-52/ London 52-62/ Delphian 62-63/ Athenian 63-75/ Barnet Yth, Hendon & Dist. Sunday 75-84/ Herts 84-89.
Record Gate: 9,555; Finchley v Bishop Auckland, FA Amateur Cup QF 49-50.
Hons: Finchley: London Snr Cup, London Charity Cup, FA Amtr Cup SF, Athenian Lg 53-54 (R-up 63-64 65-66), London Lg 36-37 (R-up 35-36, Div 2 06-07(jt with Enfield), Lg Cup 34-35, Park Royal Cup 37-38). Wingate: Middx Lg(2)(R-up(1), Lg Cup), London Lg R-up(2)(Lg Cup(1)), Middx Snr Cup 74-75, FA Vase QF 74-75, Athenian Lg Div 2 69-70, Herts Co. Lg Div 1 84-85, Herts I'mediate Cup 84-85, Herts Snr Tphy 86-87, Sth Mids Lg Div 1 89-90 (Lg Cup SF 89-90), Barnet Yth Lg 75-76, Pete Morrison Cup 82-83 83-84 (R-up 79-80 84-85).

DIVISION ONE CLUBS 1992-93

AMPTHILL TOWN

Chairman: Richard Brown   **Manager:** Tony Wright/ Neil Rodney.
Secretary: Eric Turner, 34 Dunstable Street, Ampthill, Beds MK45 2JT (0525 403128).
Ground: Woburn Road, Ampthill (0525 404440)
Directions: From Ampthill Town Centre follow signs to Woburn then 1st right into Ampthill Park.
Capacity: 500   **Seats:** 100   **Cover:** Yes   **Floodlights:** No   **Founded:** 1888.
Cols: White (red side pane, yellow sleeves/red/red   **Change Colours:** Yellow/red/yellow
Hons: Sth Mids Lg 59-60 (C'ship Shield 58-59 59-60)   **Prev. Lges:** S Mids 51-65/ Utd Co's 65-91.

ASHCROFT

Chairman: Neil Ludlow   **Manager:** Steve Wyatt
Secretary: Sandra Ludlow, 7 Hillview Crescent, Luton LU2 7AA (0582 585435).
Ground: Luton Regional Sports Centre, Stopsley, Luton. (0582 585435)
Directions: A505 from Luton to Jansel House r-about, turn left, turn right at Stopsley Memorial into St Thomas Road, ground 200 yds on right hand side.
Floodlights: No   **Previous Lg:** Luton & Dist.   **Founded:** 1970
Colours: Blue/yellow/yellow   **Change Colours:** Purple/white/purple
Previous Name: Ashcroft Co-op.   **Hons:** Sth Mids Lg Div 1 91-92 (Div 1 Tphy R-up 91-92)

BEDFORD TOWN

Chairman: Mike John   **President:** Allen J Sturgess   **Manager:** Terry King
Secretary: Penny Young, 25 Wood Lane, Cotton End, Bedford MK45 3AJ (0234 740056).
Ground: Allen Park, Queens Lane, Bedford (The club may move to a ground at Shortstown soon).
Directions: On reaching Bedford from A6 or A421 follow Ampthill Road until end. Turn left into Britannia Road, right across bridge, left into Prebend Street and at end turn left across bridge into Ford End Rd. Follow into Old Ford End Rd and Park is at end of the road on right.
Nickname: Eagles   **Floodlights:** No   **Formed:** 1908   **Reformed:** 1989.
Colours: Blue/white/blue   **Change Colours:** Red/white/red
Previous Grounds: None (predecessors: London Rd/ Gasworks/ Queens Pk/ The Eyrie, Raleigh Str.).
Record Gate: 1,227 v Bedford Utd 26/12/91. (predecessors: 18,407 v Everton, FA Cup 12/2/66).
Hons: None (predecessors: Southern Lg 58-59 (Div I 69-70), Utd Co's Lg 30-31 32-33 33-34 (R-up 11-12 12-13 13-14 29-30 31-32 34-35 36-37), FA Cup 4th Rd 63-64 65-66, FA Tphy SF 74-75).

BEDFORD UNITED

Chairman: Mr John Cleverley   **Manager:** Mark Smith
Secretary: Geoff D Seagrave, 49 Whitebeam Close, Kempston, Bedford MK42 7RW (0234 270819).
Ground: Fairhill Recreation Ground, Clapham Road, Bedford. (The club club will move to a temporary ground, equipped with floodlights, clubhouse and stand, in January 1993, and then, hopefully for 1993-94, to a permanent ground in Manton Lane, quarter of a mile north of Fairhill).   **Directions:** North West Bedford, 50 yds on the left hand side after the last r-about out of Bedford on A6 Clapham/Kettering Rd
Previous Name: Printers Diemer Reynolds (til 1972)   **Floodlights:** No   **Founded:** 1957
Colours: White/blue/blue (white trim)   **Change colours:** All red

CADDINGTON

Chairman: Peter Spowage   **Manager:** Leigh Glenister
Secretary: Paul Holmes, 124 Strathmore Avenue, Luton LU1 3QN. (0582 450293)
Ground: Caddington Recreation Club, Manor Road. (0582 696053)**Directions:** On entering village turn into Manor Road (adj to shops). Proceed 500 metres: Clubhouse and ground on LH side next to Catholic Church
Floodlights: No   **Previous Lg:** Luton & Dist.   **Colours:** Red & black stripes/black/red   **Change:** All blue

CRANFIELD UNITED

Chairman: R Thompson   **Manager:** John Alder
Secretary: T E L Corkrey, Chapel Cottage, Cranfield Rd, Moulsoe, Newport Pagnell MK16 0HB (0908 618371)
Ground: Crawley Road, Cranfield, Bedford (0234 751444)
Directions: M1 jctt 13 – A5140 to Bedford, 100 yds turn left, follow signposts. Through village, turn left into Mill Rd, continue into Crawley Rd. *Ground on left at end of houses. From Bedford – A5140, right at Marston Morteyne, turn left at end. Start of village turn right, Crane Way leads into Crawley Rd. *As above.
Capacity: 2,000   **Cover:** 200   **Floodlights:** Yes   **Founded:** 1911
Colours: Green/black/black   **Change Colours:** White/green/green
Previous League: Bedford & Dist.   **Clubhouse:** Open 6 nights and weekend lunchtimes

DE HAVILLAND

Chairman: I P Colyer   **Manager:** Mike Hollis.
Secretary: Kate Higgins, 2 St Johns Court, Beaumont Ave., St Albans, Herts AL1 4TS (0727 839896).
Ground: Comet Way, Hatfield.
Directions: From south leave A1 (M) at Hatfield turn, A1001 to Birchwood r'bout, 1st exit into car park. From north leave A1 (M) at Welwyn G.C., A1001 to Birwood r'bout and 4th exit into car park.
Previous League: Herts Snr Cup. (pre-1992)   **Floodlights:** No   **Founded:**

DELCO PRODUCTS

Chairman: Paul Shepherd   **Manager:** Alec Butler.
Secretary: Terry E Owen, 29 Elm Park Close, Houghton Regis, Dunstable, Beds LU5 5PN (0582 863273).
Ground: Delco Products Sports Ground (0582 695668)   **Directions:** On A5 Trunk Rd to the North of Dunstable. Ground entrance is approximately 100yds south of traffic lights at Chalk Cutting.
Capacity: 3,000   **Seats:** Yes   **Floodlights:** No   **Founded:** 1935.
Colours: Red (white trim)/white/red   **Change Colours:** Blue (white trim)/white/blue.
Previous League: Luton & Dist.   **Prev. Names:** AC Sphinx 46-52/ AC Delco 52-85.

EMBERTON

Chairman: R L Dugdale   **Manager:** Roger Campbell.
Secretary: R L Dugdale, 9 Stone Court, West Lane, Emberton, Olney, Bucks MK46 5ND (0234 711004).
Ground: Hulton Drive, Emberton   **Directions:** Take north route from Newport Pagnell to Olney. Emberton lies before Olney. Turn left at 2nd turning into village and 1st right Hulton Drive.
Seats: No   **Cover:** No   **Floodlights:** No   **Reformed:** 1968
Programme: 28 pages with entry   **Clubhouse:** Refreshments on matchdays.
Hons: E Northants Lg 90-91 (R-up 86-87, Lg Cup 90-91), Rushden & Dist. Lg 84-85 85-86 (Lg Cup 84-85, Jnr Shield 79-80), Nth Bucks Lg Div 3 37-38, Haynes Tphy 67-68, Hamblin Cup 90-91, Stantonbury Cup SF 91-92.

FLAMSTEAD

Chairman: Mr A Morrice   **Manager:** A Lewington
Secretary: Mrs S Hayward, Greenways, Old Watling Str., St Albans, Herts (0582 841213).
Ground: Friendless Lane, Flamstead (0582 841307).
Ground Directions: From Dunstable Town Centre travel south on A5 Trunk Road towards the M1. Follow for approximately 3 miles then turn right opposite Hertfordshire Moat House Hotel. Ground and parking approximately half a mile on the corner of the first right turn.
Floodlights: No   **Colours:** White/red/white   **Change Colours:** Gold/black/gold

ICKLEFORD

Chairman: Mr R N Austin   **Manager:** E Cumberbatch
Secretary: Roger Austin, 22 St Kathrines Close, Ickleford, Hitchin, Herts SG5 3XS (0462 457811).
Ground: Ickleford Recreation Ground, Chambers Lane, Ickleford. (0462 432249)
Directions: Two miles north of Hitchin turn right off main Bedford road signposted to Arlesey. Take 2nd left, follow road around. Ground on left hand side.
Floodlights: No   **Capacity:** 2,000   **Founded:** 1918   **Enamel Badge:** £2   **Pennants:** Yes
Colours: All green   **Change Colours:** All yellow
Previous League: North Herts   **Clubhouse:** Bar & refreshments   **Programme:** 50p

LONDON COLNEY

Chairman: Mr K Hull   **Manager:** Mr S Seabrook/ Mr H Wright.
Secretary: W G Gash, 8 Whitehorse Lane, London Colney, Herts AL2 1JX (0727 823192).
Ground: Gotslandswick, London Colney (0727 22132).
Directions: From London Colney r'bout take A414 towards Watford, after layby (300yds) turn left (marked 'Sports Ground') and follow around to gates. Three miles from St Albans (BR). Buses 84 & 358.
Capacity: 500   **Cover:** Yes   **Seats:** None   **Floodlights:** No   **Founded:** 1907.
Cols: Blue & white stripes/blue/blue   **Change Colours:** Green & white hoops/white/green
Programme: No   **Previous Leagues:** Mid Herts/ Herts Co. (pre'92).
Hons: Herts Co. Lg 56-57 59-60 86-87 88-89 90-91 (Aubrey Cup 81-82), Herts Centenary Tphy 89-90, Herts I'mediate Cup 58-59 74-75 82-83, Herts Charity Shield 61-62.   **Nickname:** Blues.

POTTERS BAR CRUSADERS

Chairman: John Metselaar   **Manager:** Clive Eldridge.
Secretary: Mark Seal, 219 Ashwood Road, Potters Bar, Herts EN6 2QF (0707 44668).
Ground: Furzefield Centre, Mutton Lane, Potters Bar (0707 50764) *(Synthetic pitch).*
Directions: A1(M)/M25 to Bignalls Corner, follow signs to South Mimms, right into A111 (Mutton Lane). King George V playing fields 1 mile on the left. (Next to Furzefield Centre).
Capacity: 100+   **Floodlights:** Yes   **Founded:** 1948
Colours: All Royal blue   **Change Colours:** All white.

RISBOROUGH RANGERS

Chairman: Jeff Gelatin   **Manager:** Frank Carter
Secretary: D J Wallace, 42 Ash Rd, Princes Risborough, Bucks HP27 0BQ (08444 5179)
Ground: Windsor's, Horsenden Lane, Princes Risborough. (08444 274176)
Directions: Rear of Princes Risborough BR Station. A4010 from Aylesbury thru Princes R'borough, fork right onto A4009, left by thatched cottage, over railway bridge, immediate right ground 150 yds on right.
Floodlights: No   **Founded:** 1971   **Previous League:** Wycombe & District.
Colours: Red & white/red/white   **Change Colours:** Yellow/blue/yellow

SANDY ALBION

Chairman: Brian Faulkner   **President:** P Brown.
Secretary: Peter Francis, 6 Willow Rise, Sandy, Beds SG19 1AY. (0767 681615)
Manager: Paul Murtagh   **Assistant Manager:** Carlos Vincent.
Ground: Recreation Ground, Bedford Road, Sandy, Beds (0767 680351).
Directions: Quarter mile off A1 junction at Sandy r-about. On B1042 road Bedford to Cambridge.
Capacity: 2,000   **Floodlights:** No   **Previous Lge:** Bedford & Dist (pre'58)   **Founded:** 1909
Colours: White/black/black   **Change Colours:** Yellow/blue/blue
Programme: 40 pages, 30p
Honours: Sth Mids Lg Div 1 59-60 (Chal. Tphy 80-81, Championship Shield 66-67), Hinchinbrooke Cup 58-59 73-74 75-76, Beds Jnr Cup 19-20, Nth Beds Charity Cup 20-21 35-36 78-79 (R-up 86-87), Beds I'mediate Cup 59-60.

SHEFFORD TOWN

Chairman: A P Rowe   **Manager:** P Hayes
Secretary: J Gilmour, 61 Lucas Way, Shefford, Beds SG17 5DU (0462 812638).
Ground: Ivel Road, Shefford, Hitchin (0462 811038).
Directions: From Hitchin right at 3rd r'bout on A507 - ground 400 yds on left. From Bedford left at 3rd r'bout on A507 - ground 400 yds on left. From Ampthill right at lights, first right into Ivel Road.
Capacity: 1,000   **Floodlights:** No   **Founded:** 1948
Prev. Lges: South Mids 49-55/ Parthenon/ Utd Co's 58-62.
Cols: Blue & white stripes/blue/blue   **Change Colours:** Black & white stripes/black/black
Hons: Sth Mids Lg 53-54 54-55 83-84 (Div 1 82-83, Lg Cup 72-73).

SHENLEY & LOUGHTON

Chairman: M J Roadnight **Manager:** TBA.
Secretary: Mick J Bartlett, 21 Dalvina Place, Hodge Lea, Milton Keynes MK12 6JF (0908 312773).
Ground: Linceslade Grove, Loughton, Milton Keynes (0908 690668).
Directions: From M1 Jct 14 follow H6, Childs Way for 5 miles until V4 Watling Way (Knowlhill r-about), right to Loughton r-about, right along H5 Portway – 1st right Linceslade Grove.
Cover: Yes **Seats:** No **Floodlights:** No **Clubhouse:** Yes **Founded:** 1946.
Colours: Red/red/royal **Change Colours:** Royal/royal/red
Previous League: Nth Bucks
Hons: Sth Mids Lg Div 1 90-91 (Lg Cup R-up 90-91), Stantonbury Cup R-up 90-91 (SF 91-92).

STONY STRATFORD TOWN

Chairman: R Gustafon **Manager:** Perry Mercer
Secretary: M J Barber, 26 Boundary Crescen, Stony Stratford, Milton Keynes MK11 1DF (0908 567930).
Ground: Sports Ground, Ostlers Lane, Stony Stratford (0908 562267)
Directions: From Dunstable old A5, Watling Street, on approaching Bletchley continue on A5 loop road (Hinkley) to end of dual c'way to A422/A508 r'bout. First exit thru lights, 2nd right into Ostlers Lane. From M1 jct 13 pick up A421 and join A5 (Hinkley) and proceed as above.
Capacity: 500+ **Floodlights:** No **Founded:** 1953 **Previous League:** North Bucks
Colours: Blue/navy/navy **Change Colours:** Red/black/navy
Programme: £1 with entry **Honours:** Sth Mids Lg R-up 70-71 71-72

TODDINGTON ROVERS

Chairman: Hugh Geddes **Manager:** Steve Loasby
Secretary: Tony H Simmonds, 5 Manor Road, Toddington, Nr Dunstable, Beds LU5 6AH (05255 2786).
Ground: Recreation Ground, Luton Road, Toddington, Nr Dunstable, Beds.
Directions: Toddington High Street A5120 Ampthill to Dunstable, off this road up one-way-street to Luton. Ground 150 yds on left.
Floodlights: No **Founded:** 1894 **Previous League:** Luton & Dist.
Colours: Black & white stripes/black with white trim/black with white trim
Change Colours: Red & black stripes/black/red with black trim

TRING ATHLETIC

Chairman: Tony Pace **Manager:** Michael Eldridge
Secretary: Ralph Griffiths, 42 Bedgrove, Aylesbury, Bucks HP21 7BD (0296 26425).
Ground & Directions: As Tring Town FC (see page 386).
Founded: 1958 **Previous League:** West Herts.
Colours: Red & black stripes/black/black **Change Colours:** Green/white/green

WALDEN RANGERS

Chairman: Mr M Garrett **Manager:** Mr C Parker
Secretary: Mr A Curran, 150 Telscombe Way, Stopsley, Luton, Beds LU2 8Qr (0582 415160).
Ground: Breachwood Green Recreation Ground (0438 833332).
Directions: From Luton Airport Gates (away from Vauxhall direction) take country road to Breachwood Green (2 miles) from Hitchin. On A602, take country road to Preston (6 miles to Breachwood Green).
Floodlights: No **Founded:** 1966
Colours: Blue/white/blue **Change Colours:** Red/white/red

WINSLOW UNITED

Chairman: J Robins **Manager:** M Foster
Secretary: David F Ward, 29 Avenue Rd, Winslow, Buckingham MK18 3DH (0296 713202).
Ground: Winslow Recreation Ground, Elmfields Gate, Winslow (0296 713057)
Directions: In Winslow High Street turn into Emeralds Gate. Ground opposite car park.
Capacity: 2,000 **Seats:** 25 **Cover:** 100 **Floodlights:** Yes **Founded:** 1891.
Colours: Yellow/blue/blue **Change Colours:** Red/black/black
Hons: S Mids Lg Div 1 74-75. **Record Gate:** 720 v Aylesbury Utd, Berks & Bucks Snr Cup.

Bedford Town, who had a happy first season in senior football following their reformation. Photo - Gavin Ellis.

BEAZER HOMES LEAGUE

President: G.E. Templeman.

Chairman: D.S.R. Gillard.

Hon. Secretary: D.J. Strudwick,

11 Welland Close, Durrington, Worthing, West Sussex BN13 3NR (0903 267788).

SECRETARY'S REPORT

£110,000 represented record gate receipts for Brighton & Hove Albion when Beazer Homes League Club Crawley Town visited the Goldstone Ground for an F.A. Cup Third Round Tie on the 4th January 1992.

Dover Athletic and Bromsgrove Rovers attracted 4035 for a Premier Division match: the highest League attendance since 1982 when 5,432, watched Bedworth and Nuneaton.

Three former Beazer League players appeared in the F.A. Cup Semi-Finals.

If any more evidence is required to illustrate the impact the Beazer Homes League has had on the country's soccer scene this year, then Sean Flynn left Halesown Town for Coventry City on 27th November, scored on his debut on Boxing Day and is ever present in the Sky Blue First Division side for the remainder of the season. Redditch United's David Farrell moved to Aston Villa for £40,000 and Moor Green sold Dave Busst to Coventry City and Ian Taylor to Port Vale for substantial fees, to name just a few.

The above observations serve as just a few of the cherries on another Beazer season laced with rich cream.

Whilst Cup success is always glamorous, pride of place must be given to the League Champions. A marathon 42 match League programme surely establishes the best team in the Competition. Certainly many of Bromsgrove Rovers' adversaries will confirm that this season proved that the best team in the League will finish top. But a look at the table on the 30th November, and your money would not have been on Bromsgrove. Rovers had collected just 16 points from their opening twelve matches, winning only four league games. The remaining 30 games, however, provided 23 victories and only two more defeats. And in a run-in that saw Bromsgrove lead the table, for the first time, on the penultimate Saturday, the macth with their nearest rivals Dover attracted a record 4,000 plus gate at the Crabble.

Apart from these two Championship Challengers, only three other Clubs topped the table throughout the season. Cambridge City and V.S. Rugby had it all their own way up to Christmas. Bashley then burst onto the scene for the first seven weeks of the new year. V.S. Rugby were never far away, however, and looked to be firm favourites as the season moved towards the 'bell'. Dover overtook them in the final straight, only to be pipped at the post. The 1990 Champions finished as runners-up.

At the foot of the table, Gravesend received an early waring that it was going to be a long season with 9-0 and 8-2 defeats at the hands of Trowbridge Town and Halesowen Town. Fisher suffered relegation for the second consecutive season and Poole Town drop back into the Southern Division after just two campaigns in the top flight. The fourth demotion spot was 'up for grabs' until the final week of the season when Wealdstone surprised everyone by falling into the bottom four. After a disastrous start to the season, Burton Albion seemed to be relegation certainties. With only two wins to their credit, Albion were three points adrift at the bottom of the table on the 21st December. A change of manager produced a change of form to championship winning proportions. Thirteen wins in the second half os the season lifted Burton to the fringe of the prize money.

The Southern Division Championship was much more clear cut. Hastings Town were the first club to be crowned having led the Southern Division section for all but three weeks of the campaign. Weymouth and Hythe Town shared the lead at the beginning of the season. And whilst Hythe's challenge fell away. Weymouth stayed 'in the frame' throughout and clinched the runners-up spot on the final day of the season. Just as the 'Terras' appeared to have thrown it all away by dropping two points to already relegated Gosport and drawing with Salisbury over Easter, the freshmen from Havant lost at home to Buckingham five days later to hand the initiative back to Weymouth. In front of 2,167 spectators on the final day, Weymouth clinched the silver medals with a 4-1 victory over Erith & Belvedere. Nobody seriously threatened Peter Silett's men from Hastings, however, who took off from the Pilot Field and landed the championship with 13 points to spare.

Bromsgrove Rovers, Premier Division Champions 1991-92. Back Row (L-R): J.Hanks (Kit Man), S.Pinfield (Trainer), L.Taliton (Physio), S.Cooper, C.Hanks, M.Crisp, P.Wardle, S.Cooksey, R.Moran, P.Masefield, S.Scott, P.Sunners (Goalkeeper trainer), D.Griffiths (Asst.Man.) B.Hewings (Secretary). Front Row: T.Daly, M.O'Connor, P.Webb, S.Brighton, K.Richardson (team captain), R.Hope (Manager), S.Burgher, J.Skelding, S.Omeara, M.Whitehouse. Trophies: League Championship Cup, League Championship Shield and Worcestershire Senior Cup.

In the Midland Division another team of new boys fared even better than Havant in the South. Despite Newport A.F.C. and Sutton Coldfield having an early flirtation with the leadership, Solihull Borough won the Championship, at their first attempt, with a six point cushion. Their only real threat came from Hednesford Town who, I feel sure, would have sustained their challenge to the end had it not been for an astonishing 6-1 defeat at the hands of the Borough on the 14th March. Notwithstanding that result, though, the Pitmen finished 17 points clear of Sutton Coldfield and will join Solihull Borough and their contemporaries from the South in next year's Premier.

By the very nature of a knock-out tournament, Cup glory is always shorter lived. But the Cup never fails to capture the imagination. With only four clubs reaching the First Round Proper of this year's F.A. Cup, it was not the best of seasons for our League, especially considering that two of the clubs were exempt until the final qualifier. Notwithstanding that, the final four performed exceedingly well. Bournemouth needed two penalties in their 3-1 defeat of a Bromsgrove side still searching for their best form. Halesowen and Atherstone took Farnborough and Hereford to replays but Crawley crushed the 'Cobblers' from Northampton 4-2 with the help of a brace from Craig Whitington, the son of the former Chelsea and Brighton centre-forward. (At this point it is pleasing to note that ground improvements carried out at Town Mead last season in order to attain the League's grading criteria gave John Maggs' club with the platform to effect further work and stage this important Cup tie). The game attracted a gate of 3,370 which followed an attendance of 3,427 for the Fourth Qualifying Round Replay with local rivals Horsham. Neither of these games could have been accommodated had not the Premier Division Ground Grading Criteria already been achieved).

In Round Two Crawley won at Hayes 2-0, with a pair from Tim Hulme, a summer signing from Hythe, to reach the Third Round for the first time in the club's history. Their reward could not have been better, for Crawley or their opponents, Brighton & Hove Albion. I'm Sussex born and bred. Never have I known a football match to generate such excitement in the county. The game was billed as the 'Sussex F.A. Cup Final' and with the Albion struggling at the foot of Division II expectations for the 'New Towners' was high, perhaps too high. On the day Albion proved far too strong in the final third of the field and won 5-0. The match attracted the Seagulls' best gate for four years (4,000 more than Albions' Cup Replay with Liverpool two years previous) and produced the Goldstone's record receipts.

Just for the record 'Beazer' participation in the F.A. Cup did not end in the Third Round. Three former Beazer League players featured in the Semi-Final, with one going a stage further. Portsmouth's Andy Awford and Guy Whittingham previously played for Worcester City and Waterlooville, repectively, and Sunderland's Paul Hardyman played for Fareham.

The F.A. Trophy once again proved to be an achilles heel for Beazer clubs. With twelve having reached the First Round, prospects for success were bright. Alas, only Bashley reached Round Two where they lost at home to a formidable Kettering outfit.

With four clubs in the last 16 of the F.A. Vase a trip to Wembley seemed a real possibility. Strong contenders, Hastings and Sittingbourne, fell at the previous hurdle. Round Five saw Hythe, Newport I.O.W. and Yate all depart leaving Sudbury to arrest the challenge of the West Midlands Police in Round Six. The prospect of facing Guiseley in the Semi-Final was daunting but with former International Brian Talbot in the Sudbury line-up, having moved back to his native Suffolk, the holders were held on their own ground in the first leg 2-2. Sadly, two goals in the last 20 minutes of the second leg dashed Sudbury's hopes of a second Wembley visit in three years. Their Semi-Final attendance (2,987) was, however, the largest of the round. Trowbridge Town achieved this feat on behalf of the Beazer League last season.

Cup success was, though, achieved by Dover Athletic and, to a large degree too, by Hednesford Town. Having won the Premier Inter League Cup last year, Dover carried off the Barclays Commercial Services Cup this season.

Dorchester held Dover to a single goal at the Crabble Ground and, therefore, stood a realistic chance in their home tie, particularly as Dover had seen their title aspirations disappear at Halesowen just three days earlier. Athletic, though, were not suffering from any hangover from that disappointment and notched three second half goals to bag the silverware.

Hednesford Town didn't actually win a Cup but they did enjoy the incredible experience of playing at Cardiff Arms Park, Wales' National Stadium in the Welsh Cup Final against Cardiff City. In front of a 10,000 crowd, most of whom were of course supporting the home team, the Pitmen from England really gave their Welsh rivlas a fright. In the end, a well balanced match was turned in favour of the Football League side by a 59th minute goal by Man of the Match, Carl Dale.

Whilst on the subject of football in Wales, it would be wrong, in a factual report, to overlook the situation concerning the eight 'Non Football League' clubs in the Principality who currently play in the English Pyramid. The formation of the proposed new League of Wales was not initially designed to prevent these Clubs from continuing their present chosen existence. Assurances had been given that the statusquo would prevail if these clubs did not wish to join the new league. However, as time went on, it appeared evident that they were expected to abandon their status and achievements in English Competitions and subsequently, permission to play in England was withdrawn from their Parent Association, the Football Association of Wales. Upon Appeal, Merthyr Tydfil were given the same privileges extended to Cardiff, Swansea and Wrexham. At the time of writing, of the remaining seven, three have decided to join the League of Wales, four including Barry Town and Newport A.F.C. have 'moved house' to English grounds.

The objective of the Welsh F.A. to have an autonomous National League, is clearly understandable and appreciated. If the proposition was so attractive and viable, in the eyes of the clubs, then I feel sure that they would wish to play in their own National Competition. At present, it would appear that the viability of the project does not suit every case. And that also applies to Clubs currently playing in Welsh Leagues. In the meantime, and until the benfits are recognised, why can't these clubs continue to exercise their freedom of choice? After all, none of them are seeking to cause disruption by moving Leagues. They simply wish to be alone where they are, and to play in the League of their choice, like Cardiff, Merthyr, Sawnsea and Wrexham.

So, although there will be no movement from Barry Town and Newport A.F.C., as was once feared, the Competition will be losing Canterbury City, and Gosport Borough who have all been relegated to Feeder Competitions. We hope that you will all be 'in the frame' for promotion at the end of the next season. There are only two relegations this season, because only three Feeder Clubs qualified for promotion. All three are Champion Clubs, however, so the Competition will be enhanced by Evesham United, Gresley Rovers, and Weston-Super-Mare. Welcome to the Beazer Homes League.

We welcome back into the fold, Cheltenham Town, from the Football Conference. We hope that our League will once again provide you with the vehicle for promotion to higher spheres. For this season that honour goes to Bromsgrove Rovers. Bobby Hope, in his second spell as Manager at the Victoria ground, deserves his success. Good luck Rovers.

To conclude this report, on behalf of everyone connected with the League, I extend my most sincere thanks to our Sponsors. Beazer Homes have now completed five years of their Association with the Southern League. One further year exists on the present Agreement and I am delighted to report that the Company has already committed itself to a further three years. The brilliant support from this magnificent Company is greatly appreciated by everyone connected with the League.

Barclays Commercial Services Limited, who stepped in at the eleventh hour last year, has already agreed to sponsor the League's Challenge Cup again next season. And Sportique has completed the hat-trick, by assuring the League of its support of the Manager of the Month Awards once again. Thank you, everyone. I look forward to working with you again next year.

Dennis Strudwick.

BARCLAYS COMMERCIAL SERVICES CUP 1991-92

PRELIMINARY ROUND FIRST LEG

Tuesday 3rd September 1991   **Res Att**
Grantham T. v Leicester Utd   1-2 1035
Waitt 40   *Liquorish 81 84*

Newport IOW v Poole Town   3-3 363
Greening 46,Deacon 52 74   Funnell 11 45,Platt 75

PRELIMINARY ROUND SECOND LEG

Wednesday 11th September 1991
Leicester Utd v Grantham Town   1-3 195
Rider 59(og)   *Randall 14(og),*
                        Whitehurst 19(og),Rolph 62

Poole Town v Newport IOW   1-5 149
Morley 51   *Hutton 9,Deacon 20,*
                        Greening 29 67,Ritchie 84

FIRST ROUND FIRST LEG

Monday 7th October 1991
Gosport Borough v Fareham Town 0-1 209
                        Camp 84(og)

Havant Town v Weymouth   0-0 214
Tuesday 8th October 1991
Alvechurch v Redditch United   1-2 180
Rogers 17(og)   *Stanton 47,P Joinson 82*

Ashford Town v Fisher Athletic   3-0 276
Ovard 32(p),Pearson 59,Stanton 65

Braintree Town v Cambridge City   2-2 296
Newbury 38,Coghlan 89   Grogan 36,Lockhart 44

Bridgnorth Town v Dudley Town   4-2 110
Meredith 16 44,   Baker 67,Horne 76
Balshaw 24,Rich 28

Bromsgrove Rvrs v Worcester City   3-3 597
O'Meara 46,   Robinson 1,Smith 45,
Wardle 52,Webb 55   Kearns 89

Buckingham Town v Burnham   3-2 94
Jenkins 46,Blencowe 46,   Argrave 14,
Sherlock 66   Cook 70

Crawley Town v Hythe Town   3-2 344
Hulme 44 88,   Warrilow 49,
Gallagher 72   Coldwell 82

Dartford v Gravesend & N'fleet   3-0 637
Leslie 25,Prutton 71,Quail 89

Dover Athletic v Sittingbourne   2-0 607
Blewden 16,Rogers 90

King's Lynn v Sudbury Town   3-4 342
O'Keefe 42,McNally 83   Day 13,Gunn 16,
Gallagher 82(p)   Parnell 29 75

Margate v Erith & Belvedere   3-2 173
Kitchen 34,Brewer 36,   Bowey 12,
Lewis 38   Cappuccio 80

Moor Green v Stourbridge   2-0 169
Taylor 57 70

Newport AFC v Barry Town   0-2 652
                    Giles 67(p),Williams 72

Newport IOW v Dorchester Town   1-2 316
Ritchie 33   Green 47,Diaz 73

R.C. Warwick v Hednesford Town   1-2 117
Deeley 22   Burr 23,Walsh 45

Stroud v Yate Town   2-3 106
Hamilton 40,   Grimshaw 55 75,
Bayliss 87   Davis 82

Tamworth v Hinckley Town   4-1 1010
Smith 13 39(p),Perry 35,Parker 63   Massey 33

Trowbridge Town v Gloucester City 1-0 478
Harris 68

Waterlooville v Bashley   4-4 108
Harvey 35 80,   Baird 30,Cole 48(og),
Moran 40,Boyce 88   Elley 55(og),Lovell 85

Witney Town v Dunstable   0-1 119
                        Campbell 42

Wednesday 9th October 1991
Atherstone Utd v Grantham Town   0-0 287

***denotes extra time played**

Canterbury City v Hastings Town   2-5 127
Bunce 33,   White 22(p),Kewley 26,
Brazil 83   Miles 27 61,Plews 58(og)

Salisbury v Andover   1-0 227
Chalk 14

Solihull Borough v Bedworth Utd   0-0 70

Sutton Coldfield T. v Burton Albion 0-0 198

V.S. Rugby v Rushden Town   3-1 432
Boyland 17,Jones 35,Fitzpatrick 90   Belfon 84

Wealdstone v Baldock Town   2-0 191
Payne 51,Donnellan 76

Monday 14th October 1991
Chelmsford City v Bury Town   1-0 398
Butler 83(p)

Monday 21st October 1991
Nuneaton Borough v Corby Town   1-1 477
Straw 89   Russell 38

Tuesday 22nd October 1991
Bilston Town v Halesowen Town   3-2 262
Richards 1,Skidmore 42,Jones 45   Harrison 58 75

FIRST ROUND SECOND LEG

Tuesday 29th October 1991
Gloucester City v Trowbridge Town 2-0 465
Lester 50(og),Eaton 64

Wednesday 30th October 1991
Yate Town v Stroud   1-3 252
Smith 37   Peacey 40,Darlaston 43,Bayliss 72

Monday 4th November 1991
Barry Town v Newport AFC   1-2 337
Giles 70   Bray 77,Lillygreen 87

Bashley v Waterlooville   0-2 152
                        Burns 63(p),Burnside 64

Fisher Athletic v Ashford Town   1-0 120
Quinn 8

Hednesford T. v R.C. Warwick   3-2* 342
Aldridge 7,   Deeley 30,
O'Connor 95,100   Wootton 65

Worcester City v Bromsgrove Rovers 1-4 620
Robinson 57   Cooper 9 73,Stott 20,Daley 79

Tuesday 5th November
Andover v Salisbury   0-1 264
                        Pearson 90(p)

Baldock Town v Wealdstone   0-5 210
Hippolyte 10 47,Brown 11,Goyette 60,Pearson 70

Bedworth Utd v Soliull Borough   1-3 191
Hardwick 49   Carter 19,Hawker 66,Wright 70

Erith & Belvedere v Margate   2-0 85
Mehmet(p),Bartley 85

Grantham Town v Atherstone Utd   3-0 302
Cook 6 74,Hurst 44

Gravesend & N'fleet v Dartford   3-1 556
Thomas 19,Flint 56,Fordred 58   Sawyer 31

Halesowen Town v Bilston Town   2-0 718
Bennett 51 68

Hastings T. v Canterbury City   1-2 197
Willard 43   Neat 32,Holmes 35

Redditch Utd v Alvechurch   1-3* 158
Williams 44   Eastoe 1,Richardson 75,Hallam 117(p)

Rushden Town v V.S. Rugby   1-4 203
Jeffrey 46(p)   Rosegreen 34 80,Boyland 59 71

Sittingbourne v Dover Athletic   0-2 430
                        Rogers 45,Ambrose 78

Sudbury Town v King's Lynn   3-1 274
Parnell 30 55,Coe 63   Gallagher 40

Wednesday 6th November 1991
Burnham v Buckingham Town   2-3 91
Jarvis 33,   Jenkins 8,
Chandler 47   Sherlock 55 58

Burton Albion v Sutton Coldfield   **Res Att** 1-0* 208
Davis 117

Bury Town v Chelmsford City   1-0 171
Balls 63   *(Chelmsford 5-3 pens)*

Cambridge City v Braintree Town   5-0 114
Tovey 1,Ryan 23 38,Spriggs 81,Wilkin 90

Corby Town v Nuneaton Borough   2-0 122
Archer 83,Diver 89

Dorchester Town v Newport IOW   5-1 187
Masters 24,Manson 28,   *Ritchie 34(p)*
Morrell 42,Diaz 47 85(p)

Dudley Town v Bridgnorth Town   3-0 56
Waring 7,Baker 30,Chambers 81

Dunstable v Witney Town   3-1 36
Cody 11,Wheeler 68,Mullins 78   *Carlisle 82*

Fareham Town v Gosport Borough   1-1 93
Swanson 90   *Rowley 33*

Hythe Town v Crawley Town   1-2 94
Carey 80   *Hulme 36,Cooper 62*

Weymouth v Havant Town   0-0 264
(Weymouth won 4-2 on penalties)

Thursday 7th November 1991
Hinckley Town v Tamworth   0-3 169
Parker 24,Green 51,Morris 82

Tuesday 12th November 1991
Stourbridge v Moor Green   0-1 201
Busst 43

SECOND ROUND FIRST LEG

Monday 25th November 1991
Barry Town v Gloucester City   1-1 239
Summers 30   *Eaton 86*

Havant Town v Fareham Town   2-1 199
Webbe 40,de Gordon 90   *Cowell 9*

Tuesday 26th November
Burton Albion v Alvechurch   2-1 238
Bottomley 20,Gee 63   *Richardson 35*

Erith & Belvedere v Dartford   0-1 400
Palmer 88(og)

Moor Green v Bromsgrove Rovers   0-0 334

Stroud v Dorchester Town   1-2 114
Darlaston 13   *Powell 40,Diaz 75*

Wednesday 27th November 1991
Buckingham Town v Chelmsford   0-1 109
Jones 30

Corby Town v Grantham Town   1-3 147
Keeble 79   *Taylor 12,Hurst 20,Marsden 72*

Dunstable v Wealdstone   2-1 186
Gyalog 22,Revel 73   *Hippolyte 88*

Tuesday 3rd December 1991
Crawley Town v Ashford Town   1-1 315
Davis 65   *McRobert 75*

V.S. Rugby v Tamworth   2-1 560
Bradder 1(p),Fitzpatrick 84   *Morris 12*

Wednesday 4th December 1991
Sudbury Town v Cambridge City   1-2 309
Ketley 14   *Grogan 45,Thorpe 86(og)*

Tuesday 10th December 1991
Waterlooville v Salisbury   1-0 90
(abandoned (frozen pitch) after 31 minutes)

Tuesday 17th December 1991
Dover Athletic v Hastings Town   0-0 393

Wednesday 18th October 1991
Solihull Borough v Dudley Town   1-2 22
Burton 55   *L Joinson 25,Wareing 65*

Monday 23rd December 1991
Hednesford Town v Halesowen   3-0 430
Walsh 52,Burr 53,O'Connor 84

Tuesday 14th January 1992
Waterlooville v Salisbury   0-2 64
Smith 47 52

*denotes extra time played

SECOND ROUND SECOND LEG

Monday 9th December 1991
Chelmsford City v Buckingham   1-1* 283
Lee 109   *Jenkins 11*

Tuesday 10th December
Dartford v Erith & Belvedere   4-0 243
Sherringham 15,Bensted 55,Prutton 40 86

Dorchester Town v Stroud   6-0 238
Diaz 70 88,Green 72 83,Manson 79,de Souza 89

Fareham Town v Havant Town   1-2 126
Hewitt 90   *Bailey 43(og),Ball 81*

Monday 16th December 1991
Wealdstone v Dunstable   4-1* 155
Payne 67,97,   *Horgan 90(p)*
Browne 85(p),Pearson 114

Tuesday 17th December
Alvechurch v Burton Albion   2-4 120
Richardson 44,   *Elliott 60,Jones 65 85,*
Hart 72   *Kurila 89*

Gloucester City v Barry Town   2-0 349
Talboys 11,Meacham 87(p)

Grantham Town v Corby Town   2-3* 237
Hurst 28 98   *Murphy 7 57(p),Edwards 45*

Tamworth v V.S. Rugby   1-5 679
Gordon 78   *Coe 10 69,Crawley 58,Fitzpatrick 61 74*

Wednesday 18th December 1991
Cambridge City v Sudbury Town   4-0 90
Wilkin 19 57,Lockhart 65,Grogan 72

Tuesday 7th January 1992
Ashford Town v Crawley Town   6-0 356
Stanton 30 75,Carlton 43 74,Ovard 56,Brignall 88

Bromsgrove Rovers v Moor Green   5-0 647
O'Connor 5 38,Crisp 30 61,O'Meara 47

Halesowen T. v Hednesford Town   1-4 519
Goodall 47   *O'Connor 79 87,Knight 86 89*

Hastings Town v Dover Athletic   1-1 465
Blondrage 59 Ambrose 54 (Dover win; away goals)

Tuesday 14th January 1992
Dudley Town v Solihull Borough   0-4 117
Pinner 19,Canning 38,Tuohy 71,Hawker 77

Wednesday 29th January 1992
Salisbury v Waterlooville   3-1 107
Chalk 30,Smith 73 75   *Sorrell 82*

THIRD ROUND FIRST LEG

Monday 13th January 1992
Havant Town v Dorchester Town   0-1 168
Diaz 24

Wednesday 15th January 1992
V.S. Rugby v Grantham Town   1-1 232
Rosegreen 11   *Whitehurst 49*

Tuesday 21st January 1992
Bromsgrove R. v Hednesford Town   1-1 603
Hanks 41   *Burr 50*

Monday 27th January
Chelmsford City v Ashford Town   2-0 517
Den. Greene 3 47

Tuesday 28th January 1992
Dover Athletic v Dartford   1-1 488
Little 26(p)   *Hennessey 52*

Wealdstone v Cambridge City   1-1 121
Donnellan 88   *Suddery 83*

Wednesday 29th January 1992
Solihull Borough v Burton Albion   0-2 77
Redfern 29,Haycock 84

Wednesday 5th February 1992
Salisbury v Gloucester City   1-2 216
Smith 34   *Penny 13,Townsend 45*

THIRD ROUND SECOND LEG

Tuesday 28th January 1992
Dorchester Town v Havant Town   2-1 323
Lovell 16,Flowers 40(og)   *De Gordon 4*

*denotes extra time played   **Res Att**

Monday 3rd February 1992

Hednesford v Bromsgrove R.   0-1 598
O'Connor 20

Tuesday 4th February 1992

Ashford Town v Chelmsford City   1-1 309
Crabbe 37   *Brown 14*

Burton Albion v Solihull Bor.   1-1 326
Gocan 16   *Tuohy 69*

Cambridge City v Wealdstone   2-1 216
Suddery 43 57   *Cordice 82*

Dartford v Dover Athletic   0-2 484
Malcolm 52,Bartlett 86

Grantham Town v V.S. Rugby   2-1 297
Whitehurst 67,Marsden 77   *Fitzpatrick 4*

Tuesday 11th February 1992

Dorchester v Havant *(replayed)* 2-2 233
Manson 2,Diaz 86   *Webb 28,Webbe 39*

Gloucester City v Salisbury   0-2 382
Pearson 24,Smith 33

QUARTER-FINALS FIRST LEG

Thursday 11th February 1992

Burton Albion v Bromsgrove   0-6 395
Crisp 22 87,Scott 67,Hanks 80 85 90(p)

Wednesday 12th February 1992

Cambridge City v Grantham Town 5-0 232
Low 4,Beattie 45,Ryan 47 85,Comfort 72

Wednesday 19th February 1992

Salisbury v Dorchester Town   0-1 244
Coates 87

Tuesday 25th February 1992

Dover Ath. v Chelmsford City   3-2 666
Rogers 22,Bartlett 73,Dyer 87 *Butler 9(p),Rolfe 88*

QUARTER-FINALS SECOND LEG

Tuesday 25th February 1992

Bromsgrove R. v Burton Albion 3-0 600
Webb 81,Crisp 26,Hanks 33

Dorchester Town v Salisbury   2-0 450
Green 63,Masters 82

Grantham T. v Cambridge City 1-2 257
Dorset 88   *Grogan 56,Lockhart 71*

Monday 2nd March 1992

Chelmsford v Dover Athletic   0-2 814
Jackson 24,Little 69(p)

SEMI-FINALS SECOND LEG

Tuesday 10th March 1992

Dorchester T. v Bromsgrove Rovers 4-1 359
Green 8,Manson 12,Diaz 47,Masters 50 *Hanks 27*

Wednesday 11th March 1992

Cambridge City v Dover Athletic 3-4 326
Grogan 20,Lockhart 71(p),Rogers 28,Malcolm 30,
Shelford 75   *Dyer 66,Jackson 87*

SEMI-FINALS SECOND LEG

Tuesday 24th March 1992

Bromsgrove Rvrs v Dorchester Town 2-1 689
Hanks 51 83   *Manson 79*

Dover Athletic v Cambridge City 2-0 541
Rogers 24 81

FINAL FIRST LEG

Tuesday 14th April 1992

Dover Athletic v Dorchester Town 1-0 906
Dyer 64   *Hippolyte 88*

FINAL SECOND LEG

Tuesday 28th April 1992

Dorchester Town v Dover Athletic 0-3 1151
Blewden 53,Rogers 68 79

Dover Athletic celebrate after winning the Barclays Commercial Services Cup with a 3-0 victory over Dorchester Town at the Avenue Stadium.

BEAZER HOMES LEAGUE ATTENDANCES 1991-92

PREMIER DIVISION ATTENDANCE CHART 1991-92

HOME TEAM	1	2	3	4	5	6	7	8	9	10	11	12	13	14	15	16	17	18	19	20	21	22
1. Atherstone U	*	304	527	440	239	264	692	298	275	256	362	156	230	326	495	376	278	314	545	301	206	301
2. Bashley	323	*	326	405	376	283	202	754	407	224	548	264	496	403	264	224	653	545	425	248	363	341
3. Bromsgrove	639	1656	*	484	603	717	564	660	806	1224	552	538	744	625	1765	867	1117	797	554	668	768	1279
4. Burton Alb.	575	768	692	*	621	594	708	642	545	637	571	429	685	943	692	574	482	706	791	595	454	541
5. Cambridge C	221	345	351	326	*	337	274	312	325	271	659	332	390	342	304	248	207	310	518	264	317	270
6. Chelmsford C	854	503	537	719	752	*	525	622	511	635	801	827	567	522	575	799	592	417	746	512	796	689
7. Corby Town	296	295	360	334	327	283	*	289	244	294	296	603	246	234	232	446	543	267	472	150	480	361
8. Crawley T.	617	424	466	431	505	511	421	*	687	379	611	606	517	463	438	475	330	453	523	677	516	418
9. Dartford	507	583	601	569	718	501	542	647	*	284	1407	406	412	1152	524	514	443	460	610	644	525	605
10. Dorchester T	579	953	622	587	401	737	468	438	480	*	562	752	1049	509	465	667	640	576	655	746	800	401
11. Dover Ath.	1087	1795	4035	1208	1093	1216	1249	901	1624	1252	*	1544	930	1441	854	1323	943	1114	1666	1024	1212	1188
12. Fisher Ath.	181	317	195	180	214	326	207	228	514	265	507	*	207	422	131	371	213	151	363	218	371	210
13. Gloucester	411	458	875	337	694	650	743	328	420	353	662	810	*	553	796	585	749	549	543	574	779	483
14. Gravesend	495	476	423	499	402	768	533	448	836	455	923	435	430	*	337	495	453	493	548	452	502	523
15. Halesowen	672	1015	1330	1112	580	713	717	914	1002	686	951	782	680	666	*	800	739	696	1276	739	1047	908
16. Moor Green	276	332	486	538	254	249	241	374	327	271	418	341	453	342	685	*	318	302	518	250	282	458
17. Poole Town	251	604	242	181	135	228	155	203	166	585	172	169	153	137	182	127	*	323	229	224	179	220
18. Trowbridge	434	878	540	530	766	404	546	266	719	516	594	310	443	448	456	515	509	*	719	556	618	498
19. V.S. Rugby	923	836	813	719	753	414	476	481	766	416	998	472	355	599	485	546	749	554	*	443	678	674
20. Waterlooville	254	236	241	114	220	210	196	245	134	153	250	294	252	125	143	174	265	256	217	*	266	224
21. Wealdstone	324	347	422	373	431	502	407	453	510	311	634	546	489	429	607	456	427	412	324	353	*	435
22. Worcester C.	756	839	2438	664	757	660	714	670	514	718	886	647	1103	893	1366	873	567	880	1215	561	680	*

MIDLAND DIVISION ATTENDANCE CHART 1991-92

HOME TEAM	1	2	3	4	5	6	7	8	9	10	11	12	13	14	15	16	17	18	19	20	21	22
1. Alvechurch	*	220	125	95	94	180	115	220	201	125	78	185	245	214	269	69	174	208	75	112	325	87
2. Barry Town	222	*	257	238	178	212	341	402	240	236	187	924	248	256	295	218	231	251	207	311	208	261
3. Bedworth U	193	258	*	221	169	259	235	220	188	222	187	338	1111	250	211	173	238	223	166	282	453	301
4. Bilston T.	124	107	125	*	153	118	143	420	139	106	82	255	228	121	135	115	131	185	93	145	214	107
5. Bridgenorth	135	115	100	125	*	118	165	320	122	115	101	225	225	95	150	125	175	135	102	112	405	165
6. Dudley T.	161	136	136	254	147	*	160	326	182	119	121	362	326	230	132	420	157	272	167	206	373	162
7. Grantham T.	208	310	273	198	379	322	*	281	291	420	254	992	382	386	314	391	404	252	359	265	425	337
8. Hednesford T	470	540	471	439	546	516	436	*	594	495	464	793	783	704	322	567	664	441	429	697	791	488
9. Hinkley T.	80	93	143	95	85	55	97	103	*	100	230	156	560	94	94	184	105	146	94	79	403	225
10. Kings Lynn	352	371	237	372	263	438	305	296	176	*	245	305	295	291	363	446	483	302	247	243	526	225
11. Leicester Utd	91	225	289	108	97	120	256	175	211	309	*	228	477	193	39	100	71	93	188	117	335	106
12. Newport AFC	1027	1051	829	1076	504	504	721	508	470	470	1071	*	653	708	511	612	496	705	608	697	485	725
13. Nuneaton B.	796	509	829	473	549	565	804	955	575	456	617	583	*	561	606	637	715	593	628	527	972	605
14. R.C.Warwick	90	107	110	66	73	85	73	144	85	72	135	191	363	*	103	83	110	110	80	275	111	
15. Redditch Utd	382	126	149	114	146	147	135	201	223	102	151	423	320	142	*	132	242	137	171	109	322	164
16. Rushden T.	163	198	234	155	219	138	208	235	201	312	164	397	410	203	145	*	259	183	182	212	326	172
17. Solihull B.	245	216	125	135	104	152	219	651	114	184	314	268	139	201	174	*	211	106	224	520	125	
18. Stourbridge	363	248	204	265	290	407	202	355	136	219	176	337	332	197	216	188	240	*	201	162	338	272
19. Stroud	69	176	63	74	145	67	110	176	96	82	68	703	190	113	72	111	138	94	*	109	329	238
20. Sutton C.	69	169	205	96	104	234	356	132	32	142	349	233	119	146	134	212	176	115		*	705	156
21. Tamworth	612	704	1089	693	532	714	504	933	943	785	509	746	1314	807	858	829	879	632	647	828	*	741
22. Yate Town	213	407		276	148	143	170	260	259	280	225	363	266	201	215	207	248	345	361	163	278	*

SOUTHERN DIVISION ATTENDANCE CHART 1991-92

HOME TEAM	1	2	3	4	5	6	7	8	9	10	11	12	13	14	15	16	17	18	19	20	21	22
1. Andover	*	156	85	212	187	271	166	112	156	184	123	158	245	111	93	192	131	363	239	146	274	204
2. Ashford T.	245	*	301	304	353	217	311	263	253	211	175	275	478	217	559	239	223	393	403	301	216	243
3. Baldock T.	212	317	*	207	273	183	305	157	257	211	197	272	287	212	205	228	219	239	327	210	237	217
4. Braintree T.	104	214	208	*	302	205	160	201	242	280	240	221	223	202	240	204	221	230	155	305	525	224
5. Buckingham	138	149	164	143	*	47	106	46	128	114	102	130	149	119	113	135	75	106	198	128	185	107
6. Burnham	97	118	101	144	121	*	104	91	141	109	114	164	108	100	103	157	102	104	172	155	119	
7. Bury Town	273	199	119	366	191	153	*	189	164	178	166	185	180	176	212	110	129	80	199	634	192	122
8. Canterbury C.	75	242	143	126	46	43	68	*	78	77	69	72	165	86	112	142	54	71	226	99	75	80
9. Dunstable	100	119	237	159	197	92	89	104	*	157	157	127	159	140	158	101	84	107	118	181	96	159
10. Erith & B.	125	192	124	154	162	99	240	138	80	*	110	60	274	103	194	95	100	75	143	154	190	108
11. Fareham T.	447	628	634	669	520	469	433	894	582	422	*	543	518	517	707	419	444	730	677	488	1200	440
12. Gosport B.	248	106	143	155	93	64	66	116	72	108	289	*	77	186	82	103	157	112	126	68	343	209
13. Hastings T	162	181	162	161	305	174	256	213	163	221	325	547	*	384	206	277	407	199	254	176	401	228
14. Havant T.	146	308	104	209	105	124	102	399	148	175	189	461	141	*	293	211	277	367	75	232	217	
15. Hythe Town	253	510	205	320	240	402	207	320	280	265	210	345	333	300	*	289	318	285	348	205	282	217
16. Margate	262	266	384	387	263	339	267	289	345	266	251	338	634	203	300	*	285	349	231	261	266	
17. Newport IOW	379	167	208	214	137	173	97	175	163	184	253	155	203	187	96	179	*	204	166	239	422	176
18. Salisbury	319	634	349	666	221	313	200	317	446	237	337	448	508	327	888	685	341	*	446	384	453	287
19. Sittingbourne	394	376	493	682	275	278	502	340	338	272	335	356	494	467	342	157	412	219	*	418	301	330
20. Sudbury T.	806	693	907	746	963	1088	706	908	650	2176	807		1598	984	790	770	801	1334	617	*	753	987
21. Weymouth	140	192	113	109	292	132	160	121	119	131	138	114	115	189	117	119	123	125	156	164	*	112
22. Witney T.																						*

Premier Division

	P	W	D	L	F	A	Pts
Bromsgrove Rovers	42	27	9	6	78	34	90
Dover Athletic	42	23	15	4	66	30	84
V.S.Rugby	42	23	11	8	70	44	80
Bashley	42	22	8	12	70	44	74
Cambridge City	42	18	14	10	71	53	68
Dartford	42	17	15	10	62	45	66
Trowbridge Town	42	17	10	15	69	51	61
Halesowen Town	42	15	15	12	61	49	60
Moor Green	42	15	11	16	61	59	56
Burton Albion	42	15	10	17	59	61	55
Dorchester Town	42	14	13	15	66	73	55
Gloucester City	42	15	9	18	67	70	54
Atherstone United	42	15	8	19	54	66	53
Corby Town	42	13	12	17	66	81	51
Waterlooville	42	13	11	18	43	56	50
Worcester City	42	12	13	17	56	59	49
Crawley Town	42	12	12	18	62	67	48
Chelmsford City	42	12	12	18	49	56	48
Wealdstone	42	13	7	22	52	69	46
Poole Town	42	10	13	19	46	77	43
Fisher Athletic	42	9	11	22	53	89	38
Gravesend & Northfleet	42	8	9	25	39	87	33

Top Scorers

A **Diaz** (Dorchester Town)	38
C **Hanks** (Bromsgrove Rovers)	30
L **Whale** (Bashley)	23
G **Manson** (Dorchester Town)	21
T **Rogers** (Dover Athletic)	21
M **Dent** (Poole Town)	19

THE BEAZER HOMES PREMIER DIVISION RESULT CHART 1991-92

HOME TEAM	1	2	3	4	5	6	7	8	9	10	11	12	13	14	15	16	17	18	19	20	21	22
1. Atherstone	*	1-3	2-0	3-2	0-1	3-0	3-4	1-2	0-0	4-2	1-1	2-2	0-3	2-1	4-0	1-1	3-0	0-3	2-0	1-4	2-0	1-3
2. Bashley	4-0	*	0-1	1-1	1-1	0-0	3-1	2-0	3-0	0-1	2-0	3-1	2-1	3-0	2-3	3-0	3-0	2-0	3-1	1-2	1-1	2-2
3. Bromsgrove	2-0	3-0	*	1-1	0-2	2-1	3-0	5-1	1-0	5-1	0-0	7-0	0-2	1-0	1-0	5-3	3-1	3-1	1-2	1-0	1-0	2-0
4. Burton	0-2	1-0	3-1	*	2-0	1-2	3-1	1-0	0-1	1-2	0-1	0-2	4-3	2-1	0-0	0-1	5-2	1-3	0-0	0-4	1-1	1-1
5. Cambridge	4-1	0-1	1-0	1-1	*	3-0	1-0	1-3	2-0	1-0	2-2	4-0	4-2	3-1	2-1	2-0	5-0	3-0	1-1	0-0	2-1	1-1
6. Chelmsford	1-0	1-1	1-1	3-1	6-1	*	1-0	0-0	1-2	0-3	0-1	3-0	0-0	2-3	0-0	3-1	1-1	1-1	3-0	3-0	0-1	
7. Corby Town	3-1	3-2	1-3	1-2	2-2	1-0	*	3-4	2-2	1-3	1-1	2-1	2-2	2-1	0-4	1-6	2-1	1-1	4-2	1-1	2-6	3-1
8. Crawley	3-1	1-3	0-3	1-2	2-2	3-0	1-1	*	1-1	1-4	0-1	0-0	5-2	0-1	2-0	1-2	3-3	1-0	1-1	2-0	0-1	2-2
9. Dartford	4-1	1-0	1-1	2-0	2-2	0-2	1-5	3-2	*	1-1	0-0	1-0	2-0	5-0	0-1	1-3	4-0	2-0	2-3	2-1	4-1	1-0
10. Dorchester	0-1	0-1	1-2	0-3	1-3	2-3	0-0	0-4	1-1	*	2-1	3-1	4-2	1-1	0-0	2-2	2-1	2-2	2-1	0-0	2-0	3-3
11. Dover A.	1-0	3-2	2-2	2-1	3-0	3-0	1-1	2-1	1-1	1-1	*	2-0	4-0	3-0	1-1	1-1	1-0	3-1	1-1	1-0	3-0	3-1
12. Fisher	0-0	2-3	1-3	1-1	1-1	3-1	2-1	2-2	0-1	6-5	2-3	*	3-0	2-2	0-1	4-0	1-0	0-4	1-3	3-2	1-0	0-1
13. Gloucester	2-0	3-1	1-2	2-2	0-0	3-1	3-2	4-1	0-0	2-1	0-4	2-0	*	0-1	1-1	5-1	2-2	1-2	2-1	3-2	2-0	
14. Gravesend	1-1	1-2	0-1	0-2	2-1	0-1	1-3	1-1	1-1	1-0	4-2	1-0	*	1-1	1-8	1-3	2-3	0-1	1-1	1-0	0-0	
15. Halesowen	1-1	1-2	1-1	4-1	3-2	2-1	1-1	4-2	1-0	2-2	2-0	3-2	0-2	1-1	*	2-0	2-2	1-0	1-2	1-2	1-1	0-0
16. Moor Green	2-3	2-0	1-1	0-2	2-2	3-2	2-0	1-1	1-3	0-1	1-0	3-0	5-1	2-0	1-1	*	1-2	1-2	0-0	0-0	0-1	2-1
17. Poole	0-1	1-1	0-1	5-3	1-1	0-2	2-2	1-1	0-0	1-1	1-1	2-1	2-0	3-2	2-2	*	1-0	0-4	0-2	0-0	1-0	
18. Trowbridge	0-1	2-0	0-2	3-0	2-1	1-1	2-0	2-1	0-0	3-4	1-1	6-0	1-1	9-0	1-1	2-1	3-1	*	0-1	1-1	3-2	3-2
19. VS Rugby	1-2	0-2	1-1	1-0	3-1	0-0	0-0	2-1	3-3	3-1	0-1	3-0	2-1	3-1	1-0	2-1	2-2	1-0	*	2-0	3-2	2-0
20. W'ville	0-1	0-0	0-1	0-4	1-1	1-1	1-4	0-2	0-5	2-2	0-2	1-1	1-0	2-1	1-0	0-1	3-1	1-0	0-4	*	0-1	3-1
21. Wealdstone	1-0	1-2	1-3	1-3	2-3	2-0	3-0	0-2	2-2	2-1	0-2	4-4	3-2	0-1	2-1	1-0	0-1	3-1	1-0	0-4	*	1-4
22. Worcester	1-1	103	1-1	1-1	2-1	2-1	1-2	2-1	2-0	5-1	1-1	1-1	0-3	6-2	1-2	1-2	0-1	1-2	2-0	0-0	1-0	*

ATHERSTONE UNITED The Adders

Atherstone United pictured at Edgar Street before their F.A. Cup First Round replay against Hereford United which resulted in a 0-3 defeat. Photo - Paul Barber.

Chairman: Mr K Haskins   **President:** Mr C Culwick
Secretary (Add & Tel): Keith Allen, 19 Hathaway Drive, Nuneaton CV11 6NU (0203 349989).
Team Manager: Graham Smith   **Asst Manager:** L Martin   **Coach:** L Martin
Press Officer: Mr D Brown   **Physiotherapist:** Mr D Looms
Newsline: 0898 446 847.   **Commercial Manager:** Wendy Gretton
Ground: Sheepy Road, Atherstone, Warks CV9 1HG (0827 717829)
Directions: Half mile north of town centre on B4116 Twycross/Ashby road.
Capacity: 3,500 (1,353 Covered)   **Seats:** 353   **Floodlights:** Y   **Shop:** Y   **Metal Badges:** Y
Colours: Red & white shirts/red/red **Change colours:** Yellow/blue/blue   **Sponsors:**
Previous Leagues: Banks' West Midlands 1979-87
Midweek home matchday: Wednesday   **Reserve Team's League:** Scoreline Comb. Res. League
Record Attendance: 2,816 v V.S. Rugby F.A. Cup 1st Round Proper 1987-88
Best F.A. Cup season: 2nd Rd Proper 1990-91 (lost 0-1 at Crewe Alexandra)
Record Fee Paid: £4,500 to Gloucester City for Gary Bradder, 1989.
Record Fee Received: £40,000 for Andy Rammell from Man. Utd.
Past Players who have progressed into The Football League: Andy Rammell (Manchester United, now Barnsley)
Clubhouse: Normal hours, all usual facilities. **Steward:** Ron Gaylor (Private owner).
Record Goalscorer: Alan Bourton, Robbie Farmer   **Record Appearances:** Lee Spencer
91-92 Captain: Steve Jackson   **91-92 P.o.Y.:** Paul Diner **91-92 Top scorer:** Kim Green
Local Newspapers(+Tel.Nos.): Tamworth Herald (0827 60741), Evening Tribune, Atherstone Herald, Coventry Telegraph (0203 382251). **Local Radio Stations:** Mercia Sound, CWR.
Honours: Southern Lg Midland Div 88-89, West Mids Lg 81-82 86-87 (Lg Cup 81-82, Premier Div Cup 86-87, Div 2 Cup (Reserves) 86-87), Walsall Snr Cup 83-84, Midland Comb Reserve Division 87-88, Birmingham Snr Cup R-up 89-90, FA Tphy 1st Rd 88-89 91-92.

GOALKEEPERS:
Wayne Starkey (Nuneaton B, Coventry Sport, Stourbridge), **Lee Keyte** (Hams Hall)
DEFENDERS: Dave Wells (Nuneaton B, Halesowen T, Tamworth, Oldbury, Harrisons, North Pk, Wolves Cas, Gresley R, Willenhall), **Leigh Everitt** (Nuneaton B), **Andy Williams** (Solihull B, Nuneaton B, Birmingham), **Dave Stringer** (Bedworth, Atherstone, Nuneaton B, Leicester C(A)), **Steve Jackson** (Bedworth), **Paul Upton** (Stafford R, Bedworth, Coventry Sport), **Alun French** (Coventry)
MIDFIELD: Steve Eccleston (Tamworth, Bridgnorth, Welshpool, GKN Sankey), **Wayne Rowley** (Sutton C, Moor Green, Kidderminster, Torquay(T), Shrewsbury(T)), **Paul Olner** (Youth), **Malcolm Randle** (Bedworth, Hurley DM), **Jeremy Bell** (Youth), **Ian Brain** (Nuneaton B, Atherstone, Bedworth, Atherstone), **Robin Judd** (Redditch, Mile Oak, Kidderminster, Birmingham), **Neil Meredith** (Nuneaton B, Bridgnorth, Telford, Poole, Shrewsbury)
FORWARDS: Kim Green (Nuneaton B, VS Rugby, Coventry Sport, MSA), **Roy Green** (Tamworth, Dudley, Oldbury, Lye, Aston Villa), **Rob Greene** (Solihull B, VS Rugby, Burton Alb, Willenhall, Oskersham(Swe), Aston V), **Marc Shilton** (Nuneaton B), **Mark Lewis** (Local), **Mark Tolley** (Blakenall, Willenhall, Hednesford), **Stuart Aubrey** (Tamworth, Mile Oak), **Lee McQuade** (Mile Oak, Tamworth, Atherstone), **Ian Gorrie** (Sweden, Atherstone, RC Warwick, Stratford), **Karl Keyte** (Youth), **Matthew Wallace** (Shepshed), **Alan**

Pages: 40 **Price:** 60p
Editor: P Bickley
WMPCC Rating: 25

BASHLEY

Bashley defend in depth at Dover Athletic on Saturday 11th April. Their 2-3 defeat that day heralded the end of their championship challenge. Photo - Roger Turner.

Chairman: Trevor Adams   **Vice Chairman:** Murray Keen   **President:** TBA
Secretary (Add & Tel): Sam Hynds, 17 Deerleap Way, New Milton BH25 5EU (0425 621280).
Team Manager: Trevor Parker   **Asst Manager:** R Badley   **Coach:** Sandy Baird
Press Officer: **Physio:** K Sturgess   **Newsline:** 0898 446 881.
Commercial Manager: Mr T Parker/ J Shippey.
Ground: Recreation Ground, Bashley, Hants BH25 5RY (0425 620280)
Directions: A35 Lyndhurst towards Christchurch, turn left down B3058 towards New Milton. Half hour walk from New Milton (BR).
Capacity: 4,250 (200 Covered)   **Seats:** 200   **Floodlights:** Y   **Shop:** N   **Metal Badges:** Y
Colours: Yellow & black/black/black   **Change colours:** Blue & White stripes/white/white
Sponsors: P.C.F. Ltd (0590 83340).
Previous Leagues: Bournemouth 50-83/ Hants 83-86/ Wessex 86-89.
Midweek home matchday: Wednesday   **Reserve Team's League:** Wessex Combination.
Record Attendance: 3,500 v Emley, F.A. Vase S.F. 1st Leg 1987-88
Best F.A. Cup season: 4th Qualifying Rd 1990-91 (lost 0-1 at Welling United)
Record Fee Paid: £7,500.
Record Fee Received: £5,000 from Havant Town for J Wilson, 1990.
Past Players who have progressed into The Football League: None
Clubhouse: Bar. Food on matchdays.   **Steward:** Tony Courtney.
Record Goalscorer: Colin Cummings   **Record Appearances:** John Bone
91-92 Captain: Sandy Baird   **91-92 P.o.Y.:** Jeremy Stagg   **91-92 Top scorer:** Leroy Whale.
Local Newspapers: Bournemouth Echo, Southern Pink, New Milton Advertiser.
Local Radio Stations: 2CR Solent, Ocean Sound.
Honours: Southern Lg Southern Division 89-90 (Lg Cup SF 89-90), Wessex Lg 86-87 87-88 88-89, Hants Lg Div 3 84-85, Hants Lg Combination 88-89, Russell Cotes Cup 88-89 90-91, FA Vase SF 87-88 (QF 88-89), FA Tphy 2nd Rd 91-92.

GOALKEEPERS:
John Simpkins (Basingstoke, East Cowes Vics)
DEFENDERS: Kevin Green (New Milton,Oxford C, Salisbury, Bournemouth), Domenyck Newman (Reading, Fareham, AFC Totton), **Barry Blankley** (Basingstoke, Farnborough, Woking, Aldershot, Southampton), **Steve Ingram** (Basingstoke, Gosport), **Sandy Baird** (Gosport, Basingstoke, Weymouth, Fareham, Horndean, Fareham, Horndean).
MIDFIELD: Jimmy Sheppard (Poole, Andover, Swindon, Peterborough), **Gareth Hughes** (Newtown, Sth Glamorgan Inst, Newtown), **Jeremy Stagg** (Andover, Woking, Southampton), **Miguel De Souza** (Dorchester, Yeovil, Bristol C, Charlton, Clapton), **Mark Redknapp** (Bournemouth(T)), **Martin Stickler** (AFC Totton), **Simon Gowans** (Yeovil, Fareham, AFC Totton, Pirelli General), **Neil Masters** (Bournemouth(T)), **Peter Conning** (Yeovil, Weymouth, Altrincham, Rochdale)
FORWARDS: Leroy Whale (Basingstoke, Southampton(T)), **Mark Skivington** (Loughboro Univ), **David Walters** (Fareham, Southwick, Gosport, Fareham, Potsmouth(J)), **Andy Case** (Bournemouth(T)), **John Chiedozie** (Barking, Chesterfield, Notts Co, Derby, Spurs, Notts Co, Leyton Orient), **Mark Barrett** (AFC Totton), **Aaron Vine** (Local football)

PROGRAMME DETAILS:
Pages: 24 **Price:** 60p
Editor: Mark Pettengell
WMPCC Rating: 22

BURTON ALBION

Burton 'keeper Nick Goodwin tips over an effort during the 0-5 FA Cup defeat at Colchester. Photo - Paul Dennis.

Chairman: Jock Gordon   **Vice Chairman:** T J Spencer   **President:**
Secretary: Tony Kirkland, 40 Hurst Drive, Stretton, Burton-on-Trent DE13 0ED (0283 36510).
Team Manager: Brian Kenning   **Asst Manager/Coach:** Alan Kurila
Press Officer: Rex Page (Burton Mail)   **Physio:** Keith Commons   **Commercial Manager:**
Newsline: 0898 884 475.
Ground: Eton Park, Princess Way, Burton-on-Trent DE14 2RU (0283 65938)
Directions: M1 - A50, turn right at island, left at next island. M42 - A38, take 2nd turn for Burton, right at island.
Capacity: 8,000 (5,000 Covered)   **Seats:** 296   **Floodlights:** Y   **Shop:** Y   **Metal Badges:** Y
Colours: All Yellow   **Change colours:** All Red   **Sponsors:** Inde Coope Brewery
Previous Leagues: West Mids 1950-58/ Southern 58-79/ Northern Premier 79-87
Midweek home matchday: Tuesday   **Previous Ground:** Wellington Street 50-57.
Record Attendance: 5,860 v Weymouth, Southern Lg Cup Final 1st leg, 1964.
Best F.A. Cup season: 3rd Rd Proper, 1955-56 and 1984-85. 1st Rd on nine occasions.
League clubs defeated in F.A. Cup: Halifax (55-56), Aldershot (84-85)
Record Fees - Paid: £21,000 to for R Jones and J Pearson (Kidderminster).
                Received: £60,000 for Darren Carr (Crystal Palace).
Past players progressing to Football League: Ray Russell (S'bury 1954), David Neville (R'dale 1955), Derek Middleton (York 1958), Tom McGlennon (Barrow 1959), Les Green & Tony Parry (H'pool 1965), George Hunter (L'coln 1965), Stan Aston (H'pool 1966), David Jones (N'port 1968), Richie Barker & Jeff Bourne & Tony Bailey (Derby 1967 & 69 & 70), Maitland Pollock & Steve Buckley (Luton 1974), Peter Ward (Brighton 1975), Tony Moore (Sheff U 1979), Carl Swan & Gary Clayton (D'caster 1980 & 86), Richard Jobson (W'ford 1982), Paul Haycock (R'ham 1986), Alan Kamara (Scarborough 1987), Paul Groves (Leic C 1988), Steve Cotterill & John Gayle (W'don 1989), Darren Carr (C Palace 1989), Darren Smith & Darren Roberts (Wolves 1990 & 92).
Clubhouse: 'The Football Tavern' - open to all on matchdays.   **Steward:** Brian Finch
Club Record Goalscorer: Ritchie Barker, 157   **Club Record Appearances:** Phil Annable, 567
91-92 Captain: **91-92 P.O.Y.:** Nick Goodwin   **91-92 Top scorer:** Rob Jones.
Local Newspaper: Burton Daily Mail (0283 43311).   **Local Radio:** Radio Derby.
Honours: Southern Lg Cup 63-64 (R-up 88-89, Div 1 (Nth) R-up 71-72 73-74), Northern Premier Lg Challenge Cup 82-83 (R-up 86-87, Presidents Cup R-up 85-86 (SF 86-87), Birmingham Snr Cup 53-54 70-71 (R-up 86-87), FA Tphy R-up 86-87 (SF 74-75), GMAC Cup SF 86-87, Bass Charity Vase 81-82 85-86, Bass Challenge Cup 84-85, West Mids Lg R-up 53-54, Staffs Senior Cup 55-56.

GOALKEEPERS:
Nicky Goodwin (Shepshed, Corby, Kettering, Shepshed, Kettering, Graham St Prims)
DEFENDERS:
Alan Kurila (Kidderminster, Stafford R, Bromsgrove, Bedford, Birmingham), Lyndon Reeves (Paget R), Ken Geelan (Shepshed, Sheff Utd), Nigel Simms (Local football), Nathan Foster (Youth), Scott Lyndsey (Stafford R, Goole), Matt Simpson (Youth), Martin Hancott (Notts Forest(T))
MIDFIELD:
Ian Straw (Grimsby, Southampton), Roger Sallis (Man Utd), Alan McLaren (Redditch, Alvechurch, Northfield, Aston Villa), Simon Redfern (Local football), Allan Davies (Man City(T)), Ian Hendry (Sutton Coldfield, Stafford R, Wealdstone, VS Rugby, Worcester, Gloucester, Redditch, Nuneaton B, Redditch, Worcester, Nuneaton B, Hibernian, Hereford, Aston Villa)
FORWARDS:
Robert Jones (VS Rugby, Burton Alb, Kidderminster, Leicester C, Walsall), Chris Meyer (Stafford R), Scott Cordner (Chesterfield), Peter Gocan (Tamworth, Nuneaton B, Stourbridge, Bath, Alvechurch, Worcester, Wolves Utd, Chasetown, Malvern, Stourbridge, Hednesford, Oldbury, Wolves Utd), Ian Doughty (Youth)

Pages: 48 **Price:** 50p
Editor: Dave Twigg
WMPCC Rating: 25

CAMBRIDGE CITY

Formed: 1908

City Devils

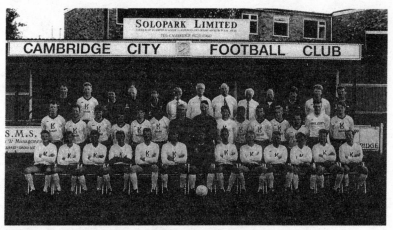

Cambridge City FC, who had a disappointing season by their recent high standards.

Chairman: D Rolph   **President:** Sir Neil Westbrook, CBE MA FRICS
Secretary: Martin Carter, 1 Coach House Ct, Hawthorn Way, Cambridge CB4 1BT (0223 312753).
Team Manager: Steve Fallon   **Asst Manager:** Peter Martin   **Coach:**
Press Officer: Secretary   **Physiotherapist:** Bill Brignell   **Commercial Manager:** Jim Mills
Newsline: 0898 122 928.
Ground: City Ground, Milton Road, Cambridge CB4 1UY (0223 357973)
Directions: 50 yards on left from beginning of A1134, Cambridge to Ely Road.
Capacity: 5,000 (1,700 Covered)   **Seats:** 400   **Floodlights:** Y   **Shop:** Y   **Metal Badges:** Y
Colours: White/black/black   **Change colours:** All Sky Blue   **Sponsors:**
Previous Leagues: Southern Amateur 1919-35/ Spartan 35-50/ Athenian 50-58. *As Cambridge Town until 1952*
Midweek home matchday: Wednesday   **Reserve Team's League:** Essex & Herts Border Comb (West)
Record Attendance: 12,500 v. Leytonstone, Amateur Cup
Best F.A. Cup season: 1st Rd Proper, v Ashford 1966, v Swindon 1946, v Walthamstow 1948
Record Fee Paid: £6,000 for A Beattie   **Record Fee Received:** £1,500 from Ipswich for Tommy Carroll.
Players who have progressing to Football League: Ken Wright (W Ham 1946), Antonio Gallego (N'wich 1947), Alf Stokes (W'ford 1961), Derek Weddle (M'boro 1961), Dave Hicksen (Bury 1962), Bryan Harvey (B'pool 1962), Robert Whitehead (Darlington 1962), George Cummins (Hull 1962), Reg Pearce & Dom Genovese (P'boro 1963 & 88), Alan Banks (Exeter 1963), Tom Carroll (Ipswich 1966), Roy Jones (Swindon), Winston Dubose (Oldham).
Clubhouse: 11am - 11pm Mon-Sat. 12 - 3pm, 7pm - 10.30pm Sun. Bingo, Dances, Pool, Stag nights, Darts.
Steward: Tony Desimone.
Club Record Goalscorer: Gary Grogan   **Club Record Appearances:** Mel Keenan
91-92 Captain: Steve Gawthrop   **91-92 P.o.Y.:** Laurence Cullum   **91-92 Top scorer:** Laurie Ryan
Local Papers(+Tel.Nos.): Cambridge Evening News 35877.   **Local Radio:** BBC Radio Cambridge
Honours: Southern Lg 62-63 (R-up 70-71,   Southern Div 85-86, Div 1 R-up 69-70, Championship Cup 62-63), East Anglian Cup 59-60 64-65 75-76, Eastern Professional Floodlit 65-66 72-73, Cambs Professional Cup 60-61 61-62 62-63 70-71 72-73 74-75, Cambs Invitation Cup 76-77 78-79 85-86 88-89 89-90, Spartan Lg 47-48 48-49 (R-up 49-50 & Eastern Div Champs 45-46), FA Trophy 2nd Rd 86-87 87-88, FA Amateur Cup SF 27-28, Addenbrookes Hospital Cup 87-88, The Munns Youth Cup 82-83 83-84 84-85, Chiltern Youth League Cup R-up 75-76, South Mids Lg Youth Trophy 82-83, Robinson Cup 87-88 89-90, Jim Digney 89-90, Essex & Herts Youth Lg 89-90.

GOALKEEPERS:
Kevin Murray (Saffron Walden, Camb City), **Barry Piggott** (Royston)
DEFENDERS: Simon Haigh (Wisbech, Holbeach, Peterborough(A)), **Steve Fallon** (Histon, Camb Utd, Kettering), **Lawrence Cullum** (Histon), **Andy Jeffrey** (Leicester C)
MIDFIELD: Steve Spriggs (Bury T, Camb Utd, Huddersfield), **Steve Gawthrop** (Youth), **Shaun Harrington** (Camb Utd(T)), **Keith Lockhart** (Hartlepool, Wolves, Camb Utd)
FORWARDS: Gary Grogan (Ely, Barnstaple, Camb City, Soham T, Camb City), **Laurie Ryan** (Camb Utd, Dunstable, Chesham), **Paul Wilkin** (Histon), **Mark Shelford** (Youth), **Chris Tovey** (Royston, Camb City, Royston, Letchworth GC)

PROGRAMME DETAILS:
Pages: 20 Price: 50p
Editor: Dave Crane
WMPCC Rating: 25

CHELMSFORD CITY

City at their Championship Shield match at Farnborough on August Bank Holiday Monday. Photo - Eric Marsh.

Chairman: Dennis Wakeling   **President:** Mrs J Coward-Talbot
Secretary: Vic Keeble, 13 Station Rd, Earls Colne, Colchester, Essex CO6 2ER (0787 222978).
Team Manager: Joe Sullivan   **Asst Manager:** Terry Harris   **Coach:** Terry Harris
Press Officer: David Ward   **Physio:** Don Stewart   **Comm. Mgr:** Steve Dorrington
Ground: The Stadium, New Writtle Street, Chelmsford CM2 0RP (0245 353052).
Directions: A1016 (Chelmsford) exit off A12, follow Colchester signs to 3rd r'bout, left (B1007, New London Rd), left at 2nd lights (signed County Cricket Ground), ground 100 yds on right.
Capacity: 2,850 (Police limit)   **Seats:** 1,296   **Floodlights:** Y   **Shop:** Y   **Metal Badges:** Y
Colours: White/claret/white.   **Change colours:** Claret/White/claret.   **Sponsors:** TBA.
Midweek home games: Monday   **Reserve Team's League:** Essex & Herts Border Comb.
Previous Name: None (Brentwood Town were incorporated in 1968).   **Previous Leagues:** None
Record Attendance: 16,807 v Colchester United, Southern League 10/9/49.
Best F.A. Cup season: 4th Rd Proper, 1938-39 (v Birmingham City). 1st Rd Proper on 25 occasions.
League clubs defeated in F.A. Cup: Darlington 38-39, Southampton 38-39, Oxford Utd 67-68
Record Fee Paid: £6,000 to Maidstone (John Bartley)   **Rec'd:** £12,000 from Wycombe (Dennis Greene).
Players progressing to Football League: Geoff Merton (W'ford 1948), George Adams (Orient 1949), William O'Neill (B'ley 1949), Brian Farley & Sid McClellan (Spurs 1949), Oscar Hold (E'ton 1950), Reuben Marden (Arsenal 1950), Cecil McCormack (B'sley 1950), Les Dicker (Spurs 1951), Dave Sexton (Luton 1951), Wally Bellet & Robert Mason & Anthony Nicholas (Orient 1961 & 63 & 65), Robin Gladwin (N'wich 1966), Brian King (M'wall 1967), Peter Collins (Spurs 1968), John O'Mara (B'ford C 1974), Nigel Spink (Villa 1977), Mark Dziadulewicz (W'don 1979), Mervyn Cawston (S'end 1984), Phil Coleman (E'ter 1984), John Keeley & Adrian Owers (B'ton 1986 & 87)
Clubhouse: Open matchdays & every evening. Pool, darts, satellite TV. Available for private hire. **Steward:** Gary Ward.
Club Record Goalscorer: Dennis Foreman   **Club Record Apps:** Colin Johnson (459 to date)
91-92 Captain: Dave Rolfe   **91-92 P.o.Y.:** Peter Locke   **91-92 Top scorer:** Dennis Greene 22.
Local Newspapers: Essex Chronicle (0245 262421), Chelmsford Weekly News (0245 493444), East Anglian Daily Times (0473 230023).
Local Radio Stations: Essex Radio/Breeze AM, BBC Essex.
Hons: Southern Lg 45-46 67-68 71-72 (R-up 48-49 60-61 63-64 65-66), Southern Div 88-89, Lg Cup 45-46 59-60 (R-up 60-61), Merit Cup 71-72, Southern Lg War-Time (East) 39-40, Essex Professional Cup(5) 57-58 69-71 73-75, Essex Snr Cup 85-86 88-89, Non-League Champs Challenge Cup 71-72, E Anglian Cup 48-49, Eastern Co's Lg(3) 46-49 (Lg Cup 59-60), Eastern F'lit Comp. (66-67 74-75 77-78 81-82 82-83 86-87 (Cup 72-73 74-75), Metropolitan Lg 67-68 (Lg Professional Cup 67-68), Autumn Shield 70-71), Essex Snr Lg Cup 84-85, Essex Snr Lg Harry Fisher Memorial Tphy 88-89.

GOALKEEPERS:
Colin Lewington (Dulwich, Corinthian, Chatham, Gravesend, Maidstone, Chelmsford, Gravesend, Erith & Belvedere), **Shane Baalham** (Northampton(T))
DEFENDERS: Ricky Cornish (St Albans, Aldershot, Camb Utd, Bury Town), **David Rolfe** (Eton Manor), **Peter Locke** (AS Solbiatese, Rovers Utd), **Colin Johnson** (Stambridge, Chelmsford, Chelmsford, Hounslow, Wealdstone, Dartford, Leyton Orient), **Liam Cutbush** (Heybridge Swifts, Aveley, Braintree, Grays, Dartford, Braintree, Tiptree), **Steve Moseley** (Enfield, Dartford, Barking, Billericay, Stambridge), **Danny Schneider** (Purfleet, Witham, Southend(T)), **Peter Reed** (Brighton)
MIDFIELD:
Steve Butler (Stambridge, East Thurrock, Basildon,Southend), **Matt Jones** (Southend, Chelsea(T)), **Ray Lee** (Redbridge F, Scarborough, Arsenal), **Gary Howard** (Brighton, Watford), **Lee Furzer** (Southend, QPR(T)), **Paul Goyette** (Wealdstone, Maidstone, Dagenham, Tilbury, West Ham), **Wayne Hannigan** (Colchester)
FORWARDS: Dave Greene (Stevenage B, Saffron Walden, Sawbridgeworth, Woodford, Basildon), **Ian Brown** (Harwich, Stowmarket, Sudbury, Felixstowe, Colchester, Birmingham), **Michael Cole** (Redbridge F, Fulham, Ipswich), **Simon Sugrue** (Southend(T)), **Steve Restarick** (Colchester, West Ham(T)), **Christian McClean** (Northampton, Bristol R, Clacton, Colchester)

Pages: 32 **Price:** 70p
Editor: Dave Williams
(0245 257648)
WMPCC Rating: 35

CHELTENHAM TOWN

Robins

Cheltenham Town's 'Player of the Year' Kevin Willetts fires an equaliser past Farnborough Town goalkeeper Peter Hucker. Cheltenham achieved a good 1-1 draw in this difficult away fixture at Cherrywood Road, but in the final reckoning they were relegated, so their seven year flirtation with Conference football has come to an end. Photo - Elaine Sarjeant.

Chairman: D Deacon **President:** E A Croker
Secretary: Reg Woodward, C/O The club (below).
Team Manager: Lindsay Parsons **Asst Manager:** **Coach:**
Press Officer: None **Physio:** Billy Sabatella **Comm. Mgr:**
Ground: Whaddon Road, Cheltenham, Gloucestershire GL52 5NA (0242 513397).
Directions: M5 jct 10, A4019 through Cheltenham centre and join A46 Prestbury Road. Whaddon Rd turning on right. M5 jct 11, A40 into Cheltenham, join A46 Bath Road, follow through town and join Prestbury Road, Whaddon Rd on right. From London; A40 into Cheltenham and join A46 at Hewlett Rd then as above. Ground 1 mile from town centre and 2 miles from Cheltenham (BR).
Capacity: 7,200 (3,000 covered) **Seats:** 1,200 **Floodlights:** Y **Shop:** Y **Metal Badges:** Y
Colours: Red & white stripes **Change colours:** Blue (white trim). **Sponsors:** Gulf Oil.
Midweek home games: Tuesday **Reserve Team's League:** Football Combination Div. 2
Previous Leagues: Birmingham Combination/ Southern 35-85/ GMV Conference 85-92.
Record Attendance: 8,326 v Reading, FA Cup 1st Rd 56-57.
Best F.A. Cup season: 3rd Rd Proper 33-34 (lost 1-2 at Blackpool).
League clubs defeated in F.A. Cup: Carlisle United 33-34.
Record Fee Paid: £20,000 to Kidderminster (Kim Casey) **Rec'd:** £45,000 from Derby (Brett Angell).
Players progressing to Football League: Paul Tester (Shrewsbury), Brett Angell (Derby), Keith Knight (Reading), Peter Shearer (Bournemouth), Simon Brain (Hereford), Chris Burns (Portsmouth).
Clubhouse: Open every evening. 3 bars; clubroom, lounge, Robin's Nest. Open before and after Saturday matches. Nest & clubroom Available for private hire.
Club Record Scorer: Dave Lewis 290 (1970-83) **Club Record Apps:** Roger Thorndale 701 (58-76)
91-92 Captain: Steve Rooks **91-92 P.o.Y.:** Kevin Willetts **91-92 Top scorer:** Kim Casey.
Local Newspapers: Echo/ Western Daily Mail.
Local Radio Stations: Radio Glos.
Hons: Southern Lg 84-85 (Midland Div 82-83, Lg Cup 57-58 (R-up 68-69 84-85, Championship Shield 58-59, Merit Cup 84-85), Nth Glos. Snr Professional Cup(28), Midland Floodlit Cup 85-86 86-87 87-88.

GOALKEEPERS:
Mark Barrett (Exmouth, Exeter)

DEFENDERS:
Kevin Willetts (Sharpness), **Mark Buckland** (Kidderminster, Wolves, AP Leamington, Cheltenham), **Anton Vircavs** (Wycombe, Pressed Steel), **Paul Bloomfield** (St Marks)

MIDFIELD:
Neil Smith (Lincoln, Redditch, Shrewsbury), **Steve Brooks** (Witney, Clanfield), **Steve Owen** (Trowbridge, Mangotsfield), **Sean Reck** (Wrexham, Oxford Utd), **Charlie Henry** (Aldershot, Swindon), **Peter Turnbull** (Youth)

FORWARDS:
Jon Purdie (Worcester, Shrewsbury, Oxford Utd, Wolves, Arsenal), **Jimmy Smith** (Salisbury, Torquay), **Darren Perrett** (Bridgend), **Jimmy Wring** (Mangotsfield, Bath C), **Darren Teggart** (Witney, Banbury, Clanfield, Moreton, Witney), **Paul Mortimore** (YTS)

PROGRAMME DETAILS:
Pages: 32 Price: 80p
Editor: Paul Godfrey
WMPCC Rating: 31

CORBY TOWN

The Steelmen

Corby's Glen Russell is forced to take evasive action as Fisher Athletic's Ronnie thumps a pile-driver during an early season fixture at the Surrey Dock Stadium. Photo - Alan Coomes.

Chairman: A Weatherall   **President:** H Hetterley.
Secretary: R Abraham, 68 Cornwall Rd, Kettering, Northants NN16 8PE (0536 522159).
Team Manager: Elwyn Roberts   **Asst Manager:** Stuart Carmichael
Commercial Manager: Jimmy Kane.   **Physio:** Mick Mackie.
Ground Address & Tel: Rockingham Triangle Stadium, Rockingham Road, Corby NN17 2AE (0536 401007).
Directions: On northern outskirts of town at junction of A6003 and A6116, opposite entrance to Rockingham Castle grounds. One and a half miles from Corby (BR).
Capacity: 3,000 (1,150 Covered)   **Seats:** 1,150   **Floodlights:** Y   **Shop:** Y   **Metal Badges:** Y
Colours: White/black/black   **Change colours:** All yellow.   **Midweek home matchday:** Monday
Previous Leagues: United Counties 35-52/ Midland 52-58.   **Previous Name:** Stewart & Lloyds 1935-48.
Previous Ground: Occupation Road 1935-85.   **Sponsors:** Mr Bips.
Record Attendance: 2,240 v Watford, pre-season friendly 86-87. At Old Ground; 10,239 v P'boro, FA Cup 52-53.
Best F.A. Cup season: 3rd Rd 65-66 (lost to Plymouth). 1st Rd on five occasions; 54-55 63-66 67-68.
League clubs defeated in F.A. Cup: Luton Town 65-66.
Record Fees - Paid: £2,700 for Elwyn Roberts (Barnet)   **Received:** £15,000 for John Flower (Sheff U).
Players progressing to Football League: Andy McCabe (C'field 1955), Les Claimers (Leics 1956), Ken Brown (Nottm F 1956), Peter Kearns (A'shot 1962), Norman Dean (S'hampton 1963), Hugh Curran (M'wall 1964), Dixie McNeil & Andy McGowan & George Reilly (N'hampton 1969 & 75 & 76), Phil Chard (P'boro 1979), Trevor Morley (W Ham), J Flower (Sheff Utd, A'shot).
Clubhouse: Open every day, usual club facilities.   **Steward:** Ernie Leaker.
Club Record Scorer: Ernie Middlemiss 135 (1949-52)   **Club Record Apps:** Derek Walker 600 (78-92).
91-92 Captain: M Lawrence   **91-92 P.o.Y.:** P Curtis   **91-92 Top scorer:** M Murphy 21.
Local Newspapers (+Tel.Nos.): Northampton Evening Telegraph (0536 81111).
Local Radio Stations: BBC Radio Northampton, Hereward and KCBC.
Hons: FA Trophy 3rd Rd 86-87, UCL 50-51 51-52 (R-up 37-38), Midland Lg R-up 52-53, Southern Lg Midland Div R-up 90-91 (Merit Cup 63-64 90-91), Northants Snr Cup 37-38 39-40 50-51 62-63 75-76 82-83, Maunsell Cup 83-84, Midland Floodlit Cup 74-75, Evans Halshaw F'lit Cup 91-92, Anglia Floodlit Trophy 68-69 72-73, Chelmsford Invitation Cup 63-64 64-65 65-66(joint), Kettering & Dist Samaritan Cup 60-61 (joint) 68-69, Wellingborough Charity Cup 50-51, Desborough Nursing Cup 48-49 50-51(joint), Bob Cunning Cup 85-86 86-87 87-88 88-89.

GOALKEEPERS:
Chris Mackenzie (Desborough)
DEFENDERS: Pat Rayment (Camb Utd, Peterborough Utd), **Jim Hamill** (Stewarts & Lloyds), **Paul Curtis** (Brixworth, Kettering, Corby, Northampton, Charlton), **Gerry McElhinney** (Peterborough, Plymouth, Bolton W, Distillery), **Lee Middleton** (Coventry), **Simon Newcombe** (Leicester C(T)), **Bryn Gunn** (Chesterfield, Peterborough, Notts Forest), **Steve Collins** (Boston Utd, Kettering, Peterborough, Lincoln, Southend, Peterborough)
MIDFIELD: **Mike Cook** (Wycombe, Camb Utd, Coventry), **Graeme Archer** (Youth), **Darren Hillier** (Cogenhoe, Long Buckby, Kettering), **Derek Walker** (Wellingborough, Corby, Kettering), **Dean Foley** (Leicester C(T)), **Dougie Keast** (Kettering, Shepshed, Hibernian)
FORWARDS: Shaun Diver (Rothwell, Desborough, Kettering), **David Hofbauer** (Kettering, Corby), **Maurice Murphy** (Irthlingborough), **Ian McInerney** (Peterborough)

Pages: 48 **Price:** 50p
Editor: D Tilley
WMPCC Rating: 25

CRAWLEY TOWN

Crawley Town FC 1991-92. Back Row (L/R): Tony Vessey (Capt), Barry Smith (now Newhaven), Damian Webber, Colin Oakes (now Three Bridges), Alan Massey, Steve Powell. Centre: Stan Markham (Sec./General Mgr), Bert Davis, Craig Whitington, Tim Hulme, Dave Venables, David Cooper (now Carshalton), Grant Gallagher, Cliff Cant, Brian Sparrow (Manager, now Wimbledon), Dave Haining (Physio/Asst Mgr). Front: Les Turnbull (Vice President), Jim Green (Director), Mick Fox (Director), John Maggs (Chairman), John Duly (Director), Ken Symons (President). Photo - Crawley Observer.

Chairman: John Maggs   **President:** K Symons
Secretary: Stan Markham, 105 Winchester Road, Tilgate, Crawley RH10 5HH (0293 522371).
Team Manager: Steve Wicks   **Asst Manager:**   **Coach:**
Press Off.: Richard Neil (081 666 8757) **Physiotherapist:** D Haining   **Commercial Manager:** F Pitts
Ground: Town Mead, Ifield Aenue, Crawley (0293 21800).
Directions: M23 exit 10, A264 for Horsham, left at 2nd island, over mini r-about, right at next island and ground 150 yards on right behind fire station. 10 mins walk from Crawley (BR).
Capacity: 2,500 (1,200 Covered)   **Seats:** 250   **Floodlights:** Y   **Shop:** Y   **Metal Badges:** Y
Colours: Re/red/white   **Change colours:** All blue   **Sponsors:** Gleave Construction.
Previous Leagues: Sussex County 1951-56/ Metropolitan 56-63
Midweek home matchday: Tuesday   **Reserve Team's League:** Suburban.
Record Attendance: 3,427 v Horsham, FA Cup 4th Qualifying Round Replay 91-92.
Best F.A. Cup season: 3rd Rd Proper 91-92 (lost 0-5 at Brighton).
League Clubs defeated in F.A. Cup: Northampton Town 91-92.
Record Fee Paid: £5,000 to Wokingham Town for David Thompson, May 1992.
Record Fee Received: £15,000 from Hythe Town for Tommy Warrilow, 1990
Players progressing to Football League: Ray Keeley (Mansfield 1968), Graham Brown (Mansfield 1969), Andy Ansah (Brentford 1987 (now Southend)), Brian Sparrow as coach to Wimbledon 1992.
Clubhouse: Open daily   **Steward:** Les Howard.
Club Record Goalscorer: Terry Robbins 51   **Club Record Apps:** John Maggs 652.
91-92 Captain: Tony Vessey   **91-92 P.o.Y.:** Steve Powell   **90-91 Top scorer:** Tim Hulme 21.
Local Newspapers: Crawley Observer (0293 526929), Crawley News (0293 526474).
Local Radio Stations: Radio Mercury, BBC Radio Sussex
Hons: Sussex Snr Cup(2) 89-91 (R-up 58-59), Sussex I'mediate Cup 26-27, Sussex Prof. Cup 69-70 (beat Brighton 1-0 in final), Southern Lg Southern Div R-up 83-84 (Merit Cup 70-71), Sussex F'lit Cup(2) 90-92, Sussex Lg Div 2 R-up 55-56, Gilbert Rice F'lit Cup 79-80 83-84, Southern Co's Comb F'lit Lg 85-86, Metropolitan Lg Chal. Cup 58-59, FA Tphy 2nd Rd 85-86 87-88

GOALKEEPERS:
Dave Winterton (Eastbourne T, Hastings T)
DEFENDERS:
Tony Vessey (Worthing, Steyning, Vassalund(Swe), Brighton), **Neil Wickens** (Canterbury, Sheppey, Gravesend, Gillingham(T)), **Damian Webber** (Worthing, Brighton), **Alan Massey** (Army), **Steve Powell** (Eastbourne Utd), **Nigel Brotherton** (Eastbourne T), **Wayne Fairchild** (Oxted), **Daren O'Neil** (Wokingham, Weybridge T)
MIDFIELD:
Jack Dineen (Bognor Regis, Brighton), **Tony Towner** (Lewes, Crawley, Gravesend, Crawley, Fisher, Gravesend, Camb Utd, Rochdale, Charlton, Wolves, Rotherham, Millwall, Brighton), **Tim Hulme** (Hythe, Ashford, Hythe, Dover, Folkestone, Hythe),, **Mike Fillery** (Oldham, Portsmouth, QPR, Chelsea, Sutton Utd), **Dale Jasper** (Crewe, Brighton, Chelsea), **Micky Turner** (Peterborough, Portsmouth)
FORWARDS:
Craig Whittington (Worthing), **Jeff Vansittart** (Youth), **Darren Cheverton** (Portsmouth(T)), **Martin Lambert** (Worthing, Wycombe, Brighton, Sedan(Fr), Volendam(Holl), Union(Bel), Torquay), **Neil Willie** (Youth), **Dave Thompson** (Wokingham, BAE Weybridge), **Paul Fishenden** (Wokingham, Crewe, Wimbledon), **Martin Chester** (C Palace)

Pages: 32 **Price:** 60p
Editor: I Hands
WMPCC Rating: 22

DARTFORD

Formed: 1888

The Darts

Dartford FC 91-92. Back Row (L/R): A Prutton, J Sherringham, J Leslie, C Tucker, P Sawyer, D Bensted, J Hunt. Front: P Hennessy, S Quail, W Barlow, C Snell, A Pask, J Shaw. Mascots: Louise Morez, Daniel Weighill.

Chairman: B L Rogers **President:** B Cussens.
Secretary: Barry Bundock, 'Dunedin', Southsea Av., Minster, Sheerness, Kent ME12 2NH (0795 876025).
Team Manager: Bobby Makin **Asst Manager:** Alan Carrington **Coach:** Micky Springer.
Press Off.: M Brett-Smith (0322 77243) **Physio:** Ted Cribbs **Comm. Manager:** Barry Bundock
Ground: Watling Street, Dartford, Kent DA2 6EN (0322 273639. Fax: 0322 284476).
Directions: From town centre (and station) go up East Hill. Watling Street is third turning right.
Capacity: 5,250 (3,000 Covered) **Seats:** 678 **Floodlights:** Y **Shop:** Y **Metal Badges:** Y
Colours: Black/black/white **Change colours:** Red/white/red
Previous Leagues: Kent 1894-96/ 97-98/ 99-1902/ 09-14/ 21-26, Southern 1896-98/ 99-1900/ 27-40/ 46-81/ 82-84, GMV Conference 1981-82/ 84-86
Midweek home games: Tuesday **Youth Team League:** Kent Yth Lg. **Sponsors:** National Power.
Record Attendance: 11,004 v Orient FA Cup 1st Rd, 1948-49
Previous Ground: Summers Meadow 1888-1920. **Newsline:** 0898 884 482.
Best F.A. Cup season: 3rd Rd Proper 1935-36 (v Derby), 1936-37 (v Darlington).
League Clubs Defeated in F.A. Cup: Cardiff (1935), Exeter (1961) Aldershot (1968)
Record Fees: Paid: £6,000 for John Bartley (Chelmsford) 1988, **Received:** £4,000 for Gary Julians (Maidstone)
Players progressing to The Football League: Riley Cullum (Charlton, 1947), Ted Croker (Charlton 1948), Frank Coombs (Bristol C 1949), James Kelly (Gillingham 1951), Tom Ritchie (Grimsby 1958), Dave Underwood (Watford 1960), Derek Hales (Luton 1972), Archie Cross (Arsenal).
Clubhouse: Players bar open matchdays. Members Social club open daily. **Steward:** Brian Edmeads.
91-92 Captain: Paul Sawyer **91-92 P.o.Y.:** Paul Sawyer **91-92 Top scorer:**
Local Newspapers(+Tel.Nos.): Dartford Times, Kent Evening Post, Kentish Times, Kent Messenger
Local Radio Stations: Coast AM, BBC Radio Kent
Hons: Southern Lg(4) 30-32 73-74 83-84 (R-up(3) 80-81 87-89, Div 1 80-81, Lg Cup(3) 76-77 87-89 (R-up 79-80 83-84 89-90), Championship Shield(2) 87-89), Kent Snr Cup(9) 30-33 34-35 47-48 69-70 72-73 86-88 (R-up 1893-94), Kent F'lit Cup(3) 64-66 70-71, Kent Lg Cup 24-25, Inter Lg Chal. 1974 (beat Boston Utd 5-3 on agg.), FA FA Tphy R-up 73-74.

GOALKEEPERS:
Craig Tucker (Leyton-Wingate, Boreham Wood, Leyton-Wingate, Haringey Boro)

DEFENDERS:
Dave Bensted (Redbridge F, Brimsdown Rov), **Andy Pask** (Redbridge F, West Ham(T)), **Paul Hennessey** (Gravesend, Corinthian, Crockenhill, Bromley, Brighton), **Paul Sawyer** (Margate, Bromley, Welling), **Peter Johns** (Redbridge F)

MIDFIELD:
Andy Prutton (Cheshunt, Wormley Rov), **Jason Shaw** (Redbridge F, West Ham(J)), **Chris Snell** (Cheshunt, Ware, Leyton-Wingate, Leytonstone & Ilford, Leyton Orient), **Jimmy Sheringham** (Grays, Barking, Walthamstow Ave, Barking, Billericay, Dagenham), **Trevor Hand** (Local football), **Steve Smith** (Youth)

FORWARDS:
John Hunt (Corinthian, Gravesend, Corinthian, Adelphi(USA), Spurs(J)), **Simon Quail** (Redbridge F, Barking, Newmont Travel, Arsenal(J), **John Leslie** (Grays, Fisher, Millwall, Gillingham, Wimbledon, Dulwich), **Paul Smith** (Youth), **Stuart Maclean** (Youth)

DARTFORD F.C.
DARTFORD
v
HALESOWEN TOWN
Saturday 29th February 1992 K.O. 3.00pm
1991 OFFICIAL MATCH
1992 PROGRAMME 80P

PROGRAMME DETAILS:
Pages: 36 **Price:** 80p
Editor: Mike Brett-Smith
WMPCC Rating: 26

474

Formed: 1880 # DORCHESTER TOWN — The Magpies

Tony Diaz (centre), the league's top scorer in 1991-92, gets one of his season's haul of 43 goals to give Dorchester a third minute lead at Worcester City. After this early strike the Magpies capitulated and lost 1-5 to the then bottom team. Photo - Keith Clayton.

Chairman: P J Aiken   **President:** J Pitfield
Secretary: A E Miller, 29 Shaston Crescent, Dorchester DT1 2EB (0305 264843)
Team Manager: Paul Arnold   **Asst Manager:** David Peach   **Coach:** Geoff Joy.
Press Officer: S Legge (0305 263799)   **Physio:** W Hall/G Dine
Commercial Manager: Keith Kellaway (0305 262451).
Ground: Avenue Stadium, Weymouth Avenue, Dorchester DT1 2RY (0305 262451).
Directions: At junction of southern bypass and Weymouth road (A35-A354).
Capacity: 7,210 (3,000 Covered)   **Seats:** 710   **Floodlights:** Y   **Shop:** Y   **Metal Badges:** Y
Colours: Black & white stripes/black/black   **Change colours:** All sky blue
Previous Leagues: Dorset/ Western (1947-72)
Previous Grounds: Recreation Ground 1880-1929/ The Avenue Ground 29-90. .
Midweek home games: Tuesday   **Reserve Team League:** Dorset Combination
Sponsors: Olds Motor Group
Record Attendance: 4,000 v Chelsea, official ground opening 1990 (at old ground 5,500 v York F.A. Cup 1954)
Best F.A. Cup season: 2nd Rd Replay 81-82. 1st Rd on seven occasions; 55-58 59-60 81-82 89-90.
Record Fees: Paid: £15,000 for Chris Townsend (Gloucester)
    Received: £35,000 for Trevor Senior (Portsmouth)
Players progressing to The Football League: Len Drake (Bristol Rov 1957), David Noake (Luton 1959), Mike Turner (Swindon 1961), Trevor Senior (Portsmouth 1981), David West (Liverpool 1983), Mike Squire (Torquay 1984), Jeremy Judd (Torquay 1984), Anthony White (Bournemouth 1985) + Graham Roberts (Spurs, Chelsea, Rangers, England) who progressed via Weymouth.
Clubhouse: Dorchester Lounge Club - open when required.   **Steward:** Geoff Green.
Club Record Goalscorer: Dennis Cheney 61   **Club Record Apps:**
91-92 Captain: Trevor Townsend   **91-92 P.O.Y.:** Gary Green   **91-92 Top scorer:** Tony Diaz 43.
Local Newspapers: Dorset Evening Echo, Western Gazette, Western Daily Press.
Local Radio Stations: Two Counties Radio (2CR Bournemouth).
Hons: Southern Lg R-up 79-80 (Div 1 (Sth) R-up 77-78, Lg Cup 86-87 (R-up 91-92), Western Lg 54-55 (R-up 60-61, Div 2 R-up 49-50), Dorset Snr Cup 50-51 60-61 67-68 68-69 71-72, FA Tphy 3rd Rd replay 71-72.

GOALKEEPERS:
Jeremy Judd (Bournemouth, Dorchester), **Gary French** (Southampton)

DEFENDERS:
Simon Browne (Swanage, Weymouth), **Darren Powell** (Poole, Bournemouth), Neil Coates (Yeovil, Bournemouth, Watford(A)), **Trevor Townsend** (Bournemouth, Poole), **Tony White** (Bournemouth, Dorchester), **Paul Thorpe** (Yeovil, Torquay, Bath, Bristol C)

MIDFIELD:
Gary Green (Eintracht Brynswick(Ger), **Ben Rowe** (Exeter, Bristol C), **Colin Sayers** (Westland Sports), **Gary Borthwick** (Weymouth, Yeovil, Weymouth, Yeovil, Bournemouth, Barnet, Aylesbury, Southend, Portsmouth)

FORWARDS:
Darren Sheppard (Westland Sports), **Paul Young** (Bournemouth Sports), **Gary Manson** (Poole, Parley Sports), **Tony Diaz** (Weymouth), **Colin Burton** (Local football), **Paul Masters** (Southampton)

PROGRAMME DETAILS:
Pages: 36 **Price:** 70p
Editor: Dave Martin
WMPCC Rating: 23

475

DOVER ATHLETIC

Dover Athletic 91-92. Back Row (L/R): Tom Terry (Asst Physio), Colin Blewden, Iain O'Connell, Jason Bartlett, Maurice Munden, Steve Chivers, Tony Dixon, Tony, McDonald, Dave Walker, Bob Jennings ((Physio)). Front: Nigel Donn, Joe Jackson, Terry Cordice, Tim Dixon (Capt), Chris Kinnear (Manager), Mark Harrop, Barry Little, Leroy Ambrose. Trophies (L/R): Beazer Homes Lg Champions Cup, Kent Snr Cup, Premier Inter-Lge Cup.

Chairman: J T Husk   **President:**
Secretary: J F Durrant, 7 Alison Close, Whitfield, Dover CT16 3HL (0304 823429).
Team Manager: C Kinnear   **Asst Manager:**   **Coach:** Kevin Raine
Press Officer: Secretary   **Physio:** B Jennings   **Comm Manager:** B Greenfield
Ground: Crabble Athletic Ground, Lewisham Road, Dover CT17 0EX (0304 822373).
Directions: From A2, 4th exit at first island, down hill and left at next island, left, right at traffic lights. 2 miles from Kearsmey (BR).
Capacity: 7,500 (2,500 Covered)   **Seats:** 1,000   **Floodlights:** Y   **Shop:** Y   **Metal Badges:** Y
Colours: White & black/black/black **Change colours:** Yellow/green/yellow **Sponsors:** Countrywide Derv
Previous Leagues: None. *(Dover United and Dover FC competed in Kent & Southern Leagues)*
Midweek home matchday: Tuesday   **Reserve Team's League:** Kent Division 2.
Record Gate: 4,035 v Bromsgrove R., Southern Lg 16/4/92 *(Dover FC: 6,900 v Folkestone, FA Cup 51-52).*
Best F.A. Cup season: 4th Qualifying Rd Replay 90-91, v Merthyr Tydfil *(Dover FC reached 2nd Rd in 1975-76 - lost 1-4 at Southend Utd)*
League clubs defeated in F.A. Cup: None *(Dover FC beat Colchester in 75-76)*
Record Fees - Paid: £12,000 for Joe Jackson (Yeovil)   **Received:** £12,000 for Knight (Brighton)
Players progressing to Football League: None. *(From predecessors; David Jones (Brentford 1951), Eric Worthington (Bradford City 1953), Eddie McManus (B'mouth 1954), Barry Rowan (M'wall 1964), Tom Horsfall (Southend 1972), Bob Bolder (Sheff Wed 1977), Ron Fearnon (Reading 1980), Gary Pugh (B'mouth 1981)).*
Clubhouse: Open Daily. Meals available.   **Steward:** G Hughes
Club Record Goalscorer: Lennie Lee, 150   **Club Record Apps:** Mark Harrop, 350
91-92 Captain: Tim Dixon   **91-92 P.o.Y.:** Jason Bartlett   **91-92 Top scorer:** Tony Rogers.
Local Newspapers: Dover Express, East Kent Mercury
Local Radio: Radio Kent, Invicta FM, Coast AM   **Newsline:** 0898 122 926.
Hons: Southern Lg 89-90 (R-up 91-92, Lg Cup 91-92, Championship Cup 90-91, Southern Div 87-88), Kent Snr Cup R-up 85-86 90-91, Premier Inter-Lge Cup 90-91, FA Tphy 3rd Rd 89-90, Knight Floodlit Competition 87-88 88-89 (R-up 86-87), Kent I'mediate Cup(Res) 88-89 91-92, Kent Lg Div 2 R-up (Res) 91-92, Eurotunnel Trophy 90-91, Kent Yth Lg 91-92, Kent Yth Cup 91-92. (As Dover Utd & Dover FC: Southern Lg Div 1 66-67 (Div 1 Sth 78-79), Kent Lg 51-52 (R-up 1898-99 1948-49 52-53 54-55), Kent Lg Cup 56-57, Kent Lg Div 2 38-39 (Div 2 East 21-22 22-23 23-24), Kent Snr Cup(7) 51-52 59-60 61-62 66-68 70-72, FA Amtr Cup 20-21, Kent Southern Shield 49-50))

GOALKEEPERS:
Maurice Munden (Welling, Folkestone, Charlton), **Steve Chivers** (Youth)
DEFENDERS:
Jason Bartlett (Folkestone), **Tony Macdonald** (Welling, Ashford), **Tony Dixon** (Tonbridge, Gravesend, Erith & Belvedere), **Mark Harrop** (Canterbury, Dover, Thanet), **Barry Little** (Fisher, Barnet, Dagenham, Charlton, Gillingham)
MIDFIELD:
Tim Dixon (Waterford, Southampton), **Nigel Donn** (Maidstone, Leyton Orient, Gillingham), **Iain O'Connell** (Southend), **Dave Walker** (West Ham), **Joe Jackson** (Yeovil, Worcester, Gresley Rov, Willenhall, Hednesford, Bilston, Wolves, Willenhall), **Kenny Dyer** (Salamina Famagusta(Cyp), Chatham, Maidstone, Charlton(A), Spurs(J), Arsenal(J))
FORWARDS:
Leroy Ambrose (Fisher, Esbjerg(Den), Kolding(Den), Hvidovre(Den), Charlton, Croydon), **Lennie Lee** (Thanet, Dover, Thanet, Ramsgate, Folkestone, Margate, Herne Bay, Margate, Ramsgate), **Colin Blewden** (Gravesend, Tonbridge, Gillingham(J)), **Paul Malcolm** (Fisher, Alma Swanley, Fisher, Millwall(J)), **Tony Rogers** (Maidstone, Barking, Dartford, Tilbury, Leytonstone & Ilford, Basildon), **Mark Rees** (Aldershot, Colchester, Bromsgrove, Walsall), **Steve Warner** (Dagenham, Burnham R)

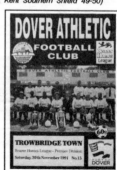

TROWBRIDGE TOWN
Beazer Homes League - Premier Division
Saturday, 30th November 1991 No.15

Pages: 36 **Price:** 60p
Editor: Chris Collings
WMPCC Rating: 27

GLOUCESTER CITY

The Tigers

Gloucester press hard during their home fixture against Dartford and force the visiting goalkeeper, Craig Tucker, into spectacular action. Photo - Keith Clayton.

Chairman: George Irvine **President:** R F Etheridge
Secretary: Ken Turner, 24 Ladysmith Road, Cheltenham, GL52 5LQ (0242 522514).
Team Manager: Brian Godfrey **Asst Manager:** TBA **Coach:** TBA
Press Off.: Brian Hobbs **Physio:** Bernard Tandy **Commercial Manager:** D Stallworthy (0452 421400)
Ground: Meadow Park, Sudmeadow Road, Hempsted, Gloucester GL2 6HS (0452 523883).
Directions: A40 to city centre towards historic docks, then Severn Road. Right into Hempsted Lane, and 2nd right again to Sudmeadow Road. Ground 50 yards on left.
Capacity: 5,000 (2,000 Covered) **Seats:** 560 **Floodlights:** Y **Shop:** Y **Metal Badges:** Y
Colours: All Yellow **Change colours:** White/white/red
Previous Lgs: Bristol & Dist. (now Western) 1893-96/ Gloucester & Dist. 97-1907/ Nth Glos. 07-10/ Glos. Nth Snr 20-34/ Birmingham Comb. 1935-39.
Previous Grounds: Longlevens 1935-1965/ Horton Road 65-86.
Previous Name: Gloucester Y.M.C.A.
Midweek home games: Tuesday **Reserve Team League:** **Sponsors:** Euroglaze
Record Attendance: 10,500 v Spurs 1952 (at Meadow Park; 3,952 v Arsenal, July 1987)
Best F.A. Cup season: 2nd Rd Proper 89-90
Record Fees: Paid: £25,000 S Fergusson (Worcester City) **Received:** £25,000 Ian Hedges (Bournemouth 1990)
Players progressing to The Football League: George Beattie & David Pugsley (N'port 1950 & 53), John Boyd & Robert Etheridge & Charlie Cook (Bristol City 1950 & 56 & 57), David Jones (Leeds 1954), Mike Johnson (Fulham 1958), William Teague & Rod Thomas (S'don 1961 & 64), John Layton (Hereford 1974), Ian Main (Exeter 1978), Mike Bruton (N'port 1979), Mel Gwinnett (Bradford 1984)
Clubhouse: Open matchdays. **Steward:** Terry Little
Club Record Goalscorer: Reg Weaver, 250 **Club Record Apps:** Stan Myers & Frank Tredgett in 1950s
91-92 Captain: Brian Hughes **91-92 P.o.Y.:** David Mogg **91-92 Top scorer:** Jason Eaton
Local Newspapers (+Tel.Nos.): Gloucester Citizen, Gloucester Express, Western Daily Press
Local Radio Stations: Severn Sound, BBC Radio Gloucestershire
Hons: Southern Lg R-up 90-91 (Lg Cup 55-56 (R-up 81-82), Midland Div 88-89), Glos Nth Snr Lg 33-34, Glos Snr Prof. Cup 37-38 49-58 65-66 68-69 70-71 74-75 78-79 79-80 81-82 82-83 83-84 90-91 (Snr Amtr Cup (Nth) 31-32), FA Tphy 3rd Rd 90-91.

GOALKEEPERS:
David Mogg (Cheltenham, Bath, Atvidaberg(Swe), Bristol City)

DEFENDERS:
Gary Kemp (Almondsbury Picksons), **Paul Dean** (Youth), **Phil Underhill** (Bath, Torquay, Swindon), **Paul Bywater** (Worcester, Shrewsbury), **Richard Criddell** (Stroud, Cinderford, Stroud, Newent, Alvechurch, Cheltenham)

MIDFIELD:
Jonathan Morgan (Merthyr Tydfil, Cardiff), **Wayne Noble** (Yeovil, Bristol Rov)

FORWARDS:
Jason Eaton (Bristol City, Bristol Rov, Trowbridge), **Shaun Penny** (Stroud, Gloucester, Forest Green Rov, Weymouth, Dorchester, Bath, KTP Kotkan(Fin), Bristol Rov, Bristol City), **Steve Crouch** (Shepshed, Stroud, Cheltenham, Frampton Utd), **Karl Bayliss** (Stroud, Sharpness, Forest Green Rov, Cheltenham)

PROGRAMME DETAILS:
Pages: 36 **Price:** 70p
Editor: Robert Kujawa
WMPCC Rating: 26

HALESOWEN TOWN

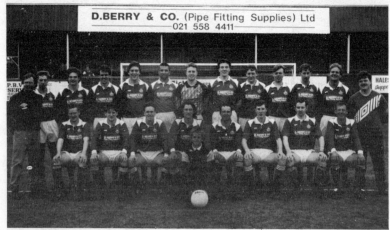

Halesowen Town - Back Row (L/R): Stuart Hall (Asst Mgr), Andrew Lunt, Andrew Bradley, Robert Shilvock, Matthew Martin, Eric Smith, Darren Steadman, Nigel Laker, Ian Bettles, Steven Moore, Malcolm Hazlewood, Richard Massey, Gavin Blackwell (Physio). Front: Shane Abell, Alan Attwood, Darren Goodall, Steven Brooks, Adam Patrick, Lee Young, Kevin Harrison, Adrian Cooper. Mascot: Ian Hipkiss.

Chairman: Ron Moseley (021 550 4310) **President:** Laurence Wood.
Secretary: Stewart Tildesley, 83 Bloomfield Street, Halesowen B63 3RF (021 550 8443).
Team Manager: John Morris   **Asst Manager:** Stuart Hall   **Coach:**
Press Officer: Paul Floud (021 550 8999)   **Physiotherapist:** Gavin Blackwell.
Commercial Manager: R E Moseley (021 550 4310)   **Newsline:** 0898 122 910.
Ground: The Grove, Old Hawne Lane, Halesowen, West Midlands (021 550 2179).
Directions: M5 jct 3, A456 to 1st island turn right, left at 2nd island, at 3rd 3rd island take 3rd exit, ground 400 yds on left.
Capacity: 5,000 (1,000 Covered)   **Seats:** 420   **Floodlights:** Y   **Shop:** Y   **Metal Badges:** Y
Colours: Blue/white/blue   **Change colours:** White/orange/orange.
Sponsors: D Berry & Co (Pipe Fitting Supplies) Ltd.
Previous Leagues: West Mids 1892-1905 06-11 46-86/ Birmingham Comb. 11-39.
Midweek home matchday: Tuesday   **Reserve Team's League:** Midland Comb. (Reserve Div)
Record Attendance: 5,000 v Hendon F.A. Cup 1st Rd Proper 1954, 18,234 v Southall Vase Final 1986 Wembley
Best FA Cup year: 1st Rd 54-55 84-85 85-86(replay) 86-87 87-88(replay) 88-89 89-90 90-91 91-92(replay)
Record Fees - Paid: £5,000 for Richard Massey (Stourbridge)   **Rec'd:** £30,000 for Dean Spink (A Villa).
Players progressing to Football League: Arthur Proudler (Aston Villa), Cyril Spiers (Aston Villa), Billy Morris (Wolves), Dean Spink (Aston Villa), Stuart Cash (Nottm Forest), Andrew Pearce & Tim Clarke & Sean Flynn (Coventry).
Clubhouse: Open lunchtimes & evenings (021 550 8907).   **Steward:** Ken Arnold.
Record Goalscorer: Paul Joinson 320   **Record Appearances:** Lee Joinson 544.
91-92 Captain: Malcolm Hazlewood **91-92 P.o.Y.:** Eric Smith   **91-92 Top scorer:** Kevin Harrison.
Local Newspapers: Sports Argus, Express & Star, Birmingham Mail, Halesowen News, Stourbridge & Halesowen Chronicle.   **Local Radio:** B.R.M.B./BBC West Mids/Beacon.
Hons: Southern Lg Midland Div 89-90, W Mids Lg(5) 46-47 82-85 85-86 (R-up 64-65, Lg Cup 82-83 84-85), Birmingham Snr Cup 83-84 (R-up 51-52 67-68), Staffs Snr Cup 88-89 (R-up 83-84), FA Vase(2) 84-86 (R-up 82-83), Worcs Snr Cup 51-52 61-62 (R-up 87-88), FA Tphy 3rd Qual. Rd 69-70, Midland Comb. Res Div 89-90.

GOALKEEPERS:
Kevan Williams (Dudley, Halesowen T, Millfields, Worcester), **Tony Rowe** (Worcester, Redditch)
DEFENDERS: Stuart Edwards (Willenhall, Stourbridge, Derby(A), Willenhall), **Bob Whittingham** (Sutton Coldfield, Northfield), **Eric Smith** (Tipton), **Dylan Adams** (Youth), **Shane Abell** (Atherstone, Alvechurch, RC Warwick, Moor Green, Northfield, Knowle, King's Heath), **Mark Penn** (Lye)
MIDFIELD: Richard Massey (Stourbridge, Kettering, Exeter), **Adrian Cooper** (Dudley, Halesowen Harriers), **Rob Shilvock** (Kidderminster, Bromsgrove, Halesowen T), **Darren Goodall** (Hereford, WBA(T)), **Andy Bradley** (Youth), **Malcolm Hazlewood** (Kidderminster, Dudley, Halesowen T, Walsall), **Ian Bettles** (RC Warwick, Southam, VS Rugby), **Steve Bourne** (Northfield), **Sean Kimberley** (Bilston, Moor Green, Bilston, Kidderminster, Hereford, Notts Co, Leicester C), **John Snape** (Stourbridge, Northfield, Bromsgrove, WBA(A)), **Lee Evans** (WBA(T))
FORWARDS: Kevin Harrison (Stourbridge, Tividale), **Frank Bennett** (Local football), **Alan Attwood** (Kidderminster), **Andy Mitchell** (Notts Forest(T)), **Matthew Martin** (Chelmsley, Alvechurch, Sandwell B), **Steve Brooks** (Youth), **Simon Robinson** (Alvechurch, Blackpool, Alvechurch, Mansfield, Aston Villa(A))

Pages: 48 **Price:** 60p
Editor: Rob Pepper & Chas Shakespeare
WMPCC Rating: 30

HASTINGS TOWN

Hastings Town, Beazer Homes League Southern Division Champions 1991-92. Back Row (L/R): Micky Crowe (Coach), Stephen Willard, Tony Burt, Peter Carman, Peter Sillett (Manager), Carlton Wynter, Terry White, Philip Henderson, Chris Emery (Physio), Keith Miles, Dean White. Front: Andy Blondrage, Paul Giles, Paul Burke, Peter Petkovic, David Scott, Jonathan Sillett.

Chairman: Dave Nessling   **Vice Chairman:** Charles Pilbeam   **President:** David Harding
Secretary: Tony Cosens, 22 Baldslow Road, Hastings TN34 2EZ (0424 427867).
Team Manager: Peter Sillett   **Asst Manager:**   **Coach:** Micky Crowe
Press Officer: Tony Cosens   **Physio:** Chris Emary   **Newsline:** 0898 664 356.
Commercial Manager: Joe Taliana (0424 715544).   **Sponsors:** Coombs Motors
Ground: The Pilot Field, Elphinstone Road, Hastings TN34 2AX (0424 444635).
Directions: From town centre take Queens Road (A2101). Right at traffic lights into Elphinstone Road - ground 1 mile on right.
Capacity: 9,100 (2,800 Covered)   **Seats:** 1,300   **Floodlights:** Y   **Shop:** Y   **Metal Badges:** £1.30
Colours: All white (red trim)   **Change colours:** All red.
Previous Lges: S. Eastern 04-05/ Southern 05-10/ Sussex Co. 21-27 52-85/ Sthern Amtr 27-46/ Corinthian 46-48.
Previous Name: Hastings & St Leonards Amateurs   **Previous Ground:** Bulverhythe.
Midweek home matchday: Tuesday   **Reserve Team's League:** Winstonlead Kent Div 2.
Record Attendance: 1,200 v Weymouth, Southern League Southern Division 15/2/92.
Best F.A. Cup season: 4th Qualifying Rd 85-86, lost 2-3 at Farnborough Town.
League clubs defeated in F.A. Cup: None.
Record Fees - Paid: £2,000   **Received:** £4,000 (twice).
Players progressing to Football League: Peter Heritage (Gillingham and Hereford United).
Clubhouse: Members' club open every night and weekend lunchtimes. Additional bar open on matchdays.
Steward: Steve Huggett.
Club Record Goalscorer: Dean White 28   **Club Record Apps:**
91-92 Captain: Andy Blondrage   **91-92 P.o.Y.:** David Scott   **91-92 Top scorer:** Terry White 25.
Local Newspapers (+Tel.Nos.): Hastings Observer & Citizen (0424 854242), Evening Argus (0273 606799).
Local Radio Stations: Radio Sussex, Southern Sound.
Hons: FA Vase 5th Rd rep. 90-91, FA Amtr Cup 3rd Rd 38-39, Southern Lg Southern Div 91-92 (Div 2 R-up 08-09 (Div 2(B) 09-10)), Sussex Co. Lg R-up 21-22 25-26 (Lg Cup 80-81, Div 2 79-80 (R-up 59-60), Div 2 Cup 79-80), Sussex Snr Cup 35-36 37-38, AFA Snr Cup 37-38, Gilbert Rice F'lit Cup 89-90.

GOALKEEPERS:
Peter Carman (Ashford, Herne Bay, Dover, Ashford, Maidstone), **Gary Gill** (Eastbourne Utd, Hastings Utd)
DEFENDERS: Jon Sillett (Ashford), **David Scott** (Canterbury, Hastings T), **Peter Petkovic** (Hastings Utd), **Tony Burt** (Local football), **Dean White** (Maidstone, Hastings T, Millwall, Gillingham, Chelsea, Hastings Utd), **Steve Smith** (Southwick, Hastings T, Brighton(A)), **Micky Crowe** (Gravesend, Welling, Leytonstone & Ilford, Maidstone, Gravesend, Hastings Utd, Gillingham, Brentford)
MIDFIELD: Andy Blondrage (Gravesend, Ashford, Gravesend), **Terry White** (Hythe, Hastings T, Bexhill, Millwall, Charlton), **Phil Henderson** (Eastbourne Utd, Wivenhoe, Northampton), **Steve Willard** (Local football), **Paul Giles** (Ashford, Dover, Ashford, Hastings Utd, Ashford, Dartford), **Kieran O'Shaughnessy** (Local football)
FORWARDS: Keith Miles (Hailsham, Hastings T, Eastbourne Utd, Hastings Utd), **Carlton Wynter** (Ashford, Bromley Green), **Paul Burke** (Gillingham), **Dean Kewley** (Local football)

Pages: 44 **Price:** 60p
Editor: Tony Cosens
WMPCC Rating: 21

479

HEDNESFORD TOWN

The Pitmen

Hednesford Town, Beazer Homes League Midland Division Runners-up and Welsh Cup Finalists 1991-92. Back Row (L/R): John Baldwin (Manager), Don Brakeley (Physio), Phil Hill, Nick Alsop, Tony Turner (Assistant Manager/Coach), Richus White, Paul Hayward, Archie King, Steve Snaith, Jim Brown, Mick Perry, Steve Austin. Front: Dale Rudge, Kevin Collins, Russell Turley, Marcus Malcolm, Andy Walsh, Terry Knight, Kevin Foster, Mark Freeman, Joe O'Connor, Steve Burr. Mascot: Mark Lomond.

Chairman: Mike Smith **Team Manager:** John Baldwin **Asst Manager/Coach:** Tony Turner
Secretary: Bob Cooper, 59 Blewitt Street, Hednesford, Staffs WS12 4BD (0543 876114).
Physio: Don Drakeley **Press Officer:** Alan Owen **Commercial Manager:** Terry Brumpton
Ground: Cross Keys Ground, Hill Street, Hednesford (05438 422870). *A move to a new, adjacent, ground is planned to take place during the next two years.*
Directions: M6 junction 11 to Cannock, A460 to Hednesford. After 2 miles turn right opposite Shell garage, ground on right at bottom of hill.
Capacity: 4,000 (1,000 Covered) **Seats:** 400 **Floodlights:** Y **Shop:** Y **Metal Badges:** Y
Colours: White/black/black **Change colours:** All yellow. **Sponsors:** British Coal - Opencast Executive.
Previous Leagees: Walsall & District/ Birmingham Combination 08-15 45-53/ West Mids 19-39 53-72 74-84/ Midland Counties 72-74.
Previous Names: None - club the result of an 1880 amalgamation between West Hill and Hill Top.
Previous Ground: The Tins (behind Anglesey Hotel) until 1904.
Midweek home matchday: Monday **Record Gate:** 10,000 v Walsall, FA Cup 1919-20.
Record Fees: Paid: £12,000 - Steve Burr (Macclesfield 1991) **Received:** £6,000 - Steve Biggins (S'sbury).
Players progressing to Football League: Norman Allsop (WBA 1948), Ron Russon & George Heseltine & John Giles & Gordon Dyas (W'sall 1948 & 49 & 50 & 55), Dennis Jackson & Gordon Lee (A Villa 1954 & 55), Brian Horton (P Vale 70), Steve Biggins (S'bury 1977), Vernon Allatt (H'fax 1979), Chris Brindley (Wolves 1986).
Clubhouse: Open every day with a matchday extension. **Steward:** Mr Glyn and Mrs Dee Cumbley.
Club Record Scorer: Tosh Griffiths **Best F.A. Cup season:** 1st Rd 19-20.
91-92 Captain: Kevin Collins **91-92 P.O.Y.:** Paul Hayward **91-92 Top scorer:** Steve Burr 42.
Local Newspapers (+Tel.Nos.): Expess & Star (W'ton 22351), Chronicle, Chase News, Hednesford Mercury.
Local Radio Stations: Radio West Mids, Beacon (Wol'ton), Radio BRMB.
Hons: Welsh Cup R-up 91-92, FA Tphy 2nd Rd 2nd rep. 77-78, Southern Lg Midland Division R-up 91-92 (Lg Cup R-up 86-87), West Mids Lg 77-78 (R-up 83-84, Lg Cup 83-84), Birmingham Combination 09-10 50-51 (R-up 12-13 52-53), Staffs Senior Cup 69-70 73-74, Birmingham Senior Cup 35-36.

GOALKEEPERS:
Paul Hayward (Bilston, Blakenall, Redditch, Kidderminster, Worcester, Paget)
DEFENDERS: Mark Freeman (Willenhall, Bilston, Wolves, Bilston), **Jason Kirkham** (Telford), **Richus White** (Dudley, Stourbridge, Dudley, Stourbridge, Dudley, Willenhall, Bilston), **Kevin Collins** (Stourbridge, Rushall Olym, Burton Alb, Kidderminster, Alvechurch, Shrewsbury, Boldmere, Causeway), **Phil Hill** (Harrisons), **Kevin Foster** (Willenhall, Hednesford, Stourbridge)
MIDFIELD: Dale Rudge (Djerv(Nor), Aldersley , Preston, Wolves), **Steve Snaith** (Tamworth, Oldbury, Harrisons, Gresley, Leicester C), **Russell Turley** (Stafford, Wolves, Notts F), **Jimmy Brown** (Newport T, Bridgnorth, Hednesfd, Bridgnorth, Willenhall), **Andy Walsh** (Harrisons, Hednesfd, Willenhall, Hednesfd, Blakenall), **Nigel Barrows** (Stourbridge, Sandwell, Oldbury, Bilston, Gresley, Dudley, **Tyrone Street** (Bilston, Cradley, Bilston, Willenhall, Blakenall)
FORWARDS: Steve Burr (Macclesfld, Stafford, Atherstone, Lichfield), **Joe O'Connor** (Stafford, Lye), **Terry Knight** (Tamworth, Stafford, Worcester, Harrisons, Rushall O), **Archie King** (Willenhall, Hednesfd, Stourbridge, Hednesfd, Darlaston), **Marcus Malcolm** (Harrisons, Willenhall, Blakenall, Wolves Utd, Bilston, Willenhall, Wednesfld), **Micky Perry** (Tamworth, Redditch, Worcester, Wealdstone, Stafford, Port V, Torquay, WBA), **Brendan Hackett** (Telford, Gloucester, Worcester, Archdales, Dudley, Stourbridge, Redditch, Bilston), **Henry Wright** (Stourbridge, Springvale, Bilston)

Pages: 40 **Price:** 50p
Editor: Chris Southall
WMPCC Rating: 23

MOOR GREEN

Moor Green proudly display the Midland Floodlit Cup, retained in May 1992. Back Back Row (L/R): Peter Allen, Andy Dwyer, Andy Dale, Nigel Watson, Darren Grocutt, Ian Taylor, Ryan Rankin, Carl Morris, Phil Davies, Stewart Talbot. Front: Richard Evans, Micky Burton, Dave Fearon, Guy Russell, Bob Coy (Capt), Graham Clegg, Steve Williams (Physio).

Chairman: Brian Smith **President:** Geoff Hood
Secretary: Martyn Davis, 22 Collingdon Ave., Sheldon, Birmingham B26 3YL (021 743 0991).
Team Manager: Bob Faulkner **Asst Manager:** Ray Monington **Coach:** Andy Dwyer
Press Officer: Peter Clynes (021 745 3262) **Physio:** Steve Williams
Commercial Manager: Rory Lynas (021 777 8961; 24 hrs).
Ground: 'The Moorlands', Sherwood Road, Hall Green B28 0EX (021 777 2757).
Directions: Off Highfield Road, which is off A34 (B'ham to Stratford). Hall Green & Yardley (BR) half mile away.
Capacity: 3,250 (1,250 Covered) **Seats:** 250 **Floodlights:** Y **Shop:** Y **Metal Badges:** Y
Colours: Blue **Change colours:** Yellow **Sponsors:** Ansells.
Previous Leagues: Birmingham & Dist Comb 1908-36/ Central Amateur 36-39/ Birmingham Comb 45-54/ West Mids 54-65/ Midland Comb 65-83.
Previous Grounds: Moor Green Lane 1901-10/ Windermere Road 1910-?.
Midweek home matchday: Tuesday **Best F.A. Cup season:** 1st Rd Proper 1979-80.
Record Gate: 5,000 v Romford, FA Amtr Cup 1951 *(15,000 v Ajax in Olympic Stadium, Amsterdam).*
Record Fees - Paid: £1,000 for Adrian O'Dowd (A'church) **Rec'd:** £15,000 - Ian Taylor (Pt Vale).
Players progressing to Football League: Herbert Smith & Ron Jefferies (A Villa 1947 & 50), Fred Pidcock (Walsall 1953), Peter Woodward (WBA 1954), Steve Cooper (Birmingham 1983), Richard Smith (Mansfield 1987), Ken Barnes (Man City), Brian Mack (WBA), Paul Grogan (Mansfield), Ian Taylor (Pt Vale 1992).
Clubhouse: Two bars and dance floor. Open nightly and weekend lunchtimes. **Steward:** Lionel Bowater
91-92 Captain: Bob Coy **91-92 P.o.Y.:** Bob Coy **91-92 Top scorer:** Ian Taylor 16.
Local Newspapers (+Tel.Nos.): Solihull News, Solihull Times, Birmingham Post & Mail, Metro News
Local Radio Stations: Radio WM, BRMB.
Hons: Southern Lg Midland Div R-up 87-88, Mids Comb 80-81 (R-up(4) 74-76 79-80 82-83), Div 1 85-86, Presidents Cup(2) 66-68 78-79), Mids Comb Challenge Cup 80-81 (R-up 69-70 82-83), Lord Mayor of B'ham Charity Cup 90-91, Mids F'lit Cup(2) 90-92, Tony Allden Tphy 81-82, B'ham Snr Cup 57-58, Worcs Snr Cup R-up 86-87, B'ham Jnr Cup 66-67, Worcs Jnr Cup 85-86, Solihull Charity Cup 85-86, Smedley Crook Memorial Cup 87-88, Central Amateur Lg 36-37 37-38 38-39, Verviers (Belg) Tphy 32-33 36-37, AFA Challenge Cup 38-39, AFA Snr Cup 26-27 35-36, Mids F'lit Yth Lg Cup R-up 87-88, B'ham County Yth Lg Cup R-up 83-84.

GOALKEEPERS:
Derek Allen (Redditch, Alvechurch, Solihull Boro, Bromsgrove Rov), **Nigel Watson** (Bromsgrove Rov, Alvechurch, Willenhall, Alvechurch, Hednesford, Rushall Olympic, Wolves(J))
DEFENDERS: Graham Clegg (Burton Alb, Moor Green, Sutton Coldfield, Blackpool), **Stewart Talbot** (Youth), **Simon Hollands** (Worcester), **Bobby Coy** (Aylesbury, Northampton, Chester, Wolves), **Ryan Rankin** (Kidderminster), **Paul Timmins** (Northfield), **Paul Brogan** (Cheltenham, Mansfield, Moor Green), **Ian Grosvenor** (Alcester)
MIDFIELD: Darren Grocutt (Northfield), **Ian Taylor** (Local football), **Dave Fearon** (Bromsgrove Rov, Earlswood, Moor Green), **Richard Evans** (Redditch, Stourbridge, Paget R, Moor Green, Sutton Coldfield, Walsall Wood, Kidderminster), **Brian McGarry** (Redditch, Moor Green, Alvechurch, Kidderminster, Bromsgrove Rov, Tamworth, Sheff Utd, Bromsgrove Rov), **Brendan Devery** (Birmingham(T))
FORWARDS: Guy Russell (Keps(Fin), Birmingham), **Carl Morris** (Atherstone, Aston Villa), **Phil Davies** (Henley Forest, Radford Senley), **Nigel Brown** (Youth), **Micky Burton** (Shrewsbury, Sheff Wed, Birmingham), **Andrew Dale** (Birmingham(T)), **Brian Duffy** (Camb City), **Michael Ayres** (Hednesford, Walsall(T)), **Peter Bennett** (Northfield)

PROGRAMME DETAILS:
Pages: 40 **Price:** 50p
Editor: Peter Denham
WMPCC Rating: 20

SOLIHULL BOROUGH

Solihull Borough, Beazer Homes League Midland Division champions 1991-92. Back Row (L/R): Dave Latchford (Coach), Steve Deakin (Youth Team Manager), Colin Holder (Reserve Team Manager), Anon., Ian Pinner, Nick Hyde, Gary Wright, Sean Bayliss, Darrell Houghton, Jan Mulders, Louis Claxton, Oliver Latchford, John Mitchell, Kirk Thomas, Ralph Punsheon (Manager), Graham Frisby (Coach), Kenny Lawrence (Assistant Manager). Front: Ian Mitchell, John Powell, Ian Tanner, Clive Boxall, Ron Morgan (Trainer/Director), Trevor Stevens (Vice Chairman), John Hewitson (Chairman), Joe McGorian (President), Alan Byrne, Andy Canning, Chris Burton, Alan Ollis.

Chairman: John Hewitson   **President:** Joe McGorian.
Secretary: John A France, 105 Coppice Walk, Cheswick Green, Shirley, Solihull B90 4HZ (05646 3011).
Team Manager: Ralph Punsheon   **Coach:** Ken Lawrence, Graham Frisby, Dave Latchford.
Physio: John Price   **Press Officer:** Richard Crawshaw (05646 2746).
Ground: Moor Green FC (see page 482). Solihull are groundsharing at Moor Green whilst awaiting planning permission for a stadium of their own
Directions & Capacity: See Moor Green FC.   **Floodlights:** Y   **Shop:** Y   **Metal Badges:** Y
Colours: Red/white   **Change colours:** Yellow and blue.
Sponsors: Mitchells & Butlers.
Previous Leagues: Mercian/ Midland Combination 69-91.
Previous Name: Lincoln FC.
Previous Grounds: Widney Stadium.
Midweek matchday: Wednesday   **Reserve Team's League:** Influence Combination Div 1.
Record Attendance: At previous ground: 400 v Moor Green, Midland Combination Division Two, 1971.
Best F.A. Cup season: Second Qualifying Round 91-92.
League clubs defeated in F.A. Cup: None.
Record Fees - Paid: £2,500 for Chris Burton (from Kidderminster Harriers).
            Received: £30,000 for Andy Williams (from Coventry City).
Players progressing to Football League: Kevin Ashley (Birmingham City, Wolverhampton Wanderers), Andy Williams (Coventry City, Rotherham United, Leeds United, Notts County), Geoff Scott (Leicester City, Birmingham City, Stoke City), Danny Conway, Alan Smith (Leicester City, Arsenal), Dean Smith (Aston Villa, Shrewsbury Town).
Clubhouse: The Borough Club, Tanworth Lane, Shirley; opened June 16th 1990. Two bars, dance floor, meeting room available for hire. Open every night, Sunday and bank holiday lunchtimes. **Steward:** Oliver Latchford.
Club Record Goalscorer: **Club Record Apps:**
91-92 Captain: Clive Boxall   **91-92 P.o.Y.:**   **91-92 Top scorer:** Chris Burton.
Local Newspapers: Solihull Times, Solihull News, Sunday Mercury, Sports Argus.
Local Radio Stations: Radio WM, BRMB.
Hons: Southern Lg Midland Div 91-92, Midland Combination R-up 90-91 (Challenge Cup R-up 74-75 90-91, Presidents Cup R-up 69-70), Lord Mayor of Birmingham Cup 91-92, FA Vase 5th Rd 74-75.

GOALKEEPERS:
Darrell Houghton (Coleshill, Kidderminster)
DEFENDERS: Alan Byrne (Stratford, Knowle), Jan Mulders (Bromsgrove, Kidderminster, Malvern), Maurice O'Connell (Bromsgrove, Sutton Coldfield, Northfield), Clive Boxall (Kidderminster, Cheltenham, AP Leamington, Cheltenham), Ian Pinner (Alvechurch, Burton Alb, Nuneaton B, Alvechurch, Moor Green, Notts Co(A)), Chris Bryan (Kidderminster), Paul Dyson (Telford, Crewe, WBA, Stoke, Coventry)
MIDFIELD: Phil Hawker (WBA, Walsall, Birmingham), Alan Ollis (Perth(Aust), Alvechurch, AP Leamington, Kidderminster, Banbury, Cheltenham, Aston Villa), John Powell (Stourbridge, Worcester, Cheltenham, Kidderminster, Corby, Notts Forest), Nick Hyde (Kidderminster), Ian Tyrell (Aston Villa(T))
FORWARDS: Chris Burton (Kidderminster), Andy Canning (Burton Alb, Willenhall, Redditch, Sutton Coldfield, Redditch, Boldmere, Port Vale, Walsall(A)), Ian Mitchell (Banbury, King's Heath, Willenhall, Nuneaton B, Highgate, Moor Green, Solihull B), Keith Bertschin (Aldershot, Chester, Walsall, Sunderland, Stoke, Norwich, Birmingham, Ipswich, Barnet), Mick Tuohy (Stafford R, Cheltenham, Kidderminster, Redditch, Southend, Worcester, Walsall), Ricky Carter (Malvern, Worcester, Kidderminster)

Pages: 24 **Price:** 50p
Editor: Richard Crawshaw
WMPCC Rating: 19

TROWBRIDGE TOWN

Dorchester's Tony Diaz puts in a shot against Trowbridge Town in the FA Trophy. Photo - Gavin Ellis.

Chairman: John Fitchen   **President:** A M Townley.
Secretary (Add & Tel): Jeff Hooper, 8 Elm Close, North Bradley, Trowbridge BA14 0SF (0225 767187).
Team Manager: John Murphy   **Asst Manager:** Bob Baird   **Coach:** P Higgins.
Ground: Frome Road, Trowbridge, Wilts BA14 0DB (0225 752076).
Directions: Follow inner relief road signs to Frome. Ground on left 100 yds past Ship Inn.
Capacity: 5,000 (2,000 Covered)   **Seats:** 200   **Floodlights:** Y   **Shop:** Y   **Metal Badges:** Y
Colours: Old gold/black/black   **Change colours:** All white.   **Sponsors:**
Previous Leagues: Somerset Senior/ Trowbridge & Dist/ Western 1892-98 1901-07 13-58/ Wiltshire/ Southern 58-81/ Alliance Premier (GMV Conference) 81-84.
Previous Name: Trowbridge.   **Previous Ground:** Bythesea Road.
Midweek home matchday: Tuesday.   **Reserve Team's League:** Wilts County.
Record Attendance: 9,009 v Weymouth, FA 4th Qualifying Rd 49-50.
Best F.A. Cup season: 1st Rd replay (v Brighton) 47-48. 1st Rd 45-46 57-58 63-64.
Record Fees - Paid: £5,000 for John Smeulders (Bournemouth).
                Received: £10,000 for Paul Compton (B'mouth), for Andy Feeley (Leicester City).
Players progressing to Football League: Alec Eisentrager (Bris C 1950), Don Townsend (Charlton 1950), Cecil Dixon (C'diff 1954), David Pyle & Jeff Meacham (Bris R 1955 & 87), Eric Weaver & Ken Skeen & Bryan Wade (S'don 1961 & 64 & 85), Paul Compton (B'mouth 1980), John Layton (N'port 1984), Andy Feeley (L'ter 1984), Ray Cashley (Chester 1985).
Clubhouse: Open matchdays and as and when required. Skittles, TV, pool, darts.   **Steward:** Committee.
91-92 Captain: Paul Rose   **91-92 P.o.Y.:** Mark Teasdale   **91-92 Top scorer:** John Freeguard 22.
Local Newspapers (+Tel.Nos.): Wiltshire Times (0225 777292), Bath Evening Chronicle, Western Daily Press.
Local Radio Stations: Radio Bristol, Wilts Radio, Wilts Sound.   **Newsline:** 0898 664 355.
Hons: FA Vase SF 90-91, FA Tphy 1st Rd rep 83-84, FA Amtr Cup 2nd Rd 30-31, Southern Lg Southern Div R-up 90-91 (Lg Cup R-up 85-86), Western Lg(7) 27-28 29-30 38-40 46-48 55-56 (R-up 1892-93 1921-22 48-49 56-57, Lg Cup 56-57), Wilts Lg Div 2 11-12 30-31(jt)(R-up 03-04 06-07 08-09 19-20 88-89), Trowbridge & Dist Lg(3) 09-11 13-14, Wilts Snr Cup 1884-85 95-96(jt with Swindon T) 97-98 1921-22 25-26 33-34 37-38 (R-up 1886-87 89-90 92-93 96-97 1906-07 07-08 12-13), Wilts Prof. Shield(6) 45-47 49-50 68-70 72-73, Wilts F'lit Cup 91-92, Bristol Charity Cup 25-26, Wilts Jnr Cup 10-11 12-13, Trowbridge & Dist Jnr Cup 19-20, Allen Palmer Cup 23-24 24-25(joint), Swanborough Cup 33-34 34-35 35-36(jt), Somerset Snr Lg 30-31 (R-up 11-12 33-34 35-36), Western Co's F'lit Cup 80-81 85-86.

GOALKEEPERS:
Mark Teasdale (Hungerford, Gloucester, Oxford C, Devizes, St Josephs)
DEFENDERS: Neil Reeves (Bath, Trowbridge, Bristol Rov), **Paul Rose** (Chippenham, Trowbridge), **Toby Jackson** (Bath, Bristol Rov(T)), **Mike Kilgour** (Stroud, Salisbury, Trowbridge, Melksham, Larkhall, Bath), **Steve Abbley** (Gloucester, Trowbridge, Wycombe, Cheltenham, Witney, Cheltenham, Swindon, Parks FC), **Dean Elliott** (Bristol Rov(T)), **Nigel Patterson** (Weston-Super-Mare, Trowbridge, Bristol MF, Trowbridge, Mangotsfield, Wokingham)
MIDFIELD: Dave Dennison (Glenavon), **Mark Adams** (Larkhall), **Neil James** (Bristol Rov), **David Webb** (Gloucester, Stroud, Devizes, Wantage, Supermarine), **Steve Lester** (Mangotsfield, Trowbridge, Backwell, Frome), **Alan Bird** (Chippenham), **Marcus Bray** (Newport AFC, Trowbridge, Gloucester, Trowbridge), **Ian Howells** (Hungerford, Trowbridge, Swindon Ath, Swindon T)
FORWARDS: John Freegard (Gloucester, Bath, Trowbridge, Chippenham, Bath), **Guiseppe Matano** (Odd Down), **Adrian Harris** (Gloucester, Aberystwyth, Llandrindod Wells, Dale Utd), **Danny Iddles** (Yate, Forest Green Rov, Yate, Sharpness), **Keith Knight** (Gloucester, Reading, Cheltenham), **Spencer Thomas** (Bristol Rov(T))

Trowbridge TOWN vs V.S. RUGBY

Pages: 36 **Price:** 50p
Editor: B Gingell, J Hooper, S H White.
WMPCC Rating: 24

V.S. RUGBY

V.S. Rugby pictured with the Birmingham Senior Cup won in 1991-92. Back Row (L/R): Graham Reed (Capt), Trevor Christie, Ian Crawley, John Coe, Gary Bradder, Mick Martin, Ian Bullions, Liam Halton, Paul Sweeney, John McGinty, Gary Fitzpatrick. Front: Barrie Fergusson (Coach), Mick Shearer, Tom McGinty, Mark Boyland, Jimmy Knox (Manager), Mark Rosegreen, Nigel Niblett, Robert Smith, Fred Todd (Physio). Photo - Rugby Advertiser.

Chairman: Roy Gallimore (0783 542414).
Secretary: Keith Coughlan, 3 Evans Road, Rugby, Warwickshire CV22 7HT (0788 814746).
Manager: Martin Martin   **Asst Mgr:** Danny Conway   **Coach:**
Press Officer: Secretary   **Physio:** Paul Miller.   **Comm. Mgr:** John Hillier (0788 540202)
Ground: Butlin Road, Rugby, Warks CV21 3ST (0788 543692).
Directions: 1 mile walk from station. Ground off Clifton (B5414) on north side of Rugby.
Capacity: 6,000 (1,000 Covered)   **Seats:** 240   **Floodlights:** Y   **Shop:** Y   **Metal Badges:** Y
Colours: Sky & navy blue stripes/navy/navy   **Newsline:** 0898 884 497.
Change colours: White (red trim)/white/white(red trim)
Previous Name: Valley Sports/ Valley Sports Rugby.   **Sponsors:** Renton Howard Wood Levin
Previous Leagues: Rugby & District 1956-63/ Coventry & Partnership/ North Warks 63-69/ United Counties 69-75/ West Midlands 75-83
Midweek matchday: Tuesday   **Reserve Team's League:** Influence Combination Reserve Division
Record Attendance: 3,961 v Northampton F.A. Cup 1984
Best F.A. Cup season: 1st Rd 84-85 85-86 86-87, 2nd Rd 87-88
League clubs defeated in F.A. Cup: None
Record Fees - Paid: £3,500 R Smith,I Crawley,G Bradder   **Received:** £15,000 T Angus (Northampton)
Players progressing to Football League: S Storer (Birmingham 1985), S Bicknell (Leicester), S Norris (Scarborough), T Angus (Northampton Town)
Clubhouse: Every night and weekend lunchtimes. Entertainment Saturday nights. Excellent facilities include Long Alley Skittles, darts and pool. **Steward:** Bob Walton.
Club Record Goalscorer: Danny Conway, 124   **Club Record Apps:** Danny Conway, 374
92-93 Captain: Nigel Niblett   **91-92 P.O.Y.:** Mick Martin   **90-91 Top scorer:** Mark Rosegreen 25
Local Newspapers: Rugby Advertiser (0788 535363), Coventry Evening Telegraph (0203 633633), Rugby Observer (0788 535147).   **Local Radio Stations:** Mercia Sound, CWR
Hons: Southern Lg Midland Div 86-87 (Lg Cup 89-90), FA Vase 82-83, Midland F'lit Cup 84-85 89-90 (R-up 86-87), Birmingham Snr Cup 88-89 91-92, Utd Co's Lg Div 3 Cup Cup 69-70. (all-time record FA Tphy win; 10-0 away to Ilkeston, Prelim. Rd 85-86.

GOALKEEPERS:
Mick Martin (Nuneaton Boro, Shepshed, Bedworth Utd, Hinckley Ath)
DEFENDERS:
Liam Halton (Telford Utd, Bedworth Utd), **Graham Reed** (Aylesbury Utd, Northampton, Frickley Ath, Barnsley), **Brian Donnelly** (Local football), **John Coe** (Rothwell, Desborough, Rothwell), **Nigel Niblett** (Stratford, Snitterfield Sports), **Tom McGinty** (Moor Green, Coventry Sporting), **Gary Redgate** (Atherstone)
MIDFIELD:
Mick Shearer (Nuneaton Boro, Coventry Sporting), **Gary Bradder** (Atherstone Utd, Gloucester, Atherstone Utd, Bedworth Utd), **Robert Smith** (Aylesbury Utd, Hillcroft), **Paul Sweeney** (Worcester, WBA(J)), **Ian Bullions** (Hinckley Town, Bedworth Utd, Hinckley Ath), **Paul Carty** (Nuneaton B, Stourbridge, Evesham, Everton(A))
FORWARDS:
Ian Crawley (Telford Utd, Kettering, VS Rugby, Nuneaton Boro, Bedworth Utd), **Trevor Christie** (Kettering, Mansfield, Walsall, Man City, Derby, Notts Forest, Notts Co, Leicester City), **Mark Boyland** (Cheltenham, Aylesbury Utd, Wycombe, Cheltenham, Witney, Banbury Utd, Oxford City), **Gary Fitzpatrick** (Leicester City)

Pages: 40 **Price:** 70p
Editor: Bob Pinks
WMPCC Rating: 16

WATERLOOVILLE

The Ville

Waterlooville FC. Back Row (L/R): E Bradwell (Manager), D Burns, W Cole, R Burnside, M Sorrel, K McArthur, S Elley, J Waugh (Coach), B Pizey (Physio). Front: A Fisher, D Boyce, K Clements, C Hore, R Burtenshaw, G Buck, S Dow.

Chairman: F P Faulkner   **Vice Chairman:** K L Ashman **President:** M Hibberd
Secretary: M C Richards, 124 Highbury Grove, Cosham, Portsmouth PO6 2RT (0705 263867).
Team Manager: Ernie Bradwell   **Asst Manager:** R Hillman   **Coach:** J Waugh.
Press Officer: **Physio:** Bill Pizey   **Comm Manager:**
Ground: Jubilee Park, Aston Road, Waterlooville PO7 7SZ (0705 263423 - office 254529).
Directions: Turn right off town by-pass (B2150) at Asda r-about. Dual carriage to next island, and return back towards town. Aston Road is first left. Nearest stations; Havant (4 miles), Cosham (5).
Capacity: 7,000 (1,500 Covered)   **Seats:** 480   **Floodlights:** Y   **Shop:** Y   **Metal Badges:** Y
Colours: White/navy/white   **Change colours:** Yellow & green/green/yellow & green.
Previous Leagues: Waterlooville & Dist/ Portsmouth 38-53/ Hants 1953-71.
Sponsors: Parkwood Developments Ltd.
Previous Grounds: Convent Ground 10-30/ Rowlands Avenue Recreation Ground 30-63.
Midweek home matchday: Tuesday   **Reserve Team's League:** Wessex Combination.
Record Attendance: 4,500 v Wycombe Wanderers F.A. Cup 1st Rd 1976-77.
Best F.A. Cup season: 1st Rd 2nd replay v Northampton, 83-84. Also 1st Rd 68-69 76-77 88-89.
League clubs defeated in F.A. Cup: None
Record Fees: Paid: £4,000 for Paul Moody (Fareham)   **Received:** For Paul Moody (Southampton).
Players progressing to Football League: Phil Figgins (Portsmouth 1973), Paul Hardyman (Portsmouth 1983), Guy Whittingham (Portsmouth via Yeovil Town 1988), Paul Moody (Southampton 1991).
Clubhouse: Jubilee Club open for all games (1st team & Res).   **Steward:** Babs Tomkins
Club Record Goalscorer: **Club Record Apps:**
91-92 Captain: D Burns   **91-92 P.o.Y.:** K Clements   **91-92 Top scorer:** Dave Boyce.
Local Newspapers (+Tel.Nos.): The News & Sports Mail.
Local Radio Stations: BBC Solent, Ocean Sound.
Hons: Southern Lg Div 1 Sth 71-72 (Lg Cup 86-87, R-up 82-83), Hants Lg R-up 69-70 (Div 2 59-60 64-65, Div 3 (East) R-up 53-54), Hants Snr Cup 69-70 72-73 84-85 (R-up 75-76 90-91), Russell Cotes Cup 88-89, P'smouth Lg 49-50 50-51 51-52 (Div 2 46-47, Div 3 38-39), P'smouth Snr Cup 68-69, P'smouth Victory Cup 59-60 69-70, FA Tphy 2nd Rd 76-77, FA Amtr Cup 1st Rd 59-60.

GOALKEEPERS:
Rob Stokes (Horndean), **Steve May** (Horndean)

DEFENDERS:
Simon Elley (Havant, Waterlooville, Havant, Portsmouth(J)), **Duncan Burns** (Waterford, Southampton), **Kevin Murphy** (Youth), **Martin Sorrell** (Havant, Fareham, Havant, Fareham), **Alex Fisher** (Aldershot), **Simon Ogbourn** (Portsmouth(J))

MIDFIELD:
Calvin Hore (Portsmouth, Waterlooville), **Steve Dow** (Local football), **Kevin McArthur** (Newport IOW, West Wight), **Paul Thomas** (Newport IOW, Fareham, Clanfield), **Russell Burtenshaw** (Basingstoke, Bognor Regis, Crawley, Dagenham, Wimbledon, Southampton), **Gary Cable** (Aldershot(T))

FORWARDS:
David Boyce (Crawley, Dover, Fisher, C Palace), **Dave Milkins** (Newport IOW, Waterlooville), **Kevin Clements** (Bognor Regis, Portsmouth(A)), **Ricky Burnside** (Bognor Regis, Waterlooville, Birkirkara(Malta), Waterlooville, Bournemouth), **Glenn Buck** (Gosport, Waterlooville, Fareham, Newport IOW)

Pages: 32 **Price:** 60p
Editor: Shaw Stenning
WMPCC Rating: 20

WEYMOUTH

Weymouth FC, Beazer Homes League Southern Division Runners-up 1991-92.

Chairman: P Sapsworth   **Team Manager:** L Drake.
Secretary: S Charlton, 74 Weymouth Bay Av, Weymouth, Dorset DT3 5AA (0305 775636).
Physio: Bob Lucas   **Press Officer:**   **Comm. Manager:** F Dunford.
Ground: Wessex Stadium, Radipole Lane, Weymouth, Dorset DT4 0TJ (0305 785558).
Directions: Arriving from Dorchester on A354, turn right at first two islands. Ground is signposted.
Capacity: 10,000 (6,000 Covered)   **Seats:** 900   **Floodlights:** Y   **Shop:** Y   **Metal Badges:** Y
Colours: Terra cotta/sky/sky   **Change colours:** All white   **Newsline:** 0898 122 924.
Previous Ground: Recreation Ground (until 1987).   **Sponsors:** Elizabethan Windows
Previous Leagues: Dorset Comb/ Western 1907-14 21-23 28-39 47-49/ Southern 23-28 49-79/ GMV Conf. 79-89.
Midweek home matchday: Wednesday   **Reserve Team's League:** Dorset Combination
Record Attendance: 5,500 v Manchester Utd, ground opening 1987.
Best F.A. Cup season: 4th Rd 61-62, 0-2 at Preston. 1st rd on 29 occasions 25-27 48-50 51-54 55-57 58-59 60-62 63-66 67-70 71-72 73-79 80-83 84-86.
League clubs defeated in F.A. Cup: Merthyr 24-25, A'shot 49-50, Shrewsbury 56-57, N'port 61-62, C'diff 82-83.
Record Fees: Paid: £15,000 for Shaun Teale (Northwich)   **Received:** £100,000 for Peter Guthrie (Spurs)
Players progressing to Football League: Reg Pickett & Brian Carter (P'smouth 1949 & 56), Stan Northover (Luton 1950), Edward Grant (Sheff U 1950), David Clelland (S'thorpe 1950), Alex Corbett (H'pool 1953), William Holt (Barrow 1954), Alex Smith (Acc'ton 1961), Graham Bond, Terry Spratt, Andy Donnelly & Micky Cave (T'quay 1961, 65, 67 & 68), Peter Leggett (Swindon 1962), Ron Fogg (A'shot 1963), Barry Hutchinson (L'coln 1965), Terry Gulliver & Richard Hill (B'mouth 1966 & 67), Alan Wool (R'ding 1971), Alan Beer (Exeter 1974), Bob Iles (C'sea 1978), Graham Roberts (Spurs 1980), Neil Townsend, Paul Morrell & John Smeulders (B'mouth 1979, 83 & 84), Tony Agana (W'ford), Andy Townsend & D Hughes (Soton), S Claridge (C Pal), B McGorry & Shaun Teale (B'mouth), Tony Pounder & R Evans (Bristol Rvrs).
Clubhouse: Public Bar & VP bar. Matchdays & functions.   **Steward:** Gordon Hollins.
Club Record Goalscorer: W Farmer, Haynes. 275   **Club Record Apps:** A Hobson 1,076
91-92 Captain: Steve Pugh   **91-92 P.o.Y.:** Gary Fullbrook   **91-92 Top scorer:** Tony Cook.
Local Newspapers (+Tel.Nos.): Dorset Evening Echo.   **Local Radio Stations:** 2CR (Bournemouth).
Honours: GMV Conf R-up 79-80 (Lg Cup 81-82), Premier Inter Lg Cup R-up 87-88 (QF 90-91), Southern Lg 64-65 65-66 (R-up 54-55 77-78, Lg Cup 72-73 (R-up 52-53 63-64 64-65 70-71 77-78), Southern Div R-up 91-92), Western Lg 22-23 (Div 2 33-34 36-37 (R-up 35-36 47-48)), Dorset Sen. Cup(24) 1893-94 98-1900 02-03 19-20 22-24 27-28 31-32 33-34 36-37 47-48 49-50 51-52 53-58 64-65 84-87 90-91, Mark Frowde Cup (12), FA Tphy 4th Rd rep. 76-77, FA Amateur Cup 1st Rd 1900.

GOALKEEPERS:
Sean Ford (Youth), **Steve Weaver** (Long term loan from Bristol City)

DEFENDERS:
Willie Gibson (Nuneaton Boro, Leicester C), **Derek Millen** (Youth), **Gary Fulbrook** (Gloucester, Bath, Carlisle, Bath, Swindon), **Steve Kidd** (Torquay(T)), **Gavin Sandrey** (Swindon(T), Weymouth), **Darren Corbridge** (Youth), **David Morris** (Poole, Bournemouth)

MIDFIELD:
Alex Browne (Youth), **Steve Pugh** (Exeter, Torquay, Wolves), **Ciaran Ryder** (Torquay(T)), **Chris Shaw** (Salisbury, Bath, Bournemouth), **Richard Bourne** (Bristol Rov(T)), **David Hughes** (Youth), **Allen Dean** (Exeter), **Graham Smith** (Paulton Rov)

FORWARDS:
Tony Cook (Bristol City(T)), **Steve Clifford** (Long term loan from Bristol City), **Darren McBride** (Youth), **Brendan King** (Youth), **Will Flint** (Dorchester, Royal Navy, Sutton Town), **Jorge Diaz** (Youth)

WEYMOUTH
Football Club.
Official Matchday Magazine
1991 - 1992

50p

Pages: 44 **Price:** 50p
Editor: F Dunford
WMPCC Rating: 29

Worcester City's Paul Bywater, who has since moved on to Gloucester, spectacularly clears a Marlow attack during the FA Cup Fourth Qualifying Round tie at St Georges Lane. Photo - Gary Cave.

Chairman: Michael Sorenson **Vice Chairman:** N Collins **President:** R H Mann
Secretary: Graham Jukes 136 Bilford Road, Worcester WR3 8PS (0905 55395).
Team Manager: Martyn Bennett **Asst Mgr:** Brian Robinson **Coach:** Mick Kearns
Press Officer: **Physio:** P O'Connell **Comm. Manager:** Christine Lines.
Ground: St Georges Lane, Barbourne, Worcester WR1 1QT (0905 23003).
Directions: A44 to Worcester from M5 junc. 7. Pass racecourse and follow A38 (to Bromsgrove). Ground on right. Foregate Street (BR) 1 mile.
Capacity: 4,749 (2,000 Covered) **Seats:** 1,223 **Floodlights:** Y **Shop:** Y **Metal Badges:** Y
Colours: Blue & white/blue/blue **Change colours:** All red **Sponsors:** Severnside Printers.
Previous Leagues: West Mids (Birmingham) 1902-38/ Southern 38-79/ Alliance Premier 79-85.
Previous Names: Worcester Rovers, Berwick Rangers (merged in 1902).
Midweek home matchday: Monday **Reserve Team's League:** No Reserves.
Record Attendance: 17,042 v Sheff Utd (lost 0-2), F.A. Cup 4th Rd 1959.
Best FA Cup year: 4th Rd 58-59. 1st Rd (10) 05-06 25-26 28-29 50-51 57-58 60-61 78-79 82-84 87-88.
League clubs defeated in F.A. Cup: Millwall, Liverpool 58-59, Plymouth 78-79, Wrexham 82-83, Aldershot 83-84.
Record Fees - Paid: £8,500 for Jim Williams (Telford) **Received:** £27,000 for John Barton (Everton)
Players progressing to Football League: John Goodwin (B'gham 1946), Tom Brown (P'smouth 1946), Gordon Medd (B'gham 1946), Henry Horton (B'burn 1947), Ron Baynham (Luton 1951), Arthur Lawiess (Plymouth 1955), Harry Knowles & Peter King (1959 & 60), Keith Ball (Walsall 1965), John Fairbrother (P'boro 1965), David Tennant (L'coln 1966), Roger Davies (Derby 1971), Neil Merrick (B'mouth 1974), John Barton (E'ton 1978), James Williams (Walsall 1979), Andy Awford (Portsmouth 1988), Andy Preece (Wrexham 1990), Mark Gayle (Walsall 1991), Des Lyttle (Swansea 1992).
Clubhouse: Two social clubs, VIP longe, bars etc. **Steward:** Mr & Mrs P Jefferies.
Club Record Goalscorer: Alex Hair **Club Record Apps:** Bobby McEwan.
91-92 Capt: Des Lyttle **91-92 P.o.Y:** Des Lyttle **91-92 Scorer:** Ollie Kearns/ Colin Robinson 24 each.
Local Newspapers: Berrows Journal, Worcester Evening News, Worcester Source.
Local Radio Stations: Radio Wyvern & BBC Hereford & Worcester **Newsline:** 0898 884 476.
Hons: Southern Lg 78-79 (Div 1 67-68, Div 1 Nth 76-77, Lg Cup R-up 45-46 59-60, Chal. Cup 39-40, Champs Cup 78-79), West Mids (B'ham) Lg(4) 13-14 24-25 28-30 (R-up(3) 31-34), Worcs Snr Cup(25) 07-14 28-30 32-33 45-46(jt) 48-49 55-59 60-61 62-63 64-65 69-70 77-78 79-80 81-82 83-84 87-88, B'ham Snr Cup 75-76, Staffs Snr Cup 76-77, Inter Lg Champs Cup 78-79, Welsh Cup SF 78-79, FA Tphy QF 69-70 73-74 80-81 81-82.

GOALKEEPERS:
Derek Dudley (Stourbridge, Sutton Coldfield, Aston Villa(T))
DEFENDERS:
Martyn Bennett (WBA), **Mark Jones** (Hereford, Shrewsbury, Birmingham, Brighton, Aston Villa), **Keiran Sullivan** (Buckingham, Banbury), **Des Lyttle** (Leicester C), **Darren Wright** (Wrexham, Wolves), **Dave Heywood** (Halesowen T, Burton Alb, Stafford R, Kettering, Wolves), **Darren Williams** (Banbury), **Martin Finn** (Tamworth, Sutton C, Paget R, Exeter, Sutton C)
MIDFIELD:
Matt Green (Wolves, Everton(Sch)), **Ronnie Walker** (Wolves Cas, Wolves Utd), **Rob Vassell** (Leicester C(T)), **Shaun Keough** (Youth), **Carl Fairhurst** (Youth), **Neil Tomlinson** (Swindon, Shrewsbury), **Paul Snowball** (Bloxwich, Paget R, Armitage)
FORWARDS:
Colin Robinson (Hereford, Birmingham, Shrewsbury, Mile Oak), **Dean Bridge** (Burton Alb, Leicester C), **Jason Wolverson** (Youth), **Stuart Stokes** (Bilston, Gresley R, Willenhall, Derby(T), Wolves(T)), **Jason Goddard** (Fairfield Villa), **Andy Widdowson** (Archdale'73), **Darren Tafft** (Bromsgrove R, Gillingham, Birmingham(T), Moor Green), **Leroy Hemans** (Walsall Wood, Halesowen T, Boldmere, Tividale, Sutton C, Solihull B, Highgate), **Paul Tester** (Cheltenham, Worcester, Hereford, Shrewsbury, Cheltenham)

WORCESTER CITY F.C.
Season 1991/92

Sutton Coldfield Town
7.30 pm Monday 2nd December
Beazer Homes League
Worcestershire Senior Cup
Second Round Replay

Pages: 32 **Price:** 70p
Editors: Pet Turrell & Julian Pugh

Beazer Homes (Southern) League Premier Division Ten Year Records

	82/3	83/4	84/5	85/6	86/7	87/8	88/9	89/90	90/1	91/2
Addlestone & Weybridge T.	20	–	–	–	–	–	–	–	–	–
Alvechurch	13	16	15	4	8	7	14	21	–	–
Ashford Town	–	–	–	–	–	12	18	19	–	–
Atherstone United	–	–	–	–	–	–	–	6	15	13
Aylesbury United	–	–	–	8	3	1	–	–	–	–
Bashley	–	–	–	–	–	–	–	–	10	4
Basingstoke Town	–	–	–	15	16	–	–	–	–	–
Bath City	–	–	–	–	–	–	9	2	–	–
Bedworth United	5	11	12	10	12	14	22	–	–	–
Bromsgrove Rovers	–	–	–	–	2	4	10	10	5	1
Burton Albion	–	–	–	–	–	16	8	4	7	10
Cambridge City	–	–	–	–	6	3	5	8	3	5
Chelmsford City	4	3	9	2	5	19	–	18	18	18
Cheltenham Town	–	8	1	–	–	–	–	–	–	–
Corby Town	15	14	11	13	9	10	16	20	–	14
Crawley Town	–	–	3	6	13	6	12	15	19	17
Dartford	6	1	–	–	4	2	2	3	13	6
Dorchester Town	9	19	–	–	–	11	13	14	11	11
Dover Athletic	–	–	–	–	–	–	6	1	4	2
Dudley Town	–	–	–	12	21	–	–	–	–	–
Enderby Town					(see Leicester United)					
Fareham Town	8	15	14	19	14	9	19	–	–	–
Farnborough Town	–	–	–	–	–	–	–	–	1	–
Fisher Athletic	–	2	8	3	1	–	–	–	–	21
Folkestone	–	7	7	9	22	–	–	–	–	–
Gloucester City	11	9	18	–	–	–	–	9	2	12
Gosport Borough	7	18	–	18	18	15	7	22	–	–
Gravesnd & Northfleet	10	4	13	20	–	–	–	7	21	22
Halesowen Town	–	–	–	–	–	–	–	–	8	8
Hastings Town	16	10	16	–	–	–	–	–	–	–
Kidderminster Harriers	2	–	–	–	–	–	–	–	–	–
King's Lynn	–	6	2	14	20	–	–	–	–	–
Leamington	1	13	20	–	–	–	–	–	–	–
Leicester United	17	–	–	–	–	8	20	–	–	–
Merthyr Tydfil	–	–	–	–	–	–	1	–	–	–
Moor Green	–	–	–	–	–	–	15	11	16	9
Nuneaton Borough	–	–	–	–	–	21	–	–	–	–
Poole Town	19	–	–	–	–	–	–	–	17	20
Redditch United	–	–	–	–	7	18	21	–	–	–
Road Sea Southampton	–	–	5	16	–	–	–	–	–	–
Rushden Town	–	–	–	–	–	–	–	–	14	–
Salisbury	–	–	–	–	19	–	–	–	–	–
Shepshed Charterhouse	–	–	10	7	11	13	–	–	–	–
Stourbridge	14	20	–	–	–	–	–	–	–	–
Sutton Coldfield Town	–	17	–	–	–	–	–	–	–	–
Trowbridge Town	–	–	19	–	–	–	–	–	–	–
V.S. Rugby	–	–	–	–	–	17	3	5	9	3
Waterlooville	18	–	–	–	–	–	17	16	20	15
Wealdstone	–	–	–	–	–	–	11	12	12	19
Welling United	3	12	6	1	–	–	–	–	–	–
Weymouth	–	–	–	–	–	–	17	22	–	–
Willenhall Town	–	–	4	11	15	20	–	–	–	–
Witney Town	12	5	17	17	17	22	–	–	–	–
Worcester City	–	–	–	5	10	5	4	13	6	16
No. of Clubs	15	16	14	12	14	13	12	16	18	20

Hastings captain Dean White receives the Southern Division championship trophy on 18th April. Photo - T S Blackman.

Midland Division

	P	W	D	L	F	A	Pts
Solihull Borough	42	29	10	3	92	40	97
Hednesford Town	42	26	13	3	81	37	91
Sutton Coldfield Town	42	21	11	10	71	51	74
Barry Town	42	21	6	15	88	56	69
Bedworth United	42	16	15	11	67	63	63
Nuneaton Borough	42	17	11	14	68	53	62
Tamworth	42	16	12	14	66	52	60
Rushden Town	42	16	12	14	69	63	60
Stourbridge	42	17	8	17	85	62	59
Newport AFC	42	15	13	14	72	60	58
Yate Town	42	14	15	13	65	64	57
Bilston Town	42	15	10	17	56	67	55
Grantham Town	42	11	17	14	59	55	50
King's Lynn	42	13	11	18	61	68	50
Hinckley Town	42	14	8	20	61	87	50
Leicester United	42	12	13	17	56	63	49
Bridgnorth Town	42	12	12	18	61	74	48
R.C. Warwick	42	11	14	17	45	61	47
Stroud	42	14	4	24	66	88	46
Redditch United	42	12	8	22	52	92	44
Alvechurch	42	11	10	21	54	88	43
Dudley Town	42	8	9	25	41	92	33

Top Scorers

C Burton (Solihull Borough)	28
S Burr (Hednesford Town)	27
M Hallam (Leicester United)	26
J O'Connor (Hednesford Town)	25
C Summers (Barry Town)	24
G Hardwick (Bedworth United)	23
K Thaws (Yate Town)	23

THE BEAZER HOMES MIDLAND DIVISION RESULT CHART 1991-92

HOME TEAM	1	2	3	4	5	6	7	8	9	10	11	12	13	14	15	16	17	18	19	20	21	22
1. Alvechurch	*	0-5	1-3	1-0	2-2	2-1	0-0	1-3	0-0	1-1	1-3	2-0	1-0	1-3	0-0	3-2	2-1	2-4	1-2	2-2	2-3	2-0
2. Barry T.	2-1	*	3-1	3-1	1-4	0-1	1-3	0-2	10-0	1-1	2-1	2-2	2-1	5-0	4-0	1-1	1-3	2-1	4-1	2-1	0-2	1-2
3. Bedworth Utd	1-2	0-4	*	3-3	0-0	2-2	3-2	1-1	3-1	2-2	0-2	3-2	0-0	2-1	1-1	0-0	0-2	1-3	3-1	1-1	1-0	0-0
4. Bilston T.	1-3	3-0	3-0	*	1-1	1-4	2-2	0-4	1-2	3-1	2-1	2-2	0-1	4-2	1-0	3-0	0-2	0-0	4-1	0-1	2-1	2-1
5. Bridgnorth T.	2-2	3-2	0-3	2-3	*	3-1	2-4	0-4	2-3	2-0	1-3	1-1	0-1	0-4	2-1	2-1	0-3	0-1	5-2	1-2	1-4	0-0
6. Dudley T.	0-0	0-6	0-3	0-2	0-1	*	1-1	1-2	0-1	2-0	0-0	2-1	2-0	2-3	1-2	1-4	0-2	2-1	0-2	1-6	3-2	2-3
7. Grantham T.	2-2	0-1	1-1	2-2	1-2	6-0	*	0-0	2-2	0-0	1-1	3-3	1-1	1-0	2-1	4-1	0-1	0-0	0-1	0-2	2-1	1-2
8. Hednesford T.	6-0	3-0	0-1	3-0	1-0	0-0	2-1	*	2-0	2-1	3-3	2-1	2-2	2-1	3-0	2-1	1-1	1-1	3-1	1-1	0-0	1-1
9. Hinckley T.	1-3	1-2	1-3	1-1	2-3	3-0	2-4	1-1	*	0-4	0-0	1-3	2-2	1-4	4-2	2-1	4-5	3-2	3-0	1-2	1-0	4-1
10. King's Lynn	4-3	3-2	1-3	0-0	0-0	2-0	4-1	0-0	1-1	*	2-5	3-1	2-1	1-0	4-0	1-3	1-2	0-2	3-1	2-2	2-4	1-2
11. Leicester Utd	2-0	1-1	2-3	0-0	3-5	2-0	1-3	0-1	2-0	4-5	*	0-0	2-1	2-1	1-2	3-3	1-1	2-2	0-1	0-1	0-1	
12. Newport AFC	3-0	1-0	1-1	0-0	1-1	3-1	1-1	0-2	5-1	3-1	0-1	*	3-2	5-0	0-1	1-3	1-1	0-4	1-0	2-2	0-3	2-2
13. Nuneaton B	5-2	0-1	3-1	1-1	2-1	5-0	1-0	1-2	2-0	1-0	2-0	2-0	*	0-1	5-0	2-1	1-1	2-2	2-0	1-1	3-3	1-2
14. R C Warwick	0-0	1-1	2-2	1-2	1-1	1-2	1-3	0-1	1-0	1-0	0-2	0-0	*	3-2	1-1	0-0	2-0	2-2	0-0	0-0	2-3	
15. Redditch Utd	1-2	0-4	1-1	4-1	3-2	1-0	1-1	1-2	2-1	0-2	0-1	0-5	0-2	4-1	*	2-2	0-4	2-1	2-1	0-2	1-3	2-0
16. Rushden T.	1-0	0-3	0-1	1-0	1-1	0-0	1-1	1-1	3-1	2-0	3-3	0-3	2-3	3-1	4-4	*	2-2	3-1	2-0	1-2	3-2	2-0
17. Solihull Boro'	2-1	2-1	0-1	3-1	2-1	33-	2-0	6-1	4-1	1-1	0-0	3-1	3-1	4-0	1-1	2-0	*	1-0	2-1	3-1	2-1	4-1
18. Stourbridge	5-1	2-2	3-1	2-1	3-3	5-1	0-2	1-3	3-1	4-0	2-1	2-3	4-1	1-2	5-0	2-3	1-1	*	2-1	2-3	4-1	1-1
19. Stroud	5-2	2-1	2-1	3-1	4-1	4-0	2-0	0-3	0-2	2-3	5-0	2-3	3-2	0-0	4-5	2-5	1-2	2-1	*	0-2	3-2	1-2
20. Sutton C'field	3-2	3-1	2-6	0-1	1-0	3-1	0-2	2-0	1-2	2-1	0-1	1-1	2-3	0-0	3-2	0-0	2-3	2-1	5-0	*	1-1	3-0
21. Tamworth	2-0	2-3	2-2	0-1	0-0	1-1	2-0	2-3	0-2	2-1	3-0	1-0	2-2	0-0	1-1	1-0	1-1	1-0	4-0	0-1	*	2-2
22. Yate T.	5-1	0-1	2-2	4-0	0-0	3-3	2-2	2-3	1-1	0-0	1-1	1-5	1-0	1-1	5-0	1-2	3-4	3-1	0-0	3-0	1-3	*

BARRI

Barry Town's Ray John and Roger Mullen jump to challenge Dorking's Carey Anderson as the Linnet's go down 1-2 in the Third Qualifying Round of the FA Trophy. Photo - Dave West.

Chairman: N O'Halloran   **President:**
Secretary: Alan Whelan, 166 Jenner Road, Barry, South Glamorgan CF6 8HR (0446 737188).
Team Manager: Ian Love   **Asst Manager:** Phil McNeil   **Coach:** Alan Curtis
Press Officer: John Lowrie   **Physio:** Johnny Prosser   **General Mgr:** C Aust.
Ground: *(Jenner Park, Barry, South Glamorgan CF6 7BG (0446 731171))* **N.B.** Until further notice, Barri will be playing at Worcester City FC - see page 487.
Directions & Ground details: As Worcester City (page 487).   **Shop:** Y   **Metal Badges:** N
Colours: Green/navy/green   **Change colours:** White/black/white.   **Sponsors:** Welsh Brewers Ltd.
Previous Leagues: Western 08-13/ Southern 13-82/ Welsh 82-89.   **Previous Name:** Barry (1891-1922).
Midweek home matchday: Wednesday   **Reserve Team's League:**
Record Attendance: 7,400 v QPR, FA Cup 1st Rd 1961 (drew 1-1 before a 1-5 defeat).
Best F.A. Cup season: 2nd Rd 29-30. 1st Rd on six occasions; 29-30 34-35 51-52 61-62 84-85.
Record Fees - Paid: **Received:** £1,000 for Derek Tapscott (Arsenal).
Players progressing to Football League: Chris Simmonds (M'wall 1947), Jack Brown (I'wich 1948), Des Tennant (B'ton 1948), Terry Elwell & Ian Love (S'sea 1948 & 86), Rob McLaren & Ron Howells (C'diff 1950), Charles Cairney & Dai Ward (Brist R 1953 & 54), D Tapscott (A'nal 1953), Jim McGhee & Laurie Sheffield & Gordon Fraser & Robert Ferguson & Roger Green & Mike Coslett & Phil Green (N'port 1954 & 62 & 66 & 69 & 72 & 78 & 84), Tom Quigley (P'smouth 1955), Brian Keating (Crewe 1956), James Hartnett (H'pool 1957), Richard Twigg (Notts C 1957), Peter Isaac (N'hampton 1962), Keith Webber (E'ton 1960), Robert Delgado & Gerry Jones (L'ton 1970 & 72), Chris Pike (F'ham 1985).
Clubhouse: Open 6-11pm Mon-Fri, 12-11pm Sat, 12-3pm & 7-10.30 Sun. Pool, darts, juke box.
Steward: Charlie Dyke.   **Previous Name:** Barry Town 1923-1992.
Club Record Goalscorer: Clive Ayres   **Club Record Apps:** Basil Bright.
91-92 Captain: **91-92 P.o.Y.:**   **91-92 Top scorer:**
Local Newspapers (+Tel.Nos.): Barry & District News, South Wales Echo.
Local Radio Stations: Radio Wales, Red Dragon Radio.   **Newsline:** 0898 122 923.
Hons: FA Tphy 3rd Qual Rd rep. 90-91, Southern Lg R-up 20-21, Western Lg R-up 11-12, Welsh Lg(6) 82-87 88-89 (R-up 87-88, Lg Cup 34-35 46-47 82-83), Welsh Cup 54-55, South Wales Snr Amtr Cup(12) 26-27 35-36 37-38 52-54 58-60 65-66 75-76 77-78 86-88, SA Brain Cup 78-79 82-83 86-87.

GOALKEEPERS:
John Roberts (Cardiff C)
DEFENDERS: Ross Knight (Northfield), **Ray John** (Ton Pentre, Happy Valley(HK), Plymouth, Cardiff Corr), **Willie Batchelor** (Worcester, Highgate Utd), **Martin Lander** (RC Warwick, Gloucester, Stourbridge, Kidderminster, Wolves(J), Aston Villa(J)), **Keith Brown** (Evesham, Stourbridge, Evesham, Alvechurch, Wolves, Birmingham(A))
MIDFIELD:
Paul Giles (Merthyr, Newport Co, Merthyr, Newport Co, Excelsior(Holl), SVV Scheidam(Holl), Cardiff C), **Dave Moreby** (Stourbridge, Highgate, Bilston, Highgate, Paget R, Highgate), **Keith Sievewright** (Redditch, Tamworth, Hinckley T, Nuneaton B, Solihull B, Stratford, Moor Green), **Ian Mitchell** (Solihull B, Banbury, King's Heath, Willenhall, Nuneaton B, Highgate, Moor Green, Solihull B), **Brian Hughes** (Gloucester, Cheltenham, Torquay, Swindon)
FORWARDS:
Hugh Ledgister (Cradley, Dudley, Willenhall, Bedworth, Dudley, Atherstone, Dudley, Oldswinford, Dudley), **Joey Dowling** (Sherwood Celtic, Moor Green), **Paul Hunter** (Cradley, Sutton C, Halesowen T, Paget R), **Michael Gray** (Highgate Utd), **Lance Morrison** (Sutton C, Gloucester, Nuneaton B, Alvechurch, Moor Green, King's Heath)

Pages: 20 **Price:** 50p
Editor: Chris Anst
WMPCC Rating: 26

BEDWORTH UNITED

Bedworth United's new £150,000 grandstand.

Chairman: Mr A Robinson **President:** Mr H Jones.
Secretary: Malcolm Wilson, 42 Arden Road, Bulkington, Nuneaton, Warwickshire (0203 490445).
Team Manager: Brendan Phillips **Asst Mgr:** Bobby Vincent **Coach:** Tim Smithers
Press Officer: Chairman **Physio:** John Roberts
Commercial Manager: Mick Stebleton
Ground Address & Tel: The Oval, Miners Welfare Park, Coventry Road, Bedworth CV12 8NN (0203 314302).
Directions: On B4113 Coventry to Bedworth road, near town centre next to swimming bath. One and a half miles from M6 junction 3.
Capacity: 2,300 (2,000 Covered) **Seats:** 300 **Floodlights:** Y **Shop:** Y **Metal Badges:** Y
Colours: Green/white/green **Change colours:** Yellow/green/yellow.
Sponsors: Elliott Sales (1990).
Previous Leagues: Birmingham Comb 47-54/ West Mids Lg 54-72.
Previous Name: Bedworth Town (47-68).
Midweek home matchday: Tuesday **Reserve Team's League:** Scoreline Combination (Reserve Div).
Record Attendance: 5,127 v Nuneaton, Southern Lg 1982.
Best F.A. Cup season: 4th Qualifying Rd 1983/89/90
League clubs defeated in F.A. Cup: None.
Record Fees - Paid: £625 for Adrian Waters **Received:** £8,000 for I Hathaway (Mansfield).
Players progressing to Football League: Phil Huffer (Derby 1953), Geoff Coleman (N'hampton 1955), Ian Hathaway (Mansfield 1989).
Clubhouse: Social club open normal hours (including weekend lunchtimes). Hot and cold food, pool, darts.
Steward: Harold Jones.
Club Record Goalscorer: Peter Spacey (1949-69) **Club Record Apps:** Peter Spacey.
91-92 Captain: **91-92 P.o.Y.:** **91-92 Top scorer:**
Local Newspapers (+Tel.Nos.): Bedworth Echo (312785/319548), Coventry Evening Telegraph (0203 633633)
Local Radio Stations: Mercia Sound, BBC CWR.
Hons: FA Tphy 2nd Rd 80-81, Birmingham Comb.(2) 48-50, Birmingham Snr Cup(3) 78-79 80-82.

GOALKEEPERS:
Paul O'Connor (Hinckley T, Leicester C), **Trevor Hopps** (Nuneaton B, Rushden, Gloucester, Rushden, Buckingham)

DEFENDERS:
Adrian Piggon (Nuneaton B), **Shaun McGrory** (VS Rugby, Burnley, Coventry C), **Dale Osborne** (Local football), **Dave Emslie** (Local football), **Peter Wilkins** (Bulkington)

MIDFIELD:
Tim Smithers (Atherstone, Nuneaton B, Oxford Utd, Nuneaton B), **Paul Thomas** (Aylesbury, Bedworth, Nuneaton B, Bedworth), **Stewart Hamill** (Spalding, Boston Utd, Scarborough, Altrincham, Nuneaton B, Kettering, Northampton, Leicester C, Pollock), **Darren Ward** (Local football), **Nicky Anderson** (Leek, Grantham, Nuneaton B, Mansfield, Lincoln, Leicester C)

FORWARDS:
Gary Hardwick (Stratford, Bedworth, Atherstone, Stratford, Coventry C(T)), **Colin Taylor** (Hinckley T, Leicester Utd, Wigston F, Anstey Nomads, Gresley R), **Peter McBean** (Atherstone, Corby, Nuneaton B, Coventry Sporting, VS Rugby, Aylesbury, Bedworth), **Paul Wilson** (Atherstone)

PROGRAMME DETAILS:
Pages: 20 **Price:** 50p
Editor: Peter Thompson
WMPCC Rating: 21

BILSTON TOWN

Bilston put Redditch United under extreme pressure during a Beazer Homes League Midland Division fixture at their Queen Street ground. Photo - Keith Clayton.

Chairman: David Cartwright **Vice Chairman:** K Nicholls.
Secretary (Add & Tel): Morris Baker, 27 Wimborne Road, Fallings Park, Wolverhampton (0902 71175).
Team Manager: Steve Bowater **Asst Manager:** Michael Babb
Commercial Manager: Terry Brumpton (Midland Sports Promotions) 0902 671171.
Ground Address & Tel: Queen Street, Bilston WV14 7EX (0902 491498).
Directions: M6 junction 10, A454 towards Wolverhampton then pick up A563 towards Bilston and turn left into Beckett Street after a little over a mile. 3 miles from Wolverhampton (BR), bus 545 passes ground.
Capacity: 7,000 (400 Covered) **Seats:** 400 **Floodlights:** Y **Shop:** Y **Metal Badges:** Y
Colours: Tangerine/black/tangerine **Change colours:** All white.
Sponsors: Second City Homes/ Cartwright Homes.
Previous Name: Bilston Utd 1895-1932/ Bilston **Previous Ground:** Pounds Lane 1895-1921.
Previous Leagues: Birmingham Comb 07-21 48-54/ West Mids 21-32 54-85.
Midweek home matchday: Tuesday **Reserve Team's League:**
Record Attendance: 7,000 v Halifax Town, FA Cup 1968.
Best F.A. Cup season: 2nd Rd replay 72-73. Also 1st Rd 68-69.
League clubs defeated in F.A. Cup: None.
Record Fees - Paid: **Received:**
Players progressing to Football League: R Ellows (Birmingham), James Fletcher (Birmingham 1950), Stan Crowther (A Villa 1955), Ron Pountney (Southend 1975), K Price (Gillingham), Campbell Chapman (Wolves 1984).
Clubhouse: Bilston Town Football & Social, Queen Street, is open every night and weekend lunchtimes. Usual club activities.
91-92 Captain: **91-92 P.o.Y.:** **91-92 Top scorer:**
Local Newspapers (+Tel.Nos.): Expess & Star, Evening Mail.
Local Radio Stations: Radio West Mids, WABC (Wol'ton), Beacon (Wol'ton), BRMB.
Honours: FA Tphy 2nd Rd 70-71 74-75, FA Vase 4th Rd 85-86, West Mids Lg 60-61 72-73 (R-up 22-23 70-71 73-74 74-75 75-76 84-85, Lg Cup 72-73 (R-up 65-66), Div 2 56-57), Birmingham Comb R-up 07-08 53-54, Staffs Senior Cup 57-58 59-60 60-61 61-62 (R-up 56-57 64-65 85-86), Birmingham Junior Cup 1895-96, Wednesbury Charity Cup 80-81 81-82 82-83 84-85 (R-up 83-84).

GOALKEEPERS:
Gary Gibbs (Bridgnorth), **Alan Pemberton** (Hednesford, Halesowen T, GKN Sankey, Shifnal, Allbrighton)
DEFENDERS:
Tommy Crook (Willenhall), **Gary Jones** (Chasetown, Bilston, Willenhall, Walsall Wood, Chasetown, Heath Hayes), **Mark Bowater** (Willenhall, Mile Oak, Rushall O, Shrewsbury), **Steve Frisby** (Newport T, Bridgnorth, Walsall(A)), **Neil Manton** (Youth), **Paul Wilde** (Wednesfield), **Paul Clarke** (Sandwell, Dudley, Boldmere)
MIDFIELD:
Simon Russon (Stourbridge, Willenhall, Bilston, Oldswinford, Wolves(A), Bilston), **Mark Hutchinson** (Sutton C, Willenhall, Nuneaton, Carlisle Utd, Leicester C, A Villa(A)), **Andy Ratcliffe** (Pelsall V), **John Rhodes** (Willenhall, Halesowen T, Tipton, Oldbury, WBA(Sch)), **Steve Mead** (Bromsgrove, Atherstone, Blakenall, Bilston, Willenhall, Redditch, Dudley, Alvechurch, A Villa(T)), **Clive Walker** (Darlaston, Bilston)
FORWARDS:
Micky Richards (Paget R, Mile Oak, Sutton C, Boldmere), **John Baker** (Willenhall, Dudley, Willenhall, Paget R, Bilston, Redditch, Banbury, Worcester, Oldbury, Redditch, Banbury, Witney, Oxford Utd), **Andy Hodgetts** (Nuneaton B, Stourbridge, Shrewsbury(A)), **Phil Bates** (Youth)

PROGRAMME DETAILS:
Pages: 32 **Price:** 50p
Editor: Jeff Calloway
WMPCC Rating: 23

Bridgnorth Town 1991-92.

Chairman: Joe Heseltine   **Vice Chairman:** Martin Lewis **President:** Mike Williams
Secretary: Gordon Thomas, 7 Meadow Close, Oldbury Wells, Bridgnorth WV16 5HY (0746 765178).
Team Manager: Billy Ball   **Asst Mgr:** Bob Macauley   **Coach:** Bob Macauley
Press Officer: Secretary   **Physio:** Carlton Leonard
Commercial Manager: Terry Brumpton (0902 671171).
Ground: Crown Meadow, Innage Lane, Bridgnorth, Salop WV16 6PZ (0746 762747/766064).
Directions: Fork left into Innage Lane off High Street, ground 200 yds on left.
Capacity: 1,600 (400 Covered)   **Seats:** 240   **Floodlights:** Y   **Shop:** Y **Metal Badges:** Y
Colours: Blue/white/blue   **Change colours:** All red.   **Sponsors:** None.
Previous Name: St Leonards Old Boys (prior to the current club's formation in 1946).
Previous Leagues: Kidderminster & District (until 68)/ Midland Combination 68-83.
Midweek home matchday: Tuesday   **Reserve Team's League:** Midland Combination (Reserve Div).
Record Attendance: 1,600 v South Shields, FA Vase 1976.
Best F.A. Cup season: 3rd Qualifying Rd 64-65.
League clubs defeated in F.A. Cup: None.
Record Fees - Paid: **Received:** £10,000 for Delwyn Humphreys (to Kidderminster Harriers).
Players progressing to Football League: Roger Davies (Derby County).
Clubhouse: Open every evening and weekend lunchtimes. Darts, pool, fruit machines, dancehall. Hot meals on matchdays.
Club Record Goalscorer: Roger Davies 157   **Club Record Apps:** Kevin Harris 426.
91-92 Captain: Kevin Harris   **91-92 P.O.Y.:** Carl Whitehouse   **91-92 Top scorer:** Billy Balshaw 14.
Local Newspapers: Shropshire Star, Bridgnorth Journal, Express & Star.
Local Radio Stations: Beacon, BBC Radio Shropshire.
Honours: FA Vase 5th Rd 75-76, Midland Combination 79-80 82-83 (R-up 76-77 80-81, Lg Cup 78-79, Tony Allden Memorial Cup R-up), Kidderminster & District Lg, Shropshire Snr Cup 85-86, Shropshire County Cup 70-71 75-76 76-77 78-79 79-80, Welsh Amateur Cup 70-71, Shropshire Junior Cup - Bridgnorth are the only Shropshire side to have won all three county cups.

GOALKEEPERS:
Carl Whitehouse (Gl(Orkney), Halesowen T, Dudley, Willenhall, Hednesford, Bilston, Ikast(Den), Boston Utd, Nuneaton B, WBA, Newport T, GKN Sankey)
DEFENDERS:
Andy Rich (Willenhall, Bridgnorth, GKN Sankey, Shrewsbury(J), Wolves(J)), **Mark Minikin** (Broseley, GKN Sankey), **Kevin Harris** (Shifnal, Stafford R, Oakengates, Madeley Utd), **Mark Duncombe** (Dudley, Stourbridge, Willenhall, Bilston, Wolves), **Carleton Leonard** (Newtown, Oswestry, Rhyl, Oswestry, Cardiff C, Hereford, Shrewsbury)
MIDFIELD:
Larry Chambers (Dudley, Bilston, Paget R, Walsall Wood, Stourbridge, Sutton C, Oldbury, Sutton C), **Andy Taylor** (Welshpool), **Mick Davidson** (Telford), **Richard Mackreath** (Broseley), **Richard Morris** (Telford), **Sam Pearce** (Broseley)
FORWARDS:
Billy Balshaw (Donnington Wood), **Paul Evans** (Bilston, Hednesford, Bridgnorth, Hednesford, Bridgnorth, GKN Sankey, WBA(A)), **Charlie Blakemore** (Chasetown, Bilston, Shifnal), **Ian Clarke** (Newtown, Caersws, Rhyl, Caernarfon, Oswestry), **John Wainwright** (Willenhall, Bilston, Hednesford, Dudley, Hednesford, Bilston, Bromsgrove, Bilston, Willenhall)

Season 1991/92
BRIDGNORTH
Town Football Club

MIDLAND DIVISION

Match Day Magazine 50p

Pages: 24 **Price:** 50p
Editor: Melvyn Morgan
WMPCC Rating: 15

DUDLEY TOWN

Dudley keeper Steve Carter makes an excellent point blank save from a header by Worcester striker Ollie Kearns as the Robins lose 2-3 at home in the Third Qualifying Round of the FA Trophy. Photo - Gary Cave.

Chairman: Mr N D Jeynes   **Treasuer:** Mr B W Woodall
Secretary: Tony Turpin, 24 Andrew Drive, Short Heath, Willenhall WV12 5PP (0922 475541).
Manager: Malcolm Woodbine   **Asst Mgr:** M Washington   **Coach:** E Whitehouse
Physio: **Press Officer:** Secretary   **Commercial Manager:** Brian Woodall.
Ground: The Round Oak Stadium, John Street, Brierley Hill (0384 263478/78560).
Directions: From Dudley take the A461 towards Stourbridge for about 2 miles and on entering Brierley Hill turn right into on B4180 into John Street, ground 200 yds on right. Two and a half miles from Stourbridge (BR).
Capacity: 3,000 (300 Covered)   **Seats:** 232   **Floodlights:** Y   **Shop:** Y   **Metal Badges:** Y
Colours: Red/white/black   **Change colours:** All yellow.   **Sponsors:** Thornleigh Freight.
Previous Leagues: West Mids (previously Birmingham) 1898-1915 35-38 53-82/ Midland (Worcs) Combination 29-32/ Birmingham Combination 32-35 45-53.
Previous Grounds: The Sports Centre, Birmingham Road, until 1985.
Midweek home matchday: Wednesday   **Record Fee Received:** £25,000 for Gary Piggott.
Record Gate: 3,000 v West Bromwich Albion, pre-season friendly 1991. *(At old ground; 16,500 for the official opening (a representative game) in 1936).*
Best F.A. Cup season: 1st Rd replay 76-77 (v York).   **League clubs defeated in F.A. Cup:** None.
Players progressing to Football League: Albert Broadbent (Notts Co 1952), Joe Mayo (W'sall 1972), Ken Price (Southend 1976), Andy Reece (Brist Rov 1987), Russell Bradley (Nottm Forest 1988), John Muir (D'caster 1989), Gary Piggott (WBA 1991).
Clubhouse: Dudley Town Sports & Social Club, John Street, Brierley Hill. Open nightly and weekend lunchtimes. Bar, lounge bar, ballroom, bowling green etc. **Steward:** Brian Woodall.
Record Scorer: Frank Treagust, 56 (47-48).   **Club Record Apps:** Brendon Hackett & John Muir, 55.
91-92 Captain: Chris Field   **91-92 P.O.Y.:** Barry Young   **91-92 Top scorer:** John Baker 12.
Local Newspapers: Express & Star, Dudley Evening Mail, Birmingham Post, Sunday Mercury.
Local Radio Stations: Beacon Radio, BRMB, BBC Radio West Midlands.
Honours: FA Tphy 2nd Rd 84-85, Southern Lg Midland Div 84-85, B'ham Comb 33-34 (R-up 34-35 47-48), Midland (Worcs) Comb 31-32 (R-up 29-30 30-31), West Mids Lg Cp R-up 75-76 (Div 2 Cp R-up 80-81), B'ham Senior Cp 85-86 (R-up 64-65 83-84), Worcs Senior Cp 45-46(joint)(R-up 84-85), Camkin Cp 64-65, Worcs Junior Cp 83-84.

GOALKEEPERS:
Ian Scarr (Stourport Swifts)
DEFENDERS: Chris Field (Lye), Kevin Hampton (Cradley), Paul Whitehead (Rushall Olympic), Alan Edwards (Oldswinford), Giles Parry (Lye), Steve Moore (Halesowen T), Anton Day (Lye, Halesowen H, Sandwell B, Stourbridge, Dudley, Boldmere), Stuart Foxall (Oldbury), Mark Clifton (Stourport S)
MIDFIELD: Neil Morgan (Wednesfield), Steve Field (Lye, Halesowen T), Matthew Green (Oldswinford), Neil Sproston (Oldswinford, Armitage, Alvechurch, Birmingham), Chris Mason (Lye), Phil Cartwright (Oldswinford), Kevin Woodbine (Oldswinford)
FORWARDS: Gary Nettleford (Tividale, Bilston, Tividale), Steve Morgan (Cradley, Willenhall, Moor Green, Wolves(T)), Andy Hodgetts (Bilston, Nuneaton B, Stourbridge, Shrewsbury(A)), Lee Young (Halesowen T, Lye, Dudley), Gavin Whitehouse (Rushall Olym, Stourbridge, Halesowen T, Alvechurch, Stourbridge, Alvechurch, Dudley, Tipton, Dudley)

DUDLEY TOWN FOOTBALL CLUB

SEASON 1991-92

Sponsored By THORNLEIGH FREIGHT LTD.

Pages: 32 **Price:** 50p
Editor: Brian Woodall
WMPCC Rating: 20

Formed: 1945

EVESHAM UNITED

The Robins

Evesham United pictured after being presented with the Influence Midland Combination championship shield at Armitage on Saturday 19th May. Evesham had trailed Armitage for the majority of the season, and had they not clinched the title with a 1-0 win at Chelmsley Town in the preceding week, the match at Armitage on FA Cup final morning would have been a championship decider. It was just as well from Evesham's point of view that it wasn't as Armitage won 3-1! Photo - James Wright.

Chairman: S G T Reeves   **Vice Chairman:** R H Stanley.   **President:** M E H Davies
Secretary: M J Peplow, 68 Woodstock Rd, St Johns, Worcester (0905 425993).
Manager: Dave Clements.   **Coach:** Ricky Harber.   **General Mgr:** Micky Brennan.
Press Officer: Graham Hill (0905 351653)   **Commercial Consultant:** Dave Boddy (0831 464517).
Ground: Common Rd, Evesham, Worcs. (0386 2303)
Ground Directions: From Evesham High Street turn into Swan Lane, then down Conduit Hill, into Common Rd, ground at end of narrow lane on right. 10 minutes walk from Evesham (BR).
Seats: 300   **Capacity:** 2,500   **Cover:** 350   **Club Shop:** Y   **Metal Badges:** Y
Clubhouse: Open Matchdays only.   **Midweek matches:** Tuesday   **Sponsors:** Safeway.
Colours: Red & white stripes/red/red   **Change Colours:** Blue & white stripes/black/black
Previous Name: Evesham Town   **Previous Ground:** The Crown Meadow
Midweek Matchday: Wednesday   **Reserve's League:** Midland Comb. Reserve Div.
Previous League: Birmingham Comb./ Midland Comb. 51-55 65-92/ West Midlands Regional 55-62.
Record Gate: 1,502 v Aston Villa, Kevin Mullen testimonial, February 12/2/92.
Record Fee Paid: £1,000; to Alcester for Kevin Mullen (Nov '91), to Malvern for Darren Bullock (June '92).
Record Fee Received: £5,000 for Simon Brain (to Cheltenham Town).
Players who have progressed to Football League: Billy Tucker, Gary Stevens (Cardiff 1977), Kevin Rose (Lincoln 1978), Andy Preece (Northampton 1986), Simon Brain (Hereford, via Cheltenham Town).
Club Record Scorer: **Club Record Appearances:**
91-92 Captain: Sean Cotterill   **91-92 P.o.Y:** Chris Taylor   **91-92 Top Scorer:** Bob Candy 26.
Local Press: Evesham Journal (0386 765678), Worcester Evening News (0905 748200), Gloucester Echo.
Local Radio Stations: Radio Wyvern, BBC Hereford & Worcester.   **Newsline:** 0891 664 388
Hons: FA Amtr Cup R-up 23-24, FA Vase QF 91-92, Worcs Snr Urn(2) 76-78 (R-up 90-91), Mids Comb.(6) 52-53 54-55 65-66 67-69 91-92 (Chal. Cup 53-54 87-88 91-92 (R-up(5) 54-55 71-72 83-84 88-90)), Worcs Comb. 52-53 54-55; B'gham Comb. R-up 30-31, Evesham Hosp. Cup 89-90

GOALKEEPERS:
Chris Taylor (Halesowen T, Bromsgrove)

DEFENDERS:
Nigel Russell (Malvern, Metal Box), **Ricky Hooman** (Malvern, Redditch, Moreton), **Trevor Whittington** (Telford Utd, Redditch, Northfield), **Sean Cotterill** (Malvern, Metal Box, Stourbridge), **Micky Rivers** (Malvern, Bromsgrove), **Nick Hyde** (Solihull B, Kidderminster)

MIDFIELD:
Ian Brown (Alcester, Bromsgrove, Alvechurch, Bromsgrove), **Chas Jones** (Malvern, Metal Box), **Tim Hall** (Malvern), **Stuart Sadler** (Redditch, Stafford R, Walsall), **Matt Forman** (Oldbury, Worcester, Moor Green, Burton Alb, Wolves, Aston Villa), **Darren Bullock** (Malvern, Redditch, Worcester, Malvern, Worcester), **Colin Day** (Hayes, Thorn EMI)

FORWARDS:
Joe Rawle (Malvern, Ledbury), **Kevin Mullen** (Alcester, Moor Green, Redditch, Moor Green, Evesham, Studley Sporting), **Rob Candy** (Moreton, Ledbury, Worcester), **Scott Crane** (Youth)

PROGRAMME DETAILS:
Pages: 36 **Price:** 50p
Editor: Graham Hill
WMPCC Rating: N/A

FOREST GREEN ROVERS Rovers

The official relaunch of Forest Green Rovers in May 1992. Photo - Gloucester Citizen.

Chairman: Andy Coburn **President:** G C Mills, MBE.
Secretary: Colin Peake, C/O Western Thermal Ltd, Unit 14, Springfield Business Centre, Stonehouse, Gloucestershire GL10 3SX (0452 523126).
Team Manager: Geoff Medcroft **Asst Manager:** Chris Gardner.
Press Officer: Andy Coburn (0453 828515). **Physio:** Adrian Tandy.
Commercial Manager: Duncan Roberts.
Ground: 'The Lawn', Nympsfield Road, Forest Green, Nailsworth, Glos. GL6 0ET (0453 834860).
Directions: About 4 miles south of Stroud on A46 to Bath. In Nailsworth turn right into Spring Hill off mini r'bout - ground approximately 1 mile up hill on left. The nearest BR station is Stroud.
Capacity: 1,995 (800 Covered) **Seats:** 200 **Floodlights:** Y **Shop:** Y **Metal Badges:**
Colours: Black & white stripes/black/red **Change colours:** Red/white/white.
Sponsors: Sheffield Insulations.
Previous Leagues: Stroud 1890-1921/ Glos Northern Snr 22-67/ Glos County 69-73 /Hellenic 75-82.
Previous Name: Stroud FC, 1989-92.
Previous Ground: None.
Midweek home matchday: Tuesday **Reserve Team's League:** None.
Record Attendance: 2,200 v Wolverhampton Wanderers, floolight inauguration 1981.
Best F.A. Cup season: 3rd Qualifying Rd 87-88.
League clubs defeated in F.A. Cup: None.
Record Fees - Paid: **Received:**
Players progressing to Football League: Graham Rogers (Newport County 1985), Mike England (Bristol Rovers 1985), Kevin Gill (Newport County 1985).
Clubhouse: (0453 833295). Bar and lounge, open every night. **Steward:** Bob Cowley.
Club Record Goalscorer: **Club Record Apps:**
90-91 Captain: Russell Wilton **90-91 P.o.Y.:** Russell Wilton **90-91 Top scorer:** Colin Peacey 21.
Local Newspapers: Stroud News & Journal, Gloucester Citizen.
Local Radio Stations: Severn Sound, BBC Radio Gloucestershire.
Honours: FA Vase 81-82, FA Trophy 3rd Rd 90-91, Hellenic Lg 81-82, Stroud & Dursley Lg 02-03, Gloucestershire Northern Senior Lg 37-38 49-50 50-51, Gloucestershire Senior Cup 84-85 85-86 86-87, Gloucestershire Senior Amateur Cup (North) 26-27 45-46 71-72 75-76 77-78, Gloucestershire Senior Professional Cup 84-85 85-86.

GOALKEEPERS:
Andy Gardiner (Tuffley R)

DEFENDERS:
Andy Pinkney (Backwell Utd), Kevin Barry (Cinderford, Malvern), Wayne Hams (Shortwood, Sharpness, Forest Green R, Cheltenham), Paul Montague (British Colleges), Darren Ford (Wotton R, Old Georgians)

MIDFIELD:
Russell Wilton (Witney, Cheltenham, Gloucester), John Hamilton (Local football), Lloyd Tucker (Cheltenham)

FORWARDS:
Simon Darlaston (Bristol C, Shortwood), Colin Peacey (Cinderford, Stroud, Sharpness, Forest Green R), Gary Eastaff (Northleach), Andy Oldknow (Cheltenham)

PROGRAMME DETAILS:
Pages: 24 **Price:** 50p
Editor: Keith Sheppard
WMPCC Rating: 24

Formed: 1874

GRANTHAM TOWN

Gingerbreads

Peter Whitehurst (stripes, centre) attempts an overhead kick under pressure from Buxton defender Robert Brown. This FA Trophy First Qualifying Round tie, played on 21st September and won 2-0 by Buxton, was one of the first matches to be played at Grantham's new ground. Photo - Colin Stevens.

Chairman: Gordon Watson **President:** Mrs Margaret Thatcher.
Secretary: Mr Pat Nixon, 2 Eskdale Road, Grantham, Lincs NG31 8EP (0476 64408).
Team Manager: Bob Duncan **Asst Mgr:** Shaughan Farrow **Coach:** Nigel Marshall, Jock Turnbull.
Press Officer: Pat Nixon **Physio:** Beverley Myers
Ground: The Meres, Trent Road, Grantham, Lincs. **Commercial Manager:** Merlin Saddleton.
Directions: Midway between A1 and A52 on edge of Earlesfield Industrial Estate.
Capacity: 5,000 (1,750 Covered) **Seats:** 750 **Floodlights:** Y **Shop:** N **Metal Badges:** Y
Colours: Black/white/black/black **Change colours:** Yellow/blue/blue **Sponsors:** Grimsby Fisheries.
Previous Lges: Central All. 11-25 59-61/ Midland Co's 25-59 61-72/ Southern 72-79/ Northern Prem. 79-85.
Previous Name: Grantham FC until 1980's **Previous Ground:** London Road until October 1990.
Midweek home matchday: Tuesday **Reserve Team's League:**
Record Attendance: 1,402 v Ilkeston Town, FA Cup Preliminary Rd 91-92 *(At London Road: 6,578 v Middlesborough, FA Cup 3rd Rd 1974).*
Best F.A. Cup season: 3rd Rd 1883-84 86-87 1973-74. Competition Proper on 23 occasions; 1877-79 80-81 83-88 1928-29 35-36 45-46 47-48 49-50 61-62 65-71 72-74 75-76.
League clubs defeated in F.A. Cup: Stockport 70-71, Rochdale 73-74.
Record Fees - Paid: £8,500 for Gary Jones (Doncaster) **Rec'd:** £20,000 for Gary Crosby (Nottm F.)
Players progressing to Football League: Archie Burgeon (Spurs 1930's), Syd Bycroft (Doncaster 1934), Ernest Morris (H'fax 1950), Peter Thompson & Robbie Cooke (P'boro 1964 & 80), James Rayner (Notts Co 1964), David Dall (S'thorpe 1979), Nick Jarvis & Hugh Wood (S'thorpe 1980), Devon White (Brist. Rvrs 1986), Terry Curran (Grimsby 1987), G Crosby (Nottm Forest 1987), Alan Kennedy (Wrexham 1987), Richard Wilson (Lincoln 1987).
Clubhouse: Open every day. Bar, darts, pool etc. Frequent entertainment. Available for functions.
Steward: Pete Down.
Club Record Goalscorer: Jack McCartney 416 **Club Record Apps:** Chris Gardiner 664.
90-91 Captain: Tony Marsden **90-91 P.o.Y.:** Adrian Speed **90-91 Top scorer:** Mark Hurst 22.
Local Newspapers: Grantham Journal (0476 62291), Nottingham Evening Post (0602 482000), Melton & Grantham Trader (0476 74433), Grantham Citizen, Lincolnshire Echo (0522 525252).
Local Radio Stations: Radio Lincolnshire, Lincs FM.
Hons: FA Tphy QF 71-72, Southern Lg R-up 73-74 (Div 1 Nth 72-73 78-79, Merit Cup 72-73), Midland Co's Lg(3) 63-64 70-72 (R-up 37-38 64-65 69-70, Lg Cup 68-69 70-71), Midland Amtr Lg 10-11 (Lg Cup R-up 10-11), Central All. 24-25 (Southern Div R-up 59-60), Lincs Snr Cup 1884-85 1936-37 (R-up(5) 34-36 39-40 45-47), Lincs Co. 'A' Cup(3) 53-54 60-62 (R-up 49-50 52-53 57-58), Lincs Co. Snr Cup 71-72 82-83 (R-up 80-81).

GOALKEEPERS:
Jon Godwin (Sheff Utd(T))
DEFENDERS:
Ged Creane (King's Lynn, Kettering, Boston Utd, Yaro(Fin), Tsun Wan(HK), Lincoln), Graham Neal (Wyberton, Spalding, Wyberton, Spalding, Grantham, Boston FC), Adrian Speed (Holbeach, Peterborough(T)), John O'Hare (Local football), Christian Penney (Brigg, Grimsby), Geoff Stephenson (King's Lynn, Eastwood T, Boston Utd, Grimsby)
MIDFIELD:
Andy Rolph (Chesterfield, Birmingham), Neil Mann (Spalding, Grimsby, Notts Forest, Notts Co), Lee Rippin (Boston FC, King's Lynn, Spalding, King's Lynn, Spalding, Boston FC),, Jim Shaw (Louth)
FORWARDS:
Mark Hurst (Huddersfield, Notts Forest), Steve McLoughlin (Notts Co, Brighton, Notts Forest), Chris Grocock (Boston Utd, Grimsby), Peter Whitehurst (Eastwood T, Ilkeston), Andy Bullimore (Melton T), Marcus Newell (Immingham, Spalding, King's Lynn, Holbeach, Grimsby(T)), Kevin Topliss (King's Lynn, Spalding, Nth Ferriby Utd, Brigg, Crewe, Scunthorpe, Grimsby), Dale Watkins (Peterborough City, Peterborough Utd)

Pages: 36 **Price:** 60p
Editor: Mr M Koranski, Mr S Clark
WMPCC Rating: 33

GRESLEY ROVERS

Gresley Rover, West Midlands (Regional) League champions 1991-92. Back Row (L/R): Frank Northwood (Manager - now retired), Paul Acklam, Scott Elliott, Gil Land, Bob Aston, Stuart Stokes, Steve Astley, Carl Rathbone, Steve Dolby (Coach), Gordon Ford (Physiotherapist). Front Row (L/R): Martin Dick, Brian Beresford, Richard Denby (Captain), Kieron Smith, Craig Weston, Ryan Venning. Mascot: Ashley Dicken. Photo - Mick Poole.

Chairman: P Hall **President:** G Duggins.
Secretary: A R Summers, 46 Ashby Road, Moira, Nr Swadlincote, Derbys DE12 6DJ (0283 217660).
Team Manager: Steve Dolby **Asst Mgr:** **Coach:**
Press Officer: **Physio:**
Commercial Manager:
Ground: Moat Street, Church Gresley, Nr Burton-on-Trent (0283 216315).
Directions: Travel to A444 via either the A5, A38, A5121 or M42 North to Appleby Magna. On reaching A444 head for Castle Gresley. Turn onto A514 to Derby; at island take second exit (Church Street), then second left (School Street) then first left into Moat Street. Five miles from Burton-on-Trent (BR). Buses from Swadlincote.
Capacity: 2,000 (500 Covered) **Seats:** 250 **Floodlights:** Y **Shop:** Y **Metal Badges:** Y
Colours: White/red/red **Change colours:** All blue **Sponsors:**
Previous Lges: Burton/ Leicestershire/ Derbyshire/ Midland 03-20s/ Central Alliance 12-25 49-53 59-67/ Birmingham Combination 25-33/ Central Combination/ West Midlands (Regional) 54-59 75-92.
Previous Names: None
Previous Grounds: Mushroom Lane 1882-95/ Church Street 95-1909.
Midweek home matchday: Tuesday **Reserve Team's League:**
Record Attendance: 3,950 v Burton Albion, Birmingham (now West Mids) Lg 57-58.
Best F.A. Cup season: 1st Rd Proper 30-31 (lost 1-3 at York City).
League clubs defeated in F.A. Cup: None.
Record Fees - Paid: **Rec'd:**
Players progressing to Football League:
Clubhouse: Inside ground, open Mon-Thurs evenings and Saturday matchdays.
Club Record Goalscorer: **Club Record Apps:**
91-92 Captain: Richard Denby **91-92 P.o.Y.:** **91-92 Top scorer:** Kieron Smith
Local Newspapers: Burton Mail. **Local Radio Stations:**
Hons: FA Vase R-up 90-91, West Mids Lg 90-91 91-92 (R-up 85-86 88-89), Derbys Snr Cup 87-88 88-89 89-90.

GOALKEEPERS:
Simon Harrison (Local football)
DEFENDERS: John Barry (Shepshed, Burton Alb, Scarborough, Kimberley, Slack & Parr), **Martin Dick** (Borrowash V, Hucknall, Long Eaton), **Jason Minton** (Willenhall, Bilston, Rushall Olympic, Willenhall), **Steve Astley** (Bilston, Gresley R, Oldbury, Wolves Utd, Smethwick, Park Rangers), **Stuart Evans** (Local football), **Dean Page** (Brereton Social), **Gil Land** (Heanor, Worksop, Burton Alb, Mickleover RBL, Notts Forest)
MIDFIELD: Richard Denby (Alfreton, Huthwaite, Sutton T, Boston Utd, Chesterfield, Notts Forest(Sch)), **Craig Weston** (Grantham, Belper, Burton Alb), **Tony Marsden** (Grantham, Belper, Burton Alb), **Neil Lovell** (Sutton T, Eastwood T, Matlock, Staveley, Sheff Wed(J)), **Jason Darkes** (Dudley, Bromsgrove, Worcester, Paget R, Everton(T)), **Richard Wardle** (Tamworth), **Steve Adcock** (Heanor, Shepshed, Borrowash V, Gresley R, Graham St Prims), **Russ Elliott** (Long Eaton)
FORWARDS: Brian Beresford (Stapenhill, Dudley, Shepshed, Corby, Worcester, Willenhall, Brereton Social, Armitage, Chesterfield, Walsall), **Paul Acklam** (Shepshed, Gresley R, Borrowash V, Hucknall, Long Eaton, Sheff Utd), **Keiron Smith** (Sutton T, Huthwaite), **Ryan Venning** (Burton Alb, Stoke(T)), **Andy Moore** (Bilston, Blakenall, Gresley, Wednesfield, Willenhall)

Pages: 28 **Price:** 50p
Editor: Brian Spare/ Derek Kinsey
WMPCC Rating: N/A

HINCKLEY TOWN

Hinckley Town. Back Row (L/R): T Hopewell, M Lee, S Scott, B Wilcox, D Hewitt, R Carey, T Robinson. Front Row (L/R): A Massey, G Williams, M Taylor, C Taylor, T Hopewell, J Borszowski. Photo - Marshall's Sports Service, Birimingham.

Chairman: David Needham **Directors:** Tony Dyer, Tony Devereux, Dave Grundy, Mike Sutton.
Secretary: Mrs Dyer, 117 Roston Drive, Hinckley, Leics (0455 238628).
Team Manager: Dave Grundy **Asst Manager:** None
Press Officer: Richard King (0455 611047) **Physio:** Alan Cooke.
Commercial Manager: Alan Esparza.
Ground: Leicester Road Sports Ground, Leicester Road, Hinckley, Leics (0455 615062).
Directions: From M69 junction 1 take A447 then A47 towards Leicester. Ground on A47 about 2 miles from town centre.
Capacity: 5,500 (326 Covered) **Seats:** 326 **Floodlights:** Y **Shop:** Y **Metal Badges:** N
Colours: White/claret/sky blue **Change colours:** Yellow/navy/navy. **Sponsors:** Under Negociation.
Previous Name: Westfield Rovers 1958-66.
Previous Grounds: Westfield Playing Field 58-60/ Granville Road Recreation Ground 60-68.
Previous Lges: Sth Leicester & Nuneaton Amtr/ Leics Snr 72-86/ Central Mids 86-88/ West Mids 88-90.
Midweek home matchday: Wednesday **Reserve Team's League:** None.
Record Attendance: 2,500 v Red Star Belgrade, summer 1990.
Best F.A. Cup season: 4th Qualifying Rd 1988-89.
League clubs defeated in F.A. Cup: None.
Record Fees - Paid: £1,600 for John Lane (VS Rugby) **Rec'd:** £1,750 for Colin Taylor (Bedworth).
Players progressing to Football League:
Clubhouse: Bar with facilities for functions. **Steward:** Mrs E Dyer.
Club Record Goalscorer: **Club Record Apps:**
91-92 Captain: Paul Purser **91-92 P.o.Y.:** Dennis Hewitt **91-92 Top scorer:** Ku Akeredolu.
Local Newspapers (+Tel.Nos.): Hinckley Times (0455 238383), Leicester Mercury (512512).
Local Radio Stations: Radio Leicester.
Honours: FA Vase 3rd Rd 85-86, West Mids (Bank's) Lg 89-90, Central Midlands Lg 86-87 (R-up 87-88, B E Webbe Cup R-up 86-87 87-88, Gerry Mills Cup R-up 87-88), Leics Senior Lg R-up 83-84 (Div 2 72-73, Div 2 Cup 72-73), Leicestershire Challenge Cup 89-90 (R-up 90-91), Leics Senior Cup (Jelson Holmes) R-up 87-88, Leics Senior Cup 88-89, M & B Floodlit Cup 88-89, Midland F'lit Cup R-up 91-92.

GOALKEEPERS:
Dennis Hewitt (Atherstone, Leicester Utd, Bedworth, Leicester Utd, Tamworth)

DEFENDERS:
Mick Brady (Hinckley FC), **Chris Macrae** (Shepshed, Grimsby), **Darren Ratcliffe** (Barwell, Hinckley T), **Paul Purser** (Hinckley Ath, Bedworth), **Barry Wilcox** (Gresley R, Nuneaton B, Hinckley Ath, Friar Lane OB, Desborough, Friar Lane OB, Shepshed, Hinckley Ath)

MIDFIELD:
Lee Harriman (Hinckley Ath, Highfield R, Lutterworth), **Carl Pears** (Hinckley FC), **Jim Childs** (Leicester Utd, Hinckley T, Hinckley Ath), **Laurie Chambers** (Local football), **Maurice Rowe** (Shepshed, Highfield R)

FORWARDS:
Kunle Akeredolu (Bedworth, Leicester Utd, Shepshed, Bedworth), **John Massey** (Hinckley FC, Leicester Utd, Hinckley T, Leicester Utd, Leicester C(A)), **Robbie Battison** (Houghton R, Lutterworth), **Tony Williams** (Wigston F)

Sponsored by
BIG CITY TYRES LTD.

HINCKLEY TOWN F.C.
v.
Sutton Coldfield Town
Wednesday, 8th April, 1992

50p

Pages: 36 **Price:** 50p
Editor: Richard King
WMPCC Rating: 26

KING'S LYNN

Two King's Lynn defenders challenge Jimmy Brown of Hednesford Town. Photo - Dennis Nicholson.

Chairman: J Dollimore.   **President:** L Rush.
Secretary: John Franks, The Lyntons, Stamford Rd, Marholm, Peterborough PE6 7HX (0733 267272).
Team Manager: John Musgrove   **Asst Manager:** TBA   **Coach:**
Press Officer: **Physio:** Andrew Thorn.   **General Manager:** J Dollimore.
Ground: The Walks Stadium, Tennyson Road, King's Lynn PE30 5PB (0553 760060).
Directions: At mini r-about arriving from A10/A47 take Vancouse Avenue. Ground on left after a quarter mile. Quarter mile from King's Lynn (BR), half mile from bus station.
Capacity: 8,200 (5,000 Covered)   **Seats:** 1,200   **Floodlights:** Y   **Shop:**   Metal Badges:
Colours: All royal blue (yellow trim)   **Change colours:** All yellow (blue trim)
Previous Leagues: Norfolk & Suffolk/ Eastern C'ties 35-39 48-54/ UCL 46-48/ Midland C'ties 54-58/ NPL 80-83.
Previous Name: Lynn Town   **Previous Ground:** None.   **Sponsors:** Skoda.
Midweek home matchday: Tuesday   **Reserve Team's League:** Jewson Eastern Division 1.
Record Attendance: 12,937 v Exeter, FA Cup 1st Rd 50-51. *(44,916 saw the Cup tie at Everton (below)).*
Best F.A. Cup season: 3rd Rd 61-62 (lost 0-4 at Everton). Competition Proper on 14 occasions; 05-06 37-38 49-50 51-52 58-63 64-65 68-69 71-72 73-74 84-85.
League clubs defeated in F.A. Cup: Aldershot 59-60, Coventry 61-62.
Players progressing to Football League: Norman Rowe (D'by 1949), Brian Taylor & Polly Ward (Brad PA 54 & 55), Tom Reynolds (Dar'ton 54), Graham Reed (S'land 55), Peter McCall (Bris C 55), John Neal (S'don 57), Tom Dryburgh (O'ham 57), John Hunter (Barrow 59), John Stevens (S'don), George Catleugh (W'ford), George Walters (C'field 64), Peter McNamee (Notts C 1966), Wayne Biggins (Burnley & Man C), Jackie Gallagher (P'boro 80), Andy Higgins (R'dale 83), Neil Horwood (G'by 86), Darren Rolph (Barnsley 87), Mark Howard (Stockport 88).
Clubhouse: Normal hours, extension for matchdays.   **Steward:** Mrs Saddleton.
Club Record Scorer: Mick Wright 1,152 (British Record)   **Club Record Apps:** Malcolm Lindsay 321.
91-92 Captain: **91-92 P.o.Y.:**   **91-92 Top scorer:**
Local Newspapers (+Tel.Nos.): Lynn News & Advertiser (0553 761188), Eastern Daily Press (0603 628311).
Honours: FA Amtr Cup R-up 1900-01, FA Tphy 2nd Rd 78-79, FA Vase 4th Rd 90-91, Southern Lg R-up 84-85 (Div 1 R-up 63-64), NPL Presidents Cup 82-83, Eastern Co's Lg 53-54 (R-up 49-50 52-53 (Lg Cup 53-54), Norfolk & Suffolk Lg8(R-up(6)), E Anglian Lg R-up(2), Norfolk Snr Cup(19) 1882-84 86-87 89-90 98-99 1907-08 23-25 31-32 33-34 36-37 38-39 51-52 53-58 (R-up(19)), Norfolk Prem. Cup 68-69(jt) 73-74, E Anglian Cup(4) 65-68 84-85 (R-up(3)), Eastern Prof. F'lit Lg 68-69.

GOALKEEPERS:
Steve Lewis (Camb Utd)

DEFENDERS:
Tim Webster (Norwich(A)), **Selwyn Shelton** (Louth Utd, King's Lynn), **Steve Bunting** (Downham T, King's Lynn), **Tim Maxwell** (Downham T, King's Lynn, Camb Utd(T))

MIDFIELD:
Tim Callaby (Downham T, King's Lynn), **Mark Lammiman** (Local football), **Neil Fryatt** (Downham T, King's Lynn, Watton Utd, King's Lynn), **Justin Elkington** (Spalding, Mansfield(T)), **Graham Thompson** (Boston Utd)

FORWARDS:
Julian Howard (Youth), **Shaughan Frohawk** (Local football), **Dave Wood** (Downham T)

PROGRAMME DETAILS:
Pages: 36 **Price:** 75p
Editor: Richard Clayton
WMPCC Rating: 29

LEICESTER UNITED

Leicester United's Danny Conway stretches Redditch United to the limits in an away Beazer Homes League Midland Division fixture. Photo - Jez Coulsdon.

Chairman: John Potter   **Directors:** N Perkins, P Dronfield, C Newcombe.
Vice Chairman: G Glover.
Secretary: John Goodman, 44 Croft Drive, Wigston, Leicester LE8 1HE (0533 882358).
Team Manager: Andy Potter   **Asst Manager:** Ivan Maile   **Coach:**
Physio: Paul Miller   **Commercial Manager:**
Ground: United Park, Winchester Road, Blaby, Leicester LE8 3HN (0533 778998).
Directions: 2 miles from junct 21 M1 & M69. 1st exit on approach road onto B582. Left at 1st r-about, right at next r-about (Everards Brewery) towards Narborough. Left at r-bout (Huntsman PH), through Whetstone village to next r-about, across A426 into Blaby, through lights and go 100 yds to next junction, right and ground on left immediately after residential area.
Capacity: 4,000 (1,300 Covered)   **Seats:** 252   **Floodlights:** Y   **Shop:** Y   **Metal Badges:** Y
Colours: Red & white/black/red   **Change colours:** All blue.   **Sponsors:**
Previous Name: Enderby Town (1900-81).   **Previous Ground:** George Street (until 1985).
Previous Leagues: Leics Senior 49-50 51-69/ East Mids 69-72.
Midweek home matchday: Tuesday   **Reserve Team's League:** Midland Combination.
Record Attendance: 1,058 v Hinckley Town, 26/12/90.
Best F.A. Cup season: 1st Rd 77-78 (lost 1-6 at AP Leamington).
Best F.A. Trophy season: 3rd Rd replay 78-79 (lost 2-4 at Bishop Auckland).
Record Fees - Paid: £1,000   **Received:** £22,500 for Keith Scott (Lincoln).
Players progressing to Football League: Richard Dixey (Burnley 1974), Cohen Griffith (C'diff), Neil Lyne & Tony Loughlan (Nottm F), Dave Puttnam & Keith Scott (L'coln), Graham Cross (L'coln 1979), Robert Atkins (Sheff Utd 1982).
Clubhouse: Open every day and evening. Meals available.   **Steward:** P Dronfield.
91-92 Captain: Ian Marsden   **91-92 P.o.Y.:** Chris Tonge   **91-92 Top scorer:** Mark Hallam 26.
Local Newspapers: Leicester Mercury. Oadby & Wigston Mail.
Local Radio Stations: Radio Leicester.
Honours: Southern Lg Midland Div R-up 86-87, Leics Senior Lg 62-63 64-65 66-67 (R-up 59-60 63-64 65-66 67-68 68-69, Div 2 58-59 (R-up 51-52)), East Mids Regional Lg 70-71 71-72 (Lg Cup 70-71), Leics Snr Cup 61-62 64-65 66-67 70-71 72-73 78-79, Leics Challenge Cup 78-79 79-80 86-87 87-88.

GOALKEEPERS:
Ian Marsden (VS Rugby, Leicester Utd, Nuneaton B, Macclesfield, Bolton W, Man City)

DEFENDERS:
Don Gethfield (Bedworth, Bromsgrove, Tamworth, Banbury, Coventry Sporting, VS Rugby, Atherstone, Coventry), **Gareth Williams** (Hinckley T, Bedworth, Wolves(A)), **Robert Wilson** (Stoke(T)), **Chris Tonge** (Highfield R), **Mark Randell** (Wigston F), **Richard Carey** (Hinckley T, Narborough), **Jason Weafer** (Youth), **Adam Beazley** (Shepshed)

MIDFIELD:
Stuart Bond (Shepshed, VS Rugby), **David Tedds** (Shepshed, Hinckley T, Atherstone, Hinckley Ath), **Andy Potter** (Youth), **David Tonge** (St Andrews), **Wayne Houghton** (Melton), **Mark Harbottle** (Ilkeston, Burton Alb, Shepshed, Oakham Utd, Scarborough, Doncaster, Notts Co), **Marc Orton** (Youth)

FORWARDS:
Alan Liquorish (Shepshed, Birstall, Leicester Utd), **Andy Beckford** (Ilkeston, Shepshed, Matlock, Shepshed, Crewe, Shepshed, Worksop, Ilkeston, Boston Utd, Leicester C, Aston Villa), **Lee Pritchard** (Youth)

MATCHDAY PROGRAMME
LEICESTERSHIRE CHALLENGE CUP
LEICESTER UNITED
v
ANSTEY NOMADS
WELCOME TO UNITED PARK
THE BEAZER HOMES FOOTBALL LEAGUE MIDLAND DIVISION

PROGRAMME DETAILS:
Pages: 20 **Price:** 50p
Editor:
WMPCC Rating: 20

NEWPORT A.F.C.

Newport AFC will bid farwell to Somerton Park (above) in 1992-93. To avoid being coerced into the new League of Wales, they have had to arrange a groundshare 'over the border' at Gloucester City. If and when the aptly nicknamed 'Exiles' do return to their home town, it could well be to new stadium that is under construction in the Gwent town. Photo - Ace Frehmen.

Chairman: Mr David Hando **President:** Brian Toms, MBE.
Secretary: Marc Williams, 2 Lakeside, Earley, Reading RG6 2PQ (0734 264559).
Team Manager: John Relish **Asst Manager:** Graham Rogers **Coach:** David Williams, Tony Gilbert
Press Off.: Wallace Brown (0633 265500/ 0222 382651) **Physio:** T Gilbert.
Ground: *(Somerton Park, Newport, Gwent NP9 0HZ (0633 271771)).* **N.B.** Until further notice, Newport will be playing at Gloucester City FC - see page 477.
Directions & Ground details: As Gloucester City (page 477).
Club Shop: Still open most weekdays at Somerton Park (contact address as above). **Metal Badges:** Yes
Colours: Amber/black/black **Change colours:** All white. **Sponsors:**
Previous Leagues: Hellenic 89-90.
Previous Grounds: London Road, Moreton-in-the-Marsh 89-90.
Previous Names: None. Newport AFC were formed after the demise of Newport County in 1988-89.
Midweek home matchday: Wednesday **Reserve Team's League:** None.
Record Attendance: 2,400 v Moreton, friendly 1990. 594 v Pegasus Juniors whilst at Moreton. *Newport County had a crowd of 24,268 against Cardiff at Somerton Park in 1937.*
Best F.A. Cup season: Entering for the first time in 1992-93.
Best F.A. Trophy season: 1st Rd Proper 91-92.
Record Fees - Paid: **Received:**
Players progressing to Football League:
Clubhouse: At Somerton Park, Newport. Members only.
Club Record Goalscorer: Chris Lilygreen 63 **Club Record Apps:** C Lilygreen.
91-92 Captain: Mark Price **91-92 P.o.Y.:** Phil Green **91-92 Top scorer:** Phil Green 27.
Local Newspapers: South Wales Argus, South Wales Echo.
Local Radio Stations: Red Dragon.
Honours: Hellenic Lg 89-90 (Lg Cup 89-90).

GOALKEEPERS:
Peter Mason (Cwmbran), **Tony Bird** (Cwmbran, Cardiff Cor)
DEFENDERS: Phil Coyne (Abergavenny Thursdays), **Rob Painter** (Cardiff C(T), Newport Co(Sch)), **Paul Towler** (Mangotsfield, Watford), **Graham Rogers** (Forest Green R, Newport Co, Barry, Minehead, Newport Co), **Chris Stanton** (Caerleon, Mangotsfield, Caerleon, Bath, Newport Co(Sch)), **Jason Prew** (Merthyr Tydfil, Swansea), **Steve Sherlock** (Stroud, AFC Cardiff, Newport Co, Cardiff C, Stockport, Luton, Man City)
MIDFIELD: Phil Williams (Cheltenham, Newport Co, Swansea), **Andrew Ellis** (Bridgend, Cardiff Cor, Swansea Univ, Cardiff Cor), **Wayne Hewitt** (Brecon, Pontllanfraith, Trelewis), **Doug John** (Barry, Cwmbran, Barry, AFC Cardiff), **Mark Price** (Albion R(Gwent)), **Darren Porretta** (Cardiff Cor)
FORWARDS: Chris Lillygreen (Ebbw Vale, Mangotsfield, Bath, Forest Green R, Yeovil, Newport Co), **David Withers** (Merthyr Tydfil, Ton Pentre, Barry, Newport Co, Ton Pentre), **Phil Green** (Merthyr Tydfil, Tung Sing(HK), Barry, Newport Co, Barry, Bridgend, Barry, Merthyr Tydfil, Barry, Cardiff Cor), **David Jarvis** (Brecon, Mangotsfield, Caerleon, Newport Co), **Will Foley** (Hereford, Newport Co, Frickley, Cardiff C, Swansea, Frickley, York)

PROGRAMME DETAILS:
Pages: 24 Price: £1.00
Editor: Wallace Brown
WMPCC Rating: 34

NUNEATON BOROUGH

The Boro

Some of the Boro' squad at the Player of the Year presentation that was attended by 300. (L/R): John Ridding, Matt Tarry, Tony Simpson, Dave Whetton, Martyn Twigger, Paul Carty, Paul Culpin, Steve Bartlett. Photo - Josie Buhain.

Chairman: Mr H Kerry **Life President:** Mr A Scattergood.
Secretary: Keith Parker, 21 the Woodlands, Hartshill, Nuneaton CV10 0SY (0203 393193).
Manager: George Rooney **Coach:** J Barton **Physio:** P Brown
Press Officer: Secretary **Commercial Manager:** Ray Dickinson (0203 491064).
Ground: Manor Park, Beaumont Road, Nuneaton, Warks CV10 0SY (0203 342690/385738).
Directions: A444 to Nuneaton from M6 junction 3. 1st exit at 1st r-about, left at 2nd r-about then 2nd right into Greenmoor Road, turn right at the end and ground is on the left. From town centre ring-road ground is at the end of Queens Road. 1 mile from Nuneaton (BR).
Capacity: 2,100 (1,500 Covered) **Seats:** 600 **Floodlights:** Y **Shop:** Y **Metal Badges:** Y
Colours: Royal blue & white stripes/royal/royal **Change colours:** Red & white **Sponsors:** M & B.
Previous Leagues: Central Amateur 37-38/ B'ham Comb 38-52/ West Mids (B'ham) 52-58/ Southern 58-79 81-82/ GM Conference (Alliance Premier & Gola) 79-81 82-87.
Midweek home matchday: Monday **Reserve Team's League:** Scoreline Comb (Reserve Division).
Record Gate: 22,114 v Rotherham, FA Cup 3rd Rd 1967 *(Best in Conference: 3,597 v Maidstone, 83-84).*
Best F.A. Cup season: 3rd Rd replay 66-67. 1st Rd on 17 occasions; 49-50 53-55 66-68 71-72 74-80 81-82 84-86.
League clubs defeated in F.A. Cup: Watford 53-54, Swansea Town 66-67, Oxford Utd 77-78.
Record Fees - Paid: £9,500 for Richard Dixey (S'boro) **Received:** £52,000 for Richard Hill (N'hampton)
Players progressing to Football League: Richard Mason & Paul Culpin (Cov C 1946 & 85), Eric Betts (W'sall 1949), Frank Cruickshank (Notts C 1950), Ken Plant (Bury 1950), John Schofield (B'ham 1950), Ron Howells (Wolves 1952), Frank Upton & Richard Hill (N'hampton 1953 & 85), Ron Dickinson & Mike Gibson (S'bury 1953 & 60), George Cattleugh (W'ford 1954), Terry Wright (Barrow 1962), Mick Hartland (Oxford 1963), Ken Satchell & Barry Holbutt (W'sall 1965), Terry Bell (H'pool 1966), Alan Morton (F'ham 1970), Reg Edwards (P Vale 1972), Kirk Stephens (Luton 1978), Trevor Peake (L'coin 1979), Paul Sugrue (Man C 1980), Malcom Shotton & Tim Smithers (Oxford 1980), Dean Thomas (W'don 1981), Paul Richardson (Derby 1984).
Clubhouse: (0203 383152). Open evenings, Sunday lunchtime and matchdays. **Steward:** Dave Radburn.
Club Record Scorer: Paul Culpin (135) **Club Record Apps:** Alan Jones (545)
90-91 Captain: D Whetton **90-91 P.O.Y.:** M Twigger **90-91 Top scorer:** M Twigger 26
Local Newspapers: Nuneaton Evening News, Nuneaton Evening Telegraph, Neaton Weekly Tribune.
Local Radio: Mercia Sound, BBC, CWRS.
Hons: FA Tphy 4th Rd rep. 76-77, GMV Conf. R-up(2) 83-85, Southern Lg R-up 66-67 74-75 81-82 (Lg Cup R-up 62-63), Birm. Lg 55-56 (Nth Div 54-55), Birm. Comb. R-up 45-46 48-49 50-51, Birm. Snr Cup 48-49 55-56 59-60 77-78 79-80.

GOALKEEPERS:
Richard Attwood (Dudley, Halesowen H, Bromsgrove, Halesowen H)
DEFENDERS: Matt Tarry (Irthlingboro D, Numneaton, Northampton), John Barton (Tamworth, Kidderminster, Derby, Everton, Worcester, Stourbridge), Dave Whetton (Atherstone, Tamworth, RC Warwick, Bedworth), John Ridding (Alvechurch, Redditch, Sutton C, Banbury, Sutton C, Worcester, Chelmsley), Adie Wilson (RC Warwick, Nuneaton, Bedworth)
MIDFIELD:
Tony Simpson (Grantham, Notts Forest(T)), Richard Smith (Local), Glenn Shepherd (Halesowen H, Stafford R, Port Vale), Andy Orberson (Paget R, Alvechurch, Worcester, Plymouth(T)), Richard Parker (Friar Lane OB)
FORWARDS: Martin Twigger (VS Rugby, Corby, Shepshed, King's Lynn, Arnold), Rob Straw (Stafford R, Derby), Ian Cotterill (Worcester, Bromsgrove, Worcester), Dave Draper (Worcester, Southam, Buckingham, RC Warwick, Brackley, Leamington, VS Rugby, Bedworth), Steve Woodfine (Youth), John Symonds (Hinckley T, Derby), Sylvester Cunningham (Bromsgrove, Halesowen T, Wednesfield, Stafford R, Wednesfield, Hednesford, Shifnal), Dale Igoe (Grantham, Bromsgrove), Paul Culpin (Hereford, Peterborough, Northampton, Coventry, Nuneaton, Leicester), Mark Rosegreen (VS Rugby, Alvechurch, Bromsgrove, Redditch, Kidderminster, AP Leamington)

Pages: 36 **Price:** 50p
Editor: Editorial Team
WMPCC Rating: 29

503

RACING CLUB WARWICK

Action from Racing Club's early season home fixture against Hednesford. Photo - Phil Grimes.

Chairman: Jim Wright   **Vice Chairman:** Jack Woolvin.
Secretary: P Murphy, 20 Dadglow Rd, Bishops Itchington, Leamington Spa CV33 0TG (0926 612675).
Team Manager: Andy Blair   **Asst Manager:**   **Coach:**
Press Officer: Secretary   **Physio:**
Commercial Manager:
Ground: Townsend Meadow, Hampton Road, Warwick CV34 6JP (0926 495786).
Directions: On the B4095 Warwick to Redditch road (via Henley in Arden) next to owners' & trainers' car park of Warwick Racecourse. Two miles from Warwick (BR).
Capacity: 1,000 (300 Covered)   **Seats:** 250   **Floodlights:** Y   **Shop:** N   **Metal Badges:** N
Colours: Red & gold/black/black   **Change colours:** Yellow/black/black.   **Sponsors:** N/A
Previous Leagues: Birmingham & West Midlands Alliance/ Warwickshire Combination/ West Midlandss 67-72/ Midland Combination 72-89.
Previous Name: Saltisford Rovers 1919-68/ Warwick Saltisford 68-70.
Midweek home matchday: Wednesday
Reserve Team's League: Scoreline Midland Combination (Reserve Division).
Record Attendance: 1,000 v Halesowen Town, FA Cup 1987.
Best F.A. Cup season:
League clubs defeated in F.A. Cup: None.
Record Fees - Paid: £1,000 for Dave Whetton (Bedworth)
         Received: £2,000 for Ian Gorrie (Atherstone Utd).
Clubhouse: (0926 495786). Open every evening and weekend lunchtimes.
Steward: Mrs Evelyn Cummings.
Club Record Goalscorer: **Club Record Apps:** S Cooper 600.
91-92 Captain: **91-92 P.o.Y.:**   **91-92 Top scorer:**
Local Newspapers: Warwick Advertiser, Leamington Courier, Coventry Evening Telegraph.
Local Radio Stations: BBC Radio Coventry.
Hons: FA Vase 4th Rd 77-78, Midland Combination 87-88 (R-up 88-89), Warwick Lg 33-34 34-35 35-36, Birmingham & West Mids Alliance 48-49, Birmingham & Dist Alliance Senior Cup 49-50, Leamington & Dist Lg 37-38 45-46 46-47 47-48, Leamington Hospital Cup 37-38 46-47, Warwick Cinderella Cup 35-36 36-37 37-38 38-39 46-47, T G John Cup 36-37, Leamington Junior Cup 38-39 46-47.

GOALKEEPERS:
Andy Russell (Coventry Sporting, Long Buckby, Coventry Sporting, Wolves(J))
DEFENDERS: Kevan Kane (Tamworth, Bedworth, Atherstone, VS Rugby, Coventry Sporting, AP Leamington, Wolves(J)), **Alec Brotherton** (Stourport S, Stourbridge, Blakenall, Redditch), **Darren Whitehouse** (Local football), **Paul Aldridge** (Redditch, R C Warwick, Moor Green), **Lennie Derby** (Coventry Sporting, Leamington, Coventry Sporting, Coventry C(Sch)), **Richard Holt** (Stratford, Henley F, Stoke(J)), **Adrian Passey** (Stratford)
MIDFIELD:
Gary Hannam (AP Leamington, RC Warwick), **Darrell White** (VS Rugby, Banbury, Birmingham), **Moreton Titterton** (Stratford), **Alan Byrne** (Stratford), **Abbey Kelly** (St Albans, RC Warwick, Stratford, Coventry Sporting), **Martin Smith** (Bedworth, RC Warwick, Moor Green, VS Rugby, Bedworth, Coventry Sporting), **Andy Blair** (Nuneaton B, Kidderminster, Aston Villa, Sheff Wed, Aston Villa, Coventry)
FORWARDS:
Darren Deeley (Banbury, Leamington, Bedworth), **Russell Jackson** (Hinckley FC, Hinckley T, Nuneaton B, Coventry C(Sch)), **Tim Emery** (Local football), **Tommy Hathaway** (Stratford, Leamington)

RACING CLUB
WARWICK F.C.
BEAZER HOMES LEAGUE

PROGRAMME DETAILS:
Pages: 40 **Price:** 40p
Editor: R Redfearn
WMPCC Rating: 23

504

REDDITCH UNITED

Hayley (right) of Redditch, and Bilston's Grant, watch a cross go in as Redditch attack. Photo - Keith Clayton.

Chairman: Mr R T Berry   **President:** R Thompson.
Secretary: M A Langfield, 174 Harport Road, Redditch, Worcs B98 7PE (0527 26603).
Team Manager: Paul Hendrie   **Asst Manager:** Colin Walsh   **Coach:** Les Healey.
Press Officer: R Newbold (0527 27516).   **Physio:** Jack Chapman.
Commercial Manager: Dave Roberts.
Ground: Valley Stadium, Bromsgrove Road, Redditch B97 4RN (0527 67450).
Directions: Access 7 on town centre ring-road takes you into Bromsgrove Road. Arriving from Redditch take first exit off dual carriageway. Ground 400 yds from Redditch (BR) and town centre.
Capacity: 9,500 (2,000 Covered)   **Seats:** 400   **Floodlights:** Y   **Shop:** Y   **Metal Badges:** Y
Colours: Red & white stripes/red/red   **Change colours:** White/black/white.
Sponsors: Windsor Carpets, Redditch.
Previous Leagues: Birmingham Combination 05-21 29-39 46-53/ West Midlands 21-29 53-72/ Southern 72-79/ GMV Conference (then Alliance Premier League) 79-80.
Previous Name: Redditch Town   **Previous Ground:** HDA Sports Grounds, Millsborough Road.
Midweek home matchday: Tuesday   **Reserve Team's League:**
Record Attendance: 5,500 v Bromsgrove, league match 54-55.
Best F.A. Cup season: 1st Rd replay 71-72 (lost 0-4 at P'boro after 1-1 draw). Also 1st Rd 71-72.
League clubs defeated in F.A. Cup: None.
Record Fees - Paid: £3,000 for Paul Joinson   **Received:** £42,000 for David Farrell (Aston Villa).
Players progressing to Football League: N Davis (Aston Villa), Hugh Evans (Birmingham 1947), Trevor Lewes (Coventry 1957), David Gilbert (Chesterfield 1960), Mike Tuohy (Southend Utd 1979), Neil Smith (Liverpool), David Farrell (Aston Villa 1992).
Clubhouse: Large clubroom and lounge boardroom.   **Steward:** Committee.
91-92 Captain: Robin Judd   **91-92 P.o.Y.:** Jimmy Williams   **91-92 Top scorer:** Steve Campbell.
Local Newspapers: Redditch Indicator (0527 63611), Redditch Advertiser, Birmingham Evening Mail, Redditch Weekly Mail.
Local Radio Stations: BBC Hereford & Worcester.
Hons: FA Tphy 1st Rd 78-79, Southern Lg Div 1 Nth 75-76 (Midland Div R-up 85-86), West Mids (B'ham) Lg Southern Sect. 54-55, Birm. Comb. 13-14 32-33 52-53 (R-up 06-07 14-15 51-52), Staffs Snr Cup 90-91, Birm. Snr Cup 24-25 31-32 38-39 76-77, Worcs Snr Cup 1893-94 1930-31 74-75 76-77 (R-up 1888-89 1929-30 52-53 73-74), Worcs Jnr Cup 90-91.

GOALKEEPERS:
Dave Adey (Boldmere)
DEFENDERS: Barry Williams (Alvechurch), **Paul Carseley** (Chelmsley), **Steve Shaw** (Youth), **Jimmy Williams** (Walsall(T)), **Bobby McDonald** (Burton Alb, Armitage, Sutton C, Worcester, Nuneaton B, Burton Alb, VS Rugby, Leeds, Oxford Utd, Man City, Coventry, Aston Villa), **Micky Andrews** (Nuneaton B, Hinckley T, Nuneaton B, Redditch, Paget R, Oldbury, Gloucester, Shrewsbury, Birmingham), **Denis Mulholland** (Tamworth, Chelmsley, Kidderminster, Nuneaton B, Solihull B, Highgate, Sutton C, Paget R, Moor Green)
MIDFIELD: Paul Bennett (Bridgnorth, Bilston, Bridgnorth), **Mark Pollard** (Tamworth, Bedworth, Nuneaton B, Coventry(T)), **Neil Brady** (Knowle), **Andy Massey** (Hinckley T, Leicester Utd), **Chris Moss** (Solihull B), **Gary Ward** (Shepshed, Arnold)
FORWARDS: Perry Blewitt (Nuneaton B, Redditch, Moor Green, Midvag(Faroe Is), Moor Green, Worcester, Tamworth, Paget R, Sutton C, Highgate, Coventry Sporting, Redditch, Mansfield(A)), **Robert Smith** (Worcester, Dudley, Halesowen T, Stourport, King's Heath), **Dean Russell** (Youth), **Paul Gibbs** (Youth), **Eric Sandiford** (Paget R, Redditch, Chelmsley, Solihull B, Paget R), **Fabian Sandiford** (Local football), **Tony Donnelly** (Paget R, Nuneaton B, Bedworth, Burton Alb, Nuneaton B, Sutton C, Alvechurch, Moor Green, Highgate)

Pages: 28 **Price:** 50p
Editor: R Newbold
WMPCC Rating: 21

Tamworth 1, Rushden Town 0; Beazer Homes League Midland Division 8/2/92. Tamworth's Russell Gordon heads against the post after 37 minutes. Two minutes from time he scored the only goal, again with a diving header. Photo - Paul Barber.

Chairman: W M Griggs
Joint Presidents: D Attley & C Jones.
Secretary: D M Joyce, 54 Ferrestone Rd, Wellingborough, Northants (0933 279466/ 0604 493161).
Team Manager: R Ashby
Asst Manager: B Jeffrey
Coach: P Brackwell
Press Officer: Secretary
Physio:
Comm Mgr: B Lake (0933 57968/317770)
Ground: Nene Park, Station Rd, Irthlingborough, Northants (0933 650345).
Directions: On A6 quarter mile from A45 junction over bridge.
Capacity: 3,500 (550 Covered)
Seats: 300
Floodlights: Y
Shop: Y
Metal Badges: Y
Colours: Red/white/blue
Change colours: All yellow
Sponsors: Pittard Garner.
Previous Names: Irthlingborough Diamonds (formed 1946), Rushden Town (formed 1889) merged in 1992.
Previous Leagues: Rushden Town: Midland 1894-1901/ Utd Co's 01-04 19-56 61-83/ Central Alliance 61-83.
Irthlingborough Diamonds: Rushden Yth/ Rushden & District/ Kettering Amtr.
Previous Ground: Rushden Town: Hayden Rd, Rushden (pre-1992).
Midweek home matchday: Tuesday
Reserve Team's League: Hereward Spts Utd Co's.
Record Attendance: 2,470 Irthlingborough Diamonds v Dagenham, FA Cup 1978
Best F.A. Cup season: 4th Qualifying Round (as Rushden Town).
League clubs defeated in F.A. Cup: None
Record Fees - Paid:
Received: From WBA to Rushden Town for Gordon Inwood.
Players progressing to Football League: From Rushden Town: Gordon Inwood (WBA 1949), Robert Peacock (Northampton 1957). *From Irthlingborough Diamonds: Scott Endersby (Ipswich, Tranmere, Swindon, Carlisle), Steve Brown & Dave Johnson (N'hampton).*
Clubhouse: Lounge facilities. Open matchdays, evenings & weekend lunctimes.
Steward: T Smith.
Club Record Goalscorer:
Club Record Apps:
92-93 Captain: Russell Lewis (91-92: Colin Waite (Rushden), Peter Clarke (Irthlingborough).
Local Newspapers: Northants Evening Telegraph (0536 81111), Chronicle & Echo (0604 231122), Herald & Post, Northants Citizen
Local Radio Stations: Radio Northampton, Radio Northampton 96.6, K.C.B.C.
Hons: As Rushden Town: Southern Lg Midland Div R-up 88-89, Utd Co's Lg(10) 02-03 26-27 29-30 31-32 34-38 63-64 72-73 (R-up(12) 01-02 24-25 28-29 30-31 33-34 38-39 49-50 62-63 71-72 77-79 82-83, Lg Cup(5) 33-35 36-38 46-47, Northants Snr Cup(9) 25-28 29-31 34-35 36-37 57-58 77-78, FA Amtr Cup 2nd Rd 1893-94, FA Tphy 3rd Qual Rd 69-70, FA Vase QF 89-90. *As Irthlingborough Diamonds: Utd Co's Lg 70-71 76-77 78-79 82-83 (KO Cup 78-79 80-81 (R-up 90-91)), Northants Snr Cup 80-81.*

GOALKEEPERS:
Kevin Fox (Wellingboro, Rushden, Kettering, Lincoln), **Darren Watts** (Northampton(T))
DEFENDERS: Andy Peaks (Northampton), **Junior Wilson** (Slough, Aylesbury, Rushden, Hitchin, Buckingham), **Darryl Page** (New Plymouth(NZ), Burton PW, Rothwell, Kettering), **Colin Waite** (Buckingham, Corby, Alvechurch, Wellingboro, Poole), **Russell Lewis** (Merthyr, Kettering, Northampton, Swindon, Bridgend), **Mark Bushell** (N'ton Spencer, Corby, Northampton T), **John Flower** (Aylesbury, Aldershot, Sheff Utd, Corby, Brixworth)
MIDFIELD: Steve Heard (Camb Utd(T)), **Billy Jeffrey** (Irthlingboro D, Rushden, Blacktown(Aust), Kettering, Northampton, Blackpool, Oxford Utd), **Steve Forbes** (St Albans, Rushden, Banbury, Hitchin, Finchley, Kingsbury, Hendon, Kingsbury), **Paul York** (Baldock, Aylesbury, Kettering, Irthlingboro D, Cogenhoe), **Andy Kirkup** (Wellingboro, Rushden, Corby, Rushden), **Glenn Beech** (Stamford, Boston Utd, Kettering, Boston Utd, Grantham, Rushden, Stamford, Aston V(A))
FORWARDS: Peter Green (Kettering, King's L, Grimsby), **Barrington Leslie** (Desboro, N'ton Spencer, N'ton T), **Frank Belfon** (Wellingboro, Buckingham, Wellingboro, Northampton, Wellingboro), **Ollie Kearns** (Worcester, Rushden, Kettering, Wrexham, Hereford, Walsall, Oxford Utd, Reading, Banbury)

RUSHDEN TOWN FOOTBALL CLUB

SEASON 1991/92

50p

Pages: 44 **Price:** 50p
Editor: Bernard Lake
WMPCC Rating: 23

Formed: 1876

STOURBRIDGE

The Glassboys

A Stourbridge forward is crowded out by Racing Club Warwick players Hannam and Aldridge. Photo - Keith Clayton.

Chairman: J C Driscoll   **Vice Chairman:** G Smith   **President:** J L Guest
Secretary: Hugh Clark, 10 Burnt Oak Drive, Stourbridge DY8 1HL (0384 392975).
Team Manager: John Chambers   **Asst Manager:** Alan Moore   **Coach:** Geoff Green
Press Officer: Secretary   **Physio:** David Thomas   **Commercial Manager:** Nigel T Pitt.
Ground: War Memorial Ground, High Street, Amblecote, Stourbridge DY8 4EB (0384 394040).
Directions: Opposite Royal Oak (PH) on left 250 yds from Stourbridge ring-road on A491 to Wolverhampton. 1 mile from Stourbridge Town (BR), buses 245/6 from Dudley, or 556 from W'ton.
Capacity: 2,000 (1,500 Covered)   **Seats:** 320   **Floodlights:** Y   **Shop:** Y   **Metal Badges:** Y
Colours: Red & white stripes/white/red   **Change colours:** White/black/white.
Previous Name: Stourbridge Standard.   **Record Fee Received:** £20,000 for Tony Cunningham (L'coln).
Previous Lges: W Mids Reg. (Prev. B'ham) 1892-1939 54-71/ B'ham Comb. 45-53. **Sponsors:** Storm Ltd.
Midweek home matchday: Tuesday   **Record Attendance:** 5,726 v Cardiff City, Welsh Cup final 1974.
Best F.A. Cup season: 4th Qual Rd 3 times this century; 67-68 (v Arnold), 84-85 & 85-86 (v VS Rugby).
League clubs defeated in F.A. Cup: Crewe 1892-93, Burslem Port Vale 94-95, Burton Swifts 1891-92.
Players progressing to Football League: Doug Pinbley & Brian Farmer (B'ham 1946 & 54), Howard Edwards (D'by 1947), James Pemberton (Luton 1947), Jack Boxley (Brist C 1950), Antonio Rowley (L'pool 1953), Colin Taylor & Keith Ball (W'sall 1958 & 72), Peter Clark (Stockport 1965), Percy Freeman (WBA 1968), Chic Bates & Ray Harwood (S'bury 1974), Les Lawrence (S'bury 1975), Steve Cooper (T'quay 1978), Tony Cunningham (L'coln 1979), Mel Gwinnet (P'boro 1981).
Clubhouse: Open every evening from 8 pm, and on Sunday lunchtimes.   **Steward:** L Tibbetts.
Club Record Goalscorer: Ron Page 269   **Club Record Apps:** Ron Page 427.
91-92 Captain: Chris Jones   **91-92 P.o.Y.:** Henry Wright   **91-92 Top scorer:** Evran Wright 30.
Local Newspapers: Stourbridge News & County Express, Express & Star, Dudley Evening Mail
Local Radio Stations: Radio West Mids, BRMB, Beacon.
Hons: Welsh Cup R-up 73-74, FA Tphy 4th Rd 70-71, Southern Lg Midland Div 90-91 (Div 1 Nth 73-74, Merit Cup 73-74), West Mids Lg 23-24 (R-up 01-02 25-26 37-38 38-39 55-56 62-63, Div 2 R-up 80-81), B'ham Comb. 51-52, B'ham Snr Cup 49-50 58-59 67-68 (R-up 10-11 45-46 75-76), Worcs Snr Cup(9) 04-06 19-20 21-22 23-24 27-28 49-50 67-68 80-81 (R-up(11) 03-04 09-11 12-13 20-21 24-26 36-37 48-49 55-56 78-79), Herefordshire Snr Cup 54-55, Camkin Cup 69-70, Camkin Pres. Cup 70-71, Kidderminster Cup 1887-88, Keys Cup 37-38 62-63, Dudley Guest Hosp. Cup 1891-92, Worcs Charity Cup 1887-88, Worcs Jnr Cup 27-28, Brierley Hill Lg R-up 44-45 (Lg Cup R-up 44-45).

GOALKEEPERS: Andy Crannage (Lye)
DEFENDERS: John Horne (Ashtree H, Oldbury, Kidderminster, Walsall), Gary Bruce (Bromsgrove), Steve Ingram (Lye, Cradley, Tividale, Halesowen T, Stourbridge), Chris Jones (Bromsgrove, Kidderminster, Stourbridge, Bilston, Halesowen T, Redditch, Telford), Mark Potter (Local football), Darren Bradburn (Wednesfield), Jason Lowe (Moor Green, Kidderminster, Birmingham)
MIDFIELD: Alan Potter (Oldswinford, Dudley, Clancey Dudley), Mick Williams (Worcester, Northfield), Seamus Roche (Stourport S), Dave Beasley (Dudley, Halesowen T, Lye), Lewis Claxton (Solihull B, Bromsgrove, Willenhall, Stourbridge, Kidderminster, Aston Villa(T))
FORWARDS: Evron Wright (Oldbury, Stourbridge, Sprinvale-Tranco), Gavin Whitehouse (Halesowen T, Alvechurch, Stourbridge, Alvechurch, Dudley, Tipton, Dudley), Toby Hall (Halesowen H), Mark Cartwright (King's Heath), Paul Joinson (Malvern, Dudley, Redditch, Worcester, Halesowen T, GEC Witton)

Pages: 28 **Price:** 60p
Editor: Nigel Gregg, Hugh Clark
WMPCC Rating: 28

SUTTON COLDFIELD TOWN

Sutton Coldfield Town FC - Back Row (L/R): P Sharp (Manager, no longer with club), S Tucker, L Morrison, S Ward, D Belford, N Richards, R Sturgeon, M Clarke, C Sharpe, A Hampton. Front: A Ling, G Smith, A Whitehouse, S McKenzie, A Biddle, P Hunter. Photo - Marshalls Sports Service, Birmingham.

Chairman: Tony Lockley   **Vice Chairman:** Kevin Holt
Secretary: Gerry Shanahan, 34 Shipton Road, Sutton Coldfield B72 1NR (021 354 5152).
Team Manager: Chris Wright   **Asst Manager:** Joe Nugent   **Coach:** Ian Cooper
Groundsman: Brian Asprey.   **Physio:** Brendan Glynn   **Comm. Mgr:** Les Woodhams.
Ground: Central Ground, Coles Lane, Sutton Coldfield B72 1NL (021 354 2997/021 355 5475).
Directions: A5127 into Sutton, right at Odeon cinema (Holland Road), then first right into Coles Lane - ground 150 yds on left. 10 mins walk from Sutton Coldfield (BR), bus 104 from Birmingham.
Capacity: 4,500 (450 Covered).   **Seats:** 250   **Floodlights:** Y   **Shop:** Y   **Metal Badges:** Y
Colours: Royal blue/white/royal blue   **Change colours:** White/royal blue/white.
Previous Leagues: Central Birmingham/ Walsall Senior/ Staffs County/ Birminghham Combination 50-54/ West Mids (Regional) 54-65 79-82/ Midlands Combination 65-79.
Reserve Team's League: Midland Combination Reserve Division.
Previous Name: Sutton Coldfield 1879-1921   **Previous Grounds:** Meadow Plat 1879-1920.
Midweek home matchday: Wednesday   **Sponsors:** DRG Construction Ltd (021 358 7040).
Record Attendance: 2,029 v Doncaster Rovers, FA Cup 80-81 (Receipts £2,727).
Best F.A. Cup season: 1st Rd 80-81 (lost 0-1 to Doncaster). **League clubs defeated in F.A. Cup:** None.
Record Fees - Paid: £1,500 for Lance Morrison (Gloucester) **Received:** £25,000 for Barry Cowdrill (WBA).
Players progressing to Football League: Arthur Corbett (W'sall 1949), Paul Cooper (Man City), Noel Blake (Leeds), Steve Cooper (Barnsley), Peter Latcford (WBA & Celtic), Mark Smith (Wolves), John Barton (E'ton), Barry Cowdrill (WBA 1979), Colin Dryhurst (H'fax 1979), Dale Belford (Notts Co 1987).
Clubhouse: Brick built lounge and concert room, fully carpeted and extensively decorated. Open daily.
Steward: Committee.
Club Record Goalscorer: Eddie Hewitt 288   **Club Record Apps:** Eddie Hewitt 465
91-92 Captain: **91-92 P.o.Y.:** Dale Belford   **91-92 Top scorer:** Gary Smith 22.
Local Newspapers: Sutton Coldfield News, Sutton Observer.
Local Radio Stations: BRMB, Radio WM.
Honours: Southern Lg Midland Div R-up 82-83, West Mids Lg 79-80 (Lg Cup 80-81), Midland Comb(2) 77-79 (R-up(2) 69-71, Lg Cup 69-70), Walsall Snr Lg 46-47, Walsall Snr Cup(3) 77-80 (R-up 80-81), Staffs Senior Cup R-up 89-90 (SF 84-85 86-87), Worcs Snr Cup SF 88-89, Walsall Challenge Cup R-up 46-47 47-48, Sutton Charity Cup 46-47 65-66 71-72 86-87 89-90, FA Trophy 1st Rd Replay 89-90, FA Amateur Cup 2nd Rd 70-71, Express & Star Cup 44-45.

GOALKEEPERS:
Dale Belford (Tamworth, Nuneaton B, VS Rugby, Notts Co, Sutton C, Aston V)
DEFENDERS: Chris Keogh (Tamworth, Sutton C, Nuneaton B, Burton Alb, Redditch, Aston V), **Andy Ling** (Wolves, Leicester C(A)), **Tony Haddon** (Paget R), **Nigel Richards** (Paget R), **Micky Clarke** (Burton Alb, Scarborough, Barnsley), **Bob Whittingham** (Paget R, Halesowen T, Sutton C, Northfield)
MIDFIELD: Rob Sturgeon (Southport, Formby, Coventry, Liverpool(A)), **Mark Caulfield** (Paget R, Oldbury, Aston V, Sandwell B, Dudley, Tamworth, Dulwich, Tamworth, Atherstone, Walsall, Birmingham), **Adam Whitehouse** (Bilston, Sutton C), **Tony Hadland** (Dudley, Nuneaton B, Alvechurch, Oldbury, VS Rugby, Sutton C, Willenhall, Mile Oak, Sutton C, Oldbury, Tamworth, Stourbridge, Tamworth, Worcester, Walsall, WBA), **Steve Buchanan** (Redditch, Worcester), **David Gibbs** (Paget R), **Matthew Carroll** (Kidderminster, Wolves), **Royston Richardson** (Moor Green, Yardley Wood Utd)
FORWARDS: John Hunt (Paget R), **Andy Biddle** (Paget R, Sutton C, Boldmere), **Gary Smith** (Paget R, Sutton C), **Carl Dwyer** (Blakenall), **Micky Carr** (Armitage, Willenhall, Sandwell B, Redditch, Evesham, Tividale, Princes End, Boldmere, VS Rugby), **Carl Rathbone** (Alvechurch, Gresley R, Bromsgrove, Tamworth, Armitage, Mile Oak)

Pages: 36 **Price:** 50p
Editor: Terry Bent
WMPCC Rating: 22

TAMWORTH

Tamworth FC: Back Row (L/R): Sammy Chung (Manager), Darren Williams, Ade Waters, John Trewick, Dean Williams, Steve Cartwright, Tony Clarke, Mark Smith, Frank Duane. Front: Darren Marsh, Russell Gordon, Martin Bodkin, Darren Dickson, Danny Martin, Steve Ross, Buster Kendall (Trainer). Photo - Paul Barber.

Chairman: M A Jones   **President:** Leon Hinton.
Directors: R Andrews, D Baxter, D Seedhouse.
Secretary: R A Hadley, 38 Godolphin, Riverside, Tamworth B79 7UF (0827 66786).
Team Manager: Sammy Chung   **Coach:** Benny Brown   **Physio:** Frank Duane
Asst Manager: John Hannah   **Reserve Manager:** Paul Wood
Yth Team Manager: Bill Jones   **General Manager:** Mr P Young (0827 53194)
Ground: The Lamb Ground, Kettlebrook, Tamworth B79 1HA (0827 65798).
Directions: From town centre follow one-way road marked South into Kettlebrook Road - ground on right opposite railway arches. From A5 to Two Gates traffic lights, left into Tamworth Road, one mile to Lamb Inn, then left into ground car park. One mile from Tamworth (BR).
Capacity: 2,500 (1,450 Covered)   **Seats:** 431   **Floodlights:** Y   **Shop:** Y   **Metal Badges:** Y
Colours: Red/black/black   **Change colours:** All yellow   **Sponsors:**
Previous Leagues: B'ham Comb 33-54/ West Midlands 54-72 84-88/ Southern 72-79 83-84/ NPL 79-83.
Previous Names: None.   **Previous Grounds:** The Jolly Sailor Ground 1933-34.
Midweek home matchday: Tuesday   **Reserve Team's League:** Midland Combination (Reserve Division).
Record Attendance: 4,920 v Atherstone Town, 1948.
Best F.A. Cup season: 2nd Rd 69-70 (lost 0-6 at Gillingham). Also 1st Rd 66-67 70-71 87-88 90-91.
League clubs defeated in F.A. Cup: Torquay 69-70.
Record Fees - Paid: For Steve Cartwright.   **Received:** £5,000 for S Cartwright (Colchester).
Players progressing to Football League: Peter Hilton (WBA 1949), Alan Godridge (Swansea 1950), Higgins (Fulham), P Weir (Cardiff), S Fox (Wrexham), Steve Cartwright (Colchester 1988).
Clubhouse: Registered club, on ground.   **Steward:** Mrs June Young.
Club Record Goalscorer: Graham Jessop 195   **Club Record Apps:** Dave Seedhouse 869.
91-92 Capt.: John Trewick   **91-92 P.O.Y.:** Adrian Waters
91-92 Top scorer: R Gordon/ M Smith 15 each.
Local Newspapers: Tamworth Herald (0827 60741).
Local Radio Stations: Radio WM, BRMB Radio.   **Newsline:** 0898 446 822.
Hons: FA Vase 88-89, West Mids Lg 63-64 65-66 71-72 87-88 (R-up(2) 67-69, Div 2 55-56, Lg Cup(5) 64-66 71-72 85-86 87-88 (R-up 70-71)), Birmingham Snr Cup 60-61 65-66 68-69 (R-up 36-37 63-64), Staffs Snr Cup 58-59 63-64 65-66 (R-up 55-56 66-67 70-71), Midland F'lit Cup R-up 71-72 72-73, Camkin Cup 71-72 (R-up 70-71).

GOALKEEPERS:
Dean Williams (Birmingham), **Darren Heyes** (Shepshed, Matlock, Shepshed, Scunthorpe, Notts Forest)
DEFENDERS: Steve Cartwright (Colchester, Tamworth), **Andy Evans** (Sutton C), **Tony Clarke** (VS Rugby, Nuneaton, Swindon, Mansfield), **Dave Butler** (Stourport Swifts, Oldswinford, Cheltenham, Wolves), **Boyd Young** (Coventry(T)), **Ade Waters** (Hinckley T, Nuneaton, Atherstone, Nuneaton, Bedworth, Atherstone, Hurley DM, Nuneaton, Mile Oak), **Jason Woodley** (Stratford), **Nigel Hollier** (Armitage, Wolves(T)), **Robbie Grant** (Bilston, Gresley R, Willenhall, Bilston, Rushall O, Bilston), **Jason Minton** (Gresley R, Willenhall, Bilston, Rushall Olympic, Willenhall)
MIDFIELD: Martin Bodkin (Atherstone, RC Warwick, Coventry Sporting, Stratford, Bedworth), **Mark Smith** (Atherstone, Stourbridge, Sutton C, Wolves, Sutton C), **John Trewick** (Gateshead, Hartlepool, Bromsgrove, Hartlepool, Birmingham, Oxford Utd, Newcastle, WBA), **Paul Baines** (Stoke), **Darren Williams** (Worcester, Leicester C), **Darren Jordan** (Youth)
FORWARDS: Darron Morris (Emley, Bradley R), **Richard Wardle** (Youth), **Russell Gordon** (Cheltenham, Stafford R, Dudley, Banbury, Brighton, Coventry), **Darren Dickson** (Coventry(T)), **Steve Thorne** (Youth), **Dean Wright** (Sutton C, Redditch), **Craig Waters** (Bloxwich, Tamworth), **Steve Ross** (VS Rugby, Bedworth, Leamington, Long Buckby), **Justin Taylor** (Kidderminster)

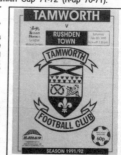

Pages: 24 **Price:** 60p
Editor: Peter Young (0827 280195)
Compiler: Stuart Turner
WMPCC Rating: 28

WESTON-SUPER-MARE

Lee Gardner (No.4) heads a goal for Weston against their neighbours, and arch rivals, Clevedon Town. Photo - Martin Wray.

President: D Usher   **Chairman:** P T Bliss
Secretary: G D Milsom, 12 Greenland Road, Milton, Weston-s-Mare BS22 8JP (0934 413059).
Manager: John Ellener   **Asst Manager:**   **Coach:** Peter Amos.
Physiotherapist: Terry Hardwell.
Ground: Woodspring Park, Winterstoke Road, Weston-super-mare (0934 21618).
Directions: From North: M5 Junct 21, to town centre 3 miles, left at Drove Rd., T. lights, 2nd exit next roundabout is Winterstoke Rd. 800 yds, ground right at next roundabout. From South: M5 Junct 22, Weston signs approx 7 miles, right at first roundabout (by Hospital), left at next roundabout, ground 1 mile on left. Twenty minutes walk from Weston-super-mare (BR).
Seats: 60   **Cover:** 500   **Capacity:** 4,000   **Club Shop:** Y   **Metal Badges:**
Midweek matches: Wednesday
Club colours: White/blue/blue   **Change colours:** Yellow/black/yellow
Previous Grounds: The Great Ground (pre-1955), Langford Road, 1955-83
Record Attendance: 692 v Cheltenham Town, 1987. *At Langford Road: 2,500 v Bridwater Town, FA Cup First Round Proper 1961-62.*
Best FA Cup season: First Round Proper replay 1961-62 (lost 0-1 at Bridgwater Town).
Players progressing to Football League: Ian Maine, John Palmer.
Previous League: Western 1948-92.
Clubhouse: Open every night, social activities, refreshments, 2 skittle alleys, 3 bars.
Club Record Goalscorer: **Club Record Apps:**
91-92 Capt.:   **91-92 P.O.Y.:**   **91-92 Top scorer:**
Local Newspapers: Bristol Evening Post, Western Daily Press.
Local Radio Stations: Somerset Sound.
Hons: Somerset Snr Cup 23-24 26-27, Western Lg 91-92 (Lg Cup 76-77 (R-up 89-90), Merit Cup 76-77 77-78).

GOALKEEPERS:
Glen Thomas (Stroud, Clevedon, Paulton R, Bristol R), **Steve Book** (Welton R, Paulton R)

DEFENDERS:
Mark Jones (Bristol Manor Farm, Bristol C), **Jon Bowering** (Bridgwater), **Jamie Boulton** (Youth), **Paul Tatterton** (Trowbridge), **Lee Rogers** (Yate, Gloucester, Exeter, Briol C)

MIDFIELD:
Ricky Chandler (Gloucester, Yeovil, Bath, Bristol C), **Paul Shrimpton** (Stroud, Paulton R, Stroud), **Julian Stearnes** (Trowbridge), **Mike Adams** (Bath, Bristol R), **Paul Terry** (Bristol C), **Alan Hooker** (Taunton, Exmouth, Bournemouth, Exeter), **Russell Priest** (Desborough)

FORWARDS:
David Payne (Clevedon, Weymouth, Bath, Gloucester, Bath), **Neil Barham** (Youth), **Paul Elson** (Minehead), **Matt Lazenby** (Minehead), **Richard Chattoe** (English Coll, Bristol R)

Pages: 44 **Price:** 40p
Editor: A Milsom
WMPCC Rating: N/A

YATE TOWN

Yate Town 91-92 - Back Row (L/R): Andy Fox, Paul Gardiner, Kevin Thaws, Terry Stevenson, Martyn Grimshaw, Dave Riley, Steve Ricketts. Front: Gary Davis, Dean Holtham, Richard Smith, Bobby Brown, Gary Hewlett, Wayne Matthews. Photo courtesy of Freelance Photos, Nailsworth.

Chairman: R G Hawkins   **President:** R Hewetson, Esq.
Secretary: T M Tansley, 1 Tyning Close, Yate, Bristol BS17 4PN (0454 324305).
Team Manager: Peter Jackson   **Asst Mgr:** Bobby Brown   **Coach:** Bobby Brown
Press Officer: **Physio:** Terry Leslie
Commercial Manager: Roger Hawkins.
Ground: Lodge Road, Yate, Bristol BS17 5LE (0454 228103).
Directions: M4 jct 18, A46 towards Stroud, then A432 to Yate. Turn left at top of railway bridge into North Road, first left past traffic lights. Five miles from Bristol Parkway (BR), buses 329, X68 and 328.
Capacity: 2,000 (200 Covered)   **Seats:** 226   **Floodlights:** Y   **Shop:** Y   **Metal Badges:** Y
Colours: White/navy blue/white   **Change colours:** All red.   **Sponsors:** Ind-Coope.
Previous Leagues: Gloucestershire County 68-83/ Hellenic 83-89.
Previous Name: Yate YMCA 46-70. **Previous Grounds:** Newmans Field 54-60/ Sunnyside Lane 60-84.
Midweek home matchday: Wednesday   **Reserve Team's League:** Bristol Suburban.
Record Attendance: 2,000 for Bristol Rovers v Bristol Rovers Past, Vaughan Jones testimonial 1990.
Best F.A. Cup season: **League clubs defeated in F.A. Cup:** None.
Record Fees - Paid: None.   **Received:** £7,500 from York City for Darren Tilley).
Players progressing to Football League: Richard Thompson (Newport County & Exeter City), Phil Purnell (Bristol Rovers), Darren Tilley (York City), Steve Winter (Walsall).
Clubhouse: Open every night and weekend lunchtimes. Skittles, darts, pool, occasional live entertainment.
Club Record Scorer   **Club Record Appearances:**
91-92 Captain: Kevin Thaws   **91-92 P.o.Y.:** Kevin Thaws (supporters' choice), Dean Holtham (players').
91-92 Top scorer: Kevin Thaws 32 (all matches).
Local Newspapers: Bristol Evening Post, Western Daily Press, North Avon Gazette.
Local Radio Stations: GWR, Radio Bristol.
Honours: FA Vase 5th Rd 91-92, Hellenic Lg(2) 87-89 (Div 1 R-up 84-85, Lg Skol Cup R-up 87-88), Glos Chal. Tphy 88-89 (R-up 78-79), Glos Snr Amtr Cup Sth 77-78, Glos Snr Chal. Cup (Nth) R-up 89-90, Stroud Charity Cup R-up 74-75 81-82 84-85 (Sect. A Winners(6) 76-78 79-80 82-83 87-89), Berkeley Hosp. Prem. Cup(3) 73-75 80-81, S.W. Co's Sutton Vase 85-86.

GOALKEEPERS:
Terry Stevenson (Berkeley)
DEFENDERS:
Jon Cordy (Youth), Gary Jones (Stokeside, Filton, Port of Bristol), Paul Gardiner (Taunton, Frome, Swindon, Yate), Steve Ricketts (Mangotsfield), Richard Bryant (Weston-Super-Mare, Forest Green R, Gloucester, Bristol C, Dry Robinsons), Dean Holtham (Ebbw Vale, Newport Co, Barry, Yeovil, Swansea, Cardiff C), Tony Dix (Local football)

MIDFIELD:
Gary Hewlett (Cheltenham, Forest Green R, Clandown, Yate), Bobby Brown (Forest Green R, Gloucester, Bath, Minehead, Weymouth, Bristol R), Kevin Thaws (Langton Court), Dean Elliott (Bristol R(T))

FORWARDS:
Richard Thompson (Salisbury, Trowbridge, Yeovil, Torquay, Newport Co, Yate), Martyn Grimshaw (Stroud, Weymouth, Yeovil, Bath, Bristol St George, Old Georgians), Kevin Hawkins (Youth), Wayne Matthews (Cheltenham, Chesham, Yate, Barry, Ton Pentre, Barry, Cardiff C), Mike Davies (Youth), Richard Smith (Stroud, Willenhall, Hednesford, Newport AFC, Stroud, Alvechurch, Stratford)

Pages: 28 **Price:** 50p
Editor: T Tansley
WMPCC Rating: 24

Beazer Homes (Southern) League Midland Division Ten Year Records

	82/3	83/4	84/5	85/6	86/7	87/8	88/9	89/90	90/1	91/2
Addlestone & Weybridge T.	–	–	–	–	–	–	–	–	20	21
Ashtree Highfield				(See Sandwell Borough)						
Atherstone United	–	–	–	–	–	4	2	–	–	–
Aylesbury United	13	5	2	–	–	–	–	–	–	–
Babbury United	7	18	17	17	12	10	16	21	–	–
Barry Town	–	–	–	–	–	–	–	5	6	4
Bedworth United	–	–	–	–	–	–	–	15	13	5
Bilston Town	–	–	–	7	18	17	13	17	14	12
Bridgend United	8	16	–	–	–	–	–	–	–	–
Bridgnorth Town	–	12	10	8	14	11	17	12	17	17
Bridgwater Town	12	–	–	–	–	–	–	–	–	–
Bromsgrove Rovers	10	3	6	1	–	–	–	–	–	–
Buckingham Town	–	–	–	–	13	12	–	–	–	–
Cheltenham Town	1	–	–	–	–	–	–	–	–	–
Corby Town	–	–	–	–	–	–	–	–	2	–
Coventry Sporting	–	15	11	18	8	20	20	–	–	–
Dudley Town	11	4	1	–	–	–	8	9	19	22
Enderby Town				(See Leicester United)						
Forest Green Rovers				(See Stroud)						
Gloucester City	–	–	–	9	7	7	1	–	–	–
Grantham Town	–	–	–	10	11	3	5	14	9	13
Halesowen Town	–	–	–	–	5	6	4	1	–	–
Hednesford Town	–	–	3	13	6	18	15	16	3	2
Hinckley Town	–	–	–	–	–	–	–	–	11	15
King's Lynn	–	–	–	–	–	13	19	13	8	14
Leamington	–	–	–	20	19	–	–	–	–	–
Leicester United	–	13	18	16	2	–	–	11	15	16
Merthyr Tydfil	4	8	12	3	3	1	–	–	–	–
Mile Oak Rovers & Youth	–	–	–	15	16	19	22	–	–	–
Milton Keynes City	17	19	–	–	–	–	–	–	–	–
Minehead	16	–	–	–	–	–	–	–	–	–
Moor Green	–	6	4	19	4	2	–	–	–	–
Newport A.F.C.	–	–	–	–	–	–	–	–	7	10
Nuneaton Borough	–	–	–	–	–	–	6	3	5	6
Oldbury United	6	14	16	21	–	–	–	–	–	–
Paget Rangers	–	–	–	–	–	22	–	–	–	–
Racing Club Warwick	–	–	–	–	–	–	–	19	16	18
Redditch United	14	9	8	2	–	–	–	18	10	20
Rushden Town	–	7	13	6	20	15	7	2	–	8
Sandwell Borough	–	–	–	–	–	–	14	22	–	–
Shepshed Charterhouse	–	2	–	–	–	–	–	–	–	–
Solihull Borough	–	–	–	–	–	–	–	–	–	1
Spalding United	–	–	–	–	–	–	8	6	22	–
Stourbridge	–	–	7	5	10	21	18	8	1	9
Stroud	3	11	14	14	9	9	12	10	18	19
Sutton Coldfield Town	2	–	9	12	17	5	10	7	12	3
Tamworth	–	20	–	–	–	–	3	4	4	7
Taunton Town	15	–	–	–	–	–	–	–	–	–
Trowbridge Town	–	–	–	–	–	16	–	–	–	–
V.S. Rugby	–	10	5	4	1	–	–	–	–	–
Wellingborough Town	9	17	15	11	15	14	21	–	–	–
Willenhall Town	5	1	–	–	–	–	11	20	21	–
Yate Town	–	–	–	–	–	–	–	–	–	11
No. of Clubs	17	20	18	21	20	22	22	22	22	22

Solihull Borough celebrate at Dudley after clinching the 1991-92 Midland Division championship.

Southern Division

	P	W	D	L	F	A	Pts
Hastings Town	42	28	7	7	80	37	91
Weymouth	42	22	12	8	64	35	78
Havant Town	42	21	12	9	67	46	75
Braintree Town	42	21	8	13	77	58	71
Buckingham Town *	42	19	15	8	57	26	69
Andover	42	18	10	14	73	68	64
Ashford Town	42	17	12	13	66	57	63
Sudbury Town	42	18	9	15	70	66	63
Sittingbourne **	42	19	10	13	63	41	61
Burnham	42	15	14	13	57	55	59
Baldock Town	42	16	10	16	62	67	58
Salisbury	42	13	16	13	67	51	55
Hythe Town	42	15	10	17	61	62	55
Margate	42	13	16	13	49	56	55
Newport IOW	42	13	10	19	58	63	49
Dunstable	42	12	12	18	55	67	48
Bury Town	42	14	4	24	52	94	46
Witney Town	42	11	12	19	55	76	45
Fareham Town	42	12	8	22	45	71	44
Erith & Belvedere	42	11	10	21	44	67	43
Canterbury City	42	8	14	20	43	69	38
Gosport Borough	42	6	9	27	32	65	27

* = 3 POINTS DEDUCTED - INELIGIBLE PLAYER.
** = 6 POINTS DEDUCTED - INELIGIBLE PLAYER.

Top Scorers

P **Odey** (Andover)		29
K **Clarke** (Witney Town)		22
S **Tate** (Havant Town)		21
D **Arter** (Sittingbourne)		19
J **Smith** (Salisbury)		19

THE BEAZER HOMES SOUTHERN DIVISION RESULT CHART 1991-92

HOME TEAM	1	2	3	4	5	6	7	8	9	10	11	12	13	14	15	16	17	18	19	20	21	22
1. Andover	*	0-2	2-0	2-5	2-4	2-1	1-2	7-1	3-1	2-0	0-2	0-0	3-1	3-1	2-7	1-3	2-2	1-1	3-2	1-2	3-0	2-1
2. Ashford T	2-2	*	2-2	3-1	0-0	1-1	0-3	1-1	1-1	2-1	1-0	2-0	3-4	0-2	2-1	1-1	2-1	2-2	3-1	5-3	0-0	3-0
3. Baldock T	2-3	1-0	*	1-3	0-0	2-1	3-2	4-3	2-1	2-0	3-0	1-4	2-1	1-1	2-3	2-1	2-0	1-1	2-3	0-3	2-1	4-1
4. Braintree T	1-0	2-0	5-0	*	0-2	4-3	1-3	1-2	7-0	2-1	2-2	1-2	0-2	4-2	2-1	1-1	3-1	2-0	1-1	1-1	0-0	1-0
5. Buckingham	3-0	0-3	2-0	0-0	*	2-2	5-1	3-0	2-1	1-0	1-0	1-1	0-1	2-0	1-1	0-2	1-0	0-0	1-0	5-0	1-1	3-1
6. Burnham	0-0	0-0	2-2	2-1	0-0	*	2-3	1-0	1-2	2-1	1-0	3-2	1-2	0-0	3-1	1-0	1-3	3-2	3-2	1-1	0-2	2-3
7. Bury Town	2-0	2-1	1-2	0-4	0-3	1-0	*	0-0	2-5	3-1	3-1	0-3	1-3	4-1	0-3	1-2	1-0	0-3	1-3	0-2	1-2	1-4
8. Canterbury C	3-3	0-2	1-6	3-4	1-1	0-1	1-1	*	1-1	1-0	1-1	2-0	1-2	0-0	1-0	2-0	3-1	1-3	0-0	1-0	0-1	2-2
9. Dunstable	2-3	1-2	1-1	1-3	1-0	3-1	2-0	1-0	*	1-3	2-1	0-1	0-4	1-2	0-0	0-0	1-1	1-1	0-1	0-2	1-2	2-2
10. Erith & Bel.	1-1	1-1	0-2	2-0	0-0	1-1	0-0	1-0	0-0	*	3-3	2-1	2-3	1-3	2-1	1-3	1-4	0-1	0-3	1-2	0-1	3-1
11. Fareham T	0-2	1-3	3-0	1-2	0-3	2-3	1-2	3-2	1-5	1-0	*	2-4	0-2	1-0	0-0	1-1	1-0	0-4	2-1	3-2	1-1	2-1
12. Gosport B	1-2	0-2	0-0	0-2	1-2	0-0	1-1	0-1	0-2	0-1	1-3	*	0-1	1-1	0-1	1-2	2-2	0-3	0-3	0-2	0-1	1-2
13. Hastings T	2-0	1-0	2-0	2-0	1-0	2-1	1-2	0-0	3-0	1-1	2-0	4-0	*	2-1	2-3	4-0	3-1	2-1	1-1	3-0	2-0	1-1
14. Havant T	2-1	1-0	1-0	3-0	0-3	1-1	5-0	3-1	4-2	1-2	1-0	2-1	3-2	*	3-1	3-1	0-3	1-1	1-0	2-2	1-2	4-1
15. Hythe T	1-1	3-1	0-0	2-2	2-0	1-3	3-1	1-0	0-4	1-3	1-1	2-0	2-1	3-3	*	0-1	2-2	3-1	0-2	1-3	0-1	3-1
16. Margate	1-2	2-2	1-1	1-3	1-1	1-2	1-0	1-0	0-0	5-0	2-2	0-1	1-1	0-0	2-1	*	3-1	1-0	0-0	0-2	1-1	4-4
17. Newport IOW	0-3	3-2	3-1	2-1	0-0	2-1	4-1	2-2	2-1	0-1	3-0	3-1	0-3	0-2	1-1	0-1	*	1-1	0-1	4-0	0-1	1-0
18. Salisbury	0-0	1-3	2-3	2-2	0-0	0-0	3-1	1-2	4-2	0-1	3-2	1-1	0-0	0-1	5-1	2-2	*	0-2	0-0	2-2	3-1	
19. Sittingbourne	1-2	3-2	1-0	4-0	0-3	0-1	3-0	2-0	2-2	2-3	1-0	0-0	2-0	0-1	1-2	1-1	0-2	2-2	*	3-0	2-1	1-0
20. Sudbury T	3-1	6-1	4-3	1-2	1-0	1-1	4-0	3-3	0-2	1-1	0-1	1-0	1-2	0-0	2-1	4-0	4-2	1-3	1-6	*	2-0	0-0
21. Weymouth	1-3	2-1	0-0	2-0	1-0	2-2	5-0	2-0	3-0	4-1	3-0	0-0	1-2	0-0	3-1	3-0	0-0	0-1	0-0	5-3	*	5-1
22. Witney T	2-2	0-2	2-0	0-1	1-1	0-2	3-6	1-1	2-2	1-0	2-1	2-0	1-2	2-2	2-0	0-0	4-2	0-3	0-0	1-0	2-1	*

ANDOVER

Andover's Mark Smith makes a spectacular headed clearance against Bashley in the FA Trophy at the Portway Stadium. Photo - Dennis Nicholson.

Chairman: K Cunningham-Brown   **President:** R Coleman
Secretary: Mr K J Stevens, 13 Eardley Avenue, Andover, Hants (0264 333052).
Team Manager: TBA   **Asst Manager:** TBA   **Coach:** TBA
Press Officer: Secretary   **Physio:** Terry Carr   **Comm Manager:**
Ground Address & Tel: Portway Stadium, West Portway Industrial Estate, Andover SP10 3LF (0264 333052).
Directions: On western outskirts - follow any sign to Portway Industrial estate. Approx 2 miles from station.
Capacity: 3,000 (250 Covered)   **Seats:** 250   **Floodlights:** Y   **Shop:** N   **Metal Badges:** Y
Colours: Red & black shirts/black/red   **Change colours:** Tangarine/white/tangarine
Sponsors: Hospital Saving Association.
Previous Leagues: Sailisbury & Dist/ Hants 1896-98/ 99-1901/ 02-62/ Southern 1898-99/ Western 1962-71.
Previous Name: Andover Town   **Previous Ground:** The Walled Meadow (until 1989).
Midweek home matchday: Tuesday   **Reserve Team's League:** None (2 youth sides).
Record Gate: 1,100 v Leicester, ground opening. *(3,484 v Gillingham at Walled Meadow, previous ground).*
Best F.A. Cup season: 1st Rd 62-63 (lost 0-1 to Gillingham).
League clubs defeated in F.A. Cup: None.
Record Fees - Paid: £8,000 for Roger Emms (Newbury)   **Received:** £6,000 for Jeremy Stagg (Bashley).
Players progressing to Football League: Keith Wilson (Southampton 1959), Nigel Spackman (B'mouth 1980), Colin Court (Reading 1981), A Kingston (Southampton), P Brown (Southampton, Walsall), Emeka Nwajiobi (Luton).
Clubhouse: As a pub, but available for private functions.   **Steward:** Bridgett Thomas.
Club Record Goalscorer: T Randall 73   **Club Record Apps:** P Pollard 469
91-92 Captain: Paul Voce   **91-92 P.o.Y.:** Kevan Bale   **91-92 Top scorer:** Paul Odey 29.
Local Newspapers: Andover Advertiser (23456), Southern Evening Echo.
Local Radio Stations: Radio 210.
Honours: FA Tphy 3rd Qualifying Rd 69-70 70-71, Western Lg R-up 69-70 70-71, Hants Lg 13-14 24-25 33-34 44-45 48-49 50-51 61-62 (R-up 42-43, Northern Div 13-14, Div 2 R-up 37-38, Combination (reserves) 87-88), Salisbury & Dist Lg 1894-95 95-96 96-97 99-1900 03-04 07-08 12-13, Hants Senior Cup 48-49 50-51 55-56 64-65, Russell Cotes Cup 23-24 31-32 37-38 44-45 52-53 58-59 60-61 61-62, Pickfords Cup 50-51, Hants Intermediate Cup 59-60 60-61, Hants Junior Cup 19-20 (R-up 1893-94 1910-11 12-13), May Lg 1899-00 00-01 01-02 07-08 08-09.

GOALKEEPERS:
Steve Osgood (Aldershot, Farnborough, Newbury)
DEFENDERS:
Darren Baldwin (Newbury, Portals, Southampton(J)), **Paul Voce** (Eastleigh, Andover, Salisbury, RS Southampton, Bemerton Ath, Willenhall), **Roger Emms** (Newbury, Swindon Ath, Devizes), **Andy Swatton** (Neweubry, Andover, Newbury, Andover, Romsey, Salisbury, Andover, Salisbury, Andover), **Stuart Thomson** (Salisbury, Andover, Basingstoke, Newbury, Andover, Reading(J)), **Lee Spalding** (Youth)
MIDFIELD:
Kevin Bale (Kintbury R, Maidenhead Utd, Newbury, Hungerford, Andover), **Keith Maddocks** (Youth), **Dean Robinson** (Basingstoke, Newbury, Basingstoke), **Jason Braidwood** (Youth), **Barry Andrews** (Salisbury, Basingstoke, Fareham, Andover, Basingstoke, Salisbury, Andover, Farnborough, Aldershot), **Vince Rusher** (Youth), **Stuart Sullivan** (Youth)
FORWARDS:
Paul Odey (Newbury, Andover), **Mark Smith** (Hamble), **Mark Hughes** (Newbury, Hungerford, Trowbridge, Chippenham, Gloucester, Swindon(A)), **Paul Cenci** (Youth)

ANDOVER F.C.

Official Programme
1991/1992 Season

(50p)

PROGRAMME DETAILS:
Pages: 20 **Price:** 50p
Editor:
WMPCC Rating: 15

Ashford Town goalkeeper Stuart Weaver produces a fine save to deny Kenny Hoyte of Erith & Belvedere. Photo - Keith Gillard.

Chairman: P G Castle   **President:** A M Batt.
Secretary: Alan Lancaster, 128 Kingsnorth Road, Ashford, Kent TN26 2HY (0233 621325).
Team Manager: Neil Cugley   **Asst Manager/Coach:** Peter McRobert
Press Officer: Secretary   **Physio:** George Sergeant
Commercial Manager: E A Warren (0233 634125).
Newsline: 0898 122 929.
Ground: The Homelands, Ashford Road, Kingsnorth, Kent TN26 1NJ (0233 611838).
Directions: In Kingsworth (4 miles south of Ashford) on A2070.
Capacity: 3,500 (500 Covered)   **Seats:** 500   **Floodlights:** Y   **Shop:** Y   **Metal Badges:** Y
Colours: White (green trim)/green/green   **Change colours:** All royal blue.
Sponsors: Sealink/ Stenna.
Previous Leagues: Kent 30-39 46-59.   **Previous Ground:** Estella Park 30-87.
Midweek home matchday: Tuesday   **Reserve Team's League:** Kent Midweek League.
Record Attendance: 6,525 (at Essella Park, previous ground), v Crystal Palace, FA Cup 1st Rd 1959.
Best F.A. Cup season: 2nd Rd 61-62 (lost 0-3 at home to QPR), 66-67 (0-5 at Swindon). Also 1st Rd 34-35 58-59 59-60 60-61 74-75.
League clubs defeated in F.A. Cup: None.
Previous Names: Ashford United/ Ashford Railway.
Record Fees - Paid: £2,000 for Tim Hulme (Hythe)   **Rec'd:** £25,000 for Jeff Ross & Dave Arter (Hythe).
Players progressing to Football League: Ollie Norris (R'dale 1961), Howard Moore (Coventry 1966), Tony Godden (WBA 1975).
Clubhouse: Licensed bar, pool, food, function room.   **Steward:** Wendy White.
Club Record Goalscorer: John Young 172   **Club Record Apps:** Peter McRobert 685.
91-92 Captain: Jed Nohilly   **91-92 P.o.Y.:** Andy Pearson   **91-92 Top scorer:** Mark Stanton 22.
Local Newspapers (+Tel.Nos.): Kentish Express (0233 623232), Ashford Citizen & Scene.
Local Radio Stations: Radio Kent, Radio Invicta.
Honours: FA Tphy SF 72-73, Southern Lg Southern Div R-up 86-87, Kent Lg 48-49 (R-up 31-32, Lg Cup 38-39), Kent Senior Cup 58-59 62-63.

GOALKEEPERS:
Stuart Weaver (Maidstone), **Paul Crocker** (Youth)
DEFENDERS:
Peter McRobert (Chelmsford, Ashford, Bromley), **Andy Pearson** (Folkestone, Chatham, Maidstone), **Jed Nohilly** (Hythe, Dulwich, Tonbridge, Gravesend, Northampton, Sheppey), **Neil Cugley** (Folkestone, Hythe, Thanet, Dartford, Hythe, Dover, Maidstone, Folkestone, Dartford, Dover, Thanet, Ashford), **Matt Gubbins** (Youth), **John Crabbe** (Canterbury, Crawley, Torquay, Crewe, Hereford, Carlisle Utd, Gillingham, Southampton)
MIDFIELD:
Jason Wheeler (Hythe, Crawley, Maidstone), **Liam Horgan** (Local football), **Mark Stanton** (Hythe), **Jamie Reilly** (Margate, Maidstone(T)), **Richard Moon** (Gillingham(J), Wimbledon(J)), **Andy Morris** (Folkestone), **James Carney** (Hythe), **Steve Brignall** (Hythe, Ashford, Gravesend, Tonbridge, Hastings Utd, Arsenal(A)), **Mick Wakeman** (Gravesend), **David Gear** (Canterbury, Thanet, Dover, Snowdown CW)
FORWARDS:
Frank Ovard (Hythe, Folkestone, Hythe, Crawley, Dover, Maidstone, Folkestone, Maidstone, Gillingham, Maidstone, Folkestone, Ashford), **Simon Bryant** (Hythe, Deal, Canterbury, Folkestone), **Lee McRobert** (Bromley Green), **Nicky Jimson** (Folkestone Invicta), **Rainbow Nelson** (Charlton(J)), **Eddie Bacon** (Local football), **Dave Jordan** (Sittingbourne, Gillingham(T))

PROGRAMME DETAILS:
Pages: 28 **Price:** 50p
Editor: Ernie Warren
WMPCC Rating: 22

515

BALDOCK TOWN

Baldock Town, Herts Charity Cup winners 1991-92. Back Row (L/R): Terry Shrieves, Steve Ward, Andy Cody, Simon Merrick, Gary Williams, Jon Bone (Captain), Alan Arber. Front: Keith Stanton, Marcelle Bruce, Kevin Phillips, Robert Sutton, Ian Allinson (Player-Manager), Paul Newman.

Chairman: Ray Childerstone **Vice Chairman:** Tony Bottomley **President:** John Pugh.
Secretary: Bob Brown, 6 Anchor Rd, Baldock, Herts SG7 6LG (0462 895355).
Team Manager: Ian Allinson **Asst Manager:** **Coach:** D Moseley
Press Officer: David Hammond (0462 892797) **Physio:** Fred Day.
Ground: Norton Road, Baldock, Herts SG7 5AU (0462 895449).
Directions: Norton Road is left off A505 Hitchin to Baldock road. From Baldock station (Kings Cross to Royston line) - left down Icknield Way, right into Norton Road and under rail bridge.
Capacity: 3,000 (1,500 Covered) **Seats:** 200 **Floodlights:** Y **Shop:** Y **Metal Badges:** Y
Colours: Red/white/red **Change colours:** Yellow/blue/yellow. **Sponsors:** Swan Garage
Previous Leagues: S Midlands 25-39 47-54 63-83/ Parthenon 54-59/ London 59-63/ United Counties 83-87.
Previous Ground: Bakers Close (until 1981).
Midweek home matchday: Tuesday **Reserve Team's League:** Essex & Herts Border Comb.
Record Attendance: 1,200 v Arsenal, floodlight opening 1984.
Best F.A. Cup season: 4th Qualifying Round 1991-92.
League clubs defeated in F.A. Cup:
Record Fees - Paid: £2,000 for Colin Hull (B Stortford) **Received:** £1,000 for Ian Ferguson (Barnet).
Players progressing to Football League: Ian Dowie (Luton & West Ham), Alan Stewart (Portsmouth).
Clubhouse: Members' bar and seperate function room. Open full licensing hours. **Steward:** John Fox.
Club Record Goalscorer: **Club Record Apps:** Paddy Stanton 440
91-92 Capt.: Jon Bone **91-92 P.o.Y.:** Kevin Phillips (supporters' choice), Marcelle Bruce (Managers').
91-92 Top scorer: Gary Williams 13.
Local Newspapers: Comet, Gazette, Herald. **Local Radio:** Radio Bedfordshire, Chiltern.
Hons: FA Tphy 2nd Qual. Rd 90-91, FA Vase 5th Rd 83-84, United Counties Lg R-up 83-84 86-87, South Mids Lg 27-28 65-66 67-68 69-70 (R-up 53-54 82-83, Lg Cup 65-66 69-70, Div 1 49-50, Reserve Div 1 66-67), Herts Charity Cup 91-92, Herts Charity Shield 57-58 69-70, Wallspan Floodlight Cup 85-86, Hinchinbrooke Cup 86-87, TSI Floodlit Cup 88-89, Woolwich Equitable Building Society Cup 83-84, Herts Intermediate Cup 86-87.

GOALKEEPERS:
Alan Arber (Gt Yarmouth, Bury T, Lowestoft, Wroxham, Hoveton, Norwich),
Keith Allinson (Local football)

DEFENDERS:
Simon Merrick (Saffron Walden, King's Lynn, Camb Utd(T)), **Kevin Phillips** (Southampton(T)), **Martin Allinson** (Stevenage B, Pirton, Hitchin, Letchworth), **Marcel Bruce** (Colchester, Spurs), **Paddy Stanton** (Arlesey, Pirton), **Gary Simpson** (Welwyn GC, Baldock), **Dave Clover** (Berkhamsted, Stevenage, St Albans)

MIDFIELD:
John Templeton (Hitchin, Stevenage B), **Steve Ward** (Spalding, Bromley, Tooting, Castleford CW), **Paul Marshall** (Buckingham, Baldock, Buckingham, Wolverton, Sydney C(Aust), Dunstable, Milton Keynes, Dunstable), **Mick Cuffle** (Dunstable, Hitchin, Dunstable, Chelmsford, Dunstable, Southall), **Paul Newman** (Luton(T)), **Andy Cody** (Dunstable, Pitstone)

FORWARDS:
Ian Allinson (Colchester, Luton, Stoke, Arsenal, Colchester), **Gary Williams** (Stevenage B, Vauxhall M, Luton(J)), **Terry Shrieves** (Buckingham, Rushden, Boreham Wood, Buckingham, Wolverton, Aylesbury, Kettering, Buckingham, Milton Keynes, Hitchin, Woking, Millwall), **Rob Sutton** Luton(T))

Pages: 48 **Price:** 50p
Editor: John Jackson
WMPCC Rating: 40

BRAINTREE TOWN

Aerial action from the Braintree (light shirts) v Sudbury Easter Monday local derby (1-1) which was watched by 525. Photo - Jon Weaver.

Chairman: George Rosling   **Vice Chairman:** Ivan Kibble   **President:** Ron Webb.
Secretary: T A Woodley, 19a Bailey Bridge Road, Braintree, Essex CM7 5TT (0376 326234).
Team Manager: Frank Bishop   **Asst Manager:**
Press Officer: Ron Webb (0376 325338)   **Physio:** Tony Last
Commercial Manager: Frank Bishop (0376 551165). Commercial Office and Shop 0376 327608).
Ground: Cressing Road Stadium, Clockhouse Way, Braintree, Essex (0376 345617).
Directions: Turn off A12 London to Yarmouth road at Witham and follow B1018 to Braintree. Floodlights visible behind 'The Sportsman' half a mile into town. Entrance next left in Clockhouse Way, then left again. 1 mile from Braintree & Bocking (BR). Bus 353 from Witham stops at 'The Sportsman'.
Capacity: 4,000 (1,300 Covered)   **Seats:** 292   **Floodlights:** Y   **Shop:** Y   **Metal Badges:** £2.00
Colours: Yellow/blue/blue   **Change colours:** Blue & white.   **Sponsors:** Chelmsford Star Co-op.
Previous Leagues: Spartan 28-35/ Eastern Counties 35-37 38-39 52-55 70-91/ London 45-52/ Suffolk Border 55-64/ Greater London 64-66/ Metropolitan 66-70/ North Essex.
Previous Names: Manor Works 1894-1918/ Crittall Ath. 18-68/ Braintree & Crittall Ath. 68-81/ Braintree FC 81-82.
Previous Grounds: Kings Head Meadow 1894-1902/ Spaldings Meadow, Panfield Lane 1902-24.
Midweek home matchday: Tuesday   **Best F.A. Cup season:** 4th Qual. Rd 69-70 85-86.
Record Attendance: 4,000 v Spurs, charity challenge match, May 1952.
Record Fees - Paid: £1,000 for Gary Hollocks (Bury T)   **Received:** £1,000 Gary Nash (Bury T).
Players progressing to Football League: J Dick (West Ham United), S Wright (Wrexham), J Cheesewright (Birmingham City), S Allen (Wimbledon - physio).
Clubhouse: Open evenings and weekends. Darts, pool etc.   **Steward:** Mrs Christine Thorogood.
Club Record Goalscorer: Chris Guy 211 (1983-90)   **Club Record Apps:** Paul Young 524 (1966-77).
91-92 Captain: Paul England   **91-92 P.o.Y.:** Paul England & Mark Cranfield (shared)
91-92 Top scorer: Neil Grice 17.
Local Newspapers: Braintree & Witham Times (0376 551551).   **Newsline:** 0898 446 883.
Local Radio Stations: BBC Essex (103.5 fm), Essex Radio (102.6 fm).
Honours: Eastern Counties Lg 36-37 83-84 84-85 (R-up 86-87 87-88 88-89 90-91, Lg Cup 87-88 (R-up 35-36 74-75)), Essex County Lg R-up 37-38, London Lg (East) R-up 45-46 (Lg Cup 47-48(joint) 48-49 51-52 (R-up 49-50)), Metropolitan Lg Cup 69-70, East Anglian Cup 46-47 68-69, Essex Senior Trophy 86-87 (R-up 90-91), Essex & Suffolk Border Lg (2), RAFA Cup 56-57, Gtr London Benevolent Cup 65-66.

GOALKEEPERS:
Adam Spicer (Heybridge S), **Paul Catley** (Youth)

DEFENDERS:
Phil Boyland (Sudbury, Bury T, Brantham, Harwich), **Shane Bailey** (Youth), **Mark Cranfield** (Brightlingsea, Colchester(J)), **Gary Culling** (Youth), **Jimmy Thomas** (Chelmsford), **Nick Maynard** (Local football)

MIDFIELD:
Russell Tanner (Chelmsford), **Duncan Coghlan** (Chelmsford), **Kevin Adams** (Writtle), **Lee Fish** (Halstead, Haverhill R), **Neil Grice** (Witham, Fisher, Braintree, Chelmsford, Braintree, Ipswich), **John Bishop** (Gt Waltham)

FORWARDS:
Paul England (Haverhill R, Bury T, Haverhill R), **Barry Roberts** (Chelmsford), **Dave King** (Stowmarket), **Kevin Newbury** (Heybridge S, Saffron Walden, B Stortford, Malden T), **Gary Hollocks** (Heybridge S, Bury T, Braintree, Silver End, Halstead), **Dean Jefferies** (Clacton)

SEASON 1991-92   CLUB SPONSORS   CHELMSFORD STAR

Pages: 36 **Price:** 45p
Editor: Ron Webb
WMPCC Rating: 26

BUCKINGHAM TOWN

The Robins

Buckingham Town. Back Row (L/R): Brian Robinson, Andy Falconer, Colin Waite, Mark Sherlock, Keith Baker, Dave Hume, Tony McGuinness, Paul Marshall, Jerry Mansfield, Sean Barker(physio). Front: Jon Blencombe, Terry Shrieves, Steve Jenkins, Phil Lines, Ian Bowyer, Kieran Sullivan, Tom Pearson.

Chairman: Chris Lawrence   **President:** Mr R B Taylor
Secretary: E J Seaton, 20 Glebe Road, Deanshanger, Milton Keynes MK19 6LT (0908 562875).
Team Manager: Keith Baker   **Asst Manager:** Adrian McKay
Press Officer: Willy   **Physio:** Willy   **Commercial Manager:** None
Ground: Ford Meadow, Ford Street, Buckingham (0280 816257).
Directions: 400 yds from town centre, off Buckingham to Aylesbury Road.
Capacity: 4,000 (150 Covered)   **Seats:** 350   **Floodlights:** Y   **Shop:** Y   **Metal Badges:** Y
Colours: All red   **Change colours:** All white.
Sponsors: Ford Tingewick Garage.
Previous Lges: Aylesbury & Dist/ Nth Bucks/ Hellenic 53-57/ Sth Mids 57-74/ Utd Co's 74-86.
Midweek matchday: Wednesday   **Reserve Team's League:** None.
Record Attendance: 2,451 v Orient, FA Cup 1st Rd 84-85.
Best F.A. Cup season: 1st Rd 84-85.
League clubs defeated in F.A. Cup: None.
Record Fees - Paid: £7,000 for Steve Jenkins (Wealdstone)   **Rec'd:** £1,000 for Terry Shrieves (Kettering).
Players progressing to Football League: None.
Clubhouse: Open every evening and weekend lunchtimes. Concert room with stage for hire, capacity 240. Bingo, dominoes, ladies and mens darts, pool, table tennis.
Club Record Goalscorer: Unknown   **Club Record Apps:** Unknown
91-92 Captain: Ian Bowyer   **91-92 P.O.Y.:**   **91-92 Top scorer:** Steve Jenkins 16
Local Newspapers: Buckingham Advertiser, MK Citizen, Herald & Post.
Local Radio Stations: Fox FM (102.6 fm).   **Newsline:** 0898 884 431.
Hons: FA Vase 6th Rd 90-91, Beazer Southern Div 90-91, Utd Co's Lg 83-84 85-86 (Div 1 R-up 75-76, Div 2 R-up 74-75, Lg Cup 83-84, Div 2 Cup R-up 74-75), Nth Bucks Lg(8) 24-25 28-29 33-34 35-37 38-39 48-49 49-50, Aylesbury & Dist. Lg 02-03, Berks & Bucks Snr Cup 83-84, Berks & Bucks Jnr Cup 02-03 48-49 (R-up 38-39 72-73), Berks & Bucks Minor Cup 32-33, Buckingham Snr Charity Cup(18) 32-33 35-36 37-38 47-50 52-55 72-73 75-77 78-79 80-81 83-87 (R-up 31-32 36-37 39-40 73-74 81-82).

GOALKEEPERS:
Keith Baker (Banbury, Aylesbury, Witney, Grimsby, Millwall, Oxford Utd)

DEFENDERS:
Mark Sherlock (Brackley, Banbury, Highgate), **Ian Bowyer** (Banbury, Wealdstone, Banbury, Brackley, Banbury, Chipping Norton), **Mark Wharton** (Witney, Kidlington), **Keith Knight** (Brackley, Thame), **Declan Cuddy** (Abingdon Utd, Witney, Osberton Rad, Abingdon T)

MIDFIELD:
Jerry Mansfield (Brackley, Banbury, Bicester), **Dave Bristow** (Banbury, Brackley, Banbury, Swindon), **Dave Hume** (Aylesbury, Buckingham, Chesham, Aylesbury), **Ricky Paul** (Local football), **Steve Bennett** (Youth), **Terry Muckelburg** (Daventry, Buckingham, Brackley, Banbury, Oxford C, Banbury, Oxford Utd)

FORWARDS:
Steve Jenkins (Wealdstone, Witney, Cheltenham, Oxford C, Limerick C, Varberg(Swe), Oxford C, Preseed Steel), **Barry Cooper** (Bicester), **Tom Pearson** (Daventry, Hinckley T, Buckingham, Long Buckby, Banbury, Irthlingborough, Buckingham, Long Buckby, Banbury, Wellingborough, Kempston R), **Jon Blencowe** (Long Buckby), **Stefan Wilson** (Youth)

BUCKINGHAM
TOWN FOOTBALL CLUB

OFFICIAL
MATCHDAY
PROGRAMME

35p

PROGRAMME DETAILS:
Pages: 36 Price: 40p
Editor:
WMPCC Rating: 24

BURNHAM

Burnham FC. Back Row (L/R): C Laver (Treasurer), D Eavis (Vice Chairman), D Clayton (Coach), M Turner, T Cook, P Tillen, N Devereux, R Dodds, R North, J Jarvis, C Cooper (Physio), C Barnes (Manager). Front: T Argrave, D Osgood, K Hughes, S Chandler, M Bennett, E Hutchinson. Photo - Slough Observer.

Chairman: Malcolm Higton   **President:** Ray Laverick.
Secretary: Michael Boxall, 39 Tockley Road, Burnham, Slough SL1 7DQ (0628 660265).
Team Manager: Colin Barnes   **Coaches:** Eddie Hutchinson, Derek Clayton.
Press Officer: Michael Boxall   **Physio:** Colin Cooper   **Comm Manager:** Neil Young, C/O the club.
Ground: Wymers Wood Road, Burnham, Slough SL1 8JG (0628 602467/602697).
Directions: North west of village centre, 2 miles from Burnham (BR), 2 miles from M4 junction 7, 5 miles from M40 junction 2. Bee Line buses 65 and 68.
Capacity: 2,500 (200 Covered)   **Seats:** 200   **Floodlights:** Y   **Shop:** Y   **Metal Badges:** N
Colours: Blue & white quarters/white/blue   **Change colours:** All yellow.
Sponsors: Rep-Tech (Herpetological Supplies).
Previous Leagues: Sth Bucks & East Berks/ Windsor, Slough & Dist./ Gt Western Comb. 48-64/ Wycombe Comb. 64-70/ Reading Comb. 70-71/ Hellenic 71-77/ Athenian 77-84/ London Spartan 84-85.
Previous Name: Burnham & Hillingdon 1985-87   **Previous Ground:** Baldwin Meadow (until 20's).
Midweek home matchday: Wednesday   **Reserve Team's League:** Suburban.
Record Attendance: 2,400 v Halesowen Town, FA Vase 1983.
Best F.A. Cup season: 3rd Qualifying Rd.   **League clubs defeated in F.A. Cup:** None.
Best F.A. Trophy season: Third Qualifying Rd replay 89-90.
Players progressing to Football League: None.
Clubhouse: Open every evening and weekend lunchtimes. Darts and pool, two bars, catering, live entertainment.
Steward: Neil Young.
Club Record Scorer: Fraser Hughes 65, 69-70   **Club Record Apps:**
91-92 Captain: Martin Turner   **91-92 P.o.Y.:** Tim Cook   **91-92 Top scorer:** Shane Chandler 14.
Local Newspapers: Slough Observer (0753 523355), South Bucks Express (0753 825111), Maidenhead Advertiser (0628 798048).
Local Radio Stations: Chiltern, Radio 210.
Hons: FA Vase SF 82-83 (QF 77-78), Athenian Lg R-up(2) 78-80, Hellenic Lg 75-76 (Div 1 R-up 72-73, Lg Cup 75-76, Div 1 Cup 71-72), London Spartan Lg 84-85 (Lg Cup 84-85), Reading Comb. Lg Cup 70-71 (All Champions Cup 70-71), Wycombe Comb. R-up(4) 65-67 68-70.

GOALKEEPERS:
Paul Tillen (Marlow, Southall, Maidenhead T, Burnham, Maidenhead Utd)
DEFENDERS: Francis Araguez (Maidenhead Utd, Windsor, Marlow, Chesham, Windsor, Burnham, Slough, Malaga(Sp), WBA(A)), **Richard North** (Maidenhead Utd, Uxbridge, Burnham, Windsor, Burnham, Maidenhead Utd), **Martin Turner** (Newbury, Hungerford, Wokingham, Bracknell, Reading), **Eddie Hutchinson** (Windsor, Burnham, Slough, Windsor, Chesham, Maidenhead Utd, Brentford, Millwall, Chelsea, QPR), **Tim Cook** (Local football), **Colin Ferguson** (Maidenhead Utd, Reading), **Paul Brett** (Local football), **Paul Taylor** (Harefield), **Noel Devereux** (Local football), **Paul Grant** (Derby)
MIDFIELD: Kenny Hughes (Reading(T)), **Andy Styles** (Flackwell H, Burnham, Flackwell H), **Shane Chandler** (Hungerford, Woking, Wokingham), **Jamie Jarvis** (Slough), **Dominic Gavin** (Local football), **Neil White** (Local football)
FORWARDS: Trevor Argrave (Chertsey), **Carl Lindo** (Chesham, Uxbridge, Dunstable, Kingsbury), **Steve Bunce** (Youth), **Tony Anglin** (Dunstable, Burnham, Ruislip, Hillingdon, Hendon), **Mick Buckley** (Local football), **Micky Creighton** (Maidenhead Utd, Windsor, Slough, Chertsey, Slough)

Burnham
Football
Club

est. 1878

ISTHMIAN
League

OFFICIAL PROGRAMME

PROGRAMME DETAILS:
Pages: 24 **Price:** 25p
Editor: Jon Adaway
WMPCC Rating: 19

BURY TOWN

Bury Town. Back Row (L/R): Simon Allen, David Lee, Richard Balls, John Pollard, George Patten, Simon Scrafe, Lou Newman. Front: Paul Marlow, Peter Coffill, Phil McCusker, Wayne Schwieso, Clive Stafford.

Chairman: V J Clark   **President:**
Secretary: Michael Parker, 18 Mill Lane, Barrow, Bury St Edunds IP29 5BS (0284 810679).
Team Manager: Chris Symes   **Asst Manager:** Brian Lafflin   **Coach:** Trevor Cox
Press Officer: A J Hall   **Physio:** John Chandler   **Comm. Manager:** V J Clark.
Ground: Ram Meadow, Cotton Lane, Bury St Edmunds, Suffolk (0284 754721/754820).
Directions: Leave A45 at sign to central Bury St Edmunds and take third exit off island. First exit at next island Northgate Street, left at 'T' junct. (2nd lights into Mustow Street and first left into Cotton Lane - ground 300 yds on right, through car park. 10 mins walk from station.
Capacity: 4,500 (1,500 Covered)   **Seats:** 300   **Floodlights:** Y   **Shop:** Y   **Metal Badges:** Y
Colours: Blue/white/blue   **Change colours:** Red/black/red.   **Sponsors:** Cowies.
Previous Lges: Norfolk & Suffolk/ Essex & Suffolk Border/ Eastern Co's 35-64 76-87/ Metropolitan 64-71.
Previous Names: Bury St Edmunds 1895-1902/ Bury Utd 02-06. **Previous Ground:** Kings Road 1872-1978.
Midweek home matchday: Wednesday   **Reserve Team's League:** Jewson (Eastern Counties) Div 1
Record Attendance: 2,500 v Enfield, FA Cup 3rd Qualifying Rd 1986. (At Kings Road, previous ground, 4,710 v Kings Lynn, 1950).
Best F.A. Cup season: 1st Rd replay 68-69 (lost 0-3 at AFC Bournemouth after 0-0 draw).
League clubs defeated in F.A. Cup: None.
Record Fees - Paid: £1,500 for Mel Springett (Chelmsford 1990).
     Received: £5,000 for Simon Milton (Ipswich).
Players progressing to Football League: D Lewis (G'ham, Preston), L Carberry (Ipswich & England), Terry Bly (N'wich 1956, P'boro), T Pearce (I'wich), Gary Stevens (Brighton, Spurs & England), Simon Milton (I'wich 1990).
Clubhouse: Members'/Public Bars open at weekends and most evenings. Darts, pool, TV snacks etc.
Steward: Charles Holden, Rosemary Soames.
Club Record Goalscorer: Doug Tooley 58.   **Club Record Apps:**
91-92 Captain: C Stafford   **91-92 P.o.Y.:** C Stafford   **91-92 Top scorer:** David Lee 19.
Local Newspapers: East Anglian Daily Times, West Suffolk Mercury, Bury Free Press.
Local Radio: BBC Radio Suffolk, Saxon Radio.   **Newsline:** 0898 884 459.
Honours: FA Vase 6th Rd 88-89, FA Trophy 2nd Rd 70-71, Eastern Counties Lg 63-64 (R-up 37-38, Lg Cup 61-62 63-64), Metropolitan Lg 65-66 (R-up 67-68 70-71, Lg Cup 67-68, Professional Cup 65-66), Suffolk Premier Cup 58-59 59-60 60-61 61-62 63-64 64-65, Suffolk Senior Cup 36-37 37-38 38-39 44-45.

GOALKEEPERS:
Lee Turner (Corinthian, Sittingbourne, Corinthian, Leyton Orient, Corinthian)

DEFENDERS:
James Crown (Leyton Orient(J)), **Simon Allen** (Newmarket, Bury T), **Richard Balls** (Earls Colne, Chelmsford), **Paul Marlow** (Billericay, Chelmsford, Harlow, Chelmsford), **Steve Barrow** (Corinthian, Gravesend)

MIDFIELD:
Trevor Collins (Stowmarket, Bury T, Colchester(J), Ipswich(J)), **Jamie Cambridge** (Mistley), **Darren Prior** (Gorleston, Sudbury, Gt Yarmouth), **Nick Guyon** (Braintree, Cornard, Wivenhoe, Hatfield, Sudbury, Clacton, Colchester), **Phil McClusker** (Chelmsford), **Paul Keys** (Cornard, Saffron Walden, Bury T, Woolongong(Aust), Bury T, Luton, Westerfield)

FORWARDS:
Mervyn Henry (Harwich, Bury T, Brantham, FC Twente(Holl), Stowmarket, Harwich, Felixstowe, Witham), **Louis Newman** (Sudbury, Chelmsford, Sudbury, Tampa Bay Rowdies(USA), Wigan, Stowmarket, Felixstowe), **Simon Dumican** (Soham Town R), **Junior Soanes** (Norwich), **Mark Radford** (Wivenhoe, Colchester)

PROGRAMME DETAILS:
Pages: 24 Price: 50p
Editor: A J Hall
WMPCC Rating: 30

CANTERBURY CITY

Canterbury City FC. Back Row (L/R): Willie Duncan (Asst Mgr), Neil Scott, Julian Holmes, Darryl Griffiths, Paul Neat, Matt Harmer, Paul Bagley, Tony Pattenden (Physio), Les Hall (Manager). Front: Steve Bunce, Kevin Smart, David Gear, Steve O'Brien, Billy Plews, Joe Latty, Peter Game. Photo - Kentish Gazette.

Chairman: Derick J Owen   **Directors:** D J Owen, C J Luckhurst, J Gallyer, W Mawdsley, J Matthews.
Secretary: Norman Walton, 55 Keats Rd, Lunsford Park, Larkfield, Maidstone ME20 6TR (0732 843630).
Team Manager: Les Hall   **Asst Mgr:** Willie Duncan   **Coach:** TBA.
Press Officer: Keith Smith (0227 456116)   **Physio:** Tony Pattenden
Ground Address & Tel: Kingsmead Stadium, Kingsmead Raod, Canterbury CT2 7PH (0227 464732).
Directions: A28 out of city centre into Military Road. At first r-about turn left into Tourtel Road, proceed to next r-about and head straight over into Kingsmead Road - stadium on right opposite Sainsbury's car park. Half mile from Canterbury West (BR). Bus service 624 or 625 from Canterbury bus station - ask for Kingsmead crossroads.
Capacity: 5,000 (200 Covered)   **Seats:** 200   **Floodlights:** Y   **Shop:** Y   **Metal Badges:** Y
Colours: Sky/navy/navy   **Change colours:** Green & white/green/green**Newsline:** 0898 800 627.
Sponsors: Cotamex Group.   **Previous Leagues:** Kent 47-59/ Metropolitan 59-60.
Previous Name: Canterbury Waverley   **Previous Grounds:** Wincheap Grove, Bretts Corner.
Midweek home matchday: Wednesday   **Reserve Team's League:** Winstonlead Kent Div 2
Record Attendance: 3,001 v Torquay, FA Cup 1st Rd 1964.
Best F.A. Cup season: 1st Rd 64-65 (lost 0-6 to Torquay), 68-69 (lost 0-1 to Swindon).
Record Fees - Paid: £2,000 for Graham Knight (M'stone)   **Received:** £2,000 for Dave Wiltshire (G'ham).
Players progressing to Football League: Ron Gawler (Southend 1949), Arthur Hughes (Grimsby 1954), Arthur Nugent (Darlington 1956), John Richardson (Southport 1956), Tommy Horsfall (Cambridge U), Jimmy Murray (Wolves), Kenny Hill (Gillingham), Terry Norton (Brighton), Mark Weatherly (G'ham), Pat Hilton (Brighton 1973), David Wiltshire (G'ham 1974), Gary Pugh (T'quay 1984).
Clubhouse: Reestaurant and lounge bars open on matchdays.   **Steward:** Nora Leach.
Club Record Goalscorer: Allan Jones   **Club Record Apps:** John Carragher.
91-92 Captain: Billy Plews   **91-92 P.o.Y.:** Paul Bagley   **91-92 Top scorer:** Paul Neat 8.
Local Newspapers: Kentish Gazette (468181), Adscene (454545).
Local Radio Stations: Radio Kent, Invicta Radio.
Honours: FA Vase Preliminary Rd 88-89, FA Trophy 2nd Rd replay 74-75, Kent Lg Cup 49-50 (Div 2 (Reserves) 90-91, Div 2 Cup (Reserves) 89-90), Kent Senior Cup 53-54, Kent Senior Trophy 79-80, Kent Intermediate Cup 73-74, Kent Messenger Trophy, Frank Norris Memorial Shield.

GOALKEEPERS:
Joe Radford (Margate, Dover, Gillingham)

DEFENDERS:
Dave Linstrem (Dover, Folkestone, Brighton(A)), **Paul Bagley** (Herne Bay, Ashford, Ramsgate, Whitstable, Thanet, Dover, Folkestone), **Darryl Griffiths** (Dover, Whitstable), **Neil Scott** (Ashford, Dover), **Jon Widdows** (Sheppey, Hastings T), **Micky Punton** (Dover), **Kevin Smart** (Folkestone Invicta, Hythe, Margate, Ashford, Hythe, Folkestone, Plymouth, Wigan)

MIDFIELD:
Gene Clout (Tonbridge, Gillingham(J)), **Matt Harmer** (Local football), **Phil Hancock** (Folkestone), **John Lineham** (Folkestone, Thanet, Canterbury, Dover, Canterbury, Folkestone), **Paul Neat** (Dover), **Peter Game** (Dover)

FORWARDS:
Joe Latty (New Romney), **Paul Brazil** (Tonbridge), **Lee Bosson** (Dover), **Julian Holmes** (Dover, Snowdown CW), **Steve Bunce** (Local football)

Pages: 24 **Price:** 40p
Editor: Keith Smith
WMPCC Rating: 26

DUNSTABLE

Totternhoe 3, Dunstable 0 - Beds Senior Cup Quarter Final 18/1/92. Hai-Ya! Time out to practise a bit of karate on the edge of the Totternhoe area! Photo - Gavin Ellis.

Chairman: Alan Fieldhouse　　　　　　　　**President:** Gerald Fox.
Secretary: Doug Simpson, 31 Carterways, Dunstable LU5 4RB (0582 666586).
Team Manager: John Wortley　　**Asst Manager:**　　　　　**Coach:**
Press Officer: D Simpson　　**Physio:** Alex Webber
Commercial Manager: Steve Brinkman.
Ground: Creasey Park, Brewers Hill Road, Dunstable (0582 606691).
Directions: Brewers Hill Road runs west from A505 at north end of Dunstable at large traffic island; turn right after 150 yds. 5 miles from Luton (BR), buses 67 and 70 (from Luton) pass 200 yds from ground.
Capacity: 10,000 (750 Covered)　　**Seats:** 500　　**Floodlights:** Y　**Shop:** Y　**Metal Badges:** Y
Colours: Royal blue/white/blue or white.　　**Change colours:** All red.
Sponsors: Fieldhouse & Husband.
Previous Leagues: Metropolitan 50-55 58-61 63-65/ Hellenic 55-58/ United Counties 61-63.
Previous Name: Dunstable Town.
Midweek home matchday: Wednesday　　　　　**Reserve Team's League:**
Record Attendance: 6,000 v Manchester United, Friendly 1974.
Best F.A. Cup season: 1st Rd 56-67 (lost 1-3 at Margate).
League clubs defeated in F.A. Cup: None.
Record Fees - Paid: £1,500 for Stuart Atkins (Wycombe 1979)
　　　　　　　　Received: £20,000 for Kerry Dixon (Reading).
Players progressing to Football League: Bill Garner (Southend, Chelsea), Keith Barber (Luton 1971), Kerry Dixon (Reading 1980), Laurie Ryan (C'bridge Utd).
Clubhouse: (0582 63800). Large clubroom and bar.　　　　　　　　**Steward:** P Williams.
Club Record Goalscorer:　　　　　　　　**Club Record Apps:**
91-92 Captain:　　　　　　**91-92 P.O.Y.:**　　　　　**91-92 Top scorer:**
Local Newspapers: Dunstable Gazette, Herald, Citzen.
Local Radio Stations: Radio Beds, Chiltern.
Honours: FA Trophy 3rd Qualifying Rd 2nd replay 71-72, Southern Lg Div 1 North R-up 74-75, Hellenic Lg R-up 57-58, Beds Senior Cup 1895-96 1956-57 59-60 79-80 82-83 85-86 86-87 87-88 88-89, Beds Premier Cup 80-81 82-83.

GOALKEEPERS:
Trevor England (St Albans, Walden R, Dunstable), **Darren Hunt** (Local football)

DEFENDERS:
Guy Kefford (Wolverton), **Paul Covington** (Local football), **Dale Hutchings** (Totternhoe), **Nick Archell** (Vauxhall M), **Seamus Horgan** (Vauxhall M, Ruislip, Dunstable, Ruislip, Chelmsford, Kingstonian, Dartford, Wealdstone, Kingstonian, Southend)

MIDFIELD:
Peter Revell (Totternhoe, Vauxhall M, Totternhoe, Dunstable), **Mick Conneely** (Arlesey), **Paul Mullings** (Vauxhall M, Barton R), **Sandor Gyalog** (Vauxhall M, Dunstable), **Neil Madden** (Vauxhall M, Dunstable, Stevenage B, Vauxhall M, Hitchin, SM Helas(Aust), Luton)

FORWARDS:
Chris Campbell (Shillington, Hitchin, Vauxhall M, Amphill), **Richard King** (Local football), **Tony Conneely** (Arlesey), **Kevin Wheeler** (Totternhoe), **Ian Edet** (Hitchin, St Albans, Letchworth GC, Caddington, Hitchin, Barking), **Paul Neufville** (Harlow, Stevenage B, Hitchin, Langford, Vauxhall M, 61FC), **Trevor Small** (Local football)

DUNSTABLE FOOTBALL CLUB

1990/1991 SEASON
OFFICIAL PROGRAMME
30p

PROGRAMME DETAILS:
Pages: 24 **Price:** 30p
Editor: D Simpson
WMPCC Rating: 22

ERITH & BELVEDERE

Erith & Belvedere FC. Graham Hall, Graham Daniels, David Mehmet, Nicky Orme, Mike Kelly (Coach), Harry Richardson (Manager), Kevin Walsh, Peter Cappuccio, David Ward, Elliott Taylor, John Palmer. Front: Tony Younng, Denis Abboh, Kenny Hoyte, John Docker, Micky Nutton, Mark Penfold, John Bartley, Tony Booth. Mascot: Daniel Joy. Photo - Mike Floate.

Chairman: TBA
President: Larry O'Connell.
Secretary: David Joy, 104 Overton Road, Abbey Wood, London SE2 9SE (081 311 0650).
Manager: Harry Richardson   **Asst Manager:** K Walsh   **Coach:** M Kelly
Press Officer: Mavis Clancy   **Physio:** Ron Bates
Commercial Manager:
Ground: Park View, Lower Road, Belvedere, Kent DA17 6DF (081 311 4444).
Directions: Entrance in Station Road, adjoining Belvedere (BR) station. Bus No. 469.
Capacity: 1,500 (1,200 Covered)   **Seats:** 250   **Floodlights:** Y   **Shop:** Y   **Metal Badges:** Y
Colours: Bliue & white/blue/white   **Change colours:** All red.
Previous Leagues: Kent 22-29 31-39 78-82/ London 29-31/ Corinthian 45-63/ Athenian 63-78.
Previous Names: Erith FC/ Belvedere & District FC (clubs amalgamated in 1922).
Midweek home matchday: Tuesday   **Reserve Team's League:** None.
Sponsors: Karlreece & Crown Communications.
Record Attendance: 8,000 v Coventry, FA Cup 1932.
Best F.A. Cup season: First Round Proper 24-25 32-33.
League clubs defeated in F.A. Cup: None.
Record Fees - Paid: **Received:**.
Players progressing to Football League: Geoff Bray (Oxford Utd 1971), Tommy Ord (Chelsea 1972).
Clubhouse: Licensed social club with seperate tea bar.   **Steward:** Bernie Chapman.
Club Record Mascot: Daniel Joy.
91-92 Captain: John Palmer   **91-92 P.o.Y.:** Tony Young   **91-92 Top scorer:** Kenny Hoyte.
Local Newspapers: Kentish Times, Kentish Independant.
Local Radio Stations: Radio Kent, Radio Thamesmead.
Honours: FA Amateur Cup R-up 23-24 37-38, FA Trophy 3rd Qualifying Rd 2nd replay 89-90, FA Vase 3rd Rd 76-77, Athenian Lg Div 1 R-up 70-71 (Lg Cup 73-74, Memorial Shield 67-68), Corinthian Lg R-up 62-63 (Lg Cup 47-48 48-49 49-50), Kent Lg 81-82 (Lg Cup R-up 81-82), London Senior Cup 44-45 (R-up 38-39), Kent Amateur Cup 23-24 47-48 65-66 66-67 68-69 69-70 (R-up 33-34 35-35 51-52 73-74), Bromley Hospital Cup 38-39, Kent Floodlit Lg R-up 67-68, Kent Intermediate Cup R-up 90-91, Kent Junior Cup 67-68, Essex & Herts Border Comb Cup 73-74, Kent County Yth Lg 90-91, Kent Yth Cup 87-88.

GOALKEEPERS:
Engin Salih (Alma S, Bromley, Tooting, Fisher, Bromley, Dulwich, Millwall)
DEFENDERS: Martin Johnson (Croydon, Chelmsford, Dulwich, Bromley, Dulwich, Erith & Belvedere, Welling), **John Palmer** (Gravesend, Hendon, Dulwich, Beckenham), **Mark Penfold** (Gravesend, Bromley, Dartford, Maidstone, Leyton Orient, Charlton), **Graham Cowley** (Hornchurch), **Chris Hiscock** (Fisher, Erith & Belvedere, Tooting, Fisher, Bromley, Fisher, Epsom & Ewell, Beckenham, Dartford, Millwall), **Wayne Barlow** (Dartford, Sittingbourne, Gillingham)
MIDFIELD: Sean McFadden (Margate, Erith & Belvedere, Auckland(NZ), Erith & Belvedere, Charlton(A)), **John Docker** (Fisher, Barnet, Maidstone, Dagenham, Enfield, Barnet, QPR), **Elliott Taylor** (Croydon), **Tony Young** (Cray W), **Dave Mehmet** (Fisher, Enfield, Barnet, Maidstone, Fisher, Millwall, Gillingham, Charlton, Tampa Bay Rowdies(USA), Millwall), **Tony Booth** (Alma S, Cray W, Gravesend, Tonbridge, Bromley, Welling, Woking, Carshalton, Oxford C, Charlton), **Mark Hobbs** (Alma S, Fisher), **Peter McKey** (Rainham, Erith & Belvedere)
FORWARDS: Peter Cappuccio (Croydon, Erith & Belvedere, Cray W, Chelmsford, Dulwich, Erith & Belvedere, Cray W, Crockenhill), **Dean Bowey** (Dover, Gravesend, Darenth Heathside), **Peter Coupland** (Crockenhill, Tonbridge), **Bobby Moyce** (Rainham, Aveley, Rainham, Erith & Belvedere, Dulwich, Erith & Belvedere)

ERITH & BELVEDERE F.C. LTD.

KARLREECE BUILDERS AND PRESERVATION LTD.

OFFICIAL PROGRAMME 40p

PROGRAMME DETAILS:
Pages: 32 **Price:** 40p
Editor: John Simpson
WMPCC Rating: 15

FAREHAM TOWN

Fareham 'keeper Shane Wheeler saves at the feet of Erith's Phil Coupland. Photo - Keith Gillard.

Chairman: Mr Roy Grant   **President:** Mr L Abraham.
Secretary: K F Atkins, 4 Cedar Close, Elson, Gosport PO12 4AT (0705 583049).
Team Manager: Keith Miller   **Asst Manager:**   **Coach:**
Press Officer: M Willis   **Physio:** G Buckner
Commercial Manager: **Newsline:** 0898 664 255.
Ground: Cams Alders, Highfield Avenue, Fareham, Hants PO14 1JA (0329 231151).
Directions: From Fareham station follow A27 towards Southampton and take second left into Redlands Avenue. Turn right at Redlands Inn then left into Highfields Avenue.
Capacity: 5,500 (500 Covered)   **Seats:** 450   **Floodlights:** Y   **Shop:** Y   **Metal Badges:** N
Colours: Red/white/red   **Change colours:** White/black/white.
Sponsors: Wiggins Homes, Hellyers Coaches.
Previous Name: Fareham FC   **Previous Leagues:** Portsmouth 47-49/ Hants 49-79.
Midweek home matchday: Wednesday   **Reserve Team's League:** Hants Combination.
Record Gate: 2,650 v Wimbeldon, FA Cup 1965. *(at Southampton FC; 6,035 v Kidderminster Harriers, FA Trophy Semi Final Second leg 86-87).*
Best F.A. Cup season: 1st Rd replay 88-89 (lost 2-3 at home to Torquay after 2-2 draw).
League clubs defeated in F.A. Cup: None.   **Previous Ground:** Bath Lane.
Record Fees - Paid: £1,000 for Peter Baxter (Poole) **Received:** £43,000 for David Leworthy (Spurs).
Players progressing to Football League: Ray Hiron (P'smouth 1964), John Hold (B'mouth), David Leworthy (Spurs 1984), Steve Claridge (B'mouth 1984), Darren Foreman (Barnsley), Kevin Bartlett (C'diff 1986), Domenyk Newman (Reading 1990).
Clubhouse: Open every evening except Sundays.   **Steward:** John Kirby.
Club Record Goalscorer: **Club Record Apps:**
91-92 Captain: **91-92 P.O.Y.:**   **91-92 Top scorer:**
Local Newspapers: Portsmouth Evening News, Southampton Evening Echo.
Local Radio Stations:
Hons: FA Tphy SF 86-87, FA Amtr Cup 2nd Rd 63-64 66-67 73-74, Hants Lg(8) 59-60 62-67 72-73 74-75 (R-up 55-56 60-61 67-68 71-72 76-77 78-79, Div 2 R-up 52-53, Eastern Div 24-25, Div 3 East 49-50), Hants Snr Cup 56-57 62-63 67-68, Russell Cotes Cup(6) 64-65 72-77, Gosport War Mem. Cup, S.W. Co's Cup(2), Pickford Cup(2), Hants I'mediate Cup (reserves), FA Sunday Cup (as Fareham Centipedes) 74-75.

GOALKEEPERS:
Shane Wheeler (Southampton(T)), Keith Bloxham (Basingstoke, Dorchester, Weymouth, Royal Navy)
DEFENDERS: Sean New (Basingstoke, Fareham, Eastleigh), **Nigel Mottashed** (Gosport, Basingstoke, Gosport, Fareham), **Miles Rutherford** (Clanfield), **John Bailey** (Andover, Fareham, Romsey, Newbury, Andover, RS Southampton, Salisbury, Basingstoke, Sholing Sports), **Martin Cunningham** (Royal Navy), **Clive Huxford** (Waterlooville, Fareham, AFC Totton, Waterlooville), **Robert Davies** (AFC Totton)
MIDFIELD: Paul Marks (AFC Totton, Pirelli General, AFC Totton), **David Morris** (Local football), **Gary Hampson** (Gosport, Knowsley, Gosport, Dorchester, Royal Navy), **Paul Joyce** (Dorchester, Puddleton), **Simon Rustell** (Waterlooville, Newport IOW, Gosport), **Mark Richardson** (Newport IOW, Bashley, Fareham, RS Southampton, Basingstoke)
FORWARDS: Mick Greeno (Dorchester, Weymouth, Dorchester, Floriana(Malta), Dorchester, Weymouth, Dorchester), **Robbie Taylor** (Dorchester, Torquay, Weymouth, Newport Co, Portsmouth), **Paul Swanson** (Local football), **Chris Miller** (Verwood), **Mick Cowell** (Locksheath, Fareham), **Anniello Iannone** (Local football, Weymouth, Dorchester), **Darren Hewitt** (Waterlooville, Gosport, Aldershot(T), Gosport)

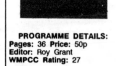

PROGRAMME DETAILS:
Pages: 36 **Price:** 50p
Editor: Roy Grant
WMPCC Rating: 27

FISHER ATHLETIC

Fisher's Dave Sansom (left) is challenged by Graham Reed of V.S. Rugby in a Premier Division fixture at the Surrey Docks Stadium. Photo - Alan Coomes.

Chairman: James Webb   **President:** Lord Mellish.
Secretary: M J Wakefield, 146 Layard Square, Drummond Rd, Bermondsey SE16 0JG (071 237 2819).
Team Manager: Dennis Sharp   **Asst Manager:**   **Coach:** Andy Massey
Press Officer: **Physio:**   **General Mgr:** Les Rowe.
Comm. Manager: Dave Gore/ Stewart Guidotti.
Ground: The Surrey Docks Stadium, Salter Road, London SE16 1LQ (071 231 5144. Fax: 231 5536).
Directions: 8 minutes walk from Rotherhithe (tube), 2 miles from London Bridge (main line). Buses 188, P11, P14.
Capacity: 5,300 (1,200 Covered)   **Seats:** 400   **Floodlights:** Y   **Shop:** Y   **Metal Badges:** Y
Colours: Black & white stripes/white/black   **Change colours:** All red.
Previous Leagues: Parthenon/ West Kent/ Kent Amateur/ London Spartan 76-82/ Southern 82-87/ GMV Conference 87-91.
Midweek home games: Monday   **Reserve Team's League:** Suburban.
Record Gate: 4,283 v Barnet, GMV Conference 4/5/91.   **Previous Grnd:** London Road, Mitcham.
Best F.A. Cup season: 1st Rd 84-85 (0-1 at home to Bristol City), 88-89 (0-4 at Bristol Rovers).
League Clubs Defeated in F.A. Cup: None.
Record Fees: Paid: £500 for Davis Regis.   **Received:**
Players progressing to The Football League: John Bumstead (Chelsea), Trevor Aylott (Bournemouth), Paul Shinners (Orient 1984), Dave Regis (Notts County - via Barnet).
Clubhouse: (071 252 0590). Luxury clubhouse, Vice-President's club, hot and cold food.
Club Record Scorer: Paul Shinners 205   **Club Record Appearances:** Dennis Sharp 720.
91-92 Captain: **91-92 P.o.Y.:**   **91-92 Top scorer:**
Local Newspapers(+Tel.Nos.):   **Local Radio Stations:**
Honours: Southern Lg 86-87 (R-up 83-84, Southern Div 82-83, Lg Cp 84-85, Championship Cup 87-88, Merit Cup), London Spartan Lg 80-81 81-82 (R-up 78-79, Senior Div 77-78, Div 2 R-up 76-77), Parthenon Lg 61-62 (Lg Cup 63-64 65-66), Kent Amateur Lg 73-74 74-75 (R-up 72-73), London Senior Cup 84-85 87-88 88-89, London Intermediate Cup 59-60 (R-up 75-76), Kent Senior Cp 83-84, Kent Senior Trophy 81-82 82-83, Surrey Intermediate Cup 61-62, FA Trophy 3rd Rd 3rd replay 87-88, FA Vase 2nd Rd replay 82-83.

GOALKEEPERS:
Jimmy Jones (Brighton(T))

DEFENDERS:
Jason Huntley (Youth), **Paul Collins** (Millwall), **Ricky Pearson** (Ashford, Gillingham), **Derek McLaren** (Local football), **Billy Edwards** (Youth), **Danny Davenport** (Beckenham, Southwark Sports, Greenwich B), **Terry Casey** (Local football)

MIDFIELD:
Jason Mummery (Brighton(T)), **Paul Foley** (Youth), **Gary Groom** (Darenth Heathside, Fisher, Gravesend, Erith & Belvedere, Greenwich B, Alma S), **Mark Hynes** (Brentford(T)), **Mark Dennehy** (Finland, Fisher, Dagenham, Kuopio Elo(Fin), Millwall), **Steve Agius** (Youth), **Terry McGinley** (Youth)

FORWARDS:
Ronnie Victor (Greenwich B), **John Bull** (Beckenham), **Dave Garratty** (Youth), **Hughie Mann** (Cray W, Molesey, Erith & Belvedere, Dulwich, Fisher, Tooting, Southwark B), **Mark Dryden** (Sheppey, Fisher)

Pages: 28 **Price:** 70p
Editor: K Wenham
WMPCC Rating: 21

The Gravesend & Northfleet side that played in the 1990-91 Kent Senior Cup final.

Chairman: L G F Ball **Vice Chairman:** D F Hockley **President:**
Secretary: Stephen Jones, 35 Laurel Avenue, Gravesend DA12 5QP (0473 365659)
Team Manager: Gary Aldous **Asst Manager:** Peter Coffil **Coach:**
Press Officer: **Physio:** Micky Ward **Comm. Manager:** Carol Sidwell
Ground: Stonebridge Road, Northfleet, Kent DA11 9BA (0474 533796)
Directions: From A2 take B262 then B2175 to junction with A226. Turn left and ground is on right after approx 1 mile. 5 mins walk from Northfleet (BR).
Capacity: 6,000 (5,000 Covered) **Seats:** 400 **Floodlights:** Y **Shop:** Y **Metal Badges:** Y
Colours: Red/white/red **Change colours:** White/blue/white
Previous Names: Gravesend Utd/ Northfleet Utd (merged in 1946). **Sponsors:** Weslyan Assurance.
Previous Leagues: Kent (as Gravesend Utd)/ Southern 1946-79/ Alliance Prem. 79-80.
Previous Ground: Central Avenue (as Gravesend United).
Midweek home matchday: Tuesday **Reserve Team's League:**
Record Attendance: 12,036 v Sunderland, F.A. Cup 4th Rd 62-63.
Best F.A. Cup season: 4th Rd Replay 1963 (lost 2-5 at Sunderland after 1-1 draw at home).
League clubs defeated in F.A. Cup: Exeter City, Carlisle United (both 62-63).
Record Fees - Paid: £3,5000 for D Blusby (Barrow). **Received:** £15,000 for Lee Smelt (Nottm Forest).
Players progressing to Football League: James Wilson (Chelsea 1947), Fred Pincott (Newport 1947), Stan Aldows & Herbert Hawkins (Orient 1950 & 51), Harry Gunning (W Ham 1952), John Hills (Spurs 1953), Norman Lewis (Newport 1954), Kevin Baron (Aldershot 1960), Roy Dwight (Coventry 1962), Robert Cameron (Southend 1963), Robert McNichol (Carlisle 1965), Alan Humphreys (Mansfield 1964), Barry Thornley (Brentford 1965), Pat Jeavons (Lincoln 1966), Barry Fry (Orient 1966), Barry Gordine (Sheff Utd 1968), Tommy Baldwin (Brentford 1977), Lee Smelt (Nottm Forest 1980), Tom Warrilow (Torquay 1987)
Clubhouse: Bar open daily (except Mondays & Wednesdays) **Steward:** Mrs Maureen O'Dell
Club Record Goalscorer: **Club Record Appearances:** Ken Burrest.
91-92 Captain: Lee Graves **91-92 P.O.Y.:** Paul Burnham **91-92 Top scorer:** Chris Fordred
Local Newspapers: Gravesend & Dartford Reporter, Kent Evening Post, Gravesend Extra, Leader
Local Radio Stations: Invicta Radio, Radio Kent. **Newsline:** 0898 122 910.
Hons: Southern Lg 57-58 (Div 1 Sth 74-75 (R-up 70-71 88-89), Lg Cup 77-78 (R-up 57-58), Champ'ship Cup 77-78), Kent Snr Cup 48-49 52-53 80-81 (R-up 47-48 76-77), Kent F'lit Cup 69-70 (R-up 72-73), Kent Snr Shield R-up 47-48, Kent I'mediate Cup R-up 87-88, Kent Yth Lg Cup 82-83 86-87, John Ullman Cup 82-83, FA Tphy 3rd Rd 88-89.

GOALKEEPERS:
Paul Burnham (Corinthian, Gravesend, Worthing, Corinthian, Gravesend, Tonbridge, Maidstone, Tonbridge, Charlton(J))
DEFENDERS: Ian Gibbs (Youth), Ian Young (Corinthian), John Cooper (Finchley, Enfield, Helsingborg(Swe), Spurs), Lee Graves (Brentford(T), Watford(Sch)), Paul Blade (Dartford, Erith, Charlton, Southend, C Palace), Jez Millbank (Chelmsford, Stambridge), Stuart Staples (Billericay, Purfleet, Southend), Dennis Abboh (Erith, Alma S, Welling, Alma S, Greenwich B)
MIDFIELD: Byron Willmott (Sittingbourne), Peter Coffill (Bury T, Brantham, Chelmsford, East Thurrock, Chelmsford, Billericay, Aylesbury, Northampton, Torquay, Watford, West Ham), Paul Lamb (Ramsgate, Margate, Dartford, Ramsgate), Jason Eede (Youth), Nicky Wren (Gillingham(T)), Simon Ullathorne (Croydon, Cleator Moor, Workington), Carl Brown (Sittingbourne, Tonbridge, Barkingside, Dulwich), Wayne Schweiso (Bury T, Corinthian, Gravesend, Corinthian, Gravesend)
FORWARDS: Micky Cotter (Dover, Erith, Welling), Mal Watkins (Folkestone, Bridgnorth, GKN Sankey, Stafford R), Chris Fordred (Local football), Leroy Bess (Sittingbourne, Cray W, Erith, Tonbridge, Gravesend, Bromley, Alma S), Mark Freeman (Sittingbourne, Tonbridge, Bromley, Corinthian, Gravesend, Dulwich, Gravesend, Greenways), Stefan Giemza (Gillingham(T)), Steve Portway (Barking, Boreham W, Witham, Brentwood, B Stortford, Walthamstow Ave, Dagenham)

Gravesend & Northfleet F.C. the Fleet 1991-92 OFFICIAL PROGRAMME — BEAZER HOMES LEAGUE PREMIER DIVISION 80p

Pages: 32 **Price:** £1
Editor: Paul Saxby (0474 361932)
WMPCC Rating: 22

526

HAVANT TOWN

Three Hastings defenders combine to keep out Havant dangerman Steve Tate. Havant eventually won this top of the table Beazer Southern Division clash by the odd goal in five. Photo - Jon Holloway.

Chairman: R R Jones   **Directors:** D A Pope, P Cummins, G Jones.
Secretary: Trevor Brock, 2 Betula Close, Waterlooville, Hants PO7 8EJ (0705 267276).
Team Manager: Tony Mount   **Coach:** Derek Edwards
Press Officer: Secretary   **Physio:** Gary Buckner
Commercial Manager: Ian Craig
Newsline: 0898 446 833.
Ground: West Leigh Park, Martin Road, West Leigh, Havant PO9 5TH (0705 455465).
Directions: Take B2149 to Havant off the A27. 2nd turning off dual carriageway into Bartons Road then 1st right into Martins Road. 1 mile from Havant (BR).
Capacity: 6,000 (1,500 Covered)   **Seats:** 240   **Floodlights:** Y   **Shop:** Y   **Metal Badges:** Y
Colours: Yellow/blue/white   **Change colours:** Blue/black/blue.
Sponsors: A T Jones Ltd.
Previous Leagues: Portsmouth/ Hants 71-86/ Wessex 86-91.
Previous Names: Leigh Park, Havant & Leigh Park.
Previous Grounds: Front Lawn 1958-83.
Midweek home matchday: Monday   **Reserve Team's League:** Hants Combination.
Record Attendance: 3,000 v Wisbech, FA Vase QF 85-86.
Best F.A. Cup season: Second Qualifying Round.
Record Fees - Paid: £5,000 for J Wilson (Bashley)   **Received:** £4,250 for P Cox (Gosport).
Players progressing to Football League: Bobby Tambling (Chelsea).
Clubhouse: Open every day, normal licensing hours.   **Steward:** Kevin Rapley.
Club Record Goalscorer: **Club Record Apps:**
91-92 Captain: C Webbe   **91-92 P.o.Y.:** G Rutherford   **91-92 Top scorer:** Steve Tate 37.
Local Newspapers: News (Portsmouth)(0705 664488).
Local Radio Stations: Ocean Sound, Radio Solent.
Honours: FA Sunday Cup 68-69, FA Vase QF 85-86, Wessex Lg 90-91 (R-up 88-89), Hampshire Lg Div 3 72-73 (Div 4 71-72), Hampshire Senior Cup R-up 91-92, Hampshire Intermediate Cup, Hampshire Junior Cup, Russell Cotes Cup 91-92, Portsmouth Senior Cup 83-84 84-85, Gosport War Memorial Cup 74-75 91-92, Southern Counties Floodlit Cup R-up 91-92, Hampshire Floodlit Cup 85-86, Portsmouth Lg.

GOALKEEPERS:
Nicky Flower (Bashley, Salisbury, Bashley, Swindon(A)), **Andy Smith** (Gosport), **Adie Chambers** (Basingstoke)
DEFENDERS: John Wilson (Bashley, Salisbury, Waterlooville, Eastleigh), **Barney Hewitt** (Horndean, Havant), **Mark Gough** (Youth), **Neil Kerton** (Locksheath, Waterlooville, Southampton(J)), **Billy Gilbert** (Maidstone, Colchester, Portsmouth, C Palace), **Gary Juryeff** (Gosport, Portsmouth, Gosport), **Paul Austin** (Youth), **Paul Askham** (Portsmouth(T)), **Stuart Hensman** (Gosport)
MIDFIELD: Cliff De Gordon (Eastleigh, King's Heath), **Richie Elmes** (Youth), **Jamie Webb** (Basingstoke, Southampton(T)), **Guy Rutherford** (Fareham, Clanfield, Portsmouth(J)), **Matt Sherry** (Horndean, Portsmouth(J)), **Colin Ball** (Horndean, Waterlooville), **John Price** (Bognor, Pagham, Bognor, Portfield), **Simon James** (Petersfield), **Dave Motteane** (Romsey, Salisbury, Basingstoke, Portsmouth(A)), **Chris Watts** (Portsmouth(T)), **Dave Taviner** (Gosport, Fleetlands), **Jocky Clark** (Gosport)
FORWARDS: Steve Tate (Lymington, Bashley, Salisbury, Bournemouth(A), QPR(A)), **Gary Joseph** (Sholing Sports, Newport IOW), **Clint Webbe** (Bashley, Basingstoke, Leyton-Wingate, Oxford C, Army), **Steve Greenwood** (Bashley, Basingstoke, Gosport, Fareham), **Neil Selby** (Southampton(T)), **Mark Tryon** (Gosport)

HAVANT TOWN
FOOTBALL CLUB LTD

A.T. JONES Ltd

Pages: 32 **Price:** 50p
Editor: Ray Webb
WMPCC Rating: 24

MARGATE

Margate prior to their 1-0 home win over Bury Town in March. Back Row (L/R): Lee Smelt, Dave Coles, Stuart Reed, Tony Harwood, Kevin Hudson, Martin Buglione, Mark Weatherly, Brian Frampton, Paul Underwood, Cliff Egan. Front: Bill Roffey, Ian Young, Mark Brewer, Mascot, Tim Page, Graham Benton. Photo - Paul Bates.

Chairman: Gordon Wallis **President:** Mr R W Griffiths
Secretary: K E Tomlinson, 65 Nash Road, Margate CT9 4BT (0843 291040).
Team Manager: Lee Smelt **Asst Manager:** **Coach:** Mark Weatherly
Press Officer: Chairman **Physio:** D Beagley **Commercial Manager:** Cliff Egan
Ground Address & Tel: Hartsdown Park, Hartsdown Road, Margate CT9 5QZ (0843 221769).
Directions: A28 into Margate, turn right opposite hospital into Hartsdown Road, proceed over crossroads and ground is on left. Ten mins walk from Margate (BR).
Capacity: 6,000 (3 sides Covered) **Seats:** 400 **Floodlights:** Y **Shop:** Y **Metal Badges:** Y
Colours: Royal blue/white/royal blue **Change colours:** All white/royal blue/white
Previous Grounds: Margate College/ Dreamland/ Northdown Rd/ Garlinge.
Previous Leagues: Kent 11-23 24-28 29-33 37-38 46-59/ Southern 33-37. **Sponsors:** TBA.
Midweek home matchday: Tuesday **Reserve Team's League:** Kent Midweek Lg.
Previous Name: Thanet United 1981-89. **Record Gate:** 14,500 v Spurs, FA Cup 3rd Rd 1973.
Best F.A. Cup season: 3rd Rd 72-73 (lost 0-6 to Spurs), 36-37 (lost 1-3 at Blackpool).
League clubs defeated in F.A. Cup: Gillingham 29-30, Queens Park Rangers, Crystal Palace 35-36, Bournemouth & Boscombe Athletic 61-62, Swansea 72-73.
Record Fees - Paid: £3,750 for Neil Cugley (F'stone) **Rec'd:** £2,000 for Paul Underwood (Fisher 91-92).
Players progressing to Football League: Pre-War; too numerous to mention, partly because Margate were Arsenal's nursery club between 1934 & 1938. Post-War: John Yeomanson (W Ham 1947), Doug Bing & George Wright (W Ham 1951), Tommy Bing (Spurs 1956), John Roche (M'wall 1957), Derek Hodgkinson (Man C 1961), Stan Foster (C Pal 1961), John Fraser (W'ford 1962), Robert Walker (B'mouth 1965), Ken Bracewell (Bury 1966), Tom Jenkins & Ray Flannigan (R'ding 1969-70), Mel Blyth (M'wall 1978).
Clubhouse: Flexible opening hours, private functions, matchday facilities. **Steward:** Mark Weatherly.
Club Record Goalscorer: John Ballagher 62 (season 1964-65). **Club Record Apps:** Bob Harrop.
91-92 Captain: Mark Weatherly **91-92 P.O.Y.:** Mark Weatherly (fans' choice) Bill Roffey (players')
91-92 Top scorer: Martin Buglione 17
Local Newspapers: Isle of Thanet Gazette, Thanet Times (0843 221313), Thanet Extra, Adscene.
Local Radio: Radio Kent, Invicta Radio. **Newsline:** 0898 800 665.
Hons: Southern Lg 35-36 (Lg Cp 67-68 (R-up 61-62 74-75), Div 1 62-63 (R-up 66-67), Div 1 Sth 77-78, East Div R-up 33-34, Merit Cp 66-67 77-78, Midweek Sect. 36-37), Kent Lg(4) 32-33 37-38 46-48 (R-up 27-28 29-30 53-54 55-56 57-58, Div 2 37-38 53-54 56-57 89-90, Lg Cp 35-36 47-48 53-54 68-69), Kent Snr Cup(3) 35-37 74-75, Kent Snr Shield(8) 20-21 30-31 35-37 47-48 52-53 61-63, Kent F'lit Cp 62-63 66-67 75-76, Kent Jnr Cup 01-02, FA Tphy 3rd Rd rep 78-79

GOALKEEPERS:
Kevin Hudson (Folkestone, Canterbury, Dover), **Adrian Clewlow** (Youth)
DEFENDERS:
Ian Young (Bromley, Gillingham(A)), **David Coles** (Phoenix Rvs, Ramsgate, Margate, Ramsgate, Thanet), **Brian Frampton** (Bromley, Coburg(Aust), Bromley), **Tony Harwood** (Coventry), **Stuart Reed** (Folkestone), **Jon Mayall** (Local football), **Andy Allon** (Hythe, Folkestone, Ashford, Folkestone, Dover, Folkestone), **David Lee** (Hythe, Ashford), **Billy Plews** (Canterbury, Dover, Thanet, Folkestone, Snowdown CW)
MIDFIELD:
Peter Jarvis (Hythe, Chelmsford, Ashford, Chatham, Sheppey), **Mark Brewer** (Maidstone(T)), **Mark Weatherly** (Hythe, Gillingham, Canterbury), **Matthew Toms** (Maidstone(T)), **Paul Golden** (Gillingham(T))
FORWARDS:
Martin Buglione (Alma S, Welling, Tonbridge, Dagenham, Walthamstow Ave, Boreham Wood, Enfield), **Graham Brenton** (IFK Mariehamn(Fin), Sheppey, Bromley, Gillingham(A)), **Roy Hales** (Welling, Brighton), **Shaun Pilbeam** (Dover), **Paul Lancaster** (Barnet, Sheff Utd, Notts Forest)

MARGATE
OFFICIAL PROGRAMME 50p

MARGATE FOOTBALL CLUB
SPONSORED BY

Pages: 28 Price: 50p
Editor: Paul Bates (0843 821032)
WMPCC Rating: 20

NEWPORT I.O.W.

Newport entertain champions Hastings on May 2nd, and go down 0-3. Photo - T S Blackman.

Chairman: Keith Newbery **President:** W H G Sunday.
Secretary: C R Cheverton, 19 Oakwood Road, Ryde, Isle of Wight PO33 3JT (0983 67355).
Team Manager: Jock Horne **Asst Manager:** Roger McCormack **Coach:** John Carragher.
Commercial Manager: Dave Hiscock. **Physio:** Steve Lambourne
Ground: St George's Park, St George's Way, Newport, Isle of Wight PO30 2QH (0983 525027).
Directions: Roads from all ferry ports lead to Coppins Bridge R-about at eastern extremity of town. Take Sandown/Ventnor exit, proceed to next r-about, St George's way is first exit. Five minute walk from Newport bus station; along Church Litten (past old ground), turn left then right at r-about.
Capacity: 5,000 (1,000 Covered) **Seats:** 300 **Floodlights:** Y **Shop:** Y **Metal Badges:** Y
Colours: Gold/royal blue/gold **Change colours:** White/red/red.
Previous Leagues: Isle of Wight 1898-1927/ Hants 27-39 45-86/ Wessex 86-90.
Midweek home matchday: Tuesday **Reserve Team's League:** Jewson Wessex Comb.
Record Attendance: 1,700 v Fulham (official ground opening). *(5,600 v Shrewsbury Town, FA Cup 58-59, at Church Litten (old ground)).*
Best F.A. Cup season: 2nd Rd 35-36 45-46. 1st Rd another seven times; 45-46 52-55 56-59.
League clubs defeated in F.A. Cup: Clapton Orient 45-46.
Record Fees - Paid: £3,000 for Stuart Ritchie (Bashley 1991)
Received: £2,250 for Mick Jenkins (Havant 1992).
Clubhouse: Open normal licensing hours. 2 bars - members' and private functions. Hot and cold snacks, entertainment every weekend, darts petanque and pool. Seperate function rooms to cater for dinner dances, conferences, meetings etc. **Steward:** Rick Guile
Club Record Goalscorer: Roy Gilfillan 220 (1951-57) **Club Record Apps:** Jeff Austin 540 (69-80).
91-92 Captain: Keith Granger **91-92 P.o.Y.:** Keith Granger **91-92 Top scorer:** Steve Greening
Local Newspapers (+Tel.Nos.): Portsmouth Evening News, I.O.W. County Press, Southampton Evening Echo.
Local Radio Stations: Solent, Isle of Wight Radio, Ocean Sound. **Newsline:** 0898 122 927.
Honours: FA Vase 5th Rd 91-92, Wessex Lg R-up 89-90 (Comb. 91-92(reserves)), Hants Lg(11) 29-30 32-33 38-39 47-48 49-50 52-54 56-57 78-81 (R-up(7) 30-32 35-36 51-52 54-55 58-59 77-78, Div 2 R-up 70-71), Hants Snr Cup(7) 31-33 54-55 60-61 65-66 79-81, Russell Cotes Cup(3) 47-50 52-53, Isle of Wight Snr (Gold) Cup(27) 29-30 35-36 37-38 39-40 44-47 48-49 52-54 55-56 57-58 65-66 67-68 70-76 77-79 80-81 86-88 89-90 91-92, Hants F'lit Cup 76-77 77-78, Isle of Wight Lg(4) 07-10 23-24, Hants I'mediate Cup 31-32, Hants Comb. Cup 38-39.

GOALKEEPERS:
Keith Grainger (Maidstone, Basingstoke, Darlington, Southampton), **Geoff Sim** (Colden Common), **Phil Moore** (RS Southampton, Fareham, RS Southampton)
DEFENDERS: Martin Brown (Andover, Basingstoke), **Mick Jenkins** (Waterlooville, Fareham, Waterlooville), **Roy Maskell** (Youth), **John Williams** (Gosport), **Richard Durham** (St Helens), **Greg Sparrow** (Shanklin, Newport IOW), **Duncan O'Rourke** (Waterlooville, Shanklin), **Andy Darnton** (Gosport, Waterlooville, Follands Sports)
MIDFIELD: Andy Butler (East Cowes V, Newport IOW), **Garry Sperry** (Ryde Sports, Colchester, Northampton, Leicester C(A)), **Stuart Ritchie** (Bashley, Waterford, Crewe, Aston Villa), **Andy Sampson** (Brading, Newport IOW), **Paul Thomas** (Fareham, Clanfield), **Chinny Taylor** (East Cowes V)
FORWARDS: Steve Greening (Basingstoke, Gosport, East Cowes V), **John Richards** (Gosport, West Wight, East Cowes V), **Mark Hutton** (East Cowes V, Westland), **Mark Deacon** (Ryde Sports, Basingstoke, East Cowes V, Gosport, East Cowes V, Newport IOW)

PROGRAMME DETAILS:
Pages: 40 **Price:** 50p
Editor: Peter Ranger
WMPCC Rating: 28

1880

POOLE TOWN

The Dolphins

Premier Division action at Poole Town, who have sadly lost their place amongst the Beazer elite after just two seasons.

Chairman: Clive Robbins **Vice Chairman:** Chris Reeves **President:** Fred Yates
Secretary: Barry Hughes, 226 Malvern Road, Bournemouth, Dorset BH9 3BX (0202 536906).
Team Manager: Brian Chambers **Asst Manager:** **Coach:**
Press Officer: Chris Reeves **Physio:** Steve Miles
Commercial Manager: Darren O'Sullivan.
Ground: Poole Stadium, Wimborne Road, Poole BH15 2BP (0202 674747).
Directions: Near centre of Poole, behind Fire Station. Adjacent to Poole station.
Capacity: 6,000 (3,000 Covered) **Seats:** 1,500 **Floodlights:** Y **Shop:** Y **Metal Badges:** Y
Colours: All blue **Change colours:** Yellow/white/yellow **Sponsors:**
Previous Leagues: Hants 1903-04 05-10 11-14 20-23 29-30 34-35/ Western 23-26 30-34 35-39 46-57.
Midweek home matchday: Wednesday **Reserve Team's League:** Dorset Comb
Record Attendance: 11,155 v Watford, F.A. Cup 1962-63
Best F.A. Cup season: 3rd Rd Proper 1926-27. (1st Rd 7 times; 26-29 46-47 62-63 66-67 83-84).
League clubs defeated in F.A. Cup: Newport County, 26-27
Record Fees - Paid: £3,000 for Phil Ferns & Gerry Pearson **Received:** £8,000 for Gary Manson.
Players progressing to Football League: Derek Stround (B'mouth & Boscombe 1950), Dave Lawrence (Bristol Rov 1951), John Thomas (B'mouth & Boscombe 1958), James Rollo (Oldham 1960), John Smeulders (B'mouth 1987), Bob Iles (Chelsea), Phil Ferns Jr (B'mouth), D Lyon (Southport).
Clubhouse: Open every evening & lunchtime. **Steward:** Committee.
Club Record Goalscorer: Tony Funnell. **Club Record Apps:** Tony Funnell.
92-93 Captain: Ashley Coobes **91-92 P.o.Y.:** Martyn Jones **91-92 Top scorer:** Nicky Dent
Local Newspapers (+Tel.Nos.): Evening Echo, Gazette.
Local Radio Stations: Radio Solent, 2CR
Honours: Southern Lg Div 1 R-up 61-62 (Southern Div R-up 88-89), Western Lg 56-57 (R-up 46-47 49-50 53-54 55-56, Lg Cup 54-55), Dorset Senior Cup 1894-95 96-97 1901-02 03-04 06-07 25-26 26-27 37-38 46-47 88-89, FA Trophy 1st Rd replay 69-70, FA Amateur Cup 2nd Rd 47-48 48-49.

GOALKEEPERS:
Martyn Jones (Bournemouth, Dorchester, Poole)

DEFENDERS:
Ade Stacey (Local football), **Andy Morley** (Youth), **Justin Spires** (Bournemouth(T)), **Lee Bradford** (Bournemouth(T)), **Sean Bartlett** (Local football), **Brian Chambers** (Swanage, Dorchester, Salisbury, Poole, Halifax, Bournemouth, Millwall, Luton, Arsenal. Sunderland)

MIDFIELD:
David Platt (Salisbury, Minehead, Wimborne, Shaftesbury, Trowbridge, Bath, Paulton R, Yeovil, Weymouth, Yeovil, Grantham, Leicester C), **Ashley Coombes** (Weymouth, Poole, Wimborne), **Paul Maloney** (Preston), **Matthew Bown** (Yeovil, Brighton)

FORWARDS:
Nicky Dent (Yeovil, Bristol C, Bristol Manor Farm), **Milton Graham** (King's Lynn, Spalding, Peterborough, Chester, Bournemouth), **Tony Funnell** (Bournemouth, Brentford, Gillingham, Southampton, Eastbourne Utd), **Craig Wilson** (Local football), **Micky Turner** (Peterborough, Portsmouth)

Pages: 24 **Price:** 50p
Editor:
WMPCC Rating: 19

530

SALISBURY

Formed: 1947   The Whites

Salisbury pictured before their FA Trophy Third Qualifying Round tie at Wokingham Town. Photo - Eric Marsh.

Chairman: Mr P R McEnhill   **President:** Mr L Whitmarsh
Secretary: Sean Gallagher, 86 Russell Road, Salisbury SP2 7LR (0722 20435).
Team Manager: Geoff Butler   **Asst Manager:** Eric Lisle   **Coach:** Bob Skutt
Press Officer: Geoff Butler   **Physio:** Bob Skutt
Commercial Manager: Geoff Butler, 52 Endless House, Salisbury (0722 26454).
Newssline: 0898 122 905.
Ground: Victoria Park, Castle Road, Salisbury SP1 3ER (0722 336689).
Directions: A345 (Amesbury) road north from city centre, Victoria Park is on the left 800 yds after the ring road. One mile from Salisbury (BR).
Capacity: 4,600 (1,000 Covered)   **Seats:** 300   **Floodlights:** Y   **Shop:** Y   **Metal Badges:** Y
Colours: White/black/black   **Change colours:** All blue.   **Sponsors:** Dunlop Hiflex.
Previous Leagues: Western 47-68.
Midweek home matchday: Monday   **Reserve Team's League:**
Record Attendance: 8,900 v Weymouth, Western League 1948.
Best F.A. Cup season: 2nd Rd 59-60, lost 0-1 at home to Newport County.
League clubs defeated in F.A. Cup:
Record Fees - Paid: £1,750 for Richard Hayson   **Received:** £18,000 for Ian Thompson.
Players progressing to Football League: Ian Thompson (B'mouth 1983), Eric Fountain (S'hampton), Graham Moxham (Exeter), Denny Mundee (B'mouth 1988).
Clubhouse: Pub hours. Main bar and function room. Snooker, darts etc.   **Steward:** Peter Rigley.
Club Record Goalscorer: Allan Green 113 (Southern Lg)   **Club Record Apps:** Barry Fitch 713.
91-92 Captain: **91-92 P.o.Y.:**   **91-92 Top scorer:**
Local Newspapers (+Tel.Nos.): Salisbury Journal, Southern Evening Echo.
Local Radio Stations: Wiltshire Sound, Radio Solent, Ocean Sound.
Honours: Southern Lg Southern Div R-up 85-86, Western Lg 57-58 60-61 (R-up 58-59 59-60 61-62 67-68, Div 2 47-48, Lg Cup 55-56), Hants Senior Cup 61-62 63-64, Alan Young Cup 59-60 60-61 62-63, FA Trophy 1st Rd 85-86 90-91, FA Amateur Cup 2nd Rd 49-50.

GOALKEEPERS:
Mark Coombe (Torquay, Colchester, Bristol C, Bournemouth), **Colin Hopkins** (Southampton(T))
DEFENDERS:
Peter Loveridge (Dorchester, Wimborne, Ringwood, Swanage, Bournemouth), **Kevin Mulkern** (Parley Sports, Poole, St Albans, Hitchin, Bournemouth), **Brett Phillips** (Bournemouth(T)), **Russell Fishlock** (Chippenham, Swindon, Pewsey V), **Nigel Tripp** (Trowbridge, Chippenham, Trowbridge, Chilpenham, Melksham, Corsham), **John Morrison** (Torquay), **Ben Prosser** (Andover), **Ian Burden** (Salisbury Manor)
MIDFIELD:
Brian O'Donnell (Bashley, Basingstoke, Farnborough, Bath, Poole, Blacktown(Aust), Torquay, Bournemouth, Blacktown(Aust), Bristol R, Bournemouth), **John Woods** (Devizes), **Sean Sanders** (Andover), **Lee Darby** (Portsmouth), **Terry Arnold** (Fareham, Andover, Waterlooville, Petersfield, Waterloovillre, Moneyfields)
FORWARDS:
Gary Fletcher (Brockenhurst, Bashley), **David Green** (Swanage, Poole, Swanage), **Ian Chalk** (Warminster, Bemerton, Peterborough, Wrexham), **Paul Turner** (Horndean), **Gordon Hobson** (Farnborough, Walsall, Exeter, Lincoln, Southampton, Grimsby, Lincoln)

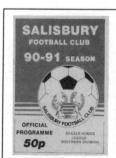

SALISBURY
FOOTBALL CLUB
90-91 SEASON

OFFICIAL
PROGRAMME   BEAZER HOMES LEAGUE SOUTHERN DIVISION
50p

PROGRAMME DETAILS:
Pages: 48 **Price:** 50p
Editor: Geoff Butler
WMPCC Rating: 18

SITTINGBOURNE

Sittingbourne FC. Back Row (L/R): Geoff Origill (Yth Team Mgr), Kevin Manser (Physio), Paul Carlton, Jeff Ross, Andy Hough, Dave Arter, Michael Harle, Ivan Haines, John Ryan (Manager), Andy Woolford (Asst Mgr). Centre: Simon Beard, Dave Bourne, Neil Emblem, Tommy Warrilow, Matt Stock, Mickey Wells. Front: Mark Miller, Steve White, Jason Fenton, Danny Tingley, Dave Ward, Phil Handford. Photo - Dave Bulley.

Chairman: Mick Fletcher   **President:** D P Robertson.
Secretary: Ian Kingsworth, c/o The Club (see below).
Team Manager: John Ryan   **Coach:** Andy Woolford
Press Officer: Dave Hollands   **Physio:** Kevin Manser
Commercial Manager: Jeff Orgill   **Newsline:** 0898 800 604.
Ground: Central Park, Eurolink, Sittingbourne, Kent (0795 475547. Fax: 0795 430776).
Directions: Through Sittingbourne on main A2, signposted from both east and west.
Capacity: 2,500 (200 Covered)   **Seats:** 200   **Floodlights:** Y   **Shop:** Y   **Metal Badges:** Y
Colours: All red.   **Change colours:** All white.   **Sponsors:** Harrisons.
Previous Leagues: Kent 1894-1905 09-27 30-39 46-59 68-91/ South Eastern 05-09/ Southern 27-30 59-67.
Previous Names: Sittingbourne United 1881-86.
Previous Grounds: The Recreation Ground 1881-90/ Gore Court Cricket Ground 90-92/ The Bull Ground 1892-1990.
Midweek home matchday: Tuesday   **Reserve Team's League:** None
Record Attendance: 5,583 v Gravesend, FA Cup 1961 (at the Bull Ground).
Best F.A. Cup season: Second Round Proper 25-26 (lost 0-7 at Swindon Town), 28-29 (lost 1-2 at Walsall). Also First Round Proper 26-27 30-31 62-63.
Record Fees - Paid: **Received:**
Players progressing to Football League:
Clubhouse: (0795 475577). Open every day, normal licensing hours.   **Steward:** R Haskell.
Club Record Goalscorer: **Club Record Apps:**
91-92 Captain: **91-92 P.O.Y.:**   **91-92 Top scorer:**
Local Newspapers: East Kent Extra.
Local Radio Stations: Invicta.
Hons: Kent Lg 1897-98 1902-03 57-58 58-59 75-76 83-84 90-91 (Lg Cup 25-26 58-59 73-74 80-81, Div 2 Cup 54-55 83-84 86-87 87-88), Kent Senior Cup 01-02 28-29 29-30 57-58, Kent Senior Shield 25-26 27-28 53-54, Kent Senior Trophy 89-90, Thames & Medway Cup 55-56 58-59, Thames & Medway Comination 02-03 07-08 11-12 24-25 25-26, Chatham Charity Cup 03-04 19-20.

GOALKEEPERS:
Andy Hough (Sheppey)
DEFENDERS: Ivan Haines (Gillingham), **Michael Harle** (Gillingham(T), Micky Wells (Canterbury, Folkestone, Chatham, Maidstone), David Ward (Erith & Belvedere, Fisher), **Tommy Warrilow** (Hythe, Crawley, Torquay, Kuopio ELO(Fin), Adelaide(Aust), Canterbury, Gravesend, Tonbridge, Millwall(A))
MIDFIELD: Phil Handford (Welling, Maidstone, Gillingham, Maidstone), Danny Tingley (Sheppey, Gravesend, Sheppey, Gillingham), **Jason Fenton** (Aylesford Paper Mills), **Matt Stock** (Durban(SA), Hastings T, Sheppey, Crawley, Ashford, Sheppey, Maidstone, Gravesend, Durban(SA), Hastings Utd, Chelmsford, Hastings Utd, Maidstone, Durban(SA), Charlton), **Dave Bourne** (Local football), **Karl Elsey** (Gillingham, Maidstone, Reading, Gillingham, Cardiff C, Newport Co, QPR, Pembroke B), Simon Beard (Local football)
FORWARDS: Neil Emblem (Tonbridge, Folkestone, Tonbridge), Dave Arter (Hythe, Ashford, Tonbridge, Herne Bay, Ashford), **Jeff Ross** (Hythe, Ashford, Gravesend, Tonbridge, Herne Bay, Welling, Ashford), **Steve White** (Youth), **Mark Miller** (Youth), **Paul Carlton** (Ashford, Sittingbourne), **Jason Lillis** (Maidstone, Gillingham)

Pages: 40 **Price:** 50p
Editor: Nina Hadaway
WMPCC Rating: 23

Formed: 1898 # SUDBURY TOWN The Borough

Knowsley United 2, Sudbury Town 4 - FA Vase 5th Round 8/2/92. Dave O'Brien of Knowsley (right) tries to dispossess Sudbury's Kevin Ketley. Photo - Colin Stevens.

Chairman: R A F Ashdown   **President:** H D J Yallop.
Secretary: David Webb, 6 Melford Road, Sudbury, Suffolk CO10 6LS (0787 72352).
Manager: Richie Powling   **Asst Manager:** Steve Barrett. **Coach:**
Press Officer: **Physio:** Tony Brightwell.
Commercial Manager:
Ground Address & Tel: Priory Stadium, Priory Walk, Sudbury, Suffolk (0787 79095).
Directions: Take Friars Street from town centre, pass cricket ground and continue to the 'Ship & Star'. Left into Priory Walk and continue to ground. Half mile and three quarters of a mile from bus and rail stations respectively.
Capacity: 5,000 (900 Covered)   **Seats:** 300   **Floodlights:** Y   **Shop:** Y   **Metal Badges:** Y
Colours: All yellow   **Change colours:** All red.
Sponsors: Wheelers (Timber & Building).
Previous Leagues: Suffolk & Ipswich/ Essex & Suffolk Border/ Eastern Counties 55-90.
Previous Ground: Friar Street (until 1951).
Midweek home matchday: Tuesday   **Reserve Team's League:** Jewson Eastern Cos. Div 1.
Record Attendance: 4,700 v Ipswich Town, testimonial 1978.
Best F.A. Cup season: 3rd Qualifying Rd replay 74-75.
League clubs defeated in F.A. Cup: None.
Record Fees - Paid: **Received:**
Players progressing to Football League: Gilbert Dowsett (Spurs 1952), John Taylor (Cambridge 1988), Steve McGavin (promoted with Colchester 1992).
Clubhouse: Open on matchdays and for other functions. Pool, darts, dancehall.   **Steward:** L Hodgson.
Club Record Goalscorer: **Club Record Apps:**
91-92 Captain: **91-92 P.o.Y.:**   **91-92 Top scorer:**
Local Newspapers: Suffolk Free Press, East Anglian Daily Times.
Local Radio Stations:
Hons: FA Vase R-up 88-89 (SF 87-88 91-92), Eastern Counties Lg 73-74 74-75 75-76 85-86 86-87 88-89 89-90 (R-up 65-66 72-73 76-77 80-81 81-82 84-85, Lg Cup 69-70 76-77 82-83 86-87 88-89 89-90, Suffolk & Ipswich Lg 34-35 52-53, Suffolk Premier Cup 72-73 73-74 75-76 80-81 81-82 82-83 84-85 86-87 87-88 88-89 89-90 91-92, Suffolk Senior Cup 56-57 86-87, East Anglian Cup 85-86 91-92.

GOALKEEPERS:
Steve Mokler (Harwich, Newmarket, Harwich, Thetford), **Dean Garnham** (Felixstowe, Colchester, Luton, Ipswich Exiles)
DEFENDERS:
Murray Osman (Harwich, Ransomes), **Marty Thorpe** (Woodbridge, Brantham, Chelmsford), **Gus Cutting** (Needham Market), **Gary Hudson** (Clacton), **Trevor Gunn** (Braintree, Brantham, Harlow, B Stortford), **Mike Henry** (Harwich, Bury T, Sudbury, Felixstowe), **Jon Reynolds** (Braintree, Lowestoft, Gorleston), **Clive Stafford** (Bury T, Colchester, Diss, Ipswich)
MIDFIELD:
Dean Barker (Brantham, Bury T, Felixstowe), **Keith Bain** (Wivenhoe, Tiptree, Wivenhoe, Colchester(J)), **Andy Crane** (Hereford, Shrewsbury, Ipswich), **Kevin Ketley** (Harwich, Bury T, Chelmsford, Braintree, Halstead), **Tony French** (Brightlingsea), **Steve Low** (Camb City, Newmarket, Soham), **David Lee** (Bury T, Basildon, Southend(J))
FORWARDS:
Steve Parnell (Halstead, Braintree, Halstead, Tiptree), **Paul Coe** (Newmarket), **Graham Powell** (Brantham, Wivenhoe, Brantham, Chelmsford, Tiptree, Chelmsford, Tiptree), **Don Cutmore** (Halstead, Sudbury, Halstead), **Dave McCoy** (Wivenhoe, Camb City, Bury T, Thetford, Bury T, Chelmsford, Sudbury, Newmarket), **Paul Smith** (Bury T, Sudbury, Felixstowe, Woodbridge)

SUDBURY TOWN FOOTBALL CLUB
PRIORY STADIUM
TEL: 79095

Wheelers Timber & Builders' Merchants

PROGRAMME DETAILS:
Pages: 24 **Price:** 50p
Editor: Brian Hender
WMPCC Rating: 28

WEALDSTONE

Wealdstone FC. Back Row (L/R): Paul Goyette, Jim Watson, Colin Tate, Steve Tapley, Grant Gallacher, Leo Donnellan. Centre: Andy Hedge, Neil Cordice, Chuck Moussaddik, Johnson Hippolyte, Steve Walford. Front: David Venables, Mark Hopson, Martin Blackler, Peter Bartlett, Russell Wilson, Tiv Lowe.

Chairman: David W Pollock   **President:** N/A
Secretary: Peter Braxton, c/o Vicarage Rd Stadium, Watford, Herts WD1 8ER (0923 212916).
Team Manager: Brian Hall   **Asst Manager:** None   **Coach:** Dennis Byatt
Press Officer: Steve Marshall   **Physio:** Terry Warren
Newsline: 0898 884 473   **Commercial Manager:** Ian Crossley (0923 210454).
Ground: Vicarage Road Stadium (Watford FC), Watford WD1 8ER (0923 212916).
Directions: Arriving on A412, turn into Harwoods Road then left at T junction into Vicarage Road. Watford Junction or Watford High Street stations.
Capacity: 23,000   **Seats:** 10,158   **Floodlights:** Y   **Shop:** Y   **Metal Badges:** Y
Colours: White(blue trim)/white/blue)   **Change colours:**   **Sponsors:** Finers.
Previous Leagues: Willesden & Dist/ Middx Senior/ London 1911-14 19-32/ Spartan 22-28/ Athenian 28-64/ Isthmian 64-71/ Southern 71-79 81-82/ GMV Conference 79-81 82-88.
Previous Grounds: College Farm 10-22/ Lower Mead Stadium 22-91.
Midweek home matchday: Wednesday   **Reserve Team's League:** Capital Football League.
Record Attendance: 13,504 v Leytonstone F.A. Amateur Cup 1949.
Best F.A. Cup season: 3rd Rd 77-78 (0-4 at Q.P.R.). 1st Rd on 13 occasions 49-50 65-67 68-69 75-80 82-84 85-87.
League clubs defeated in F.A. Cup: Hereford Utd and Reading, 77-78.
Record Fees: Paid: £15,000 for David Gipp.
Received: £25,000 for Stuart Pearce (Coventry) and Sean Norman (Chesham).
Players progressing to Football League: Edward Smith (Chelsea 1950), Phil White (Orient 1953), Tom McGhee & John Ashworth (Portsmouth 1954 & 62), Charlie Sells (Exeter 1962), Eddie Dilsworth (Lincoln 1967), Colin Franks (Watford 1969), Stuart Pearce (Coventry 1983), Vinnie Jones (W'don 1986), Danny Bailey (Exeter 1989), Francis Joseph (W'don & Brentford), Bobby Ryan.
Clubhouse: '81 Club and Aldenham Club lounges.
Club Record Goalscorer: Geo Duck, 251   **Club Record Apps:** Charlie Townsend, 514
91-92 Captain: Neil Cordice   **91-92 P.O.Y.:** Neil Cordice   **91-92 Top scorer:** Leo Donnellan.
Local Newspapers: Harrow Observer, Watford Observer.
Local Radio: LBC, Capital, Greater London Radio, Radio Bedford.
Honours: FA Tphy 84-85, FA Amateur Cup 65-66 (R-up 67-68), GMV Conference 84-85, Southern Lg 81-82 (Div 1 South 73-74, Lg Cup 81-82), Athenian Lg 51-52 (R-up 52-53 58-59 60-61), Spartan Lg R-up 22-23, London Lg Div 2 12-13 (R-up 11-12), London Snr Cup 61-62(joint)(R-up 39-40, 51-52 60-61), Middx Snr Cup(10) 29-30 37-38 40-43 45-46 58-59 62-64 67-68, Capital League 84-85 86-87.

GOALKEEPERS:
Wayne Roach (Mount Roskill(NZ)), David Hudson (Wimbledon)
DEFENDERS:
Jim Watson (Wimbledon(T)), Peter Bartlett (Staines, Hayes, Leatherhead, Epsom & Ewell, Hampton), Steve Tapley (Harrow B, Wealdstone, Yeovil, Enfield, Wealdstone, Fulham), Colin Robinson (Local football), Dermot Drummy (Boreham Wood, St Albans, Finchley, Chesham, Hendon, Enfield, Hendon, Arsenal), Martin Blackler (Wycombe, Trowbridge, Cheltenham, Witney, Swindon)
MIDFIELD:
Sean Pearson (Hitchin, Langford), Neil Cordice (Yeovil, Wealdstone, Northampton, Wycombe, Flackwell Heath), Andy Hedge (Local football), Tiv Lowe (Bath, Yeovil, Saltash, Wimborne, Dorchester, Saltash), Paul Goyette (Maidstone, Dagenham, Tilbury, West Ham), Martin Maguire (Hitchin, Shillington), Grant Gallagher (Crawley, Hythe, Crawley, Chatham, Gravesend, Thanet, Dagenham, Chatham, Dartford, Chatham)
FORWARDS:
Russ Wilson (Weymouth, Bashley, Army), Colin Tate (Hendon, Harrow B, Hendon, Slough, Wycombe, Oxford C, QPR), Dave Venables (Crawley, Eastbourne Utd), Mark Hopson (Harrow B, Brentford(J), Harrow B), Johnson Hippolyte (Chalfont, Uxbridge, Hounslow)

PROGRAMME DETAILS:
Pages: 28 **Price:** 70p
Editor: Steve Marshall
WMPCC Rating: 37

WITNEY TOWN

Witney Town 91-92 - Back Row (L/R): Dave Warner, Alan Frost, Neil Laws, Jimmy Austin, Kenny Clarke, Darren Teggart, Andy Leach, Micky Carroll, Kevin Alder. Front: Gerry O'Loughlin, Damien Maguire, Grayson Fisher, Brian Flannery, Andy Dawson, Dale Mills, Carl Wilson, Pete Osbourne. Photo - Steve Daniels.

Chairman: A N Oakey **President:** John Bury.
Secretary: Bob Watts, 16 Duabigny Mead, Brize Norton, Oxon OX18 3QE (0993 841210).
Team Manager: Andy Lyne **Asst Manager:** Peter Bridgewater
Press Officer: Adrian Bircher **Physio:** Roger Alder
Ground: Marriotts Close, Welch Way, Witney, Oxon OX8 5LZ (0993 702549/705930).
Directions: Situated in town centre adjacent to one of the main car parks. Oxford (BR) 12 miles away, bus No. 100 from Oxford bus station.
Capacity: 3,500 (1,150 Covered) **Seats:** 150 **Floodlights:** Y **Shop:** Y **Metal Badges:** Y
Colours: Yellow/royal blue/royal blue **Change colours:** Blue/white/white.
Sponsors: Western Counties Construction Ltd.
Previous Leagues: Reading & Dist/ Oxfordshire Senior/ Hellenic 53-73.
Previous Name: Witney FC.
Midweek home matchday: Tuesday **Reserve Team's League:** Mids (Scoreline) Comb Res. Div.
Record Attendance: 3,500 for Nottm Forest v West Bromwich Albion, frendly, 1979.
Best F.A. Cup season: 1st Rd 71-72 (lost 0-3 at home to Romford).
League clubs defeated in F.A. Cup: None.
Record Fees - Paid: £3,000 for Steve Jenkins (Cheltenham) **Received:** £5,000 for John Bailey (W'cester).
Players progressing to Football League: Herbert Smith, Frank Clack (Birmingham City), Arthur Hall (Bristol Rov 1959), David Moss (Swindon 1969), Jack Newman.
Clubhouse: Open Mon-Fri 18.30 - 23.00, Sat 11.00 - 14.45, 18.30 - 23.00, Sun 12.00 - 14.00, 19.00 - 22.30. Open all afternoon on matchdays.
Steward: John Drinkwater.
91-92 Captain: Andy Leach **91-92 P.o.Y.:** Andy Leach **91-92 Top scorer:** Kenny Clarke 21.
Local Newspapers (+Tel.Nos.): Witney Gazette (0993 704265), West Oxon Standard (0993 702175), Oxford Mail & Oxford Times (0865 244988).
Local Radio Stations: BBC Radio Oxford, Fox (FM) Oxford.
Hons: FA Tphy 2nd Rd 78-79, FA Amtr Cup 2nd Rd rep.(3) 66-67 71-73, Southern Lg Div 1 Nth 77-78, Hellenic Lg(8) 54-55 57-58 64-67 70-73 (R-up 53-54 67-68 69-70, Lg Cup(6) 56-57 63-65 69-70 71-73, Prem Div Benevolent Cup 59-60 63-64), Oxon Snr Lg(5) 28-30 31-32 51-53, Oxon Snr Cup(9) 1894-95 97-99 1952-53 54-56 58-59 70-71(jt) 72-73.

GOALKEEPERS:
Trevor Barefield (Coventry), **Kevin Alder** (Thame, Witney, Clanfield, Burford)
DEFENDERS:
Gary Murphy (Banbury, Oxford C, Oxford Utd(J)), **Jimmy Austin** (Abingdon Utd, Bicester, Oxford C, Bireton), **Grayson Fisher** (Youth), **Andy Leach** (Oxford C, Bicester, Kidlington, Oxford C), **Eddie Innes** (Oxford C), **Lee Hyatt** (Peterborough(T)), **Peter Hutter** (Aylesbury, Witney)
MIDFIELD:
Brian Flannery (Bicester), **Micky Carroll** (Morris Motors, Oxford Utd(J)), **Liam Carroll** (Thame, Witney, Headington Am, Oxford C, Oxford Utd(J)), **Gerry O'Loughlin** (Brackley, Abingdon T, Bicester, Oxford Utd(A)), **Mark Gee** (Banbury, Abingdon Utd), **Peter Cullen** (Banbury, Abingdon Utd)
FORWARDS:
Kenny Clarke (Banbury, Hungerford, Witney, Oxford C, Witney), **Darryl Kew** (Local football), **Darren Teggart** (Banbury, Clanfield, Moreton, Witney), **Shaun Bradbury** (Abingdon T, Abingdon Utd, Oxford C, Witney, Banbury, Abingdon T), **Rob Keates** (Local football)

WITNEY TOWN
Football Club 1991-92

Pages: 40 **Price:** 50p
Editor: Adrian Bircher
WMPCC Rating: 28

Beazer Homes (Southern) League Southern Division Ten Year Records

	82/3	83/4	84/5	85/6	86/7	87/8	88/9	89/90	90/1	91/2
Addlestone & Weybridge T.	–	5	8	–	–	–	–	–	–	–
Andover	17	15	13	20	16	6	18	18	9	7
Ashford Town	8	8	17	18	2	–	–	–	5	9
Baldock Town	–	–	–	–	–	15	6	10	4	11
Bashley	–	–	–	–	–	–	–	1	–	–
Basingstoke Town	15	3	1	–	–	–	–	–	10	4
Braintree Town	–	–	–	–	–	–	–	–	–	4
Buckingham Town	–	–	–	–	–	–	16	3	1	5
Burnham	–	–	–	11	17	8	5	11	11	10
Bury Town	–	–	–	–	–	9	4	9	12	17
Cambridge City	12	10	15	1	–	–	–	–	–	–
Canterbury City	11	11	10	12	20	20	13	15	18	21
Chatham Town	–	14	16	19	9	21	–	–	–	–
Chelmsford City	–	–	–	–	–	–	1	–	–	–
Corinthian	–	–	–	5	14	18	12	21	21	–
Crawley Town	7	2	–	–	–	–	–	–	–	–
Dorchester Town	–	–	14	21	1	–	–	–	–	–
Dover Athletic	13	13	19	4	5	1	–	–	–	–
Dunstable	4	17	18	7	13	7	15	4	17	16
Erith & Belvedere	18	16	20	9	8	10	17	20	19	20
Fareham Town	–	–	–	–	–	–	–	12	20	19
Fisher Athletic	1	–	–	–	–	–	–	–	–	–
Folkestone Town	2	–	–	–	–	17	11	17	RES	–
Gosport Borough	–	–	2	–	–	–	–	–	15	22
Gravesend & Northfleet	–	–	–	–	6	4	2	–	–	–
Hastings Town	–	–	–	3	4	12	7	8	7	1
Havant Town	–	–	–	–	–	–	–	–	–	3
Hillingdon Borough	5	7	4	–	–	–	–	–	–	–
Hounslow	10	20	–	–	–	16	8	19	–	–
Hythe Town	–	–	–	–	–	–	–	6	8	13
Margate	14	18	5	15	10	5	20	16	10	14
Newport Isle of Wight	–	–	–	–	–	–	–	–	14	15
Poole Town	–	6	3	17	18	14	3	2	–	–
Road Sea Southampton	3	1	–	–	–	–	–	–	–	–
Ruislip	–	–	–	8	19	19	22	–	–	–
Salisbury	6	9	6	2	–	3	9	5	3	12
Sheppey United	–	–	7	14	15	11	19	22	–	–
Sittingbourne	–	–	–	–	–	–	–	–	–	6
Sudbury Town	–	–	–	–	–	–	–	–	13	8
Thanet United						(See Margate)				
Tonbridge A.F.C.	9	4	12	6	7	13	21	–	–	–
Trowbridge Town	–	–	–	13	12	–	10	7	2	–
Waterlooville	–	12	9	10	11	2	–	–	–	–
Weymouth	–	–	–	–	–	–	–	–	–	2
Witney Town	–	–	–	–	–	–	14	14	16	18
Woodford Town	16	19	11	16	3	–	–	–	–	–
Yate Town	–	–	–	–	–	–	–	–	13	6	–
No. of Clubs	15	16	14	12	14	13	12	16	18	20

SPORTIQUE 'MANAGER OF THE MONTH' AWARDS

MONTH	PREMIER DIVISION	MIDLAND DIVISION	SOUTHERN DIVISION
AUG.	Jimmy Knox (V.S. Rugby)	John Relish (Newport)	Len Drake (Weymouth)
SEP.	Chris Kinnear (Dover)	Ralph Punsheon (Soluhull)	Keith Baker (Buckingham)
OCT.	Bob Makin (Dartford)	Ian Love (Barry)	Peter Sillet (Hastings)
NOV.	John Murphy (Trowbridge)	Ralph Punsheon (Solihull)	Mark Weatherly (Margate)
DEC.	Trevor Parker (Bashley)	John Baldwin (Hednesford)	Tony Mount (Havant)
JAN.	Danny O'Leary (Chelmsford)	John Baldwin (Hednesford)	Peter Collins & Brian Honeywood (Braintree)
FEB.	Bobby Hope (Bromsgrove)	Ian Love (Barry)	Any Woolford (Sittingbourne)
MAR.	Chris Kinnear (Dover)	John Chambers (S'bridge)	Tony Mount (Havant)
APR.	Bobby Hope (Bromsgrove)	Peter Eastoe (Alvechurch)	John Wortley (Dunstable)

SPORTIQUE PREMIER DIVISION MANAGER OF THE SEASON - BOBBY HOPE (BROMSGROVE)

SPORTIQUE MIDLAND DIVISION MANAGER OF THE SEASON - RALPH PUNSHEON (SOLIHULL)

SPORTIQUE SOUTHERN DIVISION MANAGER OF THE SEASON - JOHN WORTLEY (DUNSTABLE)

BODDINGTONS BITTER
WEST MIDLANDS (REGIONAL) LEAGUE

Chairman: R H Juggins
Hon. Secretary: K H Goodfellow,
11 Emsworth Grove, Kings Heath B14 6HY (021 624 3186).

ANNUAL REPORT 1992

The past season has seen a number of changes within the compilation of the league. New clubs have joined us in Divisions One and Two, and we hope their first season has been an enjoyable one and that they will remain with us for many seasons to come. The Management Committee have met regularly each month and have found it necessary to hold extra meetings in order to ensure League business is kept up-to-date.

There has been a revision of the ground-grading booklet, and all clubs have been sent a copy. The Grounds Committee have visited all Division One and Two grounds during the season, with clubs being notified of any alterations they should make to bring their facilities up to the standard required by their division by May 1993.

Fortunately, few matches have had to be postponed due to adverse weather conditions, but even so a tremendous amount of work has been necessary to re-arrange these games, particularly where clubs do not have lights or they share a ground with a club not in this league.

There have been some successes during the season, and we are pleased to note those clubs who have reached the finals of county competitions. We congratulate those who have been successful, and commiserate with the losers.

It has been confirmed by the Joint Liaison Committee that Gresley Rovers have been promoted to the Beazer Homes League, and we wish them every success. With regret, we also say 'goodbye' to Broseley Athletic, Alvechurch Reserves, K Chell, Malvern Reserves and, from the Youth Division, Halesowen Town.

The Youth Division has again been a success, and it is hoped that those players who are now over-age will move into the higher realms of football within the league. It is anticipated that this Division will be increased next season.

We are delighted to announce that on the 21st May 1992, the League acquired a Sponsorship deal with Boddingtons Bitter for next season in the sum of £25,000, and we would like to thank Tony Allen for this break-through. At the time of writing the actual breakdown of the sponsorship is being discussed by the Management Committee, but there are to be some new awards - one for Team of the Month, and another for overrall Player of the Year as well as Divisional Players of the Year.

The Management Committee would like to thank all officials for their unfailing support during the season, and would like to congratulate those who are moving to 'higher circles'. Congratulations must be extended to former referees of the League, namely Gerald Ashby who has been appointed to the FIFA Panel of Officials, and Arthur Smith who has been appointed Secretary of the National Referee's Association. In addition, Paul Rejer ran the line at the first leg of the UEFA Cup final at Torino in Italy.

On behalf of all members of the Management Committee, I would like to thank all clubs for their hospitality when we have visited them, and we look forward to their continued support in the future. I would also like to thank all members of the Management Committee for their help and support during the past season, especially as so many Ground Inspections have been carried out.

K H Goodfellow, League Secretary

Gresley Rovers pictured with the championship shield before their final game of the 1991-92 season. Back Row (L/R): Gordon Ford (Trainer), Stuart Evans, Scott Elliott, Gil Land, John Barry, Steve Astley, Simon Harrison, Jason Minton, Craig Weston, Kieron Smith, Dave Mead, Brian Beresford, Peter Hall (Chairman). Front: Martin Dick, Paul Acklam, Richard Denby (Captain), Richard Wardle, Ryan Venning, Chris Parkin. Photo - Derrick Kinsey.

Premier Division	P	W	D	L	F	A	PTS
Gresley Rovers	36	24	7	5	83	37	79
Paget Rangers	36	20	5	11	81	44	65
Stourport Swifts	36	18	10	8	62	45	64
Blakenall	36	17	10	9	67	49	61
Chasetown	36	17	10	9	47	31	61
Rocester	36	17	8	11	64	52	59
Oldbury United	36	17	7	12	61	47	58
Rushall Olympic	36	16	9	11	61	38	57
Lye Town	36	14	11	11	51	34	53
Halesowen Harr.	36	13	11	12	63	52	50
Willenhall Town	36	14	6	16	56	63	48
Pelsall Villa	36	12	11	13	52	58	47
West Brom. Town	36	11	11	14	41	60	44
Cradley Town	36	12	7	17	39	56	43
Hinckley Ath.	36	9	7	20	36	56	34
Malvern Town	36	8	9	19	39	79	33
Wednesfield	36	8	8	20	43	69	32
Westfields	36	6	12	18	48	74	30
Oldswinford	36	7	5	24	34	84	26

Division One	P	W	D	L	F	A	PTS
Ilkeston Town	38	31	6	1	121	30	99
Darlaston	38	22	11	5	83	34	77
Donnington Wood	38	21	12	5	77	43	75
Gornal Athletic	38	21	8	9	73	41	71
Knypersley Vict.	38	19	9	10	84	54	66
Ettingshall H.T.	38	15	15	8	60	47	60
Hill Top Rangers	38	17	5	16	75	76	56
Cannock Chase	38	16	7	15	68	71	55
Ludlow Town	38	16	5	17	72	71	53
Moxley Rangers	38	14	9	15	32	42	51
Wolverhampton Cas.	38	13	11	14	51	59	50
Lichfield	38	14	5	19	57	50	47
Tipton Town	38	11	12	15	51	62	45
Wem Town	38	10	10	18	63	73	40
Wolverhampton Utd	38	8	14	16	63	80	38
Tividale	38	10	6	22	46	72	36
Oldbury Utd Res	38	8	11	19	34	68	35
Great Wyrley	38	9	6	23	45	86	33
Clancey Dudley	38	8	8	22	49	90	32
Broseley Ath.	38	8	8	22	38	93	32

Division Two	P	W	D	L	F	A	PTS
K Chell	38	28	4	6	128	39	88
Gornal Sports	38	26	8	4	86	32	86
Rushall Olym. Res	38	21	8	9	91	54	71
Park Rangers	38	22	5	11	91	68	71
Mitchells & Butlers	38	21	7	10	96	48	70
Manders	38	20	9	9	70	40	69
Lye Town Res	38	19	7	12	75	51	64
Allbright & Wilson	38	18	6	14	74	56	60
Bloxwich Stroll.	38	14	10	14	81	71	52
Oldswinford Res	38	16	4	18	79	85	52
H'owen Harr. Res	38	14	6	18	63	65	48
Alvechurch Res	38	13	9	16	62	84	48
Chasetown Res	38	13	7	18	63	86	46
Cradley Town Res	38	12	9	17	74	102	45
Blackheath Motors	38	12	8	20	65	93	44
Malvern Town Res	38	10	9	19	63	68	39
Rocester Res	38	11	5	22	53	119	38
Wolves Casuals Res	38	9	5	24	58	116	32
Cheslyn Hay	38	7	9	22	62	93	30
Nuneaton Boro. Res	38	4	7	27	50	114	19

Youth Division	P	W	D	L	F	A	PTS
Halesowen T. Yth	18	13	4	1	57	23	43
Gresley Rvrs Yth	18	10	3	5	44	28	33
Redditch Utd Yth	18	8	2	8	38	31	26
Lye Town Yth	18	6	6	6	35	33	24
Wednesfield Yth	18	7	3	8	27	30	24
Boldmere SM Yth	18	6	5	7	27	24	23
Rocester Yth	18	7	2	9	24	35	23
Pelsall Villa Yth	18	6	4	8	26	43	22
Hinckley T. Yth	18	6	3	9	28	38	21
Chasetown Yth	18	4	2	12	23	44	14

PREMIER DIVISION CUP 1991-92

First Round (10-9-91)

Oldbury United v Cradley Town	0-1	
West Brom. Town v Pelsall Villa	4-0(11-9-91)	
Chasetown v Gresley	2-2,1-1(8-10-91),0-1(22-10-91)	

Second Round (24-9-91)

Oldswinford v Cradley 1-1(23-9-91),1-2(5-11-91)
Gresley Rovers v Malvern Town 2-0(12-11-91)
Wednesfield v Stourport Swifts 2-1
Willenhall Town v Hinckley A. 3-2(23-9-91)

Westfields v West Brom. Town 2-2(W'fields W/O)
Halesowen Har. v Rocester 0-0,1-2(12-11-91)
Blakenall v Rushall Olympic 1-1,5-1(1-10-91)
Paget Rangers v Lye Town 4-0(7-9-91)

Quarter Finals (15-2-92)

Cradley Town v Westfields 0-1
Blakenall v Wednesfield 2-3(3-12-91)

Rocester v Gresley Rovers 0-0,1-3(18-2-92)
Paget Rangers v Willenhall Town 2-1

Semi-Finals (1st Leg 24-3-92, 2nd Leg 14-4-92)

Westfields v Gresley Rovers 0-2,0-3

Paget Rangers v Westfields 2-0,3-2(7-4-92)

Final *(at Blakenall FC, 6-5-92)*: Gresley Rovers 1, Paget Rangers 2

The West Midlands League Representative side 1991-92. Back Row (L/R): C Rathbone, D Loughran, C Field, D Shelton, B Aston, A Crannage, M O'Sullivan, B Cullin, T Hall, S Stokes. Front: T Jones, V Scott, K Gough, N Conniff, A Box, M Brookes, C Weston. Photo - Marshalls Sports Service (Birmingham).

HOME TEAM	1	2	3	4	5	6	7	8	9	10	11	12	13	14	15	16	17	18	19
1. Blakenall	*	1-2	2-0	0-2	3-1	4-3	2-0	0-2	6-0	5-1	1-3	1-4	1-1	2-2	2-2	2-1	4-1	3-1	3-1
2. Chasetown	0-0	*	3-0	4-1	2-1	0-1	2-1	1-1	1-0	3-1	0-1	4-1	2-0	2-0	2-1	3-1	2-2	1-0	0-2
3. Cradley Town	2-2	1-0	*	0-2	0-2	1-0	0-0	2-0	0-3	3-1	1-0	1-3	0-3	1-2	0-3	3-0	3-0	2-1	1-0
4. Gresley Rovers	2-1	1-1	1-0	*	2-1	3-0	1-2	3-1	3-1	3-0	2-1	4-0	4-0	2-0	2-2	2-2	1-0	4-1	3-0
5. Halesowen H.	2-2	3-2	2-1	3-3	*	0-1	1-1	1-0	0-1	5-1	0-1	2-2	1-1	1-1	1-3	2-0	4-0	3-2	4-3
6. Hinckley Ath.	1-3	0-1	2-2	1-1	0-0	*	0-1	0-1	1-1	2-0	1-0	2-1	2-3	0-1	3-3	0-1	3-0	1-1	0-2
7. Lye Town	0-1	0-1	3-0	1-1	2-0	1-0	*	0-1	2-0	3-0	0-3	2-2	1-1	2-2	0-0	3-0	1-1	1-2	0-1
8. Malvern Town	1-1	0-1	1-1	0-4	2-5	2-1	0-4	*	0-4	0-1	2-2	0-4	0-2	0-6	1-1	1-1	3-3	5-1	1-3
9. Oldbury United	4-2	2-1	0-1	1-3	3-3	2-0	2-2	1-2	*	1-0	1-2	1-1	1-0	2-1	0-1	4-0	1-0	5-3	3-0
10. Oldswinford	1-1	2-1	1-0	1-4	1-3	0-2	1-3	1-3	0-4	*	1-5	4-1	0-0	2-0	0-1	1-2	2-2	0-5	1-2
11. Paget Rangers	1-2	0-0	4-1	3-0	0-1	0-1	2-1	4-2	0-3	4-1	*	6-1	3-3	2-1	0-1	4-1	0-0	5-1	3-0
12. Pelsall Villa	1-2	1-1	3-1	0-1	2-1	3-0	0-3	3-3	0-0	3-3	1-3	*	1-2	1-1	1-0	3-1	0-0	0-0	1-1
13. Rocester	3-0	2-0	0-3	2-3	3-2	2-0	1-2	4-0	3-3	1-2	1-5	2-0	*	2-2	4-2	3-0	2-3	3-1	0-4
14. Rushall Olym.	0-1	0-1	2-0	0-0	2-1	4-1	4-2	1-0	2-0	5-1	1-0	0-2	1-2	*	2-3	2-0	0-2	0-0	0-0
15. Stourport Sw.	1-1	1-1	4-0	3-1	2-2	3-1	0-4	5-0	3-1	3-0	1-1	2-0	4-0	0-3	*	0-0	0-1	1-0	5-1
16. Wednesfield	0-0	1-1	1-5	0-3	2-2	3-1	0-3	2-2	0-1	2-1	1-3	1-0	2-3	1-3	1-2	*	1-2	4-1	4-0
17. West Brom Town	2-1	0-0	1-1	1-7	1-0	1-2	1-0	0-2	0-4	0-1	2-0	0-1	0-0	3-3	3-0	1-0	*	3-1	0-3
18. Westfields	1-2	1-1	0-0	2-1	0-0	1-1	0-0	3-0	0-0	1-0	6-5	2-3	0-2	0-4	1-3	3-3	3-3	*	1-3
19. Willenhall T.	0-3	1-0	4-4	2-3	0-2	4-2	0-0	3-0	4-1	1-1	0-5	1-2	0-2	0-2	0-1	2-1	4-2	2-2	*

West Mids League Premier Division Ten Year Record

	82/3	83/4	84/5	85/6	86/7	87/8	88/9	89/90	90/1	91/2
Armitage	8	8	19	20	19	-	-	-	-	-
Atherstone United	5	3	3	3	1	-	-	-	-	-
Bilston Town	6	17	2	-	-	-	-	-	-	-
Blakenall	15	18	18	15	20	12	1	4	14	4
Brereton Social	18	16	14	10	14	-	-	-	-	-
Chasetown	-	19	16	17	9	5	9	10	2	5
Coventry Sporting	16	-	-	-	-	-	-	-	-	-
Cradley Town	-	20	-	-	-	-	-	-	-	14
Darlaston	-	-	-	-	-	-	-	-	4	-
GKN Sankey	-	15	11	7	11	16	-	-	-	-
Gresley Rovers	9	4	8	2	4	4	2	3	1	1
Halesowen Harriers	-	-	-	-	7	6	3	9	10	10
Halesowen Town	1	1	1	1	-	-	-	-	-	-
Harrisons	-	-	-	4	10	11	12	12	-	-
Hednesford Town	3	2	-	-	-	-	-	-	-	-
Hinckley Athletic	2	14	9	8	8	10	14	6	5	15
Hinckley Town	-	-	-	-	-	-	7	1	-	-
Ilkeston Town	-	-	-	-	-	-	-	-	7	-
Ledbury Town	19	-	-	-	-	-	-	-	-	-
Lye Town	13	5	12	6	13	3	8	5	9	9
Malvern Town	20	12	17	12	6	7	10	13	21	16
Millfields (see West Bromwich Town)										
Oldbury United	-	-	-	-	2	2	6	8	3	7
Oldswinford	17	7	10	14	17	18	19	18	18	19
Paget Rangers	-	-	-	-	-	-	4	11	17	2
Pelsall Villa	-	-	-	-	-	-	-	-	15	12
Rocester	-	-	-	-	-	-	11	2	11	6
Rushall Olympic	14	13	13	11	12	9	5	14	12	8
Shifnal Town	4	9	20	13	-	-	-	-	-	-
Stourport Swifts	-	-	-	-	-	-	21	15	13	3
Tamworth	-	-	7	9	5	1	-	-	-	-
Tipton Town	-	-	5	19	18	15	20	21	22	-
Tividale	10	11	6	16	15	13	13	19	20	-
V.S. Rugby	7	-	-	-	-	-	-	-	-	-
Wednesfield (Social)	11	10	4	5	3	8	16	7	6	17
West Bromwich Town	-	-	-	-	-	-	18	20	8	13
Westfields	-	-	-	-	-	14	17	17	19	18
Willenhall Town	-	-	-	-	-	-	-	-	-	11
Wolverhampton Casuals	-	-	-	-	-	-	15	16	16	-
Wolverhampton United	12	6	15	18	16	17	-	-	-	-
No. of clubs competing	20	20	20	20	20	18	21	21	21	19

DIVISION ONE RESULT CHART 1991-92

HOME TEAM	1	2	3	4	5	6	7	8	9	10	11	12	13	14	15	16	17	18	19	20
1. Broseley	*	2-3	2-2	2-2	1-4	1-3	2-1	2-1	0-1	0-2	1-0	2-4	2-1	1-0	1-3	1-0	1-3	2-1	0-1	2-2
2. Cannock C.	1-3	*	1-0	3-1	2-2	0-1	1-0	1-0	6-1	1-2	2-1	1-2	0-0	2-1	3-0	2-1	2-0	2-0	1-2	1-2
3. Clancey D.	4-1	2-2	*	1-1	3-3	1-2	0-4	1-1	4-1	0-3	0-4	2-1	3-2	1-4	1-2	1-3	2-1	3-2	0-1	2-2
4. Darlaston	7-0	0-0	3-0	*	2-0	2-2	4-0	6-1	1-0	2-3	5-2	6-1	1-2	0-2	3-0	1-1	2-1	2-1	2-0	1-1
5. D'ton Wood	4-0	2-0	4-2	0-0	*	1-1	1-1	3-0	2-1	1-4	5-0	2-0	0-0	3-0	3-2	2-2	2-2	3-2		
6. Ettingshall	2-2	0-1	3-2	0-3	0-0	*	1-1	7-1	2-3	0-3	1-1	2-1	3-3	1-0	0-0	0-0	0-1	1-1	1-0	2-0
7. Gornal Ath.	4-0	3-2	1-0	2-2	0-0	4-1	*	4-4	5-1	0-1	0-1	2-0	2-0	0-1	6-1	2-0	1-2	2-1	4-1	
8. Gt Wyrley	3-1	1-1	0-4	1-2	1-3	2-2	6-1	*	0-5	1-4	1-3	2-0	0-1	0-1	3-1	0-0	2-1	1-4	1-2	2-1
9. Hill Top R.	1-0	3-0	4-0	0-5	2-0	2-3	2-4	3-0	*	1-1	2-1	0-0	1-1	1-0	2-3	1-1	1-3	8-2	3-1	4-3
10. Ilkeston	11-1	7-2	3-1	1-1	2-0	1-0	0-1	4-0	3-2	*	5-3	2-1	2-1	10-0	6-1	5-0	8-1	1-0	4-0	2-2
11. Knypersley	1-1	2-4	10-0	3-1	1-1	2-0	1-3	1-2	4-1	1-2	*	3-0	1-0	2-0	1-1	2-2	4-0	3-0	2-2	2-2
12. Lichfield	2-0	5-2	3-0	0-1	1-3	1-3	0-3	3-0	4-0	0-0	0-1	*	6-1	0-0	0-1	2-1	2-2	2-2	5-2	
13. Ludlow T.	4-1	3-0	3-0	2-3	2-5	1-4	2-1	1-4	3-4	1-5	1-2	0-3	*	3-1	4-0	2-3	3-0	2-1	4-0	4-3
14. Moxley Rgrs	0-0	1-0	4-1	0-1	1-1	0-1	0-2	1-0	0-2	0-1	1-1	1-0	0-3	*	2-0	1-0	2-1	1-1	2-1	1-0
15. Oldbury Res	0-0	0-4	0-1	0-3	0-1	1-1	1-1	3-0	0-3	1-1	1-4	0-1	4-0	0-0	*	0-3	0-3	2-1	2-2	3-2
16. Tipton	5-0	4-6	2-2	0-1	1-2	2-2	3-0	1-2	0-3	2-2	1-0	2-1	1-1	0-3	*	0-3	2-1	1-3	1-1	
17. Tividale	1-0	1-1	3-2	0-2	0-5	1-1	0-1	0-2	3-1	2-2	1-4	1-4	2-2	0-1	1-1	0-1	*	4-0	2-4	0-1
18. Wem Town	6-0	8-1	3-2	1-1	1-2	1-5	0-0	1-4	3-3	0-1	3-1	0-3	1-0	0-0	2-1	1-1	1-3	*	3-0	2-2
19. Wolves Cas.	2-1	2-2	0-0	0-2	0-2	0-1	0-1	3-0	3-1	2-3	1-3	1-0	3-2	1-0	0-0	2-2	1-1	2-2	*	
20. Wolves Utd	2-2	6-5	1-0	1-1	4-1	1-1	2-2	2-2	4-2	0-3	0-2	0-4	0-2	1-1	2-1	3-1	1-2	2-3	0-2	*

DIVISION TWO RESULT CHART 1991-92

HOME TEAM	1	2	3	4	5	6	7	8	9	10	11	12	13	14	15	16	17	18	19	20
1. A & Wilson	*	2-0	0-2	1-0	1-4	4-1	1-4	0-1	1-0	2-3	5-1	3-3	1-2	2-0	3-0	4-2	0-4	1-0	1-2	3-1
2. A'church Res	2-3	*	4-2	1-1	2-2	2-2	2-2	0-3	1-3	2-0	2-3	5-1	0-3	2-3	1-0	0-3	5-0	3-1	0-3	1-2
3. B'hth Motors	2-5	2-5	*	1-1	2-0	6-2	3-4	1-1	2-5	0-3	1-3	2-1	2-2	0-4	5-1	2-0	0-1	4-3	4-4	0-1
4. B Strollers	0-2	1-1	3-1	*	1-0	4-1	2-5	1-3	2-2	0-3	2-2	3-1	3-1	1-1	2-3	1-3	0-1	0-1	0-1	7-1
5. C'town Res	2-1	1-2	1-1	1-2	*	2-2	5-3	1-3	1-0	0-5	1-1	4-2	1-4	1-5	1-1	2-4	2-3	2-1	1-0	3-3
6. Cheslyn Hay	0-2	1-2	7-1	0-2	2-3	*	3-3	1-2	2-5	1-2	0-1	2-1	1-3	1-2	3-1	0-1	1-1	1-2	2-6	4-3
7. Cradley Res	1-3	1-3	0-2	4-1	1-3	3-3	*	0-1	1-4	0-5	2-1	1-1	1-1	1-2	2-0	1-1	0-5	4-1	0-6	4-2
8. Gornal Spts	1-0	0-0	4-0	5-3	6-0	0-0	4-1	*	1-0	2-1	1-0	3-0	3-1	0-1	4-3	3-1	5-1	6-1	1-1	2-0
9. H'wen H Res	1-1	0-4	1-2	2-3	1-3	5-0	3-1	0-0	*	0-5	2-1	2-0	1-1	0-1	2-1	3-2	1-2	1-2	3-0	3-4
10. K Chell	2-1	14-0	4-1	2-2	2-3	2-0	5-0	1-0	5-0	*	0-2	2-1	2-0	4-0	5-0	5-1	2-1	2-1	9-0	4-2
11. Lye T. Res	1-2	2-0	1-0	1-1	5-1	1-2	8-0	1-4	0-1	3-3	*	2-1	0-0	1-0	6-0	5-0	2-3	0-3	1-0	3-1
12. Malvern Res	3-1	1-1	3-0	1-4	3-2	0-0	2-3	1-1	1-2	0-1	1-1	*	1-2	1-2	5-1	2-1	2-1	2-1	6-1	
13. Manders	0-0	6-0	0-1	2-2	1-0	3-2	4-1	1-2	2-1	0-2	0-1	1-0	*	1-1	2-2	7-0	1-1	7-1	1-0	4-1
14. M & Butlers	1-1	1-2	4-1	3-2	4-0	1-1	0-3	0-0	0-0	2-0	4-3	2-2	0-1	*	8-2	1-4	0-2	12-0	6-1	9-1
15. Nun'ton Res	3-3	1-1	3-3	4-4	2-3	3-1	1-4	3-2	3-1	1-6	2-4	1-2	0-1	0-2	*	1-3	2-3	0-0	1-5	0-1
16. O'winford Res	1-1	6-0	2-0	1-7	0-2	4-2	2-2	1-2	1-0	2-3	1-2	3-2	1-0	0-1	4-0	*	1-8	13-0	2-0	5-2
17. Park Rangers	3-2	1-1	5-1	2-6	4-3	5-2	3-5	2-3	2-2	4-3	1-3	2-0	0-1	2-1	4-2	3-1	*	4-0	1-3	2-1
18. Rocester Res	0-3	3-2	1-3	5-2	3-1	3-5	2-2	1-1	0-4	0-6	1-1	0-2	1-3	2-5	2-1	4-1	2-1	*	0-5	1-1
19. Rushall Res	3-2	4-1	3-1	0-1	1-1	2-2	5-1	3-0	3-0	1-1	3-0	1-1	4-0	2-1	4-1	6-1	1-1	2-1	*	5-3
20. Wolves C. Res	0-7	0-2	1-4	2-4	2-0	0-2	3-3	0-6	4-2	4-4	0-2	3-2	0-1	1-6	2-0	2-0	1-2	2-3	0-0	*

Gresley Rovers 1, Chasetown 1 - Premier Division Cup First Round replay 8-10-91. Chasetown's Simon Hyden rises to head home a corner from John Rose and take the match into extra-time. Photo - Mick Poole.

YOUTH DIVISION RESULTS 1991/92

HOME TEAM	1	2	3	4	5	6	7	8	9	10
1. Boldmere SM Yth	*	0-0	1-2	3-3	1-0	0-1	0-2	4-1	0-1	3-1
2. Chasetown	1-5	*	0-4	1-3	2-1	1-1	3-1	0-1	2-0	1-4
3. Gresley Rvrs Yth	2-1	6-3	*	0-4	4-0	4-1	4-1	1-2	3-0	0-2
4. Halesowen T. Yth	2-1	5-0	3-3	*	2-0	4-4	8-0	3-2	2-0	3-1
5. Hinckley T. Yth	2-2	3-2	1-3	0-2	*	3-2	2-3	3-2	0-1	3-1
6. Lye Town Yth	2-2	3-1	1-1	4-3	1-2	*	1-1	1-0	1-2	4-0
7. Pelsall Villa Yth	1-1	2-0	0-3	0-4	0-3	2-3	*	1-1	4-2	1-1
8. Redditch Utd Yth	0-1	2-1	4-4	3-4	6-1	2-1	5-1	*	3-0	3-2
9. Rocester Yth	1-2	2-5	1-0	0-0	4-4	3-2	2-3	1-0	*	3-1
10. Wednesfield Yth	2-0	1-0	3-0	1-2	0-0	2-2	0-3	2-1	3-1	*

DIVISION ONE CUP 1991-92

First Round

W'hampton Casuals v Darlaston	0-1(28-1-91)	Donnington Wood v Wem Town	2-1(20-8-91)
Tipton Town v Moxley Rangers	0-2(21-8-91)	Knypersley Victoria v Tividale	2-1(19-10-91)

Second Round (28-8-91)

Ludlow Town v Darlaston	1-2	Oldbury United Reserves v Donnington Wood	3-1
Cannock Chase v Clancey Dudley	1-0	Broseley Ath. v Ettingshall	5-5,1-4(5-11-91)
Moxley Rangers v Hill Top Rangers	0-1	Gornal v Knypersley	1-1,(30-11-91),2-4(21-12-91)
Ilkeston Town v Great Wyrley	4-0	Wolverhampton Utd v Lichfield	2-2,0-2(2-9-91)

Quarter Finals (15-2-92)

Darlaston v Oldbury United Reserves	3-4	Knypersley v Ilkeston Town	1-1,1-5(27-2-92)
Cannock Chase v Hill Top Rangers	3-1	Ettingshall H.T. v Lichfield	3-2(22-2-92)

Semi-Finals (1st Leg 12-3-92, 2nd Leg 11-4-92)

Oldbury Utd Res v Cannock Chase	1-1,0-1	Ilkeston Town v Ettingshall	2-1(21-3-92),2-2(7-4-92)

Final *(at Paget Rangers FC, 5-5-92):* Cannock Chase 1, Ilkeston Town 4

DIVISION TWO CUP 1991-92

First Round (20-8-91)

Bloxwich Strollers v Malvern Town Res	2-1	Allbright & Wilson v Nuneaton B. Res	2-3(21-8-91)
Mitchells & Butlers v Cheslyn Hay	2-0	Rushall Olympic Reserves v Manders	1-0(22-8-91)

Second Round (28-8-91)

Alvechurch Reserves v Lye Town Reserves	3-0	Park R. v B'heath Mtrs	1-1,2-1(28-9-91 - tie B'hth)
K Chell v Mitchells & Butlers	3-5	O'ford Res v Nun'ton Res	1-1(25-9-91),4-1aet(22-10-91)
Rocester Reserves v Halesowen H. Res	1-2	W'ton Cas. Res v Chasetown Res	2-4(28-8-91)
Rushall O. Res v Cradley Town Reserves	3-2	Gornal Sports v Bloxwich Strollers	3-1

Quarter Finals (25-2-92)

Oldswinford Res v Blackheath Mtrs	1-0(27-11-91)	Chasetown Reserves v Alvechurch Reserves	1-5
H'owen Harriers Res v Rushall O. Res	0-2	Gornal Spts v M & B.	0-0(29-2-92),0-1(28-3-92)

Semi-Finals (1st Leg 18-3-92, 2nd Leg 15-4-92)

M & B v Rushall O. Res	3-3(4-4-92),1-2(14-4-92)	O'winford Res v A'church Res	2-0,0-3(A'church default)

Final *(at Halesowen Harriers FC, 4-5-92):* Oldswinford Reserves 2, Rushall Olympic Reserves 5

YOUTH DIVISION CUP 1991-92

First Round (12-9-91)

Chastown Yth v Pelsall Villa Yth	2-1	Gresley Rovers Yth v Rocester Yth	1-3(11-9-91)

Quarter Finals (23-10-91)

Redditch Utd Yth v Chasetown Yth	4-0	Wednesfield Yth v Rocester Yth	0-1
Hinckley Town Yth v Halesowen Town Yth	3-2	Lye T. Yth v Boldmere St Michaels Yth	2-1(21-10-91)

Semi-Finals (1st Leg 18-3-92, 2nd Leg 6-4-92)

Redditch Utd Yth v Rocester Yth	1-1,0-5(8-4-92)	Lye T. Yth v Hinckley T. Yth	3-0(9-3-92),2-1(6-4-92)

Final (15-4-92): Lye Town Youth 4, Rocester Youth 1

Park Rangers FC 1991-92. Photo - Chris Bedford.

PREMIER DIVISION CLUBS 1992-93

BLAKENALL

President: F Rowley   **Chairman:** P Laneston
Secretary: P Athersmith, 46 Blakenall Lane, Leamore, Walsall (0922 479709).
Manager: Andy Keeling   **Press Officer:** F Rowley (0384 408025).
Ground: Red Lion Ground, Somerfield Rd, Bloxwich, Walsall, West Mids (0922 405835).
Directions: M6 jct 10, follow signs for Walsall centre. At 1st lights turn left (about 200yds from Motorway junction) into Bloxwich Lane. Keep following this lane to the 'T' junction and turn right into Leamore Lane, at this island turn left into Somerfield Road. Ground is approx. 400yds on the right.
Seats: Nil   **Cover:** 400   **Capacity:** 2,000   **Floodlights:** Yes   **Founded:** 1946.
Colours: Blue & white stripes/blue/blue   **Change colours:** All red
Clubhouse: Yes   **Programme:** 16 pages 25p
Previous Leagues: Bloxwich Comb./ Staffs County/ Midland Comb. 60-79.
Clubhouse Honours: Midland Comb. 76-77, Walsall Snr Cup (6)

CHASETOWN

Chairman: G Rollins   **President:** A Scorey.
Secretary: J T Bacon, 67 Hill St., Chasetown, Walsall WS7 8XU (0543 672462).
Manager: Mervyn Rowe   **Coach:** John Newell
Newsline: 0891 664 382.   **Commercial Manager:** D M Shelton.
Ground: The Scholars, Church Street, Chasetown (0543 62222/684609).
Directions: Follow Motorways M5 or M6 and follow signs for A5. A5 to Whitehorse Road, Wharf Lane, Highfields Rd (B5011) into Church Street. Ground just beyond church.
Seats: 120   **Cover:** Yes   **Capacity:** 2,000   **Floodlights:** Yes   **Founded:** 1954.
Colours: All blue   **Change colours:** All red   **Clubhouse:** Own clubhouse, bar, kitchen.
Programme: 28 pages, 40p   **Programme Editor:** David Shelton
Record Gate: 400 v Halesowen, 1984.   **Previous Name:** Chase Terrace Old Scholars 54-72.
Previous Leagues: Cannock Yth/ Lichfield & District/ Staffs County.
Hons: West Mids Lg R-up 90-91 (Lg Cup 89-90 90-91, Div 1 77-78 (R-up 73-74 74-75 75-76 80-81 82-83), Div 2 R-up 87-88, Div 2 Cup R-up 86-87), Walsall Snr Cup 90-91, Staffs Snr Cup SF 91-92.

CRADLEY TOWN

Chairman: **Manager:** John Wilson
Secretary: A Hill, 51 Meres Road, Halesowen, West Midlands B63 2HL (0384 69585).
Ground: Beeches View Avenue, Cradley, Halesowen, Cradley Heath (0384 69904).
Directions: Halesowen-Stourbridge road, left at 'Round of Beef', right at 'Smiths Arms', at end of road left and 300yds on right.
Seats: 100   **Cover:** Yes   **Capacity:** 3,000   **Floodlights:** No   **Founded:** 1948.
Colours: All red   **Change colours:** Yellow/green/green   **Programme:** Yes
Previous Name: Albion Haden United   **Previous Lges:** K'minster/ W Mids Amtr/ Mid. Comb. 71-82.
Clubhouse: Bar and other facilities
Hons: Midland Comb. Div 2 72-73 (R-up 75-76 77-78, Presidents Cup 74-75 75-76).

HALESOWEN HARRIERS

Chairman: TBA   **Manager:** Derek Beasley   **Newsline:** 0898 644 252.
Secretary: B P Beasley, 69 Bower Lane, Quarry Bank, West Mids DY5 2DU (0384 62124).
Ground: Hayes Park, Park Rd, Colley Gate, Halesowen (021 6748).
Directions: On A458 Birmingham to Stourbridge Road (B'ham 10 miles, Stourbridge 4 miles). M5 Jct 3 (towards Kidderminster), right at 1st island (towards Dudley), turn left at island (towards Stourbridge), straight over next island then 3 miles to ground on left-hand side, 200yds past Park Lane.
Seats: **Cover:** Yes   **Capacity:** 5,000   **Floodlights:** No   **Founded:** 1961
Colours: White/white or navy/white   **Change colours:** Sky/sky or navy/sky.
Programme: 20 pages, 20p   **Programme Editor:** Roy Smith
Previous League: Festival (Sunday)   **Previous Ground:** Halesowen Town FC 70-84.
Clubhouse: New social club
Hons: West Mids Lg Div 2 84-85 (Div 2 Cup 84-85), Inter City Bowl 67-68 68-69, Festival Lg(5)(R-up(9)), FA Sunday Cup SF 79-80, Midland Sunday Cup, Birmingham Sunday Cup.

HINCKLEY ATHLETIC

Chairman: M Voce
Secretary: J Colver, 22 Begonia Drive, Burbage, Hinckley, Leics LE10 2SW (0455 230263).
Ground: Middlefield Lane, Hinckley. Leics (0455 613553).
Directions: A47 Coventry Road towards Hinckley. Keep on Inner Ring Road to lights at top of Upper Bond Street at junction of Ashby Road/Derby Road. Turn left and ground is at the bottom of Middlefield Lane. Two miles from Hinckley (BR).
Seats: 300   **Cover:** 1000   **Capacity:** 5,000   **Floodlights:** Yes   **Founded:** 1879
Club colours: Red/black/red   **Change colours:** White/red/white
Programme: Yes   **Programme Editor:** Andy Gibbs   **Previous Grnd:** Hollywell Lane (pre'40)
Previous Leagues: Birmingham Comb. 14-39 47-54/ West Mids (Reg.) 54-59/ Southern 63-64.
Previous Names: Hinckley AFC, Hinckley Town, Hinckley United.
Best FA Cup season: 2nd Rd Proper 54-55 (lost 1-2 at Rochdale), 62-63 (2-7 at Queens Pk Rgrs).
Record Gate: 5,410 v Nuneaton Borough, Birmingham Combination 26/12/49.
Players progressing to Football League: John Allen (Port Vale).
Clubhouse: New social club with lounge, games room, and concert room. Open each evening, Sunday lunch and matchdays.
Hons: Leics Snr Cup 1899-1900 00-01 09-10 82-83, Leics Snr Lg 1896-97 97-98 99-1900 08-09 09-10 13-14, Birmingham Comb. 23-24 26-27 (R-up 22-23), West Mids (Reg.) Lg R-up 82-83, Birmingham Snr Cup 54-55(jt with Brush Sports), Leics Challenge Cup 57-58 58-59 59-60 60-61 61-62 67-68.

ILKESTON TOWN

Chairman: J Raynor   **President:** R Lindsay   **Manager:** Bill Fossey
Secretary: A Cuthbert, 38 Teesdale Road, Long Eaton, Nottingham NG10 3PG (0602 731531).
Ground: New Manor Ground, Awsworth Rd, Ilkeston (0602 324094).   **Floodlights:** Yes
Directions: M42 to M1 jct 23A, continue on M1 to jct 26, exit left onto A610, take 1st exit signed Awsworth and
Ilkeston (A6096), continue thru Awsworth, right at top of hill into Newtons Lane - ground quarter mile on left before
canal bridge. Or, A38 to Derby centre, A52 for Nottm to M5 jct 25, then follow as abovefrom M1 jct 26.
Colours: Red/black/black   **Change colours:** White/black/white   **Founded:** 1945.
Programme: 24 pages, 50p   **Record Gate:** 9,800 v Rochdale, FA Cup 1st Rd 1951.
Previous Leagues: Midland 1894-1902 25-58 61-71 73-82/ Central Alliance 47-61/ Central Mids 82-90.
Best FA Cup season: 1st Rd 51-52 (lost 0-2 at home to Rochdale), 56-57 (1-5 at home to Blyth).
Hons: West Mids Lg Div 1 91-92 (Lg Cup 91-92), Midland Lg 67-68 (R-up 1898-99), Central All. 52-53 53-54 54-55
(R-up 47-48 55-56), Derbys Snr Cup 1894-95 95-96 96-97 97-98 1948-49 52-53 55-56 57-58 62-63 82-83.

LYE TOWN

Chairman: W Homer   **President:** G Ball   **Comm. Manager:** Terry Brumpton.
Secretary: Mrs A Ball, 79 Aretha Close, Crestwood Park, Kingswinford, West Mids DY6 8SW (0384 79038).
Manager: Ian Cole   **Asst Manager:** Ron Corbett   **Physio:** Harry Hill.
Ground: Stourbridge Road, Lye (0384 422672).
Directions: On A458 Birmingham-Stourbridge road about 400yds after lights/crossroads at Lye. From M5 jct 3
take road marked Kidderminster as far as lights at bottom of Hagley Hill, right at island, 3rd turn off at next island,
3rd turn off at crossroads/lights, left, ground about 400yds on left. Quarter mile from Lye (BR).
Seats: 100   **Cover:** 600   **Capacity:** 5,000   **Floodlights:** Yes   **Founded:** 1930.
Colours: White/red/red   **Change Colours:** All sky   **Nickname:** Flyers.
Programme: 28 pages, 40p   **Programme Editor:** Dave Lilley
Clubhouse: Yes (0384 822672).   **Previous Leagues:** Midland Combination 31-39.
Record Gate: 6,000 v Brierley Alliance.   **Hons:** West Mids Lg R-up 76-77 78-79 79-80 80-81 (Prem. Div Cup
75-76), Midland Comb. 35-36 (R-up 32-33 34-35 37-38), B'ham Snr Cup R-up 80-81.

OLDBURY UNITED

Chairman: Frank Cooper   **Sec:** M G Stanley, 32 Junction St., Oldbury, Warley, W Mids (021 559 3528).
Ground: The Cricketts, York Road, Rowley Rgis, Warley, West Midlands (021 559 5564).
Directions: M5 jct 2, A4034 towards Blackheath, 1 mile turn left into Pencricket Lane and York Road is first left.
One and a half miles from Sandwell & Dudley (BR). Bus 140 (ask for Whiteheath).
Seats: 100   **Cover:** 500   **Capacity:** 6,000   **Floodlights:** Yes   **Founded:** 1958
Colours: Blue (white trim)/blue/blue   **Change colours:** Grey/maroon/maroon   **Nickname:** Cricketts
Programme Editor: Frank Johnson   **Record Gate:** 2,200 v Walsall Wd, W'sall Snr Cup Final 1982.
Previous Name: Queens Colts   **Previous Lges:** Midland Comb. 76-82/ Southern 82-86.
Previous Ground: Oldbury Spts Centre.   **Players progressing to Football League:** C Gordon, L Conoway, J
Scott, R O'Kelly, G Nardiello, Dakin, T Reece.
Hons: Midland Comb. R-up 78-79 (Presidents 72-73(res), Div 3 R-up 82-83(res), Chal. Vase 82-83(res)), Walsall
Snr Cup 81-82, B'ham Snr Amtr Cup.

OLDWINSFORD F. & S. C.

Chairman: D N Rees   **President:** A G Bartram   **Manager:** S Hall
Secretary: D G Dew, 148 King William Street, Amblecote, Stourbridge (0384 376902).
Ground: The Dell Sports Stadium, Bryce Rd, Pensnett, Brierley Hill, West Mids (0384 77289).
Directions: At lights in the Brierley Hill High Street turn into Bank Street by Police Station. Proceed over bridge
into Pensnett Road, ground three quarters of a mile on left Paddy's Garage. Main entrance 120yds in Bryce Road.
Seats: 300   **Cover:** 300   **Capacity:** 5,000   **Floodlights:** Yes   **Founded:** 1955
Colours: Royal Blue & sky blue   **Change colours:** Yellow or white   **Clubhouse:** Yes
Programme Editor: Secretary   **Previous Leagues:** Kidderminster/ Staffs County.
Previous Grounds: Cottage Street, Brierley Hill/ South Road, Stourbridge.
Hons: West Mids Lg Prem. Div Cup R-up 84-85 (Div 1 80-81 (Div 1 Cup 80-81)).

PAGET RANGERS

Chairman: R R Ruddick   **President:** E Angelides
Secretary: D J Culling, 5 Deveril Grove, Sutton Coldfield, West Mids B76 8FR (021 626 5000 x2576).
Manager: Keith Shrimpton   **Commercial Manager:** Paul Vanes.
Ground: Springfield Road, Walmley, Sutton Coldfield (021 3151563).
Directions: From B'gham & Gravelly Hill I'change (M6 Jct 6) via A38 Tyburn Rd & B4148 Eachelhurst Rd, over
narrow rail bridge, Walmley Rd, thru village, 500yds on right Springfield Rd. Ground 50yds past church on right
before petrol station. 2 miles from Sutton Coldfield (BR). Bus 114 from B'ham, 71 114 & 165 from Sutton.
Seats: 300   **Covered:** 300   **Capacity:** 3,500   **Floodlights:** Yes   **Founded:** 1938
Colours: Gold/black/gold   **Change colours:** All red
Programme: 24 pages, 30p   **Programme Editor:** W Dudley
Clubhouse: 6 evenings/week & weekend lunchtimes. Regular weekend entertainment, plus darts, pool etc.
Previous Grnd: Pype Hayes Pk 38-46.   **Record Gate:** 2,000 v A Villa, F'light opening 1971.
Previous Lges: Birmingham Suburban/ Central Amtr/ Mids Comb. 50-81/ Southern 86-88.
Players progressing to Football League: John Gittens (Southampton for £10,000).
Hons: West Mids Lg R-up 91-92 (Lg Cup 91-92), Midland Comb.(6) 59-61 69-71 82-83 85-86 (R-up 77-78, Lg Cup
59-60 66-67, Div 1 Cup 70-71, Div 3 82-83(res)), B'ham Jnr Cup 51-52, Walsall Snr Cup 85-86.

PELSALL VILLA

Chairman: V Dolphin   **President:** B Hill
Secretary: Gareth Evans, 72 St Pauls Crescent, Pelsall, Walsall WS3 4ET (0922 693114).
Ground: The Bush Ground, Walsall Rd Pelsall, Walsall (0922 682018 or 692748 matchdays only).
Directions: M6 jct 7 marked A34 B'gham. Take A34 towards Walsall to 1st island, turn right (marked Ring Road),
cross two islands. At large island at bottom of hill take last exit marked Lichfield, up hill, cross next island to lights.
Continue to next set of lights and turn left (B4154 Pelsall). Go over railway bridge to Old Bush house on right (next
to Pelsall Cricket and Sports Club).
Seats: Yes   **Cover:** Yes   **Capacity:**   **Floodlights:** Yes   **Founded:** 1961.
Colours: Red & black stripes/black/black **Change colours:** Blue/yellow/white   **Programme:** Yes
Previous League: Staffs County.
Hons: West Mids Lg Div 2 Cup R-up 83-84, Wednesbury Charity Cup 73-74 (R-up 87-88), D Stanton Shield(2) 73-
75 (R-up 75-76), Sporting Star Cup 76-77, Rugeley Charity Cup 78-79, Bloxwich Charity Cup(2) 81-83.

ROCESTER

Chairman: Ian Cruddas   **Manager:** Frank Northwood.
Secretary: Gilbert Egerton, 23 Eaton Road, Rocester, Staffs ST14 5LL (0889 590101).
Ground: The Rivers Field, Mill Street, Rocester, Uttoxeter, Staffs (0889 590463).
Directions: M6 to Stafford, A518 to Uttoxeter. Signs to Alton Towers (B5030). Nearing Rocester, right opposite JCB complex, over bridge to T-Junct, Red Lion on left. Right into Mill St. Ground 500yds on left past cotton mill.
Seats: 200   **Cover:** 500   **Capacity:** 4,000   **Floodlights:** Yes   **Founded:** 1895
Colours: Amber/black/black   **Change colours:** All blue   **Nickname:** Romans
Programme: 36/40 pages, 50p   **Programme Editor:** Barry Smith (0889 563989).
Shop: Yes (souvenirs & programmes)   **Clubhouse:** Open every day except Thursday
Record Transfer Fee Paid: £1,000 for Paul Ede (from Burton Albion, September 1989).
Record Transfer Fee Received: £8,000 for Tony Hemmings (from Northwich Victoria, March 1991).
Players progressing to Football League: George Shepherd (Derby County), Mark Sale (Birmingham).
Record Gate: 1,026 v Halesowen Town, FA Vase 4th Rd January 1987 (at Leek Town FC).
Previous Lges: Ashbourne/ Leek & Moorland/ Cheadle & Dist./ Uttoxeter Amtr, Staffs Co. Nth/ Staffs Snr.
Hons: West Mids Lg R-up 89-90 (Div 1 87-88, Div 1 Cup 87-88), Staffs Snr Lg(2) 85-87, Staffs FA Vase 85-86 87-88.

RUSHALL OLYMPIC

Chairman: B Greenwood   **President:** J Harris   **Press Officer:** R Beech
Secretary: J Burks, 4 Bush Grove, Heath End, Pelsall, Walsall (0922 684519).
Ground: Dales Lane, off Daw End Lane, Rushall, Nr Walsall (0922 641021).
Directions: From Rushall centre (A461) take B7154 signed Aldridge. Approx. 1 mile on right, directly opposite Royal Oak Public House, in Daw End Lane. Ground on right. Two miles from Walsall (BR).
Seats: 250   **Cover:** 100   **Capacity:** 5,000   **Floodlights:** Yes   **Founded:** 1951
Colours: Old gold/black/black   **Change colours:** White/red/red   **Nickname:** Pics.
Programme: 10 pages, 20p   **Programme Editor:** R Beech
Clubhouse: Excellent bar/lounge, kitchen, adjoining large refreshment facilities
Prev. Grnds: Rowley Place 51-75/ Aston Univ. 76-79.   **Prev. Lges:** Walsall Amtr/ Staffs County.
Players progressing to Football League: Lee Sinnott (Watford), Lee Palin (Villa, Nottm F, Bradford).
Record Gate: 2,000 v Leeds United Old Boys, charity match 1982.   **Hons:** West Mids Lg Div 1 79-80.

STOURPORT SWIFTS

Chairman: Roy Crow   **President:**   **Manager:** Phil Mullen.
Secretary: John McDonald, 65 Princes Way, Stourport-on-Severn (0299 32088).
Ground: Walsh's Meadow, off Harold Davis Drive, Stourport-on-Severn (0299 35188).
Directions: Follow one-way system through Stourport sign posted Sports Centre. Go over River Severn Bridge, turn left into Harold Davies Drive. Ground is at rear of Sports Centre.
Seats: 250   **Cover:** Yes   **Capacity:** 2,000   **Floodlights:** Yes   **Founded:** 1882.
Cols: Black & gold stripes/black/black   **Change colours:** All Red   **Nickname:** Swifts.
Previous Leagues: Kidderminster/ Worcester/ Midland Combination.   **Programme:** 30p

WEDNESFIELD

Chairman: R Thomas   **Vice Chairman:** J Massey   **President:** L W Horton
Secretary: James Highfield, 6 Soberton Close, Wednesfield, West Mids WV11 2QX (0902 724771).
Manager: P Embrey   **Physio:** M Andrews
Coach: K Hall/ B Clarke   **Commercial Manager:** J Massey (0902 781819).
Ground: Cottage Ground, Amos Lane, Wednesfield, Wolverhampton (0902 735506).
Directions: From Wolverhampton on the B4124 Wednesfield Rd. Stay on road right through Wednesfield until island. Leave island at first exit (Wood End Rd), left after about 200yds into Amos Lane. Ground is on right, approx. 400yds along. Wolverhampton (3 miles).   **Prev. Lge:** Wolverhampton & Dist. Amtr.
Seats: 200   **Cover:** Yes   **Capacity:** 1,000   **Floodlights:** No   **Founded:** 1961.
Colours: Red & white stripes/black/black   **Change colours:** Green & yellow stripes/green/yellow
Programme: 40 pages, 40p   **Record Gate:** 480 v Burton Albion, FA Cup 1981.
Previous Ground: St Georges Pk 61-71   **Previous Name:** Wednesfield Social 61-89.
Clubhouse: Yes   **Hons:** West Mids Lg Div 1 76-77 (R-up 77-78).

WEST BROMWICH TOWN

Chairman: A Brown   **President:** R Langford   **Founded:** 1962
Secretary: Gareth Stephens, 7 New Street, Hill Top, West Bromwich, West Mids (021 5566235).
Ground & directions: As Willenhall Town FC (see below).   **Programme:** Yes
Colours: Yellow/Black/Yellow   **Change colours:** All blue   **Previous Name:** Millfields FC.

WESTFIELDS

Chairman: Ron Harris   **Vice Chairman:** Roy Williams   **President:** Dennis Hartland
Secretary: Andy Morris, 17 Fayre Oaks Green, Kings Acre, Hereford (0432 264711).
Manager: Phil Emery   **Coach:** Sean Edwards
Ground: Thorn Lighting, Holme Lacy Rd, Rotherwas, Hereford (0432 268131, club-410548).
Directions: Proceed 1 mile south of Hereford, turn left in Home Lacy Rd, proceed 1 mile to Thorn Lighting Rotherwas, ground on the right. Two miles from Hereford (BR).
Seats: 100   **Cover:** 200   **Capacity:** 2,000   **Floodlights:** Yes   **Founded:** 1966
Colours: All sky   **Change colours:** All white   **Previous Grounds:** Widemarsh Common 66-74.
Programme: 16 pages, 25p   **Programme Editor:** Andy Morris
Clubhouse: Thorn lighting on ground   **Record Gate:** 1,057 v Hereford Utd, t'monial 1980.
Hons: West Mids Lg Div 2 R-up 83-84 (Div 2 Cup 79-80), Herefordshire Snr Cup 91-92.

WILLENHALL TOWN

Chairman: J Williams   **Manager:** Campbell Chapman   **Comm. Mgr:** Dave Morgan.
Secretary: Malcolm Skitt c/o The club: Noose Lane, Willenhall, Willenhall (605132-club, 636586-off.).
Directions: Noose Lane is off the main A454 Walsall to Wolverhampton road 3 miles from jct 10 (M6). Two and a half miles from Wolverhampton (BR). Buses 525, 526, 529.
Seats: 220   **Cover:** 500   **Capacity:** 4,000   **Floodlights:** Yes   **Founded:** 1953
Colours: All red   **Change colours:** White/blue/blue   **Programme:** 24 pages, 40p, **Editor:** J Davenport
Record Gate: 3,454 v Crewe Alexandra, FA Cup 1st Rd 1981.   **Nickname:** Reds.
Clubhouse: Clubhouse and ground combined, open 7 nights weekly and Sat/Sun lunchtimes.
Prev. Lges: W Mids 75-82/ Southern 82-91.   **Prev. Grnds:** Memorial Pk 55-74/ Marstons Spts Grd 74-75.
Hons: FA Vase R-up 80-81, West Mids Lg 78-79 (Prem. Div Cup 79-80, Div 1 Cup 76-77).

Lye Town FC 1991-92. Photo - Marshall's Sports Service, Birmingham.

Westfields miss with a freekick as they lose 0-1 at Wolverhampton Casuals in the FA Vase. Photo - Paul Williamson.

Willenhall Town FC 1991-92. Photo - Marshall's Sports Service, Birmingham.

DIVISION ONE CLUBS 1992-93

CANNOCK CHASE

Chairman: B Farmer   **President:** S Osborn   **Secretary:** Mark Clementson, c/o the club
Ground: West Cannock Spts Centre, Bradbury Lane, Hednesford WS12 4EP (0543 422141).
Directions: M6 jct 11, A460 thru Cannock & Hednesford, left at sign for Pye Green, ground 1 mile up hill on left.
Seats: None   **Cover:** 50   **Capacity:** 2,000   **Floodlights:** No   **Founded:** 1968.
Colours: White/black/red   **Change Colours:** Red or Yellow/red/black
Programme: 36 pages, 30p   **Programme Editor:** M Clementson/ S Pettit.
Hons: W Mids Lg Div 1 Cup R-up 91-92. **Prev. Leagues:** Cannock Chase/ Mid Staffs/ Staffs Co.

DARLASTON

Chairman: A Schofield   **Ground:** City Ground, Waverley Rd, Darlaston (021 5264423).
Secretary: Peter Evans, 8 Chandlers Close, Pendeford Park, Wolverhampton (0902 781996).
Directions: M6 Jct 10, onto A454 towards Willenhall, left at lights outside 'Lane Arms' into Bentley Road North, follow this down hill and over the railway and canal bridges to traffic lights. Cross over the lights into Richards Street and along into Victoria Rd, 1st right into Slater Street and ground on left.
Seats: Yes   **Cover:** Yes   **Programme:** Yes   **Clubhouse:** Yes   **Floodlights:** No
Colours: Blue & white hoops/blue/blue   **Change colours:** All yellow   **Founded:** 1874.
Previous Leagues: Birmingham Jnr pre-1908/ Birmingham Combination 08-11 28-54/ West Mids 11-28.
Hons: W Mids Lg Div 1 R-up 91-92, B'ham Snr Cup 72-73, B'ham Jnr Lg 07-08, B'ham Comb. 10-11 37-38 45-46.

DONNINGTON WOOD

Chairman: D Roberts   **Manager:** P Woods
Secretary: G Vater, 33 Sunbury Drive, Trench, Telford, Salop TF2 7EA (0952 612273).
Ground: Duke Street Playing Fields, St Georges, Telford.
Directions: M54 jct 4 (Telford East). From island take B5060 Priorslee Rd, follow to r'bout junction with A5. Left, follow road to next island, right B5061 to Wellington, 2nd right - St Georges and continue along Stafford Street, to mini island, straight over into Gower Street, second right Duke Street, 100yds to car park. Take lane on far side of car park down to ground.
Seats: No   **Cover:** Yes   **Capacity:**   **Floodlights:** No   **Founded:** 1910.
Colours: White (green trim)/green/green   **Change colours:** All blue.
Programme: Yes (Editor - B Harvey 0952 583002)   **Hons:** West Mids Lg Div 1 R-up 76-77.

ETTINGSHALL HOLY TRINITY

Chairman: J Humphreys   **President:** D Gadd   **Founded:** 1920.
Secretary: G Mills, 27 Ashen Close, Sedgley, Dudley, West Mids DY3 3UZ (0902 662222).
Ground: Aldersley Stadium, Aldersley Rd, Tettenhall, Wolverhampton (0902 662222).
Directions: From central Wolverhampton take A41 (Tettenhall Rd) for just over a mile, right into Lower Str., right into Aldersley Rd, ground on right.
Colours: Green & white stripes/green/green   **Change colours:** Red/Blue/Red
Previous League: Staffs County (South).   **Programme:** Yes
Hons: West Mids Lg Div 1 Cup R-up 85-86 (Div 2 R-up 84-85)

GORNAL ATHLETIC

Chairman: Ken Taylor   **Manager:** John Gwinnell
Secretary: John Gwinnell, 34/36 Hainge Road, Tividale, Warley B69 2PD (0384 257157).
Ground: Garden Walk Stadium, Lower Gornal, Dudley, West Midlands (0384 52285).
Directions: From Dudley take A459 to Sedgley past the Burton Rd Hospital. 1st on left at the Green Dragon public house on the B4175 (Jews Lane). Follow the road until you come to the Old Bull's Head, turn left into Rednall Road, 2nd left to Garden Walk.
Seats: None   **Cover:** 500   **Capacity:** 3,000   **Floodlights:** No   **Founded:** 1945.
Colours: Yellow/green/yellow   **Change colours:** Green & White stripes/black/black
Previous Name: Lower Gornal Ath.   **Previous Lge:** Midland Comb. 51-63   **Nickname:** Peacocks
Hons: West Mids Lg Div 1 R-up 83-84.

GORNAL SPORTS

Secretary: Stephen Parsonage, 16 Stanton Avenue, Woodsetton, Derby DY1 3RR (0902 676598).
Ground & Directions: Gornal Athletic FC (see above).   **Founded:** 1979.
Colours: All red   **Change colours:** White/black/black   **Hons:** W Mids Lg Div 2 R-up 91-92.

GREAT WYRLEY

Chairman: F Titley   **Manager:** F Dinham
Secretary: D Catchpole, 3 Briar Close, Pye Green, Hednesford, Cannock, Staffs WS12 4EY (0543 425883).
Ground: Hazelbrook Ground, Hazel Lane, Gt Wyrley (0922 410366).   **Clubhouse:** Yes
Directions: A34 thru Gt Wyrley until you get to Star Public House, left into Hazel Lane. Ground is on the left. **N.B.** Please park on tarmac road at side of ground.
Seats: No   **Cover:** Yes   **Floodlights:** No   **Programme:** Yes   **Founded:** 1960.
Colours: Red/black/black   **Change Colours:** All blue   **Hons:** W Mids Lg Div 2 82-83.

HILL TOP RANGERS

Chairman: Mr Scott **Ground & Directions:** Darlaston FC (see above).   **Founded:** 1980.
Secretary: Mrs A Scott, 46 James Watt St., Hill Top, West Bromwich B71 2AJ (021 556 3597).
Colours: Yellow/black/yellow   **Change Colours:** Red/navy/red   **Programme:** Yes

KNYPERSLEY VICTORIA

Secretary: P H Freeman, 30 Caton Crescent, Milton, Stoke-on-Trent ST6 8XQ (0782 543123).
Ground: Tunstall Road, Knypersley, Stoke-on-Trent, (0782 522737/ 513304).
Directions: M6 Jct 15 join A500, 4th exit, pick up A527, follow to Tunstall, on exit town centre, right into Furlong Road. At bottom rejoin A527 and continue to top of rise. Straight across at junction on A527 through Brindley Ford on to Biddulph. Ground is situated on right after Mill Hayes Sports Ground (formerly Cowlinshaw Walker).
Seats: Nil   **Cover:** 100   **Capacity:** 5,000   **Floodlights:** NO   **Founded:** 1969.
Colours: Maroon/maroon/sky   **Change Colours:** Blue/Maroon/Light Blue
Previous League: Staffs Snr (pre-1991).   **Record Gate:** 1,100 v Pt Vale, friendly '89.
Programme: 20 pages, 50p.   **Editor:** Richard Baskeyfield (S-o-T 515368).

LICHFIELD

Chairman: C Clarke **Ground:** Shortbutts Lane, Lichfield, Staffs (0543 262246).
Secretary: M Cohen, 5 Mesnes Green, Lichfield, Staffs WS14 9AB (0543 255497).
Directions: From A5 proceed to island at A5127 Birmingham Rd, right into Shortbuts Lane, ground on left approx.
300 yds after railway bridge.
Seats: No **Cover:** Yes **Floodlights:** No **Clubhouse:** Yes **Founded:** 1966.
Colours: All royal blue **Change colours:** All red **Programme:** Yes
Hons: Walsall Chal. Cup 66-67, Lichfield Charity Cup.

LUDLOW TOWN

Chairman: A Cade **Manager:** Steve Mulliner **Founded:** 1890.
Secretary: S Mulliner, 17 Henley Orchards, Ludlow, Shropshire (0584 876543).
Ground: The Riddings, Riddings Road, Ludlow, Shropshire (0584 875103).
Directions: From Kidderminster road A422; straight over r'bout into Henley Rd, 2nd left into Sandpits Rd, follow
road for a quarter mile until road bears round to the left into Ridding Road. Take 1st right to ground.
Seats: No **Cover:** 150 **Floodlights:** Yes **Clubhouse:** Yes **Programme:** No
Cols: Red (white pin stripes)/black/black (red tops) **Change colours:** Royal blue/white/royal
Previous League: Kidderminster. **Hons:** Wes Mids Lg Div 1 Cup 90-91, Presteigne-Otway Cup 90-91.

MALVERN TOWN

Chairman: R C Tandy **President:** R H Mann **Manager:** Martyn Day
Secretary: G F Knapper, 27 Alexandra Lane, Malvern, Worcs WR14 1JF (0684 574861).
Ground: Langland Stadium, Langland Avenue, Malvern, Worcs (0684 574068).
Directions: From Worcester take main road to Malvern. When reaching Malvern turn left at 1st lights into
Pickersleigh Ave., follow to Langland Arms Pub on left, left into Madresfield Rd, 2nd left into Langland Ave., ground
100yds on right. 1 mile from Malvern (BR).
Seats: 140 **Cover:** 310 **Capacity:** 4,000 **Floodlights:** Yes **Founded:** 1947.
Colours: Claret & blue/white/sky **Change colours:** White/black/claret.
Prog: 12 pages 20p (special matches) **Programme Editor:** Dave Liley
Clubhouse: 2 bars, large dance area **Previous League:** Midland Comb. 55-79.
Hons: Worcester/ Midland Comb. 55-56. **Record Gate:** 1,221 v Worcester, FA Cup

MOXLEY RANGERS

Chairman: C Aldritt. **Sec:** I Yorke, 14 Norbury Rd, Bilston, W Mids WV14 7AD (0902 459089 - mess.).
Ground: Darlaston Community Sports & Social Club, Hall Street, Darlaston (021 526 5217).
Directions: M6 jct 10, A454 Wolverhampton Rd towards Bilston, approx. 2 miles to island, round island towards
Bilston, 1st left into Darlaston Lane, over canal bridge, 2nd left into Hall Str., ground 50yds on right.
Colours: All red **Change colours:** All green **Clubhouse:** Yes **Founded:** 1966.

OLDBURY UTD RES. **Colours:** Maroon & orange/orange/maroon *(Other details as page 543)*

TIPTON TOWN

President: W Powell **Chairman:** H C Hackett **Manager:** Terry Jones
Secretary: John A Cross, 1 Moreton Close, Tipton DY4 0DG (021 556 3566).
Ground: Tipton Recreation & Community Centre, Wednesbury Oak Rd, Tipton (021 556 5067/ 502 5534).
Directions: Midway between Dudley & Wednesbury on 245 bus route, ground by ASDA superstore.
Seats: **Covered:** 200 **Capacity:** 1,000 **Floodlights:** No **Formed:** 1948
Cols: Black & white stripes/black/red **Change colours:** All blue **Programme:** Yes
Record Gate: 485 v H'owen T., 1985. **Clubhouse:** Bar, lounge, large concert room
Hons: W Mids Lg Div 1 83-84 (R-up 76-77, Div 1 Cup 83-84)

TIVIDALE

Chairman: G Lodge **President:** P Archer MP
Secretary: D Aston, 18 Hollies Rd, Tividale B69 1SX.
Ground: The Beeches, Packwood Rd, Tividale, Warley, West Midlands (0384 211743).
Directions: Dudley Port Station to Burnt tree, left towards Birmingham, ground 1 mile on right. Or, M5 jct 2, right
towards Wolverhampton - ground 2 miles on left.
Seats: 100 **Cover:** 776 **Capacity:** 3,000 **Floodlights:** No **Founded:** 1957
Colours: Yellow/yellow/yellow or red **Change colours:** Red/white/red **Nickname:** 'Dale'
Programme: 24 pages, 30p **Programme Editor:** Steve Pettit
Previous Ground: City Road. **Record Gate:** 2,400 v Telford, FA Cup.
Clubhouse: 7 nights a week, Sat/Sun lunch **Players progressing to Football League:** G Hughes.
Hons: W Mids Lg Prem. Div Cup 76-77 (Div 1 Cup 72-73).

WEM TOWN

Chairman: G Sage **Ground:** Bowensfield, Wem, Salop (0939 33287).
Secretary: Cyril Pritchard, 2 Hillside, Prees Green, Whitchurch, Salop SY13 2EB (0948 840785).
Directions: M54 jct A42 for Newport and Whitchurch, in Newport take the B5062 to High Ercall, then B5063 to
Shawbury and Wem. Entering Wem carry on to r'way bridge to T-junction, right under r'way bridge. Continue to T-
junction by church, right then left turning for Whitchurch opposite the White Lion, continue for a quarter mile and
turn left at the Hawkestone Pub into Pyms Rd; ground 2nd left.
Seats: No **Cover:** Yes **Floodlights:** No **Clubhouse:** No **Founded:** 1921.
Colours: All sky **Change colours:** White/black/red & black **Programme:**

WOLVERHAMPTON CASUALS

Chairman: G Jones **President:** Clive Hammond **Manager:** Horace Crutchley
Secretary: Michael J Green, 63 St Philip's Ave., Pennfields, Wolverhampton WV3 7GD (0902 333677).
Ground: Brinsford Lane, Coven, Wolverhampton (0902 782314).
Directions: Onto M54 jct 2 turn right (A449 to Stafford). Ground half a mile, turn right into
Brinsford Lane. 2 miles from Billbrooke (BR). Stafford-Wolverhampton buses pass ground.
Seats: 50 **Cover:** 50 **Capacity:** 2,000 **Floodlights:** No **Founded:** 1896
Colours: Green/white/green **Change colours:** White/black/white
Programme: 28 pages, 30p **Programme Editor:** G Smith
Previous Name: Staffs Casuals (pre-1981) **Previous Ground:** Aldersley Stadium.
Clubhouse: Bar and snacks, open Tues, Wed, Thurs, Sat, Sun & alternative Mon.
Players progressing to Football League: David Heywood (Wolves).
Prev. Lges: B'gham AFA, W'hampton Amtr **Hons:** W Mids Lg Div 1 R-up(3) 85-88 (Div 1 Cup 85-86).

WOLVERHAMPTON UNITED

Chairman: T Pritchard **Grnd:** Prestwood Rd Spts Centre, Prestwood Rd West, Wednesfield (0902 730881).
Secretary: C Dulstone, 34 Broadway, Finchfield, Wolverhampton WV3 9HW (0902 753644).
Directions: Situated between Nos. 44 and 46 Prestwood Rd West, approached by way of a drive between the two houses. From Wolverhampton centre Ring Road, follow round to Stafford Str., into Cannock Rd (A460), bear into Victoria Road/Thorneycroft Lane/Prestwood Lane. Ground on right.
Seats: 200 **Cover:** Yes **Programme:** Yes **Clubhouse:** Yes **Founded:** 1976.
Colours: Old gold/black/gold **Change colours:** Red & black/Black/Red
Hons: West Mids Lg Div 1 76-77 (R-up 81-82).

SECOND DIVISION CLUBS 1992-93

ALBRIGHT & WILSON

Secretary: Stephen Smith, 68 Forest Road, Oldbury, Warley B68 0EF (021 421 3211).
Ground & Directions: Tat Bank, Oldbury, Warley (021 552 1048). A4034 Oldbury Road from M5 jct 2; right at island along A457 Smethwick Road, second right into Stone Street and continue to Tat Bank.
Colours: All sky **Change colours:** Gold/black/black **Founded:** 1935.

BLACKHEATH ELECTRODRIVES

Secretary: Tito Martire, 10 Marshwood Croft, Halesowen B62 0EY (021 422 3449).
Ground & Directions: Cakemore Road, Rowley Regis, Warley (021 559 1500). A4123 towards B'ham from M5 jct 2, right at 'Hen & Chickens' (B4169) - ground half mile on left 100 yds before works entrance in Cakemore Rd.
Colours: All red **Change colours:** White (red trim)/blue/blue **Founded:** 1920

BLOXWICH STROLLERS

Secretary: George A Llewellyn, 7 Birchover Road, Walsall WS2 8TU (0922 614595). **Manager:** L Taylor.
Ground & Directions: Blakenall FC (see page 542). **Previous Name:** Little Bloxwich Strollers
Colours: White/red/red **Change colours:** All yellow **Programme:** Yes
Previous Leagues: B'ham Comb 13-32/ W Mids 52-55/ Midland Comb.
Previous Ground: T P Riley Community Centre, Lichfield Rd.
Hons: B'ham Comb. 24-25 (R-up 22-23), Staffs Co. Lg Sth, Edge Cup, Lg Shield 84-85.

CHASETOWN RESERVES (See page 542 for full club details)

CHESLYN HAY

Secretary: I J Osborne, 16 Littlewood Lane, Cheslyn Hay, Walsall WS6 7EJ (0922 414755).
Ground & Directions: Hazel Stadium, Hazel Lane, Wyrley, Walsall (0922 410366). Situated 1 mile from A5/A34 junction coming from Cannock; look for 'Star' pub.
Colours: Royal & white hoops/royal/royal **Change:** Scarlet & black stripes/black/black
Programme: Yes **Founded:** 1984.

CLANCEY DUDLEY

Secretary: Wesley Mole, Orchard Cottage, Blakedown, Nr Kidderminster (0562 824435).
Ground & Directions: As Dudley Town FC (see page 494). Club: Clanceys, Belle Vale, H'owen (0384 636131).
Colours: Red/white/black or white **Change colours:** Blue/white/blue **Founded:** 1971.

CRADLEY TOWN RES., HALESOWEN HARRIERS RES. (See page 542 for details)
HINCKLEY ATH. RES (See page 542), LYE TOWN RES. (See page 543 for details).

MANDERS

Secretary: Barry Hall, 10 Miles Meadow Close, New Invention, Willenhall WV12 5YE (0922 409017).
Ground & Directions: Wednesfield FC (see page 496) **Previous League:** Wolverhampton Works.
Colours: White/red/white **Change colours:** Red/black/red **Reformed:** 1935.
Honours: JW Hunt Cup(3), Wolverhampton Charity Cup(3).

MITCHELLS & BUTLERS

Secretary: K R Burford, 141 Cape Hill, Smethwick B66 4SH (021 565 2143).
Ground & Directions: City Road, Edgbaston, Birmingham (021 420 1576/429 2469(club)). A4252 towards Smethwick from M5 jct 1, left at 2nd island onto A457, after 3rd set of lights 1st right into Shenstone Road, right at 'T' junction into City Road - ground entrance 100 yds on left.
Colours: Sky/navy/blue **Change colours:** All red **Founded:** 1876

OLDSWINFORD RESERVES (See page 543 for full club details)

PARK RANGERS

Manager: T Jones
Secretary: Peter Worwood, 3 Speedwell Close, Aldridge, West Mids WS9 0DL (0922 56385).
Ground & Directions: Tividale Recreation & Community Centre, Lower City Road, Tividale, Warley, West Mids (021 544 8332). A4123 towards Dudley from M5 jct 2; Lower City Road is on right opposite 'Huntsman' pub and ground is signposted.
Colours: All red **Change:** Yellow/black/black **Founded:** 1968.
Previous League: Staffs County (South) until 1991.

ROCESTER RESERVES, RUSHALL OLYMPIC RESERVES (See page 544 for club details)
TIVIDALE RESERVES, WOLVERHAMPTON CASUALS RESERVES (See page 547).

SHROPSHIRE COUNTY LEAGUE 1991-92

Perkins Prem Div	P	W	D	L	F	A	PTS
Little Drayton	22	16	2	4	61	33	34
Shifnal Town	22	15	4	3	51	25	34
Morda United Res	22	14	1	7	55	34	29
Wellingtom Amtrs	22	13	1	8	48	25	27
Meole Brace	22	12	3	7	45	36	27
Snailbeach	22	8	4	10	43	43	20
Albrighton	22	8	4	10	40	44	20
Shrewsbury NH	22	6	4	12	37	55	16
Telford Jnrs	22	7	2	13	28	47	16
Admaston	22	7	1	14	35	50	15
Ellesmere	22	6	2	14	24	49	14
Oakengates Town	22	6	0	16	29	55	12

Charles Clark Div.1	P	W	D	L	F	A	PTS
Tibberton	20	14	1	5	72	33	29
H. Hill WH	20	13	2	5	50	24	28
St Georges	20	12	2	6	48	20	26
Belle Vue	20	11	4	5	42	22	26
St Martins	20	12	2	6	39	31	26
W. Rhyn Utd	20	10	3	7	56	39	23
Westn United	20	7	2	11	32	38	16
Newport	20	4	6	10	40	41	14
Wern Town Res	20	5	4	11	22	68	14
Church Stretton	20	5	2	13	29	51	12
Broseley 'C'	20	2	2	16	22	83	6

STAFFS COUNTY LEAGUE (SOUTH) 1991-92

Premier Division	P	W	D	L	F	A	PTS
Bilston C. Coll.	22	16	5	1	85	22	37
Toll End Wesley	22	14	5	3	77	34	33
Sikh Hunters	22	14	4	4	73	38	32
Lichfield Res	22	12	4	6	41	36	28
Walsall M.A.	22	11	5	6	56	38	27
Hawkins Spts	22	9	6	7	39	41	24
Brereton Social	22	8	5	9	48	56	21
Tipton Sports	22	5	5	12	36	53	15
AFC Thatch	22	6	3	13	34	62	15
GEC Stafford	22	4	5	13	28	52	12
Tipton T. Res	22	5	2	15	34	61	12
Penkridge Town	22	2	3	17	22	64	7

Lge Shield Cup Final: Walsall MA 2, Brownhill T. 1

Division One	P	W	D	L	F	A	PTS
Cannock Town	18	12	3	3	54	22	27
Brownhills Town	18	12	2	4	37	16	26
Walsall Wd Res	18	12	0	6	43	24	22
Rugeley Ath.	18	7	6	5	28	20	20
Mahal	18	9	1	8	38	38	19
Moxley Rgrs Res	18	7	3	8	29	22	17
Highfield Social	18	6	3	9	23	50	15
West Bromwich BH	18	6	1	11	23	41	13
M & Butlers Res	18	3	4	11	23	37	10
Toll End Wes. Res	18	3	3	12	19	47	9

Rugeley Moderation - record expunged.

Premier Trophy Final: Hawkins Spts 2, Lichfield Res 1
Edge Cup Final: Toll End Wesley Res 2, Mahal 0

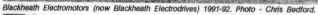

Blackheath Electromotors (now Blackheath Electrodrives) 1991-92. Photo - Chris Bedford.

Ludlow Town FC, pictured before a home Presteigne-Otway Cup tie. Photo - James Wright.

Sandwell Borough. Back Row (L/R): Steve Taylor, Bob Green, Anthony Belcher, Stuart Penrose, Anthony Davies, Rob Blakeney, Brian Carmichael, Richard Lowe, Scott Bamford, John Pearson. Front: Neil Mahoney, Jason Rhodes, Paul Brown, Alan Grainger, Paul Clark, Kevin Noakes. Photo - Kerry Miller.

West Midlands Police. Back Row (L/R): Dave Taylor (Secretary), John Southall, John Hunter (Manager), Gary Ingram, Robert Bradford, Graham Hussey, Frank Kiernan, Darren Carmell, Gary Davison, Matthew Wearing, Adam West, Steve Smith, Russell Draycott (Physio). Front: Brian Dorrian (Asst Manager), Steve Hopcroft, Darren Powney, Peter Grimshaw, David Scriven (Capt), Noel McMenamin, Sean Small, Colin Brooks (Manager), Brian Nunn (Deputy Secretary), Neil Bradley. Photo - Dave West.

Mile Oak Rovers & Youth FC 1991-92. Photo - Paul Barber.

ANSELLS MIDLAND COMBINATION

President: Mr P Fellows.
Chairman: L Wathen.
Vice Chairman: W G Eastwood.
Secretary/Treasurer: L W James,
175 Barnett Lane, Kingswinford DY6 9QA. Tel: 0384 273459.

ARMITAGE PIPPED IN THE RUN-IN

The race for the Premier Division title saw Evesham United prove their undoubted quality by winning their games in hand to clinch the title in their penultimate game. An excellent run to the last eight of the FA Vase kept things bubbling along nicely. They then cpmpleted a memorable double by getting the better of Studley in the Challenge Cup final, but the biggest prize of all came when they were accepted into the Beazer Homes League. Runners-up Armitage led the table for much of the season, and became the only team to complete the double over Evesham. By way of consolation, they did lift the Walsall Senior Cup beating Combination newcomers, Meir KA, in the final. Under new boss Gary Haynes, they will again be the team to beat next season. West Mids Police also had a memorable season, finishing third, reaching the Quarter Finals of the FA Vase, and winning the Worcestershire Senior Urn with a convincing win over Stourport and the National Police Cup.

Just six points separated the top four in Division One. Studley BKL, the success story of the season, finally clinched the title on the final day with a single goal win at Wigston Fields having stuttered for the previous few games. In a memorable season for the Bees, they also finished as runners-up in the Challenge Cup and the Presidents Cup, but were victorious in the Smedley Crooke Cup. Badsey Rangers were newly promoted at the start of the season and will be disappointed to end as runners-up having led for a long while, but overall the players have done Alex Ogg proud in their first season at the higher level. Wellesbourne looked a good bet for the title at one stage, but a poor final run saw them finish fourth. Consolation for Terry Hunt's men came when they lifted the Presidents Cup beating Studley 2-1. West Heath United could have nicked runners-up spot on the final day, but lost to Wilmcote which summed things up for them; their form against lower sides cost them dear.

In Division Two, unlike the past couple of seasons when just one or two teams have dominated, at least half a dozen clubs jostled for promotion spots. As well as the five (Marston Green, Hams Hall, Kenilworth, Sherwood and Thimblemill) who slugged out a remarkable last six weeks, others such as Monica Star, Emerald Social and Pershore Reserves hovered around the top four without actually breaking away. The real bouquet must go to Ray South's Marston Green who lost just once in 38 outings and picked up the Vase beating Thimblemill 2-1 at Boldmere. Their incredible run began at Xmas 1990 and now adds up to only three defeats in their past 55 Division Two matches.

Manager Dave Clements, General Manager Micky Brennan, and the Evesham players after picking up the Influence Combination championship shield. Photo - Marshalls Sports Service, Birmingham.

The above review was compiled using information from the **ANSELLS FOOTBALL COMBINATION MONTHLY MAGAZINE**. This superb publication provides comprehensive coverage of the competition, and details can be obtained from Editor Steve Davies at 3 Sycamore Close, Linton, Swadlincote, Derbys DE12 6PS (0283 760104).

LEAGUE TABLES 1991-92

Premier Division	P	W	D	L	F	A	PTS
Evesham United	40	28	7	5	76	31	91
Armitage '90	40	27	7	6	84	28	88
West Mids Police	40	24	8	8	86	44	80
Highgate Utd	40	22	11	7	71	34	77
Sandwell Borough	40	21	8	11	81	45	71
Pershore T. '88	40	19	11	10	76	41	68
Walsall Wood	40	18	13	9	66	42	67
Stapenhill	40	18	9	13	83	67	63
Boldmere St M.	40	17	9	14	69	52	60
Bolehall Swifts	40	15	14	11	59	47	59
Northfield Town	40	14	15	11	48	54	57
Coleshill Town	40	12	15	13	46	48	51
Alcester Town	40	11	9	20	53	74	42
Stratford Town	40	11	8	21	47	64	41
Chelmsley Town	40	12	5	23	61	111	41
Knowle	40	10	9	21	59	77	39
Barlstone St G.	40	10	9	21	39	78	39
Kings Heath	40	10	8	22	45	68	38
Hinckley	40	10	8	22	49	79	38
Bloxnorth Town	40	9	8	23	48	83	35
Mile Oak Rvys & Yth	40	3	7	30	35	114	16

TOP SCORERS: Philip Haywood (Walsall Wd) 33, Richard Lowe (Sandwell) 30, Richard Landon (Stratford) 30.

Division Two	P	W	D	L	F	A	PTS
Marston Green	38	24	13	1	87	34	85
Hams Hall	38	24	7	7	96	42	79
Kenilworth Rgrs	38	23	8	7	82	59	77
Sherwood Celtic	38	22	8	8	93	42	74
Thimblemill REC	38	20	9	9	107	62	69
Monica Star	38	17	9	12	71	51	60
Pershore '88 Res	38	18	6	14	71	57	60
Enville Ath.	38	16	7	15	60	56	55
Emerald Social	38	14	10	14	76	83	52
Shirley Town	38	13	11	14	64	56	50
Wellesbourne Res	38	14	8	16	67	67	50
Swift P.P.	38	14	8	16	56	66	50
Coleshill T. Res	38	13	9	16	60	65	48
Earlswood Town	38	12	11	15	49	65	47
Wythall	38	10	11	17	60	75	41
Archdales '73	38	11	6	21	68	88	39
Wigston Fields Res	38	8	12	18	49	93	36
Barlstone SG Res	38	8	6	24	50	91	30
Fairfield Villa	38	9	3	26	37	85	30
Dudley Spts Res	38	7	4	27	46	112	*22
* - 3 pts deducted

TOP SCORERS: Stephen Johnson (Kenilworth) 34, David Stokes (Monica Star) 34, David Keen (Marston Green) 30.

Division One	P	W	D	L	F	A	PTS
Studley B.K.L.	36	22	10	4	68	35	76
Badsey Rangers	36	22	7	7	78	37	73
Wellesbourne	36	21	8	7	76	41	71
West Heath Utd	36	21	7	8	77	37	70
Dudley Sports	36	18	8	10	57	46	62
Becketts Sporting	36	15	12	9	67	44	57
Southam United	36	13	12	11	52	50	51
Solihull B. Res	36	14	7	15	65	66	49
Kings Norton Ex-S.	36	13	9	14	55	56	48
Handrahan Timbers	36	11	14	11	45	38	47
Wigston Fields	36	12	10	14	47	45	46
Polesworth N.W.	36	13	6	17	54	65	45
Triplex	36	11	10	15	50	59	43
Upton Town	36	12	6	18	49	51	42
Wilmcote	36	11	4	21	53	64	37
W Mids Fire Service	36	8	12	16	44	61	36
Ledbury Town '84	36	10	5	21	41	91	35
Stapenhill Res.	36	7	8	21	60	106	29
Kings Hth Res.	36	5	11	20	34	80	26

TOP SCORERS: Alan Pountain (Badsey) 28, Andrew Tunnicliffe (Stapenhill Reserves) 23, Martin Preece (Studley) 22.

Reserve Division	P	W	D	L	F	A	PTS
K'minster H. Res	40	28	8	4	126	47	92
Halesowen T. Res	40	24	10	6	102	42	82
Tamworth Res	40	21	14	5	107	46	77
Bromsgrove R. Res	40	21	10	9	85	55	73
Boldmere SM Res	40	21	9	10	82	55	72
Burton Alb. Res	40	21	6	13	99	75	69
Redditch Utd Res	40	18	12	10	87	70	66
Atherstone U. Res	40	15	10	15	89	86	55
RC Warwick Res	40	16	7	17	66	69	55
Bridgnorth T. Res	40	16	6	18	80	75	54
Leicester Utd Res	40	15	8	17	76	73	53
VS Rugby Res	40	16	5	19	63	76	53
Stratford T. Res	40	16	5	19	66	91	53
Sandwell B. Res	40	13	10	17	59	75	49
Evesham Utd Res	40	13	9	18	76	89	48
Armitage '90 Res	40	13	8	19	61	89	47
Sutton C'field Res	40	11	8	21	50	83	41
Worcester C. Res	40	11	6	23	68	103	39
Northfield T. Res	40	9	11	20	58	84	38
Witney T. Res	40	8	5	27	47	103	29
Hinckley T. Res	40	8	5	27	51	112	29

TOP SCORERS: Justin Taylor (Kidderminster) 37, Stephen Ford (Tamworth) 32, Richard Cotgrave (Kidderminster) 25.

CHALLENGE CUP 1991-92 (Sponsored by Industrial Rewind Services)

First Round

Bolehall Swifts v Kings Heath	1-3
Handrahan Timbers v Upton Town	1-0(aet)
West Heath United v Wilmcote	1-1(aet),2-2(aet

Barlestone St Giles v Ledbury Town '84	6-0
Walsall Wd v Bloxwich 2-2(aet),2-2(aet W.Wd on pens)	
West Heath won on away goals)	

Second Round

Badsey Rangers v Walsall Wood	0-1
Becketts Sporting Club v Chelmsley Town	2-5
Kings Heath v Highgate United	3-0
Knowle v Alcester Town	0-3
Northfield Town v Coleshill Town	1-0
Polesworth N.W. v Stratford Town	1-2
Studley BKL v Barlestone St Giles	2-0
West Mids Fire Service v Duldley Sports	1-2

Handrahan Tim. v Boldmere St Michaels	1-1(aet),1-3
Evesham United v Triplex	3-0
Kings Norton Ex-Servicemen v Armitage '90	0-6
Mile Oak Rovers & Youth v Wigston Fields	0-2
Pershore Town '88 v Sandwell Borough	1-2
Stapenhill v Southam United	2-1
West Heath United v Wellesbourne	1-2
West Midlands Police v Hinckley	3-1

Third Round

Armitage '90 v Dudley Sports	3-0
Evesham United v Wigston Fields	3-1
Northfield Town v West Mids Police	2-1(aet)
Walsall Wood v Chelmsley Town	1-0

Boldmere St Michaels v Alcester Town	3-2
Kings Heath v Studley B.K.L.	2-2(aet),0-4
Stapenhill v Stratford Town	0-2(aet)
Wellesbourne v Sandwell Borough	0-4

Quarter Finals

Armitage '90 v Evesham United	0-1(aet)
Sandwell Borough v Walsall Wood	0-2

Northfield Town v Stratford Town	1-2
Studley B.K.L. v Boldmere St Michaels	3-2

Semi-Finals

Stratford Town v Evesham United	0-1(aet)
Studley B.K.L. v Walsall Wood	2-0(aet)

Final (at Stratford Town FC, Wednesday 13th May 1992): Evesham United 4, Studley B.K.L. 0

Midland Combination Premier Division 10-Year Record

	82/3	83/4	84/5	85/6	86/7	87/8	88/9	89/90	90/1	91/2
Alcester Town	-	-	-	-	-	-	-	-	-	13
Armitage '90	-	-	-	-	-	-	-	-	-	2
Ashtree Highfield (see Sandwell)										
Barlestone St Giles	-	-	-	-	-	-	-	-	-	17
Bloxwich Town AFC	-	-	-	5	16	19	-	7	15	20
Boldmere St.M	3	10	4	1	4	2	1	1	12	9
Bolehall Swifts	-	-	-	-	20	12	11	8	16	10
Bridgnorth Town	1	-	-	-	-	-	-	-	-	-
Chelmsley Town	-	-	-	-	-	-	13	13	18	15
Chipping Norton T.	18	14	-	-	-	-	-	-	-	-
Cinderford Town	5	16	-	-	-	-	-	-	-	-
Coleshill Town	14	2	17	11	18	7	16	16	8	12
Cradley Town	11	-	-	-	-	-	-	-	-	-
Evesham Utd	10	8	13	13	13	5	3	3	3	1
Highgate United	4	4	6	12	9	17	10	11	9	4
Hinckley	-	-	-	-	-	-	9	12	10	19
Hurley Daw Mill	9	7	14	14	-	-	-	-	-	-
Kings Heath	-	15	18	20	15	10	12	15	13	18
Kings Norton Ex S.	-	-	-	-	-	-	-	-	21	-
Knowle (North Star)	20	20	20	16	14	14	14	18	14	16
Leamington	-	-	-	-	-	15	-	-	-	-
Mile Oak Rovers	8	12	1	-	-	-	-	19	17	21
Moor Green	2	-	-	-	-	-	-	-	-	-
New World	-	-	5	15	-	-	-	-	-	-
Northfield Town	17	11	16	4	6	9	6	2	6	11
Paget Rangers	6	6	3	2	2	-	-	-	-	-
Pershore Town '88	-	-	-	-	-	-	-	-	-	6
Polesworth N.Wark	-	-	7	9	11	16	15	14	20	-
Princes End Utd	-	-	-	-	12	8	4	9	19	-
Racing C. Warwick	13	5	10	10	3	1	2	-	-	-
Sandwell Borough	16	18	12	19	10	3	-	-	4	5
Shirley Town	-	-	-	-	-	-	18	-	-	-
Smethwick Highfield (see Ashtree Highfield)										
Solihull Borough	19	13	2	7	7	11	17	10	2	2
Southam Utd	-	19	19	17	17	-	-	-	-	-
Stapenhill	-	-	-	-	-	-	-	4	7	8
Stratford Town	7	9	9	6	1	4	7	5	5	14
Streetley Celtic	-	-	-	-	-	-	-	20	-	-
Studley Sp.	-	1	15	18	19	-	-	-	-	-
Walsall (Boro) Wood	15	17	11	8	8	13	8	17	11	7
West Mids Police	12	3	8	3	5	6	5	6	1	3
Wilmcote	-	-	-	-	-	18	-	-	-	-
No. of clubs	20	20	20	20	20	19	18	21	21	21

Action from the May Bank Holiday Monday morning derby between Premier Division newcomers Alcester Town and Pershore Town '88 (striped shirts). The match finished in a 1-1 draw. Photo - Chris Bedford.

ALCESTER TOWN

President: **Chairman:** Raymond Hodgetts **Manager:** Mike Williams
Secretary: L W King, 27 Priory Road, Alcester, Warks B49 5DX (0789 765435).
Ground: Conway Playing Fields, St Faiths Road, Alcester. (763356) **Nickname:** The Town
Seats: No **Cover:** Yes **Clubhouse:** Yes **Programme:** Yes **Floodlights:** No
P.o.Y 91-92: Andrew Clear **Top Scorer 91-92:** Kevin Mullen **Founded:** 1927
Colours: Red & black hoops/black/red & black **Change Colours:** Blue & white hoops
Record Gate: 402 v Evesham Utd, Aug. Bank Holiday '91. **Previous ground:** Stratford Road (until 1991)
Hons: Midland Comb. Div 1 90-91 (Div 2 R-up 71-72, Presidents Cup 69-70), B'gham Co. Vase R-up 89-90.

ARMITAGE '90'

Chairman: Daniel McMullan **President:** S Osborn **Manager:** Gary Haynes
Secretary: K Conway, 17 Rishworth Avenue, Rugeley, Staffs.
Ground: Rugeley Road, Kings Bromley, Nr Burton-on-Trent DE13 7JG (0543 491077).
Capacity: 2,500 **Seats:** 300 **Cover:** 500 **Floodlights:** Yes **Founded:** 1990.
Programme: 36 pages, 50p **Prog. Editor/ Promotion Officer:** C Bailey. **Nickname:** 'Blues'.
Colours: Blue/white/blue **Change Colours:** White/black/black
Sponsors: Expert Roofing/ Building Co Ltd. **Previous League:** Staffs Senior 90-91.
P.o.Y. 91-92: Ian King **Top Scorer 91-92:** Tony Dawkins 23.
Players progressing to Football League: P J Devlin (Notts County), D A Roberts (Wolves).
Clubhouse: Licensed Bar, Pool. Available for hire **Hons:** Mids Comb. R-up 91-92, Walsall Snr Cup 91-92.

BARLESTONE ST GILES

Manager: John Farrington
Secretary: D Poole, 16 Kirkman Close, Barlestone, Nuneaton CV13 0HZ. (0455 291042)
Ground: Barton Road, Barlestone, Nuneaton. **Nickname:** Saints.
Colours: Gold/black/black **Previous League:** Leics Snr (until 1991)

BARWELL

Chairman: D Butlin **Manager:** Mark Lee or Pete Savage.
Secretary: Mrs Christine Goadby, 'Clevelands', 4 Elm Tree Drive, Burbage, Hinkley, Leics LE10 2TX (0455 632682).
Ground: Kirkby Rd, Barwell, Leics (0455 843067) N.B. FA Vase & Cup matches will be played at Hinckley Athletic FC
(page 542).
Capacity: **Seats:** **Cover:** **Floodlights:** Yes **Founded:** 1992.
Previous Names: Barwell Athletic FC, Hinckley FC - amalgamated in 1992.
Previous Leagues: (Barwell Athletic) Leics Snr.
Programme: 60 pages, 40p **Programme Editor:** Alan Mason (Leic. 891899).
91-92 P.o.Y: (Hinckley FC) Gary Statham **91-92 Top Scorer:** (Hinckley FC): Scott Kempin.

BLOXWICH TOWN

Manager: John Wilson. **Founded:** 1977.
Secretary: N J Smith, 124 Glastonbury Cres., Mossley Estate, Bloxwich, Walsall W5 2RQ (0922 403612).
Ground: Abbey Park, Glastonbury Crescent, Bloxwich, Walsall. (0922 77640)
Directions: A34 Walsall-Bloxwich, then west onto A4124. Ground 2-3 miles on right, s.p. Mossley Estate.
Capacity: 1,000 **Seats:** 50 **Covered:** 200 **Floodlights:** No **Nickname:** Kestrels
Midweek Matches: Tues/Thurs **Previous Name:** Bloxwich FC.
Colours: All royal blue **Change Colours:** All yellow
Programme: 16 pages 20p **Programme Editor:** Ken Moseley
Hons: Bloxwich Comb.(2), Staffs Co. Lg Div 1, Walsall Snr Cup R-up 86-87, Invitation Cup 89-90, Midland
Combination Div 1 89-90, Alan Peck Cup (3).

BOLDMERE ST MICHAELS

Manager: Alan Parsons
Secretary: John Shaw, 176 Springthorpe Rd, Erdington, Birmingham B24 0SN (021 350 5869).
Ground: Church Road, Boldmere, Sutton Coldfield (021 373 4435).
Directions: A38 & A5127 from City towards S. Coldfield, left at Yenton lights onto A452 (Chester Rd), Church Rd is 6th
turning on the right. 400yds from Chester Road (BR).
Capacity: 2,500 **Seats:** 100 **Covered:** 100 **Floodlights:** Yes **Nickname:** Mikes.
Midweek matches: Tues/Thurs **Previous Leagues:** West Mids 49-63. **Founded:** 1882
Colours: White/black/black **Change Colours:** All yellow (black trim)
Programme: 28 pages, 30p **Programme Editor:** Dave Tolley (021 382 7130)
Clubhouse: Bar & lounge, every evening and four lunchtimes.
Hons: B'ham AFA 36-37, B'ham AFA Snr Cup, B'ham Jnr Cup, FA Amtr Cup SF 47-48, AFA Snr Cup 47-48, Central Amtr
Lg 48-49, Midland Comb.(3) 85-86 88-90 (Challenge Cup 77-78 89-90, Tony Allden Memorial Cup 78-79 88-89 91-92,
Challenge Trophy 86-87).
Players who progressed to Football League: John Barton (Everton, Derby), Kevin Collins (Shrewsbury), Jack Lane
(B'ham C, Notts C), John Lewis (Walsall), Don Moss (Cardiff, C Palace), Harry Parkes (A Villa), Wally Soden
(Coventry).

BOLEHALL SWIFTS

President: Dennis Baker **Chairman:** Howard Harper
Joint Managers: Colin Middleton/ Andy Maddocks.
Secretary: M Tooley, 7 Minefoot Lane, Belgrave, Tamworth B77 2NA (0827 251973).
Ground: Rene Road, Bolehall, Tamworth (827 62637).
Ground: A51 signs south to Bolebridge Island, left under railway arches into Armington Rd, 4th left into Leedham Ave,
fork right, Rene Rd, ground on right
Capacity: 2,000 **Seats:** None **Cover:** 600 **Floodlights:** No **Founded:** 1953
Midweek matches: Tuesday **Previous League:** Staffs County **Nickname:** Swifts
Colours: White/black/black **Change Colours:** Royal blue/navy/white.
Programme: Yes **Programme Editor:** W Gould
Clubhouse: Large Social Club with lounge. Open every evening and lunchtimes.
Hons: Midland Comb. Div 2 84-85 (Challenge Vase 84-85), Ernie Brown Cup R-up 91-92.

CHELMSLEY TOWN

Secretary: M J Harris, 149 Wyckham Road, Castle Bromwich, Birmingham (021 747 4589).
Ground: The Pavilion, Coleshill Road, Marston Green, West Midlands (021 779 5400).
Directions: A452 Chester Rd towards N.E.C., right into Coleshill Heath Rd, right into Coleshill Rd (s.p. Marston Green).
Ground on right (s.p. Chelmsley Hospital). 10 mins walk from Marston Green (BR).
Capacity: 2,500   **Seats:** 50   **Cover:** 200   **Floodlights:** No   **Founded:** 1927
Midweek matches: Tuesday   **Prev. Lges:** Handsworth/ B'ham Yth O.B./ Mercian.
Colours: Sky & white stripes/sky/sky   **Change Colours:** Yellow/black/black
Programme: 24 pages 30p   **Programme Editor:** Terry Stanners
Previous Name: Christchurch (pre 1969)   **Previous Ground:** Coleshill Hall Hospital, Selly Oak
Clubhouse: One room bar and clubroom   **Record Gate:** 3,000 v A Villa Old Stars, charity game.
Players who have progressed to Football League: Bob Peyton (Port Vale)
Hons: B'ham Yth Committee Champions & B'ham Vase R-up 90-91, Handsworth Lg, Mercian Lg(3), Mids Comb 87-88
(Presidents Cup 77-78, Invitation Cup 77-78 87-88).

COLESHILL TOWN

Manager: Brian Jordan.   **Founded:** 1894.
Secretary: Mrs Sheila Davies, 46 Castle Drive, Coleshill, Birmingham B46 3LY (0675 465486).
Ground: Pack Meadow, Packington Lane, Coleshill, Birmingham B46 3JQ (0675 63259).
Directions: A446 to A4117 towards Coleshill, Packington Lane forks from A4117, south of village and ground is 150
yds on right. M6 jct 4, 1 mile away.
Capacity: 3,000   **Seats:** 50   **Cover:** 50   **Floodlights:** No   **Nickname:** Coalmen.
Midweek matches: Tues/Thurs   **Record Gate:** 1,000.
Colours: All maroon   **Change Colours:** Green/white/green
91-92 P.o.Y: Mark Hart (goalkeeper)   **91-92 Top Scorer:** Trevor Burroughs.
Clubhouse: Bar open 7 nights a week. Bar manager resident.   **Programme:** 30p, Editor: Mavis Gordon
Players who have progressed to Football League: Gary Shaw (Aston Villa, Walsall)
Hons: Mercian Lg 75-76, Walsall Snr Cup 82-83 (R-up 83-84), Midland Comb. R-up 83-84 (Div 2 69-70 (R-up 74-75),
Invitation Cup 1970, Presidents Cup R-up(2) 67-69).

HIGHGATE UNITED

Manager: Alan Campbell   **Asst Manager:** Alan Lloyd   **Founded:** 1947.
Secretary: Geoff Read, 23 Southam Rd, Hall Green, Birmingham B28 8DQ (021 777 1786).
Ground: The Coppice, Tythe Barn Lane, Shirley, Solihull B90 1PH (021 744 4194).
Directions: A34 from City through Shirley, fork right B4102 (Tanworth Lane), half mile then right into Dickens Heath
Rd, then first right and the ground is on the left. 100yds from Whitlocks End (BR).
Capacity: 5,000   **Seats:** 250   **Covered:** 750   **Floodlights:** Due   **Nickname:** The Gate
Midweek matches: Tuesday   **Record Gate:** 4,000 v Enfield, FA Amtr Cup QF '67.
Colours: All red   **Change Colours:** All white   **Programme:** 30p, Editor: Terry Bishop
91-92 P.o.Y: Trevor Mullings   **91-92 Top Scorer:** Dave Morbey.
Clubhouse: Members Club open Tues, Wed, Thurs & Sat
Players progressing to Football League: John Gayle (W'ledon), Keith Leonard (A Villa, P Vale), Geoff Scott (Leic.)
Hons: Mids Comb.(3) 72-75 (Div 2 66-67 68-69 71-72, Lg Cup(5) 72-74 75-77 84-85 (R-up 78-79), Pres. Cup 70-71 85-
86), Tony Allden Mem. Cup 74-75, Invit. Cup 68-69 71-72 85-86, W Mids All. 63-64, B'ham Snr Cup 73-74 (SF 91-92).

KNOWLE

Manager: Peter Christoforou   **Founded:** 1926.
Secretary: R Gardner, 11 Runcorn Close, Chelmsley Wood, Birmingham B37 6QX (021 770 9273).
Ground: Hampton Rd, Knowle, Solihull (0564 779807).   **Directions:** A41 Warwick Rd from City, left at
Wilsons Pub into Hampton Rd, ground 200 yds on right. 1 mile from Dorridge (BR). Buses from Solihull.
Capacity: 3,000   **Seats:** 72   **Cover:** 200   **Floodlights:** No   **Nickname:** Robins.
Midweek matches: Wednesday   **Record Gate:** 1,000 in FA Vase 1980.
Programme: 20 pages, 25p   **Editor:** Dave Radburn
Colours: Red/white/red   **Change Colours:** Yellow/black/yellow
91-92 P.o.Y: Dave Parker   **91-92 Top Scorer:** Paul Frost.
Previous Name: Knowle North Star 80-87   **Previous Ground:** Bentley Heath Village
Clubhouse: Seating for 60, tea bar   **Previous Lges:** B'ham Yth O.B./ B'ham Alliance.
Players who have progressed to Football League: Guy Russell (Birmingham City)
Hons: B'gham Jnr Cup R-up 70-71, FA Vase QF 81-82, Midland Combination Div 2 R-up 68-69.

MEIR K.A.

Manager/Chairman: Des Reaney   **Vice Chairman:** K Pickthorne.   **Commercial Mgr:** B Jones.
Secretary: Stanley Tooth, 29 Colclough Road, Meir, Stoke-on-Trent ST3 6DH (0782 310145).
Ground: Hilderstone Road, Meir Heath, Stoke-on-Trent (0543 613553)
Directions: Follow signs from Stoke to Longton, to Meir, then to Meir Heath. 2 miles from Blythe Bridge (BR).
Capacity: 500   **Seats:** None   **Cover:** 50   **Floodlights:**   **Founded:** 1976.
Colours: Old gold/black/black   **Previous Name:** Station Shoulder of Mutton.
Programme: 20 pages 35p   **Programme Editor:** Mr S Osborne.
Previous League: Staffs Snr (pre-1992)   **Clubhouse:** Built in 1982, open matchdays.
Previous Ground: Normacot Rec.   **Hons:** Staffs Snr Lg 91-92.

MILE OAK ROVERS & YOUTH

Manager: Colin Burton   **Founded:** 1958.
Secretary: Ray Earp, 515 Watling Street, Mile Oak, Tamworth B78 3NA (0827 287102).
Ground: Recreation Groundd, Price Ave., Mile Oak, Tamworth (0827 289614).   **Directions:** South on
A5 Watling Str. from Mile Oak Hotel, take 3rd right, ground 200yds on right. 2 miles from Tamworth (BR).
Capacity: 2,500   **Seats:** 60   **Cover:** 300   **Floodlights:** Yes   **Nickname:** Oaks
Midweek matches: Wednesday   **Record attendance:** 780 v Tamworth, 18.3.89
Colours: Yellow & blue stripes/blue/blue   **Change Colours:** All yellow
91-92 P.o.Y: Rob Ellison   **91-92 Top Scorer:** Rob Ellison.
Clubhouse: Large bar with separate lounge   **Programme:** 25p, Editor: Keith Wakelin
Previous Leagues: Trent Valley/ Midlamd Combination 70-85/ Southern 85-89.
Players who have progressed to Football League: Keith Downing (Notts Co, Wolves), Tony Coton (B'ham, Watford),
John Gayle (Wimbledon), Kevin Francis & Martyn Taylor (Derby), Colin Robinson (Shrewsbury, B'ham, Hereford)
Hons: Mid Comb 84-85 (Pres. Cup 73-74, Tony Allden Mem. Cup 84-85, Invit. Cup 73-74), B'ham Jnr Cup, Fazeley
Charity Cup 91-92.

NORTHFIELD TOWN

Manager: Gary Webb   **Founded:** 1966.
Secretary: Michael Rooney, 1 Woodbank Drive, Catshill, Nr Bromsgrove, Worcs B61 0HG (0527 36018).
Ground: Shenley Lane, Selly Oak, Birmingham B29 (021 478 3900).
Directions: A38 from City, past Selly Oak, opposite Woodlands/Royal Orthopaedic Hospital turn right into Whitehill Lane, right at end into Shenley Lane. Ground on right. One and a half miles from Northfield (BR).
Capacity: 3,500   **Seats:** None   **Cover:** Yes   **Floodlights:** No   **Nickname:** The Cross
Midweek Matches: Tues/Thurs   **Clubhouse:** Brick built clubhouse. (021 478 3870).
Colours: Yellow/blue/yellow   **Change Colours:** Blue & yellow/blue
Record Gate: 3,300, Charity match, 1967   **Programme:** 24 pages 25p, **Editor:** Eric Rough.
91-92 P.o.Y: John Strong   **91-92 Top Scorer:** Peter Bennett, 10.
Previous Names: Allens Cross/ Cross Castle Utd/ Northfield Town Amateur/ Northfield FC.
Players who have progressed to Football League: Clive Whitehead (WBA), Colin Brazier (Wolves, Walsall), Mark Rees (Walsall), Carlton Palmer (WBA, Sheffield Wed)
Hons: Mids Comb 61-62 75-76 (Div 2 61-62(res)) 63-64, Chal. Cup 56-57 (R-up 63-64 86-87), Pres. Cup 61-62 80-81), Tony Allden Mem. Cup 1977, B'ham Snr Amtr Cup 74-75, B'ham Jnr Cup 1958, 1962, B'ham Co. Yth Cup(3) 69-72, Worcs Co. Yth Cup(4).

PERSHORE TOWN '88

Manager: Mr Colin Shepherd.
Secretary: Alan John Barnett, 8 Croft Cottages, Cropthorne, Nr Pershore, Worcs WR10 3LX (0386 860243).
Ground: King George XI Playing Fields, High Street, Pershore, Worcs (0386 556902).
Seats: Yes   **Covered:** Yes   **Capacity:**   **Floodlights:** Yes   **Founded:** 1988.
91-92 P.o.Y: **Colours:** Blue & white stripes/blue/blue
91-92 Top Scorer: Simon Judge.   **Hons:** Worcs Jnr Cup 90-91, Bob Biggart Cup(2) 90-92

SANDWELL BOROUGH

Manager: Bob Green   **Founded:** 1918.
Secretary: Ken Jones, 19 Henn Drive, Tipton, West Mids DY4 9NN (021 557 9429).
Ground: Oldbury Sports Centre, Newbury Lane, Oldbury (021 552 1759).
Directions: Follow A4123 B'ham-Wolverhampton Rd, past island at jnt 2 M5, after half mile turn left into Newbury Lane and stadium is on the right. 2 miles from Sandwell & Dudley (BR).
Capacity: 3,000   **Seats:** 200   **Cover:** 600   **Floodlights:** Yes   **Nickname:** Trees
Midweek Matches: Wednesday   **Previous Grnd:** Londonderry, Smethwick 18-81
Colours: Green & white stripes/green/green   **Change Colours:** Amber & black
91-92 Top Scorer: Richard Lowe   **Record Gate:** 950 v Halesowen T., FA Cup 1987
Programme: 12 pages 25p   **Programme Editor:** R Unitt.
Previous Leagues: B'ham Suburban/ Central Amtr/ Worcs (Midlands Comb.) 48-88/ Southern 88-90.
Previous names: Smethwick Town, Smethwick Highfield, Ashtree Highfield
Clubhouse: Licensed bar overlooking pitch. Open everyday
Players who have progressed to Football League: Andy Micklewright (Bristol Rov, Bristol City, Swindon, Exeter), Gary Bull (Southampton, Cambridge Utd)
Hons: Mids Comb. Chal. Cup R-up(5) 49-50 51-53 67-68 74-75, Chal. Tphy R-up 88-89, Pres. Cup 79-80 (R-up 76-77), Div 2 R-up 79-80), B'ham Jnr Cup.

STAPENHILL

Manager: Bob Sykes   **Asst Manager:** John Wayte   **Founded:** 1947.
Secretary: Paul Adams, 5 Mayfield Drive, Stapenhill, Burton-on-Trent DE15 9D6 (0283 31024).
Ground: Edge Hill, Maple Grove, Stapenhill, Burton-on-Trent (0283 62471).
Directions: Three miles from Burton on A444 Measham Rd, turn right at Copperhearth Public House into Sycamore Rd for ground. Three miles from Burton-on-Trent (BR) - use buses 22, 23, 38 from opposite station.
Capacity: 2,000   **Seats:** 55   **Covered:** 150   **Floodlights:** No   **Nickname:** Swans.
Midweek matches: Mon/Tues/Thurs   **Record Gate:** 2,000 v Burton Alb. Res., 50-51
Colours: Red/white/red   **Change Colours:** Blue/white/blue
91-92 Top Scorer: Mark Barnes, 21   **91-92 P.o.Y:** Dave Carlin (fans': Dave Bolton)
Programme: 24 pages 30p   **Programme Editor:** Steve Davies
Previous Name: Stapenhill Waterside Community Centre.   **Hons:** Mids Comb. Div 1 89-90, Leics Snr Lg 59-60 86-87 88-89 (Tebbutt Brown Cup(2) 87-89), Leics Snr Cup 69-70 86-87, Derby Snr Cup R-up 88-89 91-92.

STRATFORD TOWN

Manager: Ron Mason   **Founded:** 1944.
Secretary: P W Gardner, 17 Trevelyan Crescent, Stratford-upon-Avon, Warks CV37 9LL (0789 68432).
Ground: Masons Road, off Alcester Road, Stratford-upon-Avon, Warks (0789 297479).
Directions: Follow Alcester signs from Town and Masons Rd is on the right past railway bridge. 400 yards from Stratford-on-Avon (BR).
Capacity: 4,000   **Seats:** 200   **Covered:** 200   **Floodlights:** Yes   **Nickname:** The Town
Midweek Matches: Tues/Thurs   **Clubhouse:** Open 7 nights & Sunday lunch.
Colours: Tangerine/black/tangerine   **Change Colours:** Silver/maroon/maroon
91-92 P.o.Y: M Upton   **91-92 Top Scorer:** Richard Landon, 31.
Programme: Yes   **Programme Editor:** P Gardner
Previous Name: Stratford Town Amateur   **Previous Lges:** W Mids 57-70/ Hellenic 70-75.
Record Gate: 484 v Aston Villa, Birmingham Snr Cup, Oct 1984
Players who have progressed to Football League: Martin Hicks (Charlton, Reading), Roy Proverbs (Coventry, Bournemouth, Gillingham)
Hons: Midland Comb 56-57 86-87 (Chal. Cup 86-87 88-89 (R-up 55-56), Chal. Vase 81-82, Jack Mould Tphy 81-82, Tony Allden Mem. Cup 86-87, B'ham Snr Cup 62-63.

STUDLEY B.K.L.

Chairman: D Robinson   **Manager:** Ray Richards/ John Adams   **Founded:** 1971.
Secretary: Paul Woodrow, 25 Maxstoke Close, Matchborough, Redditch, Worcs B98 0EJ (0527 24780).
Ground: 'Beehive', BKL Spts Ground, Abbeyfields, Birmingham Rd, Studley, Warks (0527 24780).
Colours: Sky/navy/navy   **Previous Name:** B.K.L. Works   **Nickname:** Bees.
Previous League: Redditch & South Warwickshire Sunday Combination 71-87.
91-92 Top Scorer: Martin Preece   **Hons:** Midland Comb. Div 1 91-92 (Chal. Cup R-up 91-92, Presidents Cup R-up 91-92, Div 2 Cup 87-88), Smedley Crooke Charity Cup 90-91 91-92.

WEST MIDLANDS POLICE

President: Chief Constable G Dear   **Chairman:** Dep Chief Constable I Sharp
Manager: C Brookes   **Coach:** Dave Scriven.
Secretary: Dave Taylor, 58 Longhurst Croft, West Heath, Birmingham B31 4SQ (021 475 7293).
Ground: West Mids Police Sports Ground, Tally Ho, Pershore Road, Edgbaston (021 472 2944).
Directions: 2 miles south west of city on A441 Pershore Road. Ground is on the left 50yds past Priory Road lights (Warks County Cricket Ground). 3 miles from Birmingham New Street (BR) - buses 41 & 45 from city.
Capacity: 1,000   **Seats:** None   **Covered:** 200   **Floodlights:** No   **Founded:** 1974
Midweek matches: Tues/Thurs.
Colours: Red & black stripes/black/red & black   **Change Colours:** All green.
Previous Names: Birmingham City Police (founded 1938), West Mids Constabulary - merged in 1974.
Previous Leagues: B'ham Wednesday 28-38/ Mercian 46-53/ B'ham Works 53-69.
Record Gate: 1,072 v Sudbury Town, FA Vase QF 29/2/92.
Clubhouse: Complex of 3 bars, snooker, ballroom, kitchen.
Hons: FA Vase QF 91-92, Mids Comb 90-91 (Chal. Cup 74-75 (R-up 85-86), Tony Allden Mem. Cup 75-76), B'ham Jnr Cup, Worcs Urn 84-85 91-92 (R-up 81-82), National Police Cup(12) 61-65 66-67 69-70 73-76 80-81 87-88 91-92 (R-up(6) 67-68 70-72 76-78 88-89), Aston Villa Cup(3).

PREMIER DIVISION RESULT CHART 1991-92

HOME TEAM	1	2	3	4	5	6	7	8	9	10	11	12	13	14	15	16	17	18	19	20	21
1. Alcester T.	*	0-3	4-0	0-2	2-2	1-2	7-0	0-0	0-3	2-1	2-0	2-2	0-0	1-0	1-1	1-1	0-2	1-2	1-0	1-2	1-3
2. Armitage	2-1	*	5-0	2-0	6-1	1-0	2-1	0-0	3-1	0-0	5-1	3-0	4-1	2-0	2-0	0-2	2-3	1-1	3-1	0-1	3-1
3. Barlestone	4-3	0-0	*	4-2	0-1	1-3	1-1	0-1	0-2	0-2	2-1	2-1	1-2	0-2	0-4	0-0	3-2	0-3	1-3	0-4	
4. Bloxwich T.	0-2	2-3	0-1	*	0-4	0-2	3-0	1-2	1-2	2-2	3-3	2-1	1-1	3-0	2-3	1-4	2-1	0-4	0-0	2-3	3-2
5. Boldmere	3-4	0-1	0-1	1-1	*	2-0	6-1	1-1	0-1	0-1	4-1	5-0	3-0	3-2	2-0	0-2	2-2	0-3	2-2	1-0	
6. Bolehall S.	2-2	2-2	0-0	3-0	0-3	*	1-1	3-2	2-3	0-2	1-0	2-0	3-1	3-3	4-0	0-0	0-0	4-0	3-0	1-1	1-2
7. Chelmsley T.	5-1	0-4	1-2	4-2	0-4	1-0	*	3-2	0-1	2-1	2-0	3-0	2-1	4-3	1-4	1-4	2-5	3-3	2-2	1-3	1-3
8. Coleshill T.	2-1	0-1	0-0	1-1	0-2	1-1	3-0	*	0-1	2-2	2-0	1-1	2-0	2-1	1-1	1-5	2-1	1-2	0-0	0-0	1-2
9. Evesham Utd	2-1	0-1	8-0	2-0	2-0	1-1	5-2	0-0	*	4-1	0-1	1-0	0-1	3-1	3-0	0-0	1-0	3-1	2-1	2-1	3-1
10. Highgate Utd	5-0	1-0	1-1	4-0	3-1	1-1	5-0	2-1	2-0	*	1-0	1-0	2-0	2-0	2-2	1-1	1-1	5-2	2-3	1-2	0-0
11. Hinckley FC	3-0	0-1	2-1	2-1	1-1	0-0	0-3	2-1	1-1	0-4	*	2-2	2-2	6-0	0-0	1-2	1-4	0-3	2-4	3-2	0-1
12. Kings Heath	1-3	0-2	3-1	0-2	1-1	1-2	3-0	0-1	1-1	0-1	2-1	*	3-1	3-1	0-0	1-2	1-0	2-4	1-0	0-3	1-3
13. Knowle	4-1	1-3	1-1	4-3	1-1	0-3	5-2	3-1	0-1	0-1	4-2	5-1	*	4-1	1-3	0-2	3-2	1-2	0-1	2-2	3-3
14. Mile Oak R.	0-3	0-7	1-1	3-2	1-2	2-2	0-5	0-2	1-1	0-0	1-0	*	0-0	1-3	0-6	3-5	1-2	2-2	0-4		
15. Northfield T.	1-0	1-0	3-1	0-0	0-1	1-1	4-3	1-1	1-3	0-0	3-0	1-0	4-2	2-1	*	1-0	2-2	1-1	1-1	0-2	1-0
16. Pershore	2-0	1-1	2-0	5-0	2-0	1-2	3-0	5-0	1-1	0-2	4-2	4-1	0-0	8-1	1-1	*	1-2	1-0	2-2	1-0	1-1
17. Sandwell B.	2-0	0-1	1-3	3-1	0-2	3-0	4-1	2-0	4-1	1-3	5-3	4-2	3-1	5-2	2-2	2-1	*	0-0	2-0	2-0	0-0
18. Stapenhill	7-0	1-4	3-1	0-0	5-3	2-1	3-1	1-2	1-2	3-1	1-2	1-3	2-2	4-0	3-0	1-1	2-1	*	2-1	1-0	2-2
19. Stratford T.	1-2	2-3	2-1	0-1	1-0	0-2	2-2	0-3	0-2	1-1	0-2	1-0	4-1	0-1	1-3	0-3	2-1	*	2-4	1-3	
20. Walsall W.	0-0	1-1	1-1	1-2	2-1	1-1	4-0	0-2	0-0	2-1	4-0	1-1	1-2	1-0	4-0	4-2	1-1	3-1	1-0	*	0-0
21. W.M. Police	2-2	1-0	3-2	4-0	1-0	5-2	8-0	0-0	2-4	0-1	4-0	1-2	3-1	2-1	3-0	2-1	1-0	4-2	3-2	2-1	*

PRESIDENTS CUP 1991-92 (Sponsored by Solihull Borough FC)

First Round

Dudley Sports v Becketts Sporting Club	1-2*(aet)*	
Kings Norton Ex-Serv. v Solihull Boro. Res	1-0	
Wigston Fields v Wilmcote		2-2*(aet)*,0-1

Second Round

Badsey Rangers v Polesworth Nth Warwick	2-1	
Ledbury Town '84 v Triplex	3-2	
Stapenhill Reserves v Handrahan Timbers	2-0	
Wellesbourne v Upton Town	1-0	
Becketts Sporting v Kings Norton Ex-Servicemen	1-2	
Southam United v West Heath United	0-1	
Studley BKL v West Midlands Fire Service	3-2	
Wilmcote v Kings Heath Reserves	3-1	

Quarter Finals

Studley BKL v Ledbury Town '84	4-0	
Wilmcote v Badsey Rangers	1-3	
Wellesbourne v Stapenhill Reserves	3-2	
West Heath United v Kings Norton Ex-Servicemen	2-4	

Semi-Finals

Kings Norton Ex-Service v Studley BKL	1-2	
Badsey Rangers v Wellesbourne		2-3*(aet)*

Final (at Redditch United FC, Wednesday 6th May 1992): Wellesbourne 2, Studley BKL 1

CHALLENGE VASE 1991-92

First Round

Archdales '73 v Dudley Sports Reserves	3-0	
Fairfield Villa v Kenilworth Rangers	1-2	
Emerald Social v Wigston Fields Reserves	4-0	
Monica Star v Marston Green	1-4	

Second Round

Earlswood Town v Wellesbourne Reserves	1-3	
Enville Athletic v Thimblemill REC	1-2	
Marston Green v Emerald Social	1-0	
Shirley Town v Swift P.P.	1-3	
Barlestone St Giles Reserves v Archdales '73	1-3	
Coleshill Town Reserves v Hams Hall	2-3*(aet)*
Pershore Town '88 Reserves v Kenilworth Rangers	2-4
Wythall v Sherwood Celtic	1-3

Quarter Finals

Archdales '73 v Wythall	1-3	
Thimblemill REC v Hams Hall	3-1	
Swift P.P. v Kenilworth Rangers	0-5	
Wellesbourne Reserves v Marston Green	0-1	

Semi-Finals

Thimblemill REC v Wythall	4-0	
Marston Green v Kenilworth Rangers		1-0*(aet)*

Final (at Boldmere St Michaels FC, Tuesday 12th May 1992): Marston Green 2, Thimblemill REC 1

ANSELLS MIDLAND COMBINATION DIVISION ONE 1992-93

BADSEY RANGERS

Manager: Alex Ogg   **Asst Manager:** Max Green   **Founded:** 1890
Secretary: M Loram, 39 Synehurst, Badsey, Evesham WR11 5UI (0386 832040).   **Seats:** Yes
Ground: Badsey Recreation Ground, Sands Lane, Badsey, Evesham (0386 830867).   **Cover:** Yes
91-92 Top Scorer: Alan Pountain.   **91-92 P.o.Y:** Malcolm Bennett (goalkeeper)
Cols: Red/black/black   **Hons:** Mids Comb. Div 1 R-up 91-92 (Div 2 90-91), Jack Mould Tphy R-up 91-92.

BECKETTS SPORTING CLUB

Chairman: Russell Moran   **Manager:** Mick Adams   **Asst Manager:** Steve Phillips
Secretary: Gerry Boyle, 19 Barberry House, Shannon Road, Kings Norton B38 9BX (021 459 9648).
Ground: Becketts Farm, Chapel Lane, Wythall, Near Birmingham (0564 822890).   **Stand:** Yes
Cols: Black & white stripes/black/black   **Hons:** B'ham Co. FA Vase SF 91-92   **Founded:** 1980
91-92 Top Scorer: Mark 'Basher' Brown   **91-92 P.o.Y:** Peter Dunbavin   **Nickname:** The Bulls.

DUDLEY SPORTS

Manager: Ollie Berry.
Secretary: Mrs J Forrest, 39 Smallshire Way, Stourbridge, West Mids DY6 9QJ (0384 378558).
Ground: High Ercal Avenue, Brierley Hill, West Mids (Brierley Hill 71260).
Directions: Just off A461 Dudley-Stourbridge Rd; coming from S'bridge, left after Silver Lane P.O.
Colours: Red/black/red   **Previous League:** Birmingham Works   **Founded:** 1978.

HAMS HALL

Manager: Gary Murray   **Asst Manager:** Steve Brooks.
Secretary: Bob Ringrose, 6 Holly Drive, Hurley, Atherstone, Warks CV9 2JY (0827 827747).
Ground: Hams Hall Generating Station, Lea Marston, Nr Coleshill B76 0BG (0675 462071 - mess. only).
Colours: White/black/black   **Programme:** Yes   **Founded:** 1930
91-92 Top Scorer: Lee Williams   **Nickname:** The Powermen.
Hons: Mids Comb. Div 2 R-up 91-92, Walsall Snr Cup SF 91-92, Fazeley Charity Cup SF 91-92.

HANDRAHAN TIMBERS

Manager: Mitchell Woods.
Secretary: E J Smith, 47 Summercourt Sqare, Kingswinford, West Mids DY6 9QJ (0384 295394).
Ground: The Mile Flat Sports Ground, Mile Flat, Wallheath, Kingswinford, West Mids (0381 484755).
Colours: Red/white/red   **Nickname:** Timbers   **Founded:** 1981.
91-92 P.o.Y: Steve Parsons   **91-92 Top Scorer:** Carl Kitching 11.
Hons: Wednesbury Charity Cup 91-2.

KENILWORTH TOWN

Manager: John Clark   **Founded:** 1936
Secretary: Richard Brooks, 33 Suncliffe Drive, Kenilworth, Warks CV8 1FH (0926 57728).
Ground: Gypsey Lane (off Rouncil Lane), Kenilworth, Warks (0926 50851).
Colours: Blue/white/blue   **Previous Name:** Kenilworth Rangers (pre-1992).
91-92 P.o.Y: Connell Gibson   **91-92 Top Scorer:** Steve Johnson, 34.

KINGS HEATH

Manager: Barry Hancox/ Paul Smith   **Founded:** 1964.
Secretary: D Ellis, 2 Willsbridge Covert, Druids Heath, Birmingham B14 5YD (021 459 7444)
Ground: As Shirley Town FC (see Div. 2). **Previous Names:** Horse Shoe FC/ Kings Hth Amateur.
Cols: Gold shadow stripes/black/gold   **Change Colours:** All red   **Nickname:** The Kings
Programme: 12 pages   **Programme Editor:** M Kite
91-92 P.o.Y: Richard Young   **91-92 Top Scorer:** Robert Trindle.
Players progressing to Football League: Geoff Scott (Stoke, Leicester, Birmingham).
Hons: Div 2 R-up 82-83 (Presidents Cup R-up 79-80 81-82), Birmingham Challenge Vase R-up 86-87.

KINGS NORTON EX-SERVICEMEN

President: M T Hickey   **Founded:** 1982
Sec: Eric Talbot, C/O Kings Norton Ex-Service Club, 185a Pershore Rd, Cotteridge B30 3DJ (021 459 1403).
Ground: Highgate Utd FC (see page 555).
Colours: All royal blue   **Change colours:** White (blue trim)/royal/white
Programme Editor: S Jesic   **Previous Ground:** Becketts Farm, Wythall.
Hons: Midland Comb. Div 2 R-up 85-86 (Chal. Vase R-up 84-85), Solihull Charity Cup R-up 84-85, Smedley Crooke Charity Cup 87-88 (R-up 89-90).

LEDBURY TOWN '84

Manager: Paul Ledbury   **91-92 Top Scorer:** Nigel Foreshew.
Secretary: M Clueit, Paladin, Bridge Street, Ledbury HR8 2AN (0531 4693).   **Founded:** 1984.
Ground: New Street, Ledbury.   **Colours:** Red/black/red   **Floodlights:** Yes.

MARSTON GREEN

Manager: Ray South   **Founded:** 1986.
Secretary: Alan Phillips, 8 Land Lane, Marston Green, Birmingham B37 7DE (021 779 3064).
Ground: Chelmsley Town FC (see page 555).   **91-92 P.o.Y:** D Grady/ P Forman (joint).
Colours: Yellow & green stripes/green/green   **91-92 Top Scorer:** D Keen.
Hons: Mids Comb. Div 2 91-92 (Chal. Vase 90-91 91-92), Jack Mould Tphy 91-92.

POLESWORTH NORTH WARWICK

Manager: David Waight.
Secretary: E Guild, 43 Station Road, Polesworth, Tamworth, Staffs B78 1BG (0827 893690).
Ground: North Warwick Sports Ground, Hermitage Hill, Tamworth Road, Polesworth (892482).
Seats: 50   **Capacity:** 1,000   **Floodlights:** No   **Founded:** 1966   **Nickname:** Poles
Colours: Green & white hoops/green/yellow   **Change colours:** Tangerine & black
91-92 P.o.Y: Simon Lilley   **91-92 Top Scorer:** Chris Marlew.
Previous League: Mercian.   **Clubhouse:** Bar, tea room and refreshments.
Hons: Mids Comb. Chal. Cup 83-84 (Pres. Cup(2) 82-84), B'ham Jnr Cup 83-84, Ernie Brown Cup 91-92.
Players progressing to Football League: Dave Tunnicliffe (Birmingham City).

Action from the table-topping Division Two game between Hams Hall and Marston Green (2-4). Photo - Paul Barber.

Halesowen Town Reserves of the Combination Reserve Division. Back Row (L/R): David Bowen, Lee Hardwick, Ian Brookes, Gary Adkins, Martin Box, Jason Hughes, David Vanes, Steve Brookes. Front: Lee Hipkiss (ball boy), Robert McLaren, Andy Mitchell, Andy Hill, Steve Moore, Sean Kimberley, Andy Lunt, Steve Shilvock (Manager).

Wilmcote (light shirts) defend a corner on the way to a 1-0 win over visiting Wigston Fields. Photo - James Wright.

SHERWOOD CELTIC

Manager: Mark Foggerty. **Founded:** 1982
Secretary: Gary Fletcher, 29 Sarehole Road, Hall Green, Birmingham B28 8DU (021 778 3807).
Ground: As Knowle FC (See page 555). **Colours:** Gold/green/gold **Programme:** Yes
91-92 P.o.Y: The Old Man, Kevin McEvoy **91-92 Top Scorer:** John Coyle, 24 in 29 games.
Previous Ground: Becketts Farm, Wythall (pre-1992).

SOLIHULL BOROUGH RESERVES

Ground: Borough Club, Tanworth Lane, Shirley, Solihull (021 745 6758) *(See page 482 for other details)*
91-92 P.o.Y: Ian Tyrell **91-92 Top Scorer:** Nick Hyde **Manager:** Mark Taylor

SOUTHAM UNITED

Manager: Ollie Berry **Founded:** 1905.
Secretary: R J Hancocks, 18 Warwick Road, Southam, Leamington Spa CV33 0HN (0926 813483).
Ground: Banbury Road Ground, Southam, Leamington Spa (0926 812091).
Directions: On righthand side of A423 Banbury Road heading south from Southam.
Seats: No **Cover:** Yes **Nickname:** Saints **Clubhouse:** Yes
Colours: Yellow/black/black **Previous League:** Coventry & North Warks.
91-92 P.o.Y.: Marcus Townsend **91 Top Scorer:** John Angove.
Hons: Mids Comb. Div 3 80-81 (Div 2 R-up 82-83, Chal. Vase 80-81).

TRIPLEX

Manager: Graham Thorn **Founded:** 1951 **Nickname:** Glassboys.
Secretary: Roy William Walters, 115 Trimpley Road, Bartley Green, Birmingham B32 3PH (021 422 1087).
Ground: T.S.A Sports Ground, Eckershall Road, Kings Norton, Birmingham (021 458 4570).
Colours: Sky (navy)/sky/navy **Hons:** Smedley Crooke Cup QF 91-92.

UPTON TOWN

Chairman: John Cook **President:** Steve Goode.
Secretary: Don G Roberts, 6 Gardens Close, Upton-on-Severn, Worcs WR8 0LT (Upton 3439).
Manager: Martin Stephens **Asst Manager:** Les Wadley.
Commercial Manager/ Programme Editor: Bosko Medakov.
Ground: Malvern Town FC (See page 547). **Founded:** 1920
Colours: Green & white stripes/green with white stripe/green & white hoops.
91-92 P.o.Y: Mark Davies **91-92 Top Scorer:** Paul Newman
Programme: 28 pages, 50p **Prev. Ground:** Old Street, Upton-on-Severn (pre'92)
Nickname: Emeralds **Hons:** Mids Comb. Div 2 89-90 (Jack Mould Tphy 89-90, Pres. Cup
R-up 89-90), Worcs Jnr Cup 73-74 88-89 (R-up 74-75), Worcs Minor Cup 24-25 86-87.

WELLESBOURNE

Manager: Terry Hunt **91-92 Top Scorer:** Ian Green **Founded:** 1932
Secretary: Terry Hunt, 20 Grange Gardens, Wellesbourne, Warks CV35 9LR (0789 840712).
Ground: The Sports Field, Loxley Road, Wellesbourne (0789 841878). **Programme:** Yes
Colours: All blue **Hons:** Midlands Comb. Presidents Cup 91-92.

WEST HEATH UNITED

Manager: Thomas Owens **Founded:** 1969.
Secretary: Brian D Fox, 189 Kingshurst Road, Northfield, Birmingham B31 2LL (021 475 4465).
Ground: Bay Tree Farm, Middle Lane, Wythall, Near Birmingham (0564 826612).
Colours: All red **Hons:** Mids Comb. Div 2 R-up 84-85, Smedley Crooke Charity Cup QF 91-92.
91-92 P.o.Y.: Bernard Murray. **91-92 Top Scorer:** Merik Kalewski.

WEST MIDLAND FIRE SERVICE

Manager: Ian Green **Colours:** All red **Founded:** 1947
Secretary: John Kempson, 16 Ganton Road, Bloxwich, Walsall WS3 3XQ (0922 408464).
Ground: 'The Glades', Lugtrout Lane, Solihull (021 705 8602).

WIGSTON FIELDS

Manager: Don Ludden **Reserves' Manager:** Stewart Ryan/ Nick Smith.
Secretary: Malc Jelley, 35 Copinger Road, Aylestone Park, Leicester LE2 6LF (0533 838475).
Ground: Windsor Avenue, Glen Parva, Leicester (0533 771039). **Nickname:** Fields
Colours: All red **Founded:** 1947 **Previous League:** Leics Snr (pre-1991).
91-92 P.o.Y.: Alan Smith **91-92 Top Scorer:** Bob Taylor.

WILMCOTE

Manager: M Flaherty **Founded:** 1971.
Secretary: Bob Adshead, 53 Aston Cantlow Road, Wilmcote, Stratford-upon-Avon CV37 9XX (0789 297895).
Ground: The Patch, Wilmcote Men's Club, Aston Cantlow Road, Wilmcote, Stratford (0789 297895).
Directions: Wilmcote signs off A34, right at T-junction opposite garage; ground on right.
Seats: No **Cover:** Yes **Clubhouse:** Yes **Programme:** No **Nickname:** Cote.
Colours: Yellow/green/yellow **Previous League:** Stratford Alliance.
91-92 P.o.Y: David Jamisson **91-92 Top Scorer:** M Flaherty 10, M O'Sullivan 10.
Players progressing to Football League: Steve Mardinbrow (Coventry City), John Smith (WBA).

ANSELLS MIDLAND COMBINATION DIVISION TWO 1992-93

ARCHDALE '73

Manager: A Grubb **Colours:** Red/white/red **Founded:** 1934
Secretary: R T Widdowson, 37 Mayfield Avenue, Worcester WR3 8LA (27866).
Ground: Windermere Drive, Worcester (51410). **Nickname:** Dales
91-92 P.o.Y.: P Scarrott **91-92 Top Scorer:** A Widdowson.

BARLESTONE ST GILES RESERVES (See page 554)

BURNTWOOD (New club 1992-93)

COLESHILL TOWN RESERVES (See page 555)

COLLETTS GREEN
Ground: Victoria Park, Malvern
Prev. Name: Three Nuns (pre-1992)   **Prev. Lge:** Worcester Sunday (pre-1992).

DUDLEY SPORTS RESERVES (See page 558)

EARLSWOOD TOWN
Secretary: Jim Jones, 22 Antony Road, Shirley, Solihull B90 2NX (021 745 3397).
Ground: Malthouse Lane, Earlswood, Solihull (05646 3989).   **Programme:** Yes
Colours: Red/black/red   **Nickname:** Earls   **Founded:** 1968
91-92 Top Scorers: Ian Sturdy 11, Graham Sturdy 10   **91-92 P.o.Y.:** Graham Sturdy

ENVILLE ATHLETIC
Manager: David Pell   **Colours:** All sky blue   **Founded:** 1890
Secretary: Graham Hingley, 24 Bramley Way, Blossom Hill, Bewdley, Worcs DY12 2PU (0299 400745).
Ground: Hall Drive Ground, Hall Drive, Enville, Stourbridge (Kinver 872368).
91-92 P.o.Y. & Top Scorer: Ian Perry.   **Hons:** B'ham Co. FA Vase QF 91-92.

FAIRFIELD VILLA
Manager: Cliff Hughes   **Founded:** 1902 (Reformed: 1959).
Secretary: C W Harris, 7 Churchill Road, Catshill, Bromsgrove B61 0PE (0527 31049).
Ground: Recreation Ground, Stourbridge Road, Fairfield, Bromsgrove (0527 77049).
Colours: All red   **Previous Leagues:** Bromsgrove/ Kidderminster   **Nickname:** Villa.
91-92 P.o.Y.: P Keasey   **91-92 Top Scorer:** Carl Forrester 11.
Hons: Bromsgrove Lg 70-71, Kidderminster Lg 81-82 83-84, Malvern Invitation Cup 77-78, Worcs Junior Cup 77-78, Smedley Crooke Charity Cup R-up 91-92.

HOLLY LANE '92 (New club 1992-93, based in Erdington)

KENILWORTH TOWN RES. (See page 558), MEIR K.A. RES. (See page 555)

MONICA STAR
Manager: Tony Carter   **91-92 Leading Scorer:** David Stokes 35   **Founded:** 1977.
Secretary: Nigel Peters, 10 Ravensdale Road, Small Heath, Birmingham B10 9HU (021 772 6871).
Ground: As Chelmsley Town (page 555).   **Colours:** Red/black/red
Previous Ground: The Glades, Lugtrout Lane, Solihull (pre-1992).

PERSHORE TOWN '88 RESERVES
Manager: Dave Connell   **91-92 Top Scorer:** Steve Andrews 15   *(Other details as page 556)*

SHIRLEY TOWN
Secretary: R Price, 6 Chestnut Close, Olton, Shirley, Solihull (021 706 3740).
Ground: Shirley Stadium, Tile House Lane, Shirley, Solihull (021 744 1560).
Directions: A34 B'gham to Shirley, right onto B4025 towards Shirley (BR) - ground one and a half miles on left.
Colours: All red   **Previous League:** B'ham Comb. 35-38.   **Founded:** 1926

STUDLEY B.K.L. RESERVES (See page 556)

SWIFT P.P.
Manager: David Baker   **Ground:** Wythall FC (see below)   **Founded:** 1982.
Secretary: John Finn, 8 Redgate Close, Kings Norton, Birmingham B38 8YT (021 459 0101).
Colours: White (red trim)/white/red   **Previous Ground:** Shirley Town FC (pre-'92).
91-92 P.o.Y.: S Brown   **91-92 Top Scorer:** Morris Costello 13.

THIMBLEMILL R.E.C.
Manager: Peter Gardiner   **Programme:** Yes   **Founded:** 1964.
Secretary: G M Houten, 68 Gower Road, Lapal, Halesowen, West Mids B62 9BT (021 442 3357).
Ground: Thimblemill Recreation, Thimblemill Road, Smethwick, Warley (021 429 2459).
Colours: White (blue trim)/white/navy blue   **Hons:** Mids Comb. Chal. Cup QF 91-92.
91-92 P.o.Y.: Chris Hunt   **91-92 Top Scorer:** T Monaghan 29.

WELLESBOURNE RESERVES
Manager: Roy Beasley   **91-92 Top Scorer:** Paul Stevens   *(Other details as page 560)*

WIGSTON FIELDS RESERVES (See page 560)

WYTHALL
Secretary: B G Thompson, 14 Rye Croft, Hollywood, Birmingham B47 5HU (00564 822276).
Ground: Wythall Park, Silver Street, Wythall, Birmingham (0564 823281).
Colours: All blue   **Founded:** 1948.

CHALLENGE TROPHY (RESERVE DIVISION CUP) 1991-92
(Sponsored by Industrial Rewind Services Ltd)

First Round

Boldmere SM Res v Racing C. Warwick Res	0-1	Evesham United Res v Atherstone Utd Res 2-6
Hinckley Town Res v Leicester Utd Res	1-2	Redditch United Res v Witney Town Reserves 1-0
Worcester City Res v Northfield Town Res	3-0	

Second Round

Atherstone Utd Res v Armitage '90 Reserves	2-1	Bromsgrove Rvrs Reserves v Tamworth Reserves 0-1
Halesowem Town Res v Redditch United Res	3-1	Kidderminster Harriers Res v V.S. Rugby Res 2-0
Racing C. Warwick Res v Bridgnorth T. Res	1-0	Sandwell Borough Res v Stratford Town Reserves 3-0
Sutton Coldfield T. Res v Burton Albion Res	1-0	Worcester City Res v Leicester United Reserves 6-2

Quarter Finals

Kidderminster Res v Worcester City Reserves	3-2	Sandwell Borough Res v R.C. Warwick Res 1-2(aet)
Tamworth Res v Halesowen Town Reserves	2-1	Sutton CT Reserves v Atherstone Res 1-1(aet),2-0

Semi-Finals

Sutton Coldfield T. Res v Tamworth Res	0-2	Racing Club Warwick Res v Kidderminster H. Res 2-4

Final (at Tamworth FC, Tuesday 28th April 1992): Tamworth Reserves 2, Kidderminster Harriers Reserves 1

Earlswood Town FC, Ansells Midland Combination Division Two. Back Row (L/R): R Powell, P Photiou, G Sturdy, B Cant, W Loughney, S Mole, A Dawes (Manager), P Robinson. Front: S Burnell, D Hind, C Saidler, P Baker, M Smyth, I Sturdy.

Neil Griffin (left) presents the Influence Midland Combination Runners-up Shield to Armitage '90 captain John Capaldi. Photo - Marshall's Sports Service, Birmingham.

HELLENIC LEAGUE

President: C J Green.
Chairman: N A S Matthews.
Treasurer: J S Russell.
Secretary/Treasurer: T G Cuss,
7 Blenheim Road, Kidlington, Oxford OX5 2HP. Tel: 08675 5920.

SHORTWOOD SNATCH TITLE WITH LATE RUN

Newly promoted Cirencester Town played like potential champions all season, but in the final reckoning were left one point short. Congratulations therefore go to Shortwood United who repeated their championship success of 1984-85. Cirencester led the table throughout from the end of September, apart from two weeks in February when they were deposed by Almondsbury, but they were finally overtaken by Shortwood, who had a fabulous run of results in their final eleven games dropping just two points and scoring 33 goals against nine conceded. At the death, Shortwood needed to win their final two games to overhaul Cirencester who had completed their fixtures. They did this with a 1-0 home win over Cinderford on Friday 8th May followed by a 2-1 success at Almondsbury the following Wednesday. To rub salt into the wound, Shortwood also beat Cirencester in the final of the Gloucestershire Challenge Trophy.

Milton United confirmed that their Premier Division title last year was no 'flash in the pan' by finishing a creditable fourth and thereby denying Gloucestershire a clean sweep of the first four places. Fairford Town, denied the championship on goal difference last season, were beset by injuries in vital matches and slipped down the table, whilst Moreton Town struggled all season to avoid relegation. They had the distinction of being the only club to concede a hundred goals - a busy time for the goalkeeper.

In Divsion One, Wollen Sports and Wantage Town proved to be the outstanding teams and duly qualified for promotion to the Premier Division. Tuffley Rovers and North Leigh maintained a strong challenge for the top places, but faltered at the end and will have to try again. Chipping Norton must be pleased with their improved position this year and will be looking forward to better results next season.

In the Reserve section, East and West Section leaders Didcot Town Reserves and Wollen Sports Reserves could not settle the championship play-off finishing 2-2 on aggregate after a two-legged final. In such a situation, competition rules allow for a replay to be contested with extra-time if necessary, but in this case no third game was arranged and it was agreed that the two clubs share the trophy.

The Hellenic League now has a pyramid system in operation. The Gloucestershire County, Wiltshire County, Oxfordshire Senior and Reading Leagues are all now recognised feeders, but this season their were no suitable candidates for promotion, and so no club has been relagated. Likewise, champions Shortwood United opted not to seek promotion to the Beazer Homes League.

An exuburant Shortwood United side indulge in a bit of ever-so-necessary carbohydrate replacement after clinching the Hellenic title championship with a 2-1 win at Almondsbury Picksons on Wednesday 13th May. Photo - Gloucester Citizen.

LEAGUE TABLES 1991-92

Premier Division

	P	W	D	L	F	A	Pts
Shortwood United	34	25	4	5	83	44	79
Cirencester Town	34	23	9	2	73	23	78
Almondsbury Pick.	34	19	7	8	63	38	64
Milton United	34	18	9	7	67	44	63
Cinderford Town	34	16	9	9	57	41	57
Abingdon United	34	17	5	12	54	40	56
Didcot Town	34	16	6	12	70	48	54
Swindon Athletic	34	15	9	10	61	44	54
Bicester Town	34	12	12	10	44	42	48
Banbury United	34	14	5	15	55	55	47
Fairford Town	34	12	9	13	72	55	45
Headingtom Amtrs	34	10	9	15	48	59	39
Pegasus Juniors	34	11	5	18	66	68	38
Kintbury Rangers	34	9	8	17	47	59	35
Rayners Lane	34	9	8	17	50	75	35
Moreton Town	34	7	4	23	38	100	25
Carterton Town	34	6	6	22	32	74	24
Bishops Cleeve	34	2	6	26	25	96	12

Division One

	P	W	D	L	F	A	Pts
Wollen Sports	32	26	4	2	96	28	82
Wantage Town	32	23	6	3	83	32	75
Tuffley Rovers	32	20	8	4	95	34	68
North Leigh	32	20	4	8	84	38	64
Cheltenham Sara.	32	15	7	10	70	45	52
Purton	32	14	7	11	48	40	49
Chipping Norton	32	13	6	13	54	56	45
Highworth Town	32	11	7	14	53	54	40
Cirencester Utd	32	11	4	17	49	55	40
Lambourn Sports	32	11	7	14	52	74	40
Yarnton	32	11	6	15	42	60	39
Wootton Bassett T.	32	10	8	14	45	59	38
Easington Sports	32	12	0	20	42	80	36
Kidlington	32	7	9	16	48	70	30
Wallingford Town	32	8	5	19	40	78	29
Clanfield	32	5	10	17	35	66	25
Supermarine	32	3	3	26	20	87	12

Reserve Division - East

	P	W	D	L	F	A	Pts
Didcot Town Res	22	15	5	2	68	20	50
Milton United Res	22	15	3	4	73	30	48
Bicester Town Res	22	14	4	4	51	32	46
Headington Res	22	13	5	4	54	28	44
Wantage Town Res	22	9	7	6	38	29	34
Abingdon Utd Res	22	9	4	9	50	43	31
North Leigh Res	22	7	4	11	49	52	25
Kintbury Rgrs Res	22	7	4	11	26	53	25
Yarnton Res	22	6	5	11	27	48	23
Easington Spts Res	22	6	4	12	32	49	22
Kidlington Res	22	4	6	12	28	40	18
Wallingford T. Res	22	0	3	19	15	87	3

Reserve Division - West

	P	W	D	L	F	A	Pts
Wollen Sports Res	20	13	4	3	51	22	43
Cirencester T. Res	20	12	4	4	56	25	40
Swindon Ath. Res	20	10	5	5	38	31	35
Cirencester U. Res	20	8	9	3	34	21	33
Almondsbury Res	20	9	5	6	39	15	32
Highworth Res	20	9	3	8	27	28	30
Cheltenham S. Res	20	8	4	8	44	30	28
Fairford Town Res	20	6	6	8	28	34	24
Carterton T. Res	20	6	5	9	19	39	23
Supermarine Res	20	2	4	14	14	58	10
Clanfield Res	20	1	3	16	11	58	6

PREMIER DIVISION RESULT CHART 1991/92

HOME TEAM	1	2	3	4	5	6	7	8	9	10	11	12	13	14	15	16	17	18
1. Abingdon United	*	0-1	1-3	2-0	2-1	1-0	4-0	0-2	1-4	3-2	0-1	2-0	1-0	10-0	0-1	1-1	1-2	
2. Almondsbury P.	2-0	*		2-2	6-0	4-1		0-1	0-2	3-2	3-0		1-1	6-2	1-0	6-1	1-2	3-2
3. Banbury United	1-2	1-2	*	0-0	2-0	4-1	3-2	0-1	1-1	2-2	0-1	1-4	1-2	3-1		1-1	5-6	4-0
4. Bicester Town	1-2	1-1	1-3	*	4-0	1-0	1-0	0-1	1-0	1-0	2-0	0-0		1-1		2-2	0-1	0-0
5. Bishops Cleeve	2-4	0-1		0-4	*	0-1		0-0	2-2	4-4	1-2	1-3	0-2	0-2	1-0	0-0	0-2	0-2
6. Carterton Town	0-2	1-2	0-1	1-4	1-1	*	2-2	0-3	1-1	1-3	0-2	3-2		0-1	1-1	0-3	1-5	0-4
7. Cinderford Town	0-0	2-0	3-1		2-0	3-1	*	0-1	1-2	3-1	1-1	1-1	1-0	4-1	1-1	2-1	1-1	
8. Cirencester Town	3-2		0-0	2-1	6-0	1-1	1-0	*	2-2		3-0	2-0	1-1	5-0	4-3	6-0	4-2	1-2
9. Didcot Town		1-2	1-2	5-0	4-3	4-1	1-2		*	1-1	0-3	3-1	4-1	2-1	3-0	2-3	3-0	
10. Fairford Town	0-1	1-2		2-0	2-1	2-2		1-1	0-1	*	2-2	6-0	5-1	9-0	4-1	3-1	0-4	1-1
11. Headington Amtrs	0-2	0-2	2-0	0-1	2-2		2-2	3-4	0-2	2-2	*	3-2	2-4	4-1	2-2	5-1	1-2	1-4
12. Kintbury Rgrs	1-3	0-0	2-0	2-2	4-1	3-0	0-2	0-2	1-1	1-4	0-1	*	1-2	0-1	1-3	4-1	1-2	0-4
13. Milton United	1-2	0-0	4-0	5-1	3-0	2-1	3-0	1-1	1-0	2-1	1-1	0-3	*	5-0	3-0	2-3	2-1	
14. Moreton Town	1-2	1-2	2-4	2-1	2-2	2-2	0-3		2-1	1-1	0-3	1-2	*		3-2	1-4	2-4	0-4
15. Pegasus Juniors	2-2	2-0	3-0	3-4	10-0		1-2	0-4	3-1	2-4	2-0		1-1	5-1	*	0-2	2-4	2-0
16. Rayners Lane	1-3	3-2	2-3	1-2	6-1	1-3	2-3	1-1	1-0	2-1	5-0	2-2	2-5	2-1	1-3	*	0-4	0-2
17. Shortwood United	5-0	1-1	1-3	2-1	3-0	1-0	1-0	1-4	5-2	0-0	2-1	2-2	1-3	3-1	2-0	3-0	*	0-0
18. Swindon Athletic	0-0	0-3	0-1	2-2	3-0	1-2	3-1	2-1	4-8	2-1	2-2	2-0	6-0	1-1	3-2		1-2	*

DIVISION ONE RESULT CHART 1991/92

HOME TEAM	1	2	3	4	5	6	7	8	9	10	11	12	13	14	15	16	17
1. Cheltenham Saracens	*		0-2	9-2		1-0	3-1	6-2	1-1		2-2	4-0	0-3		1-2	0-1	
2. Chipping Norton	0-0	*		4-2	3-1	2-1	1-1	1-1	0-2	0-2	3-0	2-3	3-1		0-4	4-1	1-0
3. Cirencester Utd	2-0	0-2	*	2-0	1-0		3-2	2-1	0-5	0-3	1-0	2-2	4-0	1-2	0-2	1-1	6-1
4. Clanfield	0-2	3-2	0-0	*	4-1		3-1	2-1	0-1	1-0	3-0	2-2	0-1	1-1	0-1	1-1	0-1
5. Easington Spts	2-4	1-0	4-2	3-1	*		5-2		0-3	1-0	2-5	0-5	1-2	0-3	0-4	1-0	1-4
6. Highworth Town	1-4	2-0	3-1	5-0	4-0	*	1-1		2-3	0-0	2-0	0-2	6-0	2-5	0-1	2-4	0-0
7. Kidlington	1-1	1-2	5-3	0-0	3-1	1-1	*	2-3	2-1	1-3		1-1	0-3	0-3	0-3	2-2	2-1
8. Lambourn Sports	1-6	3-3	1-1	1-1	1-4	2-2	4-1	*	2-1	1-3	2-1		2-2	1-0	0-2	0-3	3-2
9. North Leigh	7-1	4-1	2-1		0-1	2-3	2-1		*	3-1	7-1	4-0	6-1	2-1	2-4	4-1	4-0
10. Purton	1-0	8-1	1-1	3-1	1-2	1-1	1-4	1-0	2-1	*	1-0	0-3	2-1	1-1	2-2	2-0	
11. Supermarine	1-1	3-0	0-3	0-4	0-2	0-2	0-2	0-0	0-2	*		3-2	1-1	2-4	0-3	1-2	1-2
12. Tuffley Rovers	1-1	2-1	3-1	2-0	3-0	4-0	4-1	4-0	1-1		10-0	*		2-0		2-2	5-1	11-0
13. Wallingford T.	0-1		1-1	2-0	0-2	2-3	2-2	6-1	1-5	2-0	0-1	0-2	*	0-2			1-1
14. Wantage Town	1-1	1-1	4-3	9-0	3-1	2-3	4-1	1-0	5-1	2-1	3-1	0-0	5-1	*	1-1	3-0	2-1
15. Wollen Sports	4-3	4-0	2-0	4-1	7-1		5-0	6-1		3-1	5-1	4-3	3-0	1-2	*	4-0	2-1
16. Wootton Bassett	0-2	3-3	0-0	1-1	3-1	3-0	3-0	1-3	1-1		2-0	2-3	3-1	1-2	1-2	*	0-2
17. Yarnton	4-1	0-1	4-1	1-1	1-0	3-1	1-1		0-1	2-2		0-6	1-3	1-0	0-1	2-2	*

We apologise for these grids being incomplete, but we did not receive the requested information from the League, and had to make do as best we could from our own records, thinking some results are better the none.

PREMIER DIVISION CUP 1991-92

Preliminary Round

Cinderford Town v Milton United	4-0
Swindon Athletic v Abingdon United	0-2

First Round

Banbury United v Pegasus Jnrs	2-1
Kintbury Rgrs v Abingdon Utd	2-0
Fairford Town v Moreton Town	6-1
Cinderford Town v Bicester Town	1-0
Bishops Cleeve v Carterton Town	1-4
Rayners Lane v Cirencester Town	2-1
Almondsbury v Headington Amtrs	3-1
Didcot Town v Shortwood United	5-3

Second Round

Cinderford v Almondsbury Pick.	3-1
Carterton Town v Banbury United	1-2
Fairford v Kintbury	1-1,1-1(aet),0-1(at Fairford)
Rayners Lane v Didcot Town	0-2

Semi Finals

Didcot Town v Fairford Town	5-2(aet)
(at Abingdon United, 21st March)	
Banbury United v Cinderford Town	0-0,1-0
(both matches at Cirencester Town FC)	

Final: Didcot Town 3, Banbury United 0

FIRST DIVISION CUP 1991-92

Preliminary Round

Wootton Bassett Town v North Leigh	1-4

First Round

Kidlington v Highworth Town	0-1
Supermarine v Wollen Sports	0-4
Yarnton v Lambourn Sports	1-3
Cirencester Utd v North Leigh	0-3
Easington Sports v Purton	3-4
Wallingford Town v Clanfield	2-1
Wantage Town v Chipping Norton	2-0(ab. - fog),4-1
Tuffley Rovers v Cheltenham Saracens	4-1

Second Round

North Leigh v Wallingford Town	6-1
Purton v Wollen Sports	1-2
Highworth Town v Lambourn Sports	3-3,1-0
Tuffley Rovers v Wantage Town	2-3

Semi Finals

North Leigh v Wantage Town	0-0,1-2
(at Clanfield FC, 28th March)	
Wollen Sports v Highworth Town	3-1
(at Chipping Norton Town FC)	0-0,1-0

Final: Wantage Town 3, Wollen Sports 2

HELLENIC LEAGUE PREMIER DIVISION TEN YEAR RECORD

	81/2	83/4	84/5	85/6	86/7	87/8	88/9	89/90	90/1	91/2
Abingdon Town	3	5	11	4	1	2	-	-	-	-
Abingdon United	12	4	6	7	6	4	3	3	7	6
Almondsbury Picksons	2	1	10	17	-	-	-	7	10	3
Avon (Bradford)	-	16	-	-	-	-	-	-	-	-
Banbury United	-	-	-	-	-	-	-	-	8	10
Bicester Town	-	-	-	-	-	-	-	-	-	-
Bishops Cleeve	-	-	-	-	-	16	10	16	14	18
Carterton Town	-	-	-	-	-	-	-	-	12	17
Cinderford Town	-	-	-	-	-	-	-	-	-	5
Cirencester Town	-	-	-	-	-	-	-	-	-	2
Clanfield	11	11	18	-	-	-	-	-	-	-
Didcot Town	6	9	17	-	-	5	8	15	4	7
Fairford Town	7	14	8	13	15	8	4	5	2	11
Hazells Club (Aylesbury)	14	17	-	-	-	-	-	-	-	-
Headington Amateurs	-	-	-	-	-	-	-	12	5	12
Hounslow	-	-	5	3	2	-	-	-	9	-
Kintbury Rangers	-	-	-	-	-	-	15	8	11	14
Lambourn Sports	16	-	-	-	-	-	-	-	-	-
Maidenhead Town	13	12	13	18	-	-	-	-	-	-
Milton United	-	-	-	-	-	-	-	-	1	4
Moreton Town	1	2	2	9	8	12	7	13	17	16
Morris Motors	-	-	9	14	7	14	-	-	-	-
Newport A.F.C.	-	-	-	-	-	-	-	1	-	-
Northwood	9	13	-	-	-	-	-	-	-	-
Pegasus Juniors	-	-	-	11	12	17	5	9	15	13
Penhill					(See Swindon Athletic)					
Rayners Lane	-	6	12	6	13	13	13	11	13	15
Ruislip Park	-	-	-	-	-	-	-	18	-	-
Sharpness	-	-	4	1	5	7	2	4	-	-
Shortwood United	15	-	1	2	3	3	11	2	6	1
Supermarine	-	7	3	5	11	15	14	17	-	-
Swindon Athletic	-	-	-	-	9	6	9	10	16	8
Thame United	5	3	16	10	17	9	-	-	-	-
Viking Sports	-	-	-	-	4	11	17	-	-	-
Wallingford Town	4	10	15	12	16	18	16	-	-	-
Wantage Town	8	15	7	16	18	-	12	14	18	-
Yate Town	-	-	-	8	10	1	1	-	-	-
No. of clubs competing	**16**	**17**	**18**	**18**	**18**	**18**	**17**	**18**	**18**	**18**

ABINGDON UNITED

President: R Barlow FJMI   **Chairman:** P Evans   **Manager:** G Clark
Secretary: Terry Hutchinson, 9 Lucca Drive, Sutton Fields, Abingdon OX14 5QP (0235 523017).
Press Officer: W Fletcher (0235 20255).   **Ground:** Northcourt Road, Abingdon (0235 20255).
Directions: 1 mile north of town on A34. 2 miles from Redley (BR)
Seats: 52   **Cover:** 120   **Capacity:** 2,000   **Floodlights:** No   **Founded:** 1946
Colours: Yellow/blue/yellow   **Change colours:** White/blue
Previous leagues: North Berks
Programme: 30p   **Programme Editor:** W Fletcher, ACJI (0235 20255).
Record Gate: 500 v Abingdon Town, Berks & Bucks Senior Cup 1989-90.
Clubhouse: Two bars, membership 350. Open normal hours. New Clubhouse summer 1989.
Honours: N Berks Lg 53-54 (Lg Cup R-up 53-54, Charity Shield 52-53), Hellenic Div 1 R-up 76-77 81-82 (Lg Cup R-up 89-90, Div 1 Cup 65-66 81-82 (R-up 66-67), Berks & Bucks Snr Cup R-up 83-84.

ALMONDSBURY PICKSONS

Secretary: D W Winstone, 4 St Michaels Close, Winterbourne, Bristol BS17 1NS (0454 773771).
Manager: Steve Fey   **Ground:** Oaklands Park, Almondsbury, Bristol (0454 612220).
Directions: Adjacent to M5 junction 16 - follow A38 Thornbury - ground first left. 4 miles from Bristol Parkway (BR). County bus services to Thornbury, Stroud and Gloucester.
Seats: None   **Cover:** No   **Capacity:** 2,000   **Floodlights:** Yes   **Founded:** 1897
Colours: Blue   **Change colours:** Red   **Record Gate:** Hellenic Cup Final rep. 89-90.
Previous Leagues: Bristol Weslyan/ Bristol Suburban/ Bristol Premier Comb./ Glos Co.
Previous Names: Almondsbury/ Almondsbury Greenway/ Almondsbury '85/ Almondsbury Picksons.
Previous Ground: Almondsbury Rec. (until 1986).   **Programme:** 20 pages 25p
Nickname: Almonds. **Clubhouse:** 7 days, all sports, refreshments, function room, entertainment, skittles.
Hons: FA Vase R-up 78-79 (SF 77-78), Glos Co. Lg(4) 76-78 79-81 (R-up 75-76 81-82), GFA Chal. Tphy 78-79 (R-up 80-81), Avon Prem. Comb. 74-75, Glos Snr Amtr Cup 87-88, Hellenic Lg 83-84 (R-up 82-83, Lg Cup(2) 83-85).

BANBURY UNITED

Secretary: D K Jesson, 'Wychwood House', 3 Winchester Close, Banbury OX16 8FB (0295 257262).
Manager: Wallie Hastie   **Ground:** The Stadium, off Station Rd, Banbury Oxon (0295 3354).
Directions: Right turn down narrow lane before entering Banbury BR station forecourt; eastern end of town.
Seats: 40   **Cover:** Large terrace **Capacity:** 6,500   **Floodlights:** Yes   **Founded:** 1965
Colours: White/blue/red   **Change colours:** All yellow   **Nickname:** Gay Puritans.
Previous Leagues: Oxon Snr/ B'gham Comb. 35-54/ West Mids 54-66/ Southern 66-90.
Record Attendance: 7,000 v Oxford City, FA Cup Qualifying Competition 1947.
Best FA Cup season: 1st Rd replay 73-74 (Also 1st Rd 47-48 61-62 72-73).
Best FA Tphy year: 3rd Rd 70-71 73-74. **Clubhouse:** Match days & week-ends. Mid-week on hire.
Record Fee Paid: £2,000 P Emsden (Oxford Utd)   **Rec'd:** £20,000 K Wilson (Derby)
Previous Name: Banbury Spencer.   **Programme:** 24 pages 50p, **Editor:** Barry Worsley
Players progressing to Football League: Ollie Kearns (Reading), Kevin Wilson (Derby), Terry Muckleberg (Oxford).
Honours: Oxon Snr Cup 78-79 87-88 (R-up 35-36 82-83 86-87 88-89), Birmingham Comb. R-up 47-48, Oxon Prof. Cup 52-53(jt) 70-71(jt) 72-73 77-78 79-80(jt), Hellenic Lg Cup R-up 91-92, Birmingham Snr Cup R-up 48-49 59-60 (SF 46-47), Oxon Snr Lg 34-35 39-40, Banbury Jnr Lg 33-34, Oxon Charity Cup 34-35 (R-up 39-40), Banbury Charity Cup 34-35, Banbury Gold Cross Cup R-up 34-35, Oxon Hosp. Cup 46-47 (R-up 45-46), Oxon Benev. Cup R-up 77-78 80-81 82-83, Daventry Charity Cup 89-90, Smiths Mem. Cup 68-69 69-70 (R-up 66-67 67-68), Hitchin Centenary Cup 68-69 (R-up 67-68).

BICESTER TOWN

Secretary/Press Officer: Phil Allen, 38 Bassett Avenue, Bicester OX6 7TZ (0869 252125).
Commercial Manager: Secretary   **Manager:** Kevin Leach.
Ground: Sports Ground, Oxford Rd, Bicester (0869 241936)   **Clubhouse:** One bar
Directions: Outskirts of town on Oxford Road.   **Nickname:** Foxhunters.
Seats: 250   **Cover:** 550   **Capacity:**   **Floodlights:** No   **Founded:** 1876
Colours: Red   **Change colours:** White   **Previous Leagues:** Oxon Senior
Previous Name: Slade Banbury Road (pre-1923).   **Programme Editors:** A J Pickett/A Lyne.
Record Gate: 850 v Oxford United.   **Hons:** Hellenic Lg 60-1 77-78 (Lg Cup 90-91, Div 1 76-77).

CINDERFORD TOWN

Chairman: A J Mayo   **Manager:** Tim Harris.
Secretary: D H Gettings, 120 Estcourt Road, Gloucester GL1 3LH (0452 714147).
Ground: The Causeway, Hilldene, Cinderford, Glos (0594 22039).
Directions: From Gloucester take A40 to Ross-on-Wye, then A48 - Chepstow. In 10 miles turn right onto A4151 signed Cinderford. Ground 5 mins walk from town centre.
Seats: 100   **Cover:** 1,000   **Capacity:** 5,000   **Floodlights:** Yes   **Founded:** 1922.
Club colours: White/black/black   **Change colours:** Red/blue/blue
Record Attendance: 4,850 v Minehead, 1955-56.
Previous Lgs: Western 40-59/ Glos Northern Snr/ Warks Comb./ W Mids 65-69/ Mids Comb. 74-84/ Glos Co.
Hons: Hellenic Lg Div 1 90-91, Glos Northern Snr Lg Div 1 38-39 60-61 (R-up(6) 35-37 61-63 66-67 80-81), Nth Glos Lg Div 1 38-39 60-61, Glos Snr Amtr Cup (Nth)(6) 49-50 54-56 68-69 70-71 76-77 (R-up 34-35 57-58 60-61), Western Lg Div 2 56-57, Warwickshire Comb. 63-64, W Mids Lg Prem Div Cup 68-69, Glos Jnr Cup (Nth) 80-81, Midland Comb. 81-82, Glos Co. Lg 69-70 71-72 73-74.

CIRENCESTER TOWN

President: Alec Hibberd   **Chairman:** Robin Thompson
Secretary: Tim Bennett, 8 Purley Avenue, Cirencester, Glos GL7 1EN (0285 65302).
Ground: The Stadium, Smithsfield, Chesterton Lane, Cirencester (0285 645783).
Directions: Follow By-pass towards Bristol. The ground is on the left approx quarter of a mile from town. 3 miles from Kemble (BR).
Seats: None   **Cover:** 200   **Capacity:** 1,500   **Floodlights:** Yes   **Founded:** 1870
Colours: Red & black stripes/Black/black   **Change colours:** Yellow/blue/yellow
Record Attendance: 1,200 in 1968 FA Amateur Cup.   **Clubhouse details:** Open 5 nights
Hons: GFA Senior Amtr Cup 79-80, GFA Challenge Trophy R-up 91-92, Hellenic Lg R-up 91-92 (Div 1 73-74 (R-up 90-91), Div 1 Cup 90-91).

Abingdon United pictured before their Berks & Bucks Senior Cup tie at Sandhurst Town on November 2nd 1991. Photo - Eric Marsh.

Banbury United, Hellenic League Premier Division Cup Runners-up 1991-92.

Didcot Town, Hellenic League Premier Division Cup winners 1991-92. Back Row (L/R): Jim Charman (Chairman), Ian Miller (Programme Secretary), Trevor Mason, Freddy Stevens, John Ward, Neil Arnold, Andy Sly, Chris Fontaine, Tony Ingram, Larry Hill (Manager). Front: Jason Caffel, Phil Thomas, Simon Knight, Paul Spittle, Paul Noble, Jason Millar, Dave Bradshaw. Photo - Dave West.

DIDCOT TOWN

President: Bryan Gough   **Chairman:** Jim Charman   **Manager:** Larry Hill
Secretary: J A Gardner, 8 Green Close, Didcot OX11 8TE (0235 813884).
Ground: 58 Station Road, Didcot (0235 813212).   **Clubhouse:** Every evenings and Sunday lunchtimes.
Directions: Midway down Station Rd, Didcot, on right quarter mile from Railway Station towards town centre.
Seats: None   **Cover:** 200   **Capacity:** 5,000   **Floodlights:** No   **Founded:** 1907
Colours: Red/white   **Change colours:** White/red
Prev. Lges: Hellenic 53-57/ Metropolitan 57-63.   **Nickname:** Railwaymen.
Record Attendance: 2,000 v Wycombe Wanderers, Berks & Bucks Senior Cup 1953.
Programme: 50p   **Programme Editor:** Ian Miller.
Honours: Hellenic Lg 53-54 (Lg Cup 1965-66 66-67, Div 1 76-77, Div 1 Cup 76-77).

FAIRFORD TOWN

President: B W Wall   **Chairman:** M B Tanner
Secretary: M J Cook, "Bow Wow" Down Ampney, Cirencester GL7 1EW (0793 751240).
Ground: Cinder Lane, Fairford, Cirencester (0285 712071).
Directions: Entering Fairford from Lechlade turn left down Cinder Lane 150yds after 40mph sign. Buses from Swindon, Lechlade and Cirencester.
Seats: None   **Cover:** 200   **Capacity:** 2,000   **Floodlights:** Yes   **Founded:** 1891
Colours: Red/white   **Previous Lges:** Cirencester & District, Swindon & District.
Change colours: Blue   **Record Gate:** 1,200 v TV Entertainers XI, April 1988.
Clubhouse: Open every evening + weekend & Bank Holiday lunch.
Hons: Glos Challenge Trophy 79-80 (R-up 82-83), Hellenic Lg R-up 90-91.   **Nickname:** Town.

HEADINGTON AMATEURS

President: John Dunne   **Chairman:** P Sammons   **Manager:** J Light.
Secretary: S P Giles, 60 Glebelands, Headington, Oxford OX3 7EN (0865 60810).
Ground: Phoenix Sports & Social Club, Barton Village Road, Barton, Oxon (0865 60489).
Directions: Exit off London Rd r'bout, Headington, into Barton Estate. Grnd at bottom left side of estate.
Seats: None   **Cover:** None   **Floodlights:** No   **Founded:** 1949.
Colours: All red   **Change colours:** Blue & white
Previous Leagues: Oxford City Junior 49-66/ Oxford Senior 67-88.
Programme: 24 pages, £1 with with admission   **Programme Editor:** Stan Haksworth
Previous Ground: Romanway, Cowley (pre-1990).   **Clubhouse:** Sports & Social Club
Hons: Oxon Snr Lg 72-73 73-74 75-76 76-77 (R-up 71-72 74-75 77-78 81-82 84-85, Div 1 68-69, Presidents Cup 72-73 73-74 (R-up 71-72 77-78 84-85)), Oxon Charity Cup 75-76, Hellenic Lg Div 1 R-up 87-88, Oxon I'mediate Cup 88-89.

KINTBURY RANGERS

President: P Adamson   **Chairman:** P Adamson
Secretary: A K Plank, 26 Kennet Road, Kintbury, Newbury RG15 0XW (0488 58460).
Ground: Recreation Ground, Inkpen Road, Kintbury (0488 57001).
Directions: Turn off A4 between Newbury/Hungerford. 2nd left into Inkpen Road. 200yds on right by Jubilee Centre. Half mile from Kintbury (BR).
Seats: None   **Cover:** No   **Capacity:** 1,000   **Floodlights:** Yes   **Founded:** 1890
Colours: Amber/black   **Change colours:** White/blue   **Reformed:** 1943.
Nickname: Rangers   **Previous Leagues:** Newbury District/ North Berks.
Programme: Yes   **Programme Editor:** N Matthews (0488 84117).
Record Gate: 400 v Newport AFC, 1990.   **Clubhouse:** Open every night except Wednesday
Hons: Nth Berks Lg 77-78 81-82, Hellenic Lg Div 1 R-up 87-88, Berks & Bucks I'mediate Cup 60-61 (R-up 87-88).

MILTON UNITED

President: G Cannon   **Chairman:** J Cannon
Secretary: M James, 45 Whitehorns Way, Drayton, Abingdon OX14 4LH (0235 31789).
Ground: The Sportsfield, High Street, Milton, Abingdon, Oxon (0235) 832999   **Founded:** 1926
Directions: Use A34 bypass approx 10 miles north of M4 jct.13 & 10 miles south of Oxford. Leave A34 at Milton Hill roundabout follow signs to Milton Park Est. After roundabout follow road over railway bridge, take 1st left, ground immediately on left.
Colours: Claret & Sky/sky blue   **Change colours:** Sky blue, Claret trim or white, claret trim
Hons: Hellenic Lg 90-91 (Div 1 89-90), Nth Berks Lg(4) 85-86 87-89 (R-up 84-85 86-87, Lg Cup(3) 84-86 88-89, Div 2 80-81, Charity Shield(4) 84-86 87-89 (R-up 82-83), Nth Berks War Mem. Cup(3) 83-85 87-88, Berks & Bucks I'mediate Cup 90-91.

MORETON TOWN

President: Lord Dulverton   **Chairman:** C Miles
Secretary: Colin Hancox, 2 Keble Road, Moreton-in-the-Marsh, Glos GL56 0DZ (0608) 50972
Ground: London Road, Moreton-in-the-Marsh (0608 50861).
Directions: On main Oxford - Worcester road. Half mile from Moreton (BR).
Seats: None   **Cover:** 400   **Capacity:** 3,000   **Floodlights:** Yes   **Founded:** 1908.
Colours: White/blue/white   **Change colours:** Red/white/red   **Programme:** Yes
Nickname: Lilywhites   **Previous Leagues:** Cheltenham/ Mid Cotswold
Record Gate: 1,100 v Newport, 1963.   **Clubhouse:** Open every night except Monday
Hons: Biggart Cup 69-70, Hellenic Lg 73-74 75-76 82-83 (R-up 74-75 75-76 81-82 83-84 84-85), Beighton Cup.

PEGASUS JUNIORS

President: P S Hill   **Chairman:** R W Pasley
Secretary: R J Perks, 40 Foley Street, Hereford HR1 2SQ (0432 272524).
Ground: Essex Arms Sports Ground, Widemarsh Street, Hereford (0432 268705).
Directions: 200 yds behind Hereford Utd FC (Edgar Street) - across car park. 1 mile from Barrs Court (BR).
Seats: 20   **Cover:** 50   **Capacity:** 1,500   **Floodlights:** No   **Founded:** 1955
Colours: Red   **Change colours:** White   **Previous leagues:** Hereford/Worcester
Programme: 20p   **Programme Editor:** D.Llewellyn   **Clubhouse:** 48 Stowens Street.
Hons: Herefordshire Snr Amtr Cup 71-72, Herefordshire Co. Chal. Cup(5) 81-83 84-85 87-88 89-90, Worcs Snr Urn 85-86, Hellenic Lg Div 1 84-85.

Didcot press hard for an equaliser in their 0-1 defeat at Bicester Town. Photo - Neil Whittington.

Headington Amateurs: Back Row (L/R): J Light (Manager), D Thorne, J Hilland, G Weaving, J Cartwright, K Drackett, W Gardner, M Stevens, B McCrae (Asst Mgr). Front: C McMahon, A Penge, M Smy, D Anderson, M Roper, S Thompkins. Photo - Steve Daniels.

Kintbury Rangers pictured on the Isle of Wight before their FA Vase tie against Ryde Sports. Photo - Eric Marsh.

RAYNERS LANE

Chairman: Dave Blewitt   **Treasurer:** Danny Maher   **President:** Tom Lynn
Secretary: A N Pratt, 4 Stirling Close, Cowley, Uxbridge, Middx (0895 233853).
Manager: Don Durkin   **Assistant Manager:** Richard Hedge.
Commercial Manager: Chairman   **Press Officer:** Manager (0753 889502).
Ground: 51 Rayners Lane, Harrow, Middx (081 866 9659).
Directions: Turn right from Rayners Lane Station, take 1st turning left (Rayners Lane), ground on right.
Seats: 32   **Cover:** 70   **Capacity:** 1,000   **Floodlights:** No   **Founded:** 1933
Colours: Green/white   **Change colours:** red/black
Previous Leagues: Parthenon   **Nickname:** The Lane.
Programme: 28 pages   **Programme Editor:** Peter Ferrier.
Record Attendance: 550 v Wealdstone, Middx Senior Cup.
Clubhouse: 2 bars, entertainment, dressing rooms
Hons: Hellenic Lg 82-83 (Div 1 Cup 1980-81), Middx Lg Cup 71-72, Middx Premier Cup 83-84 (R-up 72-73), Harrow Wembley & Dist. Lg 39-40 40-41 44-45 (Lg Cup 41-42 43-44 44-45), Parthenon Lg 50-51 (R-up 52-53, Lg Cup 48-49 52-53 56-57), Middx Summer Cup 1991, West Middx Midweek Lg 36-37.

SHORTWOOD UNITED

President: J Martin   **Chairman:** P Webb   **Secretary:** TBA.
Manager: Pat Casey.   **Press Officer:** M Webb (0453 833204).
Physiotherapist: A Dodds/A Brown   **Commercial Manager:** P D Webb.
Ground: "Meadow Bank", Shortwood, Nailsworth, Gloucestershire (0453 833936).
Directions: In Nailsworth turn into Spring Hill then first left. Continue past shop and and keep left past "Britannia" (signposted Shortwood) - continue to end for ground. 4 miles from Stroud (BR).
Seats: 30   **Cover:** 200   **Capacity:** 5,000   **Floodlights:** Yes   **Founded:** 1900
Colours: Red/black/red   **Change colours:** Yellow/blue/yellow
Previous Leagues: Glos County   **Nickname:** The Wood.
Programme Editor: M Webb   **Record Attendance:** 900, FA Vase 5th Rd 81-82.
Clubhouse: Sports & Social Club on ground open before matches to 2.00pm after matches 4.00pm.
Hons: Glos Co. Lg 81-82, Glos Tphy 83-84 91-92, Hellenic Lg 84-85 91-92 (R-up 85-86 89-90, Div 1 Cup 83-84), Hungerford Merit Cup, Glos Snr Amtr Cup 85-86.

SWINDON SUPERMARINE

Secretary: E Stott, 43 Stanier Street, Swindon, Wilts SN1 5QU (0793 521301).
Ground: Highworth Road, South Marston, Swindon (0973) 824828
Directions: On A361 Swindon/Highworth road, adjoining Marston Industrial Estate. 6 miles from Swindon (BR) - buses in direction of Highworth, Fairford & Lechdale. If lost ask for Vickers Sports Ground.
Seats: 75   **Cover:** 120   **Capacity:** 1,000   **Floodlights:** No   **Founded:** 1992.
Colours: **Change colours:**   **Programme:** Yes
Previous Names: Supermarine (prev. Vickers Armstrong 46-81), Swindon Athletic (prev. Penhill Yth Centre 70-84/ Penhill 84-84-89) amalgamated in 1992.
Previous Leagues: Supermarine: Wilts, *Swindon Athletic: Wilts/ Swindon & District.*
Previous Ground: Supermarine: Vickers Airfield (until mid-1960s), *Swindon Ath.: Merton 70-84/ 'Southbrook', Pinehurst Road 84-92.*
Hons: Supermarine: Wilts Snr Cup 85-86 (R-up 74-75 84-85), Hellenic Div 1 R-Up 82-83 (Res Section West R-up 84-85 (Challenge Cup 83-84), Wilts Comb Snr 75-76, Swindon & District Lg Div 3 55-56, Dr Elliott Cup(5), Faringdon Thursday Memorial Cup(3). *Swindon Ath.: Wilts Snr Cup 82-83 86-87 89-90 (R-up 83-84 85-86 90-91), Hellenic Lg Div 1 85-86 86-87, Wilts Co. Lg 82-83 83-84).*

WANTAGE TOWN

President: **Chairman:** Ernie Smart.
Secretary: T Bolton, 15 Broadmarsh Close, Grove, Wantage, Oxon (02357 4223).
Ground: Alfredian Park, Wantage, Oxon (023 57) 4781
Directions: Take Hungerford Road from Wantage, ground signposted on right oppsite recreation ground.
Seats: 50   **Cover:** 300   **Capacity:** 1,500   **Floodlights:** No   **Founded:** 1892
Colours: Green & white/white/green   **Change colours:** Blue/white/blue
Previous Leagues: Swindon & District.   **Record Attendance:** 1,800
Programme: Yes   **Programme Editor:** Eric Pride (02357) 66608
Clubhouse: Bar open evenings, Tues, Wed, Thurs, Fri, Sat
Hons: Hellenic Lg 80-81 (R-up 81-82, Div 1 R-up 87-88 91-92, Div 1 Cup R-up 91-92), Oxon Snr Cup 82-83.

WOLLEN SPORTS

Secretary: Terry Wollen, 4 Belle Vue Road, Swindon SN1 3HQ (0793 531818).
Ground: The Barn, Blackworth, Highworth, Wilts
Directions: Leaving Highworth heading north on A361. Ground on right 300yds past Blackworth roundabout.
Seats: **Cover:**   **Capacity:**   **Floodlights:** No   **Founded:**
Colours: Green & white/green/green   **Change colours:** All blue
Clubhouse: **Hons:** Hellenic Lg Div 1 91-92 (Div 1 Cup R-up 91-92).

DIVISION ONE CLUBS 1992-93

BISHOPS CLEEVE

President: D Billingham   **Chairman:** J Davies
Secretary: Phil Tustain, 7 Dale Walk, Bishops Cleeve, Glos GL52 4PR (0242 674968).
Ground: Stoke Rd, Bishops Cleeve (084267 6752).   **Directions:** 3 miles north of Cheltenham on A435. 3rd left in village. 4 miles from Cheltenham (BR); served by Cheltenham to Tewkesbury buses.
Seats: None   **Cover:** 50   **Capacity:** 1,500   **Floodlights:** No   **Founded:** 1892.
Colours: Green/silver/silver   **Change colours:** White
Previous leagues: Cheltenham, North Gloucestershire.
Previous Grounds: The Skiller (pre-1913), Village Field (pre-1950).
Record Gate: 1,000 v Cardiff City, clubhouse opening.
Clubhouse: Full facilities, bar, dance area **Honours:** Hellenic Lg Cup R-up 90-91.

CARTERTON TOWN

President: G Fox   **Chairman:** R C Gullis
Secretary: B A Hathaway, 4 Minty Close, Carterton OX8 3LL (0993 842578).
Manager: Graham Hurn   **Press Officer:** K Rose (0993 841105).
Ground: Kilkenny Lane (0993 842410)**Directions:** At end of Swinbrook Road which is west of town centre.
Seats: No   **Cover:** No   **Capacity:**   **Floodlights:** No   **Founded:** 1922
Colours: Blue (yellow trim)/blue   **Change colours:** All yellow blue trim   **Reformed:** 1946
Previous Leagues: Witney & District   **Clubhouse:** Recently refurbished. Lounge & licensed bar facilities.
Hons: Oxon Junior Shield 85-86, Oxon Snr Cup R-up 90-91, Witney & Dist. Lg 65-66 (Div 1 84-85 76-77), Hellenic Lg Div 1 89-90 (Reserve Div 1989-90).

CHELTENHAM SARACENS

President: P Tarling   **Chairman:** J Utteridge
Secretary: R Attwood, 179 Arle Road, Cheltenham GL51 8LJ (0242 515855).
Manager: Roger Cottle   **Press Officer:** T Coates (0242 520499).
Ground: Tewkesbury Road (0242) 589134   **Previous League:** Cheltenham.
Directions: 1 mile from Cheltenham centre on A4019 Tewksbury Road (next to B & Q) - 1st left over railway bridge, 1st left and follow service road.
Seats: **Cover:** Yes   **Capacity:** 500   **Floodlights:** No   **Founded:** 1964
Colours: All blue   **Change colours:** Red/black/black.
Programme: Yes   **Programme Editor:** T Coates
Nickname: Saras   **Clubhouse:** 16-20, Swindon Road, Cheltenham
Hons: Glos Snr Cup R-up 91-92.

CHIPPING NORTON TOWN

President: Bob Tanner   **Manager:** Steve Slaughter.
Secretary: R J Tanner, 3 Cotswold Terrace, Chipping Norton, Oxon OX7 5DU (0608 641490).
Ground: Hailey Road (0608 642562).
Directions: From Swindon past school, immediately left into Waterbrush Road - ground at end. From Oxford; through town, left for Burford at Post Office, past Fire Station, next right into Waterbrush Road - ground at end.
Seats: **Cover:** 300   **Capacity:** 1,000   **Floodlights:** Yes   **Founded:** 1893
Colours: Black & white stripes/white/white   **Change colours:** Red/black/white
Programme: Adverts & fill in page with admission   **Programme Editor:** David Webb
Previous Leagues: Oxon Snr/ Hellenic 53-79/ Mids Comb. 79-84.   **Nickname:** Magpies
Clubhouse details: Well furnished bar and hall with own bar.
Hons: Oxon Jnr Shield 1899, Oxon Snr Lg 50-51, Oxon Charity Cup 48-49, Oxon Benev. Cup 49-50, Oxon Snr Cup(2) 76-78, Hellenic Lg 77-78 (Div 1 60-61 71-72, Div 1 Cup R-up 88-89), Cold Shield Cup 78-79, Mids Comb. 80-81.

CIRENCESTER UNITED

President: G Price   **Chairman:** R W Dorey
Secretary: P Spielberg, 78 Melmore Gardens, Cirencester, Glos GL7 1JW (0285 651726).
Ground: Four Acres P.F., Chesterton Lane, Cirencester (0285 651726).   **Press Officer:** D Trinder
Directions: Dual carriageway towards Bristol, under footbridge, first left after Cirencester Town FC, ground 200yds on left hand side.
Seats: No   **Cover:**   **Programme:** Yes   **Floodlights:** No   **Founded:** 1970
Colours: White/red/red   **Change colours:** Yellow & green/green/yellow
Clubhouse: Limited bar licence.   **Previous Name:** The Herd (pre-1990)

CLANFIELD

President: Brian Wallis   **Chairman:** B Court
Secretary: J Osborne, 70 Lancut Road, Witney, Oxon OX8 5AQ (0993 771631).
Manager: A Jennings   **Press Officer:** J Osborne
Ground: Radcot Road (0367 81314).**Directions:** On A4095 8 miles west of Witney, south side of Clanfield.
Seats: No   **Cover:** 300   **Capacity:** 2,000   **Floodlights:** No   **Founded:** 1890
Colours: All red   **Change colours:** Blue/white/blue   **Previous League:** Witney & Dist.
Programme: Yes, with admission   **Editor:** J Osborne   **Nickname:** Robins
Clubhouse: Open every evening & Sat/Sun lunch   **Hons:** Oxon Jnr Shield 32-33, Oxon I'mediate Cup 67-68, Witney & Dist. Lg 66-67 (Div 1 65-66, Div 2 64-65), Hellenic Lg Cup 72-73 (Div 1 Cup 69-70 85-86), Jim Newman Mem. Tphy 83-84 87-88, Faringdon Thursday Cup 69-70 71-72.

EASINGTON SPORTS

Chairman: Terry Horley   **Manager:** R Teidman
Secretary: R Cogbill, 30 Adamson Road, Banbury, Oxon OX16 9DH (0295 251374).
Ground: Addison Road, Easington Estate, Banbury, Oxon (0295 51374).
Directions: From Oxford A423. After passing under flyover on the outskirts take first turning left into Grange Road then third right into Addison Rd. Ground at top on left. One and a half miles from Banbury (BR).
Seats: 50   **Cover:** 150   **Capacity:** 1,000   **Floodlights:** No   **Founded:** 1946
Colours: Red & white stripes/white/white   **Change colours:** Yellow/white/white
Programme: Free with admission.   **Previous Ground:** Bodicote.
Record Gate: 300 v Witney, Oxon Senior Cup 1956
Previous Leagues: Banbury Junior/ Oxon Senior/ Warks Combination.
Clubhouse: Changing rooms, showers, bar facilities and food.
Honours: Oxon Snr Cup R-up, Oxon Intermediate League & Cup, Oxon Snr Lg.

HIGHWORTH TOWN

President: Alan Vockins   **Chairman:** Brian Higgs
Secretary: F Haines, 'Journeys End', Lechlade Road, Highworth, Swindon SN6 7HG (0793 763846).
Directions: Enter on A361, turn left into Green by Vet's Surgery - ground & car park 200yds on left.
Seats: No   **Cover:** No   **Capacity:** 1,000   **Floodlights:** No   **Founded:** 1904
Colours: Red/white/red   **Change colours:** Red/black/red
Programme: Yes   **Editor:** Fraser Haines (0793) 763846   **Record Gate:** 500.
Clubhouse: Bar facilities etc.   **Previous Leagues:** Wiltshire/Swindon & District
Hons: Wilts Snr Cup(2)(R-up 88-89), Hellenic Div 1 Cup 88-89, Arthur Shipway Cup 88-89.

KIDLINGTON

President: Colin Rosser   **Chairman:** A F Grose   **Manager:** Ken Fagan
Secretary: A Canning, 6 Meadow View, Kidlington, Oxford OX5 1HQ (08675 7726).
Commercial Manager: J Nicholl   **Ground:** Yarnton Rd, Kidlington, Oxford (08675 5628).
Directions: From Kidlington r'bout (junction of A4260 & A34) A423 north to Kidlington; after 1st lights take 2nd left (Yarnton Road), ground is 200yds on the left.
Colours: White/red/topaz   **Change colours:** All maroon   **Floodlights:** No
Programme: 20 pages, 20p   **Programme Editor:** M A Canning   **Founded:** 1920
Previous League: Oxon Snr 47-54.   **Clubhouse:** Two bars open after matches
Honours: Oxon Snr Lg 53-54 (R-up 47-48), Hellenic Lg Cup 74-75 (R-up 68-69 73-74 74-75), Div 1 R-up 63-64 78-79), Oxon Intermediate Cup 52-53 84-85 (R-up 68-69 73-74 74-75), FA Vase 5th last sixteen 76-77.

LAMBOURN SPORTS

President: N L Fraser   **Chairman:** A E Cripps   **Manager:** J Willoughby
Secretary: C G Bettison, Carabey House, Newbury Road, Lambourn, Berks RG16 7LL (0488 71834).
Ground: Bockhampton Rd, Lambourn, Berks (0488 71335).   **Directions:** From Lambourn Church take Newbury St, then 1st right into Station Rd, left at T junction into Bockhampton Rd, ground on left.
Seats: 150   **Capacity:** 2,000   **Floodlights:** No   **Founded:** 1889
Colours: Red & white stripes/red/red   **Change colours:** All blue   **Programme:** 12 pages
Previous Leagues: Newbury & Dist. 11-51/ Swindon & Dist. 51-61/ Hellenic 61-72/ Nth Berks 72-77.
Clubhouse: Bars, lounge, dancehall, billiard room, kitchen, open 7 nights, Saturdays from 4pm
Hons: Berks & Bucks Snr Cup 61-62 79-80, Hellenic Div 1 81-82 (R-up 61-62, Div 1 Cup 61-62 79-80).

NORTH LEIGH

President: Mrs Christine Smith   **Chairman:** Barry Norton   **Manager:** Peter King
Secretary: Peter J Dix, 8 Windmill Close, North Leigh, Nr Witney, Oxon OX8 6RP (0993) 881199
Manager: Peter King   **Press Officer:** Barry Norton (0993) 881777
Ground: Eynsham Hall Sports Ground, North Leigh, nr Witney, Oxon (0993) 881427
Simple ground directions: Ground is situated on A4095 Witney to Woodstock road 3miles East of Witney. Entrance to ground is 300yds east of Main Park Entrance.
Seats: **Cover:** No   **Capacity:** 1,000   **Floodlights:** No   **Founded:** 1908
Colours: Navy & sky.   **Change colours:** White/navy/red   **Programme:** Yes
Clubhouse: Yes with aftermatch Bar facilities   **Hons:** Oxon Jnr Shield 56-57 83-84, Oxon Charity Cup 84-85 88-89, Witney & Dist. Lg(12) 50-57 85-90 (Lg Cup(10) 47-48 51-52 53-55 56-57 81-82 85-89).

PURTON

President: Graham Price   **Chairman:** Alan Eastwood   **Manager:** Steve Paish
Secretary: Alan Eastwood, 36 Portal Road, Swindon SW21 1PY (0793) 6940361
Ground: Red House, Purton (0793 770262 - Saturday afternoons only).
Directions: Purton is on B4041 Wootton Bassett to Cricklade Road. Ground near village hall.
Seats: **Capacity**   **Cover:**   **Floodlights:** No   **Founded:** 1923
Colours: Red/white/red   **Change colours:** White/white/black & red.
Programme: 24 pages, 30p   **Programme Editor:** Alan Eastwood
Clubhouse: 4.30pm - 6pm Sat. and after matches midweek.   **Hons:** Wilts Lg 85-86 (Div 2 83-84), Wilts Snr Cup(6) 38-39 48-49 50-51 54-55 87-89, Wilts Yth Cup 77-78 85-86, Fairford Hosp. Cup(2) 87-89.

TUFFLEY ROVERS

Secretary: D M Williams, 10 Byron Avenue, Gloucester GL2 6AF (0452 305776).
Ground: Lower Tuffley Lane, Gloucester (0452 504905).
Programme: Yes   **Floodlights:** No   **Founded:** 1946   **Colours:** Claret & blue stripes/blue/blue
Previous League: Glos Co. (pre'91)   **Hons:** Glos Co. League 90-91.

WALLINGFORD TOWN

President: A Hume   **Manager:** Sean Bradford
Chairman/Secretary: Alan Brannan, 1 St Georges Green, Wallingford Oxon OX10 8JQ (0491 35751).
Ground: The Hithercroft Sports Complex, Wallingford (0491) 35044
Directions: From traffic lights at Lamb cross-roads take road into Town Square, follow oneway system then take 1st right into St Johns Road after r'bout at Green Tree pub. Left at Plough pub - ground 200yds on right past Habitat. 2 miles from Cholsey (BR).
Seats: No   **Cover:** 1,000   **Capacity:** 1,500   **Floodlights:** No   **Founded:** 1922
Club colours: White/white/red   **Change colours:** All red
Programme: 16 pages   **Programme Editor:** A Brannan
Nickname: The Town   **Previous Ground:** The Bull Croft (pre-1922)
Previous League: Reading & District   **Record Gate:** 500 v Oxford United, 1985.
Players progressing to Football League: John Dreyer (Oxford United 1985).
Clubhouse: Bar and members lounge, clubhouse open every night.   **Hons:** Hellenic Lg 68-69.

WOOTTON BASSETT TOWN

Chairman: Alan Blyth   **Manager:** Micky Woolford
Secretary: R Carter, 14 Balckthorn Close, Wootton Bassett, Swindon Wilts SN4 7JE (0793 851386).
Ground: Gerard Buxton Sports Ground, Rylands Way, Wootton Bassett, Swindon (0793) 853880
Directions: M4 jnct 16 to Wootton Bassett (A3102), left at 2nd r'bout, 2nd left into Longleaze & Rylands Way 3rd turning on right by shops. Ground 100yds on right.
Seats: 100   **Cover:** Yes   **Capacity:** 2,000   **Floodlights:** No   **Founded:** 1882
Colours: All royal blue   **Change colours:** White/white/red.
Programme: 12 pages, free   **Programme Editor:** Rod Carter
Record Gate: 1,750 v Swindon Town, friendly 20/7/91.
Hons: Wilts Lg 87-88, FA Amtr Cup QF 26-27, Hellenic Div 1 Cup 89-90.

YARNTON

Chairman: Alan Blyth   **Secretary:** B G Harris, 28 Orpwood Way, Abingdon OX14 5PX (0235 526621).
Ground: Marsh Road Sports Ground, Yarnton, Oxon (0865 842037).
Directions: North of Oxford on A44 - head for Woodstock/Chipping Norton. Ground situated behind The Grapes pub. Entrance on right before roundabout.
Colours: Blue & white stripes/blue/blue   **Change colours:** All yellow.
Previous League: Oxfordshire Senior.   **Floodlights:** No

OXFORDSHIRE
'BANBURY SPORTS' SENIOR LEAGUE

President: Mr A Search,
Chairman: Mr R A Brock,
Hon. Secretary: Mr K Rogers,
65 Bagley Close, Kenningtoon, Oxford OX1 5LT (0865 739173)

LEAGUE TABLES 91-92

Premier Division	P	W	D	L	F	A	PTS
Watlington	26	20	2	4	71	27	62
Quarry Nomads	26	17	3	6	44	19	54
Ardley United	26	16	5	5	62	33	53
Garsington	26	16	2	8	64	41	50
Woodstock Town	26	14	5	7	62	38	47
Eynsham	26	13	3	10	66	55	42
Worc. College OB.	26	10	4	12	43	55	34
Oakley United	26	10	3	13	41	65	33
Old Woodstock	26	8	6	12	48	57	30
Long Crendon	26	9	3	14	39	53	30
Bletchingdon	26	8	4	14	41	50	28
Blackbird Leys ASC	26	7	3	16	41	59	24
Kennington United	26	5	6	15	49	72	21
Marlborough	26	1	7	18	24	71	10

Division One	P	W	D	L	F	A	PTS
AP Spts & Social	28	21	3	4	86	32	66
Oxford Univ. Press	28	21	2	5	86	38	65
Launton Sports	28	20	3	5	75	31	63
Pressed St. Fisher	28	19	2	7	79	40	59
John Radcliffe	28	18	3	7	67	44	57
Northway United	28	14	6	8	85	68	48
AFC Cowley	28	13	3	12	81	61	42
Marston Saints	28	8	9	11	57	63	33
Ardley Utd Res	28	9	5	14	42	51	32
Quarry Nomads Res	28	9	3	16	45	64	30
Bicester Civil S.	28	8	3	17	50	74	27
Old Woodstock Res	28	8	3	17	38	70	27
Charlton United	28	7	1	20	34	68	22
Kennington Utd Res	28	5	4	19	40	93	19
Salesians	28	3	4	21	40	108	13

Division Two	P	W	D	L	F	A	PTS
Garsington Res	28	24	2	2	126	24	74
Eynsham Reserves	28	20	1	7	94	41	61
Bletchingdon Res	28	19	3	6	95	41	60
Long Crendon	28	18	4	6	75	33	58
Watlington Res	28	16	5	7	75	51	53
Launton Spts Res	28	14	3	11	77	55	45
AP Spts & S. Res	28	10	7	11	67	66	37
Marston Saints Res	28	10	6	12	57	66	36
Bicester CS Res	28	11	1	16	50	63	34
Woodstock T. Res	28	9	3	16	47	58	30
Marlborough Res	28	8	6	14	41	61	30
Salesians	28	8	4	16	43	96	28
Oakley Utd Res	28	5	8	15	46	92	23
Oxford U.P. Res	28	5	6	17	42	73	21
Charlton Utd Res	28	2	3	23	29	144	9

PREMIER DIVISION RESULTS 1991/92

HOME TEAM	1	2	3	4	5	6	7	8	9	10	11	12	13	14
1. Ardley United	*	6-0	3-1	3-0	1-3	5-1	1-2	1-1	1-0	4-2	2-0	0-0	3-2	3-0
2. Blackbird Leys ASC	0-0	*	0-4	0-3	0-1	2-3	4-3	4-2	7-0	2-0	2-3	0-5	2-3	3-3
3. Bletchingdon	1-4	3-1	*	3-2	2-5	1-1	0-2	2-0	0-2	2-1	0-1	2-3	2-0	1-2
4. Eynsham	1-3	3-1	6-1	*	2-0	5-3	5-1	5-1	4-1	3-1	0-2	0-2	1-3	4-7
5. Garsington	2-3	1-5	5-3	1-2	*	5-3	3-0	3-0	3-0	5-2	0-3	0-1	2-1	2-1
6. Kennington United	3-5	1-3	1-2	9-2	1-4	*	3-2	1-1	1-1	2-0	1-0	2-4	3-4	0-0
7. Long Crendon	2-1	3-0	1-6	2-2	1-1	3-1	*	3-1	1-3	1-2	0-2	1-2	3-2	0-1
8. Marlborough	2-3	0-0	0-0	3-1	3-4	2-2	0-1	*	0-3	0-5	0-0	1-5	1-9	1-2
9. Oakley United	1-2	3-1	3-2	1-4	0-4	4-3	0-5	3-1	*	4-2	1-1	1-5	0-3	2-1
10. Old Woodstock	2-2	1-2	0-0	1-1	1-3	3-1	3-1	4-3	4-4	*	0-2	2-5	2-2	3-1
11. Quarry Nomads	1-2	+	2-0	2-1	3-0	7-1	4-0	2-0	1-0	0-0	*	1-2	1-4	2-1
12. Watlington	3-2	3-1	2-1	0-2	2-1	1-1	5-1	6-0	4-0	1-2	2-1	*	4-2	0-2
13. Woodstock Town	1-0	2-1	2-1	2-2	1-1	4-0	0-0	0-0	5-2	3-0	0-1	1-0	*	2-4
14. Worcester College OB	2-2	3-0	1-1	2-5	0-5	2-1	1-0	2-1	0-2	3-5	0-2	0-2	0-4	*

+ - points awarded to Quarry Nomads.

DIVISION ONE RESULTS 1991/92

HOME TEAM	1	2	3	4	5	6	7	8	9	10	11	12	13	14	15
1. AFC Cowley	*	0-4	3-0	5-1	7-2	0-3	3-0	2-4	1-2	2-5	2-0	4-4	4-2	6-0	7-1
2. A.P. Sports & Social	1-0	*	6-0	1-2	2-1	3-2	7-2	1-3	3-1	2-1	4-1	1-1	2-1	1-3	4-1
3. Ardley Utd Reserves	3-1	1-1	*	3-1	2-4	0-1	1-2	1-2	2-2	1-1	3-0	0-3	*0-0	0-3	2-1
4. Bicester Civil Service	2-4	0-4	1-6	*	2-1	1-3	3-1	0-0	2-2	0-0	4-2	0-3	1-2	2-1	3-2
5. Charlton United	1-3	1-2	2-3	1-0	*	0-2	3-2	0-1	2-1	2-3	1-1	0-4	0-2	0-2	1-2
6. John Radcliffe	4-1	2-4	4-3	5-1	3-1	*	2-2	1-1	5-0	3-2	1-0	2-3	2-4	2-1	5-3
7. Kennington Utd Res	3-1	1-1	0-3	1-5	0-3	0-2	*	1-3	1-6	2-3	2-4	0-2	1-4	3-0	2-1
8. Launton Sports	0-0	2-4	2-1	4-3	0-1	3-1	5-0	*	3-0	5-0	2-3	2-1	3-1	3-0	4-0
9. Marston Saints	1-1	1-4	1-1	3-1	3-1	1-2	1-1	2-5	*	4-4	3-1	3-0	1-3	0-0	3-3
10. Northway United	5-2	0-3	3-2	1-5	8-3	5-1	3-3	3-5	4-0	*	2-1	3-2	3-8	4-3	11-1
11. Old Woodstock Res	3-5	0-1	2-1	4-3	2-0	0-2	4-2	0-5	0-4	0-5	*	2-7	0-3	3-1	4-0
12. Oxford University Press	4-3	2-6	4-0	4-3	1-3	3-1	7-0	2-1	6-1	4-1	2-0	*	2-0	2-1	4-0
13. Pressed Steel Fisher	3-1	3-2	1-0	3-0	5-1	1-3	5-0	3-2	3-3	1-1	4-1	3-2	*	+	5-1
14. Quarry Nomads Res	1-2	0-8	0-3	4-2	4-0	0-2	4-6	0-1	3-2	1-1	0-0	1-4	4-2	*	3-2
15. Salesians	2-11	0-4	0-0	4-2	1-2	1-1	7-2	0-4	1-6	2-3	0-0	0-3	0-7	3-5	*

* - Match abandoned and points awarded to Ardley.
+ - Points awarded to Pressed Steel.

HOME TEAM	1	2	3	4	5	6	7	8	9	10	11	12	13	14	15
1. AP Sports & Soc. Res	*	4-1	2-2	5-0	2-3	0-6	5-5	0-4	4-1	0-0	4-1	0-1	4-1	2-3	3-2
2. Bicester Civil S. Res	1-2	*	1-6	2-1	1-4	0-8	1-3	3-0	1-0	3-4	3-0	4-3	3-4	3-1	1-0
3. Bletchingdon Res	5-7	4-1	*	8-1	4-2	1-1	3-0	4-3	2-0	4-0	7-1	5-2	4-0	1-2	+
4. Charlton United Res	1-7	0-3	1-6	*	1-12	1-12	1-3	0-7	0-2	0-6	5-0	1-1	1-3	0-11	1-5
5. Eynsham Reserves	4-2	3-0	1-0	5-0	*	1-2	4-2	0-1	3-2	5-1	7-1	3-1	6-0	5-4	0-1
6. Garsington Reserves	5-0	1-0	1-3	15-0	2-0	*	2-1	2-3	5-1	10-0	6-2	2-0	4-0	5-1	5-2
7. Launton Sports Res	2-2	3-2	0-2	7-1	1-3	1-4	*	1-2	4-0	2-1	7-0	4-3	4-1	2-1	0-1
8. Long Crendon Res	4-0	2-1	1-4	6-1	2-1	1-4	1-3	*	3-1	0-1	2-0	5-0	6-0	1-1	1-0
9. Marlborough Res	2-1	1-5	1-1	5-0	1-1	3-3	2-1	0-3	*	2-6	3-0	2-1	2-3	1-2	0-4
10. Mainston Saints Res	2-2	0-2	2-5	2-0	0-2	0-2	4-1	0-0	3-3	*	0-0	4-3	5-2	3-4	3-1
11. Oakley United Res	3-3	2-0	4-3	3-3	3-4	1-6	3-4	1-5	2-1	4-4	*	3-1	2-2	2-2	0-4
12. Oxford Univ. Press Res	2-2	2-1	3-0	5-2	0-1	1-5	2-2	2-2	1-1	3-1	2-2	*	1-2	0-3	0-4
13. Salesians	2-1	1-6	4-3	2-0	1-5	0-3	0-9	0-5	1-1	1-2	1-5	3-0	*	4-4	1-1
14. Watlington Res	3-0	3-0	0-5	0-0	4-2	0-3	4-3	1-1	0-1	3-2	2-0	5-1	4-2	*	4-2
15. Woodstock Town Res	0-3	1-1	0-3	1-7	2-7	1-2	0-2	2-4	1-2	2-1	1-1	4-1	5-2	0-3	*

+ - Points awarded to Bletchingdon Reserves.

PRESIDENTS CUP 1991-92

First Round

Ardley United W/O AFC Cowley		Worcester College Old Boys v Garsington	0-3
Long Crendon v Marlborough	3-1	Bletchingdon v Watlington	2-3
Blackbird Leys ASC v Eynsham	2-5	Oakley United v A.P. Sports & Social Club	4-3
Woodstock Town v Salesians	5-0	Oxford University Press v Old Woodstock	5-0
Charlton United v Kennington United	2-4	Bicester Civil Service v Marston Saints	4-0
John Radcliffe v Pressed Steel Fisher	2-3	Northway United v Launton Sports	0-1
Oxford Stadium v Quarry Nomads	0-2		

Second Round

Pressed Steel Fisher v Ardley United	1-2	Quarry Nomads (bye)	
Watlington v Bicester Civil Service	6-0	Oxford University Press v Blackbird Leys ASC	1-2
Oakley United v Woodstock Town	2-4	Grasington (bye)	
Long Crendon (bye)		Launton Sports v Kennington United	4-2(aet)

Quarter Finals

Launton Sports v Quarry Nomads	4-2	Blackbird Leys ASC v Garsington	0-5
Ardley United v Long Crendon	4-2	Watlington v Woodstock Town	1-0

Semi-Finals

Garsington v Watlington	2-1	Launton Sports v Ardley United	0-0(3-4 penalties)

Final: Garsington 4, Ardley United 0

BEN TURNER CUP (for Presidents Cup First Round losers)

Second Round

Bletchingdon v Marlborough	3-0	A.P. Sports & Social Club v Marston Saints	1-0(aet)
John Radcliffe v A.F.C. Cowley	6-3	Charlton United v Northway United	1-4
Salesians v Worcester College Old Boys	1-4	Eynsham, Oxford Stadium, Old Woodstock	byes

Quarter Finals

Bletchingdon v Old Woodstock	3-0	Worcester College Old Boys v John Radcliffe	2-1
Oxford Stadium (w'drew) Northway United	W/O	Eynsham v A.P. Sports & Social	4-2

Semi-Finals

Bletchingdon v Eynsham	3-0	Worcester College Old Boys v Northway United	2-2(aet)

Final: Bletchingdon 3, Worcester College Old Boys 3 (Bletchingdon won 3-1 on penalties)

CLARENDON CUP 1991-92

First Round

Kennington Utd Res v Long Crendon Res	1-0	Charlton Utd Res v Marlborough Reserves	0-1
Oxford U.P. Res v Woodstock Town Res	2-1	Bletchingdon Reserves v Ardley United Reserves	0-3
Oakley United Res v Bicester Civil S. Res	2-3	Watlington Res v Marston Res	2-3(W'ton withdrawn)
Launton Sports Res v Salesians Res	1-3(aet)	Old Woodstock Reserves (bye)	
A.P. Sports & S. Res v Eynsham Res	0-5	Garsington Reserves v Quarry Nomads Reserves	4-1

Second Round

Salesians Reserves v Old Woodstock Res	2-1	Bicester Civil Service Res v Oxford U.P. Res	2-3(aet)
All other clubs - byes			

Quarter Finals

Kennington Utd Res v Eynsham Reserves	4-3	Watlington Reserves W/O Salesians Reserves	
Marlborough Reserves v Ardley Utd Reserves	2-3	Garsington Reserves v Oxford Univ. Press Res	3-0

Semi-Finals

Ardley United Reserves v Garsington Reserves	1-0	Watlington Reserves v Kennington Utd Reserves	2-1

Final: Ardley United Reserves 2, Watlington Reserves 1

IVOR GUBBINS CUP (First Round losers in Clarendon Cup)

First Round

Marston Saints Res v Charlton United Res	1-0	All other clubs received byes	0-1

Quarter Finals

Marston Saints Res v Launton Spts Res	4-1	Woodstock T. Res v AP Spts & Soc. Reserves	1-2
Oakley Utd Res v Long Crendon Reserves	3-1	Quarry Nomads Res v Bletchingdon Reserves	3-1

Semi-Finals

Marston Saints Res v Oakley Utd Reserves	2-3	A.P. Sports & Social Res v Quarry Nomads Res	2-4

Final: Quarry Nomads Reserves 2, Oakley United Reserves 1

CLUB DIRECTORY

A.F.C. COWLEY
Secretary: D Henderson, 5A Tomson Terrace, Littlemore, Oxford (0865 779595).
Colours: All red   **Change colours:** Sky & navy.   **Ground:** Roman Way, Cowley (pitch 3).

A.P. SPORTS & SOCIAL
Secretary: S Maycock, 3 The Camellias, Banbury, Oxon OX16 7YT (0295 275124).
Ground: Easington Recreation Ground, Banbury.
Colours: White/black/blue   **Reserve's colours:** Blue/white/red & black.

ARDLEY UNITED
Secretary: R Dick, 63 Halse Road, Brackley, Northants (0280 701179).
Ground: Playing Fields, Ardley.   **Colours:** All red   **Change colours:** White/navy/navy

BICESTER CIVIL SERVICE
Secretary: Mrs H Latty, 96 Churchill Rd, Bicester, Oxon OX6 7UJ (0869 240140).
Ground: Rodney House, London Road, Bicester, Oxon.
Colours: Red & white/blue/blue (Res: all blue)   **Change colours:** White/blue/red.

BLACKBIRD LEYS A.S.C.
Secretary: P Courtnage, 126 Pegasus Rd, Blackbird Leys, Oxford (0865 771137).
Ground: Pegasus Road, Blackbird Leys, Oxford.
Colours: Blue & black/black/black   **Change colours:** Yellow & red/black/black.

BLETCHINGDON
Secretary: Mrs V Willoughby, 75 Nethercote Rd, Tackley, Oxon (Tackley 521).
Ground: Oxford Road, Bletchingdon.
Colours: All red (Res: yellow & green/green/yellow)   **Change colours:** Claret & sky stripes/blue/blue

CHARLTON UNITED
Secretary: A Smith, 1 Manor Farm Buildings, Church Lane, Charlton-on-Otmoor, Oxon.
Ground: Charlton P.F.   **Colours:** Blue/blue/white   **Change colours:** All red.

EYNSHAM
Secretary: G Bailey, 8 Stratford Drive, Eynsham, Oxford OX8 1QJ (0865 882829).
Ground: Eynsham P.F., Oxford Road, Eynsham, Oxford.
Colours: White/black/black.   **Reserves' colours:** Yellow/black/yellow.

GARSINGTON
Secretary: C Moss, 8 Birch Rd, Garsington, Oxford (Garsington 704).
Ground: Off Denton Lane, Garsington (Garsington 720).
Colours: All green.   **Change colours:** White/black/black   **Res. colours:** Green & black/green/green

JOHN RADCLIFFE
Secretary: M W Welsh, 18 St Leonards Rd, Headington, Oxford OX3 8AA (0865 66240).
Ground: John Radcliffe Hospital Grounds.
Colours: Blue & white/black/black   **Change colours:** Black & white/black/black.

KENNINGTON UNITED
Secretary: Mr A Lawson, 17 Putenry Close, Abingdon.   **Ground:** Playfield Rd., Kennington, Oxford.
Colours: Green & yellow/green/yel.   **Change colours:** All yellow   **Res. colours:** All sky.

LAUNTON SPORTS
Secretary: M Ramage, 3 Sherwood Close, Launton, Bicester, Oxon (0869 24036).
Ground: Launton Playing Field, Launton, Bicester, Oxon.
Colours: Red/black/black   **Change colours:** Grey/black/black.

LONG CRENDON
Secretary: R Gower, 26 Friars Furlong Rd, Long Crendon, Aylesbury (Long Crendon 208642).
Ground: Chearsley Rd, Long Crendon, Aylesbury, Bucks.
Cols: Green/black/black (Res: Red & white/black/black)   **Change cols:** Blue & white/blue/white.

MARLBOROUGH
Sec: S Hutton, 122 Herschel Cres., Littlemore, Oxford (0865 715047)   **Ground:** Orchard Way, Littlemore.
Colours: Blue & white/white/blue (Res: all red)   **Change cols:** Yellow & blue/blue/blue.

MARSTON SAINTS
Secretary: H Devonport, 32 Elms Drive, Old Marston, Oxford OX3 0NJ (0865 249575).
Grnd: Boults Lane, Old Marston, Oxford   **Colours:** All red   **Change cols:** Yellow/blue/blue

NORTHWAY UNITED
Secretary: A Slater, 6 Old Marston Rd, Marston, Oxford (0865 245332).
Ground: Trinity College, Marston Rd, Oxford.
Colours: Red/white/red   **Change colours:** Blue & white/blue/blue.

OAKLEY UNITED
Secretary: A J Walker, 6 Brookside, Oakley, Aylesbury, Bucks HP18 9PN (Brill 238355).
Ground: Recreation Ground, Oxford Road, Oakley, Aylesbury, Bucks.
Colours: All white (Res: Orange/black/red)   **Change colours:** blue.

OLD WOODSTOCK
Secretary: T Halls, 20 Oxford Rd, Farmoor, Oxford OX2 9NN (0865 863871).
Ground: Marlborough School, Shipton Rd, Woodstock, Oxon.
Colours: Blue & white/green/green (Res: Blue & white/blue/blue)   **Change colours:** Red/black/red.

OXFORD UNIVERSITY PRESS
Secretary: I Weston, 63 Jordan Hill, Banbury Rd, Oxford OX2 8EU (0865 510500).
Ground: Oxford University Press Sports Ground, Jordan Hill, Banbury Road, Oxford.
Colours: All royal (Res: Yellow/red/red)   **Change colours:** Reverse.

PRESSED STEEL FISHER
Secretary: Mrs J A Measor, 1 Vicarage Close, Chalgrove, Oxon OX9 7RD (0865 890793).
Ground: Roman Way, Cowley.
Colours: Red/black/black   **Change colours:** Orange/white.

QUARRY NOMADS
Sec: Mrs L Dolton, 58 Pitts Rd, Headington (0865 65332).   **Grnd:** Risinghurst Est., off Grovelands Rd.
Colours: Black & white/black/white   **Change colours:** All red   **Programme:** Yes.

SALESIANS
Secretary: Mr C Nelson, 21 Trinity Street, Oxford (0865 250169).   **Ground:** Court Farm, Marston.
Colours: Yellow/blue/blue   **Reserve's cols:** Red/blue/blue (Change: reverse).

WATLINGTON
Secretary: G J Strong, 1 Watcombe Manor Cottage, Howe Rd, Watlington, Oxon (Watlington 2101).
Ground: Shirburn Road, Watlington, Oxon.
Colours: Red & black/black/black (Res: blue & white/blue/blue)   **Change:** All yellow.

WOODSTOCK TOWN
Secretary: A Hughes, 19 Great Close Rd, Yarnton, Oxon (08674 78004).   **Ground:** New Road, Woodstock.
Colours: All red (Res: Red & black/red/red)   **Change colours:** All white.

WORCESTER COLLEGE OLD BOYS
Secretary: R Oakes, 112 Leiden Rd, Headington, Oxford.   **Ground:** Roman Way, Cowley.
Colours: Sky/navy/navy   **Change colours:** Yellow/black/black.

Bletchingdon: Back Row (L/R): Gary Willoughby (Manager), Aiden Collins, Mark Greenslade, Nigel Goodgame, Mick Bockett, Peter Bradbury, Dave Gubbins, Dave Platt, anon, anon. Front: Dave Greenaway, Kevin Willoughby, Mark Cooper, Grant Slattery, Paul Palmer, Mick Nottage, anon. Photo - Steve Daniels.

WILTSHIRE COUNTY LEAGUE 1991-92

Division One	P	W	D	L	F	A	PTS
Amesbury Town	28	18	4	6	55	37	40
Sanford	28	18	3	7	56	23	39
Pewsey Vale	28	14	9	5	59	33	37
Wroughton	28	16	5	7	46	34	37
Shrewton United	28	14	6	8	52	44	34
Ferndale Athletic	28	11	8	9	46	34	30
Pinehurst	28	11	7	10	39	29	29
Bromham	28	8	10	10	40	43	26
Biddestone	28	8	9	11	29	39	25
Devizes Town Res	28	7	9	12	44	56	23
Aldbourne Park	28	7	8	13	35	47	22
Calne Town Res	28	7	8	13	34	48	22
Burmah Castrol	28	6	10	12	39	56	22
Corsham Town	28	6	9	13	36	49	21
Chippenham T. Res	28	2	9	17	26	64	13

Bottom 2 relegated, top 3 Div 2 sides promoted

Division Two	P	W	D	L	F	A	PTS
Dorcan	26	15	9	2	59	31	39
Walcot Athletic	26	15	5	6	64	31	35
Chisledon	26	13	6	7	46	37	32
Plessey Avebury	26	13	4	9	67	46	30
W'ton Bassett Res	26	10	8	8	38	35	28
Malmesbury Vic.	26	10	7	9	41	36	27
West Swindon	26	10	7	9	51	47	27
Warminster T. Res	26	11	4	11	43	45	26
Dunbar Wills	26	8	10	8	40	48	26
Marlborough Town	26	10	4	12	57	52	24
Purton Reserves	26	9	3	14	42	55	21
Westbury Utd Res	26	8	5	13	38	55	21
Stratton Red Eagles	26	6	7	13	45	68	19
Melksham T. Res	26	3	3	20	23	68	9

New to Div 2; Plessey Semics (from Div.4!), Bradford Town and Tisbury Utd (new clubs). Div 3 champs Sunray Bradbury merged with groundsharers Chisledon.

AVON COUNTY PREMIER COMBINATION 1991-92

Premier Division	P	W	D	L	F	A	PTS
Highridge United	30	24	6	0	83	24	54
Winterbourne Utd	30	21	7	2	79	23	49
Bristol St George	30	13	10	7	57	42	36
Oldland Decora	30	14	8	8	53	38	36
Hillfields Old Boys	30	12	9	9	55	42	33
Frampton Athletic	30	12	9	9	39	31	33
Iron Acton	30	11	9	10	48	45	31
Sea Mills Park	30	10	11	9	45	47	31
Hanham Athletic	30	12	5	13	55	65	29
Bitton	30	8	12	10	41	45	28
Barr United	30	10	6	14	42	52	26
Thornbury Town	30	8	6	16	35	58	22
Bristol Union	30	7	6	17	45	56	20
Brist. Spartak D'end	30	5	10	15	41	68	20
Bristol University	30	7	5	18	46	84	19
Wick Kingsway	30	5	3	22	34	78	13

Division One	P	W	D	L	F	A	PTS
Shaftesbury Crus.	30	22	3	5	78	32	47
Nicholas Wdrs	30	20	7	3	74	31	47
Sun Life	30	19	6	5	66	36	44
Hallen Reserves	30	14	8	8	61	40	36
Bristol 5 Old Boys	30	15	4	11	61	50	34
Patchway T. Res	30	11	10	9	70	63	32
Hartcliffe	30	10	9	11	54	47	29
Henbury OB Res	30	10	9	11	60	61	29
Lawrence Rovers	30	12	5	13	55	57	29
Chipping Sodbury	30	9	10	11	45	47	28
Archway St Phillips	30	12	4	14	55	61	28
Staple Hill	30	11	6	13	60	67	28
Olveston United	30	9	9	12	47	45	27
Pucklechurch Res	30	8	7	15	38	61	23
Hambrook Reserves	30	2	10	18	20	68	14
Eden Grove	30	0	5	25	25	103	5

Quarry Nomads. Back Row (L/R): D Cooper, A Bunting (Manager), J Carbon, J Jenkins, D Hutt, M Coffey, S Washington, M Fine, B Hill, M Stradley. Front: S O'Sullivan, T Chalmers, E Saunders, B Williams, G Cadle, D Graham. Photo - Steve Daniels.

A last photo of Swindon Athletic (Hellenic League) who have now joined forces with Supermarine.

Woodstock Town FC pictured before entertaining Bletchingdon in the Oxon Senior Cup. Photo - Kerry Miller.

'HAYES & GILES' EAST BERKS LEAGUE

The East Berkshire Football League, sponsored by Hayes and Giles Insurance Brokers, is a long established competition based in the Slough, Windsor, Bracknell and Maidenhead area. The League is hoping to become a feeder to the Chiltonian League and is expanding to 67 teams next season, divided into six divisions. **Stuart Bartlett, Results Secretary.**

Division One

	P	W	D	L	F	A	PTS
CBS (Bracknell)	20	13	4	3	50	26	30
Cippenham Sports	20	13	3	4	63	30	29
Running Horse	20	12	3	5	49	31	27
Bracknell Boys Club	20	12	1	7	49	38	25
Windsor Gt Park	20	9	5	6	42	34	23
Vansittart Wdrs	20	9	4	7	57	53	22
Braywick Rovers	20	5	6	9	34	46	16
Spital Old Boys	20	7	1	12	47	56	15
S. Heating (Helens)	20	6	3	11	39	51	15
Holyport	20	6	2	12	51	51	14
Hope & Anchor	20	1	2	17	22	87	4

Division Two

	P	W	D	L	F	A	PTS
Vansittart Wdrs Res	18	14	2	2	64	30	30
Prince of Wales	18	10	3	5	51	31	23
Old Windsor	18	10	2	6	37	23	22
Cippenham United	18	8	4	6	42	45	20
ICI (Jealotts Hill)	18	9	1	8	38	34	19
Maidenhead Wdrs	18	6	6	6	45	46	18
Cippenham Spts Res	18	6	5	7	31	34	17
Spital OB Res	18	7	2	9	29	33	16
Cox Green	18	5	1	12	37	66	11
Met. Office	18	1	2	15	18	50	4

Division Three

	P	W	D	L	F	A	PTS
Windsor & Eton CC	16	13	0	3	52	4	26
B.M.W.	16	11	2	3	37	20	24
Slough YCOB Res	16	11	1	4	38	20	23
Running Horse Res	16	8	4	4	45	31	20
Henley YMCA	16	8	1	7	26	26	17
Hewlett Packard	16	5	4	7	24	36	14
Bracknell Saints	16	5	0	11	25	42	10
Cargo World	16	2	1	13	20	54	5
Holyport Reserves	16	2	1	13	18	52	5

Division Four

	P	W	D	L	F	A	PTS
Waltham St Lawr.	24	19	4	1	125	31	42
Slough Heat. Res	24	19	2	3	115	41	40
Fromme Frais	24	18	2	4	80	37	38
Slough Royal Mail	24	18	1	5	95	34	37
Bracknell Exiles	24	13	3	8	65	47	29
Holyport 'A'	24	9	5	10	38	55	23
Bracknell BC Res	24	8	5	11	54	73	21
M'head Wdrs Res	24	10	1	13	73	86	21
W'sor & E. CC Res	24	8	4	12	38	58	20
Hewlett Pack. Res	24	4	5	15	59	94	13
Met. Office Res	24	5	2	17	32	82	12
Hurley	24	4	3	17	30	74	11
Bracknell Sts Res	24	2	1	21	28	120	5

DIVISION ONE RESULTS 1991/92

HOME TEAM	1	2	3	4	5	6	7	8	9	10	11
1. Bracknell BC	*	7-1	0-2	3-1	2-1	4-1	1-3	4-2	3-1	4-3	2-4
2. Braywick Rovers	2-0	*	0-3	1-2	4-1	5-1	0-2	5-1	2-1	3-3	1-4
3. C.B.S. (Bracknell)	1-2	0-0	*	4-2	4-1	4-1	1-1	4-2	4-2	4-2	4-1
4. Cippenham Sports	3-0	3-3	L-W	*	5-1	4-1	4-0	4-1	6-3	6-1	1-1
5. Holyport	0-1	3-3	2-4	1-2	*	4-1	3-6	1-2	12-0	2-2	2-0
6. Hope & Anchor	0-6	1-1	2-2	2-7	2-8	*	0-6	0-4	2-3	2-6	2-6
7. Running Horse	3-0	7-0	2-1	2-2	2-4	3-2	*	3-1	W-L	2-3	1-1
8. Slough Heating	2-4	1-1	1-3	1-2	4-1	1-0	1-2	*	4-2	4-4	3-3
9. Spital Old Boys	3-0	2-0	0-2	1-3	4-2	8-0	5-2	3-4	*	2-2	4-1
10. Vansittart Wanderers	3-4	2-1	4-2	3-2	1-2	4-1	1-2	4-0	4-3	*	1-5
11. Windsor Great Park	2-2	1-1	1-1	1-4	2-0	1-3	1-0	1-0	3-0	2-4	*

DIVISION TWO RESULTS 1991/92

HOME TEAM	1	2	3	4	5	6	7	8	9	10
1. Cippenham Spts Res	*	5-3	4-1	3-2	1-4	2-1	0-2	2-1	0-0	1-4
2. Cippenham United	2-2	*	1-3	2-1	2-1	2-2	1-0	1-3	3-0	3-7
3. Cox Green	2-6	2-6	*	3-5	3-3	4-0	0-2	1-3	1-4	1-5
4. I.C.I. (Jealotts Hill)	2-2	1-2	2-3	*	3-0	2-1	1-2	4-1	4-1	4-0
5. Maidenhead Wdrs	1-1	3-4	3-8	1-0	*	3-0	4-1	1-1	0-1	5-5
6. Met. Office	2-2	1-4	4-0	1-2	2-3	*	1-4	0-2	1-5	1-4
7. Old Windsor	4-0	3-3	1-0	3-0	3-3	5-1	*	3-0	2-3	0-1
8. Prince of Wales	3-0	2-2	12-0	2-3	4-4	2-0	2-1	*	4-1	2-1
9. Spital OB Res	W-L	3-1	2-3	0-2	2-3	1-0	L-W	2-4	*	1-1
10. Vantsittart Wdrs Res	W-L	6-0	3-2	7-0	5-3	3-0	3-1	5-3	4-3	*

DIVISION THREE RESULTS 1991/92

HOME TEAM	1	2	3	4	5	6	7	8	9
1. B.M.W.	*	2-1	3-1	3-2	3-0	7-0	1-1	3-0	W-L
2. Bracknell Saints	2-3	*	5-2	4-2	1-0	4-3	3-5	0-3	0-5
3. Cargo World	2-6	0-1	*	2-4	1-1	2-0	1-6	3-8	0-7
4. Henley Y.M.C.A.	1-0	3-0	3-0	*	3-2	1-1	0-3	2-1	W-L
5. Hewlett Packard	2-2	3-2	3-1	1-0	*	2-1	4-4	2-1	0-6
6. Holyport Reserves	0-2	4-2	2-4	0-1	3-2	*	2-5	0-2	0-6
7. Running Horse Res	0-1	2-0	2-1	3-2	1-1	6-1	*	2-3	1-2
8. Slough YCOB Res	5-1	2-0	3-0	3-1	1-0	2-4	4-0	*	W-L
9. Windsor & Eton CC	3-0	3-0	W-L	3-1	6-1	4-1	5-0	2-0	*

DIVISION FOUR RESULTS 1991/92

HOME TEAM	1	2	3	4	5	6	7	8	9	10	11	12	13
1. Bracknell BC Res	*	1-4	3-2	3-4	2-3	4-4	2-2	2-4	1-1	3-2	1-6	0-0	4-0
2. Bracknell Exiles	6-1	*	4-1	1-3	1-1	4-0	5-0	5-0	3-2	L-W	0-4	0-6	1-0
3. Bracknell Saints Res	2-6	0-5	*	0-4	4-1	0-3	2-7	0-2	1-2	7-1	1-4	2-4	
4. Fromme Frais	4-3	2-1	3-0	*	4-2	3-0	4-1	3-0	8-0	2-5	4-2	2-2	5-2
5. Hewlett Packard Res	1-3	4-5	13-2	0-6	*	1-1	6-1	0-2	1-2	2-10	2-5	3-9	2-2
6. Holyport 'A'	7-0	2-3	5-3	0-5	1-1	*	W-L	3-2	1-2	1-4	1-5	0-4	2-2
7. Hurley	1-3	2-2	1-3	1-3	3-3	0-3	*	3-1	2-1	1-6	1-4	1-3	0-3
8. Maidenhead Wdrs Res	1-3	5-3	12-1	3-4	7-4	L-W	3-0	*	4-0	1-7	2-9	4-8	4-0
9. Met. Office Res	1-5	0-3	2-2	1-3	5-2	0-2	5-1	2-4	*	1-2	1-3	0-6	2-5
10. Slough Heating Res	5-2	8-0	10-1	4-2	4-1	2-2	4-2	12-3	10-1	*	4-1	3-3	2-1
11. Slough Royal Mail	5-0	3-2	3-0	1-1	6-0	6-1	1-4	7-2	6-0	3-2	*	3-1	2-0
12. Waltham St Lawrence	7-1	2-2	10-0	4-1	9-3	4-0	7-0	8-2	4-0	7-7	2-1	*	10-0
13. Windsor & E. CC Res	1-1	0-5	8-1	1-0	0-3	0-1	2-0	0-0	4-1	0-3	2-0	0-5	*

GLOUCESTERSHIRE COUNTY LEAGUE

Chairman: Mr A C Barratt.
Honary Secretary: Mr D J Herbert,
8 Fernhurst Road, St George, Bristol BS5 7TQ (0272 517696).

	P	W	D	L	F	A	Pts
Patchway Town	32	24	5	3	87	29	77
Cadbury Heath	32	19	11	2	85	27	68
Hallen	32	19	8	5	83	46	65
D.R.G. (F.P.).	32	18	9	5	56	37	63
Ellwood	32	17	5	10	60	47	56
St Phillips Marsh	32	14	10	8	70	48	52
Pucklechurch Spts	32	11	11	10	43	49	44
Wotton Rovers	32	12	7	13	59	41	43
Henbury Old Boys	32	12	4	16	53	53	40
Campden Town	32	11	5	16	39	55	38
Stapleton	32	9	7	16	42	66	34
Old Georgians	32	9	7	16	24	50	34
Harrow Hill	32	8	9	15	41	53	33
Hambrook	32	9	6	17	43	56	33
St Marks CA	32	8	8	16	34	59	32
Dowty Dynamoes	32	8	6	18	39	71	30
Port of Bristol	32	4	2	26	33	104	14

TOWN TOPPLE HEATH

Patchway, who have added 'Town' to their name and also moved their pitch, eventually ran away with the championship for the second time in their history. The first was in 1985-86 when they had been re-elected into the League. The vital game proved to be against Cadbury Heath three weeks before the end of the season. Needing only a point to secure the title, Patchway went two up only for Heath to pull back to 2-2. A point was enough however, and Cadbury Heath needed their 4-0 win in their final game, against relegated Port of Bristol, to retain second place ahead of Hallen.

On the final day in the relegation area any one of five clubs could have joined Port of Bristol who were already down. Harrow Hill gained a 2-0 result against Hambrook which left Dowty Dynamos, who had completed their programme some two weeks before the end of the season, as the other relegated club. It was an exciting end to a tense battle for the championship and relegation.

D J Herbert, Hon. Secretary.

HOME TEAM		1	2	3	4	5	6	7	8	9	10	11	12	13	14	15	16	17
1.	CADBURY HEATH	*	1-1	5-1	2-0	2-2	0-1	6-0	2-2	1-1	1-0	2-2	4-0	0-0	5-1	2-2	2-1	0-1
2.	CAMPDEN TOWN	1-4	*	2-1	0-4	0-2	0-0	1-0	0-2	2-0	0-1	0-1	3-2	1-2	1-0	2-3	1-2	4-3
3.	DOWTY DYNAMOS	0-7	4-1	*	1-2	0-3	0-5	1-1	3-6	2-0	1-0	0-4	2-4	1-3	0-2	1-1	4-1	1-3
4.	D.R.G. (F.P.)	2-2	1-1	1-1	*	1-4	2-2	3-0	2-1	2-0	1-1	0-0	1-1	1-0	2-1	4-1	3-2	0-0
5.	ELLWOOD	0-2	1-0	3-1	2-1	*	1-3	1-0	3-0	4-1	0-0	1-3	5-2	3-1	2-0	4-3	2-1	2-3
6.	HALLEN	1-5	2-2	1-1	1-1	4-0	*	3-2	5-1	5-2	2-3	3-2	4-0	6-2	4-1	1-3	4-0	2-0
7.	HAMBROOK	1-2	3-2	2-0	1-1	1-4	0-1	*	0-2	2-3	3-0	0-3	8-0	1-1	4-1	0-0	0-2	0-0
8.	HARROW HILL	0-2	0-1	2-2	0-1	0-1	2-3	1-3	*	0-1	1-0	0-4	1-1	1-2	5-0	0-0	2-1	2-1
9.	HENBURY O.B.	0-4	1-2	1-2	5-0	3-0	4-2	3-1	2-0	*	1-0	2-3	7-1	0-0	0-1	2-1	2-3	1-3
10.	OLD GEORGIANS	0-4	1-0	2-0	0-1	1-1	1-0	1-2	0-0	2-1	*	0-3	2-0	0-1	1-2	1-8	1-1	0-5
11.	PATCHWAY TOWN	0-3	3-1	3-0	4-2	3-1	1-1	3-0	6-2	1-0	5-0	*	1-0	1-1	4-0	4-4	5-0	2-0
12.	PORT OF BRISTOL	0-4	0-4	1-2	1-2	3-1	2-3	1-2	0-3	1-4	1-3	0-3	*	1-4	2-0	0-2	1-1	2-5
13.	PUCKLECHURCH	1-4	5-0	0-1	0-3	1-1	3-3	1-0	1-1	3-1	1-0	0-5	0-2	*	2-1	2-1	0-1	2-2
14.	ST MARKS C.A.	0-0	1-1	1-5	0-3	1-1	2-1	3-1	1-1	3-0	0-1	2-1	2-2	*	2-3	2-2	0-1	1-1
15.	ST PHILIPS M.A.S.	3-3	1-2	0-0	0-2	2-1	1-2	3-0	1-1	3-2	0-2	3-1	7-2	1-1	2-1	*	5-1	0-0
16.	STAPLETON	2-2	1-2	1-0	3-1	2-3	0-3	1-5	1-2	0-0	1-0	3-4	2-1	1-1	0-1	1-4	*	1-1
17.	WOTTON ROVERS	1-2	3-1	3-1	1-2	1-2	2-4	4-0	0-0	1-2	0-0	0-2	9-0	3-0	0-1	1-2	2-3	*

GLOUCESTERSHIRE COUNTY LEAGUE 1992-93

CADBURY HEATH

Secretary: C B Trotman, 51 Deanery Rd, Warmley, Bristol BS15 4NB (0272 616446).
Ground: 'Springfield', Cadbury Heath Rd, Warmley, Bristol
Directions: A420 from Bristol through Kingswood, across new r'bout, right into Tower Rd North, past school, right into Cadbury Heath Rd, ground immediately on right down alley.
Colours: Red/black/black & red   **Change Colours:** Yellow/black/red & black
Hons: Glos Co. Lg 70-71 71-72 72-73 73-74 (R-up 74-75 90-91 91-92), Glos Amtr Cup Sth(3), FA Vase QF.

CAMPDEN TOWN

Secretary: D J Benfield, 14 Harvard Avenue, Honeybourne, Evesham, Worcs WR11 5XU. (Evesham 831935).
Ground: Recreation Ground, Catbrook, Chipping Campden, Glos. (Evesham 840124).
Directions: In Chipping Camden village, just east of Broadway, Worcs.
Colours: Amber & black trim/black/amber   **Change Colours:** White/black/white

D.R.G. (F.P.)

Secretary: J A Jacobs, 80 The Meadows, Hanham, Bristol BS15 3PB (0272 611845).
Ground: 'Shortwood', Carsons Road, Mangotsfield, Bristol
Directions: M4 jct 19 onto M32, off at jct 1 onto A4174 follow signs for Downend then Mangotsfield. Continue through town, road becomes Carsons Road, ground on right after factory.
Seats: None   **Cover:** No   **Capacity:** 1,000   **Programme:** Yes   **Founded:** 1962
Colours: Sky blue/maroon/maroon   **Change Colours:** All maroon   **Clubhouse:** Yes
Previous Name: R.W.P. (pre-1986)   **Previous Ground:** St Johns Lane 62-66.
Record Gate: 500 v Pucklechurch Sports, Bristol Combination 1/4/86.

DOWTY DYNAMOS

President: C J M Walker   **Chairman:** J Brayshaw   **Manager:** Alan Gough
Secretary: C J Brown, 25 Courtenay Street, Cheltenham, Glos. GL50 4LR (0242 511117).
Ground: Dowty Arce Court Sports Ground, Hatherley Lane, Cheltenham (0242 525515).
Directions: In Cheltenham follow signs for GCHQ. Ground adjacent.   **Clubhouse:** Yes
Colours: Navy white stripe/navy/navy   **Change Colours:** Red/navy/navy   **Founded:** 1947
Programme: 20 pages, 25p   **Previous Name:** Alstone Dynamos (1947-79).
Hons: Glos Nthn Snr Lg 90-91, Cheltenham Lg R-up 88-89 (Div 2 76-77 79-80), Winchcombe Cup 89-90 (R-up 90-91).

ELLWOOD

Secretary: R Watkins, 8 Langetts Rd, Eastbourne Estate, Coleford, Glos. GL16 8BT (0594 34845).
Ground: Bromley Rd, Ellwood, Coleford, Glos
Colours: All royal blue   **Change Colours:** Red/royal blue/royal blue

HALLEN

Chairman: Mr Roy Toye   **Manager:** Terry Hale.
Secretary: C Jones, 67 Meadowland Rd, Henbury, Bristol BS10 7FW (0272 508572).
Ground: Hallen Playing Fields, Moorhouse Lane, Hallen, Nr Bristol (0272 504610).
Directions: M5 jct 17, A4018 to Henbury r'bout, right, right again at junction, next right to Station Road, left into Avonmouth Road at r'bout. One mile to Hallen, ground first left, then right into lane to ground.
Seats: No   **Cover:** No   **Clubhouse:** Yes   **Programme:** No   **Founded:** 1949
Colours: All blue   **Change Colours:** Green & white stripes/green/green
Previous Names: Lawrence Weston Athletic (80's), Lawrence Weston Hallen (pre-1991).
Record Gate: 250   **Previous Ground:** Kings Weston (early 1980's)

HAMBROOK

Secretary: T Lansdown, 221 North Rd, Stoke Gifford, Bristol BS12 6PJ (0454 775560).
Ground: Whiteshill Common, Moorend Rd, Hambrook, Bristol   **Founded:** 1954.
Directions: M32 jct 1, A4174 towards Downend, left at lights, continue to Hambrook Common (on right).
Colours: All red   **Change Colours:** All blue
Hons: Avon Combination 60-61 61-62 62-63, Glos Snr Amtr Cup (South).

HARROW HILL

Secretary: D Boseley, Paddocks, Morse Rd, Drybrook, Glos GL17 GAT (0594 543062).
Ground: Larksfield Rd, Harrow Hill, Drybrook, Glos (0954 543873).
Directions: A40 from Gloucester for for seven miles, left onto A4136 and continue for eight miles to Harrow Hill, right into Trinity Road near Church, right into Larkfield Road after half a mile, ground on right.
Seats: No   **Cover:** Yes   **Capacity:** 2,000   **Clubhouse:** Yes   **Founded:** 1932
Colours: Claret with blue trim/blue/blue   **Change Colours:** Yellow with black trim/black/black
Record Gate: 500-600, local cup, 1960s.
Best FA Vase season: 1st Rd 88-89   **Hons:** Glos Northern Snr Lg(4) 63-65 71-72 81-82.

HENBURY OLD BOYS

Secretary: C B Barron, 126 Charlton Rd, Westbury-on-Trym, Bristol BS10 6NL (0272 504002).
Ground: Arnall Drive Playing Fields, Henbury, Bristol (0272 590475).   **Directions:** M5 jct 17, down Cribbs Causeway, into Station Road, left into Henbury Rd, ground on left.
Founded: 1962
Colours: Amber & black/black/black   **Change Colours:** Silver & black/black/silver
Hons: Avon Combination 82-83 (Lg Cup 83-84), Glos Snr Amtr Cup South.

OLD GEORGIANS

Secretary: B M Latchem, 87 Vicarage Rd, Whitehall, Bristol BS5 9AQ (0272 556292).
Ground: St George Playing Fields, Johnsons Lane, Whitehall, Bristol (0272 516888).
Directions: M32 jct 2, left, left, right at lights, right behind Kings Head. Buses 6 or 7 from central Bristol. One mile from Stapleton Road (BR).
Seats: None   **Cover:** No   **Capacity:** 1,500   **Clubhouse:** Yes   **Founded:** 1905.
Colours: Sky (navy wide stripe)/navy/navy   **Change Colours:** Red/navy/red
Record Gate: 770 v Stansted, FA Vase QF 4/3/84.   **Manager:** Brian Tufton.
Hons: Glos Co. Lg 82-83 84-85 (R-up 83-84), Glos Challenge Tphy, Glos Snr Amtr Cup Sth, FA Vase QF 83-84.

PATCHWAY TOWN

Secretary: R Stewart, 22 Arlington Way, Patchway, Bristol, BS12 5NQ (0272 792983).
Ground: 'Scott Park', Coniston Rd, Patchway, Bristol   **Hons:** Glos County Lg 91-92
Directions: M5 jct 16, A38 towards Bristol, right into Coniston Road, ground signposted Scott Park.
Colours: Black & white stripes/black/black   **Change Colours:** All royal blue

PUCKLECHURCH SPORTS

Chairman: Don Frankcom   **President:** Geoff Hobbs
Secretary: C J Bowering, 33 Cedar Way, Pucklechurch, Bristol BS17 3RN (0275 823675).
Manager: Russell Dunn   **Asst Manager:** Peter Iles
Ground: Pucklechurch Recreation Ground, Pucklechurch, Abson (0275 822102).
Directions: M32 jct 1 follow A4174 through Downend to Mangotsfield, left signposted Pucklechurch, continue to village, turn right, ground on left.
Seats: No   **Cover:** None   **Clubhouse:** Yes   **Prog:** 32 pages,40p **Editor:** M Dowse.
Colours: White with green trim/white/white   **Change Colours:** Green/white/green
Hons: Avon Comb. 77-78 78-79 87-88 (Div 2 66-67, Lg Cup 77-78 78-79 87-88), Glos Jnr Cup 65-66 82-83, Bristol & District Lg 72-73.

ST. MARKS C.A.

Secretary: W Pember, 11 Linworth Rd, Bishops Cleeve, Cheltenham, Glos GL52 4PF (0242 673800).
Ground: Cheltenham Town AFC, Whaddon Rd, Cheltenham
Directions: See Cheltenham Town.   **Hons:** Glos Northern Snr Lg 74-75 78-79 83-84.
Colours: Royal blue/royal blue/red   **Change Colours:** Red with white hoop/royal blue/red

ST. PHILIPS MARSH ADULT SCHOOL

Secretary: Mrs C Davies, 9 Banister Grove, Inns Court, Knowle, Bristol BS4 1TE. Tel. 0272 640912/0272 637861/0272 626715(Messages)
Ground: John Harvey Sports Ground, Norton Lane, Whitchurch, Bristol (0272 837271).
Directions: A37 south from Bristol, through Whitchurch, right into Norton Lane just after humped back bridge. Ground first right.
Seats: No   **Cover:** No   **Clubhouse:** Yes   **Programme:** Yes   **Founded:**
Colours: All white   **Change Colours:** All red

SMITHS ATHLETIC

Secretary: P H Jurd, 11 Shawgreen Lane, Prestbury, Cheltenham, Glos GL52 3BS (0242 529188).
Ground: The Newlands, Bishops Cleeve, Cheltenham (0242 672752).
Colours: All royal blue   **Change Colours:** All red.
Previous League: Glos Northern Snr (until 1992).

STAPLETON

Secretary: N Barnett, 35 Larkspur Close, Thornbury, Bristol BS12 1UQ. Tel. 0454 411677/0272 650994/0272 568399 **(Messages)**
Ground: Frenchay Park Playing Field, Frenchay, Bristol
Directions: M32 jct 1, A4174, follow signs to Frenchay Hospital - ground opposite. Or M32 jct 2, follow signs for Frenchay through Stapleton, ground on left.
Seats: No   **Cover:** No   **Clubhouse:** Yes   **Programme:** Yes   **Founded:** 1932.
Colours: Purple/white/purple   **Change Colours:** Red/white/red

WINTERBOURNE UNITED

Secretary: E Thornell, 17 Western Avenue, Frampton Cottrell BS17 2AJ (0454 6054).
Ground: Parkside Avenue, Winterbourne, Bristol.
Directions: Behind school, just beyond shops in Winterbourne.
Seats: No   **Cover:** Yes   **Clubhouse:** Yes   **Previous Lge:** Avon Comb. (until 1992)
Colours: White/red/red   **Change Colours:**

WOTTON ROVERS

Secretary: M P Excell, 94 Bearlands, Wotton-under-Edge, Glos. GL12 7SB (0453 845178).
Ground: Synwell Playing Field, Synwell Lane, Wotton-under-Edge (0453 842929). *NB - The club plan to move to a new ground in the near future.*
Directions: From Wotton war memorial down hill and follow Synwell Lane. Ground on left.
Seats: None   **Cover:** No   **Capacity:** 2,000   **Clubhouse:** Yes   **Founded:** 1959.
Colours: Sky blue/sky blue/navy   **Change Colours:** White/white/red
Record Gate: 2,000   **Programme:** 20 pages, 50p
Previous Names: Synwell Rovers (pre-1959)/ Wotton-under-Edge FC.

LEADING SCORERS 1991-92: Ian Day (Cadbury Heath) 27, G Britton (Cadbury Heath) 21, S Price (Hallen) 21, W Jones (Ellwood) 21, R Page (Patchway Town) 19, K Horseman (Patchway Town) 19, T Andrews (Wotton Rovers) 18, S Pinker (Henbury Old Boys, Stapleton) 17, K Morse (Hambrook) 16.

J. J. BAILEY CUP 1991-92.

	P	W	D	L	F	A	Pts
Somerset Snr Lge	2	1	1	0	2	1	3
Sth Wales Amtr Lge	2	1	1	0	1	0	3
Glos County Lge	2	0	0	2	1	3	0

RESULTS
15/10/91: Somerset Senior 2, Glos County 1
20/11/91: Glos County 0, Sth Wales Amateur 1
3/3/92: Sth Wales Amateur 0, Somerset Senior 0

BRISTOL & DISTRICT LEAGUE

Senior Div.	P	W	D	L	F	A	Pts
Longwell Green	26	19	4	3	66	19	42
Shirehampton Res	26	16	5	5	67	32	37
Highridge Utd Res	26	13	6	7	57	25	32
St Pancras	26	12	8	6	36	29	32
DRG(FP) Res	26	12	6	8	57	49	30
Soundwell Vic. Utd	26	12	4	10	52	41	28
Made for Ever	26	10	5	11	49	52	25
Hillfields Park	26	8	9	9	30	37	25
S. Bristol Central	26	10	4	12	51	46	24
Greyfriars Ath.	26	9	6	11	46	49	24
Frampton Ath. Res	26	8	8	10	28	41	24
Iron Acton Res	26	8	4	14	37	50	20
Westbury Victoria	26	6	0	20	31	88	12
Kingsgrove Utd	26	1	7	18	27	76	9

Division 1	P	W	D	L	F	A	Pts
Winterbourne U. Res	28	23	2	3	101	30	48
Langton Court Ath.	28	22	3	3	107	35	47
St Philips MAS Res	28	21	1	6	82	38	43
Hartcliffe CC	28	18	5	5	71	45	41
Parnalls	28	13	7	8	54	47	33
Tormarton	28	12	5	11	67	64	29
IML Sports	28	11	2	15	41	60	24
BAWA Aces	28	9	5	14	54	81	23
Hanham Ath. Res	28	9	4	15	41	70	22
Stapleton Res	28	9	3	16	57	65	21
Fishponds Ath.	28	8	5	15	53	68	21
Rangeworthy	28	8	4	16	44	81	20
Totterdown Utd	28	7	5	16	36	58	19
Westerleigh Spts	28	5	5	18	47	83	15

Division 2	P	W	D	L	F	A	Pts
Seymour Utd	26	18	7	1	95	50	43
St Steph. Soundwell	26	15	2	9	67	48	32
AEK Rangers	26	14	3	8	63	46	32
Imperial Courage	26	13	6	7	60	43	32
Nicholas Wdrs Res	26	13	9	10	57	45	29
Dundridge Rovers	26	11	6	9	59	49	28
Oldland Decora Res	26	13	2	11	62	68	28
Knowle United	26	12	2	12	46	46	26
Stan Butt Sports	26	10	4	12	63	65	24
Shaftesbury C. Res	26	9	4	13	41	56	22
Lawrence Rvrs Res	26	9	3	14	52	65	21
Breakaway Rgrs	26	9	2	15	52	66	20
Kingswood Carryfast	26	7	5	14	56	76	19
Wick Kingsway Res	26	2	4	20	34	84	8

Division 6 Champions: Sandringham Sports

Division 3.	P	W	D	L	F	A	Pts
Hillfields OB Res	28	20	6	2	66	16	46
Crosscourt Utd	28	19	5	4	58	29	43
Roman Glass	28	17	8	3	77	28	42
Victoria Court	28	15	7	6	81	49	37
Bristol Union Res	28	13	7	8	55	39	33
Sea Mills Pk Res	28	13	5	10	67	39	31
Bristol Univ. Res	28	10	3	15	55	56	23
Made for Ever Res	28	10	3	15	41	49	23
Cleevewood	28	9	5	14	37	56	23
Royal Table	28	9	4	15	40	63	22
Sun Life Res	28	5	11	12	43	68	21
Nicholas Wdrs 'A	28	6	8	14	47	83	20
Frampton Ath. 'A	28	6	7	15	44	76	19
Staple Hill Res	28	6	7	15	44	76	19
Eden Grove Res	28	6	6	16	44	84	18

Division 4	P	W	D	L	F	A	Pts
Ace Kitchens LT	28	22	4	2	102	36	48
Bitton Res	28	20	6	2	90	20	46
Olveston Utd Res	28	19	3	6	67	32	41
Old Sodbury	28	16	3	9	69	64	35
Bristol Albion	28	14	6	8	51	34	34
Chipping Sod. Res	28	12	5	11	57	44	29
SBC Res	28	11	6	11	75	55	28
Oldland Decora 'A	28	9	8	11	60	57	26
Long Ashton Res	28	8	9	11	56	64	25
Rangeworthy Res	28	8	7	13	44	59	23
Fry Club 'A	28	9	5	14	41	71	23
Avon St George	28	8	4	16	47	74	20
Soundwell Vic. Res	28	6	8	14	43	72	20
Wick Kingsway 'A	28	4	4	20	34	113	12
Bendix Specials	28	2	6	20	33	74	10

Division 5	P	W	D	L	F	A	Pts
Highridge Utd 'A	28	19	7	2	66	27	45
DRG (FP) 'A	28	18	3	7	61	34	39
Longwell Green Res	28	16	5	7	81	35	37
Hilton Rangers	28	16	5	7	61	36	37
Pucklechurch Spts 'A	28	14	8	6	79	39	36
AEK Rangers Res	28	13	4	11	51	49	30
Rail Bristol	28	12	6	10	46	45	30
St Pancras Res	28	13	3	12	54	47	29
Totterdown Utd Res	28	10	7	11	53	52	27
Archway St Ph. Res	28	8	9	11	56	50	25
Greyfriars A. Res	28	9	6	13	45	51	24
Bristol '5 OB Res	28	6	5	17	37	71	17
Dundridge Rvrs Res	28	6	5	17	35	72	17
Parnalls Res	28	5	4	19	43	88	14
Westerleigh Spts Res	28	6	1	21	44	115	13

GLOUCESTERSHIRE NORTHERN SENIOR LEAGUE

Division One	P	W	D	L	F	A	PTS
Smiths Athletic	30	19	7	4	64	18	45
Shortwood Utd Res	30	17	6	7	74	53	40
Kings Stanley	30	14	10	6	48	24	38
Hilldene Athletic	30	13	8	9	46	43	34
Hardwicke	30	14	5	11	59	47	33
Berkeley Town	30	11	11	8	46	38	33
Cam Bulldogs	30	12	9	9	44	49	33
Lydbrook Athletic	30	12	7	11	59	53	31
Sharpness	30	10	8	12	52	56	28
Brimscombe & T.	30	8	11	11	54	51	27
Dursley Town	30	9	9	12	51	51	27
Longford	30	10	6	14	35	53	26
Broadwell	30	9	7	14	47	57	25
Longlevens	30	9	6	15	35	58	24
I.C.I. Fibres	30	7	9	14	37	39	23
Gala-Wilton	30	4	5	21	41	102	13

Division Two	P	W	D	L	F	A	PTS
Endsleigh	30	21	7	2	91	28	49
Frampton United	30	21	3	6	88	43	45
Coleford United	30	18	4	8	53	40	40
Vikings (Stroud)	30	17	5	8	66	44	39
Worrall Hill	30	15	8	7	61	32	38
Yorkley	30	15	8	7	57	39	38
Lydney Town	30	15	5	10	51	38	35
Nuclear Electric	30	14	6	10	52	39	34
Whitecroft	30	12	4	14	36	50	28
Stonehouse F'way	30	9	5	16	54	59	23
Charfield	30	7	9	14	46	56	23
Newent Town	30	8	7	15	48	70	23
Viney St Swithins	30	8	6	16	39	56	22
Blakeney	30	8	4	18	38	72	20
Mitcheldean	30	7	3	20	40	82	17
Soudley	30	0	6	24	24	96	6

CLUB DIRECTORY

BERKELEY TOWN
Secretary: P R Young, 23 Trotman Avenue, Summerhayes, Dursley, Glos GL11 5RE (0453 547715).
Ground: Station Rd, Berkeley.　　　　**Colours:** Green & yellow.

BLAKENEY
Secretary: A Berrow, 63 Woodland Rise, Lydney, Glos GL15 5LN (0594 841392).
Ground: Blakeney Playing Fields.　　　　**Colours:** Red & black.

BRIMSCOMBE & THRUPP
Secretary: G M Phillips, 14 Grange Close, Minchinhampton, Glos GL6 9DF (0453 886155).
Ground: The Meadow, London Rd, Brimscombe　　**Colours:** All white.

BROADWELL AMATEURS
Secretary: G D Barnes, 61 North Rd, Broadwell, Coleford, Glos GL16 7BX (0594 32523).
Ground: The Hawthorns, Broadwell, Coleford.　　**Colours:** Claret & blue.

CAM BULLDOGS
Secretary: J R Jewitt, 29 Chapel Street, Cam, Glos GL11 5NX (0453 548879).
Ground: Cam Sports Club, Everlands, Cam.　　**Colours:** Green & yellow.

CHARFIELD
Secretary: P Kirby, 209 Dovecote, Yate, Bristol BS17 4PF (0454 316266).
Ground: Charfield Memorial Playing Fields.　　**Colours:** Blue & white stripes.

COLEFORD UNITED
Secretary: T Smith, 3A Lower Palmers Flat, Coalway, Coleford, Glos GL16 7LT (0594 34791).
Ground: King George V Playing Fields, Victoria Rd, Coleford.　　**Cols:** All white.

DURSLEY TOWN
Secretary: P James, 8 Meadow Vale, Tilsdown, Dursley, Glos GL11 6HJ (0453 547413).
Ground: Recreation Ground, Kingshill Road, Dursley, Glos.　　**Colours:** All red

ENDSLEIGH
Secretary: G Moss, Swindon Close, Cheltenham, Glos GL51 9HX.
Ground: The Folley, Swindon Road, Cheltenham.　　**Colours:** All royal blue.

FRAMPTON UNITED
Secretary: H G Tudor, 'Ad Extremum', Frampton-upon-Severn, Glos GL2 7EA (740224).
Ground: Bell Field, Frampton-on-Severn　　**Colours:** Blue.

G.A.L.A. WILTON
Secretary: T R Onions, 71 North Upton Lane, Barnwood, Glos (0452 616567).
Ground: Gala Club, Fairmile Gardens, Longford, Glos.　　**Colours:** Gold

HARDWICKE
Secretary: A J King, 25 Elmsgrove Road East, Hardwicke, Glos GL2 6PY (0452 728603).
Ground: Green Lane, Hardwicke.　　**Colours:** White.

HILLDENE ATHLETIC
Secretary: M J Weaving, Casa Mia, 50 Victoria Street, Cinderford, Glos GL14 2HR (0594 24737).
Ground: Technical College, Station Street, Cinderford, Glos.　　**Colours:** Sky blue.

I.C.I. FIBRES
Secretary: R Morgan, 209 Church Drive, Quedgeley, Gloucester, Glos GL2 6US (0452 728412).
Ground: I.C.I. Sports Ground, Green Street, Brockworth.　　**Colours:** Blue.

KINGS STANLEY
Secretary: R K Bassett, 8 Guildings Way, Kings Stanley, Stonehouse, Glos GL1- 3LF (0453 824012).
Ground: Markings Close, Kings Stanley.　　**Colours:** Maroon & royal blue.

LONGFORD
Secretary: T Godwin, 2 Abbotts Cottage, Sandhurst, Gloucester GL2 9NW (0452 730727).
Ground: Longford Playing Fields.　　**Colours:** Sky.

LONGLEVENS
Secretary: W G Davis, 28 Simon Road, Longlevens, Gloucester GL2 0TP (0452 422450).
Ground: The Pavilion, Longford Lane, Longlevens, Gloucester.　　**Colours:** All red

LYDBROOK
Secretary: J A Price, 'Wobage', Fourth Avenue, Greytree, Ross-on-Wye HR9 7HR (0989 63788).
Ground: Reeds, Lower Lydbrook.　　**Colours:** Black & white.

LYDNEY TOWN
Secretary: R A Sansom, 17 Woodland Rise, Lydney, Glos GL15 5LH (0594 8443210).
Ground: Lydney Recreation Ground.   **Colours:** White.

MITCHELDEAN
Secretary: B Gomery, 23 Coombs Road, Coombs Park, Coleford, Glos GL16 8AY (0594 32459).
Ground: Mitcheldean Playing Fields.   **Colours:** Red.

NEWENT TOWN
Secretary: A Bassett, Withydale Nursery, High Leadon, Newent, Glos GL18 1HG (0452 79439).
Ground: Wildsmith Meadow, Gloycester Rd, Newent, Glos.   **Colours:** Red.

NUCLEAR ELECTRIC
Secretary: P L Nurden, 52 Gambier Parry Gdns, Gloucester GL2 9RD.
Ground: As I.C.I. Fibres (page 582).   **Colours:** Yellow & green.

SHARPNESS
Secretary: J Thomas, 69 Oldminster Rd, Sharpness, Nr Berkeley, Glos GL13 9UR (0453 811397).
Ground: Berkeley Vale School.   **Colours:** Red.

SHORTWOOD UNITED RESERVES (see page 570)

SOUDLEY
Secretary: R Sladen, 1 Church Road, Soudley, Cinderford, Glos GL14 2UA (0594 24701).
Ground: Soudley Recreation Ground, Soudley, Cinderford.   **Colours:** Red.

STONEHOUSE FREEWAY
Secretary: M Smith, 2 The Cottage, The Cross, Eastington, Stonehouse, Glos GL10 3AB (0453 824214).
Ground: Oldends Lane, Stonehouse, Glos.   **Colours:** Black & white stripes.

VIKINGS (STROUD)
Secretary: A R Brown, 1 St Lawrence Rd, Barnwood, Gloucester GL4 7QR (0452 610024).
Ground: Birds Eye Walls Sports & Social Club.   **Colours:** Orange & white.

VINEY ST SWITHINS
Secretary: A R Thomas, 'Ravenscoft', 28 Allaston Rd, Lydney, Glos GL15 5ST (0594 843634).
Ground: Sports & Social Club, Viney Hill.   **Colours:** Red & black.

WHITECROFT
Secretary: R P Elsmore, Oakwood, Charleswood Rd, Whitecroft, Lydney, Glos GL15 4QW (0594 563111).
Ground: Grove Road, Whitecroft, Lydney, Glos.   **Colours:** Green.

WORRALL HILL
Secretary: B Wadley, 9 Hillside Terrace, Joys Green, Lydbrook, Glos GL17 9DY (0594 60587).
Ground: Worrall Hill, Lydbrook, Glos.   **Colours:** Red.

YORKLEY
Secretary: D Kear, Driffield Rd, Lydney, Glos GL15 4EU (0594 842785).
Ground: Yorkley Recreation Ground.   **Colours:** Blue.

BRISTOL & SUBURBAN LEAGUE

Prem. Div. One	P	W	D	L	F	A	PTS
Yate Town Res	30	26	4	0	104	27	56
Broad Plain House	30	23	3	4	94	32	49
Almondsbury FC	30	16	9	4	66	35	41
Stoke Gifford Utd	30	18	1	11	66	53	37
Stokeside Spts	30	16	4	10	66	55	36
Totterdown Ath.	30	14	5	11	65	53	33
Avonmouth	30	14	5	11	64	56	33
St Aldheims	30	10	9	11	55	48	29
Filton Athletic	30	11	6	13	50	67	28
Glenside Hosp. SC	30	9	8	13	50	61	26
Nat West Court	30	8	9	13	50	51	25
T D R Dynamo	30	9	6	15	49	68	24
Lockleaze	30	7	6	17	49	93	20
Riding High	30	6	5	18	36	63	17
Hartcliffe OB	30	4	5	21	37	81	13
Bristol Telephones	30	4	3	23	33	85	11

Prem. Div 2 Champions: P & W United
Division One Champions: Avonmouth Reserves
Division Two Champions: CTK Southside
Division Three Champions: Corinthians Spts
Division Four Champions: Totterdown Ath. Res
Division Five Champions: Imperial Saints Res
Division Six Champions: AL. Safeway Res.

TROWBRIDGE LEAGUE

Division One	P	W	D	L	F	A	PTS
Heytesbury	22	16	5	1	73	14	37
Bradford United	22	14	4	4	77	24	32
Broughton Gif.	22	12	7	3	59	24	31
Winsley	22	11	7	4	44	32	29
Airsprung '88	22	10	8	4	60	40	28
John Bull	22	10	5	7	54	45	25
Bratton	22	9	5	6	48	39	23
Hilperton United	22	5	6	11	32	53	18
Kington Langley	22	5	3	14	36	67	13
Freshford United	22	4	4	14	29	70	12
Chippenham T. 'A'	22	3	4	15	34	83	8
Audience Systems	22	2	4	16	28	83	8

TROWBRIDGE LEAGUE (cont.)

Division Two	P	W	D	L	F	A	PTS
Avon Bradford	30	20	6	4	88	35	46
Deverills	30	18	9	3	81	47	45
Melksham Har.	30	17	4	9	107	72	38
W/Lavington	30	17	4	9	107	72	38
Seend United	30	14	8	6	70	47	36
Leis Line Sports	30	18	4	10	82	61	36
Broughton Res	30	11	9	10	79	69	31
Lavington East	30	13	3	14	96	85	29
Potterne	30	11	6	13	69	76	28
Steeple Ashton	30	11	6	13	48	60	28
Bradford Utd Res	30	10	8	12	64	77	28
Lacock	30	10	4	16	64	79	24
Westbury Town	30	9	6	15	58	82	24
Crosskeys	30	9	5	16	56	83	23
Holt	30	5	6	19	54	85	16
Hilperton Utd Res	30	2	5	23	49	126	16

Division Three	P	W	D	L	F	A	PTS
Kington L'ley Res	30	26	4	0	91	22	56
Winsley Res	30	23	4	3	100	22	56
Westbury Youth	30	19	7	4	87	37	45
Atworth	30	18	3	9	103	61	39
Blue Circle	30	16	4	10	87	63	36
Melksham Legion	30	16	4	10	83	66	*34
Corsham Town Res	30	14	4	12	71	54	32
Avon Bradford Res	30	12	3	15	47	51	27
Bratton Res	30	11	4	15	68	73	26
Audience Sys. Res	30	12	2	16	69	89	26
Neston C.	30	11	3	16	66	93	*23
Ashton Rangers	30	8	4	18	59	85	20
Seend United Res	30	5	8	17	46	89	18
Waldens	30	8	1	21	46	106	17
Freshford Utd Res	30	6	2	27	36	80	14
Leis Line Res	30	5	3	22	39	107	13

* - 2 pts deducted, ineligible player

GREAT MILLS WESTERN LEAGUE

President: E K Brown.
Chairman: S G Priddle.
Treasurer: Mrs Joan Ellis.
Hon. Secretary: M E Washer,
16 Heathfield Road, Nailsea, Bristol BS19 1EB. Tel: 0395 264889.

WESTON'S YEAR

In many ways the past season saw some history made in Great Mills League Football.

First, congratulations must go to Weston-super-Mare who won the title for the very first time in their club history, and moreover, gained promotion through the Pyramid to the Beazer Homes League Midland Division. This also was a first success for this League in this respect after the disappointments of Mangotsfield United previously. It was certainly a just reward for consistency as throughout the season the pole positions were taken up by Clevedon Town, Bideford, and Weston. Tiverton Town were always threatening in the background, and must feel their chances were somewhat affected by the superb run in the FA Cup in which they reached the First Round Proper for the second year running, going out at Barnet. What is often overlooked by people is that Tiverton also had a very good run in the Vase, emulated by both Paulton Rovers and Welton Rovers who both reached the Fourth Round of that Competition. When one realises that Welton Rovers compounded their run in being relegated to the First Division, the saying that football is a funny old game takes some new meanings.

In the First Division, most experts would have tipped Torquay United, but few would have dared to suggest that they would lose out in a final run to Westbury United, who have made tremendous strides in their short history in the League. Westbury kept their heads in a tight run-in to the end of the season, whilst Torquay won only one game in the last month, drawing too many for comfort and losing their advantage. In this Division another record was created, although one not appreciated by its recipients, Heavitree United, who conceded 206 goals, the highest in the history of the League.

The Les Phillips Cup final, between Plymouth Argyle, the eventual winners, and Torrington, managed by former Argyle boss John Hore, took place at the League's weekend at Dawlish and provided some consolation for Torrington after a disappointing season.

Next year will see some hectic games in Division One in as much that the Great Mills League has now established a Pyramid under its level in which the County Leagues of Gloucestershire, Wiltshire, Devon, and Somerset will automatically feed into us, if club facilities are up to standard. This aspect has been obtained through much co-operation with the counties involved, and should give every incentive to clubs at the lower level.

Last, but not least, we are very grateful and fortunate indeed in these hard times, to retain our sponsorship with Great Mills, and to the same level as previous years. Their interest and involvement in our football is most appreciated by all our clubs, and we are now avidly looking forward to next season which heralds the Centenary of the League. Our Centenary Dinner is being held in Bristol in the Grand Hotel in Spetember, which is exactly the same place, and time of year, when our League had its inception. Not many other Leagues can boast of such a unique and perfect opportunity of celebrating the occasion.

Maurice Washer, Hon. Secretary

LEAGUE TABLES 1991-92

Premier Division	P	W	D	L	F	A	PTS
Weston-super-Mare	40	32	2	6	110	44	98
Clevedon Town	40	28	5	7	90	28	89
Tiverton Town	40	27	5	8	106	47	*85
Bideford	40	25	9	6	102	49	84
Saltash United	40	24	5	11	89	51	77
Plymouth Arg. Res	40	24	4	12	89	52	76
Taunton Town	40	17	11	12	88	56	62
Mangotsfield Utd	40	16	13	11	53	39	61
Elmore	40	17	10	13	76	72	61
Paulton Rovers	40	16	11	13	71	60	59
Minehead	40	16	10	14	65	74	58
Liskeard Athletic	40	14	10	16	68	69	52
Dawlish Town	40	15	5	20	77	76	50
Chippenham Town	40	13	7	20	58	95	46
Torrington	40	11	10	19	48	62	43
Bristol Manor Farm	40	10	10	20	42	66	40
Exmouth United	40	10	8	22	56	97	38
Chard Town	40	8	8	24	48	76	32
Frome Town	40	9	5	25	44	91	32
Welton Rovers	40	8	6	26	32	78	30
Ottery St Mary	40	2	2	36	26	156	8

Division One	P	W	D	L	F	A	PTS
Westbury United	42	27	10	5	80	39	91
Torquay Utd Res	42	26	11	5	96	32	89
Crediton United	42	20	12	10	57	32	72
Bath City Res	42	22	12	10	91	68	72
Warminster Town	42	19	13	10	80	49	70
Keynsham Town	42	19	13	10	80	69	70
Calne Town	42	20	9	13	73	49	69
Brislington	42	21	6	15	70	51	69
Bridport	42	17	16	9	61	50	67
Ilfracombe Town	42	17	14	11	76	44	65
Odd Down	42	20	5	17	58	46	65
Backwell United	42	17	10	15	64	49	61
Bishop Sutton	42	17	10	15	58	50	61
Glastonbury	42	14	8	20	52	61	50
Larkhall Athletic	42	12	12	18	58	65	48
Radstock Town	42	11	14	17	65	68	47
Barnstaple Town	42	12	8	22	42	55	44
Clandown	42	10	13	19	56	72	43
Wellington	42	9	11	22	42	70	38
Devizes Town	42	8	13	21	57	84	37
Melksham Town	42	8	12	22	44	77	36
Heavitree United	42	2	2	38	26	206	8

Combination	P	W	D	L	F	A	PTS
Taunton T. Res	26	19	4	3	84	20	61
Chard Town Res	26	16	5	5	76	43	53
Elmore Res	26	16	3	7	66	42	51
Dawlish Town Res	26	15	5	6	60	41	50
Crediton Utd Res	26	14	5	7	50	34	47
Barnstaple T. Res	26	14	4	8	56	37	46
Exmouth Town Res	26	13	6	7	82	49	45
Tiverton T. Res	26	10	4	12	65	55	34
Minehead Res	26	8	6	12	66	76	30
Bideford Res	26	7	4	15	46	68	25
Wellington Res	26	6	6	14	34	63	24
Torrington Res	26	5	4	17	37	76	19
Ilfracombe T. Res	26	5	3	18	45	74	18
Heavitree Utd Res	26	3	3	20	34	113	12

Subsidiary Zone A	P	W	D	L	F	A	PTS
Crediton Utd Res	6	5	1	0	16	5	16
Barnstaple T. Res	6	4	1	1	13	6	13
Torrington	6	2	3	1	11	7	9
Exmouth Town Res	6	3	0	3	9	11	9
Dawlish Town Res	6	2	1	3	29	11	7
Bideford Res	6	1	0	5	10	24	3
Ilfracombe T. Res	6	1	0	5	3	27	3

Subsidiary Zone B	P	W	D	L	F	A	PTS
Taunton T. Res	6	6	0	0	23	7	18
Elmore Res	6	4	0	2	18	10	12
Chard Town Res	6	3	1	2	18	13	10
Wellington Res	6	2	2	2	16	15	8
Minehead Res	6	2	1	3	19	18	7
Tiverton T. Res	6	1	1	4	14	20	4
Heavitree Utd Res	6	0	1	5	4	29	1

* - Denotes points deducted

LES PHILLIPS CUP 1991-92

First Round

Minehead v Ottery St Mary	4-2	
Elmore v Liskeard Athletic	0-3	
Saltash United v Crediton United	4-0	
Calne Town v Bristol Manor Farm	0-3	
Weston-super-Mare v Melksham Town	5-0	
Radstock Town v Warminster Town	2-1	

Taunton Town v Tiverton Town	1-0
Dawlish Town v Torquay United	3-1
Backwell United v Odd Down	3-4
Bishops Sutton v Devizes Town	1-0
Mangotsfield United v Chippenham Town	0-2

Second Round

Wellington v Bridport	0-1
Liskeard Athletic v Torrington	2-3
Saltash United v Chard Town	4-0
Dawlish Town v Minehead	3-2
Brislington v Mangotsfield United	1-2
Odd Down v Paulton Rovers	5-3
Clevedon Town v Keynsham Town	1-0
Bishops Sutton v Welton Rovers	0-2

Heavitree United v Barnstaple	2-2 (4-3 pens)
Ilfracombe v Taunton Town	2-2 (3-2 pens)
Bideford v Plymouth Argyle Reserves	0-5
Larkhall Athletic v Bath City Reserves	1-2
Radstock Town v Bristol Manor Farm	0-3
Weston-super-Mare v Frome Town	3-0
Glastonbury v Westbury United	1-2
Clandown v Exmouth Town	0-1

Third Round

Exmouth Town v Bristol Manor Farm	2-1
Dawlish Town v Heavitree United	8-1
Westbury United v Ilfracombe Town	5-3
Weston-super-Mare v Bridport	3-1

Clevedon Town v Bath City Reserves	1-2
Torrington v Odd Down	1-0
Mangotsfield United v Saltash United	2-3
Welton Rovers v Plymouth Argyle Reserves	0-4

Quarter Finals

| Bath City Reserves v Dawlish Town | 4-1 |
| Westbury United v Torrington | 0-1 |

| Saltash United v Plymouth Argyle Reserves | 0-6 |
| Exmouth Town v Weston-super-Mare | 0-1 |

Semi-Finals

| Torrington v Weston-super-Mare | 1-0 |

| Bath City Reserves v Plymouth Argyle Reserves | 0-1 |

Final (at Dawlish Town FC): Plymouth Argyle Reserves 3, Torrington 1

COMBINATION KNOCK-OUT CUP

First Round

Barnstaple Town Res v Wellington Reserves	6-1
Bideford Reserves v Chard Town Reserves	0-3
Elmore Reserves v Heavitree United Reserves	5-2

Dawlish Town Reserves v Torrington Reserves	2-0
Taunton Town Reserves v Exmouth Town Res	2-0
Tiverton Town Reserves v Minehead Reserves	3-2

Quarter Finals

| Chard Town Reserves v Ilfracombe Town Res | 3-0 |
| Taunton Town Reserves v Dawlish Town Res | 7-5 |

| Tiverton Town Reserves v Crediton United Res | 2-3 |
| Barnstaple Town Reserves v Elmore Reserves | 1-5 |

Semi-Finals

| Taunton Town Reserves v Crediton Utd Res | 1-0 |

| Chard Town Reserves v Elmore Reserves | 3-0 |

Final (at Wellington FC): Chard Town Reserves 0, Taunton Town Reserves 0 (*Chard won 4-3 on pens*)

PREMIER DIVISION RESULT CHART 1991-92

HOME TEAM	1	2	3	4	5	6	7	8	9	10	11	12	13	14	15	16	17	18	19	20	21
1. Bideford	*	3-1	4-1	3-1	1-2	1-0	3-1	5-2	3-2	3-3	2-2	2-1	12-1	2-0	0-2	3-1	2-1	1-0	1-2	2-1	3-1
2. Bristol MF	1-1	*	2-2	0-2	1-2	3-3	0-2	4-1	1-1	0-1	0-0	0-0	3-0	0-5	2-1	1-2	0-2	1-3	1-1	1-0	1-5
3. Chard Town	0-2	1-0	*	0-0	0-1	1-3	2-2	2-1	4-1	2-0	0-3	0-2	1-0	2-2	3-4	0-2	0-0	1-2	2-1	0-0	0-1
4. Chippenham	0-7	1-2	2-1	*	1-5	2-1	4-0	0-2	3-1	3-2	2-3	3-3	6-2	1-1	1-2	0-2	2-0	2-1	1-4	0-2	0-5
5. Clevedon	1-1	5-1	1-0	3-0	*	3-0	2-0	4-1	1-0	4-0	0-1	3-0	6-0	1-2	1-2	1-1	2-2	0-1	1-1	3-0	0-1
6. Dawlish	4-3	4-2	4-1	1-3	0-3	*	1-3	6-1	3-0	4-1	3-1	1-2	10-0	2-3	3-1	2-1	2-2	0-5	3-1	1-0	1-2
7. Elmore	2-5	1-2	2-1	4-4	0-1	1-0	*	5-0	4-1	1-2	1-2	2-3	2-1	3-1	2-2	3-3	2-1	0-2	1-1	1-0	3-3
8. Exmouth	1-1	2-0	1-1	1-2	1-2	1-3	4-4	*	2-2	1-2	1-1	5-1	2-0	2-2	3-2	0-0	1-4	0-5	1-6	3-0	2-4
9. Frome Town	1-6	1-1	1-0	2-1	1-2	3-0	1-5	0-1	*	2-3	0-2	2-2	2-0	0-4	1-3	1-4	1-1	1-4	2-0	0-1	2-7
10. Liskeard	1-1	3-1	4-1	2-2	2-2	1-0	1-4	5-0	1-2	*	1-1	2-3	3-1	1-4	3-1	3-1	1-1	1-2	1-2	7-0	0-2
11. Mangotsfield	1-2	0-0	2-0	2-0	0-2	1-0	5-1	1-2	1-0	1-1	*	0-0	3-0	3-1	4-1	0-0	1-1	1-0	0-0	2-2	0-1
12. Minehead	1-1	2-1	5-4	2-3	0-2	4-3	1-2	2-0	3-1	2-2	1-1	*	5-0	1-0	2-0	1-6	1-0	1-1	1-1	2-1	0-2
13. Ottery SM.	1-6	0-3	1-5	1-1	0-1	0-1	0-2	0-2	0-3	1-1	1-2	2-3	*	1-5	0-4	0-4	1-11	0-2	2-3	3-1	2-4
14. Paulton R.	0-2	0-1	3-2	1-1	0-1	2-2	2-0	2-1	1-0	0-0	1-0	1-2	1-2	*	2-2	1-1	1-1	1-1	1-0	2-2	0-4
15. Plymouth A.	4-1	1-0	3-1	7-2	1-0	3-0	0-0	3-1	4-1	4-0	1-0	3-1	3-0	3-1	*	3-0	3-1	1-2	0-0	1-2	1-3
16. Saltash	2-0	2-0	2-1	4-0	1-2	3-0	5-1	3-1	0-1	1-0	4-2	4-3	6-0	3-2	3-0	*	3-1	1-2	3-0	2-0	0-4
17. Taunton T.	1-2	0-2	1-1	3-1	3-2	0-0	4-0	2-0	3-2	2-1	5-0	7-0	2-4	3-2	1-3		*	1-1	3-1	2-0	1-3
18. Tiverton	1-2	4-1	3-2	10-0	1-6	1-1	4-4	3-2	4-0	1-3	3-0	1-0	3-0	5-0	1-3	5-1	2-4	*	4-3	3-0	4-2
19. Torrington	0-1	0-0	1-0	0-1	1-2	2-2	2-1	0-1	0-3	1-1	6-0	1-3	0-4	1-0	1-1	1-1	1-3	*	0-2	0-3
20. Welton	1-1	1-2	1-2	1-0	0-7	1-1	0-1	0-1	1-3	2-0	0-0	3-1	4-1	2-2	0-3	2-4	1-4	0-2	0-1	*	0-1
21. Weston SM	1-1	1-0	6-1	1-0	0-4	4-1	1-2	3-1	4-0	3-1	2-0	3-0	7-1	2-4	2-1	3-1	3-2	0-4	3-0	3-0	*

FIRST DIVISION RESULT CHART 1991-92

HOME TEAM	1	2	3	4	5	6	7	8	9	10	11	12	13	14	15	16	17	18	19	20	21	22
1. Backwell Utd	*	4-1	2-0	0-1	0-1	3-2	0-1	2-0	1-0	3-3	5-0	6-1	3-1	0-1	1-1	0-1	2-1	2-2	1-1	2-4	2-0	2-4
2. Barnstaple	1-2	*	1-1	3-0	1-1	2-0	0-2	0-1	0-2	2-1	3-1	0-0	1-2	2-0	1-2	2-1	0-4	0-0	1-2	3-1	0-3
3. Bath C. Res	3-2	0-2	*	1-3	1-1	1-0	3-1	1-1	0-1	3-2	2-0	8-0	2-2	2-1	2-0	1-1	2-3	2-4	1-0	1-1	1-3	3-4
4. B Sutton	1-2	0-2	1-3	*	0-0	0-1	0-2	0-0	1-1	4-1	2-1	5-0	0-2	4-2	1-2	0-0	0-1	1-1	2-2	3-0	2-0	2-2
5. Bridport	0-0	1-0	4-1	0-1	*	0-3	1-1	0-0	0-5	1-0	1-3	5-0	1-1	5-1	1-0	1-0	1-0	2-2	1-3	1-1	2-0	3-1
6. Brislington	3-1	1-0	1-0	1-2	2-2	*	2-0	2-0	0-0	3-2	0-2	6-3	4-2	2-0	3-0	1-2	1-3	3-2	2-4	1-2	1-1	1-3
7. Calne Town	0-0	1-3	2-1	1-0	1-1	2-0	*	0-1	0-1	2-0	2-0	10-0	2-2	2-2	3-2	1-0	2-1	1-1	0-3	3-3	0-2	0-1
8. Clandown	1-2	1-0	0-2	1-2	1-2	0-1	2-4	*	1-2	0-0	3-5	8-1	1-4	0-2	1-3	2-0	0-1	1-0	3-3	3-2	1-1	0-3
9. Crediton Utd	0-0	0-1	7-2	2-0	2-0	1-0	0-4	1-3	*	2-0	1-0	3-0	0-2	1-2	1-0	3-1	3-1	4-0	1-1	2-1	0-0	0-1
10. Devizes	1-1	2-1	0-5	0-2	1-1	0-1	2-3	1-1	0-0	*	2-0	3-1	2-2	2-4	2-0	2-2	3-2	3-2	0-1	0-4	1-4	0-2
11. Glastonbury	3-1	0-0	0-1	2-1	0-0	0-2	0-2	1-2	2-0	0-3	*	2-0	1-2	2-4	0-1	2-1	2-2	3-0	1-1	0-0	2-1	0-2
12. Heavitree	0-2	3-2	1-6	2-2	2-4	1-10	0-3	3-3	0-3	0-6	0-6	*	3-4	0-3	0-1	1-3	1-4	0-5	0-6	0-5	0-1	0-8
13. Ilfracombe	0-2	1-1	0-1	1-2	1-2	0-0	1-1	3-1	2-0	4-0	0-2	9-0	*	0-0	4-0	4-1	0-1	3-1	0-2	1-1	0-0	1-0
14. Keynsham T.	0-0	2-1	3-2	3-0	1-1	0-0	1-3	3-3	0-0	3-1	1-1	7-0	0-4	*	3-1	4-3	2-0	3-2	2-1	2-2	4-1	3-3
15. Larkhall	1-0	2-2	4-5	1-5	0-5	0-1	2-3	1-1	0-1	1-1	1-1	13-0	1-0	1-1	*	6-1	0-2	2-4	0-0	1-1	1-1	0-0
16. Melksham	0-3	2-0	0-4	1-1	2-2	1-2	0-5	1-1	1-1	1-1	1-2	1-2	0-5	1-3	0-3	*	0-1	3-0	0-1	1-4	5-1	0-2
17. Odd Down	1-0	0-0	2-3	2-0	1-3	1-0	2-1	0-1	0-1	5-0	2-0	4-0	1-3	2-1	0-1	1-1	*	1-1	0-3	2-0	2-0	1-2
18. Radstock	1-0	2-1	1-3	0-1	1-1	2-3	2-1	2-2	1-1	0-0	1-2	5-0	1-1	2-2	3-1	1-1	0-2	*	0-2	2-2	2-0	1-3
19. Torquay	1-1	2-0	3-1	0-0	5-0	2-1	3-0	4-3	0-2	3-3	3-1	11-0	1-1	6-0	2-0	1-0	2-1	1-0	*	1-0	6-0	2-0
20. Warminster	3-0	2-0	3-2	0-2	3-0	3-2	4-1	1-1	3-2	2-0	6-0	1-2	2-0	1-2	0-0	0-1	3-2	1-0	*	1-1	1-1
21. Wellington	0-3	1-0	1-4	2-3	1-2	0-2	0-1	1-1	1-0	3-3	1-1	2-0	1-1	5-2	1-2	0-2	0-1	0-1	0-2	1-2	*	3-1
22. Westbury	3-1	1-0	1-3	2-1	2-1	1-0	2-0	3-0	1-1	2-1	3-2	2-0	1-0	0-0	1-1	1-1	2-1	3-1	3-1	1-1	0-0	*

Bath City Reserves veteran goalkeeper Jim Preston punches the ball off the head of Dawlish striker Gidley. Bath recorded an excellent 4-1 win in this Les Phillips Cup Quarter Final at Radstock. Photo - James Wright.

END OF SEASON STATISTICS
ATTENDANCES

PREMIER DIVISION

Club	Total	Ave.	200+ gates
Bideford	4122	206	9
Bristol Mnr F.	1338	70	1
Chard Town	1279	67	
Chippenham	2118	106	
Clevedon T.	3936	179	4
Dawlish T.	921	54	
Elmore	2575	123	2
Exmouth	2602	118	2
Frome Town	1454	73	
Liskeard	2305	137	5
Mangotsfield	4608	209	6
Minehead	2956	141	3
Ottery SM	1635	82	
Paulton R.	3199	168	3
Plymouth	3943	263	15
Saltash	2894	145	3
Taunton	5709	272	19
Tiverton	4943	247	13
Torrington	2602	137	4
Welton R.	2196	105	1
Weston SM	5371	224	13
Total (419 recorded) **62651**		**149**	**103**

Top Scorers
J Durham (Bideford) 31
M Seatherton (Elmore) 30
L Cansfield (Bideford) 29
P Hunt (Taunton Town) 28
A Perrett (Clevedon Town) 28
P Everett (Dawlish Town) 26
K Smith (Tiverton Town) 25
P Elson (Weston-s-Mare) 24

FIRST DIVISION

Club	Total	Ave.	200+ gates
Backwell	1451	66	
Barnstaple	2100	100	1
Bath City	1054	48	
Bishop Sutton	1900	83	
Bridport	2167	108	
Brislington	2069	94	2
Calne Town	2001	91	
Clandown	1258	55	
Crediton Utd	2089	99	
Devizes	1072	59	
Glastonbury	1343	61	
Heavitree	770	37	
Ilfracombe	2268	103	1
Keynsham	1244	59	
Larkhall	1178	53	
Melksham	1427	75	
Odd Down	1315	63	
Radstock	1218	53	
Torquay	4909	245	13
Warminster	2601	124	2
Wellington	1343	64	
Westbury Utd	2612	114	2
Total (471 recorded) **39288**		**83**	**21**

Top Scorers
G Back (Warminster Town) 32
G Lewis (Warminster Town) 24
A McHugh (Westbury United) 24
D Slade (Ilfracombe Town) 24
S Spalding (Backwell Utd) 23
P Horwat (Calne Town) 22
D Darby (Torquay Utd Res) 22

Highest Attendances
731 - Mangotsfield United v Clevedon Town *(20/1/92)*
680 - Elmore v Tiverton Town *(30/8/91)*
600 - Clevedon Town v Weston-super-Mare *(20/4/92)*
523 - Clevedon Town v Mangotsfield United *(1/1/92)*
501 - Bideford v Torrington *(26/12/91)*
491 - Weston-super-Mare v Mangotsfield United *(11/4/92)*
480 - Tiverton Town v Elmore *(6/12/91)*
459 - Torquay United Reserves v Devizes Town *(18/4/92)*
420 - Saltash United v Liskeard Athletic *(26/12/91)*
404 - Saltash United v Plymouth Argyle Reserves *(30/3/92)*

No. of players registered: 2,054 (90-91: 2,040 89-90: 1,944 88-89: 1,727).
Transfers Actioned: 232 (90-91: 194 89-90: 241 88-89: 206).

Phil Hunt was top scorer again for Taunton Town in 1991-92. Here he torments the Ottery defence as the Peacocks cruise to a 7-0 win at Wordsworth Drive. Photo - Tony Smith.

GREAT MILLS WESTERN LEAGUE PREMIER DIVISION TEN YEAR RECORD

	82/3	83/4	84/5	85/6	86/7	87/8	88/9	89/90	90/1	91/2
Barnstaple Town	8	3	13	17	11	12	9	18	20	–
Bideford	1	6	2	3	6	10	16	16	12	4
Bridport	15	–	–	–	–	–	–	–	–	–
Bristol City Res	–	–	3	9	3	7	–	–	–	–
Bristol Manor Farm	–	8	6	11	5	8	6	12	14	16
Chard Town	–	–	11	21	22	–	15	15	16	18
Chippenham Town	13	16	7	5	9	20	12	13	17	14
Clandown	4	17	14	14	20	22	–	–	–	–
Clevedon Town	14	7	17	10	12	13	11	10	11	2
Dawlish Town	3	14	16	8	14	15	19	14	9	13
Devizes Town	12	19	22	–	–	–	–	–	–	–
Elmore	–	–	–	–	–	–	–	–	–	9
Exmouth Town	16	1	4	1	2	6	2	5	19	17
Falmouth Town	6	–	–	–	–	–	–	–	–	–
Frome Town	2	4	18	13	19	18	17	20	13	19
Keynsham Town	19	–	–	–	–	–	–	–	–	–
Liskeard Athletic	9	5	10	2	4	1	4	2	8	12
Mangotsfield Utd	–	13	8	6	10	3	18	3	1	8
Melksham Town	17	18	9	16	18	21	–	–	–	–
Minehead	–	10	12	12	21	19	21	–	–	11
Ottery St Mary	–	–	–	–	–	–	–	–	18	21
Paulton Rovers	–	–	5	19	16	14	8	11	10	10
Plymouth Argyle Res	7	9	15	20	7	4	5	7	3	6
Portway-Bristol	20	–	–	–	–	–	–	–	–	–
Radstock Town	–	–	–	–	17	16	14	19	21	–
Saltash United	5	2	1	4	1	2	1	8	6	5
Shepton Mallet Town	11	11	21	22	–	–	–	–	–	–
Swanage Town & Herston	–	–	–	–	–	11	10	9	–	–
Taunton Town	–	12	20	7	8	9	3	1	7	7
Tiverton Town	–	–	–	–	–	–	–	4	4	3
Torrington	–	–	–	15	15	17	20	17	2	15
Wellington	18	20	–	–	–	–	–	–	–	–
Welton Rovers	–	–	–	–	–	–	13	21	15	20
Weston-super-Mare	10	15	19	18	13	5	7	6	5	1
No. of Clubs	**20**	**20**	**22**	**22**	**22**	**22**	**21**	**21**	**21**	**21**

GREAT MILLS WESTERN LEAGUE DIVISION ONE TEN YEAR RECORD

	82/3	83/4	84/5	85/6	86/7	87/8	88/9	89/90	90/1	91/2
Backwell United	–	6	7	6	9	10	9	2	16	12
Barnstaple Town	–	–	–	–	–	–	–	–	–	17
Bath City Reserves	8	11	13	11	3	4	15	18	12	4
Bishop Sutton	–	–	–	–	–	–	–	–	–	13
Bridport	15	RES	–	–	–	–	3	4	6	9
Brislington	–	–	–	–	–	–	–	–	–	8
Bristol City Res.	13	1	–	–	–	–	–	–	–	–
Bristol Manor Farm	1	–	–	–	–	–	–	–	–	–
Calne Town	–	–	–	–	19	13	4	12	3	7
Chard Town	9	2	–	–	–	2	–	–	–	–
Clandown	–	–	–	–	–	–	14	13	14	18
Crediton United	–	–	–	–	–	–	–	–	10	3
Devizes Town	–	–	–	14	6	6	5	10	8	20
Elmore	14	19	14	15	14	18	20	14	2	–
Glastonbury	5	7	12	18	22	19	19	19	21	14
Heavitree United	15	16	11	10	21	16	11	11	20	22
Ilfracombe Town	–	–	21	19	20	15	8	3	9	10
Keynsham Town	–	5	8	16	13	7	10	8	13	6
Larkhall Athletic	16	14	10	5	7	5	1	6	19	15
Mangotsfield Utd	2	–	–	–	–	–	–	–	–	–
Melksham Town	–	–	–	–	–	–	12	9	15	21
Minehead	–	–	–	–	–	–	–	20	1	–
Odd Down	4	13	22	21	12	14	6	5	4	11
Ottery St Mary	19	18	9	7	11	9	13	1	–	–
Paulton Rovers	3	3	–	–	–	–	–	–	–	–
Portway-Bristol	–	9	1	1	2	–	–	–	–	–
Radstock Town	17	15	6	2	–	–	–	–	–	16
Swanage Town & Herston	6	4	4	8	1	–	–	–	–	–
Tiverton Town	18	21	17	13	16	3	2	–	–	–
Torquay Utd Res.	–	–	–	–	–	–	–	–	7	2
Torrington	–	–	2	–	–	–	–	–	–	–
Warminster Town	–	12	19	22	10	11	18	15	18	5
Wellington Town	–	–	5	12	18	12	7	17	11	19
Welton Rovers	11	8	16	17	8	1	–	–	–	–
Westbury United	–	–	20	20	15	8	16	7	5	1
Weymouth Reserves	10	20	18	9	17	–	–	–	–	–
Wimborne Town	7	10	3	4	5	–	–	–	–	–
Yeovil Town Reserves	12	17	15	3	4	17	17	16	17	–
No. of Clubs	**19**	**21**	**22**	**22**	**22**	**19**	**20**	**20**	**21**	**22**

BIDEFORD

President: Ernie Hopkins   **Chairman:** J McElwee   **Manager:** P Buckingham
Secretary: David Jewell, 75 Stukley Rd, Bideford, N Devon EX39 3EH (0237 479180).
Ground: Sports Ground, Kingsley Road, Bideford (0237 274974).
Directions: A361 for Bideford - ground on right as you enter the town.
No. of seats: New stand   **Covered Accom:** 1,000   **Capacity:** 6,000
Floodlights: Yes   **Year Formed:** 1946
Colours: All red   **Change colours:** All blue.
Previous Name: Bideford Town   **Previous Lges:** Western 49-72/ Southern 72-75
Previous Ground: Hansom Ground (one season)   **Newsline:** 0898 446 831.
Record Attendance: 6,000 v Gloucester, FA Cup 4th Qual. 1960
Programme: 16 pages, 20p   **Programme Editor:** John Hopkins
Midweek Matchday: Wednesday.   **Clubhouse:** Open lunchtimes and evenings
Hons: Western Lg 63-64 70-71 71-72 81-82 82-83 (Div 1 51-52, Lg Cup 71-72 84-85, Alan Young Cup 64-65 69-70, Merit Cup 68-69), Devon Snr Cup 79-80, Devon St Lukes Cup 81-82 83-84, FA Cup 1st Rd 64-65(replay) 73-74 77-78 81-82.

BRISTOL MANOR FARM

President: F J Wardle   **Chairman:** Laurie West   **Manager:** D Coombes
Secretary: Iain Anderson, 182 Forest Rd., Kingswood, Bristol BS15 2EN. (0272) 616426.
Ground: The Creek, Portway, Sea Mills, Bristol (0272 683571).
Directions: M5 jct 18 (Avonmouth Bridge), follow A4 for Bristol - U-turn on dual carriageway by Bristol & West sports ground and ground entrance is down narrow lane half mile on left. 5 mins walk from Sea Mills station (BR Temple Meads-Severn Beach line).
No. of seats: 150   **Covered Accom:** 400   **Capacity:** 2,500
Floodlights: Yes   **Year Formed:** 1964
Colours: Red & black stripes/white/white   **Change colours:** White/red/red.
Previous Leagues: Somerset Senior, Bristol Suburban.   **Previous Name:** Manor Farm Old Boys (1964-68)
Record Attendance: 500 v Portway, Western Lg 1978
Programme: 28 pages, 30p.   **Programme Editor:** Alex Thomas.
Clubhouse: Lounge bar, entertainments, skittle alley, bar meals Thurs.-Sat. Open every evening and lunchtime Sat & Sun.
Hons: Western Lg Div 1 82-83, Glos Tphy 87-88, Glos Amtr Cup 89-90, Somerset Snr Lg Div 1 (Lg Cup, Div 2).
Local Newspapers: Bristol Evening Post, Western Daily Press.   **Midweek Matches:** Tuesday (7.30).

CHARD TOWN

President: J Smith   **Chairman:** B D Beer   **Manager:** Royston Davies
Secretary: Colin Dunford, 27 Manor Gardens, Ilchester, Yeovil, Somerset. BA22 8LE (0935 841217).
Commercial Manager: Peter Male
Ground: Dening Sports Field, Zembard Lane, Chard (04606 61402).
Directions: 150 yards from the town centre, off Combe Street.
No. of seats: None   **Covered Accom:** 200   **Capacity:** 2,000
Floodlights: Yes   **Year Formed:** 1920   **Midweek matches:** Wednesday
Club colours: All maroon   **Change colours:** Sky/sky/navy.
Previous Leagues: Perry Street, Somerset Senior.
Programme: 28 pages, 30p   **Programme Editor:** Allan Spurway.
Hons: Somerset Snr Lg 49-50 53-54 59-60 67-68 69-70 (Lg Cup 61-62 71-72 76-77); Western Lg Div 1 R-up 83-84 87-88 (Merit Cup 82-83, Comb. Cup(Res) 91-92); Somerset Snr Cup 52-53 66-67; S W Co's Cup 88-89

CHIPPENHAM TOWN

President: G W Terrell   **Chairman:** D S Webb   **Manager:** Mel Gingell
Secretary: Arthur Wimble, 31 Southmead, Chippenham, Wilts SN14 0RT (0249 655461).
Commercial Manager: R G Terrell   **Physio:** P Christopher.
Ground: Hardenhuish Park, Bristol Road, Chippenham (0249 650400).
Directions: M4 jct 17, A429 into Chippenham, follow signs for Trowbridge/Bath until r'bout, left onto A420 into town, ground 200yds on left. 5 mins walk from railway station on main A420 Bristol Road.
No. of seats: 100   **Covered Accom:** 300   **Capacity:** 4,000
Floodlights: Yes   **Year Formed:** 1873   **Midweek matches:** Wednesday (7.30)
Club colours: Royal blue   **Change colours:** White
Previous Leagues: Hellenic, Wiltshire Senior, Wiltshire Premier.
Previous Grounds: Westmead, Lowden, Little George Lane, Malmesbury Rd
Record Gate: 4,800 v Chippenham Utd, Western Lg
Programme: 32 pages, 20p   **Programme Editor:** Sandie Webb
Clubhouse: On ground above Stand with bar, skittles etc.
Hons: FA Cup 1st Rd 51-52, Western Lg 51-52 (Div 2 52-53(Res) 80-81), Wilts Shield, Wilts Snr Cup, Wilts Snr League.
Local Newspapers: Chippenham News, Wilts Gazette

CLEVEDON TOWN

President: D Hand   **Chairman:** B Baker   **Manager:** Terry Rowles
Physio: Ken Dodd   **Assistant Manager:** David Jenkins
Secretary: Mike Williams, 34 Robinia Walk, Whitchurch, Bristol BS14 0SH. (0272) 833835
Ground: Hand Stadium, Davis Lane, Clevedon (0275 871636).
Directions: M5 Jct 20, follow signs for Equestrian Centre, first left Central Way, 1st left Kenn Rd, 2nd left Davis Lane; ground half mile on right. Or from Bristol (B3130) left into Court Lane (opposite Clevedon Court), turn right after 1 mile, ground on left.
Seats: 300   **Cover:** 1,600   **Capacity:** 3,650   **Floodlights:** Yes   **Founded:** 1880
Club colours: All blue   **Change colours:** Yellow.   **Midweek Matches:** Wednesday
Previous Lges: Weston/ Somerset Snr/ Bristol Charity.
Previous Grounds: Dial Hill (til early 1890's)/ Teignmouth Road (til 1991).
Previous Names: Clevedon FC, Ashtonians (clubs merged in 1974).
Record Gate: 2,700 v Billingham Synthonia (FA Amateur Cup, at Teignmouth Road).
Programme: 20 pages, 20p   **Programme Editor:** Nick Ball
Clubhouse: Open every midday and evening, separate skittle alley on ground.
Hons: Western Lg R-up 91-92, FA Cup 1st Rd, FA Amtr Cup 3rd Rd 52-53, Bristol Charity Lg, Somerset Snr Cup 01-02 04-05 28-29 76-77.
Local Newspapers: South Avon Mercury

Bideford enjoyed their best season for years. Here Derek Fowler heads their first in a 2-1 home success against Taunton Town. Photo - Tony Smith.

Greg Dark gets in a cross for Bristol Manor Farm in the goalless Boxing Day derby draw at Mangotsfield. Photo - David Collins.

Liskeard Athletic. Back Row (L/R): C Merrin, D Jones, R Keith, R Gibbons, W Haig, S Juniper. Front: A Wright, M Balston, B Swiggs, P Mildon, P Wilmot, R Daly. Photo - James Wright.

DAWLISH TOWN

President: M Swift   **Chairman:** Bob Webster   **Manager:** Graham Weeks
Secretary: Gerry Turner, 43 Exeter Road, Dawlish, Devon EX7 0AB (0626 862438).
Ground: Playing Fields, Exeter Road, Dawlish (0626 863110).
Directions: Approx 1 mile from centre of town, off main Exeter road (A379).
No. of seats: 200   **Covered Accom:** 200   **Capacity:** 2,000
Floodlights: Yes   **Year Formed:** 1889
Club colours: Green/white/green   **Change colours:** Blue
Previous League: Devon & Exeter.   **Previous Ground:** Barley Bank 1875-1900
Record Gate: 1,500 v Heavitree Utd, Devon Prem. Cup Q-Final
Programme: 34 pages, 30p   **Programme Editor:** Gerry Turner
Clubhouse: Open evry night, situated in car park opposite ground.
Hons: Western Lg Cup 80-81 83-84, Devon Premier Cup 69-70 72-73 80-81, Devon Snr Cup 57-58 67-68, Devon St Lukes Cup 82-83, FA Vase Quarter Finals 86-87.

ELMORE

Chairman: L M V Jones   **Manager:** Ken Freeman   **Asst Manager:** Clive Eginton
Secretary: Mike Cosway, C/O the Club (See Below) (0884 242842).
Ground: Horsdon Park, Tiverton, Devon EX16 4DE (0884 252341).
Directions: M5 Jct 27, A373 towards Tiverton, leave at sign for Tiverton Business Park, ground 500yds on right.
No. of seats: 150   **Covered Accom:** 150   **Capacity:** 1,000
Floodlights: Yes   **Year Formed:** 1947   **Midweek matches:** Wednesday (7.30)
Club colours: Green/black/green.   **Change colours:** Red/black/red.
Previous Leagues: Exeter & District, Devon & Exeter, South Western 74-78.
Editor: Mike Blackstone   **Newsline:** 0898 446823   **Programme:** 20 pages
Hons: Tiverton & District Lg; Devon Snr Cup 76-77, E. Devon Snr Cup; Western Lg Cup 90-91 (Div 1 R-up 90-91); Devon St Lukes Cup R-up 90-91

EXMOUTH TOWN

President: Brian Bradley   **Chairman:** P Marshall   **Vice Chairman:** John Disball
Secretary: Dave Richardson, 44 Whitchurch Ave., Exeter EX2 5NT (0395 430985).
Manager: John Bryan   **Assistant Manager:** Paul Dixon.
Commercial Manager: Graham Deasy (0395) 279085.
Ground: Southern Road, Exmouth (0395 279085 (Office)).
Directions: On right side of main Exeter to Exmouth road (town by-pass)
No. of seats: 150   **Covered Accom:** 300   **Capacity:** 2,500
Floodlights: Yes   **Year Formed:** 1933
Colours: Royal blue/white/white   **Change colours:** White/royal blue/red.
Programme: 24 pages   **Editor:** Phil Hiscox   **Previous Lge:** Devon & Exeter
Previous Grounds: Maer Cricket Field 33-38 48-64; Raleigh Park, Withycombe 38-39
Clubhouse: Skittles, darts, pool, open every night.
Hons: FA Vase SF 84-85; Western Lg 83-84 85-86 (R-up 86-87 88-89; Lg Cup 88-89; Div 1 R-up 81-82); Devon St Lukes Cup 84-85 88-89 89-90; Devon Snr Cup 50-51; Devon Prem. Cup 70-71 79-80; East Devon Snr Cup 50-51 82-83; Harry Wood Mem. Cup 81-82; Exmouth Chal. Cup 64-65 65-66 66-67 68-69 70-71 71-72 73-74

FROME TOWN

President: E G Berry   **Chairman:** G Morton-Norris   **Manager:** Steve Ford
Secretary: Mrs S J Merrill, 56 Nightingale Ave., Frome, Somerset BA11 2VW (0373 73820).
Ground: Badgers hill, Berkeley Road, Frome. (0373) 64087.
Directions: Locate "Vine Tree Inn", Bath Road; ground 100 yds from Inn (1 mile from town centre).
No. of seats: 250   **Covered Accom:** 800   **Capacity:** 5,000
Floodlights: Yes   **Year Formed:** 1904   **Club Shop:** Yes
Colours: Red with white trim   **Change colours:** Yellow
Previous League: Wilts Premier
Programme: 16 pages, 20p   **Programme Editor:** Sue Merrill
Clubhouse details: Modern ballroom holds 400. Open every day with two skittle alleys and three bars.
Hons: Western Lg 78-79 (Div 1 19-20, Div 2 R-up 54-55, Lg Cup 79-80 82-83, Merit Cup 82-83, Alan Young Cup 79-80, Subsidiary Cup 59-60), FA Cup 1st Rd 54-55, Somerset Prof. Cup 66-67, Wilts Premier Lg, Western Co's F'lit Lg.
Local Newspapers: Western Daily Press   **Midweek Matches:** Wednesday (7.30)

LISKEARD ATHLETIC

President: E K Brown   **Chairman:** David Hicks   **Manager:** Keith Manley
Secretary: A Wilton, Martina, Dawes Close, Dobwalls, Liskeard, Cornwall PL14 6JD. (0579) 20980
Commercial Manager: Alan Mayne (0579 43593/47644).
Ground: Lux Park, Liskeard, Cornwall (0579 42665).
Directions: Take Tavistock Road (A390) from town centre, after 1/2 mile turn left on St Cleer Road (following signs to Lux Park Sports Complex) and the ground is 200 yards on left.
No. of seats: 200   **Covered Accom:** 750   **Capacity:** 3,500
Floodlights: Yes   **Year Formed:** 1889   **Nickname:** The Blues
Club colours: All blue   **Change colours:** Green/black
Previous Leagues: East Cornwall Premier, Plymouth & District, South Western 66-79.
Players to progress to Football League: Bradley Swiggs.
Programme: 24 pages, 25p   **Programme Editor:** E K Brown & Steve Holman (0579) 21302.
Clubhouse details: Open every day, dancing, food.
Hons: South Western Lg 76-77 (R-up 75-76 77-78; Lg Cup 76-77 78-79) Western Lg 87-88 (R-up 85-86 89-90, Merit Cup 80-81); Cornwall Snr Cup 04-05 83-84 84-85 85-86 88-89 89-90 (R-up 70-71 75-76 76-77 78-79); Cornwall Charity Cup 21-22 79-80, Cornwall Jnr Cup 05-06 13-14 26-27; SW Pratten Cup 78-79; E Cornwall Prem RAOB Cup 67-68, Plymouth & Dist. Lg 60-61 (Div 1 59-60 (R-up 54-55 73-74), Div 2 76-77(Res), Victory Cup 60-61, Charity Cup 59-60), E Cornwall Prem. Lg Cup 88-89(Res).
Local Newspapers: Cornish Times   **Midweek Matches:** Tuesday (7.45)

Bideford FC. Back Row (L/R): P Buckingham (Manager), M Jenkins, P West, D Fowler, A Greene (Capt), T Fowler, J Impey, J Durham, A Morgan (Physio), K Prouse (Kit Manager). Front: P Hutchings, A Wharton, N Tucker, G Carpenter, D Palfrey, D Smith. Photo - Mark Sawbridge.

Liskeard goalkeeper Ian Simpson makes a stunning save against Frome Town. Photo - Elaine Sarjeant.

Taunton Town FC. Back Row (L/R): W Randall, D Pope, C Souness, P Shepherd, N Pugh, M Richards, D Cann. Front: P Hunt, S Mallett (Capt), N Jarvis, G Knight, A Howe, S Porter. Photo - Tony Smith.

MANGOTSFIELD UNITED

President: A J Hill   **Chairman:** Roger Coles   **Manager:** TBA.
Secretary: John Coles, 33 Jubilee Crescent, Mangotsfield B17 3BB (0202 563075).
Ground: Cossham Street, Mangotsfield (0272) 560119.
Directions: M4 jct 19, M32 jct 1; A4174 marked Downend, through lights, over double mini-r'bout to Mangotsfield. Turn left by village church onto B4465 signposted Pucklechurch, ground quarter mile on right.
No. of seats: 200   **Covered Accom:** 1,000   **Capacity:** 2,500
Floodlights: Yes   **Year Formed:** 1950
Club colours: Blue   **Change colours:** White/white/sky blue.
Players to progress to Football League: G.Megson, S.White, G.Penrice, P.Purnell, N.Tanner, M.Hooper.
Previous Leagues: Bristol & District, Avon Combination.
Record Gate: 2,386 v Bath City, FA Cup 77-78
Programme: 32 pages, 30p.   **Programme Editor:** Michael Lewis
Clubhouse: Large function room with separate lounge and kitchen facilities. Lounge bar for official functions etc.
Hons: Western Lg 90-91 (Lg Cup 73-74 (R-up 86-87) Div 1 R-up 82-83); Somerset Prem. Cup 87-88 (R-up 88-89); Glos Snr Cup 68-69 75-76; Glos FA Trophy 84-85 86-87; Hungerford Cup 74-75; Rothmans National Cup (R-up 77-78)

MINEHEAD

President: A C Copp   **Chairman:** J Walder   **Manager:** Andrew Hodgson
Secretary: Tony Smith, Marley's, Martlett Road, Minehead TA24 5QE. (0643) 703698
Ground: The Recreation Ground, Irnham Road, Minehead, Somerset (0643 704989).
Directions: Entering town from east on A39 turn right into King Edward Road at Police station, first left into Alexandra Rd and follow signs to car park; ground entrance within. Regular buses to Minehead from Taunton, the nearest railhead.
No. of seats: 250   **Covered Accom:** 700   **Capacity:** 3,500   **Floodlights:** Yes
Club colours: All blue   **Change colours:** All yellow   **Year Formed:** 1889
Programme: 24 pages, 20p   **Programme Editor:** T M Smith **Midweek Matches:** Wednesday (7.45)
Previous Leagues: Somerset Snr, Southern 72-83.
Record attendance: 3,600 v Exeter, FA Cup 2nd rnd, 17/12/1977
Hons: Southern Lg R-up 76-77 (Div 1 Sth 75-76, Merit Cup 75-76), Western Lg R-up 66-67 71-72 (Div 1 90-91, Alan Young Cup 67-68 (jt with Glastonbury), Somerset Premier Cup 60-61 73-74 76-77.

PAULTON ROVERS

President: R Carter   **Chairman:** D Bissex   **Manager:** S Gay
Secretary: John Pool, 111 Charlton Park, Midsomer Norton, Avon BA3 4BP (0761 415190).
Ground: Athletic Field, Winterfield Road, Paulton (0761 412907).
Directions: Leave A39 at Farrington Gurney (approx 15 miles south of Bristol), follow A362 marked Radstock for two miles, left at junction B3355 to Paulton, ground on right.
No. of seats: 138   **Covered Accom:** 300   **Capacity:** 4,000
Floodlights: Yes   **Year Formed:** 1881   **Midweek matches:** Tuesday
Club colours: White/white/maroon   **Change colours:** Yellow, red trim.
Previous League: Somerset Senior.   **Previous Ground:** Rec. Ground 1946-48
Record Gate: 2,000 v Crewe, FA Cup, 1906-07
Programme: 16 pages, with admission.   **Programme Editor:** Keith Simmons
Clubhouse: Bar, lounge, skittle alley, dance hall for 400.
Hons: Somerset Snr Cup 00-01 02-03 03-04 07-08 08-09 09-10 34-35 67-68 68-69 71-72 72-73 74-75, Somerset Snr Lg.
Local Newspapers: Bath Evening Chronicle, Bristol Evening Post, Western Daily Post.

PLYMOUTH ARGYLE RESERVES

President: G H Gillan   **Chairman:** Dan McAuley   **Manager:** Peter Shilton
Secretary: Mrs Elizabeth Baker, Chief Executive, Plymouth Argyle FC, Home Park, Plymouth, Devon PL2 3DQ (0752 562561).
Ground: Home Park, Plymouth, Devon PL2 3DQ (0752 562561).
Directions: From city centre to railway station, ground at top of hill behind station in Home Park.
No. of seats: 4,000   **Covered Accom:** 20,000   **Capacity:** 28,000
Floodlights: Yes   **Year Formed:** 1886   **Midweek matches:** Tuesday
Colours: Green & white stripes/black/black   **Change colours:** White & black.
Previous Leagues: Plymouth & District.
Programme: Team sheet.   **Clubhouse:** V.P. Club
Hons: Western Lg Cup 89-90 91-92.
Local Newspapers: Western Morning News, Western Evening Herald.

SALTASH UNITED

President: P Skinnard   **Chairman:** M Howard   **Manager:** Chris Harrison
Secretary: C D Phillips, 85 Lakeview Close, Tamerton Foliot, Plymouth PL5 4LT (0752 705845).
Ground: Kimberley Stadium, Callington Road, Saltash, Cornwall (0752 845746).
Directions: First left after crossing Tamar Bridge, through town centre, at top of town fork right at mimi r'bout, ground 400 yds ahead on left.
No. of seats: 250   **Covered Accom:** 250   **Capacity:** 3,000
Floodlights: Yes   **Year Formed:** 1947   **Nickname:** The Ashes
Club colours: All red   **Change colours:** Black & white stripes/black/black
Previous Leagues: Cornwall Snr/ South Western 51-59 62-76/ East Cornwall Premier 59-62.
Programme: 20 pages, 30p   **Programme Editor:** T.B.A.
Clubhouse: Club attached to stand and caters for dancing and club activities.
Hons: Cornwall Snr Lg 49-50 50-51, Western Lg 84-85 86-87 88-89 (R-up 83-84 87-88, Lg Cup 86-87 87-88 (R-up 88-89), Div 1 76-77, Merit Cup 79-80 87-88), Sth Western Lg 53-54 75-76 (R-up 52-53 73-74 74-75, Lg Cup 51-52 69-70 73-74), Cornwall Snr Cup 50-51 74-75 81-82 87-88 90-91.
Local Newspapers: Western Evening Haerald, The Cornish Times.   **Midweek Matches:** Wednesday

TAUNTON TOWN

President: T F Harris **Chairman:** T F Harris **Manager:** Keith Bowker
Secretary: Mrs Joan Ellis, c/o Taunton Town FC (0823) 278191 (W): 412423 (H)
Ground: Wordsworth Drive, Taunton, Somerset (0823 278191).
Directions: Leave M5 Jct 25, follow signs to town centre, at 2nd set of lights turn left into Wordsworth Drive; ground on left. 25 mins walk from Taunton (BR); turn left out of station and follow road through town centre bearing left into East Reach. Follow road down and turn right into Wordsworth Drive shortly after Victoria pub.
No. of seats: 250 **Covered Accom:** 1,000 **Capacity:** 4,000
Floodlights: Yes **Year Formed:** 1947 **Midweek matches:** Monday
Club colours: Sky blue & claret/claret/sky blue **Change colours:** Yellow/blue/yellow.
Record Gate: 2,960 v Torquay, Western Lg, 1958
Newsline: 0898 122 901 **Previous Lges:** Western 54-77/ Southern 77-83.
Programme: 28 pages **Editor:** Mrs Joan Ellis **Nickname:** Peacocks
Clubhouse: Social club to accommodate 300, full bar facilities, separate bar & hall for private functions.
Hons: Western Lg 68-69 89-90 (Alan Young Cup 73-74 75-76(jt with Falmouth), Charity Chall. Cup 49-50 50-51), Somerset Snr Lg 52-53, Somerset Prem. Cup R-up 82-83 89-90, FA Cup 1st Rd 81-82 (lost 1-2 at Swindon).

TIVERTON TOWN

President: Dan McCauley **Chairman:** Gordon Anderson **Manager:** John Owen
Secretary: Alan Disney, 56 Melbourne St., Tiverton, Devon EX16 5LB (0884 253829).
Ground: Ladysmead, Bolham Road, Tiverton (0884 252397).
Directions: M5 Jct 27, west towards Tiverton on A373, continue to end of dual carriageway and turn left at r'about; ground entrance 300yds on right alongside BP petrol station.
No. of seats: 300 **Covered Accom:** 300 **Capacity:** 2,000
Floodlights: Yes **Year Formed:** 1920 **Midweek matches:** Wednesday
Newsline: 0898 122 925.
Colours: Amber/amber/black **Change colours:** Blue & white/blue/blue.
Programme: 28-40 pages, 30p **Programme Editor:** Nigel Davis
Previous Leagues: Devon & Exeter. **Previous ground:** The Elms, Blundell Road 1920-39
Clubhouse: Three bars, large function room, lounge, darts, pool, real ale
Hons: FA Cup 1st Rnd 90-91 (lost 2-6 at Aldershot) 91-92 (lost 0-5 at Barnet); Western Lg Amateur Trophy 77-78 78-79 (Div 1 R-up 88-89); Devon St Lukes Cup 90-91; Devon & Exeter Lg 51-52 66-67 70-71 84-85; Devon Snr Cup 55-56 65-66; East Devon Snr Cup 35-36 37-38 52-53 55-56 60-61 62-63 66-67; North Charity Cup 72-73 86-87

TORQUAY UNITED RESERVES

Chairman: Mike Bateson **Manager:** Paul Compton.
Secretary: Dave Turner, Plainmoor, Torquay. TQ1 3PS. (0803) 38666.
Directions: Ground signed on all approaches to town.
No. of seats: 750 **Covered Accom:** Yes **Capacity:** 6,000 **Floodlights:** Yes
Club colours: Yellow **Change colours:** Blue/white/blue.
Midweek Matches: Wednesday **Programme:** Team sheet
Hons: Western Lg Div 1 R-up 91-92.

TORRINGTON

President: F Morris **Chairman:** J Cann **Manager:** John Hore
Secretary: Robert Dymond, Back Flat, 12 South Street, Torrington, Devon EX38 8HE (0805 23569).
Ground: Vicarage Field, School Lane, Great Torrington (0805 22853).
Directions: Entering town from South Molton, turn right behind church.
No. of seats: None **Covered Accom:** 2,000 **Capacity:** 4,000
Floodlights: Yes **Year Formed:** 1908 **Midweek Matches:** Wednesday
Club colours: Green/white/green **Change colours:** Blue/black/white
Programme: 48 pages, 20p **Programme Editor:** Bob Dymond
Previous League: South Western 77-84.
Clubhouse: Two bars, committee room & kitchen.
Honours: Western Lg R-up 90-91 (Div 1 R-up 84-85), South Western Lg R-up 80-81 (Lg Cup 82-83), Devon Cup.
Local Newspapers: N.Devon Journal, Bideford Gazette

WESTBURY UNITED

Chairman: Eli Manasseh **Manager:** Ian Harris
Secretary: E L Barber, 7 Farleigh Close, Westbury, Wilts. BA13 3TF. (0373) 822117.
Ground: Meadow Lane, Westbury (0373 823409).
Directions: In town centre, A350, follow signs for BR station, Meadow Lane on right. Ten mins walk from railway station (on main London-South West + South Coast-Bristol lines).
No. of seats: 150 **Covered Accom:** 350 **Capacity:** 2,000 **Floodlights:** Yes **Year Formed:** 1921'
Club colours: Green **Change colours:** White/red
Midweek Matches: Wednesday (7.30)
Previous Leagues: Wilts County, Wilts Comb.
Honours: Western Lg Div 1 91-92, Wilts Senior Cup 31-32 32-33 47-48 51-52, Wilts Combination.

DIVISION ONE CLUBS 1992-93

BACKWELL UNITED

President: W Roberts   **Chairman:** Chris Strong
Secretary: W C Coggins, 34 Westfield Road, Backwell, Bristol BS19 3ND (0275 463424).
Manager: Adrian Britton   **Coach:** Gerry Sweeney.
Ground: Recreation Ground, Backwell, Avon (0275 462612).
Directions: Near centre of Backwell on main A370 Bristol to Weston-super-Mare road. 15 mins walk from Nailsea & Backwell (BR); turn right out of station, right at traffic lights, ground quarter mile on right.
No. of seats: None   **Covered Accom:** 150   **Capacity:** 1,000   **Floodlights:** No
Club colours: All red   **Change colours:** White/blue/blue   **Year Formed:** 1911
Programme: 16 pages, 20p.   **Programme Editor:** Mike Stone   **Midweek Matches:** Tuesday
Previous Leagues: Bristol Surburban (Pre 1970); Somerset Senior 70-83
Record attendance: 400 v Robinsons, Somerset Lg, 1982
Club Honours: Somerset Snr Lg 77-78 79-80 80-81 81-82 82-83 (Lg Cup 82-83 (R-up 79-80) Div 1 72-73); Somerset Snr Cup 81-82; SW Co.'s Sutton Transformer Cup 81-82

BARNSTAPLE TOWN

President: J Symons   **Chairman:**   **Manager:** Bryan Hill
Secretary: Peter Cross, 3 Monterey Place, Water Lane, Newport, Barnstaple EX32 9LJ (0271 46591).
Ground: Mill Road, Barnstaple, Devon (0271 743469).
Directions: A361 to Ilfracombe (from M5 Jct 26), in town follow A361 Ilfracombe signs, first left after crossing bridge is Mill Road.
No. of seats: 400   **Covered Accom:** 1,000   **Capacity:** 5,000   **Floodlights:** Yes
Year Formed: 1895   **Club colours:** Red/white/red   **Change colours:** White & navy
Previous Leagues: North Devon, Exeter, Plymouth.
Previous Grounds: Town Wharf (Pre 1920's); Highfield Road (until 1935)**Previous Name:** Barnstaple Ship Yard
Record Attendance: 6,200 v Bournemouth, FA Cup 1st Rnd, 1951
Programme: 28 pages, 25p   **Programme Editor:** A Sampson
Clubhouse: Open weekday evenings, Saturday midday & evening.
Hon: Western Lg 52-53 79-80 (R-up 80-81 81-82, Div 1 49-50, Merit Cup 74-75 83-84 84-85), FA Cup 1st Rd replay 51-52, Devon Premier Cup, Devon Lg.
Local Newspapers: N Devon Journal Herald.   **Midweek Matches:** Tuesday

BISHOP SUTTON

Chairman: A J Thomas   **Manager:** Graham Bird   **Physio/Coach:** Roy Penney
Secretary: Lester Hammond, Cornerways, Church Lane, Bishop Sutton B18 4XA (0275 332673).
Ground: Football Field, Bishop Sutton. (0272) 333097
Directions: On A368 at rear of Butchers Arms Public House – Ground signposted on left entering village from the West.
No. of seats: None   **Covered Accom:** Yes   **Capacity:**   **Floodlights:** No
Club colours: All blue   **Change colours:** Yellow/Green/yellow
Midweek Matches: Tuesday
Previous Ground: Adjacent cricket field   **Previous League:** Somerset Senior (pre 1991)

BRIDPORT

President: Mrs L Parker   **Chairman:** D Fowler   **Manager:** Derek Walkey
Secretary: Keith Morgan, 95 Orchard Crescent, Bridport DT6 5HA (0308 25113).
Ground: The Beehive, St Mary's Field, Bridport, Dorset (0308 23834).
Directions: Take West Bay road from town centre, turn right immediately before Palmers Brewery.
No. of seats: 200   **Covered Accom:** 400   **Capacity:** 2,000   **Floodlights:** Yes
Club colours: Red/black/red   **Change colours:** Blue/white/blue   **Midweek Matches:** Wednesday
Founded: 1887   **Nickname:** Bees   **Prog. Editor:** P S Ennals
Previous Grounds: Pymore (pre 1930s); Crown Field (pre 1953)
Previous Leagues: Perry Street/ Western 61-84/ Dorset Combination 84-88.
Record Attendance: 1,150 v Exeter City, 1981; 3,000 v Chelsea, at Crown, 1950
Hons: Western Lg 70-71 72-73 77-78 (R-up 76-77, Merit Cup 69-70 71-72 73-74); FA Vase 5th Rd 88-89; Dorset Comb. 85-86 86-87 87-88 (Lg Cup 86-87 87-88); Dorset Snr Cup 63-64 69-70 70-71 75-76 78-79 79-80 80-81 87-88; Dorset Snr Amateur Cup 48-49 49-50 54-55 56-57 70-71 71-72; West Dorset Challenge Bowl 07-08; Perry Street Lg 22-23; Mark Frowde Cup 76-77 88-89

BRISLINGTON

President: Dick Ollis   **Chairman:** Paul Bishop   **Manager:** Jamie Patch
Secretary: F G Durbin, 52 Arlington Road, St Annes, Bristol BS4 4AJ (0272 777169).
Ground: Ironmould Lane, Brislington (0272 778531).
Directions: Four miles out of Bristol on main A4 to Bath – turn left up lane opposite Garden Centre
No. of seats: None   **Covered Accom:** Yes   **Floodlights:** None   **Previous ground:** Council pitch
Club colours: Red/black/red   **Change colours:** All blue   **Prog. Editor:** Bob Perrott

CALNE TOWN

President: P Gleed   **Chairman:** D C Syms   **Manager:** Graham Fell
Secretary: A J Brewer, 9 Fitzmaurice Square, Calne, SN11 8NL (0249 815744).
Ground: Bremhill View, Lickhill Rd., North End, Calne (0249 816716).
Directions: From Bristol to Chippenham, on entering town keep left all the way taking slip road to North End, off main Swindon Road.
No. of seats: None   **Covered Accom:** 200   **Capacity:** 2,000   **Floodlights:** Yes
Club colours: Gree/yellow/white.   **Change colours:** All red.   **Midweek Matches:** Wednesday.
Programme: 24 pages   **Programme Editor:** L Drake.
Record Gate: 1,100 v Swindon, Friendly 25.7.1987   **Previous Leagues:** Wilts County (pre-1986)
Founded: 1920 (when Calne Town (founded 1886) merged with Harris Utd to form Calne & Harris Utd).
Previous Name: Calne & Harris Utd 1920-1967   **Previous Ground:** Rec., Anchor Road 1887-1967
Hons: Wilts Snr Ghia Cup 80-81 85-86, Wilts Snr Cup 12-13 34-35 84-85 (R-up 1893-94 94-95 1911-12 49-50), Wilts Lg 33-34 (Div 2 79-80, Div 3 85-86, Div 4 81-82).

Welton Rovers. Back Row (L/R): Andrew Vause, Mike McCormack, Ian Davis, Bob Jelley, Mike Gough, Neil Parker, Milton Green. Front: John Morgan, Julian Bowen, Bill Athey, Shaun Prendeville, Simon White, Kevin Presley. Photo - Dennis Nicholson.

Minehead's highly rated No.10 Gareth Morgan capitalises on a defensive blunder and scores the first in a 3-0 success at St Blazey in the FA Cup Preliminary Round on August 31st. Photo - Ray Frith.

Bridport FC. Back Row (L/R): Patrick Ennals (Trainer), Ian Duffie, Phil Crabb, Colin Poole, Matthew Gale, Danny Kitton, Steve Crabb, Adrian Chance. Front: Sean Day, Tristan Cox, Ricky Gape, Marc Aylott, Don McAllister, Derek Walkey (Manager).

CLANDOWN

President: **Chairman:** S Button **Manager:** Gary Green
Secretary: Clive Herron, 26 Waterside Road, Radstock, Avon BA3 3YF (0761 432814).
Ground: Thyne Field, Clandown, Radstock (0761 419805).
Directions: Approx half mile from Radstock – off A367 towards Bath.
No. of seats: 300 **Covered Accom:** 300 **Capacity:** 2,000 **Floodlights:** Yes
Club colours: Black & white stripes/black/black **Change colours:** All red **Midweek Matches:** Tuesday
Founded: 1895 **Record Attendance:** 3,000 v Bath, FA Cup 1948
Hons: Western Lg Div 1 21-22 (Amateur Trophy 81-82), Somerset Snr Cup 45-46 77-78 78-79.

CLYST ROVERS

President: Mr P W Brown **Chairman:** Mr M Hale
Secretary: John Edwards, Lamorna, Pinn Lane, Pinhoe, Exeter EX1 3RF (0392 68633).
Manager: Sammy Kingdom **Asst Manager:** Mr A Carr
Commercial Manager: Mr Hookway (0884 259975).
Ground: Waterslade Park, Clyst Honito, Devon (0884 259152).
Directions: A30 following signs for Exeter Airport. Ground signposted up narrow 200yds past Duke of York Pub (on right coming from Exeter).
No. of seats: No **Covered Accom:** Yes **Capacity:** **Floodlights:** Due
Colours: Blue/white/blue **Change colours:** Red & white/blue/navy
Midweek Matches: Tuesday **Previous Leagues:** South Western 81-92.
Programme: 16 pages **Programme Editor:** Ray Dack.

CREDITON UNITED

Chairman: D J Blanchflower **Manager:** T Atkins
Secretary: Brian Maunder, 39 Geneva Close, Exeter, Devon EX2 4NH (0392 411592).
Ground: Lord's Meadow Sports Centre, Crediton (0363 24671).
Directions: A337 to Crediton from Exeter, right onto A3072 (signposted Tiverton) at White Hart Hotel, turn right into Commercial Rd for Lord's Meadow Ind. Est.- Sports Centre car park 250 metres on left.
No. of seats: 150 **Covered Accom:** 150 **Capacity:** 2,000 **Floodlights:** No
Club colours: Royal blue/white/blue **Change colours:** Red & black stripes/black/black.
Midweek Matches: Wednesday
Previous Leagues: Devon & Exeter **Hons:** Devon County Cup & Devon Snr Cup S-Final

DEVIZES TOWN

Chairman: F Giles **Manager:** A Stevens
Secretary: Chris Dodd, 69 Broadleas Park, Devizes, Wilts SN10 5JG (0380 6205).
Ground: Nursteed Road, Devizes. (0380 722817).
Directions: Off Nursteed Road (A342 signposted Andover); leaving town ground on right opposite Eastleigh Rd.
Seats: 370 **Cover:** 400 **Capacity:** 2,500 **Floodlights:** No **Founded:** 1883
Club colours: Red & white/black/red **Change colours:** Green & white/white/white
Previous Name: Southbroom (until early 1900s) **Previous Ground:** London Road (pre 1946)
Previous Leagues: Wilts Snr Cup 07-08 49-50 56-57 57-58 58-59 60-61 61-62 62-63 65-66 67-68 70-71 71-72 73-74 78-79, Wiltshire Combination, Wiltshire Premier.

GLASTONBURY

President: Mr L R Reed **Chairman:** Barry Carter **Manager:** David Baker
Secretary: David McCartney, 3 Pound Close, Paradise Estate, Glastonbury BA6 9LG (0458 31701).
Ground: Abbey Moor Stadium, Godney Road, Glastonbury, Somerset (0458 31460).
Directions: At bottom of town centre take Northload Street, first right after crossing bridge, ground immediately on right.
No. of seats: Nil **Covered Accom:** 200 **Capacity:** 1,500 **Floodlights:** Yes
Club colours: Tangerine/black/tangerine. **Change colours:** White/blue trim/white **Year Formed:** 1890
Previous Leagues: Bristol & District, Bristol Suburban **Midweek Matches:** Wednesday
Previous Ground: Abbey Park (Pre-1982).
Hons: Western Lg 48-49 50-51 69-70 (R-up 47-48 51-52, Lg Cup 65-66, Alan Young Cup 67-68 (jt with Minehead) 70-71); Somerset Professional Cup 37-38 48-49; Somerset Snr Cup 35-36; Somerset Charity Cup 32-33; Somerset Jnr Cup 12-13 13-14; Somerset Lg 49-50 50-51

HEAVITREE UNITED

President: E Drew **Chairman:** Barry Conaway **Manager:** Bill Ring
Secretary: A S Kitson, 13 Tuckfield Close, Wonford, Exeter EX2 5LR (0392 72027).
Ground: Wingfield Park, East Wonford Hill, Exeter, Devon (0392 73020).
Directions: Leave M5 at Exeter Services, follow signs for City Centre/ Heavitree for approx. 3 miles and ground is situated behind Heavitree Social Centre.
No. of seats: 150 **Covered Accom:** 150 **Capacity:** 1,000 **Floodlights:** No
Colours: All royal blue (yellow trim) **Change colours:** White/black/black **Year Formed:** 1886
Programme: 24 pages, 20p **Programme Editor:** Phil Hiscox **Previous Leagues:** Devon & Exeter
Hons: Devon & Exeter Lg, Devon Snr Cup 47-48 60-61, E Devon Snr Cup **Midweek Matches:** Tuesday

ILFRACOMBE TOWN

President: Mike Edmunds **Chairman:** TBA **Manager:** TBA
Secretary: Anthony Alcock, 2 Worth Road, Ilfracombe, N Devon EX34 9JA (0271 62686).
Ground: Marlborough Road, Ilfracombe, Devon (0271 65939).
Directions: A361 to Ilfracombe, 1st right in town after lights, follow road to top, ground on left.
No. of seats: 20 **Covered Accom:** 200 **Capacity:** 4,500 **Floodlights:** Yes
Club colours: All blue **Change colours:** All white **Year Formed:** 1902
Record attendance: 3,000 v Bristol City, Ground opening, 1924
Previous name: Ilfracombe 02-09 Ilfracombe Utd 09-14 Ilfracombe Comrades 14-20
Previous ground: Shaftesbury Field, Killacleave 02-24
Previous Leagues: East Devon, North Devon, S.Western League. **Midweek Matches:** Tuesday (7.45)
Hons: E.Devon Prem., N.Devon Senior, N.Devon Premier.

KEYNSHAM TOWN

President: E G Neal   **Chairman:** Roger Stone   **Manager:** Chris Selway
Secretary: Lester Clements, 24 Holcombe, St Giles Estate, Whitchurch BS14 0AT (0275 837698).
Ground: Crown Field, Bristol Road, Keynsham (0272 865876).
Directions: A4 from Bristol to Bath, ground on left before entering village opposite Crown Inn.
Seats: None   **Cover:** 200   **Capacity:** 2,000   **Floodlights:** Yes   **Founded:** 1896
Club colours: Amber/burgundy/amber.   **Change colours:** Blue/white/blue
Previous Grounds: The Hams 1886-1910; Gaston 1910-25; Park Road 25-30; Charlton Rd 30-39
Record Gate: 2,160 v Saltash, Amateur Cup, Oct 1952
Previous Leagues: Bristol District, Bristol Prem. Comb, Somerset Snr   **Midweek Matches:** Wednesday
Hons: Somerset Lg Div 1 77-78; Somerset Snr Cup 51-52 57-58; GFA Jnr Cup 25-26, Somerset & Avon (South)
Premier Cup 79-80, FA Cup 4th Qualifying Rd.

LARKHALL ATHLETIC

President: A J Rhymes   **Chairman:** A J Grace   **Manager:** Gerald Rich
Secretary: Mervyn Liles, 9 Eastbourne Ave., Claremont Rd., Bath BA1 6EW (0225 319427).
Ground: "Plain Ham", Charlcombe Lane, Larkhall, Bath (0225 334952).
Directions: A4 from Bath, 1 mile from city centre turn left into St Saviours Rd. In Larkhall square fork left, and right at
junction, road bears into Charlcombe Lane. Ground on right as lane narrows.
No. of seats: None   **Covered Accom:** 50   **Capacity:** 1,000   **Floodlights:** No
Club colours: All royal blue   **Change colours:** Red with white trim   **Year Formed:** 1914
Previous Leagues: Somerset Snr   **Midweek Matches:** Tuesday
Hons: Somerset Snr Cup 75-76, Somerset Snr Lg, Western Lg Div 1 88-89 (Div 1 Merit Cup 83-84 84-85 85-86 87-88(jt
with Yeovil Reserves).

MELKSHAM TOWN

President: H J Goodenough   **Chairman:** M J Harris
Secretary: Paul Macey, 30 Wellington Square, Bowerhill, Melksham SN12 6QX (0225 882888).
Manager: Nigel Brindle   **Asst Manager:** S Harvey   **Comm. Mgr:** D R Campbell
Ground: The Conigre, Melksham (0225 702843).   **Sponsors:** Hibernian plc
Directions: Turn into car park in town market-place, then left into Melksham House grounds.
Seats: None   **Cover:** 1,500   **Capacity:** 3,000   **Floodlights:** Yes   **Founded:** 1876
Colours: Old gold/black/black   **Change colours:** Green/white/green
Previous Lge: Wilts Co. 1894-1974   **Previous grounds:** Challymead, Old Brighton Rd Field
Record Gate: 2,821 v Trowbridge, FA Cup 57-58.
Clubhouse details: Open every night & Sat/Sun lunch
Hons: Wilts Lg 03-04 (R-up 24-25 29-30 59-60 67-68 68-69 71-72), Western Lg Div 1 79-80, Wilts Snr Cup 03-04 69-70
77-78 (R-up 57-58 67-68 68-69), Wilts Shield 80-81 81-82 84-85 85-86 (R-up 86-87), FA Amateur Cup 1st Rd 68-69.

ODD DOWN

President: **Chairman:** R Chandler   **Manager:** Paul Gover
Secretary: M Mancini, 36 Caledonian Rd., East Twerton, Bath BA3 2RD (0225 423293).
Ground: Combe Hay Lane, Odd Down, Bath (0225 832491).
Directions: On main Bath/Exeter road - leaving Bath turn left into Combe Hay Lane opposite Lamplighters Pub. 40
mins walk from Bath (BR).
No. of seats: None   **Covered Accom:** 50   **Capacity:** 1,000   **Floodlights:** No
Club colours: Black & white stripes/black/black   **Change colours:** All red   **Year Formed:** 1901
Previous Leagues: Wilts Premier, Bath & District, Somerset Senior   **Midweek Matches:** Tuesday
Hons: Somerset Snr Cup 91-92.

OTTERY ST MARY

President: H F Pinney   **Chairman:** G Phillips   **Manager:** David Swain
Secretary: David Swain, 26 Greendale, Ilminster, Somerset TA19 0EB (0460 54620).
Ground: Washbrook Meadows, Butts Road, Ottery St Mary, Devon (0404 813539).
Directions: From main town square, turn left following road around church, 2nd right into Butts Rd. Or, B3177 to Ottery
from A30 Honiton by-pass - ground on left past Otter workshops.
No. of seats: 120   **Covered Accom:** 120   **Capacity:** 2,000
Floodlights: Yes   **Year Formed:** 1911   **Nickname:** The Otters
Colours: Royal blue & stripes/royal/royal   **Change colours:** Red/black/black
Previous Leagues: Devon & Exeter Premier, South Western 74-76.
Record Gate: 2,500 v Nottingham Forest, 1985
Programme: 36 pages, 20p.   **Programme Editor:** Ray Dack
Clubhouse details: On ground.
Hons: E Devon Snr Cup, Devon & Exeter Lg, Western Lg Div 1 89-90
Midweek Matches: Wednesday

RADSTOCK TOWN

President: M Mitchard   **Chairman:** Ron Rendell   **Manager:** Chris Gear
Secretary: Ron Rendall, 32 Huish Court, Writhlington, Radstock, Avon BA3 3LR (0761 435573).
Ground: Southfields, Frome Hill, Radstock (0761 435004).
Directions: From Radstock centre take A362 for Frome, up hill and turn right after Fromeway Inn and right again into
ground car park.
No. of seats: 150   **Covered Accom:** 150   **Capacity:** 2,000
Floodlights: Yes   **Year Formed:** 1895
Club colours: Red/black/red.   **Change colours:** Blue
Midweek Matches: Tuesday   **Record Gate:** 2,000 v Yeovil, FA Cup, 1937
Previous Leagues: Somerset Senior League, Wiltshire County League.
Programme: 16 pages, 20p   **Programme Editor:** James Mitchard
Clubhouse details: Two bars, skittle alley and darts.
Club honours: Somerset Senior League, Wiltshire County League.

WARMINSTER TOWN

Chairman: Bob Peaty **Manager:** Dave Carpenter
Secretary: D J Saunders, 1 King Street, Warminster, Wilts BA12 8DG (0985 219356).
Ground: Weymouth Street, Warminster (0985 217828).
Directions: Take A350 for Weymouth from lights at centre of town - ground on left at brow of hill.
Seats: 200   **Cover:** 200   **Capacity:** 2,000   **Floodlights:** No   **Founded:** 1882
Colours: Red & black hoops/black/black   **Change colours:** Sky/navy blue
Previous Leagues: Wiltshire   **Midweek Matches:** Wednesday
Hons: Wilts Snr Cup 1900-01 02-03 10-11 (R-up 09-10 26-27 32-33 53-54); Wilts Prem. Lg 56-57; Wilts Jnr Cup R-up 21-22 27-28 55-56 58-59; Central Wilts Lg 08-09

WELLINGTON

President: Alan Shire   **Chairman:** Selwyn Aspin
Manager: Marino Griffiths
Secretary: Tony Brown, 6 Courtland Rd., Wellington, Somerset TA21 8ND (0823 662920).
Ground: Wellington Playing Field, North Street, Wellington, Somerset (0823 664810).
Directions: At town centre traffic lights turn into North St., then first left by Fire Station into the public car park that adjoins the ground.
Seats: None   **Cover:** 200   **Capacity:** 3,000   **Floodlights:** Yes   **Founded:** 1892
Colours: Tangerine/black/tangerine   **Change colours:** Blue & claret stripes/black/black
Previous Leagues: Taunton Saturday, Somerset Senior   **Midweek Matches:** Tuesday (7.45)
Hons: Somerset Snr Lg Div 1 R-up, Rowbarton & Seward Cup.

WELTON ROVERS

Chairman: Roy James   **Vice Chairman:** C Richardson   **Manager:** TBA
Secretary: Geoff Baker, 6 Longfellow Road, Westfield, Radstock, Bath (0761 413742).
Ground: West Clewes, North Road, Midsomer Norton, Somerset (0761 412097).
Directions: A367 Bath to Radstock – right at lights at foot of hill onto A362, ground on right.
No. of seats: 350   **Covered Accom:** 350   **Capacity:** 2,000
Floodlights: Yes   **Year Formed:** 1887   **Midweek matches:** Monday
Colours: Green & white/white/white   **Change colours:** Royal blue.   **Club Shop:** Yes
Previous Leagues: None   **Record Gate:** 2,000 v Bromley, FA Amateur Cup 1963
Programme: 28 pages, 20p   **Programme Editor:** R Richardson
Hons: Western Lg 11-12 64-65 65-66 66-67 73-74 (Div 1 59-60 87-88; Amateur Cup 56-57 57-58 58-59 59-60; Alan Young Cup 65-66 66-67 67-68(joint)); Somerset Snr Cup 06-07 11-12 12-13 13-14 19-20 24-25 25-26 60-61 61-62 62-63, Somerset I'mediate Cup 77-78, Somerset Jnr Cup 06-07(joint) 24-25 30-31, WBC Clares City of Wells Cup 78-79.

TAUNTON SATURDAY LEAGUE

Division One	P	W	D	L	F	A	Pts
Bishops Lydeard	20	16	3	1	64	21	35
Middlezoy Rovers	20	15	1	4	54	15	31
British Cellophane	20	12	3	5	51	27	27
Hulan United	20	9	3	8	45	43	21
Priorswood Utd	20	8	2	10	46	53	18
Wyvern	20	8	1	11	38	52	17
Alcombe Rovers	20	6	5	9	35	53	17
Sydenham Rangers	20	6	3	11	34	44	15
Nether Stowey	20	7	1	12	33	46	15
Westonzoyland	20	7	2	11	45	53	*12
Highbridge Town	20	3	2	15	17	55	8
* - 4 points deducted							

Division Two	P	W	D	L	F	A	Pts
Wembdon United	22	16	2	4	69	20	34
Spaxton	22	16	2	4	64	31	34
Porlock	22	12	5	5	60	41	29
Ivory Rangers	22	11	5	6	71	54	27
Middlezoy Rvrs Res	22	10	6	6	43	33	26
W Somerset Hosp.	22	11	3	8	62	53	25
B Lydeard Res	22	10	4	8	53	49	24
Hinkley Point	22	9	5	8	53	61	23
Dulverton Town	22	6	4	12	41	65	16
Norton Fitzwarren	22	6	3	13	43	46	15
Watchet Town Res	22	2	3	17	35	76	7
Bridgwater T. 'A'	22	1	2	19	32	97	4

Division Three	P	W	D	L	F	A	Pts
Priorswood Utd Res	22	17	1	4	65	25	35
Club Rangers	22	15	3	4	56	24	33
British Rail	22	12	5	5	77	42	29
B Cellophane Res	22	11	5	6	52	36	27
Avimo Eagles	22	10	7	5	51	33	27
Wyvern Res	22	9	7	6	37	42	24
Staplegrove	22	8	6	8	41	46	22
Taverners	22	7	4	11	53	51	18
Crown Dynamos	22	6	3	13	39	71	15
Marketeers	22	5	4	13	28	65	14
Williton	22	4	5	13	32	54	13
Highbridge T. Res	22	2	3	17	27	69	7

Division Four	P	W	D	L	F	A	Pts
Redgate	22	19	1	2	108	38	39
Rockwell Green	22	16	2	4	86	32	34
Forest Green	22	15	1	6	83	44	31
Civil Service	22	12	4	6	65	59	28
Quantock Pride	22	10	3	9	50	60	*21
Staplegrove Res	22	9	2	11	51	65	20
Williton Wdrs	22	8	2	12	53	56	18
Hemyock	22	6	6	10	40	52	18
North Petherton	22	6	5	11	48	66	17
Tone Vale Hosp.	22	5	4	13	47	77	14
Exmoor Rangers	22	4	5	13	38	75	13
Westonzoyland Res	22	4	1	17	45	90	9
* - 2 points deducted							

Division Five	P	W	D	L	F	A	Pts
Alcombe Rvrs Res	20	14	4	2	72	31	32
Dunster Rangers	20	14	2	4	89	51	30
Wembdon Cricketers	20	12	4	4	70	38	28
Linden	20	11	2	7	52	46	24
N. Fitzwarren Res	20	8	6	6	60	48	22
Porlock Res	20	7	4	9	48	61	18
Shepherds Wednes.	20	5	5	10	53	57	15
Nether Stowey Res	20	6	3	11	29	53	15
Stogursey Greyhounds	20	6	2	12	32	54	14
B Cellophane Colts	20	5	2	13	51	83	12
Haygrove	20	4	2	14	50	84	10

SOMERSET SENIOR LEAGUE

Hon. Secretary: C R Rose,
Sutley House, Pilton, Shepton Mallet BA4 4BL.

BRIDGWATER CLAIM THIRD CONSECUTIVE TITLE

Although Bridgwater Town '84, Portishead and Blackbrook each won their respective Divisions with points to spare, competition in other departments was keener than experienced for many seasons.

In the Premier Division Shepton Mallet Town started well, but lost ground in the closing weeks to see near neighbours Long Sutton move up to finish in third place behind Clevedon United, whose Reserves also earned promotion from the Third Division. At the foot, Larkhall Athletic's six year spell in the Premier came to an end in the final minute of their season. A one-goal defeat at Long Sutton would have kept them up, but a last-kick goal made it 3-1. So down went the Bath based side, whilst Bristol Manor Farm moved out of danger without kicking a ball. Nail-biting stuff!

Watchet Town led Division Two for most of 1992, but were pipped at the post on goal difference by Bishop Sutton. Victory at Imperial on FA Cup Final morning would have been sufficient for the title for the West Somerset side, but they could only manage a goalless draw. At the bottom Clutton performed the houdini act beating already relegated Clandown in their last match, thus condemning Farleigh Sports to join Street and Clandown in Division Three next term.

Third Division winners, newcomers Blackbrook, were favourites from around New Year, but there were numerous interchanges between the Reserves of Clevedon United, Fry Club, Paulton Rovers and Glastonbury. In the end it was the latter (enjoying their best season for eight years) and Paulton who missed out.

Sadly for Wells City, the first ever champions of the League in 1890, both their teams finished bottom. But happily the Reserves, along with Robinsons Reserves, were re-elected at a recent constitution meeting. Unfortunately for the ten new applicants, they will have to wait until next year to have another go.

At the League A.G.M. members officially rubber-stamped their future participation within the Pyramid commencing next season. Another major change next seaon will be the move from the traditional two points for a win to three points. Chairman Roy Neal, elected for his ninth term, congratulated, Bridgwater, Portishead, Bishop Sutton and Blackbrook on being winners of their respective Divisions. Particular mentions goes to the latter on gaining promotion in their first season as a senior club.
L J C Heal, League Life-Member

FINAL LEAGUE TABLES 1991-92

PREM. DIVISION	P	W	D	L	F	A	PTS
Bridgwater Town	34	25	4	5	74	37	54
Clevedon United	34	20	8	6	65	40	48
Long Sutton	34	18	9	7	77	46	45
Fry Club	34	19	5	10	60	39	43
Weston-SM Res.	34	16	6	12	56	42	38
Avon/S'set Police	34	14	10	10	57	52	38
Shepton Mallet T.	34	15	5	14	63	56	35
Frome Town Res.	34	14	6	14	64	63	34
Weston St John	34	15	3	16	68	68	33
Imperial United	34	11	11	12	43	52	33
Longwell Gr. Abb.	34	12	7	15	55	56	31
Peasedown Athletic	34	13	5	16	32	58	31
Castle Cary	34	10	9	15	45	57	29
Mangotsfield U. Res.	34	10	10	14	45	68	29*
Bristol M.F. Res.	34	7	10	17	39	58	24
Larkhall Ath. Res.	34	8	8	18	43	63	24
Nailsea United	34	7	9	18	35	55	23
Wells City	34	6	7	21	41	75	19

* - One point deducted

DIVISION ONE	P	W	D	L	F	A	PTS
Portishead	34	24	6	4	79	28	54
Brislington Res.	34	17	14	3	69	37	48
Shirehampton	34	18	11	5	75	38	47
Keynsham T. Res.	34	18	6	10	65	56	42
Westland United	34	16	7	11	77	63	39
Hengrove Athletic	34	13	10	11	51	48	36
Cheddar	34	15	5	14	70	63	35
Clevedon T. Res.	34	14	8	12	47	42	35*
Burnham United	34	13	9	12	57	58	35
Mendip Hospital	34	9	13	12	42	52	30*
Ilminster Town	34	12	5	17	44	54	29
Congresbury	34	10	9	15	40	55	29
Stockwood Green	34	11	6	17	36	51	28
Winscombe	34	10	7	17	31	43	27
Dundry Athletic '82	34	8	10	16	52	58	26
Tunley Athletic	34	8	10	16	41	63	26
St George E/Gord.	34	10	3	21	43	75	23
Wrington-Redhill	34	8	5	21	38	73	21

* - One point deducted

DIVISION TWO	P	W	D	L	F	A	PTS
Bishop Sutton Res.	34	18	8	8	53	34	44
Watchet Town	34	18	8	8	52	38	44
Portishead Res.	34	17	8	9	62	47	42
Backwell Utd Res.	34	18	6	10	66	35	41*
Bridgwater T. Res.	34	15	9	10	60	36	39
Saltford	34	14	7	13	64	45	35
Imperial Bristol	34	13	9	12	48	49	34*
Welton Rovers Res.	34	15	3	16	64	56	33
Odd Down Res.	34	11	11	12	57	56	33
Long Ashton	34	12	9	13	56	61	32*
Timsbury Athletic	34	7	18	9	39	46	32
Weston St J. Res.	34	11	10	13	41	51	32
Temple Cloud	34	13	5	16	41	41	31
Robinsons DRG	34	12	6	16	50	55	30
Clutton	34	10	11	13	37	48	30*
Farleigh Sports	34	11	8	15	35	61	30
Street	34	8	8	18	40	77	24
Clandown Res.	34	7	8	19	39	68	22

* - One point deducted

DIVISION THREE	P	W	D	L	F	A	PTS
Blackbrook	34	23	6	5	84	31	52
Fry Club Res.	34	18	10	6	74	49	46
Clevedon Utd Res.	34	20	5	9	74	39	45
Paulton Rvrs Res.	34	18	8	8	73	46	44
Glastonbury Res.	34	19	4	11	71	44	42
Nailsea Town	34	15	8	11	70	51	38
Yatton Athletic	34	12	13	9	56	59	37
Worle	34	12	12	10	70	48	36
Churchill '70	34	12	10	12	60	53	34
Banwell	34	13	4	17	65	68	30
Keynsham Cricket.	34	12	6	16	53	67	30
Hengrove Ath. Res.	34	12	6	16	60	78	30
Imperial Res.	34	9	11	14	45	58	29
Nailsea Utd Res.	34	10	8	16	40	57	28
Westland Utd Res.	34	9	7	18	51	77	25
Shepton Mallet Res.	34	9	6	19	51	75	24
Robinsons DRG Res.	34	9	6	19	34	85	24
Wells City Res.	34	7	4	23	42	88	17*

* - One point deducted

PREMIER DIVISION CLUBS 1992-93

AVON & SOMERSET CONSTABULARY
Ground: Police Sports Ground, Napier Mills Rd, Kingsweston, Bristol.   **Secretary:** A Taylor (0272 864703)
Directions: M5 jct 18, B4054 towards Shirehampton, left at crossroads up Kingsweston Lane, ground on right opposite Kingsweston House School. Half mile from Shirehampton (BR).

BRIDGWATER TOWN '84
Ground: Fairfax Park, Fairfax Road, Bridgwater.   **Secretary:** Miss Wright (0278 421189)
Directions: M5 jct 23, follow signs to Glastonbury (A39), turn right for Bridgwater (A39), turn left for Bridgwater College (Parkway), ground half mile on right; enter through college. One mile from Bridgwater (BR).

BRISLINGTON, BRISTOL MANOR FARM RESERVES (See Great Mills League section)

CASTLE CARY
Ground: Donald Pither Memorial Field, Ansford Road, Castle Cary.   **Secretary:** R J Osmond (0936 50104)
Directions: In village, one mile from Castle Cary station (main line from London Paddington).

CLEVEDON UNITED
Ground: Coleridge Vale P.F., Coleridge Vale Road, Clevedon.   **Secretary:** M Henley (0272 879096)
Directions: M5 jct 20, follow sea front signs, ground in middle of housing estate on left hand side.

FROME TOWN RESERVES (See Great Mills League section)

FRY CLUB
Ground: Cadbury Schweppes, Somerdale, Keynsham, Bristol.   **Secretary:** M G Kempster (0272 868484)
Directions: On A4175, outside Keynsham BR station in Somerdale factory complex.

IMPERIAL UNITED
Ground: Imperial Athletic Club, West Town Lane, Knowle, Bristol.   **Secretary:** D Brown (0272 716977)
Directions: A37 south of Bristol, left into West Town Lane (signed Stockwood and Brislington), ground opposite next mini r'bout. Buses 54 and 57 from Bristol Temple Meads (BR).

LONG SUTTON
Ground: Recreation Ground, Long Sutton.   **Secretary:** R Sams (0458 241395)
Directions: Ground entrance on south side of A372 about three miles east of Langport. Bus 54, Taunton-Yeovil.

LONGWELL GREEN ABBOTONIANS
Ground: Community Association, Shellards Rd, Longwell Green.   **Secretary:** R Threader (0272 670306)
Directions: From Bristol; A4175 Keynsham to Willsbridge, left up steep hill (Willsbridge Hill), across r'bout, right fork into Shellards Road, ground on right behind Community Centre.

MANGOTSFIELD UNITED RESERVES (See Great Mills League section)

PEASEDOWN ATHLETIC
Ground: Miners Welfare, Church Road.   **Secretary:** R Clark (0761 34006)
Directions: On A367 Bath-Radstock road just south of Peasedown St John, close to Red Post Inn.

PORTISHEAD
Ground: Bristol Road Playing Fields, Portishead.   **Secretary:** N Trenchard (0272 849976)
Directions: M5 jct 19, A369 towards Portishead, left at r'bout, ground on left after right hand bend.

SHEPTON MALLET TOWN
Ground: Playing Fields, West Shepton, Old Wells Rd, Shepton Mallet (07490 344609).
Secretary: K Hurrell (0749890 344037)
Directions: Into town centre and follow signs for Eye Hospital. Ground behind.

SHIREHAMPTON
Ground: Recreation Ground, Penpole Lane, Shirehampton, Bristol.   **Secretary:** D Campbell (0272 82770)
Directions: M5 jct 18, B4054 into Lower High Street, left into Penpole Lane. Ground half mile on left. Half mile from Shirehampton (BR).

WESTON ST JOHN
Ground: Coleridge Road, Bourneville, Weston-super-Mare.   **Secretary:** R Flaskett (0934 515260)
Directions: As for Weston-super-Mare FC (see Great Mills League section) then proceed up Winterstoke Road, right into Byron Road, left into Coleridge Road, ground on left.

WESTON-SUPER-MARE (See Great Mills League section)

DIVISION ONE CLUBS 1992-93

BISHOP SUTTON RESERVES (See Great Mills League section)

BURNHAM UNITED
Ground: Burnham Road Playing Field, Casis Close, Burnham-on-Sea.   **Secretary:** S Brooks (0278 785928)
Directions: M5 jct 22, ground close to Burnham town centre. Highbridge (BR), Bus 21 from Taunton.

CHEDDAR
Ground: Bowdens Park, Wells Road, Cheddar.   **Secretary:** M Higginbottom (0934 744102)
Directions: Ground on south side of A371 on eastern fringe of Cheddar.

CLEVEDON TOWN RESERVES (See Great Mills League section)

CONGRESBURY
Ground: Broadstone Playing Fields, Stonewell Lane, Congresbury (0934 832150)
Secretary: C Sherwin (0934 876083)
Directions: A38 south from Bristol, take B3133 for Congresbury at Lower Langford. Entering Congresbury turn left immediately before Post Office, bear right, ground at end of narrow lane.

DUNDRY ATHLETIC

Ground: Crabtree Lane, Dundry.   **Secretary:** S Saunders (0272 830085)
Directions: A38 south from Bristol (signed Airport), left for Dundry half mile after motel, ground unmissable in village.

HENGROVE ATHLETIC

Ground: Norton Lane, Whitchurch, Bristol (0272 832894).   **Secretary:** G Close (0272 835700)
Directions: A37 south from Bristol, through Whitchurch, right into Norton Lane just after humped-back bridge, ground half mile on left.

ILMINSTER TOWN

Ground: Recreation Ground, Ilminster.   **Secretary:** C Williams (0460 54577)
Directions: In town centre turn into Ditton Street, turn right at petrol station, ground on left.

KEYNSHAM TOWN, LARKHALL ATHLETIC RESERVES (See Great Mills League section)

MENDIP WELLS

Ground: Old Frome Road, Wells.   **Secretary:** N Church (0749 674347)
Directions: From Wells city centre follow signs to Mendip Hospital. Ground on right immediately after golf course.

NAILSEA UNITED

Ground: St Marys Grove, Old Church, Nailsea (0275 856892)   **Secretary:** J Hobbs (0275 855432)
Directions: M5 jct 20, B3130 through Tickenham to Nailsea High Street. Bear right, ground on south side of town clearly signposted Grove Sports Centre. One mile from Nailsea & Backwell (BR).

PORTISHEAD RESERVES (See previous page)

STOCKWOOD GREEN

Ground: Old Knowle Cricket Club, Stockwood Lane.   **Secretary:** R Llewellyn (0272 833460)
Directions: As Imperial (previous page) but continue up Sturminster Road. At top of hill turn right, then left into Stockwood Lane. Ground on sharp bend on right.

WATCHET TOWN

Ground: The Memorial Ground, Doniford Road (0984 31041).   **Secretary:** M Clausen (0984 31773)
Directions: On coast road, east of town.

WELLS CITY

Ground: The Athletic Grnd, Rowdens Rd, off Glastonbury Rd, Wells   **Secretary:** R Cowell (0749 676260)
Directions: Rowdens Road is a right turn off the A39 entering Wells from Glastonbury (the south).

WESTLAND UNITED

Ground: Winterstoke Road, Weston-super-Mare.   **Secretary:** C Ham (0934 814358)
Directions: As Weston-super-Mare FC (see Great Mills League section) then continue up Winterstoke Road to Westlands Helicopter complex; ground on right.

WINSCOMBE

Ground: Recreation Ground, The Lynch, Winscombe.   **Secretary:** R Liddiard (0934 843396)
Directions: A38 south from Bristol, turn right for Winscombe at Sidcot, left at sharp bend, ground at end.

DIVISION TWO CLUBS 1992-93

BACKWELL UNITED RESERVES (See Great Mills League section)

BLACKBROOK

Ground: Blackbrook Pavillion, Blackbrook Way, Taunton.   **Secretary:** R A Smith (0823 278579)

BRIDGWATER TOWN '84 RESERVES, CLEVEDON UNITED RESERVES (See previous page)

CLUTTON

Ground: Warwick Fields, Upper Bristol Road.   **Secretary:** H Marsland (0761 53064)
Directions: Ground behind Warwick Arms on right of A37 south from Bristol.

FRY CLUB RESERVES (See previous page)

IMPERIAL BRISTOL

Ground & Directions: As Imperial United (previous page)   **Secretary:** M Jones (0272 713743)

LONG ASHTON

Ground: Recreation Ground, Keedwell Hill, Long Ashton.   **Secretary:** F Richards (0272 393731)
Directions: M5 jct 19, A369 towards Bristol, at r'bout follow B3128 to Long Ashton, left into village, ground right up Keedwell Hill.

ODD DOWN RESERVES (See Great Mills League section)

ROBINSONS

Ground: D.R.G. Athletic Club, St Johns Lane, Bedminster, Bristol.   **Secretary:** D Palmer (0272 649251)
Directions: From Bristol Temple Meads follow Wells road (A37), right at lights by Y.M.C.A., across two mini r'bouts, ground 400 yards on left behing Engineers Arms. Ten minutes walk from Bedminster (BR).

SALTFORD

Ground: Norman Road, Saltford.   **Secretary:** R Denford (0272 699351)
Directions: A4 Bristol to Bath. Turn off into Norman Road in Saltford.

ST GEORGE EASTON-IN-GORDANO

Ground: Court Hay, Easton-in-Gordano.   **Secretary:** Mrs Jones (0275 372875)
Directions: M5 jct 19, A369 towards Bristol into Easton-in-Gordano village, left into St Georges Hill which joins Priory Road, ground on left.

TEMPLE CLOUD

Ground: Camley Playing Fields, Temple Inn Lane, Temple Cloud.   **Secretary:** D Flower (0272 831432)
Directions: A37 south from Bristol, left into Temple Lane at Temple Inn, ground on right.

TIMSBURY ATHLETIC

Ground: Recreation Field, North Road, Timsbury. **Secretary:** M Sage (0761 71290)
Directions: As for Tunley (following page) but continue into Timsbury. Ground at crossroads by Cricket Club.

TUNLEY ATHLETIC

Ground: Recreation Field, Tunley. **Secretary:** Mrs Fear (0761 70749)
Directions: A367 Bath-Radstock road, turn right onto B3155, through Tunley, ground on right.

WELTON RVRS RES. (See Great Mills Lge section), WESTON ST JOHN RES. (See Premier Div.)

WRINGTON-REDHILL

Ground: Recreation Ground, Silver Street, Wrington. **Secretary:** B Bull (0934 862027)
Directions: A38 south from Bristol, right towards Wrington at foot of steep hill after airport, ground in Wrington village.

DIVISION THREE CLUBS 1992-93

BANWELL

Ground: Riverside Ground, Riverside, Banwell. **Secretary:** C Gibbons (0934 512903).
Directions: A38 south from Bristol, right onto A368 at Churchill, into Banwell village, right, right again after pub into narrow lane.

CHURCHILL CLUB '70

Ground: Recreation Field, Ladymead Lane, Churchill. **Secretary:** B W Bullock (0934 834310).
Directions: A38 south from Bristol to Churchill traffic lights; ground on right.

CLANDOWN RESERVES (See Great Mills League section)

FARLEIGH SPORTS

Ground: Farleigh Hospital, Flax Bourton **Secretary:** L Cox (0272 642186).
Directions: A370 Bristol to Flax Bourton then follow signs to Farleigh Hospital.

GLASTONBURY RESERVES (See Great Mills League section), HENGROVE ATHLETIC RESERVES, IMPERIAL BRISTOL RESERVES (See previous page)

KEYNSHAM CRICKETERS

Ground: Manor Road Playing Field, Keynsham, Bristol. **Secretary:** W Howis (0272 869334)
Directions: A4175 into Keynsham, straight over 1st mini-r'bout, left at 2nd, down Bath Hill, over double mini-r'bout and next r'bout into Wells Way, left fork into Manor Road, ground on right.

NAILSEA TOWN

Ground: Fryth Way, Causeway View, Nailsea **Secretary:** C Garraway (0454 201499)

NAILSEA UTD RES. (See previous page), PAULTON RVRS RES. (See Great Mills League), ROBINSONS DRG RES. (See previous page), SHEPTON MALLET RES. (See Premier Div.)

STREET

Ground: Tannery Field, Middlebrooks, Street. **Secretary:** L Clark (0458 45869)
Directions: Near Millfields School.

WELLS CITY RESERVES, WESTLANDS SPORTS RESERVES (See previous page)

WORLE

Ground: Recreation Ground, Station Road, Worle. **Secretary:** D Brine (0934 625585)
Directions: A370 from Bristol to Worle, ground on right at junction with Station Road.

YATTON ATHLETIC

Ground: 'Hangstone', Stowey Road, Yatton. **Secretary:** A Coombes (0934 833997)

Nailsea United FC. Back Row (L/R): S McLaughlin, G Cook, C Houghton, R Parker, J Smith, R Edwards, J Pratt, L Smith (President), N Lawrence (Trainer). Front: C Wray (Player-Manager), A Micciche, J Green, P Ramplin, A Disney, D Hook. Photo - James Wright.

WESTWARD DEVELOPMENTS
DEVON COUNTY LEAGUE

Chairman: Mr B Williams,
Vice Chairman: Mr W Smale,
Hon. Secretary: Mr R D Lowe,
'Panorama', Lamerton, Tavistock PL19 8SD (0822 613516).

This is a brand new competition providing Devon with a true county league; a more logical stepping stone between local competitions and the Great Mills League.

CLUB DETAILS

ALPHINGTON
Ground: The Chronicles, Church Road, Alphington (0392 79556)   **Previous League:** Devon & Exeter.
Secretary: Mr A J Smith, 7 Cordery Rd, St Thomas, Exeter EX2 9DH (0392 438571).

BUCKFASTLEIGH RANGERS
Ground: Ducks Pond Playing Fields, Buckfastleigh, Devon   **Previous League:** South Devon.
Secretary: Mrs J Voisey, 61 Oaklands Park, Buckfastleigh TQ11 0AP (0364 42446).

CHAGFORD
Ground: **Previous League:** South Devon.
Secretary: Mrs M Cosford, West Corndon Farm, Chagford TQ13 8EE (0647 432442).

CULLOMPTON RANGERS
Ground: Speeds Meadow, Duke Street, Cullompton   **Previous League:** Devon & Exeter.
Secretary: Mr K Norman, 78 Langlands Rd, Cullompton EX15 1JB (0884 33539).

ELBURTON VILLA
Ground: **Previous League:** Plymouth & Dist.
Secretary: Mr S Matthews, 64 Wembury Rd, Elburton, Plymouth PL9 8HF (0752   492109).

E.A.F. PLYMOUTH
Ground: **Previous League:** Plymouth & Dist.
Secretary: Mr S Cadmore, 25 Dudley Gardens, Eggbuckland, Plymouth PL6 5PE (0752 782661).

IVYBRIDGE TOWN
Ground: **Previous League:** Plymouth & Dist.
Secretary: Mr B Flood, 18 St Austin Close, Ivybridge PL21 9BZ (0752 894536)

NEWTON ABBOT
Ground: Centrax Sports Field   **Previous League:** South Devon.
Secretary: Mr R Perkins, 21 Prospect Terrace, Newton Abbot TQ12 2LN (0626 61596).

NEWTON ST CYRES
Ground: Station Road, Newton St Cyres (0392 851546)   **Previous League:** Devon & Exeter.
Secretary: Mr K Baker, Sunnydene, Pinn Hill, Pinhoe, Exeter EX1 3TH (0392 69331).

NORTHERN TELECOM (PAIGNTON)
Ground: Long Road, Paignton   **Previous League:** South Devon.
Secretary: Mr J Sargent, 6 Belmont Rd, Brixham, Devon TQ5 9JH (0803 854551).

PLYMSTOCK UNITED
Ground: **Previous League:** Plymouth & Dist.
Secretary: Mr A Demuth, 35 Treveneague Gardens, Manadon PL2 (0752 782807).

STOKE GABRIEL
Ground: G J Churchward Mem. Grnd, Broadley Lane, Stoke Gabriel   **Previous League:** Sth Devon.
Secretary: Mr B Prowse, 269 Teignmouth Rd, St Marychurch, Torquay TQ1 4RT (0803 327930).

TEIGNMOUTH
Ground: Coombe Valley   **Previous League:** South Devon.
Secretary: Mr P Crawford, 6 Higher Brimley, Teignmouth TQ14 2LN (0626 772108).

TOPSHAM TOWN
Ground: Coronation Field, Exeter Road, Topsham (0392 873678).   **Previous League:** Devon & Exeter.
Secretary: Mr D G Marks, 66 Gloucester Rd, Exeter EX4 2EE (0392 58896).

WESTON MILL OAK VILLA
Ground: **Previous League:** Plymouth & Dist.
Secretary: Mr R Carpenter, 11b St Eval Place, Ernsettle, Plymouth PL5 2RN (0752 364037).

WILLAND ROVERS
Ground: Main Road (B3181), Willand   **Previous League:** Devon & Exeter.
Secretary: Mr A L Jarrett, 2 College Ct, Uffculme, Cullompton EX15 3BQ (0884 841210).

DEVON & EXETER LEAGUE

Premier Division	P	W	D	L	F	A	PTS
Exeter City 'A'	30	24	6	0	109	20	78
Willand Rovers	30	20	2	8	73	37	62
Chelston	30	19	4	7	76	36	61
Budleigh Salterton	30	16	7	7	63	42	55
Exeter Civil S.	30	15	8	7	73	36	53
Topsham Town	30	13	9	8	58	39	48
Newton St Cyres	30	14	4	12	67	53	46
Okehampton Argyle	30	11	9	10	57	59	42
Alphington	30	11	9	10	39	41	42
Exmouth Amateurs	30	11	8	11	42	59	41
Honiton Town	30	7	7	16	36	69	28
Cullompton Rgrs	30	7	6	17	53	87	27
Lapford	30	7	5	18	56	95	26
Exeter St Thomas	30	7	4	19	40	65	25
Beer Albion	30	6	2	22	30	81	20
Offwell & W'worthy	30	4	6	20	40	93	18

PREMIER DIVISION CLUBS 1992-93

BEER ALBION
Ground: Furzebrake, Stovar Long Lane, Beer (0297 24324)   **Secretary:** P Curtis (00297 20211).

BUCKLAND ATHLETIC
Ground: **Secretary:**

BUDLEIGH SALTERTON
Ground: Greenway Lane, Budleigh Salterton   **Secretary:** M Stott (0395 277039).

CHELSTON
Ground: Armada Park, Nut Bush Lane, Chelston, Torquay   **Secretary:** D Birkinshaw (0803 613445).

CLYST VALLEY
Ground: **Secretary:**

EXETER CITY 'A'
Ground: Cat & Fiddle, Sidmouth Rd, Clyst St Mary (0395 32784)   **Secretary:** M Radford (0392 424950).

EXETER CIVIL SERVICE
Ground: Foxhayes, Exwick (0392 73976)   **Secretary:** B Hooper (0626 773361).

EXMOUTH AMATEURS
Ground: Imperial Recreation Ground, Exmouth.   **Secretary:** D Cliffe (0395 270604).

HONITON TOWN
Ground: Mountbatten Park, Ottery Moor Lane, Honiton (0404 42503)   **Secretary:** P Allen (0404 43430).

LAPFORD
Ground: Edgerly Lane, Edgerly Cross, Lapford   **Secretary:** J Burrows (0363 83358).

OFFWELL & WIDWORTHY
Ground: Offwell Recreation Ground   **Secretary:** A Bennett (0404 83654).

OKEHAMPTON ARGYLE
Ground: Simmons Park, Okehampton   **Secretary:** C Beer (0837 52989).

ST MARTINS
Ground: **Secretary:**

SIDMOUTH TOWN
Ground: **Secretary:**

Senior Division 1	P	W	D	L	F	A	PTS
St Martins	28	19	6	3	79	27	63
Budleigh S'ton Res	28	17	4	7	75	34	55
Clyst Valley	28	15	3	10	60	47	48
London & Manch.	28	14	4	10	55	49	46
Buckland Athletic	28	13	6	9	58	40	45
Dawlish Town 'A'	28	13	4	11	58	44	43
East Budleigh	28	12	7	9	50	50	43
Sidmouth Town	28	13	6	9	61	36	*42
University of Exeter	28	11	6	11	52	49	39
Culm United	28	11	5	12	70	71	38
Westexe Rovers	28	11	4	13	46	70	37
Newton St C. Res	28	8	9	11	50	70	33
Newtown	28	9	4	15	50	73	31
Lympstone	28	5	4	19	47	73	19
Ottery St Mary Res	28	1	4	23	28	106	7

* - pts deducted for unregistered/ineligible players

92-93 Constitution: Budleigh Salterton Res, Culm Utd, Dawlish 'A', East Budleigh, Exeter St Thomas, Feniton, London & Manchester, Lympstone, Morchard Bishop, Newtown, Ottery St Mary Res, Rockbeare Rockets, Sidbury Utd, University of Exeter, Westexe Rovers.

Senior Division 2	P	W	D	L	F	A	PTS
Sidbury United	26	20	3	3	77	33	63
Feniton	26	19	5	3	101	35	62
Morchard Bishop	26	14	7	5	67	32	49
Rockbeare Rockets	26	10	9	7	54	40	39
Dunkeswell Rvrs	26	10	4	12	54	50	34
Exeter St T. Res	26	10	4	12	63	68	34
Cruwys United	26	10	4	12	52	76	34
Bickleigh	26	10	2	14	60	74	32
Hatherleigh Town	26	9	4	13	42	57	31
Pinhoe	26	8	6	12	48	56	30
Topsham Town Res	26	9	3	14	50	74	30
Littleham	26	8	4	14	46	55	28
Clyst Rovers Res	26	8	1	17	58	87	25
Woodbury Salterton	26	7	4	15	48	83	25

92-93 Constitution: Bickleigh, Cheriton Fitzpaine, Chulmleigh, Dunkeswell Rovers, Exeter St Thomas Res, Exmouth Amateurs Res, Hatherleigh Town, Honiton Town Res, Littleham, North Tawton, Pinhoe, University of Exeter, Village Inn (ex-Lamb Inn United), Wonford, Woodbury Salterton.

Senior Division 3	P	W	D	L	F	A	PTS
Cheriton Fitzpaine	26	19	3	4	80	34	60
Alphington Res	26	18	6	2	71	30	*57
Honiton Town Res	26	12	7	7	49	42	43
Wonford	26	13	3	10	64	56	42
Lamb Inn United	26	13	3	10	51	55	42
Exmouth Amtrs Res	26	11	5	10	50	51	38
North Tawton	26	11	3	12	62	54	36
Chulmleigh	26	10	4	12	57	63	34
University E'ter Res	26	10	5	11	59	59	*32
Kentisbeare	26	7	8	11	45	53	29
Bampton	26	8	3	15	50	64	27
Northlew	26	7	5	14	34	57	26
Bradninch	26	7	4	15	44	58	25
St Mark's	26	6	1	19	46	86	19

* - pts deducted for unregistered/ineligible players

92-93 Constitution: Bampton, Bradninch, Colyton, Culmstock, Dawlish Town 'B', Exeter CS Res, Halwill, Kentisbeare, Lympstone Res, Northlew, Queens Head, St Mark's, Sidmouth Rown Res, Tedburn St Mary, Univ. Exeter Res, Witheridge.

Senior Division 4	P	W	D	L	F	A	PTS
Tedburn St Mary	24	15	5	4	83	52	50
Queen's Head	24	14	5	5	67	36	47
Colyton	24	13	8	3	62	39	47
Willand Rvrs Res	24	14	1	9	86	73	43
Dawlish Town 'B'	24	12	5	7	53	46	41
Sidmouth T. Res	24	11	7	6	66	53	40
Lympstone Res	24	9	7	8	53	46	34
Cullompton R. Res	24	10	3	11	67	51	33
Halwill	24	8	5	11	42	54	29
Univ. Exeter 'A'	24	8	4	12	52	55	28
Folly Gate & Inward	24	6	2	16	53	71	20
London & M. Res	24	6	6	14	38	71	18
East Budleigh Res	24	2	2	20	20	95	8

92-93 Constitution: N/A

Intermediate Div. 1	P	W	D	L	F	A	PTS
Witheridge	26	21	1	4	103	38	64
Exeter CS Res	26	21	1	4	99	35	64
Culmstock	26	15	2	9	90	65	47
Bow AAC	26	15	2	9	64	45	47
Seaton Town	26	14	2	10	66	47	44
Sth Zeal United	26	12	4	10	60	55	40
Winkleigh	26	11	2	13	58	80	35
Newtown Res	26	11	1	14	59	69	34
Pinhoe Res	26	10	4	12	61	72	34
Tipton St John	26	10	3	13	55	77	*27
Broadclyst	26	8	3	15	48	71	27
Culm Valley	26	6	3	17	44	72	21
Woodbury	26	6	3	17	45	89	21
Okehampton A. Res	26	5	3	18	42	79	18

* - pts deducted for unregistered/ineligible players

92-93 Constitution: Bow AAC, Broadclyst, Dawlish Villa, East Budleigh Res, Folly Gate & Inwardleigh, London & Manchester Res, Newtown Res, Pinhoe Res, Seaton Town, Sidbury United, Silverton, South Zeal Utd, Tipton St John, Westexe Rovers Res, Winkleigh.

Intermediate Div. 2	P	W	D	L	F	A	PTS
Westexe Rvrs Res	26	22	2	2	88	31	68
Dawlish Villa	26	20	2	4	82	28	62
Sidbury United	26	15	4	7	63	31	49
Silverton	26	13	5	8	75	48	44
Culm Utd Res	26	13	4	9	50	42	43
Cruwys Utd Res	26	11	7	8	73	57	*39
Offwell & W. Res	26	11	3	12	57	68	36
Buckland Ath. Res	26	10	5	11	62	55	35
Poughill	26	10	4	12	57	51	34
Queen's Head Res	26	10	3	13	53	52	32
Morchard Bishop Res	26	8	6	12	42	59	30
Rockbeare R. Res	26	4	5	17	31	77	17
Med. Sickness Soc.	26	4	2	20	32	98	8

92-93 Constitution: Alphington Res, Buckland Ath. Res, Crediton Utd 'A', Cullompton Rgrs Res, Culm Utd Res, Honiton Town 'A', Morchard Bishop Res, Newton St Cyres Res, Offwell & Widworthy Res, Okehampton A. Res, Poughill, Queen's Head Res, Woodbury.

Intermediate Div. 3	P	W	D	L	F	A	PTS
Crediton Utd 'A'	26	22	1	3	92	33	67
Honiton Town 'A'	26	16	3	7	59	40	51
Newton Poppleford	26	15	3	8	81	56	48
Wonford Res	26	14	5	7	78	54	47
St Martin's Res	26	14	4	8	66	47	46
Newton St C. 'A'	26	13	4	9	55	47	43
Awliscombe	26	12	2	12	66	59	38
White Horse	26	12	1	13	53	70	37
Clyst Valley Res	26	11	3	12	56	43	36
Tedburn St M. Res	26	8	5	13	50	69	29
Crescent	26	9	2	15	50	70	29
Univ. Exeter 'C'	26	7	4	15	66	77	*22
Cheriton F. Res	26	4	4	18	34	58	16
Beer Albion	26	4	1	21	25	108	13

* - pts deducted for unregistered/ineligible players

92-93 Constitution: Awliscombe, Clyst Valley Res, Crescent, Dunkeswell Rovers Res, Feniton Res, King's Arms, Medical Sickness Society, Payhembury, Rockbeare Rockets Res, St Mark's Res, St Martin's Res, Sandford, Tedburn St Mary Res, White Horse, Wonford Res.

Intermiate Div. 4	P	W	D	L	F	A	PTS
King's Arms	24	23	0	1	121	21	*66
Feniton Res	24	17	1	6	84	41	52
Dunkeswell R. Res	24	16	2	6	76	35	50
Payhembury	24	14	2	8	83	50	44
St Mark's Res	24	12	7	5	68	37	43
Bampton Res	24	12	4	8	74	58	40
Colyton Res	24	12	3	9	55	49	39
Bickleigh Res	24	7	3	14	60	64	24
Bratton Clovelly	24	7	3	14	46	82	24
Hatherleigh T. Res	24	6	2	16	43	78	20
Witheridge Res	24	6	1	17	49	85	19
Kentisbeare Res	24	5	4	15	33	82	19
Bradninch Res	24	3	0	21	36	146	9

92-93 Constitution: Bampton Res, Beer A. Res, Bickleigh Res, Bratton Clovelly, Cheriton Fitzpaine Res, Colyton Res, Crediton Utd 'B', Dawlish Villa, Hatherleigh Town Res, Newton St Cyres 'A', Thorverton, University of Exeter 'B', Upottery, Winkleigh Res, Y.M.C.A.

Intermediate Div. 5	P	W	D	L	F	A	PTS
Thorverton	26	26	0	0	163	19	78
Crediton Utd 'B'	26	20	1	5	105	49	61
Winkleigh Res	26	18	2	6	73	42	56
Upottery	26	15	3	8	94	58	48
Dawlish Villa Res	26	14	4	8	77	56	46
Y.M.C.A.	26	13	3	10	89	57	42
Silverton Res	26	13	3	10	77	88	42
North Tawton Res	26	6	8	12	39	68	26
Lapford Res	26	7	5	14	55	90	26
Sampford Peverell	26	8	1	17	66	91	25
Halwill Res	26	7	2	17	53	89	23
Crescent Res	26	6	4	16	48	103	22
Seaton Town Res	26	4	3	19	42	143	15
Tipton St John	26	3	5	18	56	82	*11

* - pts deducted for unregistered/ineligible players

92-93 Constitution: Awliscombe Res, Bradninch Res, Crescent Res, Culmstock Res, Halwill Res, Kentisbeare Res, Lapford Res, Newton Poppleford Res, North Tawton Res, Okehampton Argyle 'A', Sampford Peverell Res, Seaton Town Res, Silverton Res, Tipton St John Res, Witheridge Res.

Youth Division	P	W	D	L	F	A	PTS
Exeter City	24	21	2	1	141	12	65
Budleigh Salterton	24	18	3	3	107	32	57
Clyst Rovers	24	17	2	5	122	38	53
Beacon Knights	24	16	2	6	75	43	50
Alphington	24	13	4	7	48	34	43
Crediton United	24	12	2	10	70	63	38
Topsham Town	24	11	1	12	78	49	34
Exwick	24	10	1	13	52	64	31
Twyford Spartans	24	8	5	11	37	61	29
Dawlish Generals	24	7	6	11	62	59	27
Exmouth Town	24	3	0	21	24	122	9
Rennes United	24	3	0	21	26	143	9
North Molton	24	3	0	21	24	147	9

MOD-DEC WINDOWS SOUTH DEVON LEAGUE

President: M W Benney, Esq.
Chairman: E O Benney.
Hon. Secretary: W G L Parker,
23 Higher Coombe Drive, Teignmouth (7745277)

The season was a very successful one with the league providing both finalists in the Devon Premier Cup, i.e. Upton Athletic and Stoke Gabriel, the former winning the trophy 2-1 after extra-time. It was one of the best finals seen for many years. The League were also represented, in the form of Dartmouth YMRC Reserves, in the Devon Intermediate Cup final. Dartmouth won the trophy by 2-0.

The Herald Cup final between Newton Abbot Spurs and STC Paignton was watched by a crowd of nearly 1,800 on Good Friday. Newton Abbot Spurs were the victors.

Other Cup Finals were: **Belli Cup** - Winners: Upton Athletic, R-up: Newton Abbot Spurs, **Dartmouth Cup** - Winners: Waldon, R-up: Newton Town, **Lidston Cup** - Winners: Windsor Utd, R-up Paignton Town, **Ronald Cup** - Winners: Buckfastleigh Rangers Res, R-up Newton Rangers Res, **Bill Treeby Cup** - Winners: Combined '89, R-up: Torquay Christians in Sport, **Les Bishop Cup** - Winners: Dartington United, R-up: Churston Ferrers, **Ivor Andrews Cup:** Winners: Broadhempston, R-up: Bradley Villa.

The Sportsmanship Trophies were won by; Newton Abbot 66, Waldon, Loddiswell, Ilsington Villa, Brixham Villa Res, Torquay Christians In Sport, Newton United Res.

Six clubs have moved to the new Devon County League (Stoke Gabriel, Buckfastleigh Rangers, STC Paignton, Teignmouth, Chagford and Newton Abbot), whilst Abbotskerswell, Riviera Spurs and Watcombe United are new clubs accepted into Division Seven.

W G L Parker, Hon. Secretary

Premier Division	P	W	D	L	F	A	PTS
Upton Athletic	30	25	1	4	105	27	51
Buckfastleigh Rgrs	30	23	3	4	115	46	49
N. Abbot Spurs	30	22	3	5	92	33	47
Stoke Gabriel	30	17	7	8	55	29	39
Dartmouth YMRC	30	14	9	7	65	56	37
STC Paignton	30	15	6	9	63	40	36
Upton Dale	30	12	10	8	47	44	34
Dartington United	30	11	7	12	49	49	29
Newton 66	30	8	10	12	55	76	26
Galmpton United	30	8	9	13	52	78	25
Newton Rangers	30	9	4	17	62	73	22
Dartmouth United	30	7	8	15	55	78	22
Brixham Villa	30	6	10	14	37	63	19
Teignmouth	30	6	7	17	49	87	19
Watts Blake Bearne	30	4	4	22	26	99	12
Kingsteignton Ath.	30	3	4	23	32	81	10

92-93 Constitution: Upton Athletic, Newton Abbot Spurs, Dartmouth YMRC, Upton Vale, Dartington Utd, Newton 66, Galmpton United, Newton Rgrs, Brixham Villa, Dartmouth Utd, Watts Blake Bearne, Kingsteignton Ath., Newton Town, Hele Rvrs, Waldon, Stoke Gabriel Res.

Division One	P	W	D	L	F	A	PTS
Chagford	26	14	10	2	62	24	38
Newton Town	26	16	6	4	60	28	38
Newton Spurs Res	26	15	7	4	61	22	37
Stoke Gabriel Res	26	14	8	4	54	25	36
Hele Rovers	26	14	7	5	47	26	35
Newton Abbot	26	10	12	4	58	34	32
Upton Ath. Res	26	11	7	8	59	53	29
Waldon	26	11	6	9	57	34	28
Beesands	26	10	3	13	53	61	23
Bovey Tracey	26	9	4	13	52	45	22
Liverton United	26	8	1	17	40	56	17
Victoria Rangers	26	4	5	17	28	74	13
Kingkerswell	26	4	5	17	30	81	13
St Marychurch/Gr.	26	0	3	23	28	116	3

92-93 Constitution: Newton Abbot Res, Beesands Rvrs, Upton Ath. Res, Bovey Tracey, Liverton Utd, Victoria Rgrs, Kingkerswell, Windsor Utd, Teign Village, Chelston Res, South Brent, Paignton Town, Ipplepen Ath., St Marychurch & Torquay Grammarians.

Division Two	P	W	D	L	F	A	PTS
Windsor United	26	20	5	1	84	27	45
Teign Village	18	18	3	5	70	38	39
Chelston Res	26	16	5	5	57	27	37
South Brent	26	17	1	8	85	41	35
Paignton Town	26	16	2	8	70	42	34
Ipplepen Athletic	26	11	7	8	67	47	29
B'combe Corries	26	10	6	10	44	44	26
Loddiswell	26	10	3	13	62	63	23
Moretonhampstead	26	9	4	13	47	48	22
Totnes Town	26	6	7	13	34	52	19
Galmpton Utd Res	26	6	7	13	34	57	19
STC Paignton Res	26	2	16	50	63	18	
Foxhole United	26	4	3	19	32	80	11
Kingkerswell Res	26	3	1	22	26	133	7

92-93 Constitution: Babbacombe Corries, Loddiswell, Moretonhampstead, Totnes Town, Galmpton Utd Res, Northern Telecom Paignton Res, Paignton Res, Foxhole Utd Res, Brixham Town, Newton Rgrs Res, Buckfastleigh Rgrs Res, Brixham Utd, Dittisham Utd, Kingkerswell Res.

Division Three	P	W	D	L	F	A	PTS
Brixham Town	26	20	4	2	77	29	44
Newton Rgrs Res	26	19	2	5	91	31	40
Buckfastleigh Res	26	18	3	5	96	50	39
Brixham Utd	26	14	6	6	61	39	34
Harbertonford	26	12	5	9	62	57	29
Dittisham Utd	26	13	3	10	65	64	29
Chudleigh Utd	26	11	6	9	65	43	28
Ilsington Villa	26	10	7	9	51	45	27
D'mouth YMRC Res	26	10	6	10	50	56	26
Kingsteignton Res	26	8	3	15	52	61	19
Paignton Villa	26	7	4	15	49	67	18
Ashburton	26	6	4	16	41	66	16
Centrax	26	4	6	16	42	100	14
Newton United	26	0	1	25	20	114	1

92-93 Constitution: Chudleigh Ath., Dartmouth YMRC Res, Ilsington Villa, Dartmouth Utd Res, Kingsteignton Ath. Res, Paignton Villa, Ashburton, Centrax, Brixham Villa Res, Churston Ferrers, Dartington Utd Res, Bishopsteignton Utd, Newton Utd, Newton 66 Res.

Division Four	P	W	D	L	F	A	PTS
Brixham Villa Res	26	20	3	3	101	27	43
Churston Ferrers	26	20	3	3	99	34	43
Dartington Res	26	20	2	4	78	18	42
Dartmouth Utd Res	26	10	8	8	43	42	28
Newton 66	26	12	3	11	46	38	27
Bishopsteignton	26	12	3	11	42	44	27
Staverton	26	11	4	11	52	71	26
Channings Wood	26	11	2	13	53	55	24
Watts Blabe B. Res	26	11	2	13	46	65	24
Babbacombe Rgrs	26	8	6	12	37	56	22
Paignton United	26	6	7	13	51	88	19
Meadowbrook	26	7	3	16	47	65	17
Liverton Res	26	7	0	19	26	67	14
Thurlestone	26	2	4	20	26	77	8

92-93 Constitution: Staverton, Channings Wd, Watts BB Res, Meadowbrook, Babbacombe Rgrs, Paignton Utd, Liverton Utd Res, Combined 89, Newton Town Res, Torquay Christians In Sport, Northern Telecom Paignton Saints, Windsor Utd Res, Kellaton, Thurlestone.

Division Five	P	W	D	L	F	A	PTS
Combined 89	26	24	2	0	130	14	50
Newton Town Res	26	20	3	3	87	26	43
Torquay Christians	26	16	6	4	80	29	38
NT Paignton Saints	26	12	3	11	70	58	27
Windsor Utd Res	26	12	3	11	69	66	27
Kellaton	26	12	3	11	50	53	27
Walden Res	26	11	4	11	58	56	26
Sth Brent Res	26	12	2	12	59	61	26
Bovey Tracey Res	26	8	9	9	55	54	25
Victoria Rgrs Res	26	9	5	12	60	54	23
Ipplepen Res	26	9	2	15	37	71	20
B'combe Corries Res	26	5	3	18	47	104	13
Foxhole Utd Res	26	4	2	20	26	120	10
Ashburton Res	26	3	3	20	31	93	9

92-93 Constitution: Waldon Res, Sth Brent Res, Victoria Rgrs Res, Ipplepen Ath. Res, Babbacombe Corries Res, Ashburton Res, Bovey Tracey Res, Broadhempston, Newton Abbot Res, Buckfastleigh Rgrs 'A', Torbay Gents, Teignmouth Res, Hele Rovers, Foxhole Utd Res.

Division Six	P	W	D	L	F	A	PTS
Broadhempston	26	22	3	1	108	22	47
Newton Abbot Res	26	22	3	1	97	15	47
Buckfastleigh R. Res	26	16	2	8	73	42	34
Torbay Gents	26	14	4	8	54	51	32
Teignmouth Res	26	15	1	10	86	53	31
Hele Rvrs Res	26	13	2	11	85	52	28
Teign Vil. Res	26	10	4	12	47	54	24
East Allington	26	9	5	12	51	51	23
Beesands Res	26	8	5	13	51	86	21
Brixham Utd Res	26	7	5	14	53	65	19
Paignton Villa Res	26	7	3	16	42	79	17
B'combe Rgrs Res	30	7	2	17	43	85	16
Dartington Hall	26	6	4	16	36	83	16
Harbertonford	26	3	3	20	28	116	9

92-93 Constitution: Teign Village Res, East Allington, Beesands Res, Brixham Utd Res, Paignton V. Res, Babbacombe R. Res, Dartington Hall, B'steignton Res, Newton Villa, Chagford Res, Totnes T. Res, Bradley Villa, Dittisham Res, Harbertonford Res.

Division Seven	P	W	D	L	F	A	PTS
Bishopsteignton Res	26	20	4	2	92	30	44
Newton Villa	26	20	4	2	88	32	44
Chagford Res	26	19	5	2	83	25	43
Totnes Town Res	26	17	6	3	85	27	40
Bradley Villa	26	15	3	8	56	79	33
Dittisham Res	26	15	3	8	83	57	33
Chudleigh Res	26	11	3	17	55	52	25
M'hampstead Res	26	10	0	16	64	78	20
Stoke Fleming	26	6	7	13	56	87	19
Paignton Utd Res	26	6	4	16	50	85	16
Staverton Res	26	7	1	18	64	81	15
Sth Brent 'A'	26	6	3	17	47	70	15
Newton Utd Res	26	4	4	18	25	100	12
Thurlestone Res	26	2	1	23	31	126	5

92-93 Constitution: Chudleigh Res, Stoke Fleming, Paignton Utd Res, Staverton Res, Sth Brent 'A', Newton Utd Res, Thurlestone Res, Brixham Town Res, Loddiswell Res, Combined 89, Abbotskerwell, Riviera Spurs, Watcombe Utd, Moretonhampstead Res.

BIDEFORD TOOL NORTH DEVON LEAGUE

President: Mr A S Beer.   **Chairman:** Mr W Smale

Hon. Sec: H W Bartlett, 20 Granville Av., Yeo Vale, Barnstaple EX32 7AH (43415).

Premier Division	P	W	D	L	F	A	PTS
Bradworthy	30	24	3	3	95	22	51
Braunton	30	18	7	5	102	57	43
Combe Martin	30	19	4	7	89	52	42
Morwenstow	30	18	6	6	95	62	42
Appledore Res	30	18	5	7	70	28	41
Fremington	30	13	12	5	61	41	38
South Molton	30	12	7	11	62	68	31
Chittlehampton	30	9	9	12	66	62	27
Dolton	30	10	6	14	72	79	26
Barnstaple AAC	30	9	8	13	52	74	26
Shamwickshire Rvrs	30	7	11	12	71	76	25
Putford	30	10	5	15	55	74	25
Lynton	30	9	5	16	66	86	23
Chivenor	30	8	6	16	48	84	22
Holsworthy Res	30	5	5	20	51	101	15
Northam Lions	30	1	1	28	27	116	3

Senior Division	P	W	D	L	F	A	PTS
Parkhead	24	21	1	2	87	24	43
Sporting VSW	24	14	5	5	69	44	33
Braunton Res	24	15	1	8	63	38	31
Hearts of Oak	24	12	3	9	67	42	27
Heartland	24	10	3	11	72	55	23
Barnstaple T. Colts	24	9	4	11	47	48	22
Shebbear	24	10	1	13	49	52	21
Fremington Res	24	9	3	12	50	61	21
Pyworthy	24	9	3	12	48	63	21
North Molton	24	7	6	11	52	60	20
West Down	24	8	4	12	51	79	20
Dolton Res	24	5	7	12	46	70	17
Torrington Colts	24	6	1	17	33	98	13

Premier Division Brayford Cup:
Winners: Appledore Res. R-up: Bradworthy
Senior Division Combe Martin Cup:
Winners: Hearts of Oak. R-up: Parkhead
Intermediate Division One Arlington Cup:
Winners: Admiral Vernon. R-up: Braunton
Intermediate Division Two Nth Devon Cup:
Winners: Hearts of Oak. R-up: Braunton
I'mediate Div. 3 Appledore Shipbuilders Cup:
Winners: Shapland. R-up: St Marys

Intermediate Div 1	P	W	D	L	F	A	PTS
Admiral Vernon	24	20	1	3	94	23	41
Bradworthy Res	24	19	1	4	85	35	39
Wrey Arms	24	16	2	6	79	43	34
Combe Martin Res	24	16	2	6	84	49	34
Appledore 'A'	24	15	4	5	55	32	34
Bratton Fleming	24	9	4	11	53	58	22
Shamwickshire Res	24	7	6	11	48	53	20
Sth Molton Res	24	7	4	13	48	65	18
Clovelly	24	7	4	13	46	81	18
Northam Lions Res	24	8	1	15	43	60	17
Sporting VSW Res	24	6	4	14	47	69	16
Sandpiper Inn	26	4	3	17	47	100	11
Chivenor Res	24	2	4	18	45	106	8

Intermediate Div 1	P	W	D	L	F	A	PTS
Admiral Vernon	24	20	1	3	94	23	41
Bradworthy Res	24	19	1	4	85	35	39
Wrey Arms	24	16	2	6	79	43	34
Combe Martin Res	24	16	2	6	84	49	34
Appledore 'A'	24	15	4	5	55	32	34
Bratton Fleming	24	9	4	11	53	58	22
Shamwickshire Res	24	7	6	11	48	53	20
Sth Molton Res	24	7	4	13	48	65	18
Clovelly	24	7	4	13	46	81	18
Northam Lions Res	24	8	1	15	43	60	17
Sporting VSW Res	24	6	4	14	47	69	16
Sandpiper Inn	26	4	3	17	47	100	11
Chivenor Res	24	2	4	18	45	106	8

Intermediate Div 1	P	W	D	L	F	A	PTS
Admiral Vernon	24	20	1	3	94	23	41
Bradworthy Res	24	19	1	4	85	35	39
Wrey Arms	24	16	2	6	79	43	34
Combe Martin Res	24	16	2	6	84	49	34
Appledore 'A'	24	15	4	5	55	32	34
Bratton Fleming	24	9	4	11	53	58	22
Shamwickshire Res	24	7	6	11	48	53	20
Sth Molton Res	24	7	4	13	48	65	18
Clovelly	24	7	4	13	46	81	18
Northam Lions Res	24	8	1	15	43	60	17
Sporting VSW Res	24	6	4	14	47	69	16
Sandpiper Inn	26	4	3	17	47	100	11
Chivenor Res	24	2	4	18	45	106	8

Long Sutton FC, of the Somerset Senior League, pictured before beating Larkhall Athletic Reserves 3-1 on Friday 15th May. Photo - Tim Lancaster.

Bugle FC pictured before a Cornish Senior Cup tie against Liskeard. The Molinnis club had their best South Western League season since their title year of 84-85, but tragically they have had to step down to the East Cornwall Premier League due to loss of revenue engendered by the closure of their clubhouse. Photo - James Wright.

Porthleven FC, who enjoyed their highest ever South Western League finish in 1991-92.

JEWSON SOUTH WESTERN LEAGUE

President: Mr A Jewells.
Chairman: Mr T H Scott. **Vice Chairman:** Mr P S Lee.
Hon. Secretary: Mr Melvyn Goodenough, Rose Cottage,
Horrelsford, Milton Damerel, Holsworthy EX22 7DH (0409 261402).

	P	W	D	L	F	A	PTS
Falmouth Town	34	26	5	3	91	20	57
Newquay	34	23	5	6	88	31	51
Bugle	34	16	9	9	65	46	41
Truro City	34	14	11	9	74	49	39
Bodmin Town	34	15	9	10	53	51	39
Clyst Rovers	34	15	8	11	59	60	38
Appledore/BAAC	34	16	5	13	78	56	37
Porthleven	34	14	8	12	77	69	36
St Blazey	34	15	6	13	72	67	36
Torpoint Athletic	34	14	7	13	49	50	35
Holsworthy	34	9	16	9	37	46	34
Wadebridge Town	34	12	7	15	45	52	31
St Austell	34	10	8	16	45	63	28
Millbrook	34	9	9	16	45	70	27
Launceston	34	8	6	20	45	73	22
Dev./C'wall Police	34	7	8	19	43	78	22
Tavistock	34	8	5	21	53	79	21
Penzance	34	7	4	23	35	94	18

FALMOUTH BACK IN CHARGE

Falmouth Town clinch the South Western League championship; their fifth in eight seasons since they returned to the league in 1984. In doing so they regained the title they lost to Bodmin Town last year. Falmouth's critical win was a 2-0 victory at home to Torpoint Athletic on 25th April, achieved with goals from veteran George Torrance, a free-kick, and Eric Tickle, a diving header, either side of the interval. As Falmouth notched up that win, nearest challengers Newquay lost surprisingly at Devon & Cornwall Police. Falmouth also won the League Cup to complete the double, but Newquay gained some measure of revenge by beating Falmouth in the first all-South Western League Cornish Senior Cup final for many years.

League newcomers Devon & Cornwall Police had a difficult baptism in the league, but the highlight for them was reaching of the League Cup final. Perennial whipping boys Penzance had a dream start, winning two and drawing one of their opening four games, in other words gathering more points than they had in the entire 1990-91 campaign! They ended the season with the heady total of eighteen points, but it was not sufficient to lift their very inexperienced side from its habitual bottom spot. However, manager Roger Toms has been recruiting strongly and the Magpies are predicting happier times in 1992-93.

For the new season the League loses Clyst Rovers, its most easterly club, to the Great Mills League, and Bugle who have had to resign for financial reasons. Joining the League are Mullion, the Jolly's Cornwall Combination champions who have been making unsuccessful applications for years but now make the deserved step up.

Paul Lee of Bodmin was once again the top marked referee, for the fourth year in succession. Porthleven were awarded the 'best kept ground' trophy, and Holsworthy took the Sporting Trophy by receiving no bookings at all. During the season, Launceston installed floodlighting, and Holsworthy hope to install lights in preparation for the 1993-94 season.

Leading Scorers: Mark Rapsey (Falmouth) 29, Andy Waddell (Appledore) 26, D Robison (Porthleven) 25, D Downing (Appledore) 23, G Hooper (Falmouth) 20.

LEAGUE CUP 1991-92

Preliminary Round

Bodmin Town v Holsworthy	3-0	Torpoint Athletic v Clyst Rovers	1-3

First Round

Bodmin Town v Penzance	5-1	Falmouth Town v Millbrook	5-0
Launceston v Bugle	1-0	Newquay v Truro City	1-0
St Austell v Appledore/B.A.A.C.	2-1	St Blazey v Devon & Cornwall Police	1-4
Tavistock v Wadebridge Town	3-0	Torpoint Athletic v Porthleven	4-2

Quarter Finals

Bodmin Town v St Austell	1-3	Devon & Cornwall Police v Launceston	3-2
Tavistock v Falmouth Town	0-4	Torpoint Athletic v Newquay	1-0

Semi Finals

Falmouth Town v St Austell (at St Blazey)	3-2	DC Police v Torpoint (games at Millbrook)	0-0,5-2

Final (at Bodmin Town FC, 4/5/92): Falmouth Town 5, Devon & Cornwall Police 0.

RESULT CHART 1991-92

HOME TEAM	1	2	3	4	5	6	7	8	9	10	11	12	13	14	15	16	17	18
1. Appledore	*	1-1	2-3	3-2	5-0	3-1	1-1	2-0	5-0	2-3	3-0	1-4	4-0	7-3	5-1	3-1	3-3	0-1
2. Bodmin	1-2	*	0-1	1-1	3-2	2-1	2-2	2-1	2-0	1-1	5-1	2-2	1-0	0-5	1-0	2-2	2-0	
3. Bugle	1-1	2-2	*	1-1	4-1	0-1	1-1	3-1	3-3	1-2	1-0	1-1	1-2	0-2	2-0	2-3	4-0	2-1
4. Clyst Rovers	3-2	2-1	0-2	*	3-1	0-2	1-1	4-3	0-1	1-3	2-0	1-2	5-1	0-7	3-1	1-3	3-3	2-1
5. DC Police	1-4	0-2	0-3	1-3	*	1-1	0-1	2-0	1-1	2-0	2-3	1-1	2-0	0-2	1-1	1-1	0-3	3-1
6. Falmouth	5-0	4-0	3-1	4-1	5-2	*	0-0	5-0	0-0	1-0	2-0	1-1	2-0	5-1	5-0	2-0	0-0	1-0
7. Holsworthy	1-0	1-1	2-2	3-0	1-1	1-6	*	2-1	0-4	0-5	0-1	0-3	2-3	1-1	2-1	1-1	2-2	4-2
8. Launceston	4-3	0-1	0-4	0-2	6-1	2-6	1-1	*	1-5	0-1	0-2	5-2	1-3	2-2	2-0	1-0	0-3	1-2
9. Millbrook	0-4	0-2	0-3	2-3	1-0	0-2	2-2	2-2	*	0-6	3-2	1-3	0-0	1-0	6-1	1-3	2-3	1-1
10. Newquay	3-0	4-2	1-1	2-0	1-3	2-2	1-1	6-0	5-1	*	4-0	3-1	2-1	5-0	7-0	4-1	2-3	1-0
11. Penzance	0-2	3-1	2-3	1-2	0-5	2-1	1-3	0-0	2-0	*	1-1	0-0	2-0	*	1-3	2-5	2-1	
12. Porthleven	5-4	1-2	1-4	2-3	8-3	1-5	1-0	1-1	1-0	1-2	5-0	*	2-5	4-6	2-0	2-2	2-2	1-3
13. St Austell	0-1	0-3	1-0	2-2	0-1	0-4	2-4	1-1	1-6	3-0	3-2	*	2-2	1-1	2-3	1-1	0-2	
14. St Blazey	3-1	4-2	1-1	0-1	3-1	0-3	2-1	1-0	3-6	2-2	2-0	1-0	4-1	*	5-1	2-3	0-1	0-5
15. Tavistock	1-2	0-0	1-2	2-5	2-2	0-3	0-1	0-2	5-0	0-2	4-1	2-4	0-0	2-3	*	4-0	2-1	1-2
16. Torpoint	0-0	0-1	0-5	0-1	2-1	2-1	0-0	1-0	4-0	0-1	4-2	1-3	2-3	0-0	6-1	*	1-3	2-3
17. Truro City	2-1	4-2	8-0	1-1	1-2	0-1	0-0	0-0	1-2	1-0	6-0	4-5	2-1	3-1	1-2	1-2	*	4-0
18. Wadebridge	2-1	1-3	2-1	1-1	4-2	1-2	0-0	1-1	1-1	0-1	3-1	0-3	1-1	2-1	2-4	1-0	3-2	*

APPLEDORE-BIDEFORD A.A.C.

Manager: Dave Dark   **Asst Manager:** Cliff Cann   **Coach:** Ian Mansford.
Secretary: Eddie Nichols, 14 Alexandra Terrace, Bideford EX39 2PL (0237 475993).
Ground: Marshford (0237 277099)   **Floodlights:** No   **Stand:** Yes.
Directions: Before Appledore, on right of A386 approaching town.
Colours: Yellow & blue/blue/yellow   **Change colours:** Blue/yellow/blue.

BODMIN TOWN

Manager: Richard Cardew
Secretary: Martin Mullis, 24 Jubilee Terrace, Bodmin PL31 2QE (0208 776685).
Ground: Priory Park (0208 78165)   **Directions:** Just off town centre, at rear of car park.
Cover: Yes, grandstand   **Clubhouse:** Yes   **Floodlights:** Yes
Colours: Amber & black/black   **Change colours:** Blue/black/blue.
Honours: South Western Lg 90-91 (Lg Cup R-up 77-78 88-89).

DEVON & CORNWALL POLICE

Chairman: Mr M Hale   **President:** Mr P W Brown
Secretary: Steve Bennett, C/O Police Station, Budshill Way, Crownhill, Plymouth PL6 5HT (0752 691227).
Manager: Jon Hillson.   **Asst Manager:** Peter May   **Physio:** Dave Cook
Ground: Mill Bay Park, Plymouth
Directions: Near city centre, at junction of Millbay Road and West Hoe Road. 20 mins walk from Plymouth (BR).
Seats: No   **Cover:** No   **Capacity:** 2,000   **Floodlights:** No   **Founded:** 1967.
Programme: 34 pages, with admission   **Programme Editor:** Sam Balsdon.
Colours: All royal blue   **Change colours:** White/black/red.
Previous Leagues: None   **Hons:** South Western Lg Cup R-up 91-92, South West Co's Police
Cup(4) 87-88 90-92, Falford Police Cup(12) 69-72 73-75 76-77 78-79 80-81 85-86 87-89 91-92.

FALMOUTH TOWN

Manager: Trevor Mewton   **Secretary:** Dave Donohue, 151 Longfield, Falmouth TR11 4SR (0326 316642).
Grounds: Bickland Park, Bickland Vale, Falmouth, Cornwall (0326 75156).
Directions: On west edge of town. One and a half miles from Penmere Halt (BR).
Seats: 300   **Cover:** 1,000   **Capacity:** 8,000   **Floodlights:** Yes   **Founded:** 1946.
Colours: Amber/black/amber   **Change colours:** All white.
Previous Ground: Ashfield   **Record Gate:** 8,000 v Oxford Utd, FA Cup 1966.
Hons: FA Vase QF 86-87, FA Cup 1st Rd 62-63 67-68 69-70, Cornish Snr Cup(10) 61-62 64-66 67-68 70-71 73-74
75-79, Western Lg(4) 74-78 (Lg Cup 74-75), South Western Lg(12) 60-61 65-66 67-68 70-74 85-87 88-90 91-92 (R-
up 58-59 64-65 69-70 87-88, Lg Cup(9) 57-59 61-63 67-68 70-71 85-86 90-92 (R-up(4) 59-6070-71 85-87)).

HOLSWORTHY

Manager: Terry Andrews.   **Assistant Manager:** Peter England.
Secretary: Des Masters, 10 Bodmin Street, Holsworthy, Devon EX22 6BR (0409 253995).
Ground: Upcott Field (0409 254295)   **Nickname:** Magpies   **Cover:** Yes   **Floodlights:** No.
Programme: 8 pages, £1 with entry   **Editor:** Terry Irewin.
Colours: Black & white/black/black   **Change colours:** Gold/white/gold.
Nickname: Magpies   **Hons:** Devon Snr Cup 53-54, Devon Prem. Cup 71-72 76-77

LAUNCESTON

Manager: Keith Ellacott   **Trainer:** Jock Mudie.
Secretary: Chris Martin, 3a Tavistock Road, Launceston, Cornwall PL15 9HA (0566 776175).
Ground: Pennygillam (0566 773279)
Directions: In Pennygillam Industrial Estate, just off main A30.
Clubhouse: Yes   **Programme:** Yes   **Seats:** Yes   **Cover:** Yes   **Floodlights:** Yes
Colours: Claret & blue/claret/claret   **Change colours:** Sky/blue/claret.
Hons: S. Western Lg R-up 84-85, Cornish Charity Cup R-up 88-89, Cornish Snr Cup 1899-1900 00-01 82-83.

MILLBROOK

Manager: Geoff Crudgington   **Trainer:** Murray Hyslop.
Secretary: Murray Hyslop, 14 St Andrews Street, Millbrook, Cornwall (0752 823271).
Ground: The Mill, Millbrook, Cornwall (0752 822113)   **Cover:** Yes   **Floodlights:** Yes.
Directions: B3247 through Millbrook, ground on far (east) side of village.
Colours: White/black/black   **Change colours:** Red/black/white
Hons: South Western Lg R-up 81-82.

MULLION

Ground: Clifden Parc (0326 240676)   **Manager:** Martin Smith/ Clive Biddick
Secretary: Stuart Westwood, 4 St Mellans Terrace, Mullion, Helston, Cornwall TR12 7EH (0326 240991).
Directions: Through village on B3269. Ground up hill on right (road to Polurrian Cove).
Clubhouse: Yes   **Programme:** Yes   **Cover:** No   **Floodlights:** No
Colours: Red & white/blue/red   **Change colours:** White/blue/white.
Previous League: Cornwall Comb. (pre-1992)
Hons: Cornwall Comb.(3) 85-86 90-92 (R-up(4) 80-83 86-87, Lg Cup(2) 90-92 (R-up 88-89), Suppl. Cup 85-86).

NEWQUAY

Manager: Ray Nicholls   **Secretary:** Brian Biggin, 8 Mitchell Ave., Newquay TR7 1BN (0637 875623).
Ground: Mount Wise (0637 872935)   **Nickname:** Peppermints.
Directions: From Newquay (BR) follow one-way system for 2 miles - ground signposted on left just before Windsor
Hotel.
Seats: 250   **Cover:** 500   **Capacity:** 4,000   **Floodlights:** Yes   **Founded:** 1890.
Colours: Red & white/white/white   **Change colours:** Red/black/white.
Previous Names: Newquay 1890-1903/ N'quay One & All 03-12/ N'quay Td 20-27/ N'quay Rovers 27-37.
Previous Leagues: West Cornwall/ Plymouth & District 21-27/ Cornish Senior 31-51.
Hons: FA Vase 3rd Rd 90-91, Cornish Snr Cup 34-35 52-53 54-55 56-57 91-92 (R-up(9) 05-07 08-09 25-26 33-34
35-36 57-58 69-70 84-85), S. Western Lg(7) 58-60 77-78 79-80 81-82 83-84 87-88 (R-up 57-58 85-86, Lg Cup 55-56
88-89 (R-up(4) 56-58 79-81), Cornish Charity Cup(13) 06-07 08-09 53-56 57-59 62-63 69-70 74-75 76-78 88-89 (R-
up(9) 07-08 20-21 56-57 60-61 73-74 75-76 81-82 84-86), W. Cornwall Lg 06-07 (R-up(2) 07-09), Cornish Snr Lg
Herald Cup 34-35 (R-up(7) 33-34 35-36 49-51 55-57 58-59).

Newquay 2, Falmouth Town 2 - Jewson South Western League, 24/8/91. Falmouth 'keeper David Street catches cleanly whilst Andy Street waits for any slip up. Photo - Ray Frith.

Devon & Cornwall Police. Back Row (L/R): Wayne Arthur, Chuck Shwenn, Neil Triggs, Geoff Turner, Don Pearson, Lee Dickinson, Terry Locock, Ian Dabbs, Jim Tregellas (Manager). Front: Keith Black, Steve Browmlow, Peter Small, Steve Panter, Richard Tomlin. Photo - James Wright.

Torpoint Athletic 1, Newquay 0 - Jewson South Western League Cup Quarter Final 1//92. Newquay's Sean Hooper is halted by the shirt sleeve on his way to goal. Photo - Ray Frith.

PENZANCE

President: Len Stanbury   **Chairman:** Jim Dann
Secretary: Brian Harris, Hillview Cottage, Canonstown, Hayle TR27 6ND (0736 740062).
Manager: Roger Toms   **Coach:** Charlie Coombes   **Trainer:** Ken Prowse.
Ground: Penlee Park (0736 61964)   **Floodlights:** Yes   **Seats:** Yes   **Founded:** 1888.
Directions: Seafront road past harbour, after amusement arcade turn right at r'bout (Alexander Rd), ground second right. Fifteen minutes walk from Penzance (BR); directions as above.
Colours: Black & white/black/black   **Change colours:** All blue   **Nickname:** Magpies.
Hons: Cornish Snr Cup 1892-93 95-96 97-98 98-99 1903-04 07-08 47-48 60-61 72-73 80-81 (R-up 1896-97 99-1900 00-01 48-49 49-50 54-55 56-57 74-75), South Western Lg 55-56 56-57 74-75 (Lg Cup R-up 60-61), Cornwall Charity Cup 48-49 (R-up 63-64).

PORTHLEVEN

Manager: Paul Christie   **Assistant Manager:** Andy Pascoe.
Secretary: Keith Downing, 27 Gibson Way, Porthleven, Helston TR13 9AN (0326 561160).
Ground: Gala Parc (0208 574754)   **Cover:** Yes
Floodlights: No.
Directions: Arriving from Penzance on A394, B3304 into Porthleven, ground on left immediately before town.
Colours: All yellow   **Change colours:** Blue/navy/navy.
Nickname: Fishermen.
Previous Leagues: South Western 66-77/ Cornwall Combination 77-89.
Hons: South Western Lg R-up 72-73, Cornwall Combination 88-89 (Supplementary Cup 88-89).

ST AUSTELL

Chairman: Reg Pope   **Asst Chairman:** Derek Silk
Secretary: Peter Beard, 24 Alexandra Rd, St Austell, Cornwall PL25 4QP (0726 64138).
Manager: Glyn Avery   **Asst Manager:** Colin Bunney   **Physio:** N McKenna
Ground: Poltair Park (0726 77099).   **Directions:** 5 mins walk north of St Austell (BR).
Seats: 200   **Cover:** 300   **Capacity:** 8,000   **Floodlights:** No   **Founded:** 1890.
Colours: White/black/black   **Change colours:** All sky.
Previous Leagues: Rocky Park (1890s)   **Record Gate:** 15,000 v Penzance, Senior Cup 1949.
Hons: South Western Lg 68-69 (R-up(4) 63-64 65-66 71-73, Lg Cup 64-65 71-73 87-88 (R-up 52-53 68-69 70-71 89-90)), Cornish Snr Cup(11) 11-14 33-34 38-39 45-47 63-64 68-69 71-72.

ST BLAZEY

Manager: David Pearce   **Asst Manager:** Phil Towl   **Physio:** Richy Brown
Secretary: Mike Newcombe, 29 Par Green, Par, Cornwall PL24 2AF (0726 818334).
Ground: Blaise Park, Station Road, St Blazey (0726 814110).   **Nickname:** Saints.
Directions: A390 Liskeard-St Austell road, turn into Station Road at lights in St Blazey village; ground 50 yards on left. One and a half miles from Par (BR).
Seats: 300   **Cover:** 700   **Capacity:** 4,500   **Floodlights:** Yes   **Founded:** 1896.
Colours: Green/white/green   **Change colours:** White/black/black.
Hons: South Western Lg(6) 54-55 57-58 62-64 80-81 82-83 (R-up(9) 51-52 55-57 61-62 84-85 86-87 88-91, Lg Cup 53-54 56-57 66-67(joint) 81-82 86-87 (R-up 61-62 63-64 82-83 84-85 90-91)), Cornish Snr Cup 35-36 49-50 53-54 55-56 57-58 59-60 62-63 86-87, Cornish Charity Cup 83-84.

TAVISTOCK

Manager: Mike Sloman/ Steve Metters.
Secretary: Philip Lowe, 1 Bainbridge Court, Colebrook, Plympton, PL7 4HH (0752 335273).
Ground: Langsford Park (0822 614447)   **Nickname:** Tavy   **Cover:** Yes   **Floodlights:** No.
Colours: Black & red/black/red   **Change colours:** White/white/black.   **Founded:** 1888.
Hons: Devon Snr Cup 68-69 77-78 81-82, South Western Lg Cup 68-69 (R-up 76-77 83-84).

TORPOINT ATHLETIC

Manager: Phil Cardew
Secretary: Vic Grimwood, 43 Henerdon Heights, Plympton PL7 3EY (0752 81344).
Ground: Mill Field (0752 812889)
Directions: Bear left from Torpoint ferry, ground down hill on left after half a mile.
Clubhouse: Yes   **Programme:** Yes   **Seats:** Yes   **Cover:** Yes   **Floodlights:** No
Colours: Gold & black stripes/black/black   **Change colours:** Red/black/black.
Hons: South Western Lg 64-65 66-67 (Lg Cup R-up 65-66), Cornish Snr Cup 1896-97 1905-06 06-07 08-09 09-10 19-20 28-29 32-33.

TRURO CITY

Manager: Steve Massey
Secretary: Ray Rowe, 5 Alverton Gardens, Truro, Cornwall TR1 1JA (0872 70684).
Ground: Treyew Road, Truro, Cornwall (0872 78853)   **Seats:** Yes   **Floodlights:** Yes.
Directions: On A39 by-pass south of city. 10 mins walk from BR station; up hill and left at junction.
Colours: Red & black/black/black   **Change colours:** Yellow/red/red.
Hons: South Western Lg 60-61 69-70 (R-up 54-55 62-63 66-67 67-68 70-71, Lg Cup 59-60 66-67(joint)(R-up 54-55 58-59 67-68)), Cornish Snr Cup 1894-95 1901-02 02-03 10-11 23-24 26-27 27-28 37-38 58-59 66-67 69-70, Cornish Charity Cup 19-20 28-29 29-30 30-31 49-50 64-65 80-81, Cornish Snr Lg 31-32 32-33.

WADEBRIDGE TOWN

Manager: Alan Johns.
Secretary: Barry Cudmore, 3 Marine Terrace, Wadebridge, Cornwall PL27 7AJ (0208 813826).
Ground: Bodieve Park (0208 812537)   **Seats:** Yes   **Cover:** Ample   **Floodlights:** No
Directions: At junction of A39 and B3314 to east of Wadebridge.   **Nickname:** Bridgers.
Colours: Red/white/red   **Change colours:** All blue.
Hons: South Western Lg R-up 68-69 78-79 79-80 (Lg Cup 74-75 75-76 77-78 79-80 84-85 (R-up 62-63 69-70 81-82), Cornish Snr Cup 79-80, Cornish Charity Cup 26-27 33-34 51-52 63-64 72-73 75-76 81-82 84-85.

JEWSON SOUTH WESTERN LEAGUE TEN YEAR RECORD

	82/3	83/4	84/5	85/6	86/7	87/8	88/9	89/90	90/1	91/2
Appledore/Bideford AAC	14	8	7	14	14	12	18	11	9	7
Bodmin Town	15	20	18	4	5	4	3	3	1	5
Bugle	5	4	1	5	12	20	15	5	8	3
Clyst Rovers	19	16	11	11	10	19	14	8	14	6
Devon & Cornwall Police	–	–	–	–	–	–	–	–	–	16
Falmouth Town	–	–	6	1	1	2	1	1	3	1
Holsworthy	17	15	19	20	18	17	17	17	16	11
Launceston	6	2	15	19	17	13	5	7	15	15
Millbrook	4	3	5	3	3	5	10	6	11	14
Newquay	13	1	3	2	8	1	4	4	4	2
Newton Abbot	7	6	10	10	9	11	13	–	–	–
Oak Villa	–	–	–	–	–	16	11	–	–	–
Penryn Athletic	–	–	–	15	–	–	–	–	–	–
Penzance	11	18	17	17	19	15	16	15	17	18
Plymouth Civil Service	8	11	13	–	–	–	–	–	–	–
Plymouth Command	18	19	–	–	–	–	–	–	–	–
Portleven	–	–	–	–	–	–	–	16	13	8
St Austell	10	5	16	8	6	6	12	13	5	13
St Blazey	1	7	2	9	2	3	2	2	2	9
Tavistock	16	14	12	16	16	18	9	9	12	17
Teignmouth	9	17	14	18	13	10	–	–	–	–
Torpoint Athletic	12	10	9	12	15	14	8	14	6	10
Torquay United Res	–	–	–	13	7	9	–	–	–	–
Torrington	2	12	–	–	–	–	–	–	–	–
Truro City	20	13	8	6	11	8	6	10	7	4
Wadebridge Town	3	9	4	7	4	7	7	12	10	12
No. of Clubs	**20**	**20**	**19**	**20**	**19**	**20**	**18**	**17**	**17**	**18**

Porthleven, who had a good season, defend as they win 3-0 at Wadebridge in late January. Photo - Ray Frith.

CORNISH GUARDIAN
EAST CORNWALL PREMIER LEAGUE

	P	W	D	L	F	A	PTS
St Dennis	34	27	7	0	78	23	61
Roche	34	21	8	5	80	43	50
Nanpean Rovers	34	20	6	8	85	49	46
Liskeard A. Res	34	19	5	9	82	39	43
Foxhole Stars	34	18	4	12	65	37	40
Sticker	34	16	8	10	54	53	40
Callington	34	14	9	11	68	64	37
Bodmin Town Res	34	12	10	12	55	44	34
Camelford	34	15	4	15	54	60	34
Bude	34	13	7	14	53	49	33
St Blazey Res	34	11	10	13	53	60	32
Padstow United	34	9	8	17	45	62	26
Lostwithiel	34	8	9	17	34	58	25
Wadebridge T. Res	34	7	10	17	28	50	24
Riviera Coasters	34	8	7	19	57	78	23
Tintagel	34	7	9	18	41	89	23
Bugle Reserves	34	6	9	19	46	87	21
St Breward	34	5	10	19	43	76	20

LEAGUE CUP Prel. Round

Callington v Sticker	4-2
Lostwithiel v Nanpean Rovers	1-1,0-3

First Round

Bugle Reserves v Camelford	3-1
Callington v Bude	5-1
Foxhole Stars v Roche	0-2
Padstow Utd v Bodmin Town Res	2-1
St Breward v Wadebridge T. Res	0-1
St Dennis v Tintagel	5-1
St Blazey Res v Nanpean Rovers	1-2
Riviera Coasters v Liskeard A. Res	0-4

Quarter Finals

Liskeard A. Res v Padstow Utd	3-0
Nanpean Rovers v Callington	2-1
Bugle Reserves v St Dennis	1-1,2-3
Wadebridge T. Reserves v Roche	4-2

Semi Finals

Liskeard Reserves v St Dennis	0-1
Roche v Nanpean Rovers	2-1

Final: Roche 3, St Dennis 2

JOLLY'S CORNWALL COMBINATION

Fixture Secretary: P Berryman (0736 711262)

	P	W	D	L	F	A	PTS
Mullion	34	29	2	3	117	21	60
Penryn Athletic	34	28	4	2	105	21	60
Truro City Res	34	19	6	9	89	56	44
Marazion Blues	34	18	7	9	73	45	43
Perranwell	34	17	9	8	75	50	43
Pendeen Rovers	34	19	5	10	68	50	43
St Agnes	34	17	8	9	77	50	42
Newquay Reserves	34	17	6	11	56	54	40
Porthleven	34	15	4	15	77	74	34
RNAS Culdrose	34	14	5	15	67	64	33
Mousehole	34	10	8	16	31	54	28
Ludgvan	34	8	11	15	50	67	27
Penzance Reserves	34	10	5	19	45	83	25
Helston Athletic	34	8	6	20	44	77	22
Illogan RBL	34	9	3	22	38	72	*20
St Just	34	6	8	20	36	91	20
Falmouth Town Res	34	6	2	26	50	123	14
RAF St Mawgan	34	5	3	26	48	94	13

* - 1 point deducted

COMBINATION CUP 1991-92

Preliminary Round

Falmouth Town Res v Perranwell	0-0,0-4
Penryn Athletic v Pendeen Rovers	6-0

First Round

Illogan RBL v Newquay Res	0-2
Marazion Blues v Mullion	1-3
Penryn Athletic v Helston Athletic	3-1
St Agnes v Perranwell	3-0
St Just v Penzance Reserves	1-0
RAF St Mawgan v Ludgvan	0-1
Truro City Res v Mousehole	1-0
Porthleven Res v RNAS Culdrose	1-3

Quarter Finals:

Newquay Res v RNAS Culdrose	0-3
St Just v Mullion	0-1
Penryn Athletic v Ludgvan	3-0
Truro City Res v St Agnes	1-1,1-3

Semi Finals

Mullion v Penryn Athletic	1-1,1-0	RNAS Culdrose v St Agnes	2-2,0-0,0-4

Final: Mullion 4, St Agnes 1.

HELSTON ATHLETIC
Ground: Kellaway Parc, Clodgy Lane (0326 573742) **Secretary:** S Cooper (0209 842322)
Ground Directions: On A394 Helston bypass, on right coming from Falmouth.
Clubhouse: Yes **Programme:** No **Cover:** Yes; clubhouse overhang **Colours:** Royal Blue
Hons: Cornish Senior Cup 36-37, Champ 64-65 87-88 **Reserves:** Falmouth-Helston Lg.

ILLOGAN R.B.L.
Ground: Oxland Park (0209 216488) **Secretary:** E Mills (0209 214695)
Ground Directions: Turn right for Illogan off Camborne to Redruth road. Ground on right down Richards Lane.
Clubhouse: Yes **Programme:** No **Cover:** Stand **Colours:**
Hons: Champs 70-71 71-72 73-74, Runners-up 69-70 72-73 **Reserves:** W C'wall Mining Lg.

LUDGVAN
Ground: Fairfield (0736 740774) **Secretary:** M Brownfield (0736 740603)
Ground Directions: Turn right off A30 for Ludgvan Leaze (after Crowlas). Ground on right.
Clubhouse: Village Hall **Programme:** Yes **Cover:** Yes **Colours:** Yellow and green
Formed: 1960 **Reserves:** West Penwith League
Hons: League Cup 82-83, Eveley Cup 1983, Penzance & Dist Charity Cup 89-90, West Cornwall Hosp Cup 89-90

MARAZION BLUES
Ground: Trevenner (0736 740774) **Secretary:** B Richards (0736 69327)
Ground Directions: Through Marazion village and turn up Shop Hill opposite Fire Engine Pub.
Clubhouse: Community Centre **Programme:** No **Cover:** Yes **Colours:** All Blue
Floodlights: Installed during 1990-91 **Reserves:** West Penwith Lg.

MOUSEHOLE
Ground: Trungle Park **Secretary:** R Walker (0736 68850)
Ground Directions: In Paul village, 1 mile inland from Mousehole. **Formed:** 1922-23
Clubhouse: Yes **Programme:** Yes **Cover:** Yes **Colours:** Green & white hoops **Nickname:** Seagulls
Hons: Runners-up 85-86, League Cup 75-76, Evely Cup 1976 **Reserves:** West Penwith Lg.

PENDEEN ROVERS
Ground: Borlaise Park **Secretary:** D Trezise (0736 788274)
Ground Directions: B3306 St Ives to St Just road. Ground immediately on left down road to Pendeen Lighthouse.
Clubhouse: Yes **Programme:** Yes **Cover:** No **Colours:** Amber and Black **Reserves:** West Penwith Lg.

PENRYN ATHLETIC
Ground: Kernick (0326 75182) **Secretary:** M Young (0326 74098)
Ground Directions: Turn off A394 at sign for Kernick Industrial estate. Ground on right on road into town.
Clubhouse: Y **Programme:** N **Cover:** Y **Colours:** Red & Black stripes **Reserves:** Falmouth-Helston Lg.
Hons: Champs 80-81 81-82 82-83 84-85 86-87 89-90 (R-up 83-84 88-89), League Cup 87-88 88-89 (R-up 90-91),
Evely Cup 88-89.

PERRANWELL
Ground: Village Playing Fields **Secretary:** R McLean (0326 317662)
Ground Directions: On Falmouth to Truro branch-line, or by road 1 mile off A39 (turn right at Perranaworthal).
Clubhouse: No **Programme:** No **Cover:** Yes **Colours:** Royal Blue
Hons: Champs 76-77, R-up 75-76 **Reserves:** Falmouth-Helston Lg.

R.A.F. ST MAWGAN
Ground: St Eval **Secretary:** K Edmunds (0637 831007)
Ground Directions: Follow signs for St Eval from St Columb Major. Ground in village on the right.
Clubhouse No **Programme:** No **Cover:** No **Nickname:** The Airmen **Colours:** Blue and white quarters
Hons: Supplementary Cup runners-up 88-89.

R.N.A.S. CULDROSE
Ground: Sports Field (0326 574121 ext 7167) **Secretary:** R Glennie (0326 574121 ext 2265)
Ground Directions: On A3083 Helston to Lizard Road, on right just before turning to St Keverne.
Colours: **Reserves:** Falmouth-Helston Lg.

ST AGNES
Ground: Enys Park, West Polberro (0872 553673)   **Secretary:** J Stenning (0872 552657)
Ground Directions: On cliffs to the north of the village.
Clubhouse: Yes   **Programme:** Yes   **Nickname:** Aggie   **Colours:** White/Black   **Reserves:** Falmouth-Helston Lg.

ST JUST
Ground: Lafrowda Park   **Secretary:** P Greenfell (0736 787205)
Ground Dirctions: In village take Cape Cornwall Road. First left, left again and ground at end of terrace.
Clubhouse: Yes   **Cover:** Yes   **Nickname:** The Tinners   **Reserves:** West Penwith Lg.   **Programme:** Yes
Hons: Champs 61-62, Runners-up 62-63 63-64 73-74 74-75 76-77

See also the Jewson South Western League section for details of Falmouth Town, Newquay, Penzance, Porthleven and Truro City who all field their Reserve sides in the Jollys Combination.

YEOVIL & DISTRICT LEAGUE

Premier Division	P	W	D	L	F	A	Pts
Somerton Town	22	19	2	1	88	27	40
Henstridge United	22	17	3	2	83	17	37
Langport Town	22	13	4	5	40	27	30
Wincanton Town	22	11	3	8	55	45	25
Martock	22	11	1	10	59	42	23
Bradford Sports	22	8	7	7	25	32	23
Ilchester Town	22	8	5	9	37	36	21
Milborne Port	22	8	4	10	31	41	18
St Crispin	22	6	5	11	40	45	17
Baltonsborough	22	7	3	12	45	52	17
Templecombe Rvrs	22	4	0	18	25	73	8
Chithorne Domer	22	2	1	19	17	108	5

Division One	P	W	D	L	F	A	Pts
Houndstone	20	13	6	1	61	14	32
Bishops Caundle	20	14	4	2	63	20	32
Long Sutton Res	20	13	3	4	54	21	29
Westland Spts Res	20	10	2	8	52	39	22
Henstridge Utd Res	20	9	4	7	34	44	22
Ash Rovers	20	7	6	7	31	35	20
Sherborne T. Res	20	7	5	8	34	38	19
Westland Assoc.	20	7	3	10	46	49	17
Stoke Sub Hamdon	20	6	3	11	28	44	15
Tintinhull	20	3	1	16	23	72	7
Castle Cary Res	20	1	3	16	27	77	3

Division Two	P	W	D	L	F	A	Pts
Plucknett Sports	26	18	2	6	76	46	38
Milborne Pt Res	26	14	9	3	71	30	37
Normalair	26	14	9	3	74	38	37
Keinton Mandeville	26	15	5	6	62	32	36
Corinthians	26	14	7	5	78	45	35
Trinity	26	15	5	6	56	31	35
Blatonboro. Res	26	13	4	9	51	50	30
St Crispins Res	26	8	9	9	40	51	25
Martock Res	26	7	7	12	38	48	21
Ilchester T. Res	26	4	10	12	39	61	18
Somerton Town Res	26	5	7	14	41	70	17
Street Res	26	5	2	19	42	78	12
Odcombe	26	4	4	18	41	81	12
Stoke Sub H. Res	26	3	5	18	30	80	11

Division Three	P	W	D	L	F	A	Pts
Bruton Town	26	20	6	0	109	32	46
Wincanton T. Res	26	20	2	4	86	39	42
Langport T. Res	26	19	2	5	108	44	40
Yetminster	26	18	3	5	102	42	39
Spartans	26	16	3	7	87	43	35
Barwick & Stoford	26	13	4	9	91	49	30
Ansford Rovers	26	12	2	12	79	61	26
Tintinhull Res	26	10	3	13	42	62	23
K. Mandeville Res	26	7	5	14	52	81	19
Templecombe Res	26	7	3	16	40	87	17
Kingsbury Episcopi	26	7	3	16	64	100	17
Normalair Res	26	5	5	16	43	106	15
Bradford Spts Res	26	4	4	18	47	83	12
Charlton United	26	1	1	24	26	147	3

Division Four	P	W	D	L	F	A	Pts
Long Sutton Colts	26	19	3	4	107	26	41
Camel	26	16	7	3	108	38	39
Westminster	26	17	3	6	78	49	37
Milborne Port 'A'	26	14	5	7	68	53	33
Street Colts	26	13	4	9	78	56	30
Westland Assn Res	26	11	7	8	71	54	29
Pen Mill	26	12	5	9	68	63	29
Charlton Athletic	26	11	6	8	69	60	28
Yeovil Elim	26	9	4	13	72	68	22
Yetminster Res	26	9	3	14	43	89	21
Barwick & S. Res	26	7	3	16	66	110	17
Greyhound	26	7	2	17	42	91	16
Odcombe Res	26	6	0	20	31	78	12
Montacute	26	3	4	19	42	106	10

Name changes
Houndstone are now Heron FC
Plucknett Sports now Masons Arms FC
Yeovil Elim are noe Yeovil Saints

ARKINS & ASHTON
PLYMOUTH & DISTRICT LEAGUE

Premier Division	P	W	D	L	F	A	PTS
Prince Rock	26	22	3	1	91	20	47
Saltash Utd Res	26	20	1	5	87	41	41
Elburton Villa	26	17	4	5	74	39	38
Plymstock United	34	14	7	5	49	27	36
Ivybridge United	26	12	8	6	65	47	32
Plymouth Civil Serv.	26	11	7	8	60	47	29
Tavistock Res	26	9	6	11	72	64	24
Ivybridge Town	26	11	2	13	47	63	24
Millbrook Res	26	10	3	13	50	61	23
Marjon	26	10	1	15	40	52	21
Weston Mill Oak Vil.	26	7	5	14	44	57	19
Torpoint Ath. Res	26	5	7	14	43	57	17
Wessex Rangers	26	3	2	21	27	101	8
Green Waves	26	2	2	22	39	102	6

Div. One (top)	P	W	D	L	F	A	PTS
Falstaff Wdrs	26	21	3	2	78	26	45
Woodland Fort	26	15	7	4	73	42	37
Dynamo Villa	26	15	6	5	63	47	36

BOURNEMOUTH
LEAGUE

Division One	P	W	D	L	F	A	PTS
B'mouth Post Office	24	20	2	2	84	14	42
Westover Motors	24	18	5	1	67	19	41
Hanworthy Eng. Res	24	14	7	3	82	27	35
B'mouth Electric	24	11	5	8	60	46	27
B'mouth Spts Res	24	11	4	9	52	43	26
Ferndown Sports	24	10	3	11	54	52	23
Lansdowne Res	24	8	8	8	57	56	*23
Downton Res	24	8	6	10	50	56	22
New Milton Res	24	9	4	11	38	46	22
Queens Pk Ath.	24	7	4	13	35	58	18
Parley Sports Res	24	7	4	13	32	56	18
Bournemouth 'A'	24	3	2	19	31	95	8
Bashley Stags	24	2	2	20	19	93	6

* - 1 point deducted

Bournemouth 'A' and Bashley Stags relegated. Promoted from Division Two; Stour Vale, Hamworthy Engineering 'A', Redlynch & Woodfalls. Second placed Bournemouth Post Office Reserves not promoted.

PERRY STREET LEAGUE

Premier Division	P	W	D	L	F	A	Pts
Crewkerne	20	15	2	3	57	25	32
Combe St Nicholas	22	10	6	4	45	28	26
Merriott Rovers	20	8	8	4	30	25	24
Misterton	20	11	4	5	38	26	*22
Norton Athletic	20	8	4	8	34	39	20
Lyme Regis	20	7	5	8	31	33	19
Sth Petherton T.	20	6	5	9	38	45	17
Axminster Town	20	6	4	10	25	41	16
Drimpton	20	3	9	8	28	39	15
Ilminster T. Res	20	4	5	11	29	45	13
Forton Rangers	20	4	4	12	24	33	12

* - 4 points deducted

Division One	P	W	D	L	F	A	Pts
Perry Street	22	15	6	1	82	31	36
Crewkerne Res	22	15	5	2	77	28	35
White Horse	22	11	7	4	48	37	29
Thorncombe	22	6	6	5	47	41	26
Chard W.M.C.	22	10	4	8	50	44	24
Shepton Beauchamp	22	9	6	7	37	41	24
Axmouth Town	22	7	4	11	30	42	18
Netherbury	22	6	6	10	36	50	18
Pymore	22	6	4	12	38	45	16
Hinton St George	22	5	3	14	36	61	13
Beaminster Res	22	3	7	12	26	58	13
Millwey Rise	22	3	6	13	29	58	12

Nb. White Horse now Ilminster Spartak

Division Two	P	W	D	L	F	A	Pts
Combe St Nich. Res	20	14	3	3	68	28	31
Merriott Rvrs Res	20	13	3	4	70	27	29
Winsham	20	12	4	4	54	37	28
Farway	20	9	4	7	57	38	22
Lyme Regis Res	20	7	7	6	51	58	21
Axminster T. Res	20	7	6	7	39	42	20
Barrington	20	5	7	8	35	47	17
Sth Petherton Res	20	5	5	10	35	63	15
Halstock	20	4	5	11	33	59	13
Chard United	20	3	6	11	30	50	12
Chard Youth Club	20	4	4	12	29	51	12

Division Three	P	W	D	L	F	A	Pts
Misterton	24	17	5	2	86	27	39
Hawkchurch	24	17	4	3	84	37	38
Crewkerne 'A'	24	14	4	6	74	42	32
Norton Ath. Res	24	12	7	5	63	37	31
Charmouth	24	12	6	6	65	32	30
Drimpton Res	24	11	8	5	70	39	30
Uplyme	24	13	2	9	63	45	28
Pymore Res	24	10	4	10	74	64	24
Netherbury Res	24	9	3	12	33	55	21
Dowlish Wake	24	6	3	15	47	71	15
S. Beauchamp Res	24	5	3	16	37	85	13
Millwey Rise Res	24	3	2	19	22	88	8
Chard WMC Res	24	1	1	22	20	116	3

Division Four	P	W	D	L	F	A	Pts
Powermatic	22	19	1	2	71	25	39
Crewkerne Colts	22	17	3	2	62	19	37
Axminster T. Res	22	14	3	5	54	23	31
Seavington	22	11	1	10	61	46	23
Axmouth T. Res	22	11	1	10	53	49	23
Forton Rgrs Res	22	6	6	10	37	45	18
Farway Res	22	8	2	12	53	67	18
Thorncombe Res	22	7	4	11	28	45	18
Cotley	22	7	3	12	36	55	17
Perry Street Res	22	5	4	13	38	62	14
Barrington Res	22	6	2	14	37	62	14
Hinton St G. Res	22	4	4	14	40	72	12

DORSET LEAGUE

Division One	P	W	D	L	F	A	PTS
Weymouth Taxi Co.	28	20	4	4	72	21	44
Broadmayne	28	19	4	5	92	40	42
Stourpaine	28	13	9	6	58	35	35
Hamworthy Utd Res	28	15	5	8	64	42	35
Moreton	28	12	7	9	58	50	31
Okeford United	28	13	5	10	62	59	31
Blandford U. Res	28	11	6	11	55	72	28
Bere Regis	28	10	7	11	51	57	27
Flight Ref. Res	28	10	6	12	65	68	26
Dorchester YMCA	28	9	7	12	63	60	25
Portland Wdrs	28	8	6	14	54	68	22
Chideock	28	8	5	15	41	72	21
Weston United	28	8	4	16	60	90	20
Puddletown	28	6	6	16	36	65	18
Beaminster	28	5	5	18	39	71	15

Division Two	P	W	D	L	F	A	Pts
Littlemoor Spts	30	26	2	2	103	26	54
Allendale	30	24	2	4	111	35	50
Islanders Boys C.	30	22	2	6	101	37	46
Lychett Red Triangle	30	20	6	4	84	42	46
Child Okeford	30	15	8	7	69	48	38
Poole Labour	30	14	5	11	64	68	33
Mere Town	30	12	5	13	59	61	29
Witchampton	30	12	4	16	75	63	28
Wareham Rgrs Res	30	8	9	13	51	63	25
Shaftesbury Res	30	8	9	13	34	52	25
Stalbridge	30	7	8	15	38	60	22
Sturminster Marshall	30	6	9	15	43	58	21
Gillingham T. Res	30	8	4	18	40	81	20
Albany Rovers	30	6	6	18	44	92	18
Winterborne Kingston	30	6	3	21	37	90	15
Stickland United	30	3	4	23	26	103	10

MOREYS ISLE OF WIGHT LEAGUE

Division One	P	W	D	L	F	A	PTS
Ryde Sports Res	22	16	4	2	61	24	52
Oakfield	22	14	6	2	48	19	48
East Cowes VA Res	22	11	4	7	49	28	37
Wootton B'dge Spts	22	11	4	7	45	38	37
Binstead COB	22	10	5	7	38	35	35
Shanklin	22	8	5	9	35	36	29
Sandown	22	8	4	10	47	43	28
Ventnor	22	9	1	12	39	41	28
Seaview	22	7	4	11	30	49	25
Brading Town Res	22	6	3	13	30	48	21
Bembridge	22	5	3	14	40	63	18
St Helens Blue S.	22	4	3	15	29	87	15

Division Two	P	W	D	L	F	A	Pts
Carlsbrooke Utd	22	11	8	3	58	26	41
Brighstone	22	12	4	6	35	26	40
Yarmouth Town	22	10	6	6	40	46	36
Cowes Sports Res	22	10	5	7	57	35	35
Northwood St Johns	22	9	7	6	43	32	34
Osborne Coburg	22	10	4	8	34	35	34
West Wight Res	22	8	5	9	33	33	29
Medina	22	7	6	9	35	42	27
Newport IOW 'A'	22	5	11	6	38	31	26
Niton	22	5	7	10	30	45	22
Westlans A'space	22	4	7	11	28	42	19
Wroxall	22	5	2	15	31	68	17

JEWSON WESSEX LEAGUE

Hon. Secretary: Norman Cook, 5 Holmsley Court,
Bartley Meadows, Totton, Southampton SO4 2JF (0703 865464).

WIMBORNE'S FANTASTIC SEASON

With Havant Town being promoted to the Southern League and no newcomers joining, the number of clubs in the First Division in the sixth season of the League was reduced to nineteen. The First Division championship was not decided until the final Saturday of the season when Wimborne Town won 3-2 at Dorset neighbours Swanage Town & Herston. It was the first time the title had gone outside Hampshire.

Lymington made a poor start to the season and were thirteenth at the beginning of November, but a managerial change brought a dramatic revival that saw them climb to the top of the table by February and stay in the top three for the remainder of the campaign. They lost their final match, at Bournemouth, to give Wimborne the title, and had to be content with second place. Thatcham also enjoyed an excellent second half to the season and although they led the table for a brief period at the end of March they finished a creditable third.

Romsey started the campaign well and looked capable of repeating their championship success of 1990. They led for two months just prior to Xmas, but several poor results in the New Year put paid to their bid. They did however take some consolation from having, in Mick Brockway, the division's leading scorer. Swanage had another consistent season and were never out of the top six, finishing fifth. Bournemouth were the early pace-makers and were still in contention in January, but a disappointing spell in February and March ended their challenge, and only a late flurry enabled them to finish sixth. Ryde boasted a fine home record, but fared not so well on the mainland and finished seventh, whilst Bemerton enjoyed a much improved campaign in eigth place and Aerostructures, whose home form was disappointing, did well enough to finish in their best position since joining the League.

Eastleigh made a promising start, but faded badly and could only finish in mid-table. Fleet ended in exactly the same place as last season and failed to match the progress made off the field, which was hampered when fire completely destroyed their stand. Brockenhurst did not fare so well this term, but Christchurch, and Sholing showed minor improvement. East Cowes maintained last season's position, and Totton's inexperienced squad should have learned a lot for next season. B.A.T. found it increasingly difficult to find consistency at this level, and their cause was not helped when Chairman Bryan Bailey died suddenly in February. He will be a great loss to both his club and the League. Horndean and Portsmouth R.N. struggled at the bottom, and a victory for the former when the two clashed on the final Saturday left the Navy propping up the table.

Twenty one teams entered the newly formed Combination Division but this reduced when Andover Reserves dropped out before the season started. Newport Reserves were deservedly the first champions leading for almost the entire season, apart from a brief spell when B.A.T. Reserves took over. Wimborne Reserves finished very strongly to push B.A.T. into third place. Waterlooville Reserves were always among the leaders and finished fourth, whilst Lymington Reserves also finished well to climb to fifth. Havant Reserves were among the early leaders, but tailed away in the New Year to sixth. Sholing Reserves were lumped with the wooden spoon, and Steve Hudspith of Wimborne Reserves was top scorer with 23 goals.

Thatcham Town retained the Jewson Wessex League Cup when they beat Eastleigh by a single extra-time goal at Havant in the Final. The first Wessex Combination Cup Final was staged at Brockenhurst where B.A.T. Reserves came from behind to beat Wimborne Reserves 3-2 in an entertaining match. Meanwhile, Christchurch became first winners of the 'Best Programme' award....*(continued overleaf).*

Wimborne Town FC, Jewson Wessex League Champions 1991-92. Back Row: Andy Taplin, Steve Richardson, Phil Langdown, Nicky Bridle, Robbie Beacham, Kevin Leonard. Front: Trevor Ames, Jamie Sturgess, Simon Lynn, Tommy Killick, Bradley Homer. Photo - James Wright.

Highlight of the season was undoubtedly the marvellous triumph of Wimborne Town winning the F.A. Vase at Wembley. It was not only the victory, but also the manner in which they won against very good opponents (holders Guiseley), that impressed. Wimborne are the first Wessex club to win an F.A. Competition, which, following the promotion of Bashley, Newport and Havant in recent seasons, further underlines the high standard of the League.

The League representative team played only one fixture owing to opponents pulling out of the other two matches at the last moment. The only fixture took place at Portfield FC against the Unijet Sussex County League, who recorded a 3-0 victory.

Sadly, Gosport Borough have been relegated from the Southern League, but the Jewson Wessex League are pleased to welcome them for the 1992-93 season. Applications to join the League were received from Hampshire League clubs Blackfield & Langley and Whitchurch United, with that of the latter being successful. Fleet Town Reserves are leaving the Combination and seeking a place in the Suburban League. They are replaced by Whitchurch United Reserves.

Norman Cook, League Secretary/Treasurer.

FINAL LEAGUE TABLES 1992-93

FIRST DIVISION	P	W	D	L	F	A	PTS
Wimborne Town	36	25	5	6	82	37	80
AFC Lymington	36	23	5	8	73	39	74
Thatcham Town	36	22	4	10	85	45	70
Romsey Town	36	21	6	9	72	42	69
Swanage T & H	36	20	7	9	78	38	67
Bournemouth	36	20	6	10	73	48	66
Ryde Sports	36	18	8	10	61	51	62
Bemerton Hth H.	36	17	10	9	51	38	61
Aerostructures S&S	36	18	5	13	59	40	59
Eastleigh	36	18	4	14	61	53	58
Fleet Town	36	13	10	13	59	55	49
Brockenhurst	36	12	9	15	47	52	45
Christchurch	36	9	11	16	39	54	38
East Cowes Vics	36	9	9	18	36	72	36
Sholing Sports	36	9	7	20	43	81	34
B.A.T.	36	9	4	23	41	57	31
AFC Totton	36	7	8	21	43	71	29
Horndean	36	5	3	27	33	109	18
Portsmouth R.N.	36	4	5	27	30	84	17

COMBINATION	P	W	D	L	F	A	PTS
Newport IOW Res	38	25	7	6	84	36	82
Wimborne T. Res.	38	24	6	8	106	46	78
B.A.T. Res.	38	23	6	9	92	54	75
Waterlooville Res.	38	22	9	7	72	46	75
AFC Lymington Res.	38	22	7	9	93	52	73
Havant Town Res.	38	19	13	6	95	53	70
Romsey Town Res.	38	18	6	14	74	65	60
Gosport B. Res.	38	15	10	13	80	61	39
Aerostructures Res.	38	16	8	14	86	59	55
Bournemouth Res.	38	15	7	16	77	91	52
Bashley Res.	38	15	6	17	76	79	51
Petersfield Utd Res.	37	15	6	16	69	83	51
Eastleigh Res.	38	13	6	19	69	66	45
Brockenhurst Res.	38	11	7	17	58	112	40
Fleet Town Res.	38	11	6	21	65	88	39
Horndean Res.	38	10	7	21	65	100	37
AFC Totton Res.	38	10	4	24	43	95	34
Christchurch Res.	37	5	14	18	47	67	32
Bemerton Hth Res.	38	7	10	21	55	92	31
Sholing Spts Res.	38	8	5	25	47	99	29

WESSEX LEAGUE FIRST DIVISION RECORD (SINCE FORMATION)

	86/7	87/8	88/9	89/0	90/1	91/2
Aerostructures S & S	-	13	10	12	16	9
A.F.C. Lymington	10	19	5	5	9	2
A.F.C. Totton	3	8	14	6	14	17
Bashley	1	1	1	-	-	-
B.A.T.	-	-	-	3	8	16
Bemerton Heath Harlequins	-	-	-	8	18	8
Bournemouth Poppies	15	10	12	10	3	6
Brockenhurst	17	18	16	17	7	12
Christchurst	-	5	13	15	15	13
East Cowes Victoria Athletic	-	9	8	13	13	14
Eastleigh	8	12	9	14	12	10
Fleet Town	-	-	-	18	10	11
Havant Town	5	2	2	11	1	-
Horndean	14	14	11	16	20	18
Newport Isle of Wight	4	4	3	2	-	-
Portals Athletic	12	-	-	-	-	-
Portsmouth Royal Navy	13	16	17	19	17	19
Romsey Town	16	3	7	1	4	4
Road Sea Southampton	2	-	-	-	-	-
Ryde Sports	-	-	-	-	-	7
Sholing Sports	9	7	15	9	19	15
Steyning Town	11	17	-	-	-	-
Swanage Town & Herston	-	-	-	-	2	5
Thatcham Town	6	11	4	7	6	3
Wellworthy Athletic	7	15	-	-	-	-
Wimborne Town	-	6	6	4	5	1

FIRST DIVISION RESULT CHART 1991/92

HOME TEAM	1	2	3	4	5	6	7	8	9	10	11	12	13	14	15	16	17	18	19
1. AFC Lymington	*	2-1	2-0	1-0	4-0	4-0	1-0	0-2	6-2	5-1	4-0	2-0	3-1	1-0	2-2	2-1	0-2	4-2	0-2
2. AFC Totton	1-1	*	0-4	1-0	1-2	1-1	3-1	1-1	1-1	1-2	1-3	2-0	2-1	1-5	1-2	2-0	3-4	1-2	0-3
3. Aerostructures S & S	0-1	1-0	*	2-0	1-1	1-3	0-2	3-1	3-1	0-1	1-2	6-0	1-0	1-2	3-2	1-3	2-2	0-3	2-1
4. B.A.T.	0-2	2-0	0-1	*	0-1	3-1	1-0	1-1	1-2	2-1	7-0	0-1	0-1	1-3	4-0	0-2	0-3	2-6	
5. Bemerton Heath	1-0	3-0	0-5	3-0	*	0-1	0-1	3-2	1-1	1-1	1-1	2-2	4-0	1-0	0-0	3-1	3-1	1-0	0-2
6. Bournemouth	2-0	5-0	0-0	2-1	2-1	*	0-2	6-1	4-0	1-0	0-2	3-0	5-0	4-4	2-2	4-2	2-1	0-1	3-2
7. Brockenhurst	3-0	1-1	2-3	1-2	0-0	2-3	*	1-1	1-1	1-0	1-1	3-1	2-2	0-0	2-3	2-1	0-6	1-2	0-2
8. Christchurch	1-2	3-2	2-3	0-0	1-1	2-2	0-1	*	2-0	0-1	3-0	1-0	2-0	0-0	1-0	0-0	0-2	0-2	1-5
9. East Cowes VA	1-0	2-2	1-1	1-1	0-3	2-3	1-2	1-0	*	0-2	3-1	2-0	1-0	1-1	0-1	2-1	0-2	0-4	0-1
10. Eastleigh	1-1	1-0	0-2	3-1	1-2	2-0	1-0	4-3	3-2	*	4-1	1-2	2-1	2-2	1-2	8-1	0-0	1-3	1-2
11. Fleet Town	3-3	1-2	1-2	4-1	1-1	0-0	1-2	0-2	1-1	1-0	*	4-0	2-1	0-1	4-0	3-1	0-3	1-1	1-1
12. Horndean	1-4	4-2	1-4	1-5	0-2	0-3	1-1	0-1	0-1	0-6	0-7	*	2-1	3-4	0-2	4-1	1-5	1-3	1-6
13. Portsmouth RN	2-3	2-5	0-3	0-3	2-3	0-1	2-3	0-0	1-0	0-1	1-2	1-3	*	3-0	1-2	0-0	1-0	2-4	0-3
14. Romsey Town	1-4	1-0	0-1	2-1	0-1	3-1	3-2	3-0	7-0	1-0	3-1	5-1	3-0	*	5-1	1-2	3-2	2-4	1-0
15. Ryde Sports	2-1	3-3	1-0	3-0	2-3	3-2	2-1	2-2	1-2	4-0	3-3	2-1	1-1	0-0	*	1-0	4-1	1-0	1-3
16. Sholing Sports	2-2	1-0	1-2	1-0	2-1	1-2	4-2	1-0	2-2	1-4	1-3	2-1	1-1	0-3	1-2	*	0-7	4-3	1-1
17. Swanage T & H	0-1	0-0	1-0	0-0	1-0	2-1	2-2	3-0	4-2	2-1	3-0	1-1	7-0	1-2	2-1	3-0	*	2-0	2-3
18. Thatcham Town	1-3	3-0	0-0	3-0	0-2	2-1	0-2	3-3	7-0	1-3	2-2	4-0	5-1	2-1	1-0	4-2	3-0	*	6-2
19. Wimborne Town	1-2	3-2	2-1	0-1	1-3	1-0	1-0	2-0	8-0	1-0	3-1	5-1	1-0	1-0	1-1	2-2	2-1	*	

FORSHORE WESSEX LEAGUE COMBINATION RESULT CHART 1991-92

HOME TEAM	1	2	3	4	5	6	7	8	9	10	11	12	13	14	15	16	17	18	19	20	21
1. AFC Tot. Rs	*	0-3	1-6	*	2-4	0-7	1-0	1-0	0-2	1-0	1-3	3-3	1-2	2-2	3-0	0-2	1-2	0-3	3-1	2-4	2-3
2. AFC Lym. Rs	6-0	*	2-1	*	0-3	4-1	1-1	2-2	6-0	3-1	2-0	4-0	3-0	3-0	0-2	1-3	3-2	2-0	3-5	5-0	5-1
3. Aerostr. Rs	3-0	2-2	*	*	2-3	3-3	1-1	3-2	5-0	2-2	4-1	2-0	1-3	4-3	1-3	1-2	1-2	0-3	0-0	0-1	1-0
4. Andover Rs	*	*	*	*	*	*	*	*	*	*	*	*	*	7-1	*	*	*	*	*	*	*
5. B.A.T. Rs	4-1	0-5	1-2	*	*	1-3	4-0	7-0	7-1	1-1	2-1	2-1	1-1	1-2	3-2	2-2	2-2	2-0	2-1	1-2	1-0
6. Bashley Rs	0-1	0-1	1-3	*	0-5	*	2-1	2-2	1-0	2-0	5-2	2-3	1-0	2-2	7-1	0-2	1-3	7-1	2-1	2-4	2-2
7. Bemerton Rs	1-2	2-0	2-0	*	1-3	1-1	*	6-1	3-3	2-2	1-1	4-0	1-2	3-3	0-2	1-4	1-2	1-4	3-1	0-1	1-3
8. B'mouth Rs	2-0	7-0	0-2	*	2-3	2-1	1-1	*	3-0	0-5	0-3	3-2	3-4	2-2	3-2	2-1	4-1	5-1	5-1	3-2	0-2
9. B'hurst Rs	2-1	1-3	1-7	*	4-2	1-3	7-3	6-3	*	1-0	1-0	4-2	3-3	0-1	1-7	0-0	4-3	2-2	1-0	2-2	0-3
10. C'church Rs	0-3	1-1	0-2	*	2-4	1-3	1-1	0-1	0-0	*	2-1	2-2	4-0	1-1	2-2	2-2	V	0-1	2-0	2-2	3-5
11. Eastleigh Rs	1-1	0-1	1-2	*	2-3	1-2	4-2	1-1	2-0	2-0	*	0-3	6-0	2-4	6-0	1-1	3-1	1-1	6-0	1-4	3-3
12. Fleet Rs	5-0	0-5	5-0	*	0-2	2-1	2-3	5-2	2-3	2-1	1-2	*	2-0	1-4	1-1	1-2	1-1	4-3	3-2	0-0	1-4
13. Gosport Rs	2-0	4-1	1-0	*	2-1	10-0	5-1	1-1	2-2	5-0	3-1	2-2	*	2-4	1-1	0-2	0-1	1-1	8-2	0-1	0-1
14. Havant Rs	2-2	1-1	3-0	*	0-4	3-2	5-0	10-0	5-1	2-0	4-1	1-0	1-1	*	6-0	1-3	2-2	5-0	0-0	0-2	2-2
15. Hordean Rs	2-0	3-3	2-8	*	2-3	2-1	0-1	3-4	3-1	0-5	1-3	1-3	0-7	2-2	*	1-2	2-3	3-2	1-1	2-2	1-3
16. Newport Rs	2-1	2-1	1-1	*	3-1	0-1	5-0	2-1	9-0	4-1	2-1	3-0	0-0	1-3	2-1	*	2-1	0-0	3-1	2-1	0-1
17. Peterfield Rs	3-1	1-4	3-2	*	1-1	1-1	3-1	1-3	2-1	2-2	2-3	2-0	3-1	1-4	2-4	1-4	*	3-2	4-3	0-2	1-4
18. Romsey Rs	2-3	3-4	1-1	*	2-1	5-1	2-1	1-1	4-1	3-0	0-2	4-0	3-1	3-0	3-1	0-3	0-4	*	3-2	1-0	2-0
19. Sholing Rs	0-1	0-2	0-0	*	0-2	2-5	3-1	0-4	4-2	3-3	1-0	3-2	3-2	1-3	0-4	3-2	2-1	0-6	*	1-2	0-2
20. W'ville Rs	7-2	1-1	1-2	*	1-1	2-0	3-3	4-3	1-0	0-0	2-1	3-2	2-3	0-1	2-1	1-0	1-2	2-1	0-6	*	1-1
21. Wimborne Rs	4-0	2-0	2-1	*	1-2	4-1	7-0	3-4	8-0	1-0	3-0	7-2	1-1	1-1	3-0	2-4	9-1	4-2	4-0	0-1	*

WESSEX LEAGUE CUP 1991-92

Preliminary Round

Bournemouth v BAT	0-0,1-2
East Cowes Victoria Athletic v Eastleigh	0-1,0-4
Romsey Town v Ryde Sports	5-1,3-1

First Round

AFC Lymington v Thatcham Town	3-2,1-3
BAT v Swanage Town & Herston	0-1,2-1*
Brockenhurst v Sholing Sports	1-0,0-1+
Fleet Town v Portsmouth Royal Navy	6-0,4-1
Horndean v Aerostructures S & S	0-2,0-3
Romsey Town v Eastleigh	1-1,1-2
Wimborne v AFC Totton	4-1,3-0
Bemerton Hth Harlequins v Christchurch	5-1,0-2

Second Round

Bemerton Heath Harlequins v BAT	0-1,1-0x
Eastleigh v Fleet Town	7-1,0-1
Aerostructures v Wimborne Town	3-2,2-0
Thatcham Town v Brockenhurst	3-0,3-0

Semi Finals

Thatcham Town v Bemerton Hth H.	0-0,4-1
Eastleigh v Aerostructures S & S	1-3,4-0

Final (at Havant Town FC)

Thatcham Town v Eastleigh	1-0(aet)

* - BAT won on away goals rule
+ - Brockenhurst won 5-3 on penalties
x - Bemerton won 3-2 on penalties

WESSEX COMBINATION CUP 1991-92

Preliminary Round

Wimborne Town Res v Bashley Res	3-1
Brockenhurst Res v Bournemouth Res	2-6
Newport IOW Res v Fleet Town Res	4-3
Romsey Res v Christchurch Res	1-2

First Round

Wimborne Town Res v AFC Totton Res	5-1
Gosport Borough Res v Aerostructures Res	2-1
Horndean Res v BAT Res	5-5,0-1
Sholing Sports Res v Eastleigh Res	1-3*
AFC Lymington Res v Waterlooville Res	0-4
Bemerton Hth H. Res v Newport IW Res	1-1*
Havant Town Res v Christchurch Res	3-2

Second Round

Gosport Borough Res v Newport IW Res	4-5
Havant Town Res v Sholing Spts Res	3-1(aet)
Waterlooville Res v B.A.T. Res	0-1
Wimborne Town Res v Bournemouth Res	5-2

Semi Finals

B.A.T. Res v Newport Isle of Wight Res	2-0
Havant Town Res v Wimborne Town Res	1-2

Final (at Brockenhurst FC)

B.A.T. Res v Wimborne Town Res	3-2

* - E'leigh, B'ton expelled (ineligible players)

AEROSTRUCTURES SPORTS & SOCIAL CLUB

Chairman: S. Charles   **Manager:** Paul Whitfield/Sean Mallon   **Gen. Mgr:** Nigel Kent
Secretary: James Clay, 'Tequila', Bridge Rd, Bursledon, Southampton SO3 8AH (0703 403698).
Ground: Folland Park, Kings Avenue, Hamble (0703 452173).
Directions: M27 junction 8, then B3397 to Hamble. One and a half miles from Hamble (BR); turn right out of station, proceed for one mile then turn right into Queens Avenue. Ground 50 yards on right.
Midweek Matches: Tues (1st team), Wed (Res)   **Previous Name:** Folland Sports (pre-1990).
Colours: White/white/red   **Change colours:** Maroon/black/white.   **Floodlights:** Yes
Best FA Vase season: Extra-Preliminary Round 90-91 91-92
Clubhouse: 300 capacity social club. Tennis, darts, hockey.
Honours: Hants Lg Div 3 80-81 (Div 4 79-80), Hants Intermediate Cup 79-90, Southampton Snr Cup(4).

B.A.T.

Chairman: Mr D Batt   **Sec:** D Saich, 32 Salcombe Cresc., Totton, Southampton SO4 3FP (0703 860797).
Ground: B.A.T. Sports Ground, Ringwood Road, Totton (0703 862143).
Directions: Into centre of Totton, proceed up Ringwood Rd past small r'bout, 2nd left into Southern Gardens. Half mile from Totton (BR), bus X2 (Southampton-Bournemouth).
Seats: 12-15   **Cover:** 50   **Capacity:** 3,000   **Floodlights:** Yes   **Founded:** 1925
Midweek Matches: Tue (Wed for reserves)
Colours: Blue & white/blue/blue   **Change colours:** All red.
Programme: 8-10 pages, 30p   **Best FA Vase year:** Extra-Pr. Rd 91-92
Clubhouse: Normal licensing hrs, all day for members' sports facilities. Darts, pool, juke box. Hot & cold snacks.

BEMERTON HEATH HARLEQUINS

Chairman: R Rogers   **Manager:** S Slade   **President:** P A Say
Secretary: D J Heather, 31 Hollows Close, Salisbury, Wilts SP2 8JU (0722 32600).
Ground: Western Way, Bemerton Heath, Salisbury, Wilts (0722 331925).
Directions: From central Salisbury take A30 (Wilton Rd), turn right into Roman Rd just before railway bridge, 1st left into Pembroke Rd and contine into Western Way. Ground at end. 30 mins walk from Salisbury (BR).
Seats: 200   **Cover:** Yes   **Capacity:**   **Floodlights:** Yes   **Founded:** May 1989
Previous Names: Bemerton Athletic, Moon FC & Bemerton Boys; all merged in 1989.
Previous Leagues: B'ton Ath.: Salis. & Wilts Comb., Moon: Salis. & Andover Sunday, B'ton Boys: Mid Wilts.
Midweek Matches: Tues (Wed for reserves)
Colours: Black & white diamonds/black/black   **Change colours:** Amber/white/white.
Programme: 32 pages, 30p   **Hons:** Wilts Lg(3) as Bemerton Athletic   **Clubhouse:** Yes

BOURNEMOUTH

Chairman: B Roche   **Manager:** Peter Moore   **President:** D Nippard
Secretary: A E Langworthy, 'Nesika Illahee', Castle View Drive, Wareham Rd, Lychett Matravers, Poole BH16 6DX (0202 625565).**Press Officer:** R Murphy, Flat 10 Richmond Ct, 122 Richmond Rd, Bournemouth BH8 8TH.
Ground: Victoria Park, Winton, Bournemouth, Dorset (0202 515123).
Directions: Any bus to Wimborne Road, Winton. 2 miles from Bournemouth Central (BR).
Seats: 250   **Cover:** 250   **Capacity:** 3,000   **Floodlights:** Yes   **Founded:** 1875.
Colours: Red & white/white/red   **Change colours:** All yellow   **Nickname:** Poppies.
Prog: 32 pages, 30p   **Editor:** Ray Murphy, as above (mail order service available)
Record Gate: Unknown   **Previous League:** Hants.   **Midweek Matches:** Tuesday
Previous Names: Bournemouth Rovers 1875-88/ Bournemouth Dene Park 1888-90.
Previous Ground: Dene Park 1888-90   **Local Newspaper:** Evening Echo.
Clubhouse: Open daily 11.30 -2.30 & 7-11pm.
Hons: Hants Lg 13-13 21-22, B'mouth Snr Cup 66-67 89-90, Texaco F'lit Cup R-up 91-92, Hant I'mediate Cup 49-50 69-70, Hants Yth Cup 54-55 57-58 67-68.

BROCKENHURST

Chairman: Mr B Mellor
Secretary: Mr D Chandler, 300 Salisbury Road, Totton, Southampton SO4 3LZ (0703 862957)
Ground: Grigg Lane, Brockenhurst, Hants (0590 23544).   **Newsline:** 0898 446834.
Directions: 400 yds from Brockenhurst station, just off main shopping area.
Seats: 200   **Cover:** 300   **Capacity:** 2,000   **Floodlights:** Yes   **Founded:** 1898
Midweek Matches: Tues (Wed reserves)   **Clubhouse:** Every evening plus Tues, Sat & Sun lunchtimes.
Colours: Blue & white stripes/white/blue   **Change colours:** All red.
Programme: 12 pages, 20p   **Programme Editor:** C Fisher
Prev. League: Hants 24-26 47-86   **Best FA Amateur Cup season:** 2nd Rd 73-74.
Hons: Hants I'mediate Cup 61-62, B'mouth Snr Cup 60-61, Hants Lg 75-76 (R-up 73-74 79-80, Div 2 70-71 (R-up 60-61), Div 3 59-60).

CHRISTCHURCH

Chairman: Gerry Page   **President:** D W W Hillyer   **Manager:** Roy Gater.
Commercial Mgr: P Gardner   **Asst Mgr:** Al Bryant   **Physio:** V Fulcher.
Secretary: Mrs D Page, 89 Parkway Drive, Bournemouth BH8 9JS (0202 304996).
Ground: Christchurch Sporting Club, Hurn Bridge, Avon Causeway, Christchurch (0202 473792).
Directions: From Ringwood spur road follow signs to Hurn Airport on left. Before Airport use mini roundabout & take exit signed to Sopley and ground is immediately on the right. 3 miles from Christchurch (BR).
Seats: 50   **Cover:** 50   **Capacity:** 2,000   **Floodlights:** Yes   **Founded:** 1885
Nickname: Priory   **Midweek Matches:** Thurs (Tues Reserves)
Colours: All royal blue (white trim)   **Change colours:** All green
Programme: 32 pages, 40p   **Programme Editor:** John Whiting/Pete Gardner.
Clubhouse: Normal licensing hours.   **Previous Ground:** Barrack Rd Recreation Ground (until 1984).
Honours: Hants Jnr Cup 1892-93 1911-12 20-21, Hants Int. Cup 86-87, Pickford Cup 1991, Hants Lg Div 2 37-38 47-48 85-86 (Div 3 56-57), B'mouth Snr Cup(5) 56-57 59-60 67-70.

Bournemouth FC: Back Row (L/R): Tommy Hefferman, Kiron Wall, Neil Miles, Tony Oliver, Andrew Cuddy, Shaun Munday, Darren Elmes, Steve Sharkey (Coach). Front: Richard Hill, Tony Gibney, Ossie Onuorah, Darren Mooney, Peter Moore (Manager), David Jenman, Danny Saxby, Chike Onuorah, Andy Elmes. Photo - Geoff Priest.

Fleet Town, pictured before their home match against Wimborne Town on April 4th. Photo - Eric Marsh.

Horndean, pictured before their 1-6 home thrashing at the hands of Wimborne Town on 19th October 1991. Photo - James Wright.

EAST COWES VICTORIA ATHLETIC

Chairman: Mr M Diaz   **Manager:** Gerry O'Rourke.
Secretary: Mr J H Reed, 6 Jennifer Way, East Cowes, I.O.W. (0983 293967).
Ground: Beatrice Avenue Ground, East Cowes, I.O.W. (0938 297165). *NB - As essential repairs are needed to the pitch East Cowes will commence the 1992-93 season playing home matches at Ryde Sports FC.*
Directions: From the ferry: 1 mile from town centre on lower main road to Newport or Ryde, near Whippingham Church adjacent to Osborne Middle School.
Seats: 250   **Cover:** 400   **Capacity:** 3,000   **Floodlights:** Yes   **Founded:** 1888.
Midweek Matches: Wednesday   **Previous Grounds:** Norris Castle/Old Road Ground.
Colours: Red & white stripes/black/white   **Change colours:** Yellow/blue/yellow
Programme: 12 pages,20p   **Programme Editor:** Andrew James
Record Gate: 200 v Poole Town, 1954   **Previous Name:** Vics merged with Athletic in 1954.
Honours: Hants Lg Div 1(2).   **Clubhouse:** Open every evening & Sat. after match.

EASTLEIGH

Chairman: Mr A G Froud   **Manager:** Don Gowans.
Secretary: Derik Brooks, 50 Forest Hills Drive, Townhill Park SO2 3HY (0703 557147).
Ground: 'Ten Acres', Stoneham Lane, North Stoneham, Eastleigh SO5 3HT (0703 613361).
Directions: M27 to Jct 5, to r'bout - exit marked Stoneham Lane, ground on left but carry on to r'bout and come back down Stoneham Lane, turning right opposite Concord Club. Ground 400 yds on left. Three quarters of a mile from Southampton Parkway (BR). Bus 48 (Southampton-Winchester) to Stoneham Church stop.
Seats: 150   **Cover:** 210   **Capacity:** 4,300   **Floodlights:** Yes   **Founded:** 1946.
Midweek Matches: Tues (Wed Reserves)   **Previous Leagues:** Southampton 46-59/Hants 50-86.
Colours: All royal blue   **Change colours:** All white.
Programme: 32 pages, 30p   **Programme Editors:** John Pothecary
Record Gate: 2,500 v Southampton, floodlight opener 30/9/75.
Previous Names: Swaythling Ath. 46-73/ Swaythling 73-80   **Newsline:** 0898 664351.
Previous Grounds: Southampton Common 1946/ Walnut Avenue, Swaythling 46-75.
Clubhouse: Every evening plus Sat & Sun lunchtimes. 2 lounges with 2 bars, catering, skittle alley.
Honours: Wessex Lg Cup R-up 91-92, Hants Lg Div 2 69-70 (R-up 54-55 60-61 62-63 64-65(Res), Div 3 West 50-51 53-54 70-71(Res), Comb Div 86-87(Res)), Hants Midweek F'lit Cup 78-79, Soton Snr Lg West 49-50 (R-up 51-52(Res), Div 1 56-57(Res) 57-58(Res)), Russell Cotes Cup R-up 76-77 80-81 89-90, Hants Int. Cup 49-50, 56-57(Res) 74-75(Res)(R-up 73-74(Res)), Soton Snr Cup (all Res) 74-75 78-79 87-88 (R-up 55-56 57-58 58-59 60-61 66-67 71-72 80-81 87-88), Soton Jnr Lg Div 2 (Res) 47-48, Reg Mathieson Tphy (Res) 74-75 78-79 87-88.

FLEET TOWN

Chairman: A Cherry
Secretary: Mr S Lunt, 'Alcudia', 156 Kings Road, Fleet, Hants GU13 9DT (0252 615303).
Ground: Calthorpe Park, Crookham Road, Fleet, Hants (0252 623804).
Directions: From Fleet town centre at crossroads, Crookham 200 yds roght turn.
Seats: 100   **Cover:** Yes   **Capacity:**   **Floodlights:** Yes   **Founded:** 1896.
Midweek Matches: Tuesday
Colours: Navy & sky stripes/navy/navy   **Change colours:** White & red/red/white & red.
Programme: **Programme Editor:**   **Clubhouse:** Yes
Previous Leagues: Hants/ Athenian/ Combined Counties.   **Honours:**

GOSPORT BOROUGH

Chairman: I T Hay   **President:** W J Adams.
Secretary: B V Cosgrave, 2 Cavanna Close, Gosport PO13 0PE (0329 285087).
Manager: Roger Sherwood   **Asst Manager:** Paul Smith   **Coach:** Alan Williams
Press Officer: Glen Perry (0705 502070)   **Physio:** George Bramble.
Ground: Privett Park, Privett Road, Gosport, Hants (0705 583986).
Directions: M27 junct 11, then A32 Fareham to Gosport. At Brockhurst r-about (after about 3 miles) right into Military Road (signposted Alverstoke, Stokes Bay), left into Privett Road at next r-about, ground 300 yds on left. 2 miles from Portsmouth Harbour (BR).
Capacity: 5,000 (500 Covered)   **Seats:** 500   **Floodlights:** Y   **Shop:** Y   **Metal Badges:** Y
Programme: 24 pages, 50p
Colours: Yellow/blue/blue   **Change colours:** Blue/white/red.   **Sponsors:** TBA.
Midweek matchday: Wed (Mon Res.)   **Previous Leagues:** Portsmouth 44-45/ Hants 45-78.
Previous Name: Gosport Borough Athletic   **Record Gate:** 4,770 v Pegasus, FA Amtr Cup 1951.
Best F.A. Cup season: 4th Qualifying Rd 80-81 (lost to Windsor & Eton).
Record Fees - Paid: £3,000   **Received:** £10,000 for Gareth Williams (A Villa).
Players progressing to Football League: Peter Harris (P'smouth, N'castle & Scotland), B Sherwood, D Dimmer, S Berry, Ron Blackman (Reading 1947), Richard Pearson (P'smouth 1949), Albert Mundy & Mike Barnard (P'smouth 1951), Peter Smith (G'ham 1954), Alan Grant (Brighton 1956), Brian Gibbs (B'mouth 1957), Gary Juryeff (P'smouth), Robert Carroll (Brentford 1986), Gareth Williams (A Villa 1988).
Clubhouse: (0705 525460). Open evenings and all day Saturday. Darts,pool, hot and cold snacks on matchdays.
Steward: A J Brickwood.
Club Record Scorer: Richie Coulbert 192   **Club Record Apps:** Tony Mahoney 764.
91-92 Captain: Dave Tauwer   **91-92 P.o.Y.:** Nicky Goater   **91-92 Top scorer:** Nick Goater
Local Newspapers: Portsmouth Evening News, Southampton Evening Echo.
Local Radio Stations:
Honours: FA Trophy 1st Rd 88-89, FA Amateur Cup 3rd Rd 47-48 66-67, FA Vase 6th Rd replay 77-78, Southern Lg Div 1 South R-up 84-85, Hants Lg 45-46 76-77 77-78 (Div 3 (Reserves) 70-71 75-76), Portsmouth Lg R-up 44-45, Hants Senior Cup 87-88, Hants Intermediate Cup 70-71, Portsmouth Senior Cup 61-62 69-70 70-71, South West Counties Pratten Challenge Cup 77-78.

HORNDEAN

Chairman: Mr J Knight **President:** Ron Coldrick
Vice Chairman: John Knight **Treasurer:** Rosmarie Crouch.
Secretary: Mrs G Berry, 74 Five Heads Road, Horndean PO8 9NZ (0705 591698).
Ground: Five Heads Park, Five Heads Road, Horndean (0705 591363).
Directions: 8 miles north of Portsmouth, just off A3. Five Heads Road is a turning off main road. 2 miles from Rowlands Castle (BR).
Seats: 50 **Cover:** 200 **Capacity:** 3,200 **Floodlights:** Yes **Founded:** 1887
Midweek Matches: Wed (Tues Reserves) **Previous Ground:** Horndean Rec. 1887-1969.
Colours: Red/black/black **Change colours:** Green & white/green/green.
Programme: 16 pages, with admission **Programme Editor:** Derek Usher
Record Gate: 1,560 v Waterlooville, Victory Cup April 1971.
Best FA Cup season: 1st Qualifying Round replay 1982-83.
Best FA Vase season: 1sr Round 85-86 88-89.
Clubhouse: Open every evening plus Sat & Sun lunctimes
Honours: Hants Div 2 79-80 (Div 3 75-76, Div 4 74-75), Portsmouth Snr Cup 75-76 79-80 (R-up 86-87, Portsmouth Lg 69-70 70-71 71-72, Wessex Lg Cup R-up 86-87, Portsmouth Jnr Cup 64-65.

(A.F.C.) LYMINGTON

Chairman: John Mills **Vice Chairman:** Ian Snook
Manager: Trevor Williams **Coach:** **Asst Mgr:** Alan Keats
Secretary: John Osey, 9 Samphire Close, Lymington Meadows, Lymington, Hants SO41 9LR (0590 676995).
Ground: Lymington Sports Ground, Southampton Road, Lymington (0590 671305).
Directions: From M27 follow signs to A337 to Lymington. Ground on left (signposted) just before town centre. 1 mile from Lymington Town (BR).
Seats: 200 **Cover:** 200 **Capacity:** 3,000 **Floodlights:** Yes **Founded:** 1988
Midweek Matches: Mon (Wed Reserves) **Record Gate:** 1,098 v Southampton, stand opening 1987.
Colours: White (red trim) **Change colours:** Sky & white/sky/sky. **Nickname:** Linnets
Best FA Vase season: **Clubhouse:** Sat 2-7pm and training and match nights.
Programme: 32 pages, 30p **Programme Editor:** John Mills.
Previous Name: Lymington Town (until 1988 when the club merged with Wellworthy Athletic).
Previous Ground: Ampress Ground (Wellworthy Athletic)
Honours: Wessex Lg R-up 91-92 (Lg Cup R-up 88-89), Hants Snr Cup R-up 89-90. As Lymington: Russell Cotes Cup 35-36, B'mouth Snr Cup 83-84 (R-up(2) 69-71 84-85), Hants Lg Div 3 67-68 (Div 2 R-up 83-84), Pickford Cup 52-53. As Wellworthy: B'mouth Snr Cup 87-88 (R-up 53-54), Hants Int. Cup 56-57 84-85, Pickford Cup 84-85, B'mouth Lg 84-85, Hants Lg Div 3 R-up 85-86.

PORTSMOUTH ROYAL NAVY

Chairman: Commander J Molloy RN
Secretary: Lt. G R Howells RN, 20 Redlands Lane, Fareham, Hants PO14 1EY (0329 221146).
Ground: RN Stadium, Burnaby Road, (West) Portsmouth (0705) 822351 Ext. 24235).
Directions: From Portsmouth Harbour (BR), drive towards Southsea along The Hard Pass under the rail bridge, road is now St George Rd, and ground is on the left.
Seats: 500 **Cover:** Yes **Capacity:** **Floodlights:** Yes **Founded:**
Midweek Matches: Monday
Colours: All blue **Change colours:** All red
Programme: No **Clubhouse:** Yes **Honours:** Basingstoke Lg Div 2, Hants Lg Div 1 & 3.

ROMSEY TOWN

Chairman: Mr D Edwards **President:** Mr Don Smith
Secretary: Mr R Willcock, 2 St Swithens Close, Romsey, Hants SO51 9AP (0794 523659).
Manager: Allan Stones **Press Officer:** S Judd
Ground: The By-Pass Ground, South Front, Romsey, Hants SO51 8GJ (0794 512003).
Directions: Adjacent to roundabout at junction of A31 and A27. Three quarters of a mile from Romsey (BR).
Seats: 50 **Cover:** 150 **Capacity:** 1,200 **Floodlights:** Yes **Founded:** 1925
Midweek Matches: Wednesday **Previous Ground:** Priestlands (pre-1956).
Colours: Green/white/green **Change colours:** Red.
Programme: 28 pages, 30p. **Programme Editor:** M Clouder
Best FA Vase season: **Best FA Cup season:** 4th Qual Rd 90-91.
Previous Leagues: Eastleigh & Dist/ Hants 31-64 71-87/ Southampton 64-71.
Clubhouse: Open every evening & weekend lunchtimes.
Honours: Wessex Lg 89-90 (Lg Cup R-up 87-88), Hants Lg Div 2 78-79 (R-up 30-31 47-48, Div 3 R-up 46-47 77-78, Div 4 75-76), Sotom Prem Lg 80-81 83-84, Soton Snr Lg 26-27 (R-up 10-11, West Lg 51-52, Div 2 72-73 (R-up 68-69), Romsey Div 27-28), Soton Jnr Lg Div 3 R-up 24-25 (Div 4 74-75), Eastleigh & Dist Lg(3) 22-24 28-29, Salisbury & Dist Lg 1898-99, Sth Hants Lg R-up 00-01, Hants Snr Cup 78-79 (R-up 48-49, Int. Cup 25-26 30-31 77-78, Jnr Cup 00-01 09-10 23-24 (R-up 1898-99 99-00)), Soton Snr Cup 73-74 (R-up(3) 27-30, Jnr Cup 22-23 23-24, Charity Cup R-up 82-83, Travers Cup 29-30), Russell Coates Cup R-up 32-33 88-89, Reg Mathieson Tphy R-up 81-82 83-84, Sth Hant Hosp Cup R-up 22-23 (R-up 21-22 23-24), Romsey Hosp Cup R-up 33-34, Warminster Cup 99-00, New Forest Invit. Cup R-up(2) 79-81, Andover Cup 1895-96 98-99, Winchester Cup R-up 08-09, Salisbury Cup 29-30, Geoff Hattersley Shield 74-75 84-85, Romsey Carnival Plate 1985.

AFC Lymington. Back Row (L/R): Alan Keats (Asst Mgr), Graham Pardey, Glen Limburn, Derek Holloway, Martin Coffin, David Mills, Lee Rankin, Graham Kemp, Neil Broomfield, Trevor Williams (Coach). Front: Dave Perrett, Danny Adams, Ian Knight, Ian Snook (Vice Chairman), George Putman (Manager), John Mills (Chairman), Kevin Dalby, Peter Kelly (no longer with club), Keith Collier.

Ryde Sports, pictured before their FA Vase victory at home to Kintbury. Photo - Eric Marsh.

Thatcham Town. Back Row (L/R): Eurshall Fearon, David Hobbs, Steve McCartney, Chris Edmonds, Neil Baker (Captain), Mickey Hurdwell, Simon Hargreaves, Kevin Rowe, Howard Dini (Physio). Front: Louis Barrett, David Yates, Hughie Worriskey, Darren Kupieck, Barry Grant, Des McMahon (Player-manager). Photo - Dave West.

RYDE SPORTS

President: John Keynes   **Chairman:** Mr S Rann
Secretary: Mr Mark Firmin, c/o The club (see below).
Manager: Graham Daish   **Asst Manager:** Len Cade.
Ground: Smallbrook Stadium, Ashey Rd, Ryde (0983 812906).   **Previous Ground:** Partlands (pre-1990).
Directions: From the Pier Head follow directions to the Royal Isle of Wight Hospital, carry on past the hospital turning left at the Partlands Hotel - ground is one mile along Ashey Road. Not served by public transport.
Seats: 450   **Cover:** 1,500   **Capacity:** 5,000   **Floodlights:** Yes   **Founded:** 1888.
Midweek Matches: Wednesday   **Previous League:** Hants.
Colours: Red/white/red   **Change colours:** White/blue/blue.   **Metal Badges:** Yes.
Programme: 32 pages, 50p.   **Programme Editor:** Secretary   **Nickname:** The Reds.
Travel Sponsors: Hovertravel   **Club Sponsors:** Colemans Carpet Superstore.
Best FA Vase season: Prel. Rd 90-91   **Best FA Cup season:** 3rd Rd Proper 35-36.
Record Gates: 3,100 v Aston Villa 17/12/90. 2,400 v Sheffield Wednesday 26/3/90.
Players progressing to Football League: Roy Shiner (Sheff Wed), Keiron Baker & Kevin Allen (Bournemouth).
(Also Wally Hammond played for Ryde before achieving fame in cricket).
Clubhouse: Open everyday. Large bar, restaurant, fitness centre, gym, treatment room.   **Club shop:** Yes.
Honours: FA Atr Cup 47-48 (2-4 v Clevedon) 48-49 (1-2 v Cheshunt), Hants Lg 1899-00 25-26 89-90 (Div 2 88-89, Div 3 64-65), Hants Snr Cup(8) 1899-00 03-04 25-26 34-39, IOW Gold Cup(7) 26-27 46-47 48-49 55-56 61-64, IOW Snr Challenge Cup 1898-99, IOW Gold Cup(7) 26-27 46-47 48-49 55-56 61-64, IOW Challenge Cup 27-28 80-81, P'mouth Snr Cup 1899-00 00-01 05-06 19-20 53-54 66-67 89-90, IOW Charity Cup(7) 18-22 44-47, Ryde & Dist Cup 89-90, Westwood Cup 84-85, IOW Lg 20-21 (Div 2 80-81).

SHOLING SPORTS

President: Mr George Dunn   **Chairman:** Mr B P Sivier.
Secretary: Mr B F Nash, 74 The Grove, Sholing, Southampton SO2 9LU (0703 445444).
Manager: Steve Clarke   **Asst Manager:** Ian Knight   **Coach:** Bill Moore.
Ground: Birch Lawn, 137 North East Road, Sholing, Southampton (0703 449381).
Directions: M27 Jct 8, A3024 then 6th turning on left - ground on right. One and a half miles from Sholing (BR).
Seats: 150   **Covered Accom:** 300 **Capacity:** 1,500   **Floodlights:** Yes   **Founded:** 1901.
Midweek Matches: Wed (Tues Res)   **Clubhouse:** Daily, normal licensing hours.
Colours: Black & white/black/black & white   **Change:** Red & black/white/red.
Programme: 12 pages, with admission   **Programme Editor:** Ward Puddle
Record Gate: 1,200 v Gosport Borough, Hants Snr Cup 1983.
Best FA Vase season: Quarter Final
Honours: Russell Cotes Cup 71-72 82-83 84-85, Hants Snr Cup 22-23 73-74 82-83, Hants Lg 73-74 82-83 83-84 (East Div 62-63 69-70), S'hampton Snr Cup(6) 19-22 38-39 61-62 79-80, S'hampton Snr Lg(4) 19-21 37-39, S'hampton Jnr Lg(4) 33-34 38-39 59-61, S'hampton Jnr Cup 59-60, Hants Int. Cup 37-38.

SWANAGE TOWN & HERSTON

Chairman: Mr P McLeod
Secretary: Mr C Smith, 110 Kings Rd, Swanage, Dorset BH19 1HS (0929 426362).
Ground: Days Park, off De Moulhem Road, Swanage, Dorset (0929 424633).
Directions: At north end of town adjacent to north beach car park in De Moulhem Road.
Seats: 150   **Cover:** 150   **Capacity:** 1,500   **Floodlights:** Yes   **Founded:** 1895.
Midweek Matches: Tuesday   **Previous League:** Western.
Colours: White/black/black.   **Change colours:** Blue/yellow/blue.
Programme: 12-14 pages, 30p.   **Programme Editor:** Eric Webster
Clubhouse: Open match days & special functions.
Previous Name: Swanage FC (merged with Herston in late 1960s)

THATCHAM TOWN

Chairman: Mr A E Hyde   **President:** Dave Quaintance
Secretary: Mr K Lovitt, 42 Pear Tree Lane, Newbury, Berks RG13 2LX (0635 44528).
Manager: Des McMahon   **Press Off:** Phil Liles (0635 66018)   **Coach:** Dave Cox
Ground: Lancaster Close, Thatcham, Berks (0635 862016). *A move to a new ground is imminent.*
Directions: Leave A4 on road from Thatcham to Newbury turning right at lights by Northfield Row. Turn right after shops and 1st right into Lancaster Close. 3 miles from Thatcham (BR).
Seats: 48   **Cover:** 100   **Capacity:** 3,000   **Floodlights:** Yes   **Founded:** 1896.
Midweek Matches: Tuesday   **Best FA Vase season:** QF 88-89
Colours: Blue & white stripes/blue/blue   **Change colours:** White/white/red
Programme: 20 pages, 30p   **Programme Editor:** Dave Ware
Previous Ground: Station Road 51-52   **Record Gate:** 600 v Fulham, floodlight opening
Clubhouse: Open every evening & weekend lunchtimes.   **Honours:** Wessex Lg Cup 90-91 91-92.

(A.F.C.) TOTTON

Chairman: Mr P Maton
Secretary: Mr C Bushby, 66 The Drive, Hounsdown, Totton, Southampton SO4 4EN (0703 867358).
Ground: Testwood Park, Testwood Place, Totton, Southampton (0703 868981).
Directions: 5 mins walk from Totton station. Turn off r'bout in Totton centre.
Seats: 200   **Cover:** 200   **Capacity:** 1,000   **Floodlights:** Yes   **Founded:** 1906
Record Gate: 800 for local cup final.   **Midweek Matches:** Wednesday (Monday for Reserves)
Colours: Blue & white stripes/blue (white trim)/blue   **Change colours:** Red/white/red
Previous Name: Totton FC (until 1979)   **Previous Grounds:** Downs Park/ Mayfield Park.
Clubhouse: 8-11pm every evening, after games, and 12-2pm at weekends.
Hons: Hants Lg(2)

WHITCHURCH UNITED

Chairman: Mr C Varndell.
Secretary: Mr N Spencer, 54 Winchester Rd, Whitchurch, Hants RG28 7HP (0256 896895).
Ground: Long Meadow, Winchester Road, Whitchurch (0256 892394).
Directions: From Whitchurch (BR) station; turn left after Railway Inn, follow road to end, turn right into main road, arriving in town turn left along Winchester Road. Ground three quarters of a mile on left.
Seats: 200 **Cover:** Yes **Capacity:** **Floodlights:** Yes **Founded:**
Midweek Matches: Wednesday (Monday for Reserves).
Colours: Red & black/black/white **Change colours:** Blue & white/white/blue.
Programme: 28 pages **Previous Leagues:** Hants (pre-1992).
Clubhouse: Hot food on matchdays. Sports hall incorporating squash courts and indoor bowling green

WIMBORNE TOWN

Chairman: Mr B Maidment **President:** Sir Michael Hanham, Bart
Manager: Alex Pike. **Asst Manager:**
Secretary: Mr K Holloway, 1 Laburnum Close, Ferndown, Dorset BH22 9TX (0202 892795).
Ground: Cuthbury, Cowgrove Road, Wimborne, Dorset BH21 4EL (0202 884821).
Directions: Wimborne to Blandford Road, behind Victoria Hospital.
Seats: None **Cover:** 300 **Capacity:** 3,000 **Floodlights:** Yes **Founded:** 1878
Midweek Matches: Wed (Tues Res)
Record Gate: 3,250 v Bamber Bridge, FA Vase Semi Final 2nd Leg, 28/3/92.
Colours: Black & white stripes/black/black**Change colours:** Green & white/white/gree & white.
Programme: 20 pages, 20p. **Programme Editor:** Commitee.
Best FA Vase season: SF 90-91 **Best FA Cup season:** 1st Rd Proper 82-83.
Previous Leagues: Dorset/ Western 81-86.**Clubhouse:** Every evening & Mon, Fri + weekend lunchtimes.
Honours: FA Vase 91-92, Wessex Lg 91-92 (Lg Cup R-up 90-91), Hants Snr Cup SF 89-90, Dorset Lg Div 1(2) 80-81 81-82 (R-up 38-39 72-73, Div 2 31-32 34-35 36-37 (R-up 35-36), Lg Cup R-up(4) 72-74 80-82), Dorset Snr Cup(4) 80-82 85-86 91-92, Dorset Snr Amateur Cup 36-37 63-64, Dorset Jnr Cup 31-32 36-37 (R-up 13-14 34-35), Dorset Minor Cup 12-13, Dorset Jnr Amateur Cup(4) 34-36 38-39.

Kevin Winchcombe of East Cowes Vics is set to save a header from Ryde's Andy Rayner during an Isle of Wight Centenary Cup Quarter Final at Cowes Sports's Westwood Road. Photo - Dan Draper.

DORSET COMBINATION

President: A P Humphries, Esq.
Chairman: R H Green, Esq.
Hon. Secretary: G A Theobald, Esq.,
41 South Road, Corfe Mullen, Wimborne BH21 3HZ (0202 697994).
Press Officer: T Scorah.

	P	W	D	L	F	A	PTS
Blandford Utd	36	22	10	4	54	29	76
Westland Sports	36	21	8	7	74	47	71
Parley Sports	36	20	10	6	60	37	70
Dorchester Res.	36	18	9	9	78	48	63
Shaftesbury	36	18	9	9	81	56	63
Sturm. Newton U.	36	18	8	10	48	42	62
Hamworthy Utd	36	17	10	9	92	55	61
Bournemouth S.C.	36	16	9	11	69	49	57
Flight Refuelling	36	15	12	9	59	42	57
Sherborne Town	36	16	8	12	63	47	56
Weymouth Res.	36	16	5	15	66	52	53
Bridport Res.	36	13	6	17	53	59	46
Portland Utd	36	11	8	17	59	72	41
Gillingham Town	36	8	11	17	55	62	35
Wareham Rangers	36	8	9	19	46	64	33
Swanage T&H Res	36	9	5	22	39	69	32
Cranborne	36	8	6	22	46	102	30
Poole Town Res.	36	4	12	20	34	69	24
Holt United	36	2	8	26	26	99	14

LEADING SCORERS 1991-92

John Inglis (Sherborne (+ 13 for Westland))	29
Colin Burton (Dorchester Town Reserves)	24
Steve Manuel (Hamworthy United)	24
Billy Cannie (Flight Refuelling)	19
Steve Barfoot (Wareham Rangers)	18
Paul Toomer (Shaftesbury)	18
Kevin Manson (Blandford United)	17
Danny Alford (Shaftesbury)	16
John Cluett (Cranborne)	15
Steve Paradise (B'mouth (+ 7 for Sherborne))	15
Mike Satterley (Hamworthy United)	15
Jimmy Fry (Parley Sports)	14
Andy Walters (Parley Sports)	14
Martin Shepherd (Westland Sports)	13

COMBINATION LEAGUE CUP 1991-92

First Round. 19/10/91.

Dorchester Reserves v Poole Town Reserves 7-0
Wareham Rangers v Holt United 1-0
Swanage Town & Herston Res. v Blandford Utd 1-3

Second Round. 23/11/91.

Sherborne v Sturminster Newton (16/11/91) 5-0
Bridport Reserves v Westland Sports 1-2
Gillingham Town v Parley Sports 0-3
Shaftesbury v Weymouth Reserves 2-0
Bournemouth Sports Club v Portland United 4-0
Cranborne v Blandford United 1-4
Hamworthy United v Wareham Rangers 1-4
Dorchester Res. v Flight Refuelling (30/11/91) 5-1

Quarter Finals. 1/2/92.

Dorchester T. Reserves v Bournemouth SC 2-1
Shaf'bury v Parley (8/2,22/2,&14/3/92) 0-0,1-1,1-3
Sherborne Town v Wareham Rangers 4-1
Westland Spts v Blandford United (29/2/92) 2-0

Semi Finals

Dorchester Reserves v Sherborne (28/3/92) 7-2
Parley Sports v Westland Sports (11/4/92) 3-1

Final (at The County Ground, Hamworthy United FC, Tuesday 12th May):
Dorchester Town Reserves 3, Parley Sports 0.

RESULT CHART 1991-92

HOME TEAM	1	2	3	4	5	6	7	8	9	10	11	12	13	14	15	16	17	18	19
1. Blandford	*	2-1	3-0	4-4	4-3	0-0	1-0	1-0	4-0	1-0	1-0	3-2	1-1	2-0	0-0	2-1	4-3	1-2	2-0
2. B'mouth SC	1-1	*	5-1	4-0	1-3	1-0	2-1	1-2	3-1	3-2	6-1	4-2	1-1	0-2	1-0	3-1	2-4	1-0	0-1
3. Bridport Res	0-3	1-0	*	7-2	2-3	1-2	1-2	2-0	2-0	1-3	4-1	0-0	0-1	1-1	2-0	0-0	2-1	0-2	
4. Cranborne	0-1	2-0	4-4	*	4-1	0-1	2-3	0-5	2-1	1-1	1-1	0-5	1-7	1-9	0-1	1-0	1-3	2-3	0-0
5. Dorch. Res	3-0	1-1	2-1	3-1	*	1-1	3-0	3-1	1-1	1-2	0-0	1-4	5-2	1-0	1-1	6-0	3-2	5-0	5-1
6. Flight Ref.	2-1	2-2	1-1	5-1	2-1	*	4-0	2-1	0-0	2-3	1-1	6-1	2-0	0-1	0-1	3-2	0-2	0-2	3-2
7. Gillingham	0-2	1-2	2-3	3-0	4-2	1-1	*	1-1	8-1	0-1	2-2	0-1	3-3	1-0	2-2	2-3	3-0	1-1	1-0
8. Hamworthy	0-1	2-2	3-0	1-1	1-1	1-1	3-2	*	3-0	2-4	2-3	3-0	6-2	5-2	6-0	2-2	3-1	3-3	2-0
9. Holt United	0-1	1-3	0-2	0-4	0-6	0-1	1-1	2-4	*	0-2	3-2	2-2	1-3	2-2	0-5	0-3	0-3	2-1	0-7
10. Parley Spts	0-0	1-1	3-1	1-0	1-1	1-1	2-0	3-3	2-0	*	2-1	2-2	0-0	3-1	1-2	2-3	2-1	0-3	2-1
11. Poole T. Res	1-1	0-2	0-3	0-3	0-1	1-2	2-2	1-4	0-0	0-2	*	1-0	0-2	1-2	1-3	0-0	2-2	2-4	3-2
12. Portland Utd	1-1	1-1	3-3	3-1	0-5	2-2	4-2	2-0	1-2	0-0		*	0-5	1-2	1-2	0-2	2-0	2-4	2-0
13. Shaftesbury	0-2	2-2	6-2	3-0	0-1	4-3	1-0	2-5	3-3	0-2	2-3	3-1	*	4-0	2-2	1-0	2-1	2-1	1-6
14. Sherborne	0-0	2-1	0-0	3-1	2-2	0-2	3-1	1-6	0-0	3-1	3-1	0-4	*	1-1	1-3	1-0	0-1	2-0	
15. Stur. Newton	0-1	2-1	2-0	2-3	0-1	0-0	0-0	0-4	1-0	2-0	2-1	0-1	0-0	0-6	*	5-2	3-0	2-0	1-2
16. Swanage Res	0-1	0-3	1-2	1-2	2-1	1-0	2-1	1-4	2-0	0-2	0-0	0-4	5-1	1-2	1-2	*	1-1	0-3	1-1
17. Wareham R.	0-1	0-3	0-2	4-0	0-4	1-1	3-1	1-1	3-3	1-3	1-1	2-2	0-3	2-1	0-1	2-1	*	1-1	0-1
18. Westland	1-1	3-2	1-1	9-1	3-0	2-2	4-2	3-2	3-1	1-1	1-0	4-2	1-1	2-0	1-0	1-0	2-1	*	1-0
19. Weym. Res	3-0	3-3	1-2	3-0	1-1	5-1	1-1	2-4	2-1	0-2	3-1	4-1	1-3	0-4	2-0	2-0	3-1	4-1	*

REPRESENTATIVE MATCH

Wiltshire County League 1, Dorset Combination 3 - at Chippenham Town FC, Tuesday 8th March.
Dorset Scorers: C Burton, K Newman, A Walters.
Team: K Horder (Bournemouth Spts), R Wigmore & K Newman (Flight Refuelling), S Harris, C Butcher, C Burton & C Stranger (Dorchester Town Reserves), R Churchill (Shaftesbury), L Bright (Sturminster Newton Utd), P Watts (Weymouth Reserves), T Benjafield (Gillingham Town), A Walters (Parley Sports).
Manager: G Joy (Dorchester Town Reserves)
Trainer: F Voss (Dorchester Town Reserves)

DORSET COMBINATION CLUBS 1992-93

BLANDFORD UNITED

Secretary: David A Thomas, 45 Badbury Drive, Blandford Forum, Dorset DT11 7UJ (0258 456570).
Ground: Recreation Ground, Park Lane, Blandford Forum, Dorset. (HQ Tel: 0258 456374).
Colours: Royal blue   **Change colours:** All red
Cover: No   **Programme:** Yes   **Clubhouse:** No
91-92 Top Scorers: Kevin Manson 17, Peter Owen 9.

BOURNEMOUTH SPORTS CLUB

Secretary: Mike Ewings, 21 Monsal Avenue, Ferndown, Dorset BH22 8LA (0202 873286).
Ground: Chapel Gate, East Parley, Christchurch, Dorset BH23 6BD (0202 581933).
Colours: Gold/black/black   **Change colours:** All red
Cover: No   **Programme:** Yes   **Clubhouse:** Yes
91-92 Top Scorers: Michael McDonnell 8, Steve Paradise 8, Paul Spence 8.

BRIDPORT RESERVES

91-92 Top Scorers: Jason Hawker 12, Robert Thom 7 *(See Great Mills League section for other info.)*

CRANBORNE

Secretary: Allen F Ambrose, 45 Castle Street, Cranborne, Wimborne, Dorset BH21 5PZ (0725 54648).
Ground: Cranborne Recreation Ground, Penny's Lane, Cranborne, Wimborne (0725 4616).
Cols: Black & white stripes/black/black   **Change colours:** Yellow/yellow/red
Cover: No   **Programme:** Yes   **Clubhouse:** Yes
91-92 Top Scorers: John Cluett 15, Mark McGrath 10.

DORCHESTER TOWN RESERVES

91-92 Top Scorers: Colin Burton 24, Martin Harvey 9 *(See Beazer League section for other info.)*

FLIGHT REFUELLING

Secretary: Harry W Doyle, 27 Fairview Cres., Broadstone, Poole BH18 9AP (0202 698393).
Ground: Merley Park, Merley, Wimborne, Dorset (0202 885773).
Colours: Sky/navy/sky   **Change colours:** All yellow
Cover: No   **Programme:** Yes   **Clubhouse:** Yes
91-92 Top Scorers: Billy Cannie 19, Keith Newmann 9.

GILLINGHAM TOWN

Secretary: David J Ayles, 37 Sylvan Way, Bay Road, Gillingham SP8 4EQ (0747 822065).
Ground: Hardings Lane, Gillingham (0747 823673).
Colours: Yellow/black/black   **Change colours:** All blue
Cover: Yes   **Programme:** Yes   **Clubhouse:** Yes
91-92 Top Scorers: Robin Knobbs 10, Tim Benjafield 7, Matthew Turner 7.

HAMWORTHY ENGINEERING

Secretary: Mr R J Harris, 150 Rempstone Rd, Merley, Wimborne BH21 1SX (885999).
Ground: Hamworthy Rec. Club, Magna Rd, Canford Magna, Wimborne, Dorset BH21 3AE (881922).
Colours: All green   **Change colours:** White/blue/blue
Cover: No   **Programme:**   **Clubhouse:** Yes

HAMWORTHY UNITED

Secretary: Roy R Mitchener, 68 St Mary's Rd, Poole, Dorset BH15 2LL (0202 676128).
Ground: The County Ground, Blandford Close, Hamworthy, Poole, Dorset (0202 674974).
Colours: Maroon & sky/sky/maroon   **Change colours:** Green & white/green/green
Cover: Yes   **Programme:** Yes   **Clubhouse:** Yes
91-92 Top Scorers: Steve Manuel 24, Mike Satterley 15.

HOLT UNITED

Secretary: Ian Bradley, 251 King John Ave., Bournemouth, Dorset BH11 9SJ (0202 593732).
Ground: Gaunts Common, Holt, Wimborne, Dorset (0258 840379).
Cols: Red & black stripes/black/red   **Change colours:** Blue & yellow stripes/blue/yellow
Cover: No   **Programme:** No   **Clubhouse:** Yes
91-92 Top Scorers: Colin Brown 8, Stuart Rendell 7.

PARLEY SPORTS

Secretary: Malcolm Whitfield, 10 Briar Way, Wimborne, Dorset BH21 2LB (0202 841467).
Ground: Parley Sports Club, Christchurch, West Parley, Bournemouth, Dorset (0202 573345).
Colours: Yellow/blue/yellow   **Change colours:** Blue/yellow/blue
Cover: No   **Programme:** No   **Clubhouse:** Yes
91-92 Top Scorers: Jimmy Fry 14, Andy Watts 14.

POOLE TOWN RESERVES

91-92 Top Scorers: Shane Loader 7, Nicholas Lanaham 4 *(See Beazer League section for other info.)*

PORTLAND UNITED

Secretary: David M Camp, 23 Four Acres, Weston, Portland DT5 2LG (0305 821816).
Ground: Grove Corner, Portland (0305 823690).
Colours: All blue   **Change colours:** Red/white/red
Cover: Yes   **Programme:** Yes   **Clubhouse:** Yes
91-92 Top Scorers: Raymond Cody 12, Darren Whyton 11.

SHAFTESBURY

Secretary: Terry J Warder, 7 The Knapp, Enmore Green, Shaftesbury SP7 8LT (0747 52336).
Ground: Cockrams, Coppice Street, Shaftesbury (0747 53990).
Colours: Red & white/black/red   **Change colours:** All green
Cover: Yes   **Programme:** No   **Clubhouse:** Yes
91-92 Top Scorers: Paul Toomer 18, Danny Alford 16

SHERBORNE TOWN

Secretary: Roger V Woolmington, 23 Harbour Rd, Sherborne DT9 4AL (0935 813048).
Ground: Raleigh Grove, The Terrace Playing Fields, Sherborne (0935 816110).
Colours: Tangerine/black/tangerine   **Change colours:** White/white/black
Cover: Yes   **Programme:** Yes   **Clubhouse:** Yes
91-92 Top Scorers: Inglis 16, Pete Hooper 14.

STURMINSTER NEWTON

Secretary: Richard J Frear, 44 Green Close, Sturminster Newton, Dorset DT10 1BL (0258 73036).
Ground: Ricketts Lane, Sturminster Newton, Dorset. (HQ (RBL) Tel: 0258 72437).
Colours: Red/black/black   **Change colours:** Yellow/white/red
Cover: Yes   **Programme:** Yes   **Clubhouse:** No
91-92 Top Scorers: Robert Fox 9, Richard Peters 6.

SWANAGE TOWN & HERSTON RESERVES

91-92 Top Scorers: Steven Bolton 7, Richard Fox 5 *(See Jewson Wessex League section for other info.)*

WAREHAM RANGERS

Secretary: Mrs Carol White, 9 Bere Road, Wareham, Dorset BH20 4DB (0929 551765).
Ground: Wareham Recreation Ground, Worgret Rd, Wareham, Dorset.
Cols: Amber/black/amber   **Change colours:** Sky/blue/sky
Cover: No   **Programme:** Yes   **Clubhouse:** No
91-92 Top Scorers: Steven Barfoot 18, Trevor Dando 8.

WEYMOUTH RESERVES

91-92 Top Scorers: Barry Holmes 11, Paul Watts 8   *(See Beazer League section for other info.)*

Peter Richards (nearest camera) goes close for Sturminster Newton at home to Westland Sports. Stur's 2-0 victory, on a Tuesday evening, effectively ended their opponents' title aspirations. Photo - Tim Lancaster.

Wareham Rangers 2, Portland United 2 - Saturday 29th February. Portland's Simon Browne attacks the home goal on Wareham Rec. Photo - Tim Lancaster.

LEADING AGENCIES HAMPSHIRE LEAGUE

Division One	P	W	D	L	F	A	PTS
Colden Common	34	20	10	4	56	33	70
Blackfield & Langley	34	20	8	6	70	32	68
Whitchurch Utd	34	18	10	6	71	39	64
Pirelli General	34	18	9	7	54	30	63
Malshanger	34	16	8	10	52	41	56
DCA Basingstoke	34	15	9	10	55	41	54
Alton Town Bass	34	15	8	11	48	41	53
A.C. Delco	34	15	6	13	50	42	51
Fleetlands	34	15	6	13	58	54	51
Locksheath	34	13	9	12	44	41	45
Downton	34	13	5	16	44	41	44
Bishops Waltham T.	34	12	6	16	51	61	42
Cowes Sports	34	9	12	13	40	51	39
ISL Midanbury	34	10	6	18	58	71	36
Alresford Town	34	8	5	21	46	74	29
Awbridge	34	7	8	19	38	70	29
Brading Town	34	8	4	22	37	73	28
West Wight	34	6	7	21	27	59	25

Division Two	P	W	D	L	F	A	PTS
Winchester City	28	18	8	2	53	24	62
Overton United	28	17	7	4	56	21	58
New Milton	28	16	4	8	53	36	52
Paulsgrove	28	14	6	8	46	31	48
Verwood Town	28	14	5	9	48	38	47
Otterbourne	28	13	7	8	62	44	46
Ringwood Town	28	10	6	12	52	43	36
Braishfield	28	10	6	12	42	49	36
Nutfield United	28	10	6	12	44	54	36
Basing Rovers	28	9	7	12	54	55	34
Broughton	28	9	7	12	50	52	34
Netley Central	28	8	6	14	33	52	30
Liss Athletic	28	7	8	13	42	45	29
Winchester Castle	28	4	10	14	39	66	22
Compton	28	3	3	22	28	92	12

Division Three	P	W	D	L	F	A	PTS
P'mouth Civil Serv.	26	20	4	2	74	22	64
New Street	26	18	2	6	71	26	56
Fleet Spurs	26	16	4	6	64	42	52
AFC Aldermaston	26	14	4	8	83	43	46
Netley Vic. Ath.	26	12	6	8	59	51	42
Hayling United	26	11	8	7	41	35	41
Hedge End	26	12	5	9	61	56	41
Covies	26	10	4	12	35	58	34
Stockbridge	26	9	5	12	63	54	32
Lansdowne	26	9	6	11	31	39	*32
Vosper Thorneycroft	26	7	5	14	44	58	26
Alton T. Bass Res	26	6	2	18	31	66	20
Ecchinswell	26	4	3	19	34	78	15
Netley Central Res	26	3	4	19	26	89	13

* - One point deducted

DIVISION ONE CLUBS 1992-93

A.C. DELCO
Ground: Stoneham Lane, Eastleigh (0703 613334). **Secretary:** D Freeman (0703 777618).

ALRESFORD TOWN
Ground: Arlebury Park, Alresford (0962 735100). **Secretary:** R Lane (0962 51797).

ALTON TOWN BASS
Ground: Bass Sports Ground, Alton, Hants. **Secretary:** A Hillman (0420 87103).

AWBRIDGE
Ground: Village Ground, Crossroads. **Secretary:** J Moody (0794 514073).

BISHOPS WALTHAM TOWN
Ground: Hoe Road, Bishops Waltham. **Secretary:** Mrs Weavil (0489 894952).

BLACKFIELD & LANGLEY
Ground: Gang Warily, Newlands Rd (0703 893603). **Secretary:** K Bevis (0703 891854).

COLDEN COMMON
Ground: Rec. Ground, Main Rd, Colden Common (0962 712365). **Secretary:** C Banford (0703 730206).

COWES SPORTS
Ground: Westwood Pk, Reynolds Close, Cowes, Isle of Wight (0983 293793).
Secretary: P Jeffery (0983 296091).

DOWNTON
Ground: Brian Whitehead Spts Grnd, Wick Lane, Downton (0725 22162). **Sec.:** R Hillman (0725 20815).

FLEETLANDS
Ground: Lederle Lane, Gosport (0329 239723). **Secretary:** G Cox (0703 693021).

I.S.L. MIDANBURY
Ground: Blackfield & Langley Spts & Soc. Club, Netley View, Hardley Lane, Hythe, Hants.
Secretary: W Mew (0703 583970).

LOCKSHEATH
Ground: Locksheath Rec., Warsash Road (0489 581021). **Secretary:** K Smith (0703 442542).

MALSHANGER
Ground: Malshanger Sports Field. **Secretary:** F Norris (0256 781679).

NEW MILTON
Ground: Fawcett Fields, Christchurch Rd, New Milton. **Secretary:** J Wyatt (0425 611670).

OVERTON UNITED
Ground: Recreation Ground, Bridge Str., Overton (0256 770561). **Secretary:** R Taylor (0256 770835).

PIRELLI GENERAL
Ground: Chesnut Avenue, Eastleigh (0703 612725). **Secretary:** R Hawkins (0703 612721).

WINCHESTER CITY
Ground: Abbots Barton, Winchester (0703 693021). **Secretary:** G Cox (0703 693021).

DIVISION TWO CLUBS 1992-93

A.F.C. ALDERMASTON
Ground: Recreational Society, A.W.E. Aldermaston.   Secretary: G Dew (0734 811271).

BASING ROVERS
Ground: Recreation Ground, The Street, Old Basing.   Secretary: C Dale (0256 26604).

BRADING TOWN
Ground: Vicarage Lane, Brading, Isle of Wight (0983 405217).   Secretary: F Powell (0983 611891).

BRAISHFIELD
Ground: Recreation Ground, Braishfield.   Secretary: B Reid (0794 517991).

BROUGHTON
Ground: The Sports Field, Buckholt Rd, Broughton.   Secretary: A Hammerton (0794 301495).

FLEET SPURS
Ground: Peter Driver Spts Grnd, Bourley Rd, Church Crookham.   Secretary: P Hampshire (0252 622307).

HAYLING UNITED
Ground: Hayling Park, Hayling Island.   Secretary: Mrs Westfield (0705 463305).

LISS ATHLETIC
Ground: Newman Collard P.F., Liss (0730 894022).   Secretary: L Heath (0730 892017).

NETLEY ATHLETIC VICTORIA
Ground: Castle Grnd, Victoria Rd, Netley (0703 453319).   Secretary: I Herding (0703 435196).

NETLEY CENTRAL SPORTS
Ground: Rec. Ground, Station Rd, Netley.   Secretary: Mrs Ellis (0703 453744).

NEW STREET
Ground: TBA.   Secretary: Mrs Waterman (0264 362751).

NUTFIELD
Ground: Nursling Rec, Nursling Str., Nursling.   Secretary: P Hurst (0703 734061).

OTTERBOURNE
Ground: Oakwood Pk, off Oakwood Av., Otterbourne (0962 714681)   Secretary: R Broom (0703 612045).

PAULSGROVE
Ground: The Grove Club, Marsden Road (0705 324102).   Secretary: V Collins (0705 829164).

PORTSMOUTH CIVIL SERVICE
Ground: Copnor Rd, Hilsea (0705 662538).   Secretary: P Shires (0705 751994).

RINGWOOD TOWN
Ground: The Clubhouse, Long Lane, Ringwood (0425 473448).   Secretary: N Crewe (0202 398975).

VERWOOD TOWN
Ground: Potterne Park, Potterne Way, Verwood.   Secretary: Mrs Moon (0202 823182).

WEST WIGHT
Ground: Camp Rd, Freshwater, Isle of Wight (0983 754780).   Secretary: S Willis (0983 753912).

DIVISION THREE CLUBS 1992-93

ALTON TOWN BASS RESERVES (See page 632)

COMPTON
Ground: Shepherds Lane, Compton (0962 712083).   Secretary: M Allerton (0962 869574).

COVIES
Ground: Queens Rd Rec, North Camp, Farnborough (0252 373137)   Secretary: J McKane (0252 541980).

DRAYTON PARK (New entrant)

ECCHINSWELL
Ground: Ecchinswell Football Grnd, Ecchinswell, Newbury.   Secretary: R Francis (0635 48139).

ESSO FAWLEY (New entrant)

FLEETLANDS RESERVES (See page 632)

HEDGE END
Ground: Norman Rodway PF, Hedge End, Southampton   Secretary: A Draper (0489 785487).

LANSDOWNE
Ground: Winton Rec, Fitzharris Av., Winton, Bournemouth.   Secretary: S Smith (0202 528162).

LAVERSTOCK & FORD (New entrant)

NETLEY CENTRAL SPORTS RESERVES (See above)

STOCKBRIDGE
Ground: Rec. Ground, High Street, Stockbridge.   Secretary: Mrs Webb (0264 810819).

SWANMORE (New entrant)

VOSPER THORNEYCROFT
Ground: Portsmouth Rd, Sholing (0421 213829).   Secretary: A Fox (0703 443961).

WINCHESTER CASTLE
Ground: Hants CC Spts Grnd, A31, Petersfield Rd, Chilcomb (0962 866989)
Secretary: M Finch (0489 786303).

WINCHESTER CITY RESERVES (See page 632)

Alresford Town, Hampshire League Division One. Photo - Eric Marsh.

A.F.C. Aldermaston, Hampshire League Division Two. Photo - Eric Marsh.

Covies FC, Hampshire League Division Three. Photo - Eric Marsh.

UNIJET SUSSEX COUNTY LEAGUE

Chairman: P R Bentley
Vice Chairman: L Ralph
Hon. Secretary: P Wells,
37 Bewley Road, Angmering BN16 4JL (0903 771146).

PEACEHAVEN MAKE AMENDS FOR 1991

A record number of points saw Peacehaven win the League Championship, for the first time since 1982-83, which they supplemented with League Cup final success on Good Friday evening at Burgess Hill against Littlehampton by a 3-0 scoreline. This makes five years out of seven that the 'double' has been achieved, all by different teams. Peacehaven were only defeated in one league match, at Wick on February 4th. After that date they played nineteen matches in all competitions with only a 0-0 against Oakwood on March 3rd denying them a 100% run-in.

Littlehampton suffered some reaction from their previous season's successes, and although they maintained close touch throughout they were destined to finish third in the League and League Cup runners-up. Second place went to Langney Sports who thus improved their past two season's performances by one place, and also created the biggest day in the club's history when they reached the Sussex Senior Cup final and were beaten by Brighton by only the narrowest of margins.

In Division Two Portfield won the title, their points total falling just three short of the record for the Division, set by themselves in 83-84. They thus regain their Division One status after three seasons, and joining them will be Midhurst, returning after five years. The Division Two Cup final, held for the second consecutive season on Good Friday morning at Broadbridge Heath, saw Redhill defeat Horsham YMCA in front of 400.

Division Three champions were Hassocks, who have spent five years in this Division following relegation due to inadequate facilities. Extensive work and efforts have been put in effect to enable them to be re-graded for senior football at a new ground. They will be joined by runners-up Mile, entering senior football for the first time. The Division Three Cup final at Littlehampton saw Sidlesham gain success in their first season defeating holders Withdean by the only goal.

The Reserve Section Premier Division title was won by Burgess Hill, repeating their success of two years ago, with Peacehaven, who looked likely champions for most of the season, finishing second. In the final of the Reserve Cup, after a drawn match at Wick, the replay at Arundel saw third placed Portfield defeat fourth placed Horsham YMCA after two matches of high quality. Reserve Section East was won by Crawley Reserves, in their first season since formation, by a single point from Lewes, with Hassocks third on goal difference. Had the champions not won their last match they would have finished third. In the Reserve Section West, Worthing were runaway winners, some ten points ahead of second placed Bognor.

I am pleased to report the further advances made by our clubs with their facilities, and it must be even more pleasing for Peacehaven to be one of the clubs to have added floodlights in the year they completed the 'double'. I feel confident that I can speak with knowledge, having visited all Division One, Two and Three clubs on matchdays. In times like our current recession it is pleasing to observe the desires and intentions of most of our clubs not to stand still. It is equally important that whatever upgradings are necessary, it is essential to ensure that improvements are not allowed to lead clubs into debts they can never afford.

Next season will see the return of two former clubs, Eastbourne United and Southwick, to the senior fold within the League. Although both clubs were within an alternative structure to ours, when a plea was made to try to assist both clubs from disintegration, we felt an obligation to open a door in their hour of need.

Peter Bentley, League Chairman

Peacehaven & Telscombe pictured before their F.A. Vase tie at Chertsey Town. In 1991-92 the Piddinghoe Avenue side were pushed into second place on goal difference by Littlehampton. However, now they have won the championship with ease, and iced their cake by beating Littlehampton in the League Cup Final. Photo - Eric Marsh.

UNIJET SUSSEX LEAGUE CUP 1991-92

Preliminary Round (24-8-91)

East Grinstead v Three Bridges	1-2	Little Common Albion v Bexhill Town		0-6
Seaford Town v Newhaven	3-1			

First Round (21-9-91)

Crowborough Ath. v Littlehampton *(24-8-91)*	1-3	Lancing v Pagham *(24-8-91)*		5-2
Saltdean United v Hailsham Town *(24-8-91)*	0-1	East Preston v Whitehawk *(31-8-91)*		1-0
Stamco v Peacehaven & Telscombe *(31-8-91)*	0-2	Seaford Town v Bexhill Town		1-6
Bosham v Shoreham	1-9	Broadbridge Heath v Chichester City *(AET)*		5-2
Burgess Hill Town v Worthing United	7-2	Eastbourne Town v Midhurst & Easebourne *(AET)*		7-4
Langney Sports v Sidley United	4-2	Oakwood v Horsham YMCA *(Rep 12-11-91)*	2-2,2-0	
Portfield v Haywards Heath Town	2-1	Redhill v Arundel		2-6
Selsey v Wick	3-1	Ringmer v Three Bridges *(14-1-92)*		0-1

Second Round (14-12-91)

Broadbridge Heath v Littlehampton *(AET)*	2-4	East Preston v Arundel *(AET)*		3-4
Hailsham Town v Bexhill Town	1-2	Langney Sports v Oakwood		2-3
Selsey v Burgess Hill Town *(30-11-91)*	0-5	Lancing v Eastbourne Town *(9-11-91)*		0-3
Portfield v Peacehaven & Telscombe *(9-11-91)*	1-2	Shoreham v Three Bridges *(17&22-1-92)*	3-3,0-1	

Third Round (21-12-91)

Oakwood v Burgess Hill *(AET)*	3-2	Peacehaven & Telscombe v Bexhill *(25-1-91)*	3-2
Littlehampton v Eastbourne Town *(1-1-92)*	3-1	Three Bridges v Arundel	2-0

Semi-Finals

Littlehampton Town v Oakwood	2-0	Peacehaven & Telscombe v Three Bridges	6-2
At Horsham YMCA		At Burgess Hill Town	

Final (at Burgess Hill Town FC, 17-4-92)

Peacehaven & Telscombe v Littlehampton Town	3-0

Peacehaven & Telscombe celebrate their 3-0 victory over Littlehampton in the League Cup. Photo - Eric Marsh.

More action from the all-conquering Peacehaven; Paul Thomsett (nearest the camera) tries to find a way round the Bexhill Town defence during the 1-0 win at the Polegrove.

DIVISION ONE 1991-92

	P	W	D	L	F	A	PTS
Peacehaven & Tel.	34	29	4	1	115	24	91
Langney Sports	34	22	10	2	96	36	76
Littlehampton T.	34	23	7	4	95	42	76
Pagham	34	18	9	7	85	53	63
Wick	34	16	11	7	61	50	59
Burgess Hill Town	34	16	7	11	64	46	55
Three Bridges	34	14	11	9	66	51	53
Hailsham Town	34	14	8	12	73	63	50
Ringmer	34	13	7	14	57	60	46
Newhaven *	34	13	6	15	63	73	45
Arundel	34	10	10	14	43	49	40
Eastbourne Town	34	12	4	18	33	63	40
Whitehawk	34	9	7	18	36	56	34
Oakwood	34	7	9	18	50	70	30
Chichester City	34	7	5	22	37	96	26
Bexhill Town	34	5	10	19	33	71	25
Shoreham	34	5	9	20	34	71	24
Haywards Hth T.	34	2	8	24	29	96	14

* - 1 gl deducted (v Peacehaven) ineligible player

Manager of the month awards

Aug	Alan Pook (Peacehaven & Telscombe)
Sept	Jim Thompson (Burgess Hill Town)
Oct	Carl Stabler (Littlehampton Town)
Nov	Dave Kew (Pagham)
Dec	Alan Pook (Peacehaven & Telscombe)
Jan	Micky French (Hailsham Town)
Feb	Norman Cairns (Wick)
Mar	Peter Cherry (Langney Sports)
Apr/May	Alan Pook (Peacehaven & Telscombe)

Manager of the Season:
Alan Pook (Peacehaven)

LEADING SCORERS
(League matches only)

Nigel Hole (Langney Sports) 40
Mark Vickers (Pagham) 28
Paul Bennett (Littlehampton Town) 25

Roy Hayden Trophy *(10-8-91 at Crawley)*
Crawley Town 6, Littlehampton Town 0

Norman Wingate Trophy *(17-8-91 at Peacehaven)*
Peacehaven & Telscombe 2, Littlehampton T. 0

UNIJET SUSSEX COUNTY LEAGUE DIVISON ONE RESULTS 1991/92

HOME TEAM	1	2	3	4	5	6	7	8	9	10	11	12	13	14	15	16	17	18
1. ARUNDEL	*	1-1	1-0	2-0	2-0	1-2	1-0	1-2	2-2	2-0	2-2	1-3	1-2	1-0	3-1	1-1	1-2	1-1
2. BEXHILL TOWN	0-2	*	1-0	0-2	0-2	2-0	1-1	0-4	2-2	2-3	2-2	1-1	0-1	2-2	1-1	1-5	1-0	0-3
3. BURGESS HILL T.	6-2	3-0	*	1-1	0-1	0-0	1-0	0-2	2-5	6-1	2-1	3-2	1-2	1-1	4-0	1-1	0-1	3-1
4. CHICHESTER CITY	2-1	0-0	1-2	*	1-3	3-2	3-0	0-3	0-3	1-2	1-4	3-4	1-8	0-1	2-0	0-5	0-3	1-2
5. EASTBOURNE TOWN	0-2	0-3	0-1	1-1	*	1-2	4-1	1-1	1-5	0-1	2-1	0-3	1-5	3-1	1-0	1-5	1-0	0-0
6. HAILSHAM TOWN	2-0	5-1	1-3	9-0	2-0	*	8-0	3-3	2-4	6-2	3-1	1-1	2-2	3-2	3-2	0-0	2-1	0-2
7. HAYWARDS HEATH T.	1-1	1-0	1-2	1-1	1-2	0-2	*	3-4	1-4	2-4	3-1	1-2	1-8	2-2	0-3	0-4	0-0	3-3
8. LANGNEY SPORTS	1-1	4-2	1-0	1-1	0-0	1-0	10-1	*	5-1	4-1	3-1	2-2	2-2	1-1	4-0	2-1	3-0	5-1
9. LITTLEHAMPTON T.	2-1	5-0	1-1	4-0	4-0	6-0	3-0	5-3	*	3-1	2-1	3-2	0-5	6-0	2-2	1-1	4-1	1-1
10. NEWHAVEN	3-0	6-1	1-5	3-4	2-0	6-2	2-1	2-2	1-2	*	4-0	1-1	0-4	1-1	3-0	2-1	0-0	0-1
11. OAKWOOD	1-1	3-1	0-0	2-3	0-1	4-3	4-0	0-3	0-3	1-1	*	4-1	0-7	4-1	1-1	0-1	4-2	1-3
12. PAGHAM	3-1	4-2	2-2	6-0	4-0	5-1	6-1	1-1	2-0	4-0	3-3	*	1-5	3-1	1-2	3-1	1-0	2-2
13. PEACEHAVEN & T.	2-1	1-0	3-2	8-1	5-0	4-1	3-1	2-1	2-1	0-0	2-0	2-0	*	2-1	3-0	8-1	3-0	0-0
14. RINGMER	2-0	2-0	5-3	4-0	1-0	3-0	0-0	1-7	1-2	2-2	3-1	1-2	0-1	*	3-1	0-1	5-1	2-4
15. SHOREHAM	0-0	3-3	0-2	2-1	2-4	1-1	2-1	0-2	1-2	0-3	0-0	3-6	0-4	1-3	*	3-1	0-2	0-1
16. THREE BRIDGES	3-2	2-1	1-1	3-2	3-0	1-1	1-1	0-3	0-0	4-1	3-0	1-1	2-6	2-3	1-1	*	4-1	1-2
17. WHITEHAWK	1-3	0-2	1-3	4-0	0-1	1-1	1-0	1-2	0-4	3-2	2-1	0-1	1-5	3-1	1-2	3-1	*	1-1
18. WICK	1-1	0-1	0-0	2-3	2-1	4-2	0-3	3-0	0-4	1-3	6-2	3-2	4-2	2-1	0-1	2-1	1-1	2-2	*

(Peacehaven v Newhaven finished 2-1, but Newhaven had goal deducted so result 2-0)

Sussex County League Division One Ten Year Record

	82/3	83/4	84/5	85/6	86/7	87/8	88/9	89/90	90/1	91/2
Arundel	15			5	9	1	12	16	8	11
Bexhill Town									15	16
Burgess Hill Town	11	15	8	7	11	9	5	4	6	6
Chichester City	16				13	15				15
Eastbourne Town	9	10	3	3	5	4	15	15	16	12
Hailsham Town	10	9	14	11	14	6	4	13	13	8
Hastings Town Reserves	3	6	9							
Haywards Heath Town					3	7	13	12	14	18
Horsham YMCA			11	11	15	13	16			
Lancing			13	12	10	10	13	12	17	
Langney Sports							10	3	3	2
Littlehampton Town	6	2	2	6	6	14	7	2	1	3
Midhurst & Eastbourne	14	12	15	14	16					
Newhaven										10
Oakwood							17		9	14
Pagham	12	16				1	1	8	4	4
Peacehaven & Telscombe	1	7	10	5	7	8	8	5	2	1
Portfield			7	8	12	15	18			
Redhill							11	18		
Ringmer	13	8	13	16				10	12	9
Seaford Town							11	17		
Selsey						11	9	14	18	
Shoreham					12	8	10	14	9	11	17
Southwick	2	4								
Steyning Town	4	3	1	1						
Three Bridges	8	5	6	2	4	2	2	7	7	7
Whitehawk	5	1	4	4	2	5	3	6	10	13
Wick	7	14	16		9	3	6	1	5	5
No. of clubs competing	16	16	16	16	16	16	18	18	18	18

DIVISION TWO 1991-92

DIVISION TWO 1991-92

	P	W	D	L	F	A	PTS
Portfield	32	22	8	2	73	27	74
Midhurst & Ease.	32	21	3	8	88	53	66
Stamco	32	18	7	7	76	46	61
Redhill	32	18	6	8	70	40	60
Worthing United	32	18	5	9	73	49	59
Horsham YMCA	32	17	7	8	72	44	58
Selsey	32	16	5	11	63	48	53
Seaford Town	32	15	6	11	68	53	51
Crowborough A.	32	14	4	14	58	56	46
Sidley United	32	12	3	17	60	80	39
Broadbridge Hth	32	10	5	17	50	63	35
Little Common A.	32	10	5	17	52	66	35
Saltdean United	32	9	4	19	40	68	31
East Grinstead	32	7	7	18	43	69	28
Lancing	32	7	6	19	46	58	27
Bosham	32	7	5	20	41	106	26
East Preston	32	4	8	20	39	86	20

Manager of the month awards

Aug	Ken Ireland (Redhill)
Sept	Vijay Korgaokar (Portfield)
Oct	Micky Reed (Stamco)
Nov	Brian Woolmer (Worthing United)
Dec	John Suter (Horsham YMCA)
Jan	Vijay Korgaokar (Portfield)
Feb	Brian Woolmer (Worthing United)
Mar	Vijay Korgaokar (Portfield)
Apr/May	Vijay Korgaokar (Portfield)

Manager of the Season:
Vijay Korgaokar (Portfield)

LEADING SCORERS
(League matches only)

Anton Romasz (Midhurst & E'bourne) 33
John Daughters (Seaford Town) 31
Nigel Waller (Worthing United) 26

UNIJET SUSSEX COUNTY LEAGUE DIVISON TWO RESULTS 1991/92

HOME TEAM	1	2	3	4	5	6	7	8	9	10	11	12	13	14	15	16	17
1. BOSHAM	*	1-1	1-1	0-2	4-2	1-7	1-2	2-1	3-1	1-3	0-3	2-0	1-6	1-4	2-1	1-2	1-5
2. BROADBRIDGE HEATH	3-1	*	4-1	1-0	2-2	0-1	2-1	4-2	1-2	0-0	1-3	4-2	0-3	5-1	4-1	1-0	2-3
3. CROWBOROUGH ATH.	9-0	3-1	*	2-1	0-2	1-0	2-0	3-4	3-2	0-0	0-1	4-2	4-1	0-2	1-0	1-2	3-4
4. EAST GRINSTEAD	1-5	1-1	1-1	*	4-1	2-3	2-0	1-2	2-2	0-1	1-2	3-1	1-7	1-4	1-2	2-2	5-1
5. EAST PRESTON	2-2	1-0	0-2	1-3	*	1-4	2-3	0-5	0-5	0-1	0-2	2-4	2-0	0-2	1-2	0-3	1-1
6. HORSHAM Y.M.C.A.	4-0	3-1	4-2	1-0	2-0	*	0-0	2-0	4-2	3-3	2-3	1-2	2-0	4-1	2-2	4-0	1-2
7. LANCING	9-2	1-0	0-3	2-3	1-2	0-2	*	0-2	1-3	1-1	1-1	0-0	3-1	0-2	0-2	0-2	1-2
8. LITTLE COMMON A.	1-2	1-0	0-2	3-3	1-1	0-2	0-2	*	2-1	0-3	1-3	2-1	0-2	3-3	1-3	1-1	3-0
9. MIDHURST & E.	7-1	4-3	3-1	2-0	2-0	6-1	3-3	2-1	*	3-2	0-1	4-0	3-1	4-1	3-1	3-0	1-1
10. PORTFIELD	1-0	2-0	2-1	0-0	6-1	1-1	2-2	1-0	6-2	*	1-0	4-1	3-3	2-1	4-0	4-0	4-2
11. REDHILL	5-0	3-1	0-2	5-1	3-0	2-2	3-1	1-1	4-1	4-2	*	1-2	4-1	3-1	1-2	2-3	1-3
12. SALTDEAN UNITED	4-1	4-2	0-1	3-0	1-1	0-3	1-7	1-3	1-2	0-3	1-1	*	1-0	0-4	2-3	0-2	0-1
13. SEAFORD TOWN	2-2	2-0	1-1	4-0	4-4	2-2	2-0	4-1	1-2	0-3	3-1	1-2	*	1-0	2-1	1-1	2-0
14. SELSEY	1-1	7-1	3-0	1-1	4-1	2-1	2-1	6-1	0-3	0-1	2-1	1-1	2-4	*	1-0	1-3	1-0
15. SIDLEY UNITED	5-1	2-3	3-2	5-1	6-6	2-0	3-1	2-8	2-4	0-1	1-3	1-0	2-4	1-3	*	2-6	1-2
16. STAMCO	4-1	1-3	9-2	1-0	5-2	2-2	3-2	3-2	4-3	0-2	1-1	1-2	4-0	0-0	9-1	*	1-0
17. WORTHING UTD	7-0	4-1	3-0	3-0	2-2	4-2	2-1	5-0	2-3	2-4	2-2	3-1	1-3	3-0	1-1	2-1	*

UNIJET SUSSEX COUNTY LEAGUE DIVISION TWO CUP 1991-92

Preliminary Round (7-11-91)

East Grinstead v East Preston	2-1

First Round (4-1-92)

Little Common Albion v Saltdean United	1-0	Stamco v Sidley United (AET)	1-0
Worthing United v Bosham	8-0	Horsham YMCA v Broadbridge Hth (7-1-92)	3-1
Selsey v Portfield (8-1-92)	1-2	Crowborough Athletic v Seaford Town (11-1-92)	1-3
Redhill v Midhurst & Easebourne (11-1-92)	5-2	East Grinstead v Lancing (8-2-92)	0-1

Second Round (25-1-92)

Portfield v Worthing United (AET)	3-2	Horsham YMCA v Seaford Town (1-2-92)	3-1
Little Common Albion v Stamco (1-2-92)	3-0	Redhill v Lancing	2-0

Semi-Finals

Horsham YM v Portfield (at Littlehampton)	2-1	Redhill v Little Common (at Ringmer)	5-0

Final (at Broadbridge Heath FC)

Redhill v Horsham YMCA	2-1

UNIJET SUSSEX COUNTY LEAGUE SUSSEX FIVES (5-A-SIDE)

HELD AT THE BRIGHTON CENTRE, MONDAY FEBRUARY 3rd 1992
SPONSORED BY THE EVENING ARGUS AND PHONESPORT (SUSSEX SPORTSLINE)

First Round

Newhaven v Eastbourne Town	1-2	Littlehampton Town v Horsham YMCA	1-0
Langney Sports v Midhurst & E'bourne	1-2	Ringmer v Portfield	0-1
Peacehaven & Telscombe v Wick	0-4	Burgess Hill Town v Three Bridges	0-1
Pagham v Selsey	1-0	Redhill v Stamco	0-0 (1-0 pens)

Second Round

E'bourne Town v L'hampton 1-1 (6-5 pens)		Midhurst & Easeborne v Portfield	0-0 (0-1 pens)
Wick v Three Bridges 0-0 (1-2 pens)		Pagham v Redhill	2-1

Semi Finals

Portfield v Eastbourne Town	1-0	Three Bridges v Pagham	1-1 (2-1 pens)

Final

Portfield v Three Bridges	0-0 (4-5 on penalties)

NB - Penalty competitions were sudden death

DIVISION THREE 1991-92

DIVISION THREE 1991-92

	P	W	D	L	F	A	PTS
Hassocks	26	22	1	3	72	14	67
Mile Oak	26	17	6	3	61	25	57
Sidlesham	26	13	8	5	48	36	47
Ifield	26	13	6	7	49	37	45
Withdean	26	12	6	8	50	40	42
Hurstpierpoint	26	10	6	10	46	49	36
Lindfield Rangers	26	10	4	12	48	50	34
Ferring	26	10	4	12	44	53	34
Storrington	26	9	6	11	36	40	33
Franklands Village	26	7	7	12	33	42	28
Buxted	26	7	5	14	43	64	26
Forest	26	5	7	14	31	45	22
Rottingdean '89	26	5	5	16	33	70	20
Leftovers Sports	26	3	7	16	19	53	16

Manager of the month awards

Aug	N/A
Sept	Norman Johnson (Ferring
Oct	Joe Laidlaw (Sidlesham)
Nov	Nick Greenwood/Peter Liddell (H'socks)
Dec	Dave Richardson (Lindfield Rangers)
Jan	Nick Greenwood/Peter Liddell (H'socks)
Feb	Tony Gratwicke (Mile Oak)
Mar	Tony Gratwicke (Mile Oak)
Apr/May	Nick Greenwood/Peter Liddell (H'socks)

Manager of the Season:
Nick Greenwood/Peter Liddell (Hassocks)

LEADING SCORERS
(League matches only)

Steve Hards (Hassocks) 24
Robert Kitchen (Lindfield Rgrs) 16
Adrian Haines (Forest) 14
Gavin Tanner (Mile Oak) 14

UNIJET SUSSEX COUNTY LEAGUE DIVISON TWO RESULTS 1991/92

HOME TEAM		1	2	3	4	5	6	7	8	9	10	11	12	13	14
1.	BUXTED	*	3-4	1-0	2-2	0-6	1-1	3-0	3-0	4-1	1-2	2-3	2-3	2-1	4-1
2.	FERRING	3-0	*	0-1	0-1	2-1	3-2	1-2	0-0	2-1	4-3	5-1	1-1	2-2	2-3
3.	FOREST	1-3	1-1	*	3-1	0-2	3-0	1-2	3-0	1-2	3-2	3-3	1-3	0-2	1-5
4.	FRANKLANDS VIL.	4-1	4-0	1-0	*	0-1	1-2	0-3	3-2	1-3	0-4	4-1	1-1	1-2	1-1
5.	HASSOCKS	2-1	4-0	3-0	3-0	*	1-0	2-1	6-0	2-1	0-1	4-0	1-0	4-0	3-0
6.	HURSTPIERPOINT	3-2	2-3	3-2	3-0	1-5	*	2-2	1-1	3-2	0-0	3-1	2-2	3-0	1-3
7.	IFIELD	6-2	4-1	0-0	2-1	2-1	3-0	*	0-1	5-1	1-1	1-0	3-2	2-3	1-3
8.	LEFTOVERS	2-2	0-3	1-0	0-0	0-2	1-6	1-2	*	1-2	0-2	2-5	0-2	1-1	3-1
9.	LINDFIELD RGRS	6-0	5-3	3-2	1-1	1-2	3-0	1-1	2-2	*	0-4	4-0	3-3	1-0	0-2
10.	MILE OAK	1-1	2-0	4-2	2-1	2-2	2-2	1-0	2-0	2-0	*	5-1	0-2	2-1	5-1
11.	ROTTINGDEAN	1-1	5-0	1-1	2-3	0-6	1-3	2-0	0-0	0-3	0-4	*	0-0	2-3	3-1
12.	SIDLESHAM	3-1	2-1	1-1	1-0	0-4	0-1	0-4	2-1	4-2	1-1	5-1	*	3-0	3-2
13.	STORRINGTON	3-1	1-2	0-0	2-2	0-2	4-1	0-0	2-0	4-0	1-5	2-0	1-2	*	1-1
14.	WITHDEAN	5-0	2-1	1-1	0-0	2-3	3-1	2-2	1-0	1-0	1-2	5-0	2-2	1-0	*

UNIJET SUSSEX COUNTY LEAGUE DIVISION THREE CUP 1991-92

First Round

Buxted v Ifield	0-3	Ferring v Lindfield Rangers	3-1
Franklands Village v Forest	2-1	Leftovers Sports v Hurstpierpoint	1-2
Mile Oak v Rottingdean '89	4-2	Storrington v Sidlesham	0-3

Second Round (25-1-92)

Ferring v Withdean	0-2	Ifield v Franklands Village	2-0
Mile Oak v Hurstpierpoint	5-0	Sidlesham v Hassocks	4-1

Semi-Finals (all three matches at Shoreham FC)

Ifield v Sidlesham	0-2	Mile Oak v Withdean	3-3,2-3
			5-0

Final (at Littlehampton Town FC)

Sidlesham v Withdean   1-0

Hassocks FC - Unijet Sussex County League Division Three Champions 1991-92. Photo - Eric Marsh.

FIRST DIVISION CLUBS 1991-92

ARUNDEL

President: Michael Monk   **Chairman:** Michael Peters   **Manager:** Paul Croft
Secretary: Peter Wells, 37 Bewley Road, Angmering BN16 4JL (0903 771146).
Ground: Mill Road, Arundel (0903 882548)**Press Officer:** Brian Sellers (0903) 787468
Directions: Into Arundel, look for Mill Road car park. 1 mile from Arundel (BR).
Seats: 100   **Cover:** Yes   **Capacity:** 2,000   **Floodlights:** Yes   **Founded:** 1889
Colours: Red/white/red   **Change colours:** All yellow   **Nickname:** Mulletts
Programme: Yes   **Programme Editor:** Secretary   **Admission:** £1.50/75p
Record Gate: 2,200 v Chichester, League 67-68   **Previous League:** West Sussex.
Clubhouse: 2 bars, pool, darts, juke box, phone, toilets
Local Press: Arun Gazette, Evening Argus **91-92 Top Scorers:** Shaun Berrett 8, Danny Levy 8.
91-92 Gates: Total: 1,444   **Average:** 85   **Highest Gate:** 370 (v Littlehampton Town 20/4/92)
Hons: Sussex County Lg 57-58 58-59 86-87 (Lg Cup 86-87, Div 2 76-77, Reserve Section 78-79, Reserve Section Cup 78-79), Sussex RUR Charity Cup 68-69 72-73 78-79 79-80, Sussex Jnr Cup 07-08.

BEXHILL TOWN

President: Barry Woodcock   **Chairman:** Mr A J Hammond   **Manager:** J Lambert
Secretary: Mr E N Hughes, 5 Badgers Way, Hastings, East Sussex TN34 2QD (0424 427967).
Ground: The Polegrove, Brockley Rd, Bexhill-on-Sea, East Sussex (0424 220732).
Directions: At Little Common r'bout take 3rd exit to Cooden Sea Rd, left into Cooden Drive for one and a half miles, Brockley Rd on the right. Three quarters of a mile from Bexhill Central (BR).
Seats: 250   **Cover:** 250   **Capacity:** 2,000   **Floodlights:** No   **Founded:** 1926
Colours: Green & white   **Change colours:** Black & white   **Nickname:** Green Machine
Previous Name: Bexhill Town Athletic.
Programme: Yes   **Programme Editor:** Mr G Sully   **Admission:** £1.50/£1/50p
Record Gate: 2,000   **Clubhouse:** New clubroom and bar facilities
Local Press: Bexhill Observer   **91-92 Top Scorers:** Paul Balch 8.
91-92 Gates: Total: 1,293   **Average:** 76   **Highest Gate:** 250 (v Langney Sports 20/8/91)
Hons: S'sex Co. Lg 56-57 65-66 (Invit. Cup 55-56), S'sex RUR Char. Cup 57-58 73-74, S'sex Midweek Cup 25-26.

BURGESS HILL TOWN

President: Jack Lake   **Manager:** Jim Thompson   **Chairman:** Roy McKey
Secretary: David McKechnie, 20 Junction Rd, Burgess Hill RH15 0JD (0444 241790).
Ground: Leylands Park, Burgess Hill (0444 242429).
Directions: Wivelsfield Station (BR out of Victoria), turn right, first left, ground on right.
Seats: 100   **Cover:** Yes   **Capacity:** 2,000   **Floodlights:** Yes   **Founded:** 1882
Colours: Green & black stripes/black/black   **Change colours:** All yellow
Programme: Yes   **Programme Editor:** Peter Strange   **Admission:** £1.50   **Nickname:** Hillians
Record Gate: 600 v Carshalton A., FA Cup 3rd Qual. 1981.   **Sponsors:** Herbert Sports
Previous Leagues: **Clubhouse:** Members social club
Local Press: Mid Sussex Times   **91-92 Top Scorers:** Paul Harris 20, Ashley Carr 12.
91-92 Gates: Total: 2,212   **Average:** 130   **Highest Gate:** 368 (v Haywards Heath Town 26/12/91)
Hons: Sussex County Lg 75-76 (Div 2 74-75, Lg Cup 73-74 79-80 (R-up 90-91), Div 2 Cup 73-74), Sussex Snr Cup 1883-84 84-85 85-86, Sussex RUR Charity Cup R-up 91-92, Sussex I'mediate Cup 76-77, Sussex Jnr Cup 1889-90.

CHICHESTER CITY

Manager: R Reynolds   **Chairman:** G Redford   **President:**
Secretary: J F Hutter, 28 Stockbride Gdns, Donnington, Chichester PO19 2QT (0243 785839).
Ground: Oaklands Park, Chichester (0243 785978).   **Press Officer:** T Wallis (0705 464438).
Directions: Half mile north of city centre adjacent to Festival Theatre. Turn into Northgate car park from Oaklands Way and entrance is beside Tennis and Squash club. 1 mile from Chichester (BR) - walk north through city centre.
Seats: 50   **Cover:** 500   **Capacity:** 2,500   **Floodlights:** No   **Founded:** 1873
Colours: White/black/white   **Change colours:** All yellow   **Nickname:** Lilywhites
Programme: Yes   **Editor:** T Wallis (0705 464438)   **Admission:** £1.50   **Metal Badges:** No
Record Gate: 2,500 v Dorchester, FA Cup 1960   **Previous Name:** Chichester FC (pre-1960)
Previous Grounds: New Park Rec. 1873-81/ Priory Park 1881-1956.
Best FA Cup year: 1st Round Proper 60-61 (lost 0-11 at Bristol City).
Clubhouse: Open matchdays and some evenings   **Sponsors:** D & R Engineering
Local Press: Chichester Observer   **Previous Lgs:** Chichester/ West Sussex 1886-1920)
91-92 Top Scorers: Trevor Ashburner 7, David Kelly 7.
91-92 Gates: Total: 1,476   **Average:** 87   **Highest Gate:** 180 (v Littlehampton Town 20/8/92)
Hons: Sussex Co. Lg(5) 59-61 67-68 72-73 79-80 (Lg Cup 47-48 54-55 56-57 63-64, Div 2 R-up 84-85 90-91, Div 2 Cup 84-85 87-88 90-91, Invitation Cup 47-48 53-54 56-57 63-64), Sussex Snr Cup 25-26, Sussex RUR Charity Cup 60-61(Jt) 63-64, Sussex I'mediate Cup 67-68, West Sussex Lg (reserves) 45-46 66-67, Chich. Charity Cup 73-74, G C Hillier Mem. Tphy 1984+85+88+89+90, Coronation Cup 1989+90, Simmonds Cup 46-47 49-50 64-65 66-67.

EASTBOURNE TOWN

President: **Chairman:** K Twort   **Manager:** D Guy
Secretary: S R Myall, 9 Ringwood Close, Eastbourne, East Sussex BN22 8UH (0323 655565).
Ground: The Saffrons, Compton Place Road, Eastbourne, East Sussex (0323 23734).
Directions: Turn south west off A22 into Grove Road (opposite BR station). Ground quarter mile on right.
Seats: 50   **Cover:** 50   **Capacity:** 4,500   **Floodlights:** No   **Founded:** 1881
Colours: Yellow/blue/blue   **Change colours:**   **Nickname:** 'Town'
Programme: Yes   **Programme Editor:** K Winterton   **Admission:**   **Metal Badges:**
Previous Leagues: Southern Amtr 07-46/ Corinthian 60-63/ Athenian 63-76.
Record Gate: 7,378 v Hastings U. 1953   **Previous Ground:** Devonshire Park 1881-85
Previous Name: Eastbourne FC (until 1970) **Clubhouse:** Open every night and Sat. lunctimes.
Local Press: **91-92 Top Scorers:** Steve Loughton 13
91-92 Gates: Total: 2,129   **Average:** 129   **Highest Gate:** 513 (v Langney Sports 28/12/91)
Hons: Sussex County Lg 76-77, Sussex Snr Cup(12) 1889-91 93-95 98-1901 02-03 21-22 31-33 52-53, Sussex RUR Charity Cup 32-33 47-48 49-50, Southern Amtr Lg(2), AFA Snr Cup 21-22 24-25 (R-up 22-23 23-24), AFA Invitation Cup 69-70 (R-up 56-57 68-69 70-71).

Bexhill 'keeper Dave Bilsby claims under pressure against Peacehaven on 28th December. Photo - Colin Stevens.

Burgess Hill Town before their FA Cup 3rd Qualifying Round clash with Gravesend & Northfleet. Photo - Eric Marsh.

Eastbourne Town's Graham Evenden catches, but Peacehaven win 5-1 at the Saffrons. Photo - Roger Turner.

HAILSHAM TOWN

President: M Walker, Esq   **Chairman:** John Whippy, Esq   **Manager:** Mick French
Secretary/Press Officer: Derek York, 59 Anglesey Avenue, Horsebridge, Hailsham BN27 3BQ (0323 848024).
Ground: The Beaconsfield, Western Road, Hailsham, East Sussex (0323 840446).
Directions: A22 to Arlington Road, turn east, then left into South Road - left into Diplocks Way until Daltons. Four miles from Polegate (BR - Brighton-Eastbourne line); regular bus service from Eastbourne.
Seats: None   **Cover:** 300   **Capacity:** 2,000   **Floodlights:** Yes   **Founded:** 1885
Colours: Yellow & green   **Change colours:** White or red   **Nickname:** None
Programme: Yes   **Programme Editor:** Secretary   **Admission:** £1.50
Previous League: E Sussex, Southern Comb.   **Previous Ground:** Western Rd Rec.
Record Gate: 1,350 v Hungerford, FA Vase Feb '89   **Metal Badges:** No.
Clubhouse: Hot and cold snacks. Open every evening, matchdays and Sundays.   **Sponsors:**
Local Press: Hailsham Gazette, Eastbourne Herald, Sussex Express
91-92 Top Scorers: John Kemp 17, David Rowe 12, Steve Marsh 11, Russell Saunders 10.
91-92 Gates: Total: 3,844   **Average:** 226   **Highest Gate:** 480 (v Langney Sports 28/12/91)
Hons: FA Vase 5th Rd 88-89, Sussex County Lg Div 2 R-up 80-81, Southern Co's Comb. 74-75, Sussex I'mediate Cup, Hastings Snr Cup, Sussex Jnr Cup, Sussex Lg Cup, Hailsham Charity Cup.

LANGNEY SPORTS

President: Mr J Stonestreet   **Chairman:** Mr L Smith   **Manager:** P Cherry
Secretary: Mrs J Field, 17 Montague Way, Westham, East Sussex BN24 5NB (0323 765859).
Ground: Priory Lane, Eastbourne, East Sussex (0323 766265).
Directions: A22 to Polegate, A27 to Stone Cross, right onto B32104 to Langney Shopping Centre, then left and first right. One mile from Pevensey & Westham (BR). Buses from Eastbourne.
Seats: None   **Cover:** 200   **Capacity:** 1,000   **Floodlights:** Yes   **Founded:** 1966
Colours: Red & white/red/red   **Change colours:** White/blue/white   **Nickname:** None
Midweek Matchday: Wednesday
Programme: Yes   **Editor:** T Dawes (0323 764218)   **Admission:** £1.50/75p
Record Gate: 1,000+ v Crystal Palace, f'light opener 90-91.   **Sponsors:** Hotchkiss
Clubhouse: Every evening & lunchtime   **Previous League:** Eastbourne & Hastings
Previous Grounds: Princes Park, Wartling Rd, Eastbourne/ Adjacent pitch.   **Metal Badges:** No
Local Press: Eastbourne Gazette & Herald **91-92 Top Scorers:** Nigel Hole 40, Derrick Smith 16
91-92 Gates: Total: 3,590   **Average:** 211   **Highest Gate:** 400 (v Eastbourne Town 1/1/92)
Hons: Sussex Co. Lg R-up 91-92 (Div 2 87-88, Lg Cup 89-90, Div 3 86-87, Div 3 Cup 86-87, 5-aside comp. 1990), Sussex I'mediate Cup 85-86, Eastbourne Challenge Cup 85-86 86-87.

LITTLEHAMPTON TOWN

President: T Stabler   **Manager:** Carl Stabler   **Chairman:** B Suter
Secretary/Press Officer: Jim Owen, 6 Seafield Rd, Littlehampton, West Sussex BN16 2SE (0903 776832).
Ground: The Sportsfield, St Flora's Road, Littlehampton (0903 713944).
Directions: 10 minutes walk from Littlehampton station (BR) - turn left along Terminus Rd, continue through High Street and Church Rd to junction with St Flora's Rd (left).
Seats: 300   **Cover:** 400   **Capacity:** 3,000   **Floodlights:** Yes   **Founded:** 1894
Colours: Gold (black trim)/black/gold   **Change colours:** All white   **Nickname:** Marigolds
Programme: Yes   **Programme Editor:** C Scrimshaw   **Local Press:** Arun Gazette
Record Gate: 4,000 v Northampton, FA Cup 1st Rd Proper 90-91   **Sponsors:** Nicholson
Midweek Matches: Wednesday   **Clubhouse:** Sportsman (Private Club)   **Admission:** £1.50
91-92 Top Scorers: Paul Bennett 25, Steve Guilee 22, Mark Bennett 21, Terry Withers 11, Barry Rishman 11 (including 10 for Selsey).
91-92 Gates: Total: 3,360   **Average:** 198   **Highest Gate:** 310 (v Arundel 26/12/91)
Hons: FA Vase SF 90-91, FA Cup 1st Rd 90-91, Sussex Co. Lg 90-91 (Lg 58-59(jt with Shoreham) 75-76 76-77 84-85 90-91 (R-up 91-92)), Sussex Snr Cup 73-74 (R-up 90-91).

MIDHURST & EASEBOURNE

Manager: Stuart Groves   **Chairman:** Robert Boxall   **President:** TBA.
Secretary: E S Dummer, 14 Nine Acres, June Lane, Midhurst, West Sussex GU29 9EP (0730 813887).
Ground: Rotherfield, Dodsley Lane, Midhurst (0730 816557)   **Press Officer:** Rex Lane.
Directions: Ground one mile out of Midhurst on London Road.
Seats: 60   **Cover:** 200   **Capacity:** 1,000   **Floodlights:** No   **Founded:** 1946
Colours: All royal blue   **Change colours:** All red   **Nickname:** None
Programme: Yes   **Editor:** Secretary   **Admission:** £1   **Metal Badges:**
Record Gate: **Clubhouse:** Bar and canteen   **Sponsors:** Midhurst and Fernhurst Builders.
Local Press: Observer Series & West Sussex Gazette
Previous Lgs: West Sussex 46-79/ Southern Co's Combination 79-81.
91-92 Top Scorers: Anton Romasz 33, Robert Pearce 18.
91-92 Gates: Total: 950   **Average:** 59   **Highest Gate:** 150 (v Horsham YMCA 1/1/92)
Hons: Sussex Co. Lg Div 2 R-up 81-82 91-92, Southern Co's Comb. Div 2 80-81 (Chal. Cup 80-81), W Sussex Lg 67-68 76-77 79-80 (Div 1 55-56 62-63 64-65, Malcolm Simmonds Cup 59-60 73-74 77-78 79-80, Bareham Tphy 70-71), Sussex I'mediate Cup(5) 54-57 62-63 77-78.

NEWHAVEN

President: **Chairman:** M Godden   **Manager:** M Rosers
Secretary: F D Dixon, 39 Southdown Avenue, Peacehaven, East Sussex BN10 8RX (0273 585514).
Ground: Fort Road, Newhaven, East Sussex (0273 513940).
Directions: A275 from Lewes, or A259 coast rd, to Newhaven 1-way system. 1 mile from Newhaven Town (BR).
Seats: 50   **Cover:** Yes   **Capacity:** 4,000   **Floodlights:** Yes   **Founded:** 1887
Colours: All red   **Change colours:** All white (blue flash)   **Nickname:** Dockers
Programme: Yes   **Editor:** Mike Taylor (0273 515232)   **Admission:** £1.50   **Metal Badges:** N
Previous Leagues: None (founder members of SCFL)   **Previous Name:** Newhaven Town.
Record Gate: 3,000   **Previous Ground:** None (Lewes FC temporarily 90-91)
Midweek Matchday: Tuesday   **Clubhouse:** Being redeveloped   **Sponsors:** Lojex.
Local Press: Evening Argus, Sussex Express   **91-92 Top Scorers:** Andy Blythe 17, Michael Ring 15.
91-92 Gates: Total: 2,342   **Average:** 138   **Highest Gate:** 475 v (Peacehaven & Telscombe 27/8/91)
Hons: Sussex County Lg 53-54 (Div 2 71-72 90-91, Invitation Cup 48-49), Sussex Snr Cup R-up 53-54.

Hailsham Town. Back Row (L/R): Dick Jenner, Graham Bishop, Gary Holder, Tobi Hutchinson, Graham Richards, Dave Rowe, Shaun Chator-Grubb, John Kemp, Simon Fenner, Rob Gellatey, Mick French (Manager). Front: Phil Comber, Neil Thornicroft, Howard Stevens, Richard Booth, Steve Marsh, Paul Charlton. Photo - Dave West.

Langney Sports, Runners-up 1991-92. Back Row (L/R): Pete Cherry (Manager), Simon Haynes, Nigel Jones, Paul Callaghan, Mick Green, Steve Dell, Matt Jones, Paul Filsell, Pete Roberts, Pete Andrews (Physio), Eddie Woods (Coach). Front: Joe O'Neill, Derrick Smith, Paul Stevens, Jason Morley, Danny Ashworth, Nigel Hole. Mascot: Joe Green. Photo - Roger Turner.

Midhurst & Easebourne. Back Row (L/R): Paul Dowdell, Wayne Hyde, Graham Nutting, Andy Claydon, Simon Gibson, Andy Woodward, Dave Rowe, Micky Shotter (Captain), Stuart Groves (Manager), Bernard Penny (Trainer). Front: Peter Hill, Mark Sills, Adie Holden, Micky Taylor, Daren Chiverton, Robbie Pearce. Photo - Dave West.

643

OAKWOOD

President: R G Britts **Chairman:** A T Bridges
Secretary: Gerry Martin, 'Singlegate', Tinsley Green, Crawley RH10 3NS (0293 882400).
Manager: Brynn Marshall **Press Officer:** R Conley
Ground: Tinsley Lane, Three Bridges, Crawley, West Sussex (0293 515742).
Directions: From A23 to Gatwick, take 1st set of lights into Manor Royal, pass next lights, over r'bout to warehouse marked Canon, turn right signposted Oakwood. Last clubhouse down lane. Two miles north of Three Bridges (BR).
Seats: None **Cover:** Yes **Capacity:** 3,000 **Floodlights:** Yes **Founded:** 1962
Colours: Red/white/red **Change colours:** White/red/white **Nickname:** Oaks
Programme: Yes **Editor:** A T Bridges (0293 533982) **Admission:** £1.50
Previous Lgs: Crawley & Dist., Southern Co's Comb. **Previous Ground:** Park pitches.
Record Gate: 527 **Midweek Matchday:** Wednesday **Metal Badges:** No
Clubhouse: Pool tables, multidart boards, large bar area **Sponsors:** Bryant Homes
Local Press: Crawley Observer, Crawley News
91-92 Top Scorers: Gary Chandler 10, David Rowe 10.
91-92 Gates: Total: 822 **Average:** 48 **Highest Gate:** 222 (v Three Bridges 20/4/92)
Hons: Sussex Co. Lg Div 2 R-up 89-90 (Div 2 Cup 89-90, Div 3 84-85), Southern Comb. Cup 83-84.

PAGHAM

Chairman: John Allen **Manager:** Graham Peach **President:** A Pearce
Secretary/Press Officer: Mr Eric G Nunn, 8 West Drive, Aldwick, Bognor Regis PO21 4LY (0243 262879).
Ground: Nyetimber Lane, Pagham, West Sussex (0243 266112).
Directions: Turn off A27 Chichester by-pass (signposted A259 Pagham). Ground in village of Nyetimber. Three miles from Bognor (BR). Buses 260 & 240.
Seats: 180 **Cover:** Yes **Capacity:** 2,000 **Floodlights:** Yes **Founded:** 1903
Colours: White & black **Change colours:** Red & yellow **Nickname:** None
Midweek Matchday: Wednesday
Programme: Yes **Programme Editor:** Secretary **Admission:** £1.50
Record Gate: 1,200 v Bognor 1970. **Sponsors:** Viking Toyota.
Clubhouse: Members and visitors club open evenings and matchdays.
Previous League: West Sussex **Previous Grounds:** None **Metal Badges:** No
Local Press: Observer **91-92 Top Scorers:** Mark Vickers 28, Neil Darnley 15, Christopher Sibley 10.
91-92 Gates: Total: 1,725 **Average:** 101 **Highest Gate:** 260 (v Littlehampton Town 21/1/92)
Hons: Sussex Co. Lg R-up 80-81 87-88 88-89 (Div 2 78-79 86-87, Lg Cup 88-89, Div 2 Cup 71-72 85-86, Res. Sect. West 80-81, Res Sect. Cup 80-81, Sussex F'lit Cup R-up 88-89, Sussex RUR Charity Cup 88-89, West Sussex Lg 65-66 68-69 69-70, Malcolm Simmonds Cup 67-68, Sussex I'mediate Cup 66-67.

PEACEHAVEN & TELSCOMBE

President: Mr W Parris **Chairman:** Mr J Edwards **Manager:** Mr A Pook
Secretary/Press Officer: Mr K Parris, 12 Abbey Close, Peacehaven, East Sussex BN10 7SD (0273 585173).
Ground: Piddinghoe Avenue, Peacehaven, East Sussex (0273 582471).
Directions: Arriving from Brighton on A259, cross r'bout and Piddinghoe Avenue is next left after 2nd set of lights - ground at end. From Newhaven Piddinghoe Avenue is first right after first set of lights. Three miles from Newhaven (BR). Peacehaven is served by Brighton to Newhaven and Eastbourne buses.
Seats: None **Cover:** 250 **Capacity:** 3,000 **Floodlights:** Yes **Founded:** 1923
Colours: White/black/black **Change colours:** All sky **Nickname:** The Tye
Programme: Yes **Programme Editor:** Secretary
Local Press: Evening Argus/ Sussex Express
Record Gate: 1,420 v Littlehampton, League 11/5/91. **Sponsors:** Fine Bookmakers
Previous Ground: Telscombe Tye **Previous Leagues:** Lewes/ Brighton
Previous Names: Peacehaven Rangers merged with Telscombe Tye in 1923/ Peacehaven & Telscombe Cliffs (for one season only in early 1980's).
Midweek Matches: Wednesday **Clubhouse:** Every evening. Pool, darts **Admission:** £1.50
91-92 Top Scorers: Mark Taylor 23, Adie Chipper 14, Lee Butler 13 (including 8 for Shoreham), Graham Farmer 11, Darren Newman 11, Paul Thomsett 10.
91-92 Gates: Total: 3,661 **Average:** 215 **Highest Gate:** 572 (v Littlehampton Town 28/1/92)
Hons: Sussex Co. Lg 78-79 81-82 82-83 91-92 (R-up 77-78 80-81 90-91, Lg Cup 91-92, Div 2 R-up 75-76, Div 2 Cup 75-76, Norman Wingate Tphy 91-2, Hayden Tphy 81-82, Div 2 Invitation Cup 69-70, Res. Sect. 83-84, Res Sect. Cup 81-82 83-84 85-86 86-87 87-88), Sussex Snr Cup R-up 81-82, Sussex RUR Charity Cup 77-78 81-82 (R-up 80-81 89-90), FA Cup 4th Qual. Rd 90-91.

PORTFIELD

Manager: Vijay Korgaokar **President:** E W White **Chairman:** T Rustell
Secretary: Mr G Rustell, The Den, Priors Leaze, Hambrook, Chichester, West Sussex PO18 8RQ (0243 572675).
Ground: Church Road, Chichester (0243 779875) **Press Officer:**
Directions: A27 from Arundel to Chichester, take road to signposted city centre then 1st left (Church Rd) after supermarket r'bout. 1 mile from Chichester (BR).
Seats: 30 **Cover:** 200 **Capacity:** 2,000 **Floodlights:** Yes **Founded:** 1896
Colours: Amber and black **Change colours:** All white **Nickname:**
Programme: Yes **Editor:** R Saxton **Admission:** **Metal Badges:**
Record Gate: Unknown **Midweek Matchday:** Wednesday **Sponsors:**
Clubhouse: 2 bars, pool, snooker, dance floor, stage - open every night and weekend lunchtimes.
Local Press: **Previous League:** West Sussex.
Previous Grounds: Downers (until 1952)/ Florence Road (until 1959).
91-92 Top Scorers: Adrian Miles 22 (including 2 for Chichester City), Sean Forry 15.
91-92 Gates: Total: 779 **Average:** 49 **Highest Gate:** 102 (v Selsey 26/12/91).
Hons: Sussex Co. Lg Div 2 72-73 83-84 91-92 (Div 2 Cup 70-71 72-73), W Sussex Lg 46-47 48-49 (Malcolm Simmonds Cup 46-47), Sussex Jnr Cup 45-46.

RINGMER

President: Sir G Christie   **Chairman:** Richard Soan
Secretary: Pam Howard, 39 Springett Avenue, Ringmer BN8 5HD (0273 813818).
Manager: Derek Southouse   **Press Officer:** Alan Harper (0323 764263)
Ground: Caburn Pavillion, Anchor Field, Ringmer (0273 812738).
Directions: Turn into Springett Avenue opposite Ringmer village green. Anchor Field first left. Five miles from Lewes (BR).
Seats: No   **Cover:** Yes   **Capacity:** 2,000   **Floodlights:** Yes   **Founded:** 1910
Colours: Sky & navy blue   **Change colours:** All white   **Nickname:** None
Programme: Yes   **Editor:** Alan Harper (0323 764263)   **Admission:** £1.30/70p/40p
Previous League: Brighton   **Previous Names:** None.   **Metal Badges:** No
Record Gate: 1,200 in FA Cup   **Previous Grounds:** None.
Midweek Matchday: Tuesday   **Clubhouse:** Two bars, function room   **Sponsors:**
Local Press: Sussex Express   **91-92 Top Scorers:** Darren Brown 13, Pip Parris 11.
91-92 Gates: Total: 1,730   **Average:** 102   **Highest Gate:** 243 v (Newhaven 1/1/92).
Hons: FA Cup 1st Rd Proper 70-71 (lost 0-3 at Colchester Utd), Sussex Co. Lg 70-71 (Div 2 68-69, Div 2 Invitation Cup 66-67, Res. Sect. 80-81, Res. Sect. East 79-80 80-81), Sussex Snr Cup 72-73 (R-up 80-81), Sussex Jnr Cup 25-26.

THREE BRIDGES

President: Mr Jim Steele   **Chairman:** Mr Mick Yearwood
Secretary: Mr Martin Clarke, 18 Mannings Close, Pound Hill, Crawley RH10 3TX (0293 883726).
Manager: Mr Bobby Nash   **Press Officer:** Mr Alf Blackler
Ground: Jubilee Field, Three Bridges, Crawley, West Sussex (0293 530540).
Directions: 200yds from Three Bridges (BR) - towards Crawley town centre.
Seats: None   **Cover:** 400   **Capacity:** 3,500   **Floodlights:** Yes   **Founded:** 1901
Colours: Amber & black   **Change colours:** All white   **Nickname:** None
Programme: Yes   **Editor:** Mark Stacy (0293 885864)   **Admission:** £1.50
Previous Lgs: Mid Sussex/ Redhill & District   **Previous Grounds:** None.
Record Gate: 2,000 v Horsham, 1948   **Midweek Matchday:** Tuesday   **Metal Badges:** No
Clubhouse: Bar, dance floor, pool, darts   **Sponsors:** Auto Body Care
Local Press: Crawley Observer, Crawley News
91-92 Top Scorers: Sean Smith 15, Neil Elson 11, John Malthouse 10.
91-92 Gates: Total: 1,472   **Average:** 87   **Highest Gate:** 227 (v Oakwood 26/12/91)
Hons: Sussex Co. Lg R-up 85-86 87-88 88-89 (Div 2 54-55, Invitation Cup 70-71, Div 2 Invitation Cup 62-63), Sussex RUR Charity Cup 82-83.

WHITEHAWK

Manager: Butch Reeves   **President:** Ron Wiltshire   **Chairman:** Ken Powell
Secretary: John Rosenblatt, 25 Arundel Street, Brighton BN2 5TH (0273 680322).
Ground: The Enclosed Ground, East Brighton Park (0273 609736).
Directions: Follow Brighton seafront road towards Newhaven, turn inland (Arundel Road) opposite Marina, 3rd right into Roedean Road, 1st left into Wilson Avenue. Three miles from Brighton (BR); take Newhaven, Eastbourne or Saltdean bus to Marina, then as above.
Seats: None   **Cover:** 500   **Capacity:** 3,000   **Floodlights:** Yes   **Founded:** 1945
Colours: All red   **Change colours:** All blue   **Nickname:** Hawks
Midweek Matchday: Wednesday
Programme: Yes   **Editor:** Tony Kelly (0273 698203)   **Admission:** £1.50   **Sponsors:**
Record Gate: 2,200 v Bognor Regis Town, FA Cup 4th Qualifying Rd replay 88-89.
Clubhouse: Licensed bar, hot and cold food, pool, darts.
Previous League: Brighton Hove & Dist.   **Previous Grounds:** None
Previous Name: Whitehawk & Manor Farm Old Boys (until 1958).   **Metal Badges:** No
Local Press: Evening Argus   **91-92 Top Scorer:** Dale Mills 6.
91-92 Gates: Total: 1,119   **Average:** 66   **Highest Gate:** 259 (v Peacehaven & Telscombe 20/4/92)
Hons: Sussex Co. Lg 61-62 63-64 83-84 (Div 2 67-68 80-81, Lg Cup 82-83, Invitation Cup 60-61 69-70, Div 2 Cup 80-81), Sussex Snr Cup 50-51 61-62, Sussex RUR Charity Cup 54-55 58-59 90-91, Sussex I'mediate Cup 49-50, Sussex Jnr Cup 48-49 51-52, Brighton Charity Cup 51-52 59-60 61-62 82-83 87-88 88-89, Worthing Charity Cup 82-83.

WICK

Chairman: Norman Cairns   **Manager:** Norman Cairns   **President:** M Hood
Secretary/Press Officer: Andy Blackwood, 10 Dean Close, Littlehampton, West Sussex BN17 7ND (0903 731024).
Ground: Crabtree Park, Coombes Way, Littlehampton, West Sussex (0903 713535).
Directions: A27 to Crossbush, left at Howards Hotel, after 1 mile cross level crossing, turn left into Coombes Way next to Locomotive PH - ground at end. One and a half miles from Littlehampton (BR).
Seats: None   **Cover:** 300   **Capacity:** 2,000   **Floodlights:** Yes   **Founded:** 1892
Colours: Red & black hoops/black/black   **Change colours:** Green & white hoops/white white
Programme: Yes   **Editor:** Les Page (0903 260837)   **Local Press:** Littlehampton Gazette.
Record Gate: 900.   **Sponsors:** Body Shop International   **Nickname:** Wickers
Previous Grounds: None   **Previous Leagues:**
Previous Names: None.   **91-92 Top Scorer:** Rod Wood 10.   **Metal Badges:** No.
Midweek Matches: **Clubhouse:** First floor. Capacity 120   **Admission:** £1.50
91-92 Gates: Total: 1,427   **Average:** 84   **Highest Gate:** 300 (v Littlehampton Town 20/12/92)
Hons: Sussex Co. Lg 89-90 (Lg Cup 87-88, Div 2 81-82 85-86, Div 2 Cup R-up 82-83, Norman Wingate Tphy 88-89 90-91, Res. Sect West 87-88 90-91, Sussex 5-aside R-up 85-86), Sussex RUR Charity Cup 89-90, Gilbert Rice F'llt Cup R-up 80-81 81-82, Sussex Jnr Cup 59-60, Brighton Charity Cup 85-86.

SECOND DIVISION CLUBS 1991-92

BROADBRIDGE HEATH

President: T Beech   **Chairman:** K Soames   **Manager:** J Laker (0403 730944).
Secretary: B P Nagle, The Briars, 59A Millfield, Southwater, Horsham RH13 7HT
Ground: Broadbridge Heath Sports Centre, Wickhurst Lane, Horsham (0403 65871).
Directions: Alongside A24, Horsham north/south bypass.
Seats: 250   **Cover:** Yes   **Capacity:** 2,000   **Floodlights:** No   **Founded:** 1919
Colours: All royal blue   **Change colours:** All red   **Nickname:**
Programme: Yes   **Programme Editor:** G Street   **Admission:**
Previous Leagues: Horsham, West Sussex, Southern Co's Comb.
Clubhouse: Bar. Meals, pool, darts, social club etc.
91-92 Top Scorers: Richard Camps 9 (including 4 for Horsham YMCA).
91-92 Gates: Total: 676   **Average:** 42   **Highest Gate:** 140 (v Horsham YMCA 1/1/92).

CROWBOROUGH ATHLETIC

President: Mr Peter Taylor   **Chairman:** Mr Barry Sykes
Secretary: Mr Roddy Harman, Flat 6, 3 Carlton Rd, Tunbridge Wells, Kent TN1 2JS   (0892 518808).
Manager: Mr Roger Crouch   **Press Officer:** Mr Harry Smith
Ground: Alderbrook Recreation Ground, Fermor Road, Crowborough (0892 661893).
Directions: Turn east off A26 at Crowborough. Cross traffic lights, through High Street, right into Croft Rd, continue into Whitehall Rd and Fermor Rd, Alderbrook is second right after mini-r'bout.
Seats: None   **Cover:** 200   **Capacity:** 1,000   **Floodlights:** No   **Founded:** 1894
Colours: White/navy/navy   **Change colours:** All yellow   **Nickname:** Crows.
Programme: Yes   **Programme Editor:** Mr Harry Smith   **Sponsors:** Blackden Enterprises Ltd.
Previous League: Brighton   **Clubhouse:** Function room and bars   **Admission:** £1
Midweek Matchday: Wednesday   **Local Press:** Kent & Sussex Courier, Sussex Express
Previous Grounds: None   **91-92 Top Scorers:** Richard Dorrill 16.
91-92 Gates: Total: 1,046   **Average:** 65   **Highest Gate:** 143 (v Sidley United 20/8/91)
Hons: Sussex Co. Lg Div 2 Cup 77-78 (Div 3 R-up), Sussex Intermediate Cup.

EAST GRINSTEAD

President: Peter Paice   **Chairman:** Peter Cadman   **Manager:** Mark Arnold
Secretary: Gary Bullen, 4 Churchfields, East Grinstead TN22 3NA (0825 713138).
Ground: East Court, East Grinstead (0342 325885).   **Press Officer:** Bruce Talbot (0293 543809).
Directions: A264 Tunbridge Wells road, turn off to right opposite Blackwell Farm Road, follow lane on left 200yds past rifle club.
Seats: None   **Cover:** 300   **Capacity:** 2,000   **Floodlights:** Yes   **Founded:** 1890
Colours: Gold/black/black   **Change colours:** Red/white/red   **Metal Badges:** Yes
Programme + Admission: £1.50   **Programme Editor:** Press Officer   **Nickname:** Wasps
Record Gate: 2,002 v Lancing 8/11/48   **Sponsors:** Rydon Construction.
Previous Lgs: Mid S'sex/ Sthern Amtr   **Midweek Matchday:** Wednesday.
Previous Grounds: West Street Cricket Ground/ King George's Field.
Clubhouse: Bar, kitchen (hot food on matchdays), darts, pool, dance floor.
Local Press: East Grinstead Courier, Observer.   **91-92 Top Scorers:** Simon Doran 14.
91-92 Gates: Total: 1,710   **Average:** 107   **Highest Gate:** 250 (v Midhurst & Easebourne 4/10/91)
Hons: Sussex RUR Charity Cup 74-75, Sussex Co. Lg Invitation Cup 51-52, Sussex Jnr Cup (jointly) 07-08.

EASTBOURNE UNITED

Chairman: Andrew Curry   **President:**
Secretary: Mrs Myra Stephens, 7b Erica, Langney, Eastbourne BN23 8BT (0323 766050).
Manager: Nicholas Stephens   **Press Officer:** Steve Dorling (0323 24541).
Ground: The Oval, Channel View Rd, Eastbourne, East Sussex (0323 269989).
Directions: To seafront and turn left. Turn left into Channel View Rd at Princes Park and ground 1st right. 2 miles from Eastbourne (BR).
Seats: 200   **Cover:** 250   **Capacity:** 3,000   **Floodlights:** Yes   **Founded:** 1894
Colours: White/black/white   **Change colours:** All tangerine   **Nickname:** The "U's"
Programme: Yes   **Programme Editor:** Steve Dorling   **Admission:** £2   **Metal Badges:** Yes
Record Gate: 3,000   **Previous Ground:** Lynchmere   **Previous Name:** Eastbourne Old Comrades
Previous Leagues: Sussex Co. 21-28 35-56/ Metropolitan 56-64/ Athenian 64-77/ Isthmian 77-92.
Clubhouse: Club licence - for members   **Sponsors:** Planahead
Local Press: Eastbourne Gazette + Herald, Evening Argus   **Midweek Matchday:** Tuesday
Players progressing to Football League: B Salvage, T Funnell, M French.
91-92 Top Scorers: John Craig 5.
91-92 Gates: Total: 1282   **Average:** 64   **Highest Gate:** 117 (v Horsham 21/8/91)
Hons: Sussex Snr Cup 60-61 62-63 63-64 66-67 68-69 (R-up 89-90), Sussex RUR Charity Cup 55-56, Athenian Lg Div 2 66-67 (Div 1 R-up 68-69), Sussex Intermediate Cup 65-66 68-69.

HASSOCKS

President: Maurice Boxall   **Chairman:** Jim Goodrum
Secretary: Bob Preston, 65 Oak Hall, Burgess Hill, West Sussex RH15 0DA (0444 245695).
Manager: Nick Greenwood/ Peter Liddell   **Press Officer:** Paul Elphick (Haywards Hth 454492)
Ground: Adastra Park, Hassocks (0273 842668) *Move to new ground imminent - check before travelling*
Directions: Orchard Lane off Grand Avenue from B2116 (Albourne - Ditchling Road). Third of a mile from Hassocks (BR); walk east from station along Keymer Rd, ground on left.
Seats: None   **Cover:** None   **Capacity:**   **Floodlights:** No   **Founded:** 1902
Colours: Red/white/red   **Change colours:** Blue & white stripes/white/red
Programme: Yes   **Programme Editor:** Paul Elphick   **Admission:** N/A   **Metal Badges:** No.
Previous Leagues: Mid Sussex/ Brighton Hove & Dist./ Southern Co's Comb.   **Nickname:** Robins
Record Gate: 400 v Nottingham University, AFA Snr Cup January 1978
Midweek Matchday: Wednesday   **Clubhouse:** Lounge with adjoining bar & kitchen.
Sponsors: Burgess Hill Glass   **Local Press:** Mid Sussex Times, Evening Argus
91-92 Top Scorers: Steve Hards 24, Neil Smith 13, David Smith-Phillips 10.
Hons: Sussex County Lg Div 3 91-92, Southern Counties Comb. 76-77 (Lg Cup 79-80), Brighton Hove & Dist. Lg 71-72, Sussex Intermediate Cup 74-75 (R-up 80-81).

646

HAYWARDS HEATH TOWN

Manager: Gary Croydon   **President:** Tony Lander   **Chairman:** Frank Hall
Secretary: Stan Barnes, 'Fairfields', London Rd, Hassocks, West Sussex BN6 9NE (0444 235192).
Ground: Hanbury Park Stadium, Allen Road, Haywards Heath, West Sussex (0444 412837).
Directions: A272 to Haywards Heath town centre. At Sussex r'bout, north on B2078 (Hazelgrove Road), first right into New England Road, 4th right into Allen Road which leads to ground. 1 mile from Haywards Heath (BR).
Seats: 490   **Cover:** 490   **Capacity:** 5,000   **Floodlights:** Yes   **Founded:** 1888
Colours: White (blue trim)/blue/blue   **Change colours:** All yellow   **Nickname:** Bluebells
Programme: Yes   **Editor:** Pat Bucknell (0444 457726)   **Admission:** £1.50   **Sponsors:**
Previous Leagues: Mid Sussex/ Metropolitan 52-61.   **Metal Badges:** No.
Previous Grounds: Muster Green/ Haywards Heath Recreation Ground/ Victoria Park.
Previous Names: Haywards Heath Junior/ Haywards Heath Excelsoir/ Haywards Heath FC 1895-1988.
Record Gate: 4,000 v Horsham, Metropolitan League, 1952.
Local Newspaper: Mid Sussex Times   **Clubhouse:** Bar, small dance floor, pool.
91-92 Top Scorers: Russell Barnard 5, Jason Rutherford 5.
91-92 Gates: Total: 1,245   **Average:** 73   **Highest Gate:** 150 (v Burgess Hill Town 20/4/92)
Hons: Sussex Snr Cup 57-58, Sussex RUR Charity Cup 66-67 74-75 75-76, Sussex Co. Lg 45-46 49-50 50-51 69-70 (R-up 74-75, Lg Cup 72-73), Mid Sussex Lg 11-12 19-20 22-23 23-24 24-25, Montgomery Cup 19-20 22-23 24-25.

HORSHAM Y.M.C.A.

President: J Smith   **Chairman:** D Cherriman   **Manager:** J Suter
Secretary: W Bower, 5 Patching Close, Ifield, Crawley, West Sussex RH11 0ES (0293 533831).
Ground: Gorings Mead, Horsham, West Sussex (0403 52689).
Directions: At end of lane at rear of Horsham FC (see Diadora League section). Half mile from Horsham (BR).
Seats: 125   **Cover:** 200   **Capacity:** 800   **Floodlights:** Yes   **Founded:** 1898
Colours: White/black/red   **Change colours:** All red   **Nickname:** "YM's"
Programme: Yes   **Editor:** B Denyer (0403 741401)   **Metal Badges:** No (ties + jumpers)
Record Gate: 600 v Horsham, FA Cup   **Previous Ground:** Lyons Field, Kings Rd   **Admission:** £1
Clubhouse: Snooker room, dancehall, bar, committee room.
Previous League: Horsham & District/ Brighton Hove & District/ Mid Sussex.
Sponsors: Principal Copiers/ Swift Surveying Services Ltd.   **Midweek Matchday:** Tuesday
Local Newspaper: West Sussex County Times
91-92 Top Scorers: Duane Read 18, Barry Burden 16, David Smith 16.
91-92 Gates: Total: 1,333   **Average:** 83   **Highest Gate:** 139 (v Broadbridge Heath 20/4/92)
Hons: Sussex Co. Lg Div 2 65-66 82-83 (Lg Cup 81-82, Invitation Cup 66-67 67-68, Div 2 Invitation Cup 59-60 61-62).

LANCING

President: R G Steele, Esq   **Chairman:** R J Brown   **Manager:** R Culley
Secretary: W J Chisnell, 15 Orchard Way, Lancing, West Sussex BN15 9ED (0903 763048).
Ground: Culver Road, Lancing, West Sussex (0903 764398).
Directions: Third turning left north of Lancing station (BR).
Seats: 300   **Cover:** 300   **Capacity:** 3,000   **Floodlights:** Yes   **Founded:** 1941
Colours: Yellow/blue/yellow   **Change colours:** All red   **Nickname:** None
Programme: Yes   **Editor:** Len Ralph (0903 763913)   **Sponsors:** Churchill Windows.
Previous Name: Lancing Athletic   **Previous Ground:** Croshaw Rec, Sompting.
Previous League: Brighton Hove & Dist.   **91-92 Top Scorers:** Alan Herbert 12.   **Metal Badges:** No.
Record Gate: 2,591 v Tooting, FA Amtr Cup 22/11/47. At Culver Road: 2,340 v Worthing 25/10/52.
Midweek Matches: Wednesday   **Clubhouse:** Run by Sussex County FA   **Admission:** £1.50p
91-92 Gates: Total: 1,193   **Average:** 74   **Highest Gate:** 178 (v Worthing United 26/12/91)
Hons: Sussex Co. Lg R-up 49-50 64-65 (Div 2 57-58 69-70 (R-up 82-83), Div 2 Cup 81-82, Invitation Cup), Sussex RUR Charity Cup 65-66, Brighton Lg 46-47 47-48, Sussex Intermediate Cup 46-47, Brighton Charity Cup 83-84 84-85 86-87.

LITTLE COMMON ALBION

Chairman: Mr K E Cherry   **President:** Councillor Ivor Brampton.
Secretary: Mrs M Cherry, 11 Bidwell Avenue, Bexhill-on-Sea, East Sussex TN39 4DB (0424 217191).
Manager: K Cherry/ R Eldridge
Ground: Little Common Rec, Pear Tree Lane, Little Common, East Sussex (0424 35861)
Directions: A259 from Brighton.
Seats: None   **Cover:** 250   **Capacity:**   **Floodlights:** No   **Founded:** 1966
Colours: Claret & blue   **Change colours:** White & blue   **Nickname:** None
Programme: Yes   **Editor:** D Comerford (0424 218695)   **Admission:** £1   **Metal Badges:** Yes
Record Gate: 251   **Clubhouse:** Bar, clubroom   **Midweek Matchday:** Wednesday
Local Newspapers: Bexhill Observer   **Previous League:** East Sussex   **Sponsors:** Poolcare.
91-92 Top Scorers: Gary Barker 16.
91-92 Gates: Total: 568   **Average:** 36   **Highest Gate:** 151 (v Sidley United 20/4/92)
Hons: E Sussex Lg(2) 75-77, Hastings I'mediate Cup, Hawkhurst Chal. Cup 76-77, Sussex Minor Cup 75-76.

MILE OAK

Manager: A Gratwicke   **President:** E J Earle   **Chairman:** R Kerly
Secretary: C D Brown, 19 The Crescent, Southwick, West Sussex BN42 4LB (0273 591346).
Ground: Mile Oak Recreation Ground, Graham Avenue, Mile Oak (No telephone).
Directions: From A27 take Mile Oak Road or Locks Hill & Valley Road to Chalky Road, ground 500yds on right along Graham Avenue which runs up valley from centre of Chalky Road.
Seats: None   **Cover:**   **Capacity:**   **Floodlights:** No   **Founded:** 1960
Colours: All tangerine   **Change colours:** All white   **Nickname:** The Oak
Programme: Yes   **Editor:** C Tew (0273 416668)   **Admission:**   **Metal Badges:** No
Previous Leagues: Southern Counties Combination/ Brighton Hove & District
Record Gate: Unknown   **Previous Ground:** Victoria Rec., Portslade.
Midweek Matchday: **Clubhouse:** Mile Oak Pavillion; Hall and tea bar.
Sponsors: Lancing Glass Works Ltd   **Metal Badges:**
91-92 Top Scorers: Gavin Tanner 14   **Local Newspapers:** Brighton Evening Argus, Adur Herald
Hons: Southern Counties Combination 86-87, Brighton Hove & District Lg 80-81, Vernon Wentworth Cup 85-86.

REDHILL

President: Mr Ray Ward **Chairman:** Mr John Park **Manager:** Ken Ireland
Secretary: Mr B S Thomas, Surrey View, The Green, Godstone, Surrey RH9 8DY (0883 742502).
Ground: Kiln Brow, Three Arch Road, Redhill, Surrey (0737 762129).
Directions: On left hand side of A23, two and a half miles south of Redhill.
Seats: 150 **Cover:** 150 **Capacity:** 2,000 **Floodlights:** Yes **Founded:** 1900
Colours: All red **Record Gate:** 1,200 v Crystal Palace, Brian Medlicott Testimonial 1989
Programme: Yes **Programme Editor:** John Parks **Admission:** **Sponsors:**
Previous Leagues: East West Surrey/ Spartan 09-10/ Southern Suburban/ London 21-23/ Athenian 23-84.
Local Newspaper: **Previous Grounds:** Memorial Sports Ground 1894-1986.
Clubhouse: Evenings (except Wednesday), weekend lunchtimes **Nickname:** Reds
91-92 Top Scorers: Steve Turner 19, Ricky Kidd 17, John Holman 12. **Metal Badges:**
91-92 Gates: Total: 1,983 **Average:** 123 **Highest Gate:** 168 (v Horsham YMCA 20/8/91)
Hons: FA Amtr Cup SF 25-25, FA Cup 1st Rd 57-58, Athenian Lg 24-25 83-84 (Lg Cup 69-70 70-71), Surrey Snr Cup 28-29, Gilbert Rice F'llt Cup 80-81, Sussex County Lg Div 2 Cup 91-92.

SALTDEAN UNITED

Chairman: Trevor Clarke **Manager:** John Bolingbroke **President:** Jim Bower
Secretary: Ken Ades, 93 Greenbank Avenue, Saltdean, Brighton BN2 8QQ (0273 304625).
Ground: Hill Park, Combe Vale, Saltdean, Brighton (0273 309898).
Directions: A259 coast road east from Brighton to Saltdean, left into Arundel Drive West, and Saltdean Vale to bridle path at beginning of Combe Vale. Club 200yds along track.
Seats: 50 **Capacity:** 2,500 **Floodlights:** No **Founded:** 1966
Colours: Red & black/stripes/black/black **Change colours:** Blue & white stripes/sky/sky
Programme: Yes **Programme Editor:** Secretary **Admission:** £1 (OAPs etc 50p)
Record Gate: Unknown **Previous Grounds:** None **Sponsors:** Sunley
Clubhouse: Most evenings & weekends. Licensed bar, lounge, pool table **Nickname:** Tigers
Previous League: Brighton Hove & Dist. **Local Press:** Brighton Evening Argus. **Metal Badges:** No
91-92 Gates: Total: 366 **Average:** 23 **Highest Gate:** 48 (v Redhill 7/9/91)
91-92 Top Scorer: Danny Shine 9. **Hons:** Sussex Co. Lg Div 3 88-89.

SEAFORD TOWN

President: J Tanner, Esq **Chairman:** J Rolf, Esq
Secretary: S R Francis, 40 Stafford Rd, Seaford, East Sussex BN25 1UB (0323 891885).
Manager: P Hubbard, J Kingswood **Press Officer:** Secretary.
Ground: Crouch Gardens, East Street, Seaford, East Sussex (0323 892221).
Directions: Enter Seaford on A259 and turn into Warwick Road (opposite Library), continue into East Street. Ground along Crouch Lane (by phone box). Third of a mile from Seaford (BR).
Seats: None **Cover:** 150 **Capacity:** 1,000 **Floodlights:** No **Founded:** 1889
Colours: All red **Change colours:** All blue **Nickname:** Town
Programme: Yes **Editor:** M Webster (0328 899218) **Sponsors:** Fell Clean Air.
Previous Name: None **Previous Grounds:** None.
Previous Leagues: S'sex 01-02/ Mid S'sex 02-52/ S'sex Co. 52-78/ Southern Co's Comb./ Brighton Hove & Dist.
Midweek Matches: Tuesday **Record Gate:** 800 v Brighton & H.A. 16/8/89.
Clubhouse: Tuesdays, Thursdays, matchdays. Pool, darts. **Admission:** £1
Local Newspapers: Seaford Gazette, Sussex Express, County Shield. **Metal Badges:** No.
91-92 Top Scorers: John Daughters 31, Barry Knight 18.
91-92 Gates: Total: 957 **Average:** 60 **Highest Gate:** 124 (v Saltdean United 20/4/92)
Hons: Sussex Co. Lg Invitation Cup 58-59 (Div 2 88-89 (R-up 63-64), Div 3 85-86, Div 3 Cup 85-86), Sussex Jnr Cup 09-10, Brighton Lg Div 1 80-81, Sussex RUR Charity Cup R-up 73-74, Montgomery Cup 35-36 38-39.

SELSEY

Chairman: D Longworth **Manager:** N Hider/ I Lee **President:**
Secretary: D W Lee, 47 Sunnymead Drive, Selsey, Chichester, West Sussex PO20 0DG (0243 605163).
Ground: High Street Ground, Selsey, Chichester, West Sussex (0243 603420)
Directions: B2145 from Chichester to Selsey, turn right by Fire Station. Regular buses from Chichester.
Seats: 100 **Cover:** 200 **Capacity:** 2,000 **Floodlights:** Yes **Founded:** 1903
Colours: Blue/white/blue **Change colours:** White/red/red **Metal Badges:** Yes
Programme: Yes **Editor:** Secretary **Admission:** £1.20 **Nickname:** Seasiders
Record Gate: 750-800 v Chichester or Portfield, 1950's **Midweek Matchday:**
Clubhouse: Bar, lounge, snooker room. **Sponsors:** Allslade Welding & Fabrications Ltd
Local Newspapers: Chichester Observer, Evening Argus, Portsmouth Evening News.
Previous Lgs: Chich. & Dist./ W Suss. **91-92 Top Scorers:** Jeffery Marshall 18, Marc Agostinelli 13.
91-92 Gates: Total: 1,263 **Average:** 80 **Highest Gate:** 140 (v Portfield 20/4/92)
Hons: Sussex Co. Lg R-up 89-90 (Div 2 63-64 75-76 (R-up 86-87), Div 2 Cup 86-87 (R-up 84-85), Div 2 Invitation Cup 63-64, Sussex 5-aside), Sussex Snr Cup R-up 63-64, Sussex l'mediate Cup 58-59, Sussex Jnr Cup(Reserves) 76-77, West Sussex Lg 54-55 55-56 57-58 58-59 60-61 (Malcolm Simmonds Cup 55-56 56-57 57-58 58-59).

SHOREHAM

President: Mr A Bloom **Chairman:** Mr J Linfield
Secretary: Mr G Hilton, 67 Test Rd, Sompting, West Sussex BN15 0EP (0903 763024).
Manager: Mr K Keehan **Press Officer:** Mr M Wenham (0273 596009).
Ground: Middle Road, Shoreham-by-Sea, West Sussex (0273 454261).
Directions: Half mile from Shoreham-by-Sea (BR) - east across level crossing, up Dolphin Road, ground 150yds on right. Or, A27 to Southlands Hospital - south down Hammy Lane, left at end, ground opposite.
Seats: None **Cover:** 1 stand **Capacity:** 1,500 **Floodlights:** Yes **Founded:** 1892
Colours: Blue & white **Change colours:** Red & white **Nickname:** None
Programme: Yes **Editor:** Mr M Wenham (0273 596009) **Admission:** £1.20 (60p OAP/children)
Previous League: West Sussex **Midweek Matchday:** Wednesday **Metal Badges:** No
Record Gate: 1,342 v Wimbledon (floodlight opening 1986). **Sponsors:** Ballamys
Clubhouse: Seats 70. Bar, pool, darts. **Previous Ground:** Buckingham Pk (pre-1970)
Local Press: Shoreham Herald **91-92 Top Scorers:** Lee Butler (now Peahaven) 8.
91-92 Gates: Total: 1,084 **Average:** 64 **Highest Gate:** 120 (v 3 Bridges 22/4/92, v L'hampton 86/2/92)
Hons: Suss. Co. Lg 51-52 52-53 77-78 (R-up 34-35, Div 2 61-62 76-77, Div 2 Cup 74-75 82-83, Invitation Cup 57-58), Sussex Snr Cup 01-02 05-06, Sussex F'llt Cup R-up 89-90, Sussex RUR Charity Cup 02-03 05-06, Vernon Wentworth Cup 86-87.

Redhill. Back Row (L/R): Mickey Joyce (Asst Mgr), Keith Grimestone, Ricky Kidd, Mark Sestanovich, Terry Burns, Mark Endsleigh, Roy Jellow, Roger Moss (Trainer), Ken Ireland (Manager), John Costick (Physio). Front: Dave Savage, Steve Tucker, Jim Parle, Richard Ungar, Perry Williams, Paul Daubeney, Decon Monger, Nigel Smith. Photo - Dave West.

Tim Edwards, the Horsham YMCA goalkeeper dashes from his goal to smother at Steve Turner's feet. The Redhill striker had the last laugh scoring the winner in the last minute of this Division Two Cup Final. Photo - Dennis Nicholson.

Selsey FC pictured before their FA Cup tie against Romsey Town. Photo - Eric Marsh.

SIDLEY UNITED

President: Mr T Adams   **Chairman:** Mr Peter Snow   **Secretary:** TBA
Manager: Dave Shearing   **Press Officer:** Mr Peter Snow (0424 210974).
Ground: Gullivers Sports Ground, North Road, Glovers Lane, Sidley, Bexhill-on-Sea (0424 217078).
Directions: From Brighton on A259 to Bexhill bypass traffic lights, left into London Road, continue into Sidley, right into Glovers Lane and 1st left into North Road. One mile from Bexhill (BR).
Seats: None   **Cover:** 150   **Capacity:** 1,500   **Floodlights:** No   **Founded:** 1906
Colours: Royal & sky blue   **Change colours:** All red   **Nickname:** Blues
Programme: Yes   **Editor:** Mr Peter Snow (0424 210974)   **Admission:** £1 (50p OAP)
Previous Leagues: East Sussex/ Hastings & District   **Metal Badges:** Yes
Record Gate: 1,300 in 1959   **Previous Grounds:** None.   **Sponsors:** J Burke
Midweek Matchday: Tues/ Thurs   **Clubhouse:** Large bar area & function room.
Local Press: Bexhill Observer, Argus, Citizen   **91-92 Top Scorers:** Robert Warner 12, Guy Bentley 11.
91-92 Gates: Total: 1,880   **Average:** 117   **Highest Gate:** 376 (v Little Common Albion 26/12/91)
Hons: Suss. Co. Lg Div 2 58-59 64-65 (Div 2 Invit. Cup 57-58), Suss. I'mediate Cup 47-48, Suss. Jnr Cup 24-25.

SOUTHWICK

Chairman: Dennis Perry   **President:** Dr D W Gordon, MBBS Dr.COG
Secretary: Mr A J Edwards, 26 Church Green, Shoreham-by-Sea, West Sussex BN43 6JQ (0273 596577).
Manager: Micky Fogden   **Assistant Manager:** Dennis Bowen.   **Press Officer:** Sec.
Newsline: 0898 800 624   **Commercial Manager/Physiotherapist:** Tony Dineen
Ground: Old Barn Way, off Manor Hall Way, Southwick, Brighton BN43 4NT (0273 591744).
Directions: Five minutes walk from either Fishergate or Southwick BR stations. By A27 from Brighton take 1st left after 'Southwick' sign to Leisure Centre. Ground adjacent.
Seats: 220   **Cover:** 1,220   **Capacity:** 3,500   **Floodlights:** Yes   **Founded:** 1882
Colours: Red & black stripes/black/black   **Change Colours:** Yellow (blue pin stripe)/blue/blue
Record Gate: 3,200 v Showbiz side 1971   **Midweek matchday:** Tuesday   **Metal Badges:** Yes.
Programme: 30p   **Editor:** Paul Symes (0273 594142)   **Sponsors:** Power Tools Ltd.
Previous Leagues: West Sussex 1896-1920/ Sussex County 20-52 54-84/ Metropolitan 52-54/ Combined Counties 84-85/ Isthmian 85-92.
Previous Grounds: Croft Avenue/ The Green/ Oldfield Crescent.   **Nickname:** Wickers
Players progressing to Football League: Charles & William Buttenshaw (Luton 1948).
Best FA Cup season: 1st Rd Proper 74-75 (lost 0-5 at AFC Bournemouth).
Best FA Amateur Cup season: 3rd 28-29 **Best FA Vase season:** 3rd Rd 79-80 85-86
Local Newspaper: Evening Argus (0273 606799), Shoreham Herald (0273 455104)
Clubhouse: Evenings & weekend lunchtimes. Members bar & VIP lounge. Snacks on matchdays.
91-92 Top Scorer: Paul Smith 6.
91-92 Gates: Total: 1,522   **Average:** 72   **Highest Gate:** 257 (v Worthing 1/1/92).
Hons: Isthmian Lg Div 2 Sth 85-86, Sussex Co. Lg 25-26 27-28 29-30 47-48 68-69 74-75 (R-up 23-24 28-29 36-37 39-40 70-71 76-77 78-79 79-80 82-83, Lg Cup 77-78, Div 1 Invitation Cup 65-66, Div 2 R-up 65-66), Combined Co's Lg R-up 84-85, Sussex Snr Cup 1896-97 1910-11 12-13 24-25 27-28 29-30 30-31 36-37 47-48 67-68, Sussex RUR Charity 1896-97 1908-09 10-11 24-25 25-26 27-28 28-29 29-30 37-38 76-77, West Sussex Lg 1896-97 97-98 1908-09 10-11, Sussex Jnr Cup 1891-92.

STAMCO

Chairman: Leon Shepperdson   **President:** Mrs K Shepperdson
Secretary: Alan Ramsay, 8 Montgomery Rd, Hastings, East Sussex TN35 4LA (0424 712395).
Manager: Micky Reed   **Press Officer:** Terry Henham.
Ground: Pannel Lane, Pett, Hastings, East Sussex (0424 813757).
Directions: A259 from Hastings towards Rye, right at White Hart pub, down Friars Hill for two miles to Trompett church, left into Pannel Lane.
Seats: 20   **Cover:** Yes   **Capacity:** 1,5000   **Floodlights:** No   **Founded:** 1971
Colours: Blue & white/blue/blue   **Change colours:** All yellow   **Metal Badges:** No
Programme: Yes   **Editor:** Michael James (0424 852926)   **Admission:** £1   **Nickname:** None
Record Gate: 166   **Previous Grounds:** None   **Sponsors:** Sussex Turnery & Moulding Co.
Previous Leagues: Southern Counties Combination/ East Sussex/ Hastings.
Clubhouse: Bar/ lounge   **Midweek Matchday:**
Local Newspaper: Hastings Observer.   **91-92 Top Scorer:** Kevin Bevis 16, Kevin Clee 15.
91-92 Gates: Total: 538   **Average:** 34   **Highest Gate:** 78 (v Little Common Albion 2/5/92).
Hons: Sussex Co. Lg Div 2 Cup R-up 89-90 90-91, Hastings Snr Invitation Cup 89-90, Hastings Intermediate Cup 79-80 81-82 82-83 85-86 86-87 87-88.

WORTHING UNITED

President: N/A   **Chairman:** Mr L Newbon
Secretary: Mr B A Withers, 7 Guildford Rd, Rustington, West Sussex BN16 3JB (0903 772416).
Manager: Mr Brian Woolmer   **Press Officer:** Secretary.
Ground: Beeches Avenue, Worthing, West Sussex (0903 234466).
Directions: From west on A27, Beeches Avenue is 4th left past Barn Hill r'bout. From east take 2nd left past lights at Downlands Hotel and proceed to Beeches Avenue - go to and follow concrete road to cap park.
Seats: 100   **Cover:** Yes   **Capacity:** 500   **Floodlights:** No   **Founded:** 1948
Colours: Sky & white stripes/navy/white   **Change colours:** All white   **Nickname:** None
Programme: Yes   **Editor:** N Woolmer (0903 772698)   **Sponsors:** Tinsley Robor.
Previous Name: Wigmore Athletic   **Previous Grounds:** Harrison Road, Worthing.
Previous Leagues:
Midweek Matches: **Record Gate:** 180 v Northwood, FA Vase 3rd Rd 91-92.
Clubhouse: Bar, refreshment facilities   **Admission:** £1 (50p OAP & children).
Local Newspapers: Worthing Herald.   **Metal Badges:** Yes
91-92 Top Scorers: Nigel Waller 26, Steve Gurney 25 (including 3 for Lancing).
91-92 Gates: Total: 823   **Average:** 51   **Highest Gate:** 91 (v Sidley United 17/8/91).
Hons: Sussex Co. Lg Challenge Cup 74-75 (Invitation Cup 59-60, Div 2 52-53, Div 2 Invitation Cup 59-60, Div 3 89-90), Sussex Jnr Cup 49-50.

Lancing defend during their home league fixture with Little Common Albion.

Nigel Sopp of Worthing United (right) is pursued by Lancing's Mark Collins in a Boxing Day derby. Photo - Colin Stevens.

Worthing United FC. Back Row (L/R): Jerry Webb (Asst Manager), Nick Smith, Darren Tracey, Nigel Waller, Paul House, Graham Waller, Steve Jones, Lee Newbon (Chairman), Brian Woolmer (Manager). Front: Howard Albon, Mark Jackson, Nigel Sopp, Jamie Houslop (Mascot), Jason Monger, Steve Murphy, John Marion, Wai Lam Yau. Photo - Dave West.

THIRD DIVISION CLUBS 1991-92

BOSHAM

President: D G Phillips   **Chairman:** D M Fowler   **Manager:** R L Collyer
Secretary: R D Probee, 39 Arnold Way, Bosham, West Sussex PO18 8NJ (0243 572570).
Ground: Walton Lane, Bosham, West Sussex PO18 8QF (0243 574011).
Directions: Half mile from Bosham (BR) - walk south down station road, over A27 r'bout, left at T-junction, ground entrance 50 yds on left.
Seats: None   **Cover:** 50   **Capacity:** 2,000   **Floodlights:** No   **Founded:** 1901
Colours: Red/white/red   **Change colours:** White/black/red   **Nickname:** Robins
Programme: Yes   **Programme Editor:** Secretary   **Admission:** £1   **Metal Badges:** No
Previous Leagues: Chichester & Dist Jnr/ Chichester & Bognor/ Chichester & Dist./ West Sussex
Midweek Matchday: Tuesday.   **Clubhouse:** Club bar. Open throughout week and weekends.
91-92 Top Scorers: Lloyd Fowler 5.   **Local Press:** Portsmouth News, Chichester Observer.
91-92 Gates: Total: 620   **Average:** 39   **Highest Gate:** 82 (v Portfield 1/1/92).
Hons: Sussex Co. Lg Div 3 Cup 84-85, Sussex Jnr Cup 55-56, West Sussex Lg 77-78 (Div 2 56-57), Chichester & Dist. Jnr Lg 06-07, Chichester & Bognor Lg 11-12 12-13 (Lg Cup 11-12), Chichester & Dist. Lg 53-54 55-56, Chichester Charity Cup 55-56.

BUXTED

President: K Nicholls, Esq   **Chairman:** C C Winter, Esq   **Manager:** Sam Coates
Secretary: P J Durrant, 'Haven', Station Rd, Isfield, East Sussex TN22 5XB (0825 750449).
Ground: Buxted Recreation Ground (0825 812431).
Directions: A272 to Buxted, first right into Framfield Rd opposite Buxted Inn, ground 500 yds on right.
Seats: None   **Cover:** No   **Capacity:**   **Floodlights:** No   **Founded:** 1918
Colours: Red/black/black   **Change colours:** All blue   **Nickname:** The Bux.
Programme: Yes   **Editor:** A Cornford (0825 765422)   **Sponsors:** Top Title Video.
Previous Leagues: Brighton Hove & District/ Mid Sussex.   **Admission:**
Midweek Matchday: **Clubhouse:** Pavillion with social area and bar.
Local Newspapers: The Courier, Sussex Express
Previous Grounds: **91-92 Top Scorers:** Michael Turner (now Hassocks) 12.

EAST PRESTON

President: Greg Stanley   **Chairman:** Greg Stanley   **Manager:** Phil Green.
Secretary: Mrs E C Brett, 20 Holly Drive, Toddington Lane, Littlehampton, West Sussex (0903 725316).
Ground: Roundstone Rrecreation Ground, East Preston, West Sussex (0903 776026).
Directions: 1 mile from Angmering (BR). A259 from Worthing to Roundstone Hotel (6 miles), turn south over level crossing, 1st right is Roundstone Drive.
Seats: **Cover:**   **Capacity:**   **Floodlights:** No   **Reformed:** 1966
Colours: Jade/sky/yellow   **Change colours:** All red   **Nickname:**
Programme: Yes   **Programme Editor:** W Tomlinson Snr   **Midweek Matchday:**
Sponsors: **Previous Leagues:** Worthing/ W Sussex   **91-92 Top Scorer:** David Croft 8.
Clubhouse details: 4 dressing rooms, licensed bar, kitchen   **Metal Badges:**
91-92 Gates: Total: 558   **Average:** 35   **Highest Gate:** 69 (v Midhurst & Easebourne 26/8/91).
Hons: Sussex Co. Lg Div 2 83-84 (Div 3 R-up 90-91, Div 3 Cup 87-88), West Sussex Lg 77-78 80-81 81-82 82-83 (Malcolm Simmonds Cup 80-81 82-83), Vernon Wentworth Cup 80-81.

FERRING

Manager/Press Officer: N Johnson   **Chairman:** H W McIlwain   **President:** P Seaby
Chairman: H W McIlwain
Secretary: Malcolm Gamlen, 46 Sunningdale Road, Durrington, Worthing BN12 2NE (0903 263655).
Ground: Glebelands, Greystoke Road, Ferring (0903 53618).
Directions: Turn SE from the A259 Worthing/Littlehampton road into either Ferring Lane or Langbury Lane. Cross Ferring Railway crossing turn right in to Rife Way, then left into Greystoke Road. 1 mile from Goring (BR) - walk south, then right for 1 mile on main road.
Seats: None   **Cover:** 200   **Capacity:** 500   **Floodlights:** None   **Founded:** 1952
Colours: Royal blue/white   **Change colours:** Yellow & green   **Nickname:** None
Programme: Yes   **Editor:** Chairman   **Sponsors:** Mason Pearce   **Metal Badges:** No
Midweek Matchday: **Previous Leagues:** W Sussex/ Worthing   **Record Gate:** 150
Clubhouse: Separate changing/showers accomodation for both teams and officials, Ladies & Gents toilets inside and out.
90-91 Top Scorer: William Pearce 11   **Local Newspapers:** Worthing Herald, Argus.
Hons: Sussex Co. Lg Div 2 Invitation Cup 64-65 (Div 2 Cup R-up 86-87, Div 3 Cup 83-84), Worthing Lg 61-62 (Div 1 60-61), West Sussex Lg 80-81 (Div 2 Sth 79-80).

FOREST

President: **Chairman/Press Off.:** Michael Robinson   **Manager:** Graham Powell.
Secretary: Mrs Sandra Robinson, 51 Cook Road, Horsham RH12 5GJ (0403 62513).
Ground: Roffey Sports Social Club, Spooners Road, Roffey (0403 210223).
Directions: Spooners Road is off the main Crawley Road, approx 100yds from the Star Public House heading towards Crawley.
Seats: No   **Cover:** 250   **Capacity:** 1,500   **Floodlights:** No   **Founded:** 1958
Colours: Blue/white   **Change colours:** Yellow/green   **Metal Badges:**
Programme: 16 pages   **Programme Editor:** Mick Robinson (0403 62513)
Previous Leagues: Crawley/ Southern Co's Comb./Mid Sussex **Midweek Matchday:**
Local Newspapers: West Sussex County Times.   **Previous Ground:** Forest Boys School.
Sponsors: Roffey Sports & Social Club   **Record Gate:** Unknown.   **Nickname:** None
Clubhouse: 2 large bars, snooker tables, pool room etc   **91-92 Top Scorer:** Adrian Haines 14
Hons: Mid Sussex Snr Charity Cup 76-77 84-85 85-86 86-87 89-90, Sussex I'mediate Cup 87-88.

FRANKLANDS VILLAGE

President: J Rutherford   **Chairman:** P Gaston
Secretary: Mr N J Worsfold, Flat 3, 5 Sydney Rd, Haywards Heath, West Sussex RH16 1QQ (0444 415331).
Manager: P Batchelor/P Gaston   **Press Officer:** Mr R Collins.
Ground: Hardy Memorial Playing Fields, Franklands Village, Haywards Heath, West Sussex (0444 440138).
Directions: A272 Haywards Heath to Uckfield Road turn left at Birch Service Station which leads down to the village.
Seats: No   **Cover:** 400 sq ft.   **Capacity:** N/A   **Floodlights:** No   **Founded:** 1956
Colours: All royal blue   **Change colours:** Gold/black/black   **Nickname:** None.
Programme: Yes   **Editor:** Mrs L Worsfold (0444 416475)   **Midweek Midweek:** Wednesday
Previous Leagues: Mid Sussex/ Crawley/ Brighton Hove & District/ Southern Counties Combination.
Clubhouse details: Franklands Village Social Club. Bar, function room, pool, darts, television.
Local Newspapers: Mid Sussex Times, Brighton Evening Argus
Previous Grounds: None   **Record Gate:** 150   **Admission:** £1   **Metal Badges:** No
Sponsors: TBA.   **90-91 Top Scorer:** Mark Ormanroyd 17.
Hons: Brighton Lg 76-77 78-79, Sussex Co. Lg Div 3 Cup, Southern Counties Combination 82-83, Mid Sussex Charity Cup 79-80 80-81 82-83, Sussex Intermediate Cup.

HURSTPIERPOINT

President: **Chairman:** W Marchant   **Manager:** Steve Chambers
Secretary/Press Officer: Paul Joun, 16 Church Close, Burgess Hill, Sussex (0444 247183).
Ground: Pavilion, Fairfield Recreation Ground, Cuckfield Road, Hurstpierpoint, Sussex (0273 834785).
Directions: At Hurst crossroads (mini r'bout) proceed north into Cuckfield Rd (B2117) for 1km. Entrance to ground between houses Nos 158 & 160.
Seats: None   **Cover:** No   **Floodlights:** No   **Nickname:** The Point **Founded:** 1886
Colours: Blue & black stripes/black/black   **Change colours:** Yellow & red
Programme: Yes   **Editor:** Matthew Bosher (0273 835290)   **Midweek Matchday:** Tuesday
Previous Leagues: Mid Sussex/ Brighton Hove & District/ Southern Counties Combination.
Clubhouse: Facilities for refreshments including licenced premises
Local Newspapers: Mid Sussex Times, Brighton Evening Argus   **Metal Badges:** No
91-92 Top Scorer: Mark Stafford 12   **Sponsors:** Picket & White.

IFIELD

President: D Whinder   **Chairman:** B Crossley   **Manager:** S Reed
Secretary: R S Anderson, 15 Sissington Close, Pound Hill, Crawley (0293 886215).
Ground: Ifield Green, Rusper Rd, Ifield, Crawley (0293 536569).
Directions: From Ifield BR station follow Ifield Drive, 2nd left into Rudgwick Rd, turn right, ground 600 yds on left.
Seats: None   **Cover:** No   **Nickname:** None   **Floodlights:** No   **Founded:**
Cols: Red & white stripes/black/black   **Change colours:** Blue & white stripes   **Metal Badges:** No
Programme: Yes   **Editor:** Geoff Thornton (0293 531911)   **Midweek Matchday:** Wednesday
Previous Leagues: Mid Sussex 73-74/ Crawley & Dist.
Clubhouse: Located within football and sports field. Two changing rooms & showers, referee's changing room & shower, bar, kitchen.
Local Press: Crawley News, Crawley Observer   **Sponsors:** Jardine DFS Air Cargo.
91-92 Top Scorer: Des Lyons (including two for Broadbridge Heath).
Hons: Mid Sussex Snr 73-74, Crawley Premier Lg 73-74, Crawley Snr Cup 83-84.

LINDFIELD RANGERS

Manager: Mr Dave Richardson   **Chairman:** Squadron Ldr B F Ryan   **President:** N Fisk
Secretary: Mr P Fisk, Dormer Cottage, 64 Oathall Rd, Haywards Heath (0444 412112).
Press Officer: R Tilford (0825 763737).
Ground: Underhill Lane, Clayton, East Sussex.
Directions: A23 from Brighton to Pycombe Garage, right onto Burgess Hill Rd, at bottom of Pycombe Hill turn right into ground.
Seats: None   **Cover:** No   **Nickname:** None   **Floodlights:** No   **Founded:** 1983.
Colours: Red/white/red   **Change colours:** Blue & white hoops   **Metal Badges:** No
Programme: **Midweek Matchday:**   **Sponsors:** Trident Copiers.
Previous Leagues: Crawley & District/ Mid Sussex (pre-1991).
Previous Ground: Hickmans Lane, Lindfield.   **Clubhouse:** Tea bar.
90-91 Top Scorers: Robert Kitchen 16, Gareth Rees 10.
Local Newspapers: **Hons:** Mid Sussex Lg 90-91
91-92 Top Scorer: Des Lyons (including two for Broadbridge Heath).
Hons: Mid Sussex Snr 73-74, Crawley Premier Lg 73-74, Crawley Snr Cup 83-84.

ST FRANCIS HOSPITAL

President: **Chairman:** P Gaffney   **Manager:**
Secretary: C O'Prey, 2 Hatchgate Lane, Cuckfield RH13 5DU (0444 450403).
Ground: Colwell Lane, Haywards Heath.
Seats: None   **Cover:** None   **Nickname:** None   **Floodlights:** No   **Founded:**
Colours: Green   **Local Newspaper:** Mid Sussex Times.
Programme: **Editor:**   **Midweek Matchday:** TBA
Previous League: Mid Sussex (pre-1992).
Clubhouse: Bar, changing rooms, tea bar, boardroom.

SHINEWATER ASSOCIATION

President: **Chairman:** S Courtney   **Manager:** A Walsh/ K Rogers.
Secretary: 79 Harebeating Drive, Hailsham, East Sussex (0323 442488).
Ground: Shinewater Lane, Langney, Eastbourne, East Sussex.
Seats: None   **Cover:** None   **Nickname:** None   **Capacity:** 2,000   **Floodlights:** No
Colours: Sky blue   **Previous Leagues:** East Sussex.   **Metal Badges:**
Sponsors: British Gas   **Midweek Matchday:** TBA
Local Newspaper: Eastbourne Gazette.   **Clubhouse:** Bar, dressing rooms, tea bar.

SIDLESHAM

President: Mr Cyril Cooper   **Chairman:** Mr Roy Parker
Secretary: Mr Peter Taylor, 14 Ashurst Close, North Bersted, Bognor Regis PO21 5UJ (0243 867970).
Manager: Mr Joe Laidlaw   **Press Officer:** Mr David Arnell-Smith.
Ground: The Recreation Ground, Sidlesham, West Sussex (0243 641538).
Directions: Signposted Hunston/Selsey (B2145) - from r'bout travel south towards Selsey for four miles; ground on right between houses.
Seats: None   **Cover:** Yes   **Nickname:** None   **Floodlights:** Yes   **Reformed:** 1946.
Colours: Yellow & green stripes/black/black   **Change colours:** All blue
Programme: Yes   **Editor:** Mr Patrick Phillips (0243 603028)   **Midweek Matchday:** Wednesday
Previous Leagues: West Sussex (pre-1991).   **Local Newspaper:** Chichester Observer.
Clubhouse: Large bar, separate function room, snooker room.   **Metal Badges:** No
Sponsors: Stearns Builders Merchants Ltd   **Admission:** 50p including programme.
91-92 Top Scorer: Mark Bailey 10.   **Previous Grounds:** None.
Hons: West Sussex Lg Malcolm Simmonds Cup 78-79 90-91, Sussex Intermediate Cup 90-91.

STORRINGTON

President: D Medhurst   **Chairman:** M Baker.
Secretary: K Dalmon, 4 End Cottages, Storrington Rd, Amberley, Arundel, West Sussex BN18 9LX (0798 831887).
Manager: A Massimo/ F Massimo/ R Howley   **Press Officer:** T Brookes.
Ground: Recreation Ground, Pulborough Road, Storrington (0903 745860).
Directions: Turn west on A283 (off A24). Ground opposite pond to the west of the village
Seats: None   **Cover:** Yes   **Nickname:** Swans   **Floodlights:** No   **Founded:** 1920
Colours: All blue   **Change colours:** White/navy/navy
Metal Badges: No
Programme: Yes   **Editor:** Mike Wenham (0273 596009)   **Previous Leagues:** Worthing/ W Sussex.
Previous Grounds: No   **Sponsors:** The White Horse, The Square, Storrington
Clubhouse: Clubroom with bar, dressing rooms & toilets
Local Newspapers: Chanctonbury Herald, Horsham County Times.
91-92 Top Scorer: David Scott 7   **Hons:** Worthing Lg(3).

WITHDEAN

Chairman: Keith Turrell   **President:** Graham Spicer
Secretary: D J Gunstone, 285 Brighton Rd, Lancing, West Sussex BN15 8JR (0903 750063).
Manager: Steve Nealgrove.
Ground: Withdean Stadium, off Valley Drive, Brighton (0703 551638).
Directions: Off main London - Brighton road.
Seats: 1,000   **Cover:** None   **Capacity:** 10,000   **Floodlights:** No   **Founded:** 1987.
Colours: All red   **Change Colours:** All white   **Clubhouse:** Pub on ground
Programme Editor: K Turrell (0273 591530).
Previous Leagues: Brighton Hove & District   **Previous Grounds:** None
Local Newspaper: Brighton Evening Argus   **Midweek Matchday:**
91-92 Top Scorer: Bill Collinson 13.   **Sponsors:** Express Computers.
Hons: Sussex Co. Lg Div 3 Cup 91-92.   **Metal Badges:** No.

P.G. CUNNINGHAM SPORTSMANSHIP TROPHY 1991-92:

Little Common Albion 80.31 points, East Grinstead 76.25, Horsham YMCA 75.93, Peacehaven & Telscombe 75.88, Pagham 74.41, Shoreham 74.41, Portfield 74.37, Burgess Hill Town 74.11, Lancing 74.06, Selsey 73.43, Eastbourne Town 73.23, Three Bridges 73.23, East Preston 73.12, Arundel 72.94, Langney Sports 72.64, Bosham 72.50, Broadbridge Heath 72.50, Wick 71.76, Crowborough Athletic 71.56, Stamco 71.56, Sidley United 71.25, Whitehawk 70.88, Littlehampton Town 70.58, Saltdean United 70.31, Haywards Heath Town 70.00, Oakwood 69.70, Midhurst & Easebourne 69.06, Redhill 68.12, Seaford Town 67.81, Hailsham Town, 66.47, Worthing United 65.93, Chichester City 64.41, Bexhill Town 63.23, Ringmer 62.23, Newhaven 62.64.

DIVISION THREE SPORTSMANSHIP MARKS 1991-92:

Franklands Village 80.76%, Storrington 78.46, Ferring 77.69, Mile Oak 76.75, Lindfield Rangers 76.53, Buxted 75.76, Ifield 75.00, Hurstpierpoint 74.61, Leftovers Sports 74.23, Hassocks 73.84, Forest 73.07, Rottingdean '89 72.30, Sidlesham 71.15, Withdean 67.30.

Sidlesham FC, Unijet Sussex County League Division Three Cup Winners 1991-92. Photo - Eric Marsh.

UNIJET SUSSEX COUNTY LEAGUE RESERVE & YOUTH SECTIONS

RESERVE SECTION PREMIER DIVISION

	P	W	D	L	F	A	PTS
Burgess Hill Town	30	19	6	5	55	26	63
Peacehaven & T.*	30	19	5	6	66	27	62
Portfield *	30	17	9	4	79	36	60
Horsham YMCA	30	16	7	7	52	33	55
Pagham	30	15	7	8	56	42	52
Littlehampton	30	13	10	7	52	42	49
Ringmer	30	13	7	10	62	46	46
Eastbourne Town	30	13	4	13	58	65	43
Langney Sports	30	11	7	12	37	40	40
Oakwood #	30	10	7	13	42	45	37
Arundel	30	11	4	15	48	67	37
Wick *	30	10	5	15	41	53	35
Shoreham	30	8	4	18	49	57	28
East Grinstead	30	5	9	16	38	56	24
Hailsham Town	30	6	4	20	36	72	22
Haywards Hth ##	30	4	5	21	30	94	17

RESERVE SECTION EAST

	P	W	D	L	F	A	PTS
Crawley Town	26	17	4	5	60	24	55
Lewes *	26	16	6	4	72	22	54
Hassocks	26	16	6	4	66	34	54
Saltdean United	26	12	4	10	52	64	40
Stamco	26	11	6	9	60	47	39
Bexhill Town *	26	11	5	10	44	44	38
Crowborough A. #	26	10	7	9	43	31	37
Little Common Alb.	26	10	7	9	47	60	37
Whitehawk	26	9	7	10	49	39	34
Seaford Town	26	9	6	11	51	45	33
Sidley Utd	26	8	1	17	41	63	25
Newhaven	26	7	2	17	31	53	23
Franklands Village #	26	7	2	17	23	60	23
Eastbourne Utd	26	5	5	15	29	82	20

RESERVE SECTION WEST

	P	W	D	L	F	A	PTS
Worthing	26	18	6	2	87	33	60
Bognor Regis Town	26	15	5	6	78	45	50
East Preston # *	26	15	2	9	43	38	47
Steyning Town	26	12	7	7	45	32	43
Bosham +	26	13	3	10	55	53	42
Broadbridge Hth *	26	11	8	7	51	38	41
Southwick	26	11	8	7	38	32	41
Selsey *	26	11	6	9	50	39	39
Worthing United	26	10	9	7	56	46	39
Lancing	26	9	4	13	41	55	31
Ferring	26	9	1	19	33	48	28
Midhurst & E.	26	6	4	16	42	52	22
Chichester City #	26	4	5	17	36	67	17
Storrington	26	3	2	22	21	98	11

YOUTH SECTION EAST

	P	W	D	L	F	A	PTS
Lewes	20	17	3	0	105	18	54
Peacehaven & Tel.	20	13	5	2	68	18	44
Whitehawk	20	14	1	5	52	24	43
Ringmer	20	13	2	5	51	30	41
Langney Sports	20	12	2	6	50	31	38
Newhaven *	20	8	4	8	55	61	28
Sidley Utd	20	7	4	9	54	59	25
Franklands Village	20	5	2	13	32	62	17
Buxted	20	4	2	14	48	64	14
Eastbourne Town	20	2	1	17	27	101	7
Hailsham Town	20	2	0	18	24	98	6

YOUTH SECTION WEST

	P	W	D	L	F	A	PTS
Burgess Hill Town	24	22	1	1	87	31	67
Worthing	24	19	2	3	83	38	59
Horsham YMCA	24	13	3	8	55	42	42
Littlehampton T. *	24	12	4	8	74	35	40
Midhurst & E.	24	12	4	8	60	45	40
Chichester City	24	12	2	10	48	38	38
Shoreham *	24	11	3	10	64	58	36
Worthing Utd *	24	11	0	13	53	59	33
Southwick *	24	10	2	12	49	53	32
Wick	24	8	4	12	47	60	28
Steyning Town	24	7	6	11	39	49	27
Forest	24	1	3	20	36	77	6
Selsey	24	1	0	23	11	117	3

YOUTH SECTION PLAY-OFF (at Peacehaven)
Lewes v Burgess Hill Town — 3-0

YOUTH SECTION CUP FINAL (at Whitehawk)
Worthing v Langney Sports — aet 7-5

Throughout the above tables (*) denotes match and pts awarded, # denotes goals and pts deducted, + denotes match and pts conceded.

RESERVE SECTION CUP 1991-92

First Round

Crowborough Athletic v Broadbridge Hth	3-2
East Preston v Little Common Albion	3-0
Eastbourne United v Hailsham Town	0-2
Ferring v Hassocks	0-2
Lewes v Shoreham	2-3
Newhaven v Midhurst & Easebourne	aet 3-2
Peacehaven & Telscombe v Bexhill Town	1-0
Portfield v Worthing United	aet 3-2
Selsey v Littlehampton Town	2-1
Southwick v Saltdean United	3-1
Storrington v Franklands Village	2-1

Second Round

Bosham v Arundel	4-5
Crowborough Athletic v Hailsham Town	5-3
Haywards Heath Town v Worthing	2-1
Horsham YMCA v Worthing United	2-1
Lancing v Eastbourne Town	5-1
Langney Sports v Whitehawk	1-2
Newhaven v East Preston	0-4
Oakwood v Chichester City	8-0
Pagham v Bognor Regis Town	4-3
Portfield v Shoreham	3-0
Seaford Town v Burgess Hill Town	1-5
Selsey v Peacehaven & Telscombe	1-2
Southwick v Hassocks	3-0
Stamco v East Grinstead	2-4
Steyning Town v Wick	2-0
Storrington v Ringmer	2-4

Third Round

Burgess Hill Town v Peacehaven & Telscombe	1-2
East Grinstead v Lancing	aet 1-1,aet 2-1
East Preston v Haywards Heath Town	2-0
Oakwood v Steyning Town	aet 1-1, aet 2-1
Portfield v Pagham	2-1
Ringmer v Crowborough Athletic	2-4
Southwick v Arundel	aet 3-5
Whitehawk v Worthing United	0-1

Fourth Round

East Preston v Arundel	0-3
Horsham YMCA v Crowborough Athletic	3-0
Peacehaven & Telscombe v Oakwood	1-0
Portfield v East Grinstead	3-0

Semi Finals

Arundel v Portfield *(at Wick)*	0-1
H'ham YM v P'haven *(at B. Hill)* 2-1*(aban. in ET)*	
Horsham YMCA v Peacehaven *(at Burgess Hill)*	2-0

Final

Horsham YMCA v Portfield *(at Wick)*	2-0
Horsham YMCA v Portfield *(at Arundel)*	0-2

RESERVE SECTION PREMIER DIVISION RESULTS 1991/92

HOME TEAM	1	2	3	4	5	6	7	8	9	10	11	12	13	14	15	16
1. Arundel	*	0-1	1-1	2-1	2-2	1-1	0-3	3-0	1-1	2-3	0-2	0-7	3-1	2-0	3-2	3-0
2. Burgess Hill	5-0	*	4-1	2-0	2-0	2-0	3-0	2-2	2-2	3-0	1-1	2-0	0-0	0-2	1-0	3-1
3. Eastbourne Town	3-4	2-2	*	5-1	3-0	3-1	1-1	2-2	1-0	3-1	2-0	2-3	2-3	2-3	0-4	2-1
4. East Grinstead	2-3	1-3	2-3	*	1-4	1-1	0-1	1-0	2-0	2-0	0-1	0-4	1-1	2-2	0-2	6-0
5. Hailsham Town	2-4	1-1	0-3	1-1	*	2-1	2-0	3-4	1-2	2-4	1-2	2-5	2-2	0-3	0-2	
6. Haywards Heath	1-8	0-2	1-3	0-0	1-3	*	0-4	0-3	4-0	0-2	1-4	0-1	0-11	1-4	3-2	L-W
7. Horsham YMCA	4-1	2-1	4-2	2-0	3-1	7-0	*	2-0	2-2	4-0	1-1	1-0	0-2	1-3	2-0	0-0
8. Langney Sports	1-0	2-4	1-3	2-1	2-0	3-0	0-0	*	3-1	2-0	1-3	0-2	1-1	2-0	1-0	1-3
9. Littlehampton	1-0	4-0	2-1	1-1	3-1	1-2	4-2	0-0	*	1-0	1-1	0-1	1-1	3-3	4-1	1-1
10. Oakwood	4-0	1-2	1-2	4-2	1-0	2-4	0-0	0-0	2-2	*	3-1	2-2	0-1	0-1	1-3	1-0
11. Pagham	2-0	0-2	1-0	1-1	6-0	3-3	6-0	0-1	1-3	2-3	*	2-1	3-3	3-2	1-2	2-0
12. Peacehaven & T.	5-1	1-0	5-0	3-1	6-0	W-L	3-0	1-0	1-2	2-0	1-1	*	2-1	2-3	2-2	2-2
13. Portfield	3-1	1-2	6-1	3-1	3-2	6-1	0-0	2-0	1-0	4-1	*	5-2	2-2	3-1		
14. Ringmer	6-0	0-1	5-4	1-1	1-0	3-3	0-1	2-1	1-3	0-0	6-0	1-3	0-0	*	5-0	0-2
15. Shoreham	3-2	1-2	6-0	1-2	1-2	6-0	0-1	1-3	4-0	0-1	1-2	0-3	1-4	0-3	*	0-2
16. Wick	0-1	1-0	0-1	1-4	1-2	7-1	1-4	3-1	2-1	0-4	2-3	0-0	2-3	2-2	4-2	*

NB - Oakwood v Portfield ended 2-1, but 0-1 recorded. Ringmer v Burgess Hill 1-1, but 0-1 recorded.

RESERVE SECTION EAST RESULTS 1991/92

HOME TEAM	1	2	3	4	5	6	7	8	9	10	11	12	13	14
1. Bexhill Town	*	0-3	0-0	3-0	2-0	2-1	0-4	0-0	2-0	1-3	1-3	6-1	1-1	2-2
2. Crawley Town	4-1	*	2-0	2-1	4-1	5-1	0-0	2-2	2-0	7-0	1-2	2-0	3-0	1-0
3. Crowborough Ath.	2-2	3-2	*	3-0	4-1	1-0	1-1	1-2	1-2	1-1	6-0	3-1	1-1	
4. Eastbourne United	1-2	2-2	1-1	*	0-4	1-3	1-1	1-1	2-1	2-1	0-0	3-0	0-3	0-7
5. Franklands Village	0-1	0-3	0-4	3-1	*	1-4	0-2	0-1	0-2	0-3	1-0	3-2	1-6	0-3
6. Hassocks	3-1	2-2	3-1	2-4	4-1	*	3-1	4-1	4-1	2-0	2-2	5-2	2-2	2-0
7. Lewes	2-3	0-1	1-0	5-0	1-1	2-2	*	7-0	6-1	6-0	2-0	1-0	1-1	2-1
8. Little Common Albion	0-2	2-7	4-2	4-1	1-3	2-2	1-4	*	3-0	2-2	2-2	2-0	5-3	1-1
9. Newhaven	2-4	1-2	1-1	2-3	2-0	0-2	0-2	6-0	*	3-1	2-4	2-1	0-3	1-1
10. Saltdean United	3-2	2-0	2-1	3-2	0-0	0-2	1-10	1-3	2-1	*	6-1	2-7	2-6	5-1
11. Seaford Town	4-2	1-2	0-2	13-0	2-0	0-2	2-3	1-3	0-1	1-1	*	2-1	3-1	5-1
12. Sidley United	2-1	1-0	0-1	8-0	0-2	1-3	0-5	4-2	1-0	1-6	2-2	*	1-4	1-0
13. Stamco	1-0	0-1	1-2	3-2	3-2	0-1	1-6	2-3	3-1	5-0	3-0	2-1	*	2-2
14. Whitehawk	2-3	2-0	1-0	5-1	8-0	0-0	1-0	1-2	1-0	0-2	3-0	1-4	4-4	*

NB - C'borough v E'bourne ended 3-1, but 3-0 recorded. Franklands v Bexhill 1-1, 0-1 recorded, Lewes v Crowborough 1-4, 1-0 recorded.

RESERVE SECTION WEST RESULTS 1991/92

HOME TEAM	1	2	3	4	5	6	7	8	9	10	11	12	13	14
1. Bognor Regis Town	*	4-0	6-1	4-3	9-2	3-2	4-2	6-2	1-1	3-3	1-0	4-0	1-3	6-1
2. Bosham	2-3	*	2-1	7-3	4-3	3-0	4-1	2-1	2-5	0-0	1-3	3-0	3-3	4-4
3. Broadbridge Heath	3-0	2-4	*	1-0	2-0	1-0	3-4	1-1	2-2	3-0	1-1	8-3	1-1	5-0
4. Chichester City	0-7	0-1	L-W	*	0-1	2-3	1-4	2-2	2-1	0-2	1-1	0-1	2-4	4-4
5. East Preston	1-0	W-L	0-0	2-1	*	3-2	1-1	1-0	0-1	0-1	1-0	3-0	1-5	2-0
6. Ferring	3-0	0-1	0-2	2-1	2-4	*	0-1	1-0	2-3	1-0	1-0	5-0	0-4	0-2
7. Lancing	1-1	4-0	3-1	1-0	1-2	1-4	*	0-2	0-1	0-3	1-1	4-1	1-6	2-5
8. Midhurst & E'bourne	3-1	1-3	2-3	2-0	1-2	4-1	1-2	*	2-4	2-2	0-1	2-1	1-2	1-4
9. Selsey	2-2	0-1	1-0	8-0	0-3	0-0	3-0	2-1	*	1-2	2-4	5-0	1-2	2-2
10. Southwick	3-3	3-1	2-2	1-3	0-2	1-0	0-2	4-0	2-0	*	1-4	2-0	3-0	0-0
11. Steyning Town	0-1	3-1	1-5	2-4	2-0	3-0	2-0	2-1	3-1	4-1	*	0-1	2-2	1-0
12. Storrington	1-4	0-4	1-1	1-5	1-7	1-2	4-1	2-8	0-2	0-1	2-2	*	0-5	0-3
13. Worthing	3-4	6-2	3-1	5-1	3-1	4-1	4-4	1-0	3-0	0-0	2-2	9-0	*	5-1
14. Worthing United	3-0	3-0	1-2	1-2	4-2	1-0	2-2	2-2	1-1	1-1	8-0	1-2	*	

NB - East Preston v Selsey ended 2-1, but 0-1 recorded.

Three Bridges 'keeper Tony Dugdale is beaten by a superb 35 yard free-kick from Bexhill Town's Andy Taylor at the Polegrove. However, his side still won 5-1. Photo - Roger Turner.

UNIJET SUSSEX COUNTY LEAGUE FEEDERS 1991-92

BRIGHTON HOVE & DIST. LEAGUE

	P	W	D	L	F	A	PTS
AFC Falcons	20	16	4	0	71	23	52
Old Varndeanians	20	12	3	5	55	39	39
La Roma	20	9	4	7	44	37	31
Legal & General	20	9	4	7	33	39	31
Portslade Ath.	20	8	5	7	42	36	29
Midway	20	8	1	11	43	44	25
Mile Oak Res.	20	7	4	9	35	41	25
Preston Village	20	7	3	10	32	48	24
Brighton BBOB	20	6	3	11	27	42	21
Withdean Res.	20	5	3	12	32	41	18
Grenadier	20	6	0	14	38	62	18

EAST SUSSEX LEAGUE

	P	W	D	L	F	A	PTS
Shinewater AFC	18	17	0	1	60	7	34
Hollington Utd	18	13	2	3	63	24	28
Tenterden & St M.	18	10	2	6	47	33	22
Bodiam	18	10	2	6	35	25	22
Rock-a-Nore	18	8	4	6	31	38	20
Wadhurst Utd	18	7	3	8	39	38	17
Firehills	18	8	1	9	31	37	17
Hawkhurst Utd	18	3	5	10	25	49	11
Icklesham Cas.	18	1	3	14	25	57	5
Westfield	18	1	2	15	15	63	4

WEST SUSSEX LEAGUE

	P	W	D	L	F	A	PTS
South Bersted	24	18	4	2	61	16	40
Sunallon	24	17	3	4	76	24	37
West Chiltington	24	16	4	4	68	32	36
North Holmwood	24	13	5	6	66	34	31
Steyning O Gram.	24	14	3	7	68	38	31
Lanc. & Somp. RBL	24	9	8	7	43	38	26
L'don & Edin. Spts	24	10	5	9	56	54	25
Barns Green	24	9	1	14	43	66	19
Rustington	24	5	6	13	40	56	16
Henfield Ath.	24	6	4	14	35	70	16
Old Collyerians	24	6	2	16	37	78	14
Milland	24	3	6	15	32	59	12
Horndean 'A'	24	4	1	19	24	84	9

CRAWLEY & DISTRICT LEAGUE

	P	W	D	L	F	A	PTS
Longley	21	15	4	2	48	21	49
M.E.L.	21	15	3	3	58	23	48
Thomas Bennett	21	12	3	6	56	38	39
Rediffusion	21	8	3	10	35	40	27
Town Mead	21	9	0	12	33	48	27
Edwards Sports	21	7	3	11	37	37	24
Phoenix	21	6	2	13	32	49	20
Horley T. Cas.	21	2	2	17	24	67	8

KETCHEN KING WORTHING & DIST. LGE

	P	W	D	L	F	A	PTS
Swan	18	14	4	0	68	16	32
Sompting	18	11	2	5	54	34	24
Eurotherm	18	9	4	5	45	31	22
Russell Bourne	18	9	4	5	49	41	22
West Tarring WMC	18	8	4	6	47	44	20
Northbrook	18	8	4	6	34	41	20
St Theresa's	18	3	5	10	18	35	11
Ristington Res.	18	4	3	11	23	47	11
Becket	18	2	6	10	32	63	10
L & Sompt RBL Res	18	3	2	13	32	50	8

Dolphin Athletic withdrew - record expunged

UNIJET MID-SUSSEX LEAGUE

	P	W	D	L	F	A	PTS
St Francis Hospital	24	18	3	3	73	21	57
Plumpton Ath.	24	15	7	2	60	22	52
Cuckfield	24	14	6	4	70	34	48
Wisdom Sports	24	13	4	7	62	38	43
Newick	24	13	3	8	56	43	42
Southwater	24	11	4	9	50	45	37
Crawley Down Utd	24	9	4	11	54	46	31
Lewes Rovers	24	9	4	11	39	51	31
Lingfield	24	8	4	12	42	44	28
Lindfield Res	24	9	1	14	51	60	28
Maresfield Village	24	8	3	13	41	53	27
Leftovers SC Res	24	3	6	15	23	64	15
Forest Row	24	1	1	22	17	118	4

REDHILL & DISTRICT LEAGUE

PREMIER DIVISION

	P	W	D	L	F	A	PTS
Tadworth	20	14	3	3	52	23	31
Godstone	20	14	1	5	62	32	29
Charlwood	20	12	2	6	54	29	26
South Park	20	8	4	8	56	53	20
Smallfield	20	6	8	6	38	35	20
Horley United	20	8	4	8	39	42	20
Nork Soc.	20	8	4	8	45	50	20
Westcott '35	20	7	4	9	34	35	18
Mickleham	20	4	7	9	29	38	15
C.O.B.	20	4	5	11	27	60	13
Watsons	20	2	4	14	28	67	8

DIVISION ONE

	P	W	D	L	F	A	PTS
Nutfield	20	16	2	2	90	36	34
Hollands Sports	20	15	2	3	73	32	32
Limpsfield Blues	20	13	2	5	62	41	28
Walton Heath	20	9	3	8	47	42	21
Paris G.S.	20	10	0	10	51	42	20
Beechams	20	9	1	10	43	44	19
Westcott 35 Res.	20	6	5	9	29	43	17
Brockham	20	7	3	10	36	52	17
Godstone Res.	20	7	1	12	41	49	15
Woodland Alb.	20	3	3	14	13	64	9
Nork Soc. Res	20	2	4	14	26	66	8

DIVISION TWO

	P	W	D	L	F	A	PTS
Horley Utd Res	22	18	4	0	82	23	40
Oddfellows	22	17	3	2	103	30	37
Whyteleafe 'A'	22	13	4	5	56	25	30
Charlwood Res	22	11	4	7	58	43	26
South Park Res	22	10	5	7	47	42	25
Sth Godstone Ath.	22	8	6	8	46	60	22
Coulsdon Mitre	22	8	3	11	59	55	19
Woodmansterne 'A'	22	5	7	10	37	60	17
Warlingham 'A'	22	6	3	13	38	70	15
Cheam V.W. 'A'	22	5	4	13	37	68	14
Merstham Newton	22	3	4	15	22	73	10
Fox Yox	22	3	3	16	29	65	9

DIVISION THREE

	P	W	D	L	F	A	PTS
Griffin Albion	20	14	5	1	71	25	33
NEL Britannia	20	15	1	4	89	28	31
Bookham 'A'	20	13	3	4	78	21	29
Tadworth Res	20	11	4	5	41	31	26
Limpsfield B. Res	20	9	4	7	48	41	22
Godstone 'A'	20	8	4	8	43	56	20
Monotype 'A'	20	7	3	10	38	44	17
Warlingham 'B'	20	7	3	10	40	56	17
Paris GS Res	20	6	3	11	21	46	15
Smallfield Res.	20	3	2	15	37	61	8
Oxted 'A'	20	0	2	18	18	115	2

DIVISION FOUR

	P	W	D	L	F	A	PTS
Walton Hth Res	20	14	4	2	63	20	32
C.O.B. Res	20	12	5	3	59	23	29
Horley Utd 'A'	20	11	5	4	49	30	27
Godstone 'B'	20	10	5	5	64	37	25
Hoilands Spts Res	20	8	6	6	57	40	22
Bletchingley 'A'	20	9	4	7	51	52	22
Brockham Res.	20	9	3	7	53	47	21
South Park 'A'	20	7	2	11	37	56	16
Bookham 'B'	20	6	2	12	39	66	14
Fox Yox Res.	20	3	3	14	37	77	9
Paris GS 'A'	20	1	1	18	21	82	3

DIVISION FIVE

	P	W	D	L	F	A	PTS
Horley Utd 'B'	20	18	2	0	81	21	38
Cheam V.W. 'B'	20	16	1	3	73	31	33
Oddfellows Res	20	12	5	3	54	40	29
Lingfield 'A'	20	11	1	8	77	44	23
Woodmansterne 'B'	20	8	3	9	43	59	19
Nutfield Res	20	7	4	9	48	54	18
Beechams Res.	20	9	0	11	42	51	18
Merstham New. Res	20	6	3	11	41	60	15
C.O.B. 'A'	20	6	1	13	38	55	13
Sth Godstone 'B'	20	3	2	15	18	46	8
Westcott '35 'A'	20	2	2	16	38	92	6

MISCELLANEOUS LEAGUES

EAST SUSSEX LEAGUE
(See page 657 for Premier Division)

DIVISION ONE

	P	W	D	L	F	A	PTS
E'bourne Fishermen	22	20	1	1	74	19	41
Willingdon	22	14	3	5	57	24	31
Herstmonceaux	22	15	1	6	59	28	31
Polegate	22	13	4	5	59	27	30
Wadhurst Toc. H.	22	11	3	8	73	57	25
Rye United Res	22	10	2	10	45	43	22
Rusthall Res	22	8	5	9	33	38	21
Hastings Rangers	22	7	2	13	38	59	16
Old Hastonians	22	6	3	13	48	87	15
Ninfield United	22	6	2	14	34	56	14
Sandhurst	22	6	0	16	36	72	12
Hooe Sports	22	3	0	19	25	70	6

WEST SUSSEX LEAGUE
(See page 657 for Premier Division)

DIVISION ONE

	P	W	D	L	F	A	PTS
Cowfold	24	17	5	2	72	31	39
S.B. Sports	24	16	5	3	60	24	37
Stedham United	24	16	2	6	76	49	34
Roffey	24	15	3	6	59	24	33
Ifield Reserves	24	13	3	8	54	47	29
Worthing BCOB	24	9	5	10	32	44	23
Emsworth	24	7	6	11	45	40	20
Horsham Olympic	24	7	6	11	54	55	20
Eastergate Utd	24	4	10	10	32	45	18
Lavant	24	5	7	12	42	72	17
Brackleham	24	6	4	14	39	65	16
Billinghurst Utd	24	5	3	16	32	66	13
Pulborough	24	5	3	16	29	63	13

PORTSMOUTH LEAGUE

PREMIER DIVISION

	P	W	D	L	F	A	PTS
P'mouth Civil S Res	18	14	2	2	58	23	30
Fleetlands Res	18	10	3	5	39	29	23
Jubilee	18	10	3	5	67	52	23
Hilsea	18	10	2	6	41	34	22
Drayton Park	18	8	1	9	43	45	17
Sportique	18	6	4	8	40	52	16
Greyhound	18	6	1	11	37	47	13
Portchester Utd	18	5	3	10	31	45	13
Wicor Mill	18	5	2	11	33	44	12
Paulsgrove Res	18	5	1	12	34	52	11

Senior Div Champions: Norma Jeans
Junior Div 1 Champions: Clanfield
Junior Div 2 Champions: Mayflower

PORTSMOUTH NORTH END LEAGUE

DIVISION ONE

	P	W	D	L	F	A	PTS
Bellevue	20	15	3	2	100	28	33
Grant Thornton	20	14	4	2	89	35	32
Anmore	20	14	4	2	87	34	32
Sparta '89	20	14	1	5	90	58	29
Hadleys	20	9	3	8	58	55	21
St Helena	20	7	4	9	59	64	18
Old Canal	20	7	3	10	38	68	17
Cosmos '87	20	4	4	12	48	80	12
Kingston	20	4	4	12	49	92	12
Oakville	20	2	3	15	38	81	7
P.S.G.	20	3	1	16	34	93	7

Division 2 Champions: Dunham Bush
Division 3 Champions: Beltax Wingard

SOUTHAMPTON SENIOR LEAGUE

PREM. DIVISION

	P	W	D	L	F	A	PTS
Brendon	26	18	6	2	71	25	41
Swanmore	26	14	10	2	50	24	38
Esso (Fawley)	26	14	5	7	63	31	33
Fair Oak	26	12	8	6	49	32	32
Colden Com. Res	26	9	10	7	39	32	28
West End	26	11	5	10	38	36	27
Old Tauntonians	26	9	6	11	60	47	24
Queens Keep	26	9	6	11	39	35	24
AC Delco Res	26	8	7	11	35	45	23
Hamble Club	26	8	6	12	53	58	22
Bishopstoke Soc.	26	9	4	13	39	52	22
Hythe & Dibden	26	6	7	13	38	52	19
B Waltham T Res	26	7	5	14	28	72	19
Botley	26	3	5	18	24	85	11

DIVISION ONE

	P	W	D	L	F	A	PTS
Pirelli Gen. Res	26	19	3	4	67	22	41
BTC Southampton	26	19	2	5	66	26	40
Millbrook & May.	26	13	6	7	45	37	32
Cadnam United	26	12	7	7	65	44	31
Durley	26	12	7	7	46	35	31
Netley	26	11	8	7	50	36	30
Nth Baddesley	26	11	7	8	46	40	29
Otterbourne Res	26	10	6	10	46	45	26
Sarisbury Green	26	8	7	11	47	53	23
Ordnance Survey	26	7	9	10	34	43	23
C.H.B.	26	7	7	12	47	58	21
Ampfield	26	5	7	14	24	46	17
West End Res	26	2	7	17	24	69	11
Warsash	26	2	5	19	33	86	9

Eastleigh FC of the Jewson Wessex League. Photo - Bruce D Williams.

HEREWARD SPORTS
UNITED COUNTIES LEAGUE

Chairman: T N Bates,
Hon. Secretary: R J Gamble,
8 Bostock Avenue, Northampton.

SPENCER COMPLETE FIRST TITLE WIN

The 1991-92 season was a memorable one for Northampton Spencer who lifted the Premier Division championship for the first time in their history. In doing so they became the first Northants side to take the crown since Irthlingborough in 1983. Spencer fully deserved their title; they were the only team to show consistency during the run-in, edging clear of the other contenders, Raunds Town, who took the runners-up medals for the first time, Rothwell, who had topped the division through February, and outgoing champions Bourne, who had the league's most potent attack, but never looked as solid in defence as they had the previous year. Other clubs to feature in the title race were Stotfold, who finally slipped out of the reckoning under a massive fixture pile-up caused by their cup success, and newcomers Boston, who had a poor end to the campaign and finished eigth.

At the bottom Brackley and Holbeach, both fielding very young squads, occupied the bottom two places with Wellingborough and Spalding, both recently relegated from the Beazer Homes League, also ending in the bottom four. With Irthlingborough merging with Beazer Homes League neighbours Rushden Town, and Arlesey returning to the South Midlands League after a decade of UCL football, both Brackley and Holbeach live to fight another day in the Premier. Not so Peterborough City, who drop down to Division One after failing to bring their new Phorpres ground up to Premier standards.

The Division One crown went to Harrowby in only their second season in the League. They pipped Newport Pagnell on goal difference, but it is the Bucks club who step up to the top flight after a six year absence, Harrowby failing to bring their ground up to Premier Division requirements. Consistent Division One performers Ramsey were back in third place ruing their poor start, while St Ives enjoyed their best UCL season finishing fourth. Basement club Irchester finished well adrift with their only victory of the season being recorded in their final match. Towcester, who lost many matches by the odd goal, finished second bottom, but both clubs will continue in the league next year.

Rothwell won the League Knockout Cup for the first time in twenty years beating first-time finalists Stotfold 5-2 in the final, while Northampton Spencer added the Benevolent Cup to their array of silverware beating Harrowby 3-1 in the final.

Mirrlees Blackstone enjoyed their best FA Cup run reaching the Second Qualifying Round with a win over former FA Trophy winners Bishop's Stortford on the way. Raunds were our best Vase performers, reaching Round Three, while County Cup winners were Kempston Rovers (Beds Senior), Stotfold (Beds Premier), Eynesbury (Hunts Senior), Potton (Hunts Premier) and Harrowby (Lincs Senior 'B').

The 1992-93 season will see the start of a new era with the Premier Division all floodlit for the first time.

Jeremy Biggs, League Press Liaison Officer

Another goal and another win for champions-elect Northampton Spencer. Here their Adam Sandy (No.10) scores the first in a 2-0 win away to Wootton Blue Cross on March 21st 1992. Photo - Gavin Ellis.

FINAL LEAGUE TABLES 1992-93

Premier Division	P	W	D	L	F	A	PTS
Northampton Spen.	46	31	8	7	101	44	101
Raunds Town	46	27	14	5	94	38	95
Rothwell Town	46	29	6	11	100	51	93
Bourne Town	46	27	8	11	113	57	89
Stotfold	46	26	8	12	93	52	86
Mirrlees B'stone	46	23	12	11	77	60	81
Eynesbury Rovers	46	22	12	12	82	58	78
Boston	46	21	11	14	79	62	74
Hamlet S & L	46	21	11	14	76	60	74
Arlesey Town	46	20	12	14	76	65	72
APV P'borough C.	46	22	5	19	81	66	71
Cogenhoe	46	19	13	14	92	63	70
Potton United	46	20	9	17	76	61	69
Daventry Town	46	18	10	18	71	65	64
Kempston Rovers	46	16	15	15	54	51	63
Long Buckby	46	18	9	19	66	67	63
Irthlingborough	46	17	8	21	73	88	59
Desborough T.	46	13	10	23	57	85	49
Wootton Blue X	46	15	3	28	57	85	48
Stamford	46	11	8	27	60	85	41
Spalding United	46	10	11	25	59	104	41
Wellingborough T.	46	7	5	34	45	130	26
Holbeach United	46	4	9	33	44	133	21
Brackley Town	46	3	7	36	39	135	16

Division One	P	W	D	L	F	A	PTS
Harrowby United	34	25	5	4	92	30	80
Newport Pagnell	34	25	5	4	86	44	80
Ramsey Town	34	23	6	5	95	36	75
St Ives Town	34	22	6	6	78	32	72
Bugbrooke St Mich.	34	21	5	8	78	42	68
Higham Town	34	19	7	8	73	45	64
Ford Sports	34	18	6	10	74	48	60
O.N. Chenecks	34	16	9	9	61	47	57
Cottingham	34	16	8	14	62	68	46
Thrapston Venturas	34	11	6	17	54	70	39
Blisworth	34	11	4	19	50	65	37
Olney Town	34	10	6	18	53	61	36
Whitworths	34	10	6	18	41	70	36
British Timken	34	9	4	21	65	107	31
Sharnbrook	34	8	5	21	51	77	29
Burton Pk Wdrs	34	6	10	18	38	58	28
Towcester Town	34	6	6	22	38	72	24
Irchester United	34	1	2	31	27	144	5

Reserve Div. One	P	W	D	L	F	A	PTS
Stotfold Res	38	30	3	5	103	33	93
Raunds T. Res.	38	29	4	5	97	35	91
Corby Town Res	38	21	11	6	94	42	74
M. B'stone Res.	38	20	9	9	88	57	69
N'hampton Sp. Res.	38	21	5	12	103	64	68
Irthlingboro. Res.	38	19	8	11	85	63	65
Rothwell Town Res.	38	18	9	11	86	66	63
APV P'boro. Res.	38	18	3	17	75	76	57
Kempston Rvrs Res.	38	17	5	16	90	86	56
Desborough Res.	38	15	9	14	80	79	54
Wootton BC Res	38	15	7	16	65	73	52
Rushden Town Res.	38	14	8	16	58	58	50
Long Buckby Res.	38	12	5	21	65	82	41
ON Chenecks Res.	38	12	5	21	47	83	41
Cogenhoe Res.	38	12	5	21	53	94	41
Eynesbury Res.	38	9	9	20	54	78	36
Stamford	38	9	5	24	59	103	32
Cottingham Res.	38	8	7	23	51	102	31
N'port Pagnell Res	38	7	9	22	42	72	30
Wellingboro. Res	38	6	10	22	49	98	28

Reserve Div. Two	P	W	D	L	F	A	PTS
Hamlet S & L Res	38	32	6	0	152	31	102
Arlesey T. Res.	38	27	6	5	127	34	87
Higham T. Res.	38	38	3	10	109	51	78
Boston Res.	38	23	5	10	122	62	74
Ford Sports Res.	38	20	9	9	93	57	69
Bugbrooke SM Res.	38	21	4	13	88	50	67
Buckingham T. Res.	38	20	3	15	96	69	63
Harrowby Utd Res.	38	18	6	14	76	53	60
Olney Town Res.	38	17	9	12	58	50	60
Bourne Town Res.	38	16	8	14	107	70	56
Blisworth	38	15	9	14	90	96	54
Thrapston V. Res.	38	15	9	14	71	84	54
Spalding Utd Res.	38	14	11	13	76	64	53
Burton PW Res.	38	11	10	17	63	80	43
Sharnbrook Res.	38	12	6	20	60	118	42
Whitworths Res	38	8	9	21	63	95	33
Brackley T. Res.	38	8	7	23	62	88	31
Daventry T. Res.	38	8	6	24	52	133	30
Towcester T. Res.	38	4	2	32	37	190	14
Irchester Utd Res.	38	0	4	34	29	156	4

Stotfold, destined to have a fine season, take on an Arsenal X1 on July 20th and win 2-1. Photo - Gavin Ellis.

RESULTS 1991/92

PREMIER DIVISION

	1	2	3	4	5	6	7	8	9	10	11	12	13	14	15	16	17	18	19	20	21	22	23	24
1. Arlesey Town	*	1-3	3-0	2-0	3-4	0-1	2-2	1-2	0-2	6-2	0-0	1-1	1-0	4-1	0-6	1-0	0-1	1-1	2-1	1-1	1-0	4-3	2-0	1-0
2. Boston	0-0	*	1-1	2-1	1-3	1-1	3-1	1-1	2-0	3-0	2-0	0-0	1-1	3-3	0-2	0-1	0-1	2-2	1-2	3-0	0-0	1-0	2-1	4-1
3. Bourne Town	2-1	0-1	*	8-0	4-0	1-1	5-1	1-2	0-2	3-2	4-1	2-1	3-0	1-1	5-1	3-1	2-2	1-0	3-0	3-1	3-1	1-1	9-0	4-2
4. Brackley Town	0-2	1-4	1-4	*	1-5	0-6	2-0	2-3	0-3	0-0	1-5	1-2	4-4	2-2	0-5	2-4	0-2	0-1	1-3	1-1	0-1	0-1	0-0	0-0
5. Cogenhoe United	1-1	2-3	1-2	1-1	*	0-2	1-0	1-1	2-0	4-1	0-0	0-1	2-1	1-0	0-1	1-1	2-4	5-1	1-1	4-0	2-2	6-0	2-0	2-2
6. Daventry Town	1-3	2-4	0-1	3-1	1-0	*	1-0	2-3	1-2	2-1	1-1	1-1	1-2	2-0	1-0	1-0	1-2	1-1	2-1	0-2	4-2	4-3	3-0	4-0
7. Desborough Town	1-0	2-3	1-1	0-3	0-1	0-0	*	2-2	1-1	4-1	2-1	0-0	0-3	2-3	0-2	3-1	0-2	0-4	2-0	0-0	1-0	0-1	4-0	
8. Eynesbury Rovers	3-3	2-2	2-0	6-2	4-2	2-1	4-2	*	0-0	6-0	0-2	0-1	0-1	0-0	0-2	1-2	1-1	2-1	1-2	2-1	1-1	0-1	2-1	1-0
9. Hamlet Stewart & Lloyds	2-0	2-1	0-6	2-0	3-3	2-1	4-1	0-1	*	2-1	2-2	1-2	2-2	5-0	1-0	4-1	5-2	0-0	3-1	3-0	1-2	0-2	2-2	0-2
10. Holbeach United	0-6	0-4	1-4	0-2	2-2	1-1	1-2	1-2	2-2	*	1-3	2-3	2-1	1-2	3-4	0-1	1-6	0-3	0-1	2-0	0-3	2-2	2-1	
11. Irthlingborough Diamonds	1-2	1-2	0-3	2-0	1-3	2-2	2-2	2-2	3-2	4-0	*	0-2	0-3	4-1	1-3	1-4	3-2	4-0	3-1	1-3	2-4	0-3	5-3	2-1
12. Kempston Rovers	2-4	3-2	0-1	4-1	3-3	1-1	2-1	1-1	2-3	3-0	0-1	*	0-0	1-2	1-3	0-1	0-0	0-3	1-0	2-0	1-2	1-2	1-1	
13. Long Buckby	2-0	2-1	0-1	2-0	1-4	2-2	2-1	0-3	1-0	6-0	4-1	1-1	*	0-2	0-2	3-1	1-0	0-0	1-4	5-1	1-2	1-2	3-2	3-1
14. Mirrlees Blackstone	3-1	1-0	1-0	4-1	3-2	2-1	0-0	3-2	2-1	1-1	3-0	0-0	1-0	*	1-1	1-2	2-1	2-2	5-0	4-2	1-3	3-2	3-0	
15. Northampton Spencer	3-0	1-2	0-0	4-1	1-0	2-1	7-0	1-5	1-0	3-0	3-0	2-2	1-1	2-0	*	3-1	0-0	1-2	2-0	1-0	1-1	1-1	3-2	4-2
16. Peterborough City	0-1	3-1	1-1	5-1	4-1	0-0	2-0	1-2	2-1	0-1	8-0	2-1	2-1	1-1	2-0	*	1-1	1-2	4-0	1-3	3-1	1-3	3-0	
17. Potton United	0-1	1-2	4-3	3-1	5-2	2-1	1-1	0-0	1-1	1-2	1-2	2-1	2-1	2-4	4-2	*	1-1	0-3	3-0	0-1	2-1	5-0	4-1	
18. Raunds Town	4-1	3-1	3-2	2-0	0-0	5-1	3-0	0-1	0-0	2-1	4-0	0-0	1-0	4-1	4-2	0-0	1-1	*	2-0	4-0	3-3	2-1	4-0	3-1
19. Rothwell Town	2-2	4-1	2-1	8-2	2-1	2-1	4-3	2-0	1-1	5-0	1-2	1-0	5-0	1-1	1-1	2-1	2-0	0-0	*	6-0	1-0	0-2	5-0	3-0
20. Spalding Utd	2-2	2-4	0-3	2-1	0-3	4-0	1-1	2-0	1-3	4-4	0-2	0-2	2-2	1-1	1-6	1-2	1-0	0-1	1-2	*	2-1	1-1	3-0	2-4
21. Stamford	1-3	1-1	1-7	7-1	0-1	0-2	2-5	1-3	1-2	1-1	2-3	0-1	0-1	0-3	0-2	1-0	1-2	1-4	4-1	2-2	*	2-1	5-1	2-0
22. Stotfold	1-1	4-1	5-0	6-1	2-0	2-0	0-1	5-0	3-1	3-0	1-1	4-0	1-0	2-2	1-1	2-1	1-2	3-1	3-3	1-0	*	2-0	1-3	
23. Wellingborough Town	3-3	1-2	2-2	4-0	0-8	1-4	4-0	1-3	1-4	1-2	0-3	0-1	1-0	0-1	1-8	0-1	0-5	0-6	0-1	1-5	0-2	1-5	*	1-0
24. Wootton Blue Cross	0-2	0-2	3-1	1-0	1-4	0-1	0-3	3-2	2-1	4-0	1-3	2-0	2-0	0-3	0-2	0-1	1-0	0-2	2-1	3-4	3-1	2-1	3-0	*

DIVISION ONE

	1	2	3	4	5	6	7	8	9	10	11	12	13	14	15	16	17	18
1 Blisworth	*	3-1	0-3	1-3	1-3	1-1	0-10	3-1	0-0	0-2	3-0	2-1	1-3	0-1	0-1	3-0	1-0	1-3
2. British Timken	2-5	*	1-0	4-4	2-3	1-4	6-2	5-6	1-0	3-6	4-4	1-5	2-5	0-5	0-0	3-3	2-1	2-1
3. Bugbrooke St Michaels	2-1	4-0	*	2-0	4-1	1-0	2-2	2-0	2-0	2-4	1-1	1-2	3-2	0-0	7-2	3-0	3-0	3-1
4. Burton Park Wanderers	3-3	3-1	2-2	*	4-0	1-1	0-2	0-2	4-0	0-4	0-1	1-1	1-1	0-2	0-1	2-2	1-1	4-0
5. Cottingham	1-4	3-5	1-2	2-0	*	3-1	1-2	2-3	2-2	0-1	2-2	1-2	0-3	2-1	4-1	2-0	2-0	3-1
6. Ford Sports	3-2	1-0	5-2	0-0	2-0	*	4-2	2-0	3-2	2-0	1-1	5-1	2-4	2-1	3-2	9-0	3-0	
7. Harrowby United	2-0	6-1	3-1	6-0	4-0	3-2	*	3-1	4-1	2-1	2-0	3-1	5-0	2-1	4-1	1-1	2-0	0-0
8. Higham Town	1-0	2-3	0-0	3-0	2-2	2-0	1-0	*	6-0	2-3	2-1	4-2	1-0	2-3	2-0	2-0	3-2	5-1
9. Irchester United	1-4	2-6	0-8	2-0	2-6	1-3	0-3	1-5	*	0-5	2-4	0-8	0-2	1-9	2-3	2-3	2-3	0-2
10. Newport Pagnell Town	2-1	1-0	2-0	4-3	2-0	3-1	0-4	1-1	6-0	*	1-1	3-2	2-3	1-3	2-1	6-1	3-2	2-1
11. Northampton O.N. Chenecks	2-1	4-2	0-2	1-0	2-2	5-0	1-1	0-3	5-0	3-4	*	2-0	0-0	1-2	2-0	3-1	2-1	2-1
12. Olney Town	1-0	1-2	0-2	2-0	2-1	0-0	0-1	1-1	6-1	1-2	1-2	*	0-1	0-2	1-6	2-1	0-0	2-3
13. Ramsey Town	2-1	6-0	4-1	3-0	4-1	2-1	1-1	0-1	1-8	2-4	4-1	4-0	*	0-0	4-0	6-1	3-0	5-0
14. St Ives Town	2-0	2-0	2-1	1-0	5-2	0-2	1-4	2-3	9-0	0-0	0-3	3-1	0-0	*	2-1	1-1	2-0	4-0
15. Sharnbrook	1-3	4-1	2-3	0-0	1-2	1-5	1-3	1-2	2-2	1-2	1-3	2-3	1-3	1-3	*	2-0	1-1	3-0
16. Thrapston Venturas	3-0	6-3	1-4	1-0	1-2	4-2	1-3	1-0	5-0	0-2	0-1	4-1	0-7	1-1	3-0	*	2-3	0-0
17. Towcester Town	1-3	2-1	2-3	0-1	0-4	1-2	0-1	1-1	4-1	1-2	0-0	1-1	1-3	1-2	1-3	1-2	*	2-0
18. Wellingborough Whitworths	1-1	3-0	1-2	2-1	0-2	1-0	0-0	2-1	2-0	1-1	1-2	3-2	2-2	0-3	5-3	0-4	3-5	*

PREMIER DIVISION - TEN YEAR RECORD

	81/82	82/83	83/84	84/85	85/86	86/87	87/88	88/89	89/90	90/91
Ampthill Town	15	10	20	14	21	-	-	-	-	-
Arlesey Town	9	11	1	9	15	9	14	9	18	10
APV Peterborough City	-	-	-	-	-	15	17	13	11	11
Baker Perkins							(See Baker Perkins)			
Baldock Town	-	2	8	3	2	-	-	-	-	-
Boston	-	-	-	-	-	-	-	-	-	8
Bourne Town	4	4	10	17	20	21	20	4	1	4
Brackley Town	-	-	16	16	11	14	2	20	20	24
Buckingham Town	10	1	3	1	-	-	-	-	-	-
Burton Park Wanderers	-	-	-	-	-	-	-	17	22	-
Cogenhoe United	-	-	-	-	-	11	16	5	8	12
Daventry Town	-	-	-	-	-	-	-	-	-	14
Desborough Town	6	18	6	15	13	7	11	16	7	18
Eynesbury Rovers	17	16	17	20	17	16	12	21	3	7
Hamlet Stewarts & Lloyds							(See Stewarts & Lloyds)			
Holbeach United	13	15	18	10	8	20	3	1	13	23
Irthlingborough Dia.	1	7	4	4	4	13	4	12	14	17
Kempston Rovers	18	-	-	-	16	19	19	22	15	15
Long Buckby AFC	7	8	2	7	9	10	9	10	9	16
Mirrlees Blackstone	-	-	-	-	-	-	18	8	12	6
Newport Pagnell	11	12	12	21	-	-	-	-	-	-
Northampton Spencer	-	-	-	11	12	8	13	7	5	1
Potton United	5	5	7	6	1	4	1	14	4	13
Raunds Town	-	14	13	13	6	3	6	3	6	2
Rothwell Town	16	13	15	12	18	2	5	2	2	3
Rushden Town	2	-	-	-	-	-	-	-	-	-
St. Neots Town	-	19	19	18	19	18	-	-	-	-
Spalding United	-	-	-	-	7	1	-	-	-	21
Stamford AFC	3	3	5	5	10	12	7	15	21	20
Stevenage Borough	12	6	-	-	-	-	-	-	-	-
Stewart & Lloyds	14	17	11	2	5	6	15	11	17	9
Stotfold	-	-	14	19	3	5	10	6	10	5
Wellingborough Town	-	-	-	-	-	-	-	19	16	22
Wootton Blue Cross	8	9	9	8	14	17	8	18	19	19
No. of clubs competing	18	19	20	21	21	21	20	22	22	24

HEREWARD SPORTS

UNITED COUNTIES LEAGUE

U.C.F.L.

NEWSLINE

0891 122 960

☎ BE ON THE BALL FOR

☎ LATEST NEWS

☎ 24 HOURS A DAY

☎ 7 DAYS A WEEK

☎ INTERVIEWS

☎ MATCH OF THE DAY

☎ RESULTS & FIXTURES

☎ UPDATED DAILY

0891 122 960

Calls cost 36p per minute cheap rate & 48p per minute at all other times
Marketed by Sportslines (0386) 47302 or (0831) 464517
Call costing correct at time of going to press

LEAGUE KNOCKOUT CUP 1991-92

Preliminary Round
Potton United 2 *(Albone, Cox)*, APV Peterborough City 1 *(Scotcher)*
Holbeach United 2 *(Reeson, Gray)*, Desborough Town 0
Brackley Town 1 *(Sawyer)*, Daventry Town 3 *(O'Neill, Geary, Bunn)*
Raunds Town 1 *(Murphy)*, Northampton Spencer 0
Wellingborough Whitworths 2 *(Wilkins 2)*, Boston 4 *(Gibbons 3, Cook)* AET
Newport Pagnell Town 0, Wellingborough Town 1 *(Harrold)*
Higham Town 0, Eynesbury Town 2 *(Jackson, Kandekore)*
Mirrlees Blackstone 1 *(Hand)*, Harrowby 1 *(Gee)* AET
Spalding United 2 *(Graham, Tarrant)*, British Timken 0
Wootton Blue Cross 1 *(Kyle)*, Sharnbrook 1 *(Spall)* AET
Replays
Harrowby United 0, Mirrlees Blackstone 1 *(P Sharp)*
Sharnbrook 1 *(G Smith)*, Wootton Blue Cross 2 *(Kyle, Marshall)*

First Round
Ford Sports 3 *(McKay, Calvey 2)*, Burton Park Wanderers 2 *(Amos, Stewart)*
Cottingham 3 *(N Pask, Rogers, Cruickshank)*, Spalding United 0
Wootton Blue Cross 1 *(Marshall)*, Rothwell Town 4 *(Beazeley, McDonald, McIlroy 2)* AET
Bugbrooke St Michaels 1 *(Pacey)*, Kempston Rovers 5 *(Neil, Carter, Farthing, Davy, Dazeley)*
O.N. Chenecks 1 *(Barford)*, Hamlet Stewart & Lloyds 3 *(Farr, Baxter, Bogle)* AET
Blisworth 2 *(Ryall, Holmes)*, Arlesey Town 1 *(Simmonds)*
Long Buckby 2 *(Emms, Gee)*, Stotfold 4 *(M Taverner, Vessey 2, Parker)* AET
Eynesbury Rovers 2 *(Humphrey, Meeds)*, St Ives Town 1 *(Taylor)*
Cogenhoe United 5 *(Knibb, Shelswell, Westland, Cunningham 2)*, Wellingborough Town 1 *(Westley)*
Irthlingborough Diamonds 2 *(Medlin 2)*, Thrapston Venturas 1 *(James)*
Olney Town 0, Bourne Town 4 *(Munton 2, Scotney 2)*
Towcester Town 1 *(Preston)*, Irchester United 0
Boston 1 *(Potts)*, Mirrlees Blackstone 0
Potton United 5 *(Cox 2, Seekings 2, Beddall)*, Ramsey Town 2 *(Stonnell, Findlay)* AET
Raunds Town 1 *(Lewis)*, Holbeach United 0
Stamford 1 *(Ward)*, Daventry Town 2 *(Pearson, Geary)*

Second Round
Stotfold 1 *(Murphy)*, Kempston Rovers 0 AET
Towcester Town 0, Boston 4 *(Rodwell, Holleran, N Timby, Cook)*
Eynesbury Rovers 1 *(McCreanor)*, Ford Sports 4 *(Tarbuck, R Green, Hough, A Green)*
Cottingham 0, Potton United 3 *(Branch, Seekings 2)*
Raunds Town 3 *(Beards 2, Murphy)*, Hamlet Stewart & Lloyds 1 *(Torrance)* AET
Rothwell Town 3 *(McDonald 2, Hornby)*, Daventry Town 0
Bourne Town 4 *(Ireland, Langford, Munton 2)*, Blisworth 0
Irthlingborough Diamonds 4 *(Clarke, Paine, Shiavi, Thompson)*, Cogenhoe United 5 *(Hillier, Glennon, Berridge, Shelswell 2)*

Quarter Finals
Stotfold 2 *(Bennett, Boon)*, Ford Sports 1 *(Hough)*
Raunds Town 2 *(Bird, Torrance)*, Cogenhoe United *(Heslop)*
Bourne Town 3 *(Hall, Harradine, Munton)*, Potton United 2 *(Albone, Seekings)*
Rothwell 3 *(Beazeley, McIlroy, Own goal)*, Boston 1 *(Vaughan)*

Semi Finals
Stotfold 2 *(Murphy, Boon)*, Raunds Town 0
Rothwell Town 1 *(Keech)*, Bourne Town 1 *(Mitchell)* AET
Replay
Bourne Town 0, Rothwell Town 1 *(Keech)*

Final
1st Leg
Rothwell Town 2 *(McHutchison, McDonald)*, **Stotfold** 2 *(Cox, Boon)*
Rothwell: Liquorish, McHutchison, Sheerin, Bailey, Bates, Davies, McDonald, P O'Keefe, Kelly, McIlroy, Hornby.
Subs: Smith, Keech.
Stotfold: Hawkins, Redmond, Bambrick, Brown, Hull, O'Brien, Cox, Vessey, Bennett, Cook, Boon. Sub: S Taverner.
2nd Leg
Stotfold 0, **Rothwell Town** 3 *(Hornby, McIlroy 2)*
Stotfold: Hawkins, Brown, Bambrick, S Taverner, Hull, O'Brien, Cox, Vessey, Bennett, Cook, Boon. Sub: Parker.
Rothwell: Liquorish, McHutchison, Geohegan, Bailey, Bates, Davies, McDonald, Sheerin, O'Keefe, McIlroy, Hornby.

BENEVOLENT CUP 1991-92

Semi Finals
Northampton Spencer 5 *(Inwood 3, Jelley, Wilson)*, Newport Pagnell Town 1 *(Daniels)*
Raunds Town 1 *(Murphy)*, Harrowby United 2 *(Jenas, Johnson)*

Final
Northampton Spencer 3 *(Inwood, O'Meara OG, Wilson)*, **Harrowby United** 1 *(Jenas)*
Spencer: Mallett, Agutter, Briggs, Bushell, Jelley, Gage, Heap, Mann, Inwood, Sandy, Wilson. Subs: McGuire, Francis.
Stotfold: Newham, Cook, Liburd, Spencer, Ryder, Durham, Bredan, O'Meara, Scotcher, Jenas, Johnson. Subs: North, Goldsmith.

LEADING SCORERS 1991-92

PREMIER DIVISION	Club	League	KO Cup	Ben. Cup	Total
Darren Munton	Bourne Town	34	5		39
Roy Boon	Stotfold	30	3		33
Jon Inwood	Northampton Spencer	25		4	29
Dave Scotney	Bourne Town	27	2		29
Billy Horn	Eynesbury Rovers	27			27
Paul Murphy	Raunds Town	22	2	1	25
Paul Sharp	Mirrlees Blackstone	24	1		25
Jamie Cunningham	Cogenhoe United	22	2		24
Terry O'Keefe	Rothwell (inc 7 for Raunds)	24			24
Russell Brown	Daventry (inc 20 for B Timken)	23			23
Mick Bennett	Stotfold	21	1		22
Ian Locke	Mirrlees Blackstone	22			22
Adrian Marlow	Desborough Town	21			21
David Rogers Desboro. (inc 18 & 1 KO cup for Cottingham)		20	1		21
Peter Cox	Potton United	17	3		20
Chris Cook	Boston	17	2		19
Nick Keeble	Spalding United	19			19
Dave Torrance	Hamlet S & L	18	1		19
Dale Watkins	Peterborough City	19			19
Sean Giddens	Arlesey Town	18			18
Chris Goodchild	Long Buckby	18			18
Steve McIlroy	Rothwell Town	13	5		18
Danny Nicholls	Wootton BC (inc 7 for Olney)	17	1		18
Neil Kane	Arlesey Town	16			16
Kevin McGuire	N Spencer (inc 12 for Rothwell)	16			16
Phil McHutchison	Hamlet (inc 3 for Rothwell)	16			16
Jim Barron	Stamford	15			15
Nick Green	Cogenhoe United	15			15
Adam Sandy	Northampton Spencer	15			15
Dave Albone	Potton United	12	2		14
Gary Baines	Boston (inc 2 for Holbeach)	14			14
Mark Shiavi	Irthlingborough	13	1		14
Paul Cashin	Wootton Blue Cross	13			13
Neil Donovan	Daventry Town	13			13
John McFarlane	L Buckby (in 10 for Bugbrooke)	13			13
Neil Bird	Raunds Town	11	1		12
Chris Cotwell	Peterborough City	12			12
Dave Gregory	Spalding (inc 3 for Holbeach)	12			12

DIVISION ONE	Club	League	KO Cup	Ben. Cup	Total
Andy Calvey N. Pagnell (inc 11 & 2 KO Cup for Ford)		23	2		25
Mike Findlay	Ramsey Town	24	1		25
Derek Atkinson	Higham Town	22			22
Steve Medlin Higham (inc 2 & 2 KO Cup for Irthlingboro)		17	2		19
Rick Ranshaw	Harrowby United	18			18
Gary Hartwell	Newport Pagnell Town	17			17
Gary Holmes	Ramsey Town	16			16
Dennis Jenas	Harrowby United	14		2	16
Neil Tipper	St Ives Town	16			16
Craig Goldsmith	Harrowby United	15			15
Mark James	Thrapston Venturas	14	1		15
Gary Kiernan	Bugbrooke St Michaels	15			15
Neil Mattinson	Thrapston Venturas	15			15
Richard McGrath	Bugbrooke St Michaels	14			14
Dave Taylor	St Ives Town	13	1		14
Tony Hamilton	Newport Pagnell Town	13			13
Dave Liddle	Newport Pagnell Town	13			13
Trevor Cadden	O.N. Chenecks	12			12
John McCabe	British Timken	12			12
Shay O'Riordan	Bugbrooke St Michaels	12			12

RESERVE DIV. ONE	Club	League	KO Cup	Total
Matt Sanderson	Northampton Spencer	33	3	36
Steve Barrett	Stotfold	23	6	29
Shaun Dodson	Irthlingborough Dia.	20	7	27
Ian Richardson	Mirrlees Blackstone	20	5	25
Paul Davey	Kempston Rovers	23		23
Stuart Creed	Raunds Town	20	1	21
Mel Payne	O.N. Chenecks	19	1	20
Terry Williams	Wootton Blue Cross	19		19
Mark Tilley Mirrlees B. (inc 7 & 1 KO Cup for Raunds)		17	1	18
Phil Coe	Desborough Town	15	2	17
Nick Green	Cogenhoe (all for N. Spencer)	15	2	17
Darren Hempson	Peterborough City	13	3	16
Dave Kenney Rothwell (inc 1 KO Cup for L Buckby)		15	1	16
Tony Gilbert	Stotfold	14	1	15
Dave Hofbauer	Corby Town	15		15
Dave Breakell	Mirrlees Blackstone	9	5	14
Steve White	Eynesbury Rovers	14		14
Steve Dowing	Irthlingboro (inc 4 for Rothwell)	13		13
Carl Pask	Cottingham	13		13
Steve Till	Raunds Town	12	1	13
Paul Attfield	Mirrlees Blackstone	11	1	12
Mark Hilton	Stamford	10	2	12
Paul Daldy	Wellingborough Town	10	2	12

HAT-TRICKS 1991-92

PREMIER DIVISION

Five Goals
Paul Murphy (Raunds) at Holbeach 5/10/91

Four Goals
Mark Thompson (Irthling.) v Wellingboro. 12/10/91
Jon Inwood (Spencer) at Potton 13/11/91
Neil Donovan (Daventry) at Brackley 14/3/92

Three Goals
Terry O'Keefe (Raunds) at Wellingborough 24/8/91
Andy McGowan (Hamlet) v Desborough 27/8/91
Steve Cook (Stotfold) v Brackley 31/8/91
Billy Horn (Eynesbury) v Brackley 14/9/91
Jamie Cunningham (Cogenhoe) at Wootton 21/9/91
James Westley (Wellingboro) v Desboro. 28/9/91
Gary Marshall (Arlesey) at Wellingboro. 22/10/91
Sean Giddens (Arlesey) v Holbeach 26/10/91
Wayne Digby (Arlesey) at Holbeach 16/11/91
Dave Torrance (Hamlet) v Spalding 19/11/91
Darren Munton (Bourne) v Spencer 23/11/91
Steve Scott (Eynesbury) v Holbeach 7/12/91
Mick Keall (Desborough) at Rothwell 26/12/91
Darren Munton (Bourne) at Stamford 26/12/91
Robbie Cooke (Spencer) at Brackley 4/1/92
Jon Inwood (Spencer) at Arlesey 1/2/92
Steve McIlroy (Rothwell) v Brackley 15/2/92
Paul Sharp (Mirrlees) at Irthlingborough. 18/2/92
Nick Green (Cogenhoe) at Wellingboro. 29/2/92
Steve Marshall (APV P'boro) v Rothwell 7/3/92
Darren Munton (Bourne) v Wellingborough 7/3/92
Darren Munton (Bourne) v Spalding 21/3/92
Neil Donovan (Daventry) v Spalding 28/3/92
Nick Green (Cogenhoe) v Stotfold 28/3/92
Danny Nicholls (Wootton) v Holbeach 28/3/92
Neil Birds (Raunds) at Stamford 4/4/92
Andy Adam (Long Buckby) v Spalding 18/4/92
Sean Giddens (Arlesey) v Stotfold 20/4/92
James Westley (Wellingboro.) v Brackley 20/4/92
Adrian Marlow (Desboro.) v Wootton 5/5/92
Phil McHutchison (Hamlet) v Spalding 6/5/92

DIVISION One

Five Goals
Neil Brough (Ford) v Towcester 20/4/92

Four Goals
Dave Taylor (St Ives) at Irchester 28/8/91
Shaun Hubbard (Ramsey) v Whitworths 19/10/91
Mike Findlay (Ramsey) v Irchester 16/11/91
Derek Atkinson (Higham) v Irchester 21/12/91
Rick Ranshaw (Harrowby) v Burton PW 21/12/91
Dennis Jenas (Harrowby) v Timken 28/3/92

Three Goals
Graham Smith (Chenecks) at Irchester 16/8/91
Russell Brown (Timken) v Harrowby 17/8/91
Andy Calvey (Ford) v Bugbrooke 27/8/91
Neil Tipper (St Ives) v Irchester 21/9/91
Mark O'Neill (Burton PW) at Blisworth 5/10/91
Craig Smithsmith (Harrowby) at Blisworth 19/10/91
Rick Ranshaw (Harrowby) at Blisworth 19/10/91
Paul Roberts (Olney) v Irchester 19/10/91
David Rogers (Cottingham) v Irchester 2/11/91
Paul Roberts (Olney) at Timken 23/11/91
Dave Liddle (N Pagnell) v Irchester 30/11/91
Pete Mitchell (Olney) at Irchester 7/12/91
Derek Atkinson (Higham) v Timken 14/12/91
Russell Brown (Timken) at Cottingham 21/12/91
Rick Ranshaw (Harrowby) v Cottingham 26/12/91
Jon Ogden (Sharnbrook) at Olney 28/12/91
David Rogers (Cottingham) v Ford 11/1/92
Mike Findlay (Ramsey) at Thrapston 18/1/92
Gary Holmes (Raunds) v Olney 25/1/92
Peter Orton (Whitworths) v Sharnbrook 25/1/92
Martin Jennings (Timken) at Irchester 1/2/92
Neil Tipper (Ford) v Ford Spts 8/2/92
Roger Amos (Burton PW) v Irchester 14/3/92
Andy Calvey (N Pagnell) at Bugbrooke 25/4/92
Neil Brough (Ford) v Harrowby 2/5/92

LEAGUE KNOCKOUT CUP
Three goals
Darren Gibbons (Boston) at Whitworths 21/9/91

BENEVOLENT CUP
Three goals
Jon Inwood (Spencer) v N Pagnell 5/5/92

1991-92 RESULTS ANALYSIS

	PREMIER DIVISION	DIVISION ONE
Biggest Home Win	Bourne 9, Wellingborough 0 (7/3/92)	Ford 9, Towcester 0 (20/4/92)
Highest Score Draw	Brackley 4, Long Buckby 4 (20/8/91)	B Timken 4, Burton PW 4 (7/12/92)
	Spalding 4, Holbeach 4 (24/9/91)	B Timken 4, ON Chenecks 4 (21/3/92)
Highest Aggregate	Rothwell 8, Brackley 2 (15/2/92)	B Timken 5, Higham 6 (14/12/92)
Longest Unbeaten Run	21 games - Northampton Spencer	20 games - Ramsey Town
" run without win	30 - Brackley Town	33 - Irchester United
Most consecutive wins	11 - Stotfold	20 - Harrowby United
Most consecutive draws	5 - Mirrlees Blackstone	4 - Burton PW, ON Chenecks
" " defeats	10 - Holbeach United	19 - Irchester United
" " scoring games	24 - Stotfold	14- Ford, Newport Pagnell
" " without scoring	5 - Arlesey, Brackley, Desboro., Holbeach	4 - Olney, Irchester
" " matches conceding	19 - Holbeach, Wellingborough	33 - Irchester United
" " not conceding	4 - Arlesey, Hamlet, Kempston, Spencer, Rothwell Town, Stotfold	4 - Harrowby Utd, Ramsey Town

---

MANAGER OF THE MONTH AWARDS

	PREMIER DIVISION	DIVISION ONE
August/September	Frank Reynolds (Arlesey Town)	Mick Durrant (Newport Pagnell)
October	Keith Burt (Raunds Town)	Derek Andrews (Higham Town)
November	Mark Mitchell (Bourne Town)	Dave Harris (Thrapston Venturas)
December	Mark Mitchell (Bourne Town)	Gordon Higgins (Bugbrooke St Mich.)
January	Jack Murray (Rothwell Town)	Steve Hurry (Ramsey Town)
February	Jan Czarnecki (APV P'boro. City)	Alan O'Meara (Harrowby United)
March	Steve Taverner (Stotfold)	Dave Harris (Thrapston Venturas)
April/May	Gary Sargent (Northampton Spencer)	Steve Hurry (Ramsey Town)

Manager of the Year   Gary Sargent (Northampton Spencer)

OTHER HONOURS (NOT MENTIONED ELSEWHERE IN SECTION)

Reserve KO Cup: Stotfold (R-up: Irthlingborough), **Highest Aggregate Scoring Trophy:** Bourne Town, **Fair Play Award:** Holbeach, **Reserve Fair Play Award:** Corby Town/ON Chenecks, **Beds Senior Cup:** Kempston, **Beds Premier Cup:** Stotfold (R-up: Kempston), **Hunts Senior Cup:** Eynesbury (R-up: Ramsey), **Hunts Premier Cup:** Potton, **Beds Intermediate Cup:** Stotfold Reserves (R-up: Sharnbrook Reserves), **Northants Junior Cup:** Raunds Reserves, **Northants Lower Junior Cup:** Bugbrooke Reserves, **East Anglian Cup R-up:** Eynesbury, **Hinchingbrooke Cup:** Potton.

PREMIER DIVISION CLUBS 1992-93

BOSTON

Chairman: Mick Vines   **President:** W Jackson
Secretary: Roger Timby, 38 York Street, Boston, Lincs (0205 354638)
Manager: Percy Freeman   **Asst Manager:** Dick Creasey
Ground: Tattershall Road, Boston, Lincs (0205 65470).
Directions: A52 Grantham - Sleaford, 2nd left into Brothertoft Road, Argyle Street to bridge, immediately over left into Tattershall Road, ground three quaters of a mile.
Capacity: 6,000   **No. seats:** 450   **Covered Accom:** 950   **Floodlights:** Yes
Programme: 16 pages, 25p   **Editor:** Keith Sandell   **Press Officer:** Pete Massam
Club Colours: All blue   **Change Colours:** All white
Clubhouse: Open matchdays and special functions.   **Previous Ground:** Mayflower.
Year formed: 1963   **Nickname:** Poachers   **Midweek matchday:** Tuesday
Record Attendance : 2,700 v Boston Utd, FA Cup 1970.
Previous Leagues: Lincs/ Central Alliance 65-66/ Eastern Co's 66-68/ Midland 68-82/ Northern Co's East 82-87/ Central Midlands 87-91.
Major Honours: Midland Co's Lg 74-75 78-79 80-81 (Lg Cup 76-77), Lincs Snr 'A' Cup (5), Central Mids Lg,.
Club Captain 1991-92: Jamie Rodwell   **Player of the Year 1991-92:** Martin King.
Leading Scorers 1991-92: Chris Cook 19, Gary Baines 12, Kevin Hunt 10, Scott Kent 10.
Leading Appearances 1991-92: Martin King 45, Chris Cook 42, Jamie Rodwell 38.

BOURNE TOWN

Chairman: Jim Brown   **President:** Ray Ferrer
Secretary: Don Mitchell, 55 West Road, Bourne, Lincs PE10 9BS (0778 423382).
Manager: Mark Mitchell   **Asst Manager:** Jimmy Jackson   **Coach:** Martin Henderson.
Ground: Abbey Lawn, Abbey Road, Bourne, Lincs (0778 422292).
Directions: In market place take Spalding Road, ground 500 yds on right
Capacity: 3,000   **No. seats:** 300   **Covered Accom:** 750   **Floodlights:** Yes
Programme: 24 pages, 30p   **Editor:** Pauline Jackson   **Press Officer:** Derek Bontoft
Club Colours: Claret & white   **Change Colours:** White & red.
Local Newspapers: Stamford Mercury, Lincs Free Press, Peterborough Evening Telegraph.
Clubhouse details: Small, open matchdays and specific events
Year formed: 1883   **Nickname:** The Wakes   **Midweek matchday:** Tuesday
Record Attendance: 3,000 v Chelmsford, FA Tphy 1970   **Previous Ground:** Cricket Field.
Previous Leagues: Peterborough/ UCL 47-56/ Central Alliance 58-61/ Midland Counties 61-63.
Players to progress to Football League: Peter Grummit (Nottm Forest), Shaun Cunnington (Wrexham, Grimsby), David Palmer (Wrexham).
Major Honours: Utd Co's Lg 68-69 69-70 71-72 90-91 (KO Cup 69-70, Benevolent Cup 90-91), Lincs Snr 'A' Cup 71-72, Central Alliance Division 1 South 59-60, Lincs Intermediate Cup 85-86.
Club Captain 1991/92: Paul Langford   **Player of the Year 1991/92:** Darren Munton
Leading Scorers 1991-92: Darren Munton 39, Dave Scotney 29, Rob Harradine 10.
Leading Appearances 1991-92: Brendan Blythe 50, Darren Munton 49, Gavin Smith 49.

BRACKLEY TOWN

Chairman: Kim Golding   **President:** Miss C Billingham
Secretary: Pat Ashby, The Cottage, The Green, Moreton, Pinkney, Daventry NN11 6SG (0295 768283).
Manager: John Randall   **Press Officer:** Phil Rogers
Ground: St James Park, Churchill Way, Brackley, Northants (0280 704077).
Directions: Churchill Way, east off A43, south end of town
Capacity: 3,500   **No. seats:** 400   **Covered Accom:** 50   **Floodlights:** Yes
Programme: 16-20 pages, 25p   **Editor:** Pat Ashby
Local Newspapers: Brackley Advertiser, Banbury Guardian, Herald & Post.
Club Colours: Red, black & white   **Change Colours:** All yellow
Clubhouse details: Lounge & main hall. Open all week
Year formed: 1890   **Nickname:** Saints   **Midweek matchday:** Tuesday
Record Attendance: 650 v Kettering, Northants Senior Cup 1989
Previous Leagues: Banbury & District/ North Bucks/ Hellenic 77-83.
Previous Grounds: Banbury Road, Manor Road, Buckingham Road (upto 1974).
Players to progress to Football League: Jon Blencowe (Leicester)
Major Honours: Utd Co's Lg 88-89 (Div 1 83-84), Northants Snr Cup R-up, Buckingham Charity Cup, Hellenic Lg Div 1 Cup 82-83.
Club Captain 1991-92: John Thorne   **Player of the Year 1991-92:** Steve Wilkes.
1991-92 Top Scorers: Andy Ashton 9, Phil Ross 5, John Thorne 4.
1991-92 Leading Appearances: Steve Wilkes 38, Andy Ashton 37, Richard Blossom 37, Derek Purves 37.

COGENHOE UNITED

Chairman: Derek Wright   **President:** Steve Brockwell
Secretary: Mick Marriott, 14 Kiln Corn Close, Cogenhoe, Northants NN7 1NX (0604 890043).
Asst Manager: Stuart Robertson   **Manager:** Dave Conlon
Ground: Compton Park, Brafield Rd. Cogenhoe (0604 890521).   **Press Officer:** Mick Marriott
Directions: Turn off A428 at Brafield-on-the-Green, first turn right to Cogenhoe or A45 to Billing Aquadrome. Carry on, take second Cogenhoe turn on left.
Capacity: 5,000   **No. seats:** 100   **Covered Accom:** Yes   **Floodlights:** Yes.
Programme: 24 pages with admission   **Editor:** Mick Marriott
Club Colours: Sky blue & white   **Change Colours:** Maroon
Clubhouse details: Bar & changing room block, open all week   **Major Honours:** UCL Div 1 R-up
Year formed: 1967   **Nickname:** Cooks   **Midweek matchday:** Tuesday
Record Attendance: 1,000 v Eastenders XI   **Previous League:** Central Northants Combination
Players to progress to Football League: Darren Bazeley (Watford), Darren Harmon (Notts Co.).
Club Captain 1991-92: Neil Heslop   **Player of the Year 1991-92:** Jeff Gilmore
1991-92 Leading Scorers: Jamie Cunningham 24, Neil Westland 18, Nick Green 15.
1991-92 Leading Appearances: Pete Bulliman 49, Neil Westland 49, Guy Glennon 47.

Boston attack during their home fixture against Kempston Rovers. Photo - Martin Wray.

Dave Scotney turns in his second goal as Bourne win 4-0 at Olney in the K.O. Cup. Photo - Neil Whittington.

Cogenhoe 'keeper Pete Bulliman on his way to a clean sheet at Stamford on the opening day of the season.

DAVENTRY TOWN

Chairman: Alan Hills   **President:** Malcolm Hobbs
Secretary: Brian Calvey, 9 The Pasture, Daventry NN11 4AU (0327 705184).
Manager: Willie Barrett   **Asst Manager:** Russ Ashenden.
Ground: Elderstubbs Farm, Leamington Way, Daventry, Northants (0327 706286).
Directions: Adjacent to A45 by-pass.
Capacity: 2,000   **Seats:** 250   **Cover:** Yes   **Floodlights:** Yes   **Founded:** 1886.
Programme: 16 pages   **Editor:** Brian Calvey   **Press Officer:** Brian Calvey
Local Newspapers: Daventry Weekly Express, Herald & Post.
Club colours: Black & white stripes   **Change colours:** Red & white
Midweek Matchday: Tuesday   **Nickname:** None.
Record Attendance: 350 v Ford Sports 1991.   **Clubhouse:** Large Bar.
Previous Leagues: Northampton Town, Central Northants Combination.
Major Honours: UCL Div 1(2), Highest Aggregate Cup, Northants Junior Cup(3).
Players Progressing to Football League: Martin Aldridge (Northampton).
Club Captain 1991-92: Gary Wall   **Player of the Year 1991-92:** Simon Williams
1991-92 Leading Scorers: Neil Donovan 13, Shane Geary 11, Ian Pearce 11.
1991-92 Leading Appearances: Shane Geary 49, Ian Pearce 46, Andy Stoker 46, Simon Williams 46.

DESBOROUGH TOWN

Chairman: Bryan Walmsley   **President:** Ernie Parsons.
Secretary: John Lee, 85 Breakleys, Daventry, Northants NN14 2PT (0536 760002).
Manager: Pat Coe   **Asst Manager:** Mick Keall.   **Press Officer:** John Lee
Ground: Waterworks Field, Braybrooke Rd, Desborough (0536 761350).
Directions: Half a mile west of A6 following signs for Braybrooke.
Capacity: 8,000   **No. seats:** 250   **Covered Accom:** 500   **Floodlights:** Yes
Programme: 20 pages   **Editor:** Craig Labudek   **Price:** With admission
Local Newspapers: Evening Telegraph, Northants Post, Chronicle & Echo, Harborough Mail.
Club Colours: All blue   **Change Colours:** Old gold.
Clubhouse details: Lounge & main hall, 2 bars, games room. Open every evening, weekend lunchtimes.
Year formed: 1896   **Nickname:** Ar Tarn   **Midweek matchday:** Tuesday
Record Attendance: 8,000 v Kettering   **Previous Leagues:** None.
Players progressing to Football League: Wakeley Gage (Northampton, Chester, Peterborough and Crewe), Jon Purdie & Campbell Chapman (Wolves), Andy Tillson (Grimsby & QPR).
Hons: Utd Co's (Prev. Northants) Lg 00-01 01-02 06-07 20-21 23-24 24-25 27-28 48-49 66-67 (R-up 02-03 10-11 19-20 22-23 79-80 (Div 2 10-11(Res) 28-29(Res) (R-up 09-10(Res) 26-27(Res) 51-52(Res)), KO Cup 77-78), Northants Snr Cup 10-11 13-14 28-29 51-52.
Club Captain 1991-92: Dean McAlwane   **Player of the Year 1991-92:** Dean McAlwane
1991-92 Leading Scorers: Adrian Marlow 21, Sean McPolin 6, Simon Reilly 5.
1991-92 Leading Appearances: Dean McAlwane 46, Ian Carvell 42, Adrian Marlow 42.

EYNESBURY ROVERS

Chairman: Ian Kavanagh   **Vice Chairman:** R Parr   **President:** W Stephenson
Secretary: Deryck Irons, 12 Hadleigh Close, Bedford MK41 8JW (0234 268111).
Manager: Alan Day   **Asst Manager:** Barry Cavilla   **Press Officer:** Deryck Irons
Ground: Hall Road, Eynesbury, St Neots (0480 74041).
Directions: Approx 2 miles from A1, on South side of St Neots urban area, near Ernulf School.
Capacity: 3,000   **No. seats:** 270   **Covered Accom:** 270   **Floodlights:** Yes
Programme: 24 pages   **Editor:** Patrick Worrall   **Price:** 25p
Local Newspapers: Hunts Post, Cambridge Evening News, St Neots Weekly News, St Neots Citizen.
Club Colours: Royal blue & white   **Change Colours:** All yellow.
Clubhouse details: Large bar, capacity 150, committee room
Year formed: 1897   **Nickname:** Rovers   **Midweek matchday:** Tuesday
Record Gate: 5,000 v Fulham 1953   **Previous Lges:** Sth Mids 34-39/ UCL 46-52/ Eastern Co's 52-63.
Players to progress to Football Lge: Chris Turner (P'boro, Luton, Cambridge), Denis Emery (P'boro)
Hons: UCL Div 1 76-77, Hunts Snr Cup(10) 13-14 46-47 48-51 54-55 56-57 69-70 84-85 90-91, Hunts Premier Cup 50-51 90-91, Hinchinbrooke Cup(7) 46-47 48-52 57-58 66-67, Cambs Invitation Cup 61-62, E Anglian Cup R-up 90-91 91-92, Scott Gatty Cup 35-36 56-57 84-85 89-90, Hunts Jnr Cup 21-22 26-27, S Mids F'lit Cup 90-91(Res).
Club Captain 1991-92: Dave Jackson   **Player of the Year 1991-92:** Billy Horn
1991-92 Leading Scorers: Billy Horn 27, Maurice Kandekore 11, Mark Humphrey 8.
1991-92 Leading Apps: Warren Brown, Billy Horn, Ian Kavanagh, Mick McCreanor, Graham McMillan all 44.

HOLBEACH UNITED

Chairman: Alan Mitchell   **President:** J King
Secretary: Ian Lovell, 86 London Rd, Long Sutton, Lincs (0406 362139).
Manager: Carl Russell   **Assistant Manager:** Paul Greenaway.
Ground: Carters Park, Park Road, Holbeach (0406 24761).
Directions: Second left at traffic lights in town centre, 220 yds down road on left. From King's Lynn; sharp right at traffic lights.
Capacity: 4,000   **No. seats:** 200   **Covered Accom:** 450   **Floodlights:** Yes
Programme: 20 pages, 30p   **Editor:** Alan Wright   **Press Officer:** Ian Lovell
Local Newspapers: Lincs Free Press, Spalding Guardian, Peterborough Evening Telegraph.
Club Colours: Old gold & black   **Change Colours:** Blue & white
Clubhouse details: Large enough to hold dances. Lounge & kitchen, open every night.
Year formed: 1929   **Nickname:** Tigers   **Midweek matchday:** Wednesday
Record Attendance: 4,094 v Wisbech 1954.   **Previous Name:** Lily Whites.
Previous Leagues: Peterborough/ Utd Co's 46-55/ Eastern Co's 55-62/ Midland Co's 62-63.
Players progressing to Football League: Peter Rawcliffe (Lincoln).
Major Honours: Utd Co's Lg 89-90 (KO Cup(2), Benevolent Cup), Lincs Snr Cup 'A'(3), Lincs Senior Cup 'B', FA Cup 1st Rd Proper 82-83 (lost 0-4 v Wrexham at Peterborough).
Captain 1991-92: Dean Elston**Player of the Year 1991-92:** Lyndon Secker/ Dean Elston/ Andy Crunkhorn.
1991-92 Leading Scorers: Mark Melson 7, Andy Gray 5, Kevin Reeson 4, Lyndon Secker 4.
1991-92 Leading Appearances: Andy Crunkhorn 44, Dean Elston 42, Brian Small 41.

KEMPSTON ROVERS

Chairman: Dai Williams   **President:** H Gilbert
Secretary: Alan Scott, 26 King William Rd, Kempston, Bedford MK42 7AT (0234 854875).
Manager: Alan Wright   **Assistant Manager:** Bobby Folds.
Ground: Hillgrounds Rd, Kempston, Bedford (0234 852346).
Directions: M1 junction 13 to Bedford, ground opposite Sainsburys in Kempston.
Capacity: 2,000   **No. seats:** 100   **Covered Accom:** 250   **Floodlights:** Yes
Programme: 48 pages, 30p   **Editor:** Ian Davis   **Press Officer:** Ian Davis.
Local Newspapers: Bedfordshire Times, Herald & Post.
Club Colours: Red, white & black   **Change Colours:** White & black.
Clubhouse details: Bar & Lounge, built 1986, extended 1989
Year formed: 1884   **Nickname:** Walnut Boys   **Midweek matchday:** Wednesday
Record Attendance: unknown   **Previous League:** Sth Mids 27-53.
Previous Grounds: Hillgrounds Road, Bedford Road.
Major Honours: Utd Co's Lg 73-74 (R-up 56-57 59-60 (Div 2 55-56 (R-up 67-68), KO Cup 57-58 59-60 76-77), Beds Senior Cup(3)
Club Captain 1991-92: Russell Shreeves   **Player of the Year 1991-92:**
1991-92 Leading Scorers: Steve Farthing 10, Dave Farrar 7, Paul Davey 5, Martin Dazeley 5, Darren King 5.
1991-92 Leading Appearances: Steve Farthing 47, Richard Evans 43, Martin Baker 40, Stuart Holmes 40.

LONG BUCKBY

Chairman: Ted Thresher   **President:**
Secretary: Dave Austin, 6 Jubilee Close, Long Buckby NN6 7NP (0327 843286).
Manager: Mick Emms   **Asst Manager:** Les Thurbon
Ground: Station Rd, Long Buckby (0327 842682).
Directions: On Daventry - Long Buckby road. 400 yds from station (Northampton - Rugby line).
Capacity: 1,000   **No. seats:** 50   **Covered Accom:** 150   **Floodlights:** Yes
Programme: 16 pages, 20p   **Editor:** Rod Pryor   **Press Officer:** Rod Bryor
Local Newspapers: Chronicle & Echo, Daventry Weekly Express.
Club Colours: Blue & white   **Change Colours:** Yellow & black
Clubhouse details: Bar & concert room.
Year formed: 1945   **Nickname:** Bucks   **Midweek matchday:** Tuesday
Record Attendance: 750 v Kettering, NFA Senior Cup Final
Previous Name: Long Buckby Nomads 1936.
Previous Leagues: Rugby & District, Central Northants Combination.
Past Players to progress to Football League: Gary Mills (Nottingham Forest, Derby, Notts County, Leicester), Vince Overson (Burnley, Birmingham), Des Walcock (Northampton), Steve Norris (Scarborough, Carlisle, Halifax).
Major Honours: UCL KO Cup 84-85 (UCL Div 2 70-71 71-72, Div 3 69-70, Div 2 KO Cup 71-72).
Club Captain 1991-92: Steve Gee   **Player of the Year 1991-92:** Matt Clarke
1991-92 Top Scorers: Chris Goodchild 18, Peter Walker 11, Andy Adam 10.
1991-92 Leading Appearances: Les Thurbon 45, Steve Gee 44, Jimmy Rogers 44.

MIRRLEES BLACKSTONE

Chairman: Bill Sewell   **President:**
Secretary: Ian McGillivray, 20 New Road, Ryhall, Stamford, Lincs PE9 4HL (0780 62263).
Manager: Steve Blades   **Asst Manager:** John Greenwood.
Ground: Lincoln Road, Stamford (0780 57835).
Directions: A6121 Stamford to Bourne road, 2nd left past MB works.
Capacity: 1,000   **No. seats:** 50   **Covered Accom:** Yes   **Floodlights:** Yes
Programme: 20 pages, 20p   **Editor:** Kevin Boor   **Press Officer:** Secretary
Local Newspapers: Stamford Mercury, Herald & Post, Peterborough Evening Telegraph.
Club Colours: Blue & white   **Change Colours:** Red
Clubhouse details: Open evenings, lunchtimes & matchdays.
Year formed: 1910   **Nickname:** Stones   **Midweek matchday:** Tuesday
Previous Leagues: Peterborough Works/ Peterborough/ Stamford & District.
Previous Names: Rutland Ironworks/ Blackstone (until 1975).
Players to progress to Football League: Craig Goldsmith (Peterborough, Carlisle), Alan Neilson (Newcastle & Wales).
Major Honours: UCL Div 1 R-up 87-88 (Benevolent Cup R-up).
Captain 1991-92: Stan Hardy   **Player of the Year 1991-92:** Stan Hardy/ Trevor Smith
1991-92 Leading Scorers: Paul Sharp 25, Ian Locke 21, Neil Seconde 7.
1991-92 Leading Appearances: Eric Bolster 48, Stan Hardy 48, Steve Blades 47, Paul Collin 47.

NEWPORT PAGNELL TOWN

Chairman: Ernie Print   **President:** Ken Inch.
Secretary: John Anderson, 29 De Ferneus Drive, Raunds, Northants NN9 6SU (0933 623734).
Manager: Mick Durrant   **Asst Manager:** Chris Hullet   **Coach:** Terry Ashton.
Ground: Willen Road, Newport Pagnell (0908 611993).
Directions: Adjacent to A442 Newport Pagnell by-pass.
Capacity: 2,000   **Seats:** 100   **Cover:** 100   **Floodlights:** Yes   **Founded:** 1963.
Prog: 20 pages   **Editor:** Jim Bean   **Press Officer:** Barry Cook.
Clubhouse: Open every evening   **Local Newspapers:** Milton Keynes Citizen.
Club colours: Green & white   **Change colours:** Yellow & black
Previous Leagues: Nth Bucks/ Sth Mids 71-73   **Nickname:** Swans
Hons: UCL Div 1 81-82 (R-up 91-92, Div 1 Cup 77-78).
Captain 1991-92: Chris Hullett   **Player of the Year 1991-92:** Gary Hartwell.
1991-92 Leading Scorers: Gary Hartwell 17, Tony Hamilton 11, Dave Liddle 13.
1991-92 Leading Appearances: Tony Hamilton 32, Gary Hartwell 32, Chris Hullett 32.

NORTHAMPTON SPENCER

Chairman: Graham Wrighting   **President:** Barry Rumford
Secretary: Paul Robinson, 84 Coppice Drive, Parklands, Northampton NN3 1NF (0604 643834).
Manager: Gary Sargent   **Asst Manager:** Keith Bowen
Ground: Kingsthorpe Mill, Studland Rd, Northampton NN3 1NF (0604 718898).
Directions: Turn off Kingsthorpe Rd at traffic lights into Thornton Rd, 1st right into Studland Rd, ground at end.
Capacity: 2,000   **No. seats:** 100   **Covered Accom:** 350   **Floodlights:** Yes
Programme: 40 pages   **Programme Editor/Press Officer:** Andy Goldsmith
Local Newspapers: Chronicle & Echo, Northampton Post, Northants Advertiser.
Club Colours: Yellow & green   **Change Colours:** White & green
Clubhouse details: Large lounge and bar, open matchdays
Year formed: 1936   **Nickname:** Millers   **Midweek matchday:** Tuesday
Record Attendance: 800, English Schools Semi-Final 1991, Kingsthorpe v Erith.
Previous League: Northampton Town   **Previous Name:** Spencer School Old Boys.
Previous Grounds: Dallington Park 1936-70, Duston High School 70-72.
Players to progress to Football League: Paul Stratford (Northampton), Wakeley Gage (Northampton, Chester, Peterborough, Crewe)
Hons: Utd Co's Lg 91-92 (Div 1 84-85, KO Cup Winners & R-up, Benevolent Cup 91-92), Northants Snr Cup R-up
Club Captain 1991-92: Paul Jelley   **Player of the Year 1991-92:** Wakeley Gage.
1991-92 Leading Scorers: Jon Inwood 29, Adam Sandy 15, Adrian Mann 11.
1991-92 Leading Apps: Paul Jelley 49, Jon Inwood 48, Tim Agutter 47, Dick Briggs 47, Adam Sandy 47.

POTTON UNITED

Chairman: Claude Munns   **President:** P Hutchinson.
Secretary: Derek Inskip, 3 Bellevue Close, Potton, Beds SG19 2QA (0767 260355).
Manager: Andy Lloyd   **Asst Manager:** Mark Humphrey   **Coach:** Andy Dunn
Ground: The Hollow, Biggleswade Road, Potton (0767 261100).
Directions: Outskirts of Potton on Biggleswade Road (B1040). Three and a half miles from Sandy (BR). United Counties buses from Biggleswade.
Capacity: 2,000   **Seats:** 180   **Cover:** 250   **Floodlights:** Yes   **Founded:** 1943
Programme: 48 pages, 30p   **Programme Editor/ Press Officer:** Keith Mayhew
Local Newspapers: Biggleswade Chronicle, St Neots Weekly News.
Club Colours: Blue & white   **Change Colours:** Yellow.   **Nickname:** Royals
Clubhouse details: Large (capacity for 100), opened 1985.   **Midweek matchday:** Tuesday
Record Attendance: 470 v Hastings Town, FA Vase 1989
Previous Lges: Sth Mids 46-55/ Central Alliance 56-61 **Previous Ground:** The Recreation Grnd until 1947.
Hons: Utd Co's Lg 86-87 88-89 (KO Cup 72-73, Benevolent Cup 89-90), Beds Snr Cup(5) 47-49 63-64 75-76 77-78, Wallspan Floodlit Cup 87-88, Hinchinbrooke Cup 51-52 84-85 89-90 90-91 91-92, Hunts Premier Cup 89-90, Beds I'mediate Cup 43-44, Nth Beds Charity Cup(9) 58-60 65-67 70-72 85-86 87-88 89-90, FA Vase 5th Rd 89-90.
Club Captain 1991-92: Gary Branch   **Player of the Year 1991/92:** Dave Albone.
1991-92 Leading Scorers: Ray Seekings 24, Peter Cox 20, Dave Albone 14.
1991-92 Leading Appearances: Steve Young 50, Dean Beddall 47, Darren Marsh 45.

RAUNDS TOWN

Chairman: George Hagan   **President:** R Woods
Secretary: Frank Matson, 44 Holmes Avenue, Raunds, Northants NN9 6SX (0933 624765).
Manager: Keith Burt   **Asst Manager:** Glen Burdett
Ground: Kiln Park, Brick Kiln Road, Raunds (0933 623351).
Directions: Take Raunds turning at r'bout on A605 and ground is first left.
Capacity: 3,000   **No. seats:** 100   **Covered Accom:** 1,000   **Floodlights:** Yes
Programme: 48 pages 30p   **Press Officer & Programme Editor:** Mick Jones
Local Newspapers: Northants Evening Telegraph, Wellingborough Post, Chronicle & Echo.
Club Colours: Red & black   **Change Colours:** White.
Clubhouse details: On ground, open every day
Year formed: 1896   **Nickname:** Shopmates   **Midweek matchday:** Tuesday
Record Attendance: 1,500 v Crystal Palace, ground opening 23/7/91.
Previous Leagues: Rushden & District, Central Northants Combination.
Previous Grounds: Greenhouse Field (until 1948), The Berristers (1948-91).
Past Players to progress to Football League: Greg Downs (Norwich, Coventry, Birmingham).
Major Honours: UCL Div 1 82-83 (KO Cup 90-91), Northants Snr Cup, Northants Jnr Cup.
Club Captain 1991-92: Tony Boatswain   **Player of the Year 1991-92:** Neil Bird
1991-92 Leading Scorers: Paul Murphy 25, Neil Bird 12, Martin Lowe 11.
1991-92 Leading Appearances: John Arundel 52, Gary Torrance 51, Ade Cooksley 50, Ian Jordan 50.

ROTHWELL TOWN

Chairman: Stuart Andrews   **President:** Jack Covington.
Secretary: Roger Barratt, 18 Norton Street, Rothwell, Northants (0536 711244).
Manager: Jack Murray   **Asst Manager:** Graham Simmonds
Ground: Cecil Street, Rothwell (0536 710694).
Directions: Enter Rothwell on A6, turn into Bridge Street at Midland Bank, turn 3rd left into Tresham Street, ground is at top. Three miles from Kettering (BR); Rothwell is served by Kettering to Market Harborough buses.
Capacity: 3,000   **No. seats:** 460   **Covered Accom:** 700   **Floodlights:** Yes
Programme: 20 pages, 20p   **Programme Editor/Press Officer:** Peter Bradley
Local Newspapers: Northants Evening Telegraph, Chronicle & Echo.
Club Colours: Blue   **Change Colours:** All white
Clubhouse: Large Sportsmans Bar, 'Top of the Town Ballroom', lounge for 200.
Year formed: 1896   **Nickname:** Bones   **Midweek matchday:** Tuesday
Record Attendance: 2508 v Irthlingborough 1971   **Previous Name:** Rothwell Town Swifts.
Previous Leagues: Kettering Amateur, Leicestershire Senior, Central Alliance 56-61.
Players to progress to Football League: Lee Glover (Nottm Forest, Barnsley & Scotland under-21), Matty Watts (Charlton)
Hons: UCL KO Cup(5) (Div 2(2) 52-54, Div 2 Cup(2) 52-54, Northants Lg 1899-1900, Northants Snr Cup(3)
Club Captain 1991-92: Adrian Sheerin   **Player of the Year 1991-92:** Adrian Sheerin.
1991-92 Leading Scorers: Steve McIlroy 18, Terry O'Keefe 17, Kevin McGuire 12.
1991-92 Leading Appearances: Glyn Davies 53, Adrian Sheerin 53, Cliff Bailey 51, Dave McHutchison 51.

Potton United. Back Row (L/R): Paul Smith, Colin Young, Stuart Ives, Steve Young, Paul Beattie, Darren Marsh. Front: Peter Cox, Dean Beddall, Gary Branch (Capt), David Albone, Ray Seekings. Photo - Gavin Ellis.

Mirrlees Blackstone Player-Manager Steve Blades shields the ball from Bishop's Stortford's John Lawford during the 1-1 FA Cup First Qualifying Round draw at the George Wilson Stadium. Photo - Mike Floate.

Eynesbury concede an own goal and lose 0-2 at home to Northampton Spencer. Photo - Neil Whittington.

SPALDING UNITED

Chairman: Rod Quinton   **President:**
Secretary: Sue Anderson, 23 West Parade, Spalding, Lincs (0775 711134).
Manger: Martin Henderson   **Asst Manager:** Dave Arnold
Ground: Sir Halley Stewart Field, Winfrey Avenue, Spalding (0775 724957).
Directions: Town centre off A16, adjacent to bus station. 250 yds from Spalding (BR).
Capacity: 7,000   **Seats:** 350   **Cover:** 2500   **Floodlights:** Yes   **Founded:** 1921
Programme: 16 pages   **Editor:** J Grimwood   **Press Officer:** Ray Tucker
Club Colours: Blue & white   **Change Colours:** All white
Clubhouse details: Open matchdays, and events.   **Midweek matchday:** Tuesday
Record Attendance: 6,972 v Peterborough, FA Cup 1952.   **Nickname:** Tulips
Previous Leagues: Peterborough/ Utd Co's 31-55 68-78 86-88/ Eastern Co's 55-60/ Central Alliance 60-61/ Midland Co's 61-68/ Northern Co's East 82-86/ Southern 88-91.
Players progressing to Football League: Carl Shutt (Sheffield Wednesday, Bristol City, Leeds).
Local Newspapers: Lincs Free Press, Spalding Guardian, Peterborough Evening Telegraph.
Hons: Utd Co's Lg 54-55 74-75 87-88 (R-up 50-51 51-52 52-53 72-73 75-76, KO Cup 75-76), Northern Co's East Lg 83-84, Lincs Snr Cup 52-53, Lincs Snr 'A' Cup 87-88, Lincs Snr 'B' Cup 50-51, Evans Halshaw F'lit Cup 89-90.
Club Captain 1991-92: Jeremy Moulds   **Player of the Year 1991-92:** Jeremy Moulds
Leading Scorers 1991-92: Nick Keeble 19, Dave Gregory 9, Dean Tarrant 9.
Leading Appearances 1991-92: Jeremy Moulds 46, Nick Keeble 45, Dave Whisker 45.

STAMFORD

Chairman: Arthur Twiddy   **Vice Chairman:** Bill Warrington.
Secretary/Press Officer: Andrew Eason, 36 Queens Walk, Stamford, Lincs (0780 54510).
Manager: Chris Corby   **Asst Manager:** Mick Reilly
Coach: Stuart Chivertob   **Commercial Mgr:** Bob Ford/ George Bennett
Ground: Wothorpe Road, Stamford, Lincs (0780 63079).
Directions: Off A43 Kettering Rd, 1 mile east of A1. 200 yds from station.
Capacity: 5,000   **No. seats:** 250   **Covered Accom:** 1,250   **Floodlights:** Yes
Programme: 40 pages, 40p   **Editor:** Andrew Eason   **Club Shop:** Dave Salisbury (0780 52377)
Local Newspapers: Stamford Mercury, Peterborough Evening Telegraph, Herald & Post.
Club Colours: Red & blue   **Change Colours:** All white
Year formed: 1896   **Nickname:** Daniels   **Midweek matchday:** Tuesday
Record Attendance: 4,200 v Kettering, FA Cup 1953.
Previous Leagues: Peterborough/ Northants (UCL) 08-55/ Central Alliance 55-61/ Midland Co's 61-72.
Players to progress to Football League: Alan Birchenall (Chelsea, Crystal Palace, Leicester), Reg Chester (Aston Villa), Teddy Tye (Chelsea), Gerry Fell (Brighton, Southend, Torquay, York), Campbell Chapman (Wolves), Steve Collins (Peterborough), Keith Alexander (Grimsby, Stockport, Lincoln), Andy Tillson (Grimsby, QPR), Brian Stubbs (Notts Co.), Domenico Genovese (Peterborough).
Hons: FA Vase 79-80 (R-up 75-76 83-84), Utd Co's Lg 75-76 77-78 79-80 80-81 81-82 (KO Cup 51-52 75-76 79-80 81-82 85-86, Northants Lg 11-12, Lincs Snr 'A' Cup 78-79 82-83, Lincs Snr 'B' Cup 51-52 53-54, Hinchingbrooke Cup, William Scarber Mem. Cup 70-71 82-83 85-86 88-89, Stamford Chal. Cup 89-90, Lincs Jnr Cup 48-49.
Club Captain 1991-92: Wayne Arthur   **Player of the Year 1991-92:** Dave Parker.
1991-92 Leading Scorers: Jim Barron 15, Glenn Beech 10, Dave O'Boyle 5.
1991-92 Leading Appearances: Wayne Arthur 41, Tony Dunn 41, Glenn Beech 36, Martin Bonner 36.

STEWART & LLOYDS

Chairman: John Hamill   **President:**
Secretary: Phil Mackay, 207 Rockingham Road, Kettering, Northants NN16 9JA (0536 410840).
Manager: Kevin Byrne   **Assistant Manager:** Mick Bihanycz.
Ground: Recreation Ground, Occupation Road, Corby (0536 401497).
Directions: On Occupation Road at rear of Stewart & Lloyds Leisure Club.
Capacity: 1,500   **No. seats:** 100   **Covered Accom:** 200   **Floodlights:** Yes
Programme: 8 pages with admission   **Programme Editor/Press Officer:** Dave Foster
Clubhouse details: Licensed bar.   **Local Press:** Northants Evening Telegraph
Club Colours: Yellow & blue   **Change Colours:** Red & white
Year formed: 1935   **Nickname:** None   **Midweek matchday:** Tuesday
Record Attendance: Unknown   **Previous Leagues:** Kettering Amateur
Previous Name: Hamlet Stewart & Lloyds (until 1992).
Players to progress to Football League: Andy McGowan (Northampton), Willie Graham (Brentford)
Hons: UCL R-up 85-86 (KO Cup, Div 1(2) 73-75, Div 1 Cup(2) 73-75, Div 2(Res) 76-77, Div 2 KO Cup(2) 75-77)
Club Captain 1991-92: P J Hamill   **Player of the Year 1990/91:** Graham Leech.
1991-92 Leading Scorers: Dave Torrance 19, Phil McHutchison 13, Steve Farr 8.
1991-92 Leading Appearances: P J Hamill 48, Graham Leech 48, Adrian Ringrose 45.

STOTFOLD

Chairman: Gerry Watson   **Vice Chairman:** G Jarman   **President:** C Hyde
Secretary: Bill Clegg, 12 Common Rd, Stotfold, Hitchin, Herts SG5 4BX (0462 730421).
Manager: Steve Taverner   **Asst Manager/Coach:** Tony Martin
Press Officer: Julie Longhurst   **Physiotherapists:** J Page, I Taylor.
Ground: Roker Park, The Green, Stotfold (0462 730765).
Directions: A507 from A1, right at lights, right at T-jct. A507 from Bedford via Shefford, left at lights, right at T-jct.
Capacity: 5,000   **Seats:** 50   **Cover:** 300   **Floodlights:** Yes   **Nickname:** Eagles
Programme: 32 pages   **Editor:** Julie Longhurst   **Price:** With admission
Local Newspapers: Hitchin Gazette, Biggleswade Chronicle.
Club Colours: Amber & black   **Change Colours:** Sky blue
Clubhouse details: Clubroom, bar, dressing rooms, physio room.   **Midweek matchday:** Tuesday
Year formed: 1904, reformed 1945   **Record Attendance:** 1,000 v Letchworth Town, FA Vase.
Previous Leagues: Biggleswade & District/ North Herts/ South Midlands 51-84.
Hons: Utd Co's Lg KO Cup R-up 91-92 (Res Div 1 87-88), Sth Mids Lg 80-81 (R-up 55-56 57-58 58-59 59-60 63-64 65-66 77-78, Div 1 53-54, Chal. Tphy 81-82, Beds Snr Cup 64-65, Beds Premier Cup 81-82, Beds I'mediate Cup 58-59, Nth Beds Charity Cup 55-56 56-57 61-62 81-82 87-88 90-91, Beds Colts Lg 88-89.
Club Captain 1991-92: Gary Redmond   **Player of the Year 1991-92:** Mick Bennett
1991-92 Leading Scorers: Roy Boon 33, Mick Bennett 22, Steve Cook 11.
1991-92 Leading Appearances: Roy Boon 51, Gary Bambrick 50, Mick Bennett 49, Gordon Brown 49.

Stamford. Back Row (L/R): Simon Davis, Tony Dunn, David Jackson, Scott Miller, Paul Downs, John Rawdon. Front: Karl Richardson, Ken Roworth, Wayne Arthur (Capt), Simon Laws, Nick Green, Dave Parker. Photo - Gavin Ellis.

Two APV Peterborough forwards hassle goalie Martin Lakin in a 2-1 win at troubled Spalding. Photo - Martin Wray.

Stamford's Dave Parker-Meadows (2) disposses Potton's Steve James, but his side slipped to a 1-2 home loss.

WELLINGBOROUGH TOWN

Chairman: Mike McNamee   **President:** Brian Abbott
Secretary: Mike Walden, 5 Fernie Way, Wellingborough, Northants NN8 3LB (0933 279561).
Manager: Peter Garbutt   **Assistant Manager:** Paul Barratt
Ground: Dog & Duck, London Rd, Wellingborough (0933 223536).
Directions: 200 yds off A45 by-pass, by Dog & Duck public house. 1 mile from Wellingborough (BR).
Capacity: 5,000   **Seats:** 300   **Cover:** 500   **Floodlights:** Yes   **Founded:** 1867
Programme: 16 pages, 30p   **Editor:** Nick Dzyka   **Press Officer:** Secretary.
Local Newspapers: Northants Evening Telegraph, Chronicle & Echo.
Colours: White & blue   **Change Colours:** All red   **Clubhouse details:** On ground, full facilities.
Nickname: Doughboys   **Midweek matchday:** Tuesday   **Record Attendance:** 4,013 v Kettering
Previous Leagues: Midland 1895-97 98-1901/ Southern 01-05 79-82/ Northants (Utd Co's) 19-34 36-56 61-68/ Central Alliance 56-61/ Metropolitan 68-70/ West Mids 70-71.
Players to progress to Football League: Phil Neal (N'hampton, L'pool & Eng.), Fanny Walden (Spurs & Eng.).
Major Honours: UCL(3), Metropolitan Lg 69-70, Northants Senior Cup(7).
Club Captain 1991-92: Dino Cirelli   **Player of the Year 1991-92:** James Westley
1991-92 Leading Scorers: James Westley 24, Ian Garrett 5, John Cowper 4.
1991-92 Leading Appearances: James Westley 48, Mark Cowper 35, Paul Shopland 34.

WOOTTON BLUE CROSS

Chairman: B Keens   **President:** J Clarke
Secretary: Trevor Templeman, 67 Glenwoods, Newport Pagnell, Bucks MK16 0NG (0908 611053).
Manager: John Horsley   **Asst Manager:** Derek Williamson.
Ground: Weston Park, Bedford Rd, Wootton (0234 767662).
Directions: 4 miles south of Beford on main road through village, at rear of Post Office.
Capacity: 2,000   **No. seats:** 50   **Covered Accom:** 250   **Floodlights:** Yes
Programme: 12 pages, 20p   **Press Officer & Programme Editor:** Trevor Templeman.
Local Newspapers: Bedfordshire Times, Bedford Herald, Beds Express, Beds On Sunday.
Club Colours: Blue & white   **Change Colours:** All white
Clubhouse: Main hall, bar, darts, pool, bingo. Open every evening, Sat & Sun lunchtimes
Year formed: 1887   **Nickname:** Blue Cross   **Midweek matchday:** Tuesday
Record Attendance: 838 v Luton Town, Beds Premier Cup 1988
Previous Leagues: Bedford & District, South Midlands 46-55.
Players to progress to Football League: A Biggs (Arsenal).
Hons: Utd Co's Lg Div 2 67-68 69-70 (KO Cup 82-83, Div 2 Cup 64-65), Sth Mids Lg 47-48 (R-up 49-50), Beds Snr Cup 70-71, Hinchinbrooke Cup(5).
Club Captain 1991-92: Paul Ewart   **Player of the Year 1991-92:** Paul Cashin.
1991-92 Leading Scorers: Danny Nicholls 14, Paul Cashin 13, Mick Marshall 9.
1991-92 Leading Appearances: Andrew Carey 45, Tony Brittain 38, Paul Cashin 38.

DIVISION ONE CLUBS 1992-93

A.P.V. PETERBOROUGH CITY

Chairman: Tony Zirpolo
Secretary: Margaret Lamb, 205 Welland Rd, Peterborough PE1 3SY (0733 340199).
Manager: Jan Czarnecki   **Asst Manager:** John McKie   **Coach:** Jim Walker
Ground: Phorpres Sports Ground, London Road, Peterborough (0733 343501).
Directions: Off A1 to A1139 Fletton Parkway, take 3rd exit and turn into Phorpres Way, left at r'bout, ground 100yds on left.
Press Officer: Derek Hall   **Clubhouse:** Phorpres Sports Club.
Capacity: 1,000   **Seats:** Due 92-93   **Cover:** 100   **Floodlights:** No.   **Founded:** 1904
Programme: 8 pages, 20p   **Editor:** Dave Lamb   **Previous Name:** Baker Perkins (until 1991).
Colours: All red   **Change Colours:** All white   **Nickname:** The Bakers
Local Newspapers: Peterborough Evening Telegraph, Peterborough Standard.
Record Attendance: 450 v Ramsey, UCL 1/2/87 (at Alma Road)   **Midweek matchday:** Tuesday
Previous Grounds: West Wood (until mid-1960s), Alma Rd (until 1991), Ringwood PF, Sth Bretton (91-92).
Previous Leagues: Northants, Peterborough   **Hons:** UCL Div 1, Hinchinbrooke Cup
Club Captain 1991-92: Andy Hamilton   **Player of the Year 1991-92:** Martin Porter
1991-92 Leading Scorers: Dale Watkins 19, Chris Crotwell 12, Dave Bonner 10.
1991-92 Leading Appearances: Clive Foster 41, Paul Kirby 40, Jason Walker 38.

BLISWORTH

Chairman: Pete Edwards   **Manager:** Gary Knibbs   **Asst Manager:** Brian Oldham.
Secretary: Phil Holding, 19 Highfield Rd, Northampton NN1 4SR (0604 715093).
Ground: Blisworth Playing Field, Courteenhall Rd, Blisworth (0604 858024).
Directions: Courteenhall Rd off A43.
Capacity: 1,000   **Seats:** None   **Cover:** None   **Floodlights:** No   **Clubhouse:** Yes
Colours: Yellow & green   **Change colours:** White & blue   **Programme:** 16 pages
Previous Leagues: Central Northants Combination.   **Major Honours:** Northants Junior Cup
Club Captain 1991-92: Geoff Pallett   **Player of the Year 1991-92:** Gary Edwards.
1991-92 Leading Scorers: Steve Holmes 11, Mick Matthews 7, Nigel Roberts 5.
1991-92 Leading Appearances: Gary Edwards 36, Geoff Pallett 32, Mark Duckett 31.

BRITISH TIMKEN

Chairman: A Watts   **Manager:** Bernie Franklin   **Asst Manager:** Steve Essex
Secretary: Trevor Burrows, 40 Brockwood Close, Duston, Northampton NN5 6LY (0604 583059).
Ground: Braunston Road, Daventry (0604 581588).   **Programme:** 16 pages
Directions: A45 from Northampton to outskirts of Daventry, works entrance at top of Braunston Road.
Capacity: 2,500   **Seats:** 150   **Cover:** Yes   **Floodlights:** No   **Clubhouse:** Yes
Previous Leagues: None   **Hons:** UCL Div 1 (Div 2, Div 2 Cup, Benevolent Cup)
Club Captain 1991-92: Des Magee   **Player of the Year 1991-92:** Martin Jennings
1991-92 Leading Scorers: Russell Brown 20, John McCabe 12, Martin Jennings 10.
1991-92 Leading Appearances: Steve Hardy 32, Martin Jennings 31, Russell Brown 30.

APV Peterborough City. Back Row (L/R): Jan Czarnecki (Manager), Des Lawrence, Scott Miller, Paul Johnson, Ian Pledger, Gary Scotcher, Clive Foster, Andy Hamilton, Tony Zirpolo (Chairman). Front: John McKie (Physio), Darrin Clarke, Jason Walker, Mark Amps, Chris Crotwell, Paul Kirby, Dale Watkins. Photo - Martin Wray.

The big Division One match of the season - Harrowby win 4-0 at Newport Pagnell. Here Goldsmith's wind assisted corner is helped into the net by Scotcher for the second goal. Photo - Neil Whittington.

Mark Newton scores for Higham in a 5-1 home win over Wellingborough Whitworths. Photo - Neil Whittington.

BUGBROOKE ST MICHAELS

Chairman: John Curtis   **Manager:** Gordon Higgins   **Asst Manager:** Nick Verity
Secretary: Roger Geary, 31 Kislingbury Rd, Bugbrooke, Northampton NN7 3QG (0604 831678).
Ground: Birds Close, Gayton Rd, Bugbrooke (0604 830707).
Directions: A45 Northampton to Daventry road, turn onto B4525 (Banbury Lane) at Kislingbury, turn left to Gayton, ground on left.
Capacity: 1,500   **Seats:** None   **Cover:** Yes   **Floodlights:** No   **Nickname:** Badgers
Founded: **Programme:** 8 pages   **Clubhouse:** Yes
Club colours: Yellow & navy   **Change colours:** Blue & grey
Previous Leagues: Central Northants Combination   **Major Honours:** Northants Junior Cup
Club Captain 1991-92: Gavin Hough   **Player of the Year 1991-92:** Dale Williams.
1991-92 Leading Scorers: Gary Kiernan 15, Richard McGrath 14, Shay O'Riordan 12.
1991-92 Leading Appearances: Mark Coleman 35, Steve Eborall 34, Gary Kiernan 34, Richard McGrath 34.

BURTON PARK WANDERERS

Chairman: Bernard Lloyd   **Manager:** Ian Lawson.
Secretary: Stuart Coles, 216 Bath Rd, Kettering NN16 9LZ (0536 520349).
Ground: Latimer Park, Polwell Lane, Burton Latimer (0536 723639).
Directions: Entering Burton Latimer, turn off A6 Station Rd and right into Powell Lane; ground on the right.
Capacity: 1,000   **Seats:** 100   **Cover:** 150   **Floodlights:** No   **Founded:** 1961
Local Newspapers: Northants Evening Telegraph, Northants Post.
Club Colours: Red & black stripes   **Change Colours:** Green & yellow
Prog: 16 pages with entry   **Nickname:** The Wanderers   **Midweek matchday:** Tuesday
Record Attendance: 253 v Rothwell, May 1989   **Previous Leagues:** Kettering Amateur
Past Players to progress to Football League: Shaun Wills (Peterborough)
Major Honours: UCL Div 1 R-up, Benevolent Cup R-up
Club Captain 1991-92: John Sadler   **Player of the Year 1991-92:** John Reed.
1991-92 Leading Scorers: Steve Bones 8, Roger Amos 6, Chris Meagan 4, Angelo Negri 4.
1991-92 Leading Appearances: Steve Bones 34, John Sadler 30, John Reed 28.

COTTINGHAM

Chairman: Mike Beadsworth   **Manager:** Neil Newlands   **Asst Manager:** John Sneddon
Secretary: Lindsay Brownlie, 30 Bancroft Rd, Cottingham, Market Harborough LE16 8XA (0536 771009).
Ground: Berryfield Rd, Cottingham (0536 770051).
Directions: One and a half miles from Corby on A427 turn right to Cottingham. At junction of B670 turn left; Berryfield Road 200 yds on right.
Capacity: 1,000   **No. of seats:** None   **Covered Accommodation:** Yes
Floodlights: No   **Programme:** No   **Clubhouse:** Bar & changing rooms
Club colours: White & navy blue   **Change colours:** Blue, white & green.
Previous Leagues: East Mids Alliance, Kettering Amateur, Market Harborough
Major Honours: UCL Div 1 runners-up, Northants Junior Cup
Club Captain 1991-92: Neil Pask   **Player of the Year 1991-92:**
91-92 Top Scorers: Dave Rogers 19, Ally Reid 6, Brendan Furey, Dave Haddon, Bob Owen, Neil Pask all 4.
1991-92 Leading Appearances: Neil Pask 33, John Knowles 30, Bobby Owen 30.

FORD SPORTS

Chairman: Dave Taylor   **Manager:** Gary Graham   **Asst Manager:** Richard Green.
Secretary: David Taylor, 96 The Medway, Grange Estate, Daventry NN11 4QU (0327 706512).
Ground: Royal Oak Way South, Daventry (0327 709219).
Directions: Enter Daventry on A45 or A361 and follow signs for Royal Oak Way
Capacity: 1,000   **Seats:** Yes   **Covered Accommodation:** Yes
Floodlights: No   **Programme:** 12 pages   **Clubhouse:** Yes
Club colours: All blue   **Change colours:** White & black.
Previous Leagues: Central Northants Combination
Club Captain 1991-92: Richard Green   **Player of the Year 1991-92:** Rob McKay.
1991-92 Leading Scorers: Andy Calvey 13, Neil Brough 10, Richard Green 7, Rod Hough 7.
1991-92 Leading Appearances: Rob McKay 37, Richard Green 34, Brian Blakeman 29.

HARROWBY UNITED

Chairman: Chris Whitehead   **Manager:** Alan O'Meara   **Assistant Mgr:** Graham Bredan
Secretary: Steve Cullington, 6 Scotney Drive, Grantham, Lincs NG31 9UA (0476 60831).
Ground: Harrowby Playing Fields, Harrowby Lane, Grantham (0476 590822).
Directions: From A1 take B6403, go past A52 roundabout, past Ancaster turn and take road to Harrowby. Continue into Grantham, ground opposite Cherry Tree public house.
Capacity: 1,500   **No. of seats:** 100   **Covered Accommodation:** Yes.
Floodlights: No   **Programme:** 12 pages   **Clubhouse:** Yes
Club colours: Blue & white   **Change colours:** Red & white.
Previous Leagues: Mids Regional Alliance, East Mids, Lincolnshire, Grantham.
Hons: Utd Co's Lg Div 1 91-92 (Benevolent Cup R-up 91-92), Mids Regional Alliance Lg & Cup, Lincs Snr 'B' Cup.
Club Captain 1991-92: Mick Spencer   **Player of the Year 1991-92:** Andy Ryder
1991-92 Leading Scorers: Rick Ranshaw 18, Dennis Jenas 16, Craig Goldsmith 15.
1991-92 Leading Appearances: Gary Bredan 37, Mick Spencer 36, Russ Gee 35.

HIGHAM TOWN

Chairman: Phil Palmer   **Manager:** Gary Savage   **Asst Manager:** Graham Benwell/ Alan Strickla
Secretary: Chris Ruff, 23 Queensway, Higham Ferrers NN9 8BU (0933 58862).
Ground: Vine Hill Drive, Higham Ferrers (0933 53751).
Directions: From Kettering 1st right on A6 after A45 junction to St Neots. From Bedford, 3rd left after A45 junction to Northampton
Capacity: 1,000   **No. of seats:** Yes   **Covered Accommodation:** 100
Floodlights: No   **Programme:** 12 pages   **Clubhouse:** Yes
Colours: Sky blue & navy   **Change colours:** White & black   **Previous Lge:** Rushden & Dist.
Major Honours: Northants Lg 21-22 22-23, Northants Snr Cup 21-22, Maunsell Cup.
Club Captain 1991-92: Mark Newton   **Player of the Year 1991-92:** John Perry.
1991-92 Leading Scorers: Derek Atkinson 22, Steve Medlin 15, Trevor Forward 5, Nick Shelton 5.
1991-92 Leading Appearances: Mark Newton 35, Derek Atkinson 33, Trevor Forward 33.

Olney Town. Back Row (L/R): Mark Lancaster, Paul Roberts, Paul Banks, Alan Brown, Andy McCabe, Lee Bearman, Rob Wardell, Dave Tooley (Manager). Front: Paul Breeze, Gary Sands, Adrian North, Lee Griffiths, Andy Kinchington. Photo - James Wright.

Ramsey Town, Huntingdonshire Senior Cup Finalists 1991-92. Photo - Gavin Ellis.

St Ives attack during their home fixture with Wellingborough Whitworths on February 1st. Mist eventually caused abandonment with the score at 2-0 to the visitors. When the match was replayed ten days later the home side prevailed 4-0!. Photo - Martin Wray.

IRCHESTER UNITED

Chairman: Geoff Cotter   **Manager:** Alan Ambridge.   **Asst Manager:** Martin Batley.
Secretary: P Mayhew, 25 Finedon Street, Burton Latimer, Northants, (0536 723341).
Ground: Alfred Street, Irchester (0933 312877).
Directions: Off Rushden Road to Wollaston Road, next to recreation ground.
Capacity: 1,000   **No. of seats:** None   **Covered Accommodation:** Yes
Floodlights: No   **Programme:** No   **Clubhouse:** Yes
Club colours: Red & white   **Change colours:** Yellow & black
Previous Leagues: Rushden & District   **Hons:** Northants Lg Div 2 30-31 31-32.
Club Captain 1991-92: Glen Finch   **Player of the Year 1991-92:** Andy Cotter.
1992-92 Leading Scorers: Andy Cotter 4, Andy Smart 4, Gary Cotter 3, Matt Tompkins 3.
1991-92 Leading Appearances: Glen Finch 34, Gary Cotter 32, Matt Tompkins 32.

NORTHAMPTON O.N. CHENECKS

Chairman: John Wilson   **Manager:** Jim Tate   **Asst Manager:** Malcolm Wincott.
Secretary: John Goodger, 74 Beech Avenue, Northampton NN3 2JG (0604 717224).
Ground: Billing Road, Northampton (0604 34045).
Directions: South ring road, exit A43 Kettering, left at lights, top of hill, ground 200 yds on right.
Capacity: 1,350   **Seats:** Yes   **Covered Accommodation:** Yes
Floodlights: No   **Programme:** 16 pages   **Clubhouse:** Yes
Club colours: All blue   **Change colours:** All red
Previous Leagues: Northampton Town   **Hons:** UCL Div 1 77-78 79-80.
Club Captain 1991-92: Andrew Kevan   **Player of the Year 1991-92:** Stuart Fitzhugh
1991-92 Leading Scorers: Trevor Cadden 12, Jessell Dore 11, Tom O'Connell 10
1991-92 Leading Apps: Stuart Fitzhugh 35, Robert Powell 35, Roy Anderson 34, Jessel Dore 34.

OLNEY TOWN

Chairman: Terry Finney   **Manager:** Dave Tooley   **Asst Manager:** Barry Simons
Secretary: Andrew Baldwin, 49 Midland Road, Olney, Bucks MK46 4BP (0234 711071)
Ground: East Street, Olney (0234 712227)
Directions: Enter Olney on A509 from Wellingborough, 100yds on left enter East St, ground 200 yds on left.
Capacity: 2,000   **No. of seats:** None   **Covered Accommodation:** Yes
Floodlights: No   **Programme:** 32 pages   **Clubhouse:** Yes
Club colours: White & black   **Change colours:** Claret & blue.
Previous Leagues: North Bucks   **Major Honours:** UCL Div 1 72-73.
Club Captain 1991-92: Paul Banks   **Player of the Year 1991-92:** Pete Miller
1991-92 Leading Scorers: Paul Roberts 9, Wayne Bellamy 6, Adrian North 5.
1991-92 Leading Appearances: Alan Brown 34, Pete Miller 32, Paul Banks 31.

RAMSEY TOWN

Chairman: John Slack   **Manager:** Neil King.
Secretary: Mike Baldwin, 10 Slade Close, Ramsey (0487 814084).
Ground: Cricketfield Lane, Ramsey (0487 814218)
Directions: 100 yds off B1040 Ramsey to Warboys road.
Capacity: 1,000   **No. of seats:** None   **Covered Accommodation:** Yes
Floodlights: Yes   **Programme:** 12 pages   **Clubhouse:** Yes
Club colours: Amber & black   **Change colours:** Red & white.
Previous Leagues: Peterborough & District   **Honours:** UCL Div 1, Hunts Senior Cup(3).
Club Captain 1991-92: Roy Blake   **Player of the Year 1991-92:** Ian Edmonds
1991-92 Leading Scorers: Mike Findlay 25, Gary Holmes 16, Peter McCrudden 8, Ray Stonnell 8.
1991-92 Leading Appearances: Gary Holmes 34, Charlie Walker 33, Mike Findlay 32.

ST IVES TOWN

Chairman: Mick Tacchi   **Manager:** Dave Donaldson   **Asst Manager:** Dave Taylor.
Secretary: John Parker, 2 Priory Gardens, New Rd, St Ives, Cambs PE17 4BE (0480 64549).
Ground: Westwood Rd, St Ives, Cambs (0480 63207) **Directions:** Adjacent to St Ivo Sports Centre.
Capacity: 5,000   **Seats:** Due 92-93   **Covered Accommodation:** Yes
Floodlights: Yes   **Programme:** 8 pages   **Clubhouse:** Bar and entertainment room.
Club colours: White & black   **Change colours:** Yellow & black
Previous Leagues: Peterborough, Cambs   **Major Honours:** Hunts Senior Cup(8).
Club Captain 1991-92: Cliff Miles   **Player of the Year 1991-92:** Cliff Miles.
1991-92 Leading Scorers: Neil Tipper 16, Dave Taylor 14, Tony Flisher 8, Mark Shiels 8.
91-92 Leading Apps: Warren Everdell, Shane Gibbs, Cliff Miles, Rob Moore, Dave Taylor all 34.

SHARNBROOK

Chairman: S P Butler   **Manager:** Dick Williams   **Asst Manager:** Bob Perez
Secretary: Bill Edwards, 8 Towns End Rd, Sharnbrook, Beds MK44 1HY (0234 781584).
Ground: Lodge Rd, Sharnbrook (0234 781080).
Directions: Second sign to Sharnbrook from Rushden on A6, under railway bridge, right at T-junction, left past church, right into Lodge Road.
Capacity: 1,000   **No. of seats:** None   **Covered Accommodation:** Yes
Floodlights: No   **Programme:** 12 pages   **Clubhouse:** Yes
Cols: Maroon & white   **Change colours:** White & black.   **Previous Leagues:** Bedford
Club Captain 1991-92: Steve Guerin   **Player of the Year 1991-92:** Grant Smith
1991-92 Leading Scorers: Jon Ogden 8, Paul Hoogstraten 7, Steve Smith 7.
1991-92 Leading Appearances: Steve Guerin 35, Grant Smith 32, Phil Spall 31.

THRAPSTON VENTURAS

Chairman: David Morson **Manager:** Gary Petts **Asst Manager:** Mark James.
Secretary: D Pickard,: 9 Springfield Ave, Thrapston, Northants (08012 4102)
Ground: Chancery Lane, Thrapston, Northants (08012 2470).
Directions: Chancery Lane off A605 in town centre.
Capacity: 1,000 **No. of seats:** None **Covered Accommodation:** Yes
Floodlights: No **Programme:** Yes **Clubhouse:** Yes
Club colours: All light blue **Change colours:** Yellow & black
Previous Leagues: Kettering & District **Major Honours:** Northants Junior Cup
Club Captain 1991-92: Mark James **Player of the Year 1991-92:** Paul Stringer
1991-92 Leading Scorers: Mark James 15, Neil Mattinson 15, Dave Harris 10.
1991-92 Leading Appearances: Mark Brown 35, Dave Harris 33, Mark James 33.

TOWCESTER TOWN

Chairman: Bob Kightly **Manager:** Jim Henderson **Secretary:** Teresa Porter, 79 Brackley Rd,
Towcester, Northants NN12 7DH (0327 51290).
Ground: Castle Park, Towcester (0327 51487).
Directions: On A5, on the left arriving from the south.
Capacity: 1500 **No. of seats:** None **Covered Accommodation:** Yes
Floodlights: No **Programme:** Yes **Clubhouse:** Yes
Club colours: All red **Change colours:** Amber & black
Previous Leagues: South Midlands **Major Honours:** Northants Junior Cup(3).
Club Captain 1990/91: Mark Townsend **Player of the Year 1990-91:** Mark Townsend.
1991-92 Leading Scorers: Liam Hynes 4, Trevor Pannell 4, Steve Preston 4.
1991-92 Leading Appearances: Mark Townsend 28, Brian Watts 28, Trevor Pannell 25.

WELLINGBOROUGH WHITWORTHS

Chairman: B Jarvis **Manager:** John Mayes **Asst Manager:** Martin Goodes.
Secretary: Ron Edwards, 15 James Rd, Wellingborough NN8 2LR (0933 227765).
Ground: London Road, Wellingborough, Northants (0933 227324).
Directions: Off London Road at Dog & Duck public house
Capacity: 700 **No. of seats:** None **Covered Accommodation:** Yes
Floodlights: No **Programme:** No **Clubhouse:** Yes
Club colours: Green & white **Change colours:** Blue
Previous Leagues: East Midlands Alliance, Rushden & District
Club Captain 1991-92: Steve Grant **Player of the Year 1991-92:** Shaun Grant.
1991-92 Leading Scorers: Darren Wilkins 10, Steve Whitehead 7, Steve Grant 5, Peter Orton 5.
1991-92 Leading Appearances: Steve Grant 34, Mark Downing 32, Shaun Grant 32.

Towcester (lighter shirts) attack during their 3-2 win at Thrapston on March 14th. Photo - Martin Wray.

NORTH BUCKS LEAGUE

With just a few weeks to go before the end of the season, Leighton Athletic looked set to stroll to the championship, but they ended up blowing their games in hand and needed to beat Deanshanger Athletic 19-0 in their final game of the season to take the title on goal difference. Winning 8-0, they made a valiant effort, but it was not enough and the title went to Roade.

Premier Division	P	W	D	L	F	A	PTS
Roade	28	22	3	3	101	37	47
Leighton Athletic	28	22	3	3	83	27	47
Scot FC	28	17	8	3	90	35	42
Westbury	28	15	7	6	68	48	37
Silverstone	28	14	7	7	73	42	35
Earls Barton	28	12	9	7	76	50	33
Deanshanger Ath.	28	14	2	12	57	58	30
Old Bradwell Utd	28	10	7	11	54	59	27
Yardley Gobion	28	10	7	11	54	59	27
Pottersbury	28	10	5	13	78	67	25
Padbury United	28	9	4	15	51	78	22
Wicken Sports	28	5	7	15	44	62	19
St Claydon	28	4	7	17	39	80	15
MK Civil Service	28	2	4	22	36	106	8
Syresham	28	2	2	24	25	127	6

Intermediate Div.	P	W	D	L	F	A	PTS
Newport Athletic	24	19	4	1	88	29	42
Marsh Gibbon	24	16	3	5	66	27	35
Gawcott FC	24	15	4	4	73	32	34
Mercedes Benz	24	14	2	8	63	34	30
British Legion	24	13	2	9	62	39	28
Audi Voltswagon	24	9	6	9	37	46	24
Leighton A. Res	24	8	6	9	36	47	24
Grendon Rangers	24	6	6	12	27	49	18
Abbey National	24	5	7	12	27	38	17
Hanslope	24	6	5	13	41	57	17
Deanshanger A. Res	24	7	3	14	38	62	17
Scot FC Res	24	5	5	14	51	87	15
Tingewick Sports	24	4	3	17	25	87	11

Division One	P	W	D	L	F	A	PTS
Sherington	26	21	4	1	107	22	46
Eaton United	26	19	5	2	92	32	43
Tesco FC	26	15	6	5	70	36	36
Stoke Bruerne	26	14	3	9	68	60	31
Old Bradwell Res	26	14	2	10	61	44	30
Roade Res	26	11	6	9	64	37	28
MK Dynamos	26	5	14	7	52	50	24
Yardley Gobion Res	26	8	5	13	48	70	21
Oldbrook	26	9	2	15	67	76	20
Thornborough	26	7	6	13	43	74	20
Earls Barton Res	26	8	3	15	43	46	19
Finmere	26	6	6	14	47	96	18
Silverstone Res	26	7	3	16	52	95	17
Wicken Sports Res	26	4	3	19	30	106	11

Division Two	P	W	D	L	F	A	PTS
Gawcott Res	26	20	3	3	82	40	43
Wincanton	26	20	1	5	111	33	41
Potterspury Res	26	15	2	9	68	54	32
Abbey National Res	26	13	5	8	51	37	31
Padbury Res	26	13	2	11	70	53	28
S. Claydon Res	26	11	6	9	64	53	28
Bow Brickhill	26	12	1	13	43	46	25
Marsh Gibbon Res	26	8	8	10	36	38	24
Grendon Rgrs Res	26	10	4	12	42	49	24
Tesco Res	26	9	6	11	46	63	24
Hanslope Res	26	9	4	13	42	50	22
Tingewick Spts Res	26	8	5	13	32	71	21
Leighton Pipers	26	4	6	16	45	84	14
Syresham Res	26	2	3	21	31	91	7

NORTHAMPTON TOWN LEAGUE

Premier Division	P	W	D	L	F	A	PTS
Rosebery Rangers	24	18	6	0	75	15	42
Pitsford Eagle	24	14	5	5	65	31	33
Queen Eleanor	24	13	5	6	63	22	31
Bective Wanderers	24	14	3	7	58	25	31
Sileby Rangers	24	13	3	8	68	32	29
Queens Park WMC	24	12	4	8	47	35	28
N'ton Park	22	12	3	9	57	38	27
Crusaders	24	8	7	9	57	38	27
St Georges O.B.	24	6	5	13	37	53	17
St Marys	24	5	6	13	47	71	16
Strollers	24	4	7	13	21	67	15
Delapre Old Boys	24	2	3	19	28	114	7

Top Scorers: Jim Plumpton (Queen Eleanor) 23, Mick Harris (St Marys) 20, Conrad Vigo (Sileby Rangers) 19, Ady Akano (Park) 19

Division One	P	W	D	L	F	A	PTS
Pitsford Reserves	26	16	9	1	76	19	41
Duston United	26	16	6	4	75	26	38
Queen Eleanor Res	26	12	7	7	61	42	34
Foundry Generals	26	14	4	8	65	35	32
N'ton Spencer 'A'	26	13	4	9	55	56	30
Hard'stone Ath.	26	11	5	10	53	49	27
St Crispin	26	12	3	11	63	61	27
ON Chenecks 'A'	26	10	5	11	49	49	25
N'ton Park Res	26	10	4	12	51	49	24
Ashley Rovers	26	9	6	11	41	48	24
Sileby Rgrs Res	26	10	2	14	54	61	22
Nomads	26	6	5	15	48	81	17
St Marys Res	26	3	7	16	26	72	13
Vic. Rangers	26	4	4	18	35	102	12

Top Scorers: Ady Franklin (St Crispin) 24, Ricki Pyke (Ashley Rovers) 19, Russ Merrick (Duston United) 18.

Division Two	P	W	D	L	F	A	PTS
Crusaders Res	22	15	4	3	79	29	34
Qu. Pk WMC Res	22	16	0	6	93	53	32
Foundry Gen. Res	22	15	1	6	64	46	31
Rosebery Rgrs Res	22	10	7	5	72	41	27
Kingsthorpe Wdrs	22	11	3	8	57	47	25
Bective Wdrs Res	22	9	6	7	58	55	24
St Georges OB Res	22	10	2	10	45	49	22
New Duston Ath.	22	8	4	10	46	49	20
N'ton Amateurs	22	7	5	10	50	80	19
Cue Sports	22	6	6	10	31	34	18
S.P.A.	22	3	3	16	45	81	9
Wootton Res	22	0	3	19	22	100	3

Top Scorers: Peter Canavan (Queens Park WMC Res) 42, Mark Handley (Kingsthorpe Wanderers) 31.

Division Three	P	W	D	L	F	A	PTS
Duston Utd Res	20	15	4	1	64	22	34
British Timken 'A'	20	14	2	4	89	30	30
Duston Mag. Res *	19	13	4	2	65	24	30
Kingsthorpe W. Res	20	11	1	8	49	43	23
Park/Tigers	20	9	4	7	39	47	22
Ashley Rvrs Res	20	9	1	10	39	43	19
Delapre OB Res	20	9	1	10	29	48	19
Strollers Res	20	6	4	11	19	33	16
Nomads Res *	19	4	2	13	33	60	10
Cue Sports Res	20	3	4	13	25	69	10
Hard'stone Ath. Res	20	0	5	15	15	47	5

Top Scorers: Roy Cuthbert (Timken) 25, Hugh Dillon (Duston Magpies) 24.

WESTAWAY CENTRAL NORTHANTS COMBINATION

Westaway Premier	P	W	D	L	F	A	PTS
Woodford	30	25	1	4	138	33	53
Harpole	30	23	2	5	107	42	48
Heyford	30	20	5	5	94	40	45
Milton	30	19	2	9	87	38	40
Brington	30	17	0	13	58	43	34
Wollaston	30	15	2	13	74	57	32
Country Cons.	30	13	6	11	65	58	32
Police	30	14	3	13	66	89	31
Long Buckby 'A'	30	13	4	13	65	69	30
Kislingbury	30	12	4	14	54	51	28
Brown Brothers	30	12	4	14	68	74	28
Moulton	30	10	8	12	51	69	28
West Haddon	30	8	7	15	48	84	23
Flore	30	4	4	22	47	106	12
Byfield	30	3	4	23	40	127	10
Bugbrooke SM 'A'	30	1	6	23	35	123	8

Charade Division	P	W	D	L	F	A	PTS
Braunston	18	15	0	3	75	21	30
Yardley	18	12	3	3	58	28	27
Welford Victoria	18	11	4	3	49	23	26
Emerald	18	9	4	5	55	37	22
Crick. Athletic	18	7	6	5	50	40	20
Heyford Res	18	8	3	7	42	48	19
Cold Ashby	18	4	3	11	25	47	11
Ravensthorpe	18	3	5	10	28	56	11
Milton Res	18	2	3	13	32	60	7
Brington Res	18	2	3	13	32	81	7

EAST NORTHANTS LEAGUE

Premier Division	P	W	D	L	F	A	PTS
Finedon Volta	20	15	4	1	64	22	34
Wellingboro. Alb.	20	13	3	4	64	28	29
Weavers	20	11	4	5	58	26	26
Harrowden	20	11	3	6	56	44	25
St Peters	20	11	2	7	53	30	24
Royal Oak	20	10	2	8	58	47	22
Wanderers	20	8	4	8	39	38	20
Lavenden	20	7	1	12	45	51	15
Bridgemans	20	6	3	11	45	72	15
Bozeat	20	3	1	16	30	100	7
Wollaston Res	20	1	1	18	29	83	3

LEICESTER & DISTRICT LEAGUE

Premier Division	P	W	D	L	F	A	PTS
Cottesmore	26	19	5	2	75	31	62
Fosse Imps	26	18	3	5	73	23	57
Croxton Kerrial	26	17	3	5	59	40	54
Uppingham Town	26	16	2	8	67	35	50
Greetham	26	16	2	8	75	50	50
Thurmaston Utd	26	13	3	8	48	37	44
Blaby United	26	10	3	13	44	53	33
Stoney Stanton	26	8	7	16	39	49	31
Glenfield Town	26	9	2	14	59	60	29
Dunton Bassett	26	8	4	14	55	74	28
Cosby United	26	7	6	13	43	57	27
Newbold Jubilee	26	5	6	15	37	63	21
City Gas	26	5	6	15	34	63	21
Fleckney	26	2	2	22	29	102	8

Kevin White, captain of East Northants League champions Finedon Volta, receives the league Trophy from League Chairman Richard Dugdale before the final game of the season at Eastfield Park, Wellingborough, on April 22nd. Photo - Martin Wray.

EAST MIDLANDS FOOTBALL ALLIANCE

Chairman: J Shooter.

Hon. Secretary: W Morris,
30 Exeter Street, Kettering.

BRIXWORTH COMPLETE DOUBLE

Brixworth All Saints became the eigth club in forty years to achieve a League Championship and Munton Cup 'double' just a year after Corby Strip Mills picked up both honours. It was no forgone conclusion, however, the title not being decided until the final match of the season. Up till then Strip Mills, and fellow Corby side Locomotives, were both in with a chance of wresting the 'Sportsworld' County Division title from Brxsworth's grip, but while the two Corby clubs could manage only draws in the last week of the campaign, Brixworth made sure by taking two points off Corby Pegasus in a tense match. Three days later they had little trouble in defeating Stanion United by three goals to nil in the replayed 'R Griggs & Co.' Munton Cup final to complete their most successful season since joining the League 23 years ago. The replay, staged at Irthlingborough Diamonds' Nene Park, was made necessary when the first match, staged at Kettering's Rockingham Road, was deadlocked at two apiece with Brixworth perhaps a shade lucky to get a second chance; midway County Division side Stanion showed scant respect for their highly placed opponents, taking the game to them and having the better of the first half, but they were just not able to keep up the pressure and extra-time saw them drawing on reserves of energy to keep Brixworth at bay.

Elsewhere in the County Division, Corby Locomotives gained the runners-up consolation, a fitting reward to mark the 25th anniversary of their formation as works team in the then Stewarts & Lloyds steelworks. Corby Strip Mills, who were formed from the same roots, finished third separated from Locomotives on goal difference only. In fact Corby clubs claimed four of the top five places to emphasise the wealth of talent in the town.

Kettering teams did not have such a happy year, the town's five representatives occupying 10th, 12th, 13th, 15th and 16th places in the sixteen-strong division, with Kettering Generals claiming the foremost position.

The only Leicestershire club in membership of the E.M.F.A., Medbourne, became champions of the 'Alliance & Leicester' Intermediate Division, and along with runners-up, Corby Grampian Association, have gained promotion to the top flight for 92-93. For Medbourne, it was their first League title in a membership that dates back to the early fifties, and the enthusiasm generated by the club at their presentation evening recently suggests they have the ability and determination to do well in the higher sphere.

In the lower divisions, Stanwick Rangers captured the Division One crown just twelve months after collecting the Division Two title, whilst Wellingborough AFC 2000 repeated a similar feat by winning Division Two a year after triumphing in Division Three. Newly formed Corby Earlstree had a six point margin in Division Three to lift the title at their first attempt.

Corby F.C. Maple of Division One were 'Airwair' Cup winners, whilst the competition for the Reserve teams, the 'Doug Fairwey' trophy, was won for the second year running by Corby Danesholme reserves.

1992-93 sees a decrease of four teams as Spratton and Wilby, each with two sides, have resigned. Due to administrative problems, Kettering Avondale and Kettering Harlequins have been forced to amalgamate and play as Avondale-Harlequin, the first team retaining County Division status and the reserves to participate in Division Two. The County Division will again comprise sixteen clubs, the Intermediate and Division One each have fourteen, but with no new teams joining, Division Three will be scrapped and Division Two reconstituted into two sections of nine; a unique formula will see a cross-matching of teams from both sections playing each other once, and then home and away within their own section to ensure a programme of 25 games.

At the A.G.M. in June, Roy Reddaway, a former Football League referee, received an illuminated display from League Chairman John Shooter to mark his 28th year as League Treasurer.

Walter Morris, Hon. Secretary

'Sportsworld (N'ton)' County Division	P	W	D	L	F	A	PTS
Brixworth	30	21	5	4	66	27	47
Corby Locomotives	30	21	4	5	84	35	46
Corby Strip Mills	30	20	6	4	70	33	46
Corby Danesholme	30	20	3	7	82	38	43
Corby Pegasus	30	15	5	10	56	48	35
Weldon	30	15	3	12	78	54	33
Rothwell Corinth.	30	12	8	10	54	40	32
Stanion United	30	11	7	12	49	45	29
Corby FC Fisher	30	11	6	13	64	66	28
Kettering Generals	30	9	7	14	53	66	25
Gretton	30	10	5	15	47	62	25
Kettering Nomads	30	7	10	13	45	48	24
Kettering Avondale	30	4	10	16	41	85	18
Spratton	30	6	5	19	30	84	17
Barton Seagrave	30	4	8	18	33	65	16
Kett. Orchard Park	30	5	6	19	41	97	16

'Alliance & Leicester' Intermediate Division	P	W	D	L	F	A	PTS
Medbourne	26	15	6	5	63	39	36
Grampian Assoc.	26	15	5	6	66	36	35
Corby St Brendans	26	16	3	7	70	46	35
Geddington WMC	26	14	5	7	61	38	33
Corby Strip M Res	26	11	6	9	60	46	28
Corby D'holme Res	26	11	6	9	50	42	28
Brixworth Res	30	11	2	13	46	44	24
Corby Loco Res	26	11	1	14	38	54	23
Rothwell Com. Ctre	26	8	6	12	42	61	22
Wellingboro. Gram.	26	7	7	12	46	58	21
Irthlingboro Rgrs	26	8	5	13	39	60	21
Gretton Reserves	26	9	3	14	34	55	21
Rothwell Cor. Res	26	6	7	13	36	44	19
Kettering Nom. Res	26	7	4	15	35	63	18

JEWSON EASTERN COUNTIES LEAGUE

President: Derek I Needham.
Hon. Secretary: Colin Lamb,
3 Land Close, Clacton-on-Sea, Essex CO16 8UJ (0255 436398).

1991-92 DIARY/ ROUND-UP

1991-92 was a historic season for the League; its 50th playing season. However, it started with an almost new line-up of officers. Secretary Martin Davis had resigned to be succeeded by Assistant Secretary Colin Lamb, Keith Johnson being appointed Assistant Secretary, Graham Chell Fixtures Secretary and John Tythcott Referees Appointments Secretary.

The opening day saw defending champions Wisbech go down 1-4 to Division One champions Norwich United in the first ever League match at United's new stadium. The other promoted side, Brightlingsea, opened their account with a solitary goal success over Great Yarmouth. Harwich smashed seven past luckless Thetford, a defeat which set the seal on what was to be the one of the Norfolk club's worst ever seasons; they won just three matches finishing in bottom slot, and were relegated. Manager Tony Lyes, with the club since January 1986, resigned at the end of 1991 to be succeeded by David Low. Of the League newcomers, Sudbury Wanderers opened with a 5-1 win over Clarksteel Yaxley, Cambridge City Reserves on their return to the League beat Swaffham 1-0, whilst Hadleigh went down 0-1 to Fakenham. Halstead set a strange record in the opening month by playing a goalkeeper of different nationality in their first three games; Mark Cook (English), Eric Wilson (New Zealander) and Douglas Coetzee (South African).

The second Saturday saw Harwich winning 9-0 at Haverhill with Glen Hepburn getting seven for the season's highest individual tally. In contrast, Ipswich Wanderers had great difficulty in opening their account. It was some 380 minutes of playing time before striker Jon Anderson netted their first of 91-92, against Sudbury Reserves on 4th September.

The first managerial casualty came on just three weeks, Chatteris' Keith Payne resigning after five straight opening defeats. He was succeeded by the partnership of Lester Kent and Steve Bedford. During the night of September 9/10, Brantham's main stand was gutted by fire. On September 26th, Huntingdon with just one win from twelve, sacked Peter Mynch, Eric Cheesewright taking over as player-manager for the remainder of the campaign. Two days later, Clacton became only the third club to complete 1,500 Jewson League matches; a goalless draw with Haverhill in torrential rain! It was Cornard who led the Premier by the end of September, albeit narrowly from Harwich and Wroxham. Diss led from Ely in Division One, whilst Tiptree, Chatteris and Warboys all still awaited a League win. Surprisingly though, Tiptree had beaten Diadora Leagers Hitchin and Dagenham in the FA Cup.

October saw the League's last survivors in the FA Cup, Lowestoft, bow out to Grays in the Third Qualifying Round. By the end of the month Cornard still led the Premier, from Wroxham and Norwich United, but Cambridge City Reserves, with a run of twelve straight wins including a 9-1 drubbing of Clarksteel Yaxley, headed Division One from Fakenham and Diss. Tiptree and Warboys, however, still awaited that first win.

Into November, and on the eleventh Chatteris became the 16th club to complete 1,000 matches in the League, beating Brightlingsea 2-1. The same day, Tiptree and Warboys both notched their first wins beating Watton and Ipswich Wanderers respectively. The fifth saw Collwyn Rowe resign as Halstead's manager to be succeeded until the end of the season by former boss Jimmy Holder. At the end of the month Cornard still topped the Premier, from Wroxham and Stowmarket, with Fakenham leading Division One from Diss and Cambridge City Reserves....*(continued overleaf).*

Wroxham FC, Jewson Eastern Counties League Premier Division Champions 1991-92.

On 3/12/91, the League's two clubs with unbroken membership, Lowestoft and Great Yarmouth, played their 100th League match, drawing 1-1. Overall Yarmouth lead their rivals with 40 wins to Lowestoft's 38. December saw the League's longest serving manager with one club, Alan Doyle, part company with Histon. Boxing Day saw the first 1,000+ crowd at a League match for several years, 1,200 turning out for the March v Wisbech derby. At the turn of the year, Cornard, Wroxham and Stowmarket still held the top Premier Division spots, with Diss heading Division One from Fakenham and Long Sutton. Diss would go on to win the title with eight points to spare.

January 1992 saw Brightlingsea boss Steve Dowman resign, rejoin, and then part company again with his club. He was succeeded by Adrain Webster. Tiptree boss Phil Whettell also resigned, to be succeeded by Steve Sutton, and the Jam Makers went on to make their now almost traditional second half of the season recovery. By December 31st they were bottom with two wins. They ended 16th, losing only two of their last twenty. On January 16th Wroxham recorded the third highest score in the League's history; 15-2 v Thetford. For the fifh successive month Cornard led the Premier with Wroxham and Stowmarket still in pursuit.

In February Gorleston lost the services of manager Jimmy Landamore, with Chairman Peter Self taking charge of team affairs. Clacton also had a change, Tony Kinsella being replaced by the trio of Tony Armstrong, Dave Reynolds and former Ipswich star Kevin Beattie. John Musgrove, manager of Swaffham, also resigned. By the end of the month Wroxham overtook Cornard, a position they were not to relinquish; the clinched the Premier Division with a 2-1 win against Histon on 11th April with four matches still to play. Manager Brian Cunningham is reputed to have worn the same pair of lucky underpants for every match.

Lowestoft manager Jimmy Campbell resigned in March, with former Ipswich 'keeper Laurie Sivell stepping in for the rest of the season. Wisbech boss Dave Eldred stepped down in late March, as did Cornard's Keith Martin in an attempt to stop his side's disappointing run-in; to no avail as the club won only one of their last nine to finish third, being overtaken by Stowmarket who despite losing their opening three matches had come good to record their highest ever placing. Stowmarket also became the first recipients of the League's latest award, which carries a £1,000 cash prize courtesy of Jewson; the Fair Play Trophy. Based on disciplinary records over 38 matches, clubs receive one point per caution, and five per dismissal. Fakenham booked promotion in the final week of March, and a superb 'off-the-field' effort saw them attain the ground standard criteria to enable them to go up. For the second successive campaign the League's last FA Vase survivor reached the Quarter Finals, Diss going down in a replay to eventual winners Wimborne. Two Division Two sides, Cambridge City Reserves and Sudbury Reserves, reached the Semis of the League Cup but lost to Norwich United and Gorleston respectively.

With two going up, for the first time since 89-90 two sides were relegated. The battle to avoid the drop with Thetford went to the final weekend. Chatteris won their last game against Harwich, and Brightlingsea took a point at Gorleston to pip Clacton on goal difference. The Seasiders will therefore celebrate their centenary in 92-93 one flight down. In Division One, Woodbridge, losing just once in their last fourteen, pipped Ely for the third promotion spot.

The final action was the League Cup final, held at Norwich City on 6th May. Last minute goals in normal time and extra time saw the score end 2-2 and Norwich United take Gorleston to a replay at Diss nine days later. Gorleston led there 2-0 after 21 minutes, but United again forced extra time and this time emerged 5-2 winners.

Clubs starting 92-93 with new managers include Brightlingsea, Bury Town Reserves, Ely (one former Cambridge City player, Alan Biley, replacing another, Tom Finney), Halstead, Lowestoft, Mildenhall and Wisbech. Outside of the League, the Norfolk Senior Cup was an all-Jewson affair, Fakenham beating Diss in a replay. Wisbech beat Cambridge City to win the Cambs Invitation Cup, whilst Stowmarket were runners-up in the Suffolk Premier Cup, and Harwich and Parkeston runners-up in the Eastern Floodlit Competition. 1992-93 sees one new arrival, Stanway Rovers - runners-up in the Essex & Suffolk Border League. They replace Clarksteel Yaxley whose membership was terminated through inadequate facilities. Division One will however be one club short, Huntingdon having resigned due to financial difficulties. **Colin Lamb**, League Secretary.

Premier Division	P	W	D	L	F	A	PTS
Wroxham	42	31	6	5	113	41	99
Stowmarket Town	42	26	9	7	86	50	87
Cornard United	42	24	8	10	85	47	80
Norwich United	42	23	7	12	72	53	76
Wisbech Town	42	23	6	13	86	62	75
Harwich & Park.	42	24	2	16	106	61	74
Newmarket Town	42	19	14	9	66	50	71
Haverhill Rovers	42	18	11	13	70	61	65
Halstead Town	42	18	6	18	79	72	60
March Town Utd	42	15	12	15	64	49	57
Lowestoft Town	42	16	9	17	67	64	57
Gorleston	42	16	8	18	62	64	56
Felixstowe T.	42	14	11	17	55	61	53
Gt Yarmouth T.	42	15	6	21	60	71	51
Histon	42	15	5	22	61	89	50
Tiptree United	42	11	16	15	54	70	49
Brantham Ath.	42	12	12	18	51	69	48
Watton United	42	12	9	21	57	70	45
Chatteris Town	42	12	7	23	49	72	43
Brightlingsea Utd	42	11	9	22	60	83	42
Clacton Town	42	11	9	22	50	90	42
Thetford Town	42	3	4	35	31	135	13

Division One	P	W	D	L	F	A	PTS
Diss Town	38	28	6	4	105	28	90
Fakenham Town	38	25	7	6	80	35	82
Woodbridge Town	38	19	10	9	70	34	67
Ely City	38	20	6	12	66	52	66
Downham Town	38	19	5	14	68	61	62
Long Sutton Ath.	38	18	7	13	70	58	61
Sudbury T. Res.	38	17	8	13	72	55	59
Soham Town Rgrs	38	16	11	11	70	58	59
Cambridge C. Res.	38	17	7	14	84	74	58
Somersham Town	38	16	9	13	75	56	57
Hadleigh United	38	17	6	15	59	61	57
Sudbury Wanderers	38	16	6	16	63	62	54
King's Lynn Res.	38	12	11	15	58	61	47
Warboys Town	38	13	8	17	60	69	47
Ipswich Wanderers	38	10	9	19	47	70	39
Bury Town Res.	38	10	9	19	45	74	39
Clarksteel Yaxley	38	11	6	21	49	79	39
Swaffham Town	38	11	5	22	53	80	38
Huntingdon Utd	38	7	7	24	34	90	28
Mildenhall Town	38	2	9	27	31	102	15

Diss captain Marcus Oliver receives the Division One Championship Cup from Mr Sam Lawrence, its donator.

Doug Wade, joint manager of Stowmarket Town, receives £1,000 from Martin Sizeland, along with Jewson Fair Play Trophy. Geoff Porter and Chairman John Kerridge look on. Stowmarket are the first winners of the award.

Thetford Town captain, Dave Lowe, receiving a cheque for £100 from Jewson Managing Director Mr Les Morrell in recognition of their winning the Good Behaviour award for October. They also won the award in January, becoming the first club to win it twice in one season.

PREMIER DIVISION RESULT CHART 1991-92

HOME TEAM	1	2	3	4	5	6	7	8	9	10	11	12	13	14	15	16	17	18	19	20	21	22
1. Brantham A.	*	1-3	0-2	3-0	0-0	2-2	1-0	3-1	1-1	1-4	1-2	2-1	1-1	0-1	0-0	1-1	0-2	7-0	1-3	1-1	0-1	0-1
2. Brightlingsea	2-0	*	1-1	2-0	0-4	1-1	0-1	1-0	2-2	2-3	2-0	1-2	0-3	2-2	0-0	2-4	0-2	5-1	2-3	3-2	1-2	1-3
3. Chatteris	2-3	2-1	*	1-2	3-3	2-0	1-1	0-1	0-1	2-0	2-1	3-0	1-0	0-1	0-1	0-0	1-1	3-4	2-3	4-1	0-3	2-5
4. Clacton	1-2	1-2	0-3	*	1-1	3-1	0-1	3-2	2-4	2-1	0-0	0-3	0-3	1-0	1-3	1-1	0-3	3-1	1-1	2-0	0-0	1-4
5. Cornard	0-1	2-1	4-1	3-1	*	1-0	2-1	3-0	1-4	0-3	1-0	1-1	1-1	2-0	1-0	1-2	6-0	4-1	1-1	2-3	1-1	
6. Felixstowe	0-0	0-3	2-0	1-1	2-1	*	1-1	3-1	3-1	2-1	1-1	3-0	0-2	0-0	1-2	5-1	0-0	2-0	2-1	1-1	0-2	2-3
7. Gorleston	4-1	3-3	1-0	2-0	0-1	1-3	*	0-1	3-4	3-1	1-3	3-0	1-3	0-1	3-1	1-1	0-3	1-1	2-0	2-2	3-0	0-2
8. Gt Yarm.	1-1	2-1	1-2	3-3	2-1	3-1	2-1	*	0-3	1-2	3-0	4-3	0-1	2-1	0-0	1-2	2-2	5-0	1-3	3-2	0-1	1-2
9. Halstead	1-2	0-2	6-2	3-1	0-2	3-2	3-1	1-2	*	0-1	1-2	1-2	4-3	0-0	2-3	1-2	1-0	4-0	1-0	1-1	3-0	0-3
10. Harwich	5-2	1-1	0-1	2-3	2-1	4-0	5-0	2-0	3-4	*	3-1	6-1	2-2	2-1	1-0	2-1	2-3	7-0	3-0	3-4	6-1	1-2
11. Haverhill	1-1	2-2	2-1	2-0	2-4	3-0	1-1	2-1	3-0	0-9	*	0-1	4-0	3-2	1-1	1-1	1-1	3-0	4-0	2-2	1-1	3-0
12. Histon	2-2	2-4	0-1	4-1	0-5	1-0	4-1	2-1	1-4	2-6	1-4	*	0-2	3-3	2-3	1-2	4-3	1-0	2-2	3-2	0-2	1-2
13. Lowestoft	2-0	7-3	3-1	2-1	0-4	2-3	2-0	1-1	4-2	1-2	1-1	1-2	*	1-1	0-1	0-2	1-2	4-0	1-1	1-0	1-3	1-2
14. March T.	5-0	2-0	5-0	2-3	1-2	1-1	1-3	4-2	1-0	2-0	1-0	0-1	1-2	*	0-1	1-2	0-0	4-1	2-2	3-0	2-1	2-2
15. Newmarket	1-0	1-1	3-1	3-3	0-1	0-0	2-2	4-1	3-1	0-4	5-1	2-0	3-0	1-1	*	3-2	1-3	2-1	1-1	3-0	2-2	2-2
16. Norwich U	4-3	3-1	0-0	5-1	0-2	3-1	0-3	0-2	4-1	1-0	1-2	0-3	3-1	2-1	3-1	*	0-1	2-1	0-1	1-0	4-1	1-1
17. Stowmarket	6-1	5-0	3-0	2-0	1-0	2-0	0-2	1-0	3-1	3-0	3-0	4-0	2-1	2-0	1-1	2-6	*	1-0	1-1	2-1	5-3	2-4
18. Thetford	0-1	2-0	2-0	1-2	3-5	0-2	0-4	0-3	2-1	0-2	1-1	0-3	0-4	0-1	2-2	1-2		*	1-2	0-2	0-2	1-4
19. Tiptree	1-2	2-0	0-0	2-2	1-3	0-2	6-2	1-1	1-1	2-3	1-5	1-1	0-0	0-1	0-2	1-1	2-2	*	1-0	1-0	1-1	
20. Watton	2-0	3-1	2-1	3-0	1-3	0-2	1-2	2-2	3-1	1-3	1-0	3-2	1-1	1-0	2-1	1-2	6-0	1-2	*	0-4	0-1	
21. Wisbech	1-1	3-1	1-1	2-3	2-2	3-2	0-1	1-0	0-3	3-1	4-2	4-1	1-2	1-1	1-2	4-1	6-1	5-1	3-0	*	3-2	
22. Wroxham	1-2	1-0	2-0	6-0	3-1	3-1	2-0	6-1	2-1	2-0	2-1	2-0	0-1	3-2	4-0	0-1	7-1	15-2	3-1	0-0	2-0	*

DIVISION ONE RESULT CHART 1991-92

HOME TEAM	1	2	3	4	5	6	7	8	9	10	11	12	13	14	15	16	17	18	19	20
1. Bury Res	*	0-1	2-2	0-2	0-3	1-3	2-1	1-3	2-1	3-1	2-1	0-1	5-1	2-2	1-0	1-1	1-2	3-0	1-1	0-1
2. Camb C Res	1-1	*	9-1	1-3	4-4	5-4	1-2	3-2	6-0	6-1	3-1	2-3	2-2	0-3	1-2	3-2	2-1	1-2	1-0	3-1
3. C'steel Y.	4-0	4-0	*	2-2	0-1	2-1	0-1	1-2	3-0	1-2	1-0	1-3	1-0	0-2	2-0	3-3	2-0	1-4	4-0	2-2
4. Diss Town	5-0	4-2	3-0	*	0-1	2-0	3-1	2-1	3-0	8-0	2-1	0-0	5-0	2-0	3-0	1-1	3-0	3-1	3-3	1-1
5. Downham	1-1	3-0	5-0	1-4	*	3-1	1-1	2-0	4-0	0-4	2-1	3-2	4-1	1-2	1-0	3-4	2-0	3-2	1-3	0-2
6. Ely City	2-0	5-0	2-0	2-1	2-1	*	1-1	1-0	2-0	1-0	1-2	0-2	3-1	1-2	1-1	3-2	0-0	2-0	3-1	3-2
7. Fakenham	4-0	3-5	5-1	0-3	2-0	4-0	*	7-1	3-0	2-1	4-1	1-0	3-0	6-2	1-1	0-1	1-0	2-1	1-0	1-1
8. Hadleigh	2-3	1-1	2-0	1-3	2-1	0-2	0-1	*	2-3	3-0	2-1	2-0	3-2	0-2	3-1	1-4	1-1	2-0	5-3	0-2
9. Huntingdon	0-2	1-1	0-1	2-1	2-3	1-3	0-2	2-3	*	0-2	1-3	1-4	1-0	1-1	1-1	0-2	1-2	0-1	1-1	0-0
10. Ipswich W.	2-2	2-2	2-1	1-3	3-3	0-5	0-2	0-0	4-0	*	1-3	1-1	4-1	0-2	0-2	3-1	1-2	4-0	0-1	1-3
11. K Lynn Res	4-1	3-4	1-1	0-0	1-1	0-0	2-2	0-0	2-2	0-0	*	1-3	5-0	2-1	1-1	1-0	1-4	0-4	3-0	1-4
12. L Sutton	5-3	2-1	2-0	1-2	2-1	3-0	1-2	3-0	1-2	0-0	1-3	*	0-2	3-1	0-3	4-4	3-3	0-0	2-3	2-1
13. Mildenhall	1-2	0-3	1-3	0-5	0-3	0-2	0-3	0-4	1-2	1-1	0-1	2-2	*	3-3	1-1	2-0	1-3	1-4	0-1	0-3
14. Soham T.R.	2-1	2-0	3-0	1-4	3-1	3-4	1-1	3-0	2-2	1-1	5-1	1-2	0-0	*	1-3	1-0	4-3	0-0	3-1	1-1
15. Somersham	5-0	4-0	3-1	1-4	3-0	5-3	2-2	2-3	1-2	1-0	1-1	2-4	6-0	1-1	*	3-2	3-0	6-0	2-0	0-4
16. Sudbury Res	5-0	4-3	2-1	1-0	5-0	1-0	0-1	1-1	0-2	0-2	3-3	3-0	4-1	1-0	2-1	*	2-0	5-1	2-2	2-0
17. Sudbury W.	1-1	1-3	5-1	0-3	0-1	4-0	2-1	0-2	4-2	4-0	1-0	2-1	4-0	2-2	4-1	2-0	*	3-2	0-6	0-3
18. Swaffham	1-0	0-1	6-1	1-5	1-2	2-2	0-3	1-2	5-0	0-2	2-6	0-3	3-3	2-0	3-2	2-0	1-1	*	0-1	0-2
19. Warboys	1-1	0-3	2-0	0-4	2-0	0-1	1-2	2-2	3-1	3-1	0-1	1-4	0-0	4-6	2-3	2-2	2-1	5-1	*	3-1
20. Woodbridge	1-0	0-0	1-1	1-3	1-2	0-1	0-1	0-1	9-0	2-0	1-0	4-0	3-3	2-1	1-1	2-0	2-1	3-0	3-0	*

Histon 'keeper Vince Garner tips the ball over at home to Wroxham on April 11th. The visitors won 2-1 to seal the championship. Photo - Clive Pearson.

JEWSON EASTERN COUNTIES LEAGUE CUP 1991-92

Preliminary Round *(Attendances in parentheses)*

Brightlingsea United v Halstead Town *(145)*	0-2	Cambridge City Reserves v Haverhill Rovers *(54)*	4-2
Chatteris Town v Bury Town Reserves *(65)*	2-0	Cornard United v Stowmarket Town *(102)*	1-3
Ely City v Clacton Town *(41)*	0-2	Great Yarmouth Town v Downham Town *(120)*	1-0
Histon v Thetford Town *(58)*	7-1	Soham Town Rangers v Swaffham Town *(58)*	1-2
Sudbury Wanderers v Norwich United *(94)*	1-3	Warboys Town v Woodbridge Town *(30)*	1-2

First Round

Brantham Ath. v Chatteris Town *(61)*	1-2	Clarksteel Yaxley v Huntingdon *(59 & 35)*	2-2,4-1
Gorleston v Halstead Town *(98)*	2-1	Great Yarmouth Town v Clacton Town *(59)*	2-1
Harwich & P. v Lowestoft *(151 & 147)*	0-0,5-4	Histon v Sudbury Town Reserves *(60)*	1-2
Ipswich Wdrs v Long Sutton Athletic *(45)*	3-1	King's Lynn Reserves v Hadleigh United *(84)*	2-0
March Town United v Diss Town *(120)*	0-1	Mildenhall Town v Swaffham Town *(48)*	1-6
Newmarket Town v Norwich United *(55)*	2-4	Tiptree United v Cambridge City Reserves *(32)*	2-6
Watton United v Somersham Town *(65)*	7-1	Wisbech Town v Fakenham Town *(274)*	3-1
Woodbridge Town v Stowmarket Town *(122)*	1-0	Wroxham v Felixstowe Town *(74)*	2-0

Second Round

Cambridge City Reserves v Diss Town *(72)*	2-1	Chatteris Town v Swaffham Town *(61)*	0-2
Clarksteel Yaxley v Ipswich Wanderers *(31)*	0-2	Great Yarmouth Town v Watton United *(76)*	2-1
King's Lynn Reserves v Gorleston *(96)*	1-2	Subd. Res v W'bech *(239 & 336)* 3-3*(ab.fog 92m)*,2-1
Wroxham v Harwich & Parkeston *(88)*	4-1	Woodbridge Town v Norwich Utd *(108 & 97)* 1-1,0-2

Third Round

Gt Yarmouth v Sudbury Res *(81)*	0-2	Cambridge C Res v Ipswich W. *(47 & 70)* 1-1*(ab. 99m fog)*,2-0
Wroxham v Gorleston *(211)*	1-2	Norwich v Chatteris *(35 & 118)* 1-1*(ab. 90m fog)*,3-3*(6-5 pens)*

Semi-Finals

Cambridge City Res v Norwich United *(77)*	0-3	Sudbury Town Res v Gorleston *(183 & 429)* 0-0,3-6

Final (at Norwich City FC, 6-5-92): Gorleston 2, Norwich United 2 *(AET, att: 767)*
Rep: (at Diss, 15-5-92): Norwich U. 5 *(Money 2,McKenchie 2,Sayer)*, Gorleston 2 *(Carter,Bannant) (AET, att: 550)*

An Ipswich Wanderer shields the ball during the First Round win over Long Sutton. Photo - Gavin Ellis.

Former Norwich City manager David Stringer presents the League Cup to United captain Tony Tuddenham.

JEWSON EASTERN ATTENDANCES 1991/92

Club	Games	Total	Ave		Best Gate 91-92
Brantham Athletic	26	2,150	85	351	(25/9 - League v. Harwich)
Brightlingsea Utd	24	2,489	104	322	(28/8 - League v. Harwich)
Chatteris Town	26	3,070	118	264	(21/8 - League v. Wisbech)
Clacton Town	27	2,380	88	230	(20/8 - Lg v. B'sea, 14/9 FAC v B'ricay)
Cornard United	29	2,998	103	330	(4/2 - E Flood v. Halstead)
Felixstowe Town	24	2,278	95	202	(9/10 - League v. Harwich)
Gorleston	27	4,030	149	422	(20/4 - League v. Gt Yarmouth)
Gt Yarmouth Town	28	3,313	118	365	(26/12 - League v. Gorleston)
Halstead Town	31	5,186	167	319	(24/9 - KFL v. Sudbury)
Harwich & Parkeston	29	5,270	182	315	(26/12 - League v. Clacton)
Haverhill Rovers	22	2,086	95	539	(23/11 - FA Cup v. Sudbury)
Histon	27	1,916	71	362	(26/9 - Camb Cup v. C'bridge City)
Lowestoft Town	27	4,810	178	679	(12/10 - FA Cup v. Grays A.)
March Town Utd	25	4,393	176	1,200	(26/12 - League v. Wisbech)
Newmarket Town	25	2,992	120	230	(27/8 - League v. Wisbech)
Norwich United	26	2,862	110	401	(2/10 - League v. Wroxham)
Stowmarket Town	27	3,176	118	180	(14/9 - FA Cup v. Hendon)
Thetford Town	23	2,248	98	176	(2/10 v Wisbech, 9/10 March, 22/1 v Watton, all League)
Tiptree United	29	1,873	65	163	(14/9 - FA Cup v. Dagenham)
Watton United	23	1,507	65	120	(24/9 - League v. Gt Yarmouth)
Wisbech Town	29	9,895	341	1,017	(14/9 - FA Cup v. Kettering)
Wroxham	27	4,863	180	725	(3/9 - League v. Norwich Utd)
Division One					
Bury Town Reserves	19	1,369	72	177	(25/9 - League v. Diss)
Cambridge C. Reserves	23	1,173	51	81	(22/2 - League v. Soham)
Clarksteel Yaxley	22	1,062	48	91	(4/4 - League v. Diss)
Diss Town	28	8,019	286	1,528	(29/2 - FA Vase v. Wimborne)
Downham Town	23	2,314	101	292	(3/3 - League v. Diss)
Ely City	25	1,594	64	147	(26/12 - League v. Soham)
Fakenham Town	22	4,159	189	388	(15/10 - E Ang Cup v. Wroxham)
Hadleigh United	19	2,090	110	271	(25/3 - League v. Sudbury Wdrs)
Huntingdon United	23	1,139	50	115	(20/4 - League v. Warboys)
Ipswich Wanderers	23	1,355	59	180	(26/12 - League v. Woodbridge)
King's Lynn Res.	23	2,267	99	196	(18/1 - Norf. Snr Cup v. Overstrand)
Long Sutton Ath.	23	1,511	66	141	(22/10 - E Ang Cup v King's Lynn)
Mildenhall Town	21	1,397	67	150	(26/12 - League v. Diss)
Soham Town Rgrs	20	1,784	89	175	(20/4 - League v. Ely)
Somersham Town	22	1,381	63	136	(15/10 - League v. Huntingdon)
Sudbury Town Reserves	21	2,226	101	239	(7/12 - Lge Cup v. Wisbech)
Sudbury Wanderers	24	1,867	78	142	(2/5 - League v. Diss)
Swaffham Town	19	1,797	95	250	(8/10 - League v. Downham)
Warboys Town	20	1,298	65	127	(1/5 - League v. Somersham)
Woodbridge Town	24	3,894	162	1,010	(17/1 - Suf. Snr C. v. Framlingham)

The above includes Jewson League and League Cup matches and, where notified, FA Cup, FA Vase, East Anglian Cup, Knight Floodlit Competition and County Cup ties. Attendance totals; Premier Division - 75,793 (581 matches - average gate: 130), Division One - 43,696 (445 matches - average gate: 130), Total - 119,489.

PREMIER DIVISION - TEN YEAR RECORD

	82/83	83/84	84/85	85/86	86/87	87/88	88/89	89/90	90/91	91/92
Braintree Town	18	1	1	6	2	2	2	3	2	-
Brantham Athletic	4	11	16	16	19	20	17	8	19	17
Brightlingsea Utd	-	-	-	-	-	-	-	-	-	20
Bury Town	12	13	9	4	3	-	-	-	-	-
Chatteris Town	16	10	15	19	15	7	19	21	21	19
Clacton Town	20	21	17	22	12	12	18	20	12	21
Colchester U. Res.	6	3	7	2	7	14	-	-	-	-
Cornard United	-	-	-	-	-	-	-	-	8	3
Ely City	22	20	18	20	22	22	20	-	-	-
Felixstowe Town	8	14	14	12	17	17	11	13	13	13
Gorleston	2	7	11	13	18	18	10	5	17	12
Gt. Yarmouth Town	3	9	3	3	6	4	5	6	18	14
Halstead Town	-	-	-	-	-	-	-	14	3	9
Harwich & Parkes.	-	-	21	17	14	13	14	4	5	6
Haverhill Rovers	15	17	20	14	13	10	7	15	4	8
Histon	19	16	8	10	21	5	6	7	10	15
Lowestoft Town	7	4	4	11	9	8	12	18	9	11
March Town Utd.	11	15	6	7	4	1	4	9	15	10
Newmarket Town	10	12	19	21	16	15	16	17	20	7
Norwich United	-	-	-	-	-	-	-	-	-	4
Saffron Walden T.	1	6	-	-	-	-	-	-	-	-
Soham Town Rang.	17	18	12	18	20	21	21	-	-	-
Stowmarket Town	14	19	10	8	10	19	8	11	11	2
Sudbury Town	5	5	2	1	1	3	1	1	-	-
Thetford Town	21	22	22	15	23	16	9	2	14	22
Tiptree United	13	8	13	5	5	11	15	19	16	16
Watton United	-	-	-	-	8	9	13	16	6	18
Wisbech Town	9	2	5	9	11	6	3	10	1	5
Wroxham	-	-	-	-	-	-	-	12	7	1
Teams Competing	**22**	**22**	**22**	**22**	**23**	**22**	**21**	**21**	**21**	**22**

PREMIER DIVISION STATISTICS

LEAGUE STATISTICS
1991/92 STATISTICS

Club	Season Joined		Championships or Best Placing	Leading Appearances League & Lge. Cup	Leading Goalscorers League & Lge. Cup
Brantham	1978/79	14	4th - 1983	43 - Jason Foxhall 42 - Jason Burman - Terry Clarke 39 - Kevin Steggles	8 - Terry Clarke - Stephen Morgan 6 - David Ellis
Brightlingsea	1990/91	1	20th - 1992 Div 1 runners-up 1991	42 - Lloyd Pentney 35 - Kevin Harris 33 - Peter Frost	9 - Dean Jeffries 8 - Peter Frost 7 - Scott Young
Chatteris	1966/67	26	3rd - 1968	39 - Mark Hilliard 39 - Steve Bedford 36 - Steve Hudson	12 - Tommy Gross - Steve Hudson 10 - Kevin Malle
Clacton	1935/36 1938/39 1964/65	2 13 28	2nd - 1937, 1954, 1965 & 1975	43 - Sid Edwards 37 - Paul Fraser 32 - Darren Critchell	6 - Chris Roll - Dave McGregor 4 - Lee Neale
Cornard Utd	1989/90	3	3rd - 1992 Div 1 1990	41 - Andy Smiles 40 - Aaron Gardiner 38 - Lee Wilson	25 - Andy Smiles 15 - Tony Hall 11 - Dave Hubbick
Felixstowe	1976/77	16	8th - 1983	43 - Mick Smith 41 - Stuart Swift 40 - Daniel Cattermole	12 - Nigel Wallis 11 - Stuart Swift 8 - Graham Fuller
Gorleston	1935/36 1969/70	18 23	1953, 1973 1980, 1981	49 - Steve Foyster 46 - Steve Driver 45 - Steve King	12 - Kelly Barth 11 - Steve King 7 - Dean Bamment
Gt. Yarmouth	1935/36	50	1969	46 - Tim Harrison 44 - Shaun Wright 44 - David Hatch	21 - Colin Danby 12 - Mark Grealy 7 - Stephen Cockrill
Halstead	1988/89	4	3rd - 1991 Div 1 runners-up 1988/89	39 - John Bibby 35 - Brendan Tuck 32 - Shaun Curtis	15 - Shaun Curtis 9 - Julian Lamb 8 - Paul Barker
Harwich	1935/36 1938/39 1984/85	2 19 8	1935 (Jt)	45 - Chris Tracey 44 - John Kemp 38 - Glen Hepburn	34 - Glen Hepburn 19 - John Kemp 9 - Ian Brown
Haverhill	1964/65	28	1979	43 - Gerald Sylvester - Paul Blackburn 42 - Andy Ince	14 - Alistair Suddery 8 - John McLean 7 - Andy Ince
Histon	1965/66	27	4th - 1975	44 - Vince Garner - Kevin Crisp 42 - Duncan Confrey	13 - Darren Hayward 11 - Salvatore Maiorana 9 - Daren Haylock
Lowestoft	1935/36	50	1936, 1938 1963, 1965-68 1970-71, 1978	43 - Matthew Barbrook 41 - Micky Chapman - Micky Shade	17 - Micky Chapman 12 - Micky Pratt 9 - Matthew Barbrook
March Town	1954/55	38	1988	42 - Crispin Morgan 40 - Paul Allen 37 - Clive Death	27 - Clive Death 8 - Mark Wales 7 - Steven Bailey
Newmarket	1937/38 1959/60	8 33	2nd - 1967	43 - Colin Vowden - Martin Marris 42 - John Black	17 - Colin Sinclair 10 - Dean McGill 7 - Dave Burton
Norwich United	1989/90	1	4th - 1992 Div 1 Winners 1991	51 - Paul Hartle 49 - Martin Moy 48 - Mick Money	29 - Mick Money 11 - Bob McKechnie 10 - Martin Moy
Stowmarket	1952/53	40	2nd - 1992	44 - Graham Pooley - Cameron Smith - Martin Bennett - Simon Morris	32 - Martin Bennett 19 - David King 6 - Mark Clarke
Thetford	1935/36 1963/64	2 29	2nd - 1990	41 - Alan Banthorpe 40 - David Lowe 39 - Colin Grant	7 - Julian Bussell 3 - Harvey Bussell 3 - Philip Jones
Tiptree	1979/80	13	1982	42 - Vincent Wood 41 - Gary Nash 40 - Nicholas Lee	11 - Spencer Smith 9 - Chris Guy 8 - Nicholas Lee

	LEAGUE STATISTICS			**1990-91 STATISTICS**	
Club	**Season Joined**	**Championships or Best Placing**		**Leading Appearances League & Lge. Cups**	**Leading Goalscorers League & Lge. Cups**
Watton	1986/87 6	8th - 1987		43 - Tim Warner 41 - Mark Blockwell 40 - Ian Manning	14 - Mark Blockwell 8 - George Wilson - Mark Groves
Wisbech	1950/51 2 1970/71 22	1972 & 1977 & 1991		38 - Ian Jones - Ian Williams - Jamie Brighty	24 - Mark Garwood 15 - Les Lawrence - Ian Williams
Wroxham	1988/89 4	1992		45 - Ryan Lemmon 42 - Martin Woolsey 40 - Mark Crowe	37 - Jon Rigby 20 - Martin Woolsey 18 - Scott McIntosh

LEADING SCORERS 1990-91

Premier Division

37 - Jon Rigby (Wroxham)
34 - Glen Hepburn (Harwich & Parkeston)
32 - Martin Bennett (Stowmarket Town)
29 - Mick Money (Norwich United)
27 - Clive Death (March Town United)
25 - Andy Smiles (Cornard United)
24 - Mark Garwood (Wisbech Town)
21 - Colin Danby (Gt Yarmouth Town)
20 - Martin Woolsey (Wroxham)
19 - John Kemp (Harwich & Parkeston)

Division One

25 - Brendan Doe (Somersham Town)
- Matthew Metcalfe (Diss Town)
21 - Brian Duffy (Cambridge City Reserves)
- Simon Fryatt (Woodbridge Town)
20 - Simon Barnes (Fakenham Town)
19 - Darren Theobald (Soham Town Rangers)
18 - Jon Anderson (Ipswich Wanderers)
17 - James McCullum (Clarksteel Yaxley)
- Karl Simper (Ely City)
16 - Donnie Davis (Hadleigh United)
- Andrew Hollis (Warboys Town)

Individual Scoring Feats:

7 goals: Glen Hepburn (Harwich) 24/8/91 v. Haverhill Rovers.
4 goals: Paul Carmen (Swaffham) 24/8/91 v. Clarksteel Yaxley.
: Neil Pope (Cambridge City Reserves) 11/10/91 v. Ipswich Wanderers.
: Colin Danby (Gt Yarmouth Town) 5/11/91 v. Thetford Town.
: Adrian Bullett (Soham Town Rangers) 21/12/91 v. Warboys Town.
: Dave King (Stowmarket Town) 11/1/92 v. Histon.
: Martin Woolsey (Wroxham) 17/1/92 v. Thetford Town.
: Michael Eves (Swaffham Town) 18/1/92 v. Huntingdon United.
: David Claxton (Woodbridge Town) 22/2/92 v. Huntingdon United.
: Kelly Barth (Gorleston) 20/3/92 v. Sudbury Town Reserves.
: Jon Rigby (Wroxham) 28/3/92 v. Clacton Town.

There were a total of 26 hat-tricks recorded during the season 1991-92 in the Premier Division, and 22 in Division One. Clive Death of March Town United hit most; four.

MONTHLY AWARDS 1991-92

Month	Premier Division Club of the Month	Division One Club of the Month	Good Conduct
September	Cornard United	Diss Town	Felixstowe Town
October	Wisbech Town	Cambridge C. Res	Thetford Town
November	Harwich & Parkeston	Soham Town Rangers	Woodbridge Town
December	Newmarket Town	Long Sutton Athletic	Lowestoft Town
January	Wroxham	Diss Town	Thetford Town
February	Watton United	Warboys Town	Clacton Town
March	Tiptree United	King's Lynn Reserves	Gorleston
April	Wroxham	Woodbridge Town	Diss Town

PREMIER DIVISION CLUBS 1992-93

BRANTHAM ATHLETIC

Chairman: Alan Clarke   **President:** D White   **Manager:** Keith Norton.
Secretary: Linda Norton, 20 Annbrook Road, Ipswich, Suffolk IP2 9JN (0473 684126).
Ground: B.A.S. Club, New Village, Brantham, Manningtree, Essex (0206 392506).
Directions: Leave A12 at B1070 junction signposted Manningtree. Ground just off A137.
Seats: 100   **Cover:** 200   **Capacity:** 1,500   **Floodlights:** Yes   **Founded:** 1887.
Colours: Blue & white   **Change colours:** Red & black   **Pennants:** Yes.
Midweek Matches: Wednesday   **Previous League:** Essex & Suffolk Border.
Programme: 24 pages, 25p   **Record Gate:** 1,500 v VS Rugby, FA Vase 5th Rd 82-83.
Clubhouse details: Open daily, licensing hours. 2 bars, dancing, snooker, pool, refreshments.
Matchday food & drink: Tea, coffee, cold drinks, confectionary, burgers(after), chips(after), soup, rolls.
Honours: Suffolk Senior Cup, Essex Border Lg(4), Essex & Suffolk Border League Cup(2), Suffolk Premier Cup, Jewson Sportsmanship Award 88-89.

BRIGHTLINGSEA UNITED

Chairman: Michael Cole   **Manager:** Graham Carter.
Secretary: H J Beere, 108 Regent Road, Brightlingsea, Essex CO7 0NZ (0206 303122).
Ground: North Road, Brightlingsea, Essex (0206 304199).
Directions: B1027 Colchester-Clacton, B1029 from Thorrington Cross - follow Church Road into town, left into Spring Road, left into Church Road. Nearest station; Colchester then bus 78 to Brightlingsea.
Seats: 50   **Cover:** 250   **Capacity:** 2,000   **Floodlights:** Yes   **Club Shop:** Yes.
Colours: All red   **Change colours:** All blue   **Nickname:** Oystermen.
Previous Leagues: Tendring Hundred, Essex & Suffolk Border, Essex Senior 1972-90.
Midweek Matches: Wednesday   **Record Gate:** 1,200 v Colchester, friendly 68-69.
Programme: 24 pages, 30p   **Prog. Editor:** M Cole (0206 304430)   **Founded:** 1887
Clubhouse details: Open matchadays and all evenings bar Sunday.
Matchday food & drink: Tea, coffee, cold drinks, confectionary, hotdogs, sandwiches, rolls.
Local Newspapers: Essex County Standard, Evening Gazette.
Honours: Essex Snr Lg 88-89 89-90 (Harry Fisher Mem. Tphy 89-90 (R-up 88-89), Lg Cup R-up 78-79), Eastern Co's Lg Div 1 R-up 90-91, Essex & Suffolk Border Lg Prem. Div Cup 71-72, Harwich Charity Cup 87-88, Worthington Evans Cup 76-77 77-78 78-79.

CHATTERIS TOWN

Chairman: Colin Cornwell   **President:** J Chambers   **Manager:** Lester Kent/ Dave Eldred
Secretary: Anthony Summers, 41 The Elms, Chatteris, Cambs PE16 6JN (0354 692062).
Ground: West Street, Chatteris (03543 2139).
Directions: Entering Chatteris on A141 from Huntingdon turn right into West Street after by-pass roundabout.
Seats: 250   **Cover:** 400   **Capacity:** 2,000   **Floodlights:** Yes   **Founded:** 1920.
Colours: All white   **Change colours:** All red   **Nickname:** Lillies.
Previous League: Peterborough   **Midweek Matches:** Wednesday   **Pennants:** Yes.
Clubhouse details: Bar & tea bar.   **Record Gate:** 2,000 v March, League 87-88.
Programme: 12 pages, 20p   **Previous Ground:** First Drove
Matchday food & drink: Tea, coffee, cold drinks, confectionary, burgers, hotdogs, sandwiches, soup, rolls.
Players progressing to Football League: Andy Rogers (Reading, Southend, Plymouth), Dave Gregory (Plymouth).
Honours: Eastern Counties Lg Cup 67-68, Peterborough Premier Lg(3).

CORNARD UNITED

Chairman: L Hodgson   **President:** K Martin   **Vice Chairman:** D Nicholls
Secretary: R J Powell, 14 North Rise, Great Cornard, Sudbury, Suffolk CO10 0DE (0787 71671).
Manager: Keith Martin.   **Asst Manager:** D Hill   **Coach:** A Row.
Address & Tel No. of ground: Blackhouse Lane Sportsfield, Great Cornard, Suffolk (0787 76719).
Directions: Left off r'bout on A134. Follow signs for Country Park - ground is immediately opposite along Blackhouse Lane.
Seats: 250   **Cover:** Yes   **Capacity:** 2,000   **Floodlights:** Yes   **Founded:** 1964.
Colours: Blue/white/blue   **Change colours:** Red   **Pennants:** Yes.
Previous Leagues: Bury St Edm. & Dist. 66-71/ Colchester 71-78/ Essex & Suffolk Border 78-89.
Record Attendance: 330 v Sudbury Town, Eastern Floodlit League 91-92.
Midweek Matches: Wednesday   **Prog.:** 16 pages, 30p **Programme Editor:** M Vincent
Clubhouse details: Open matchadays   **Local Newspaper:** Suffolk Free Press.
Matchday food & drink: Tea, coffee, cold drinks, confectionary, hotdogs, burgers, soup, sandwiches, rolls.
Honours: Eastern Co's Lg Div 1 89-90, Essex & Suffolk Border Lg 88-89 (Lg Cup 88-89), Suffolk Snr Cup 89-90.

DISS TOWN

Chairman: D A Tebble   **President:** R A Gooderham   **Manager:** Bill Punton.
Secretary: R S Upson, Bamburgh House, Brewers Green Lane, Diss, Norfolk IP22 3QP (0379 642923).
Ground: Brewers Green Lane, Diss (0379 651223).
Directions: Just off B1066 Diss-Thetford road, near Roydon School. One and a half miles from Diss (BR).
Seats: 260   **Cover:** Yes   **Capacity:** 2,000   **Floodlights:** Yes   **Founded:** 1886.
Colours: Tangerine/black   **Change colours:** White/navy/tangerine.   **Pennants:** Yes.
Previous Leagues: Norwich & District/ Norfolk & Suffolk 35-64/ Anglian Combination 64-82.
Midweek Matches: Tuesday   **Previous Ground:** Roydon Road 1886-1982.
Record Gate: 1,528 v Wimborne, FA Vase QF 29/2/92   **Nickname:** Tangerines.
Programme: 10 pages, 30p   **Programme Editor:** G Enderby
Clubhouse details: Open evenings (except Sunday), Sat/Sun lunchtimes, and matchdays.
Matchday food & drink: Tea, coffee, cold drinks, confectionary, burgers, hotdogs, soup, rolls.
Players progressing to the Football League: Alec Thurlow (Man City), Mervyn Cawston (Norwich), Trevor Whymark (Ipswich), Clive Stafford (Colchester).
Honours: Eastern Co's Lg Div 1 91-92, FA Vase QF 91-92, Anglian Comb. 76-77 78-79 (R-up 74-75, Div 1 67-68 73-74, Lg Cup 67-68 79-80 81-82), Norfolk & Suffolk Lg R-up 55-56 (Applegate Cup 56-57 57-58(joint)(R-up 55-56)), Norfolk Jnr Cup 1891-92.

FAKENHAM TOWN

Chairman: J Day　　　**President:** B E Woodhouse　　**Manager:** Nolan Keeley
Secretary: E V Linnell, 40 Warren Avenue, Fakenham, Norfolk NR21 8NP (0328 855445).
Ground: Barons Hall Lawn, Norwich Road, Fakenham (0328 862939).
Directions: Adjacent to Police Station in Norwich Road.
Seats: 80　　　**Cover:** 300　　　**Capacity:** 1,500　**Floodlights:** Yes　　**Founded:** 1884.
Colours: Amber & black　　　　**Change colours:** Red & white　　　**Club Shop:** Yes.
Previous Leagues: Anglian Comb.　　**Midweek Matchday:** Tuesday.
Record Gate: 1,000 v Norwich City, floodlight inauguration.
Clubhouse details: Bar, colour TV and pool table.
Matchday food & drink: Tea, coffee, cold drinks, confectionary, soup.
Programme: 32 pages (Barnes Print), 20p **Local Newspapers:** Fakenham & Wells Times.
Players progressing to the Football League: Nolan Keeley (Scunthorpe & Lincoln).
Honours: Norfolk Snr Cup 70-71 72-73 73-74 91-92, Eastern Co's Lg Div 1 R-up 91-92, Anglian Comb. Cup 78-79.

FELIXSTOWE TOWN

Chairman: Dave Ashford　　**President:** TBA　　　　　　　**Manager:** Paul Adams.
Secretary: Norman Howlett, 139 Ashcroft Rd, Ipswich, Suffolk (0473 749137).
Ground: Dellwood Avenue, Felixstowe (282917).
Directions: A45 to Felixstowe. Turn right at 3rd r'bout then 1st left - ground 100 yds on left. 5 mins from Felixstowe (BR) and town centre.
Seats: 200　　　**Cover:** 200　　　**Capacity:** 2,000　**Floodlights:** Yes　　**Founded:** 1890.
Colours: Red/white & black　　　**Change colours:** All blue　　　　**Nickname:** Seasiders.
Prev. Leagues: Essex & Suffolk Border/ Ipswich & Dist.　**Midweek Matches:** Tuesday
Record Attendance: 1,500 v Ipswich Town, floodlight inauguration 25/1/91.
Programme: 16 pages, 30p　　　　**Programme Editor:** P Griffiths.
Clubhouse details: Bar, snack bar, TV, darts, pool table.　**Local Newspaper:** East Anglia Daily Times.
Matchday food & drink: Tea, coffee, cold drinks, confectionary, hotdogs, burgers, soup, rolls.
Honours: Suffolk Senior Cup 66-67 74-75.　　　**Club Shop:** Yes **Enamel Badges & Pennants:** Yes.

GORLESTON

Chairman: A Norton　　　**President:** J Jones　　　**Manager:** Peter Self.
Secretary: Kevin Antcliffe, 62 Englands Lane, Gorleston, Gt Yarmouth, Norfolk NR31 6BE (0493 668475).
Ground: Emerald Park, Woodfarm Lane, Gorleston, Great Yarmouth (0493 602802).
Directions: On Magdalen Estate - follow signs to Crematorium, turn left and follow road to ground. Five and a half miles from Great Yarmouth Vauxhall (BR).
Seats: 100　　　**Cover:** 5,000　　　**Capacity:** 5,000　**Floodlights:** Yes　　**Founded:** 1884.
Colours: Green & white　　　　**Change colours:** All white.　　　**Nickname:** Greens.
Prev. Ground: Recreation Ground.　　**Prev. Leagues:** Norfolk & Suffolk/ Anglian Comb.
Record Attendance: Not known.　　　**Midweek Matchday:** Tuesday.
Programme: 30p　　　　　　　**Programme Editor:** D Benson
Clubhouse details: Bar, colour TV, pool table, darts, snacks.
Matchday food & drink: Tea, coffee, cold drinks, confectionary, burgers, hotdogs, soup, rolls.
Past players progressing to the Football League: Billy Bailey (Wolves & England), Dave Stringer (Norwich), R Carter (Aston Villa), D Carter (Man City), A Brown (Charlton, S Morgan (Cambridge).
Honours: Eastern Co's Lg 52-53 72-73 79-80 80-81 (R-up 82-83, Lg Cup 55-56 (R-up 91-92)), Norf. Snr Cup(13)(R-up(24)), Anglian Comb. 68-69, Norf. & Suf. Lg(7) 20-21 25-26 29-30 31-35, E Anglian Lg 52-53(res.).

GREAT YARMOUTH TOWN

Chairman: Colin Smith　　**President:** Derek Needham　　**Manager:** B Cockrill/J Cogger.
Secretary: Michael Capon, 16 Orchard Way, Fleggburgh, Gt Yarmouth, Norfolk NR29 3AY (0493 369530).
Ground: Wellesey Recreation Ground, Wellesey Road (0493 842936).
Directions: Just off Marine Parade, 200 yds north of Britannia Pier. Half a mile from Vauxhall (BR).
Seats: 500　　　**Cover:** 2,100　　　**Capacity:** 3,600　**Floodlights:** Yes　　**Founded:** 1897.
Colours: Amber & black/black　　　**Change colours:** White/red　　　**Nickname:** Bloaters.
Previous Leagues: Norfolk & Suffolk　　**Midweek Matches:** Tuesday　　　**Club Shop:** No.
Record Attendance: 8,944 v Crystal Palace, FA Cup 1st Rd 52-53.　　　　**Pennants:** Yes
Record Victory: 13-0 v Cromer, FA Cup 1st Qualifying Rd 52-53.　　　　**Prog.:** 20 pages, 50p
Clubhouse details: (0493 8443373). Dancehall, Committee Room, darts, pool.
Matchday food & drink: Tea, coffee, cold drinks, confectionary, hotdogs, burgers, soup, sandwiches, rolls.
Local Newspapers: Yarmouth Mercury (844201), Eastern Football News (Norwich 283111).
Players progressing to the Football League: Roy Hollis (Norwich), Mel Blyth & Nolan Keeley (Scunthorpe), Steven Davy (West Ham), Kevin Ready (Aston Villa), Gary Butcher (Blackburn).
Honours: Eastern Co's Lg 68-69 (R-up 56-57 67-68 77-78 78-79, Lg Cup 37-38 74-75 80-81), East Anglian Cup(3), Norfolk Snr Cup(12)(R-up(22)), Norfolk Premier Cup(twice shared), Norfolk & Suffolk Lg 13-14 26-27 27-28, FA Vase SF 82-83, FA Cup 2nd Rd(2)(1st Rd(1)), Anglian Comb. Cup 65-66(res), E Anglian Lg 56-57(res).

HALSTEAD TOWN

Chairman: M Gage　　　**President:** T Burrett　　　**Manager:** Adrian Webster.
Secretary: Michael Gage, 3 Bois Hall Gdns, Halstead, Essex CO2 2HX (0787 475110).
Ground: Rosemary Lane, Halstead, Essex (0787 472082).
Directions: A131 Chelmsford to Braintree - follow signs to Halstead. In Halstead, 1st left after Police Station, then 1st right, and first left to ground.
Seats: 492　　　**Cover:** 500　　　**Capacity:** 2,000　**Floodlights:** Yes　　**Founded:** 1879.
Colours: White & black　　　　**Change colours:** Red & white
Previous Lges: Nth Essex/ Halstead & Dist./ Haverhill/ Essex & Suffolk Border/ Essex Snr 80-88.
Previous Grounds: Three Gates 1879-1948, Coggeshall Pieces, Ravens Meadow, King George Playing Field.
Record Attendance: 4,000 v Walthamstow Avenue, Essex Senior Cup 1949.
Clubhouse details: Open evenings and matchdays.　　**Programme:** 30p　　　**Editor:** D Osborne.
Matchday food & drink: Tea, coffee, cold drinks, confectionary, burgers, hotdogs, sandwiches, rolls.
Players progressing to the Football League: Steve Allen (Wimbledon Physio).
Midweek Matches: Tuesday　　　　**Local Newspaper:** Halstead Gazette.
Honours: Eastern Co's Lg Div 1 R-up 89-90, Knight F'lit Cup R-up 90-91, Essex & Suffolk Border Lg 57-58 58-59 77-78 (R-up 49-50 54-55 60-61, Lg Cup 57-58 58-59 73-74), Essex Snr Lg Cup R-up 79-80, Essex Jnr Cup 01-02 46-47 (R-up 00-01).

Brantham Athletic 1991-92.

Felixstowe Town 1991-92. Photo - Gavin Ellis.

Great Yarmouth Town 1991-92. Back Row (L/R): Brian Cockrill (Joint Manager), Tim Harrison, Shaun Wright, Steve Cockrill, Steve Blacklett, Mark Grealy, Mark Chandler. Front: Mark Potter, John Scott (Captain), Tim Fox (now left club), Kevin Barnes, Julian Bussell (now Thetford), John Alexander, David Hatch. Photo - B G Bunn.

HARWICH & PARKESTON

Chairman: J Coleman   **President:** J Whitmore   **Manager:** Martin Head.
Secretary: Graham Firth, 24 Glebe Close, Wix, Essex CO11 2SD (0255 870805).
Ground: Royal Oak, Main Road, Dovercourt, Harwich (503649).
Directions: Main road into Dovercourt. 600 yds from Dovercourt (BR).
Seats: 350   **Cover:** 1,000   **Capacity:** 5,000   **Floodlights:** Yes   **Founded:** 1877.
Colours: Black & white stripes/black   **Change colours:** Red   **Nickname:** Shrimpers.
Previous Lges: Eastern Co's 35-37 38-64/ Essex County 37-38/ Athenian 64-73 83-84/ Isthmian 73-83.
Midweek Matches: Tuesday   **Previous Ground:** Phoenix Field, Seafront.
Record Attendance: 5,649 v Romford, FA Amateur Cup 4th Rd 19/3/38.
Programme: 20 pages, 30p   **Editor:** A Schooler   **Club Shop:** Yes
Newsline: 0898 664 250.   **Pennants & Enamel Badges:** Yes
Clubhouse details: Open every day. Dances, bingo, darts, pool, function room.
Matchday food & drink: Tea, coffee, cold drinks, confectionary, hotdogs, burgers, soup.
Players progressing to the Football League: I Gillespie (C Palace, Ipswich), G Waites, K Sanderson.
Local Paper: Harwich & Manningtree Standard.
Honours: FA Amateur Cup R-up 1898-99 1952-53, FA Vase QF 90-91, Eastern Counties Lg 35-36(joint)(Lg Cup 35-36 36-37), Essex County Lg 37-38, Athenian Lg Div 1 R-up 65-66 (Div 2 64-65, Lg Cup 64-65), Essex Senior Cup 1898-99 1936-37, Essex Senior Trophy 89-90, AFA Senior Cup 35-36 36-37, Worthington Evans Cup 80-81.

HAVERHILL ROVERS

Chairman: R Esdale   **President:** R C Carter   **Manager:** N Farlie/ S Hubbard.
Secretary: C Davies, 8 Helions Park Avenue, Haverhill, Suffolk CB9 8BL (0440 705472).
Ground: Hamlet Croft, (0440 702137).   **Directions:** Centre of Haverhill.
Seats: 200   **Cover:** 200   **Capacity:** 3,000   **Floodlights:** Yes   **Founded:** 1886.
Colours: All red   **Change colours:** All yellow   **Prev. League:** Essex & Suffolk Border.
Record Attendance: 1,537 v Warrington Town, FA Vase QF 86-87.   **Nickname:** Rovers.
Programme: 24 pages, 30p   **Editor:** R Esdale
Clubhouse details: Open matchdays and function. Country & Western evening Saturday.
Matchday food & drink: Tea, coffee, cold drinks, confectionary, burgers, hotdogs.
Midweek Matches: Tuesday   **Local Paper:** Haverhill Echo.
Players progressing to the Football League: R Wilkins (Colchester).
Honours: Eastern Co's Lg 78-79 (Lg Cup 64-65), E & S Border Lg 62-63 63-64, East Anglian Cup 90-91.

HISTON

Chairman: Gareth Baldwin   **President:** G P Muncey   **Manager:** Roy Johnson
Secretary: Mrs Eunice Joel, 7 Roselea, Impington, Cambs CB4 4LB (0223 234279).
Ground: Bridge Road, Impington, Cambridge (0223 232301).
Directions: Leave A45 northern Cambridge bypass on B1049 (signposted Histon and Cottenham). Ground half a mile on right. 5 miles from Cambridge (BR). Bus No. 104.
Seats: 250   **Cover:** 200   **Capacity:** 2,250   **Floodlights:** Yes   **Founded:** 1904.
Colours: Red & black stripes/red/black   **Change colours:** Blue/black/blue.
Previous Leagues: Cambridgeshire 04-48/ Spartan 48-60/ Delphian 60-63/ Athenian 63-65.
Midweek Matches: Wednesday   **Previous Name:** Histon Institute 04-51.
Programme: 16 pages, 50p   **Editor:** Kevin Woollard.
Record Gate: 2,400 v K. Lynn, FA Cup.   **Local Newspaper:** Cambridge Evening News.
Clubhouse details: Bar/lounge open Tues-Sun evenings, Sun lunctimes and matchdays.
Matchday food & drink: Tea, coffee, cold drinks, confectionary, soup, rolls.
Honours: Eastern Co's Lg Cup 90-91, Cambridge Invitation Cup 77-78 79-80 (R-up 50-51 52-53 53-54), Spartan Lg Div 1 (East) 50-51, Cambs Chal. Cup, Cambs Lg Section 'A'.

LOWESTOFT TOWN

Chairman: Roy Harper   **President:** S Matley   **Manager:** Colwyn Rowe.
Secretary: Terry Lynes, 156 Denmark Road, Lowestoft, Suffolk NR32 2EL (0502 564034).
Ground: Crown Meadow, Love Road, Lowestoft (0502 573818).
Directions: Just off A12, 10 mins walk from Lowestoft (BR).
Seats: 466   **Cover:** 500   **Capacity:** 4,000   **Floodlights:** Yes   **Founded:** 1890.
Colours: Blue & white   **Change colours:** Yellow/red/yellow   **Nickname:** Blues.
Previous Leagues: Norfolk & Suffolk   **Midweek Matches:** Tuesday   **Metal Badges:** Yes
Record Attendance: 5,000 v Watford, FA Cup 1st Rd 9/12/67.
Programme: 20 pages, 30p   **Programme Editor:** T Lynes
Clubhouse details: Pub hours
Matchday food & drink: Tea, coffee, cold drinks, confectionary, hotdogs, burgers, soup.
Honours: Eastern Co's Lg(8) 35-36(joint) 37-38 62-63 64-65 67-68 69-71 77-78 (Lg Cup(7) 38-39 54-55 65-67 68-69 75-76 83-84), Norf. & Suffolk Lg(8) 1897-99 1900-04 28-29 30-31, Suffolk Prem. Cup(5) 66-67 71-72 74-75 78-80, Suffolk Snr Cup(10) 02-03 22-24 25-26 31-32 35-36 46-49 55-56, E Anglian Cup(10), FA Cup 1st Rd 26-27 38-39 66-67 77-78, Anglian Comb. (Reserves) 77-78 79-80 (Lg Cup 76-77), E Anglian Lg (Reserves) 57-58 63-64.

MARCH TOWN UNITED

Chairman: M Miller   **President:** D Wilkinson   **Manager:** Clive Death.
Secretary: C R Woodcock, 24 Grounds Avenue, March, Cambs PE15 8BG (0354 54817).
Ground: GER Sports Ground, Robin Goodfellows Lane, March (0354 53073).
Directions: 5 mins from town centre, 10 mins from BR station.
Seats: 500   **Cover:** 2,000   **Capacity:** 4,000   **Floodlights:** Yes   **Founded:** 1885.
Club colours: Yelow/blue   **Change colours:** Blue & black stripes/white.
Previous Ground: The Avenue (prior to 1946).   **Nickname:** Hares
Previous Leagues: Peterborough/ Isle of Ely/ Utd Co's 48-54.
Midweek Matches: Tuesday   **Record Gate:** 7,500 v King's Lynn, FA Cup 1956.
Programme: 30p   **Editor:** S Snell c/o Secretary
Clubhouse details: On ground, seating 150.
Matchday food & drink: Tea, coffee, cold drinks, soup, sandwiches, rolls.
Local Newspapers: Cambs Times, Fenland Advertiser, Peterborough Evening Telegraph.
Honours: Eastern Co's Lg 87-88 (Lg Cup 60-61), Utd Co's Lg 53-64, FA Cup 1st Rd 53-54 (lost to Brentford) 77-78 (to Swindon), Cambs Invitation Cup 54-55, East Anglian Cup 53-54(jt with Barking).

NEWMARKET TOWN

Chairman: K Sheppard   **President:** M J Nicholas
Manager: Peter Graham/ David Pinkowski.
Secretary: Mr John E How, 25 Highwood Cres., Gazeley, Newmarket, Suffolk CB8 8RU (0638 750852).
Ground: Cricketfield Road, off New Cheveley Road, Newmarket (0638 663637).
Directions: 400 yds from Newmarket (BR) - turn right into Green Road, right at crossroads New Cheveley Road - ground at top on left.
Seats: 200   **Cover:** 150   **Capacity:** 3,000   **Floodlights:** Yes   **Founded:** 1877.
Colours: Yellow/navy/yellow   **Change colours:** All red   **Nickname:** Jockeys.
Previous Grounds: The Severals 1877-78/ Sefton Lodge 1878-85   **Previous Names:** Newmarket FC.
Prev. Lges: Bury Snr/ Ipswich Snr/ Essex & Suffolk Border/ Utd Co's 34-37/ Eastern Co's 37-52.
Record Attendance: 2,701 v Abbey Utd (now Cambridge Utd), FA Cup 1st Qualifying Rd 1/10/49.
Midweek Matches: Tuesday   **Clubhouse details:** Matchdays only.
Programme: 30p   **Programme Editor:** G Eales.
Matchday food & drink: Tea, coffee, cold drinks, confectionary, burgers, hotdogs, soup, sandwiches, rolls.
Players progressing to the Football League: Mick Lambert (Ipswich), M Wright (Northampton), G Tweed (Coventry), R Fuller (Charlton).
Honours: Suffolk Snr Cup 34-35, Cambs Invitation Cup 58-59, Cambs Challenge Cup 21-22 26-27, Cambs Snr Lg, 19-20, Ipswich Snr Lg 30-31 31-32 32-33 33-34, Peterborough Lg 57-58.

NORWICH UNITED

Chairman: John Hilditch   **President:** Michael Miles   **Manager:** Paul Chick.
Secretary: Mick Alexander, Plantation Park, Plantation Rd, Blofield, Norwich NR13 4PL (0263 721943).
Ground: Plantation Road, Blofield, Norwich, Norfolk NR13 4PL (0603 716963).
Directions: Half a mile from Blofield village.
Seats: 100   **Cover:** Yes   **Capacity:** 3,000   **Floodlights:** Yes   **Founded:** 1903.
Club colours: Yellow & blue   **Change colours:** Red   **Metal Badges:** Yes
Programme: 12 pages, 40p   **Programme Editor:** Secretary   **Pennants:** Yes
Midweek Matches: Tuesday   **Previous Leagues** Anglian Comb.   **Nickname:** Planters.
Previous Ground: Gothic Club, Heartsease Lane, Norwich (until end of 90-91).
Record Attendance: 401 v Wroxham, League match, 2/10/91.
Clubhouse details: All facilities.   **Local Newspaper:** Eastern Counties Newspapers.
Matchday food & drink: Tea, coffee, cold drinks, confectionary, hotdogs, burgers, soup, sandwiches, rolls.
Honours: Eastern Co's Lg Div 1 90-91 (R-up 89-89, Lg Cup 91-92), Anglian Combination 88-89.

STOWMARKET TOWN

Chairman: John Kerry   **President:** David Hunting   **Manager:** Doug Wade/Geoff Porter.
Secretary: John Doward, Deepland House, Stowupland, Stowmarket, Suffolk IP14 1LD (0449 612003).
Ground: Green Meadows Stadium, Bury Road, Stowmarket (0449 612533).
Directions: Take Bury Street from lights in town centre - continue r'bout, ground on right. 880 yds from Stowmarket (BR).
Seats: 200   **Cover:** 450   **Capacity:** 2,000   **Floodlights:** Yes   **Founded:** 1883.
Colours: Gold & black   **Change colours:** Red   **Nickname:** Stow
Midweek Matches: Wednesday   **Previous League:** Essex & Suffolk Border **Club Shop:** Yes
Record Gate: 2,500, FA Cup 50-51   **Pennants & Metal Badges:** Yes.
Programme: 20 pages, 30p   **Programme Editor:** John Gillingham
Previous Names: Stowmarket Corinthians, Stowmarket FC
Local Press: East Anglian, Bury Free Press.
Clubhouse: Bar, meeting rooms, kitchen, entertainment Saturdays, snooker.
Matchday food & drink: Tea, coffee, cold drinks, confectionary, hotdogs, burgers, soup, sandwiches, rolls, ice cream, cream cakes.
Players progressing to Football League: Craig Oldfield (Colchester), Les Tibbett & Brian Klug (Ipswich).
Honours: Eastern Co's Lg R-up 91-92, Suffolk Premier Cup(?), Suffolk Snr Cup(10), Suffolk Jnr Cup.

TIPTREE UNITED

Chairman: F Byles   **President:** L Foakes   **Manager:** Steve Sutton.
Secretary: Peter G Fidge, 77 Chelmer Road, Chelmsford, Essex CM2 6AA (0245 353667).
Ground: Chapel Road, Tiptree, Essex (0621 815213).
Directions: Enter town on B1023 - Chapel Road is left at second crossroads. 3 miles from Kelverdom (BR). Served by Eastern National Colchester to Maldon bus.
Seats: 150   **Cover:** 250   **Capacity:** 2,500   **Floodlights:** Yes   **Founded:** 1933.
Club colours: Red & white   **Change colours:** White.   **Nickname:** Jam Makers.
Midweek Matchday: Tuesday.   **Previous Lges:** Essex & Suffolk Border/ Essex Snr 71-79
Record Attendance: 1,289 v Spurs, floodlight inauguration Dec 1990.
Programme: 30 pages, 30p   **Programme Editor:** Secretary
Local Newspapers: Colchester Evening Gazette, Essex County Standard.
Clubhouse details: Sports Hall & licensed bar, snooker, pool, darts, badminton. Open every day.
Matchday food & drink: Tea, coffee, cold drinks, confectionary, burgers, hotdogs, soup.
Honours: Essex Snr Tphy 80-81, Eastern Co's Lg 81-82 (Lg Cup 81-82 84-85), Essex Snr Lg R-up 75-76 77-78, Harwich Charity Cup(4).

WATTON UNITED

Chairman: R Neave   **President:** Malcolm Warner   **Manager:** Mick Simmons.
Secretary: Tim Warner, 9 Spinney Close, Beech Road, Beetley, Dereham NR20 4EZ (0362 860016).
Ground: Dereham Road, Watton, Norfolk (0953 881281).
Directions: On A1075 towards Dereham about half a mile from junction with B1108.
Seats: 50   **Cover:** 150   **Capacity:** 2,000   **Floodlights:** Yes   **Founded:** 1888.
Colours: All white   **Change colours:** Green/black/green   **Nickname:** Brecklanders.
Midweek Matches: Tuesday   **Previous Leagues:** East Anglian/ Anglian Comb.
Record Gate: 1,200 v Norwich C., floodlight opener 1985.
Programme: 25p   **Programme Editor:** Rick Neave   **Clubhouse:** Watton 881281
Matchday food & drink: Tea, coffee, cold drinks, confectionary, burgers, soup, sandwiches, rolls.
Players progressing to Football League: Chris Watts & Robert Taylor (Norwich).
Honours: Anglian Comb. 66-67 67-68 85-86 (Lg Cup 66-67 69-70).

WISBECH TOWN

Chairman: M E Davis   **President:** J W A Chilvers   **Vice Chairman:** A Buchan.
Secretary: M E Davis, Ely House, 158 Lynn Road, Wisbech, Cambs PE13 3EB (0945 583567).
Manager: J Gallagher/ K Rudd.   **Newsline:** 0898 446 887.
Ground: Fenland Park, Lerowe, Wisbech, Cambs (0945 584176).
Directions: On Lerowe Road, a right turn off the A47 Lynn Road. 20 mins walk from town centre, irregular bus service to Wisbech from Peterborough or March.
Seats: 258   **Cover:** 3,000   **Capacity:** 7,500   **Floodlights:** Yes   **Founded:** 1920.
Colours: Red/white   **Change colours:** Blue/white.   **Nickname:** Fenmen
Previous Lges: Peterborough/ Utd Co's 35-50/ Eastern Co's 50-52/ Midland 52-58/ Southern 58-70.
Previous Grounds: Wisbech Park 20-21, Waisoken Rectory 21-22, Harecroft Road 22-47.
Record Attendance: 8,044 v Peterborough Utd, Midland Lg 25/8/57.   **Metal Badges:** Yes.
Midweek Matchay: Tuesday.   **Clubhouse:** Open every day.   **Pennants:** Yes
Matchday food & drink: Tea, coffee, cold drinks, confectionary, burgers, hotdogs, soup, sandwiches, rolls.
Programme: 36 pages, 40p   **Programme Editor:** Secretary   **Club shop:** Yes
Honours: FA Cup 2nd Rd 57-58 (1st Rd(5) 45-46 58-60 64-66), FA Vase SF 84-85 85-86, Southern Lg Div 1 61-62, Utd Co's Lg(4) 46-48 49-50 61-62(reserves) (R-up 48-49, Lg Cup 35-36 (R-up 46-47)), Midland Lg R-up 57-58, Eastern Co's Lg 71-72 76-77 90-91 (R-up 70-71 73-74 83-84, Lg Cup 50-51 70-71 71-72 (R-up 73-74 76-77 86-87), Cambs Invitation Cup(8) 52-53 55-56 57-58 74-76 81-83 91-92, East Anglian Cup 87-88 (R-up 40-41 48-49), Peterborough Lg 24-25 27-28 28-29 31-32 32-33, Peterborough Snr Cup 32-33 76-77 89-90.

WROXHAM

Chairman: T Jarrett   **President:** L King   **Manager:** Bruce Cunningham.
Secretary: Chris Green, 24 Keys Drive, Wroxham, Norfolk NR12 8SS (0603 783936).
Physio: G Christmas   **Press Officer:** Chris Green   **Commercial Manager:** Tom Jarrett
Ground: Trafford Park, Wroxham (0603 783583).
Directions: Arriving from Norwich turn left at Castle PH and keep left to ground. Two and a half miles from Hoveson (BR). Buses 722, 724 and 717.
Seats: 50   **Cover:** 250   **Capacity:** 2,500   **Floodlights:** Yes   **Founded:** 1892.
Colours: Blue/white   **Change colours:** All white.   **Nickname:** Yatchtsmen.
Previous League: Anglian Comb.   **Midweek Matchday:** Tuesday.
Record Attendance: 750 v Arbroath, friendly August 1987.
Programme: 24 pages, with entry   **Programme Editor:** Chris Green
Local Newspapers: North Norfolk, Eastern Football (Norwich 28311).
Clubhouse details: Bar, pool, darts etc.
Matchday food & drink: Tea, coffee, cold drinks, confectionary, burgers, hotdogs, soup, sandwiches, rolls.
Honours: Eastern Co's Lg 91-92 (Div 1 88-89, Lg Cup R-up 90-91), Anglian Comb. (5)(Lg Cup (6)).

DIVISION ONE CLUBS 1992-93

BURY TOWN RESERVES (See page 520 for full details)

CAMBRIDGE CITY RESERVES (See page 469 for full details)

CLACTON TOWN

Chairman: Fred Lawrence   **President:** R Manning   **Manager:** Tony Armstrong.
Secretary: George Hardwick, 1 Munnings Drive, Clacton-on-Sea, Essex CO16 8YJ (0255 435232).
Ground: The Rushgreen Bowl, Rushgreen Road, Clacton-on-Sea (0255 432590).
Directions: A133 to Clacton, at r'bout right into St Johns Rd, 4th left Cloes Lane, 3rd right Rushgreen Rd, ground approximatly half mile on right. From B1027 take main Jaywick turn off (Jaywick Lane), then 2nd left (after about a mile) into Rushgreen Rd. Ground 400 yds. 2 miles from Clacton (BR), buses 3, 5 or 5a to Coopers Lane/Rushgreen Rd.
Seats: 200   **Cover:** Yes   **Capacity:** 2,500   **Floodlights:** Yes   **Founded:** 1892.
Colours: Royal blue   **Change colours:** All red   **Club Shop:** Yes
Previous Grounds: Clacton Stadium, Old Road 06-87/ Gainsford Av (temp).   **Metal Badges:** Yes.
Midweek Matches: Tuesday   **Pennants:** Yes.
Record Attendance: 3,505 v Romford, FA Cup 1st Qualifying Rd 1952 (at Old Road).
Previous Leagues: Eastern Co's 35-37 38-58/ Southern 58-64.
Programme: 40 pages, 30p   **Local Paper:** Clacton Gazette   **Nickname:** Seasiders.
Clubhouse details: Licensed club. Open 7-11pm Mon-Sat, 12-3pm Sat-Sun.
Matchday food & drink: Tea, coffee, cold drinks, confectionary, burgers, hotdogs, soup, rolls.
Players progressing to Football League: Vivian Woodward (Spurs, Chelsea, England), Mick Everitt (Arsenal, Northampton), Christian McLean (Bristol Rovers).
Honours: Southern Lg Div 1 59-60, Eastern Co's Lg R-up 36-37 53-54 64-65 74-75 (Lg Cup 73-74), East Anglian Cup 53-54, Worthington Evans Cup 56-57 67-68 74-75, FA Cup 1st Rd (v Southend) 60-61.

DOWNHAM TOWN

Chairman: C Knott   **President:** T G Barker   **Manager:** Kevin Bunn.
Secretary: B Connor, 02, Bungalow, Windsor Street, Downham Market, Norfolk PE38 9EG (0366 383179).
Ground: Lynn Road, Downham Market, Norfolk (0366 388424).
Directions: One and a quarter miles from Downham Market (BR) - continue to town clock, turn left and ground is three quarters of a mile down Lynn Road.
Seats: None   **Cover:** Yes   **Capacity:** 1,000   **Floodlights:** Yes   **Founded:** 1881.
Colours: Red & white   **Change colours:** All yellow   **Nickname:** Town
Midweek Matches: Tuesday   **Previous Leagues:** Peterborough
Record Attendance: 292 v Diss Town, Jewson League Division One 1991/92.
Clubhouse: Open matchdays   **Programme:** By Barnes Promotions, with entry
Matchday food & drink: Tea, coffee, cold drinks, confectionary, hotdogs, burgers, soup, sandwiches, rolls.
Honours: P'boro Lg(5) 62-63 73-74 78-79 86-88, Norfolk Senior Cup 63-64 65-66 (R-up(3) 66-69).

ELY CITY

Chairman: Roger Pauley   **President:** Doug Unwin   **Manager:** Alan Biley.
Secretary: Derek Oakey, 37 Fordham Road, Soham, Nr Ely, Cambs CB7 5AH (0353 722141).
Ground: Unwin Sports Ground, Downham Road (0353 662035).
Directions: A10 Ely by-pass turn off for Downham. 3 miles (approx) from Ely (BR).
Seats: 50   **Cover:** 150   **Capacity:** 1,500   **Floodlights:** Yes   **Founded:** 1885
Colours: All red   **Change colours:** Blue   **Midweek Matches:** Tuesday
Previous Leagues: Peterborough/ Central Alliance 58-60.
Record Gate: 220 v Cambridge Utd, Hunts Premier Cup 15/11/88.   **Nickname:** Robins
Clubhouse details: Open matchdays   **Local Press:** Ely Standard (0353 667831). **Metal Badges:** Yes
Matchday food & drink: Tea, coffee, cold drinks, confectionary, hotdogs, burgers, sandwiches, rolls. **Programme:** 20p
Hons: Cambs Snr Cup 47-48, Eastern Co's Lg R-up 69-70 (Lg Cup 79-80), FA Cup 1st Rd 54-55 (2-6 v Torquay).

HADLEIGH UNITED

Chairman: Peter Vardon   **Manager:** Alan Dilloway/ Les Tibbott.
Secretary: Alvin Jarrald, 2 Waterworks Cottages, Raydon, Ipswich, Suffolk IP7 6SB (0473 311798).
Ground: Millfield, Duke Street, Hadleigh, Suffolk (0473 822165).
Directions: Follow signs to Hadleigh off A12. Duke Street is off the High Street - turn by Library.
Seats: None   **Cover:** 100   **Capacity:** 2,000   **Floodlights:** Yes   **Founded:** 1892.
Colours: White/navy/white   **Change colours:** All red   **Programme:** 20p
Midweek Matches: Wednesday.   **Previous League:** Suffolk & Ipswich (pre-1991).
Record Gate: 271 v Diss Town, Jewson Eastern Counties League Division One 1991-92.
Clubhouse details: Open matchdays, Fridays & Sundays.
Matchday food & drink: Tea, coffee, cold drinks, confectionary, soup, rolls.
Honours: Suffolk & Ipswich Lg(5)(Lg Cup(4)), Suffolk Senior Cup(3).

IPSWICH WANDERERS

Chairman: J Barker   **President:**   **Manager:** Brian Swift.
Secretary: Keith Bassett, 15 Heathercroft Road, Ipswich, Suffolk IP1 6QG (0473 48458).
Ground: Humberdoucey Road, Ipswich, Suffolk (0473 728581).
Directions: A12 north of Ipswich Rushmere Golf Club. Players Road into Humberdovey Lane.
Seats: None   **Cover:** Yes   **Capacity:** 2,000   **Floodlights:** No   **Founded:** 1983.
Colours: Blue/blue/white   **Change colours:** Red & white/red/red.   **Nickname:** Wanderers.
Previous Leagues: Little David Sunday   **Previous Names:** Loadwell Ipswich.
Midweek Matches: Wednesday   **Record Gate:** 276 v Woodbridge, Jewson Lg 18/3/91.
Programme: With admission   **Clubhouse details:** Bar, refreshments.
Matchday food & drink: Tea, coffee, cold drinks, confectionary, burgers, hotdogs, sandwiches, rolls.
Local Newspapers: East Anglian Daily Times, Evening Star.

KING'S LYNN RESERVES (See page 500 for full details)

LONG SUTTON ATHLETIC

Chairman: P Childs   **President:** V W Day   **Manager:** B L Wilson.
Secretary: Simon Caney, 2 Bleak Cottages, Garners Lane, Sutton Bridge, Spalding, Lincs (0406 350553).
Ground: London Road, Long Sutton, Spalding, Lincs (0406 364208).
Directions: On left hand side of A17 entering village from Wisbech or King's Lynn.
Seats: None   **Cover:** 100   **Capacity:** 1,000   **Floodlights:** Yes   **Founded:** 1922.
Club colours: Black & white   **Change colours:** Red & blue.   **Nickname:** Magpies
Previous League: Peterborough.   **Prev. Name:** Long Sutton Town 1922-55. **Programme:** 20p
Clubhouse: Open matchdays   **Record Gate:** 537 v Grimsby, friendly.
Matchday food & drink: Tea, coffee, cold drinks, pies, pasties, sandwiches.
Local Press: Wisbech Standard, Spalding Guardian, Lincs Free Press.   **Midweek Matchday:** Tuesday.
Honours: Lincs Junior Cup 85-86 (R-up 87-88), Lincs 'B' Snr Cup 88-89, TSLB Challenge Cup 88-89.

MILDENHALL TOWN

Chairman: B Brigden   **President:** J E Butcher   **Manager:** Mark Goldsack.
Secretary: B W Hensby, 14 Sanderling Close, Mildenhall, Suffolk IP28 7LF (0638 715772).
Ground: Recreation Way, Mildenhall, Suffolk (0638 713449).
Directions: Next to swimming pool/car, quarter of a mile from town centre.
Seats: None   **Capacity:** 2,000   **Midweek Matchday:** Tuesday   **Founded:** 1890.
Club colours: Amber/black   **Change colours:** All white   **Nickname:** Town or yellows.
Previous Leagues: Bury & District/ Cambs Lg 2B, 1B & Premier.
Record Attendance: 350 v Norwich City, friendly 22/7/89.
Programme: Free with admission   **Editor:** D Isaac   **Clubhouse:** Open matchdays & functions.
Matchday food & drink: Tea, coffee, cold drinks, confectionary, sandwiches, rolls.
Local Newspapers: Bury Free Press, Newmarket Journal, Cambridge Evening News.
Honours: Suffolk Junior Cup 1899-1900.

SOHAM TOWN RANGERS

Chairman: C J Murfitt   **President:** B E Owers   **Manager:** Adrian Davis.
Secretary: A J Issacson, 16 Hall Street, Soham, Cambs CB7 5BS (0353 721163).
Ground: Julius Martins Lane, Soham, Cambs (0353 720732).
Directions: A142 between Newmarket and Ely - Julius Martins Lane.
Seats: 200   **Cover:** Yes   **Capacity:** 2,000   **Floodlights:** Yes   **Founded:** 1947.
Colours: Green/white   **Change colours:** Red/black/green   **Nickname:** Town or Rangers.
Previous Leagues: Peterborough & District.
Record Attendance: 3,000 v Pegasus, FA Amateur Cup 1963.
Previous Names: Soham Town and Soham Rangers amalgamated in 1947.
Previous Ground: Soham Rangers: Brook Street 1919-47.
Programme: With admission   **Programme Editor:** Secretary
Midweek Matchday: Wednesday   **Clubhouse:** General bar, Stud Bar, Lounge Bar.
Matchday food & drink:
Local Newspapers: Ely Standard, Newmarket Journal, Cambridge Evening News.
Honours: Peterborough League(3) *plus 6-0 defeat of renowned Pegasus in 1963 FA Amateur Cup.*

SOMERSHAM TOWN

Chairman: David Hardy   **President:** Jack Marjason   **Comm. Mgr:** Norman Ward (0487 840181).
Secretary: John Lyon, 'Molineux' 1 Asplins Avenue, Needingworth, Huntingdon PE17 3SX (0480 64411).
Manager: Norman Hudson   **Asst Manager:** John Scarborough   **Physio:** Alan Magnus
Ground: West End Ground, St Ives Road, Somersham, Cambs (0487 843384).
Directions: On A604 St Ives to Somersham on right as you enter town.
Seats: None   **Cover:** 200   **Capacity:** 1,500   **Floodlights:** Yes   **Founded:** 1893.
Colours: All amber   **Change colours:** Sky blue   **Midweek matchday:** Tuesday.
Previous League: Peterborough & Dist.   **Record Gate:** 538 v Norwich City, floodlight inauguration 19/11/91.
Programme: 76 pages, 30p   **Programme Editor:** Dave Hardy (0487 840441)
Sponsors: T S Frozen Foods   **Clubhouse:** Open Friday, Sat/Sun lunchtimes.
Matchday food & drink: Tea, coffee, cold drinks, confectionary, rolls.
Local Newspapers: Hunts Post, Cambs News, Citizen Express, St Ives Weekly.
Honours: Hunts Snr Cup 72-73, P'boro Snr Cup 84-85, Hinchinbrooke Cup 34-55.

STANWAY ROVERS

Chairman: Alan Buck   **Manager:** Alan Smith   **President:**
Secretary: Richard Degville, 5 Old Heath Road, Colchester, Essex CO3 4AU (0206 792599).
Ground: 'Hawthorns', New Farm Road, Stanway, Colchester, Essex (0206 578187).
Directions: Take turn off marked Stanway off A12. Turn right and go over flyover, left at r'bout, 1st right into Villa
Rd, after 25 yards turn left into Church Rd, 200 yards on left into New Farm Rd, ground 400 yards on left.
Seats: None   **Cover:** Yes   **Capacity:** 1,500   **Floodlights:** No   **Founded:**
Colours: Blue/white/blue   **Change colours:** Yellow/black/black   **Nickname:** Rovers.
Record Attendance: Unknown   **Previous League:** Essex & Suffolk Border (pre-1992).
Programme: Yes   **Clubhouse:** Normal licensing hours.
Midweek matchday: Tuesday.   **Local Newspaper:** Essex County Standard.
Honours: Essex Intermediate Cup R-up 89-90 90-91, Essex & Suffolk Border Lg R-up 91-92.

SUDBURY TOWN RESERVES (See page 533 for full details)

SUDBURY WANDERERS

Chairman: N Smith   **President:**   **Manager:** M Mills.
Secretary: Brian Tatum, 4 Beaconsfield Close, Sudbury, Suffolk CO10 6JR (0787 75840).
Ground: Brundon Lane, Sudbury, Suffolk (0787 76213).
Directions: From Sudbury centre follow Halstead/Chelmsford signs for about 1 mile. Take 1st right after railway
bridge at foot of steep hill, and 1st right after sharp lefthand bend.
Seats: None   **Cover:** 150   **Capacity:** 2,500   **Floodlights:** No   **Founded:** 1958
Midweek Matchday: Tuesday   **Programme:** With admission   **Nickname:** Wanderers
Record Attendance: 142 v Diss Town, Jewson Eastern Counties League Division One 2/5/92.
Clubhouse details: Open matchdays/ training nights.
Matchday food & drink: Tea, coffee, cold drinks, confectionary.
Honours: Essex & Suffolk Border Lg 89-90 90-91 (R-up 88-89), Suffolk Senior Cup 90-91.

SWAFFHAM TOWN

Chairman: S G Bartrum   **President:**   **Manager:** Adrian Hewitt.
Secretary: David Ward, 2 Princes Street, Swaffham, Norfolk PE37 7BX (0760 22516).
Ground: Shoemakers Lane, Swaffham, Norfolk (0760 22700).
Seats: None   **Cover:**   **Capacity:** 2,000   **Floodlights:** Yes   **Founded:** 1892.
Colours: White/black/red   **Change colours:** Yellow   **Nickname:** Pedlars
Midweek Matchay: Tuesday.   **Previous Leagues:** Dereham, Anglian Combination
Record Attendance: 250 v Downham Town, Jewson Eastern Co's League Cup 3/9/91.
Clubhouse details: Open Tuesday, Thursday, Saturday & Sunday lunchtimes & evenings.
Matchday food & drink: Tea, coffee, cold drinks, confectionary, rolls (occasionally).
Programme: 36 pages, 30p   **Hons:** Norfolk Snr Cup(2), Anglian Comb. 89-90 (Div 1 88-89).

THETFORD TOWN

Chairman: K Newman   **President:** F Huson   **Manager:** David Low.
Secretary: John Wordley, 4 Claxton Close, Thetford, Norfolk IP24 1BA (0842 762530).
Ground: Mundford Road, Thetford (0842 66120).
Directions: On Mundford Road, signposted via Lynn, Downham Market on A143 of A11.
Seats: 400   **Cover:** 400   **Capacity:** 2,000   **Floodlights:** Yes   **Founded:** 1964.
Colours: Claret/blue   **Change colours:** White/black
Previous Leagues: Norfolk & Suffolk   **Midweek Matches:** Tuesday   **Club Shop:** Yes.
Local Press: Thetford & Watton Times, Bury Free Press.   **Programme:** 28 pages, 30p
Clubhouse details: Bar, teas, refreshments, light meals.   **Pennants:** Yes.
Matchday food & drink: Tea, coffee, cold drinks, confectionary, hotdogs, burgers, sandwiches, rolls.
Players progressing to Football League: Dick Scott (Norwich City, Cardiff City), Kevin Seggie (Leeds United),
Simon Milton (Ipswich Town).
Honours: Eastern Co's Lg R-up 89-90, Norfolk & Suffolk Lg 54-55, Norfolk Snr Senior Cup 47-48 90-91.

WARBOYS TOWN

Chairman: Trevor Chamberlain   **President:** G C Bowd   **Manager:** Tony Godden.
Secretary: R O England, 39 High Street, Warboys, Huntingdon PE17 2TA (0487 822312).
Ground: Sports Field, Forge Way, off High Street, Warboys, Cambs (0487 823483).
Directions: Access through Forge Way, half way along south side of High Street.
Seats: None   **Cover:** 200   **Capacity:** 2,000   **Floodlights:** No   **Founded:** 1885.
Colours: Red/white   **Change colours:** Blue & maroon/blue   **Nickname:** Witches.
Midweek Matches: Tuesday   **Previous Leagues:** Utd Co's/ Peterborough & Dist.
Record Attendance: 500 v Ramsey Town, Hunts Senior Cup Semi Final.
Programme: 12 pages, 20p   **Programme Editor:** M England
Local Newspaper: Hunts Post (0480 411481).
Clubhouse: Bar, lounge, function hall. Open every evening & Sunday lunchtime. Various entertainments.
Matchday food & drink: Tea, coffee, cold drinks, confectionary, sandwiches, rolls.
Past Players progressing to Football League: Alex Chamberlain (Ipswich, Everton, Colchester).
Honours: Utd Co's Lg Div 2 R-up, P'boro Lg R-up(2), P'boro Snr Cup, Hunts Snr Cup.

Ipswich Wanderers FC before their League Cup First Round tie against Long Sutton Athletic. Photo - Gavin Ellis.

Somersham Town. Back Row (L/R): Ian Boon (Captain), Mark Scott, Chris Western, Ian Magnus, Brendan Doe, Chris Bailey, Adrian Hayward. Front: Paul Smith, Barry Stimson, Ian Wilson, James Gwilt (Mascot), Mark Furness, Iain Bell, Michael Cuthbert. Photo - Gavin Ellis.

Stanway Rovers, runners-up in the Essex & Suffolk Border League in 1991-92, and the only newcomers to the ranks of the Jewson Eastern Counties League for the current campaign. Photo - Leo Heonig.

WOODBRIDGE TOWN

Chairman: K Dixon   **President:** J Coates   **Manager:** David Dixon/ Les Simmons
Secretary: Ralph Coxall, 5 Orchard Close, Melton, Woodbridge, Suffolk IP12 1LD (0394 387839).
Ground: Notcutts Park, Seckford Hall Road, Woodbridge, Suffolk (0394 385308).
Directions: Turning into Woodbridge off last r'bout from Lowestoft, or 1st r'bout from Ipswich. Take 1st turning left and 1st left again. Drive to ground at end of road on left.
Seats: None   **Cover:** 250   **Capacity:** Unknown   **Floodlights:** Yes   **Founded:** 1885.
Colours: Black & white stripes/white/white   **Change colours:** Yellow/navy.
Nickname: The Bridge or Woodpeckers.
Midweek Matches: Tuesday   **Previous Leagues:** Suffolk & Ipswich
Record Gate: 3,000 v Arsenal, floodlight inauguration 2/10/90.
Local Newspapers: East Anglian Daily Times.
Programme: 36 pages, 20p   **Programme Editor:** K Dixon
Clubhouse details: Visitors bar, lounge bar, function hall.
Matchday food & drink: Tea, coffee, cold drinks, confectionary, hotdogs, soup, burgers, sandwiches, rolls. Also small cooked meals after match.
Honours: Suffolk Senior Cup(3).

Haverhill Rovers. Back Row (L/R): Andy Salter, Ian Fish, Andy Ince, John NcLean, Gerald Sylvester, Mick Gower, Ian Goddard. Front Row: Dave Hedley, Neil Farlie, Shaun Harrington, Paul Blackburn, Lee Fish, 'Alf' Ramsey. Photo - Cambridge Newspapers Ltd.

Ely City FC 1991-92.

ANGLIAN COMBINATION

Chairman: A J Dickerson, Esq.
Hon. Secretary: J C Harpley,
4 Harlington Avenue, Hellesden, Norwich NR6 5LJ (Norwich 408803).

TITLE GOES TO OVERSTRAND

Overstrand won the Premier Division (the Sterry Trophy) for the first time since joining the Combination in 1964, and completed the double by defeating Dereham Town in the final of the Senior K.O. Cup, this after a replay at Diss. They are sixth club to do the double, Watton United being the first followed by Gorleston, CNSOBU, St Andrews and Wroxham, the latter on no fewer than three occasions. Overstrand were far and away the most talented team in Division One, and were worthy champions. Runners-up Mulbarton threatened at one stage to thwart Overstrand, but in the final run-in they lost some vital points. They can however be proud of their first season in the Premier having worked hard to come up from our Junior Divisions, and now have one of the best grounds in the Combination. It was a tight competition right to the final games with only nine points separating the runners-up and four of the bottom teams.

In the Norfolk Senior Cup, Blofield and Overstrand put in some sterling performances. In the Second Round, Blofield disposed of Norwich United from the Jewsom Premier Division, and Overstrand defeated Great Yarmouth Town at the Wellesley by 1-0. In the Semis, Blofield had an incredible match at Fakenham sharing ten goals after extra-time, but they went out to the eventual winners 1-0 in the replay. Overstrand had an excellent game in their Semi Final with Diss, but lost 1-2, Peter Mendham getting the winner near the end.

In Division One, Horsford and Wortwell made all the running with only Lowestoft Reserves looking possible challengers until they went down 1-2 at Wortwell and then lost to lowly Hellesdon in their final game. Horsford and Wortwell return to the Premier after just one season in Division One. Sadly, in this Division Bungay Town finished in the bottom two and are relegated to Junior football after 57 years in the Senior game. Bungay were one of the leading amateur clubs in the Eastern region during the 40's and 50's, but now join some other past distinctive clubs in the lower divisions such as CNSOBU, Cromer Town, Sheringham and Norwich CEYMS.

J C Harpley, Hon. Secretary

PREMIER DIVISION	P	W	D	L	F	A	PTS
Overstrand	30	18	6	6	75	40	42
Mulbarton Utd	30	13	10	7	58	40	36
St Andrews	30	13	9	8	61	53	35
Wymondham Town	30	13	9	8	54	47	35
Blofield Utd	30	13	8	9	55	41	34
Kirkley	30	13	6	11	53	44	32
Coltishall SV	30	11	9	10	57	45	31
Newton Flotman	30	11	8	11	40	45	30
Carrow	30	13	3	14	46	40	60
Lakeford Rangers	30	10	8	12	57	60	28
Ashlea	30	11	6	13	43	61	28
Beccles Town	30	12	3	15	70	73	27
Gt Yarmouth Res.	30	9	9	12	50	53	27
Dereham Town	30	9	9	12	44	52	27
Bradenham	30	9	9	12	48	58	27
Hempnall	30	3	6	21	29	68	12

DIVISION ONE	P	W	D	L	F	A	PTS
Horsford United	30	21	7	2	58	27	49
Wortwell	30	21	5	4	69	42	47
Lowestoft T. Res.	30	19	5	6	79	39	43
Mattishall	30	12	10	8	52	40	34
Loddon United	30	12	8	10	58	44	32
Watton Utd Res.	30	12	7	11	40	40	31
Gorleston Res.	30	13	7	10	55	57	31*
Wymondham OB	30	11	7	12	47	44	29
Norwich Union	30	9	8	13	49	55	26
Hellesdon	30	11	4	15	52	62	26
Reepham	30	11	4	15	50	61	26
Oulton Broad	30	9	7	14	42	51	25
Brandon Town	30	9	5	16	45	61	23
Harleston Town	30	8	6	16	40	60	22
Bungay Town	30	8	4	18	52	71	20
Stalham Town	30	4	6	20	34	68	14

* - Two points deducted.

SENIOR KNOCK-OUT CUP 1991-92

First Round

Stalham Town v Wortwell	4-1
Mattishall v Hempnall	0-1
Newton Flotman v Wymondham Town	0-2
Harleston v Gorleston Reserves	0-2
Oulton Broad v Carrow	0-5
Hellesdon v Hempnall	3-1
Loddon United v Watton United Reserves	4-3
Blofield Utd v Lowestoft Town Res.	2-2(aet),2-4

Coltishall HV v Overstrand	0-4
Kikley v St Andrews	1-0
Mulbarton United v Bungay Town	10-0
Brandon Town v Great Yarmouth Reserves	1-0
Ashlea v Lakeford Rangers	1-2(aet)
Horsford United v Norwich Union	1-1(aet),4-0
Wymondham Old Boys v Dereham Town	1-3
Beccles Town v Bradenham	2-2(aet),1-0

Second Round

Hempnall v Mulbarton Utd	3-3(aet),3-3(aet),3-1
Hellesdon v Stalham Town	2-0
Horsford United v Gorleston Reserves	3-1
Brandon Town v Wymondham Town	0-5

Dereham Town v Carrow	5-0
Kirkley v Beccles Town	2-1
Lowestoft Town Res. v Loddon Utd	2-2(aet,4-6 pens)
Lakeford Rangers v Overstrand	0-3

Quarter Finals

Horsford United v Dereham Town	1-3
Hellesdon v Loddon United	1-0

Overstrand v Kirkley	2-0
Hempnall v Wymondham Town	2-4

Semi-Finals

Overstrand v Wymondham Town	1-0

Dereham Town v Hellesdon	1-1(aet),3-0

Final (at Norwich United FC)

Overstrand v Dereham Town	2-2(aet)

Replay (at Diss Town FC)

Overstrand v Dereham Town	2-1

PREMIER DIVISION RESULTS 1991/92

HOME TEAM	1	2	3	4	5	6	7	8	9	10	11	12	13	14	15	16
1. Ashlea	*	4-1	0-1	3-2	1-3	1-5	3-1	3-1	0-6	3-1	1-1	2-0	0-2	3-2	1-0	1-2
2. Beccles Town	1-1	*	1-1	4-1	4-3	0-3	4-0	6-1	1-2	6-2	2-3	3-1	3-5	7-1	1-0	2-4
3. Blofield United	3-0	7-1	*	1-1	1-1	2-1	1-0	0-2	2-1	3-4	1-3	1-2	4-2	1-1	2-2	2-1
4. Bradenham	1-1	4-0	0-2	*	2-1	1-1	3-2	0-2	3-1	1-4	2-2	1-2	2-2	1-1	1-1	3-1
5. Carrow	1-3	2-1	2-1	3-4	*	1-1	1-0	1-0	0-1	3-2	0-3	2-0	1-0	1-4	1-1	2-1
6. Coltishall HV	0-2	1-1	0-0	6-1	5-2	*	1-1	4-1	0-3	1-3	1-0	2-2	3-1	1-2	0-0	4-1
7. Dereham Town	1-0	0-4	1-4	3-2	3-0	4-1	*	0-0	1-3	3-3	1-1	4-1	2-2	0-2	2-5	6-2
8. Hempnall	0-2	2-1	1-3	2-3	0-2	2-3	0-2	*	0-1	1-2	1-2	1-2	1-6	2-3	0-3	1-1
9. Kirkley	1-1	3-2	4-1	0-1	2-4	1-0	1-1	1-1	*	3-1	3-5	2-2	0-2	3-1	2-1	3-0
10. Lakeford Rangers	4-1	1-2	1-1	2-1	0-1	0-4	4-2	1-1	1-1	*	1-2	0-2	1-1	3-1	1-2	1-2
11. Mulbarton United	7-2	2-5	2-0	1-1	3-1	2-2	0-0	0-0	3-0	0-2	*	0-0	1-2	4-2	2-1	4-0
12. Newton Flotman	2-2	1-3	1-1	2-1	3-0	3-2	0-2	3-1	1-0	2-2	3-2	*	1-2	0-3	1-1	2-0
13. Overstrand	5-0	5-1	4-2	0-0	0-2	0-2	4-1	4-2	2-1	6-1	3-2	2-0	*	1-1	0-0	1-3
14. St Andrews	2-2	2-1	1-0	4-2	4-2	4-1	0-0	4-2	5-3	1-1	0-0	0-0	1-2	*	1-2	2-2
15. Wymondham Town	2-0	6-2	1-5	2-0	3-2	2-2	0-1	4-0	2-1	1-6	0-0	1-0	3-1	5-4	*	2-2
16. Yarmouth Reserves	3-0	5-0	0-2	2-3	7-1	2-0	0-0	1-1	0-0	2-2	3-1	2-1	0-0	1-2	1-1	*

DIVISION ONE RESULTS 1991/92

HOME TEAM	1	2	3	4	5	6	7	8	9	10	11	12	13	14	15	16
1. Brandon Town	*	1-2	0-1	1-1	3-1	0-1	1-3	2-2	3-1	1-0	1-0	0-1	2-5	1-1	4-0	0-1
2. Bungay Town	2-1	*	1-1	1-2	1-3	1-3	2-5	2-6	1-1	1-3	2-3	4-1	3-1	0-1	3-4	1-4
3. Gorleston Reserves	5-5	3-2	*	3-2	2-2	2-1	2-0	1-1	1-3	1-1	5-3	1-2	1-4	1-3	1-1	2-1
4. Harleston Town	3-1	4-5	3-0	*	0-4	1-3	0-6	0-2	0-2	2-2	0-3	2-4	1-0	2-0	0-2	2-0
5. Hellesdon	3-1	4-1	1-4	2-0	*	1-2	3-4	2-1	0-1	1-4	4-2	1-3	0-2	1-1	0-3	1-3
6. Horsford United	3-1	1-0	3-0	2-1	2-0	*	3-2	1-1	2-2	1-1	2-0	4-2	3-1	1-0	3-1	2-1
7. Loddon United	4-2	0-0	2-2	1-1	2-3	0-0	*	2-4	2-1	8-0	1-0	1-2	4-3	1-2	0-1	2-1
8. Lowestoft Town Res.	6-0	1-0	1-2	4-0	8-2	1-1	3-1	*	1-0	3-2	1-0	2-0	5-1	3-1	3-3	2-3
9. Mattishall	3-3	2-0	0-1	3-1	3-1	0-1	0-0	4-1	*	3-3	5-2	1-3	3-0	2-1	3-4	1-1
10. Norwich Union	4-0	1-4	1-4	3-1	3-2	1-4	2-0	0-1	0-0	*	4-1	0-1	4-0	1-0	2-3	0-0
11. Oulton Broad	2-0	4-3	2-0	0-4	0-0	2-2	0-1	0-2	0-1	3-1	*	2-2	2-0	2-0	0-1	1-1
12. Reepham Town	0-1	3-2	6-1	1-2	1-3	1-1	1-5	2-3	3-3	2-3		*	0-1	0-3	0-5	2-1
13. Stalham Town	1-4	2-3	0-3	0-0	0-3	0-2	1-1	2-4	1-1	2-2	1-1	2-3	*	0-1	0-2	0-2
14. Watton United Reserves	2-1	4-2	1-3	0-2	0-0	2-2	1-1	2-1	2-0	1-0	1-1	1-1	3-0	*	0-2	4-3
15. Wortwell	2-3	3-2	3-1	3-3	1-2	2-0	2-1	2-1	2-2	2-0	3-2	3-2	3-3	2-0	*	2-0
16. Wymondham Old Boys	1-2	0-0	2-1	1-1	4-2	1-2	1-2	2-3	1-1	2-1	1-1	2-1	2-1	3-4	1-2	*

CLUB DETAILS

ASHLEA
Ground: Pitch 1, Normaston Park, Lowestoft.   **Secretary:** E Peek (0502 568716).

BECCLES TOWN
Ground: College Meadow, Beccles (0502 712016).   **Secretary:** J Humby (0502 713776).

BLOFIELD UNITED
Ground: Great Yarmouth Road, Blofield.   **Secretary:** G Hambling (0603 716893).

BRADENHAM WANDERERS
Ground: Bradenham Village Green.   **Secretary:** R Ayers (0603 762575).

BRANDON TOWN
Ground: Remenbrance PF, Church Rd, Bradenham (0842 813177). **Secretary:** C Marchant (0842 812123).

CARROW
Ground: Lakenham Cricket Ground, Norwich.   **Secretary:** P Bugdale (0603 483283).

COLTISHALL H.V.
Ground: Rectory Road, Coltishall.   **Secretary:** Mrs Batch (0603 400065).

DEREHAM TOWN
Ground: Recreation Ground, Commercial Rd, Dereham.   **Secretary:** M Henman (0362 692242).

HARLESTON TOWN
Ground: Recreation Ground & Memorial Leisure Centre, off Wilderness Lane, Harleston (0379 85088) **Secretary:** F Coleman (0379 853815).

HELLESDON
Ground: Coronation Playing Fields, Hellesdon (0603 427675).   **Secretary:** J Watson (0603 868937).

HEMPNALL
Ground: Bungay Road, Hempnall.   **Secretary:** R Youngman (0508 44237).

HORSFORD UNITED
Ground: St Faiths Sports Centre, St Faiths (0603 898069)   **Secretary:** P Bates (0603 897837).

KIRKLEY
Ground: Kirkley Rec. Ground, Kirkley, Lowestoft (0502 560442)   **Secretary:** J Dale (0502 560442).

LAKEFORD RANGERS
Ground: Cringleford Rec. Ground, Oakfields, Cringleford, Norwich.   **Secretary:** R Watling (0603 405032).

LODDON UNITED
Ground: George Lane Playing Field, Loddon.   **Secretary:** B Edwards (0508 28497).

MATTISHALL
Ground: Mattishall PF, Sth Green, Mattishall.   **Secretary:** R Kaye (0362 850489).

MULBARTON UNITED
Ground: Mulberry Par, Mulbarton.   **Secretary:** B Tungate (0508 78460).

NEWTON FLOTMAN
Ground: Newton Flotman Village Centre, Grove Way.   **Secretary:** N Harrod (0603 746507).

NORWICH UNION
Ground: Pinebanks, School Lane, off Harvey Lane, Thorpe. **Secretary:** C McCulloch (0603 402242).

OVERSTRAND
Ground: Sports Ground, High Street, Overstrand. **Secretary:** R Rounce (0263 513715).

OULTON BROAD
Ground: Normaston Park, Lowestoft. **Secretary:** D Rackham (0502 563353).

REEPHAM TOWN
Ground: Stimpsons Place Rec., Reepham. **Secretary:** D Norris (0603 870634).

ST ANDREWS
Ground: Thorpe Rec., Laundry Lane, Thorpe (0603 300316). **Secretary:** I Bishop (0603 720737).

WORTWELL
Ground: Wortwell PF (opposite Bell pub). **Secretary:** I Fisher (0379 852936).

WYMONDHAM OLD BOYS
Ground: Browick Rd Rec., Wymondham. **Secretary:** M Musk (0953 603421).

WYMONDHAM TOWN
Ground: Kings Head Meadow, Wymondham (0953 607326). **Secretary:** M Utting (0953 453146).

(See Jewson Eastern Counties League section for details of Reserve sides)

Dereham Tow, Knock-Out Cup Finalists 1991-92. Back Row (L/R): T Gedge (Trainer), D Seaton, K Bristow, N Starling, A Bemrose, D Hitchcock, S Fletcher, M Goreham, P Annison, P Jarvis, R Symonds (Manager). Front: K Robinson, M Henman, M Bond, G Roberts, M Symonds, P Colman.

Wimpey Homes Essex & Suffolk Border League action; Ian Fish of Haverhill Rovers Reserves heads goalwards during his team's 1-1 draw at Dedham Old Boys on 5th May. Photo - Richard Brock.

WIMPEY HOMES
ESSEX & SUFFOLK BORDER LEAGUE

President: B R Tatum Esq.
Hon. Secretary: K G Bulow Esq.,
13 Kingswood Road, Mile End, Colchester CO4 5JX Tel: 0206 851733

Harwich & Parkeston Reserves must take pride of place with their outstanding performance in that they remained top of the Premier from October 19th and were never displaced. The other divisional leaders (see tables below) are all to be congratulated, and each take their rightful place in higher spheres for 1992-93.

Domestic Cups produced their usual intense struggles. Stowmarket Reserves had a conclusive victory over Long Melford in the K.O. Cup, whilst Long Melford Reserves lost to a lower division club in the Reserve K.O. Cup. Halstead Town Reserves won the Tommy Thompson Cup for the second year running, Tiptree Heath being the luckless finalists.

County Cups saw West Bergholt Reserves win the Essex Junior Cup which brought further prestige to themselves and this Competition. This was no mean feat considering the huge number of entries this particular Cup attracts. Also, Long Melford reached the Suffolk Senior Cup final only to fall at that hurdle.

H G Martin, Press Officer.

Premier Division 1991-92

	P	W	D	L	F	A	PTS
Harwich & P. Res	30	19	7	4	76	42	64
Stanway Rovers	30	18	4	8	49	39	58
Dedham Old Boys	30	17	5	8	57	41	56
Hatfield Peverel	30	17	2	11	59	39	53
West Bergholt	30	16	5	9	58	38	*53
Little Oakley	30	16	2	12	65	46	50
Stowmarket Res	30	13	7	10	63	49	46
Gas Recreation	30	12	6	12	49	50	42
Alresford Colne R.	30	12	5	13	53	58	41
Long Melford	30	11	7	12	46	52	40
Clacton T. Res	30	10	5	15	39	56	35
St Johns Clacton	30	9	6	15	48	61	33
Haverhill R. Res	30	9	3	18	43	58	30
Mistley United	30	7	9	14	38	53	30
Boxted Lodgers	30	7	3	20	34	61	24
Felixstowe Res	30	6	6	18	38	72	24

* - 3 points awarded

Division One

	P	W	D	L	F	A	PTS
Kelvedon Social	30	20	5	5	81	39	65
Mersea Island	30	19	6	5	66	26	63
Sudbury Athletic	30	18	8	4	74	38	*62
Cornard Utd Res	30	17	6	7	51	31	57
Anchor Press	30	14	5	11	52	43	47
Rowhedge	30	12	10	8	51	43	46
Bramston C.M.L.	30	13	4	13	37	34	43
Ryl London (Colc.)	30	12	5	13	40	41	41
Lawford Lads	30	12	5	13	47	55	41
Long Melford Res	30	12	3	15	49	56	39
Stanway Rvrs Res	30	11	3	16	45	70	36
Sudbury Wdrs Res	30	9	8	13	53	46	35
Brantham Res	30	10	2	18	62	68	32
Little Oakley Res	30	10	1	19	45	81	31
Great Bantley	30	5	6	19	32	65	21
Silver End United	30	6	3	21	43	92	21

* - 3 points awarded

Division Two

	P	W	D	L	F	A	PTS
Tiptree Heath	26	19	5	2	73	18	62
W Bergholt Res	26	17	5	4	78	36	*56
Weeley Athletic	26	15	6	5	82	40	51
Halstead T. Res	26	16	3	7	58	30	+51
Alresford CR Res	26	13	5	8	74	39	44
Woods-West End	26	13	4	9	60	49	43
Bures United	26	11	7	8	60	55	40
Gas Recreat. Res	26	10	5	11	55	60	35
Walton Town	26	10	4	12	44	62	34
St Johns (C) Res	26	7	7	12	44	67	*28
Cavendish	26	6	4	16	33	75	*22
Boxted Lodg. Res	26	6	0	20	30	84	*18
Mersea Island Res	26	3	7	16	39	72	16
Hatfield Pev. Res	26	3	4	19	26	69	*13

* - 3 points awarded
+ - 6 points awarded

Division Three

	P	W	D	L	F	A	PTS
Foxash	26	21	3	2	92	26	66
Earls Colne	26	16	4	6	87	41	52
Wormingford Wdrs	16	16	4	6	61	46	*52
Sudbury Ath. Res	26	15	5	6	74	49	50
Dedham OB Res	26	12	6	8	70	40	42
Rowhedge Res	26	13	2	11	57	44	41
Mistley Utd Res	26	12	4	10	48	33	*40
Anchor Press Res	26	12	3	11	54	61	39
Kelvedon S. Res	26	10	4	12	44	62	34
Bramston CML Res	26	8	6	12	54	55	30
Severalls Ath	26	8	3	15	41	58	27
Lawford L. Res	26	7	3	16	39	57	24
Coggeshall Res	26	6	2	18	31	74	20
Bures Utd Res	26	1	1	24	19	125	4

* - 3 points awarded

Divisional Constitutions for 1992-93:

Premier Division: See Club Directory on page 706.

Division 1: Anchor Press, Bramston CML, Brantham Athletic Res., Cornard United Res., Halstead Town Res., Lawford Lads, Little Oakley Res., Long Melford Res., Mersea Island, Rowhedge, Royal London (Colchester), Stanway Rovers Res., Sudbury Wanderers Res., Tiptree Heath, Weeley Athletic, West Bergholt Res.

Division 2: Alresford Colne Rangers Res., Boxted Lodgers Res., Bures United, Cavendish, Clacton St Johns Res., Earls Colne, Foxash Social, Gas Recreation Res., Great Bentley, Mersea Island Res., Silver End United, Walton Town, Woods-West End, Wormingford Wanderers.

Division 3: Anchor Press Res., Bramston CML Res., Bures United Res., Coggeshall Town, Dedham Old Boys Res., Hedingham United, Kelvedon Social Res., Lawford Lads Res., Mistley United Res., Rowhedge Res., St Osyth, Severalls Athletic, Sudbury (Lucas) Athletic Res., Tiptree Heath Res..

#	HOME TEAM	1	2	3	4	5	6	7	8	9	10	11	12	13	14	15	16
1.	Alresford	*	3-0	0-1	2-5	3-0	1-0	2-5	2-0	2-0	3-3	1-1	3-1	1-0	1-2	2-2	1-0
2.	Boxted Lodg.	5-2	*	3-0	1-3	1-2	2-3	0-2	0-3	1-1	1-4	1-0	1-0	5-1	0-2	0-1	2-3
3.	Clacton Town Res	1-1	1-0	*	1-1	1-4	1-1	1-1	3-1	0-2	0-5	2-0	2-1	5-1	3-2	4-3	1-4
4.	Dedham Old B.	3-3	5-1	2-0	*	3-2	3-2	1-2	3-0	1-1	0-1	5-1	1-0	0-0	0-1	4-1	1-0
5.	Felixstowe Res	0-4	1-1	4-1	0-2	*	1-2	0-2	0-1	1-2	2-0	1-1	1-1	3-1	1-2	1-3	1-2
6.	Gas Recreation	0-2	3-1	2-1	4-0	5-2	*	1-1	0-2	0-2	2-1	1-3	1-1	1-2	2-1	3-1	3-2
7.	Harwich & P. Res	2-0	5-0	4-2	2-0	3-3	4-1	*	5-1	2-4	2-0	2-2	3-0	2-1	1-1	1-1	4-5
8.	Hatfield Peverel	4-2	1-0	1-1	4-0	2-1	2-1	1-2	*	4-0	1-2	4-1	3-1	4-1	3-1	2-3	3-0
9.	Haverhill Res	1-2	2-1	2-0	0-2	1-2	2-1	2-4	1-2	*	0-3	2-3	0-1	3-3	1-3	3-1	0-2
10.	Little Oakley	4-2	1-2	3-2	3-0	5-0	4-1	1-3	0-2	3-1	*	3-0	3-0	1-3	4-0	2-4	3-1
11.	Long Melford	2-1	4-1	1-0	5-1	2-2	1-1	5-3	0-0	1-3	0-2	*	2-2	0-2	0-1	2-1	3-0
12.	Mistley United	3-0	1-1	2-1	1-2	1-1	0-1	1-3	2-1	5-3	4-0	3-0	*	3-3	1-1	1-5	1-1
13.	St Johns (C'ton)	2-5	1-2	0-3	1-3	3-0	3-3	1-2	1-4	3-1	2-2	1-2	2-0	*	4-0	1-0	1-2
14.	Stanway Rovers	2-0	1-0	3-0	1-2	4-0	1-0	1-2	3-2	3-2	3-0	3-1	2-0	1-0	*	0-0	0-0
15.	Stowmarket Res	7-1	3-0	0-1	0-3	3-2	2-2	2-2	2-1	2-1	2-0	3-2	5-0	3-3	1-2	*	0-1
16.	West Bergholt	2-1	1-2	2-0	1-1	10-0	1-2	2-0	1-0	W-L	3-2	0-1	1-1	1-0	8-2	2-2	*

W-L; West Bergholt awarded three points.

#	HOME TEAM	1	2	3	4	5	6	7	8	9	10	11	12	13	14	15	16
1.	Anchor Press	*	2-1	0-1	3-1	1-2	1-1	4-0	2-2	0-3	1-1	0-1	4-0	4-1	2-4	2-4	
2.	Bramston CML	2-3	*	2-1	0-1	0-1	0-1	1-0	2-1	0-2	2-3	2-1	0-1	2-1	0-1	0-0	1-0
3.	Brantham A. Res	0-3	0-1	*	3-1	1-0	2-6	1-2	1-5	4-0	0-2	0-6	2-0	8-0	8-0	2-5	3-6
4.	Cornard U. Res	3-0	2-1	3-2	*	0-0	1-2	4-1	1-0	4-1	0-0	1-2	2-0	4-1	1-0	L-W	4-0
5.	Great Bentley	1-1	1-3	0-3	4-2	*	3-0	0-1	0-4	1-1	1-2	1-1	0-4	1-2	1-3	1-1	1-2
6.	Kelvedon Social	3-2	1-2	1-1	4-1	2-0	*	3-1	3-0	4-2	2-2	0-1	1-1	3-1	6-3	3-0	5-0
7.	Lawford Lads	3-1	2-2	6-2	0-0	3-2	0-6	*	0-2	0-2	1-4	2-0	1-1	1-0	2-0	1-1	1-5
8.	L. Oakley Res	1-2	1-2	2-4	2-0	3-1	0-3	1-7	*	1-5	1-5	2-2	3-1	1-4	2-1	2-5	1-0
9.	L. Melford Res	1-0	0-1	2-5	0-2	5-0	1-4	1-4	1-3	*	1-0	1-1	0-1	6-2	2-3	3-1	3-1
10.	Mersea Island	1-2	1-0	2-1	1-2	1-2	1-3	5-0	4-1	3-0	*	3-1	2-0	4-3	4-1	1-0	3-0
11.	Rowhedge	0-0	1-0	1-0	3-3	4-2	4-2	2-1	6-3	3-0	0-0	*	1-5	1-2	1-1	2-2	1-1
12.	Ryl London (Colc.)	1-2	0-0	1-2	0-2	2-1	2-0	4-0	0-1	0-3	3-1		*	0-2	2-1	1-3	0-3
13.	Silver End Utd	1-3	3-1	3-2	2-3	1-1	4-5	0-1	1-3	1-3	0-4	0-1	3-4	*	3-3	1-6	2-2
14.	Stanway R. Res	2-1	0-6	3-1	0-1	1-3	3-2	0-0	0-3	2-2	2-0	3-1	2-2	2-0	*	2-5	3-1
15.	Sudbury Ath.	2-3	2-1	0-1	1-1	5-0	2-2	4-3	3-0	2-0	0-0	3-2	2-1	7-0	2-1	*	1-1
16.	Sudbury Wdrs Res	0-1	1-1	1-2	1-1	2-3	0-0	0-2	6-0	3-0	0-0	0-1	1-1	6-0	5-0	1-3	*

L-W; 15/1/92 - Cornard fielded illegible players - 3 points to Sudbury Athletic.

#	HOME TEAM	1	2	3	4	5	6	7	8	9	10	11	12	13	14
1.	Alresford Res	*	8-2	4-0	7-0	3-1	4-1	4-1	6-1	3-0	1-1	2-4	3-2	1-1	3-1
2.	Boxted Lodgers Res	3-6	*	1-3	0-3	0-2	3-2	L-W	1-3	0-3	0-5	4-3	2-5	2-0	2-3
3.	Bures United	2-1	4-0	*	5-0	3-3	2-2	4-1	7-2	3-1	2-2	1-0	2-4	1-5	2-1
4.	Cavendish	W-L	3-1	2-2	*	2-4	0-3	1-0	4-1	3-3	0-5	0-4	2-1	1-3	1-4
5.	Gas Rec. Res	1-1	4-1	2-1	2-0	*	L-W	4-1	6-3	4-1	0-7	2-2	0-5	2-4	1-3
6.	Halstead Town Res	3-1	0-1	6-1	2-0	6-1	*	2-0	0-0	3-0	W-L	1-2	0-3	0-1	2-1
7.	Hatfield Peverel Res	0-1	2-3	2-3	5-0	2-3	1-8	*	2-1	1-2	0-1	0-2	1-6	0-4	3-1
8.	Mersea Isl. Res	3-1	L-W	1-1	2-2	2-2	1-3	1-1	*	1-3	0-3	1-2	2-2	2-3	1-2
9.	St John (C) Res	3-2	3-2	4-5	2-0	2-2	0-0	W-L	2-5	*	1-3	1-6	2-3	0-3	1-1
10.	Tiptree Heath	0-0	3-0	2-1	2-2	3-4	4-0	3-1	4-0		*	6-0	3-2	2-1	5-0
11.	Walton Town	1-6	2-1	3-1	4-3	1-6	0-2	1-1	2-0	3-3	0-2	*	0-0	0-8	0-4
12.	Weeley Ath. Res	2-2	7-1	3-1	4-2	2-0	1-4	1-1	4-0	3-3	0-1	4-1	*	4-2	6-2
13.	W Bergholt Res	3-2	7-0	2-2	3-1	4-1	3-0	4-0	7-2	3-3	2-2	W-L	1-6	*	3-1
14.	Woods-West End	3-2	3-0	1-1	6-1	2-1	1-4	7-1	3-2	4-1	0-2	3-1	2-1	1-1	*

#	HOME TEAM	1	2	3	4	5	6	7	8	9	10	11	12	13	14
1.	Anchor Press Res	*	2-3	6-1	3-1	3-5	1-0	2-5	4-2	0-1	2-2	1-4	0-4	1-1	1-1
2.	Bramston Res	3-1	*	13-0	3-1	2-2	3-3	3-5	1-1	0-3	2-1	0-2	0-0	1-2	1-3
3.	Bures Utd Res	2-5	0-3	*	1-3	0-6	2-9	0-10	0-3	3-1	1-4	1-1	0-3	1-2	L-W
4.	Cogeshall Town	3-4	2-0	3-2	*	0-7	0-7	0-3	0-4	0-0	1-3	1-4	2-0	0-4	2-3
5.	Dedham Old B. Res	2-3	1-1	4-0	6-2	*	2-0	2-3	6-0	4-1	1-4	3-1	3-2	3-0	1-1
6.	Earls Colne Res	4-1	5-5	7-2	2-1	4-2	*	2-2	4-2	11-0	1-2	4-2	5-0	4-2	1-0
7.	Foxash	4-1	3-1	8-0	5-1	1-0	3-2	*	9-0	3-1	2-0	4-0	2-0	2-3	2-2
8.	Kelvedon S. Res	1-2	1-2	4-0	0-0	2-1	0-1	0-4	*	0-7	2-1	4-0	4-3	1-1	3-2
9.	Lawford Lads Res	2-3	2-1	4-0	1-2	2-2	1-2	0-2	1-0	*	0-2	1-2	2-1	1-2	2-2
10.	Mistley Utd Res	0-1	4-0	2-1	0-2	1-0	1-1	2-0	1-2	3-0	*	W-L	0-0	2-2	2-3
11.	Rowhedge Res	4-0	3-0	7-2	4-0	1-1	2-1	0-3	4-0	2-1	3-2	*	2-3	0-2	0-1
12.	Severalls Ath.	1-2	1-3	3-0	1-0	1-1	1-3	0-2	2-3	4-2	4-3	1-5	*	2-1	1-3
13.	Sudbury Ath. Res	3-4	5-2	6-0	3-1	5-3	0-3	3-3	3-3	3-2	1-0	5-3	6-2	*	3-3
14.	Wormingford Wanderers	2-1	2-1	7-0	4-3	0-2	4-1	1-2	3-2	4-1	1-6	3-1	4-2	3-3	*

ESSEX & SUFFOLK BORDER PREMIER DIVISION 1992-93

ALRESFORD COLNE RANGERS
Secretary: R Wood, 33 Broomfield Crescent, Wivenhoe, Colchester (0206 222983).
Headquarters: The Clubhouse, Ford Lane, Alresford, Colchester.
Colours: Red & black quarters/black/black & red   **Change Colours:** Yellow/black/black.
Ground: Village Playing Fields, Ford Lane

BOXTED LODGERS
Secretary: G R Scott, 6 Home Dale Cottages, Boxted CO4 5SJ (0206 272596).
Headquarters: Boxted Sports & Social Club, Playing Field, Cage Lane, Boxted, nr Colchester (0206 271969).
Colours: White (Royal trim)/Royal/white   **Change Colours:** Royal or yellow/navy or royal/royal or white
Ground: as Headquarters

CLACTON TOWN RESERVES
Secretary: A R Harvey, 4 Fairlop Close, Clacton-on-Sea, Essex CO15 4UU (0255 420219).
Colours: White/blue/blue   **Change Colours:** All red.
Please refer to page 696 for other details

DEDHAM OLD BOYS
Secretary: H G Martin, 16 Southfield Close, Colchester, Essex CO4 4QH (0206 842531).
Headquarters: Dedham Sports Club, Duchy Field, Recreation Ground, Dedham, Essex.
Colours: Red & white stripes/black/black   **Change Colours:** Blue & white stripes/blue/black.
Ground: Old Grammar School, at HQ, Dedham

FELIXSTOWE TOWN RESERVES
Secretary: D Foskett, 16 Quantock Close, Rushmere, Ipswich, Suffolk IP5 7AS (0473 611303).
Colours: Red & black stripes/black/black   **Change Colours:** White/black/black.
Please refer to page 692 for other details.

GAS RECREATION
Secretary: G McKillop, 'Four Seasons', Mumford Close, West Bergholt, Colchester CO6 3HY (0206 241501).
Headquarters: British Gas Sports Club, Bromley Road, Colchester, Essex (0206 860383).
Colours: Red & black stripes/black/black   **Change Colours:** All blue.
Ground: as Headquarter

HARWICH & PARKESTON RESERVES
Please refer to page 694 for full details.

HAVERHILL ROVERS RESERVES
Please refer to page 694 for full details.

KELVEDON SOCIAL
(Newly promoted from Division One).

LITTLE OAKLEY
Secretary: D Chopping, 1 Laurel Avenue, Dovercourt, Essex CO12 4HP (0255 553025).
Headquarters: Little Oakley Club, Memorial Ground, Little Oakley (0255 880370).
Colours: Blue/navy/blue   **Change Colours:** Red/black/black & white
Ground: as Headquarters

LONG MELFORD
Secretary: P Hurrell, 17 Butt Road, Great Cornard, Sudbury CO10 0DS (0787 78829).
Headquarters: The Clubhouse, 'Stonylands', via St Catherines Road, Long Melford, Suffolk (0787 312187).
Colours: white & black stripes/white/black & white   **Change Colours:** Red/black/black & white.
Ground: as Headquarters

MISTLEY UNITED
Secretary: D Bird, 5 Kings Close, Lawford, Manningtree, Essex CO11 1EP (0206 392866).
Headquarters & Ground: Shrubland Road, Furze Hills, Mistley, Essex (0206 393350).
Colours: Amber/black/amber   **Change Colours:** White, green or blue/black or blue/black or blue.

ST JOHN'S (CLACTON)
Secretary: C Garrod, 20 Gilders Way, Clacton-on-Sea, Essex CO16 8UU (0255 434621).
Headquarters: The Clubhouse, Dulwich Road, Holland-on-Sea, Essex.
Colours: Red/black/black   **Change Colours:** Green & white hoops/green/black.
Ground: Eastcliff Sports Ground, Dulwich Road, Holland-on-Sea (0255 814874)

STOWMARKET TOWN RESERVES
Please refer to page 695 for full details.

SUDBURY (LUCAS) ATHLETIC
(Newly promoted from Division One)

WEST BERGHOLT
Secretary: P Thompson, 54 Erle Way, West Bergholt CO6 3LH (0206 241227).
Headquarters: West Bergholt FC Clubhouse, Lexden Road, West Bergholt (0206 240180).
Colours: Sky blue/navy/navy   **Change Colours:** Red/black/red.
Ground: Rear of Orpen Hall, Lexden Road, West Bergholt

ESSEX & SUFFOLK BORDER LEAGUE SPORTSMANSHIP AWARDS 1991-92.

Average marks out of 10

Premier Division		Division 1		Division 2		Division 3	
Alresford Colne	8.36	Silver End Utd	8.67	Bures United	8.88	Bures United	9.08
Boxted	8.31	Long Melford	8.63	Alresford	8.84	Coggeshall	8.38
Dedham Old B.	8.31	Sudbury Wdrs	8.27	Boxted	8.68	Foxash	8.35
Stowmarket	8.22	Stanway	8.17	Tiptree Hth	8.65	Dedham OB	8.27
Long Melford	8.15	Ryl London	8.13	Walton Town	8.56	Kelvedon S.	8.12
Harwich & P.	7.90	Lawford Lads	8.03	Halstead Town	8.54	Bramston CML	7.92
Stanway Rvrs	7.81	Bramston CML	7.93	Gas Recreation	8.28	Anchor Press	7.81
Little Oakley	7.79	Little Oakley	7.86	Weeley Ath.	8.00	Lawford Lads	7.69
Clacton Town	7.74	Brantham Ath.	7.82	Woods-West End	8.00	Rowhedge	7.68
St Johns (C'ton)	7.54	Sudbury Ath.	7.67	W Bergholt	7.92	Sudbury Ath.	7.68
Haverhill	7.50	Gt Bentley	7.59	St Johns (C'ton)	7.88	Wormingford	7.60
Felixstowe	7.43	Kelvedon S.	7.53	Cavendish	7.85	Severalls	7.42
W Bergholt	7.36	Mersea Island	7.45	Mersea Island	7.85	Mistley Utd	7.33
Mistley Utd	6.96	Anchor Press	7.43	Hatfield P.	7.65	Earls Colne	7.27
Hatfield P.	6.69	Cornard Utd	7.40				
Gas Rec.	6.61	Rowhedge	7.23				

Dedham Old Boys FC. Back Row (L/R): Peter Licence, John Lynch, Simon Smith, David Bird, Martyn Chater, Grant Matthews, John Jones, Roy Walsh (Manager), Terry Duffett (Physio). Front: Barry Nunn, Lee Wooldridge, Barrie Tingley, Ian Loughton, Sean Ketteridge, Paul Harrison. Photo - Richard Brock.

Haverhill Rovers Reserves. Back Row (L/R): D Franklin (Physio), M Gorner, I Fish, David Green, M Bavester, T Beavis, P Eady, D Goodman, S Stoten. Front: Daniel Green (Coach - father of David), T Botten, S Halls, N Gaffan, B Abery. Photo - Richard Brock.

PUBMASTERS
SUFFOLK & IPSWICH LEAGUE

President: G Harper.
Patron: Mr W Snook.
Hon. Secretary: Alan Gorham,
179 Cauldwell Hall Road, Ipswich, Suffolk IP4 5DA Tel: 723685.

When at the League's A.G.M. Fiona Whatling, the secretary of Framlingham Town, was crowned Senior Administrator of the Year, it really put the finishing touch to what for Framlingham had been a wonderful season. Having led the Senior Division from the early weeks, they finally finished three points ahead of Grundisburgh, and Whitton United, with a long run of drawn matches, slipped to third.

Framlingham completed the double when they defeated B.T. Research in the Mick McNeil Leeague K.O. Cup. This competition is run along the same lines as the F.A. Cup with Senior Clubs entering at the Third Round stage. The 'McNeil Giant-Killer Trophy' award went to Kesgrave who also won the League's Fina Fairplay Trophy which is a competition based on referee's marks.

Back to Framlingham one last time; they of course won the 'Senior Club of the Year' award. The Junior Award went to Division Two champions Fisons who won their fourth consecutive championship. Division One champions and runners-up were respectively Westerfield and Willis Corroon who both return to Senior Football.

The League Chairman retired and became the competition's first Patron. Bill Snook played in the league in the 1930's, was a referee by 1951, became Referee's Appointment Secretary in 1961 and Chairman in 1977. He had held the chairmanship of the Suffolk County F.A. during the same period.

Alan Gorham, Hon. Secretary.

LEAGUE TABLES 1991-92

Senior Division	P	W	D	L	F	A	PTS	Division One	P	W	D	L	F	A	PTS
Framlingham Town	28	17	8	3	51	17	42	Westerfield	26	21	2	3	84	17	44
Grundisburgh	28	16	7	5	57	29	39	Willis Corroon	26	16	4	6	77	37	36
Whitton United	28	12	11	5	53	39	35	Achilles	26	16	4	6	63	35	36
Needham Market	28	14	5	9	52	44	33	Ipswich Athletic	26	13	7	6	62	38	33
Melton St Aubreys	28	13	6	9	63	47	32	Crane Sports	26	13	3	10	60	59	29
B. Sugar F. Ath.	28	13	5	10	46	41	31	Walton United	26	11	6	9	52	43	28
Halesworth Town	28	12	6	10	49	41	30	Wenhaston	26	11	5	10	57	50	27
B.T. Research	28	10	7	11	49	51	27	Elmswell	26	12	3	11	59	65	27
Haughley	28	10	7	11	43	51	27	Coplestonians	26	8	7	11	45	53	23
Stutton	28	8	9	11	35	42	25	Ipswich Exiles	26	9	5	12	39	52	23
Old Newton	28	10	5	13	39	49	25	Bramford Utd	26	9	5	12	39	57	23
Stonham Aspal	28	10	4	14	37	57	24	Elmsett	26	8	6	12	46	61	22
Walsham	28	9	5	14	41	51	23	Sproughton	26	3	2	21	35	91	8
RSSC Ransomes	28	4	6	18	33	53	14	Leiston St Marg.	26	1	3	22	26	86	5
Leiston	28	4	5	19	21	57	13								

SENIOR DIVISION RESULTS 1991/92

HOME TEAM	1	2	3	4	5	6	7	8	9	10	11	12	13	14	15
1. B.S. Fonnereau	*	1-2	1-3	4-2	1-1	3-1	0-1	2-1	2-4	2-3	1-0	0-1	1-0	2-1	1-0
2. B.T. Research	2-2	*	1-1	2-2	3-1	5-2	3-1	1-2	0-0	0-1	0-0	4-3	2-2	0-1	2-1
3. Framlingham Town	1-0	1-0	*	2-1	3-1	5-1	3-0	2-2	1-0	6-0	1-1	6-0	2-0	1-0	0-1
4. Grundisburgh	2-1	5-0	1-1	*	3-2	1-1	4-0	1-0	4-1	0-2	2-1	2-2	1-2	3-0	0-0
5. Halesworth Town	1-2	1-0	1-0	1-1	*	1-1	2-1	3-1	5-3	2-1	1-0	0-2	0-1	3-0	1-1
6. Haughley United	1-2	4-1	2-1	0-5	2-3	*	1-0	2-0	2-3	2-1	1-0	3-0	1-1	2-2	2-3
7. Leiston	0-1	1-3	0-5	0-1	0-4	1-1	*	1-3	3-1	0-1	3-0	0-2	1-1	2-3	0-2
8. Melton St Audrys	2-2	2-2	2-3	0-2	1-0	1-2	1-2	*	5-2	3-1	3-2	6-1	2-0	5-2	4-4
9. Needham Market	0-2	4-0	0-0	0-2	2-2	2-0	1-1	2-1	*	5-0	0-2	2-1	2-0	4-2	1-1
10. Old Newton Utd	1-1	1-5	0-0	2-3	2-0	1-1	1-1	2-4	1-0	*	5-0	1-2	1-1	4-2	2-5
11. RSSC Ransomes	2-3	2-4	0-2	0-3	3-4	3-1	1-1	0-1	2-3	1-2	*	4-0	0-1	1-4	3-1
12. Stonham Aspal	3-2	1-2	0-1	2-0	1-5	2-1	4-1	1-2	2-4	0-2	1-1	*	2-0	0-0	0-3
13. Stutton	2-2	2-0	0-2	2-2	3-2	0-1	2-0	2-6	0-1	2-0	2-2	4-1	*	1-2	1-1
14. Walsham-le-Will.	2-4	3-2	1-1	1-2	2-1	0-1	3-0	1-1	1-2	2-0	1-1	0-2	4-2	*	0-1
15. Whitton United	2-1	4-4	1-1	0-2	1-1	4-4	3-0	2-2	2-3	3-1	2-1	1-1	1-1	3-1	*

MICK McNEIL LEAGUE KNOCK-OUT CUP

Quarter Finals

Ipswich Exiles* v B.T. Research	1-3	Saxmundham Sports* v Grundisburgh	0-1
Framlingham Town v Whitton United	2-0	Westerfield United* v Halesworth Town	2-3

Semi-Finals

B.T. Research v Grundisburgh	2-1	Framlingham Town v Halesworth Town	1-0

Final

British Telecom Research v Framlingham Town   0-3

* - denotes Junior club.

First half action from BT Research's 3-1 home win over Halesworth on April 25th. Photo - Martin Wray.

Haughley United FC. Photo - Martin Wray.

Ransomes desperately defend a corner as they lose 0-5 at Old Newton United on 21st March. Photo - Martin Wray.

SUFFOLK & IPSWICH LEAGUE SENIOR DIVISION 1992-93

BRITISH SUGAR FONNEREAU ATHLETIC
Secretary: Nigel Spurling, 16 Thanet Rd, Ipswich, Suffolk IP4 5LB (0473 716018).
Ground: British Sugar Plc, Sproughton Road, Ipswich, Suffolk.
Colours: All royal blue   **Change Colours:** All white.
Previous Names: Silent Youth/ Fonnereau Ath./ YMCA Fonnereau Ath.

B.T. RESEARCH
Secretary: Mrs Dee Haste, 48 Dobbs Lane, Kesgrave, Suffolk IP5 7PX (0473 622431).
Ground: The Hollies, Straight Road, Bucklesham.
Colours: Yellow/blue/blue   **Change Colours:** All red.
Previous Names: British Telecom   **Programme Editor:** Julian Catt (0473 252239).

FRAMLINGHAM TOWN
Secretary: Mrs Fiona Whatling, 46 College Rd, Framlingham, Woodbridge IP13 9ES (0728 723524).
Ground: Sports Field, Badlingham Road, Framlingham, Woodbridge, Suffolk.
Colours: Green & white/white/white   **Change Colours:** Maroon & blue/blue/blue.

GRUNDISBURGH
Secretary: Malcolm Harris, 70 Post Mill Gardens, Grundisburgh, Woodbridge IP13 6UP (0473 35422).
Ground: The Playing Field, Grundisburgh, Woodbridge.
Colours: All rblue   **Change Colours:** Red/red/black.

HALESWORTH TOWN
Secretary: John Stannard, 87 Bedlingfield Cres., Halesworth IP19 8ED (0986 873529).
Ground: Playing Fields, Dairy Hill, Bungay Road, Halesworth.
Colours: White/navy/red   **Change Colours:** Maroon & royal/royal/royal.

HAUGHLEY UNITED
Secretary: Mark Mead, 44 Hillside, Stowmarket, Suffolk IP14 2BA (0449 674100).
Ground: British Sugar Plc, Sproughton Road, Ipswich, Suffolk.
Colours: All white   **Change Colours:** Red/white/red.

MELTON ST AUDRYS
Secretary: David Spink, Flat 3, The Square, Martlesham Heath, Ipswich (0473 611669).
Ground: St Audrys Hospital Sports Field, Melton, Nr Woodbridge, Suffolk.
Colours: Red/black/black   **Change Colours:** Grey & white stripes/black/black.
Programme Editor: Michael Milbourne (Woodbridge 380146).

NEEDHAM MARKET
Secretary: Ian Croft, 30 Masefield Rd, Stowmarket, Suffolk IP14 1TH (0449 676517).
Ground: Barretts Lane, Needham Market, Suffolk.
Colours: Red/red/black   **Change Colours:** Green/green/grey.
Programme Editor: Alan Parson (0449 720468).

OLD NEWTON UNITED
Secretary: John Thorndyke, 13 Winchester Close, Stowmarket, Suffolk IP14 1SH (0449 675653).
Ground: Playing Field, Church Road, Old Newton.
Colours: Amber/amber/blue   **Change Colours:** All blue.
Programme Editor: Rob Atherton (0449 673105).

R.S.S.C. RANSOMES
Secretary: John Gorham, 16 Ranwell Close, Ipswich, Suffolk IP4 5ES (0473 713876).
Ground: Sidegate Avenue, Ipswich.   **Programme Editor:** Darren Richardson (0473 231402).
Colours: Red/black/black   **Change Colours:** All blue.
Previous Names: Orwell Works/ Ransomes FC.

STONHAM ASPAL
Secretary: Eric Cousins, 2 Holly Green, Mickfield, Stowmarket, Suffolk IP14 5LH (0449 711884).
Ground: Delsons Meadow, Three Crossways, Stonham Aspal.
Colours: Blue/blue/white   **Change Colours:** All yellow.

STUTTON
Secretary: Barry Felgate, 20 Pine Close, Brantham, Manningtree, Essex CO11 1TP (0206 393029).
Ground: Hall Park, Stutton.   **Programme Editor:** Ivan Ransby (0473 47645).
Colours: White/black/black   **Change Colours:** Gold/black/black.

WALSHAM-LE-WILLOWS
Secretary: Mark Howlett, Jasmine, The Street, Coney Weston, Bury St Edmonds IP31 1HG (0359 21726).
Ground: Walsham Sports Club, Sumner Road, Walsham-le-Willows.   **Programme Editor:** Julie Smith.
Colours: Blue/blue/navy   **Change Colours:** White/navy/blue.

WESTERFIELD UNITED
Secretary: Mrs Jan Mitchell, 12 Fairfield Rd, Ipswich, Suffolk IP3 0LD (0473 714692).
Ground: S.E.H. Sports Centre, Humber Doucy Lane, Rushmere.
Colours: All blue   **Change Colours:** Red & black stripes/black/red.

WHITTON UNITED
Secretary: David Gould, 7 Karen Close, Ipswich, Suffolk IP1 4LP (0473 253838).
Ground: King Geore V Playing Field, Norwich Road, Ipswich, Suffolk.
Colours: Green & white hoops/white/green **Change Colours:** Blue/white/green.
Previous Name: Whitton FC   **Programme Editor:** Ian Vernau (0473 680592).

WILLIS CORROON
Secretary: Alan Butler, 326 Hawthorn Drive, Ipswich, Suffolk IP2 0RX (0473 683037).
Ground: The Street, Rushmere St Andrew, Ipswich, Suffolk.
Colours: Purple/white/sky   **Change Colours:** Yellow/navy/navy.

PEARL ASSURANCE
PETERBOROUGH & DISTRICT LEAGUE

President: R Leigh.
Hon. Secretary: M J Croson, 44 Storrington Way,
Werrington, Peterborough PE4 6QP. Tel: 0733 73122.

Premier Division	P	W	D	L	F	A	PTS
Molins	34	27	4	3	90	23	85
Whittlesey Utd	34	23	7	4	97	49	76
Ortonians	34	23	6	5	96	27	75
Perkins Sports	34	23	5	6	118	43	74
Pinchbeck Utd	34	19	6	9	72	42	63
Deeping Rangers	34	16	9	9	64	39	57
March T. Utd Res	34	17	6	11	64	46	57
Alconbury	34	14	8	12	64	46	50
Oundle Town	34	13	6	15	48	62	45
Thomas Cook FC	34	12	8	14	75	66	44
Eye United	34	11	8	15	67	63	41
Brotherhoods	34	10	7	17	45	63	37
P'borough BRAD	34	9	8	17	46	67	35
Leverington Spts	34	8	6	20	44	80	30
Chatteris T. Res	34	10	3	21	59	99	*30
Wisbech T. Res	34	7	7	20	50	70	28
Stamford Belvedere	34	8	4	22	41	73	28
Holbeach U. Res	34	2	0	32	25	198	*3

* - 3 points deducted

Relegated from Premier: Holbeach Reserves

Division One	P	W	D	L	F	A	PTS
Deeping Rgrs Res	30	23	4	3	74	32	73
Hotpoint	30	21	3	6	85	37	66
Moulton Harrox	30	19	4	7	73	30	61
Thurlby United	30	19	3	8	64	39	60
Ortonians Res	30	14	7	8	67	40	49
Rythall United	30	15	3	12	72	64	48
Stanground Utd	30	12	8	10	48	51	44
Stilton United	40	12	6	12	47	55	42
Manea United	30	11	8	11	59	58	41
Crowland Town	30	11	6	13	67	76	39
Juventus	30	9	9	12	38	44	36
Peterborough Rvrs	30	9	4	17	32	51	31
Pinchbeck Utd Res	30	6	6	18	26	53	24
Leverington S. Res	30	6	6	18	32	75	17
Ramsey Town Res	30	3	8	19	32	75	17
Whittlesey Res	30	5	3	21	32	83	15

Promoted to Premier: Moulton Harrox
Relegated from Div. One: bottom three
Promoted to Div. One: Outwell, Pearl, Newgate.

Deeping Rangers Reserves, Peterborough & District League Division One champions. The first team came sixth in the Premier Division and won the Peterborough FA Senior Cup for the first time. A stand is being built, and the club have ambitions to join the United Counties League. There is also a third senior side, which finished in mid-table in Division Two, and eight junior sides from under-10 to under-18. Photo - P J Beuken.

Whitton United FC of the Suffolk & Ipswich League Senior Division. Photo - Gavin Ellis.

C. & G. BURY (ST EDMUNDS) & DISTRICT LEAGUE

Division One	P	W	D	L	F	A	PTS
Newbury United	20	19	1	0	111	21	39
Thurston	20	13	2	5	64	40	28
Fornham St M. YC	20	11	4	5	61	43	26
Hundon	20	10	3	7	53	35	23
Lakenheath Res	20	8	6	6	46	48	22
Thomas Ridley	20	8	3	9	43	51	19
Sporting '87	20	8	2	10	45	46	18
St Edmunds (1965)	20	7	3	10	48	47	17
Cockfield United	20	4	4	12	32	77	12
Eriswell	20	3	2	15	24	53	8
Bury Town 'A'	20	3	2	15	19	85	8

Division Two	P	W	D	L	F	A	PTS
Chicago Rock Cafe	26	22	2	2	105	32	46
Pot Black Utd	26	21	2	3	83	26	44
Beck Row	26	14	4	8	58	30	32
Old Burians	26	14	3	9	61	53	31
Stanton Res	26	11	8	7	91	50	30
Hepworth	26	13	3	10	77	77	29
Macebearer	26	11	5	10	64	58	27
Tostock '85	26	9	3	14	48	72	21
Eastbury	26	8	4	14	26	54	20
Priors Inn	26	9	1	16	49	94	19
Brandon Town Res	26	6	5	15	48	59	17
Lakenheath 'A'	26	6	5	15	40	68	17
Barons	26	7	3	16	42	72	17
Cockfoeld Utd Res	26	3	8	15	33	80	14

Division Three	P	W	D	L	F	A	PTS
Eriswell Res	26	18	4	4	100	34	40
Wanderers S.C.	26	17	4	5	87	44	38
Newbury Utd Res	26	17	4	5	77	44	38
Next Installations	26	17	3	6	76	33	37
Sporting '87 Res	26	13	7	6	66	55	33
Cadogan Arms	26	12	6	8	72	68	30
Helmsman	26	8	6	12	52	56	22
Beck Row Res	26	8	4	14	54	67	20
Fornham St Mart.	26	7	6	13	45	61	20
Silver Spoon	26	8	4	14	51	76	20
Hundon Res	20	6	5	15	41	72	17
Barrow	26	7	3	16	37	83	17
Ixworth	26	6	4	16	40	65	16
Lucky Break	26	4	8	14	37	76	18

Captain Neil Brown (with trophy) leads the festivities as Herne Bay celebrate their Winstonlead Kent League championship success. Photo - Gavin Ellis.

THE WINSTONLEAD
KENT LEAGUE

President: D D Baker, Esq.
Chairman: P C Wager, Esq.
Vice Chairman: E V Ward, Esq.
Hon. Secretary: A R Vinter, Esq., The Smithy,
The Square, Chilham, Canterbury, Kent CT4 8BY Tel: 0227 730884.

HERNE BAY ACHIEVE SURPRISE SUCCESS

Herne Bay won their first ever Kent League Division One title, and although well enough did they do themselves, rivals Faversham Town, Alma Swanley, Deal Town and Tonbridge did their best to help them with some indifferent end of season results. Managed by Trevor McGowan, Herne Bay eventually pulled away from the rest following a good 1-1 draw at Alma Swanley two days before the end of the season. Bay then comfortably beat struggling Danson 4-1 at Winch's Field despite having goalkeeper Lol Wright sent off after 51 minutes.

McGowan's squad includes many players with experience at Beazer Homes League level. Strikers Gary Pugh, Andy Ballantyne and Steve Tapp, defenders Tommy Sloan, John Love and Simon Kingsfield and Mark and John Munday have all played for clubs such as Canterbury, Margate and Ashford. Unfortunately Herne Bay's Winch's Field ground currently falls below the standard necessary for promotion to the Beazer Homes League, but planning permission has been sought from Canterbury City Council for the erection of floodlights and plans are also in hand for further ground improvements.

Division One was won at the first attempt by Folkestone Invicta, who seem to be successfully filling the void left in the sizeable town by the sad demise of Folkestone FC, the Southern League club, during the 1990-91 season. Invicta completed a fabulous treble by also carrying off the Second Division Cup and the Kent Intermediate Shield. Another ex-Southern League name apparently heading back for the big time appears to be Tonbridge; the Angels won the League Cup beating Whitstable Town 2-1 in the final at Dover's Crabble ground, finished a creditable fourth in the League, and reached the final qualifying round of the F.A. Cup breaking their ground record attendance three times in the space of ten days in doing so.

Following the League's Annual General Meeting on Thursday 25th June, Danson Furness United and Darenth Heathside were both re-elected into Division One, while Folkestone Invicta having obtained full senior status were promoted from the Second Division. Alas Thames Polytechnic, that famous old club whose past players included Charles Buchan and Olympic sprinter John Regis, were unable to meet the ground grading requirements now laid down by the Kent League. Having subsequently failed in their attempts for adequate ground-sharing arrangements elsewhere, 'Poly' have decided to switch to the F.C.N. Music Kent County League for next season, meaning that Division One now comprises 21 teams. Groundsharing arrangements elsewhere will see Sheppey United playing at Faversham Town's Salters Lane ground, Danson Furness United moving into Green Court Road with with landlords Alma Swanley, and Greenwich Borough joining Erith & Belvedere of the Beazer Homes League at their Park View Stadium in North West Kent.

For a while, it appeared that Canterbury City would be joining the ranks of the Winstonlead Kent League after finishing second from bottom in the Southern Division of the Beazer Homes League, but they won a last minute reprieve following the resignation of Hythe Town due to financial difficulties.

LEAGUE TABLES 1991-92

Division One	P	W	D	L	F	A	PTS
Herne Bay	40	29	6	5	91	34	93
Faversham Town	40	25	11	4	78	33	86
Deal Town	40	26	6	8	119	43	84
Tonbridge AFC	40	26	6	8	93	44	84
Alma Swanley	40	24	11	5	92	49	83
Sheppey United	40	21	11	8	69	44	74
Whitstable Town	40	21	8	11	70	38	71
Slade Green	40	15	12	13	68	56	57
Greenwich Borough	40	15	10	15	77	62	55
Ramsgate	40	16	7	17	62	58	55
Kent Police	40	14	11	15	60	63	53
Corinthian	40	14	8	18	57	63	50
Tunbridge Wells	40	15	8	17	61	68	50
Beckenham Town	40	13	10	17	52	67	49
Thames Polytechnic	40	8	11	21	43	78	36
Crockenhill	40	7	13	20	48	83	34
Thamesmead Town	40	9	7	24	44	100	34
Cray Wanderers	40	8	7	25	38	84	31
Chatham Town	40	7	10	23	41	89	31
Danson Furness U.	40	8	6	26	38	95	30
Darenth Heathside	40	6	7	27	42	96	25

Division Two	P	W	D	L	F	A	PTS
Folkestone Invicta	36	29	5	2	122	33	92
Dover Ath. Res	36	27	4	5	114	30	85
Hastings T. Res	36	24	4	8	117	46	76
Ashford T. Res	36	19	6	11	59	45	63
Sittingbourne Res	36	20	7	9	98	51	61
Deal Town Res	36	16	5	15	84	87	53
Herne Bay Res	36	16	4	16	70	86	52
Whitstable Res	36	15	6	15	61	62	51
Ramsgate Res	36	15	6	16	62	66	47
Thames Poly Res	36	14	5	17	62	70	47
Cray Wdrs Res	36	13	8	15	58	66	47
Darenth H'side Res	36	13	6	17	63	79	45
Canterbury C. Res	36	12	6	18	62	84	42
Chatham Town Res	36	10	11	15	49	65	41
Thamesmead Res	36	11	7	18	53	74	40
Sheppey Utd Res	36	11	6	19	60	89	39
Beckenham T. Res	36	8	5	23	51	83	29
Faversham T. Res	36	6	7	23	41	95	25
Hythe Town Res	36	8	3	25	44	138	24

DIVISION ONE RESULT CHART 1991-92

HOME TEAM	1	2	3	4	5	6	7	8	9	10	11	12	13	14	15	16	17	18	19	20	21	22
1. Alma S.	*	2-1	3-0	2-1	2-2	2-0	6-1	1-0	1-1	0-4	3-0	1-1	2-0	5-0	0-0	2-2	3-0	5-1	3-2	4-2	2-0	3-2
2. Beckenham	0-4	*	4-0	2-0	5-1	3-0	2-0	2-1	0-6	1-1	0-1	2-2	3-1	3-1	1-1	1-0	2-1	5-1	1-1	1-3	0-0	0-1
3. Chatham	0-1	1-0	*	0-0	2-0	2-2	1-0	1-2	2-5	1-3	0-4	0-1	3-3	1-0	0-2	2-3	0-3	2-4	1-1	1-3	1-1	1-1
4. Corinthian	0-2	2-0	1-2	*	3-1	3-0	2-3	3-2	1-2	1-2	1-1	1-0	1-1	2-0	4-0	0-3	4-3	3-4	1-1	1-4	1-1	0-2
5. Cray	1-4	0-0	2-1	1-2	*	2-2	0-2	1-1	0-1	2-3	0-0	1-2	0-2	0-3	1-2	0-4	2-1	2-0	1-2	1-5	1-0	0-3
6. Crockenhill	2-5	0-5	1-1	0-0	2-5	*	3-1	1-1	2-4	1-4	3-3	0-2	1-1	*	2-0	2-3	2-0	3-1	1-1	1-2	1-0	2-0
7. Danson	1-2	0-1	4-1	0-2	1-0	0-2	*	1-1	0-4	0-4	1-3	0-4	3-2	0-1	1-3	0-1	0-0	3-0	2-2	0-2	3-2	0-4
8. Darenth	0-6	2-1	2-3	2-4	4-0	2-1	0-0	*	2-9	1-6	1-3	0-1	0-1	*	0-1	1-4	0-3	1-1	0-1	2-4	2-4	0-0
9. Deal	7-2	4-0	2-0	2-0	1-1	1-0	4-0	2-0	*	2-2	3-3	4-0	6-0	4-0	3-2	3-0	0-1					
10. Faversham	1-1	1-0	1-1	1-0	4-0	1-1	1-2	3-0	5-5	*	1-1	3-2	4-2	*	3-1	2-0	0-0	1-0	2-1	2-0	3-0	1-0
11. Greenwich	0-0	5-2	4-1	5-2	2-0	5-1	6-0	6-2	1-3	0-2	*	1-1	5-0	5-0	3-0	0-3	0-2	3-2	0-1	1-3	1-2	0-3
12. Herne Bay	1-0	3-3	8-0	1-0	3-0	5-0	4-1	1-0	2-1	1-1	3-1	*	0-1	3-0	3-1	1-2	1-1	2-0	4-2	1-0	4-0	2-0
13. Kent Pol.	5-3	1-3	3-0	0-4	1-2	1-0	2-2	4-0	1-0	0-0	3-1	0-3	*	1-1	1-2	2-1	1-1	1-1	6-0	1-2	1-1	1-1
14. Met P. (Hayes)	*	*	*	*	2-3	*	*	*	*	*	*	*	*	*	*	*	*	*	1-1	2-6	0-2	1-3	*
15. Ramsgate	1-1	5-0	2-3	0-1	1-2	1-1	3-2	1-0	2-1	0-2	3-1	2-3	2-3	*	*	1-1	1-2	5-1	2-0	2-3	1-0	0-1
16. Sheppey	1-1	3-0	1-2	2-2	1-0	1-1	5-1	0-2	0-5	0-0	3-2	1-4	2-1	5-0	1-0	*	2-0	1-0	3-0	1-1	4-2	1-0
17. Slade G.	2-4	6-0	2-0	1-1	2-0	2-2	3-1	2-0	2-5	3-1	2-2	0-2	0-0	*	2-1	1-1	*	6-0	0-1	1-1	3-1	3-1
18. Thamesmead	1-0	1-1	1-1	1-2	3-2	2-2	1-0	3-2	0-5	0-1	2-2	3-2	0-3	*	0-4	0-3	1-2	*	2-2	3-2	1-3	0-4
19. Thames Poly	1-3	1-1	1-1	1-2	2-3	2-1	1-1	2-2	2-4	1-3	1-0	0-1	0-1	*	3-0	0-0	1-0	0-1	*	1-3	0-5	0-1
20. Tonbridge	1-1	4-0	3-1	1-0	5-0	5-1	6-1	4-1	1-0	0-0	2-0	1-3	2-0	*	1-2	0-0	4-2	1-0	2-1	*	4-0	2-2
21. Tun. Wells	2-2	1-0	2-1	5-2	1-1	1-0	3-1	1-3	2-1	3-0	0-1	1-2	3-3	*	0-4	2-1	2-2	6-2	3-2	0-1	*	1-0
22. Whitstable	2-3	0-0	3-1	2-0	2-0	3-1	2-0	4-0	2-4	1-0	2-2	2-3	2-0	3-0	1-1	0-1	2-2	1-0	7-2	2-1	3-0	*

Nb. Metropolitan Police (Hayes) withdrew in mid-season. Record expunged and shown for interest only.

WINSTONLEAD KENT LEAGUE DIVISION ONE CUP 1991-92

First Round

Greenwich Borough v Thamesmead Town	0-2	Beckenham Town v Danson Furness United	1-0
Kent Police v Darenth Heathside	1-2	Whitstable v Sheppey	0-0*(aet)*,2-2*(aet, 6-5 pens)*
Crockenhill v Chatham T.	3-3*(aet)*,4-0	Slade Green v Corinthian	2-3

Second Round

Cray Wanderers v Thamesmead Town	2-2*(aet)*	Beckenham Town v Tonbridge A.F.C.	0-2
Ramsgate v Darenth Heathside	3-2	Metropolitan Police (Hayes) v Faversham Town	0-3
Tunbridge Wells v Herne Bay	1-0	Whitstable Town v Corinthian	4-1
Deal Town v Alma Swanley	1-2*(aet)*	Crockenhill v Thames Polytechnic	3-0

Third Round

Thamesmead Town v Tonbridge A.F.C.	1-3	Ramsgate v Faversham Town	0-1*(aet)*
Tunbridge Wells v Whitstable Town	2-5*(aet)*	Alma Swanley v Crockenhill	0-1

Semi-Finals

Tonbridge A.F.C. v Faversham Town	2-1	Whitstable Town v Crockenhill	1-0

Final (at Dover Athletic FC)

Tonbridge A.F.C. v Whitstable Town   2-1*(aet)*

Tonbridge celebrate their League Cup final victory over Whitstable Town at the Crabble.

WINSTONLEAD KENT LEAGUE DIVISION TWO CUP 1991-92

First Round

Faversham Town Res v Dover Ath. Res	1-2	Deal Town Res v Hastings Town Res	0-5
Sittingbourne Res v Folkestone Invicta	0-5		

Second Round

Chatham Town Res v Sheppey Utd Res	3-5	Canterbury City Res v Hastings Town Res	3-2
Folkestone Invicta v Beckenham Town Res	12-0	Darenth Heathside Res v Ashford Town Res	0-1
Cray Wdrs Res v Thamesmead T. Res	4-5*(aet)*	Whitstable Town Res v Hythe Town Res	1-0*(aet)*
Thames Polytechnic Res v Ramsgate Res	3-4	Dover Ath. Res v Herne Bay Res	2-0

Third Round

Dover Athletic Res v Sheppey United Res	5-1	Canterbury City Res v Folkestone Invicta	1-3
Ashford Town Res *W/O* Cray Wanderers Res		Whitstable Town Res v Alma Swanley Res	5-1

Semi-Finals

Dover Athletic Res v Folkestone Invicta	0-3	Ashford Town Res v Whitstable Town Res	0-2

Final

Folkestone Invicta v Whitstable Town Reserves   1-0

ALMA SWANLEY

Chairman: Mike Dougherty   **President:** Margaret Isley.
Secretary: Ron Moore, 11 Oaklands Close, West Kingsdown, Kent TN15 6EA (0474 85215).
Manager: Franny Fitzpatrick   **Asst Manager:** John Mears   **Press Officer:** Dave Clark.
Ground: Green Court Road, Crockenhill, Kent (0322 666120).
Directions: From junction of M25 & M20 follow signs for Swanley. Left at Crockenhill turning, then first right after motorway crossing. 500 yards from Swanley (BR).
Seats: 100   **Cover:** 200   **Capacity:** 1,500   **Floodlights:** No   **Founded:** 1963.
Colours: Red & black   **Change Colours:** Red/white/red   **Nickname:** Alma.
Midweek matchday: Tuesday   **Record Gate:** 1,500 v Enfield, London Snr Cup 76-77.
Sponsors: Hanover Park Group PLC   **Previous Lges:** Gtr London 65-71/ L'don Spartan 75-82
Programme: 12 pages, 20p   **Programme Editor:** Mike Dougherty
Clubhouse: Open every day.   **Previous Ground:** Swanley Rec.   **Hons:** Spartan 73-74
(Lg Cup 73-74, Benevolent Cup 73-74), Kent Snr Tphy 75-76, Kent Lg 85-86 (Lg Cup 88-89 (R-up 90-91)).

BECKENHAM TOWN

President: Fred Starmer   **Chairman:** Les Chandler.
Vice-President: Pat Quinn   **Treasurer:** Bernie Holloway.
Secretary: Peter J Palmer, 107 Wentworth Rd, West Croydon, Surrey CR0 3HZ (081 689 2134).
Manager: Kevin Sugrue   **Asst Manager:** Bob Chilvers
Ground: Eden Park Avenue, Beckenham, Kent (081 650 1066).
Directions: 1 mile west of town off A214, 2 mins walk from Eden Park (BR), 194 & 366 LT buses stop nearby.
Seats: 60   **Cover:** 60   **Capacity:** 2,000   **Floodlights:** No   **Founded:** 1971.
Colours: All red   **Change Colours:** Blue & white   **Nickname:** Town.
Midweek matchday: Wednesday   **Record Gate:** 692 v Greenwich Borough, League 1988.
Sponsors: F M Conway Ltd   **Previous Ground:** Stanhope Grove, Beckenham.
Previous Leagues: South East London Amtr 71-73/ Metropolitan 73-75/ London Spartan 75-82.
Programme: 24 pages, 20p   **Programme Editor:** Craig Ralph.
Clubhouse: Open Tuesday and Thursday evenings, Sunday lunchtimes, and matchdays. Bar and dance area. Pool tables and fruit machines.   **Hons:** London Spartan Lg Cup R-up 77-78 78-79, Kent Snr Tphy R-up 81-82, Kent Lg Cup R-up 84-85 (Div 2 Cup R-up 90-91).

CHATHAM TOWN

Chairman: P Enright   **President:**
Secretary: Brian Burcombe, 4 Hallwood Close, Parkwood, Rainham, Kent ME8 9NT (0634 363419).
Manager: Barry Zilwood   **Asst Manager:** Les Warren.
Ground: Maidstone Road Sports Ground, Maidstone Road, Chatham, Kent (0634 812194).
Directions: M2, A229 Chatham turn-off, follow signs to Chatham, ground one and a half miles on right opposite garage. 1 mile from Chatham (BR).
Seats: 500   **Cover:** 1,000   **Capacity:** 5,000   **Floodlights:** Yes   **Founded:** 1882.
Colours: Red & white hoops/black   **Change Colours:** Yellow & green   **Nickname:** Chats.
Midweek matchday: Tuesday   **Record Gate:** 5,000 v Gillingham, 1980.
Sponsors: Topps Scaffolding   **Previous Ground:** Great Lines, Chatham 1882-90.
Previous Lges: Southern (several spells)/ Aetolian 59-64/ Metropolitan 64-68/ Kent (Sev. spells).
Programme: 12 pages, 50p   **Programme Editor:** Trevor Busby
Clubcuse: Matchdays and functions   **Previous Names:** Chatham FC/ Medway FC (1970s).
Hons: Kent Lg(9) 1894-95 03-05 24-25 26-27 71-72 73-74 76-77 79-80 (R-up 02-03 23-24 25-26 70-71 74-75 80-81, Lg Cup 71-72 76-77 (R-up(3)), Thames & Medway Comb.(5) 1896-97 04-06 19-20 23-24, FA Cup QF (beat Nottm Forest 2-0 en route) 1888-89, FA Tphy 3rd Rd 70-71, Kent Snr Cup 1888-89 1904-05 10-11 18-19, Kent Snr Shield 19-20.

CORINTHIAN

Chairman: **President:**
Secretary: Mr Ron Brown, 10 Pincroft Wood, New Barn, Longfield, Kent DA3 7HB (0474 707186).
Manager: Tony Sitford   **Asst Manager:**
Ground: Gay Dawn, Valley Road, Fawkham, Nr Dartford, Kent DA3 8LZ (0474 7559).
Directions: A2 off Longfield, take Fawkham Road - ground one mile on left. Or, A20 to Fawkham Green then ground one and a half miles on right. One and a quarter miles from Longfield (BR).
Seats: 134   **Cover:** 175   **Capacity:** 2,000   **Floodlights:** Yes   **Founded:** 1972.
Colours: Green & white/white   **Change Colours:** All royal blue   **Nickname:** None.
Midweek matchday: Tuesday   **Record Gate:** 480 v Spurs, friendly 1979.
Sponsors: None   **Clubhouse:** Bar, kitchen, large lounge.
Programme: 12 pages, 30p   **Programme Editor:** TBA
Previous Grounds: None.   **Previous League:** Southern 85-91.
Hons: Essex AFA Snr Cup 82-83, Kent Snr Tphy 83-84 86-87, Fort Lauderdale International Tournament 84-85, Kent Intermediate Cup 90-91.

CRAY WANDERERS

Chairman: B W Faukner   **President:** A C Walker   **Press Officer:** Greg Mann
Secretary: Mr Kerry Phillips, 15 Watling Street, Bexleyheath, Kent DA6 7QJ (0322 554108).
Manager: Eddie Davies   **Comm. Mgr:** John Linton   **Physio:** John Dunbar.
Ground: Oxford Road, Sidcup, Kent (081 300 9201).
Directions: Between Sidcup High Street and Footscray High Street. Three quarters of a mile from Sidcup (BR).
Seats: 20   **Cover:** 1,000   **Capacity:** 3,000   **Floodlights:** No   **Founded:** 1860.
Colours: Amber & black   **Change Colours:** Navy & white   **Nickname:** Wands.
Midweek matchday: Tuesday   **Record Gate:** 1,500 v Stamford, FA Vase 79-80.
Sponsors: Mobike Bromley   **Clubhouse:** Open matchdays, Tuesdays & Thursday.
Programme: 20 pages for donation   **Programme Editor:** Robert McCarthy
Previous Leagues: Kent Amtr/ West Kent/ Southern Suburban/ London 20-34 51-59/ Aetolian 59-64/ Gtr London 64-66/ Metropolitan 66-71/ London Metropolitan 71-75/ London Spartan 75-78.
Previous Grounds: Star Lane/ Tothills/ Twysden/ Fordcroft/ Grassmeade, St Mary Cray.
Hons: London Lg(2) 56-58 (Lg Cup 54-55), Aetolian Lg 62-63 (Lg Cup 63-64), Gtr London Lg 65-66 (Lg Cup(2) 64-66), Metropolitan Lg Cup 70-71 (Amtr Cup(2) 66-68), London Spartan Lg(2) 76-78, Kent Lg 01-02 80-81 (R-up 79-80 90-91, Lg Cup 83-84), Kent Amtr Cup(4) 30-31 62-65.

Alma Swanley FC 1991-92. Photo - Dave West.

Beckenham Town FC 1991-92. Photo - Dave West.

Corinthian 0, U.S. Graveslines 2 - Friendly 3/8/91. The bounce of the ball beats Frenchman Emmanuel Deheunick, but Dave Penton reads it correctly and beats his man. Photo. Photo - Mike Floate.

CROCKENHILL

Chairman: Alan Parker   **President:** H Miller   **Treasurer:** V M Nicholls.
Secretary: TBA.
Manager: Tim Kite   **Asst Manager:**
Ground: 'Wested', Eynsford Road, Crockenhill, Kent (0322 62097).
Directions: Just off M25 junction 3, off Swanley by-pass. Just over a mile from Swanley (BR). Bus 477.
Seats: 100   **Cover:** 100   **Capacity:** 1,500   **Floodlights:** No   **Founded:** 1946.
Colours: Red/white/black   **Change Colours:** All blue   **Nickname:** Crocks.
Midweek matchday: Tuesday   **Record Gate:** 800 v Maidstone, Kent Amtr Cup 1948.
Sponsors: Erith Sports   **Previous Lges:** Kent Amtr/ Aetolian 59-64/ Gtr London 64-68
Programme: 12 pages, 20p   **Programme Editor:** Secretary.
Players progressing to Football League: Tony Cascarino.
Clubhouse: Friday & Saturday nights and matchdays. On-ground licensed bar.
Hons: Kent Lg 82-83 (R-up 84-85), Kent Snr Tphy 80-81, Kent Amtr Cup R-up, West Kent Snr Cup, Sevenoaks Charity Cup.

DANSON FURNESS UNITED

President: Steve Brown   **Treasurer:** Paul Roberts.
Secretary: Alan H Nicholls, 16 Blackthorn Grove, Bexleyheath, Kent DA7 4EH (081 304 3121).
Manager: Alan Sutherland   **Asst Manager:** Dave Hamer
Ground & Directions: As Alma Swanley FC (see page 716).   **Founded:** 1991.
Colours: Sky/navy/white   **Change Colours:** All red   **Nickname:** None.
Midweek matchday: Tuesday   **Record Gate:** 350 v Newport I.O.W., FA Vase 1980.
Sponsors: S H E Printers
Previous Names: Danson (Bexley Borough)(founded 1941), Furness United. Clubs merged in 1991.
Previous Grounds: Randell Down Road 41-53/ Eltham Road 53-60/ Crook Log, Brampton Road 60-92.
Previous Leagues: Sidcup & District/ South East London Amateur/ London Spartan 82-87. *Furness Utd: South London Alliance (pre-1991).*
Programme: 8 pages, 20p   **Programme Editor:** Fabio Rossi.
Clubhouse: Matchdays and functions   **Hons:** S.E. Amtr Lg Cup R-up 60-61.

DARENTH HEATHSIDE

Chairman: Dave Munn   **Press Officer:** Martin Wiseman (0689 833083).
Secretary: Tony Kingshott, 67 Avondale Rd, Bromley, Kent BR1 4HS (081 460 4834).
Manager: Andy Sawyer   **Asst Manager:** Dave Wadhams.
Ground: Heathside Club, Horton Road, South Darenth, Dartford, Kent (0322 863554).
Directions: A2 or A20, then A225 and turn off opposite Farningham Road BR station (5 minutes walk). Ground opposite 'The Sun' PH next to brick viaduct.
Seats: 140   **Cover:** 140   **Capacity:** 2,000   **Floodlights:** No   **Founded:** 1951.
Colours: Blue & white   **Change Colours:** All yellow   **Nickname:** None.
Midweek matchday: Tuesday   **Previous Name:** Heathside Sports.
Sponsors: Geoffrey Osborne Ltd   **Clubhouse:** Tuesdays, matchdays and other events.
Previous Lges: Dartford/ Gtr London 68-71/ London Spartan 75-78.
Record Gate: 900 v Internationals XI, Silver Jubilee match, 1976.
Programme: 8 pages, 10p   **Programme Editor:** Martin Wiseman
Hons: Kent Lg Cup R-up 80-81 85-86 (Div 2 Cup R-up 78-79), Kent Intermediate Cup 74-75.

DEAL TOWN

Chairman: J M Ullman   **Treasurer:** Colin Adams.
Secretary: Jim Nokes, 51 Celtic Road, Deal, Kent CT14 9EF (0304 36847).
Manager: Jim Nokes   **Asst Manager:** Eddie Pickford   **Physio:** Steve Trice
Ground: Charles Sports Ground, Mill Road, Deal, Kent (0304 375623).
Directions: A258 through Walmer, left into Cornwell Road, into Hamilton Road, into Manor Road, then right into St Leonards Road. Ground 100 yards on right.
Seats: 500   **Cover:** 1,500   **Capacity:** 2,000   **Floodlights:** Yes   **Founded:** 1908.
Colours: All yellow   **Change Colours:** Black & white hoops   **Nickname:** Town.
Midweek matchday: Wednesday   **Record Gate:** 4,000 v Billy Wright showbiz XI 1979.
Sponsors: Franks Snooker Club   **Clubhouse:** Matchdays & functions. Supporters Club, bar.
Programme: 20 pages, 20p   **Programme Editor:** Dave Clements.
Previous Grounds: **Prev. Lges:** Aetolian 59-63/ Southern 63-66/ Gtr London 66-71
Hons: Kent Lg 52-53 (R-up 88-89, Lg Cup 55-56 81-82 (SF 88-89 89-90), Kent Snr Tphy R-up 82-83 90-91, Gtr London Lg Cup 67-68, Aetolian Lg R-up 59-60.

FAVERSHAM TOWN

Chairman: Terry Rowland   **President:** R Neame
Secretary: Mr R C Yorke, 27 Churchill Way, Faversham, Kent ME13 7QX (0795 534328).
Manager: Paul Prior   **Assistant Manager/Physio:** Roger Stephen.
Ground: Salters Lane, Faversham, Kent (0795 532738).
Directions: On A2 (Canterbury road) just west of town.
Seats: 350   **Cover:** 1,000   **Capacity:** 2,000   **Floodlights:** Yes   **Founded:** 1901.
Colours: Blue & white   **Change Colours:** Red & white   **Nickname:** Town.
Midweek matchday: Tuesday   **Record Gate:** 1,400 v Sheppey United, 1949.
Sponsors: Motogold U.K.   **Clubhouse:** Matchdays, Tuesdays & Thursdays and functions.
Programme: 10 pages with entry   **Programme Editor:** C Young.
Previous Ground: Gordon Square (pre'47)
Previous Leagues: Aetolian 59-64/ Metropolitan 64-71/ Athenian 71-76.
Hons: Kent Lg 69-70 70-71 77-78 89-90 (R-up 87-88, Lg Cup 70-71 90-91 (R-up 82-83)), Kent Snr Tphy 76-77 77-78 (R-up 87-88 88-89), Kent Amtr Cup 56-57 58-59 71-72 72-73 73-74.

Crockenhill FC 1991-92. Photo - Dave West.

Danson Furness United 1991-92. Photo - Dave West.

Faversham Town, pictured at the start of the season with the League Cup (won in 1990-91), and the League Charity Shield. Photo - Dave West.

FOLKESTONE INVICTA

Chairman: T R Gulver   **President:**
Secretary: B Goodsell, 20 Longfield, Smallhythe Rd, Tenterden, Kent TN30 7HH (0580 4725).
Manager: Gary Stanliforth   **Asst Manager:** Terry Collins   **Coach:** Curly Russell
Ground: The New Pavilion, Cheriton Road, Folkestine, Kent CT20 5JU (0303 57461).
Directions: On the A20 behind Presto foodstore, midway between Folkestone Central and Folkestone West BR stations.
Seats: 900   **Cover:** 3,500   **Capacity:** 4,000   **Floodlights:** Yes   **Founded:** 1946.
Colours: Amber & black/black/black   **Change Colours:** Red & white/white/red **Nickname:**
Midweek matchday: Tuesday
Record Gate: 1,211 v Brighton, friendly 26/9/91. *Ground record; 7,801 Folkestone v Margate, Kent Senior Cup 1958.*
Sponsors: **Previous Lges:** FCN Kent County (pre-1991).
Programme: Yes   **Programme Editor:**
Previous Ground: South Road, Kent (pre-1991).
Clubhouse:
Hons: Kent Lg Div 2 90-91.

GREENWICH BOROUGH

President: T H M Edwaards   **Chairman:** B Thompson.
Secretary: Ms Denise Richmond, 7 Castlecombe Rd, Mottingham, London SE9 4AU (081 851 4169).
Manager: Dave Waight   **Asst Manager:** Doug Francis
Ground & Directions: As Erith & Belvedere FC (see page 523).   **Founded:** 1928.
Colours: Red & black   **Change Colours:** Black & white   **Nickname:** Boro.
Midweek matchday: Tuesday   **Previous Ground:** Harrow Meadow, Eltham (pre'92).
Record Gate: 2,000 v Charlton, floodlight opening, 1978 (at Harrow Meadow).
Sponsors: Pelgary Ltd   **Previous Names:** London Borough of Greenwich.
Previous Leagues: South London Alliance/ Kent Amateur/ London Spartan 77-84.
Programme: 8 pages, 20p   **Programme Editor:** Denise Richmond.
Clubhouse:
Hons: London Spartan Lg 79-80 (Lg Cup 82-83), Kent Lg 86-87 87-88 (Lg Cup 84-85 86-87), Kent Snr Tphy 84-85, FA Vase 5th Rd 89-90.

HERNE BAY

Chairman: M Todd   **President:** J Hodkinson   **Treasurer:** R Bates.
Secretary: Tim Knibb, 57 Beatrice Rd, Margate, Kent CT9 5SW (0843 227215).
Manager: Trevor Gowan   **Asst Manager:** D Elliot   **Physio:** J Hodkinson.
Ground: Winch's Field, Stanley Gardens, Herne Bay, Kent (0227 374156).
Directions: Leave A299 at Herne Bay r'bout, 2nd left, 1st left. Half mile from Herne Bay (BR); down Station Approach, 1st right (Spencer Road), 2nd right.
Seats: 250   **Cover:** 1,500   **Capacity:** 5,000   **Floodlights:** No   **Founded:** 1886.
Colours: Blue & white stripes/blue   **Change Colours:** White (claret trim)   **Nickname:** The Bay.
Midweek matchday: Tuesday   **Previous Ground:** Memorial Park 1886-1953.
Sponsors: Herne Bay Snooker Club, Waterways Caravan Park.
Clubhouse: Open most evenings and matchdays.
Previous Lges: Kent Amtr/ Thanet/ East Kent/ Aetolian 59-64/ Athenian 64-74.
Record Gate: 2,303 v Margate, FA Cup 1970.
Programme: 28 pages, 35p   **Programme Editor/Press Officer:** Secretary.
Hons: Kent Lg 91-92 (Div 2 62-63 63-64, Lg Cup R-up 78-79, Div 2 Cup 53-54), Kent Snr Tphy 78-79, Kent Amtr Cup 57-58 (R-up 58-59 33-64 68-69 72-73), Aetolian Lg Div 2 62-63 63-64 (Lg Cup R-up 62-63, Div 2 Cup 62-63 63-64), Athenian Lg Div 2 70-71 (Lg Cup 66-67), Kent Amtr Lg Cup 53-54 54-55, Thames & Medway Comb. Cup R-up 61-62, FA Cup 4th Cup Qual. Rd 70-71 86-87.

KENT POLICE

Chairman: P Hermitage   **President:** P Condon, Chief Constable.
Secretary: J C Bateman, Christmas Cottage, Lavender Square, Hawkhurst TN18 4DX (0580 752809).
Manager: Duncan McLachlan   **Asst Mgr/Coach:** Staurt McFaden   **Press Officer:** Secretry
Ground: Police H.Q., Sutton Rd, Maidstone, Kent (0831 845163).
Directions: Leave Maidstone on Hastings Road, then onto A274 to Rye Road.
Seats: 40   **Cover:** 60   **Capacity:** 3,000   **Floodlights:** No   **Founded:** 1951.
Colours: Royal blue   **Change Colours:** Blue & white   **Nickname:** None.
Midweek matchday: Tues/Wed.   **Record Gate:** Unknown.
Sponsors: **Previous League:** Kent Amateur.
Programme: 6 pages, £1 with entry   **Programme Editor:** Secreatary.
Clubhouse: Use HQ bar on matchdays. New changing room/ refreshment facilities adjacent to pitch.
Hons: Kent Lg R-up 69-70 (Lg Cup 69-70).

RAMSGATE

Chairman: R Lawson   **President:**
Secretary: T Atkins, 8 Manston Rd, Ramsgate, Kent CT11 0RB (0843 595632).
Manager: Bob Wickens   **Press Officer:** Ivor Thomas (0843 587047).
Ground: Southwood Football Ground, Prices Avenue, Ramsgate, Kent (0843 591662).
Directions: Coming from London on A229, join A253 into Ramsgate - left into Netherhill at r'bout. Right into Ashburnham Rd, then right into Southwood Rd. 1 mile from Ramsgate (BR).
Seats: 500   **Cover:** 1,000   **Capacity:** 5,000   **Floodlights:** Yes   **Founded:** 1946.
Colours: Red & white   **Change Colours:** Green & white   **Nickname:** Rams.
Midweek matchday: Tues/Wed   **Record Gate:** 5,200 v Margate, 56-57.
Sponsors: Godden & Lawson Civil Engineers.
Clubhouse: Open matchdays & functions. Two bars, two pool tables, darts.
Programme: 16 pages, 20p   **Programme Editor:** Ivor Thomas (0843 587047).
Previous Name: Ramsgate Athletic   **Previous Leagues:** Southern 59-75.
Hons: Kent Lg 49-50 55-56 56-57 (Lg Cup 48-49), Kent I'mediate Cup 54-55, Kent Snr Cup 63-64, Thames & Medway Cup 60-61, Kent Snr Shield 60-61, Kent Floodlit Tphy 69-70, Kent Snr Tphy(2) 87-89.

Folkestone Invicta, Winstonlead Kent League Division Two Champions 1991-92. Photo - Folkestone Herald/Citizen.

Greenwich Borough. Back Row (L/R): Dave Waight (Manager), Paul Challis, Phil Yardley, Mick Potter, Danny Keable, Jeff Hindmarsh, Vic Barton, Dave Piggott, Barry Poole, Danny Gee (Physio). Front: George Henning, Gary Kitt, Mark Edwards, Brian Inglis, Paul Roberts, Stuart Kitt, Steve Davis, Dean Levy. Photo - Dave West.

Herne Bay celebrate their Kent League championship with an exciting 4-2 win against Thames Polytechnic in front of a bumper crowd at Winch's Field. Here Andy Ballantyne nets the Bay's second, past the desperate lunge of Poly's Steve Fribbens. Photo - Gavin Ellis.

SHEPPEY UNITED

Chairman: Dave Whitton   **President:**
Secretary: P R Sharrock, 35 Summerhill Ave., Minster, Sheerness, Kent ME13 3LB (0795 872336).
Manager: Tommy Sampson   **Press Officer:** Secretary.
Ground & Directions: As Faversham Town FC (see page 718).   **Founded:** 1890.
Colours: Red & white/white   **Change colours:** All blue
Midweek matchday: Tuesday   **Nickname:** Islanders or Ites.
Sponsors: **Previous Name:** Sheppey Athletic.
Programme: 16 pages, 20p   **Programme Editor:** TBA.
Previous Ground: Botany Road, St Georges Avenue, Sheerness (pre-1992).
Record Gate: 4,000 v Sittingbourne, Kent Senior Trophy 1927 (at Botany Road).
Previous Leagues: Southern 1894-1901 84-91/ Kent 01-27 32-59 72-84/ Aetolian 59-64/ Gtr London 64-65/ Metropolitan Lg 65-71.
Players progressing to Football League: E C Harper (England, Blackburn, Spurs, Preston).
Hons: Kent Lg(6) 05-07 27-28 72-73 74-75 78-79 (R-up 03-04 04-05 77-78 83-84, Lg Cup 75-76 78-79, Div 2(reserves) 32-33 84-85 (R-up 1894-95 1979-80)), Thames & Medway Comb. 08-09 12-13 22-23 25-26 28-29 55-56, Kent Amtr Cup 45-46 51-52, Kent Snr Shield 77-78, Kent Snr Cup R-up(3), Gtr London Lg 64-65, FA Cup 6th Qual. Rd 19-20, FA Tphy 1st Rd Proper 85-86.

SLADE GREEN

President: W Dudley   **Chairman:** B B Smith.
Secretary: Bruce W Smith, 15 Gumping Rd, Orpington, Kent BR5 1RX (0689 58782).
Manager: Todd Dowling   **Asst Manager:** Tony Carley   **Press Officer:** Robert Smith
Ground: The Small Glen, 35 Moat Lane, Slade Green, Erith, Kent (0322 349018).
Directions: 300 yards from Slade Green BR station.
Capacity: 2,000   **Seats:** 20   **Cover:** 200   **Floodlights:** Yes   **Founded:** 1946.
Colours: White & green   **Change Colours:** All yellow   **Nickname:** The Green
Midweek matchday: Tuesday   **Clubhouse:** Every evening & matchays.
Sponsors: Russell Stoneham Estates   **Previous Name:** Slade Green Athletic.
Clubhouse: Every evening, matchdays   **Previous Leagues:** Dartford/ Kent Amtr/ London 61-64.
Programme: 24 pages, £1.50 with entry   **Programme Editor:** Fred Stokes, Robert Smith.
Hons: Kent Snr Tphy 91-92 (R-up 80-81), Kent Lg Cup 82-83.

THAMESMEAD TOWN

Chairman: Jim Adie   **Treasurer:** Vic Smith   **President:**
Secretary: Paul Bayne, 313 Raymond Postgate Ct, Tawney Rd, Thamesmead, London SE28 8DR (081 311 1276).
Manager: Gerry Bright   **Asst Manager:** Kelvin Bright   **Physio:** Alan Martin.
Ground: Bayliss Avenue, Thamesmead, London SE28 8NS (081 311 4211).   **Directions:** From Abbey Wood (BR) north east along Harrow Manor Way, into Crossway at 3rd r'bout, Bayliss Av. is 3rd right.
Seats: 100   **Cover:** 100   **Capacity:** 1,000   **Floodlights:** Due   **Founded:** 1969.
Colours: Green & black   **Change Colours:** Red & white   **Nickname:** The Mead.
Midweek matchday: Tuesday   **Previous Ground:** Meridian Ground, Greenwich.
Sponsors: Woolwich Building Society/ Thamesbank Insurance Brokers.
Clubhouse: Open every evenings and weekend afternoons and matchdays. Double bar, lounge, dancefloor, children's games room, video machines, kitchen.
Prev. Lge: London Spartan 80-91.   **Record Gate:** 300 v Wimbledon, ground opening 1988.
Programme: **Programme Editor:**
Hons: Four promotions, and nine trophies (including London FA and Kent FA Cups) during progress through London Spartan Intermediate Divisions, 1980-87.

TONBRIDGE A.F.C.

Chairman: Ken Shellito   **President:** Phil Emblem.
Secretary: Steve Wardhaugh, 39 Badger Rd, Lordswood, Chatham, Kent ME5 8TY (0634 669154).
Trainer: Peter Battell   **Coach:** Carl Laraman   **Newsline:** 0898 800 661.
Ground: Longmead Stadium, Darenth Avenue, Tonbridge, Kent TN10 3JW (0732 352417/ 358868).
Directions: From Tonbridge BR station, through High Street, up Shipbourne Rd (A227) to 'The Pinnacles' pub. Darenth Avenue immediately left, ground at bottom approx. 1 mile.
Seats: 200   **Cover:** 1,000   **Capacity:** 5,000   **Floodlights:** Yes   **Founded:** 1948.
Colours: Royal blue & white   **Change Colours:** Yellow & blue   **Nickname:** Angels.
Sponsors: Crest Sporting Entreprises.   **Midweek matchday:** Tuesday   **Club Shop:** Yes.
Previous League: Southern 48-89.   **Prev. Ground:** The Angel 48-80.   **Metal Badges:** Yes.
Programme: 20 pages, 30p   **Editors:** Ian White, Tom Spence, Steve Wardhaugh, Nigel Clark
Record Gate: 1,463 v Yeovil Town, FA Cup 4th Qualifying Round 26/10/91. *At the Angel Ground: 8,236 v Aldershot, FA Cup 1st Round 1951.*   **Previous Names:** Tonbridge Angels, Tonbridge FC.
Clubhouse: Licensed bar, tea bar, open matchdays, Tues/Thurs evenings and Saturday lunchtimes.
Hons: Kent Lg Cup(2), Southern Lg Cup R-up(2)(SF(1)), Kent Snr Cup 64-65 74-75 (R-up(2)), Kent Snr Shield 51-52 55-56 57-58 58-59 63-64, FA Cup 1st Rd Proper 50-51 51-52 52-53 67-68 72-73.

TUNBRIDGE WELLS

Chairman: P C Wager   **Team & Commercial Manager:** Mark Higgs.
Secretary: P C Wager, 46 Mereworth Rd, Tunbridge Wells, Kent TN4 9PL (0892 24182).
Coach: Tom Mead/ Tony Atkins   **Press Officer:** R Bonny (0892 31898).   **Physio:** George Piper
Ground: Culverden Stadium, Culverden Down, Tunbridge Wells, Kent (0892 20517).
Directions: Leaving town on main Tonbridge road (A26), turn left opposite 'Red Lion' pub. 1 mile from Tunbridge Wells Central (BR). Served by any Tunbridge Wells-Tonbridge bus.
Seats: 300   **Cover:** 700   **Capacity:** 5,000   **Floodlights:** No   **Club Shop:** Yes.
Colours: Red & white   **Change Colours:** All blue   **Nickname:** Wells.
Midweek matchday: Wednesday   **Record Gate:** 967 v Maidstone United, FA Cup 1969.
Sponsors: Private Patients Plan.   **Clubhouse:** Open matchdays & functions.
Founded: 1886 (present club 1967)   **Previous Leagues:** None.
Programme: 16 pages, 20p   **Programme Editor:** Secretary.
Previous Names: None. *predecessors: Tunbridge Wells 1886-1910 47-50/ Tunbridge Wells Rangers 03-09 63-67/ Tunbridge Wells United 51-62.*   **Previous Grounds:** Down Lane 1906/ Combley Park 06-10/ Swiss Cottage 06-14/Down Farm 19-39/ St Johns 47-50/ Eridge Road 50-51.
Hons: Kent Lg 84-85 (R-up 68-69, Lg Cup 74-75 77-78 85-86 87-88), Kent Snr Tphy R-up 85-86.

Thamesmead Town FC 1991-92. Photo - Dave West.

Tonbridge A.F.C., Kent League Cup winners 1991-92. Back Row (L/R - players' names only): Gary Valli, Dean Finch, Steve Clarke, Wayne Finch, Billy Thompson, Paul Collins, G Wallace. Front: Lloyd Hurne, Roly Graham, Matt Broadway, P Brazil, Alan Baber, Lee Thompson. Photo - Mike Floate.

Thames Poly's Peter Ellis is beaten by a 25 yard shot in a 0-3 home defeat by Tonbridge. Photo - Keith Gillard.

WHITSTABLE TOWN

Chairman: J C Brownett   **President:** James Lambie
Secretary: Mrs Sylvia J Davies, 5 Old Bridge Rd, Whitstable, Kent CT5 1RJ (0227 265646).
Manager: Peter Merritt   **Asst Mgr/Coach:** Malcolm Ainsley   **Physio:** Andy Harman
Ground: Belmont Road, Belmont, Whitstable, Kent (0227 266012).
Directions: From Thanet Way (A299) to Millstrood Rd. Ground at bottom of road, 400yds from Whitstable (BR).
Capacity: 2,000   **Cover:** 1,500   **Seats:** 500   **Floodlights:** Yes   **Founded:** 1885.
Colours: Red & white   **Change colours:** All green
Midweek matchday: Tuesday   **Nickname:** 'Oystermen', 'Reds', or 'Natives'.
Sponsors: D & J Tyres   **Previous Ground:** Saddlestons Field 1885-88.
Programme: 40 pages, 30p   **Programme Editor:** Paul Rivers.
Clubhouse: Social & Recreation Ground (substantially rebuilt & modernised in 1991), tea bar, hot & cold food.
Previous Names: Whitstable United (pre-1886)/ Whitstable Swifts 93-95/ Whitstable Town 95-1905/ Whitstable FC 08-66.
Previous Leagues: Kent 09-14 20-39 47-50/ East Kent/ Thanet/ Aetolian 59-60/ Gtr London 64-67/ Kent 01-27 32-59 72-84/ Aetolian 59-64/ Gtr London 64-65.
Hons: Kent Lg Div 2 27-28 33-34 49-50 (Lg Cup 79-80 (R-up 89-90 91-92)), Kent Amtr Lg East 60-61, Kent Amtr Cup 28-29, Kent Snr Tphy R-up 78-79 89-90, Gtr London Lg Cup R-up 65-66.

Whitstable Town, Kent League Cup Runners-up 1991-92. Back Row (L/R): P Merritt (Manager), W Godden, G Clark, D Walton, P Lawrence, S Cairns, G Record. Front: P Venn, K Rolls, L Spokes, L Horton, T Timms, R Mason, D Down. Photo - Dennis Nicholson.

KENT LEAGUE DIVISION ONE TEN-YEAR RECORD

	82/3	83/4	84/5	85/6	86/7	87/8	88/9	89/90	90/1	91/2
Alma Swanley	11	13	11	1	3	12	6	5	8	5
Beckenham Town	9	8	4	15	15	8	17	12	14	14
Chatham Town	7	-	-	-	-	-	19	16	12	19
Cray Wanderers	8	4	5	14	10	7	7	18	2	18
Crockenhill	1	6	16	3	2	19	13	15	15	16
Danson Furness United	-	-	-	-	-	15	14	17	18	20
Darenth Heathside	14	12	8	4	9	11	4	10	13	21
Deal Town	3	9	12	18	16	16	2	4	5	3
Faversham Town	13	10	7	6	17	2	3	1	6	2
Greenwich Borough	-	-	6	7	1	1	16	6	17	9
Herne Bay	6	7	13	11	5	18	20	14	3	1
Hythe Town	2	3	2	12	11	5	1	-	-	-
Kent Police	16	14	15	9	18	6	12	11	19	11
Medway (See Chatham Town)										
Metropolitan Police (Hayes)	-	-	9	13	14	13	15	19	20	w/d
Ramsgate	17	16	17	8	4	10	9	20	10	10
Sheppey United	10	2	-	-	-	-	-	-	21	6
Sittingbourne	4	1	3	2	6	4	5	2	1	-
Slade Green	12	11	14	17	12	14	10	9	9	8
Thames Polytechnic	-	-	-	10	13	17	18	13	16	15
Thamesmead Town	-	-	-	-	-	-	-	-	-	17
Tonbridge A.F.C.	-	-	-	-	-	-	-	-	3	4
Tunbridge Wells	5	5	1	5	7	9	11	7	11	13
Whitstable Town	15	15	10	16	8	3	8	8	7	7
Number of clubs	**17**	**16**	**17**	**18**	**18**	**19**	**20**	**20**	**21**	**22**

F.C.N. MUSIC KENT COUNTY LEAGUE

President: A E Farmer.
Chairman: C T C Windiate.
Hon. Secretary: J C Mugridge,
14 Cherry Tree Road, Tunbridge Wells, Kent TN2 5QA (0892 5211578).

Major changes have taken place in the League's constitution for 1992-93 with the formation of a new all-region Premier Division. Regional Divisions will now be numbered from one downwards, and talks are continuing with the Winstonlead Kent League with a view to the two leagues entering the Pyramid.

For the second season running, Oakwood won the Western Region Senior Division, with the Eastern Section Division being won by Lydd Town, also for the second successive year. One again the competition competed in the South Eastern Intermediate Inter-League competition, and despite a number of set-backs with players, they came second to Surrey having beaten both Essex and Sussex, drawn with Surrey and lost to Middlesex.

FCN Music, of Morley Road, Tonbridge, presented sponsorship monies to winning clubs at the AGM, and St Georges (Wrotham) from the Western Region won the top award of £500; £400 for being the overall fair-play winners with no sendings-off or cautions during the entire season, and £100 for being their division's fair-play winners. Oakwood were also among the winners collecting £100 for their championship success, the same amount for their division's fair-play award and £50 for being Challenge Cup runners-up.

The final of the FCN Music Challenge Cup took place at Gillingham's Priestfield Road, and Stansfeld Oxford & Bermondsey Club defeated Oakwood 4-2. Early in the season when Tonbridge were near the top of the Winstonlead Kent League, Stansfeld took them on in the Kent Senior Trophy and were not disgraced in losing 0-2. Stansfeld also played Erith & Belvedere in the Semi Finals of the West Kent Challenge Shield and lost by only the odd goal in three.

Manager of the Year was Martin Atkins of Western Region First Division side Wellcome (Saturday). His team played 37 Cup and League games winning the Kent Junior Cup Group B, never losing in the League, and losing only in the final of the Western Region Junior Cup competition.

J C Mugridge, League Secretary

Western Senior	P	W	D	L	F	A	PTS
Oakwood	24	14	8	2	39	24	50
Edenstone	24	14	5	5	49	30	*44
Stansfeld O & B.	24	13	3	8	51	37	42
Scott Spts & Soc.	24	12	4	8	42	36	40
V.C.D. Athletic	24	12	3	9	53	41	39
Sevenoaks Town	24	9	7	8	35	28	34
Aylesford P.M.	24	8	9	7	39	35	33
Bearsted	24	9	5	10	48	36	32
Greenways	24	9	4	11	49	51	31
Otford United	24	6	7	11	24	39	25
Borough United	24	8	1	15	28	63	25
Moonshot Athletic	24	5	6	13	33	51	21
Lordswood	24	4	4	16	30	49	16

* - Denotes 3 points deducted

Eastern Senior	P	W	D	L	F	A	PTS
Lydd	20	17	0	3	70	20	51
Phoenix Rovers	20	15	1	4	51	24	46
New Romney	20	13	2	5	51	28	41
Bromley Green	20	11	5	4	49	32	38
Woodnesborough	20	9	3	8	43	34	30
Rye United	20	7	3	10	29	32	24
Teynham & Lynsted	20	7	2	11	36	44	23
Kennington	20	6	4	10	35	52	22
Knatchbull	20	5	4	11	33	56	19
University of Kent	20	5	3	12	33	62	18
Walmer Rovers	20	0	3	17	11	57	3

Western Premier	P	W	D	L	F	A	PTS
Knockholt	24	14	7	3	61	29	49
Colts '85	24	14	6	4	58	35	48
Ex-Blues	24	12	9	3	57	30	45
Westerham	24	11	4	9	60	45	37
Sutton Athletic	24	10	7	7	41	34	37
Ten Em Bee	24	10	7	7	47	48	37
Rusthall	24	9	8	7	60	44	35
Platt United	24	7	6	11	43	55	27
Eltham Palace	24	7	6	11	39	64	27
Eynsford	24	6	8	10	40	40	26
Edenbridge Utd	24	5	8	11	46	62	23
Halstead	24	5	4	15	33	74	19
Paddock Wood T.	24	4	4	16	39	64	16

Eastern Premier	P	W	D	L	F	A	PTS
Broomfield Utd	22	18	2	2	87	20	56
Headcorn	22	15	4	3	95	26	49
Folkstone Inv. Res	22	14	3	5	60	31	45
Snowdon C.W.	22	12	4	6	62	43	40
Lydd Res	22	10	4	8	49	31	34
Sturry	22	10	4	8	56	41	34
Kennington Res	22	9	5	8	53	57	32
Bromley Green Res	22	7	3	12	58	71	24
New Romney Res	22	4	9	9	42	54	21
Knatchbull Res	22	4	2	16	32	100	14
Dymchurch	22	4	1	17	35	91	13
Swingfield & Dist.	22	3	3	16	38	92	12

Western Div. One	P	W	D	L	F	A	PTS
Wellcome (Sat.)	24	21	3	0	87	18	66
Fleetdown Utd	24	15	5	4	81	26	50
AFC Egerton	24	14	2	8	62	36	44
Stansfeld OB Res	24	11	6	7	41	33	39
Bearsted Res	24	13	5	6	41	47	*38
St Georges	24	11	4	9	50	52	37
Swanscombe Utd	23	11	3	9	54	52	36
Chislehurst	24	9	7	8	44	34	34
Lordswood Res	24	10	3	11	43	49	33
Tonbridge Invicta	24	9	1	14	35	47	28
Brasted/Sundridge	24	5	1	18	38	76	16
Chipstead	24	4	3	17	24	77	15
Sevenoaks T. Res	24	1	5	18	24	77	8

* - Denotes 3 points deducted

Western Div. Two	P	W	D	L	F	A	PTS
Strood County	23	20	2	1	88	23	62
The Railway (TW)	24	16	6	2	60	28	54
Tonbridge Rangers	24	16	6	2	59	29	54
Scott S. & S. Res	24	11	4	9	52	45	37
V.C.D. Ath. Res	24	9	6	9	53	41	33
Halls	24	10	1	13	57	58	31
Dunton Green	24	10	1	13	63	77	31
Old Bexleians	24	8	4	12	41	65	28
N.P.I.	24	8	3	13	47	49	27
Joyce Green	24	7	3	14	44	53	24
Edenstone Res	23	6	6	11	42	56	24
Otford Utd Res	24	4	5	15	28	66	17
Wickham Park	24	4	5	15	31	75	17

Strood County v Edenstone Reserves unplayed.

WESTERN SENIOR DIVISION RESULT CHART 1991/92

HOME TEAM		1	2	3	4	5	6	7	8	9	10	11	12	13
1.	Aylesford PM	*	2-2	0-1	2-2	2-2	4-1	2-2	0-0	3-0	2-1	2-2	0-3	2-0
2.	Bearsted	2-2	*	1-1	2-3	3-0	3-0	4-1	1-2	0-3	0-1	0-2	0-2	3-2
3.	Borough United	0-3	0-7	*	3-1	1-3	1-0	3-0	0-1	1-2	1-5	1-0	0-8	1-3
4.	Edenstone	1-1	2-1	4-1	*	3-3	3-1	1-0	0-2	3-0	1-0	2-2	4-1	3-0
5.	Greenways	1-2	4-3	4-0	1-4	*	4-0	1-0	0-1	0-4	0-3	1-3	1-1	6-2
6.	Lordswood	1-1	1-0	3-1	3-1	1-3	*	2-3	0-0	6-0	1-2	1-3	2-3	1-3
7.	Moonshot	5-3	0-2	4-1	2-3	4-2	2-2	*	0-0	1-1	2-2	0-3	0-3	0-2
8.	Ooakwood	1-3	2-2	3-1	0-0	4-3	2-0	3-1	*	3-1	4-3	1-0	2-4	0-0
9.	Otford United	0-3	0-3	0-1	1-0	3-2	0-0	0-0	2-3	*	0-2	2-2	1-1	1-0
10.	Scott Spts & Social	3-0	0-3	0-4	2-1	2-4	1-0	4-1	0-0	1-1	*	2-1	2-1	4-3
11.	Sevenoaks Town	1-0	3-2	4-0	0-2	0-1	2-0	1-0	1-1	1-1	0-0	*	0-2	0-2
12.	Stansfeld Ox. & Berm.	1-0	1-2	2-3	0-2	1-1	4-2	0-4	0-1	2-1	2-1	5-4	*	3-1
13.	V.C.D. Athletic	3-0	2-2	5-2	2-3	4-2	3-2	6-1	2-3	1-0	4-1	0-0	3-1	*

EASTERN SENIOR DIVISION RESULT CHART 1991/92

HOME TEAM		1	2	3	4	5	6	7	8	9	10	11
1.	Bromley Green	*	2-2	3-1	1-2	2-1	1-5	0-0	5-1	2-2	4-0	5-2
2.	Kennington	1-5	*	3-0	0-5	0-6	1-4	3-2	5-3	3-2	1-1	1-5
3.	Knatchbull	1-1	0-0	*	1-2	2-4	0-5	4-4	2-0	5-6	1-0	2-1
4.	Lydd	5-1	2-1	3-0	*	1-3	6-0	4-2	4-0	3-1	2-1	4-1
5.	New Romney	1-3	2-1	5-1	0-4	*	1-2	1-0	2-0	2-2	3-1	5-1
6.	Phoenix Rovers	2-1	1-1	6-1	2-3	2-0	*	2-3	2-0	2-0	2-0	2-1
7.	Rye United	0-0	1-2	4-0	0-1	0-1	1-2	*	2-1	0-1	2-0	1-0
8.	Teynham & Lynsted	1-3	2-1	3-3	3-2	1-3	0-4	3-1	*	3-0	4-1	0-3
9.	University of Kent	1-2	5-2	4-3	1-7	2-5	2-3	2-3	0-9	*	1-0	1-5
10.	Walmer Rovers	1-3	2-6	0-3	0-9	1-4	1-3	0-3	1-2	0-0	*	0-3
11.	Woodnesborough	3-5	2-1	2-3	2-1	2-2	1-0	5-0	0-0	3-0	1-1	*

WESTERN PREMIER DIVISION RESULT CHART 1991/92

HOME TEAM		1	2	3	4	5	6	7	8	9	10	11	12	13
1.	Colts '85	*	6-4	5-2	2-0	3-0	2-0	2-2	3-2	1-1	2-1	0-0	0-1	2-2
2.	Ednebridge United	1-0	*	2-3	0-0	2-2	2-2	1-1	4-1	3-1	4-3	1-5	3-3	0-1
3.	Eltham Palace	2-2	0-0	*	0-3	1-1	0-2	1-3	4-2	3-2	2-2	2-4	0-2	2-1
4.	Ex Blues	1-4	3-3	1-0	*	1-1	4-2	1-1	3-1	2-2	5-1	1-1	5-0	2-1
5.	Eynsford	0-1	5-4	2-0	1-1	*	1-2	0-2	1-0	8-1	3-2	1-3	2-2	0-1
6.	Halstead	0-2	3-2	3-3	2-2	0-5	*	0-4	1-3	4-2	0-6	0-2	2-2	3-5
7.	Knockholt	0-2	1-0	11-1	2-1	2-1	7-1	*	5-1	4-2	2-2	1-1	1-1	2-1
8.	Paddock Wood Town	4-3	3-6	2-3	1-4	1-0	2-3	1-3	*	0-0	3-3	3-4	1-3	2-1
9.	Platt United	3-4	4-2	4-2	1-5	4-1	3-0	1-1	3-2	*	2-5	1-1	1-1	2-0
10.	Rusthall	1-4	1-1	2-2	1-3	1-1	6-0	3-0	0-0	2-1	*	1-1	6-0	2-4
11.	Sutton Athletic	0-3	3-0	1-2	2-2	0-0	2-1	0-1	3-1	1-0	2-3	*	1-2	3-1
12.	Ten Em Bee	5-2	7-1	2-3	0-4	1-1	3-1	1-2	2-1	2-0	1-3	2-1	*	2-2
13.	Westerham	3-3	4-0	5-1	1-3	5-3	4-1	4-3	2-2	1-2	1-3	5-0	5-2	*

EASTERN PREMIER DIVISION RESULT CHART 1991/92

HOME TEAM		1	2	3	4	5	6	7	8	9	10	11	12
1.	Bromley Green Res	*	2-2	4-2	2-4	4-4	3-0	4-2	1-6	3-3	3-2	5-0	5-3
2.	Broomfield United	7-0	*	9-0	3-0	3-0	3-0	8-0	4-1	4-1	4-1	2-1	5-1
3.	Dymchurch	3-2	0-1	*	1-4	0-9	0-7	5-1	1-7	1-1	0-4	7-4	7-4
4.	Folkestone Invicta Res	5-1	1-0	1-0	*	0-1	4-1	7-1	1-1	5-3	1-4	0-0	6-0
5.	Headcorn	4-2	0-2	6-0	5-1	*	4-0	7-0	2-1	6-2	6-3	2-0	12-2
6.	Kennington Res	2-1	4-3	8-3	2-1	2-7	*	3-3	2-5	4-3	3-3	1-0	1-1
7.	Knatchbull Res	1-7	1-11	4-3	0-2	0-11	1-5	*	1-3	1-1	1-7	0-5	5-3
8.	Lydd Res	1-0	0-0	5-1	1-4	1-1	0-1	2-3	*	0-0	2-0	2-1	2-0
9.	New Romney Res	5-2	2-4	3-1	1-1	0-0	3-1	4-0	1-6	*	3-4	1-1	1-1
10.	Snowdon Colliery Welfare	4-2	1-3	1-0	1-2	1-1	3-3	7-1	1-0	4-1	*	3-3	3-1
11.	Sturry	4-3	4-5	3-0	2-3	2-0	4-1	2-0	5-3	3-3	2-3	*	8-1
12.	Swingfield & District	7-2	0-4	3-5	1-7	0-7	2-2	3-6	1-0	2-0	1-2	1-2	*

WESTERN DIVISION ONE RESULT CHART 1991/92

HOME TEAM		1	2	3	4	5	6	7	8	9	10	11	12	13
1.	A.F.C. Egerton	*	6-1	4-3	1-0	2-1	5-2	3-2	0-1	4-1	2-3	6-0	3-1	2-3
2.	Bearsted Res	0-3	*	3-2	1-1	2-2	2-8	1-2	2-5	2-0	1-2	2-2	0-2	1-2
3.	Brasted & Sundridge	1-9	1-2	*	1-2	1-3	2-4	5-1	1-1	5-1	0-1	2-5	0-1	2-4
4.	Chipstead	0-2	3-4	1-2	*	0-2	2-2	0-7	1-3	5-1	0-2	2-6	2-1	0-6
5.	Chislehurst	3-3	0-2	1-4	3-0	*	1-1	2-4	3-0	3-1	4-1	2-2	0-0	0-1
6.	Fleetdown United	3-1	1-2	5-1	10-0	1-0	*	1-1	5-1	11-1	0-0	7-2	4-0	0-0
7.	Lordswood Res	1-0	0-1	5-1	3-1	1-0	0-4	*	2-3	4-1	0-0	3-1	1-2	1-6
8.	St Georges (Wrotham)	4-0	1-6	4-1	1-1	1-3	0-1	5-2	*	2-2	1-1	3-1	4-1	1-9
9.	Sevenoaks Town Res	0-2	1-1	0-3	1-2	2-2	0-2	0-0	0-4	*	1-2	2-3	0-1	2-6
10.	Stansfeld O. & Berm. Res	3-1	0-1	6-0	3-0	1-1	0-4	2-0	1-2	2-2	*	1-4	4-2	0-1
11.	Swanscombe United	1-2		5-0	4-1	0-3	2-0	3-2	4-1	2-2		*	3-2	0-2
12.	Tonbridge Invicta	2-1	1-2	3-0	5-0	1-4	0-2	4-0	2-0	0-4	1-3	2-4	*	1-3
14.	Wellcome (Saturday)	0-0	2-2	5-0	6-0	3-1	3-2	6-1	4-1	7-0	3-1	2-0	3-0	*

WESTERN DIVISION TWO RESULT CHART 1991/92

HOME TEAM	1	2	3	4	5	6	7	8	9	10	11	12	13
1. Dunton Green	*	2-4	5-3	3-4	4-3	3-5	3-2	2-5	2-3	3-5	0-4	1-0	7-2
2. Edenstone Res	1-6	*	2-2	1-1	3-4	4-1	1-2	1-0	1-3	0-3	2-5	0-4	2-2
3. Halls	3-0	5-3	*	0-5	2-0	2-4	5-0	1-3	2-3	0-2	0-4	2-1	10-0
4. Joyce Green	1-4	0-1	2-3	*	1-0	2-4	6-1	3-0	0-5	1-4	1-3	3-4	2-2
5. N.P.I.	2-3	1-0	3-0	4-1	*	3-1	0-2	1-3	1-5	0-0	1-2	3-7	1-2
6. Old Bexleians	2-2	3-6	3-1	0-3	1-8	*	0-1	1-3	0-4	1-3	2-1	3-3	2-2
7. Otford United Res	3-4	1-1	1-4	3-2	0-4	2-3	*	1-5	0-3	1-2	0-0	0-1	
8. Scott Spts & Soc. Res	6-2	2-1	1-3	2-0	3-0	2-0	2-2	*	2-5	2-2	1-3	1-4	5-1
9. Strood County	7-1		2-1	3-1	1-1	5-0	8-0	4-0	*	1-1	5-2	2-0	2-1
10. The Railway (T. Wells)	2-1	2-2	5-1	2-0	2-1	2-0	3-1	3-1	2-5	*	3-2	2-1	0-1
11. Tonbridge Rangers	5-0	4-2	2-1	1-1	3-2	2-2	2-1	2-0	2-1	1-1	*	1-1	2-0
12. V.C.D. Athletic Res	4-2	2-2	5-1	3-0	2-2	0-1	3-0	2-2	1-2	1-5	0-2	*	5-2
13. Wickham Park	1-3	1-2	2-5	0-4	1-2	1-2	3-3	1-5	1-7	1-3	1-1	2-0	*

F.C.N MUSIC INTER REGIONAL CHALLENGE CUP 1991-92

First Round

Aylesford Paper Mills v Eltham Palace	3-1		Bearsted v Edenbridge United	7-2
Borough United v Sevenoaks Town	1-7		Dymchurch v Lydd	0-12
Ex Blues v Platt United	0-3		Colts '85 v Vickers Crayford/Dartford Athletic	4-3
Greenways v Westerham	3-2		Halstead v Edenstone	2-4
Knockholt v Eynsford	1-2		Knatchbull v Snowdown Colliery Welfare	3-1
Phoenix Rovers v Headcorn	1-1,5-1		Scott Sports & Social v Oakwood	1-2
Sturry v University of Kent	5-2		Stansfeld Oxford & Bermondsey v Ten Em Bee	2-1

Second Round

Colts '85 v Moonshot	1-1,0-1		Bromley Green v Teynham & Lynsted	3-7
Lydd v Sturry	6-1		Platt United v Sevenoaks Town	6-5
Greenways v Edenstone	0-2		Knatchbull v Phoenix Rovers	2-1
Lordswood v Bearsted	0-7		New Romney v Broomfield United	3-1
Otford United v Paddock Wood Town	3-3,2-4		Royal Oak Ravens *withdrew* Walmer Rovers W/O	
Oakwood v Rusthall	2-1		Sutton Athletic v Eynsford	0-1
Woodnesborough v Kennington	2-0		Stansfeld Ox. & B.C. v Aylesford Paper Mills	2-2,3-1

Third Round

Rye United v Folkestone Invicta Reserves	4-2		Lydd v New Romney	3-2
Woodnesborough v Knatchbull	5-0		Walmers Rovers v Teynham & Lynsted	2-0
Platt United v Bearsted	0-6		Oakwood v Eynsford	6-0
Paddock Wood Town v Moonshot	3-2		Stansfeld Oxford & Bermondsey v Edenstone	2-1

Quarter Finals

Lydd Town v Bearsted	5-0		Stansfeld Oxford & Bermondsey v Rye United	2-0
Walmer Rovers v Woodnesborough	3-2		Paddock Wood Town v Oakwood	1-5

Semi Finals

Walmer Rovers v Oakwood	1-3		Stansfeld Oxford & Bermondsey v Lydd Town	6-2

Final (at Gillingham FC): Stansfeld Oxford & Bermondsey Club 4, Oakwood 2

PREMIER DIVISION CLUBS 1992-1993

AYLESFORD PAPER MILLS
Secretary: Mr E Best, 40 Priory Grove, Ditton, Aylesford, Kent ME20 6BB (0622 710300)
Ground: Cobdown, Station Road, Ditton, Nr. Maidstone (0622 717771) **Founded:** 1979
Colours: Black & white stripes/black/black   **Change Colours:** All yellow

GREENWAYS
Secretary: Mr W Miller, 14 Cygnet Gardens, Northfleet, Kent DA11 7DN (0474 560913)
Ground: Blue Circle Spts Ground, via Springhead Road, Northfleet (0474 534625) **Founded:** 1965
Colours: All green   **Change Colours:** All blue

KNOCKHOLT
Secretary: Mr L Benham, 72 Reedham Drive, Purley, Surrey (081 660 5377)
Ground: Knockholt Village Club, Main Road, Knockholt (0959 32468) **Founded:** 1967
Colours: Red/black/black   **Change Colours:** Orange/black/black

LORDSWOOD
Secretary: Mr S Lewis, Sunnybrook, Gorsewood Road, Hartley, Longfield (0474 708233)
Ground: Lordswood Spts & Social Club, North Dane Way, Walderslade (0634 669138)
Colours: Amber/black/black   **Change Colours:** White/black/black **Founded:** 1968

NEW ROMNEY
Secretary: Mr H Payne, 'Stonecrop', Grand Parade, Littlestone, New Romney, Kent TN28 8NQ (0679 66425)
Ground: Station Road, New Romney (0679 64858) **Founded:** 1895
Colours: All blue   **Change Colours:** White/blue/blue

OAKWOOD
Secretary: Mr P Mannering, 24 Ellenswood Close, Otham, Maidstone, Kent ME15 9QA (0622 862482)
Ground: Honey Lane, Otham, Maidstone **Founded:** 1924
Colours: All red   **Change Colours:** White/white/red

OTFORD UNITED
Secretary: Mr R Gulliver, 22 Berwick Way, Sevenoaks, Kent TN14 5EY (0732 459064)
Ground: Recreation Ground, High Street, Otford **Founded:** 1900
Colours: Amber/black/black   **Change Colours:** Red/black/black

SCOTT SPORTS & SOCIAL
Secretary: Mr R Taylor, 24 Sun Lane, Gravesend, Kent DA12 5HG (0474 332208)
Ground: Scott Sports & Social Club, Nelson Road, Northfleet (0474 336456) **Founded:** 1927
Colours: Black & silver stripes/black/black   **Change Colours:** Blue & white hoops/white/blue

SEVENOAKS TOWN
Secretary: Mr E Diplock, 23 Holly Bush Lane, Sevenoaks, Kent TN13 3TH (0732 454280)
Ground: Greatness Park, Seal Road, Sevenoaks **Founded:** 1883
Colours: Royal/royal/red **Change Colours:** Amber/black/black

STANSFELD OXFORD & BERMONDSEY CLUB
Secretary: Mr A Rigby, 70 Roundtable Road, Bromley, Kent BR1 5LG (081 698 5641) **Founded:** 1897
Ground: St James Squash & Leisure Club, Marvels Lane, Grove Park SE12 (081 851 3522)
Colours: Blue & yellow stripes/blue/blue **Change Colours:** Green & white/green/green

TEYNHAM & LYNSTED
Secretary: Mr M Ashworth, 74 Harold Road, Sittingbourne, Kent ME10 3AJ (0795 423986)
Ground: Frognal Lane, Teynham, Off A2 **Founded:** 1961
Colours: Sky & white stripes/maroon/sky **Change Colours:** Red & black/black/black

THAMES POLYTECHNIC
Secretary: Derek A Ingram, 8 St Josephs Close, Orpington, Kent BR6 9TY (0689 977162)
Ground: Kidbrooke Lane, Eltham, London SE9 (081 850 1221) **Founded:** 1888.
Directions: Off South Circular, near Eltham Well Hall r'bout. 250 yards from Eltham (BR).
Colours: Yellow & green **Change Colours:** White & green

VICKERS CRAYFORD/DARTFORD ATHLETIC
Secretary: Mr R Bond, 97 Birkbeck Road, Sidcup, Kent DA14 4DJ (081 300 9943)
Ground: Oakwood, Old Road, Crayford (0322 524262) **Founded:** 1916
Colours: Green & white hoops/white/white **Change Colours:** All blue

WOODNESBOROUGH
Secretary: Mr G Hunt, Hillcross Farm, Eastry, Sandwich, Kent CT13 0NY (0304 611311)
Ground: "Hillborough", Woodnesborough Road, Eastry (0304 614721) **Founded:** 1961
Colours: Yellow/blue/blue **Change Colours:** All blue

EASTERN FIRST DIVISION CLUBS 1991-1992

BROMLEY GREEN
Secretary: Mr A Barham, 218 Cheriton High Street, Folkestone, Kent (0303 277240)
Ground: Carters Field, Bromley Green Road, Upper Ruckinge, Ashford, Kent **Founded:** 1930
Colours: All green **Change Colours:** All red

BROOMFIELD UNITED
Secretary: Mr J Edgington, 4 Damerham Close, Canterbury, Kent CT2 7SB (0227 452323)
Ground: Bridge Recreation Ground, Patrixbourne Road, Bridge, Nr Canterbury **Founded:** 1925
Colours: Red & black stripes/black/red & black **Change Colours:** Sky blue/navy/navy

HEADCORN
Secretary: Mr A Purvis, 5 Newlands, Bridewell, Ashford, Kent (0233 631365)
Ground: Grigg Lane, Off Oak Lane, Headcorn **Founded:** 1920
Colours: Ambler/black/black **Change Colours:** All blue

HOUCHIN ROVERS
Secretary: Mr M Robinson, 76 Hawks Way, Ashford, Kent TN23 2UW (0233 624226).
Ground: Bybrook Road, Kennington. **Founded:** 1962
Colours: Blue & white/navy/sky **Change Colours:** Grey/black/black.

HYTHE (New entrant, no details available)

KENNINGTON
Secretary: Mr R Lancaster, 'Totternhoe', Goat Lees, Faversham Road, Kennington, Ashford (0233 624858)
Ground: Spearpoint Rec. Grnd, opposite Spearpoint Hotel, The Ridge, Kennington **Founded:** 1880
Colours: Amber/black/black **Change Colours:** All red

KNATCHBULL
Secretary: Mr D Howie, 13 Charminster, Washford Farm, Ashford, Kent TN23 2UH (0233 611207)
Ground: Hatch Park, Off A20, Mersham, Nr. Ashford **Founded:** 1981
Colours: White/maroon/maroon **Change Colours:** Maroon/white/maroon

LYDD TOWN
Secretary: Mr P Sisley, 52 Skinner Road, Lydd, Kent TN29 9HP (0679 21194)
Ground: The Rype, Manor Road, Lydd **Founded:** 1885
Colours: Red/green/green **Change Colours:** All green

RYE UNITED
Secretary: Mr S Williams, 'Grovewood', Grove Lane, Iden, East Sussex TN31 7PX (0797 280509)
Ground: Rye Football and Cricket Salts **Founded:** 1938
Colours: Red & black/black/red & black **Change Colours:** All white

SANDWICH SPORTS
Secretary: Mr K Clapton, 17 Glenfield Rd, Dover, Kent CT16 2AL (0304 211922)
Ground: The Sandwich Sports & Leisure Centre, Deal Road, Sandwich, Kent. **Founded:** 1992
Colours: Sky/navy/navy **Change Colours:** Red/white/white.

SNOWDOWN COLLIERY WELFARE
Secretary: Mrs A Norton, 26 Burgess Road, Aylesham, Canterbury, Kent (0304 841706)
Ground: Spinney Lane, Aylesham, Canterbury (0304 840278) **Founded:** 1907
Colours: Black & white stripes/black/black **Change Colours:** White/blue/blue

TENTERDEN & ST MICHAELS
Secretary: Mr S Stevens, Kent House, Ashford Rd, St Michaels, Tenterden.
Ground: The Recreation Ground, Tenterden. **Founded:** 1890
Colours: Blue/navy/black **Change Colours:** Maroon/sky/maroon

The most famous club to join the FCN League this summer are Thames Polytechnic whose ground is no longer up to the standard required by the Winstonlead League. Above they are pictured before their last match in the Winstonlead League. Back Row (L/R): Colin Mace, Tony Slater, Dean Wordsworth, Peter Ellis, Garry Dreher, Ryan George. Front: Craig Bevis, Paul Skates, Chris Ovens, Frank Attard, Steve Fribbens. Photo - Gavin Ellis.

Bruce Marchant (left) & Terry Mahoney, joint bosses of Lydd, accept December's 'Manager of the Month' award.

Edenstone entertain Platt United in a cup tie at their old ground at Hayes Lane. The big crowd are awaiting the kick-off of Bromley v Woking on Bromley's adjacent ground. Photo. Photo - Mike Floate.

UNIVERSITY OF KENT
Secretary: Mrs J Nevett, Sports Federation, Sports Centre, University of Kent, Canterbury, Kent CT2 7NL (0227 768027)
Ground: The Playing Fields, University of Kent, Canterbury **Founded:**
Colours: Black & white stripes/black/black **Change Colours:** Red/black/black

WHITE LION (CHERITON)
Secretary: Mr R Matthews, 41 Brambley Cres., Folkestone, Kent CT20 3PU (0303 276151)
Ground: Cheriton Recreation Ground, Weymouth Rd, Folkestone **Founded:** 1990
Colours: Red/blue/red **Change Colours:** All green.

WESTERN FIRST DIVISION CLUBS 1991-1992

BEARSTED
Secretary: Mr J Scannel, 24 Fauchons Lane, Bearsted, Maidstone, Kent (0622 39072)
Ground: Bearsted Green, The Street, Bearsted **Founded:** 1895
Colours: White/white/blue **Change Colours:** Blue & yellow/blue/blue

BOROUGH UNITED
Secretary: Mr M G Bennett, 29a Princes Road, Dartford, Kent DA1 3HJ (0322 270231)
Ground: Dartford Sports & Social Club, Darenth Road, Dartford **Founded:** 1945
Colours: Blue/navy/navy **Change Colours:** Yellow/navy/yellow

COLTS '85
Secretary: TBA. **Founded:** 1985
Ground: Swanmead Sports Ground, Swanmead Way, off Cannon Lane, Tonbridge (0732 350473)
Colours: Blue/white/blue **Change Colours:** White/white/blue

EDENSTONE
Secretary: Mrs C Jones, 84 Southlands Road, Bromley, Kent BR2 9QS (081 290 6034)
Ground: The Grove Sports Club, Oakley Road, Bromley **Founded:** 1965
Colours: Blue/white/white **Change Colours:** Silver grey/black/grey

EX BLUES
Secretary: Mr M Harvey, 29 Crown Lane Bromley, Kent BR2 9PG (081 464 4815)
Ground: 118 Pickhurst Rise, Off Pickhurst Lane, Hayes, West Wickham, Kent (081 777 9904)
Colours: White/blue/blue **Change Colours:** All blue **Founded:** 1945

MOONSHOT ATHLETIC
Secretary: Mr R Collymore, 37 Vaughan Williams Close, London SE8 4AW (081 691 2543)
Ground: Fordham Park, Pagnell Street, New Cross, SE14 (081 691 8935) **Founded:** 1970
Colours: All yellow **Change Colours:** All blue

PHOENIX SPORTS
Secretary: Mr A Pearson, 4 Gainsborough Avenue, Dartford, Kent (0322 228625)
Ground: Phoenix Sports Ground, May Road East, Barnehurst. **Founded:** 1895
Colours: Red/white/red **Change Colours:** Green/red/red.

RUSTHALL
Secretary: Mr R Forbes, 27 Ashenden Walk, Tunbridge Wells, Kent TN2 3HR (0892 545075)
Ground: Jockey Farm, Newington Road, Rusthall **Founded:** 1899
Colours: All green **Change Colours:** Claret & blue/sky/sky.

SUTTON ATHLETIC
Secretary: Mr J Willis, 6 Somerset Road, Dartford, Kent DA1 3DP (0322 222540)
Ground: The Roaches, Parsonage Lane, Sutton At Hone, Nr.Dartford **Founded:** 1928
Colours: All green **Change Colours:** Blue/black/black

TEN EM BEE
Secretary: Mr G Davies, 65 Killearn Road, Catford, London SE6 1BN (081 461 1477)
Ground: Old Bromley Road Playing Fields, Old Bromley Road (081 460 0652) **Founded:** 1975
Colours: Blue stripes/blue/red **Change Colours:** Yellow/black/black

WESTERHAM
Secretary: Mr A Noad, 25 Croydon Road, Westerham, Kent (0959 62658)
Ground: King George Playing Fields, Costells Meadow, off Quebec Avenue, Westerham (0959 61106)
Colours: Red/black/black **Change Colours:** Green/black/black **Founded:** 1888

LOWER DIVISION CONSTITUTIONS 1992-93

Eastern Second	Western Second	Western Third
Bromley Green Res	A.F.C. Egerton	Chipstead
Castle Tavern	Chislehurst	Dunton Green
Dymchurch	Edenbridge United	Empire
Folkestone Invicta Res	Eltham Palace	Halls
Kennington Res	Eynsford	Joyce Green
Knatchbull Res	Fleetdown	N.P.I.
Lydd Town Res	Halstead	Nomads
New Romney Res	Paddock Wood Res	Old Bexleians
Royal George Folkestone	Platt United	Snodland
Sandwich Sports Res	St Georges Wrotham	Swanscombe United
Sturry	Strood County	The Railway (T'bridge Wells)
Teynham & Lynsted	Tonbridge Invicta	Tonbridge Rangers
University of Kent Res	Wellcome Saturday	Wickham Park
Walmer Rovers		

Western Reserve Division One: Bearsted Res, Edenstone Reserves, Lordswood Res, Otford United Res, Scott Sports & Social Res, Sevenoaks Town Res, Stansfeld Oxford & Bermondsey Club Res, Vickers Crayford/Dartford Athletic Res.

Western Reserve Division Two: Aylesford Paper Mills Res, Borough United Res, Colts '85 Res, Greenways Res, Oakwood Res, Rusthall Res, Westerham Res.

H.F.S. LOANS LEAGUE

Chairman: K Marsden, Esq.

Hon. Secretary: R D Bayley,
22 Woburn Drive, Hale, Altrincham, Cheshire WA15 8LZ (061 980 7007).

STALYBRIDGE'S CONSISTENCY PAYS DIVIDENDS

The HFS Loans League Premier Division title looked set to be a close battle with Frickley Athletic, Buxton, Leek Towm and Goole Town all having tasted life at the top by mid-October, but once Stalybridge took the lead their sheer consistency proved to be the telling factor and they were never headed again, with only Marine being serious challengers in the latter stages. They won the title in an anti-climax on Easter Monday when, in spite of losing their unbeaten home record to local rivals Hyde, Marine failed to secure the three points at Southport that would have kept them in touch. Never-the-less, Stalybridge equalled the League record of only two defeats in a season, set by Wigan Athletic in 1970, their only other set-back being at Gainsborough Trinity in December.

Marine's demanding fixture schedule meant they lost their way in the chase for the title as exciting runs in both the FA Trophy and League Challenge Cup took their toll. After Trophy victories over Stafford Rangers, Kettering Town and Redbridge Forest, the Mariners just missed out on a Wembley appearance when they faltered at the last hurdle against last season's HFS champions Witton Albion. However they were more successful in the League Challenge Cup at Manchester City when an 86th minute goal by Eddie Murray was enough to lift the trophy at the expense of Frickley Athletic. Pre-season favourites in many people's view were Southport and Morecambe, but neither put in a serious challenge after disastrous starts - Southport winning only one of their opening ten games, and Morecambe just five of their first thirteen. However, Morecambe had the benefit of a good FA Cup run in which they reached the First Round Proper, and they overcame a first leg deficit against Stalybridge Celtic to take the President's Cup, their first domestic trophy during a 24 year membership of the league. Together with Gainsborough Trinity and Goole Town they remain one of only three founder members from back in 1969.

In the First Division all the newly promoted clubs faired well. Indeed, Knowsley positively exploded onto the HFS scene scoring within thirty seconds of their debut and adding another three within the next five minutes! Guiseley reached the First Round Proper of the FA Cup and made a return trip to Wembley in the FA Vase, but failed to hold onto the trophy going down 3-5 to Wimborne Town. Colwyn Bay achieved the most success with a League and Cup double, also reaching the Semi-Finals of the Welsh Cup before going down to Hednesford Town. Their 3-1 Cup Final victory was over Worksop Town, whilst with just two league games to go, Winsford United had the championship in their grasp but slipped up at home to Netherfield allowing 'The Bay' to clinch the title in their final game.

The annual representative game against the Football Association ended in a 3-1 success for Roley Howard's HFS Loans League team to put them ahead on results over the past twelve seasons. Chris Camden with two and Brian Ross were the League's scorers, with Malcolm O'Connor getting the opening goal for the FA XI.

Once again in the elusive search for success, over a third of the 44 clubs changed managers, but an even more serious shadow was cast by the threat to the five Welsh member clubs by the proposed League of Wales. The shameful outcome sees Colwyn Bay and Caernarfon Town forced from their homeland due to the inflexible attitude of the F.A. of Wales, and their determination to remain within the Pyramid sees them groundsharing at Northwich Victoria and Curzon Ashton respectively. Meanwhile, Bangor City, Newtown and Rhyl all felt obliged to resign from the League even though this was against their wishes. Another departure was that of Irlam Town who resigned at the end of the season due to the financial pressures.

However, the strength of the League was again demonstrated by many players departing the HFS scene to make an impact in the Football League. In particular, Fleetwood pocketed nearly £50,000 for the sale of Steve Macauley to Crewe, and Bridlington a similar amount for the sale of striker Mike Norbury to Second Division Championship contenders Cambridge United.

R D Bayley, Secretary

H.F.S. LOANS LEAGUE CHALLENGE CUP 1991-92

Preliminary Round

Alfreton Town v Netherfield	1-2	Congleton Town v Workington	2-1

First Round

Colwyn Bay v Rhyl	1-1,7-0	Farsley Celtic v Bridlington Town	4-2
Guiseley v Congleton Town	2-0	Knowsley United v Eastwood Town	3-1
Lancaster City v Harrogate Town	0-3	Radcliffe Borough v Caernarfon Town	4-1
Rossendale United v Irlam Town	3-0	Warrington Town v Curzon Ashton	0-0,0-1
Winsford United v Newtown	4-1	Worksop Town v Netherfield	1-0

Second Round

Accrington Stanley v Southport	1-2	Bishop Auckland v Hyde United	1-0
Chorley v Winsford United	1-3	Colwyn Bay v Matlock Town	1-2
Curzon Ashton v Farsley Celtic	6-2	Fleetwood Town v Emley	1-0
Frickley Athletic v Worksop Town	2-1	Guiseley v Bangor City	6-2
Harrogate Town v Buxton	1-2	Knowsley United v Horwich R.M.I.	2-1
Narine v Gainsborough Trinity	2-0	Morecambe v Shepshed Albion	3-1
Radcliffe Borough v Goole Town	0-2	Rossendale United v Mossley	2-1
Stalybridge Celtic v Leek Town	4-1	Whitley Bay v Droylsden	1-0

Third Round

Buxton v Knowsley United	3-2	Curzon Ashton v Bishop Auckland	4-3
Frickley Athletic v Whitley Bay	2-1	Morecambe v Guiseley	1-1,3-3(aet 2-4 pens)
Goole Town v Southport	1-0	Rossendale United v Matlock Town	1-1,0-1
Stalybridge Celtic v Fleetwood Town	5-0	Winsford United v Marine	1-3

Quarter Finals

Buxton v Guiseley	1-2	Curzon Ashton v Marine	2-3
Matlock Town v Goole Town	3-2	Stalybridge Celtic v Frickley Athletic	0-2

Semi-Finals

Guiseley v Marine	1-0,0-2	Matlock v Frickley 3-2,0-1(aet, Frickley on away goals)	

Final (at Manchester City FC): Marine 1, Frickley Athletic 0

H.F.S. LOANS LEAGUE PRESIDENT'S CUP 1991-92

Third Round

Eastwood Town v Buxton	2-1	Emley v Fleetwood Town	0-0,3-2
Marine v Warrington Town	2-1	Morecambe v Lancaster City	2-0
Rhyl v Leek Town	0-2	Southport v Worksop Town	2-3
Stalybridge Celtic v Accrington Stanley	3-0	Whitley Bay v Bishop Auckland	0-0,1-2

Quarter Finals

Bishop Auckland v Emley	4-0	Eastwood Town v Stalybridge Celtic	0-2
Marine v Morecambe	1-1,3-4(aet)	Worksop Town v Leek Town	3-5

Semi-Finals

Leek Town v Morecambe	0-0,0-2	Stalybridge Celtic v Bishop Auckland	3-2,1-0

Final: Morecambe 1, Stalybridge 2; Stalybridge 0, Morecambe 2 *(Morecambe won 3-2 on aggregate)*

H.F.S. LOANS LEAGUE FIRST DIVISION CUP 1991-92

First Round

Caernarfon Town v Farsley Celtic	2-1	Curzon Ashton v Irlam Town	2-1
Guiseley v Radcliffe Borough	2-2,1-2	Knowsley United v Bridlington Town	4-1
Rhyl v Winsford United	1-2	Rossendale United v Eastwood Town	4-1

Second Round

Colwyn Bay v Caernarfon Town	2-0	Congleton Town v Worksop Town	2-4
Knowsley United v Curzon Ashton	3-4	Lancaster City v Workington	0-2
Newtown v Harrogate Town	4-0	Radcliffe Borough v Netherfield	1-5
Rossendale United v Winsford United	4-2	Warrington Town v Alfreton Town	4-0

Quarter Finals

Colwyn Bay v Netherfield	5-2	Curzon Ashton v Workington	2-0
Worksop Town v Warrington Town	2-0	Rossendale v Newtown	4-4,2-2(aet, 3-4 pens)

Semi-Finals

Newtown v Colwyn Bay	0-2,0-5	Worksop Town v Curzon Ashton	2-1,2-2

Final (at Stalybridge Celtic FC): Colwyn Bay 3, Worksop Town 1

H.F.S. LOANS LEAGUE ATTENDANCES 1991-92

PREMIER DIVISION ATTENDANCE CHART 1991-92

HOME TEAM	1	2	3	4	5	6	7	8	9	10	11	12	13	14	15	16	17	18	19	20	21	22
1. Accrington	*	482	709	485	261	832	352	385	358	385	392	365	640	704	628	484	721	385	561	502	632	338
2. Bangor City	305	*	215	303	275	192	279	214	211	195	209	152	321	257	223	270	278	218	245	282	211	212
3. B Auckland	247	199	*	221	249	251	357	206	414	192	229	202	289	315	217	208	207	216	239	230	225	439
4. Buxton	402	257	298	*	351	301	389	206	320	434	387	354	360	1153	384	611	343	507	351	359	735	255
5. Chorley	340	301	289	279	*	208	197	334	322	148	273	539	282	374	280	204	329	218	296	297	329	223
6. Droylsden	423	310	213	304	307	*	333	201	241	203	203	204	325	229	274	288	294	352	309	254	580	198
7. Emley	389	354	453	354	558	465	*	314	562	605	272	542	289	359	423	251	274	218	308	326	501	429
8. Fleetwood	130	163	196	184	180	207	187	*	155	201	168	215	241	220	224	105	349	234	119	179	251	194
9. Frickley	415	222	208	371	197	202	316	219	*	242	496	151	238	276	228	229	276	264	217	176	374	174
10. G Trinity	343	335	336	335	315	278	363	219	494	*	307	258	321	308	261	386	230	320	252	204	369	319
11. Goole Town	195	415	275	278	335	365	390	195	418	345	*	215	505	235	285	225	285	216	355	210	325	405
12. Horwich	252	263	206	258	566	236	220	269	249	237	169	*	254	227	259	208	210	198	277	410	243	214
13. Hyde United	489	325	325	352	537	418	427	369	404	405	402	438	*	297	307	301	503	887	319	425	1117	277
14. Leek Town	415	455	246	678	604	502	565	354	549	427	456	411	430	*	585	490	532	438	602	634	675	532
15. Marine	507	405	314	339	510	403	451	280	409	305	317	281	402	439	*	322	377	387	349	1029	433	451
16. Matlock	417	285	303	748	308	367	463	313	447	377	569	254	418	542	421	*	397	309	427	382	523	275
17. Morecambe	424	308	402	363	451	320	399	422	286	318	375	368	350	407	350	304	*	365	274	403	660	305
18. Mossley	288	257	278	353	266	405	402	241	243	202	252	296	571	322	238	230	334	*	224	436	605	317
19. Shepshed	291	203	219	271	218	201	286	248	337	205	280	309	185	293	313	367	249	224	*	387	288	247
20. Southport	458	311	342	440	552	280	427	411	206	272	327	408	341	409	509	275	413	337	301	*	388	306
21. Stalybridge	687	471	405	587	717	726	679	606	544	577	338	628	1225	629	411	303	405	739	631	523	*	364
22. Whitley B.	423	233	123	179	353	166	252	221	222	440	460	253	402	432	164	183	397	183	216	174	333	*

FIRST DIVISION ATTENDANCE CHART 1991-92

HOME TEAM	1	2	3	4	5	6	7	8	9	10	11	12	13	14	15	16	17	18	19	20	21	22
1. Alfreton	*	208	58	102	121	77	169	135	159	120	156	97	95	79	71	62	140	122	121	119	63	215
2. Bridlington	126	*	101	147	173	205	225	227	160	251	147	118	153	86	107	117	162	195	140	197	161	264
3. Caernarfon	195	228	*	414	177	256	229	215	190	222	210	234	169	237	286	180	273	317	240	305	213	175
4. Colwyn Bay	417	495	732	*	373	311	491	652	444	449	469	546	425	448	629	404	458	338	603	617	374	505
5. Congleton	125	209	112	132	*	129	164	153	173	163	120	142	163	188	245	154	132	120	148	372	127	235
6. Curzon Ash.	97	187	192	137	105	*	212	112	177	107	98	216	107	128	110	147	172	109	177	179	127	192
7. Eastwood T.	299	201	86	110	98	97	*	154	158	162	94	94	77	135	97	122	73	75	110	145	93	250
8. Farsley	119	179	153	187	115	112	167	*	417	246	102	243	131	86	129	84	103	111	94	169	127	151
9. Guiseley	636	684	403	786	697	467	411	571	*	510	578	433	650	580	411	480	460	513	401	568	482	720
10. Harrogate	190	219	187	203	246	194	140	310	768	*	147	215	206	239	154	268	206	246	301	212	191	247
11. Irlam T.	74	84	103	150	75	52	80	65	85	93	*	75	77	82	72	45	65	74	102	130	55	76
12. Knowsley	34	93	94	183	72	164	96	85	75	75	84	*	59	146	218	40	99	109	130	133	115	131
13. Lancaster	125	134	184	103	112	83	165	110	187	112	154	156	*	287	107	165	112	166	215	182	178	114
14. Netherfield	137	112	132	178	113	137	134	161	353	152	112	115	317	*	108	274	133	147	195	148	176	114
15. Newtown	167	231	307	278	204	145	109	214	143	179	157	237	207	261	*	217	210	207	107	227	142	177
16. Radcliffe	52	114	78	122	114	117	112	105	162	80	70	73	102	62	63	*	82	142	140	158	100	59
17. Rhyl	140	122	438	438	109	197	93	117	136	161	194	128	164	102	272	145	*	105	149	189	129	146
18. Rossendale	122	218	191	218	215	174	215	211	241	325	152	216	288	169	160	154	202	*	183	230	160	256
19. Warrington	173	217	228	135	154	148	150	144	222	169	168	253	149	171	133	154	197	209	*	414	125	178
20. Winsford	316	421	429	963	240	311	308	405	557	204	353	309	415	523	326	246	661	359	458	*	359	246
21. Workington	97	105	144	151	111	121	142	102	165	141	101	151	150	156	102	94	123	109	103	193	*	93
22. Worksop	102	154	115	123	85	100	120	83	183	107	90	88	101	84	108	108	91	113	111	154	88	*

Stalybridge Celtic receive the H.F.S. Loans League Premier Division Championship on 20th April. They had just suffered a surprise home defeat, their first of the season, at the hands of local rivals Hyde United, but Marine's result meant their lead was now unassailable. Photo - Colin Stevens.

Premier Division

	P	W	D	L	F	A	Pts
Stalybridge Celtic	42	26	14	2	84	33	92
Marine	42	23	9	10	64	32	78
Morecambe	42	21	13	8	70	44	76
Leek Town	42	21	10	11	62	49	73
Buxton	42	21	9	12	65	47	72
Emley	42	18	11	13	69	47	65
Southport	42	16	17	9	57	48	65
Accrington Stanley	42	17	12	13	78	62	63
Hyde United	42	17	9	16	69	67	60
Fleetwood Town	42	17	8	17	67	64	59
Bishop Auckland	42	16	9	17	48	58	57
Goole Town	42	15	9	18	60	72	54
Horwich	42	13	14	15	44	52	53
Frickley Athletic	42	12	16	14	61	57	52
Droylsden	42	12	14	16	62	72	50
Mossley	42	15	4	23	51	73	49
Whitley Bay	42	13	9	20	53	79	48
Gainsborough Trinity	42	11	13	18	48	63	46
Matlock Town	42	12	9	21	59	87	45
Bangor City	42	11	10	21	46	57	43
Chorley	42	11	9	22	61	82	42
Shepshed Albion	42	6	8	28	46	79	26

Top Scorers

C **Camden** (Stalybridge C)	40
S **Holden** (Morecambe)	31
B **Ross** (Marine)	28
J **Coleman** (Morecambe)	25
P **Beck** (Accrington Stanley)	21
C **Madden** (Fleetwood Town)	20
E **Priest** (Stalybridge Celtic)	20

THE H.F.S. LOANS PREMIER DIVISION RESULT CHART 1991-92

HOME TEAM	1	2	3	4	5	6	7	8	9	10	11	12	13	14	15	16	17	18	19	20	21	22
1. Accrington	*	1-0	2-2	1-1	3-2	2-2	2-1	3-0	1-2	1-1	4-0	1-1	1-1	1-0	0-3	2-2	3-1	5-1	3-1	1-1	0-3	3-2
2. Bangor C	4-3	*	1-1	0-1	1-1	4-0	2-0	0-2	2-1	1-3	2-0	1-2	2-2	0-1	0-2	2-3	0-1	4-0	1-0	1-1	0-1	1-2
3. Bishop A.	0-6	0-0	*	2-0	3-0	1-0	1-1	3-0	1-0	3-1	1-2	1-3	0-1	0-2	3-0	1-1	0-2	1-2	4-1	0-1	1-4	1-1
4. Buxton	0-1	2-0	2-1	*	4-2	2-0	1-3	1-0	3-0	2-1	1-1	5-0	2-0	3-0	0-3	3-1	1-3	1-3	1-0	1-0	1-2	3-1
5. Chorley	2-1	4-3	1-0	0-2	*	1-2	0-1	1-0	2-2	3-1	4-4	0-0	2-0	0-2	3-1	2-1	1-2	1-2	1-2	2-2	2-3	1-3
6. Droylsden	3-2	2-0	1-2	0-0	2-0	*	4-0	1-4	4-2	0-0	3-2	5-1	3-2	2-2	1-1	2-2	0-1	1-4	3-2	1-1	2-2	1-1
7. Emley	3-1	0-2	4-1	1-2	5-0	1-2	*	4-0	2-0	6-0	2-0	0-0	0-0	0-0	0-1	4-0	3-3	2-1	0-0	3-2	2-3	3-1
8. Fleetwood T	2-1	2-1	3-4	1-1	5-0	2-1	1-1	*	2-1	0-1	2-3	1-2	5-1	2-2	0-0	4-0	1-1	3-1	2-0	5-1	0-2	5-0
9. Frickley A	1-1	2-1	2-0	1-1	1-0	1-1	0-0	3-2	*	0-0	1-2	0-2	3-0	0-1	0-4	2-1	1-1	3-0	6-1	2-0	1-1	4-0
10. Gainsborough	0-4	1-1	0-1	0-0	3-1	0-0	1-0	1-1	1-1	*	0-2	4-0	1-0	1-2	0-0	0-1	5-1	0-1	3-1	0-2	3-1	1-3
11. Goole Town	2-4	2-1	1-2	2-2	3-1	2-2	0-1	2-1	2-2	4-1	*	1-0	0-1	1-2	1-2	3-0	1-2	3-1	0-1	2-1	1-1	1-0
12. Horwich RMI	1-1	0-1	2-0	0-0	2-2	1-0	3-0	0-1	1-3	3-0	2-1	*	0-2	1-1	1-0	2-1	0-2	1-2	0-0	1-1	0-0	1-2
13. Hyde United	2-1	2-2	4-0	2-1	1-2	3-1	5-3	7-0	1-1	2-1	1-3	1-1	*	1-0	0-4	3-2	2-2	4-1	3-1	4-0	1-2	0-1
14. Leek Town	1-0	0-0	1-1	4-1	2-0	2-0	1-1	0-3	2-1	0-1	1-1	3-1	3-3	*	3-2	2-1	0-4	3-2	3-0	3-0	2-3	2-2
15. Marine	0-1	1-0	0-1	2-0	2-1	3-1	2-0	5-0	1-0	2-1	2-0	2-1	2-0	3-0	*	1-3	0-1	2-1	1-1	1-1	0-0	3-0
16. Matlock T	0-4	2-0	0-1	0-2	2-2	3-2	0-3	1-1	1-1	3-4	1-1	0-2	1-3	0-0	0-1	*	1-2	0-2	4-3	3-3	0-3	5-3
17. Morecambe	4-1	3-0	3-0	2-1	2-1	1-1	0-1	1-2	2-0	1-1	1-1	0-0	3-0	2-2	2-1	3-3	*	1-0	0-2	0-1	0-0	0-1
18. Mossley	0-1	1-3	0-2	1-3	1-0	3-0	0-3	4-1	1-1	2-1	3-1	1-1	1-1	1-2	0-1	0-1	1-4	*	2-1	0-0	0-1	3-2
19. Shepshed A	4-0	0-0	0-0	2-3	2-3	2-3	3-2	0-1	1-3	1-1	0-1	1-3	1-2	1-2	0-0	4-1	2-4	0-1	*	0-1	3-3	0-1
20. Southport	2-2	4-0	3-0	2-1	1-1	2-2	2-3	1-0	3-2	2-2	1-1	1-1	2-0	1-0	0-0	2-0	1-1	1-0	3-0	*	0-0	2-0
21. Stalybridge	2-1	1-1	0-0	2-2	3-3	2-0	1-0	2-0	2-2	3-0	7-0	2-0	1-2	1-0	3-1	4-0	1-0	5-0	2-1	1-0	*	3-1
22. Whitley Bay	2-2	0-1	0-2	0-2	0-6	3-1	0-0	0-0	2-2	3-3	2-0	1-3	4-1	0-3	2-2	3-1	1-1	2-1	2-1	1-2	0-2	*

Stewart Owen heads clear for Accrington in an away match at Marine. Owen had an eventful afternoon - he scored the only goal of the match and was subsequently sent off!

Chairman: John S Alty   **President:** J C Prescott.
Directors: J S Alty, M Clay, S Adams, Mrs C Booth, P J Stanley (Marketing).
Secretary: Joe E Daly, 49 Lowergate Road, Huncoat, Accrington BB5 6LN (0254 33096).
Team Manager: Phil Staley   **Asst Manager:**   **Physio:** Alan Crane
Press Officer: John S Alty   **Comm. Mgr:** John Guilfoyle. **Coach:** Tony Keyes.
Ground: Crown Ground, off Livingstone Road, Accrington (0254 383235).
Directions: Arriving on A680 from Clayton-le-Moors Livingstone Road is on left 50 yds past Crown Hotel. From M62/M66, through town centre on A680 - Livingstone Road 500 yds on right after Victoria Hospital. One and a half miles from Accrington (BR).
Capacity: 2,420 (1,650 Covered)   **Seats:** 200   **Floodlights:** Y **Shop:** Y **Metal Badges:** Y
Colours: Red/white/red   **Change colours:** All sky
Previous Leagues: Lancs Combination 70-78/ Cheshire County 78-82/ North West Counties 82-87.
Midweek home matchday: Wednesday   **Reserve Team's League:** East Lancs Lg.
Record Attendance: 2,096 v Fleetwood Town, FA Cup 4th Qualifying Rd 27/10/90.
Best F.A. Cup season: 4th Qualifying Rd 74-75 (lost 1-2 at Altrincham), 90-91 (lost 0-2 v Fleetwood).
Record Fees - Paid: £2,250 for Bernie Hughes (Droylsen 90-91).
        Received: £1,000 for David Hargreaves (Blackburn Rovers).
Players progressing to Football League: David Hargreaves (Blackburn Rovers 1977), Ian Blackstone (York City).
Clubhouse: Open two nights and matchdays. Private functions.   **Steward:** Valerie Wade.
Club Record Goalscorer: David Hargreaves 318   **Club Record Apps:** David Hargreaves 310.
91-92 Captain: Mark Walsh   **91-92 P.O.Y.:** Mark Pye   **91-92 Top scorer:** Paul Beck 21.
91-92 Average Attendance: 520.   **Sponsors:** Hollands Pies, Baxenden.
Local Press: Accrington Observer (0254 871444), Lancashire Evening Telegraph (0254 63588).
Local Radio Stations: Radio Lancashire, Red Rose Radio.   **Newsline:** 0898 122 921.
Honours: North West Counties Lg R-up 86-87, Cheshire County Lg Div 2 80-81 (R-up 79-80), Lancs Combination 73-74 77-78 (R-up 71-72 75-76, Lg Cup 71-72 72-73 73-74 76-77), George Watson Trophy 71-72 73-74 74-75, John Duckworth Trophy 85-86, Lancs Junior Cup (now ATS Trophy) R-up 85-86, FA Trophy 1st Rd 72-73 78-79, Lancs under-18 Yth Cup 89-90.

GOALKEEPERS:
Mark Pye (Irlam)
DEFENDERS: Andy Damjanovic (Eastwood H, Rocester, Nuneaton, Tamworth, Eastwood H, Trent R), **Steve Lampkin** (Rossendale Utd, Chorley, Colne D, Oswestry, Bradford City), **Alec Davies** (Stalybridge, Marine, Runcorn), **Paul Wilson** (Irlam, St Helens, Ashton Town), **Stewart Owen** (Rossendale), **James McComb** (Irlam, St Helens, Sth Liverpool, Witton Alb, Southport, Witton Alb, Sth Liverpool, Formby), **Steve Mills** (Leek, Shepshed, Lincoln, Mansfield, Sheff Wed, Man City), **Eddie Johnston** (Bangor, Sth Liverpool, Almathak)
MIDFIELD: Mark Walsh (Workington, Morecambe, Auckland(NZ), Exeter, Preston), **Dave Galloway** (Newtown, Runcorn, Irlam, Dundee Utd, Everton), **Jimmy Collins** (Morecambe, Fleetwood, St Helens, Derby(A)), **Clive Evans** (Caernarfon, Leek, Stalybridge, Bangor, Lincoln, Stockport, Crewe, Wigan, Tranmere), **Harvey Cunningham** (Mossley, Ashton Utd), **John Burns** (Droylsden, Buxton), **Charlie Cooper** (Emley, Chorley, Horwich, Chorley, Horwich, Chorley, Huddersfield)
FORWARDS: Bernie Hughes (Droylsden, Stalybridge, Glossop), **Paul Beck** (Rossendale, Clitheroe, Accrington, Rossendale, ROF Blackburn), **Terry Williams** (Grove Utd), **Darren Schofield** (Droylsden, Curzon A, Horwich), **Dean Pritchard** (Emley, Ovenden West Riding)

THE STANLEY SCENE

PROGRAMME DETAILS:
Pages: 32 **Price:** 70p
Editor: Lesley Crossley
WMPCC Rating: 25

Barrow's interest in the 1991-92 FA Trophy was curtailed by this 0-1 defeat at Gateshead. Here Neil Doherty rides the challenge of a Gateshead defender. Photo - Ged Rule.

Chairman: S Morgan   **President:** W A McCullough.
Directors: P G M Cowing, W Carradus, M Wilcox, C H Whiteside, S McCullough.
Secretary: C H Whiteside, Queens Arms, Biggar Village, Walney Island, Barrow, Cumbria (0229 471113).
Team Manager: **Asst Manager:**   **Physio:** M Cloudsdale
Press Officer: **Comm. Mgr:**   **Coach:** T Rhodes.
Ground: Holker Street, Barrow-in-Furness, Cumbria (0229 820346/823839).
Directions: M6 to junction 36, A590 to Barrow, right at 4th set of lights (next to station), ground 400 yards on left.
Capacity: 6,500 (All Covered)   **Seats:** 1,200   **Floodlights:** Y   **Shop:** Y   **Metal Badges:** Y
Colours: White/navy/white   **Change colours:** All red
Previous Leagues: Lancs Lg 01-03/ Lancs Combination 03-05 08-11/ Football League 11-72 / Northern Premier 72-79 83-84/ GMV Conference 79-83 84-86 89-92.
Midweek home matchday: Tuesday   **Reserve Team's League:** Northern Comb.
Record Attendance: 16,840 v Swansea Town, FA Cup Third Round 1954.
Best F.A. Cup season: As a Non-League club: Third Round 90-91 (lost 0-1 at Bolton).
Record Fees - Paid: Undisclosed   **Received:** £40,000 for Kenny Lowe (Barnet, January 1991).
Players progressing to Football League: I McDonald, N McDonald, J Laisby, B Diamond, F Gamble, B Knowles, G Skivington, P Byron, L Edwards, K Lowe.
Clubhouse: Barrow Sports & Leisure centre next to ground (0229 23839). Snack bars around ground.
Club Record Goalscorer: Colin Cowperthwaite 650+   **Club Record Apps:** Colin Cowperthwaite 250+
91-92 Captain: **91-92 P.O.Y.:**   **91-92 Top scorer:**
91-92 Average Attendance: **Sponsors:** Kitchen Design Studio.
Local Press: North West Evening Mail (0229 821835), Barrow & West Cumberland Advertiser (0229 832032).
Local Radio Stations: BBC Radio Furness, BBC Radio Cumbria, Red Rose.   **Newsline:** 0898 122 921.
Honours: FA Trophy 89-90 (SF 87-88), Northern Premier Lg 83-84 88-89 (Lg Cup R-up 87-88, Lg Shield 84-85), Bord Lord Trophy R-up 90-91, Cumbrian Cup 82-83 83-84 (R-up 86-87), Lancs Floodlit Cup R-up 86-87, Lancs Snr Cup 54-55 (R-up 51-52 65-66 66-67 69-70), Lancs Chal. Trophy 48-49(reserves) 80-81 (R-up 81-82 84-85), Lancs Comb. 20-21 (R-up 13-14, Div 2 R-up 04-05 10-11).

GOALKEEPERS:
Peter McDonnell (Morecambe, Barrow, Hong Kong R, Oldham Ath, Dallas Tornadoes(USA), Liverpool, Bury, Netherfield), **John Armfield** (Blackpool Rvrs, Fleetwood, Runcorn, Wren Rvrs, Fleetwood, Blackpool, Man Utd(J))
DEFENDERS:
Gary Messenger (Workington, Newcastle Blue Star, Workington), **Paul Rowlands** (Altrincham, Mt Maunganui(NZ), Bangor C, Runcorn, West Kirby, Heswall, Tranmere), **Steve Knox** (Youth), **Glen Skivington** (Southend, Derby, Barrow), **Stuart Todhunter** (Preston, Workington), **Mark Rutter** (Macclesfield, Winsford, Caernarfon, Northwich V, Caernarfon, Telford), **Shaun McHugh** (Blackpool), **Harry Wiggins** (Altrincham, Telford)
MIDFIELD:
Neil Kelly (Altrincham, Stockport), **Paddy Atkinson** (Newcastle Blue Star, Gateshead, Hartlepool, Sheff Utd), **Kevin Proctor** (Dalton Utd, Holker OB, Barrow), **Dave Burgess** (Vickers SC), **Paul Slater** (Holker OB)
FORWARDS:
Neil Doherty (Watford), **John Brady** (Altrincham, Chorley, Buxton, Southport, Altrincham, Southport, Burscough, Preston), **Mike Friars** (Youth), **Ken McKenna** (Altrincham, Telford, Tranmere, Runcorn, Telford, Tranmere, Poulton V)

Pages: 48 **Price:** £1
Editor: C H Whiteside
WMPCC Rating: 40

BISHOP AUCKLAND

Bishop Auckland FC. Back Row (L/R): Ralph Petitjean, Andrew Shaw, Brian Healey, Andrews Sams, Paul Harnett, Bryan Magee, Glen Liddle. Front: Keith Gorman, Andrew Sinclair, Paul Walker, Richie Watson, Gavin Liddle, John Deacy. Photo - Barry Lockwood.

Chairman: C Townsend **Vice Chairman:** M Hodgson **President:** W B Botcherby
Secretary: A J Russell, 21 Ramsey Crescent, Bishop Auckland DL14 6TN (0388 661568).
Team Manager: Harry Dunn **Asst Manager:** T Boylan **Coach:** J Deacey
Press Officer: Secretary **Physio:** **Comm Manager:** H Young
Ground: Kingsway, Bishop Auckland, County Durham (0388 603686).
Directions: A1 to Scotch Corner then follow signs to Bishop Auckland. Ground in town centre (rear of Newgate Str). Half mile from station.
Capacity: 5,000 (1,500 Covered) **Seats:** 600 **Floodlights:** Y **Shop:** Y **Metal Badges:** £3.00
Colours: Sky & Navy blue **Change colours:** Red & white. **Sponsors:** H Banks & Co.
Previous Leagues: N East Counties 1889-90/ Northern Alliance 1890-91/ Northern 1893-1988.
Midweek home matchday: Wednesday **Reserve Team's League:** None.
Record Attendance: 17,000 v Coventry, FA Cup 2nd Rd 6/12/52.
Best FA Cup season: 4th Rd 54-55. **League clubs beaten in Cup:** C Palace, I'wich 54-55, T'mere 56-57.
Record Fees - Paid: **Received:** £6,000 for Andy Toman.
Players progressing to Football League: Bob Paisley (L'pool), Fred Richardson & Seamus O'Connell (C'sea 1946 & 54), Robert Hardisty & Ken Williamson (D'ton 1946 & 52), William Shergold (N'port 1947), Norman Smith (F'ham 1948), Ron Steel & Ken Murray (D'ton 1950), Arthur Adey (D'caster 1950), Frank Palmer & Alan Stalker (G'head 1951 & 58), Arthur Sewell (B'ford C 1954), Gordon Barker (S'end 1954), Jack Major (Hull 1955), Harry Sharratt (O'ham 1956), Frank McKenna (Leeds 1956), John Barnwell (A'nal 1956), Derek Lewis (A Stan 1957), Corbett Cresswell (C'lisle 1958), Warren Bradley (Man U), Laurie Brown (N'hampton), Paul Baker (S'hampton), Micky Gooding (R'ham), Keith Nobbs & Andy Toman (H'pool), Peter Hinds (Dund U).
Clubhouse: Open every lunchtime and evening. Large bar, pool, juke box. **Steward:** I Taylor.
Club Record Goalscorer: **Club Record Apps:** Bob Hardisty
91-92 Captain: Brian Magee **91-92 P.o.Y.:** David Lobb **91-92 Top scorer:** Glen Liddle 14.
Local Newspapers (+Tel.Nos.): Northern Echo, Evening Gazette, N'castle Journal.
Local Radio Stations: Radio Cleveland, Radio Tees.
Honours: FA Amat Cp(10) 1895-96, 1899-1900 13-14 20-22 34-35 38-39 54-56 57-58 (R-up(8) 01-02 05-06 10-11 14-15 45-46 49-51 53-54), FA Tphy 4th Rd 78-79 88-89, N'thern Lg(19) 1898-99 1900-02 08-10 11-12 20-21 30-31 38-39 46-47 49-52 53-56 66-67 84-86 (R-up(16) 03-04 05-06 14-15 19-20 21-23 36-38 39-40 47-49 52-53 60-61 72-73 78-79 86-87, Lg Cp(7) 49-51 53-55 59-60 66-67 75-76), D'ham Chall Cp 1891-92 98-99 1930-31 38-39 51-52 55-56 61-62 66-67 84-85 85-86 87-88, HFS Loans Lg Div 1 R-up 88-89.

GOALKEEPERS: Gareth McNary (Crook), **Andy Dolphin** (Crook Town Rangers), **Matt Donnelly** (Hexham), **Andrew Sams** (Sunderland)
DEFENDERS: Paul Harnett (Ferryhill, Black & Decker), **Garry Parle** (Shildon, Bishop Auckland, **Bryan Magee** (Newcastle Blue Star, Scarborough, Horden), **Richie Watson** (Billingham T, Whitley Bay, Billingham T), **Mark Linighan** (Crook, Billingham T, Hartlepool, Wingate, North Shields), **Gavin Liddle** (Chester-le-Street, Brandon, Durham, Seaham, Gateshead, Spennymoor, Darlington, Hartlepool(A))
MIDFIELD:
David Lobb (Hartlepool), **John Deacey** (Harrogate T, Goole, Chesterfield), **James Sharkey** (Whitby), **Brian Healey** (Billingham T), **Andy Fothergill** (Crook, Bishop Auckland, Crook, Torrington), **Geoff Thompson** (Kingstonian, Newton Aycliffe, Crook, Spennymoor, Middlesbrough(T)), **John Ainsley** (Spennymoor, Guisborough), **Gary Lockwood** (Goole, Bridlington Town, Hatfield Main)
FORWARDS: Trenton Wiggan (Gainsborough Trin, Matlock, Frickley, Matlock, Gainsborough Trin, Burton Alb, Scarborough, Gainsborough Trin, Sheff Utd), **Glen Liddle** (Chester-le-Street), **Andy Sinclair** (Consett), **Tony Deane** (Frickley, Boston Utd, Emley), **Brian Crawley** (South Bank), **Paul Otley** (Garforth), **Steve Cuthbert** (Billingham T), **Wayne Noteman** (Bridlington Town, Frickley, Harrogate T, Farsley C, Goole, Harrogate RA, Yorkshire Main)

BISHOP AUCKLAND F.C. 1886-1991

KINGS WAY GROUND BISHOP AUCKLAND

HFS LOANS LGE—Premier Div.
EMLEY Sat. Dec. 28th, 1991

HFS LOANS LEAGUE

Pages: 28 **Price:** 50p
Editor: Nick Postma
WMPCC Rating: 21

737

BUXTON

Buxton's Robert Brown (6) heads clear a corner as the Bucks slip to a surprise 0-1 defeat at Ilkeston Town in the Derbyshire Senior Cup. Photo - James Wright.

Chairman: David Mellor **President:** Eddie Lampard
Secretary: D Belfield, 20 Hereford Road, Buxton SK17 9PG (0298 26033).
Team Manager: Bob Murphy **Coach:** K Perrin **Press Officer:** Tony Tomlinson (0484 718097)
Ground: The Silverlands, Buxton, Derbyshire (0298 25303).
Directions: Within 200 yards of Buxton Market Place, opposite County Police HQ. Half mile from Buxton (BR).
Capacity: 4,000 (2,500 Covered) **Seats:** 594 **Floodlights:** Y **Metal Badges:** Y
Colours: All white **Change colours:** Yellow/royal blue/royal blue.
Sponsors: Wards.
Previous Leagues: The Combination 1891-99/ N Derbys / E Ches./ Manchester 1907-32/ Ches.County 32-73.
Midweek home matchday: Tuesday **Record Attendance:** 6,000 v Barrow, FA Cup 1st rd 51-52.
Best F.A. Cup season: 3rd Rd 51-52. Also 2nd Rd 58-59, 1st Rd 62-63.
League clubs defeated in F.A. Cup: Aldershot 51-52.
Best F.A. Trophy season: Quarter Finals 70-71 71-72.
Record Fees - Paid: £5,000 for Gary Walker (Hyde 1989) **Received:** £16,500 for A Pickering (Rotherham).
Players progressing to Football League: Peter Robinson (Notts Co 1950), John Higgins (Bolton 1950), Maurice Brooks (Stockport 1951), Ray Parker (Bradford C 1951), Fred Marlow (Grimsby 1951), Ian Greaves (Man Utd 1953), John Brindley (Chesterfield 1953), Les Ferriday (W'sall 1954), John Good (T'mere 1955), Jimmy Anders (B'ford PA 1956), William Haydock (Man C 1959), Anthony Parkes (B'burn 1970), Andy Proudlove (Sheff W 1975), Graham Collier (York 1978), Harry Charlton (D'lington 1979), Ally Pickering (R'ham 1990).
Clubhouse: (0298 3197). Open nightly + Sunday lunchtimes. Wards beers, all sprits, bingo, darts and dominoes.
Steward: Committee.
Club Record Goalscorer: Dave Herbert **Club Record Apps:** Mick Davis.
91-92 Captain: Leroy Dove **91-92 P.o.Y.:** Steve Bunter **91-92 Top scorer:** Jimmy Clarke 19.
91-92 Attendances: **Highest:** 1,153 **Lowest:** 206 **Average:** 415
Local Newspapers (+Tel.Nos.): Buxton Advertiser (0298 22118/22119), Matlock Mercury (M'lock 2432/3).
Local Radio Stations: Radio Derby.
Honours: Northern Premier Lg Cup 90-91 (Presidents Cup R-up 81-82), Cheshire County 72-73 (R-up 46-47 62-63, Lg Cup 56-57 57-58 68-69), Manchester Lg 31-32 5-60(reserves)(R-up 04-05 28-29 29-30 30-31, Lg Cup 25-26 26-27), Derbyshire Senior Cup 38-39 44-45 45-46 56-57 59-60 71-72.

GOALKEEPERS:
Jimmy O'Donnell (Crewe, Man Utd)
DEFENDERS:
Robert Brown (Irlam, Astro), Colin Julian (Alfreton, Heanor, Alfreton, Eastwood T, Belper, Bolehill), Paul Daughtry (Portsmouth(T)), Lee Broomhead (Cheadle, Crewe, Stockport), Les Hunter (Matlock, Chesterfield, Lincoln, Scunthorpe, Chesterfield, Scunthorpe), Mark Howard (Stockport, King's Lynn, Norwich)
MIDFIELD:
Leroy Dove (Droylsden, Prestwich), Paul Hardman (Mossley, Rossendale, Ashton Utd, Stalybridge, Salford), Nicky Bentham (Bolton W(T)), Paul Egerton (Local football), Andy Robinson (Glossop, Rossendale, Helmshore), Marcus Harper (Stockport(T)), Andy Woodcock (Northwich V, Oldham Ath)
FORWARDS:
Paul Allen (Fleetwood, Southport, Preston, Southport, Preston, Bolton W), Andy O'Connor (Leek, Macclesfield, Shrewsbury, WBA(J)), Steve Bunter (Hyde, Curzon Ashton), Stuart Thompson (Glossop, Bacup Boro, Rochdale), Mark Hilditch (Rochdale, Wigan, Tranmere, Rochdale)

Buxton
AFC
SEASON 1991-92

HFS
LOANS
LEAGUE

Pages: 36 **Price:** 40p
Editor: Tony Tomlinson
WMPCC Rating: 19

CHORLEY

The Magpies line up for new manager Glen Buckley's first game in charge, against Shepshed on Saturday 25th April. Back Row (L/R): Fred Eyre (Coach), Danny Kent, Paul Moss, Carl Dyson, Des Christie, Declan Duke, Derek Goulding, Paul Cuddy, Lee Harvey, John Cunliffe (Trainer). Front: Tony Ward, Barry Knowles, Glen Buckley (Manager), Paul Willis, Neil Williams, Graham Harston. Photo courtesy of Chorley Guardian.

Chairman: David Murgatroyd   **President:** Dr Peter Wren.
Secretary: Jack Heyes C/O The Club (below). Home Tel: 061 702 8854.
Team Manager: Glen Buckley   **Asst Manager:** Fred Eyre   **Coach:**
Club Doctor: Dr Philip Earl   **Press Officer:** Ged Scott, Chorley Guardian (0257 264911x212)
Ground: Victory Park, Duke Street, Chorley, Lancs (0257 263406).
Directions: Just off A6, heading south out of town towards Manchester. Quarter mile from Chorley (BR).
Capacity: 4,400   **Seats:** 700   **Floodlights:** Y **Shop:** Y **Metal Badges:** Y
Colours: White & black stripes/white/black   **Change colours:** All yellow
Previous Leagues: Lancs Alliance 1890-94/ Lancs 94-1903/ Lancs Comb. 03-68 69-70/ Northern Premier 68-69 70-72 82-88/ Cheshire County 72-82/ GMV Conference 88-90.
Previous Grounds: Dole Lane 1883-1901/ Rangletts Park 01-05/ St George's Park 05-20.
Midweek home matchday: Tuesday   **Reserve Team's League:** Northern Comb.
Sponsors: O.B.G. Construction.   **Record Gate:** 9,679 v Darwen, 1931-32.
Best F.A. Cup year: 2nd Rd 86-87 (lost in replay at Preston), 90-91 (lost at Shrewsbury).
League clubs defeated in F.A. Cup: Accrington 46-47/ Wolves 86-87/ Bury 90-91.
Record Fees - Paid: £900 for Geoff Twentyman (Formby)   **Received:** £22,500 for Paul Mariner.
Players progressing to Football League: Charles Ashcroft (L'pool 1946), William Healey (Arsenal 1949), Stan Howard (H'field 1952), Derek Hogg (Leicester 1952), William Norcross (Southport 1959), Micky Walsh (Blackpool 1971), Paul Mariner (Plymouth 1973), Graham Barrow (Wigan 1976), Steve Galliers (W'don 1977), Kevin Tully (Bury 1980), Geoff Twentyman (Preston 1983), Gary Buckley (Bury 1984), Chris Hunter (Preston 1984).
Clubhouse: (0257 275662). Mon-Fri 7-11pm, Sat 12-11pm, Sun 7-10.30pm.   **Steward:** Ann Hodge.
Club Record Goalscorer: Dave Herbert   **Club Record Apps:** Mick Davis.
91-92 Captain: Barry Knowles   **91-92 P.o.Y.:** Paul Moss
90-91 Top scorer: Brian Ross, Carl Dyson (both 11).
Local Newspapers (+Tel.Nos.): Lancs Evening Post, Chorley Guardian (0257 264911 - Ged Scott ext 211).
Local Radio Stations: Radio Lancs, Red Rose.
Honours: Northern Premier Lg 87-88, Cheshire Co. Lg 75-76 76-77 81-82, Lancs Comb. 19-20 22-23 27-28 28-29 32-33 33-34 45-46 59-60 60-61 63-64 (R-up 21-22 26-27 48-49 62-63 64-65 65-66, Lg Cup 24-25 58-59 62-63), Lancs Lg 1896-97 98-99, Lancs Alliance 2892-93 (R-up 93-94), Lancs Jnr Cup 1893-94 1908-09 23-24 39-40 45-46 57-58 58-59 60-61 63-64 64-65 75-76 79-80 81-82 82-83, FA Tphy QF (replay) 76-77.

GOALKEEPERS:
Des Christie (Leyland Motors, Multipart, Royal Ordnance), **Robin Simpson** (Leek, Witton A, Hyde, Witton A, Stalybridge, Macclesfield, New Mills, Macclesfield, Stockport)
DEFENDERS: Derek Goulding (Bangor, Chorley, Bangor, Oswestry, Stafford R, Bangor, Altrincham, Prescot Cables, Everton(J)), **Barry Knowles** (Fleetwood, Altrincham, Colne D, Wigan, Barrow, Runcorn, Southport, Chorley), **Paul Willis** (Southport, Swindon, Stalybridge, Darlington, Halifax), **Paul Cuddy** (Witton A, Altrincham, Chorley, Blackpool, Huddersfield, Rochdale, Bolton W, Man City), **Russell Proctor** (Bacup Boro, Clitheroe, Glossop, Darwen, Rossendale, Darwen, Rossendale, Haslingden)
MIDFIELD:
Graham Houston (Skelmersdale, Leyland DAF, Morecambe, Colne D, Northwich V, Carlisle Utd, Wigan, Preston, Burnley, Preston), **Danny Kent** (Bury), **John Wills** (Man City), **Tony Griffiths** (Leek, Stafford R, Telford, Leek, Winsford, Leek, Port Vale), **David Glenn** (Fleetwood, Chester, Blackburn, Wigan), **David Murray** (Mauberge(Fr), Chester, Wigan), **Ian Salisbury** (Local football)
FORWARDS: Neil Williams (Local football), **Declan Duke** (Emley, Ovenden West Riding, Halifax), **Chris Patterson** (Local football), **Paul Marsden** (Local football)

Pages: 24 **Price:** 60p
Editor: S Seymour
WMPCC Rating: 29

COLWYN BAY

Colwyn Bay FC, H.F.S. Loans League Division One champions and Cup Winners 1991-92.

Chairman: G Owens   **President:** I G Grant.
Secretary: A J Banks, 15 Smith Avenue, Old Colwyn, Clwyd LL29 8BE (0492 516941).
Team Manager: Bryn Jones   **Asst Mgr:** Steph Rush   **Coach:**
Press Officer: **Physio:** John Carmichael.
Ground & Directions: As Northwich Victoria FC (See G.M.V. Vauxhall Conference Section).
Capacity, Seats etc: As Northwich Victoria.   **Metal Badges:** Yes
Colours: Sky blue/maroon/sky blue   **Change colours:** Red/white/red.
Sponsors: D J Construction.
Previous Ground: Eiras Park 1930-82/ Llanelian Road 82-92.
Previous Leagues: Nth Wales Coast 01-21 33-35/ Welsh National 21-30/ Nth Wales Comb. 30-31/ Welsh Lg (Nth) 45-84/ North West Counties 84-91.
Midweek home matchday: Tuesday   **Reserve Team's League:** O.C.S. Clwyd Lg.
Record Attendance: 5,000 (at old ground) v Borough United, 1964.
Best F.A. Cup season: First Round Proper 87-88.
League clubs defeated in F.A. Cup: None.
Record Fees - Paid: **Received:**
Players progressing to Football League:
Clubhouse: Not on ground.
Club Record Goalscorer: **Club Record Apps:**
91-92 Captain: Dave Brett   **91-92 P.o.Y.:** Mark Woods   **91-92 Top scorer:** Mark Williscroft.
Local Newspapers: North Wales Weekly News, North Wales Pioneer.
Local Radio Stations:
Honours: HFS Loans Lg Div 1 91-92 (Div 1 Cup 91-92), North West Counties Lg R-up 90-91 (Floodlit Cup 90-91), Welsh Cup SF 91-92, Welsh National Lg R-up 27-28 29-30, Nth Wales Comb. 30-31, Welsh Lg Nth 64-65 82-83 83-84 (R-up 35-36 45-46 63-64, Lg Cup 27-28), Alves Cup 63-64, Cookson Cup 73-74 79-80 80-81 81-82 83-84, Barritt Cup 79-80 81-82 83-84, Nth Wales Coast Chal. Cup 30-31 31-32 81-82 82-83 83-84, Nth Wales Coast Jnr Cup 1898-99.

GOALKEEPERS:
Trevor Ball (Northwich V, Bangor, Rhyl), **Colin Darcy** (Warrington, Sth Liverpool, Hyde, Chorley, Sydney C(Aust), Hyde, Altrincham, Bury, Everton)
DEFENDERS:
Bryn A Jones (Rhyl, Colwyn Bay, Oswestry, Winsford, Portmadoc, Denbigh), **Damian McKeown** (Skelmersdale), **Darren Tinson** (Connah's Quay), **Mark Chaloner** (Brymbo Steelworks, New Boughton), **Jamie Williams** (Wrexham(T)), **Lee Harley** (Flint), **Gary Wynne** (Flint, Mold Alex), **Mark Joseph** (Caernarfon, Savon Pallo(Fin), Caernarfon, Rhyl, Oswestry, Wrexham)
MIDFIELD:
Timmy Williams (Rhyl, Flint), **Dave Brett** (Chester), **Mark Woods** (Flint, Utd Services), **Terry Cooke** (Chester), **Bruce Urquhart** (Rhyl, Bangor, Rhyl, Bangor, Wrexham)
FORWARDS:
Mark Williscroft (Brymbo Steelworks), **Steve Jones** (Rhyl, Colwyn Bay, Bethesda, Pilkingtons), **Peter Donnelly** (Rhyl, Oswestry, Chester), **Graham Roberts** (Flint, Mold Alex, British Steel FC), **Stefan Rush** (Rhyl, Flint)

BAY REVIEW

COLWYN BAY FC.

OFFICIAL MATCH DAY MAGAZINE
Season 88-89   25p

Pages: 28 **Price:** 50p
Editor: D Orme
(0492 531758)
WMPCC Rating: 33

DROYLSDEN

As did most H.F.S. League defences in 1991-92, the Droylsden back line have trouble contending with Stalybridge's Chris 'Buffalo' Camden (9). Photo - Rob Ruddock.

Chairman: D Sterling   **President:** J Kennedy
Secretary: Gordon Hargreaves, 44 Morar Road, Dukinfield SK16 4BB (061 344 2075).
Team Manager: John Cooke   **Asst Mgr:** Kevin Gorman   **Coach:**
Press Officer: **Physio:**   **Comm Manager:**
Ground: The Butchers Arms Ground, Market Street, Droylsden, Manchester (061 370 1426).
Directions: 4 miles east of Manchester via A662 Ashton New Road, behind Butchers Arms Hotel.
Capacity: 3,500 (1,000 Covered)   **Seats:** 450   **Floodlights:** Y   **Shop:** Y   **Metal Badges:** Y
Colours: All red   **Change colours:** All yellow
Previous Leagues: Manchester/ Lancs Com 36-39 50-68/ Cheshire County 39-50 68-82/ NW Counties 82-87.
Midweek home matchday: Tuesday   **Reserve Team's League:**
Record Attendance: 4,250 v Grimsby, FA Cup 1st rd 1976.
Best F.A. Cup season: 2nd Rd 78-79.   **League clubs defeated in F.A. Cup:** Rochdale 78-79.
Record Fees - Paid: **Received:** £11,000 for Tony Naylor (Crewe).
Players progressing to Football League: Albert Butterworth & F Letchford (Blackpool 1931), William Davies & Maurice Randall (Crewe 1947), William Mellor (Accrington 1950), Geoff Tonge (Bury 1960), David Campbell (WBA 1962), Kevin Randall (Bury 1965), Peter Litchfield (Preston 1979), Tony Naylor (Crewe 1990).
Clubhouse: Open nightly and matchdays. Pool and darts.   **Steward:** Derek Balaam.
Club Record Scorer: E Gillibrand 78 (1931-32)   **Club Record Apps:**
91-92 Captain: John Burns   **91-92 P.o.Y.:** Ian Johnson   **91-92 Top scorer:** Steve Wood.
Local Newspapers (+Tel.Nos.): Droysden Reporter (061 303 1910), Advertiser.
Local Radio Stations: BBC Manchester.
Honours: Northern Prem Lg Div 1 R-up 89-90 (Div 1 Cup 87-88), NW Counties Lg Div 2 86-87, Cheshire County Lg R-up 39-40 45-46 (Lg Cup 77-78 (R-up 76-77)), Lancs Comb Div 2 R-up 55-56 58-59 62-63, Manchester Lg 30-31 32-33 (Lg Cup 23-24 33-34), Manchester Premier Cup 80-81 (R-up 83-84 90-91), Manchester Senior Cup 72-73 75-76 78-79 (R-up 72-73 75-76 78-79), Manchester Intermediate Cup 59-60 64-65 69-70, Manchester Challenge Shield 46-47.

GOALKEEPERS:
Ian Senior (Ashton Utd, Chorley etc)

DEFENDERS:
Ray Sidderley (Accrington, Droylsden, Stockport Georgians, Droylsden), **Ian Johnson** (Altrincham, Rochdale, Curzon Ashton, Chadderton), **Dave Pick** (Rylands), **Nigel Hart** (York, Chesterfield, Stockport, Bury, Crewe, Blackpool, Leicester City, Wigan)

MIDFIELD:
Dave Kershaw (Oldham Town, Whitworth Valley), **Colin Booth** (Stalybridge, Cheadle, Stalybridge, Curzon Ashton, Stalybridge, Bacup Boro), **Ian Henderson** (Accrington), **Dave Howes** (Cheadle, Stalybridge, Mossley), **Eamonn Mulvey** (Altrincham, Man City(T))

FORWARDS:
Jez Rowson (Ashton Utd, Droylsden, Ashton Utd, Droylsden), **Tony Plant** (Warrington), **Graeme Ham** (Abbey Hay, Hyde, Abbey Hay), **Tony Jones** (North Trafford, Flixton), **Mark Cullen** (Southport), **Malcolm Wagstaffe** (Stalybridge, Winsford, Hyde, Witton Alb, Winsford, Warrington, Marine, Mossley, Marine, Irlam, Urmston), **Wayne Lattie** (Local football)

PROGRAMME DETAILS:
Pages: 20 **Price:** 50p
Editor: John Schofield
WMPCC Rating: 28

Formed: 1903

EMLEY

Emley pictured before their first game in the H.F.S. Loans League Premier Division last August. Back Row (L/R): Ronnie Hudson (Physio), Gerry Quinn (Manager), Nicky Brammald, Mark Stephenson, Russell Green, Ray Dennis, Mick Farrar, Mally Wright (now Guiseley), Graham Broadbent, Steve Codd, Simon Beaumont (Coach). Front: Peter Maguire, John Balmer, Charlie Cooper, Robert Mellor, Shuan Smith (now Crewe Alexandra). Photo courtesy of the Huddersfield Daily Examiner.

Chairman: Roy Shirley   **President:** P Maude
Secretary: Gordon Adamson, 219 RowleyLane, Lepton, Huddersfield HD8 0EH (0484 602720).
Team Manager: Steve Codd   **Asst Manager:** Stephen Dyson **Coach:** Daryl Brook/Simon Beaumont
Press Officer: **Physio:** Ronnie Hudson
Ground: Emley Welfare Sports Ground, Huddersfield (0924 848398).
Directions: Follow Huddersfield signs from M1 junction 38, left onto A636, then right after about three quarters of a mile for Emley. Seven miles fron Huddersfield (BR).
Capacity: 3,000 (800 Covered)   **Seats:** 250   **Floodlights:** Y   **Shop:** Y **Metal Badges:** Y
Colours: Sky Blue/maroon/sky blue   **Change colours:** Amber/black/amber
Previous Leagues: Huddersfield/ Yorkshire 69-82/ Northern Counties East 82-89.
Midweek home matchday: Monday   **Reserve Team's League:** Northern Co's Reserve Div.
Record Attendance: 5,134 v Barking, FA Amateur Cup 1969. *9,035 v Bolton Wanderers, FA Cup First Round Proper 17/11/92; matched staged at Huddersfield Town FC.*
Best F.A. Cup season: First Round Proper 91-92 (lost 0-3 at home to Bolton Wanderers).
Record Fees - Paid: **Received:** £10,000.
Players progressing to Football League: Alan Sweeney (Hartlepool United 1979), Graham Cooper (Huddersfield Town 1984), John Francis (Sheffield United 1988), Shaun Smith (Crewe Alexandra 1992).
Clubhouse: (0924 848398). Open every day. Bingo, dancing, artists.   **Steward:** Rod Marriott.
Club Record Goalscorer: Mick Pamment 305   **Club Record Apps:** Ray Dennis 711.
91-92 Captain: Robert Mellor   **91-92 P.o.Y.:** Nicky Bramald   **91-92 Top scorer:** John Balmer 21.
91-92 Average Attendance: 390.   **Sponsors:** Perrys.
Local Newspapers (+Tel.Nos.): Huddersfield Examiner (0484 430000), Huddersfield & District Chronicle.
Local Radio Stations: Radio Leeds, Radio Sheffield.
Honours: FA Vase R-up 87-88 (SF 86-87), FA Trophy 4th Rd 90-91, FA Amateur Cup 3rd Rd replay 69-70, Northern Premier Lg Div 1 R-up 90-91, Northern Counties East Lg(2) 87-89 (R-up 85-86), Yorkshire Lg 75-76 77-78 79-80 81-82 (R-up(5) 72-74 76-77 78-79 80-81, Lg Cup 69-70 78-79 81-82, Div 2 R-up 69-70), Sheffield & Hallamshire Senior Cup 75-76 79-80 80-81 83-84 88-89 90-91 91-92, Huddersfield Lg(4).

GOALKEEPERS:
Ray Dennis (Local football)

DEFENDERS:
Steve Codd (Denaby, Guiseley, Boston FC, Long Eaton), **Nicky Bramald** (Local football), **Robert Mellor** (Birkby), **Neil Wilson** (Local football), **Frank Harrison** (Halifax, Lincoln, Middlesbrough)

MIDFIELD:
Mick Carmody (Tranmere, Emley, Huddersfield), **Lee Burrows** (Guiseley, Bradley R, Southampton(Sch)), **Simon Jones** (Netherton), **Shaun Joyce** (Local football)

FORWARDS:
Peter Maguire (Huddersfield, Leeds), **Ian Tunnacliffe** (Storthes Hall), **Chris Wood** (Bradley R), **John Balmer** (Bradley R, Emley), **Graham Broadbent** (Halifax, Emley)

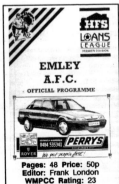

Pages: 48 **Price:** 50p
Editor: Frank London
WMPCC Rating: 23

FLEETWOOD TOWN

Fishermen

Fleetwood's Peter Farrell fires in a shot as the Fishermen over-run fellow strugglers Hyde United 5-1 at the Highbury Stadium. Photo - Steve Daniels.

Chairman: P Murfin **Vice Chairman:** T Lowery
Secretary: A Dickinson, 10 Loxley Place, Whiteholme, Blackpool FY5 3HH (0253 866004).
Team Manager: Micky Taylor **Asst Manager:** Kevin Byrne **Coach:** Barry Knowles
Press Officer: S Presnail **Physio:** Alan Dallas **Comm Manager:** S Kennedy.
Ground: Highbury Stadium, Park Avenue, Fleetwood (0253 876443).
Directions: M6 junction 32 or M55 junction 3, then A585 to Fleetwood. Follow signs to Docks - ground on far side of tramtracks behind fire station. Nearest BR station is Poulton-le-Fylde, seven miles distant. Tram stop - Nansen Road (40 yds).
Capacity: 9,500 (700 Covered) **Seats:** 200 **Floodlights:** Y **Shop:** Y **Metal Badges:** Y
Colours: Red & white/white/red **Change colours:** White/black/black
Previous Leagues: Cheshire County 78-82/ North West Counties 82-87.
Previous Grounds: None *(Predecessors Fleetwood FC played at Euston Ground 1937-38).*
Midweek home matchday: Wednesday **Reserve Team's League:**
Record Attendance: 3,000 v Exmouth Town, FA Vase Semi Final 2nd leg, 84-85. Ground Record: 6,000 - Fleetwood v Rochdale, FA Cup 1965.
Best F.A. Cup season: 1st Rd 80-81 (lost 0-4 at Blackpool), 90-91 (lost 1-4 at Atherstone Utd).
League clubs defeated in F.A. Cup: None.
Record Fees - Paid: £5,000 for Rob Wakenshaw (Southport)
Received: £25,000 for Steve Macauley (Crewe).
Players progressing to Football League: Paul Sanderson (Manchester City 1983), Phil Clarkson & Steve Macauley (Crewe Alexandra 1991). *Frank Swift (Manchester City) from predecessors Fleetwood FC.*
Clubhouse: Open normal licensing hours. **Steward:** John Hamilton.
Club Record Scorer: Dave Barnes 101 **Club Record Apps:** Stuart Robinson 388.
91-92 Captain: Paul Byron **90-91 P.o.Y.:** **91-92 Top scorer:**
Local Newspapers (+Tel.Nos.): West Lancs Evening Gazette, Fleetwood Weekly News.
Local Radio Stations: Radio Lancs, Red Rose Radio.
Honours: FA Vase R-up 84-85, FA Trophy 1st Rd 88-89 90-91, Northern Premier Lg Div 1 87-88 (Presidents Cup 89-90 (R-up 90-91), Lg Cup R-up 88-89), North West Counties Lg Div 2 83-84.

GOALKEEPERS:
Mark Thornley (Matlock, Stafford R, Alfreton, Sutton T, Belper)
DEFENDERS: Simon Woollerson (Blackpool R, Morecambe, Fleetwood, Blackpool Rangers), **Steve Haydock** (Mossley, Blackpool Rvs, Morecambe, Fleetwood), **Kevin Gerrard** (Wren Rvs, Blackburn), **Mark Simms** (Bury, Preston, Blackburn), **Gary Haslem** (Wyre Villa), **Matt Hilton** (Burnley(T)), **Loz Walsh** (Blackpool R, Morecambe, Fleetwood, Penrith, Lancaster, Workington, Southport, Morecambe, Blackpool, Preston), **Carl Lancashire** (Blackpool Mech, Feetwood, Southport, Blackpool)
MIDFIELD: Wayne Aspinall (Leyland Daf, Lancaster, Runcorn, Northwich V, Barrow, Wigan, Tranmere), **Glenn Walker** (Horwich, Warrington, Horwich, Marine, Horwich, Crewe, Burnley), **David Gough** (Chorley, Morecambe, Wyre V), **Ben Lavelle** (Morecambe, Blackpool R, Morecambe, Southport, Wren R), **Peter Farrell** (Barrow, Apoel(Cyp), Keflavik(Ice), Goteborg(Swe), Crewe, Rochdale, Shrewsbury, Port Vale, Bury), **Dave Windridge** (Blackpool R, Morecambe, Colne D, Rochdale, Bury, Cork C, Northwich V, Galatasaray(Turk), Blackpoll, Chesterfield, Sheff Utd)
FORWARDS: Craig Madden (York, Blackpool, WBA, Bury), **Alan Hughes** (Blackpool, Watford(Sch)), **Robbie Wakenshaw** (Southport, Crewe, Rochdale, Carlisle, Hamilton Zelos(NZ), Everton), **Andy Lyons** (Blackpool R, Morecambe, Fleetwood, Morecambe), **Steve Hazlehurst** (Local football), **Andy Howard** (Local football), **Stuart Diggle** (Blackpool R, Morecambe,

FRICKLEY ATHLETIC

Frickley Athletic are beaten by the aerial power of Morecambe's Steve Holden who rises to head the second goal in the Shrimps' 2-0 home win on 11th April. Photo - Andrew Mollitt.

Chairman: M Twiby. **President:** M High.
Secretary (Add & Tel): R L Bates, 2 Lincoln Crescent, South Elmsall, Pontefract WF9 2TJ (0977 644575).
Team Manager: Ronnie Glavin **Physio:** T McCroakam **Coach:** A Miller.
Financial Secretary: D Fisher.
Ground Address & Tel: Westfield Lane, South Elmsall, Pontefract (0977 642460/644453).
Directions: Follow signs for South Elmsall from A1 and A638. Left at Superdrug warehouse, right at T junction and immediately left up Westfield Lane (signposted Frickley Colliery). Left into Oxford Road (opposite Westfield Hotel) - ground on right. Two miles from South Elmsall (BR).
Capacity: 6,000 (2,500 Covered) **Seats:** 800 **Floodlights:** Y **Shop:** Y **Metal Badges:** £1.10
Colours: Blue/whites/blue **Change colours:** Yellow & black.
Previous Leagues: Sheffield/ Yorkshire 22-24/ Midland Counties 24-33 34-60 70-76/ Cheshire County 60-70/ Northern Premier 76-80/ GMV Conference (Alliance Premier) 80-87.
Midweek home matchday: Tuesday **Previous Name:** Frickley Colliery Athletic 1910-74.
Record Attendance: 6,500 v Rotherham United, FA Cup 1971. **Sponsors:** Ramset Construction.
Best F.A. Cup season: 3rd Rd 1985-86 (lost 1-3 at home to Rotherham). 2nd Rd 84-85 (0-1 at Darlington). 1st Rd 36-37 57-58 63-64 71-72 73-74 83-84 86-87 88-89.
League clubs defeated in F.A. Cup: Hartlepool United 85-86.
Record Fees - Paid: £1,800 **Received:** £12,500 for Paul Shirtliff (Boston Utd).
Players progressing to Football League: Dennis Smith & Jack Brownsword (Hull 1946), Stan Scrimshaw (H'fax 1947), William Callaghan (A'shot 1949), Leo Dickens 1950/ John Ashley & Graham Caulfield (York 1950 & 67), Ron Barritt (Leeds 1951), John Pickup (Bradford PA 1955), Tom Hymers & Arthur Ashmore & Stewart Gray (D'caster 1958 & 66 & 78), Colin Roberts (Bradford City 1959), Derek Downing (M'boro 1965), Graham Reed & Russell Wilcox (N'hampton 1985 & 86), Will Foley (S'sea 1986), Gary Brook (N'port 1987).
Clubhouse: Harlequin Club outside ground. TV, pool, other facilities. **Steward:** D Fisher.
Club Record Scorer: K Whiteley **Club Record Apps:**
91-92 Captain: P Heaney **91-92 P.O.Y.:** W Campbell **91-92 Top Scorer:** G Brook 18.
91-92 Attendance Figures: **Highest:** 496 **Lowest:** 174 **Average:** 278.
Local Newspapers (+Tel.Nos.): S Yorks Times (0977 642214), Hemsworth & S Elmsall Express (0977 640107).
Local Radio Stations: Radio Sheffield, Radio Hallam, Radio Leeds.
Hons: GMV Conf. (Gola Lg) R-up 85-86, Midland Co's Lg R-up 72-73 (Lg Cup 75-76), Yorks Lg R-up 23-24, Sheff. & Hallamshire Snr Cup 27-28 56-57 60-61 62-63 66-67 78-79 85-86 87-88 89-90, Sheffield Assoc. Lg 20-21 (R-up 11-12), FA Tphy QF 84-85.

GOALKEEPERS:
Ian Wardle (Maltby MW, Barnsley)
DEFENDERS: Neil Lacey (Goole, Denaby Utd), Mike Thompson (Goole, Scunthorpe, Barnsley), David Kitchen (Goole, Stafford R, Goole, Yorkshire Main), Peter Heaney (Goole), Gary Barnsley (Local football), Nicky Legdon (Local football), Mick Pickering (Goole, Hallam, Stockport, York, Rotherham, Sheff Wed, Southampton, Barnsley), Malcolm Shotton (Hull, Barnsley, Huddersfield, Portsmouth, Oxford Utd, Nuneaton B, Leicester C)
MIDFIELD: Winston Campbell (Boston Utd, Stafford R, Boston Utd, Rotherham, Barnsley), Ian Thompson (Goole, Worksop, Goole, Worksop, Gainsborough Trin), Mark Wilson (Huddersfield, Rotherham), Wayne Scargill (Worsbrough Bridge), Tony Holgate (Brodsworth MW, Armthorpe Welfare, Bridlington Town, Armthorpe Welfare, Doncaster, Sheff Wed), Gary Hatto (Ossett T, Frickley, Doncaster, Huddersfield(A))
FORWARDS: Simon Lowe (Goole, Scarborough, Colchester, Hartlepool, Halifax, Barnsley, Ossett Alb, York), Simon Fuller (Ossett T, Bradford C), Gary Brook (Blackpool, Scarborough, Newport Co, Frickley, Ossett Alb), Andy Kiwomya (Sheff Wed, Barnsley), Tommy Graham (Halifax, Scarborough, Scunthorpe, Doncaster, Halifax, Barnsley, Aston Villa, Arthurlie), Andy Hayward (Pontefract Coll), Andy Phillott (Harrogate T, Yorkshire Am), Chris Audsley (Ossett Alb)

1873 GAINSBOROUGH TRINITY Blues

The Gainsborough Trinity defence sprint back but cannot prevent Marine's Steve Haw capitalising on an open goal oppunity to score his side's first in a 2-1 win. Photo - Rob Ruddock.

Chairman: Mr John Davis, M.Inst.M.   **Vice Chairman:** Mr C C Anyan.
President: Ken Marsden   **Secretary:** TBA.
Team Manager: Gary Simpson.   **Asst Manager:**   **Coach:** P Barker
Commercial Manager: R Hearn (Gainsborough 614307 or 613295).
Ground: The Northolme, Gainsborough, Lincs (0427 613295).
Directions: Ground situated in town centre, 250 yds from the Post Office and magistrates court. Two miles from Lea Road (BR).
Capacity: 9,947 (4,000 Covered)   **Seats:** 290   **Floodlights:** Y   **Shop:** Y   **Metal Badges:** Y
Colours: Royal blue (white trim)/white/blue & white   **Change colours:** White/black/red
Previous Leagues: Mids Counties 1889-96 1912-60 61-68/ Football League 1896-1912/ Central Alliance 60-61.
Midweek home matchday: Tuesday   **Record Gate:** 9,875 v Scunthorpe United, 1948.
Best F.A. Cup season: 3rd Rd 1886-87. 1st Rd on 33 occasions; 1885-86 97-98 1905-14 27-34 35-36 37-39 45-47 48-49 50-54 59-60 66-67 83-84.
League clubs defeated in F.A. Cup: Rotherham United 1894-95/ Stockport County 1913-14/ Crewe 28-29 31-32/ Port Vale 37-38/ Gateshead 38-39/ Mansfield Town 45-46.
Record Fees - Paid: £3,000 for Stuart Lowe (Buxton 89-90)   **Received:** £20,000 for Tony James.
Players progressing to Football League: A Morton & S Foxall & J Cockcroft (W Ham), Arthur Hall (C'field 1947), Jack Haigh (L'pool 1949), Norman Curtis (Sheff W 1950), Des Thompson & Steve Richards (York 1951 & 86), Terry Farmer & Barry Webster & John Woodall (R'ham 1952 & 56 & 74), Maurice Robinson & Roy Brown (D'caster 1952 & 53), John Burnett & Robert Ham (G'by 1958 & 64), Robert Pashley & Mike Woldworth (S'thorpe 1959 & 76), Simon Jones (R'dale 1963), William Purton (Brad C 1975), Keith Ripley (H'field 1978), Stewart Evans (Sheff U 1980), Tony James & Ian Bowling & John Scofield (L'coln 1988), David Redfearn (S'kport).
Clubhouse: Executive 'Club on the Park' (0427 615625) open nightly and Saturday matchday lunctimes. Full license and restaurant facilities.
Club Record Scorer: Monty Brown   **Club Record Apps:** Monty Brown.
Local Newspapers: Gainsborough News, Lincolnshire Echo.
Local Radio Stations: BBC Radio Lincs.
Hons: Northern Premier Lg Cup 81-82 (R-up 71-72), Midland Co's Lg 1890-91 1927-28 48-49 66-67 (R-up 1891-92 95-96 1913-14 28-29), Lincs Snr Cup(15) 1889-90 92-93 94-95 97-98 1903-05 06-07 10-11 46-49 50-51 57-59 63-64, FA Tphy 2nd Rd 2nd rep. 86-87.

GOALKEEPERS:
Giles Newcombe (Rotherham)
DEFENDERS: Chris Gaffney (Burton Alb, Grantham, Gainsborough Trin, Denaby, Goole, Worksop, Scunthorpe, Sheff Utd(A)), Gary Middleton (Belper, Barnsley, Rotherham(T)), Paul Watson (Ossett T), Neil Horwood (Grantham, King's Lynn, Kettering, Spalding, Camb Utd, Grimsby, King's Lynn, Grantham), Darren Rolph (Frickley, King's Lynn, Barnsley), Gavan Walker (Frickley, Hallam), Ian Webster (Goole, Frickley, Mqabba(Malta), Scunthorpe)
MIDFIELD: Gary Simpson (Altrincham, Boston Utd, Stafford R, Weymouth, Stafford R, Boston Utd, Stoke), Gary Mallender (Frickley, Boston Utd, Barnsley), Andy Shaw (Worksop), Richard Logan (Belper, Worsbrough Bridge MW), Steve Kaye (Barnsley), Darrell Fox (Sheffield FC)
FORWARDS: Kevin Eley (Chesterfield, Rotherham), Neil Jenkinson (Worksop), Simon Dwyer (Sutton T, Ossett T, Denaby, Gainsborough Trin, Matlock, Nelson Utd(NZ), Jomala(Fin), Mexborough, Sheff Wed(A)), Calvin Plummer (Chesterfield, Plymouth, Notts Forest, Barnsley, Derby, Chesterfield, Notts Forest)

Formed: 1900

GOOLE TOWN

Town or Vikings

Goole Town full-back Gary Lee is given a torrid time by Morecambe winger Ian Cain. Goole lost 1-2 in this home fixture on February 8th. Photo - Andrew Mollitt.

Chairman: Christopher J Raywood
President:
Vice President: E Shaw
Vice Chairman: D O'Hearne.
Secretary: Graeme Wilson, 12 Thorntree Close, Goole, North Humbs DN14 6LN (0405 763316).
Team Manager: Dale Banton/ Terry Burdass
Asst Mgr: Peter Brown
Physio: Colin Naylor
Commercial Mgr: Mr T Burdass (0302 831650).
Coach: Richard Dawson
Press Officer: Secretary.
Newsline: 0898 446 825.
Ground: The Victoria Pleasure Ground, Carter Street, Goole (0405 762794 - matchdays).
Directions: M62 junction 36, then A614. On entering Goole turn left at second set of lights - Carter Street is the sixth right. 400 yds from Goole town (BR).
Capacity: 4,500 (4,000 Covered)   **Seats:** 200   **Floodlights:** Y   **Shop:** Y   **Metal Badges:** Y
Colours: Blue & red stripes/blue/red
Change colours: All green.
Previous Leagues: Yorkshire 24-48/ Midland Counties 48-60 61-68/ Central Alliance 60-61.
Midweek home matchday: Tuesday
Record Fee Received: £10,000 for Tony Galvin (Spurs).
Record Attendance: 8,700 v Scunthorpe United, Midland Counties Lg 1950.
Best F.A. Cup season: 3rd Rd 1956-57 (lost at Nottm Forest). Also 1st Rd on eight other occasions; 14-15 49-50 51-52 55-56 57-58 67-69 76-78 84-85.   **League Clubs defeated in F.A. Cup:** Workington 56-57.
Players progressing to Football League: Eric Binns (Burnley 1949), Arthur Hall & Les Bloadley & John Kaye & Steve Shutt (S'thorpe 1951 & 52 & 60 & 85), William Linacre & Malcolm Thompson & David Stewart (H'pool 1953 & 68 & 83), Bernard Shaw (L'coln 1953), Eric Cousans (W'sall 1954), Brian Handley (A Villa 1957), Gordon Robbins (Crewe 1958), Alan Darby (D'caster 1959), Mitchell Dournie (Bradford City 1959), Arthur Taylor (Hull 1962), Stan Marshall (M'boro 1963), John Woodall (York 1967), Ian Pearson (Plymouth 1974), Tony Galvin (Spurs 1978), Brian Ferguson (Southend 1983), Chris Maples (C'field 1986), I Sampson (Sunderland), J Smith (Wigan).
Club Record Scorer: Brian Howard
Club Record Apps: Jimmy Kelly 475.
91-92 Captain: Dave Travis   **91-92 P.o.Y.:** Dave Travis   **91-92 Top scorer:** Peter Collier 19.
Local Newspapers (+Tel.Nos.): Goole Times (763391), Hull Mail (762647), Goole Courier (763073).
Local Radio Stations: BBC Radio Humberside, Viking FM.
Honours: Northern Premier Lg Cup 87-88, Yorkshire Lg 27-28 36-37 47-48 (Lg Cup 33-34 48-49), West Riding County Cup 38-39 50-51 51-52 56-57 68-69 69-70 75-76 76-77 77-78 86-87 88-89 91-92, West Riding Snr Cup(1), FA Trophy 3rd Rd 74-75.

GOALKEEPERS:
Paul Allen (Bradford PA, Pontefract Coll, Frickley Ath, Goole, Scunthorpe Utd, Doncaster R, Bradford City), **Gary Copley** (Maltby MW)
DEFENDERS: Tony Nicholson (Selby, York City(J)), **David Burr** (Bridlington Trinity, Goole, Hull City), **Grenville Shorte** (Leeds Utd), **Doug Saunders** (Bradford PA, Pontefract Coll), **Steve Daniels** (Black-a-Moor, Selby), **Richard Dawson** (Northwich V, Chorley, Goole, Boston Utd, Frickley Ath, Scarborough, York City), **Dave McAughtrie** (Harrogate Town, Bishop Auckland, Northwich V, Darlington, York City, Carlisle Utd, Stoke)
MIDFIELD: Chris Redhead (Doncaster R), **Chris Collier** (Selby, York Rl, Selby, York Rl, Selby), **Kevin Kelly** (Huddersfield(T)), **David Travis** (Bridlington Town, Gainsborough Trinity, Chesterfield, Gainsborough Trinity, Scunthorpe Utd, Doncaster R, Hatfield Main), **Nigel Thompson** (Alfreton, Gainsborough Trinity, Colne D, Leeds Utd, Chesterfield), **Paul Neville** (Bridlington Town, Denaby Utd, Harrogate Town, Eastwood Town, Bentley V), **Mark Preston** (Leeds Utd(T))
FORWARDS: Dale Banton (Aldershot, Walsall, York City, Aldershot, West Ham), **Gary Hurlstone** (Bridlington Town, York City, Hatfield Main, Worksop, Gainsborough Trinity), **Max Nicholson** (Doncaster R), **John Duffy** (Hatfield Main), **Steve Shutt** (Scunthorpe Utd, Goole, Barnsley), **Darryl Franklin** (Harrogate Town)

HFS LOANS LEAGUE

GOOLE TOWN A.F.C.
v
BANGOR CITY
SATURDAY 12th OCTOBER

HFS LOANS LEAGUE

VICTORIA PLEASURE GROUNDS, GOOLE
SEASON 1991/92
Pages: 16 **Price:** 50p
Editor: G Wilson, A Lawson
WMPCC Rating: 20

Formed: 1896

HORWICH R.M.I.

Railwaymen

Horwich goalkeeper John Henry claims well under pressure as the Railwaymen achieve a 2-2 draw at Emley in the Second Qualifying Round of the FA Cup. Photo - Barry Lockwood.

Chairman: P J O'Berg, Esq   **President:** G H Fisher, Esq.
Secretary: L Hamer, 6 Moorside Avenue, Horwich, Bolton BL6 8EZ (0204 691155).
Team Manager: K Wright   **Asst Manager:**   **Coach:** D Haslam
Press Officer: P O'Berg   **Physio:**   **Commercial Manager:**
Ground: Grundy Hill, Victoria Road, Horwich, Bolton (0204 696908).
Directions: M61 junction 6, follow Horwich signs at r-about, bear left then right, just before zebra crossing, into Victoria Road. Ground along side road on left. 3 miles from Blackrod (BR). Buses - 126 from Preston, 517 from Wigan, 575 from Bolton.
Capacity: 5,000 (3 sides covered)   **Seats:** 500   **Floodlights:** Y   **Shop:** Y   **Metal Badges:**
Colours: Blue & white stripes/blue/blue   **Change colours:** Maroon & white/maroon/maroon.
Sponsors: Dunhall Financial Services, Horwich.
Previous Leagues: Lancs Alliance 1891-97/ Lancs 1897-1900/ Lancs Combination 17-18 19-39 46-68/ Cheshire County 68-82/ North West Counties 82-83.
Midweek home matchday: Monday   **Reserve Team's League:** Northern Football Combination.
Record Attendance: 4,500.
Best F.A. Cup season: 1st Rd 28-29 82-83.   **League clubs defeated in F.A. Cup:** None.
Record Fees - Paid: **Received:** £2,000 for Tony Caldwell (Bolton).
Players progressing to Football League: Harold Lea & David Holland & Jim Cunliffe (Stockport 1958 & 59 & 60), Frank Wignall (Everton 1958), Gary Cooper (Rochdale 1973), Tony Caldwell (Bolton 1983), Raymond Redshaw (Wigan 1984), Tony Ellis (Oldham 1986).
Clubhouse: Open every evening.   **Steward:** John Kirby.
91-92 Captain: **91-92 P.o.Y.:**   **91-92 Top scorer:**
Local Newspapers (+Tel.Nos.): Bolton Evening News (Bolton 22345).
Local Radio Stations: Radio Lancs, Red Rose Radio.
Honours: FA Trophy QF 90-91, Premier Inter League (GMAC) Cup 87-88, Cheshire County Lg 78-79 (Challenge Shield 78-79), Lancs Combination 57-58 (R-up 29-30 55-56 66-67, Lg Cup 28-29 53-54 56-57 65-66, Div 2 R-up 48-49 50-51), West Lancs Lg 10-11 11-12, Lancs Junior Cup 24-25 29-30 (R-up 53-54 57-58 62-63 82-83), Lancs Floodlit Trophy 84-85 (R-up 83-84), Lancs FA Cup 84-85.

GOALKEEPERS:
John Henry (Salford, Irlam, Leek), **Sean Bradley** (Youth)
DEFENDERS: Paul Booth (Crewe, Bolton W), **Ian Lloyd** (Mossley, Chorley, Bolton W), **Craig Wardle** (Morecambe, Chorley, Mossley, Macclesfield, Bolton W), **Andy Westwell** (Leyland Motors), **Neil Peters** (Hyde, Chorley, Witton Alb, Horwich RMI, Irlam)
MIDFIELD: Graham Haddon (Radcliffe B, Leyland Motors, Horwich RMI), **Graham Bell** (Mossley, Hyde, Mossley, Hyde, Tranmere, Bolton W, Carlisle, Preston, Oldham, Chadderton), **Alan Sixsmith** (Stockport, Blackburn(T)), **Allan Tonge** (Man Utd), **Mike Gregory** (Southport), **John Hughes** (Darwen, Winsford, Chorley, Witton Alb, Altrincham, Bury, Winsford), **Peter Cottam** (Westhoughton)
FORWARDS: **Neil McLachlan** (Chorley, Horwich RMI, Morecambe, Wrexham), **Tony McDonald** (Radcliffe), **Andy Gayle** (Naxxar Lions(Malta), Horwich RMI, Bury, Crewe, Oldham Ath), **Paul Griffin** (Mossley, Hyde, Chorley, Mossley, Chorley, Bolton W), **Ray Redshaw** (Rossendale, Salford, Chorley, Northwich V, Auckland(NZ), Northwich V, Wigan, Horwich RMI, Glossop, Southport, Hyde, Glossop, Prestwich Heys, Salford), **Paul Moss** (Chorley, Horwich, Winsford, Stalybridge, Darwen)

PROGRAMME DETAILS:
Pages: 28 **Price:** 50p
Editor: G Culshaw
WMPCC Rating: 24

HYDE UNITED

Hyde United 1991-92. Back Row (L/R): T Sutton (Trainer), M Wrench, R Harris, S Marsh, C Hodgert, P Hughes, P Kirkham, A Graham, M McGlyn (Coach). Front: I Callaghan, L Edwards, T Megram, A Coyle, C Downs, P Chadwick. Photo - Calvin Palmer, Reporter Group Newspapers.

Chairman: S Hartley   **Directors:** S Hartley, A Slater, A Beard, D Walker, F Whyatt.
Secretary: Alan Slater, 83 King Edward Road, Hyde, Cheshire SK14 5JJ (061 368 3687).
Team Manager: Cliff Roberts   **Physio:** C I Wych.   **Comm Manager:** K Clements.
Ground: Tameside Stadium, Ewen Fields, Walker Lane, Hyde SK14 5PL (061 368 1031).
Directions: On entering Hyde follow signs for Tameside Leisure Park - in Walker Lane take second car park entrance near Leisure Pool and follow road around to the stadium. Quarter of a mile from Newton (BR).
Capacity: 4,000 (2,000 Covered)   **Seats:** 400   **Floodlights:** Y   **Shop:** Y   **Metal Badges:** Y
Colours: Red/white/black   **Change colours:** Yellow/blue/blue.
Sponsors: Clarendon Square, Hyde.
Previous Leagues: Manchester 21-30/ Cheshire County 30-68 70-82/ Northern Premier 68-70. *Predecessors, Hyde FC: Lancs Lg 1889-90/ Lancs Combination 1906-17.*
Midweek home matchday: Monday   **Record Attendance:** 9,500 v Nelson, FA Cup 1952.
Best F.A. Cup season: 1st Rd 54-55 (v Workington), 83-84 (v Burnley). *Hyde FC: 1st Rd 1887-88.*
Record Fees - Paid: £8,000 for Jim McCluskie   **Received:** £17,500 for Simon Rudge.
Players progressing to Football League: Charles McClelland & John Webber & Patrick Barry (B'burn 1946 & 47 & 48), L Battrick (Manc. City 1968), Jack Hilton (Wrexham 1950), David Teece (Hull 1952), Ray Calderbank & William Bell & Neil Colbourne (R'dale 1953 & 74 & 80), Jeff Johnson (Stockport 1976), David Constantine & Donald Graham (Bury 1979), George Oghani (Bolton 1983), Kevin Glendon (Burnley 1983), Peter Coyne (Swindon 1984).
Clubhouse: (061 368 1621). Open most nights, full facilities, 150 seats.   **Stewards:** Lil & Doug.
Club Record Goalscorer: P O'Brien 247   **Club Record Apps:** S Johnson 623.
91-92 Captain: W Goodison   **91-92 P.o.Y.:** G Hodgert   **91-92 Top scorer:** P Kirkham 20.
91-92 Attendance Figures: **Highest:** 1,117   **Lowest:** 277   **Average:** 444.
Local Newspapers (+Tel.Nos.): North Cheshire Herald & Hyde Reporter (061 368 3595).
Local Radio Stations: GMR, Piccadilly.
Hons: FA Tphy SF 88-89, Prem. Inter-Lg Cp R-up(2) 88-90, NPL R-up(2) 87-89 (Lg Cp 85-86 88-89 (R-up 83-84), Chal Shield R-up 86-87 90-91), Ches County Lg(3) 54-56 81-82 (Lg Cp 33-34 52-53 54-55 72-73 81-82, Lg Chal Shield(2) 80-82 Manc. Lg(5) 20-23 28-29 29-30 (Lg (Gilgryst) Cp(4) 27-29 49-50 70-71), Ches Sen Cp 45-46 62-63 69-70 80-81 89-90, Manc. Sen Cp 74-75 (Int Cp 55-56 56-57(jt), Junior Cp 21-22 68-69), Lancs & Ches F'lit Cp(2) 54-56, Ashton Chal Cp(6) 30-34 39-40 47-48, Hyde Chal Cp(2) 27-29, Reporter Cp(3) 72-74 75-76, Gavin Nicholson Mem Tphy 79-80, Lancs F'lit Tphy(2) 86-88, Edward Case Cp(4) 56-8 59-60 80-81.

GOALKEEPERS:
Simon Marsh (Blackpool(T))
DEFENDERS: Wayne Goodison (Rochdale, Crewe, Barnsley), **John Bramhall** (Scunthorpe, Halifax, Rochdale, Bury, Tranmere), **Terry Megram** (Witton Alb, Curzon Ashton, Northwich V, Sheff Utd), **Chris Downes** (Crewe, Stockport, Sheff Utd), **Mark Wrench** (Northwich V, Wrexham), **Mick Hardman** (Droylsden, Macclesfield, Altrincham, Runcorn, Warrington)
MIDFIELD: Jamie Shields (Curzon Ashton, Man Utd(T)), **Colin Murphy** (Runcorn), **Paul Hughes** (Runcorn, Bolton), **Ian Callaghan** (Northwich V, Bolton), **Gary Vaughan** (Northwich V, Port Vale), **Steve Holland** (Northwich V, Rochdale, Crewe), **Richard Harris** (Runcorn, Hyde, Altrincham, Ashton Utd), **Steve Curley** (Southport, Radcliffe, Droylsden, Morecambe, Accrington, Curzon Ashton, Flixton, Mossley, Witton Alb, Hyde, Stalybridge), **Tony Coyle** (Northwich V, Stockport, Chesterfield, Stockport, Albion R), **Paul Kirkham** (Huddersfield, Man Utd(A), East Manchester)

PROGRAMME DETAILS:
Pages: 32 **Price:** 50p
Editor: R Stanley
WMPCC Rating: 19

LEEK TOWN

Leek Town 0, Morecambe 4 - Premier Division 21/3/92. Gary Dullaghan (5) heads just over for Morecambe, in front of Leek's impressive new stand. Photo - Andrew Mollitt.

Chairman: TBA   **President:** TBA
Secretary: Mike Rowley, 62 London Rd, Chesterton, Newcastle, Staffs ST5 7DY (0782 562890).
Team Manager: Neil Baker   **Asst Mgr:** Trevor Mullet   **Coach:** Steve Norris
Press Officer: Mike Cope
Commercial Manager: N Biddulph   **Physio:** M Rowley
Ground: Harrisons Park, Macclesfield Road, Leek ST13 8LD (09538 399278. Fax 0538 399826).
Directions: Opposite chemical works on A53 Macclesfield road half a mile north west of Leek.
Capacity: 3,500 (3,000 Covered)   **Seats:** 400   **Floodlights:** Y   **Shop:** Y   **Metal Badges:** Y
Colours: Blue/white/blue   **Change colours:** Red/yellow/red   **Sponsors:** TBA.
Previous Leagues: Staffs County/ Manchester 51-54 57-73/ West Mids (B'ham) 54-56/ Cheshire County 73-82/ North West Counties 82-87.
Previous Names: Abbey Green Rovers/ Leek Lowe Hamil.
Midweek home matchday: Tuesday   **Record Attendance:** 3,512 v Macclesfield, FA Cup 73-74.
Best F.A. Cup season: 2nd Rd replay 90-91 (lost 0-4 at Chester after 1-1 draw).
League clubs defeated in F.A. Cup: Scarborough 90-91.
Record Fees - Paid: £2,000 for Simon Snow (Sutton T)   **Received:** £2,500 Tony Griffiths (Telford).
Players progressing to Football League: Geoff Crosby (Stockport 1952), Bill Summerscales & Mark Bright & Martyn Smith (P Vale 1970 & 81 & 84), Paul Edwards (Crewe 1989).
Clubhouse: (0538 383734). Open nightly + weekend lunchtimes.   **Steward:** Mrs C Carter.
Club Record Goalscorer: Alan Vickers   **Club Record Apps:** Gary Pearce 447.
91-92 Captain: Steve Norris   **91-92 P.o.Y.:** Allan Somerville   **91-92 Top scorer:** Dave Sutton 15.
Supporters' P.o.Y. 91-92: Dave Bainbridge.
91-92 Attendances: **Highest:** 678   **Lowest:** 249   **Average:** 502
Local Newspapers: Leek Post & Times (0538 399599), Evening Sentinel (0782 289800).
Local Radio Stations: Radio Stoke, Signal Radio.   **Newsline:** 0898 664 353.
Honours: FA Trophy R-up 89-90 (QF 85-86), NPL Div 1 89-90 (Div 1 Cup R-up 88-89, Lg Shield 90-91), NW Co's Lg Cup 84-85 (Charity Shield 84-85), Cheshire Co. Lg 74-75 (Chal. Shield 74-75), Manchester Lg 51-52 71-72 72-73 (Lg Cup 72-73), Staffs Snr Cup R-up 54-55 81-82 (Jnr Cup 51-52 70-71 (R-up 47-48 48-49 49-50)), Staffs Co. Lg 50-51 69-70 70-71 73-74 (R-up 47-48 49-50, Lg Cup 70-71 73-74), Leek Post Charity Shield 46-47, Leek Cup 47-48 52-53 70-71 71-72 (R-up 46-47), May Bank Cup 47-48 50-51 71-72, Hanley Cup 48-49 70-71 (R-up 49-5), Mid Cheshire Lg Div 2 87-88 (Div 2 Cup 87-88).

GOALKEEPERS:
Bob Aston (Gresley R, Eastwood Hanley, Congleton, Welshpool, Oswestry, Hanley, Port Vale, Stoke(J)), **Rod Bates** (Irlam, Glossop)
DEFENDERS:
Dave Bainbridge (Stalybridge, Buxton, Biggin R), **Gary Pearce** (Stoke), **Andy Holmes** (Doncaster, Stoke), **Steve Norris** (Eastwood Hanley, Leek), **Chris McMullen** (Local football), **Paul Clowes** (Port Vale(J)), **Paul Wood** (Glossop, Accrington Stanley, Hyde, Sheff Utd)
MIDFIELD:
Iain Sankey (Bangor, Telford, Ipswich), **Brian Mellor** (Eastwood Hanley, Leek), **Allan Somerville** (Rocester, Hednesford, Stafford R), **Jon Laws** (Nuneaton B, Gresley R, Willenhall, Mansfield, Wolves), **Matthew Beeby** (Port Vale(T)), **Rob Myatt** (Port Vale(T))
FORWARDS:
Darren Twigg (Eastwood Hanley, Audley), **Stuart Lowe** (Gainsborough Trin, Buxton, Sheffield FC, Goole, Huddersfield), **Savvas Anastasi** (Hednesford, Stafford R, Rocester, Wolves Utd), **Martin Devaney** (Tamworth, Gresley R, Hanford, Ilkeston), **Keith Mountford** (Altrincham, Macclesfield, Eastwood Hanley, Milton Utd, Port Vale), **Dave Sutton** (Crewe, Stoke(A)), **Mark Fisher** (Congleton)

Pages: 40 **Price:** 60p
Editor: Mike Cope
WMPCC Rating: 36

MARINE

Formed: 1894   The Mariners

Marine FC, with the H.F.S. Loans League Cup won in 1992. Back Row: (L/R): Roger Patience (trainer), Graham Rowlands, Brendan Grant, Andy Rooney, Kevin O'Brien, Brian Ross, Keith Johnson, Peter King, Roly Howard (Manager). Front Row: Steve Haw, Eddie Murray, Terry McDonagh, Jon Gautrey, John Roche, Keith Proctor, John Bradshaw (Physio).

Chairman: P T Culshaw   **President:** D Hargreaves.
Secretary: John Wildman, 4 Ashbourne Avenue, Crosby, Liverpool (051 924 5248).
Manager: Roly Howard - 22 yrs at Marine, manager since March 1972 - 1,219 games in charge (625 won)!
Asst Manager/Coach: Roger Patience   **Press Officer:** David Wotherspoon
Physio: John Bradshaw
Ground: Rossett Park, College Road, Crosby, Liverpool (051 924 1743).
Directions: Ten minutes walk from Crosby & Blundell Sands (Mersey Rail). Bus No. 92.
Capacity: 2,500 (1,900 Covered)   **Seats:** 400   **Floodlights:** Y   **Shop:** Y   **Metal Badges:** Y
Colours: White/black/black   **Change:** Yellow/green/green   **Sponsors:** Boddingtons & Higsons.
Previous Leagues: L'pool Zingari/ L'pool County Comb/ Lancs Comb 35-39 46-69/ Cheshire County 69-79.
Previous Name: Waterloo Melville 1894-1903   **Previous Ground:** Waterloo Park 1894-1903.
Midweek home matchday: Tuesday   **Record Gate:** 4,000 v Nigeria, Friendly 1949.
Best FA Cup year: 2nd Rd rep. (v Hartlepool) 75-76. Also 1st Rd 32-33 45-46 46-47 47-48 74-75 89-90.
League clubs defeated in F.A. Cup: Barnsley 75-76.
Record Fees - Paid: None   **Received:** £12,250 for Ian Nolan to Tranmere Rovers, 1991.
Players progressing to Football League: James Veacock & Anthony Sharrock & Steve Brooks (Southport 1947 & 73 & 77), Sam Parker (Accrington 1948), Harry Conner (Stoke 1953), Alf Jones (Leeds 1960), Gary Williams (Preston 1972), John Lacy (Fulham & Spurs), Paul Beesly (Sheff Utd), Mark Kearney (Everton 1981), Alan Finlay (Shrewsbury 1981), Paul Cook (Norwich), Paul Edwards (Crewe & Coventry), Ian Nolan (T'mere).
Clubhouse: Open daily. Concert Hall (250 seats), Members Lounge (100 seats). Snooker room with bar.
Steward: John Barry.
Club Record Goalscorer: Paul Meachin 200   **Club Record Apps:** Peter Smith 952
91-92 Captain: Jon Gautrey   **91-92 P.o.Y.:** Jon Gautrey (Players' P.o.Y.: Keith Proctor)
91-92 Top scorer: Brian Ross 24.
91-92 Attendance Figures: **Highest:** 1,029   **Lowest:** 261   **Average:** 413.
Local Newspapers (+Tel.Nos.): Crosby Herald, Liverpool Echo, Daily Post (051 227 2000).
Local Radio Stations: BBC, Radio Merseyside, Radio City.
Hons: FA Amtr Cup R-up 31-32 (SF 46-47), FA Trophy SF 83-84 91-92, Northern Prem Lg R-up 85-86 91-92 (Lg Cup 84-85 91-92 (R-up 80-81 85-86), Presidents Cup R-up 83-84 86-87), Cheshire Co. Lg 73-74 75-76 77-78 (R-up 72-73), Lancs Comb. R-up 46-47 (Lg Cup 46-47 63-64 68-69), L'pool Comb. 27-28 30-31 33-34 34-35 (Lg Cup 30-31), Lancs Tphy 87-88 90-91, Lancs Jnr Cup 78-79, Lancs Amtr Cup 21-22 25-26 30-31 31-32 32-33, L'pool Snr Cup 78-79 84-85 87-88 89-90, L'pool Non-Lge Cup 68-69 75-76 76-77, L'pool Chal. Cup 42-43 44-45 71-72.

GOALKEEPERS:
Kevin O'Brien (Sth Liverpool, Runcorn, Chorley, Oswestry, Burscough, Rhyl, New Brighton, Maghull, Everton)
DEFENDERS: Keith Johnson (Prescot Cables), **Danny Maddox** (Bamber Bridge, Fleetwood, Wigan(T)), **Keith Proctor** (Youth), **Andy Rooney** (Altrincham, Runcorn, Crewe, Everton), **Andrew Draper** (Local football), **Phil Fisher** (Tranmere), **Mike Atkinson** (Youth), **Paul Dawson** (Witton Alb, Marine, Winsford), **Graham Rowlands** (Southport, Preston, Formby)
MIDFIELD:
Jon Gautrey (Southport, Bolton W), **John Roach** (Caernarfon, Warrington, Kirkby T), **Joey Murray** (Wrexham, Liverpool), **Tony Ward** (Chorley, Wigan Athletic, Everton, Doncaster-loan), **David Roberts** (Bolton W), **Gareth Drury** (Knowsley, Vauxhall GM)
FORWARDS: Chris Camden (Stalybridge, Cheltenham, Macclesfield, Stafford, Sth Liverpool, Ellesmere Port, Tranmere, Chorley, Oswestry, Chester, Poulton Vics), **Brendan Grant** (Warrington, Marine, Caernarfon, Southport, Burscough), **Steve Haw** (Altrincham, Marine, Kirkby T, Runcorn, Wigan), **Eddie Murray** (Altrincham, Tranmere, Stork), **Steve O'Neill** (Stantondale Utd), **Brian Ross** (Chorley, Winsford, Northwich V, Rochdale, Man Utd(A))

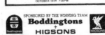

MARINE A.F.C. 🏠 LOANS LEAGUE

FORTY PENCE

1991/92

MARINE v MOSSLEY

SPONSORED BY THE WINNING TEAM
Boddingtons   **HIGSONS**
SUPPLIERS OF TRADITIONAL CASK CONDITIONED BEERS

Pages: 24 **Price:** 50p
Editor: David Wotherspoon
WMPCC Rating: 25

750

MATLOCK TOWN

Bangor City's Jason Welsh bursts through the Matlock Town defence. However, the Gladiators had the last laugh as they won 3-2; the first time they had beaten Bangor at Farrar Road for 22 years. Photo - Allan Monument.

Chairman: C Britland   **Vice Chairman:** G Worth   **President:**
Secretary: K F Brown, 'Barncroft', 1 Malvern Gardens, Matlock DE4 3JH (0629 584231).
Team Manager: Ron Reid   **Physio:** G Buckner   **Coach:**
Press Officer: G M Tomlinson (0629 3763)   **Commercial Manager:** Mrs S Tomlinson.
Ground: Causeway Lane, Matlock, Derbyshire (0629 55362/583866).
Directions: On A615, 500 yds from town centre and Matlock (BR).
Capacity: 7,500 (2,000 Covered)   **Seats:** 240   **Floodlights:** Y   **Shop:** Y   **Metal Badges:** Y
Colours: Royal blue/white/royal blue   **Change colours:** All yellow.
Sponsors: Panasonic.
Previous Ground: Hall Leys (last century).
Previous Leagues: Midland Counties 1894-96 1961-69/ Matlock & District/ Derbys Senior/ Central Alliance 24-25 47-61/ Central Combination 34-35/ Chesterfield & District 46-47.
Midweek home matchday: Tuesday   **Reserve Team's League:**
Record Attendance: 5,123 v Burton Albion, FA Trophy 1975.
Best F.A. Cup season: 3rd Rd 76-77. Also 1st Rd 1885-86 86-87 86-87 87-88 1959-60 74-75 75-76 89-90.
League clubs defeated in F.A. Cup: Mansfield Town 76-77.
Record Fees - Paid: £300 for Mick Chambers (Grantham)   **Received:** £10,000 for Ian Helliwell (York).
Players progressing to Football League: Keith Haines (Leeds 1959), Wayne Biggins (Burnley 1984), Darren Bradshaw (Chesterfield 1987), Les McJannet (Scarborough 1987), Ian Helliwell (York 1987).
Clubhouse: Gladiators Social Club, on ground, open six nights per week.   **Steward:** Steve Flitter.
Club Record Goalscorer: **Club Record Apps:**
91-92 Captain: **91-92 P.o.Y.:**   **91-92 Top scorer:**
Local Newspapers (+Tel.Nos.): Matlock Mercury, Derbyshire Times.
Local Radio Stations: Radio Derby.
Honours: FA Trophy 74-75, Northern Premier Lg R-up 83-84 (Lg Cup 77-78, Shield 78-79), Midland Counties Lg 61-62 68-69, Central Alliance (North) 59-60 60-61 (R-up 61-62 62-63, Div 1 Cup R-up 61-62, Div 2 59-60, Div 2 Cup 59-60 60-61), Derbyshire Senior Cup 74-75 76-77 77-78 80-81 83-84 84-85 91-92 (R-up 60-61 72-73 73-74 75-76 80-81 81-82 82-83 89-90), Derbshire Divisional Cup (North) 61-62 (R-up 62-63), Evans Halshaw Floodlit Cup 88-89, Anglo-Italian Non-League Cup 1979.

GOALKEEPERS:
Stewart Wilson (Dronfield, Rotherham)
DEFENDERS: Stuart Franklin (Shepshed, Grantham, Belper, Alfreton), **Steve Myles** (Boston Utd, Frickley, Worksop, Chesterfield, Sheff Wed), **Carl Fuller** (Shepshed, Matlock, Frickley, Matlock, Barnsley), **David Vaughan** (Boston Utd, Burton Alb, Mossley, Boston FC), **Paddy McGeeney** (Gainsborough Trin, Chesterfield, Sheff Utd), **Greg Mitchell** (Sheffield FC, Gainsborough Trin, Crookes, Matlock, Sheff Utd(A)), **Gordon Simmonite** (Gainsborough Trin, Lincoln, Blackpool, Boston Utd, Sheff Wed, Rotherham(A)), **Chris James** (Scarborough, Matlock)
MIDFIELD: John Sheppard (Sheffield FC), **Everton Marsh** (Stafford R, Worksop, Grantham, Ruddington), **Craig Thompson** (Gainsborough Trin, Worksop, King's Lynn, Gainsborough Trin, Boston Utd), **Marcus Brameld** (Hatfield Main, Bridlington Town, Man Utd(T)), **John Harker** (Local football), **Andy Glenister** (Rossington Main)
FORWARDS: Graham Hoyland (Goole, Gainsborough Trin, Spalding, Matlock, Gainsborough Trin, Frickley, Worksop, Canberra(Aust), Doncaster, Grimsby), **Nick Tilly** (Belper, Matlock, Sheffield FC, Matlock, Crookes), **Mark Mullins** (Staveley, Alfreton, Chesterfield), **Kevin Gee** (Rainworth MW, Oakham Utd), **David Mossman** (Boston Utd, Stafford R, Boston Utd, Lincoln, Brad City, Stockport, Rochdale, Sheff Wed), **Stacey Reed** (Local football)

MATLOCK TOWN FC
CAUSEWAY LANE GROUND, MATLOCK
SEASON 1991/92
Panasonic
SHIRT SPONSORS
WESTON'S of WIRKSWORTH
HFS
LOANS LEAGUE
Official programme 40p

Pages: 32 **Price:** 35p
Editor: D Phillips (0629 55035)
WMPCC Rating: 23

MORECAMBE

Ian Cain - outstanding again for Morecambe in 1991-92.

Chairman: Eddie Weldrake   **Vice Chairman:** Fred O'Brien.
Secretary: Brian Cowburn, 11 Windsor Road, Hyde, Cheshire SK14 5JB (061 368 2126).
Team Manager: Bryan Griffiths   **Asst Mgr:** Billy Rodaway   **Physio:** David Edge
Press Officer: **Lottery Manager:** Percy Mitton.
Ground: Christie Park, Lancaster Road, Morecambe LA4 4TJ (0524 411797/832230).
Directions: Ground on main town centre road. Two miles from Morecambe Promenade (BR).
Capacity: 2,500   **Seats:** 3,050   **Floodlights:** Y   **Shop:** Y   **Metal Badges:** Y
Colours: Red/white/black   **Change colours:** All white
Sponsors: Lancaster & Morecambe Newspapers.   **Newsline:** 0898 446 826.
Previous Leagues: Lancs Combination 20-68.   **Previous Ground:** Woodhill Lane 1920.
Midweek home matchday: Tuesday   **Record Attendance:** 9,383 v Weymouth, FA Cup 3rd Rd 13/1/62.
Best FA Cup year: 3rd Rd 61-62. 1st Rd(13) 36-37 56-57 58-59 61-63 66-67 68-69 74-77 78-80 85-86 91-92.
League clubs defeated in F.A. Cup: Chester 61-62.
Record Fees - Paid: £7,500 to Fleetwood for Ian Cain, 1988
             Received: £6,000 from Colne Synamoes for Barrie Stimpson.
Players progressing to Football League: Fred Blondel & Malcolm Darling (Bury 1946 & 78), Herbert Harrison (Accrington 1947), Gordon Milne (Preston 1956), Ray Charnley (B'pool 1957), Ron Mitchell (Leeds 1958), Derek Armstrong (Carlisle 1961), Alan Taylor (Rochdale 1973), John Coates (Southport via Burscough & Skelmersdale 1975), Keith Galley (Southport 1975), Brian Thompson (West Ham 1977), David Eyres (Blackpool), Kevin Lowe (Barnet via Barrow), Steve Gardner (Bradford City), Dave Lancaster (Chesterfield).
Clubhouse: The Shrimps Club (0524 417849). Open every evening.   **Steward:** R Long.
Club Record Scorer: Keith Borrowdale 289   **Club Record Apps:** Steve Done 579.
91-92 Captain: Paul Lodge   **91-92 P.o.Y.:** Ollie Parillon **91-92 Top scorer:** John Coleman.
91-92 Attendances: **Highest:** 692   **Lowest:** 304   **Average:** 409
Local Newspapers (+Tel.Nos.): Morecambe Visitor (0524 414531).
Local Radio: Radio Lancs, Red Rose Radio.
Hons: FA Tphy 73-74, Lancs Comb.(5) 24-25 61-63 66-68 (R-up 25-26, Lg Cup 26-27 45-46 64-65 66-68), Lancs Jnr Cup (now ATS Tphy)(7) 25-27 61-63 68-69 85-87, Lancs Snr Cup 67-68, Lancs Lg Div 2 83-84.

GOALKEEPERS:
Mike Allison (Chesterfield, Horwich RMI), **Geoff Thornton** (Southport, Runcorn, Burscough, Prescot Cables, Southport0
DEFENDERS: Steve Horrocks (Local football), **Paul Tomlinson** (Mossley, Burscough), **Robbie Armstrong** (Rhyl, Southport, Kirkby T), **Gary Dullaghan** (Rhyl, Oswestry, Witton Alb, Ford Motors), **Ollie Parillon** (Horwich RMI, Leyland Motors), **Richard Scanlon** (Marine), **Jamie McGowan** (Netherfield)
MIDFIELD: Jimmy Brown (Vauxhall GM), **John McMahon** (Altrincham, Runcorn, Witton Alb, Altrincham, Sth Liverpool, Southport, Everton), **Ian Murphy** (Formby, Altrincham, SV Hasel(Ger)), **Alex Russell** (Sth Liverpool, Liverpool(T)), **Paul Lodge** (Witton Alb, Macclesfield, Southport, Barrow, Stockport, Bolton W, Preston, Everton), **Paul McNally** (Vauxhall GM, Warrington, Southport, Stalybridge, Runcorn, Oswestry)
FORWARDS: Ian Cain (Fleetwood, Blackpool Mech, Fleetwood), **Stuart Mellish** (Witton Alb, Altrincham, Rochdale, Blackpool), **Steve Holden** (Southport, Morecambe, Fleetwood, Takapuna City(NZ), Blackpool, Northwich V, Runcorn, Blackpool Mech, Blackpool Rangers, Wren R), **Ian McInerney** (Northwich V, Stockport, Huddersfield, Newcastle Blue Star), **Richard Close** (Netherfield), **John Coleman** (Witton Alb, Rhyl, Macclesfield, Runcorn, Southport, Marine, Burscough, Kirkby T)

Pages: 36 **Price:** 60p
Editor: P Oldrieve
WMPCC Rating: 34

MOSSLEY

Mossley FC (including Peter Barnes, top right) 19910-92. Photo - Barry Lockwood.

Chairman: Roger Finn   **President:** J Anderson.
Secretary: Les Fitton, 25 Rushmere, 18th Fairway, Ashton-under-Lyme OL6 9EB (061 330 2182).
Team Manager: Ged Coyne   **Asst Mgr:** Tommy Martin   **Physio:** Tony Sutton
Coach: **Press Officer:**
Ground: Seel Park, Market Street, Mossley, Ashton-under-Lyme (0457 832369).
Directions: Off M62; from west via Oldham, Lees and Grotton; from east via Saddleworth. From M1 or Sheffield via Stalybridge then Mossley. Half mile from Mossley (BR), buses 153 from Manchester, 343 from Oldham or 350 from Ashton.
Capacity: 4,500 (1,500 covered)   **Seats:** 200   **Floodlights:** Y   **Shop:** Y   **Metal Badges:** Y
Colours: White/black/black   **Change colours:** Yellow/blue/yellow.   **Sponsors:**
Previous Leagues: Ashton/ South East Lancs/ Lancs Combination 18-19/ Cheshire County 19-72.
Previous Names: Park Villa 03-04/ Mossley Juniors 04-09.   **Previous Ground:** Luzley.
Midweek home matchday: Tuesday   **Record Attendance:** 7,000 v Stalybridge, 1950.
Best F.A. Cup season: 2nd Rd replay 49-50. Also 2nd Rd 80-81, 1st Rd 69-70 77-78 78-79 79-80 81-82 83-84.
League clubs defeated in F.A. Cup: Crewe Alexandra, 80-81.
Record Fees - Paid: £2,300.   **Received:** £25,000 for Eamon O'Keefe.
Players progressing to Football League: John Wright (Blackpool 1946), Tom Bell & Albert Wadsworth (Oldham 1946 & 49), Albert Lomas (Rochdale 1950), Arthur Tyrer (Leeds 1946), Eric Williams (Halifax 1951), John Willis (A Villa 1958), Mike Eckershall (Torquay 1959), Alan Roberts (Bradford PA 1969), Gary Pierce (Huddersfield 1971), Eamon O'Keefe (Everton 1979), David Young (Wigan 1983).
Clubhouse: Open nights and matchdays.   **Steward:** Ms Easey and McConnell.
91-92 Captain: John Imrie   **91-92 P.o.Y.:**   **91-92 Top scorer:**
91-92 Attendance Figures: **Highest:** 605   **Lowest:** 224
Local Newspapers (+Tel.Nos.): Oldham Evening Chronicle, Saddleworth & Mossley Reporter.
Local Radio Stations: Radio Manchester, Piccadilly.
Honours: FA Trophy R-up 79-80, Northern Premier Lg 78-79 79-80 (R-up 80-81 81-82 82-83, Lg Cup 78-79 88-89 (R-up 75-76 81-82), Challenge Shield 88-89 (R-up 78-79 79-80 80-81 81-82)), Cheshire County Lg R-up 19-20 69-70 (Lg Cup 20-21 60-61), Manchester Premier Cup 88-89 90-91, Manchester Intermediate Cup 60-61 66-67 67-68 (R-up 58-59 63-64 70-71 78-79), Manchester Challenge Shield 14-15 33-34 37-38 48-49 (R-up 36-37 38-39 50-51), Reporter Floodlit Cup 74-75 88-89, North West Floodlit Cup R-up 76-77.

GOALKEEPERS:
Andy Newell (Witton Alb, Accrington, Witton Alb, Wren R), **Martin White** (Accrington S, Hyde, Man City(T))

DEFENDERS:
Russ Hooton (Witton Alb, Hyde, Oswestry, Runcorn, Northwich V, Witton Alb, Droylsden, Mossley, Sth Liverpool, Stockport), **Chris Molloy** (Altrincham, St Helens, Witton Alb, York(T)), **Robert Price** (Oldham Ath(T)), **David Blow** (Radcliffe, Hyde, Flixton, Hyde, Glossop, Hyde, Horwich RMI, Glossop, Bury, Oldham Ath(J))

MIDFIELD:
John Imrie (Runcorn, Macclesfield, Altrincham, Runcorn, Northwich V, Nantwich, Bury), **Colin Heywood** (Hyde, Sheff Utd(T)), **Mark Butterworth** (East Manchester), **Steve Milligan** (Rochdale)

FORWARDS:
Paul Bowler (Chadderton, Chorley, Chadderton), **Colin Small** (Stalybridge, Rochdale, Man City), **John Waring** (Runcorn, Telford), **Peter Sivori** (Hyde), **Lee Butterworth** (Ashton Utd, Accrington Stanley, Hyde, Ashton Utd), **Mark Aston** (Loughborough)

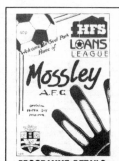

PROGRAMME DETAILS:
Pages: 28 **Price:** 50p
Editor: Julian Thomas
WMPCC Rating: 19

SOUTHPORT

Southport FC: Back Row (L/R): David Gamble, Tony Jarvis, Kevin McCormack, Chris Pile, Paul Moore, Dave Fuller, Bobby Howard, Steve Curley. Centre: Ian Baines, Neil Rigby, Mark Brennan, Ian Baker, Steve Joel, Les Blasberry (Former Asst Manager), Brian Kettle (Manager), Kevin Mooney, Steve Baines, Jon Senior, Jimmy Blackhurst. Front: Steve Porter, Andy Pope, Tim Medcroft (Directors), Jack Carr (President), Charles Clapham (Chairman), Roy Morris (Secretary), Mick Morgan (Director), Charlie Powell (Groundsman). Macol: Paul Morris.

Chairman: Charles Chapman **Directors:** A Pope, M Morgan, T Medcroft, S Porter, R Morris.
Secretary: Roy Morris, Manikata, 3 Stretton Drive, Southport PR9 7DR (0704 211428).
Team Manager: Brian Kettle **Asst Manager:** **Coach:**
Press Officer: Secretary **Physio:** **Commercial Manager:**
Ground: Haig Avenue, Southport PR8 6JZ (0704 533422).
Directions: M6 then M58 to Ormskirk, then Southport. Haig Avenue is a right turn off Scansbrick New Road half mile before town centre. Ground signposted from all entrances to town. One and a half miles from the station.
Capacity: 6,500 **Seats:** 1,890 **Floodlights:** Y **Shop:** Y **Metal Badges:** Y
Colours: Old gold/black/old gold & black **Change colours:** All white. **Sponsors:** Apollo Leisure.
Previous Leagues: Lancs 1889-1903/ Lancs Combination 03-11/ Central 11-21/ The Football Lg 21-78.
Previous Names: Southport FC & Southport Wanderers; clubs amalgamated in 1886. Southport Central 1888-1918, Southport Vulcan 1918-19.
Previous Ground: New Scarisbrick Road (pre-1904)/ Ash Street now renamed Haig Avenue.
Record Gate: 20,010 v Newcastle Utd, FA Cup 1932. *At old ground; 5,000 v Everton, FA Cup 1894-95.*
Midweek home matchday: Tuesday **Best F.A. Cup season:** 6th Rd 30-31.
League clubs defeated in F.A. Cup (as a non-league club): Blackpool 1898-99 1901-02 & 03-04.
Record Fees - Paid: £6,000 for Malcolm Russell. **Received:** £16,000 for Tony Field.
Players progressing to Football League: Ian Workman (Chester), Andy Mutch (Wolves), Shaun Teale (B'mouth, Aston Villa), Tony Rodwell (Blackpool), D Eyres (Blackpool), Ian Gore (Blackpool), Graham Barrow (Chester, Wigan), Tommy Wheeldon (Torquay), Steve Whitehall (Rochdale).
Clubhouse: (0704 530182). On ground. **Steward:** TBA.
91-92 Captain: Kevin Mooney **91-92 P.O.Y.:** Bob Howard **91-92 Top scorer:** Jimmy Blackhurst 23.
91-92 Attendance Figures: **Highest:** 552 **Lowest:** 2-6 **Average:** 365.
Local Newspapers: Southport Visitor, Southport Star.
Local Radio Stations: Radio Merseyside, Red Rose, Radio City. **Newsline:** 0898 446 836.
Hons: Football Lg Div 4 72-73 (R-up 66-67, Div 3 Nth Cup 37-38), FA Tphy 3rd Rd rep. 85-86, Premier Inter Lg Cup R-up 90-91, NPL Cup 90-91 (Presidents Cup 87-88 88-89), Lancs Comb. Div 2 03-04, Lancs Lg 02-03 (R-up(3) 1898-99 1900-02), Lancs Snr Cup 04-05 (Jnr Cup 19-20), L'pool Snr Cup 30-31 31-32 43-44 57-58(Jt) 63-64(Jt) 74-75 90-91.

GOALKEEPERS:
Paul Moore (Alvechurch, Morecambe, Alvechurch, Worcester, Rhyl)
DEFENDERS:
Gray Bradley (Sth Liverpool, Gen Chemicals, Runcorn, Gen Chemicals), Dave Fuller (Witton Alb, Bangor City, Gainsborough Trinity, Bangor City), Ian Baines (Knowsley Utd, Rhyl, Knowsley Utd, Southport, Kirkby), Peter Daley (Redbridge F, Chelmsford, Southend Utd, Tranmere R, Liverpool(A)), Bob Howard (Sth Liverpool), Kevin Mooney (Bangor City, Stafford R, Tranmere R, Telford Utd, Bury, Bangor City), Steve Baines (Newton), Mark Schofield (Horwich, Wigan)
MIDFIELD: Mark Brennan (Morecambe, Sth Liverpool, Bootle, Sth Liverpool), David Gamble (Altrincham, Grimsby), Jon Senior (Horwich RMI, Northwich V, Horwich RMI, Bolton W(T)), Ian Baker (Sth Liverpool, Bootle, Sth Liverpool, Altrincham, Sth Liverpool), Chris Walmesley (Fleetwood, Horwich RMI, Atherton LR, Horwich RMI, Daisy Hill), Alistair Monk (Everton), Alan McDonald (Altrincham, Witton Alb, Accrington Stanley, Southport, Gen Chemicals, Vauxhall GM, St Helens)
FORWARDS: Tony Jarvis (Witton Alb, Colne D, Crewe, Oldham Ath, Irlam), Jimmy Blackhurst (Sth Liverpool, Marine, Formby), Kevin McCormack (Formby, Droylsden, Southport, Skelmersdale, Southport), Gary Martindale (St Dominics), Steve Hanson (Youth team), Ian Joinson (Bootle), Peter Withers (Runcorn, Sth Liverpool)

PROGRAMME DETAILS:
Pages: 40 Price: 70p
Editor: Derek Hitchcock
WMPCC Rating: 28

WHITLEY BAY

Whitley Bay pictured before their first home match in 1991-92. Back Row (L/R): Billy Johnson, Warren Teasdale, Peter Robinson, Gregg Young, Ian Chandler, Chris Scott, Steve Veitch. Front: Danny Olsen, Perry Briggs, John Carver, Tony Dawson, Peter Embleton, Paul Ferris. Cups: HFS Loans Division One championship and Cup, both won previous season.

Chairman: Alan Lingwood　　**Vice C'man:** W Rodgerson　　**President:** C E Fuller, MBE.
Secretary: Rob Harding, 22 Cambridge Avenue, Whitley Bay NE26 1BB (091 251 5179).
Team Manager: Bobby Graham　　**Physio:** Dave Ashton　　　　　　**Press Officer:** Secretary
Commercial Manager: W Dixon/ A Lingwood.
Ground: Hillheads Park, Hillheads Road, Whitley Bay, Tyne & Wear (091 2513680).
Directions: 1 mile walk from bus station - leave St Pauls Church southward, turn right at r-about, ground 3rd left at rear of ice rink. Whitley Bay or Monkseaton metro stations, both 1 mile.
Capacity: 4,500 (500 Covered)　　**Seats:** 350　　**Floodlights:** Y　**Shop:** Y　**Metal Badges:** Y
Colours: Blue & white stripes/blue/blue　　**Change colours:** All yellow
Record Fee (Paid & Received): £500　　**Sponsors:**
Previous Leagues: Tyneside 09-10 Northern Alliance 50-55/ North Eastern 55-58/ Northern 58-88.
Previous Name: Whitley Bay Athletic 1950-58.
Midweek home matchday: Wednesday　　**Record Attendance:** 7,301 v Hendon, FA Amateur Cup 1965.
Best F.A. Cup season: 3rd Rd 89-90 (lost 0-1 at Rochdale). 2nd Rd 90-91 (lost 0-1 at home to Barrow).
League clubs defeated in F.A. Cup: Scarborough, Preston North End 89-90.
Players progressing to Football League: William Dodd (Burnley 1956), William Younger (Nottm F 1957), Ron Brown (B'pool 1965), John Ritchie (P Vale 1965), John Brodie & Aiden McCaffery (C'lisle 1967 & 88), Mike Spelman (Wolves 1969), Tony Harrison (Southport 1977), Mark Miller (Gillingham 1981), Garry Haire (Bradford City 1983 Stewart Ferebee (Darlington 1987).
Clubhouse: Bar and concert room. Lounge, darts, pool, 5-a-side courts.　　**Steward:** Run by directors.
Club Record Goalscorer: Billy Wright 307　　**Club Record Apps:** Bill Chater 640.
91-92 Captain: Warren Teasdale　　**91-92 P.o.Y.:**　　**91-92 Top scorer:** Ian Chandler 21.
91-92 Attendances:　　**Highest:** 505　　**Lowest:** 123　　**Average:** 257
Local Newspapers: The News, Guardian, Herald & Post.
Local Radio: Radio Newcastle, Metro.
Honours: FA Amateur Cup SF 65-66 68-69, FA Trophy 3rd Rd 86-87, Northern Premier Lg Div 1 90-91 (Div 1 Cup 88-89 90-91), Northern Lg 64-65 65-66 (R-up 59-60 66-67 68-69 69-70, Lg Cup 64-65 70-71 (R-up 67-68)), Northern Alliance 52-53 53-54 (Lg Cup 52-53 53-54), Northumberland Senior Cup 52-53 60-61 63-64 64-65 67-68 68-69 69-70 70-71 72-73 86-87 (R-up 53-54 54-55 55-56 65-66 76-77 85-86 90-91).

GOALKEEPERS:
Steve Toth (Nth Shields, Spennymoor, South Bank, Whinney Bank, **Paul Leeming** (Gretna, Penrith, Netherfield, Blackburn R)
DEFENDERS: Pete Embleton (Brandon Utd, Blyth S, Sunderland), **Mark Liddle** (Sunderland(A)), **Chris Scott** (Lincoln, Northampton, Blyth S, Nth Shields, Whitley B), **Warren Teasdale** (Brandon Utd, Morpeth), **Gary Lormor** (B Auckland, Chester-le-St, B Auckland, Horden CW), **Tony Dawson** (Weymouth, Blyth S, Whitley B, WBA), **Pete Harrison** (Gateshead, Barrow, Charleroi(Belg), Gateshead), **Simon Jeffels** (Carlisle Utd, Barnsley)
MIDFIELD: Billy Johnson (Ashington, Whitley B, Nth Shields, Brandon Utd), **Perry Briggs** (Gateshead, Nth Shields, Gateshead, Newcastle Utd), **Billy Lees** (Spennymoor), **Chris Hutchinson** (Nth Shields, Newcastle B Star, Newcastle Utd), **John Carver** (Barrow, Gateshead, Newcastle Elm St, Newcastle B Star, Cardiff, Newcastle Utd), **Dave Willis** (Bedlington T, Alnwick, Newcastle Utd), **Paul Walker** (B Auckland, Whitley B, Blyth S, Horden CW, Newcastle B Star, Blyth S, Scarborough, Horden CW, Hull, Sunderland(A))
FORWARDS: Ian Chandler (Aldershot, Barnsley), **Andy Shaw** (B Auckland, Crook), **Gary Boagey** (Spennymoor), **Keith McNall** (Barrow, Eppleton, Gateshead, B Auckland, Gateshead, Crook), **Darren Barker** (Tow Law, Nth Shields, Whickham, Winlaton), **Danny Olson** (Colchester, Ipswich, Whitley B), **Joe Olabode** (Gateshead, South Bank, Gateshead, SC Vaux), **Mark Eagling** (Gretna, Whitley Bay, Carlisle(T))

THE BAY BULLETIN

OFFICIAL MATCHDAY PROGRAMME OF WHITLEY BAY F.C.

WHITLEY BAY
V
NEWCASTLE UTD. RES.
NORTHUMBERLAND SENIOR CUP
QUARTER FINAL
SATURDAY, 18th JANUARY 1992
KICK OFF 3.00 p.m.
50p

PROGRAMME DETAILS:
Pages: 48 **Price:** 50p
Editor: Len Bone
WMPCC Rating: 26

WINSFORD UNITED

Winsford United FC, H.F.S. Loans League Division One runners-up 1991-92. Back Row (L/R): Mike McKenzie, Mark Leacock, Jason McCoy, Archie Lloyd, Osher Williams, Cec Edey, Alex Mayfield, Peter Prince, Jimmy Cameron, Bevon Blackwood, Dave Maynard, Jackie McDonald, Dave 'Taffy' Jones. Front: Dave Esdaile, Barry Downer, Wayne Grant, John Whitney, Chris Winwood, Andy Taylor, Neil Hall, Darrem Sheridan, Gary Thomas.

Chairman: M Gaskill **President:** J Deans.
Secretary: B D Redmond, 51 Esk Road, Winsford, Cheshire CW7 3JJ (0606 552841).
Team Manager: Mike McKenzie **Asst Manager:** Taffy Jones **Coach:** None
Press Officer: **Physio:** None
Ground: Barton Stadium, Wharton, Winsford, Cheshire CW7 3EU (0606 593021).
Directions: From north; M6 junction 19, A556 towards Northwich to Davenham, then A5018 to Winsford. From south; M6 junction 18, A54 through Middlewich to Winsford. Ground quarter mile off main road in Wharton area of town. 1 mile from Winsford (BR).
Capacity: 6,000 (5,000 Covered) **Seats:** 250 **Floodlights:** Y **Shop:** N **Metal Badges:** N
Colours: Royal blue/white/royal blue **Change colours:** Maroon/white/white.
Sponsors: Dickson Motors Ltd, Winsford (Ford).
Previous Name: Over Wanderers (prior to 1914). **Previous Leagues:** The Combination 02-04/ Cheshire County 19-40 47-82/ North West Counties 82-87.
Midweek home matchday: Wednesday **Record Attendance:** 7,000 v Witton Albion 1947.
Best F.A. Cup season: 2nd Rd 1887-88. Also 1st Rd 1975-76 1991-92.
League clubs defeated in F.A. Cup: None.
Record Fees - Paid: Nil
  Received: £6,000 for Neville Southall from Bury.
Players progressing to Football League: William Foulkes (Chester 1948), Cliff Marsh (Leeds 1948), Bennett Nicol (Rochdale 1949), Eric Johnson (Coventry 1952), Walter Hughes (Liverpool 1954), Reg Lewis (Luton 1954), William Heggie (Accrington 1955), Joe Richardson (Birmingham City 1959), John Abbott (Crewe Alexandra 961), Robert Walters (Shrewsbury 1962), Phil Mullington (Rochdale 1978), Neville Southall (Bury 1980), Mark Came (Bolton Wanderers 1984), Dave Bamber (Blackpool), Bob Sutton (West Ham United), J Richardson (Sheffield United), Stanley Wood (West Bromwich Albion), R Pearce (Luton Town).
Clubhouse: Mon-Sat 8-11pm, Sun 8-10.30pm **Steward:** Mr E Welsh.
Club Record Goalscorer: Graham Smith 66 **Club Record Apps:** Edward Harrop 400.
91-92 Captain: Cec Edey **91-92 P.o.Y.:** **91-92 Top scorer:** Bevon Blackwood.
Local Newspapers: Winsford Chronicle, Winsford Guardian.
Local Radio Stations: Signal, Piccadilly.
Honours: Northern Premier Lg Div 1 R-up 91-92 (Div 1 Cup SF 89-90), Cheshire County Lg 20-21 76-77 (R-up 74-75 79-80, Lg Cup 49-50 55-56 59-60 76-77 78-79 79-80 80-81 (R-up 36-37 68-69 77-78)), Cheshire Senior Cup 58-59 79-80, Mid Cheshire Cup 90-91 (R-up 88-89), Cheshire Amateur Cup 00-01 02-03, Lancs Comb/Cheshire County Inter-Lg Cup 62-63, FA Trophy QF 77-78.

GOALKEEPERS:
Alex Mayfield (Crewe), **Curwen Searle** (Congleton, Alsagar, Kidsgrove Ath)
DEFENDERS: Cec Edey (Morecambe, Lancaster, Chorley, Lancaster), **John Whitney** (Skelmersdale, Wigan), **Duncan Akin** (Droylsden, Curzon Ashton, Droylsden), **Archie Lloyd** (Caernarfon, Knowsley, Mossley, Knowsley, Southport), **Andy Taylor** (Liverpool(T)), **Gary Maunsall** (Local football)
MIDFIELD: Peter Tilley (Glossop, Radcliffe B, Clitheroe, Hyde, Droylsden, Accrington S, Prestwich, Curzon Ashton, Mossley, Blackpool), **Kojo Taylor** (Mossley, Winsford), **Tony Camilleri** (Southport, Hyde, Lancaster, Buxton, Clitheroe, Radcliffe B, Irlam, Salford), **Gary Thomas** (Buxton, Maine Road, Luton, Bury), **Dave Maynard** (Army), **Dave Esdaile** (Buxton, Flixton), **Darren Sheridan** (Local football), **Neil Hall** (Local football), **Levi Edwards** (Hyde, Stockport, Altrincham, Crewe, Oldham Ath, Man Utd, Ashton Utd, Barrow), **Ossie Smith** (Fleetwood, Southport, Northwich V, Altrincham, Runcorn, Altrincham, Grays, Wimbledon, Bolton, Man Utd(J)), **Wayne Grant** (Lancaster, Maine Road)
FORWARDS: Jimmy Cameron (Runcorn, Winsford, Accrington S, Buxton, Maine Road), **Bevan Blackwood** (Lancaster, Hyde, Astro, Salford), **Richard Owusu** (Mossley), **Jimmy Cookson** (Middlewich), **Tony Farnsworth** (Westhoughton, Congleton, Ashton Town), **Mark Platt** (Local football), **Colin Finch** (Burnage), **Warren Thompson** (Chadderton, Fleetwood, Accrington S, Droylsden, Rossendale, Crewe, York)

UNITED REVIEW

HFS LOANS LEAGUE

WINSFORD UTD
v
MACCLESFIELD TOWN

Pages: 20 **Price:** 50p
Editor: Andrew Maylor
WMPCC Rating: 26

Northern Premier (H.F.S. Loans) League Premier Division Ten Year Records

	82/3	83/4	84/5	85/6	86/7	87/8	88/9	89/90	90/1	91/2
Accrington Stanley	–	–	–	–	–	–	–	–	–	8
Bangor City	–	–	10	13	2	7	4	10	18	20
Barrow	–	1	–	–	15	5	1	–	–	–
Bishop Auckland	–	–	–	–	–	–	–	11	7	11
Burton Albion	3	5	6	5	12	–	–	–	–	–
Buxton	12	21	22	19	13	16	15	16	8	5
Caernarfon Town	–	–	–	17	3	3	12	21	–	–
Chorley	4	14	19	20	9	1	–	–	14	21
Colne Dynamoes	–	–	–	–	–	–	–	1	–	–
Droylsden	–	–	–	–	–	–	–	–	13	15
Emley	–	–	–	–	–	–	–	–	–	6
Fleetwood Town	–	–	–	–	–	–	7	8	4	10
Frickley Athletic	–	–	–	–	–	10	9	13	10	14
Gainsborough Trinity	17	9	11	4	20	20	17	12	20	18
Gateshead	1	–	–	1	–	18	21	2	–	–
Goole Town	16	18	16	22	16	12	6	19	12	12
Grantham Town	14	4	21	–	–	–	–	–	–	–
Horwich R.M.I.	–	8	9	16	22	13	20	14	16	13
Hyde United	8	11	4	10	11	2	2	4	11	9
King's Lynn	9	–	–	–	–	–	–	–	–	–
Leek Town	–	–	–	–	–	–	–	–	9	4
Macclesfield Athletic	5	6	2	9	1	–	–	–	–	–
Marine	6	12	5	2	4	9	5	9	6	2
Matlock Town	10	2	13	21	7	19	13	6	17	19
Morecambe	13	19	18	3	6	4	16	15	3	3
Mossley	2	22	15	12	10	17	10	18	15	16
Netherfield	22	–	–	–	–	–	–	–	–	–
Oswestry Town	18	20	14	18	17	21	–	–	–	–
Rhyl	–	7	17	14	18	8	8	22	–	–
Shepshed Albion	–	–	–	–	–	–	18	20	21	22
South Liverpool	19	3	20	15	5	15	11	5	19	–
Southport	15	16	12	6	8	14	14	7	5	7
Stafford Rangers	–	10	1	–	–	–	–	–	–	–
Stalybridge Celtic	–	–	–	–	–	–	19	17	2	1
Tamworth	20	–	–	–	–	–	–	–	–	–
Whitley Bay	–	–	–	–	–	–	–	–	–	17
Witton Albion	11	13	3	11	14	11	3	3	1	–
Workington	7	15	8	8	21	22	–	–	–	–
Worksop Town	21	17	7	7	19	6	22	–	–	–
No. of Clubs	**22**	**22**	**22**	**22**	**22**	**22**	**22**	**22**	**21**	**22**

Mossley 3, Whitley Bay 2 - 7/9/91. Goalkeeper Greg Young scampers back but cannot prevent Brendan Burke from finding an empty net to give Mossley a 1-0 lead. Photo - Barry Lockwood.

Division One

	P	W	D	L	F	A	Pts
Colwyn Bay	42	30	4	8	99	49	94
Winsford United	42	29	6	7	96	41	93
Worksop Town	42	25	5	12	101	51	80
Guiseley	42	22	12	8	93	56	78
Caernarfon Town	42	23	9	10	78	47	78
Bridlington Town	42	22	9	11	86	46	75
Warrington Town	42	20	8	14	79	64	68
Knowsley United	42	18	10	14	69	52	64
Netherfield	42	18	7	17	54	61	61
Harrogate Town	42	14	16	12	73	69	58
Curzon Ashton	42	15	9	18	71	83	54
(1)Farsley Celtic	42	15	9	18	79	101	53
(3)Radcliffe Borough	42	15	9	18	67	72	51
Newtown	42	15	6	21	60	95	51
Eastwood Town	42	13	11	18	59	70	50
Lancaster City	42	10	19	13	55	62	49
Congleton Town	42	14	5	23	59	81	47
Rhyl	42	11	10	21	59	69	43
Rossendale United	42	9	11	22	61	90	38
Alfreton Town	42	12	2	28	63	98	38
(1)Irlam Town	42	9	7	26	45	95	33
(1)Workington	42	7	8	27	45	99	28

(-) points deducted for breach of rule

Top Scorers

K Clark (Worksop Town)	42
M Williscroft (Colwyn Bay)	34
B Blackwood (Winsford United)	32
P Donnelly (Colwyn Bay)	32
G McDonald (Warrington Town)	26
S French (Harrogate Town)	25
M Tennison (Guiseley)	24
P Coyne (Radcliffe Borough)	21
A Radford (Bridlington)	21
I Howat (Rhyl)	20

THE H.F.S. LOANS FIRST DIVISION RESULT CHART 1991-92

HOME TEAM	1	2	3	4	5	6	7	8	9	10	11	12	13	14	15	16	17	18	19	20	21	22
1. Alfreton	*	2-3	2-4	0-1	1-0	3-1	0-1	2-4	1-2	2-3	5-1	0-3	1-2	0-1	4-3	2-3	3-2	0-1	1-6	2-3	1-3	3-0
2. Bridlington	8-0	*	0-3	2-0	1-2	2-0	5-0	1-0	4-0	1-1	3-1	1-1	2-0	0-2	0-1	1-1	4-1	4-0	4-0	3-1	3-2	1-3
3. Caernarfon	5-2	0-2	*	3-2	2-2	201	4-1	0-1	3-0	3-0	3-0	1-3	3-2	2-1	2-1	2-0	1-1	2-0	0-1	1-0	5-0	1-3
4. Colwyn Bay	5-3	1-4	1-2	*	2-1	4-3	2-0	4-1	1-2	1-1	3-0	3-1	2-0	0-1	3-2	3-0	2-1	1-1	1-0	1-0	6-1	4-2
5. Congleton	3-1	0-3	0-2	0-1	*	2-4	1-2	4-2	0-2	0-1	2-1	0-2	0-0	1-2	1-2	3-0	2-0	2-0	2-3	0-2	3-0	2-1
6. Curzon A	4-1	0-0	0-4	2-5	2-0	*	2-0	1-2	2-2	2-2	3-1	2-0	3-1	1-1	1-1	1-0	2-1	4-1	1-1	1-5	6-1	0-3
7. Eastwood	3-1	0-1	0-0	2-2	3-4	1-1	*	1-2	2-0	0-1	2-3	1-0	1-1	6-4	2-2	0-2	2-1	4-4	1-3	1-2	3-1	1-2
8. Farsley	2-3	2-1	2-5	0-2	1-1	4-3	2-3	*	1-1	2-3	2-1	0-5	1-1	3-2	3-2	2-2	3-3	2-4	2-5	4-5	2-2	2-1
9. Guiseley	3-1	1-1	6-1	2-0	3-1	3-2	1-1	5-0	*	2-4	5-0	2-0	0-1	1-1	3-1	5-2	2-2	2-1	1-4	6-0	1-1	
10. Harrogate T	0-2	1-1	3-1	1-4	1-1	1-2	3-2	1-1	0-1	*	4-2	3-1	1-1	2-2	2-2	1-1	2-2	4-2	1-2	1-1	0-2	1-1
11. Irlam T	1-0	2-2	2-1	2-3	3-5	0-1	0-4	2-0	0-1	0-3	*	1-0	1-1	1-0	1-3	3-3	1-1	1-2	0-1	1-4	1-0	2-1
12. Knowsley Utd	0-1	2-1	1-0	0-2	0-0	2-2	2-0	5-3	0-0	2-3	2-2	*	0-0	0-0	5-0	4-1	3-0	2-3	2-1	1-2	3-1	0-2
13. Lancaster C	0-2	2-2	2-2	0-2	5-2	0-1	1-1	0-0	2-2	2-0	4-3	0-0	*	0-1	0-2	2-2	1-1	2-2	3-0	0-2	5-1	1-2
14. Netherfield	3-1	2-1	2-2	0-2	3-1	1-0	1-1	1-2	2-2	0-4	1-1	1-2	0-2	*	2-0	1-2	0-1	1-0	2-1	0-1	4-2	2-1
15. Newtown	0-1	0-4	0-2	1-4	5-1	3-1	2-1	2-4	1-6	0-5	1-0	1-4	5-1	0-1	*	2-0	1-0	0-0	2-0	1-3	2-1	1-2
16. Radcliffe B	3-0	3-1	1-2	1-4	3-0	1-0	1-1	4-1	1-6	1-1	1-2	4-2	2-3	3-1	3-1	*	2-3	3-2	2-2	1-1	0-1	4-1
17. Rhyl	3-3	1-2	0-0	0-2	1-2	3-4	0-1	0-1	1-2	2-0	1-0	1-1	0-0	4-0	2-3	2-1	*	5-1	3-1	1-2	1-0	1-4
18. Rossendale	1-2	1-1	1-0	1-5	1-2	7-0	0-1	2-1	2-1	1-1	3-1	0-1	1-1	0-1	5-1	1-2	1-3	*	3-3	3-5	1-1	0-2
19. Warrington	2-1	2-1	0-1	3-3	3-1	4-1	3-1	1-4	2-2	1-5	4-0	3-3	2-0	2-1	1-1	1-2	2-1	4-0	*	0-1	2-2	2-1
20. Winsford Utd	1-0	2-3	0-0	0-4	4-1	1-1	3-1	2-4	3-1	2-0	4-1	0-2	2-2	0-1	7-0	1-0	0-0	5-0	1-0	*	3-0	5-0
21. Workington	3-2	0-3	0-0	1-2	0-2	2-4	0-1	2-2	2-2	5-2	0-0	0-2	5-1	1-3	0-2	1-0	1-3	1-1	0-2	0-3	*	0-1
22. Worksop T	1-0	1-3	1-1	1-3	6-2	3-0	0-0	6-2	3-2	5-0	6-0	4-0	1-1	5-0	9-0	1-0	1-0	5-1	3-0	1-2	4-0	*

758

Formed: 1959

ALFRETON TOWN

The Reds

Alfreton's young goalkeeper Kevin Bedford reacts well under pressure from league leaders Winsford. Alfreton went down by the odd goal in five in this home fixture on 9th November. Photo - Colin Stevens.

Chairman: Shaun Egan
Directors: S Egan, T McRoy, I Wright, C Atkinson.
Secretary (Add & Tel): T McRoy, 12 Alma Street, Alfreton, Derby DE5 7HX (0773 834707).
Team Manager: Danny Hague   **Asst Mgr:** Paul Mitchell   **Coach:**
Ground Address & Tel: North Street, Alfreton. (0773 832819).
Directions: M1 junction 28 and follow A38 towards Derby for 1 mile, left onto B600, right at main road to town centre and after half a mile turn left down North Street - ground on right. Half mile from Alfreton & Mansfield Parkway (BR).
Capacity: 6,000 (1,000 covered)   **Seats:** 160   **Floodlights:** Y   **Shop:** Y   **Metal Badges:** Y
Colours: Red & white stripes/black/red   **Change colours:** All white.
Previous Leagues: Central Alliance *(before reformation 21-25)* 59-61/ Midland (Counties) 25-27 61-82/ Northern Counties (East) 82-87.
Midweek home matchday: Wednesday **Record Attendance:** 5,023 v Matlock Town, Central Alliance 1960.
Best F.A. Cup season: 1st Rd 3rd replay 69-70. Also 1st Rd 73-74.
League clubs defeated in F.A. Cup: Lincoln 24-25, but none since club's reformation in 1959.
Record Fees - Paid: £1,000 for R Mountain (Matlock)   **Received:** £1,500 for T Henson (Chesterfield).
Players progressing to Football League: Martin Wright (Chesterfield 1968), Alan Woodward (Grimsby 1970), Alan Taylor (Chelsea 1972), Andy Kowalski (Chesterfield 1973), Tony Henson (Chesterfield 1981), Ricky Greenhough (Chesterfield City 1985), Philip Greaves (Chesterfield 1986), Keith Smith (Exeter 1989).
Clubhouse: Normal evening hours. Monday, Friday and weekend lunchtimes.   **Steward:** Joe Pearson.
Record Goalscorer: J Harrison 303.   **Record Appearances:** J Harrison 560.
91-92 Captain: **91-92 P.o.Y.:**
91-92 Top scorer: **91-92 Average Attendance:**
Local Newspapers (+Tel.Nos.): Derbyshire Times, Derby Evening Telegraph, Nottingham Evening, Ripley/Heanor News, Mansfield Chad.
Local Radio Stations: Radio Derby.
Honours: FA Trophy 3rd Qualifying Rd replay 83-84 85-86, Northern Counties (East) Lg 84-85 (Lg Cup 84-85), Midland (Counties) Lg 69-70 73-74 76-77 (R-up 71-72 80-81 81-82, Lg Cup 71-72 72-73 73-74), Derbyshire Senior Cup 60-61 69-70 72-73 73-74 81-82, Derbyshire Divisional Cup (North) 64-65, Evans Halshaw Floodlit Cup 87-88. *Before reformation in 1959:* Central Alliance 23-24 (Lg Cup 22-23).

GOALKEEPERS:
Andy Cutts (Sheffield Aurora, Hyde, Accrington Stanley), **Steve Chadbourne** (Sutton T, Oakham Utd, Arnold, Mansfield, Notts Forest, Notts Co), **Kevin Bedford** (Borrowash V, Derby)
DEFENDERS: Lee Walshaw (Sheffield Aurora, Gainsborough Trin, Crookes, Gainsborough Trin, Sheffield FC, Worksop, Sheff Utd), **Simon Copeland** (Eastwood T, Gainsborough Trin, Rochdale, Sheff Utd), **Tim Atkinson** (Rotherham, Sheff Utd), **Paul Baker** (Ilkeston, Alfreton, Belper), **Dave Markham** (Ilkeston, Alfreton, Arnold), **Jason Maybury** (Worksop, Frickley, Crookes, Goole, Hull(T), Sheff Wed(T)), **Paul Bicknell** (Eastwood T, Ilkeston), **Rob Robinson** (Chesterfield(T)), **Steve Cam** (Matlock, Buxton, Matlock, Shepshed, Matlock, Norton Woodseats)
MIDFIELD: Richard Holmshaw (Denaby, Sheff Wed(T)), **Carl Hutchinson** (Sheffield Aurora, Worksop, Crookes), **Mark Clarke** (Eastwood T, Grimsby(T), Notts Forest(J)), **David Hoole** (Chesterfield), **Dave McCarthy** (Gainsborough Trin, Crewe), **Neil Webster** (Ripley), **Steve Pell** (Chesterfield(T))
FORWARDS: Darren Stevenson (Ilkeston, Heanor), **Graham Millington** (Sutton T, Ilkeston, Leek, Eastwood T, Alfreton, Belper, Clay Cross), **Matthew Walsh** (Leek, Alfreton, Sutton T, Worksop, Stafford R, Bradford C, Arsenal), **Bob Newton** (Goole, Evargoras(Cyp), Goole, Bristol R, Hartlepool, New England Teamen(USA), Chesterfield, Port Vale, Hartlepool, Huddersfield), **Keith Ward** (Rainworth MW, Ilkeston)

ALFRETON TOWN
FOOTBALL CLUB

SEASON 1991 - 1992

OFFICIAL PROGRAMME

50p

B.F.S. LOANS LEAGUE FIRST DIVISION
V WARRINGTON TOWN
SATURDAY 5th OCTOBER 1991

Pages: 24 **Price:** 50p
Editor: Joint Effort
WMPCC Rating: 23

759

ASHTON UNITED

Ashton United attack in a Bass North West Counties League Premier Division fixture at Nantwich Town, and force the home goalkeeper, Chris Holmes, into a good catch.

Chairman: J N Milne   **Patron:** Sid Sykes.
Secretary: E Jones, 2 Anderton Grove, Hurst Cross OL6 9EF (061 3399987).
Manager: Dave Denby   **Asst Manager:** Garry Riley   **Coach:**
Commercial Manager: Ray Lee
Ground: Surrey Street, Hurst Cross, Ashton-u-Lyne, Tameside (061 339 4158. Fax-061 652 6413).
Directions: M62 to junction 20 A627(M) follow signs for Oldham/Ashton-u-Lyne, leave at Ashton sign passing Belgrade Hotel, follow signs for Stalybridge (B6194) until you reach Hurst Cross, ground on right behind Royal Oak P.H. BR to Charles Street (Ashton), or Stalybridge. Buses 331, 332, 337, 408 (Ashton-Stalybridge) all pass ground.
Seats: 250   **Cover:** 3,000   **Capacity:** 7,000   **Floodlights:** Yes   **Club Shop:** Yes
Colours: Red/black/red.   **Change colours:** Blue/white/blue
Record Attendance: 11,000 v Halifax, FA Cup 1952.
Midweek matches: Monday.
Previous Leagues: Manchester/ Lancs Combination 12-23 48-64 66-68/ Midland 64-66, Cheshire Co. 23-48 68-82/ North West Counties 82-92.
Clubhouse: Open normal licensing hours. Steward: Mr E Jones (061 330 1511/339 4158).
Record fee paid: £1,000 to Knowsley United for Peter McDonnell (1992).
Best FA Cup season: 1st Rd replay 52-53 (lost 1-2 at Halifax after 1-1 draw). Also 1st Rd 55-56 (lost 1-6 at Southport).
Previous Name: Hurst (pre-1912)
Hons: Manchester Snr Cup 1884-85 13-14 75-76 77-78, Manchester Lg 11-12, Lancs Comb. Div 2 60-61 (Lg Cup 62-63), Manchester Prem. Cup 79-80 82-83, North West Counties Lg 91-92 (Challenge Cup 91-92, Div 2 87-88, Floodlit Lg 90-91), Manchester Challenge Shield 35-36 38-39 49-50 53-54 (R-up 34-35 39-40), Manchester Intermediate Cup 58-59 62-63 65-66 (R-up 60-61 64-65), Manchester Jnr Cup(4) 1893-94 10-12 32-33.

GOALKEEPERS:
Chris Holmes (Nantwich)
DEFENDERS: Ian Boyle (Droylsden, Ashton Utd, Stalybridge, Altrincham, Cork Celtic, Ashton Utd, Blackpool), **Nigel Cudworth** (Darwen, Leyland Daf), **Phil Hulme** (East Manchester, Chadderton, Atherton LR), **Mark Hilton** (Accrington Stanley, Ashton Utd, Mossley, Ashton Utd, Witton Alb, Bury, Oldham), **Micky Boyle** (Stalybridge, Ashton Utd, Waterloo Dock), **Garry Riley** (Mossley, Hyde, Stalybridge, Hyde, Salford Am, Droylsden, Oldham(A)), **David Lees** (Oldham T, Mossley, Curzon Ashton, Mossley, Ashton Utd, Chorley, Ashton Utd, Hyde, Stoke(A))
MIDFIELD: Gary Butterworth (Accrington Stanley, Stalybridge, Curzon Ashton, Rochdale, Man Utd(A)), **Gordon Woods** (Maine Road), **Leon Schofield** (GM County, Droylsden), **Dave Aspinall** (St Helens, Wigan, Bolton W), **Terry Stubbs** (Mossley, ICI Blackley, Winsford), **Geoff Jones** (Mossley, Chamber Coll), **David Lake** (Curzon Ashton, Droylsden, Curzon Ashton), **Mike Coffey** (Warrington)
FORWARDS: Chris Shaw (Oldham T, Radcliffe B), **Gary Laird** (St Helens, East Sutton), **Steve Morgan** (Abbey Hay, Maine Road), **Karl Marginson** (Curzon Ashton, Stockport), **Peter Mc Conville** (Knowsley, Oldham), **Jimmy Bell** (Knowsley, Rhyl, Winsford, Kirkby, Sth Liverpool, Burscough)

ASHTON UNITED F.C.

THE BASS NORTH WEST COUNTIES FOOTBALL LEAGUE

DIVISION ONE
Matchday Magazine

SEASON 1991/92   50p

PROGRAMME DETAILS:
Pages: 26 **Price:** 50p
Editor: K Whickham
WMPCC Rating: N/A

BRIDLINGTON TOWN

Alan Radford (nearest camera) looks favourite to beat Netherfield's Malcolm Jackson to the ball in a League fixture played on Sunday 5th April. Photo - Colin Stevens.

Chairman: Charles Dunn.   **Directors:** Barry Garton.
Secretary: Alan Proudlock, 49 Starhill Rd, Driffield, Nth Humbs YO25 7EY (0377 241821).
Team Manager: Neil Brandon   **Asst Manager:**   **Coach:**
Press Officer: Graham Proudlock   **Physio:** George Halley   **Comm Manager:** Colin Matheson.
Ground: Queensgate, Bridlington YO16 5LN (0262 670391).
Directions: A166 to Bridlington, through first lights, over island signed town centre, left at second set of lights, Queensgate ground on right.
Capacity: 3,000   **Seats:** 740   **Floodlights:** Y **Shop:** Y **Metal Badges:** N
Colours: All red   **Change colours:** All white   **Sponsors:** East Riding Sacks Ltd.
Previous Leagues: Driffield & District Minor/ Driffield & District/ East Riding Amateur/ Yorkshire 24-39 59-82/ Northern Counties East 82-90.
Previous Name: Bridlington Central (until 1959).
Midweek home matchday: Tuesday   **Reserve Team's League:** Northern Co's (East) Reserve Div.
Record Attendance: 2,102 v Scarborough, FA Cup.
Best F.A. Cup season: 1st Rd 60-61 (lost 2-3 at Bishop Auckland) 91-92 (1-2 at home to York City).
League clubs defeated in F.A. Cup: None.
Record Fees - Paid: **Received:**
Players progressing to Football League: Mick Head (Hull 1953), Phillip Stubbins (Mansfield), Gary Brattan (Cambridge Utd), David Bowman (Scarborough 1983), Andy Shaw (York 1988), Ian Taylor (Carlisle), Neil Grayson (York), Mick Norbury Cambridge Utd (1991).
Clubhouse: (0262 606879). Open 7-11pm. Hot and cold food.   **Steward:** Paul & Sally Jones.
Club Record Goalscorer: **Club Record Apps:**
91-92 Captain: Steve Brentano   **91-92 P.O.Y.:**   **91-92 Top scorer:** Alan Radford 29.
91-92 Average Attendance: 188.
Local Newspapers: Hull Daily Mail, Bridlington Free Press, Scarborough Evening News.
Local Radio Stations: Humberside - Viking.
Honours: FA Vase R-up 89-90, Northern Counties East Lg 89-90 (Lg Cup 88-89), Yorkshire Lg R-up 66-67 (Lg Cup 59-60 60-61 65-66, Div 2 74-75), East Riding Senior Cup 20-21 21-22 22-23 30-31 52-53 56-57 60-61 64-65 66-67 69-70 71-72 88-89.

GOALKEEPERS:
Gary Ingham (Goole, Shepshed, Frecheville Comm, Heanor, Gainsborough Trin, Rotherham), **Ian Taylor** (Scarborough, Carlisle Utd, Bridlington Town)
DEFENDERS:
Bobby McNeil (Carlisle Utd, Preston, Lincoln, Hull), **Steve Brentano** (Hull, North Ferriby), **Andy Smith** (Winterton R), **Ricky Warburton** (Farsley Celtic, Gainsborough Trin, Bridlington Trin), **Barry Gallagher** (Farsley Celtic, Naxxar Lions(Malta), Hamrun Spartans(Malta), Halifax, Bradford C), **Paul Bottomley** (Guiseley, Garforth, Yorkshire Am), **Tim Wragg** (Armthorpe Welfare, Belper, Ossett T, Denaby, Belper, Gainsborough Trin, Matlock, Goole, Worksop)
MIDFIELD:
Paul Stevenson (Farsley Celtic, Blackpool, Farsley Celtic, Harrogate T, Farsley Celtic), **Colin Bishop** (Frickley), **Lee Harvey** (Goole, Grimethorpe Coll, Gainsborough Trin, Huddersfield), **Malcolm Connor** (Harrogate T, Scarborough), **Jason Hopkinson** (Local football)
FORWARDS:
Vinny Archer (Farsley Celtic, York RI, Garforth, Yorkshire Am), **Alan Radford** (Emley, Ossett T, Lincoln, Barnsley, Huddersfield), **Rick Ranshaw** (Harrowby), **Alan Tyrell** (Knowsley, Wrexham), **Peter Collier** (Goole, Selby, York, Plymouth)

PROGRAMME DETAILS:
Pages: 44 Price: 50p
Editor: Barry Garton
WMPCC Rating: 26

CAERNARFON TOWN

Caernarfon Town. Back Row (L/R): Ian Humphreys (Physio), Neil Wilson, Steve Edwards, Dave Cockram, Tony Livens, Ian Haigh, Martin Baldry, Shaun Fallon, Stuart Pickthall, John T Roberts (Manager). Front: Alan Schumacker, Les Armor, Reggie McGuire, Dave Barnett, Paul Allen, Mark Shirley. Mascots: Michael & Anwen with Harry Williams Challenge Cup.

Chairman: Dr Emrys Price-Jones **Directors:** E Angel, W Gray-Thomas, J E Watkins, V Orritt, E Price-Jones, G Denham, E W Jones, G Lloyd-Owen, C Jones, E Watkins, J Edwards.
Secretary: J E Watkins, 20 South Penrallt, Caernarfon, Gwynedd LL55 1NS (0286 4045).
Team Manager: John T Roberts **Physio:** ian Humphreys **Comm Manager:** Jimmy Edwards.
Ground & Directions: As Curzon Ashton FC (see page 764).
Capacity, Seats etc: As Curzon Ashton. **Metal Badges:** Y
Colours: Yellow/green/yellow **Change colours:** Red/white/red **Sponsors:**
Previous Leagues: North Wales Coast 06-21/ Welsh National 26-30/ North Wales Combination 32-33/ Welsh Lg (North) 37-76 77-80/ Lancs Combination 80-82/ North West Counties 82-85.
Previous Ground: The Oval, Marcus Street, Caernarfon (ground vacated to avoid playing in League of Wales).
Previous Name: Caernarfon Athletic. **Reserve Team League:** Sain Caernarfon & Dist.
Midweek home matchday: Wednesday **91-92 Average Attendance:** 236.
Record Attendance: 6,002 v Bournemouth, FA Cup 2nd Rd 1929.
Best F.A. Cup season: 3rd Rd replay 86-87 (lost 0-1 at Barnsley). Also 2nd Rd 29-30.
League clubs defeated in F.A. Cup: Darlington 29-30/ Stockport County, York City 86-87.
Record Fees - Paid: **Received:** £2,500.
Players progressing to Football League: Ernie Walley (Spurs), Gwyn Jones (Wolves 1955), Wyn Davies & Haydn Jones (Wrexham 1960 & 64), Tom Walley (Arsenal 1964), Paul Crooks (Stoke 1986), David Martindale & Steve Craven & David Higgins (T'mere 1987).
Clubhouse: (at The Oval, Marcus Street, Caernarfon) 2 snooker tables, darts, fruit machines and entertainment, pool. **Steward:** Emrys Williams.
Club Record Goalscorer: Walter Jones 255 (1906-26) **Club Record Apps:** Walter Jones 306.
91-92 Captain: Dave Barnett **91-92 P.o.Y.:** Alan Schumacker **91-92 Top scorer:** Reggie Magiure 22.
Local Newspapers (+Tel.Nos.): Caernarfon Herald, Liverpool Daily Post.
Local Radio Stations: Radio Cymru/Wales.
Honours: FA Tphy 1st Rd replay 87-88, NW Co's Lg R-up 84-85 (Div 2 R-up 82-83), Lancs Comb 81-82 (Lg Cup 80-81), Welsh Lg (North)(4) 46-47 65-66 77-79 R-up(4) 56-58 72-73 79-80, Alves Cup(4) 38-39 74-75 77-79, Cookson 56-57 77-78), N Wales Comb 32-33, Welsh National Lg 26-27 29-30 (R-up 28-29), N Wales Coast Lg 11-12.

GOALKEEPERS:
Ian Haigh (Bethesda Ath, Mossley, Runcorn, Rhyl, Southport, Bethesda Ath, Sth Liverpool, Wrexham), **Steve Lawrenson** (Southport Am)

DEFENDERS:
Paul Allen (Rhyl, Flint T, Rhydymwyn), **Martin Baldry** (Nantlle V, Notts Co(T)), **Russell Sang** (Runcorn), **Alan Schumaker** (Vauxhall GM, Witton Alb, Ellesmere Pt), **Steve Edwards** (Bangor, Oswestry, Tranmere, Crewe, Oldham), **Andrew Evans** (Leek)

MIDFIELD:
Shaun Fallon (Skelmersdale, Bangor, Wigan), **Dave Barnett** (Witton Alb, Rhyl, Runcorn, Sth Liverpool, Telford, Stafford R, Bangor, Oldham), **Les Armor** (Stalybridge, Bangor, Rhyl, Colwyn B), **Reg McGuire** (Stalybridge, Southport, Witton Alb, Bangor, Tranmere), **Darren Baker** (Bangor, Caernarfon, Rhyl, Bangor, Wrexham), **Mark Shirley** (Netherley RBL, Notts Forest(T)), **Ian Murphy** (Maghull), **Carl Smyth** (Bangor), **Chris Williams** (Vauxhall GM)

FORWARDS:
Viv Williams (Bangor, Caernarfon, Rhyl, Bethesda Ath, Bangor, Llanerchymedd), **Neil Wilson** (Bangor, Flint T), **Chris Bennett** (Chester Coll), **Dave Cockram** (Poulton V), **Brian Evans** (Newtown), **Tony Livens** (Southport, Bangor, Marine, Oswestry, Ellesmere Pt)

PROGRAMME DETAILS:
Pages: 44 **Price:** 50p
Editor: Emrys Price-Jones
WMPCC Rating: 23

CONGLETON TOWN *Humbugs/Bears*

Congleton Town 2, Warrington Town 3 - 4/4/92. Three Congleton Town defenders gaze in admiration at Joe Rice, scorer of Warrington's winning goal. Photo - Rob Ruddock.

Chairman: Peter Warren   **Directors:** P Warren, A Warren, J V Pullen, D G Wilcock, P P Farrow, K Barlow, S W Foden, G Warren, G A McClory, S P Goel,JP.
Secretary: J V Pullen, 70 Belgrave Avenue, Congleton CW12 1HT (0260 277128).
Team Manager: **Physio:** B Harper   **Press Officer:** Chris Phillips (0260 271713)
Asst Manager: David Bell   **Commercial Manager:**
Ground Address & Tel: Booth Street Ground, Crescent Road, Congleton, Cheshire (0260 274460).
Directions: On approach to Congleton via Clayton bypass take second right after fire station, into Booth Street. Two miles from Congleton (BR).
Capacity: 5,000 (1,200 Covered)   **Seats:** 250   **Floodlights:** Y **Shop:** N **Metal Badges:** N
Colours: White/black/black   **Change colours:** All red   **Sponsors:**
Previous Leagues: Crewe & Dist/ North Staffs/ Macclesfield/ Cheshire 20-39 46-65 78-82/ Mid Cheshire 68-78/ North West Counties 82-87.
Previous Name: Congleton Hornets *(prior to current club's formation in 1901).*
Reserve Team: Congleton Town Hornets - Sportscene International (Staffs Senior) League.
Midweek home matchday: Wednesday   **Record Attendance:** 7,000 v Macclesfield, League 53-54.
Best F.A. Cup season: 1st Rd 89-90 (lost 0-2 at Crewe).
League clubs defeated in F.A. Cup: None.
Record Fees - Paid: **Received:** £5,000 for D Frost (Leeds).
Players progressing to Football League: Ron Broad (Crewe 1955), Jack Mycock (Shrewsbury 1958), Steve Davies (Port Vale 1987), L Hamlet (Leeds), Jimmy Quinn (West Ham, N Ireland), Ian Brightwell (Man City).
Clubhouse: Open every day.   **Steward:** Peter Warren.
Club Record Goalscorer: Mick Biddle (150+)   **Club Record Apps:** Ray Clack (600+)
90-91 Captain: **91-92 P.o.Y.:**   **91-92 Top scorer:**
91-92 Average Attendance:
Local Newspapers (+Tel.Nos.): Congleton Chronicle (0260 273737), Staffs Evening Sentinel (0782 289800).
Local Radio Stations: Radio Stoke, Signal.
Honours: North West Counties Lg R-up 85-86, Cheshire County Lg R-up 20-21 21-22 (Div 2 81-82), Mid Cheshire Lg 73-74 75-76 77-78 (R-up 69-70 71-72 76-77, Lg Cup 71-72), Cheshire Senior Cup 20-21 37-38, FA Trophy 3rd Qualifying Rd 89-90 90-91, FA Vase 4th Rd 76-77 80-81.

GOALKEEPERS:
Andy Daniels (Local football)
DEFENDERS: Ian Elsby (Leek, Macclesfield, Port Vale), **Peter Wilcox** (Newcastle T, Warwicks Police, Kidsgrove), **Ray Clack** (Winsford, Congleton, Leek, Congleton), **Martin Cranmer** (Chester(T)), **Steve Goldstraw** (Leek, Buxton, Leek), **Don Nicely** (Droylsden, Leek), **Aidan Brodigan** (Cheadle), **Graham Evans** (Leek)
MIDFIELD: Shaun Elder (Winsford, Eastwood Hanley, Leek, Congleton, Wilmslow Alb), **Mark Jones** (Leek, Congleton), **Nicky Craig** (Port Vale(T)), **Darren Washington** (Eastwood Hanley, Knypersley V), **Gary Davenport** (Local football), **Graham Harrison** (Rolls Royce), **Andy Morgan** (Leek, Eastwood Hanley, Leek, Stalybridge, Stafford R, Stoke), **Steve Oliver** (St Albans, Hitchin, Vauxhall M, St Albans, Sandridge R)
FORWARDS: Steve Piggott (Winsford, Nantwich, Winsford, Nantwich), **Ivan Lodge** (Nantwich, Leek, Stafford R, Crewe), **Matt Cunliffe** (Chester(T)), **Mike Biddle** (Eastwood Hanley, Witton Alb, Congleton, Port Vale, Stoke(A)), **Nigel Deeley** (Rhyl, Stalybridge, Witton Alb, Congleton, Winsford, Congleton, Runcorn)

PROGRAMME DETAILS:
Pages: 32 **Price:** 50p
Editor: P Warren (0260 275994)
WMPCC Rating: 24

CURZON ASHTON

Curzon Ashton. Back Row (L/R): John Robinson, Ray Silous, Graham Sanders, Mark Lilliston, Steve Jones, Dave Ridings, Barry Diamond. Front: Malcolm Cunningham, Dave Grimbaldeston, Andy Raines, Dave Liptrot, Kenny Quigg, Steve Blake. Photo - Ashton Reporter.

Chairman: Harry Twamley   **Directors:** P Booth, A Sykes, A Jones, I Seymour, D Lees, H Twamley, H Gallaway, R Cooper, T Spruce, J Hughes, R Walker, P Cross, P Kelly, D Murray.
Secretary: Alun Jones, 36 Forrest Road, Denton, Manchester M34 1RL (061 336 8004).
Team Manager: S Waywell   **Physio:** Dave Pover   **Press Officer:** David Murray (061 7757509)
Asst Manager/Coach: Ray Silous   **Commercial Manager:** Alan Sykes (0457 863049).
Ground: National Park, Katherine Street, Ashton-under-Lyne (061 330 6033).
Directions: Behind Ashton police station, one and a half miles from Ashton-under-Lyme (BR).
Capacity: 5,000 (630 Covered)   **Seats:** 330   **Floodlights:** Y **Shop:** N **Metal Badges:** N
Colours: All blue   **Change colours:** Silver grey/black/black.
Sponsors: Byford Computer Services.
Previous Lges: Manchester Amtr/ Manchester (until 1978)/ Cheshire Co. 78-82/ North West Co's 82-87.
Midweek home matchday: Monday   **Record Attendance:** 1,826 v Stamford, FA Vase SF 1980.
Best F.A. Cup season: Never beyond qualifying rounds.
Record Fees - Paid: Nil   **Received:** £3,000 for Steve Wigley (Nottm Forest).
Players progressing to Football League: Gordon Taylor (Bolton Wanderers 1962), Steve Wigley (Nottm Forest 1981), Malcolm O'Connor (Rochdale 1983), Eric Nixon (Manchester City 1983).
Clubhouse: Open Tuesday - Thursday, matchdays and for private functions.   **Steward:** Phil Cross.
Club Record Goalscorer: Alan Sykes   **Club Record Apps:** Alan Sykes 600.
91-92 Captain: Jimmy Birch   **91-92 P.o.Y.:** Dave Liptrot
91-92 Top scorer: Andy Bainer, Dave Liptrot 20 each.
Local Newspapers (+Tel.Nos.): Ashton Reporter, Ashton Advertiser.
Local Radio Stations: Manchester Radio, Piccadilly.
Honours: FA Vase SF 79-80, Cheshire County Lg Div 2 R-up 78-79 (Reserve Div 81-82), Manchester Lg 77-78 (R-up 74-75 75-76), Lg Cup 77-78 (R-up 74-75 75-76), Murray Shield R-up 75-76, Reserve Div 74-75 75-76 76-77 77-78), Manchester Amateur Lg 63-64 65-66 (R-up 64-65 79-80(Res) 80-81(Res)), Manchester Premier Cup 81-82 83-84 85-86 86-87 89-90, Manchester Intermediate Cup 71-72 72-73 73-74 (R-up 70-71), Manchester Amateur Cup R-up 63-64, Ashton Challenge Cup 64-65 67-68, Philips F'lit Cup R-ups 77-78, FA Trophy 2nd Qualifying Rd 82-83 84-85, North West Counties Reserve Div 82-83 84-85 (R-up 83-84, Lg Cup 84-85 (R-up 83-84 85-86)), Northern Combination Supplementy Cup 87-88 88-89, South East Lancs Lg Shield R-up 84-85.

GOALKEEPERS:
Mark Lillistron (Droylsden), Andy Mulliner (Newtown, Accrington Stan, Bangor, Telford, Port Vale)
DEFENDERS: Benny Phillips (Mossley, Rossendale, Droylsden, Stalybridge, Chorley, Witton Alb, Buxton, Barrow, Witton Alb, Mossley, Stalybridge, Winsford, Macclesfield, Bury, Crewe), Ross Moore (Westhoughton), Dave Grimbaldeston (Rochdale(T)), Dave Constantine (Glossop, Hyde, Northwich V, Witton Alb, Winsford, Altrincham, Bury, Hyde)
MIDFIELD: Graham Sanders (Irlam, Flixton, Atherton LR, Colne D), Kenny Quigg (Accrington Stan, Highfield Utd), Jamie Birch (Mossley, Droylsden, Curzon A, Stalybridge, Altrincham, Stalybridge), Dave Ridings (Macclesfield, Curzon A), Andy Baines (Hyde, Stalybridge, Ashton Utd), Keith Evans (Irlam), Mark Thomas (Horwich, Radcliffe, Stalybridge, Prestwich, Maine Road)
FORWARDS: Dave Liptrot (Horwich RMI, Atherton LR, Chorley, Horwich RMI, Stockport), Steve Jones (Local football), Barry Diamond (Stalybridge, Chorley, Altrincham, Hyde, Mossley, Colne D, Morecambe, Gainsborough Trin, Halifax, Rochdale, Olun Pallo(Fin), Barrow, Workington, Barrow, Dumbarton, Gillingham(A)), Colin McCrory (Droylsden, Rossendale, Droylsden, Curzon A, Irlam, Horwich RMI, Curzon A), Ian Lunt (Droylsden, Curzon A, Winsford, Witton Alb, Altrincham), Steve Blake (Accrington Stan, Macclesfield, Stalybridge, Curzon A, Stalybridge, Winsford, Altrincham, Hyde)

Pages: 32 **Price:** 45p
Editor: Ian Seymour
WMPCC Rating: 21

Formed: 1953   # EASTWOOD TOWN   The Badgers

Eastwood Town. Back Row (L/R): John Adams, Stuart Wiggins, Russell Leatherland, Neil Stafford, Lee Wilkinson, Mark Plaice, John Knapper, Mark Richardson, John Gray, John Brooks (Trainer). Front: Clayton Woods, Lee Howard, Chris Freestone, Russell Downing, Geoff Hall, Simon Osborne. Photo - James Wright.

Chairman: George Belshaw   **President:** John Holmes.
Secretary: Paddy Farrell, 7 Primrose Rise, Newthorpe, Notts NG16 2BB (0773 715500).
Team Manager: Bryan Chambers   **Asst Mgr:** Jimmy McGowan   **Physio:** Derek Myatt.
Press Officer: Paddy Farrell   **Commercial Mgr:** John Holmes (0773 531591).
Ground Address & Tel: Coronation Park, Eastwood, Notts (0773 715823).
Directions: From North - M1 junction 27 then follow Heanor signs via Brinsley to lights in Eastwood. Turn left then first right after Fire Station. From South - junction 26, B6010 to first exit, left at lights, first left at 'Man in Space'.
Capacity: 5,500 (1,000 Covered)   **Seats:** 200   **Floodlights:** Y   **Shop:** N   **Metal Badges:** Y
Colours: Black & white stripes/black/black   **Change colours:** All yellow.
Previous Leagues: Notts Alliance 53-61/ Central Alliance 61-67/ East Midlands 67-71/ Midland Counties 71-82/ Northern Counties (East) 82-87.
Previous Names: None - predecessors Eastwood Collieries disbanded in 1953.
Midweek home matchday: Tuesday **Record Attendance:** 2,723 v Enfield, FA Amateur Cup, February 1965.
Best F.A. Cup season: Final Qualifying Rd replay 75-76 (lost 0-1 at Wycombe Wanderers).
Record Fees - Paid: **Received:** £10,000 for Simon Hutchinson (Wycombe Wanderers 90-91).
Players progressing to Football League: John Butlet (Notts County 1957), Tony Woodcock, Paul Richardson, Alan & Steve Buckley.
Clubhouse: Daily 11-2.30pm, 7.30-11pm (Sat 11am-11pm). Snacks always available, meals by arrangement.
Steward: Mr Alan Cheetham (0773 715823)
Club Record Goalscorer: Martin Wright
Club Record Apps: Arthur Rowley (1st team only), David Williams (1st team and reserves).
91-92 Captain: Stuart Wiggins   **91-92 P.o.Y.:** Stuart Wiggins   **91-92 Top scorer:** Mark Richardson
91-92 Average Attendance: 173.   **Sponsors:** Melfin (UK) Ltd.
Local Newspapers (+Tel.Nos.): Eastwood Advertiser (0773 713563), Nottingham Evening Post (0602 482000), Derby Telegraph (0332 291111).
Local Radio Stations: Radio Nottingham, Radio Trent.
Honours: Northern Counties (East) Lg R-up 82-83 84-85, Midland Counties Lg 75-76 (R-up 74-75 77-78, Lg Cup 77-78 79-80), Central Alliance 63-64 (R-up 64-65), Notts Alliance 56-57 (R-up 53-54 54-55 55-56 57-58 58-59 59-60, Lg Cup 55-56), East Midlands Lg R-up 68-69, Notts Senior Cup 75-76 77-78 78-79 79-80 82-83 83-84 88-89 89-90 91-92 (R-up 57-58 63-64 65-66), Evans Halshaw Floodlit Cup R-up 89-90, Notts Intermediate Cup 86-87, Ripley Hospital Charity Cup(6) 76-81, FA Trophy 1st Rd 78-79, FA Amateur Cup 3rd Rd replay 67-68.

GOALKEEPERS:
Lee Wilkinson (Local football), **Richard Wilson** (Spalding, Lincoln C, Grantham, Chesterfield, Notts Co)

DEFENDERS:
John Gray (Belper), **Mark Place** (Doncaster, Mansfield), **Geoff Hall** (Mansfield(T)), **Kevin Elshaw** (Leek, Eastwood T, Sheff Wed), **John Adams** (Burton Alb, Shepshed, Arnold, Eastwood T, Sutton T, Mansfield(J)), **Neil Stafford** (Local football)

MIDFIELD:
Stuart Wiggins (Belper, Matlock, Ilkeston), **Jason Milner** (Gainsborough Trin, Mansfield(T), Scunthorpe(T)), **Andy Gilliver** (Boston Utd, Alfreton, Goole, Doncaster), **Tony Burton** (Shirebrook), **Phil Greaves** (Matlock, Stafford R, Worksop, Chesterfield, Alfreton, Staveley, Grantham)

FORWARDS:
Simon Osborne (Shepshed, Army), **John Knapper** (Belper), **Mark Richardson** (Matlock, Eastwood T, Worksop, Stafford R, Boston Utd, Derby, Eastwood T), **Russell Downing** (Burton Alb, Heanor, Albany Capitals(USA), Alfreton, Belper), **Chris Freestone** (Local football)

HFS LOANS LEAGUE

BADGERS REVIEW
EASTWOOD TOWN
CORONATION PARK
TELEPHONE 0773 715823

Pages: 28 Price: 40p
Editor: John Brooks (719005)
WMPCC Rating: 22

FARSLEY CELTIC

Farsley Celtic 0, Colwyn Bay 2 - 28/3/92. Farsley goalkeeper Trevor punches clear against the league leaders. Photo - Colin Stevens.

Chairman: Alun Jones   **President:** J E Palmer.
Secretary: E Hardcastle, C/O The Club (see below).
Team Manager: D Metcalf   **Asst Manager:**   **Coach:**
Press Officer: A Jones   **Physio:** Tong Gregg
Commercial Manager:
Ground: Throstle Nest, Newlands, Farsley, Pudsey, West Yorks (0532 561517).
Directions: From M62 junction 28, right into Leeds ring-road to A647, right at r-about, left down New Street into Newlands. Ground at bottom of road. 1 mile from New Pudsey (BR). Buses 17, 72 and 508 from Leeds.
Capacity: 5,000 (1,500 Covered)   **Seats:** 750   **Floodlights:** Y   **Shop:** Y   **Metal Badges:** Y
Colours: All blue   **Change colours:** All white.
Sponsors: Various.
Previous Grounds: Red Lane, Calverley Lane (prior to 1948).
Previous Leagues: West Riding County Amateur/ Leeds Red Triangle/ Yorkshire 49-82/ Northern Counties (East) 82-87.
Midweek home matchday: Wednesday   **Reserve Team's League:** Northern Counties (E) Reserve Div.
Record Attendance: 11,000 (at Elland Road) v Tranmere Rovers, FA Cup 1st Rd 1974.
Best F.A. Cup season: 1st Rd 74-75 (see above). Lost 0-2.
League clubs defeated in F.A. Cup: None.
Record Fees - Paid: **Received:**
Players progressing to Football League: Barry Smith (Leeds 1951), Paul Madeley (Leeds 1962), William Roberts (Rochdale 1988).
Clubhouse: Lounge and games room (for 350). New multi-purpose sports hall, open every evening and weekend lunchtimes.
Steward: S Shaw.
91-92 Captain: Martin Haresign   **91-92 P.O.Y.:** Kevin Taylor   **91-92 Top scorer:** Martin Haresign
Local Newspapers (+Tel.Nos.): Yorkshire Evening Post, Telegraph & Argus, Pudsey Times.
Local Radio Stations: Radio Leeds, Radio Aire, Radio Pennine.
Honours: FA Vase QF 87-88, FA Amateur Cup 3rd Rd 34-35, West Riding County Cup 57-58 59-60 66-67 70-71 83-84 86-87, Yorkshire Lg 59-60 68-69 (R-up 57-58 58-59 70-71 71-72, Div 2 51-52, Lg Cup 62-63 63-64 66-67).

GOALKEEPERS:
Richard Harrison (Frickley, Sheff Utd), **Wayne Baker** (Frickley, Whitby, Darlington, Notts Forest, Sheff Wed)
DEFENDERS: Martin Pattison (Guiseley, Bradford C), **Richard Harrison** (Lincoln C(T)), **Graham Sanderson** (Local football), **Floyd Peltier** (Accrington Stanley, Redditch, Coventry Sporting, Nuneaton B, Bedworth, Coventry Sporting), **Tony Clegg** (Radcliffe B, Chorley, IFK Trelleborg(Swe), York, Bradford C), **Kevin Taylor** (Fryston CW, Scunthorpe, C Palace, Derby, Sheff Wed), **Rick Canavan** (Youth)
MIDFIELD: Justin Sumner (Harrogate T, Harrogate RA, Goole, Doncaster, Leeds), **Simon Fell** (Guiseley, Farsley Celtic, Yorkshire Am), **Kevin Farrelly** (Local football), **Peter Craven** (Eccleshill), **Steve Howley** (Thackley), **Micky Adams** (Guiseley, Garforth, Sheff Wed(A)), **Keith Sanderson** (Local football)
FORWARDS:
Martin Haresign (Harrogate RA, Farsley Celtic, Thackley, Barnleigh, Swinnow V), **Mark Hamilton** (Harrogate T, Guiseley, Harrogate T, Farsley Celtic, Harrogate RA, Goole, Leeds Ashley Road, Farsley Celtic), **Gordon Owen** (Frickley, Blackpool, Mansfield, Bristol C, Barnsley, Cardiff C, Sheff Wed), **Steve Daykin** (Thackley, Eccleshill), **Craig Norrie** (B Auckland, North Ferriby), **Russell Doig** (Harrogate T, Nuneaton B, Halifax, Hartlepool, Leeds, East Stirling, St Mirren), **Robbie Whellans** (Harrogate RA, Frickley, Harrogate T, Rochdale, Bradford C, Leicester C(Sch))

FARSLEY
CELTIC A.F.C.

EMLEY
THROSTLE NEST GROUND

FARSLEY,
PUDSEY,
WEST YORKSHIRE.
OFFICIAL
PROGRAMME.

HFS
LOANS
LEAGUE

PROGRAMME DETAILS:
Pages: 32 **Price:** 40p
Editor: T Becton (0532 564206)
WMPCC Rating: 16

GREAT HARWOOD TOWN

Great Harwood Town celebrate their victory in the Lancashire ATS Challenge Trophy final.

Chairman: C Hickey   **Vice Chairman:** D Cook
Secretary: S A Brown, 50 Water Str, Great Harwood, Blackburn, Lancs BB6 7QR (0254 883170).
Manager: Eric Whalley   **Asst Mgr:** D Cook
Coach: M Eatough
Ground: The Showground, Wood Street, Great Harwood, Lancs (0254 883913).
Directions: M66 from Manchester to Haslingden exit, A680 through Baxeneden, Accrington to Clayton-le-Moors, left at the Hyndburn Bridge Hotel into Hyndburn Road and right into Wood Street to ground. Or M6 jct 31, A59, A677 towards Blackburn, A678 to Rishton, left at lights (B6536) to Gt Harwood, past Whiteheads mini-market, left into Wood Street. 3 miles from Rishton (BR), 6 miles from Blackburn (BR). Various buses from Heyes Lane & Park Road to Blackburn & Accrington.
Seats: 250   **Cover:** 750   **Capacity:** 2,500   **Floodlights:** Yes   **Club Shop:** No
Reserves' League: Northern Comb.
Record Gate: 5,397 v Manchester Utd 1980
Colours: All red   **Change colours:**
Midweek Matches: Tuesday   **Clubhouse:** Normal licensing hours
Previous Name: Great Harwood Wellington.
Previous Leagues: West Lancashire/ Lancs Combination 79-82/ North West Counties 82-92.
Previous Ground: Park adjacent to the Showground until demise of Great Harwood FC in 1978.
Best FA Cup season: 1st Qualifying Round 91-92
Best FA Vase season: Quarter Finals 90-91.
Hons: North West Counties Lg R-up 91-92 (Div 2 90-91, Lamot Pils Tphy 89-90 (R-up 90-91)), Lancs ATS Challenge Trophy 91-92 (R-up 90-91).

GOALKEEPERS:
Denis Underwood (Clitheroe)
DEFENDERS: Dave Tattersall (Clitheroe, Accrington Stanley), Neil Baron (Local football), Neil Rowbotham (Horwich RMI, Rossendale, Morecambe, Accrington Stanley, Haslingden), Duncan Seddon (Accrington Stanley), Martin Eatough (Fleetwood, Accrington Stanley, Clitheroe, Morecambe, Southport, Barrow, Morecambe, Great Harwood), Russell Whalley (Local football)
MIDFIELD: Lee Rogerson (Morecambe, Wigan, Clitheroe), Dave Sharples (Darwen, Morecambe, Accrington Stanley, Clitheroe, Chorley, Clitheroe, Padiham, Blackburn R), Paul Rigby (Radcliffe B, Accrington Stanley, Radcliffe B, Chorley, Glossop), Paul Whalley (Accrington Stanley, Clitheroe), Wayne Haworth (Glossop, Rossendale, Haslingden), Andrew Taylor (Cutwood Rangers)
FORWARDS: John Taylor (Darwen, Accrington Stanley, Clitheroe, Great Harwood), Paul Baker (Clitheroe), Peter Smith (BAC Preston, Barrow), Daryl Adams (Accrington Stanley, Darwen, Winsford, Accrington Stanley, Bamber Bridge), Mark Heyes (Clitheroe, Great Harwood, Accrington Stanley, Clitheroe, Whinney Hill, Padiham, Preston NE)

THE BASS
Bass NORTH WEST
COUNTIES FOOTBALL LEAGUE

**GREAT HARWOOD TOWN
FOOTBALL CLUB**

THE SHOWGROUND, WOOD STREET

THE BASS NORTH WEST COUNTIES LEAGUE
LAMOT PILS TROPHY WINNERS
1989/90

OFFICIAL PROGRAMME 30p

Pages: 20 **Price:** 30p
Editor: Barry Marsden

GRETNA

Gretna FC, Northern League Champions 1991-92. Back Row (L/R): Geoff Fell, Mark Eagling, Allan Carruthers, Paul O'Hagan, Paul Leeming, Marc Irwin, Kenny Goodrick, Paul Gorman, Geoff Bell, Les Armstrong. Front: Billy Bentley, Andy Pratt, Gary Bell, Mike McCartney, Ian Wilson, Chris Pickford, Jim Mulholland, Alan Shoulder. Photo - Alan Watson.

Chairman: Ian Dalgleish   **Press Officer:** Secretary
Secretary: Keith Rhodes, 8 Graitney, Gretna, Carlisle, Cumbria CA6 5AR (0461 37447).
Ground: Raydale Park, Domminion Rd., Gretna, Carlisle (0461 37602).
Directions: 9 miles north of Carlisle on A74.
Seats: 100   **Cover:** 300   **Capacity:** 3,000   **Floodlights:** Yes
Club colours: Black & white hoops/black/black with white turnover
Change colours: All red
Midweek Matches: Tuesday
Record Gate: 2,307 v Rochdale, FA Cup First Round Proper, 16/11/92.
Previous Leagues: Carlisle & District 47-51/ Cumberland 51-52/ Northern 83-92.
Previous Ground: MacKay's Field.
Best season in F.A. Cup: 1st Round Proper 1991-92 (lost 1-3 in replay at Rochdale).
Players progressing to Football League: John Hamilton (Hartlepool United 1982), Russell Black & Don Peattie (Sheffield United).
Souvenir Shop: No
Clubhouse details: Mon - Wed 11am-11pm, Thur - Sat 11am-12pm & Sun 12.30 -11pm
Snooker & pool; entertainment on Sat.
Local Newspapers: Cumberland News
Honours: Northern Lg 90-91 91-92 (Lg Cup 90-91), Cumberland Cup; Last 16 F.A. Trophy

GOALKEEPERS:
Bill Bentley (Kello Rov, Auchinleck Talbot)

DEFENDERS:
Marc Irwin (Spennymoor, Gateshead), **Jim Mulholland** (Wigton), **Paul O'Hagan** (Gateshead, Port Vale, Sunderland), **Mike McCartney** (Carlisle, Plymouth, Southampton, Carlisle, WBA), **Ian Wilson** (Workington, Penrith, Carlisle City), **John Wilson** (Annan Ath)

MIDFIELD:
Kenny Goodrick (Ferryhill), **Ken Nelson** (Haltwistle), **Willie Armstrong** (Penrith, Gretna, Penrith, Netherfield, Carlisle), **Allan Carruthers** (Morecambe, Workington, Penrith, Netherfield, Carlisle Spartans, Coventry(A))

FORWARDS:
Chris Pickford (Ferryhill, Newcastle Blue Star, Coundon TT, Spennymoor), **Geoff Fell** (Penrith, Workington, Carlisle), **Mark Wilson** (Carlisle City, Penrith, Carlisle)

UNFORTUNATELY

NO PROGRAMME

COVER AVAILABLE

PROGRAMME DETAILS:
Pages: **Price:**
Editor: N Hampson

Formed: 1909

GUISELEY

Guiseley pictured before their FA Vase Semi Final victory at Sudbury on March 21st. Back Row (L/R): D Heely (Coach), B Roberts, P Wilson, D Morgan, P Maxted, M Tennison, A Roberts, B Colville, G Rayner (Manager). Front: I Noteman, M Nagey, V Brockie, C Hogarth, R Annan, P Atkinson. Photo - Dennis Nicholson.

Chairman: Mr D Brotherton   **Treasurer:** Mr A Spinks.
Secretary: Mr D Martin, 2 Mulberry Avenue, Adel, Leeds LS16 8LL (0532 677867).
Team Manager: Gordon Rayner   **Asst Mgr:** David Heeley   **Coach:**
Press Officer: Secretary   **Physio:** John Rhodes
Commercial Manager: Mrs A Ellis (0943 878884).
Ground: Nethermoor Ground, Otley Road, Guiseley (0943 872872).
Directions: Via M1 to M62 junction 28, follow Leeds road to junction of A65 at Horsforth. At r-about turn left onto A65 through Rawdon to Guiseley centre. Ground quarter of a mile past traffic lights, on the right. Half a mile from Guiseley (BR/Metro).
Capacity: 3,000 (800 Covered)   **Seats:** 400   **Floodlights:** Y   **Shop:** Y   **Metal Badges:** Y
Colours: All white   **Change colours:** All yellow.
Sponsors: Abbey Hire.
Previous Grounds: None.
Previous Leagues: West Riding Co. Amtr/ West Yorks/ Yorkshire 68-82/ Northern Co's (East) 82-91.
Midweek home matchday: Monday   **Reserve Team's League:** Northern Counties (E) Reserve Div.
Record Attendance: 2,486 v Bridlington Town, FA Vase Semi Final 1st Leg 89-90.
Best F.A. Cup season: First Round Proper 1991-92 (lost 0-1 at Chester City).
League clubs defeated in F.A. Cup: None to date.
Record Fees - Paid: **Received:**
Players progressing to Football League: Keith Walwyn (York City), Frank Harrison (Halifax Town), Dean Walling (Carlisle United), Richard Annan (Crewe Alexandra).
Clubhouse: Open evenings and Sunday lunchtimes. Non-League club parties welcome if booked in advance.
91-92 Captain: Martin Telley   **91-92 P.O.Y.:**   **91-92 Top scorer:** Ian Noteman.
Local Newspapers (+Tel.Nos.): Yorkshire Evening Post, Bradford Telegraph & Argus, Airedale & Wharfdale Observer, Wharfe Valley Times.
Honours: FA Vase 90-91 (R-up 91-92, SF 89-90), Northern Counties (East) Lg 90-91 (Lg Cup 90-91), West Riding County Cup(4), Yorkshire Lg R-up 79-80 81-82 (Lg Cup 79-80).

GOALKEEPERS:
Paul Maxted (Goole, Harrogate RA, Frickley, Pontefract Coll, Doncaster)

DEFENDERS:
Peter Atkinson (Otley), **Martin Tetley** (Harrogate T, Goole, Leeds Ashley Road, Harrogate RA), **Calvin Allen** (Farsley C, Harrogate RA, Farsley C), **Phil Wilson** (Witton Alb, Stafford R, Scarborough, Macclesfield, York, Huddersfield, Bolton)

MIDFIELD:
Richard Annan (Doncaster, Leeds), **Vince Brockie** (Goole, Doncaster, Leeds), **Steve Boothroyd** (Harrogate RA, Ossett T), **Allan Roberts** (Bradford PA, Harrogate T, Birkenshaw R, Thackley, Pontefract Coll), **Michael Nagy** (Ventue Yeadon)

FORWARDS:
Billy Roberts (Farsley C, Rochdale, Farsley C), **Bob Colville** (Barrow, Bangor, Northwich V, Darlington, York, Stockport, Bury, Oldham, Rossendale), **Mark Tennison** (Bridlington Trin), **John Hudson** (Eccleshill)

GUISELEY A.F.C.
(F.A. VASE WINNERS 1991)
Official Programme
Season 1991-92

OFFICIAL SPONSORS

Abbey
HIRE

PROGRAMME DETAILS:
Pages: 20 **Price:** 50p
Editor: Phil Rogerson
WMPCC Rating: 22

HARROGATE TOWN

Harrogate Town in front of their smart new stand. Back Row (L/R): David Harvey (Coach), Graham Shepherd (Asst Manager), Chris Annan, Jim Wright, Justin Sumner, Gary Edmunds, Mark Fenton (Goalkeeper), Dave McAughtrie, Ricky Greenough, Alan Smith (General Manager). Front: Mark Fenton, Steve Templeton, Tony Outhart, Paul Williamson, Mark Hamilton, Mick Varley, Dave Whitehead (Physio). Mascots: Jack Miller, Paul Smith. Photo - Phil Cartledge.

Chairman: George Dunnington   **President:** C Margolis.
Secretary: Roy Dalby, 123a Dene Park, Harrogate, HG1 4JX (0423 567973).
Team Manager: Alan Smith   **Asst Manager:** Graham Shepherd   **Coach:** David Harvey
Press Officer: **Physio:** Dave Whitehead
Commercial Manager: **Sponsors:** Crystal (Ford).
Ground: Whetherby Road, Harrogate. (0423 883671 (880675-press)).
Directions: From Leeds turn right at traffic lights (Appleyard's) into Hookstone Road, continue to Woodlands Hotel (traffic lights) turn left into Wetherby Road. The ground is on the right. From Harrogate (BR), over bridge to North Park Road and junction of Knaresborough Road. Left to lights, right into Wetherby Road.
Capacity: 3,800 (700 Covered)   **Seats:** 350   **Floodlights:** Y   **Shop:** Y   **Metal Badges:** Y
Colours: Amber & black/amber   **Change colours:** All blute.
Prev. Names: Harrogate FC 26-34/ Harrogate Hotspurs 36-50.   **Prev. Ground:** Starbeck Lane 1919-20.
Previous Leagues: Yorkshire 20-21 22-31 51-82/ Midland 21-22/ Northern 31-32/ Harrogate & District 36-46/ West Yorkshire 46-51/ Northern Counties (East) 82-87.
Midweek home matchday: Tuesday   **Reserve Team's League:** Northern Counties (E) Reserve Div.
Record Attendance: 3,208 v Starbeck LNER, Whitworth Cup final 1948.
Best F.A. Cup season: 3rd Qualifying Rd 87-88 (lost 0-2 after a 1-1 draw).
League clubs defeated in F.A. Cup: None.
Record Fees - Paid: **Received:**
Players progressing to Football League: Stewart (York City 1979), Tim Hotte (Halifax Town 1985), Andy Watson (Halifax Town 1988).
Clubhouse: On ground, open Tuesday, Wednesday, Thursday, Saturday).   **Steward:** Ken Reardon.
91-92 Captain: **91-92 P.O.Y.:**   **91-92 Top scorer:**
Local Newspapers: Yorkshire Post, Harrogate Herald Advertiser.
Local Radio Stations: Radio Leeds, Radio York, local hospital radio.
Honours: FA Vase 4th Rd 89-90, Northern Premier Lg Div 1 Cup 89-90, Northern Counties (East) Div 1 (Nth) R-up 84-85 (Reserve Div 85-86, Reserve Div Cup 86-87), Yorks Lg Div 1 26-27 (Div 2 81-82, Div 3 R-up 71-72 80-81), West Riding Co. Cup 62-63 72-73 85-86, West Riding Chal. Cup 24-25 26-27.

GOALKEEPERS:
Mark Fenton (Eastwood T, Guiseley, Harrogate, T, Halifax), **Mark Wright** (Knaresborough)

DEFENDERS:
Gary Edmunds (Youth), Paul Williamson (Harrogate RA, Bradford C, Leeds(J)), Middlesbrough(Sch), **Mark Fenton** (Tadcaster Alb), **Ricky Greenough** (Matlock, Bridlington Town, York, Scarborough, Chester, Alfreton), **Mick Varley** (Harrogate RA, Harrogate T, Harrogate RA), **Kenny Dennis** (Harrogate RA, Scarborough), **Brian Duffy** (Local football)

MIDFIELD:
Keith Heblich (Pickering), **Chris Camm** (Farsley Celtic, Guiseley), **Paul Slade** (Winterton R), **Paul Vincent** (Youth), **Alan Higgins** (Northallerton), **Mark Clifton** (Harrogate RA, Harrogate T), **Lee Swales** (Local football)

FORWARDS:
Tony Outhart (Harrogate RA, Scarborough, Bridlington Trin), **Chris Annan** (Tadcaster Alb), **Robbie Turnbull** (Harrogate RA, Harrogate T), **Steve French** (Whitby), **Paul Brown** (Darwen)

Pages: 36 **Price:** 50p
Editor: K Welford (0423 889186)
WMPCC Rating: 24

Formed: 1984

KNOWSLEY UNITED

The Reds

Knowsley United's Joey Barton sees his shot pushed onto the bar by Buxton goalkeeper Jimmy O'Donnell as Knowsley lose 2-3 away in the League Cup Third Round on January 4th. Photo - Rob Ruddock.

Chairman: Mr P G Orr   **President:** The Mayor of Knowsley.
Secretary TBA.
Team Manager: Max Thompson   **Asst Manager/Coach:** Mr P Campbell
Press Officer: J Richards/S Gore   **Physio:** Mr M Thompson
Commercial Manager: J Richards.
Ground: Alt Park, Endmoor Road, Huyton, Merseyside (051 480 2529).
Directions: Come off M62 at junction 6 onto M57. Leave at junction 3 for Huyton, go straight across r-about onto Huyton link road and ground is on the left.
Capacity: 9,000 (5,000 Covered)   **Seats:** 350   **Floodlights:** Y   **Shop:** N   **Metal Badges:** N
Colours: Red (white trim)   **Change colours:** Grey & white   **Sponsors:**
Previous Name: Kirkby Town until 1988.
Previous Leagues: Bass North West Counties until 1991.
Midweek matchday: Thursday.   **Reserve Team's League:** Liverpool Co. Comb.
Women's Team League: FA National League, Premier Division.
Record Attendance: 900 v Everton, Liverpool Senior Cup 85-86.
Best F.A. Cup season: 4th Qualifying Round 91-92 (lost 0-1 at Telford United).
Record Fees - Paid: **Received:**
Players progressing to Football League: Phil Daily (Wigan), Mick Marsh (Liverpool), Rodney McDonald (Walsall), Steve Farrelly (Chester City).
Clubhouse: Lounge, 2 Function Suites, Sponsors Box, Directors Room. Matchday refreshment bar.
Club Record Goalscorer: **Club Record Apps:**
91-92 Captain: **91-92 P.O.Y.:**   **91-92 Top scorer:**
Local Press: Liverpool Daily Post/Liverpool Echo (051 227 2000), Knowsley Challenger (051 548 0710).
Local Radio Stations: Radio Merseyside (051 708 5500), Radio City.
Hons: FA Vase 5th Rd 90-91 91-92, North West Counties Lg 90-91 (R-up 88-89 89-90, Div 2 85-86, Div 3 84-85, Raab Karcher Cup 89-90, Champions v Cup Winners Trophy 89-90).

GOALKEEPERS:
Andy Johnson (St Helens, Wigan)
DEFENDERS: Peter Orr (Southport, Northwich V, Prescot Cables), **Dave Pennell** (Morecambe, Paulton V, Knowsley, Bootle, Witton Alb, Runcorn, Witton Alb, Southport, Burscough, Runcorn), **Dave O'Brien** (Southport, Marine, Everton(T)), **Steve Jackson** (Southport, Sth Liverpool, Buxton, Southport, Prescot Cables, Ellesmere Pt), **Chris Seagraves** (Winsford, Southport, Caernarfon, Hong Kong Rangers, Kingstonian, Walton & Hersham, Wealdstone, Grimsby, Liverpool), **Les Halverson** (Local football)
MIDFIELD: Chris Lee (Ford Motors), **Mark Fletcher** (Boston Utd, Loughboro Univ), **Alan Fahy** (Local football), **Paul Duncan** (Local football), **Steve Hall** (Local football), **Paul Boardman** (Wrexham), **Ian Henesy** (Runcorn)
FORWARDS: Neil Parker (Caernarfon, Waterloo Docks), **Owen Brown** (Prescot, Bootle, Chester, Tranmere, Crewe, Tranmere, Carlisle Utd, Liverpool), **Paul Wilson** (Local football), **Dave Siddell** (Local football), **Billy Parry** (Local football)

KNOWSLEY UNITED
FOOTBALL CLUB

KNOWSLEY UNITED
vs
EASTWOOD HANLEY

WEDNESDAY 24th APRIL 1991

PROGRAMME DETAILS:
Pages: 36 **Price:** 40p
Editor: J & S Richards
WMPCC Rating: 20

LANCASTER CITY

Lancaster attack in a League Cup First Round tie against Harrogate Town at the Giant Axe on October 19th, but they could find no way through this massed defence and went down 0-3. Photo - Alan Watson.

Chairman: John Bagguley
Vice Chairman: K Lancaster.
President: M Woodhouse.
Secretary: Barry Newsham, 9 Addle Street, Scotforth, Lancaster LA1 4EQ (0524 35774).
Team Manager: Keith Brindle
Asst Secretary: Don Smith (0524 52229)
Physio: Dave Hughes
Commercial Manager: Mike Hoyle.
General Mgr: R Danson
Press Officer: Andy Satterthwaite.
Ground: Giant Axe, West Road, Lancaster (0524 382238).
Directions: M6 junction 33 to Lancaster. Follow signs for railway station turning left at lights. Take second right and follow road down hill - ground on right. Quarter mile from Lancaster Castle (BR), 5 mins walk from bus station.
Capacity: 5,000 (1,000 Covered)   **Seats:** 500   **Floodlights:** Y   **Shop:** N   **Metal Badges:** Y
Colours: Blue/white/blue   **Change colours:** All yellow   **Sponsors:** Reebok UK.
Previous Leagues: Lancs Combination 05-10 11-15 19-70/ Northern Premier 70-82/ North West Counties 82-87.
Reserve Team's League: Northern Combination.
Previous Names: Lancaster Town
Previous Ground: Quarry Meadow 05-06 (just 2 games!)
Midweek home matchday: Wednesday
Record Attendance: 7,500 v Carlisle, FA Cup 1936.
Best F.A. Cup season: 2nd Rd 46-47 (0-4 v Gateshead) 72-73 (1-2 v Notts County). Also 1st Rd on 8 other occasions: 28-29 29-30 30-31 31-32 33-34 37-38 38-39 47-48.
League Clubs defeated in F.A. Cup: Barrow, Stockport County 21-22.
Players progressing to Football League: John McNamee (Workington 1975), Brendan O'Callaghan (Stoke City), Ian Stevens (Stockport County 1986).
Clubhouse: Open matchdays.
Steward: D Redding.
Club Record Goalscorer:
Club Record Apps: Edgar J Parkinson.
91-92 Captain:
91-92 P.O.Y.:
91-92 Top scorer:
91-92 Average Attendance:
Local Newspapers (+Tel.Nos.): Lancaster Guardian, Morcambe Visitor, Lancaster Evening Post.
Local Radio Stations: Lancaster Radio, Red Rose.
Honours: Northern Premier Lg Cup R-up 79-80 (Div 1 Cup R-up 90-91), Lancs Combination 21-22 29-30 34-35 35-36 (R-up 19-20 22-23 27-28 51-52, Lg Cup 21-22, Div 2 R-up 14-15), Lancs Junior Cup (ATS Challenge Trophy) 27-28 28-29 30-31 33-34 51-52 74-75 (R-up 06-07 08-09 19-20 26-27), FA Vase 2nd Rd 86-87 90-91, FA Trophy 3rd Rd 74-75 75-76, Lancs Yth (under 18) Cup 87-88 88-89 (R-up 86-87 89-90).

GOALKEEPERS:
Glen Johnstone (Preston, Blackpool, Blackburn)
DEFENDERS: Brian Curwen (Wyre Villa), **Martin Clark** (Preston(T)), **Barrie Stimpson** (Barrow, Colne D, Morecambe, Gateshead, Hartlepool, Chesterfield, Hartlepool), **Shaun Allen** (Morecambe, Chorley, Morecambe, Preston), **Dave Morgan** (Guiseley, Accrington Stanley, Witton Alb, Guiseley, Colne D, Morecambe, Thackley, Huddersfield, Phoenix Pk, Bradley R), **Colin Hogarth** (Guiseley, Harrogate T, Guiseley, Otley, Thackley), **Lee Doody** (Radcliffe B, Preston, Man Utd(T))
MIDFIELD: **Graham Gill** (Leyland Daf, Barrow, Colne D, Morecambe, Workington, KTV Kokkola(Fin), Lancaster, Netherfield, Leyland M), **Vaughan Williams** (Colne D, Morecambe, Workington, Lancaster, Everton(J)), **Ashley Cross** (Youth), **Steve Anderton** (Prerston), **Len Breakell** (BAC Preston), **Dave Woodburn** (Morecambe, Dalton Utd, Barrow, Burnley(J)), **Billy Gilmour** (Barrow, Newcastle Blue Star, Barrow, Workington, Gretna, Penrith)
FORWARDS:
Colin Coppin (Luton), **Stuart Darley** (Bamber Bridge, Morecambe, Horwich RMI, Burnley(A)), **Martin Horsfield** (Darwen, Clitheroe, Gt Harwood), **Steven Roe** (Morecambe, Lancaster), **Peter McCrae** (Ghent(Bel), Northwich V, Lancaster, Runcorn, Oldham, Blackburn), **Dave Smith** (Netherfield, Barrow, Netherfield, Workington, Barrow), **Peter Rigby** (Local football), **Ian Noteman** (Guiseley, Garforth, Yorkshire Am)

PROGRAMME DETAILS:
Pages: 50 Price: 60p
Editor: Dave Woodburn
WMPCC Rating: 35

Formed: 1920

NETHERFIELD

Netherfield's Brian Dawson clears the ball against Irlam Town watched by team-mates Chris Ward and Mick Fuller. Photo courtesy of the Westmorland Gazette.

Chairman: David Willan   **President:** Ty Power.
Secretary: Peter Savage, 46 Hayclose Road, Kendal (0539 726488).
Team Manager: Tony Hesketh   **Coach:** Keith Galley
Physio: **Commercial Manager:**   **Press Officer:** Secretary.
Ground Address & Tel: Parkside Road, Kendal, Cumbria (0539 722469).
Directions: M6 junction 36, follow Skipton sign for 200 yds, left at r-bout, straight into Kendal. Turn into Parkside Road opposite 'K' shoe factory - ground 400 yds. One and a half miles from Oxenholme (BR).
Capacity: 4,800 (1,000 Covered)   **Seats:** 280   **Floodlights:** Y   **Shop:** N   **Metal Badges:** Y
Colours: Black & white/black/red   **Change colours:** Yellow/green/yellow.
Previous Leagues: Westmorland/ North Lancs/ Lancs Combination 45-68/ Northern Premier 68-83/ North West Counties 83-87.   **Sponsors:** 'K' shoes.
Midweek home matchday: Tuesday   **Reserve Team's League:** Westmorland Lg.
Record Attendance: 5,184 v Grimsby Town, FA Cup 1st Rd 1955.
Best F.A. Cup season: 2nd Rd replay 63-64 (lost 1-4 at Chesterfield after 1-1 draw). Also 2nd Rd 49-50, 1st Rd 45-46 48-49 52-53 54-55 55-56 64-65.
Players progressing to Football League: John Laidlaw (Carlisle 1946), Louis Cardwell (Crewe 1947), Herbert Keen (Barrow 1953), Alec Aston (Preston 1955), Horace Langstreth (T'quay 1956), John Simpson (Lincoln 1957), Dennis Rogers (Accrington 1959), Tom Brownlee (Bradford City 1965), Peter McDonnell (Bury 1973), Keith Silken (Workington 1973), Roger Wicks (Darlington 1981), Andy Milner (Man City).
Clubhouse: The Park Leisure Club. Open daily 11am-11pm (till 2am at weekends).
Club Record Goalscorer: Tom Brownlee   **Club Record Apps:**
91-92 Captain: Graham Byram/ Chris Ward   **91-92 P.o.Y.:** Malcolm Jackson
91-92 Top scorers: M Jackson, W Maddock, S McCullough, C Ward.   **91-92 Average Gate:** 164.
Local Newspapers (+Tel.Nos.): Westmorland Gazette (0539 720555), Lancaster Evening Post.
Local Radio Stations: Radio Cumbria, Red Rose.
Hons: FA Vase 3rd Rd 89-90, FA Tphy 2nd Rd 80-81, Lancs Comb. 48-49 64-65 (R-up 45-46 53-54 61-62 63-64, Lg Cup 55-56 60-61), Westmorland Snr Cup(12) 24-25 31-33 35-36 46-48 63-64 65-66 71-72 86-87 89-89 90-91.

GOALKEEPERS:
Graham Byram (Colne D, Morecambe, Penrith, Lancaster, Workington, Morecambe)
DEFENDERS:
Alan Kennedy (Morecambe, Wrexham, Colne D, Wigan, Grantham, Hartlepool, Sunderland, Liverpool, Newcastle Utd), **Micky Fuller** (BAC Preston), **Malcolm Jackson** (Workington, Barrow, Netherfield, Bolton W(A)), **Graham Jones** (Morecambe, Gainsborough Trin, Bradford C), **Gary Moss** (BAC Preston), **Peter Whitehead** (Hull(T)), **Graham Dewhurst** (BAC Preston), **Gary Knowles** (Lancaster, Netherfield, Morecambe, Netherfield), **Mick Crabbe** (Bamber Bridge)
MIDFIELD:
Les Breakell (Bamber Bridge), **Gary Moffatt** (Holker OB), **Brian Dawson** (Millom), **Steve McCullough** (Barrow, Nautical), **Chris Ward** (BAC Preston), **Tony Jackson** (Droylsden, Mossley, Man Utd(T)), **Ian Smith** (Bamber Bridge), **Jamie Dunne** (Maghull, Flint T, Tranmere)
FORWARDS:
Keith Galley (Morecambe, Netherfield, Morecambe, Netherfield, Morecambe, Southport, Rochdale, Telford, Morecambe, Netherfield), **Brian Fleming** (Lancaster, Netherfield), **Leroy Allen** (Bamber Bridge), **Wayne Maddock** (Marine, BAC Preston, Leyland M), **Mel Tottoh** (Accrington Stanley, Preston, Lytham)

50 pence

NETHERFIELD

1991 1992

HFS LOANS LEAGUE

Pages: 40 **Price:** 60p
Editor: Peter Savage
WMPCC Rating: 27

NORTH SHIELDS

North Shields FC, Northern Counties (East) League champions 1991-92. Back Row (L/R): George Cook (Asst Manager), Ian MacKenzie, Dave Woodcock, Shaun Dunn, Graham Mole, Bobby Strong, Dave Callaghan, Graham Jones, Ted Collingson. Front: Gary Nicholson, Steve Pyle, Neil Howie, Martin Hamilton, Barrie Wardrobe, Ged Parkinson, Brian Jennings. Photo - James Wright.

Chairman: G Vasey **President:**
Secretary: R D Wilkinson, 72 Albatross Way, The Links, Blyth, Northumberland NE24 3QH (0670 352237).
Manager: Colin Richardson **Assistant Manager:** George Cook.
Press Officer: Ken Green **Commercial Manager:** Vic Halom.
Ground & Directions: As Whitley Bay FC (see page 755).
Colours: All red **Change colours:** All yellow
Midweek matches: Monday
Previous Leagues: North Eastern 28-58/ Midland 58-60/ Northern Counties 60-65/ Northern 65-89/ Northern Counties (East) 89-92.
Previous Names: North Shields Athletic/ Preston Colliery (pre-1928).
Previous Ground: Appleby Park, Hawkeys Lane (pre-1992).
Record Attendance: 12,800 v South Shields, North Eastern Lg October 1936
Best FA Trophy season: 2nd Round 83-84.
Best FA Cup season: 2nd Round Proper 33-34 82-83.
League Clubs beaten in FA Cup: Halifax Town 82-83.
Sponsors: Drymill Builders Merchants.
Club Record Scorer: Tom Cole 244 (1930-39) **Club Record Apps:** Ron Tatum 515 (63-75)
Local Newspapers: Newcastle Journal, Evening Chronicle, Shields New Guardian, Weekly Courier
Hons: FA Amateur Cup 68-69, Northern Lg 68-69 (R-up 65-66 83-84, Northern Lg Cup 68-69 71-72), Northern Counties (East) Lg 91-92 (R-up 90-91, Presidents Cup 91-92), Northumberland Snr Cup 37-38 45-46 47-48 53-54 57-58 59-60 65-66 75-76 78-79 90-91), Northern Counties Lg 60-61 (Lg Cup 60-61), Midland Lg R-up 59-60, North Eastern Lg 49-50 (R-up 51-52, Div 2 28-29, Lg Cup 44-45 56-57), European Amateur Cup Winners Cup (joint with Almas of Rome) 68-69

GOALKEEPERS:
Bobby Strong (Dunstan Fed, Ryhope CA, Seaham Red Star, Eppleton CW, Annfield Plain, Ryhope CW)
DEFENDERS:
Martin Hamilton (Chester-le-Street, Eppleton CW, Durham, Sunderland), **Ian McKenzie** (Stockport, Barnsley, Newcastle Utd), **Graham Mole** (Newcastle Blue Star, Ryhope CW, Annfield Plain), **John Elliott** (Spennymoor, Newcastle Utd, Aston Villa), **Dave Woodcock** (Newcastle Blue Star, Darlington, Sunderland), **Shaun Dunn** (Bury, Blackpool, North Shields), **Dave Callaghan** (Ferryhill, B Auckland, Vuax SC, Peterlee, Newcastle Blue Star, Blyth S, Newcastle Blue Star, Spennymoor)
MIDFIELD:
Barrie Wardrobe (Gateshead, Arcadia(SA), St Mirren, Hartlepool, Sunderland), **Tony Burgess** (Whitley Bay, Bedlington, Ashington), **Ged Parkinson** (Seaham Red Star, Dawdon CW), **Neil Howie** (Blyth S, Brandon Utd, Chester-le-Street), **Justin Robson** (Newcastle Blue Star, Gateshead, Newcastle Utd), **Tony Howarth** (Roker, Annfield Plain), **Steve Houlden** (Ashington, Bedlington, Whitby, Middlsbrough)
FORWARDS: Steve Pyle (Blyth S, Kumu(Fin), Torquay, Camb Utd), **Graeme Jones** (Bronstjarns BK(Swe), North Shields, Newcastle Blue Star, Millwall(J)), **Gary Nicholson** (Gateshead, North Shields, Whitley Bay, Blyth S, Halifax, York, Mansfield, Newcastle Utd)

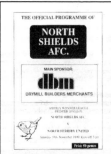
PROGRAMME DETAILS:
Pages: 20 **Price:** 50p
Editor: David Thompson
WMPCC Rating: N/A

RADCLIFFE BOROUGH

Boro'

Radcliffe Borough put pressure on Rossendale United's Carl Parker (nearest camera) and record a 3-2 win. Photo - Anthony Brown

Chairman: Ian Wood **President:** A A Swarbrick.
Secretary: Graham E Fielding, 93 Callender Street, Ramsbottom, Bury, Lancs BL0 9DU (0706 825299).
Team Manager: Kevin Glendon **Asst Manager:** Paul Webb **Coach:** Jimmy Golder
Press Officer: M Collins **Physio:** Derek Miles
Commercial Manager: None.
Ground: Stainton Park, Pilkington Road, Radcliffe, Lancs M26 0PE (061 725 9197).
Directions: M62 junction 17 - follow signs for Whitefield and Bury then A665 to Radcliffe. Through town centre, turn right into Unsworth Street, ground on left, Colshaw Close. Half a mile from Radcliffe (BR).
Capacity: 5,000 (1,000 Covered) **Seats:** 350 **Floodlights:** Y **Shop:** N **Metal Badges:** N
Colours: All blue **Change colours:** All red.
Sponsors: The Sport.
Previous Ground: Bright Street 1949-70. **Previous Leagues:** South East Lancs/ Manchester 53-63/ Lancs Combination 63-71/ Cheshire County 71-82/ North West Counties 82-87.
Midweek home matchday: Tuesday **Reserve Team's League:** Northern Comb.
Record Attendance: 1,468 v Caernarvon Town, North West Counties League 1983.
Best F.A. Cup season: Never beyond qualifying rounds.
League clubs defeated in F.A. Cup: None.
Record Fees - Paid: £5,000 for Gary Walker (Buxton) **Rec'd:** £5,000 for Kevin Hulme (Bury).
Players progressing to Football League: Jim Hayman (Bury 1950), Ian Wood (Oldham Athletic 1965), Robert Hutchinson (Rochdale 1974), Gary Hawarth (Rochdale 1984), Kevin Hulme (Bury 1989).
Clubhouse: (061 723 4181). 'The Footballers' - public house on ground.
Club Record Goalscorer: Gary Howarth **Club Record Apps:** Chris Lilley.
91-92 Captain: Nigel Smith **91-92 P.o.Y.:** Nigel Smith **91-92 Top scorer:** Peter Coyne.
Local Newspapers (+Tel.Nos.): Radcliffe Times, Bolton Evening News, Manchester Evening News.
Local Radio Stations: Greater Manchester Radio (GMR), Piccadilly.
Honours: North West Counties Lg 84-85 (Div 2 82-83), Lancs Combination Lg Cup 69-70), Manchester Lg R-up 55-56 (Lg Cup 58-59(joint)), FA Trophy 1st Rd 72-73.

GOALKEEPERS:
Gary Walker (Buxton, Hyde, Man City, Stockport, Ashton Utd), **Paul Horridge** (Walshaw)

DEFENDERS:
Gary Curtis (Newtown, Northwich V, Grimsby(T)), **Peter Mellor** (Hyde), **Lee Doody** (Preston, Man Utd(T)), **Steve Guest** (Bradford PA, Accrington Stanley, Hyde, Oswestry, Netherfield, Everton(A)), **Simon Whittle** (Netherfield, Cheadle, Accrington Stanley, Chorley, Irlam, Horwich, Bolton W), **Nigel Smith** (Hyde, Flixton, Stalybridge, Hyde, Northwich V, Stockport)

MIDFIELD:
Paul Newton (Cheadle, Stockport, Flixton, Man City), **Simon Mooney** (Oldham), **David Moran** (Hyde), **Kevin Glendon** (Macclesfield, Chorley, Hyde, Northwich V, Mossley, Witton Alb, Burnley, Crewe, Man City), **John Secker** (Charlton(T))

FORWARDS:
John Saxon (Highfield Utd, Radcliffe B), **Stuart Cunningham** (Buxton), **John Bottomley** (Man Utd(T)), **Peter Coyne** (Glossop, Colne D, Swindon, Hyde, Crewe, Ashton Utd, Man Utd)

PROGRAMME DETAILS:
Pages: 36 Price: 50p
Editor: M Collins
WMPCC Rating: 20

ROSSENDALE UNITED

The Stags

Rossendale United 1991-92: Back Row (L/R): Ian Lang, Dave Stafford, Neil Wright, Lloyd Green, Jon Pacey, Steve Bentley, Ian Pilkington, Chris Rouine, Billy Greenan (Asst Manager). Front: Duncan McFadyen, Peter Devine, Simon Westwell (Captain), Ray Davies, Carl Parker. Photo - Lancashire Evening Telegraph.

Chairman: Steve Conaghan.   **President:** C Barcoft.
Secretary: Hughie Cairney, 9 Cloister Drive, Darwen, Lancs BB3 3JX (0254 773642).
Team Manager: Steve Conaghan   **Assistant Manager:** Billy Greenan.
Directors: C Sims, J Heyworth, M Hobson, E Roult, K Holt, C Doody, D Hutchinson, S Conaghan, A Saunders, W Carlton, B Kemp.
Commercial Manager: Steve Hobson.
Ground: Dark Lane, Newchurch, Rawtenstall, Rossendale, Lancs (0706 215119).
Directions: M66, then A682 to Rawtenstall. From town centre follow signs to Burnley (A682). After 1 mile turn right into Newchurch Road, after another mile and a half turn right into Staghills Road - through council estate to ground (half mile).
Capacity: 5,000 (900 Covered)   **Seats:** 400   **Floodlights:** Y   **Shop:** N   **Metal Badges:** N
Colours: Blue & white stripes/white/blue   **Change colours:** All yellow
Sponsors: C.R.G. Signs.   **Reserve Team's League:** Northern Comb.
Previous Leagues: Lancs 1889-97/ Lancs Comb 1903-16 19-70/ Cheshire County 70-82/ NW Counties 82-89.
Midweek home matchday: Monday   **Record Attendance:** 3,400 v Shrewsbury, FA Cup 75-76.
Best F.A. Cup season: 2nd Rd 71-72 (1-4 v Bolton). Also 1st Rd 75-76.
Record Fees - Paid: **Received:** £1,500 for Dave O'Neill (Huddersfield).
Players progressing to Football League: Tommy Lawton, Geoff Smith (B'ford C 1952), Edmund Hartley & William O'Loughton (Oldham 1956 & 60), Colin Blunt (Burnley 1964), Fred Eyre (B'ford PA 1969), Dave O'Neill (H'field), Carl Parker (Rochdale 1992).
Clubhouse: Open nightly & weekend lunchtimes. Snooker, pool, darts, dominoes.   **Steward:** A Saunders.
Club Record Goalscorer: Bob Scott   **Club Record Apps:** Johnny Clarke 770.
91-92 Captain: Simon Westwell   **91-92 P.o.Y.:** Duncan McFadyen.
91-92 Top scorer: Ian Pilkington 23   **91-92 Average Attendance:** 192.
Local Newspapers (+Tel.Nos.): Rossendale Free, Lancs Evening Telegraph, Rossendale Herald & Post, Rossendale Mail.
Local Radio Stations: Red Rose, Radio Lancashire.
Honours: NW Counties Lg 88-89 (Div 2 R-up 85-86), Lancs Comb 26-27 (R-up 54-55, Lg Cup 28-29, Div 2 56-57), Cheshire County Lg(2) 70-72 (R-up 73-74, Lg Cup 73-74), Lancs Junior Cup (ATS Challenge Tphy) 11-12 72-73, FA Vase 5th Rd 86-87 88-89, FA Tphy 2nd Rd 81-82.

GOALKEEPERS:
Jon Pacey (Runcorn, Rossendale, Glossop)
DEFENDERS: Dave Feeney (Accrington Stanley, Everton(T)), **Simon Westwell** (Accrington Stanley, Colne D, Chorley, Preston), **Duncan McFadyen** (Accrington Stanley, Colne D), **Tony Flanagan** (Glossop, Rossendale, Haslingden), **Steve Bentley** (Salford, Mossley, Colne D, Salford, Stalybridge), **Gary Rishton** (Haslingden)
MIDFIELD: Lloyd Green (Haslingden), **Neil Wright** (Radcliffe B, Chorley), **Chris Halstead** (Oldham Ath(T)), **Ian Lang** (Clitheroe, Atherton LR, Accrington Stanley), **Chris Rouine** (Helmshore, Haslingden), **David Leigh** (Local football), **Mark Kayley** (Salford, Rossendale, Haslingden, Bacup B), **Andy Darbyshire** (Haslingden)
FORWARDS: **Colin Yeomans** (Haslingden, Clitheroe), **Ian Pilkington** (Whinney Hill), **Andy Rouine** (Haslingden), **Craig Dewhurst** (Accrington Stanley), **Alex Binnie** (Bacup B, Glossop, Rossendale, Witton Alb, Rossendale, Blackburn), **Steve Whitehead** (Accrington Stanley, Salford, Rossendale, Colne D, Burnley Utd), **Chris Grimshaw** (Accrington Stanley, Colne D, Morecambe, Accrington Stanley, Bury, Crewe, Burnley), **Jimmy Clarke** (Buxton, Bacup B, Rossendale, Colne D, Rossendale, Haslingden, Hyde, Haslingden)

OFFICIAL PROGRAMME
Pages: 36 **Price:** 50p
Editor: Tony Brown/John Dunn
WMPCC Rating: 23

SHEPSHED ALBION Albion or Raiders

Rammal Korpal head Shepshed's first goal in their excellent 3-3 draw against already promoted Premier Division leaders Stalybridge Celtic on 18th April. Photo - Colin Stevens.

Chairman: Tony Greenwood **Directors:** Patrick Concannon, David Heap, David Levitt, Brian Edwards, Claire Woodward, Lyn Howden, Mike Knaggs.
Secretary: Brian Edwards, 35 Woodbrook Road, Loughborough, Leics LE11 3QB.
Manager: John T Martin **Public Relations:** Barry F Perkins.
Press Officer: Maurice Brindley (0509 267922)
Ground: The Dovecote, Butthole Lane, Shepshed, Leics (0509 502684).
Directions: M1 junction 23, A512 towards Ashby, right at first lights, right at garage in Forest Street, right into Butthole Lane opposite Black Swan. Five miles from Loughborough (BR).
Capacity: 5,000 (1,500 Covered). **Seats:** 209 **Floodlights:** Y **Shop:** N **Metal Badges:** N
Colours: White (red & black trim)/black (red & white trim)/red
Change colours: All green (gold trim). **Sponsors:** I.S.S. Security Group.
Previous Leagues: Leics Senior 07-16 19-27 46-50 51-81/ Midland Counties 81-82/ Northern Counties (East) 82-83/ Southern 83-88.
Previous Names: Shepshed Albion 1890-1975/ Shepshed Charterhouse 75-91.
Midweek home matchday: Tuesday **Reserve Team's League:** Midland Comb.
Record Attendance: 1,672.
Best F.A. Cup season: 1st Rd 82-83 (lost 1-5 at Preston North End).
League clubs defeated in F.A. Cup: None.
Record Fees - Paid: £2,000 for Doug Newton **Received:** £10,000 for John Deakin.
Players progressing to Football League: Neil Grewcock (Burnley 1984), Gordon Tucker (Huddersfield 1987), Devon White (Bristol Rovers 1987), John Deakin (Birmingham City).
Clubhouse: Accomodates 120 in main room, 50 in others. **Steward:** TBA.
Club Record Goalscorer: Jeff Lissaman **Club Record Apps:** Austin Straker 300.
91-92 Captain: Mick Williamson **91-92 P.o.Y.:** Tim Griffin **91-92 Top scorer:**
Local Newspapers (+Tel.Nos.): Nottingham Forest, Leicester Mercury, Loughborough Echo.
Local Radio Stations: BBC Radio Leicester.
Honours: Southern Lg Midland Division R-up 83-84, Northern Counties (East) Lg 82-83 (Lg Cup 82-83), Midland Counties Lg 81-82 (Lg Cup 81-82), Leics Senior Lg 10-11 20-21 78-79 79-80 80-81 (R-up 21-22, Div 2 53-54 65-66 77-78, Div 2 Cup 77-78), Leics Senior Cup 77-78 79-80 81-82 83-84 84-85 85-86 87-88, FA Vase SF 78-79, FA Tphy 1st Rd Replay 85-86 89-90.

GOALKEEPERS:
Darren Heyes (Matlock, Shepshed, Scunthorpe, Notts Forest), **Paul Robbins** (Lincoln, Notts Co, Shepshed)
DEFENDERS: John Jenkins (Shrewsbury, Aston Villa(T)), **Tim Griffin** (Leicester Utd), **Mick Collins** (Frickley), **John Tatham** (Ilkeston, Shepshed, Ilkeston), **Peter Leebrook** (VS Rugby, Aldershot, Burnley), **Steve Sims** (Stafford R, Boston FC, Lincoln, Aston Villa, Watford, Notts Co, Watford, Leicester C), **Tony Barratt** (Local football), **Wayne Oxley** (Burton Alb, Shepshed, Burton Alb, Buxton, Hallam)
MIDFIELD: Tim Watts (Quorn, Friar Lane OB), **Ramman Korpal** (Loughboro Dynamo), **Robin Taylor** (Camb City), **Ian Turner** (Grantham, Shepshed, Kettering, Burton Alb, Chesterfield), **Dave Reddin** (Boston Utd, Kettering, Bourne), **Jason Glover** (Bedworth, Shepshed, Quorn)
Brentford), **Nicky Ryder** (Brentford(T)), **Darren Seabrook** (Kelmscott(Aust)),
FORWARDS:
Scott Machin (Burton Alb, Shepshed, Notts Co), **Martin Roderick** (Blackpool, Harrogate T, Leeds Carnegie Coll, Wycombe, Farnborough, Portsmouth), **Keith Dakin** (Hinckley, Leicester Utd, Shepshed), **Richard Flint** (Alfreton, Sutton T), **Shaun Hession** (Local football), **Dave Cockayne** (Local football)

PROGRAMME DETAILS:
Pages: 24 **Price:** 50p
Editor: Maurice Brindley
WMPCC Rating: 19

Warrington Town 1991-92. Back Row (L/R): Dennis Smith (Physio), Richard Harvey, Gavin McDonald, Gary Finley, Steve Parsonage, Chris Coulson, Steve Hughes, Ian Thompson, Frank O'Brien (Asst Manager). Front: Aiden Warder, Joey Dunn, Neil Whalley (Captain), Derek Brownbill (Manager), Neil Williams, Kevin Gratton, Paul Meachin. Photo - D Hollinsworth.

Chairman: R Smith **Treasurer:** Rosa Dale.
Secretary: Graham Ost, 120 Warrington Rd, Penketh, Warrington, Cheshire WA5 2JZ (0925 722540).
Team Manager: D Brownbill **Asst Manager:** F O'Brien **Coach:**
Physio: D Smith **Press Off.:** Colin Serjent **Commercial Manager:** Joan Gleave.
Ground: Cantilever Park, Common Lane, off Loushers Lane, Latchford, Warrington WA4 2RS (0925 31932).
Directions: M6 junction 20, then A50 towards Warrington. After 2 miles turn left immediately after swing bridge into Station Road. Ground quarter of a mile. 2 miles from Warrington Bank Quay (BR).
Capacity: 2,500 (500 Covered) **Seats:** 200 **Floodlights:** Y **Shop:** N **Metal Badges:** N
Colours: Yellow/blue/yellow **Change colours:** Red/white **Sponsors:** Whitbread Plc.
Previous Name: Stockton Heath 1949-62. **Best F.A. Cup season:** 3rd Qual. Rd 88-89.
Previous Leagues: Warrington & Dist. 49-52/ Mid-Cheshire 52-78/ Cheshire Co. 78-82/ North West Co's 82-90.
Midweek home matchday: Wednesday **Reserve Team's League:** Northern Combination.
Record Attendance: 3,000 v Halesowen Town, FA Vase Semi Final 1st leg 85-86.
Record Fees - Paid: **Received:**
Players progressing to Football League: Sam Morris (Chester 1951), John Green (Tranmere 1958), Roger Hunt (Liverpool 1959), John Richards (Wolves), John Bramhall (Tranmere 1976), Mark Leonard (Everton, Stockport, Bradford City).
Clubhouse: Weekdays 1pm-11pm, Sat. noon-11pm, Sun. 12-3pm, 7pm-10.30pm. **Steward:** D Gleave.
Club Record Goalscorer: L Arnold 60 **Club Record Apps:**
91-92 Capt: Neil Whalley
91-92 P.o.Y.: Steve Parsonage (management choice), Gavin McDonald (fans'), Gary Finley (players').
91-92 Top scorer: Gavin McDonald 26 **91-92 Average Attendance:** 188.
Local Newspapers (+Tel.Nos.): Warrington Guardian (0925 33033), Warrington Mercury, Manchester Evening News, Liverpool Post & Echo.
Local Radio Stations: Radio Merseyside, Radio Manchester (GMR).
Honours: FA Vase R-up 86-87 (SF 85-86), North West Counties Lg 89-90 (Lg Cup 85-86 87-88 88-89 (R-up 89-90), Div 2 R-up 86-87, Div 3 R-up 82-83, Reserve Div West 89-90), Mid Cheshire Lg 60-61 (R-up 57-58, Lg Cup 54-55 55-56) 11-12 72-73, FA Vase 5th Rd 86-87 88-89, FA Tphy 2nd Rd 81-82.

GOALKEEPERS:
Mark Whittaker (Accrington Stanley, Droylsden, Warrington, Chester), **Steve Parsonage** (Christleton, Colwyn B)
DEFENDERS: Alan Blair (Droylsden, Rylands, Warrington, Chester), **Ian Thompson** (Knowsley, Ellesmere Pt, Prescot C, Skelmersdale, Kirkby, St Helens), **Neil Williams** (Eagle Sports), **Gary Finley** (Vauxhall GM, Warrington, Marine), **John McInnes** (Sth Liverpool, Southport), **Chris Coulson** (Interox, Walkers, Droylsden, Runcorn), **Ian Reid** (Youth), **Kevin Gratton** (Bolton W(A)), **David Lomax** (Irlam, Radcliffe B, Salford, Flixton)
MIDFIELD: Neil Cook (Altrincham, Warrington, Monks Sports, Bolton(Sch)), **Richard Harvey** (Youth), **Neil Whalley** (Local football), **Mike Tandy** (Interox, Warrington), **Aiden Warder** (Sth Liverpool, London Univ), **Colin Beck** (Marine, Burscough, Marine), **Alan Richards** (Runcorn)
FORWARDS: Gavin McDonald (Irlam, Chesterfield), **Joey Dunn** (Marine, Burscough, Altrincham, Formby, Sth Liverpool, Earle), **Colin Russell** (Droylsden, Morecambe, Bangor, Colne D, Wigan, Scarborough, Doncaster, Bournemouth, Huddersfield, Liverpool), **Joe Rice** (Caernarfon, Formby, Sth Liverpool, Caernarfon, Sth Liverpool, Mossley, Bootle, Southport, Prescot C, Bootle, Sth Liverpool, Burscough), **Darren Beales** (Marine), **Paul Meachin** (Marine, New Brighton, Southport), **Steve Hughes** (Crewe, Man City(A)), **Liam Watson** (Burscough), **Tony Plant** (Droylsden, Warrington), **Kenny Saunders** (Knowsley, Mossley, Marine, St Helens, Burnley, Tranmere)

Pages: 20 **Price:** 50p
Editor: Jim Dale
WMPCC Rating: 28

WORKINGTON

Workington 1991-92. Back Row (L/R): George Norrie (Manager), Lee O'Keefe, Danny Foley, Alan Stewart, Graham Emerson, Lee Copeland, Martin Scarborough, Peter Davis, Darren Mahone. Front Row: Sean Sunderland, Jason Brierley, Jackie Hather, Graham Flynn, Graham Caton.

Chairman: J J Donald   **President:** E Fisher.
Secretary: Tom Robson, 12 Derwent Bank, Seaton, Workington CA14 1EE (0900 605208).
Team Manager: George Norrie   **Asst Manager:** Jackie Hather **Coach:** Martin Gaffney
Press Officer: Steve Durham   **Physio:** Danny Foley.
Ground: Borough Park, Workington, Cumbria CA14 2DT (0900 602871).
Directions: A66 into town, right at 'T' junction, follow A596 for three quarters of a mile. Quarter of a mile from Workington (BR).
Capacity: 2,500 (1,000 Covered)   **Seats:** 200   **Floodlights:** Y   **Shop:** Y   **Metal Badges:** Y
Colours: Red/white/red   **Change colours:** White/red/white.
Sponsors: TBA.   **Previous Ground:** Lonsdale Park 1884-1937.
Previous Leagues: Lancs Combination 04-10/ North Eastern 10-11 21-51/ Football League 51-77.
Midweek home matchday: Tuesday   **Record Attendance:** 21,000 v Manchester United, FA Cup 1958.
Best F.A. Cup season: 4th Rd, 1933-34. Competition Proper on 53 other occasions.
Record Fees - Paid: £6,000 for Ken Chisholm, 1956
           Received: £33,000 for Ian McDonald (Liverpool 1974).
Players progressing to Football League: Numerous, the best known being John Burridge.
Clubhouse: Open matchdays and for private functions only.
Club Record Goalscorer: Billy Charlton 193   **Club Record Apps:** Bobby Brown 419.
91-92 Captain: Graham Flynn   **91-92 P.O.Y.:** Nigel Park
91-92 Top scorer: Keith Glover 7   **91-92 Average Attendance:** 129.
Local Newspapers (+Tel.Nos.): Evening News & Star, Times & Star (John Walsh 0900 601234).
Local Radio Stations: BBC Radio Cumbria (0228 31661).
Honours: Football League Cup QF 63-64 64-65, Football Lg: 5th Div 3 65-66, 3rd Div 4 63-64, Northern Premier Presidents Cup 83-84, North Eastern Lg R-up 38-39 (Lg Cup 34-35 36-37 (R-up 37-38)), Cumberland County Cup 1886-87 87-88 88-89 89-90 90-91 95-96 96-97 97-98 98-99 1906-07 07-08 09-10 24-25 34-35 36-37 37-38 49-50 53-54 67-68 85-86 (R-up 1885-86 91-92 1899-1900 00-01 02-03 08-09 11-12 23-24 26-27 29-30 46-47 68-69 78-79), FA Trophy 1st Rd replay 77-78.

GOALKEEPERS:
Keith Hunton (Newcastle Blue Star, Workington, Carlisle Utd, Workington)

DEFENDERS:
Jackie Hather (Penrith, Horden CW, Blackpool, Aberdeen, Annfield Plain), Martin Scarborough (Carlisle Utd(J)), Darren Mahone (Local football), Malcolm Rice (Youth), John George (Cleator Moor, Workington), Dean Kennedy (Morecambe), Marcus Thomson (Carlisle Utd(T)), Danny Foley (Local football)

MIDFIELD:
Graham Flynn (Local football), Scott Middlemass (Preston), Neil Douglas (Youth), Keith Glover (Cleator Moor, Workington, Penrith, Workington), Graham Caton (Youth), Nigel Park (Windscale Utd), Alan Stewart (Windscale Utd, Cleator Moor, Workington), Jason Brierley (Local football)

FORWARDS:
Sean Sunderland (Lancaster, Morecambe), Peter Davies (Lancaster), Kevin McClaughlin (Local football), Lee O'Keefe (Morecambe), Lee Butterworth (Morecambe)

Pages: 16 Price: 40p
Editor: Steve Durham
WMPCC Rating: 25

WORKSOP TOWN

Worksop Town FC 1991-92. Back Row (L/R): Tommy Watson (Trainer), Darren Brookes, Tony Morris, Dave Cunnington, Paul Norton, Paul Mainwaring, Dave Moss, Tommy Spencer (Manager). Front: Kenny Clark, Gary Waller, Gary Thorpe, Neil Pickering, Lee Howard, Ian Clark, Adrian Shaw.

Chairman: Mel Bradley
Directors: John Ellis, Wally Peace, Tony Ridsdale, Chris Smith, Brian Vickers, Mel Bradley.
Secretary: W E Peace, 72 Woodburn Drive, Chapeltown, Sheffield S30 4YT (0742 468160).
Team Manager: Tommy Spencer   **Asst Manager:**   **Coach:**
Press Officer: Mel Bradley   **Physio:** Tommy Watson
Ground: Babbage Way, Sandy Lane, Worksop, Notts.
Directions:
Capacity: 3,000   **Seats:** 350   **Floodlights:** Y **Shop:** Y **Metal Badges:** Y
Colours: Amber & black/black/amber   **Change colours:** Blue/white.
Previous Grounds: Central Avenue (prior to 1989)/ The Northolme, Gainsborough (shared) 89-92.
Previous Leagues: Midland Counties 1896-97 1900-30 49-60 61-68 69-74/ Central Combination 34-35/ Yorkshire 35-39/ Central Alliance 47-49 60-61/ Northern Premier 68-69.
Midweek home matchday: Tuesday   **Sponsors:** Eyres of Worksop
Record Attendance: 8,171 v Chesterfield, FA Cup 1925 (at Central Avenue).
Best FA Cup year: 3rd Rd 55-56 (lost 0-1 at Swindon). 2nd Rd 25-26. 1st Rd 07-08 21-22 22-23 26-27 61-62 78-79.
League Clubs defeated in F.A. Cup: Rotherham Town 1893-94/ Grimsby Town 94-95/ Nelson 1921-22/ Chesterfield 22-23/ Coventry City 25-26.
Record Fees - Paid: None.   **Received:** £10,000 for Martin Hardy (Boston United).
Players progressing to Football League: Jack Brown (Sheff Wed & England), Gordon Dale (C'field 1948), Alan Daley (D'caster 1950), Kevin Wood (Grimsby 1951), Harry Jarvis (Notts C 1951), Brian Taylor (Leeds 1951), Stan Rhodes & Dennis Gratton & Alan Hodgkinson & John Harrison (Sheff U 1951 & 52 & 53 67), Stanley Lloyd & Peter Marshall (S'thorpe 1954), Albert Rhodes (QPR 1954), Robert Moore (R'ham 1955), Harold Mosby (Crewe 1956), Les Moore (Derby 1957), Herbert Bowery (Nottm F 1975), Tony Moore (R'dale 1984), Steve Adams (S'boro 1987).
Club Record Goalscorer: Paul Fisher 100+ (HFS Loans Lg).
91-92 Captain: Neil Pickering
91-92 P.o.Y.: Kenny Clark (supporters' choice), Gary Thorpe (players'), David Cunnington (committee's).
91-92 Top scorer: Kenny Clark 48.   **91-92 Average Attendance:** 140.
Local Press: Worksop Guardian (500500), Worksop Star (486335), Nottingham Football Post (0602 475221).
Local Radio Stations: Radio Sheffield, Radio Hallam, Radio Lincoln.
Hons: Northern Prem. Lg Presidents Cup 85-86, Midland Co's Lg 21-22 65-66 72-73 (R-up 62-63 66-67 73-74, Sheff. & Hallamshire Snr Cup 23-24 54-55 65-66 69-70 72-73 81-82 84-85, FA Trophy 2nd Rd replay 73-74.

GOALKEEPERS:
Paul Norton (Bridlington Town, Hartlepool, Sheff Utd), **Phil Yeomans** (Kiveton Pk, Denaby)

DEFENDERS:
Tony Morris (Local football), **Neil Pickering** (Sutton T, Crookes), **Adrian Shaw** (Chesterfield, York, Halifax, Notts Forest), **Jamie Shearman** (Chesterfield), **Dave Cunnington** (King's Lynn, Harworth Cl, Worksop), **Mark Hall** (Frickley, Grantham, Doncaster), **Paul Barnett** (Eastwood T, King's Lynn, Harworth Cl)

MIDFIELD:
David Moss (Rossington Haslam, Doncaster), **Gary Thorpe** (Kiveton Pk), **Darren Cox** (Rotherham(T)), **Paul Mainwaring** (Gainsborough Town), **Linden Whitehead** (Alfreton), **Gary Waller** (ABM), **Kevin Scott** (Denaby)

FORWARDS:
Ian Clarke (Rotherham), **Kenny Clark** (Alfreton, Worksop, Davy McKee), **Lee Howard** (Eastwood T, King's Lynn, Harworth Cl, Mansfield(T)), **Darren Brookes** (ABM)

WORKSOP
TOWN F.C.

HFS LOANS LEAGUE DIVISION ONE 1991/92 SEASON

50p

HFS LOANS LEAGUE

Official match day programme sponsor Worksop Guardian

Pages: 20 **Price:** 50p
Editor: M Bradley
WMPCC Rating: 22

BASS NORTH WEST COUNTIES LEAGUE

President: Canon J R Smith.
Chairman: J E Hinchliffe.
Vice Chairman: A R McCombe.
Hon. Secretary: N A Rowles, 'Westhaven',
845 Liverpool Rd, Peel Green, Eccles, Manchester M30 7LJ (061 707 1091).

ASHTON SNATCH TITLE AT THE DEATH

The title race went right to the wire. Great Harwood Town finished their fixture list with a comfortable cushion over Ashton United, but then had to sit back and wait as Ashton played out their three games in hand. The first, potentially a tricky one against fourth placed Blackpool Rovers, proved difficult. Goals from Ian Boyle and the highly rated Darren Lyons, who had returned from Bury for the run-in, gave United a two goal cushion. However, ex-Blackpool forward Dave Windridge pulled one back to give United a nervous finish, but they held out for three valuable points.

Two days before their penultimate game, at Maine Road, Ashton had the little matter of the Raab Karcher Cup final at Bury's Gigg Lane against Burscough, and this they won 1-0 to ensure silverware in the cabinet whatever the outcome of the title race.

The game at Maine Road saw Ashton take a second minute lead through Chris Shaw only for Ged Byrne to put the home side level three minutes later. Again there was a frantic finale, and Maine Road looked set to deny Ashton the title until that man Ian Boyle popped up again to score the winner in the very last minute. Boyle, formerly with Blackpool, Cork Celtic, and Stalybridge, returned from Droylsden recently for his third spell at Hurst Cross, and he has a proved a vital signing for manager Dave Denby.

So to the final match, at Bacup Borough on Monday 4th May. Ashton had to win to overtake Great Harwood, but managerless Bacup put up a tremendous fight in front of their largest crowd of the season, and were beaten by a solitary goal from Steve Morgan just before the interval. So what a season it proved to be for Ashton with the Bass North West Counties League Championship, the Raab Karcher Cup, and the Manchester Premier Cup all ending up in the Hurst Cross boardroom. There was a lot of sympathy for Great Harwood. They had battled so hard and looked favourites for most of the season, but in the end will be far from disappointed with their lot; they created a major surprise by beating Southport in the final of the Lancashire ATS Trophy, and have been admitting to the H.F.S. Loans League, along with Ashton, due the resignation of the Welsh clubs.

In Division Two, all the headlines were grabbed by Bamber Bridge. The progressive Preston outfit went all the way from the Extra-Preliminary Round to the Semi Finals of the F.A. Vase, reached the final of the Tennants Floodlit Cup, yet still found time to win their domestic championship. Some season!

With Ashton United and Great Harwood Town leaving for higher spheres, Bootle being relegated and Vauxhall G.M. folding, there is much change within the league for the 1992-93 season. Accompanying Bamber Bridge and runners-up Newcastle Town from Division Two to Division One are no fewer than six other clubs; Blackpool Mechanics, Burscough, Glossop, Salford City, Kidsgrove Athletic and Chadderton. All this upward movement has created a number of vacancies, and newcomers to the League are Irlam Town, who have found the financial burden of H.F.S. football too great, K Chell who arrive from the West Midlands League, Nelson and Burnley Bank Hall, both from the West Lancs League, the newly formed Ellesmere Port Town, North Trafford from the Mid-Cheshire League, and Stanton Dale from the Liverpool Combination.

Bamber Bridge FC, Bass North West Counties Division Two Champions 1991-92. Photo - Francis Short.

LEAGUE TABLES 1991-92

Division One	P	W	D	L	F	A	PTS
Ashton United	34	24	5	5	61	31	77
Gt Harwood Town	34	22	8	4	68	38	74
Eastwood Hanley	34	18	9	7	54	35	63
Blackpool Rovers	34	16	7	11	73	57	55
Prescot	34	15	6	13	48	43	51
Penrith	34	15	5	14	57	58	50
Skelmersdale Utd	34	11	11	12	48	52	44
Flixton	34	11	9	14	46	50	42
Clitheroe	34	11	9	14	44	55	42
Darwen	34	10	11	13	56	55	41
Atherton L.R.	34	11	8	15	38	45	41
Nantwich Town	34	11	10	13	44	49	*40
Vauxhall G.M.	34	10	10	14	42	51	40
Bacup Borough	34	9	11	14	41	45	38
St Helens Town	34	9	9	16	49	55	36
Maine Road	34	9	9	16	40	60	36
Bradford Pk Ave.	34	10	5	19	57	68	35
Bootle	34	9	8	17	41	61	35

* - points deducted.

Division Two	P	W	D	L	F	A	PTS
Bamber Bridge	34	25	3	6	97	39	78
Newcastle Town	34	23	6	5	69	26	75
Blackpool Mech.	34	20	9	5	75	34	69
Burscough	34	19	7	8	82	46	64
Formby	34	17	5	12	49	39	56
Glossop	34	15	9	10	61	44	54
Salford City	34	14	9	11	57	41	51
Castleton Gab.	34	14	9	11	54	43	51
Cheadle Town	34	15	6	13	53	50	51
Kidsgrove Ath.	34	14	7	13	44	45	49
Chadderton	34	14	6	14	50	48	48
Oldham Town	34	11	8	15	49	62	41
Atherton Coll.	34	12	4	18	51	64	40
Squires Gate	34	11	5	18	45	60	38
Holker Old Boys	34	10	6	18	37	53	36
Maghull	34	7	2	25	38	90	23
Ashton Town	34	4	7	23	47	101	19
Westhoughton T.	34	5	4	25	33	106	19

Reserve Div.	P	W	D	L	F	A	PTS
Flixton Res	34	28	3	3	107	34	87
Chadderton Res	34	22	9	3	102	36	75
Atherton LR Res	34	20	5	9	87	50	65
Salford City Res	34	20	1	13	96	65	61
Darwen Res	34	18	6	10	64	48	60
Ashton Utd Res	34	16	7	11	66	44	55
Maine Road Res	34	15	9	10	58	46	54
Ashton Town Res	34	15	8	11	65	68	53
Blackpool M. Res	34	14	10	10	73	60	52
Maghull Res	34	15	5	14	61	57	50
Prescot Res	34	14	7	13	65	65	49
Squires Gate Res	34	11	5	18	51	73	38
Cheadle Town Res	34	10	6	18	56	69	36
Holker O.B. Res	34	8	6	20	48	81	30
Glossop Res	34	7	9	18	45	85	30
Castleton Res	34	7	4	23	46	93	25
Atherton C. Res	34	6	5	23	37	91	23
Westhoughton Res	34	5	5	24	31	91	20

LEADING SCORERS 1991-92:

Division One:

L - League, C - Cup, T - Total.

	L	C	T
Stuart Diggle (Blackpool Rvrs)	20	12	32
Phil Hulme (Eastwood Hanley)	19	9	28
Chris Shaw (Ashton United)	17	11	28
Kieran Hughes (Flixton)	16	7	23
Darren Wardman (Bradford Pk Ave.)	18	2	20
Paul Baker (Gt Harwood Town)	11	9	20
Karl Marginson (Ashton United)	11	9	20
Gary Laird (St Helens/ Ashton Utd)	17	1	18
Brent Hetherington (Penrith)	10	7	17
Gary Washington (Vauxhall G.M.)	16		16
Lee Bedson (Skelmersdale/ Prescot)	15	1	16
Peter Smith (Gt Harwood Town)	11	5	16
Brian Kilshaw (Skelmersdale Utd)	15		15
Geoff Young (Clitheroe)	12	2	14
Alan Gallagher (Blackpool Rvrs)	8	6	14
Peter Hall (Newcastle/ Nantwich)	10	3	13
Eddie Kennedy (Penrith)	10	3	13
Mark Stewart (Atherton L.R.)	8	5	13
Peter Muncey (Eastwood Hanley)	6	7	13

Division Two

	L	C	T
Andy Whittaker (Bamber Bridge)	27	13	40
Shaun Parker (Atherton Collieries)	14	12	26
Dave Ritchie (Newcastle Town)	14	12	25
Ian Hodge (Burscough)	17	7	24
Paul Hession (Chadderton)	17	7	24
Mike Batholomew (Salford City)	16	4	20
Dave Whiteman (Bamber Bridge)	11	9	20
Shaun Wade (Newcastle Town)	16	3	19
Kevin Still (Burscough)	14	3	17
Paul Cameron (Atherton Collieries)	12	5	17
Paul James (Kidsgrove Athletic)	10	7	17
Sean Togher (Burscough)	8	8	16
Peter Borrowdale (Blackpool Mech.)	14	1	15
Tom McKenna (Castleton Gabriels)	14	1	15
Dave Brown (Castleton Gabriels)	11	4	15
Carlton Dove (Salford City)	9	6	15
Gary Dalgleish (Bamber Bridge)	10	4	14
Keith Ingram (Glossop)	11	2	13
Gary Davenport (Glossop)	10	3	13
Neil Pestridge (Newcastle Town)	9	4	13

HOME TEAM	1	2	3	4	5	6	7	8	9	10	11	12	13	14	15	16	17	18
1. Ashton United	*	2-0	1-1	2-1	5-1	2-0	1-0	2-0	1-2	4-1	1-0	2-1	2-0	1-0	2-1	1-0	2-0	2-0
2. Atherton L.R.	0-1	*	2-3	1-1	2-0	0-1	1-2	0-4	1-2	1-1	1-1	2-2	0-3	3-1	2-1	4-2	2-2	2-1
3. Bacup Borough	0-1	3-1	*	0-1	0-1	1-2	1-4	0-1	0-0	4-1	1-4	0-2	3-0	1-1	0-3	3-0	0-0	2-0
4. Blackpool Rovers	1-3	0-2	1-1	*	2-2	5-3	3-3	0-0	3-1	2-3	2-1	1-0	2-2	5-1	5-3	4-0	1-0	0-1
5. Bootle	2-3	1-1	3-1	5-4	*	1-3	1-1	1-1	1-1	3-0	0-1	3-0	0-0	0-4	0-2	2-4	1-4	0-3
6. Bradford Park Av.	1-1	0-1	2-2	1-2	0-1	*	2-1	3-2	0-5	1-1	2-3	0-1	5-1	0-2	1-3	1-2	2-2	5-0
7. Clitheroe	0-0	0-1	0-0	2-2	2-0	0-5	*	0-0	1-2	1-0	0-2	1-4	2-2	1-2	2-1	2-0	1-0	2-0
8. Darwen	1-3	0-0	3-3	6-1	1-3	2-2	4-0	*	2-2	2-2	0-3	2-3	1-3	2-1	1-3	2-0	3-1	2-2
9. Eastwood Hanley	1-0	3-1	1-0	2-1	3-2	3-2	1-0	3-2	*	0-0	5-2	2-1	1-0	0-0	1-2	1-0	0-0	1-1
10. Flixton	1-2	0-1	0-1	1-3	0-0	5-2	0-2	2-0	3-1	*	0-1	2-3	1-1	2-1	3-0	2-0	3-2	1-1
11. Great Harwood T.	2-0	2-0	2-2	2-0	1-0	3-1	2-1	3-1	0-0	3-0	*	3-2	1-1	2-1	3-2	1-0	1-3	3-2
12. Maine Road	1-2	1-3	0-2	3-2	2-0	0-3	1-0	2-2	0-6	1-3	1-1	*	1-2	1-2	1-1	3-3	0-2	0-0
13. Nantwich Town	1-1	1-0	1-0	2-4	1-3	3-3	4-2	2-1	0-0	1-3	2-3	2-1	*	0-1	1-1	1-1	1-1	2-1
14. Penrith	0-3	2-1	2-0	0-5	4-0	3-1	1-1	2-2	0-1	3-1	1-6	3-0	1-0	*	1-3	1-3	5-2	4-2
15. Prescot A.F.C.	1-0	1-0	1-0	1-0	2-3	3-0	1-4	0-1	0-4	1-1	0-1	0-0	2-0	0-1	*	2-1	2-0	2-2
16. St Helens Town	0-0	0-0	2-2	1-2	1-1	2-1	0-1	0-1	4-1	1-2	2-2	0-0	3-1	4-3	1-1	*	1-2	2-1
17. Skelmersdale U.	3-3	2-1	1-1	2-5	1-0	1-2	2-2	1-4	3-0	1-1	1-1	0-1	2-1	3-1	0-3	2-1	*	2-0
18. Vauxhall G.M.	0-1	1-0	1-3	0-2	1-0	4-2	5-2	2-0	2-0	2-1	2-2	1-1	0-2	1-1	1-0	2-2	0-0	*

Bass North West Counties Division One 10-Year Record

	82/3	83/4	84/5	85/6	86/7	87/8	88/9	89/90	90/1	91/2
Accrington Stanley	10	7	15	11	2	-	-	-	-	-
Ashton United	13	19	-	-	-	-	17	9	3	1
Atherton Laburnam Rovers	-	-	-	-	-	17	14	14	18	11
Bacup Borough	-	-	-	-	-	-	-	-	14	14
Blackpool Rovers	-	-	-	-	-	-	-	-	-	4
Bootle	14	16	14	15	5	13	9	11	13	18
Bradford Park Avenue	-	-	-	-	-	-	-	-	-	17
Burscough	1	4	3	9	12	10	10	17	-	-
Caernarfon Town	-	14	2	-	-	-	-	-	-	-
Chadderton	-	-	-	-	-	-	-	18	-	-
Clitheroe	-	-	-	1	3	3	12	5	15	9
Colne Dynamoes	-	-	-	-	-	1	-	-	-	-
Colwyn Bay	-	-	-	-	-	4	4	3	2	-
Congleton Town	8	9	10	2	11	-	-	-	-	-
Curzon Ashton	12	5	6	8	19	-	-	-	-	-
Darwen	6	20	-	-	-	7	5	6	16	10
Eastwood Hanley	-	-	5	3	14	-	-	-	4	3
Ellesmere Port & Neston	-	-	-	-	-	6	11	-	-	-
Fleetwood Town	-	-	8	5	8	-	-	-	-	-
Flixton	-	-	-	-	-	-	7	12	7	8
Formby	16	13	17	20	-	14	18	-	-	-
Glossop	18	15	16	18	20	18	-	-	-	-
Great Harwood Town	-	-	-	-	-	-	-	-	-	2
Horwich R.M.I.	3	-	-	-	-	-	-	-	-	-
Irlam Town	-	-	-	6	18	-	-	-	-	-
Kirkby Town (See Knowsley United)										
Knowsley United	-	-	-	-	4	9	2	2	1	-
Lancaster City	7	6	19	-	-	-	-	-	-	-
Leek Town	11	11	9	7	16	-	-	-	-	-
Leyland Motors	17	17	11	12	13	11	8	13	12	-
Maine Road	-	-	-	-	-	-	-	-	9	16
Nantwich Town	20	-	-	-	-	-	-	7	11	12
Netherfield	-	18	18	17	17	-	-	-	-	-
Penrith	9	2	20	16	9	-	-	-	17	6
Prescot A.F.C.	15	10	13	19	-	12	15	10	6	5
Prescot Cables (see Prescot A.F.C.)										
Radcliffe Borough	-	3	1	14	15	-	-	-	-	-
Rhyl	2	-	-	-	-	-	-	-	-	-
Rossendale United	-	-	-	-	10	2	1	-	-	-
St Helens Town	19	8	12	10	6	5	3	8	8	15
Salford (City)	-	-	-	-	-	15	16	16	19	-
Skelmersdale United	-	-	-	-	-	16	13	15	10	7
Stalybridge Celtic	4	1	4	4	1	-	-	-	-	-
Vauxhall G.M.	-	-	-	-	-	-	-	4	5	13
Warrington Town	-	-	-	-	-	8	6	1	-	-
Winsford United	5	12	7	13	7	-	-	-	-	-
No. of clubs competing	20	20	20	20	20	18	18	18	19	18

DIVISION TWO RESULT CHART 1991/92

HOME TEAM	1	2	3	4	5	6	7	8	9	10	11	12	13	14	15	16	17	18
1. Ashton Town	*	1-3	3-4	2-8	3-4	1-4	2-0	0-1	0-2	0-2	2-2	1-1	5-2	0-3	1-1	1-5	2-1	4-0
2. Atherton Col.	4-1	*	1-4	0-3	1-1	0-1	0-1	1-2	0-1	0-1	0-2	0-2	4-3	1-2	0-0	2-0	4-0	3-1
3. Bacup Borough	5-0	4-1	*	0-2	2-3	1-1	7-4	1-0	2-0	3-1	6-1	1-0	9-2	3-0	3-1	0-2	4-0	3-1
4. Blackpool Mech.	6-1	2-1	1-1	*	0-2	2-1	1-1	1-1	0-3	3-2	1-0	4-3	3-0	1-1	1-1	2-2	1-1	2-0
5. Burscough	3-1	1-2	1-2	1-0	*	1-2	1-0	1-1	1-1	6-1	4-1	6-1	1-1	9-2	6-2	2-0	4-0	
6. Castleton Gabriels	3-1	3-4	3-2	0-3	3-0	*	0-0	2-2	0-1	1-2	1-2	2-0	1-2	1-0	2-2	0-0	4-1	0-0
7. Chadderton	6-4	1-0	1-3	2-2	1-1	1-2	*	2-1	2-1	1-0	1-0	2-0	3-0	0-1	4-0	1-1	1-3	2-0
8. Cheadle Town	4-0	5-3	0-4	0-3	2-3	1-0	2-0	*	3-1	1-5	2-1	1-2	1-1	1-0	4-1	0-2	3-2	4-1
9. Formby	1-0	1-1	2-4	1-2	0-1	4-2	2-0	2-0	*	0-0	1-4	3-0	4-1	0-1	0-0	2-1	1-0	3-1
10. Glossop	2-2	4-2	2-2	1-2	1-3	3-0	2-1	2-1	5-2	*	1-1	1-1	3-2	1-2	2-0	1-3	1-2	4-0
11. Holker Old Boys	4-0	2-2	0-1	0-2	0-1	1-1	2-3	1-0	0-1	0-0	*	0-1	3-0	1-8	1-2	1-3	0-2	0-1
12. Kidsgrove Ath.	2-0	3-1	1-4	0-1	1-1	1-3	2-1	1-1	1-0	3-2	1-0	*	1-2	0-0	0-2	0-2	1-2	1-1
13. Maghull	2-1	1-2	0-4	0-2	1-6	0-1	1-2	2-1	2-0	0-2	0-1	0-1	*	0-3	0-3	1-1	0-3	4-2
14. Penrith	5-0	6-1	1-0	3-1	2-0	4-2	1-1	1-0	2-2	1-1	2-0	0-3	3-2	*	0-1	2-1	2-0	6-0
15. Oldham Town	3-0	2-3	0-3	0-4	1-1	1-1	2-1	1-3	0-2	2-1	0-0	0-2	3-0	1-2	*	2-4	2-0	7-1
16. Salford City	1-1	1-3	1-2	1-1	1-1	0-0	2-1	1-2	0-0	1-3	0-1	0-1	1-0	0-2	3-0	*	2-0	5-2
17. Squires Gate	3-3	1-2	2-1	2-1	3-4	0-1	2-1	1-1	2-1	1-1	1-3	2-2	1-3	0-1	3-1	0-3	*	3-0
18. Westhoughton T.	4-4	0-2	1-3	0-7	4-2	0-6	0-2	2-2	1-2	0-1	0-2	1-5	5-3	0-1	1-5	0-5	2-1	*

Bass North West Counties Division Two 10-Year Record

	82/3	83/4	84/5	85/6	86/7	87/8	88/9	89/90	90/1	91/2
Ashton Town	-	-	-	-	-	10	17	10	15	17
Ashton United	-	-	4	14	3	1	-	-	-	-
Atherton Collieries	-	-	-	-	-	8	11	8	18	13
Atherton L.R.	13	9	10	11	17	-	-	-	-	-
Bacup Borough	-	-	-	-	-	22	9	2	-	-
Bamber Bridge	-	-	-	-	-	-	-	-	4	1
Blackpool Mechanics	-	-	-	-	12	15	16	3	5	3
Blackpool Wren Rovers	3	10	6	3	4	3	4	4	2	-
Bradford Park Avenue	-	-	-	-	-	-	-	-	3	-
Burscough	-	-	-	-	-	-	-	-	9	4
Caernarfon Town	2	-	-	-	-	-	-	-	-	-
Castleton Gabriels	-	-	-	-	-	-	-	-	11	8
Chadderton	7	8	8	6	7	13	3	-	12	11
Cheadle Town	-	-	-	-	-	12	14	6	7	9
Clitheroe	-	-	1	-	-	-	-	-	-	-
Colne Dynamoes	-	6	9	7	8	-	-	-	-	-
Colwyn Bay	-	-	-	5	5	-	-	-	-	-
Daisy Hill (see Westhoughton Town)										
Darwen	-	-	16	15	6	-	-	-	-	-
Droylsden	17	5	5	10	1	-	-	-	-	-
Eastwood Hanley	4	2	-	-	-	-	-	-	-	-
Ellesmere Port & Neston	10	7	18	13	10	-	-	-	-	-
Fleetwood Town	12	1	-	-	-	-	-	-	-	-
Flixton	-	-	-	-	-	2	-	-	-	-
Ford Motors	9	12	12	17	-	17	-	-	-	-
Formby	-	-	-	-	11	-	-	12	17	5
Glossop	-	-	-	-	-	-	13	14	8	6
Great Harwood Town	15	16	7	8	15	14	7	5	1	-
Holker Old Boys	-	-	-	-	-	-	-	-	-	15
Irlam Town	6	3	2	-	-	-	-	-	-	-
Kidsgrove Athletic	-	-	-	-	-	-	-	-	14	10
Kirkby Town/Knowsley Utd	5	-	-	1	-	-	-	-	-	-
Lancaster City	-	-	-	12	13	-	-	-	-	-
Lytham	14	14	-	-	-	-	-	-	-	-
Maghull	-	-	-	-	-	6	8	7	13	16
Maine Road	-	-	-	-	-	5	2	1	-	-
Nantwich Town	-	18	11	18	-	21	5	-	-	-
Nelson	-	-	-	-	-	16	-	-	-	-
Newcastle Town	-	-	-	-	-	4	6	13	6	2
New Mills	20									
Newton	-	-	-	-	-	20	18	16	-	-
Oldham Town	-	-	-	-	16	11	15	9	16	12
Padiham	19	-	17	-	-	19	12	11	-	-
Prescot B.I.	18	13	-	-	-	-	-	-	-	-
Prescot Cables	-	-	-	-	14	-	-	-	-	-
Radcliffe Borough	1	-	-	-	-	-	-	-	-	-
Rossendale United	8	15	14	2	-	-	-	-	-	-
Salford City	16	17	15	16	18	-	-	-	-	7
Skelmersdale United	11	11	13	9	9	-	-	-	-	-
Squires Gate	-	-	-	-	-	-	-	-	-	14
Vauxhall G.M.	-	-	-	-	-	7	1	-	-	-
Warrington Town	-	4	3	4	2	-	-	-	-	-
Westhoughton Town	-	-	-	-	-	18	10	15	10	18
Whitworth Valley	-	-	-	-	-	9	-	-	-	-
No. of clubs competing	20	18	18	18	18	22	18	16	18	18

RAAB KARCHER CUP 1991-92

Preliminary Round

Oldham Town v Kidsgrove Athletic		0-6	Squires Gate v Holker Old Boys	1-1,2-1
Maghull v Atherton Collieries		4-3	Formby v Ashton Town	0-1

First Round

Bootle v Ashton United	2-2,0-1	Great Harwood Town v Kidsgrove Athletic	1-0
Cheadle Town v Westhoughton Town	2-1	Newcastle Town v Prescot A.F.C.	0-1
Squires Gate v Blackpool Rovers	2-5	Clitheroe v Castleton Gabriels	0-1
Vauxhall G.M. v Maghull	0-1	Bacup Borough v Salford City	1-3
Chadderton v Glossop	0-0,1-2	Skelmersdale United v Burscough	0-2
Penrith v Bamber Bridge	1-3	Blackpool Mechanics v Maine Road	1-1,0-2
Nantwich Town v Bradford Pk Avenue	1-1,3-1	Ashton Town v St Helens Town	3-4
Eastwood Town v Darwen	0-0,2-1	Flixton v Atherton L.R.	0-2

Second Round

Ashton United v Great Harwood Town	3-0	Cheadle Town v Prescot A.F.C.	0-1
Blackpool Rovers v Castleton Gabriels	1-5	Maghull v Salford City	1-2
Glossop v Burscough	1-1,2-3	Bamber Bridge v Maine Road	1-2
Nantwich Town v St Helens Town	3-0	Eastwood Town v Atherton L.R.	2-1

Third Round

Ashton United v Prescot A.F.C.	3-1	Castleton Gabriels v Salford City	3-1
Burscough v Maine Road	4-0	Nantwich v Eastwood Hanley	1-1,0-1

Semi-Finals

Ashton Utd v Castleton Gabriels	1-1,3-0	Burscough v Eastwood	2-0,1-3(Burs. on away goals)

Final (at Bury FC, 30-4-92): Ashton United 1, Burscough 0

LAMOT PILS TROPHY FINAL (at Ashton Utd, 6-5-92): Newcastle Town 2, Atherton Collieries 0 *(aet)*

Dave Davies heads past Atherton Collieries' goalkeeper Andy Hassall to score his first in a 4-3 home win in the Preliminary Round of the Raab Karcher Cup. Photo - Rob Ruddock.

Penrith 0, Vauxhall GM 0 - Division One 19/1/91. Brent Hetherington tests the Vauxhall wall. Photo - Alan Watson.

ATHERTON LABURNUM ROVERS

President: P Eckersley   **Chairman:** H Dainton
Secretary: Trevor Bennett, 47 Chestnut Av., Wallden, Worlsey, Manchester M28 5EE (061 7994008).
Manager: Dave Morris   **Vice Chairman/Treasuer:** A Grundy
Ground: Crilly Park, Greendale, Greater Manchester (0942 883950).
Directions: M61 to Jct 5, follow signs for Westhoughton, left onto A6, right onto A579 (Newbrook Rd/Bolton Rd) over the railway bridge, right into Upton Rd passing Atherton Central Station, left into Springfield Rd and left again into Hillside Rd into Spa Rd and ground.
Seats: 300   **Cover:** 600   **Capacity:** 2,000   **Floodlights:** Yes   **Founded:** 1954
Record Gate: 500 v Accrington Stanley, FA Cup 1989.
Colours: White/navy/white   **Change colours:**
Previous leagues: Bolton Comb., Cheshire Co. 80-82.
Previous Name: Laburnam Rvrs 54-79   **Previous Grounds:** Laburnam Rd 54-56, Hagfold 56-66
Programme: 48 pages   **Programme Editor:** John Bullen   **Club Shop:** No
Clubhouse: Open normal licensing hours. **Midweek Matches:** Tuesday
Local Newspaper: Bolton Evening News.

BACUP BOROUGH

President: Bill Shufflebottom   **Chairman:** W Heywood
Secretary: F Manning, 14 Osborne Terrace, Stacksteads, Bacup OL13 8JZ (0706 873664).
Manager: Sean Coleman.
Ground: West View, Cowtoot Lane, Blackthorn, Bacup, Lancashire (0706 878655).
Directions: From M62, M66 onto A681 through Rawtenstall to Bacup centre, left onto A671 towards Burnley, after approx 300 yds right (immed. before the Irwell Inn) climbing Cooper Street, right into Blackthorn Lane then first left into Cowtoot Lane to ground.
Seats: 200   **Cover:** Yes   **Capacity:** 2,000   **Floodlights:** No   **Founded:** 1875
Record Gate: 4,980 v Nelson 1947
Colours: Black & white stripes/black/black   **Change colours:** Sky blue/sky blue/red
Previous league: Lancs Comb. 03-82.   **Midweek Matches:** Wednesday.
Previous Name: Bacup FC.   **Hons:** Lancs Jnr Cup 10-11 (R-up 22-23 74-75), Lancs Comb. 46-47 (Lg Cup R-up 46-47 80-81, NW Co's Lg Div 2 R-up 89-90.

BAMBER BRIDGE

President: Harold Hargreaves   **Chairman:** Arthur Jackson
Secretary: D G Spencer, 11 Tennyson Place, Walton-le-Dale, Preston, Lancs PR5 4TT (0772 34355).
Manager: Barrie Massie   **Coach:** Tony Greenwood   **Asst Mgr:** Dave May
Ground: Irongate, Brownedge Road, Bamber Bridge, Preston, Lancs (0772 627387).
Directions: M6 Junct 29, A6 (Bamber Bridge Bypass) towards Walton-le-Dale, to r'bout, A6 London Road to next r'bout, 3rd exit signed Bamber Bridge (Brownedge Road) and first right. Ground 100 yds at end of road on left. Just over a mile from Bamber Bridge (BR).
Seats: 50   **Cover:** 200   **Capacity:** 3,000   **Floodlights:** Yes   **Founded:** 1952
Record Gate: 2,241 v Preston North End 1988
Colours: White/black/white.   **Sponsors:** MPH Windows Ltd.
Programme: 32 pages, 30p   **Programme Editor:**   **Club Shop:** No
Midweek Matches: Tuesday   **Clubhouse:** Matchdays & evenings.
Best FA Vase season: SF 91-92   **Previous League:** Preston & Dist. (pre 1991)
Hons: FA Vase SF 91-92, North West Co's Lg Div 1 91-92 (F'lit Cup R-up 9-92), Preston & Dist Lg(4) 80-81 85-87 89-90 (R-up 78-79 82-83 84-85), Guildhall Cup 78-79 80-81 84-85 89-90 (R-up 77-78 79-80 87-88), Lancs Amtr Shield 81-82 (R-up 80-81 89-90), Lancastrian Brigade Cup 76-77 89-90 90-91.

BLACKPOOL MECHANICS

Chairman: Mr Thomas Baldwin   **Vice Chairman:** T McNamee   **President:** P Sutton
Secretary: W Singleton, 'Circular Quay', 36 Colwyn Ave., Blackpool, Lancs FY4 4EU (0253 68105).
Manager: Bobby Thomson (ex-Hibernian, Middlesbrough, Blackpool)
Physio: J Streetley   **Coach:** R Thomas
Ground: Back Common Edge Rd, Blackpool, Lancs (0253 61721).
Directions: M6 to M55, follow Airport signs. Left at r'bout along A583 (Preston New Rd) to lights, right into Whitehill Rd, becomes School Road, to lights. Straight over main road & follow signs for Blackpool Mechanics to ground.
Seats: 240   **Cover:** 750   **Capacity:** 2,000   **Floodlights:** Yes   **Founded:** 1947
Record Gate: 1,200 v Morecambe, Lancs Comb. 62-63   **Club colours:** All green
Programme: 20 pages, 20p   **Programme Editor:** Steve Goss   **Metal Badges:** Yes
Club Shop: Yes, Managed by Steve Goss. Ties, jerseys, old programmes, metal badges.
Clubhouse: Open match days, training nights & Sunday lunchtime. Dancehall.
Previous Leagues: Blackpool & Fylde Combination, West Lancs, Lancs Comb. 62-68.
Hons: Lancs Comb. R-up 74-75 (Bridge Shield 72-73, George Watson Tphy 75-76), NW Co's. Lg Div 3 85-86, W Lancs Lg 62-63 (R-up 59-60), Fylde & Dist Lg 53-54 56-57 (R-up(3) 54-56 57-58, Div 2 50-51, Lg Cup 52-53 57-58 (R-up 55-56 58-59)), Bannister Cup 52-53 56-57 (R-up(3) 55-56 57-59), Evening KO Cup 61-62, B'pool & Dist Amtr Lg Brackwell Cup R-up(2) 57-59, Lancs Jnr Shield 57-58 60-61 (R-up 54-55), Richardson Cup(2) 60-62, Den Haag Cup R-up 53-54, Dordrecht R-up 55-56, Rotterdam R-up 59-60.

BLACKPOOL (WREN) ROVERS

Chairman: S Hopwood   **Manager:** John Dodd.
Secretary: P Kimberley, 34 Priory Gate, South Shore, Blackpool, Lancs FY4 2QE (0253 49853).
Ground: Bruce Park, School Road, Marton, Blackpool, Lancs (0253 60570).
Directions: M6 to M55, leave at Jct 4, left onto A583, sharp right at 1st lights (Whitehill Rd)., follow signs for Airport. Ground approx 1.5 miles on right. 6 miles from Blackpool North (BR).
Seats: 250   **Cover:** 750   **Capacity:** 1,000   **Floodlights:** Yes   **Founded:** 1931
Record Gate: 800 v Manchester City, floodlight opener October 1991.
Colours: All red   **Change colours:** All blue
Programme: 20 pages, 20p   **Programme Editor:** P Kimberley   **Club shop:** No
Clubhouse: Open matchdays only   **Midweek matches:** Tuesday.
Previous Name: Wren Rovers   **Prev. Lges:** Blackpool Amtr, West Lancs, Lancs Comb. 72-82.
Hons: W Lancs Lg 69-70 70-71 (Lg Cup(2)), Lancs FA Shield 69-70 70-71, Lancs Comb. 78-79 80-81 (R-up 77-78, Lg Cup 78-79, Bridge Shield 76-77).

Neil Wade scores Maghull's only goal in a 1-3 defeat at Bamber Bridge. Photo - Rob Ruddock.

Blackpool Rovers defender John Hay heads a goal against Maine Road on April 4th. It was Rovers' 699th in the League, and with two against Great Harwood the following Tuesday they became the first club to score 700 in the ten year history of the League. Photo - Kevin Taylor.

Formby's Alan Powell saves in a home tie against promotion-bound Blackpool Mechanics. Photo - C J Sumner.

BRADFORD PARK AVENUE

Chairman: J Russell   **President:** C Atkinson.
Secretary: R Griffiths, 59 Sandygate Terrace, Bradford, West Yorks BD4 8PF (0274 668825).
Manager: Jim MacKay   **Asst Manager:** D Richmond.
Commercial Mgr: R S V Thompson   **Press Officer:** T R Clapham.
Ground: McLaren Field (Bramley RLFC), Town Street, Leeds, W Yorks (0532 564842).
Directions: M62 Jct 27, onto M621, A643 Wetherby exit directly opposite Leeds Utd ground. At foot of slip road take 1st exit & continue to r'bout taking 2nd exit (A647 Bradford). A647 for 2 miles until left turn for Bramley, Shipley A657. Right at top of slip road, 2nd exit at next r'bout, ground 400 yds on left. Half mile from Bramley (BR), bus 72 from Bradford to Town End or 16 or 17 from Leeds to ground.
Seats: 1,400   **Cover:** 1,900   **Capacity:** 3,500   **Floodlights:** Yes   **Reformed:** 1988
Record Gate: 1,740 v Leeds Utd 1989   **Midweek Matches:** Tuesday
Colours: White/green/white   **Club Shop:** Yes (G Sawyer, esq)
Programme: 32 pages, 60p   **Clubhouse:** Run by rugby club, open matchdays. Tea bar, snacks.
Previous Leagues: West Riding Co. Amtr 88-89, Central Mids 89-90.
Best FA Vase season: Ex-Prelim. 91-92   **Hons:** W Riding Co. FA Snr Cup 90-91.

BURSCOUGH

President: John Mawdsley   **Vice President:** Derek Watkinson   **Chairman:** F Parr
Secretary: M J Woods, 14 Melrose Av., Marshside, Southport, Merseyside PR9 9UY (051 2002067).
Manager: Russell Perkins   **Press Officer/Comm.Mgr:** Mark Parr (0704 24667).
Ground: Victoria Park, Mart Lane, Burscough, Ormskirk, Lancs (0704 893237).
Directions: M58 Jct 27, follow signs for Parbold A5209, right into Junction Lane (signed Burscough & Martin Mere) to lights, right onto A59 from Ormskirk to Burscough Village, 2nd left over canal bridge into Mart Lane to ground. Half a mile from Burscough Bridge (BR).
Seats: 200   **Cover:** 500   **Capacity:** 3,000   **Floodlights:** Yes   **Founded:** 1946
Colours: Green/white/white   **Change colours:** All yellow   **Nickname:** Linnets
Programme: 24 pages, 40p   **Programme Editor:** Mark Parr   **Club Shop:**
Midweek Matches: Tuesday   **Best FA Cup season:** 1st Rd(4) 59-60 77-78 79-81
Clubhouse: None   **Record Gate:** 3,500 v Crewe Alexandra, FA 1st Rd 1959
Previous Leagues: L'pool Co. Comb., Lancs Comb. 53-70, Ches. Co. 70-82.
Hons: Cheshire Co. Lg R-up 70-71 (Lg Cup 74-75 (R-up 73-74)), L'pool Snr Non-Lg Cup 71-72, Lancs Comb. 55-56 69-70, Lancs Jnr Cup 47-48 49-50 66-67, Nth West Co's Lg 82-83 (Lg Cup R-up 91-92, Chal. Shield 82-83), Bill Tyrer Mem. Tphy 1990.

CHADDERTON

President: Derek Glynn   **Chairman:** Harry Mayall   **Manager:** Peter Evans
Secretary: Dave R Ball, 9 Roxbury Avenue, Salem, Oldham, Lancs OL4 5JE (061 678 9624).
Ground: Andrew Street, Chadderton, Oldham, Lancs (061 624 9733).
Commercial Mgr: Tony Lynch   **Assistant Mgr:** Steve Willcock   **Coach:** Mick McKay
Directions: M62 Jct 20, A627(M) to Oldham. Motorway then becomes dual carriageway. Turn left at first major traffic lights A669 (Middleton Road), then first left opposite 'Harlequin' P.H. into Burnley Street - ground at end. 1 mile from Oldham Werneth (BR), buses 458 & 459 (Oldham-Manchester) stop at the Harlequin.
Seats: 200   **Cover:** 700   **Capacity:** 2,500   **Floodlights:** Yes   **Founded:** 1947
Best Gates: 1,500 v Guinness Exports 1969 & 1,257 v Oldham Athletic, pre-season friendly 1991.
Colours: Red/white/red.   **Change colours:** All blue.   **Nickname:** Chaddy
Programme: 36-40 pages, 30p   **Programme Editor:** Dave Ball   **Club Shop:** Yes
Midweek Matches: Wednesday   **Clubhouse:** Matchdays & training nights.
Players progressing to Football League: David Platt (Crewe, Villa, Bari).
Previous Leagues: Oldham Amateur, Manchester Amateur, Manchester 64-80, Lancs Comb. 80-82
Hons: Oldham Atr Lg Cup 54-55, Manc. Atr Lg 62-63 (North Div 55-56), Manc. Prem Cup R-up 82-83 (Chal. Tphy 71-72 (R-up 72-73)), Manc. Lg Div 1 66-67 (Div 2 64-65, Gilgryst Cup. 69-70, Murray Shield 65-66), Lancs Comb. Cup R-up 81-82, Alfred Pettit & Hulme Celtic Cup 61-62, Nth West Co's Res. Div 85-86 (R-up 90-91, Res. Cup 91-92), Manc. Yth Cup 59-60 (R-up 60-61).

CLITHEROE

Chairman: C Murphy   **President:** Jer Aspinall
Secretary: C Wilson, 4 Moss Street, Clitheroe, Lancs BB7 1DP (0200 24370).
Manager: Alan Bradshaw.   **Ground:** Shawbridge, Clitheroe, Lancs (0200 23344).
Directions: M6 jct 31, A59 to Clitheroe (17 miles), pass 'Visit Historic Clitheroe' sign, left into Pendle Rd for 1 mile, ground behind 'The Bridge Inn' on the right. 11 miles from BLackburn (BR).
Seats: 200   **Cover:** 750   **Capacity:** 4,000   **Floodlights:** Yes   **Founded:** 1877
Record Gate: 1,600 v Atherstone Utd, FA Vase 82-83.   **Club Shop:** No
Colours: Blue with white pin stripe/blue/blue   **Change colours:** All red
Previous Leagues: Blackburn & Dist./Lancs Comb. 03-04 05-10 25-82.
Clubhouse: Matchday only.   **Previous Name:** Clitheroe Central 1877-1914.
Programme: 4 pages, 20p   **Programme Editor:** Ian Rimmer   **Hons:** Lancs Comb. 79-80 (Lg Cup 34-35), Lancs Chal. Tphy 1892-93 1984-85, NW Co's Lg 85-86 (Div 2 84-85, Div 3 83-84).
Local Newspapers: Clitheroe Advertiser, Citizen, Lancs Evening Tele.   **Midweek Matches:** Tuesday

DARWEN

President: E Devlin   **Chairman:** M Elsworth
Secretary: H Cairney, 9 Cloister Drive, Darwen, Lancs BB3 3JX (0254 773642).
Manager: Ian McGarry   **Commercial Mgr:** Mick Rathbone
Ground: Anchor Ground, Anchor Road, Darwen, Lancs (0254 705627).
Directions: A666 Blackburn/Bolton road, 1 mile north of Darwen town centre, turn right at Anchor Hotel, ground 100 yds on left. One and a half miles from Darwen (BR), bus 51 to Anchor Hotel.
Seats: 250   **Cover:** 2,000   **Capacity:** 4,000   **Floodlights:** Yes   **Founded:** 1875
Record Gate: 9,000 v Luton, FA Cup 1909   **Previous Ground:** Barclay Bank.
Colours: Red & white/white/red   **Change colours:** All blue
Prev. Lges: Football Alliance 1889-91, Football Lg 91-99, Lancs Lg 99-03, Lancs Comb. 03-75, Ches. Co. 75-82.
Programme: 20 pages, 20p   **Programme Editor:** N Walsh   **Club Shop:** No
Clubhouse: Matchday only.   **Best FA Cup season:** Semi Finals
Hons: NW Co's Lg 82-83, Lancs Lg 01-02, Lancs Comb. 30-31 31-32 72-73 74-75 (Lg Cup 29-30 30-31 74-75, Lancs Jnr Cup 72-73, George Watson Tphy 72-73, Lancs FA Yth Cup 74-75, Lancs F'lit Tphy 89-90.
Local Newspapers: Darwen Advertiser, Lancs Eve. Tele.   **Midweek Matches:** Wednesday

Bradford Park Avenue FC 1991-92.

Formby 3, Kidsgrove Athletic 0 - Division Two 11/9/91. Paul Byrne heads Formby's second. Photo - Rob Ruddock.

Eastwood Hanley 3, Bootle 2 - Division One 21/9/91. Bootle's Graham Stamper heads over. Photo - Rob Ruddock.

EASTWOOD HANLEY

Chairman: Alan P Key   **Joint Managers:** Jim Wallace/John Ridley
Secretary: John L Reid, 2 Northam Rd, Sneyd Green, Stoke-on-Trent, Staffs ST1 6DA (0782 279062).
Press Officer/Commercial Mgr: Geoff Eccleston (0782 636828).
Ground: Berryhill Fields, Trentmill Rd, Hanley, Stoke-on-Trent, Staffs (0782 274238).
Directions: M6 Jct 16, A500 to r'bout, first exit (under bridge), 100 yds turn right (Cauldon Rd), to end and turn left, forward at mini r'bout and Trentmill Rd is 400 yds on right. 1 mile from Stoke-on-Trent (BR).
Seats: 200   **Cover:** 2,500   **Capacity:** 5,000   **Floodlights:** Yes   **Founded:** 1946
Record Gate: 5,000 v Stoke City (Brooks Bros Testimonial) 1978
Colours: All blue   **Change colours:** All red
Previous leagues: Mid Ches., Manchester, W. Mids 68-78, Ches. Co. 78-82, NW Co's Lg 82-87, N. Prem. 87-90.
Programme: 32 pages, 35p   **Programme Editor:** Geoff Eccleston   **Club Shop:** Yes
Previous Names: Eastwood (Hanley added to contrast with Town), Trent Rovers (incorporated in 1982).
Players progressing to League: Melia Alecksic (Spurs), Maurice Doyle (QPR).
Clubhouse: Open matchdays, weekends & special evenings.
Hons: Manc. Lg Gilgryst Cup 67-68, Staffs Snr Cup 85-86, Staffs FA Vase 81-82.
Local Newspapers: Evening Sentinel, S-o-T Herald & Post.   **Midweek Matches:** Monday

FLIXTON

President: Councillor F H Eadie   **Chairman:** Mr A Fowler
Secretary: Mrs C A Entwistle, 14 Woodhouse Rd, Davyhulme, Urmston, Manchester M31 2DJ (061 747 9937).
Manager: Brian Griffin   **General/Commercial Manager:** Peter Dentith.
Ground: Valley Road, Flixton, Manchester (061 748 2903).
Directions: M63 Jct 3, B5214 (signed Urmston), follow Trafford General Hosp. signs, at 4th r'bout take 3rd exit (Woodbridge Rd), ground at top. One and a quarter miles from Flixton (BR), buses 257 & 256 from Manchester.
Seats: 200   **Cover:** 400   **Capacity:** 2,000   **Floodlights:** Yes   **Founded:** 1960.
Record Gate: 1,145 v Manchester Utd 1989-90, Inauguration of Floodlights
Colours: Blue & white stripes/white/blue   **Change colours:** Red & black stripes/black/red
Previous leagues: S. Manc. & Wythenshawe 60-63, Lancs & Ches. 63-73, Manchester 73-86.
Programme: 36 pages, 25p   **Programme Editor:** T Entwistle   **Club Shop:** No
Best FA Cup season: 1st Qual. 91-92   **Best FA Vase season:** 3rd Rd 91-92
Clubhouse: Open every evening & Sat matchday afternoons   **Midweek Matches:** Tuesday
Hons: NW Co's Lg Div 2 R-up 87-88 (Div 3 R-up 86-87, Div 3 Cup SF 86-87, Res. Chal. Cup 87-88 (R-up 89-90 91-92), Res. Div East 89-90), Manc. Lg R-up 78-79 81-82 85-86 (Div 1 77-78, Div 2(res) 82-83 85-86, Open Tphy 80-81), Lancs Amtr Cup 79-80 (R-up 80-81), Manc. Chal. Tphy 83-84 (R-up(2) 84-86), Manc. Prem. Cup R-up 86-87 91-92, Manc. Amtr Cup R-up 88-89.

GLOSSOP NORTH END

Chairman: P Heginbotham   **President:** C T Boak
Secretary: P. Hammond, 15 Longmoor Road, Simmondley, Glossop, Derbys SK13 9NH (0457 863852).
Manager: R W T Soule.   **Ground:** Surrey Street, Glossop, Derbys (0457 855469).
Directions: A57 to Glossop town centre, left at 'Peak Auto Spares' into Shrewsbury Street. Ground at the top of the hill, turn left after approx. 60 yds. 700 yds from Glossop (BR). Buses 236 & 237 from Manchester.
Seats: 209   **Cover:** 509   **Capacity:** 2,374   **Floodlights:** Yes   **Founded:** 1886
Record Attendance: 10,736 v Preston North End, FA Cup 1913/14
Colours: Blue/blue/red.   **Change colours:** All yellow with blue trim.
Programme: 20 pages, 30p   **Programme Editor:** Mr P Heginbotham.
Midweek Matches: Tuesday   **Clubhouse:** Open matchdays & training nights.
Previous Names: Glossop North End 1886-1946/ Glossop FC 46-92.
Previous Leagues: Midland 1896-98/ Football League 1898-1915/ Manchester 15-56 66-78/ Lancs Combination 56-66/ Cheshire County 78-92.
Hons: Nth West Co's Lg Lamot Pils Trophy 90-91, Manchester Lg 27-28 (Gilgryst Cup 22-23 29-30 34-35 74-75).

KIDSGROVE ATHLETIC

Chairman: H Thomas   **Manager:** Phil Yeomans.
Secretary: Mrs A Camm, 1 Lyneside Road, Knypersley, Stoke-on-Trent, Staffs ST8 6SD (0782 511101).
Ground: Clough Hall, Hollinwood Road, Kidsgrove, Stoke-on-Trent, Staffs (0782 782412).
Directions: M6 Jct 16, A500 towards Stoke, 2nd junction onto A34 towards Manchester, turn right at 1st set of lights into Cedar Ave., 2nd right into Lower Ash Rd., and 3rd left into Hollinwood Road to ground.
Seats: Yes   **Cover:** Yes   **Capacity:**   **Floodlights:** Yes   **Year Formed:** 1952
Club colours: All blue   **Record Attendance:** 538
Clubhouse details: Yes   **Midweek Matches:** Monday or Wednesday
Prev. Leagues: Staffs Co./ Mid Cheshire (pre-1991).   **Hons:** Mid Cheshire Lg 70-71 78-79 86-87 87-88 (R-up 68-69 85-86, Lg Cup 67-68 69-70 85-86 (R-up 84-85 86-87)), Staffs Co. FA Vase 78-79 88-89, Sentinel Cup 66-67 76-77 84-85 (R-up 58-59 78-79 79-80 83-84), Leek Cup 84-85, Hanley Cup 65-66.

MAINE ROAD

Chairman: R Meredith   **Manager:** D Barber
Secretary: K Hunter, 157 Aston Ave., Fallowfield, Manchester M14 7HN (061 226 9937).
Ground: Manchester County FA Ground, Brantingham Rd., Chorlton-cum-Hardy, Manchester (061 862 9619).
Directions: M63 Jct 7, A56 towards City Centre, right onto A5145, onto A6010 to Chorlton, through lights, left at next lights, left into Withington Rd, left into Branthingham Rd, ground 400 yds on left. 2 miles from Stretford (Metroline), 3 miles from Piccadilly and Victoria (BR). Buses 85, 102, 103, 188, 244, 260, 261.
Seats: 200   **Covered Accom:** 900 **Capacity:** 2,000   **Floodlights:** Yes   **Founded:** 1955
Record Gate: 875 v Altrincham, FA Cup 1990
Colours: Royal & navy blue stripes/royal/royal   **Change colours:** All yellow
Previous Name: City Supporters Rusholme   **Clubhouse:** Open matchdays.
Previous Grounds: Total Sports Ground, Ward Street O.B., Hough End Playing Fields.
Previous leagues: Rusholme Sunday, Manchester Sunday, Manchester Amtr.
Programme: 50 pages, 50p   **Programme Editor:** R Baber   **Souvenir Shop:** None
Best FA Cup season: 2nd Qual. 89-90 90-91   **Best FA Vase season:** 2nd Rd 89-90 91-92.
Hons: Manc. Prem. Lg(4) 82-86 (Lg Cu(2) 82-84)), Manc. Prem. Cup 87-88, Manc. Chal. Cup(4) 82-83 84-87, NW Co's. Lg Div 2 R-up 88-89.
Midweek Matches: Tuesday

NANTWICH TOWN

President: E J Davies   **Chairman:** J F Lindop   **Manager:** Peter Ward.
Secretary: J Davies, 7 Mount Close, Nantwich, Cheshire CW5 6JJ (0270 626170).
Ground: Jackson Avenue, off London Road, Nantwich, Cheshire (0270 624098).
Directions: M6 Jct 16, A500 for Nantwich (about 8 miles), continue on A52 over railway crossing (London Rd), first right into Jackson Avenue. From Chester take A51. 3 miles from Crewe (BR).
Seats: 150   **Cover:** 550   **Capacity:** 1,500   **Floodlights:** Yes   **Founded:** 1894
Record Gate: 1,500 v Altrincham 1965 (Charity Match) & v Liverpool (floodlight opener) 30/7/91.
Colours: Green & white hoops/white/green   **Change colours:** All yellow.
Nickname: The Dabbers   **Previous leagues:** Cheshire County
Programme: 18 pages, 50p   **Programme Editor:** Che Kerin   **Club Shop:** Yes
Clubhouse: Mon, Wed, Fri & Sat evenings - social, Tues + Thurs - players training nights.
Previous Leagues: Ches. Comb. 19-38 68-82, The Comb. 1892-94 01-10, Manch., Lancs Comb. 12-15, Mid Ches.
Midweek Matches: Tuesday   **Previous Name:** Nantwich FC (pre 1973)
Hons: Cheshire Co. Lg 80-81 (R-up 00-01), Ches. Snr Cup 32-33 75-76 (R-up 1898-99 13-14 29-30), Ches. Jnr Cup 1895-96 (R-up 1890-91 96-97), Manc. Lg R-up 66-67 (Gilgryst Cup R-up 67-68), Crewe & Dist Cup 97-98 98-99 01-02 61-62 (R-up 1889-90 90-91 04-05 51-52 60-61), The Combination R-up 02-03, Crewe Amtr Comb. 46-47, Shropshire & Dist Lg R-up 1891-92, Mid Ches. Lg 63-64 (R-up 61-62 64-65, Lg Cup 61-62 63-64 (R-up 64-65)), Ches. Amtr Cup 63-64 (R-up 61-62), Ches. Jnr Cup 1895-96 (R-up 90-91 96-97), Mid Ches. Cup 48-49.

NEWCASTLE TOWN

Chairman: J W Walker   **Manager:** Alan Sides.
Secretary: J F Cotton, 293 Weston Road, Weston Coyney, Stoke-on-Trent, Staffs ST3 6HA (0782 333445).
Ground: 'Lyme Valley Parkway Stadium', Lilleshall Road, Clayton, Newcastle-under-Lyne, Staffs (0782 662351).
Directions: M6 Jct 15, A500 for Stoke, left at r'bout A519 for Newcastle, right at 2nd r'bout into Stafford Ave., 1st left into Tittensor Road to ground. 3 miles from Stoke-on-Trent (BR).
Seats: 350   **Cover:** 1,350   **Capacity:** 3,000   **Floodlights:** Yes   **Founded:** 1964
Midweek Matches: Tuesday   **Record Attendance:** 3,586 v Stoke City, August 1991
Colours: Royal blue/white/blue   **Change colours:** White/blue/white.
Programme: 40 pages, 30p   **Programme Editor:** Bill Johnson   **Clubhouse:** Yes
Previous Names: Parkway (founded 1964), Newcastle Town (founded 1981) merged in 1985.
Previous Lges: Newcastle/ Staffs Co./ Mid Cheshire.   **Hons:** Nth West Co's Lg Div 2 R-up 91-92 (Lamot Pils Tphy 91-92), FA Vase 5th Rd 91-92, Mid Cheshire Lg Div 2 & Div 1 & Lg Cup.

PENRITH

Chairman: D Johnson   **Manager:** Mike Herring
Secretary: W Brogden, 47 Folly Road, Penrith, Cumbria CA11 8BU (0768 62551).
Ground: Southend Road Ground, Penrith, Cumbria.
Directions: M6 Jct 40, onto dual carriageway to Appleby & Scotch Corner, turn off at next r'bout approx half a mile into Penrith, follow A6 into town, take 1st left for ground. Three quarters of a mile from Penrith (BR).
Seats: 250   **Cover:** 1,250   **Capacity:** 4,000   **Floodlights:** Yes   **Founded:** 1894
Colours: Blue/white/blue   **Change colours:** White/blue/white
Previous leagues: Carlisle & Dist., Northern 48-82, NW Co's 82-87, Northern Prem. 87-90
Programme: 20 pages, 25p   **Programme Editor:** P Johnson   **Club Shop:** No
Players progressing to Football League: K Sawyers, G Fell, G Mossop (all Carlisle).
Best FA Cup season: 2nd Rd 81-82   **League Clubs beaten in FA Cup:** Chester 81-82.
Midweek Matches: Wednesday   **Clubhouse:** Open all matchdays & Fri & Sat evenings.
Record fee paid: A Carruthers from Netherfield   **Received:** B Brown (Queen of South)
Record Gate: 4,000 v W. Auckland   **Local Press:** Cumberland & Westmorland Herald, Cumberland News.
Hons: Northern Lg R-up 61-62, NW Co's Lg R-up 83-84, Cumberland Snr Cup 60-61 61-62 62-63 63-64 64-65 65-66 70-71 72-73 74-75 80-81.

PRESCOT A.F.C.

President: Mr B F Taylor   **Chairman:** Mr G Glover
Comm. Mgr: John Richards (0744 57613).   **Secretary:** Mr G H Hayward, C/O The Club (below).
Manager: Joe Gibiliru   **Asst Manager:** Lee Madin
Ground: 'Sandra Park', Hope Street, Prescot, Knowsley, Merseyside (051 430 0507).
Directions: M62 Jct 7, A57 to Prescot town centre (3 miles), right into Hope Street. Three quarters of a mile from Prescot (BR). Buses 10, 10A, 10C from Liverpool & Wigan.
Seats: 400   **Cover:** 2,000   **Capacity:** 8,000   **Floodlights:** Yes   **Founded:** 1884
Record Gate: 8,122 v Ashton National, 1932   **Metal Badges:** Yes.
Colours: Gold/black/black   **Change colours:** All red   **Nickname:** Tigers.
Prev. Names: Prescot Ath./ Prescot Town, Prescot Cables.   **Previous Leagues:** Liverpool Co. Comb./ Lancs Comb. 1897-98 18-20 27-33 36-67/ Ches. Co. 33-36 78-82/ Lancs Lg 01-02/ Mid Cheshire 67-78.
Programme: 30 pages, 40p   **Programme Editor:** S Richards   **Club Shop:** No
Midweek Matches: Tuesday   **Best FA Cup season:** 2nd Rd 57-58 59-60
Clubhouse: Refreshment bar, open matchdays/evenings for hot & cold refreshments.
Hons: Lancs Comb. 76-77 (Lg Cup 47-48), Ches. Co. Lg 78-79, Mid Ches. Lg 76-77, L'pool Non-League Cup(4) 51-53 58-59 60-61, L'pool Chal. Cup(6) 27-30 48-49 61-62 77-78, Lancs Int. Cup 1895-96, George Mahon Cup 23-24 25-27 36-37, Lord Wavertree Cup 65-66.

ST HELENS TOWN

President: A Kelsall   **Chairman:** J Barrett
Secretary: W J Noctor, 95 Sutton Park Drive, Marshalls Cross, St Helens WA9 3TR (0744 816182).
Manager: Mick Holgate   **Asst Manager:** Peter Smith
Ground: Houghton Road, Sutton, St Helens, Merseyside (0744 812721).
Directions: M62 Jct 7, follow St Helens signs for two and a half miles, right to St Helens Junction BR station - ground 150 yards from station alongside railway line. Buses 121, 122, 5D, 41, 6 to St Helens Junction.
Seats: 200   **Cover:** 700   **Capacity:** 4,500   **Floodlights:** Yes   **Founded:** 1946
Colours: Blue (white trim)/white/blue   **Change colours:** All yellow   **Record Gate:** 4,000
Previous Leagues: Liverpool Co. Comb., Lancs Comb. 03-14 49-75, Cheshire Co. 75-82.
Programme: 32 pages, 30p   **Programme Editor:** Committee
Clubhouse: Evenings, match afternoons   **Club Shop:** Yes (contact George Smith 0744 59737)
Midweek Matches: Tuesday   **Local Newspapers:** Reporter, Star, Leader,Echo.
Hons: FA Vase 86-87, George Mahon Cup 51-52, Lancs Comb. 71-72, Bass Charrington Cup 71-72, St Helens Comb. Hosp. Cup Winners & R-up.

SALFORD CITY

Chairman: H Brearley   **Manager:** Billy Garton.
Secretary: Mr Frank McCauely, 22 Beverley Road, Pendlebury, Swinton, Manchester (061 7360021).
Ground: Moor Lane, Kersal, Salford, Manchester (061 792 6287).
Directions: M62 jct 17, A56 Bury New Road to Manchester, continue thro' 4 sets of lights, right into Moor Lane, 1st left into Neville Road to ground. 4 miles from Manchester Victoria (BR). Buses 96, 139, 94, 95 to Moor Lane.
Seats: 260   **Cover:** 600   **Capacity:** 8,000   **Floodlights:** Yes   **Founded:** 1940
Midweek Matches: Tuesday   **Record Attendance:** 3,000 v Whickham FA Vase 1981
Colours: Tangerine/black/black   **Prev. Lges:** Manchester 63-80/ Cheshire Co. 80-82.
Programme: 20 pages, 25p   **Editor:** Alan & John Pawson   **Souvenir Shop:** Yes
Clubhouse: Open match days only   **Previous Ground:** Crest, Salford.
Prev. Names: Salford Central 40-63/ Salford Amateurs 1963 until merger with Anson Villa/ Salford FC.
Hons: Lancs Amtr Cup 72-73 74-75 76-77, Manc. Snr Cup(4) 73-77, Manc. Chal. Cup(3) 73-76, Manc. Lg(4) 74-77 78-79 (Div 1 68-69, Open Tphy 75-76, Murray Shield 68-69), Manc. I'mediate Cup. *As Anson Villa: Manc. Lg Div 2 62-63 (Open Tphy 77-78(res)).*

SKELMERSDALE UNITED

Chairman: D Tomlinson   **President:** C R Bailey   **Manager:** Tommy O'Neill.
Secretary: K Hilton, 58 Higgins Lane, Burscough, Ormskirk, Lancs L40 7SD (0704 894504).
Ground: White Moss Park, White Moss Road, Skelmersdale, Lancs (0695 22123).
Directions: M58 Jct 3, at 2nd r'bout take 3rd exit towards Skelmersdale, continue for approx 1 mile, ground on the right. 4 miles from Ormskirk (BR).
Seats: 250   **Cover:** 2,000   **Capacity:** 10,000   **Floodlights:** Yes   **Founded:** 1882
Record Gate: 7,000 v Slough FA Amateur Cup 1967
Colours: Blue/white/white.   **Change colours:** All yellow   **Prev. Lges:** L'pool Co.
Comb., Lancs. Comb. 1891-93 03-07 21-24 55-68 76-78, Ches. Co. 68-71 78-82, Northern Prem. 71-76.
Programme: 50p   **Programme Editor:** Dave Donaldson   **Club Shop:** No   **Clubhouse:** None
Best FA Cup year: 1st Rd 67-68 (0-2 at Scunthorpe), 68-69 (0-2 at Chesterfield), 71-72 (0-4 at Tranmere).
Midweek Matches: Tuesday   **Local Press:** Ormskirk & Skelmersdale Advertiser.
Hons: FA Amtr Cup 70-71 (R-up 66-67), Ches. Co. Lg(2) 68-70 (Jubilee Cup 69-70), Lancs F'lit Cup 69-70, Lancs Jnr Cup(2) 69-71, Ashworth Cup 70-71, Barassi Cup 70-71, Lancs Co. FA Non-League Cup(2) 73-75, NW Co's Lg Cup R-up 82-83.

Holker Old Boy Andy Forbes heads just wide as his side lose 1-8 at home to Newcastle Town. Photo - Andrew Mollitt.

St Helens keeper Andy Almond in trouble away to League leaders Great Harwood in February. Photo - Colin Stevens.

DIVISION TWO CLUBS 1992-93

ASHTON TOWN

President: W Pomfrett   **Chairman:** G Messer
Secretary: C G Ashcroft, 8 Mason Close, Ashton-in-Makerfield, Wigan WN4 8SD (0942 717565).
Manager: Tommy Lawson
Ground: Edge Green Street, Ashton-in-Makerfield, Wigan WN4 8SY (0942 719168).
Directions: M6 Jct 23, A49 to Ashton-in-M. Right at lights onto A58 towards Bolton. After 3/4 mile turn right at 'Rams Head' P.H. into Golbourne Rd. After 200 yds right into Edge Green Str. Ground at end.
Record Gate: 600 v Accrington Stanley 76-77   **Floodlights:** No   **Founded:** 1965
Colours: Red with white pin stripe/red/red   **Change colours:** All sky blue
Best FA Vase season: Prelim. Rd 84-85
Previous Leagues: Warrington, Lancs Comb. 03-11 71-78, Ches. Co. 78-82.
Midweek Matches: Tuesday   **Hons:** Warrington Lg Guardian Cup.

ATHERTON COLLIERIES

Chairman: Steve Neal   **Manager:** Alan Kirkman   **Asst Mgr:** Brian Hart
Secretary: A G Farnworth, 34 Drake Hall, Westhoughton, Lancs BL5 2RA (0942 814754).
Ground: Alder House, Alder Street, Atherton, Gt Manchester (0942 884649).
Directions: M61 Jct 5, follow sign for Westhoughton, left onto A6, right onto A579 (Newbrook Rd/Bolton Rd) into Atherton. At 1st set of lights left into High Street, then 2nd left into Alder St. to ground. Quarter of a mile from Atherton Central (BR).
Seats: No   **Cover:** 600   **Capacity:** 3,500   **Floodlights:** Due   **Founded:** 1916
Record Gate: 3,300 Lancs Comb. 1920's   **Nickname:** Colls
Colours: Black & white stripes/black/black.   **Midweek Matches:** Tuesday
Change colours: Yellow & red stripes/yellow/yellow.   **Clubhouse:** Evenings & matchdays.
Programme: 20-30 pages, 30p   **Programme Editor:** B Taylor   **Club Shop:** No
Previous Leagues: Bolton Comb., Lancs Comb. 50-52 71-78, Ches. Co. 78-82.
Hons: NW Co's. Lg Div 3 86-87, Bridge Shield 85-86, Lancs Co. FA Shield 19-20 22-23 41-42 56-57 64-65.

BOOTLE

Chairman: J McCornish   **President:**
Secretary: P Carr, 58 Orchard Hey, Old Run, Bootle, Merseyside L30 8RY (051 526 9228).
Manager: Tommy Fagan   **Asst Manager:** Tommy Barry
Ground: Bucks Park, Northern Perimeter Road, Netherton, Merseyside (051 526 1851 - matchdays only).
Directions: At end of M57 & M58 follow signs to Bootle/All Docks. Ground on right so turn right at next lights by Police station after bend. Entrance 150 yds on right. 300 yds from Old Roan (BR), buses 3 & 55 (100yds), 25, 300, 341, 345, 350 (350yds).
Seats: 350   **Cover:** 1,100   **Capacity:** 4,000   **Floodlights:** Yes   **Founded:** 1953
Record Gate: 750 v Carshalton Athletic, FA Trophy 2nd Rd 1981.
Colours: All blue   **Change colours:** Amber/black/amber.
Previous Grounds: Edinburgh Park 1953-73, Orrell Mount 1973-79
Previous leagues: Liverpool Shipping, Liverpool County Comb., Lancs Comb. 74-78, Cheshire Co. 78-82.
Programme: 24 pages, 30p   **Programme Editor:** A McCumiskey   **Club Shop:** No
Previous Name: Langton 1953-73   **Clubhouse:** (051 526 1850). Normal licensing hours.
Hons: L'pool Chal. Cup 64-65 75-76 78-79, L'pool Amtr Cup 65-66 67-68 73-74, Lancs Amtr Cup 69-70, L'pool Co. Comb. 64-65 65-66 67-68 68-69 69-70 70-71 71-72 72-73 73-74, George Mahon Cup 66-67 67-68 68-69 69-70 72-73 73-74, Lancs Comb. 75-76 76-77 (Lg Cup 75-76), Cheshire Co. Lg Div 2 76-77 (Lg Cup 76-77).
Local Newspapers: Bootle Times   **Midweek Matches:** Tuesday

BURNLEY BANK HALL

Chairman: John Howarth   **Secretary:** Mrs Howarth (0282 26695).
Manager: Ian Britton   **Asst Manager:** Kevin Robinson.   **Ground:** (0282 26695).
Previous League: West Lancs   **Hons:** West Lancs Lg 91-92.

CASTLETON GABRIELS

President: Mr R Murphy   **Chairman:** T E Butterworth
Secretary: D Lord, 34 Fairway, Castleton, Rochdale OL11 3BU (0706 522719).
Manager: Terry White/ Dave Grimbaldeston.
Ground: Butterworth Park, Chadwick Lane, off Heywood Rd., Castleton, Rochdale (0706 527103).
Directions: M62 Jct 20, A6272M to r'bout. Left towards Castleton (A664 Edinburgh Way) to next r'bout, keeping Tesco Superstore to the left, take 1st exit to next r'bout, take 2nd exit into Manchester Rd (A664), right at 'Top House' P.H. into Heywood Rd., to end & ground on right.
Seats: **Cover:**   **Capacity:**   **Floodlights:** No   **Founded:** 1924
Record Gate: 450 v Bamber Bridge 86-87, Lancs Shield   **Colours:** Blue/navy blue/blue.
Midweek Matches: Tuesday   **Previous Leagues:** Rochdale Alliance, Manchester League
Hons: Manc. Lg 86-87 (Murray Shield 86-87), Nth West Co's Lg Cup SF 91-92.

CHEADLE TOWN

President: Freddie Pye   **Chairman:** C Davies   **Manager:** TBA.
Secretary: G Cliffor, 18 The Hawthorns, Corporation Rd, Audenshaw, Manchester M34 5LU (061 336 6045).
Ground: Park Road, Cheadle, Cheshire SK8 2AN (061 428 2510).
Directions: M63 Jct 11 to r'bout, A560 (Stockport Road) towards Cheadle, 1st left after lights into Park Rd to ground. 1 mile from Gatley (BR), buses from Stockport & Altrincham.
Seats: 300   **Cover:** 300   **Capacity:** 2,500   **Floodlights:** No   **Founded:** 1961
Record Gate: 550 v Stockport County, 1988   **Midweek Matches:** Tuesday
Colours: All White   **Change colours:** Green & black stripes/black/black.
Programme: 20 pages, 25p   **Programme Editor:** Chris Davies   **Club Shop:** No
Clubhouse: Normal weekday hours plus lunch on Sunday and from 2.15pm on Sat.
Previous Grounds: Hyde United 5yrs, Glossop 3yrs
Previous Name: Grasmere Rovers 1961-83   **Previous Leagues:** Manc. (pre 1987).
Hons: Manc. Lg Div 1 79-80 (R-up 80-81 81-82), Manc. Amtr Cup 79-80, Manc. Chal. Cup R-up(3) 79-82, Derbys Cup 80-81 (R-up 81-82).

ELLESMERE PORT TOWN '92

Chairman: Mr T Andrews   **Vice Chairman:** Mr P Furlong   **President:** Mr J Rigg.
Secretary: Mrs A Nicholson, 23 Masseyfield Rd, Brookvale, Runcorn, Cheshire WA7 6AE (0928 716911).
Manager: Mr P Bartley   **Asst Manager:** Mr C Bellis/ Mr S Furlong.
Coach: Mr Alan Ainscow   **Comm. Mgr:** Mr Jim Jones   **Promotions Mgr:** Mr David Johnson
Ground: Ellesmere Port Stadium, Thornton Rd, Ellesmere Port, South Wirral (051 357 1594).
Directions: M56, M53 (Ellesmere Port, Birkenhead) then junction 10, A5117 signed Queensferry, then B5132
signed Ellesmere Port centre. After about a mile turn right following Thornton Rd Ind. Estate and Stadium signs
onto Wolverham Rd, carry on down Wolverham Rd across r'bout to bottom, right into Thornton Rd, stadium
quarter mile on left.
Seats: 300   **Cover:** 499   **Capacity:**   **Floodlights:** Yes   **Founded:** 1992
Programme: 32p   **Programme Editor:** Mr P A Nicholson.
Midweek Matches: Tuesday.   **Clubhouse:** Open matchdays.

FORMBY

Chairman: C Welsh   **Manager:** Peter Henerty/Mike Scott
Secretary: C Welsh, 38 Greenloom Walk, Formby, Merseyside L37 2LE (07048 77414).
Ground: Brows Lane, Formby, Merseyside (07048 72603).
Directions: A565 L'pool-Southport, turn for Formby at lights opposite Payless DIY into Altcar Rd, fork left at
junction to r'bout, take 2nd exit then sharp left into Duke Street, 1st right into Elbow Lane, ground entrance 50yds
on left. Half a mile from Formby (BR), buses from Formby & Southport stations.
Seats: 200   **Cover:** 300   **Capacity:** 2,000   **Floodlights:** Due   **Founded:** 1919
Record Gate: 2,500 v Oldham, FA Cup 1973   **Midweek Matches:** Wednesday.
Programme: 30p   **Editor:** John McNally & Paul Lawler   **Club Shop:** No
Best FA Cup season: 1st Rd 73-74   **Clubhouse:** Open Tues, Thur & matchdays.
Previous Leagues: L'pool Co. Comb., Lancs Comb. 68-71, Ches. Co. 71-72.
Hons: L'pool Co. Comb. 48-49, George Mahon Cup 64-65 67-68, L'pool Snr Cup 77-78 (Chal. 63-64, Amtr Cup(3)
29-30 47-49).

HOLKER OLD BOYS

Chairman: R Moffatt   **Manager:** TBA.
Secretary: A Wilson, 56 Fairfield Lane, Barrow-in-Furness, Cumbria LA13 9AL (0229 822983).
Ground: Rakesmoor Lane, Howcoat, Barrow-in-Furness, Cumbria (0229 828176).
Directions: M6 Jct 36, A590 to Barrow-in-Furness, on entering Barrow, continue across r'bout, 1st right (Dalton
Lane) to top of road, right into Rakesmoor Lane, ground on right.
Seats: **Cover:**   **Capacity:**   **Floodlights:** Due   **Founded:** 1936
Colours: White (green trim)/green (white trim)/green (white trim).
Midweek Matches: Tuesdays   **Clubhouse:** Yes.
Previous Leagues: North Western/ Furness Premier/ West Lancs (pre-1991).
Hons: West Lancs Lg 86-87, Lancs Co. FA Shield 88-89 90-91.

IRLAM TOWN

Chairman: George Parker   **Vice Chairman:** E Keiller.   **Secretary:** TBA.
Manager: Stuart Parker   **Press Officer:** D W Murray
Ground: Silver Street, Irlam (061 775 5599).
Directions: M6 jct 21 then east on A57 - Silver Street is opposite the Sports pub after five and a half miles. Or, M63
jct 2 and west on A57 for two and a half miles - turn right after Nags Head (PH). 1 mile from Irlam (BR).
Capacity: 3,000 (500 Covered)   **Seats:** 250   **Floodlights:** Yes **Shop:** No **Metal Badges:** No
Colours: All royal blue   **Change colours:** Red & black.
Programme: 28 pages, 50p   **Programme Editor:** D W Murray
Prev. Lges: Manc. (until 1978)/ Cheshire Co. 78-82/ Nth West Co's 82-87/ Northern Prem. 87-92.
Midweek matchday: Tuesday   **Record Attendance:** Unknown.
Record Fees - Paid: **Received:** £8,000.
Players progressing to Football League: Tony Caldwell (Bolton Wanderers), Tony Jarvis (Oldham Athletic 1986),
Graham Leishman (Mansfield Town 1988).
Clubhouse: Lounge, vault, kitchen, dressing rooms, committee.   **Steward:** C Duckworth.
Local Newspapers (+Tel.Nos.): Advertiser, Manchester Evening News.
Local Radio: Piccadilly, Key 103.   **Sponsors:** P M Communications, M L Electro Optics.
Hons: FA Vase 5th Rd 81-82, FA Amateur Cup 1st Rd 70-71, North West Counties Div 2 R-up 84-85, Manchester Lg
73-74 (R-up 76-77, Gilgryst Cup 73-74), Manchester Premier Lg 84-85 (R-up 78-79 81-82 87-88). *Reserves:
Manchester Amateur Cup 81-82, North West Counties Lg Reserve Div 83-84 (Lg Cup 82-83 85-86), Northern
Combination 88-89 (Lg Cup 87-88 88-89 89-90).*

K. CHELL

Secretary: Reg Barnsley, 41 Scotia Road, Burslem ST6 4EP (0782 836315).   **Founded:** 1991
Ground: Kay's Sports & Social Club, Uplands Avenue, Chell, Tunstall, Stoke-on-Trent (0789 837607).
Directions: M6 jct 15, A500, A50 to Tunstall, follow signs to Chatley, Whitfield Mining Museum and Congleton
(A527) - at top of hill island after 1.5 miles take small lane on left (Uplands Avenue) - ground at top (if in trouble ask
for Chell Cricket Ground).
Colours: All blue   **Change colours:** All red   **Previous League:** West Midlands (Regional) 1991-92.

MAGHULL

Chairman: L Jacques   **Manager:** Ronnie Young.
Secretary: D Sherlock, 14 Alexander Drive, Lydiate, Merseyside L31 2NJ (051 526 2306).
Ground: Hall Lane, Maghull, Merseyside (051 526 7320).
Directions: M57 or M58 to end (Switch End), A59 towards Preston (Northway) to lights at Hall Lane, turn right
following signs for Maghull Station. Ground 200 yds on the left. Half mile from Maghull (BR).
Seats: None   **Cover:** 200   **Capacity:** 3,500   **Floodlights:** No   **Founded:** 1921
Record Gate: 500 v Marine, Liverpool Challenge Cup 1982/83
Club colours: Royal blue with white flashing/blue/blue   **Change colours:** Red/black/black
Programme: Pages vary, 20p   **Programme Editor:** A M Boyd   **Midweek Matches:** Tuesday
Previous Ground: Pimbley Recreation Ground 1921-59.
Previous Leagues: I Zingara/ Liverpool Co./ Lancs Comb. 72-78/ Cheshire Co. 78-82.
Hons: Liverpool Co. Amtr Cup, Liverpool Co. Chal. Cup 79-80 80-81, Lancs FA Amtr Cup, Lancs Comb. Cup 77-
78.

Holker Old Boys FC 1991-92.

Atherton Collieries defend as they go down 3-5 at Cheadle Town on 9th September. Photo - Colin Stevens.

Maghull's Mick Feeney (10) takes on Formby defender Paul Byrne in their Bass North West Counties League fixture at Hall Lane, Maghull, on 3rd September 1991. Photo - Andrew Mollitt.

795

NELSON

Secretary: C King (0282 66394)
Ground: Victoria Park, Lomesway, Nelson, Lancs (0282 63820).
Colours: Blue & white.
Previous Leagues: Lancashire 1889-98 1900-01/ Football League 1898-1900/ Lancashire Combination 01-16 46-82/ Nth West Counties 82-88/ West Lancashire 88-92.
Hons: Lancs Lg 1895-96 (R-up 97-98), Lancs Comb. 1949-50 51-52 (R-up 47-48 50-51 60-61, Lg Cip 49-50 50-51 59-60, Bridge Shield 75-76, George Watson Tphy 78-79, Div 2 R-up(res) 47-48 51-52), Lancs Jnr Cup 07-08 54-55, FA Cup 2nd Rd Proper 30-31(replay) 50-51 (1st Rd 32-33 51-52 53-54).

NORTH TRAFFORD

Chairman: Mr J Ackerley   **Manager:** David Law.
Secretary: David Brown, 5 The Avenue, Sale, Cheshire M33 4PB (061 976 2560).
Ground: Shawe View, Chassen Road, Flixton.
Directions: M63 jct 5, to Urmston, 2nd lights into Flixton Rd, 2nd left into Chassen Rd, Shawe Rd 2nd right.
Colours: All white   **Change Colours:** All red.
Previous League: Mid-Cheshire (pre-1992).

OLDHAM TOWN

Chairman: K Hughes   **Manager:** Harold Hazard/ Steve Braithwaite.
Secretary: Mr R A Manton, 24 Whitegate Lane, Chadderton, Oldham Lancs OL9 8LS (061 620 0368).
Coach: Jimmy McIlwraith.
Ground: Nordens Road, off Middleton Road, Chadderton, Oldham, Lancs (061 624 0914).
Directions: M62 Jct 20, A627(M) Broadway, right into Middleton Rd A669 and right at Nordens Rd to ground. 2 miles from Werneth Oldham (BR). Buses 59, 181, 182, 184.
Seats: 50   **Cover:** 200   **Capacity:** 500   **Floodlights:** No   **Founded:** 1964
Record Gate: 250 v Mossley, Manchester Premier Cup 1987/88
Colours: Blue/white/blue.   **Midweek Matches:** Wednesday
Programme: 16 pages, 25p   **Programme Editor:** M Kirfoot.
Previous Ground: National Park   **Clubhouse:** Open evenings and matchdays.
Previous Names: Dew Construction/ Oldham Dew.
Previous Leagues: Manchester Amateur League, Lancashire Combination 81-82.

SQUIRES GATE (BLACKPOOL)

Chairman: W Carr   **Vice President:** Brian Addison.
Secretary: J Maguire, 4 Garton Avenue, Blackpool, Lancs FY4 2JW 0253 407597
Manager: Mark Spedding.
Ground: School Road, Marton, Blackpool, Lancs 0253 798584
Directions: M6 to M55 jct 4, left onto A583, at 1st lights turn right (Whitehall Rd) follow signs for airport. Ground approx. one and a half miles on right.
Seats: 2 rows   **Cover:** One side   **Capacity:**   **Floodlights:** No   **Formed:** 1948
Club colours: All royal blue   **Midweek Matches:** Tuesday
Clubhouse: Yes
Programme: 20 pages   **Previous Leagues:** West Lancs (pre-1991).
Hons: West Lancs Lg Div 2 80-81 (Richardson Cup).

STANTON DALE

Ground: Orrell Lane, Bootle, Merseyside L20.
Previous League: Liverpool County Combination (pre-1992).
Hons: Liverpool County Comb. 90-91, Liverpool Jnr Cup 90-91.

WESTHOUGHTON TOWN

Chairman: D Haworth   **Manager:** Steve Walton/ Alan Cord.
Secretary: Mrs Haworth, 50 Parkway, Westhoughton, Bolton, Lancs (0942 840730).
Ground: New Sirs, St James Street, Westhoughton, Bolton, Lancs (0942 818544).
Directions: M61 Jct 5, A58 (Snydale Way/Park Road) for 1.5 miles, left into Leigh Road (B5235) for 1 mile, right fork to Daisy Hill. Straight forward between Church and School into St James Street. Ground 250 yds on the left. Half mile from Daisy Hill (BR).
Seats: 200   **Cover:** 450   **Capacity:** 2,000   **Floodlights:** No   **Founded:** 1952
Colours: Red & white stripes/black/red & black.   **Change colours:** All royal blue.
Programme: 8 pages, 20p.   **Programme Editor:** Barry Young
Previous Name: Daisy Hill   **Midweek Matches:** Tuesday (Reserve Wednesday)
Previous Grounds: Various   **Clubhouse:** Open normal licensing hours.
Record Attendance: 2,000 v Horwich R.M.I, Westhoughton Charity Cup final May 1980.
Previous Leagues: Westhoughton/ Bolton Comb./ Lancs Combination. 78-82.
Hons: Bolton Comb. 62-63 72-73 75-76 77-78 (Prem. Div Cup(4) 59-60 61-62 71-73), Lancs Shield 61-62 71-72 86-87.

SPORTSCENE INTERNATIONAL
STAFFORDSHIRE SENIOR LEAGUE

President: P Keller.
Chairman: F Askey.
Vice Chairman: A Key.
Hon. Secretary: J K Johnson
149 St Nicholas Avenue, Norton, Stoke-on-Trent ST6 8JW.   Tel: 0782 534866

REDGATE CHAMPIONS WITH THEIR FINAL KICK

Drama and excitement was the name of the game as three clubs battled it out for the title, the climax coming on Wednesday 6th May when the final fixtures were played. It was a night when the League's Newsline became swamped with calls, and it ended with the first two clubs being divided only by goal difference, Redgate Clayton pipping Stafford MSHD, three points ahead of Meir KA.

Redgate went into their final game at Eccleshall aware that victory would see them champions, and in a match described as the most exciting ever seen at Pershall Park, the visitors twice had to claw their way back into the game. Five minutes from time they again fell behind, but the remaining minutes brought high drama as Redgate drew level and then snatched the winner with the very last kick of the match.

Yet the clubs who failed could claim they threw the title away, particularly Stafford who led the table from 14th September to 4th April at one point having a ten point lead over the eventual champions. With nine games to go they still had points and games in hand, but they won just three, the points lost over this period equalling those lost over their previous 25 games. Their only consolation was gates of over 350 against Meir and Redgate, and of over 250 against Brocton and Eccleshall.

Going into their eighteenth game undefeated, it was not surprising that Meir KA kept in touch with the leaders, but they had a disastrous April losing succesive games against Rists, Hanford and Norton and failing to score. They finished badly as well, twice losing a two goal advantage at Brocton in their final fixture.

Not all attention was focussed on the top of the table. Six clubs were still in danger of having to apply for re-election with only three games remaining. Victories by Congleton Hornets and Goldenhill Wanderers in their final games saw them edge clear and ensure the bottom places were occupied by Hanford and Ball Haye Green. Of the others, Milton United, holding seventeenth place with just two wins from their opening nine, improved to such an extent that they finished fourth losing just one of their next 25. On the other hand, Audley, never out of the top five until late February, won just one of their last ten to finish twelvth. Rists United were the best of the newcomers, with Brocton three places behind.

The League Cup too was not without its surprises, Meir being taken to a replay by Brocton in the First Round and then being beaten on their own ground by second bottom Goldenhill in the Second. Stafford MSHD scored five in extra-time against neighbours Eccleshill in a replay, and strongly fancied Milton lost to Norton in a battle of the United's in the Third Round. In the Semis, Stafford came from two down against Norton before going out in the replay. In the Final, Norton equalised against Redgate with just a minute to go, and did likewise in the replay, from the penalty spot, before going on to clinch the Cup in extra-time.

J K Johnson, Hon. Secretary

FINAL LEAGUE TABLE 1991-92

	P	W	D	L	F	A	Pts
Redgate Clayton	34	24	6	4	94	33	78
Stafford M.S.H.D.	34	23	9	2	71	27	78
Meir K.A.	34	23	6	5	72	32	75
Milton United	34	19	7	8	53	38	64
Leek C.S.O.B.	34	12	10	12	47	46	46
Staffordshire Police	34	13	7	14	37	43	46
Norton United	34	13	6	15	53	51	45
Rists United	34	12	9	13	47	62	45
Eccleshall	34	11	11	12	44	49	44
Heath Hayes	34	11	9	14	64	60	42
Brocton	34	12	6	16	48	50	42
Audley	34	11	8	15	53	63	41
Eastwood Hanley Reserves	34	10	8	16	38	52	38
Stafford Rangers Reserves	34	11	5	18	39	58	38
Goldenhill Wanderers	34	11	3	20	47	63	36
Congleton Hornets	34	10	5	19	43	58	35
Ball Haye Green	34	10	4	20	36	61	34
Hanford	34	8	5	21	30	70	29

SPORTSCENE INTERNATIONAL RESULT CHART 1991/92

HOME TEAM	1	2	3	4	5	6	7	8	9	10	11	12	13	14	15	16	17	18
1. Audley	*	1-3	2-2	2-1	4-0	2-4	4-1	3-2	3-1	1-1	0-3	1-3	1-1	0-3	3-3	1-4	1-2	2-0
2. Ball Haye Green	1-3	*	1-3	1-3	2-0	2-0	2-1	3-1	1-1	1-0	0-1	1-2	3-6	1-2	0-1	0-2	0-2	0-2
3. Brocton	2-0	3-1	*	0-2	0-1	2-0	1-3	2-0	3-0	1-1	3-3	4-0	4-1	0-2	2-4	1-2	0-1	1-2
4. Congleton Hornets	1-1	1-2	1-2	*	1-3	1-1	3-0	5-1	2-2	0-2	0-1	0-2	1-3	1-0	5-4	1-3	4-0	2-1
5. Eastwood Hanley Res.	2-4	0-2	1-2	1-1	*	1-1	3-0	1-0	1-3	1-2	0-0	2-4	0-2	0-0	1-0	1-1	3-1	1-1
6. Eccleshall	1-0	3-0	1-1	1-1	0-3	*	2-0	4-0	2-1	1-1	0-1	1-1	1-3	3-4	3-2	0-0	1-1	0-0
7. Goldenhill Wanderers	2-3	4-1	2-1	1-0	0-2	1-2	*	1-2	2-0	2-0	1-3	1-2	1-0	0-3	0-0	0-3	4-3	0-1
8. Hanford	1-1	1-0	1-0	3-1	1-0	0-2	2-6	*	1-1	3-2	1-0	0-1	0-2	1-6	0-0	1-2	1-3	2-0
9. Heath Hayes	1-2	6-1	4-0	3-0	1-1	4-0	5-5	3-0	*	1-1	3-4	0-2	0-4	3-4	3-1	0-0	0-3	4-1
10. Leek C.S.O.B.	4-1	2-0	1-2	2-0	3-1	2-1	0-0	3-0	1-1	*	1-1	2-3	1-0	1-3	0-0	0-3	3-1	4-1
11. Meir K.A.	1-0	1-0	2-0	2-3	3-1	2-1	2-1	3-0	5-0	1-2	*	2-0	3-2	3-1	6-1	2-2	4-1	3-0
12. Milton United	1-0	0-2	2-1	1-0	1-0	2-1	1-0	3-1	5-4	3-0	0-0	*	1-1	1-1	8-1	0-1	1-3	0-2
13. Norton United	1-0	3-1	1-2	3-0	0-3	1-1	1-2	1-1	0-3	2-3	2-0	0-0	*	0-4	0-1	1-2	3-1	1-2
14. Redgate Clayton	3-0	1-1	3-2	6-0	5-1	3-0	2-0	4-0	1-2	4-1	1-2	1-1	3-1	*	3-3	4-2	2-0	4-1
15. Rists United	1-1	2-2	2-1	1-0	0-2	1-2	1-5	2-0	0-2	3-0	2-0	3-0	2-0	0-3	*	2-1	1-0	0-0
16. Stafford M.S.H.D.	3-1	3-0	0-0	2-0	4-1	5-0	4-0	2-1	3-2	1-0	2-2	0-0	2-0	2-2	3-3	*	2-1	1-0
17. Stafford Rgrs Res.	2-2	0-1	2-1	0-2	1-1	0-3	1-0	2-2	0-0	2-0	0-5	2-1	2-3	0-3	2-1	0-1	*	0-1
18. Staffordshire Police	2-3	0-0	1-1	4-0	2-0	1-1	3-1	1-0	1-0	1-1	1-1	3-4	0-1	2-0	0-2	0-2	0-2	1-0 *

LEAGUE CUP RESULTS 1991-92

First Round

Brocton v Meir K.A.	2-2,0-2		Redgate Clayton v Staffordshire Police	2-0
Second Round				
Audley v Hanford	3-1		Ball Haye Green v Eccleshall	2-4
Heath Hayes v Milton United	1-3		Leek C.S.O.B. v Redgate Clayton	1-2
Meir K A v Goldenhill Wanderers	1-2		Norton United v Eastwood Hanley Reserves	4-4,3-1
Rists United v Congleton Hornets	0-0,0-3		Stafford Rangers Reserves v Stafford M.S.H.D.	0-2
Third Round				
Goldenhill Wand. v Congleton Hornets	3-0		Milton United v Norton United	0-1
Redgate Clayton v Audley	1-0		Eccleshall v Stafford M.S.H.D.	2-2,1-6(aet)
Semi-Finals				
Goldenhill Wanderers v Redgate Clayton 0-2			Stafford M.S.H.D. v Norton United	2-2,1-2

Final (both matches played at Eastwood Hanley FC)
Norton United v Redgate Clayton   1-1(aet),2-1(aet)

CLUB DIRECTORY 1992-93

AUDLEY

Ground: Old Road, Bignall End.   **Founded:** 1985
Secretary: Michael Shaw, 25 Wood Street, Bignall End ST7 8QL (0782 722086).   **Programme:** Y
Manager: Terry Greer   **Colours:** Red/navy/red   **Hons:** Lg Cup 89-90

BALL HAYE GREEN

Ground: Rear Balle Haye Green WMC, Leek.   **Founded:** 1880
Secretary: Michael Naylor, 27 Wallbridge Close, Leek ST13 8HZ (0538 383711).   **Programme:**
Manager: Neil Gilmore   **Colours:** Green & yellow/green/yellow   **Hons:** Lg Cup R-up 89-90

BRERETON SOCIAL

Ground: Armitage Lane, Rugeley (0889 585526).   **Founded:** 1899
Secretary: David J Rowley, 32 Lodge Rd, Brereton, Rugeley WS15 1HG (0889 583000).
Manager: Michael Morris   **Colours:** Red & white/red/red &white   **Programme:** Y

BROCTON

Ground: Rowley Park Stadium, Stafford (0785 51060).   **Founded:** 1937
Secretary: T J Homer, 124 John Street, Chadsmoor, Cannock WS11 2HR (0543 571964).
Manager: T R Cook   **Colours:** Green & white/white/green & white   **Programme:** Y

CONGLETON TOWN HORNETS

Ground: Booth Street, Congleton (0260 274460).   **Founded:** 1896
Secretary: David Wilcock, 9 Maxwell Road, Congleton, Cheshire CW12 3HY (0260 276347).
Manager: Alan Hughes   **Colours:** Green & white/white/green & white.

ECCLESHALL

Ground: Pershall Park, Near Eccleshall.   **Founded:** 1971
Secretary: Jed C Atkins, 30 School Road, Eccleshall ST21 6AS (0785 851016).   **Programme:** Y
Manager: Ken Roberts   **Colours:** Green & white/green/green   **Hons:** Champs 89-90.

GOLDENHILL WANDERERS

Ground: Shelford Road, Sandyford (0782 811977).   **Founded:** 1885
Secretary: Michael J Goodwin, 4 Russell Road, Sandyford ST6 5LS (0782 824838).   **Programme:** Y
Manager: Bryan Finney   **Colours:** Yellow/blue/yellow   **Hons:** Lg Cup R-up 85-86

HANFORD

Ground: Trentmill Road, Hanley.   **Founded:** 1959
Secretary: Ian Bradbury, 9 Frenchmore Grove, Lightwood, Longton ST3 7SF (0782 341877).
Manager: Michael J Clewes   **Colours:** All red   **Programme:**

HEATH HAYES

Ground: Newlands Lane, Heath Hayes.   **Founded:** 1965
Secretary: Peter J Francis, 191 Hednesford Road, Heath Hayes (0543 274212).
Manager: John Davies   **Colours:** Blue & white/white/blue   **Programme:** Y

LEEK C.S.O.B.

Ground: Leek Town FC (see H.F.S. Loans League).   **Founded:** 1945
Secretary: Neil Ogden, 11 Moorfields, Leek ST13 5LU (0538 384281).
Manager: Michael Nettle   **Colours:** Orange & white/black/black   **Programme:** Y

Brocton FC 1991-92.

Stafford M.S.H.D. - Runners-up 1991-92. Back Row (L/R): Mark Poole, Ian Spence, Mark Morris, Peter Ingram, Dave Hall, Steve Kenney, Neale Kirkland, Colin Clayton (Trainer). Front: Andy Geoghagen, Nicky Dunne, Matt Smith (Captain), anon, Tony Dale, Joe Handley. Photo - Staffordshire Sentinel.

Hanford FC 1991-92. Photo - Chris Bedford.

MILTON UNITED

Ground: Leek Road, Milton End.
Secretary: Maurice Sherratt, 3 Clifford Avenue, Norton Green (0782 533775).
Manager: Simon Bullock · **Colours:** Sky & white stripes/black/sky
Founded: 1985
Programme: Y
Hons: Lg Cup 88-89

NORTON UNITED

Ground: Community Drive, Smallthorne (0782 838290).
Secretary: Keith Sutton, 110 Hanley Road, Sneyd Green ST1 6BE (0782 214120).
Manager: Neil Dundas · **Colours:** Red & black/black/black
Founded: 1989
Programme: Y
Hons: Lg Cup 91-92

REDGATE CLAYTON

Ground: Northwood Lane, Clayton, Newcastle-under-Lyme (0782 717409).
Directions: M6 jct 15, left for Newcastle, past Post House Hotel, ground on right at 1st r'bout.
Secretary: Roger Farr, 9 Winnipeg Close, Trentham ST4 8UE (0782 641334).
Manager: Bernard Bramwell · **Colours:** Red/blue/red
Previous Name: Manor Park
Founded: 1969
Programme: Y
Nickname: Gate
Prev. Grounds: St Josephs College 84-87/ Oldfields Spts Grnd
Hons: Champs 87-88 91-92 (Lg Cup 90-91 (R-up 87-88 91-92)), Walsall Snr Cup 87-88, Staffs Vase 91-92.

RISTS UNITED

Ground: Lower Milehouse Lane, Newcastle-under-Lyme (0782 563366).
Secretary: Graham Michael Rutter, 46 James Street, Wolstanton ST5 0BX (0782 619567).
Manager: Stephen Smith · **Colours:** Yellow/blue/yellow
Founded: 1956
Programme: Y

STAFFORD TOWN

Ground: Riverway, Stafford (0785 51660)
Secretary: Ian Clark, 21 Cull Avenue, Stafford ST16 3UX (0785 49640).
Manager: Chris Curtiss · **Colours:** All red
Previous Names: Stafford Town 74-90/ Stafford M.S.H.D. 90-92.
Founded: 1974
Programme: Y
Hons: Lg R-up 91-92

STAFFORD RANGERS RESERVES

Manager: Desmond Lyons · **Programme:** Y · *(For all other details see G.M.V. Conference section).*

STAFFORDSHIRE POLICE

Ground: Silkmore Lane, Stafford (0785 58386).
Secretary: D F Wooler, 2 Kentmere Close, Weston Drowns, Stafford ST17 9HZ (0785 44192).
Manager: Peter Dent · **Colours:** Red/black/red
Programme: Y
Founded: 1953
Hons: Lg Cup 87-88 (R-up 86-87)

WALSALL WOOD

Ground: Oak Park, Lichfield Rd, Walsall (0543 361084).
Directions: Off A461 Walsall-Lichfield Rd, 100yds south of jnt with A4152 Aldridge-Brownhills.
Secretary: Stuart J Rousell, c/o 6 Pool Green, Aldridge, Walsall WS9 0JH (0902 368621-work).
Manager: Michael Speake · **Colours:** Red/black/red
Previous Names: Walsall Wood, Walsall Sportsco merged to form Walsall Borough. Name later reverted.
Programme: Y
Founded: 1928
Prev. Lg: Mids Comb. (pre'92)
Hons: Mids Comb. 51-52 (R-up53-54 54-55 57-58 58-59 60-61, Lg Cup 54-55 60-61 (R-up 56-57 58-59)), B'ham Jnr Cup 76-77. *Walsall Sportsco: Mids Comb. Lg Cup 79-80.*

MANCHESTER FOOTBALL LEAGUE

Hon. Secretary: F Fitzpatrick, 102 Victoria Rd, Stretford, Manchester M32 0AD(061 865 2726)

Premier Division	P	W	D	L	F	A	PTS
East Manchester	34	24	4	6	107	41	76
Wythenshawe Amtrs	34	21	9	4	71	18	72
Abbey Hey	34	20	8	6	94	49	68
Little Hulton	34	21	4	9	69	56	67
Gtr Man. Police	34	17	8	9	67	42	59
Springhead	34	16	8	10	64	49	56
Mitchell Shackleton	34	15	9	10	58	46	54
Ramsbottom Utd	34	16	5	13	58	48	53
B.T. Cables Leigh	34	12	11	11	63	66	47
Highfield Utd	34	10	13	11	53	54	43
Silcoms Woodside	34	11	8	15	61	70	41
I.C.I. Blackley	34	9	11	14	55	62	38
Dukinfield Town	34	8	12	14	45	52	36
S'kport Georgians	34	8	8	18	47	78	32
Wythenshawe Town	34	7	9	18	34	63	30
Prestwich Heys	34	6	11	17	39	78	29
+ Crompton Town	34	7	3	24	32	102	24
+ Avro	34	3	9	22	39	82	18

Gilgryst Cup: GM Police (R-up: Springhead)
Murray Shield: Sacred Heart (R-up W'worth Valley)
Open Tphy: Monton Amtrs (R-up: Abbey Hey)
Manc. Chal Tphy: E Manchester (R-up: Heywood SJ)

Division Two	P	W	D	L	F	A	PTS
E Manchester Res	28	19	5	4	64	29	62
Abbey Hey Res	28	18	5	5	83	39	59
Springhead Res	28	18	4	6	75	34	58
Dukinfield Res	28	17	5	6	65	38	56
Wyth. Amtrs Res	28	16	7	5	67	35	55
Mitchell S. Res	28	11	10	7	53	39	43
Monton Amtrs Res	28	12	7	9	61	51	43
$ Urmston Res	28	9	6	13	60	68	33
Prestwich Res	28	8	6	14	44	82	30
S. Georgians Res	28	7	7	14	26	39	28
Highfield U. Res	28	7	7	14	58	74	28
Wyth. Town Res	28	7	6	15	36	48	27
Ramsbottom U. Res	28	5	9	14	44	70	24
BT Cables Res	28	5	8	15	44	87	23
ICI Blackley Res	28	2	6	20	43	90	12

Division One	P	W	D	L	F	A	PTS
* Woodley Sports	36	29	2	5	95	46	89
* Whitworth Valley	36	27	6	3	119	46	87
O Altrinchamians	36	22	2	12	82	51	68
Atherton Town	36	20	5	11	95	48	65
Monton Amateurs	36	19	8	9	79	51	65
Sacred Hearts	36	17	12	7	85	55	63
Waterloo	36	18	9	14	75	62	58
$ Urmston	36	18	4	14	72	63	58
Gorton	36	15	9	12	77	64	54
Pennington	36	15	8	13	69	67	53
Milton	36	12	11	13	59	66	47
New Mills	36	12	8	16	64	72	44
Whalley Range	36	12	7	17	67	69	43
Breightmet United	36	10	10	16	64	80	40
Ashton Athletic	36	10	6	20	65	85	36
Hollinwood	36	8	7	21	55	90	31
Little Lever	36	6	6	24	53	96	24
$ Oldham Victoria	36	6	6	24	49	117	24
British Vita	36	4	1	31	39	144	13

Division Three	P	W	D	L	F	A	PTS
Waterloo Res	30	25	4	1	111	30	79
Whalley Range Res	30	19	6	5	92	49	63
O Altrinch. Res	30	16	10	4	66	39	58
Pennington Res	30	17	5	8	51	37	56
Breightmet Res	30	14	5	11	69	67	47
Woodley Spts Res	30	14	4	12	68	68	46
Atherton T. Res	30	14	3	13	61	55	45
Crompton Res	30	12	8	10	55	48	44
Whitw. Valley Res	30	10	11	9	53	42	41
New Mills Res	30	11	5	14	47	56	38
Hollingwood Res	30	10	5	15	52	56	35
Gorton Res	30	9	7	14	49	65	34
Gtr M. Police Res	30	8	6	16	44	52	30
Milton Res	30	7	3	20	39	82	24
Sacred Heart Res	30	5	7	18	40	80	22

* - Promoted, **+** - Relegated, **$** - Resigned

New Clubs in Div 1: Manchester Royal, Winton Utd
New Clubs in Div 3: Manchester Royal Res, Winton Utd Res, Avro Res, British Vita Res

JOHN SMITHS WEST LANCASHIRE LEAGUE

Division One	P	W	D	L	F	A	PTS
Burnley Bank Hall	34	28	4	2	107	37	88
Vickers Spts Club	34	26	3	5	110	35	81
B.A.C. Preston	34	22	8	4	93	44	74
Feniscowles	34	21	9	4	62	30	72
Eagley	34	16	5	13	65	53	53
Poulton Town	34	14	10	10	66	53	52
Dalton United	34	15	6	13	61	53	51
Burnley United	34	15	5	14	61	51	50
Lytham St Annes	34	11	15	8	63	60	48
Royal Ordnance	34	13	4	17	53	54	43
Vernon Carus	34	12	7	15	54	61	43
Wigan College	34	12	4	18	58	58	40
Turton Bolton	34	10	9	15	66	81	39
Norcross & Warbeck	34	9	5	20	47	90	32
Blackpool Rgrs	34	7	7	20	36	86	28
Freckleton	34	6	7	21	38	81	25
Springfields	34	6	6	22	30	82	24
Carnforth Rgrs	34	4	4	26	26	87	16

Richardson Cup Final (at Turf Moor, Burnley)
Burnley Bank Hall 3, Eagley 1

Division Two	P	W	D	L	F	A	PTS
I.C.I. Thornton	34	23	4	7	104	49	73
Colne Brit. Legion	34	23	4	7	90	63	73
Claxo Ulverston	34	22	5	7	98	43	71
Blackrod Town	34	22	5	7	95	52	71
Multipart (Chorley)	34	20	7	7	75	43	67
Longridge United	34	19	5	10	120	64	62
Lansil Lancaster	34	18	5	11	79	53	59
Padiham	34	16	8	10	68	49	56
Blackpool Rvrs Res	34	16	6	12	75	53	*51
Kirkham & Wesham	34	13	9	12	61	67	48
Hesketh Bank	34	14	6	14	71	77	48
Barrow Wanderers	34	12	5	17	65	67	41
Haslingden	34	9	7	18	49	68	34
Wigan Rovers	34	9	4	21	57	81	31
Fleetwood Hesketh	34	6	8	20	51	81	26
Nelson	34	6	7	21	61	95	25
BAE Warton	34	7	5	22	62	93	*23
Lucas SC Burnley	34	1	0	33	19	192	3

* - 3 points deducted

Presidents Cup Final (at Leyland DAF FC)
Blackrod Town 2, I.C.I. Thornton 1

Burnley Bank Hall, Division One Champions and Richardson Cup Winners 1991-92. Back Row (L/R): John Dawson (Physio), Kevin Robinson (Asst Manager), Jason Harris, Kiko Rodriguez, Graham Howarth, Keith Blackman, Steve Whitehead, Phil Malley, Trevor Hanson, Ian Britton (Manager), John Howarth (Chairman). Front: Geoff Smith, Ashley Hoskin, Andy Baker, Derek Scott (Captain), Gary Norwood, Neil Grewcock. Photo - Burnley Express.

DIVISION ONE CLUBS 1992-93

B.A.C. PRESTON
Ground: Riverside Spts Grnd, South Meadow Lane, Preston (0772 51009)   **Sec:** I Fraser (0772 861648).

BLACKPOOL RANGERS
Ground: Fleetwood Road, Bispham (0253 853308)   **Secretary:** T Dickinson (0253 866004).

BURNLEY UNITED
Ground: Barden Lane Spts Grnd, Burnley.   **Secretary:** R Greenwood (0282 34739).

COLNE BRITISH LEGION
Ground: Holt House, Colne (0282 862335)   **Secretary:** W Alexander (0282 866638).

DALTON UNITED
Ground: Railway Meadow, Beckside Rd, Dalton-in-Furness (0229 62799)   **Sec:** D Lacey (0229 64202).

EAGLEY
Ground: Eagley Sports Complex (0204 54191)   **Secretary:** M Hackin (0204 595863).

FENISCOWLES
Ground: Livsey Branch Road, Feniscowles, Blackburn (0254 208210)   **Sec:** A Akeroyd (0254 706931).

FRECKLETON
Ground: Hodgson Memorial Grnd, Bushey Lane, Freckleton, Nr Preston   **Sec:** Mrs Bell (0772 632036).

I.C.I. THORNTON
Ground: Gamble Road.   **Secretary:** J Wright (0253 868430).

LYTHAM ST ANNES
Ground: Lytham Cricket & Sports Club, Lytham St Annes (0253 734137)   **Sec:** P Shearer (0253 738676).

NORCROSS & WARBRECK
Ground: Norcross Lane **Secretary:** B Roberts (0253 825179).

POULTON TOWN
Ground: Cottam Hall PF, Blackpool Old Rd, Poulton-le-Fylde **Secretary:** D Sponder (0253 890284).

SPRINGFIELDS
Ground: S.S.R.A. Spts Grnd, Dodney Drive, Lea, Preston **Secretary:** T Threlfall (0772 718959).

TURTON
Ground: Thomasson Fold, Turton **Secretary:** L Donlan (0204 593387).

VERNON CARUS
Ground: Factory Lane, Penwortham (0772 744006) **Secretary:** T Beswick (0772 745007).

VICKERS SPORTS CLUB
Ground: Hawcoat Park, Barrow-in-Furness (0229 825296) **Secretary:** Mrs Else (0229 834766).

WIGAN COLLEGE
Ground: Christopher Park, Standish (0257 41140) **Secretary:** D Stott (0257 423531).

Wigan College. Back Row (L/R): S Dean (Asst Sec.), T Berry (Coach), S McNally, G Cuncliffe, I Taylor, G McCrae, P Tate, D Booth, G Hatton, P Cooper, M Liptrot (Trainer). Front: J Wilson, D McMullan, D Fields, G Read (Manager), S Phoenix (Capt), J Culshaw (Asst Mgr), G Moore, D Parkinson.

DIVISION TWO CLUBS 1992-93

B.A.E. CANBERRY (New entrant 92-93)

B.A.E. WARTON
Ground: British Aerospace Spts Grnd, Bank Lane, Warton (0772 632134)**Sec:** S Broomfield (0772 632392).

BARROW WANDERERS
Ground: Lesh Lane (0229 830125) **Secretary:** I Parkinson (0229 830125).

BLACKPOOL ROVERS RESERVES (See page 786)

BLACKROD TOWN
Ground: Blackrod Community Centre, Vicarage Rd, Blackrod (0204 692614)**Sec:** D Almond (0942 818663).

CARNFORTH RANGERS
Ground: **Secretary:** K Webster (0524 735322).

FLEETWOOD HESKETH
Ground: Fylde Road, Fleetwood (0704 27968) **Secretary:** Mrs Hibbott (0704 214630).

GLAXCO SPORTS CLUB
Ground: Glaxco Spts Club, Ulverston (0229 52804/52300) **Secretary:** M Simpson (0229 54981).

HASLINGDEN
Ground: Ewood Road, Rossendale **Secretary:** J Mead (0706 225988).

HESKETH BANK
Ground: Hesketh Spts Field, Station Road **Secretary:** C Taylor (0772 815844).

KIRKHAM & WESHAM
Ground: Coronation Rd Recreation Ground **Secretary:** R Davey (0772 33962).

LANSIL LANCASTER
Ground: Lansil Sports Ground, Caton Rd, Lancaster **Secretary:** M Miller (0524 33962).

LEYLAND
Ground: Thurston Road, Leyland, Lancs (0772 422400) **Secretary:**

LONGRIDGE UNITED
Ground: Recreation Grnd, Barclay Rd, Longridge **Secretary:** A Wilson (0772 798256).

LUCAS SPORTS CLUB
Ground: Raedale Avenue, Burnley, Lancs (0282 695796) **Secretary:** B Bennett (0282 34061).

MULTIPART (CHORLEY)
Ground: St Georges Park, Duke Street, Chorley (0257 270103) **Secretary:** D Jolly (0257 270518).

PADIHAM
Ground: Well Street, Padiham, Lancs (0282 73742) **Secretary:** D Howarth (0282 22983).

TEMPEST (New entrant 92-93)

WIGAN ROVERS

Ground: St James Park, Poolstock   **Secretary:** J Hulton (0942 53113).

WYRE VILLA (New entrant 92-93)

LANCASHIRE AMATEUR LEAGUE

Premier Division	P	W	D	L	F	A	PTS
Burnley Belvedere	24	21	1	2	80	14	43
Rochdale St Clem.	24	18	4	2	57	21	40
Old Gregorians	24	12	5	7	41	30	29
Burnley G.S.O.B.	24	9	9	6	49	47	27
Walshaw	24	9	7	8	39	35	25
Old Blackburnians	24	9	6	9	40	38	24
Hesketh Casuals	24	8	7	9	46	42	23
Old Rivingtonians	24	8	5	11	37	46	21
Old Mostonians	24	8	5	11	33	50	21
Southport Amtrs	24	7	4	13	33	47	18
Fulwood Amtrs	24	6	4	14	34	58	16
Broughton Amtrs	24	6	2	16	27	57	14
Bury Amateurs	24	3	5	16	29	60	11

Division One	P	W	D	L	F	A	PTS
Leigh Athletic	28	22	3	3	103	33	47
Royton Town	28	22	3	3	99	40	47
Rossendale Amtrs	28	19	5	4	80	45	43
Ashtonians	28	11	10	7	55	51	32
Tarleton Corinthians	28	13	5	10	60	56	31
Old Smithillians	28	11	7	10	60	52	29
Ainsdale United	28	12	5	11	55	54	29
Bolton Wyresdale	28	10	7	11	60	67	27
Old Sladians	28	7	11	10	39	67	25
Thornleigh	28	9	6	13	60	66	24
Old Boltonians	28	9	6	13	48	54	24
Lymm	28	9	3	16	59	72	21
Preston G.S.A.	28	5	10	13	50	67	20
Little Lever S.C.	28	3	7	18	47	89	13
Nth Manch. HSOB	28	1	6	21	22	84	8

Southport based side Hesketh Casuals, of the Lancashire Amateur League Premier Division.

Division Two	P	W	D	L	F	A	PTS
Oldham Hulmeians	28	18	5	5	68	30	41
Chaddertonians	28	18	5	5	67	41	41
Newman College	28	17	6	5	61	39	40
Old Choritonians	28	15	9	4	84	57	39
Old Mancunians	28	15	7	6	69	38	37
Bolton County	28	12	7	9	73	53	31
Hayward	28	12	5	11	64	64	29
Bury G.S.O.B.	28	11	5	12	66	70	27
Roch Valley	28	10	5	13	70	74	25
Burnage H.S.O.B.	28	9	7	12	51	59	25
Radcliffe Amtrs	28	10	4	14	51	51	24
Hathershaw	28	9	4	15	56	56	22
Accrington Amtrs	28	6	4	18	53	80	16
Spotland Methodists	28	7	2	19	44	82	16
Old Salfordians	28	3	1	24	42	125	7

Reserve Div. One	P	W	D	L	F	A	PTS
Burnley G.S.O.B.	26	19	1	6	81	45	39
Ashtonians	26	16	5	5	72	45	37
Preston G.S.A.	26	14	8	4	76	50	36
Ainsdale United	26	15	4	7	68	48	34
Little Lever SC	26	12	7	7	74	57	31
Newman College	26	13	4	9	53	58	30
Old Smithillians	26	12	5	9	58	47	29
Walshaw S.C.	26	11	4	11	59	49	26
Tarleton Corinthians	26	10	4	12	50	54	24
Royton Town	26	8	7	11	61	63	23
Bolton Wyresdale	26	7	7	12	43	52	21
Old Mancunians	26	6	2	18	29	66	14
Chaddertonians	26	4	3	19	48	80	11
Lymm	26	4	1	21	44	106	9

Prem. Reserves	P	W	D	L	F	A	PTS
Old Gregorians	26	17	5	4	77	34	39
Old Rivingtonians	26	18	3	5	74	46	39
Rochdale St Clem.	26	17	4	5	79	28	38
Burnley Belvedere	26	14	4	8	69	48	*30
Rossendale Amtrs	26	11	7	8	64	43	29
Old Blackburnians	26	10	9	7	47	44	29
Old Mostonians	26	10	7	9	52	49	27
Leigh Athletic	26	9	5	12	53	52	23
Bury Amateurs	26	10	3	13	47	52	23
Southport Amtrs	26	8	4	14	45	74	20
Fulwood Amtrs	26	5	9	12	35	59	19
Old Boltonians	26	6	5	15	41	68	17
Broughton Amtrs	26	7	3	16	30	62	17
Oldham Hulmeians	26	4	4	18	43	97	12

*— 2 points deducted

Reserve Div. Two	P	W	D	L	F	A	PTS
Hesketh Casuals	28	21	3	4	95	30	45
Roch Valley	28	17	6	5	77	46	40
Burnage H.S.O.B.	28	14	10	4	63	43	38
Old Choritonians	28	14	8	6	80	47	36
Bolton County	28	16	2	10	78	51	34
Hathershaw	28	13	6	9	60	45	32
Bury G.S.O.B.	28	14	3	11	74	57	31
Old Sladians	28	12	7	9	61	48	31
Thornleigh	28	11	6	11	62	68	28
Radcliffe Amtrs	28	11	4	13	52	58	26
Hayward	28	8	5	15	55	70	21
Nth Manch. HSOB	28	7	7	14	64	84	21
Accrington Amtrs	28	5	6	17	44	88	16
Old Salfordians	28	3	5	20	33	108	11
Spotland Methodists	28	2	6	20	49	104	10

(continued overleaf)

North - 3A	P	W	D	L	F	A	PTS
O Blackburnians 'A'	26	20	3	3	106	43	43
O Smithillians 'A'	26	17	5	4	84	32	39
Fulwood Amtrs 'A'	26	16	2	8	76	59	34
Burnley Bel. 'A'	26	13	7	6	69	46	33
Rossendale A. 'A'	26	13	6	7	69	50	32
O Rivingtonians 'A'	26	12	5	9	65	50	29
O Boltonians 'A'	26	8	8	10	45	47	24
Little Lever SC 'A'	26	9	6	11	72	86	24
O Rivingtonians 'B'	26	7	7	12	60	80	21
Burnley GSOB 'A'	26	9	3	14	47	70	21
Broughton Amtrs 'A'	26	5	11	10	53	81	21
Southport Amtrs 'A'	26	8	3	15	57	89	19
Burnley GSOB 'B'	26	5	5	16	65	88	15
Broughton 'B'	26	2	5	19	33	100	9

North - 3B	P	W	D	L	F	A	PTS
Hesketh Casuals 'A'	26	18	5	3	79	34	41
O Sladians 'A'	26	16	6	4	59	28	38
Fulwood Amtrs 'B'	26	16	5	5	82	34	37
Burnley Bel. 'B'	26	13	5	8	66	43	31
Preston GSA 'A'	26	13	3	10	68	57	29
Burnley B'dere 'C'	26	12	3	11	56	62	27
O Boltonians 'B'	26	10	5	11	48	48	25
O Rivingtonians 'C'	26	10	4	12	69	79	24
O Blackburnians 'B'	26	9	6	11	42	55	24
Rossendale A. 'B'	26	10	3	13	54	61	23
Little Lever SC 'B'	26	7	5	14	60	76	19
Newman College 'A'	26	6	6	14	57	95	18
Tarleton Cor. 'A'	26	5	4	17	52	72	14
Burnley GSOB 'C'	26	5	4	17	33	81	14

North - 3C	P	W	D	L	F	A	PTS
Hesketh Casuals 'B'	26	18	5	3	103	43	41
Newman Collage 'C'	26	17	5	4	82	38	39
O Smithillians 'B'	26	14	3	9	82	42	31
Southport Am. 'B'	26	11	7	8	73	66	29
Newman College 'B'	26	11	7	8	55	52	29
Thornleigh 'A'	26	12	4	10	61	67	28
O Sladians 'B'	26	12	3	11	46	47	27
Burnley B'dere 'D'	26	10	5	11	78	62	25
Accrington Amtrs 'A'	26	11	3	12	67	76	25
Accrington Amtrs 'B'	26	9	5	12	59	70	23
Burnley GSOB 'D'	26	9	5	12	60	80	23
Thornleigh 'B'	26	9	4	13	48	68	22
Preston GSA 'B'	26	7	2	17	59	83	16
Southport Amtrs 'C'	26	2	2	22	29	108	6

HALLMARK LIVERPOOL COUNTY COMBINATION

Division One	P	W	D	L	F	A	PTS
Yorks Cop. Tubes	30	22	4	4	96	45	70
St Dominics	30	21	4	4	96	32	69
Stanton Dale	30	18	7	5	76	42	61
Ayone	30	18	5	7	68	47	59
Waterloo Dock	30	16	9	5	73	58	57
Crawfords U.B.	30	15	7	8	69	43	52
Littlewoods Ath.	30	15	5	10	63	47	50
Speke	30	14	4	12	67	60	46
Earle	30	14	2	14	61	62	44
Ford Motors	30	11	6	13	46	60	39
B.R. Nth End S.C.	30	11	4	15	47	55	37
Electric Supply	30	9	5	16	41	53	32
Mossley Hill	30	7	6	17	41	69	27
Crystal Villa	30	6	3	49	80	21	8
Cheshire Lines	30	2	2	26	35	115	8
Bootle Reserves	30	1	5	24	23	80	*5

* - 3 points deducted

Division Two	P	W	D	L	F	A	PTS
Lucas Sports	28	24	0	4	97	30	72
B.R.N.E.S.C. Res	28	17	6	5	90	56	57
Eldonians	28	17	3	8	59	38	54
Beesix	28	16	5	7	67	53	53
Ford Motors Res	28	14	4	10	77	50	46
Camadale	28	12	3	13	53	52	39
Royal Seaforth	28	12	3	13	54	60	39
Knowsley Utd Res	28	13	0	15	60	63	*36
Halewood Town	28	8	10	10	46	52	34
Merseybus FC	28	9	7	12	52	67	34
Speke Reserves	28	9	5	14	54	68	32
Mersey Dock H.C.	28	8	6	14	43	67	*27
Mossley Hill Res	28	5	10	13	47	69	*22
Plessey G.P.T.	28	6	4	18	55	91	22
Electric Supply Res	28	5	4	19	38	76	19

* - 3 points deducted

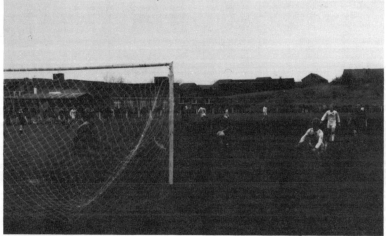

Dave Hewitson of champions-elect Yorkshire Copper Tubes dives to head his side's third in a 3-0 win at Waterloo Dock on 17th April. Photo - Rob Ruddock.

GREEN INSULATION
MID-CHESHIRE LEAGUE

President: W Salt, Esq.
Hon. Secretary: E B Davies,
34 Ryebank Road, Firswood, Manchester M16 0FP (061 881 5732).

GROVE CANTER TO EASY SUCCESS

The early months of the 1991-92 season saw Grove United and Linotype vying for the top spot, but a torrid second half to the season by the Altrincham based side gave Grove United the edge and they cantered to an easy championship. Garswood United and Knutsford both kept in touch, but was the former that fell away leaving Knutsford needing to win their last game of the season. An injury time goal gave them the point that saw them pip Linotype for the runners-up position.

There was a two horse race in the Second Division, and the issue was only decided on the last match when Broadheath pipped Beechams thus winning the title by three points.

The Division One Cup final was between Barnton and Chorlton Town with the former squandering a two goal half-time lead. Extra-time was followed by a penalty shoot-out in which Barnton came out on top winning 4-3.

Broadheath completed a Division Two League and Cup double with a 2-0 win over Knutsford Reserves place, a worthy feat in their first season in the League.

The annual challenge match against the Tetley Walker West Cheshire League was played at the end of the season and was won by the West Cheshire League, who celebrate their centenary this season.

For season 1992-93 the League await the outcome of applications to the Bass North West Counties League by Chorlton Town and North Trafford. If they are successful there will be no relegation from the First Division, with Broadheath Central and Beechams (now to be renamed 'The Beeches') being promoted. Should neither club leave, Styal and Winnington Park will drop to Division Two joining newcomers Littlemoor, Warrington Town Reserves and Grove United Reserves.

E B Davies, Hon. Secretary

LEAGUE TABLES 1991-92

Division One	P	W	D	L	F	A	PTS
Grove United	30	23	2	5	74	21	71
Knutsford	30	18	6	6	47	29	60
Linotype	30	18	5	7	67	30	59
North Trafford	30	16	7	7	56	37	55
Barnton	30	15	4	11	60	48	49
Hanley Town	30	14	5	10	42	36	48
Garswood United	30	14	4	12	48	42	46
Poynton	30	14	4	12	57	55	46
Bramhall	30	13	6	11	62	56	56
Rylands	30	11	6	13	50	43	39
Whitchurch	30	10	5	15	38	57	35
Newcastle T. Res	30	9	5	16	41	48	32
Chorlton Town	30	8	8	14	41	52	32
Wilmslow Albion	30	6	7	17	41	66	25
Winnington Park	30	5	7	18	40	67	22
Styal	30	4	2	24	33	100	14

Division Two	P	W	D	L	F	A	PTS
Broadheath Central	32	24	4	4	85	31	76
Beechams	32	23	4	5	78	24	73
ICI Pharms.	32	20	5	7	93	43	65
Pilkington	32	17	7	8	69	46	58
Alsager	32	16	5	11	48	42	53
Middlewich Ath.	32	14	8	10	54	46	50
Malpas	32	14	5	13	68	60	47
Bramhall Res.	32	13	8	11	55	58	58
Linotype Res.	32	13	5	14	60	72	44
Rylands Res.	32	10	5	14	59	74	44
Garswood Utd Res	32	11	7	14	60	47	40
Knutsford Res	32	10	9	13	40	42	39
Poynton Res	32	11	6	15	40	62	39
Chorlton Town Res	32	9	3	20	45	75	30
Bollington	32	7	7	18	36	78	28
Wilmslow Alb. Res	32	4	7	21	38	77	19
Grove Utd Res	32	3	5	24	38	87	14

DIVISION ONE RESULTS 1991/92

HOME TEAM		1	2	3	4	5	6	7	8	9	10	11	12	13	14	15	16
1.	Barnton	*	2-0	3-2	5-1	1-0	4-0	2-0	1-3	6-2	1-3	2-2	0-0	4-0	1-0	3-2	5-1
2.	Bramhall	5-0	*	1-0	0-1	1-1	1-1	2-2	2-5	2-0	3-0	3-3	2-1	6-2	4-0	0-3	4-0
3.	Chorlton Town	2-5	1-1	*	2-1	1-0	0-0	2-3	1-0	2-1	0-0	2-3	2-5	4-1	1-1	2-1	2-2
4.	Garswood United	1-3	2-3	2-1	*	1-0	1-0	0-1	2-0	0-0	0-2	3-0	2-0	4-1	2-1	0-0	4-2
5.	Grove United	2-0	7-0	5-1	2-1	*	3-0	3-0	3-0	2-1	3-0	1-0	1-1	4-1	2-1	3-1	4-0
6.	Hanley Town	1-0	5-1	1-0	0-2	0-2	*	0-1	1-0	1-1	0-1	4-1	1-0	2-0	3-1	2-0	1-4
7.	Knutsford	3-1	1-0	2-1	1-0	3-0	0-0	*	1-0	2-2	1-3	2-0	2-2	1-1	2-3	0-1	2-0
8.	Linotype	5-1	1-0	1-1	1-5	2-4	1-1	2-1	*	2-1	2-1	1-0	3-2	5-4	3-0	3-0	3-3
9.	Newcastle Town Res	0-1	2-2	0-1	1-1	0-2	2-1	1-2	0-1	*	1-2	1-0	1-2	2-1	2-0	5-1	1-0
10.	North Trafford	1-1	3-5	1-0	2-0	2-1	4-0	1-2	0-0	3-0	*	4-0	1-5	6-1	2-2	3-0	0-0
11.	Poynton	2-1	2-1	2-1	5-2	0-3	1-1	0-4	1-4	2-1	4-1	*	3-2	8-1	5-0	3-1	0-0
12.	Rylands	3-0	2-0	1-3	1-0	1-3	1-2	0-0	1-1	2-4	1-2	5-3	*	1-0	1-2	5-1	1-0
13.	Styal	0-3	4-1	2-1	2-2	1-5	1-5	0-1	1-5	0-3	0-3	1-3	3-1	*	2-3	0-6	1-3
14.	Whitchurch Alport	3-2	3-4	2-0	3-0	0-1	1-2	1-4	0-7	3-2	1-1	0-1	1-0	3-0	*	0-0	0-2
15.	Wilmslow Albion	2-2	1-5	2-2	1-2	0-3	2-4	1-2	2-5	2-1	2-2	2-0	0-0	1-2	0-2	*	3-2
16.	Winnington Park	2-0	1-3	3-3	2-6	1-4	0-3	0-1	0-1	2-3	1-2	1-3	0-3	4-0	1-1	3-3	*

DIVISION TWO RESULTS 1991/92

HOME TEAM	1	2	3	4	5	6	7	8	9	10	11	12	13	14	15	16	17
1. Alsager	*	1-2	2-0	3-0	2-5	2-1	2-1	2-0	1-0	2-1	0-0	2-1	1-2	2-0	3-1	2-2	2-0
2. Beechams	1-2	*	5-0	5-0	3-0	3-0	2-0	6-0	3-0	2-0	1-1	4-0	1-0	2-0	2-1	2-0	7-1
3. Bollington Athletic	1-0	2-2	*	1-1	0-3	1-0	0-3	2-2	4-2	0-0	0-2	3-4	2-4	1-2	1-1	1-4	3-2
4. Bramhall Res	2-0	1-0	5-2	*	0-3	2-0	2-1	4-2	1-3	2-0	3-3	1-0	2-2	0-0	3-1	5-0	3-3
5. Broadheath Central	4-0	2-0	1-1	5-0	*	2-3	4-1	5-1	1-2	2-1	4-0	5-0	2-0	4-1	1-0	1-3	1-1
6. Chorlton Town Res	1-2	0-5	1-4	2-2	2-3	*	4-3	3-0	0-1	0-2	2-3	4-2	0-4	1-4	1-1	1-2	3-1
7. Garswood Utd Res	2-1	0-3	8-0	2-1	0-1	5-1	*	4-0	2-1	5-0	4-2	1-1	0-2	0-2	5-0	0-2	1-1
8. Grove United Res	1-0	4-0	1-1	0-2	2-3	2-3	1-1	*	0-3	0-2	1-4	2-2	1-2	1-2	1-1	4-5	4-1
9. ICI Pharmaceuticals	0-0	4-2	3-0	6-1	2-3	5-1	1-1	5-3	*	4-1	8-3	3-1	0-0	1-1	7-0	2-0	3-0
10. Knutsford Res	2-2	1-1	4-0	2-1	1-3	0-1	1-1	4-1	2-0	*	0-0	0-1	0-1	0-2	1-1	1-1	0-3
11. Linotype Res	5-2	1-3	1-0	1-3	0-5	2-1	0-2	3-1	3-2	1-2	*	4-2	3-0	2-2	1-3	5-1	2-1
12. Malpas	1-2	1-2	0-2	4-3	1-2	5-1	1-1	5-1	3-4	0-2	3-0	*	1-0	4-1	2-1	6-0	3-1
13. Middlewich Athletic	1-4	1-1	4-1	0-1	2-2	2-2	1-1	3-0	1-4	0-2	2-1	2-2	*	3-2	1-3	4-3	3-2
14. Pilkington	2-1	0-2	8-1	1-0	0-3	4-1	3-1	2-0	2-2	1-1	3-1	2-3	1-0	*	5-1	6-3	6-3
15. Poynton Res	1-0	0-3	0-2	2-0	1-3	2-1	1-0	2-1	1-5	1-1	4-2	1-2	0-3	1-1	*	2-3	3-0
16. Rylands	0-1	0-1	1-0	2-2	1-1	0-2	4-3	3-1	1-7	1-0	6-2	2-2	1-4	1-3	1-2	*	3-0
17. Wilmslow A. Res	2-2	1-2	2-0	2-2	0-1	1-2	2-1	2-0	1-3	2-6	1-2	1-5	0-0	0-0	0-1	1-3	*

DIVISION ONE CUP 1991-92

First Round

Grove United v Linotype	4-0		Styal v North Trafford	0-3
Newcastle Town Reserves v Barnton	1-2		Knutsford v Garswood United	1-3
Chorlton Town v Bramhall	3-1		Rylands v Whitchurch Alport	2-4
Wilmslow Albion v Winnington Park	4-1		Hanley Town v Poynton	0-1

Second Round

Grove Utd v North Trafford	2-2 (7-8 pens)		Barnton v Garswood United	2-1
Chorlton Town v Whitchurch Alport	3-0		Wilmslow Albion v Poynton	0-1

Semi-Finals

North Trafford v Barnton	2-5		Chorlton Town v Poynton	1-0

Final: Barnton 2, Chorlton Town 2 (4-3 pens)

DIVISION TWO CUP 1991/92

Preliminary Round

Broadheath Central v Rylands Res.   6-3

First Round

Broadheath Central v ICI Pharms.	4-4,4-1		Middlewich Athletic v Malpas	0-0,3-0
Wilmslow Albion Res v Grove Utd Res	1-3		Linotype Res v Alsager	2-2,4-2
Knutsford Res v Bramhall Res	1-0		Pilkington v Beechams	4-1
Chorlton Res v Garswood Utd Res	1-1,0-1		Bollington Ath v Poynton Res	0-0,0-2

Second Round

Broadheath Central v Middlewich Ath.	3-1		Grove Utd Reserves v Linotype Res	1-6
Knutsford Res v Pilkington	2-0		Garswood Utd Res v Poynton Res	(7-8 pens)

Semi Finals

Broadheath Central v Linotype Res	6-0		Knutsford Res v Poynton Res	2-0

Final: Broadheath Central 2, Knutsford Reserves

CLUB DETAILS

ALSAGER

Chairman: Kevin Dean   **Manager:** David Nixon.
Secretary: John Dykes, 7 Dairylands Rd, Church Lawton, Stoke-on-Trent ST7 3FU (0270 877722).
Ground: The Town Ground, Wood Park, Alsager.
Directions: M6 jct 16, A500 towards Stoke, turn left for Alsager after half mile, follow lane to lights, in village centre turn right into Lawton Rd, 3rd left Moorhouse Avenue, 2nd right Woodland Court, ground entrance on righthand corner.
Colours: Black & white/black/black   **Change Colours:** Blue/black/black.

BARNTON

Chairman: William Perrin   **Manager:** A Woods.
Secretary: Peter Stanley, 10 Westfield Grove, Barnton, Nr Northwich, Cheshire CW8 4QB (0606 782305).
Ground: Townfield, Townfield Lane, Barnton.
Directions: Turn off A553 (Northwich-Runcorn) at Beech Tree Inn in Barnton village into Beech Lane. Right at T-junction with Townfield Lane - ground 200yds on left.
Colours: Black & amber stripes/black/black   **Change Colours:** Amber/black/amber.

BEECHES

Chairman: Gordon Rigby   **Manager:** D Corrigan.
Secretary: David Corrigan, 7 Burrows Avenue, Haydock, St Helens WA11 0DE (0744 572273).
Ground: Beechams Social Club, Sutton Rd, St Helens (0744 25906).
Directions: Approach from Widnes on A570, right at lights after St Helens Hospital into Sutton Rd, right at next lights, ground 200yds on left.
Colours: All blue   **Change Colours:** Claret & blue/claret/claret

BOLLINGTON ATHLETIC

Chairman: A Deery   **Manager:** Michael McKernan.
Secretary: Anthony Holmes, 79 Parkgate Rd, Macclesfield, Cheshire SK11 7SZ (0625 615044).
Ground: Recreation Ground, Bollington.
Directions: Turn off A523 (Macclesfield-Stockport) at 1st sign for Bollington. Follow for one and a half miles to Dog & Partridge, left into Adlington Rd, ground 100yds on right.
Colours: Jade & silver/silver   **Change Colours:** Tangerine/black.

Hanley Town. Back Row (L/R): Ken Wood (Trainer), Andy Hawkesworth, Mark Gribble, Paul Simpson, Karl Bamford, Ashley Webb, Paul Goodstadt, John Whalley, John Hulme. Front: Bobby Dalkin, Ade Stevenson, Doug Bell, Ade Tilstone, Dave Bell, Dean Challinor.

Pilkington. Back Row (L/R): Lol Stanton (Manager), Mark Ventre, John Beckett, John Potter, Lee Dyer, Aidan Barratt, Ray Wilson, Steve Oadmore, John Dawson (Manager). Front: Robbie Watson, Paul Bolan, John Wright (Capt), Steve Palfrey, Wally Lunt, Phil Dixon, Barry McCabe.

Wilmslow Albion. Back Row (L/R): M Cunningham, J Dippnall, S Bennett, A Lamon, D Bradshaw, P Booth. Front: G Tolen, M Partington, B Kabbani, J Bostock, M Paolo, S Cundliffe.

BRAMHALL

Chairman: B Wood   **Manager:** Glyn Williams (Peter Murphy: Res).
Secretary: Bernard Johnson, 25 Bean Leach Rd, Hazel Grove SK7 4LD (061 456 2542).
Ground: Lumb Lane, Bramhall.
Directions: Centre of Bramhall take Lumb Lane (pizza shop on corner), grnd 300yds on right behind village club.
Colours: Red/black/black   **Change Colours:** Yellow/blue/blue (All blue:Res)

BROADHEATH CENTRAL

Chairman: Robert German   **Manager:** Michael Merry.
Secretary: David Murphy, 10 Green Drive, Timperley, Altrincham WA15 6JW (061 980 1925).
Ground: Viaduct Road, Broadheath, Altrincham.
Directions: One and a half miles north of Altrincham on A56 Manchester Road; turn right immediately after B & Q and Halfords. A-Z ref. 2D 79.
Colours: Black & red stripes/black/black   **Change Colours:** All blue.

CHORLTON TOWN

Chairman: Mr H Ennis   **Manager:** I R Jarratt (Simon King:Res).
Secretary: Ronald Anderson, 34 Jenny Lane, Woodford, Stockport SK7 1PE (061 440 9112).
Ground: Longford Stadium, Longford Park.
Directions: A-Z ref. P58 4C. From M63 take A56 Chester Road towards Manchester, right into Edge Lane shortly after passing under M63, left into Ryebank Rd after a few hundred yds, ground 400yds on left.
Cols: Black & red stripes/white/white (Blue & black stripes/black/black:Res)   **Change Colours:** All white.

GARSWOOD UNITED

Chairman: D Finnegan   **Manager:** John Moriarty.
Secretary: Joseph McCann, 11 Foxfold, Fosters Green, Skelmersdale, Lancs WN8 6UE (0942 723243).
Ground: Simms Lane Ends, Garswood Road, Garswood, Nr Wigan (0744 892258).
Directions: A580 towards Liverpool, right into Liverpool Rd (A58), left into Garswood Rd (signposted Garswood), follow round, left at triangle, upto crossroads, straight ahead, entrance 100yds on left.
Colours: Blue & white stripes/blue/blue   **Change Colours:** All red.

GROVE UNITED

Chairman: J J Murphy   **Manager:** S Crowther.
Secretary: Mark Boothby, 68 Deneside Cres., Hazel Grove, Cheshire SK7 4NU (061 456 7610).
Ground: Half Moon Lane, Alfreton Rd, Offerto/ Lisburne Lane, Stockport.
Directions: Lisburne Lane is a continuation of Cherry Tree Lane off the A6 or Dialstone Lane. M56 jct 13, 4th exit at r'bout A626, at 2nd lights after one and a half miles turn right at Golden Hind pub.
Colours: Red/black/black   **Change Colours:** All blue.

HANLEY TOWN

Chairman: A Mountford   **Manager:** Terrence Lees.
Secretary: Mrs Ann Hassall, 38 Sandwick Cres., Birches Head, Stoke-on-Trent ST1 7HW (0782 289191).
Ground: Abbey Lane, Abbey Hulton, Hanley, Stoke-on-Trent (0782 267234).
Directions: M6 jct 16, A500 (5th exit), left under bridge, 6th right, go to bottom, left to lights (2 miles), turn right and through next lights, 2nd left is Fellbroke Lane, ground quarter mile on left (after houses).
Colours: Navy/navy/white   **Change Colours:** Red/red/white.

I.C.I. PHARMACEUTICALS

Chairman: David Black   **Manager:** Glyn H Ingham.
Secretary: Ian Merrill, 26 St Pauls Rd, Godley, Hyde, Cheshire SK14 2SW (061 368 0950).
Ground: I.C.I. Cals Social Centre, Alderley Park (0625 512902).
Directions: From A537 (Knutsford-Macclesfield) turn left at Monks Heath traffic lights (jct with A34). 1st right after 200yds in Matthews Garden Centre, immediate right, then left and follow road to Sports Centre.
Colours: All royal blue   **Change Colours:** Red & black/black/red.

KNUTSFORD

Chairman: Richard Walker   **Manager:** Kenneth Harrison (P McCurry:Res)
Secretary: Michael Binnie, The Bungalow, 145 Manchester Rd, Wilmslow SK9 2JN (0625 537909).
Ground: Manchester Road, Knutsford.
Directions: Situated on Knutsford to Altrincham & Warrington road.
Colours: Red/white (All blue:Res)   **Change Colours:** All blue (White or red:Res)

LINOTYPE

Chairman: G Smith   **Manager:** K Gardner (Bradley Smith:Res)
Secretary: Graham Fothergill, 11 St Marys Rd, Sale, Cheshire M33 1SB (061 969 4999).
Ground: British Airways Club, Clay Lane, Timperley, Altrincham (061 980 7354).
Directions: Clay Lane off Thorley Lane. Off A560 Altrincham-Stockport road (Timperley, Altrincham). corner.
Colours: White/black/red   **Change Colours:** Red & black/black/black.

MALPAS

Chairman: Peter Downey   **Manager:** Bernard Lloyd.
Secretary: Bernard Lloyd, 15 Springfield Avenue, Malpas, Cheshire SY14 8QD (0948 860812).
Ground: Malpas & District Sports Club, Oxheys, Wrexham Rd, Malpas, Cheshire (0948 860662).
Directions: On arrival in Malpas, up Church Str., carry on into Wrexham Rd, right into ground which is signposted.
Colours: Red/blue/red   **Change Colours:** All blue.

MIDDLEWICH ATHLETIC

Chairman: B Fletcher   **Manager:** P McAleer.
Secretary: Brian Longley, 16 Northway, Holmes Chapel CW4 7EF (0477 373310).
Ground: Seddon Street, Middlewich, Cheshire.
Directions: St Michaels Way to Webb Street, Seddon Street on left.
Colours: Red/white/red   **Change Colours:** All blue.

PILKINGTON RECREATION

Chairman: G Barlow   **Manager:** J Dawson.
Secretary: Dave Johnson, 4 Darent Rd, Haydock, Merseyside WA11 0HH (0744 34734).
Ground: Ruskin Drive, St Helens (0744 22893).
Directions: M6 jct 23, A580, left at 3rd lights, continue to Hope Anchor pub, right into Bishop Rd, continue to halt sign, follow road around to Ruskin Rd (2nd left). Ground in Ruskin Rd.
Colours: Green & yellow/green/green   **Change Cols:** Maroon & grey/maroon/maroon & grey.

POYNTON

Chairman: J Malam   **Manager:** Harry Daniels (I Cook:Res)
Secretary: Paul Burch, 24 Brooklands Avenue, Poynton, Cheshire SK12 1HZ (0625 871205).
Ground: London Road North, Poynton (0625 875765).
Directions: On main A523 between Macclesfield and Hazel Grove, approx 300yds from Poynton village centre traffic lights.
Colours: Red/black/black   **Change Colours:** White & blue/blue/blue.

RYLANDS

Chairman: Fredrick Bibby   **Manager:** T Selby.
Secretary: Ian Finchett, 31 Elizabeth Drive, Padgate, Warrington WA1 4JQ (0925 816911).
Ground: Gorsey Lane, Warrington (0925 35700).
Directions: M6 jct 21, A57 to Warrington, through two sets of lights, right at the Chevvies Rock'n Roll Cafe, carry straight on, ground on right.
Colours: Maroon & grey/maroon/grey   **Change Colours:** All yellow.

STYAL

Chairman: Ben Hurren   **Manager:**
Secretary: Sydney Plumley, 28 Strawberry Lane, Wilmslow SK9 6AQ (0625 532560).
Ground: Altrincham Road, Styal (0625 529303).
Directions: From M56 take A538 towards Wilmslow, 1st left after tunnel, before the Valley Lodge Hotel, ground two miles up on left.
Colours: Amber & yellow/red/white   **Change Colours:** All blue.

WHITCHURCH ALPORT

Chairman: J Jackson   **Manager:** P Wainwright.
Secretary: Andrew Mitchell, 8 Mill Cottages, Grindley Brook, Whitchurch, Salop SY13 4QH (0948 6150).
Ground: Yockings Park, Whitchurch, Shropshire.
Directions: To lights on A41 main through road, left up Talbot Street to Ready Mix concrete plant; ground 200yds further on left.
Colours: Claret/blue/claret   **Change Colours:** All green.

WILMSLOW ALBION

Chairman: Geoff Thornton   **Manager:** Tom Doodson (P Smith:Res).
Secretary: John Smith, 3 Holly Farm House, Isherwood Rd, Carrington, Urmston M31 4BH.
Ground: Oakwood Farm, Styal Rd, Styal, Wilmslow (0625 535823).
Directions: M56 jct 6, A538 towards Wilmslow, 1st left for Styal (Altrincham Rd) after Airport tunnel, and procced to T-junction passing Styal FC and Ship Inn - ground 2nd left opposite Quarry Bank Mill. A-Z ref 982A.
Colours: Yellow/blue/yellow   **Change Colours:** All blue.

WINNINGTON PARK

Chairman: A Blower   **Manager:** S Moore.
Secretary: Raymond Burrows, 43 Greenback Lane, Northwich CW8 1JP (0606 77195).
Ground: Moss Farm, Northwich (0606 79987)   **Previous Name:** I.C.I. Alkali.
Directions: A559 towards Chester, 1 mile outside Northwich turn left into Moss Rd which leads to Moss Farm.
Colours: Blue & white hoops/blue/blue   **Change Colours:** White/navy/white.

BURNLEY & DISTRICT LEAGUE

PREM. DIVISION	P	W	D	L	F	A	PTS
Trinity I.D.L.	22	17	4	1	75	28	55
Worsthorne A.	22	12	7	3	58	33	43
British Rail A.	22	13	4	5	47	27	43
Michelin	22	10	7	5	54	48	37
Ultra A.	22	9	6	7	41	39	33
Hapton	22	9	5	8	43	46	32
Brunshaw Hotel	22	9	3	10	41	36	30
Wellington Brit.	22	8	5	9	52	54	29
Bacup C.C.	22	8	1	13	51	60	25
Burnley Wood	22	5	1	16	35	57	16
Market Hotel	22	4	3	15	24	65	15
St Josephs	22	4	2	16	33	61	11

DIVISION ONE	P	W	D	L	F	A	PTS
Wellington United	20	16	0	4	65	31	48
British Rail B.	20	13	3	4	52	29	42
Warburton C.V.	22	13	2	5	59	24	41
Bank Hall	20	12	3	5	58	33	39
Ultra B.	20	9	6	5	54	41	33
B.B.C.O.B. A.	20	9	3	8	50	44	30
Worsthorne B.	20	7	4	9	47	50	25
Dickie Pinks	20	7	3	10	39	54	24
Bacup United	20	3	5	12	36	53	14
Padiham	20	3	2	15	22	60	11
Lucas	20	1	3	16	22	72	6

DIVISION TWO	P	W	D	L	F	A	PTS
Goodshaw Utd 'A	26	20	2	4	99	38	62
Falkland Engineering	26	19	4	3	115	50	61
Brunshaw Res.	26	18	4	4	92	39	58
Hapton Res	26	15	3	8	92	62	48
Marden Alers	26	14	4	8	91	67	46
Michelin Res	26	12	5	9	70	65	41
Cliviger	26	10	6	10	58	52	36
Generals	26	10	3	13	57	64	33
Duke of York	26	9	3	14	62	75	30
B.B.C.	26	7	8	11	61	62	29
B'field Feathers	26	7	5	14	51	78	26
Free Gardeners	26	7	2	17	57	111	23
Ashworth Arms	26	6	4	16	44	80	22
B.B.C.O.B. 'B.	26	1	1	24	34	140	4

DIVISION THREE	P	W	D	L	F	A	PTS
Padiham S.C.	24	17	4	3	111	44	55
P.H.P.	24	16	5	3	87	35	53
Read United	24	14	6	4	68	35	48
Riverside	24	13	5	6	56	35	44
Jovial Hatters	24	13	2	9	53	55	41
K.S.C. 'B.	24	11	5	8	68	54	38
Bly Wood Res	24	10	3	11	72	59	33
St Leonards	24	8	6	10	62	57	30
Express Gifts	24	8	6	10	56	52	30
Goodshaw Utd 'B.	24	8	6	10	57	64	30
Laund Rovers	24	6	8	10	37	50	26
Y.C.W.	24	1	3	20	30	127	6
Mission United	24	1	1	22	40	140	4

TETLEY WALKER
WEST CHESHIRE A.F. LEAGUE

President: Ken Halsall

Secretary: Les Bullock, 8 Cambridge Road, Bronborough, Wirral L62 7JA

DIVISION ONE	P	W	D	L	F	A	Pts
CAMMELL LAIRD	20	20	5	5	72	32	45
SHELL	30	18	5	7	54	34	41
HESWALL	30	15	10	5	70	36	40
CHRISTLETON	30	14	10	6	60	36	38
BROMBORO. P.	30	14	9	7	59	37	37
MERSEY POLICE	30	16	4	10	69	45	36
POOULTON V.	30	14	7	9	56	44	35
MERSEY ROYAL	30	13	4	13	45	44	30
GEN. CHEMICALS	30	12	6	12	37	49	30
ASHVILLE	30	11	5	14	47	52	27
STORK	30	9	7	14	44	47	25
VAUXHALL MTRS	30	7	9	14	38	48	23
NEWTON	30	8	7	15	40	62	23
UPTON ATH. A.	30	8	3	19	34	82	19
CAPENHURST	30	4	8	18	34	68	16
MORETON	30	4	7	19	24	67	15

DIVISION TWO	P	W	D	L	F	A	Pts
POULTON RES.	34	23	7	4	74	35	53
CAMMELL L. RES	34	23	6	5	106	42	52
HESWALL RES	34	20	10	4	85	58	50
BROMBORO. RES	34	18	10	6	75	50	46
BLACON Y.C.	34	18	7	9	86	63	43
MOND RANGERS	34	14	8	12	67	61	36
M.ROYAL R.	34	10	15	9	72	61	35
ASHVILLE RES	34	13	9	12	52	52	35
MANOR ATH.	34	13	5	16	61	65	31
WILLASTON	34	10	9	15	52	62	29
VAUXHALL RES	34	11	6	17	57	68	28
CHRISTL. RES	34	10	8	16	52	72	28
ST WERBURGHS	34	8	11	15	58	59	27
RIVACRE SC	34	11	6	17	71	87	*28
MERSEY P. RES	34	8	9	17	45	76	25
WEST KIRBY	34	7	10	17	55	73	24
STORK RES	34	7	10	17	57	86	24
SHELL RES	34	4	10	20	47	102	18

PLAYER OF THE YEAR: T FARRELL (CHRISTLETON)

* - 2PTS DEDUCTED RULE INFRINGEMENT

DIVISION ONE

Home Club	1	2	3	4	5	6	7	8	9	10	11	12	13	14	15	16
1. Ashville	xxx	0-2	0-3	5-1	0-3	2-1	0-0	2-3	3-1	0-0	1-2	2-0	0-1	4-3	7-2	2-0
2. Bromborough P.	3-3	xxx	1-1	3-2	3-3	1-2	2-2	2-1	2-0	3-0	3-0	1-1	0-0	1-2	3-0	5-0
3. Cammell Laird	5-0	3-2	xxx	0-1	2-1	2-0	2-1	3-2	1-1	5-0	3-2	2-1	2-3	3-1	3-0	3-1
4. Capenhurst	0-1	2-5	1-1	xxx	0-4	2-3	0-4	1-0	1-0	4-0	2-2	1-4	0-2	0-0	0-1	1-2
5. Christleton	3-0	1-1	0-0	5-0	xxx	0-0	1-1	3-0	1-1	2-0	3-0	2-2	3-0	1-1	2-1	2-1
6. General Chem.	2-1	0-1	0-5	3-2	2-1	xxx	1-4	2-1	0-2	2-1	1-1	1-1	1-0	1-3	1-3	2-1
7. Heswall	2-1	0-1	3-3	2-2	6-1	2-0	xxx	2-0	4-2	1-2	3-1	2-1	6-2	3-1	7-0	2-2
8. Mersey Royal	0-1	1-0	2-1	3-2	2-0	4-1	2-0	xxx	1-1	2-1	2-0	2-2	1-0	0-2	2-1	1-1
9. Merseyside Pol.	3-0	1-0	1-4	5-2	3-1	1-2	1-1	2-3	xxx	2-3	3-0	4-1	6-1	3-1	2-0	2-0
10. Moreton	2-5	2-2	0-2	2-2	0-3	1-1	1-3	0-3	2-5	xxx	0-1	0-2	0-2	3-1	0-2	2-0
11. Newton	3-1	1-3	3-4	1-1	2-2	2-0	3-3	0-2	0-3	4-0	xxx	1-0	0-4	1-0	1-1	2-4
12. Poulton Victoria	1-2	0-2	1-2	5-2	3-2	3-0	1-1	2-1	3-2	2-1	3-2	xxx	0-0	2-1	3-2	3-1
13. Shell	1-0	2-0	1-3	1-0	1-2	1-1	1-0	4-1	4-1	1-1	6-2	2-2	xxx	2-0	4-0	2-0
14. Stork	2-2	4-4	1-0	1-1	1-1	1-2	0-1	2-0	1-4	5-0	1-2	2-0	0-1	xxx	3-1	0-4
15. Upton Ath. Assn	2-2	2-0	1-4	2-0	2-4	0-5	1-1	3-2	1-4	1-0	3-1	0-5	1-3	0-4	xxx	1-7
16. Vauxhall Motors	1-0	1-3	1-0	1-1	1-3	0-0	1-3	2-2	2-2	0-0	0-0	1-2	1-2	0-0	2-0	xxx

DIVISION TWO

Home Club	1	2	3	4	5	6	7	8	9	10	11	12	13	14	15	16	17	18
1. Ashville Res	xxx	1-1	0-3	1-2	3-1	1-2	1-3	2-1	2-2	0-3	1-1	2-2	1-0	4-2	2-0	1-0	2-0	0-0
2. Blacon Y.C.	2-3	xxx	1-0	0-4	2-1	6-2	3-1	1-1	1-2	3-2	1-2	5-2	2-2	6-2	2-2	2-1	3-3	2-0
3. Bromboro. Res	3-1	1-1	xxx	1-0	4-1	2-3	3-2	4-2	1-0	1-1	1-1	2-3	2-0	4-1	0-0	3-1	3-1	3-1
4. Cammell L. Res	2-1	1-3	4-2	xxx	3-0	1-1	3-1	4-1	4-1	1-2	0-0	4-1	2-2	3-2	4-4	3-2	5-0	6-1
5. Christleton Res	3-0	2-3	2-2	3-8	xxx	0-2	3-2	1-1	0-0	2-2	0-1	1-4	1-1	0-1	5-4	3-2	4-2	0-0
6. Heswall Res	4-3	3-2	3-0	0-5	4-1	xxx	1-0	0-2	3-0	3-2	5-0	3-3	1-1	4-2	2-0	2-2	2-3	3-3
7. Manor Athletic	0-3	1-4	0-3	3-7	3-1	1-1	xxx	1-0	3-2	5-0	1-2	4-0	2-5	2-1	1-1	2-2	2-1	1-0
8. Mers. Royal Res	1-2	1-1	3-3	3-3	2-1	3-5	2-3	xxx	6-2	1-1	1-1	1-1	2-1	0-0	2-2	0-0	0-2	1-1
9. M Police Res	0-0	4-3	2-2	0-7	1-1	1-2	2-1	0-2	xxx	1-1	0-2	1-1	2-1	4-2	4-2	0-3	4-1	0-2
10. Mond Rangers	1-0	1-3	2-2	0-2	0-1	1-1	2-1	2-6	3-0	xxx	2-2	2-4	2-1	4-1	4-1	5-1	1-0	1-0
11. P Victoria Res	2-0	5-2	1-2	1-0	4-0	1-4	1-0	2-2	1-0	xxx	4-1	3-1	2-3	4-2	3-1	3-0	2-1	
12. Rivacre SC	3-3	2-6	3-4	0-4	2-4	4-5	2-3	0-4	0-3	2-1	0-4	xxx	1-1	1-0	3-1	2-3	6-0	5-1
13. St Werburghs	2-3	2-3	3-0	0-1	3-0	1-1	4-2	2-1	4-1	3-3	2-3	3-2	xxx	3-3	3-0	1-4	0-0	1-3
14. Shell Res	0-0	2-5	2-2	2-3	1-4	1-5	1-1	4-8	3-3	1-5	0-1	0-5	1-1	xxx	1-3	3-1	1-1	1-8
15. Stork Res	1-4	2-1	0-4	3-2	0-1	1-1	1-5	3-3	0-4	1-5	0-3	1-0	4-1	xxx	2-2	2-2	3-1	
16. Vauxhall M. Res	1-3	4-0	5-2	0-6	1-2	1-2	1-0	3-5	3-0	4-1	1-3	1-1	2-1	0-0	2-1	xxx	2-2	3-1
17. West Kirby	2-2	1-4	0-2	0-1	2-1	0-3	2-2	2-3	3-0	6-3	1-1	2-3	1-1	7-1	2-2	3-0	xxx	4-1
18. Willaston	2-0	0-2	0-1	1-1	2-2	2-1	0-2	1-1	2-2	1-3	0-2	3-2	1-0	1-2	4-4	3-0	3-2	xxx

WEST CHESHIRE LEAGUE CLUBS 1992-93
(Divisional Constitutions Unchanged From 1991-92)

ASHVILLE
Chairman: Kenny Baker
Secretary: E W Parker, 26 Mere Heath, Moreton, Wirral L46 3SH.
Ground & Directions: Villa Park Cross Lane, Wallasey Village, Wallasey (051 638 2127). Cross Lane is off Leasowe Road, entrance behind Wallesey Rugby Club. Merseyrail to Wallesey Village - cross road to Mosslands Drive, School Lane on right, ground under bridge.
Colours: White/black/black.   **Club Sponsors:** Wager.   **Founded:** 1949

BLACON YOUTH CLUB
Chairman: Peter Barnes
Secretary: Colin Lawson, 54 Adelaide Road, Blacon, Chester CH1 5SZ (0244 375508).
Ground & Directions: Cairns Crescent Playing Fields, Blacon, Chester. Parkgate Road to the Ben Whitehouse Garage, approach new island, 3rd exit into Blacon, along Blacon Avenue to Parade Shops (RHS), left opposite, 1st right, Western Avenue 2nd right, Melbourne Road, 1st right, Cairns Crescent. Buses 1,2,2a,2e to Blacon from Chester bus station.
Colours: Black & white stripes/black/black   **Founded:** 1964

BROMBOROUGH POOL
Chairman: Harry W Bevan
Secretary: Alan Pringle, 3 Willow Grove, Moreton, Wirral L46 0TU (051 677 0055).
Ground & Directions: The Green, South View Road, Bromborough Pool (051 645 3476). A41 from Ellesmere Port and Chester to Bromborough. Into Dock Road at Port Sunlight Works, past Fire Station, left into Pool Village, 1st right down Village Green - pavilion on far left of green. Buses C1,C3,C4 from Chester - alight at Bromborough Pool Lane. 41 MPTE from Birkenhead.
Colours: All blue   **Club Sponsors:** Ocean Software   **Founded:** 1884

CAMMELL LAIRD
Chairman: Arthur Parker
Secretary: Ray Steele, 46 Croft Avenue, Bromborough, Wirral L62 2BR.
Ground & Directions: Kirklands, St Peters Road, Rock Ferry, Birkenhead (051 645 5991). A41 New Chester Road to Rock Ferry - turn down Proctor Road - ground behind Crosville Bus Station.
Colours: All blue   **Club Sponsors:** MET ARC   **Founded:** 1900

CAPENHURST
Chairman: Dave Kilfoyle
Secretary: Roger Knight, 8 Wenlock Gardens, Great Sutton, South Wirral L66 2QZ (051 355 5736).
Ground & Directions: Capenhurst Sports Ground, Capenhurst Lane, Capenhurst (051 339 4101). A41 Birkenhead/Chester road to Capenhurst lights, down Capenhurst Lane, over railway, past BNLF factory, ground on right. Crosville bus C1 to Capenhurst lights on A41. Train to Capenhurst (Wirral Line).
Colours: Claret & sky   **Club Sponsors:** BNF Capenhurst   **Founded:** 1952

CHRISTLETON
Chairman: Ron Mayers
Secretary: Kenneth Price, 35 Canadian Avenue, Hoole, Chester CH2 3HQ (0244 313513).
Ground & Directions: Little Heath, Christleton (0244 332153). Turn off A51 Chester/Northwich road at sign to Littleton and Christleton - follow road to pond on the left and turn left. Bus from Chester to Christleton.
Colours: Red/black/red   **Covered Accom:** Y   **Founded:** 1966

GENERAL CHEMICALS
Chairman: Michael Jacques
Secretary: Roy Nickson, 44 York Street, Runcorn, Cheshire WA7 5BA (0928 576632).
Ground & Directions: ICI (Weston) Club, Sandy Lane, Weston Point, Runcorn. M56 to Runcorn Expressway - take Castner Kellner turn off. 1 mile from Runcorn (BR). Bus to Weston Point.
Previous Name: Castner Kellner   **Covered Accomdation:** 100   **Floodlights:** Y
Colours: Navy & white stripes   **Founded:** 1958

HESWALL
Chairman: Robbie Allen
Secretary: Jake Horan, 13 Reedville, Bebington, Wirral L63 2HS (051 644 0459).
Ground & Directions: Gayton Park, Brimstage Road, Heswall, Wirral (051 342 7523). From Birkenhead; Barnston Road, left into Brimstage Road, then first right. From Chester; Chester High Road to Gayton r-bout, Brimstage Rd then 1st right. From West Kirkby; Telegraph, left at Gayton r-bout then 1st right. 1 mile from Heswall Hills (BR).
Colours: Yellow/blue/yellow   **Club Sponsors:** Allied Dunbar   **Founded:** 1891
Record Attendance: 1,000 v Sheffield Wednesday 7/8/87.

MANOR ATHLETIC
Chairman: Tony Bell
Secretary: Stewart Galtress, 3 Centurion Close, Meols, Wirral L47 7BZ (051 632 3211).
Ground & Directions: Unilever Sports Ground, Bromborough. A41 Chester New Road to Candy (Kelvinator) factory, left (from Birkenhead) into Old Hall Road, 1st right. Buses to Green Lane, Bromborough.
Colours: White/black/red   **Club Sponsors:** SDM Computer Services **Founded:** 1968

MERSEY ROYAL
Chairman: Tony Nelson   **Secretary:** Billy Morris, 28 Charlwood Close, 3rd Avenue, Manor Green, Beechwood, Birkenhead L43 9XF (051 678 7161).
Ground & Directions: (See note below) Valley Road, Bidston, Birkenhead (051 652 0339). M53 jct 1, signs to Birkenhead A533, left at r-bout, up hill, 1st left after lights. Buses 18,98,99 to Hurrell Road, Bidston.
Important Note: Due to ground reconstruction Mersey Royal may play elsewhere during 92-93.
Colours: Red & white/red/red   **Founded:** 1946

MERSEYSIDE POLICE
Chairman: Pat Carraghan.
Secretary: George Todd, 14 Crowther Street, St Helens WA10 4NH (0744 55845).
Ground & Directions: Fairfield Sports Ground, Prescot Road, Liverpool L7 0JD (051 709 6010). From city travel via Kensington towards Old Swan, into Prescot Road - ground on corner with Fairfield Street. One and a half miles from Limestreet (BR).
Colours: Blue/white/blue   **Club Sponsors:** Davies & Co, surveyors **Founded:** 1885
Record Attendance: 1,500 v Kent Police, National Police Final 22/5/73.

MOND RANGERS

Chairman: Roy Roberts
Secretary: John Worthington, 5 Bellingham Drive, Runcorn WA7 4XN (0928 567477).
Ground & Directions: Ground-share at General Chemicals FC (see preceding page).
Colours: Sky/blue/blue.　　　　**Club Sponsors:** Comid Engineering　　**Founded:** 1967

MORETON

Chairman: Tommy Potter
Secretary: A Heffernan, 30 Appleton Drive, Upton, Wirral L49 1SJ.
Ground & Directions: 73 Upton Road, Moreton, Wirral (051 677 3235). M53 jct 2, follow signs to Moreton - ground quarter mile on right. MPTE bus 3 passes ground.
Colours: Jade & navy stripes/navy/navy　**Club Sponsors:** Cuemasters　　**Founded:** 1900

NEWTON

Chairman: Fred Sherlock
Secretary: Alan Dabner, 41 St David Road, Claughton, Birkenhead L43 8SW (051 652 5648).
Ground & Directions: Millcroft, Frankby Road, Greasby, Wirral (051 677 8382). M53 to West Kirby, left at lights, right at lights at Upton Cross, ground 3 miles on left in Frankby Road. MPTE bus 96 from Birkenhead Woodside passes ground, MPTE 78 terminus 3 mins walk.
Colours: Yellow/green/yellow　　　**Club Sponsors:**　　　　　　　　**Founded:** 1933

POULTON VICTORIA

Chairman: Tom Quinn
Secretary: H Deery, 15 Dorset Drive, Irby, Wirral L61 8SX.
Ground & Directions: Victoria Park, Rankin Street, Wallesey (051 638 3559). Wallesey Docks signs off M53, right into Limelin Lane by Vics Club, Rankin Street 6th left. Buses 10 & 11 to Gorsey Lane from Birkenhead. 20 mins from Birkenhead North (BR).
Colours: All royal blue　　　　　　**Club Sponsors:** Windsors (Wallesey)　**Founded:** 1935
Previous Ground: Wallace Park 1935-72

RIVACRE ROSSFIELD

Chairman: D Harvey
Secretary: K R Hornby, 310 Chester Road, Whitby, Ellesmere Port L66 2NY.
Ground & Directions: Rivacre Sports & Social Club, Rivacre Road, Overpool, Ellesmere Port (051 355 2574). From lights at junction of Rossmore and Overpool Roads (cemetery gates), proceed down Rivacre Road - club on right. Crosville buses C3 & C4 to Overpool Cemetery.
Colours: Gold/black/black　　　　　**Club Sponsors:** Rivacre Social Club　**Founded:** 1954

ST WERBURGHS

Chairman: John Kenyon
Secretary: John Beresford, 2a Cedar Grove, Hoole, Chester CH2 3LQ (0244 346792).
Ground & Directions: Catholic High School, Old Wrexham Road, Handbridge, Chester. From M53 end; right, right at 2nd r'bout onto dual carriageway, right at 2nd r'bout over Grosvenor Bridge, left into Overleigh Road after 400 yds, Old Wrexham Road on right 200 on. Handridge bus every 15 mins from Chester; ask for Catholic High School.
Colours: Blue & black stripes/navy/yellow　**Club Sponsors:** McEwans Lager　　**Founded:** 1958

SHELL

Chairman: Roy Jones
Secretary: Joseph Davies, 35 Glencoe Road, Great Sutton, South Wirral L66 4NA (051 339 0652).
Ground & Directions: Chester Road, Whitby, Ellesmere Port (051 355 2704/2364). A5117 turn right at 3rd island coming from M53 jct 10 (4th coming from jct 10); club on right. All buses to Ellesmere Port (BR), or C3 from Chester.
Colours: Yellow/red/red　　　　　**Sponsors:** Shell Uk/Portions Control Ltd　**Founded:** 1924

STORK

Chairman: Gerry Brown
Secretary: S Carter, 7 Elm Rd, Bebington, Wirral L43 8PH.
Ground & Directions: Unilever Sports Ground Bromborough (see Manor Athletic opposite).
Colours: All green　　　　　　　**Club Sponsors:** Quartz Cleaning Services **Founded:** 1920

UPTON ATHLETIC ASSOCIATION

Chairman: Peter Upton
Secretary: Barry Gaulton, St Marks Crescent, Whitby, Ellesmere Port L66 2XD (051 339 1504).
Ground & Directions: Cheshire County Council Sports & Social Club, Plas Newton Lane, Chester CH2 1PR (0244 318167). At end of M53, right, right at A41 r'bout (signed Zoo). Car park and clubhouse on left after half mile; ground over bridge. C42 from Chester bus station to Plas Newton Lane - ground 200 yds down lane.
Colours: All blue　　　　　　　**Club Sponsors:** Durwen Group　　　**Founded:** 1964

VAUXHALL MOTORS

Chairman: Tony Woodley　　　　　　　　　　**Floodlights:** Y
Secretary: S M McInerney, 12 Merton Rd, Gt Sutton, South Wirral L66 2SW.
Ground & Directions: Vauxhall Sports Ground, Rivacre Road, Ellesmere Port (051 327 2115). Turn into Hooton Green off A41 at Hooton crossroa, left at 'T' junction, right at next 'T' junction, ground 100 yds on right.
Colours: All sky　　　　　　　　**Club Sponsors:** James Edwards　　**Founded:** 1963

WEST KIRBY

Chairman: Ken Raine.
Secretary: Mrs Carole Paisey, 80a Banks Road, West Kirby L48 0RE (051 625 6936).
Ground & Directions: Marine Park, Greenbank Road, West Kirby (051 625 7734). From Concourse, West Kirby, along Orrysdale Road and Anglesey Road into Greenbank Road.
Colours: White/black/black　　　　**Club Sponsors:** Don Walker Insurance　**Founded:** 1895

WILLASTON

Chairman: Martin Collins
Secretary: Harvey Rushton, 31 Moss Close, Willaston, South Wirral L62 2XQ (051 327 7419).
Ground & Directions: Recreation Ground, Neston Road, Willaston, South Wirral. Off A41 at Hooton crossroads, along Hooton Road and through Willaston; ground on right behing Primary School.
Colours: All white　　　　　　　**Club Sponsors:** Andrew Meadows Ltd　**Founded:** 1962

WEST CHESHIRE LEAGUE, AND OTHER LOCAL CUPS 1991-92

PYKE CUP
First Round

Capenhurst v Upton Athletic Assoc.	1-2	Cammell Laird v Bromborough Pool	2-1
Mersey Royal v Poulton Victoria	0-1	Christleton v General Chemicals	4-2
Stork v Vauxhall Motors	1-5	Newton v Heswall	1-2
Merseyside Police v Moreton	5-1	Shell v Ashville	2-1

Quarter Finals

Christleton v Upton Athletic A.	0-0,5-4	Poulton Victoria v Heswall	3-4
Shell v Cammell Laird	1-4	Mersey Police v Vauxhall Mtrs	0-0,5-5,4-2

Semi-Finals

Heswall v Christleton	2-1	Merseyside Police v Cammell Laird	0-5

Final: Cammell Laird 4, Heswall 0

CASTELMAINE XXXX COMPETITION
Semi-Finals (Divisional Winners)

Capenhurst v Christleton	3-4	Ashville v Bromborough Pool	3-4

Final: Bromborough Pool 4, Christleton 3

BILL WEIGHT MEMORIAL TROPHY
Semi-Finals

Cammell Laird Reserves v Cammell Laird	0-1	Poulton Victoria v Heswall Reserves	2-3*(aet)*

Final: Heswall Reserves 2, Cammell Laird 1

WIRRAL SENIOR CUP
First Round

Mersey Royal v Vauxhall Motors	0-2	Poulton Victoria v Shell	1-3
Capenhurst v Newton	2-0	Stork v Ashville	2-2,2-0
Rivacre Sports Club v Moreton	1-0		

Quarter Finals

Bromborough Pool v Stork	2-1	Capenhurst v Vauxhall Motors	0-6
Cammell Laird v Shell	5-1	Heswall v Rivacre Sports Club	4-1

Semi-Finals

Vauxhall v Bromborough Pool 2-2,1-1*(away goals)*		Heswall v Cammell Laird	1-0

Final: Heswall 2, Bromborough Pool 1

DURWEN GROUP WEST CHESHIRE LEAGUE BOWL
First Round

West Kirby v Merseyside Police	2-1	Vauxhall Motors v Stork	2-2,1-0

Second Round

Willaston v Cammell Laird	0-1	Mersey Royal v Blacon Youth Club	2-1
Christleton v West Kirby	0-1	Manor Athletic v Rivacre SC	4-1
Bromborough Pool v Poulton Victoria	2-1	Vauxhall Motors v Mond Rangers	3-4
St Werburghs *w/o* Ashville *(disqualified)*		Shell v Heswall	1-5

Quarter Finals

Heswall v West Kirby	2-3	Mersey Royal v Cammell Laird	3-1
Mond Rangers v Manor Athletic	3-2	Bromborough Pool v St Werburghs	2-3

Semi-Finals

Mersey Royal v Mond Rangers	1-1,1-1,0-1	West Kirby v St Werburghs	0-1

Final: Mond Rangers 3, St Werburghs 1

WIRRAL AMATEUR CUP
Second Round

Manor Athletic v Mersey Royal	3-1	Poulton Victoria v Heswall	2-1
Rossfield United v Cammell Laird	0-3	Capenhurst v Stork	1-2
Shell v Vauxhall Motors	1-3	Ashville v West Kirby	2-3
Willaston v Bromborough Pool	0-2	Bronze Social v Great Eastern	4-0

Quarter Finals

Manor Athletic v Poulton Victoria	1-3	Cammell Laird v Stork	2-0
Vauxhall Motors v West Kirby	1-2	Bromborough Pool v Bronze Social	5-0

Semi-Finals

West Kirby v Bromborough Pool	2-0	Poulton Victoria v Cammell Laird	2-0

Final: Bromborough Pool 2, Poulton Victoria 0

CHESTER SENIOR CUP
Quarter Finals

Blacon Youth Club v Bromfield Victoria	4-1	Manweb v Christleton	1-2
Sunblest v St Werburghs	1-3	Upton Athletic Association v Cholmondeley Arms	3-1

Semi-Finals

Christleton v Blacon Youth Club	3-0	St Werburghs v Upton Athletic Association	1-2

Final: Christleton 2, Upton Athletic Association 1

LANCASHIRE AMATEUR CUP
Final: Merseyside Police 3, Rochdale St Clements 1

RUNCORN DISTRICT CUP
Final: General Chemicals 3, Cholmondeley Arms 2

WEST CHESHIRE LEAGUE CENTENARY FIXTURES
Tetley Walker West Cheshire League 1, Guiseley 1
Tetley Walker West Cheshire League 2, Green Insulation Mid-Cheshire League 0

Prescot 2, Bootle 3 - Bass North West Counties League Division One, 26/12/91. Desperate Bootle defending as Prescot seek a late equaliser. Photo - Rob Ruddock.

Penrith 1, Nantwich Town 0 - Bass North West Counties League Division One, 21/9/91. With a penalty, Dave Phizacklea scores the only goal of the game. Photo - Alan Watson.

The Crystal Villa keeper saves in a 1-2 defeat at Earle in the Liverpool Combination. Photo - Bob Jones.

NORTHERN COUNTIES EAST LEAGUE

President: H F Catt, Esq.

Chairman: C Morris.

Hon. Secretary: B Wood,
6 Restmore Avenue, Guiseley, Leeds LS20 9DG (0943 874558).

THIRD TIME LUCKY FOR NORTH SHIELDS

After suffering the disappointment of finishing as runners-up to Bridlington Town and then Guiseley in their first two seasons in the Northern Counties East Football League, North Shields finally made it third time lucky by running away with the title, winning the championship by a large margin of 24 points.

The North East side lost only two matches all season, one to local neighbours and rivals Spennymoor United in early September, and then to Winterton Rangers in Mid-February. That second defeat proved to be to Winterton's cost; the following week they travelled to Appleby Park to play Shields again, and were beaten 10-0! In addition to the League title, North Shields also collected the Presidents Cup, beating Brigg Town 2-1 in the final at Harrogate Town's Wetherby Road ground, and the 'G & W' Engineering League Challenge Cup in which they defeated Armthorpe Welfare 5-0 in the final at Ossett Albion FC. It was a truly remarkable season for manager Colin Richardson and his team, and let's hope that the club can overcome their admininistration difficulties and take up their rightful place in the H.F.S. Loans League next season.

Sutton Town finished as runners-up in the League with Denaby United pipping North Ferriby United for third place - a turn around for the South Yorkshire club under manager John Reed, after experiencing a traumatic twelve months prior to the start of the season.

The First Division title was a closer affair, with Stocksbridge Park Steels winning the race only one point ahead of Pickering Town and Bradley Rangers. Stocksbridge and Pickering have now obtained promotion to the Premier Division, but Bradley suffered a bad blow towards the end of the season when their clubhouse and dressing rooms were totally burnt down.

In national competitions, we were pleased to see our previous three champion clubs, Guiseley, Bridlington Town and Emley all reach the First Proper of the F.A. Cup, along with the League's newboys for 1992-93, Lincoln United. However, after being spoilt by success in the F.A. Vase in previous seasons, this year we could only manage to reach the Fourth Round with Brigg Town, who lost to eventual Semi-Finalists Bamber Bridge after two nail-biting matches.

Kevin Motley, Publicity Officer.

North Shields FC, Northern Counties (East) League champions 1991-92. Back Row (L/R): George Cook (Asst Manager), Ian MacKenzie, Dave Woodcock, Shaun Dunn, Graham Mole, Bobby Strong, Dave Callaghan, Graham Jones, Ted Collingson. Front: Gary Nicholson, Steve Pyle, Neil Howie, Martin Hamilton, Barrie Wardrobe, Ged Parkinson, Brian Jennings. Photo - James Wright.

Premier Division	P	W	D	L	F	A	PTS
North Shields	36	31	3	2	109	14	96
Sutton Town	36	21	9	6	79	41	72
Denaby United	36	22	3	11	78	47	*68
Nth Ferriby Utd	36	19	8	9	63	45	65
Spennymoor Utd	36	17	8	11	61	45	59
Sheffield	36	16	9	11	71	48	57
Maltby Miners W.	36	16	8	12	61	61	56
Brigg Town	36	15	7	14	44	42	52
Thackley	36	14	9	13	45	45	51
Ossett Albion	36	14	8	14	40	51	50
Belper Town	36	12	11	13	48	50	47
Ossett Town	36	11	12	13	48	57	45
Armthorpe Welfare	36	12	9	15	57	67	45
Liversedge	36	11	8	17	54	72	41
Winterton Rgrs	36	10	5	21	53	78	35
Pontefract Coll.	36	9	7	20	36	71	34
Eccleshill Utd	36	7	10	19	38	83	31
Harrogate R'way	36	5	8	23	31	60	23
Glasshoughton Wf.	36	5	8	23	35	74	23

* - One point deducted.

Leading Scorers:
M Culley (Sutton Town) 36
S Pyle (North Shields) 28
R Spotswood (Sheffield) 26

Division One	P	W	D	L	F	A	PTS
Stocksbridge PS	30	19	5	6	71	34	62
Pickering Town	30	19	4	7	84	46	61
Bradley Rangers	30	18	7	5	59	26	61
Yorks Amateur	30	18	3	9	56	27	57
Hallam	30	17	6	7	57	36	57
Hall Road Rgrs	30	17	5	8	68	36	56
Rossington Main	30	13	5	12	44	48	44
R.E.S. Parkgate	30	12	5	13	41	59	41
Immingham Town	30	12	4	14	48	64	40
Worsbrough Bridge	30	11	6	13	44	43	39
Garforth Town	30	10	5	15	48	44	35
Tadcaster Albion	30	8	4	18	37	62	28
Selby Town	30	8	4	18	32	67	28
York R'way I.	30	6	7	17	32	77	25
Brodsworth M.W.	30	6	6	18	45	72	24
Hatfield Main	30	7	2	21	36	71	*22

* - One point deducted

Leading Scorers:
T Jones (Stocksbridge) 20
R L Mills (Stocksbridge) 18
S A Frith (Stocksbridge) 16

Reserve Div.	P	W	D	L	F	A	PTS
Emley Res	28	22	3	3	101	29	69
Guiseley Res	28	19	6	3	67	30	63
Nth Ferriby Res	28	17	7	4	70	43	58
Hall Rd Rgrs Res	28	13	7	8	54	45	46
Tadcaster A. Res	28	12	8	8	59	46	44
Yorks Amtr Res	28	13	5	10	54	43	44
Armthorpe W. Res	28	12	8	8	50	49	44
Eccleshill U. Res	28	13	4	11	53	44	43
Liversedge Res	30	11	6	11	42	50	39
Thackley Res	28	9	10	9	46	47	37
Frasley C. Res	28	8	12	8	35	37	36
Bradley Rgrs Res	28	11	2	15	44	49	35
Brodsworth MW Res	28	9	6	13	43	45	33
Harrogate T. Res	28	9	4	15	54	56	31
Pontefract Res	28	8	5	15	33	65	29
Glasshoughton Res	28	8	3	17	34	62	27
Ossett Town Res	28	7	5	16	37	58	26
Ossett Alb. Res	28	4	8	16	34	63	20
Garforth Town Res	28	4	5	19	20	62	17

Leading Scorers:
L Corbally (Guiseley Res) 25
J E Forman (Hall Road Res) 22
A Rae (Eccleshill Utd Res) 21

'G & W' ENGINEERING LEAGUE CUP 1991-92

First Round

Bradley Rangers v R.E.S. Parkgate	0-1
Yorkshire Amateur v Garforth Town	2-0

Immingham Town v Rossington Main — 0-2

Second Round

Armthorpe Welfare v Tadcaster Albion	5-0
Hallam v Eccleshill	1-1,1-1,1-2 *(at Ecc.)*
Liversedge v Thackley	2-1
North Ferriby United v Pickering Town	3-0
Sheffield v Stocksbridge Park Steels	2-1
Spennymoor United v Belper Town	2-1
Winterton Rangers v North Shields	0-6
Yorkshire Amateur v Ossett Albion	2-1

Glasshoughton Welfare v Hall Road Rangers	0-1
Hatfield Main v Denaby United	0-2
Maltby Miners Welfare v R.E.S. Parkgate	4-3
Ossett Town v Selby Town	2-0
Pontefract Collieries v Harrogate Railway Athletic	0-5
Sutton Town v Brodsworth Miners Welfare	10-0
Worsbrough Bridge Miners Welfare v Brigg Town	1-0
York Railway Institute v Rossington Main	0-4

Third Round

Eccleshill United v North Shields	2-1
Sheffield v Liversedge	2-0
Rossington Main v Maltby Miners Welfare	1-2
Spennymoor United v Sutton Town	2-5

Harrogate Railway Athletic v Armthorpe Welfare	0-1
North Ferriby Utd v Yorkshire Amateur	0-0,3-2
Hall Rd v Denaby	2-1 *(Cup-tied player-tie to Denaby)*
Worsbrough Bridge Miners Welfare v Ossett Town	4-1

Fourth Round

Maltby Miners Welfare v Sheffield	3-1
Sutton Town v North Ferriby United	2-1

Armthorpe Welfare v Worsborough Bridge Miners	W-0
Denaby United v North Shields	0-3

Semi-Finals

Sutton Town v North Shields	0-3

Maltby Miners Welfare v Armthorpe Welfare — 0-1

Final (at Ossett Albion FC): North Shields 5, Armthorpe Welfare 0

PRESIDENT'S CUP 1991-92

Semi-Finals

North Shields v Spennymoor United — 5-0   Stocksbridge Park Steels v Brigg Town — 2-3

Final (at Harrogate Town FC): North Shields 2, Brigg Town 1

RESERVE CHALLENGE CUP: Winners: Guiseley Reserves. Runners-up: Ossett Town Reserves.

PREMIER DIVISION RESULT CHART 1991-92

HOME TEAM	1	2	3	4	5	6	7	8	9	10	11	12	13	14	15	16	17	18	19
1. Armthorpe	*	3-4	0-2	0-4	1-2	5-1	1-0	1-1	0-0	2-2	0-2	1-2	1-2	1-1	2-4	2-1	1-0	2-0	2-1
2. Belper Town	0-0	*	0-2	4-0	3-2	0-0	2-0	4-3	0-0	1-1	1-2	0-1	1-3	2-2	3-0	1-3	1-3	1-1	1-1
3. Brigg Town	2-1	0-1	*	0-2	0-1	1-0	1-0	4-0	3-1	2-0	2-4	1-1	2-2	0-0	2-3	0-2	2-3	1-0	1-0
4. Denaby Utd	5-1	4-1	2-0	*	4-0	2-1	2-0	2-0	3-1	1-1	0-1	1-3	1-0	1-0	2-1	2-1	2-2	2-1	4-2
5. Eccleshill	3-2	1-1	0-3	4-3	*	2-2	0-2	2-4	0-0	0-3	0-2	1-1	0-1	0-4	1-5	2-2	1-3	1-1	4-4
6. G'houghton	2-2	1-1	2-0	0-3	0-1	*	3-1	3-2	1-2	0-1	0-3	1-2	0-2	3-1	0-2	0-1	2-2	1-1	0-4
7. H'gate RA	2-0	1-2	0-0	0-0	0-2	1-3	*	1-0	2-2	1-1	1-3	2-4	2-0	0-1	0-5	2-2	1-1	0-1	3-0
8. Liversedge	2-4	3-2	1-1	3-1	2-1	3-2	1-0	*	2-3	2-2	0-4	2-1	1-1	4-2	1-1	0-0	0-6	2-2	2-1
9. Maltby	2-2	0-1	2-0	2-1	4-0	3-1	2-1	1-0	*	3-4	0-1	2-4	2-1	2-1	0-1	3-1	1-1	0-1	4-3
10. Nth Ferriby	0-0	3-0	4-1	1-4	2-2	3-1	2-1	4-2	7-0	*	0-4	3-0	1-0	2-0	1-2	1-0	0-1	1-0	2-1
11. Nth Shields	1-1	0-0	2-0	5-0	5-0	7-0	4-0	2-0	5-2	7-1	*	3-0	0-0	3-0	4-0	0-1	1-0	2-0	10-0
12. Ossett Alb.	0-1	1-0	0-1	0-6	0-0	2-0	3-1	1-0	3-4	1-0	0-3	*	0-3	1-2	1-1	1-1	3-1	0-1	2-0
13. Ossett Town	1-3	1-0	1-1	1-3	6-1	2-1	3-1	1-1	1-6	1-1	0-5	1-1	*	2-3	0-0	1-1	1-1	0-1	2-2
14. Pontefract	3-2	0-3	1-3	0-4	1-1	1-0	1-0	2-1	1-3	0-2	0-2	1-1	1-0	*	1-2	0-4	1-4	0-1	2-4
15. Sheffield	2-3	1-1	4-0	1-4	2-0	2-2	2-1	2-1	6-0	0-2	2-3	0-1	5-0	4-0	*	0-1	1-1	1-1	4-0
16. Spennymoor	1-3	2-0	2-1	3-0	2-1	3-1	2-2	1-2	0-2	1-2	1-2	2-0	4-0	1-1	1-1	*	2-3	4-2	3-1
17. Sutton T.	5-1	2-3	1-0	2-1	5-0	2-0	3-2	4-3	1-0	2-0	1-3	2-0	2-2	4-1	2-2	1-2	*	2-1	4-1
18. Thackley	5-3	3-1	0-0	3-2	1-2	1-1	1-0	1-3	1-1	1-0	0-4	0-1	1-2	3-0	3-0	4-1	0-0	*	2-1
19. Winterton	2-3	0-2	1-3	2-0	2-0	1-2	2-1	2-0	1-1	1-3	2-0	3-0	1-4	1-1	3-2	1-2	0-2	3-0	*

FIRST DIVISION RESULT CHART 1991-92

HOME TEAM	1	2	3	4	5	6	7	8	9	10	11	12	13	14	15	16
1. Bradley	*	1-1	1-1	3-1	3-0	4-1	2-1	1-0	0-0	1-1	4-0	3-1	3-2	0-1	7-0	1-1
2. Brodsworth	0-1	*	2-3	1-1	1-3	0-3	3-1	2-0	2-3	1-3	2-2	2-4	1-3	2-2	0-2	4-0
3. Garforth	4-0	0-4	*	1-2	1-4	2-0	7-0	0-2	2-2	0-1	1-0	1-2	4-0	3-1	1-1	1-2
4. Hallam	2-1	4-3	1-1	*	2-0	2-1	2-0	3-4	4-3	1-2	0-3	2-1	1-2	0-0	5-0	1-1
5. Hall Rd R.	0-0	4-2	2-0	1-0	*	2-1	1-3	0-2	3-1	0-0	6-0	2-3	4-0	1-3	8-0	2-0
6. Hatfield	0-2	2-0	2-1	0-1	2-1	*	2-3	1-2	1-2	0-3	4-3	1-5	2-2	4-2	2-3	0-2
7. Immingham	0-6	4-1	3-2	0-1	1-1	4-1	*	1-3	4-0	1-2	0-1	0-5	6-0	2-1	3-0	1-0
8. Pickering	2-3	5-2	2-0	0-2	3-8	5-0	8-0	*	5-0	3-2	5-0	5-1	3-1	4-4	2-2	2-1
9. Parkgate	3-2	1-1	1-0	0-2	2-2	3-2	1-2	3-1	*	3-1	1-1	0-2	2-0	2-1	1-2	2-0
10. Ross. Main	0-1	1-1	1-0	2-4	1-3	0-0	0-4	1-0	3-0	*	1-2	1-2	0-1	1-2	1-2	1-1
11. Selby T.	1-4	0-2	0-3	3-3	1-0	3-0	3-2	1-2	1-2	0-3	*	0-1	0-1	0-5	2-0	2-0
12. Stocksbr.	2-2	5-1	2-2	0-0	1-1	4-0	6-0	2-1	5-1	0-2	3-1	*	2-0	2-0	3-2	0-1
13. Tadcaster	0-1	4-1	0-1	0-4	1-2	4-0	1-1	1-3	4-0	3-0	1-1	0-3	*	1-3	4-2	0-4
14. W'boro BMW	0-1	2-1	3-1	0-1	1-2	1-3	0-0	2-2	0-1	1-3	2-1	2-1	3-0	*	0-0	0-2
15. York RI	0-1	1-2	0-4	1-4	1-3	0-3	2-2	2-2	2-1	1-5	0-2	1-1	2-2	2-1	*	0-2
16. Yorks Amtr	1-0	7-0	3-1	2-1	0-2	2-0	3-0	0-3	5-0	1-2	6-1	2-0	2-0	0-1	3-1	*

Daral Pugh of Denaby United (left) tries to cut out a Glasshoughton Welfare cross in match at Denaby on 19th October. Photo - J Hanson.

ARMTHORPE WELFARE

President/Chairman: Alan Bell   **Vice Chairman:** Jimmy Houston   **Manager:** Carl Leighton
Secretary: Mr E Cottam, 'Roydean', Whiphill Lane, Armthorpe, Doncaster, South Yorks DN3 3JP (0302 832514).
Asst. Manager: J McKeown   **Coach:** Dave Lister.
Ground: Church Street, Armthorpe (0302 833674-Welfare, 0302 831247-Club No.).
Directions: From north turn left at roundabout in centre of Doncaster, straight across next r/about on to Wheatley Hall Rd. Right at Mines Rescue Station, go to top of hill on to Armthorpe Rd. From south go to Racecourse on right, right at next roundabout on to Armthorpe Rd. Two and a half miles from Doncaster (BR). Buses A2, A3 & 181 pass ground.
Formed: 1926   **Disbanded:** 1974   **Reformed:** 1976
No. of seats: 120   **Covered accomm.:** 200   **Capacity:** 3,000   **Floodlights:** Yes
Midweek matches: Tuesday   **Record Att.:** 2,500 v Doncaster Rvrs, Charity match 85-86
Colours: White/navy/white & navy   **Change colours:** Navy/white/navy & white
Programme: 24 pages, 30p   **Programme Editor:** Miss Sharon Morgan
Previous League: Doncaster Senior   **Record attendance:** 1,500
Local Newspaper: Doncaster Evening Star   **Clubhouse:** Wheatsheaf Hotel (after matches).
Club honours: Northern Co's East Lg R-up 87-88 (Lg Cup R-up 91-92, Div 1 R-up 83-84, Central Div 1 84-85); Doncaster & Dist. Lg 82-83 (Div 1 81-82, Div 2 79-80, Div 3 78-79; Lg Cup 79-80 80-81 81-82 82-83; Challenge Cup 82-83); West Riding Chall. Cup 81-82 82-83; Goole & Thorne Dist. Cup 82-83

BELPER TOWN

President: Alan Benfield   **Chairman:** Phil Varney   **Manager:** Steve Powell
Secretary: P E Wainwright, 11 Stanton Ave, Belper, Derbys DE5 1EE. Tel: 0773 825675
Asst Manager: Mick Williamson   **Press Officer:** D R Laughlin/S Wilton
Ground: Christ Church Meadow, Bridge Street, Belper (0773 825549).
Directions: From M1 North, Jnct. 28 onto A38 towards Derby, turn off at A610 (s.p. Ripley/Nottingham), then 4 exit at roundabout towards Ambergate. At junction with A6 (Hurt Arms Hotel) left to Belper. Ground on right past traffic lights. 400 yards from Belper (BR).
No. of seats: 200   **Covered accomm.:** 1,500   **Capacity:** 6,000   **Floodlights:** Yes
Year formed: 1883   **Nickname:** Nailers   **Midweek matches:** Tuesday
Club colours: Gold/black/gold   **Change colours:** Sky & white
Programme: 16 pages, 30p   **Programme Editor:** David Laughlin.
Prev. Lges: Central Alliance 57-61/ Midland Co's 61-82   **Record Gate:** 3,600 v Ilkeston Town 1951
Clubhouse details: Bar (Tetley and Castlemaine). Hot & cold food.
Previous Ground: Acorn Ground – pre 1951
Local newspapers: Derby Evening Telegraph, Belper News
Club honours: Midland Counties Lg 79-80, Central Alliance League 1958-59, N. Counties East League 1984-85, Derbys Snr Cup 58-59 60-61 62-63 79-80, FA Cup 1st Round Proper 1887-88 (4th Qual. Rnd 1964-65).

BRIGG TOWN

President: B Robins   **Chairman:** H Williams   **Manager:** Ralph Clayton
Secretary: R B Taylor, 'Highfield House', Barton Rd, Wrawby, Brigg DN20 8SH (0652 652284).
Coach: John Kaye   **Commercial Manager:** H Williams
Ground: The Hawthorns, Hawthorn Avenue, Brigg (0652 652767).
Directions: From M180 Scunthorpe East, A18 through Brigg leaving on Wrawby Rd, left into East Parade/Woodbine Ave, follow houses on right into Hawthorn Ave. One mile from Brigg (BR).
No. of seats: 250   **Covered accomm.:** 2 Stands   **Capacity:** 4,000   **Floodlights:** Yes
Year formed: 1864   **Nickname:** Zebras   **Midweek matches:**
Club colours: Black & white stripes/black/black   **Change colours:** Orange shirts
Programme: 16 pages   **Programme Editor:** Secretary
Previous Leagues: Lindsey / Lincs 48-76/ Midland Counties 76-82
Previous Grounds: Manor House Convent, Station Rd (pre 1939); Brocklesby Ox 1939-59
Record attendance: 2,000 v Boston Utd 1953 (at Brocklesby Ox).
Clubhouse details: Licensed social club open matchdays
Honours: Northern Co's East Lg Presidents Cup R-up 91-92, Lincs Lg 49-50 53-54 73-74 75-76 (Div 1 68-69 69-70 70-71 71-72, Lg Cup 49-50 65-66 68-69 69-70 72-73); Mids Co's Lg 77-78 (Lg Cup 77-78), Lincs 'A' Snr Cup 75-76 76-77, Lincs 'B' Snr Cup 54-55 56-57 66-67 68-69 84-85.

DENABY UNITED

President: Alan Wilson   **Chairman:** Frank Martin   **Manager:** John Reed.
Secretary: Terry Ashford, 'Pedlars Green', , Conisbrough, Doncaster DN12 3NX. 0709 861893
Asst. Manager: John Kirk   **Coach:** Daral Pugh.
Ground: Tickhill Square, Denaby Main, Doncaster (0709 864042).
Directions: From Conisbrough take first left in Denaby along Wadworth St. From Mexborough take first right after Reresby Arms, left on to Bolton St. then left on to Wheatley Street. Rail to Conisbrough.
No. of seats: 250   **Covered accomm.:** 350   **Capacity:** 6,000   **Floodlights:** Yes
Year formed: 1895   **Midweek matches:** Tuesday or Wednesday
Club colours: Red/white/red   **Change colours:** Yellow/green/yellow
Programme: 32 pages 20p   **Programme Editor:** Barrie Dalby (0709 851283)
Previous Leagues: Midland 20-60 61-65/ Central Alliance 60-61/ Yorks 65-82.
Clubhouse: None.
Record attendance: 3,801 v Oldham Athletic, FA Cup 1st Rnd Proper 15/11/58
Local newspapers: South Yorks Times, Doncaster Free Press.
Honours: Yorks Lg R-up 67-68 (Div 2 R-up 66-67, Div 3 R-up 81-82, Lg Cup 71-72); Northern Counties East Div 1 South R-up 83-84; Midland Lg R-up 07-08; Sheffield & Hallamshire Snr Cup 05-06 09-10 32-33, 35-36, 86-87

Armthorpe Welfare FC 1991-92.

Brigg goalkeeper Gawthorpe is challenged for a cross by Liversedge's Murphy during a 1-1 draw at Liversedge on 12th October. Photo - Barry Lockwood.

The Belper goalkeeper is pressurised by Wayne Ali during a fixture at North Ferriby.

ECCLESHILL UNITED SPORTS CLUB

President: Vacant   **Chairman:** Keith Firth   **Manager:** John Price
Secretary: Lewis N Dixon, 61 Mount St., Eccleshill, Bradford BD2 2JN (0274 638053).
Asst. Manager: Ray Price   **Press Officer:** Mick Couzens (0274 663591).
Ground: Plumpton Park, Kingsway, Wrose, Bradford BD2 1PN (0274 615739).
Directions: M62 jct 26 onto M606, right on Bradford Ring Road A6177, left onto A650 for Bradford at 2nd r'bout. A650 Bradford Inner Ring Road onto Canal Rd, branch right opposite Woodheads Builders Merchants into Kings Rd, fork right after 30mph sign to junction with Wrose Rd, across junction - continuation of Kings Rd, 1st left onto Kingsway - ground 200 yds on roght. 2 miles from Bradford (BR). Buses 686 or 687 for Wrose.
No. of seats: 220   **Covered accomm.:** 220   **Capacity:** 2,000   **Floodlights:** Yes
Year Reformed: 1948   **Nickname:** Eagles   **Midweek matches:** Wednesday
Colours: Royal blue & white stripes   **Change colours:** Yellow
Programme: 34 pages 30p   **Programme Editor:** Bill Rawlings
Previous Ground: Myers Lane   **Record Gate:** 600 v Bradford City 90-91.
Previous Leagues: Bradsford Amateur/ West Riding County Amateur.
Previous Names: Phoenix Park, Eccleshill FC; clubs merged in 1985.
Clubhouse details: Bar, lounge, games room, kitchen (hot & cold snacks), committee room
Local newspapers: Bradford Telegraph & Argus, Bradford Star Free Press.
Club honours: Northern Counties East Div 2 R-up 86-87 (Reserve Div 86-87 89-90 (R-up 87-88)); Bradford Amtr Lg Cup 61-62; Bradford & Dist. Snr Cup 84-85; Bradford & Dist. FA Snr Cup 85-86; West Riding County Amateur Lg 76-77

GLASSHOUGHTON WELFARE

President: R Rooker   **Chairman:** Mr G Day
Secretary: E Jones, 'Marrica', Westfields Ave., Cutsyke, Castleford W10 5JJ (0977 556257).
Manager: Mr Wayne Day   **Asst Manager/Coach:** Mr M Ripley.
Ground: Glasshoughton Welfare, Leeds Rd, Glasshoughton, Castleford (0977 518981).
Directions: M62 junct. 31 or 32 towards Castleford. From exit 32 the road comes into Glasshoughton. From exit 31 turn right at 2nd roundabout at Whitwood Tech. College. Ground is on left in Leeds Road. Car park on ground. 1 mile from Castleford (BR).
Club colours: All blue   **Change colours:** All yellow
Seats: None   **Covered accom.:** 250   **Capacity:** 2,000   **Floodlights:** Yes
Founded: 1964   **Record Att.:** 300 v Bradford C – F'light opening 1990
Previous Name: Anson Sports 1964-76   **Previous Ground:** Saville Park 1964-76
Previous League: West Yorkshire   **Clubhouse:** Bar & refreshment facilities.
Programme: 20 pages, 20p   **Programme Editor:** Mr G Day.

HARROGATE RAILWAY ATHLETIC

President: Coun. J Blakey   **Chairman:** P Render   **Manager:** Barry Statham
Secretary: W D Oldfield, 80 Stonefall Ave, Harrogate, N Yorks HG2 7NP (0423 888941).
Coach: Barry Statham   **Publicity Sec:** C W Robinson (0423 880022).
Ground: Station View, Starbeck, Harrogate (0423 885539).
Directions: A59 Harrogate to Knaresborough road. After approx 1.5 miles turn left just before railway level crossing. Ground is 150 yds up the lane. Adjacent to Starbeck (BR). Served by any Harrogate to Knareborough bus.
No. of seats: None   **Covered accomm.:** 350   **Capacity:** 4,000   **Floodlights:** Yes
Year formed: 1935   **Nickname:** The Rail
Club colours: White/white/red   **Change colours:** White/blue/blue
Programme: 28 pages   **Programme Editor:** Committee
Previous leagues: W. Yorks, Harrogate District   **Record attendance:** 1,400 in 1962 (FA Amateur Cup)
Clubhouse details: Games, TV room, lounge, open normal public house hours
Sponsors: Robinsons of Knaresborough.   **Local Newspaper:** Pontefract & Castleford Express.

LIVERSEDGE

Chairman: Bob Gawthorpe   **Treasurer:** B Prendergast.
Secretary: M Balmforth, 5 Victoria Rd., Gomersal, Cleckheaton BD19 4RG (0274 862123).
Manager: Colin Penrose   **Asst Manager:** Stuart Harrison.
Ground: Clayborn Ground, Quaker Lane, Hightown Rd, Cleckheaton, West Yorks (0274 862108).
Directions: M1 & M62 to junct. 26, then A638 into Cleckheaton. Right at lights on corner of Memorial Park through next lights & under railway bridge. Then first left (Hightown Rd) and Quaker Lane is approx quarter mile on left which leads to ground. Bus 220 Leeds-Huddersfield passes top of Quaker Lane.
Seats: None   **Cover:** 250   **Capacity:** 2,000   **Floodlights:** Yes   **Founded:** 1919.
Colours: Royal blue & white   **Change colours:** Gold & black
Programme: 24 pages, 30p   **Editor:** Secretary   **Midweek Matches:** Tuesday
Previous Leagues: Spen Valley/ West Riding County Amateur 22-72/ Yorkshire 72-82.
Nickname: The Sedge   **Previous Ground:** Primrose Lane, Hightown.
Players progressing to Football League: Garry Briggs (Oxford), Martin Hirst (Bristol City).
Clubhouse details: Bar open matchdays plus Tuesday & Thursdays during season. Pool table, TV.
Local Press: Yorkshire Evening Post, Telegraph & Argus, Cleckheaton Reporter, Spenborough Guardian.
Club honours: West Riding Co. Chal. Cup 48-49 51-52 69-70; West Riding County Cup 89-90; North Counties East Lg Div 1 R-up 89-90 (Div 2 R-up 88-89); West Riding Co. Amtr Lg(6).

MALTBY MINERS WELFARE

President: TBA   **Chairman:** Mr H Henson
Secretary: Mr S Mallinder, 109 Sycamore Avenue, Bramley, Rotherham, Sth Yorks S66 0PA (0709 549958).
Manager: Mr Colin Walker   **Asst Manager:** Mr M Walker.
Ground: Muglet Lane, Maltby (0709 812462 (match days)).
Directions: Exit M18 at junct with A631. Two miles into Maltby, right at crossroads at Queens Hotel corner on to B6427. Ground 3/4 mile on left
No. of seats: None   **Covered accomm.:** 200   **Capacity:** 2,000   **Floodlights:** Yes
Year Reformed: 1970   **Record Gate:** 940 v Thackley, Yorks Lg Cup 77-78.
Club colours: White/black/white   **Change colours:** Yellow/blue/yellow
Midweek Matches: Tuesday   **Clubhouse:** None.
Programme: 16 pages, 50p   **Programme Editor:** Dave Brennan.
Previous name: Maltby Main   **Previous leagues:** Sheffield Co. Snr/ Yorks 73-82.
Hons: Sheff. & Hallamshire Snr Cup 77-78, Northern Counties East Lg Presidents Cup SF 90-91.

Eccleshill United FC. Back Row (L/R): John Price (Manager), Adrian Tate, Martin Dolan, Kent Noble, David Bramhill, Paul Sunter, John Brown, Colin Moody, Alan Dakin (Physio). Front: Martin Stergiopoulis, Andrew Shanks, Richard Dakin, David Jeng, Raymond Price, Subtan Nazir. Photo - Dave West.

Dave Callaghan heads North Shields' third in an Easter Monday 3-0 win at Harrogate Railway. Photo - James Wright.

North Ferriby United 1991-92. Photo - Hamlyn Photographic.

NORTH FERRIBY UNITED

President: Brian Thacker **Chairman:** Jeff Frank **Vice Chairman:** Roy Wallis
Secretary: S Tather, 16 Peasholme, Heads Lane, Hessle, E Yorks HU13 0NY (0482 642046).
Manager: Peter Daniel **Asst Mgr:** Dave Robinson **Press Officer:** Roy Wallis
Ground: Church Road, North Ferriby (0482 634601).
Directions: Main Leeds-Hull road A63 or M62. Into North Ferriby thorugh village past the Duke of Cumberland Hotel, right down Church Rd, ground half mile on left. Half mile from North Ferriby (BR).
Seats: 200 **Cover:** 2,000 **Capacity:** 5,000 **Floodlights:** Yes **Founded:** 1934.
Club colours: White/green/white **Change colours:** All red **Midweek matches:** Tuesday
Programme: 28 pages 25p **Programme Editor:** Jeff Frank
Previous leagues: East Riding Church/ East Riding Amateur/ Yorks 69-82.
Record attendance: 1,800 v Tamworth, FA Vase Semi-Final, 1989
Clubhouse details: Bar, lounge, TV, pool – open every night **Local newspapers:** Hull Daily Mail
Club honours: FA Vase SF 88-89 (QF 89-90, 5th Rd 87-88); Yorkshire Lg R-up 75-76 (Lg Cup 74-75, Div 2 70-71), Northern Counties East Div 1 85-86 (Lg Cup R-up) 90-91, Presidents Cup 90-91, Div 1 (North), R-up 82-83, Reserve Div R-up 90-91); East Riding Snr Cup 70-71 76-77 77-78 78-79 90-91; East Riding Church Lg 37-38.

OSSETT ALBION

President: Miss Helen Worth **Chairman:** N A Wigglesworth **Manager:** David Cope
Secretary: A Carter, 10 Oxford Drive, Gomersal, Cleckeaton BD19 4TU (0274 861008).
Asst Mgr: Peter Eaton **Coach:** Brian Crowther **Physio:** Stuart Gayside/John Hirst
Ground: Dimple Wells, Ossett (0924 273618-club, 0924 280450-ground (matchday only)).
Directions: M1 jct 40. Take Wakefield road, right at Post House Hotel down Queens Drive. At end right then second left down Southdale Rd. At end right, then first left down Dimple Wells (cars only). Coaches take second left following the road for 200yds bearing left twice. Four miles from both Wakefield and Dewsbury BR stations. Buses 116 and 117.
No. of seats: 200 **Covered accomm.:** 350 **Capacity:** 3,000 **Floodlights:** Yes
Year formed: 1944 **Nickname:** Albion **Midweek matches:** Tuesday
Club colours: Old gold/black/black **Change colours:** Blue/white/blue
Programme: 44 pages **Programme Editor:** N Wigglesworth (0924 275630).
Prev. Lges: Heavy Woollen Area/ Yorks 57-82 **Record Gate:** 1,200 v Leeds Utd, 1986
Clubhouse details: Full bar facilities open 7 days and catering
Sponsors: Giedhill of Ossett **Local newspapers:** Wakefield Express
Club honours: Yorks Lg 74-75 (R-up 59-60 61-62, Lg Cup 75-76, 76-77, Div2 2 78-79, 80-81 (R-up 58-59)); Northern Co. East Div 1 86-87 (Lg Cup 83-84); West Yorks Lg 53-54 55-56 (Div 2 52-53, Lg Cup 52-53); West Riding County Cup 64-65 65-66 67-68; Wheatley Cup 56-57 58-59

OSSETT TOWN A.F. & S.C.

President: John Carter **Chairman:** Graham Firth
Secretary: F Lloyd, 27 Park Close, Mapplewell, Barnsley S75 6BY (0226 382415).
Manager: Dave Leadbeater **Asst. Manager:** Terry Gray
Ground: Ingfield, Prospect Road, Ossett, Wakefield (0924 272960).
Directions: M1 jct. 40 to Ossett town centre, turn left opposite bus station on ring road. Three miles from Wakefield (BR).
Seats: None **Cover:** 500 **Capacity:** 4,000 **Floodlights:** Yes **Founded:** 1936
Colours: All red **Change colours:** All sky **Midweek matches:** Tuesday
Programme: 20 pages, 30p **Programme Editor:** Bruce Saul
Clubhouse details: Bar, pool, darts. **Record attendance:** 3,200 v Manchester Utd 1988
Local Newspapers: Dewsbury Reporter. **Previous League:** Yorkshire 45-82.
Club honours: West Riding County Cup 81-82, Northern Co's Lg Cup.

PICKERING TOWN

President: S P Boak, esq **Chairman:** M T Jones, esq **Manager/Coach:** Nigel Tate
Secretary: K W Sales, 4 Northway, Pickering, N. Yorks YO18 8NN (0751 73348).
Asst. Manager: Michael Hudson **Press Officer:** Secretary
Ground: Recreation Club, Mill Lane (off Malton Rd), Pickering, North Yorkshire (0751 73317).
Directions: A169 from Malton, first turn left past Pickering Police Station.
No. of seats: 50 **Cover:** 300 **Capacity:** 2,000 **Floodlights:** Yes **Founded:** 1888
Nickname: Pikes **Midweek matches:** Tuesday
Programme: 32 pages, 50p **Programme Editor:** Secretary.
Club colours: Royal blue/white/royal blue **Change colours:** All yellow.
Sponsors: Hargreaves Quarries Ltd. **Record Gate:** 1,412 v Notts County, friendly, August 1991.
Previous leagues: Beckett/ York & District/ Scarborough & District.
Clubhouse: Various beers, light refreshments at half-time, pool, darts etc. Food after games.
Players progressing to Football League: Chris & Craig Short (both Scarborough & Notts County).
Local Press: Pickering Gazette & Herald, Yorkshire Evening Press, Mercury, Scarborough Evening News.
Hons: Northern Co's East Div 2 1987-88 (Div 1 R-up 91-92), Yorks Lg Div 3 73-74, Nth Riding County Cup 90-91.

PONTEFRACT COLLIERIES

President: R Blatherwick **Chairman:** Anthony Dunwell, JP **Manager:** Ged Elliott
Secretary: Sid Mason, 16 Harefield Rd, Pontefract, West Yorks WF8 2HX (0977 707756).
Asst Mgr: Andrew Butterwick **Coach:** Roland Lanes. **Physio:** Andy Dean/Neil Beavers
Ground: Skinner Lane, Pontefract, West Yorkshire (0977 702180).
Directions: M62 jct 32 into Pontefract. Left at traffic lights opposite Racecourse entrance. Vehicles travelling through Pontefract follow Racecourse/Leeds signs to traffic lights and turn right to ground. 1 mile from Monkhill (BR). All Leeds and Castleford buses stop near ground.
No. of seats: None **Covered accomm.:** 500 **Capacity:** 2,000 **Floodlights:** Yes
Founded: 1958 **Nickname:** The Colls **Midweek matches:** Tuesday
Club colours: All blue **Change colours:** All yellow
Programme: 8 pages, 25p **Programme Editor:** Shaun Nash
Previous leagues: West Yorks League/ Yorkshire 79-82.
Record attendance: 1,200 v Hull – friendly 1987
Clubhouse: Open matchdays. Fully licensed. Hot & cold food. **Local Press:** Pontefract & Castleford Express
Hons: Northern Co's East Lg Div 1 83-84 (Div 2 R-up 82-83, Floodlit Comp 87-88 88-89); Yorks Lg Div 3 81-82; West Riding Co. Cup R-up 87-88 90-91; Embleton Cup 82-83 86-87; Castleford FA Cup 82-83 86-87; West Yorks Lg.

SHEFFIELD

President: J K Healey   **Chairman:** Alan Methey   **Manager:** R Evans
Secretary: S Hall, 24 Crofton Ave., Sheffield S6 1WF (0742 344553).
Asst. Mgr: D Moxon   **Coach:** John Bramhall   **Physio:** Paul Foster.
Press Officer: Alan Methley (0742 884608)
Ground: Don Valley Stadium
Directions: From the north M1 to jnt 34. Straight on at traffic island (directly underneath motorway). At next island take 6th exit following City Centre signs. Don Valley Stadium is approx 1 mile on left. From South M1 to jnt 34. Take 2nd exit from traffic island at bottom of slip road, following City Centre signs. As from north.
Seats: All seater   **Covered:** Yes   **Capacity:** 20,000   **Floodlights:** No
Club colours: Red & black quarters/black/black   **Change colours:** Blue & white
Year formed: 1857   **Programme:** 24 pages   **Editor:** John Stainrod
Previous leagues: Yorks 49-82   **Previous grounds:** Sheffield Amateur Sports Club, Hillsborough Park Stadium
Hons: FA Amtr Cup 03-04, FA Vase R-up 76-77, Northern Co's East Lg Div 88-89 90-91, Yorks Lg Div 2 76-77.

SPENNYMOOR UNITED

President: Mr T Beaumont   **Chairman:** Mr J B Hindmarch   **Vice Chairman:** J Norman
Secretary: Mrs Joyce Hindmarch, Bedford House, 7 Green Lane, Spennymoor, Co. Durham DL16 6HD (0388 815168).
Manager: Matty Pearson   **Asst Mgr/Coach:** Dave Barton   **Physio:** Jacquie Moore
Commercial Manager: D Beamson   **Press Officer:** Chairman
Ground: Brewery Field, Durham Road, Spennymoor, County DL16 6JN (0388 814100/811934).
Directions: From A167 South – leave at Tinford (Black & Decker factory), straight on at mini-r'bout, 3rd left at next large r'bout, keep left at church, pass Asda on left, straight on at junction, pass Salvin Arms (Durham Rd), ground 200 yds on left. From A167 North - leave at Croxdale (N.E.S.S. factory), right at cemetary on left - this is Durham Rd - ground half mile on right.
Seats: 300   **Cover:** 1,500   **Capacity:** 7,000   **Floodlights:** Yes   **Founded:** 1901.
Nickname: The Moors   **Midweek matches:** Wednesday
Club colours: Black & white stripes/black/black   **Change colours:** All red
Programme: 30 pages, 50p   **Programme Editor:** Ed Minto
Previous leagues: Northern 05-08 60-90/ North Eastern 08-37 38-58/ Wearside 37-38/ Midland 58-60.
Record Gate: 7,202 v Bishop Auckland, Durham County Challenge Cup 30/3/57.
Local Press: Northern Echo/ The Journal.   **Clubhouse:** Normal licensing hours, catering available.
Best FA Cup season: 3rd Rd 36-37   **Best FA Trophy season:** Semi Final 77-78.
Players progressing to Football League: Jack Oaks, Tommy Dawson, Bert Johnson (all Charlton Athletic).
Hons: Northern Lg(6) 67-68 71-72 73-74 76-79 (R-up(3) 74-75 79-81, Lg Cup(5) 65-66 67-68 79-81 86-87, Turney Wylde Cup 80-81, J R Cleator Cup 80-81 86-87); Durham Chal. Cup 45-46 52-53 62-63 67-68 72-73 73-74 74-75 75-76 82-83; Durham Benevolent Bowl 26-27 29-30 31-32 47-48; North Eastern Lg(4) 09-10 44-46 56-57.

STOCKSBRIDGE PARK STEELS

President: C D Sedgwick   **Chairman:** A Bethel
Secretary: M Grimmer, 48 Hole House Lane, Stocksbrige, Sheffield S30 5BP (0742 886470).
Manager: Alan Watson   **Asst Manager:** Trevor Gough
Ground: Bracken Moor Lane, Stocksbridge, Sheffield. 0742 882045
Directions: From Sheffield on main Manchester road A616 (9 miles) from M1 jnt 36 – on arriving at Stocksbridge turn left into Nanny Hill under the Clock Tower and continue up the hill for about 500 yds.
Colours: Royal blue/yellow   **Change colours:** All yellow
Seats: 700   **Covered accom.:** 800   **Capacity:** 3,500   **Floodlights:** Yes
Nickname: Steels   **Midweek matches:** Wednesday   **Metal badges:** Yes (£1.75)
Programme: 44 pages, 50p   **Editor:** David Webster (Sheffield 337457)
Record Gate: 2,000 v Sheffield Wednesday, Floodlight opening 90-91.
Previous Names: Stocksbridge Works, Oxley Park; clubs merged in 1986.
Previous Leagues: Sheffield Amateur/ Sheffield Association/ Yorkshire 49-82.
Local newpapers: Sheffield Trader, Green'un, The Star
Clubhouse: Open seven days (lunchtime & evenings)
Club honours: Northern Co's East Lg Div 1 91-92 (Presidents Cup SF 91-92), Sheffield & Hallamshire Snr Cup 51-52, Yorks Lg 51-52 54-55 55-56 56-57 57-58 61-62 62-63 (R-up 60-61, Div 2 50-51 64-65, Div 3 70-71 74-75 (R-up 78-79) Lg Cup 61-62).

SUTTON TOWN

President: Frank Haynes M.P.   **Chairman:** Roy Gregory   **Treasurer:** Gillian Gregory
Secretary: W Roper, 82 Columbia St., Huthwaite, Sutton-in-Ashfield, Notts. NG17 2JA (0623 554657).
Manager: John Ramshaw   **Coach:** Paul Smalley   **Physio:** Ken Burton
Commercial Manager: Paul Smalley   **Press Officer:** Steve Jarvis. 0623 34466
Ground: Lowmoor Road, Kirkby-in-Ashfield, Notts (0623 752181).
Directions: From M1 jct. 38 at 5th lights turn right onto B6021 (s.p. Kirkby-in-Ashfield). After half mile turn right immediately after crossing railway lines. Ground is on left approx 1 mile (before Lowmoor Inn and opposite Texas)
Seats: 200   **Cover:** 500   **Capacity:** 8,000   **Floodlights:** Yes   **Founded:** 1885.
Club Shop: Yes (contact Leighton Morris).
Nickname: Snipes   **Midweek matches:** Wednesday
Club colours: Blue/claret/blue   **Change colours:** White/black
Programme: 36 pages, 30p   **Programme Editor:** Gordon Foster (0623 794281).
Previous leagues: Notts & District, Notts & Derbys, Midland Comb., Derbys Senior, Central Comb., Notts Alliance, Central Alliance, Midland League, NE Counties, Northern Premier.
Previous Grounds: Dog & Duck 1885-97/ New Cross 98-1919/ Avenue Ground 19-39/ Skegby MW 49-51/ Prestic Rd 51-77.
Record attendance: 1,562 v Leeds, floodlight opening, 1980. *At Priestic Rd: 6,000 v Peterborough Utd, 1958. At The Avenue: 8,000 v Reading, FA Cup 1933.*
Local newspapers: Notts Free Press, Sutton & Kirkby News
Club honours: Notts Snr Cup 08-09 12-13 13-14 23-24 55-56 57-58 59-60 61-62 62-63 63-64 67-68 69-70 71-72 72-73 73-74 74-75 76-77; Notts & Dist Lg 05-06 06-07; Derby Snr Lg 30-31 31-32 32-33; Central Alliance 50-51; Northern Co. East Lg R-up 91-92 (Lg Cup 85-86); Mansfield Charity Cup 1892-93 05-06 23-24; Sutton Charity Cup 29-30 30-31 31-32; Byron Cup 30-31 31-32; FA Cup 2nd Rnd 1933-34

THACKLEY

President: P Hockney **Chairman:** Vacant **Manager/Coach:** Warren Rayner
Secretary: Stewart Willingham, 3 Kirklands Close, Baildon, Shipley, W. Yorks BD17 6HN (0274 598589).
Asst. Man: Jan Kudelinitzky **Press Officer:** Jamie Scott
Ground: Dennyfield, Ainsbury Avenue, Thackley, Bradford (0274 615571).
Directions: On main Leeds/Keighley A657 road, turn off at Thackley corner which is 2 miles from Shipley traffic lights and 1 mile from Greengates lights. Ainsbury Avenue bears to the right 200yds down the hill. Ground is 200yds along Ainsbury Avenue on the right. 3 miles from Bradford Interchange (BR), one and a half miles from Shipley (BR). Buses to Thackley corner (400 yds).
Seats: 100 **Cover:** 100 **Capacity:** 3,000 **Floodlights:** Yes
Founded: 1930 **Club colours:** Red & white/white/red **Change colours:** All white
Midweek matches: Tuesday **Programme:** 20 pages, 30p **Programme Editor:** S L Willingham
Club Shop: No, but old programmes and metal badges available.
Previous leagues: Bradford Amateur, W. Riding County Amateur, W. Yorks, Yorks 67-82.
Record Att.: 1,500 v Leeds United, 1983 **Previous name:** Thackley Wesleyians 1930-39.
Players progressing to Football League: Tony Brown (Leeds, Doncaster, Scunthorpe, Rochdale), Ian Ormondroyd (Bradford City, Aston Villa, Derby, Leicester).
Clubhouse details: Hot & cold snacks on matchdays. Open Tues-Sunday evenings, matchdays and weekend lunchtimes. Boardroom, committee room, dancefloor, darts, pool, gaming machines.
Local Press: Bradford Telegraph & Argus, Bradford Str, Aire Valley Target. **Hons:** Yorks Lg Div 2 73-74, West Yorks Lg 66-67, West Riding Co. Amtr Lg 57-58 58-59 59-60, West Riding Co. Cup 73-74 74-75, West Riding Co. Chal. Cup 63-64 66-67, Bradford & Dist. Snr Cup(10) 38-39 49-50 55-56 57-60 65-67 78-79 87-88.

WINTERTON RANGERS

President: J W Hiles **Chairman:** D Waterfall **Manager/Coach:** Mick Wild
Secretary: G Spencer, 2 Dale Park Ave., Winterton, Scunthorpe, S. Humbs DN15 9UY (0724 732039).
Asst Mgr: K Rooney **Ground:** West Street, Winterton (0724 732628).
Directions: From Scunthorpe take A1077 Barton-on-Humber road for 5 miles. On entering Winterton take second right (Eastgate), third left (Northlands Road) and first right (West Street). Ground 200yds on left
Seats: 200 **Covered:** 200 **Capacity:** 3,000 **Floodlights:** Yes
Founded: 1934
Club colours: White/navy/white **Change colours:** All red **Midweek:** Wednesday
Programme: 28-36 pages, 50p **Editor:** M Girdham
Best FA Cup year: 4th Qual. Rd 71-72 76-77 **Best FA Vase year:** Quarter Finals 76-77.
Previous League: Scunthorpe & Dist. 45-65/ Lincs 65-70/ Yorkshire 70-82.
Record attendance: 1,200 v Sheffield Utd – Official opening of floodlights, October 1978.
Clubhouse: Evenings & matchdays, hot & cold food available on matchdays. Pool and snooker rooms.
Local Press: Scunthorpe Evening Telegraph **Players progressing to Football League:** Henry Smith (Leeds, Hearts), Keith Walwyn (Chesterfield, York, Carlisle), Rick Greenhough (Chester, York)
Record transfer fee received: £5,000 from Leeds Utd for Henry Smith, 1979
Hons: Lincs Jnr Cup 47-48 61-62; Lincs Snr 'B' Cup 69-70; Yorks Lg 71-72 76-77 78-79 (Lg Cup 80-81); Northern Co's East Lg Div 2 89-90; S'thorpe Lg & Cup many times; Philips National F'light 6-aside 76-77.

Northern Counties East Premier Division Ten Year Record

	82/3	83/4	84/5	85/6	86/7	87/8	88/9	89/90	90/1	91/2
Alfreton Town	13	4	4	6	1	–	–	–	–	–
Appleby Frodingham	11	14	16	18	–	–	–	–	–	–
Armthorpe Welfare	–	–	–	13	12	2	11	7	9	13
Arnold	8	2	7	1	–	–	–	–	–	–
Belper Town	3	11	1	9	15	16	10	12	13	11
Bentley Victoria	19	18	15	14	14	–	–	–	–	–
Boston	16	12	17	17	19	–	–	–	–	–
Bridlington Town	–	–	–	–	10	4	3	1	–	–
Bridlington Trinity	17	16	9	19	17	13	16	4	–	–
Brigg Town	–	–	–	–	18	15	14	10	5	8
Denaby United	–	–	6	11	6	3	6	3	15	3
Eastwood Town	2	5	2	5	13	–	–	–	–	–
Eccleshill United	–	–	–	–	–	–	–	–	–	17
Emley	10	3	8	2	4	1	1	–	–	–
Farsley Celtic	–	–	–	8	2	–	–	–	–	–
Glasshoughton Welfare	–	–	–	–	–	–	–	–	–	19
Grimethorpe Miners Wf.	–	–	–	–	–	9	15	17	–	–
Guisborough Town	12	8	5	–	–	–	–	–	–	–
Guiseley	5	7	3	3	16	7	5	11	1	–
Hallam	–	–	–	–	–	10	12	14	–	–
Harrogate Railway Ath.	–	–	–	–	–	12	8	5	7	18
Harrogate Town	–	–	–	–	9	–	–	–	–	–
Hatfield Main	–	–	–	–	–	11	2	18	–	–
Heanor Town	9	17	18	15	–	–	–	–	–	–
Ilkeston Town	15	6	13	20	–	–	–	–	–	14
Liversedge	–	–	–	–	–	–	–	–	–	–
Long Eaton United	–	–	–	4	11	14	13	–	–	–
Maltby Miners Welfare	–	–	–	–	–	–	–	–	6	7
Mexborough Town	20	15	19	–	–	–	–	–	–	–
North Ferriby United	–	–	–	–	3	6	4	6	4	4
North Shields	–	–	–	–	–	–	–	2	2	1
Ossett Albion	–	–	–	–	–	17	17	16	14	10
Ossett Town	–	–	–	–	–	–	–	–	8	12
Pontefract Coll	–	–	14	12	8	8	7	13	16	16
Sheffield	–	–	–	–	–	–	–	9	–	6
Shepshed Charterhouse	1	–	–	–	–	–	–	–	–	–
Skegness Town	18	–	–	–	–	–	–	–	–	–
Spalding United	4	1	11	16	–	–	–	–	–	–
Spennymoor United	–	–	–	–	–	–	–	–	3	5
Sutton Town	14	13	12	7	5	–	–	8	12	2
Thackley	7	9	10	10	7	5	9	15	11	9
Winterton Rangers	6	10	–	–	–	–	–	–	10	15
No. of Clubs	**20**	**18**	**19**	**20**	**19**	**17**	**17**	**18**	**16**	**19**

BRADLEY RANGERS

President: G Pearson   **Chairman:** J Finn
Secretary: Christopher Walker, 4 College Street East, Crosland Moor, Huddersfield HD4 5DN (0484 658789).
Manager: Jim Martin   **Asst Manager:** C Mear   **Coach:** Jimmy Martin.
Ground: Warrenside, Deighton, Huddersfield (0484 542044).
Directions: M1 jct 38 on to A637 – Huddersfield until coming to major crossroads. Go across onto the main Huddersfield-Wakefield Rd A642. Follow B6118 Brighouse through contryside to 2nd traffic lights on main A62 Huddersfield-Leeds Rd, follow A640 Rochdale, *take 2nd left by bus shelter through housing estate to tree-lined area on left hand bend, then take 1st left Warrenside. Entrance to club 50 yds on left. From M62 jct 25;, A644 for 1 mile, turn right at r'about onto the A62 towards Huddersfield. At lights turn A640 Rochdale, then follow as above*. 1 mile from Deighton (BR).
Colours: Black & white.   **Change colours:** Gold & sky.
Seats: None   **Covered Accom.:** 500   **Capacity:** 1,000   **Floodlights:** No
Founded: 1946   **Previous Ground:** Leeds Rd Playing Fields 1962-80
Programme: £1 with entry   **Programme Editor:** Mrs Helen Finn.
Clubhouse: Being built   **Record Gate:** 600 v Emley, League Cup 1983
Local Press: Huddersfield Examiner   **Previous Leagues:** Huddersfield/ Huddersfield Sunday/ Yorks 80-82.
Hons: Yorks Lg Div 3 80-81, Northern Co's East Lg Cup R-up 89-90, West Riding Co. Cup R-up 91-92.

BRODSWORTH MINERS WELFARE

Chairman: Mr J Mounsey   **Treasurer:** Mr A Pawson
Secretary: T Ashman, 53 Wroxham Way, Scawsby, Doncaster DN5 8JY (0302 785429).
Manager: B Orwin   **Coach:** J Bedford.
Ground: Welfare Ground, Woodlands, Nr. Doncaster (0302 728380).
Directions: Adjacent to the old A1 (Great North Rd), 3 miles north of Doncaster at Woodlands. Ground entrance approx 30 yds into Welfare Rd. Left turn into Car Park.
Seats: No   **Cover:** Yes   **Floodlights:** No   **Prog.:** 28 pages   **Founded:** 1912
Colours: Scarlet & white halves/black/black with red & white trim
Previous Name: Brodsworth Main   **Previous Leagues:** Doncaster Snr/ Sheffield/ Yorks.
Hons: Yorks Lg 24-25, Donc. & Dist. Lg 84-85 (Lg Cup 85-86, Div 2 78-79, Div 2 Cup 78-79), Sheffield Jnr Cup 83-84.

GARFORTH TOWN

President: George Thompson   **Chairman:** Ken Payne   **Manager:** Peter Bush
Secretary: Paul Bracewell, 24 Coupland Rd, Garforth, Leeds LS25 1AD (0532 863314).
Asst. Manager: Fred Bennett   **Coach:** Paul Dooley
Press Officer: J Griffiths (0532 871702).
Ground: Brierlands Lane, Aberford Road, Garforth, Leeds (0532 864083).
Directions: From South, A642 thru Garforth, ground 200yds past Aberford Rd Junior School. From East & West turn off A63 at Hilton Hotel on to A642, then as from South. Three quarters of a mile from Garforth (BR).
Seats: None   **Cover:** 100   **Capacity:** 2,000   **Floodlights:** No   **Founded:** 1965
Club colours: Red/black/red   **Change colours:** Blue/white/blue
Prog.: 28 pages, glossy print, 50p   **Programme Editor:** Kevin Strangeway.
Previous leagues: Leeds Sunday Combination/ West Yorks/ Yorks 78-82.
Clubhouse: Opening August 1992.   **Previous names:** Miners Arms 64-78, Garforth Miners 78-79
Midweek matches: Wednesday   **Record attendance:** 817 v Leeds, friendly 1987
Club honours: FA Vase QF 85-86; Northern Co's East Lg Div 2 R-up 85-86; Yorks Lg Div 3 R-up 79-80, Barkeston Ash Snr Cup 80-81 84-85 85-86 86-87.

HALL ROAD RANGERS

President: Mr R Pugh   **Chairman:** Mr J Urbanowicz
Secretary: E Richardson, 35 Hall Road, Hull, Nth Humbs HU6 8QW (0482 43781).
Manager: Ted Richardson   **Asst Manager:** Pete Smith   **Coach:** Pat Heard
Ground: Dene Park, Dene Close, Dunswell, Nr. Hull (0482 850101).
Directions: Hull-Beverley road (A1079 and A1174). Dunswell is first village from the Hull boundary. Entrance to ground on A1174 is 20 yds past large r'about and opposite Dunswell Village road sign. Four & a half miles from Hull (BR).
Seats: None   **Cover:** 300   **Capacity:** 600   **Floodlights:** No   **Founded:** 1959.
Colours: Blue & white hoops/blue/blue   **Change colours:** All green
Prev. ground: Hull Co-Op (until 1968)   **Record Gate:** 345v Hull City XI, August '91.
Programme: 8 pages, 25p   **Programme Editor:** E Richardson.
Midweek Matches: Thursday
Clubhouse: Open all week for drinks and snacks. Meals at weekends. Snooker, pool, darts.
Local Press: Hull Daily Mail   **Prev. Leagues:** East Riding/ Yorks 68-82.
Hons: Northern Co's East Lg Div 2 90-91, Yorks Lg Div 3 72-73 79-80, East Riding Snr Cup 72-73.

HALLAM

President: Mr T Stones   **Chairman:** Mr A Scanlan   **Vice Chairman:** A Cooper
Secretary: G L Holland, 34 Standon Crescent, Sheffield S9 1PP (0742 421899).
Manager: Glyn Kenny   **Treasurer:** N Webster.
Sponsors: Hallam Incorporated Services
Ground: Sandygate Road, Crosspool, Sheffield S10 (0742 309434).
Directions: A57 Sheffield to Glossop Rd, left at Crosspool shopping area signed 'Lodge Moor' on to Sandygate Rd. Ground half mile on left opposite Plough Inn
No. of seats: None   **Covered accomm.:** 250   **Capacity:** 2,000   **Floodlights:** Yes
Year formed: 1860   **Nickname:** None   **Press Officer:** M Radford 0742 434529
Club colours: Blue/white/blue   **Change colours:** All red
Programme: 8 pages with admission   **Programme Editor:** Mark Radford (0742 434529).
Midweek Matches: Monday   **Previous leagues:** Yorks 52-82.
Record Gate: 2,000 v Hendon, FA Amtr Cup 3rd Rd 1959. (13,855 v Dulwich at Hillsborogh, FA Amtr Cup 1955).
Clubhouse details: Licensed bar   **Local Press:** Star, Green'Un, Sheffield Telegraph.
Hons: Northern Co's East Lg Div 1 R-up 90-91, Yorks Lg Div 2 60-61 (R-up 56-57), Sheffield & Hallamshire Snr Cup 50-51 61-62.

HATFIELD MAIN

President: D Gardiner   **Chairman:** D Willis
Secretary: Mr Bruce Hatton, 92 Ingram, Dunscroft, Doncaster, Sth Yorks DN7 4JE.
Manager: Neil Harie   **Asst. Manager:** Neil Derbyshire.
Ground: Dunscroft Welfare Ground, Dunscroft, Doncaster, Sth Yorks (0302 841326).
Directions: From Doncaster (A18) Scunthorpe Rd to Dunsville. Left at Flarepath Hotel down Broadway. Ground half mile on right. Half mile from Stamforth & Hatfield (BR). Buses every fifteen minutes from Doncaster.
No. of seats: None   **Covered accomm.:** 300   **Capacity:** 4,000   **Floodlights:** Yes
Year formed: 1936   **Programme details:** 24 pages 20p
Club colours: Yellow/blue/yellow   **Change colours:** All red
Clubhouse: Open every evening   **Previous League:** Yorkshire 55-82.
Hons: West Riding Co. Cup.   **Record Gate:** 750 v B. Auckland, FA Amtr Cup

HUCKNALL TOWN

President: Andy Stewart   **Chairman:** Robert Spray
Secretary: B Scothern, 95 Brookfield Avenue, Hucknall, Notts NG15 6FF (0602 634208).
Manager: Edward Mullane   **Asst Mgr:** John H Coleman   **Coach:** Mick Vinter
Ground: Watnall Road, Hucknall, Notts (0602 641292).
Directions: M1 jct 27, A608 to lights, right onto A611 to town centre, left at lights in market place, down High Street, right into Watnall Rd at lights - follow to island and entrance on right after. From M1 jct 26 follow Nottm signs to lights on island, left onto A610, right at Three Ponds Pub onto B600 towards Watnall, 200 yds past Queens Head turn right signed Hucknall, follow over motorway and past Rolls Royce - ground on left. 7 miles from Nottingham (BR) - bus 344.
Capacity: 2,000   **Seats:** 100   **Cover:** 1,100   **Floodlights:** No   **Founded:** 1946.
Colours: Yellow/black/yellow   **Change:** White/red/red   **Midweek matches:** Tuesday
Programme: 50p   **Programme Editor:** Robert Spray
Prev. Ground: Wigham Park 46-54   **Clubhouse:** Every night and weekend lunchtimes
Prev. Name: Hucknall Colliery Welfare (until closure of pit in 1988).
Prev. Lges: Notts All./ Central Mids.   **Record Gate:** 1,300 v Arnold Town, Central Mids Lg 26/12/89.
Local Newspapers: Hucknall & Bulwell Dispatch/ Nottm Evening Post/ Nottm Football Post.
Hons: Central Mids Lg(2) 89-91 (R-up 91-92, Lg Cup(3) 89-92), Notts All.(4) 76-78 87-89 (Lg Cup 78-79, Div 1 72-73, Div 2 70-71, Intermediate Cup 72-73); Notts Snr Cup 84-85 90-91 (R-up 83-84 85-86 87-88 89-90); FA Vase QF 85-86.

IMMINGHAM TOWN

President: Steve Davies   **Chairman:** Alan Morrish   **General Mgr:** John Spreckley
Secretary: T Paul, 28 Anglian Way, Market Rasen, Lincs LN9 3RP (0673 843654).
Manager: Micky Duffy   **Physio:** Steve Howard
Ground: Woodlands Avenue, Immingham (0469 75724).
Directions: M180 & A180 – 1st exit to Immingham. Straight on at r/about, through lights and right a 2nd r/about. Entrance on right between ATS Tyres and Lectec Services. 3 miles from Habrough (BR). Buses from Grimsby.
Colours: Maroon & sky blue stripes/maroon/maroon   **Change:** White with black pinstripe/black/black
Seats: None   **Cover:** 100   **Capacity:** 2,500   **Floodlights:** Yes   **Founded:** 1969.
Prev. Lges: Grimsby/ Lincs   **Record attendance:** 1,200 v Grimsby Town, 8/8/89.
Programme: 32 pages, 40p   **Programme Editor:** Rob Hart.
Hons: Northern Co's East Lg Div 2 R-up 86-87, Lincs Snr 'B' Cup 73-74 80-81 (R-up 81-82 83-84), Lincs Lg Cup 71-72 86-87 (Chal. Cup 84-85, Div 2 Cup R-up 76-77), Grimsby Lg 70-71, Lincs Cup 70-71, War Mem. Cup R-up 71-72, Lambert Cup 72-73 74-75, Tom Fox Cup 83-84, Bill Allinson Cup R-up 86-87, Grimsby Suppl. Cup 86-87.

LINCOLN UNITED

President: A Simpson   **Chairman:** K Roe
Secretary: K J Weaver, 22 Grainsby Close, Lincoln LN6 7QF (0522 531832).
Manager: Allen Crombie   **Assistant Manager/Coach:** John Wilkinson.
Ground: Ashby Avenue, Hartsholme, Lincoln (0522 690674).
Directions: From Newark A46 onto Lincoln relief road, at 2nd r'bout turn right for Birchwood (Skellingthorpe Rd), proceed for 1 mile passing lake and Country Park, 1st right at 30mph sign into Ashby Avenue - ground entrance 200 yds, opposite Old Peoples home. From north proceed along A57 via Saxilby until reaching A46 Lincoln Relief Road - continue on this and turn left at r'bout signed Birchwood then proceed as above. 3 miles from Loncoln Central (BR).
Capacity: 3,000   **Seats:** 150   **Covered:** 250   **Founded:** 1938   **Floodlights:** Yes
Midweek matches: Tuesday
Colours: White & red/white/white   **Change Colours:** Yellow
Programme: 50p   **Programme Editor:** John Wilkinson.
Clubhouse: Open every night, and Football season Saturdays 12-3, 4.30-6.
Previous Leagues: Lincs/ Yorks 67-82/ Northern Co's East/ Central Mids (pre'92).
Prev. Grounds: Skew Bridge (1940's)/ Co-op Spts Ground (til mid-60's)/ Hartsholme Cricket Grnd (til '82).
Prev. Names: Lincoln Amateurs (until an ex-professional signed in 1954).
Record Gate: 2,000 v Crook Town, FA Amateur Cup 1st Rd Proper, 1968.
Best FA Cup season: First Round Proper 91-92 (lost 0-7 at Huddersfield Town).
Local Newspapers: Lincolnshire Echo, Lincoln Standard.
Hons: NCE Div 1 Sth 82-83 (Div 2 85-86); Yorks Lg 70-71 73-74 (Lg Cup 70-71), Lincs Lg 63-64, Lincs Snr 'A' Cup 72-73 85-86 ('B' Cup 63-64 70-71), Central Mids Lg 91-92 (Wakefield Cup 90-91), Lincs I'mediate Cup(7) 67-73 80-81.

R.E.S. PARKGATE

President: T L Dabbs   **Chairman:** A T Dudill   **Manager:** A J Senior
Secretary: Bruce Bickerdike, 2 Cardew Close, Rawmarsh, Rotherham S62 6LB (0709 522305 (tel & fax)).
Asst Manager: Paul Greaves   **Coach:** Alan Stringer.
Ground: Roundwood Sports Complex, Green Lane, Rawmarsh, Rotherham (0709 523471).
Directions: From Rotherham A633 to Rawmarsh. From Doncaster A630 to Conisbrough, then A6023 through Swinton to Rawmarsh. Ground at Green Lane – right from Rotherham, left from Conisbrough at the Earl Grey Hotel, then right at Crown Inn. Ground 800yds on right
Seats: 100   **Cover:** 200   **Capacity:** Unknown   **Floodlights:** Yes   **Founded:** 1969
Colours: White & blue/black/white   **Change colours:** All sky.   **Nickname:** The Gate
Midweek matches: Tuesday   **Programme:** 20 pages, 50p (Editor: Secretary)
Previous leagues: Yorkshire 74-82   **Record attendance:** v Worksop 1982
Previous Name: B.S.C. Parkgate (until mid-eighties).
Clubhouse: Licensed bar, 2 lounges, including dance floor. Meals Wed. to Sat. lunchtimes.
Local Newspapers: Star/ Green'Un/ Rotherham Advertiser/ Sth Yorks Times/ Dearne Valley Weekender.

Stocksbridge Park Steels, North West Counties League Division One Champions 1991-92. Back Row (L/R): T Gough (Asst Mgr), P Nazim, S Thomas, T Jones, L Mills, J Pringle, S Frith, G Littlewood (Physio). Front: A Denton, M Dawson, S Howe, C Chadburn (Capt), M Horne (Manager), R Evans, P Sykes.

Garforth Town 1991-92. Photo - Ian Prentis.

Hallam FC 1991-92. Back Row (L/R): G Kenny (Manager), C Wilson, P Quigley, S Tighe, G Glover, I Walker, A Sharman, J Beachell (Physio). Front: S Begara, S Connelly, G Slack, S Sidebottom, I McMillan, S Lawrence, I Coe.

ROSSINGTON MAIN

Chairman: Mr S Tagg   **Manager/Coach:** Mr D Carlin   **Asst Mgr/Coach:** Mr S Downing
Secretary: Mr Malcolm Day, 3 Coronation Way, Rossington, Doncaster DN11 0RL (0302 863516).
Ground: Welfare Ground, Oxford St, Rossington, Doncaster (0302 865524).
Directions: Enter Rossington and go over the railway crossings. Pass the Welfare Club on right, Oxford Street is next right - ground is at bottom. 8 miles from Doncaster (BR).
Seats: 200   **Covered accomm.:** 500   **Capacity:** 1,200   **Floodlights:** Yes
Founded: 1925   **Midweek matches:** Tuesday
Club colours: All blue   **Change colours:** All white.
Programme: 32 pages, 50p   **Programme Editor:** Mr S Tagg.
Record attendance: 1,200 v Doncaster Rovers (date unknown).
Previous leagues: Yorkshire/ Central Midlands.
Clubhouse: Rossington Miners Welfare.
Local Newspapers: Village Life - own newspaper.
Club honours: Central Mids Lg Prem. Div 84-85 (Prem. Div Cup 84-85, Div 1 Cup 83-84).

SELBY TOWN

President: R Coultish   **Chairman:** J Vause   **Manager:** R Pearse
Secretary: T Mitchell, 9 Portholme Drive, Selby, N. Yorks YO8 0QF (0757 708035).
Asst. Manager: J Storey   **Coach:** W Carpenter.
Ground: Flaxley Road Ground, Richard Street, Selby, North Yorkshire YO8 0BN.
Directions: From Leeds, left at main traffic lights in Selby down Scott Rd. then 1st left into Richard St. From Doncaster go straight across main traffic lights into Scott Road then 1st left. From York right at main traffic lights into Scott Rd, and 1st left. 1 mile from Selby (BR).
Seats: 100   **Cover:** 750   **Capacity:** 5,000   **Floodlights:** Yes   **Founded:** 1911
Club colours: All white   **Change colours:** All red.
Programme: 12 pages, 30p   **Programme Editor:** M Limbert
Nickname: The Robins   **Main Sponsors:** Irwin & Co Builders
Prev. League: Yorkshire (1920-82)   **Prev. ground:** Bowling Green, James St. 1920-51
Past players to progress to Football League: Numerous
Best FA Cup performance: Second Round Proper 1954-55
Best FA Vase performance: Preliminary Round 1989-90
Record attendance: 7,000 v Bradford Park Avenue (FA Cup 1st Rnd 1953-54)
Clubhouse: Bar at ground open first and second team matchdays
Midweek Matches: Wednesday   **Local Newspaper:** Selby Times.
Club honours: Yorkshire Lg 32-33 34-35 35-36 52-53 53-54 (R-up 24-25 25-26 27-28 28-29 30-31 31-32 50-51 55-56, Div 3 R-up 74-75, Lg Cup 37-38 53-54 54-55 62-63); Northern Co. East Div 2 R-up 89-90; West Riding Snr Cup 37-38; West Riding Co Cup 27-28 48-49; West Riding Chall. Cup 34-35 35-36

TADCASTER ALBION

Chairman: A Rose   **Vice Chairman:** J Learoyd.
Secretary: E Brown, 35 Calcaria Crescent, Tadcaster, N. Yorks LS24 9LN (0937 832844).
Manager: S Alford   **Treasurer:** M Burnett.
Ground: The Park, Ings Lane, Tadcaster. 0937 832844
Directions: From West Riding and South Yorks, turn right off A659 at John Smith's Brewery Clock. From East Riding turn left off A659 after passing over river bridge and pelican crossing (New Street).
Colours: Red with white trim/white/red   **Change colours:** White/black/black
Programme: 20 pages.

WORSBROUGH BRIDGE M.W. & ATHLETIC

Chairman: Mr J Wright   **Press Officer:** Mr A Wright (0226 243418).
Secretary: D Smith, 18 Shield Avenue, Worsbrough Bridge, Barnsley, S. Yorks S70 5BQ (0226 243418).
Manager: G Bedford   **Asst Manager:** K Paddon.
Ground: Park Road, Worsbrough Bridge, Barnsley (0226 284452).
Directions: On the A61 Barnsley-Sheffield road two miles south of Barnsley, 2 miles from M1 jnt 36 opposite Blackburns Bridge. Two and a half miles from Barnsley (BR). Yorkshire Traction run buses every 10 mins thru Worsbrough Bridge.
Seats: 175   **Covered:** 175   **Capacity:** 2,000   **Floodlights:** Due   **Founded:** 1921
Colours: All red   **Change colours:** Yellow/blue   **Reformed:** 1947
Record attendance: 2,300 v Blyth Spartans, FA Amateur Cup 1971
Previous Leagues: Barnsley 52-61/ County Snr 62-70/ Yorks 71-82.
Programme: 20 pages, 20p
Hons: Northern Co's East Lg Div 1 R-up 90-91 (Div 3 R-up 85-86), Sheffield Snr Cup R-up 72-73, County Snr Lg 65-66 69-70 (R-up 62-63, Lg Cup 65-66), Barnsley Lg 52-53 58-59 59-60 (Lg Cup 56-57 58-59 (R-up 53-54)), Beckett Cup 57-58.

YORKSHIRE AMATEUR

President: Rayner Barker   **Chairman:** W Ellis
Secretary: B Whaley, 50 Moseley Wood Walk, Leeds LS16 7HG (0532 679806).
Manager: M White   **Asst Mgr:** S Jeffery   **Coach:** B Richardson
Ground: Bracken Edge, Sycamore Avenue, Leeds LS8 4DZ (0532 624093).
Directions: From South M1 to Leeds, then A58 Wetherby Road to Fforde Green Hotel. Turn left and proceed to Sycamore Ave. From East A1 to Boot & Shoe Inn then to Shaftesbury Hotel, turn right into Harehills Lane, then to Sycamore Avenue. Two and a half miles from Leeds (BR).
Seats: None   **Cover:** None   **Capacity:** 3,000   **Floodlights:** Yes
Colours: White/blue/red   **Change colours:** All red   **Founded:** 1919
Midweek Matches: Tuesday   **Previous ground:** Elland Road 1919-20
Record Gate: 4-5,000 v Wimbledon, FA Amateur Cup 1932.
Programme: 16 pages, 30p   **Programme Editor:** Ian White.
Previous League: Yorks 20-24 30-82.   **Clubhouse:** Bar, tea bar, games room, lounge.
Local Newspapers: Yorkshire Post/ Yorkshire Evening Post/ North Leeds Advertiser.
Hons: FA Amtr Cup SF 31-32, West Riding Co. Cup(3), Yorks Lg 31-32 (Div 2 58-59 (R-up 52-53 71-72), Div 3 77-78, Lg Cup 32-33), Leeds & Dist. Snr Cup.

Rossington Main's D Ridley scores the final goal in a 5-1 win at York Railway Institute, who have now left the League, on Easter Monday morning. Photo - James Wright.

Worsbrough Bridge Miners Welfare & Athletic. Back Row (L/R): Keith Paddon (Coach), Dave Bursztyn, Paul Hardcastle, Gary Parkin, Steve Morfitt, Wayne Scargill, Neil Broadhead, Martin Beaumont, Geoff Bedford (Manager), Barry Snape (Trainer). Front: Carl Kendrick, Paul Hodgson, John Rushforth, Darrell Pickering, Geoff Horsefield, Kevin Holmes. Photo - Dave West.

Yorkshire Amateur FC 1991-92. Back Row (L/R): Malcolm White (Manager), Danny O'Hearn, James Anderson, Kevin Smith, Mick Whaley, Paul Lowery, Vernal Blair, Gary Jackson, Terry Davis (Physio). Front: Paul Bowland, Darren Nicholson, Anthony Holt, Jamie Steel (Capt), Peter Cusic, David Hope. Photo - Dave West.

Hallam's Sidebottom flicks on a header as Immingham's Fisher challenges in an NCEL clash at Woodlands Avenue.

Hucknall Town FC, Websters Central Midlands League Runners-up and League Cup Winners, who have deservedly earned promotion under the Pyramid system to the Northern Counties East League. Back Row (L/R): Mick Vinter (Player/Physio), Paul Hancock, Gavin Ottewell, Stuart Harding, Tim Preece, Paul Tomlinson, Graham Harrod, Nigel Bailey, Phil Towle. Front: John Chamberlain, Keith Ward, Mick Hodgson, Pete Fletcher, Steve Hare (Capt), Glenn Grantham, Carl Steggles. Photo - Gavin Ellis.

BASS DERBYSHIRE SENIOR LEAGUE

Bass Prem. Div.	P	W	D	L	F	A	Pts
Malt Shovel	24	20	2	2	69	34	42
Little Easton	24	17	5	2	87	34	39
Ockbrook	24	11	9	4	68	33	31
Castle Donnington T.	24	13	5	6	62	44	31
Allestree	24	13	3	8	55	45	29
Nottingham House	24	11	5	8	53	39	27
Santos	24	10	5	9	84	49	25
Mickleover Sports	24	8	7	9	37	54	29
Allenton Athletic	24	5	8	11	51	58	18
Aston	24	7	4	13	43	57	18
T/S Rail Freight	24	4	6	14	27	61	14
Greyhound Kestrels	24	4	3	17	33	68	11
Belper St Johns	24	1	2	21	24	117	4

Carling Black L. D1	P	W	D	L	F	A	Pts
Stanley Common	26	19	3	4	82	37	41
Melbourne Dynamos	26	18	4	3	88	33	40
Alfreton Athletic	26	19	1	6	69	33	39
Ashbourne Town	26	16	3	6	71	44	35
Smalley Villa	26	10	9	6	41	36	29
Grenville Ath.	26	13	2	10	67	45	28
Allenton RBL	26	12	2	11	53	43	26
Hemington	26	7	9	10	48	54	23
Concorde Utd	26	9	5	12	47	65	29
Qualcast	26	7	6	13	42	62	20
Findern	26	8	3	15	45	58	19
FC Turbines	26	7	4	14	43	82	18
Denby Villa	26	4	4	18	42	79	12
T/S Rail Fr. Res	26	2	3	21	29	101	7

Worthington D2	P	W	D	L	F	A	Pts
Tutbury Hawthorns	20	15	4	1	87	18	34
Sudbury Park	22	14	5	3	70	33	33
Bargate Rovers	22	14	5	3	62	41	33
Alestree Res	22	8	9	5	50	36	25
AC Rolls Royce	20	11	2	7	63	39	24
Allestree Rovers	22	9	5	8	50	38	23
Alvaston OB	22	8	5	9	29	35	21
Shipley	22	9	1	12	59	64	19
Punjab United	22	5	6	11	32	58	16
Mickleover S. Res	22	5	5	12	26	55	15
Christians	22	4	4	14	36	92	12
Severn Trent	22	1	3	18	30	85	5

Lamot Pils D3	P	W	D	L	F	A	Pts
Spa Inn	24	17	2	5	97	41	36
Belper Thorntons	24	16	4	4	92	42	36
New Pondeross	24	15	1	8	64	48	31
St Marys	24	12	6	6	75	56	30
Little Eaton	26	11	7	6	65	42	29
Qualcast Res	24	10	5	9	49	44	25
Belper St J. Res	24	10	4	10	65	61	24
Sth Wingfield	24	8	7	9	49	57	23
Bargate Rvrs Res	24	7	5	12	46	64	19
Aston Res	24	6	6	12	44	58	18
Castle Donn. Res	24	7	4	13	58	79	18
Derventio	24	5	5	14	39	71	15
Scholl	24	4	0	20	37	117	8

WEBSTERS CENTRAL MIDLANDS LEAGUE

President: L Nowicki, Esq.
Chairman: F A Harwood.
Hon. Secretary: Mr A E Goodacre,
6 Maddison Avenue, Chaddesden, Derby DE2 6HZ.

LINCOLN AND HUCKNALL EARN PROMOTION

If the plans and provisions made in season 1991/92 come into being it could well go down in the annals of time as the year the Central Midlands League came of age. Sterling efforts were made to produce a 'Working Plan' for full incorporation in the Northern Pyramid feeding into Division One of the Northern Counties East League, and it appears that this plan is acceptable to all concerned.

To mark this, and to assist in removing some of the void created by certain Welsh clubs leaving English football, two clubs have been promoted to the Northern Counties East League for 1992/93. There can be little doubt that both have earned their elevation. Lincoln United became the first Central Midlands League club to reach the First Round Proper of the F.A. Cup, and, although losing heavily at Leeds Road to Huddersfield, achieved some notable 'scalps' on the way with Gainsborough Trinity (home) and Leek Town (away) amongst them. The club took over the leadership of the League's Supreme Division back in October and never looked likely to be caught, ending the season as worthy champions. Even twice champions and League Cup winners Hucknall were unable to close the gap despite valiant efforts, and had to be content with retaining the Cup for the third successive year with a 1-0 win over Nettleham at Derby County's Baseball Ground. Nevertheless, they have earned their promotion, and both clubs have completed extensive ground improvements over the last twelve months.

There were two other results in the F.A. Cup which captured the imagination of Non-League followers the country over. Borrowash gained a Second Qualifying Round victory at Conference club Macclesfield before losing to Emley, and Oakham United won at Goole Town who were then leading the H.F.S. Loans League, before falling as another of Lincoln United's victims. The progress and high expectations of our clubs, however, were not maintained in the F.A. Vase.

Domestically, the League was dominated by Lincoln United with their superb run of results, with Louth United temporarily threatening. Newly promoted clubs Stanton Ilkeston, Glapwell and Shirebrook Colliery struggled to find their feet, but they will have enjoyed the experience and will be all the better for it. The main success was Mickleover Royal British Legion who must qualify for the nickname 'Nomads'. Their own ground being unsuitable for Supreme Division football, they groundshared with Gresley Rovers, and ended up playing home games at both Belper Town and Burton Albion, yet still finished in a remarkable sixth place.

Premier Division North was dominated by new arrivals Fryston Colliery Welfare, Kiveton Park and Norton Woodseats, the former eventually claiming the title with a bit to spare and winning the Castleford Cup in the process. Down and almost out before the season started and with no league to play in, Fryston enquired about membership of the C.M.L., were accepted, and went from strength to strength. Kiveton Park and Norton Woodseats made great efforts to catch them and were involved in one of the tightest 'scraps' the League has witnessed for second spot. Off the field, South Normanton Athletic made greater strides than on it, leaving their chase for a top six place very late indeed. However, here is a club to watch for the future. *(continued overleaf)...*

Lincoln United FC, Websters Central Midlands League champions 1991-92. Back Row (L/R): Allen Crombie, Stuart Park (capt), Paul Ward, Simon Waby, Gary Goddard, Warren Ward, Rick Wright. Front: Fraser Hinchcliffe, Steve Carter, Tony Simmons, Alfie Park, Darren Dye, Justin Elkington. Photo - T Sandell-Codd.

Premier Division South was led for a long while by Gedling Town until Slack & Parr came through to dominate the latter stages and win by a sizeable margin. Long Eaton United took another step forward off the field towards bringing back their former glories, and Kimberley probably did more than most, in achieving both the grading and floodlighting to return to the top Division. Newhall, through a land sale, gained the money to finance their future destiny and this is another club to look out for.

The League's Wakefield Floodlight Cup was won by Harworth Colliery Institute with a 3-0 win over Louth at Lincoln City's Sincil Bank, and Sharlow St James of Premier Division South take the League Cup acolades as the Premier Division's last survivor. In other areas, Arnold Town supplied most of the Notts F.A. team which won the F.A. County Youth Cup beating Surrey in the final, Louth United won the Lincs Senior 'B' Cup, and Highfield Rangers came close to providing a shock in the Leicestershire & Rutland F.A. Senior Cup.

Season 1992/93 looks to be full of interest if progress can be maintained.

Stan Wilton, Retiring General Secretary.

Supreme Division	P	W	D	L	F	A	PTS
Lincoln United	34	26	5	3	95	26	83
Hucknall Town	34	22	3	9	86	44	69
Louth United	34	20	6	8	72	41	66
Harworth C.I.	34	20	5	9	76	51	65
Sheffield Aurora	34	22	2	10	68	33	*62
Mickleover R.B.L.	34	19	3	12	77	54	60
Blidworth Welfare	34	16	5	13	46	46	53
Arnold Town	34	15	7	12	73	60	52
Priory (Eastwood)	34	14	7	13	50	56	49
Nettleham	34	13	8	13	49	52	47
Heanor Town	34	13	6	15	48	54	45
Oakham United	34	13	6	15	52	59	45
Borrowash Victoria	34	8	11	15	49	63	35
Shirebrook Coll.	34	10	5	19	51	68	35
Wombwell Town	34	10	4	20	52	71	+31
Melton Town	34	7	5	22	42	93	26
Stanton Ilkeston	34	7	4	23	29	78	25
Glapwell	34	7	4	23	29	78	25

* - Six points deducted
+ - Three points deducted

Leading Scorers:
Christopher Shaw (Arnold) 28
Alan Park (Lincoln Utd) 27
Allan Cooper (Louth Utd) 25
Neal Farrow (Harworth) 24
Jason Farrow (Heanor) 24
Peter Fletcher (Hucknall) 22
Gary Wells (Nettleham) 22
Simon Gamble (Harworth) 21
Michael Taplin (Mickleover) 20

Premier North	P	W	D	L	F	A	PTS
Fryston C.W.	26	20	2	4	75	33	62
Kiveton Park	26	17	4	5	63	29	55
Norton Woodseats	26	14	7	5	58	33	49
Mexborough Town	26	12	8	6	46	31	44
Sth Normanton Ath.	26	13	5	8	42	32	44
Blackwell M.W.	26	11	6	9	38	44	39
Rossington	26	11	4	11	42	50	37
Linc. Moorlands	26	9	6	11	44	40	33
Holbrook Miners W.	26	8	9	9	35	42	33
Kilburn Miners W.	26	8	6	12	56	60	30
Biwater	26	8	4	14	43	41	28
Selston	26	6	6	14	33	60	24
Retford Rail	26	3	6	17	33	70	15
Nuthall	26	4	3	19	34	77	15

Leading Scorers:
Richard Hazelhurst (Fryston) 21
Barry Davies (Mexorough Town) 20
Stephen Gisborne (Norton W'seats) 20
Andrew Fitzmaurice (Fryston) 15
Kevin Martin (Lincoln Moorlands) 15

Premier South	P	W	D	L	F	A	PTS
Slack & Parr	30	24	3	3	81	23	75
Gedling Town	30	19	6	5	91	42	63
Kimberley Town	30	17	6	7	66	40	57
Highfield Rgrs	30	15	8	7	48	28	53
Newhall United	30	17	2	11	63	49	53
Shardlow St James	30	15	4	11	49	38	49
Long Eaton Utd	30	13	5	12	67	49	44
Derby C & W Reck.	30	14	2	14	47	42	44
Alvaston & Boulton	30	12	6	12	45	44	42
Derby Rolls Royce	30	11	7	12	48	62	40
Redford	30	12	3	15	49	72	39
Leicester Nirvana	30	11	1	18	37	65	*31
Brailsford	30	8	5	17	43	74	29
West Hallam	30	7	2	21	38	73	23
Bulwell United	30	6	4	20	46	85	22
Attenborough	30	5	4	21	37	69	19

* - Three points deducted

Leading Scorers (Premier South):
Kevin Joyce (Newhall Utd) 21
Darren Terry (Gedling Town) 20
Neil Wallace (Slack & Parr) 18
David Harbottle (Gedling Town) 16

Reserve Premier	P	W	D	L	F	A	PTS
Hucknall Res	30	24	5	1	92	28	77
Borrowash Res	30	18	6	6	61	29	60
Priory (E'wood) Res	30	18	6	6	57	44	60
Shirebrook Res	30	17	3	10	71	45	54
Wombwell T. Res	30	14	4	12	53	41	46
Arnold Town Res	30	13	7	10	48	36	46
Highfield R. Res	30	13	7	10	53	42	46
Oakham Utd Res	30	11	7	12	51	53	40
Bulwell Utd Res	30	9	7	14	56	71	34
Derby Rolls R. Res	30	8	10	12	43	61	34
Rossington Res	30	6	13	11	33	44	31
Alvaston & B. Res	30	7	9	14	36	55	30
Melton T. Res	30	8	5	17	42	73	29
Blidworth Res	30	8	4	18	44	80	28
Mickelover Res	30	6	9	15	36	45	27
Derby C & W Res	30	6	6	18	34	63	24

Leading Scorers:
Marc Smoczyk (Hucknall Res) 25
Paul Tomlinson (Hucknall Res) 20
Mark McGraw (Priory Res) 19
Chris Darby (Shirebrook Res) 17
Peter Evans (Arnold Town Res) 17
David Blackband (Shirebrook Res) 16

Reserve Div. One	P	W	D	L	F	A	PTS
Norton W'seats Res	32	25	3	4	109	39	78
Biwater Res	32	22	9	1	98	29	75
Kimberley T. Res	32	19	7	6	79	54	64
Harworth Res	32	19	6	7	81	48	63
Slack & Parr Res	32	17	4	11	95	55	55
Stanton Ilk. Res	32	14	7	11	82	67	49
Holbrook MW Res	32	15	4	13	49	52	49
Brailsford Res	32	14	7	11	62	64	*45
Attenborough Res	32	12	5	15	64	76	41
Radford Res	32	11	8	13	60	83	41
Arnold T. 'A'	32	9	6	15	50	62	35
Kilburn MW Res	32	7	10	15	45	63	31
Derby RR 'A'	32	8	7	17	44	100	31
Borrowash Vic. 'A'	32	8	5	19	65	70	29
Selston Res	32	7	7	18	48	77	28
Nuthall Res	32	8	1	23	50	92	25
Shardlow SJ Res	32	7	2	23	44	94	23

* - Four points deducted

Leading Scorers:
Terence Griffin (Harworth Res) 43
Michael Gabbitas (Norton W. Res) 40
David Martin (Biwater Res) 29
Andrew Neilson (Kimberley Res) 19
Ashley Potts (Slack & Parr Res) 19
Darren Heithus (Slack & Parr Res) 18
Steven Corrall (Stanton Ilk. Res) 17

SUPREME DIVISION RESULT CHART 1991/92

HOME TEAM	1	2	3	4	5	6	7	8	9	10	11	12	13	14	15	16	17	18
1. Arnold Town	*	3-0	2-5	4-0	4-3	2-2	2-1	0-1	2-5	4-5	2-0	1-1	1-1	1-1	0-3	2-1	5-0	4-2
2. Blidworth Wf.	1-3	*	1-1	1-0	1-3	0-3	0-1	2-1	0-2	1-1	2-1	0-1	2-0	1-4	0-0	2-1	2-0	1-0
3. Borrowash	1-0	2-2	*	5-2	0-1	2-4	4-4	2-2	1-3	3-1	2-2	1-1	1-1	1-1	0-1	1-2	0-2	2-0
4. Glapwell	1-6	3-4	1-1	*	3-4	1-3	1-3	1-5	1-7	6-1	1-2	5-0	1-2	0-6	0-4	1-5	2-1	2-6
5. Harworth C.I.	3-2	0-1	4-0	3-1	*	1-0	2-0	2-3	1-3	2-3	3-2	3-1	3-0	7-1	4-1	1-1	2-0	2-1
6. Heanor Town	0-1	0-2	0-1	1-1	1-0	*	1-2	0-4	0-0	2-2	0-2	1-1	2-1	3-1	0-2	2-3	2-0	2-1
7. Hucknall Town	5-2	0-3	6-2	4-0	1-2	3-1	*	1-1	1-2	7-3	3-1	3-1	2-0	3-0	0-3	1-0	6-0	6-0
8. Lincoln United	1-0	1-0	3-0	3-0	2-2	8-0	1-1	*	0-2	7-1	2-0	2-1	4-0	3-1	0-0	6-1	4-0	1-0
9. Louth United	3-1	0-1	1-0	2-0	0-1	1-1	2-1	0-6	*	8-0	2-2	0-1	5-3	1-1	0-1	1-5	2-0	5-0
10. Melton Town	1-4	0-1	0-2	2-2	1-1	0-2	0-2	1-2	1-2	*	2-3	0-5	0-5	0-4	1-3	4-0	3-1	3-2
11. Mickleover RBL	2-2	2-3	2-0	6-0	6-4	1-2	2-4	2-1	0-2	5-2	*	2-1	0-2	2-1	0-3	2-1	3-1	1-2
12. Nettleham	1-3	1-0	4-1	2-1	1-1	1-0	3-2	2-4	2-2	1-1	0-3	*	1-1	1-2	1-0	4-0	1-0	3-1
13. Oakham United	2-2	0-2	2-2	4-1	3-1	3-1	1-2	1-3	3-1	0-1	0-7	2-0	*	1-1	0-2	1-0	3-0	3-1
14. Priory Eastwood	1-1	2-1	0-4	4-2	0-1	1-0	0-3	1-2	0-2	2-0	0-4	1-1	2-1	*	3-1	1-0	2-1	1-2
15. Sheffield Aurora	3-0	3-2	3-0	1-0	4-0	1-0	0-1	0-1	3-1	0-1	2-3	4-0	3-2	1-2	*	4-1	4-0	0-4
16. Shirebrook C.	1-3	2-3	1-1	6-3	2-5	2-3	0-1	0-1	1-2	1-0	1-2	2-1	3-0	1-1	4-3	*	0-3	2-0
17. Stanton Ilkeston	3-2	1-1	2-0	1-1	0-2	0-4	1-4	0-6	0-2	2-1	0-3	2-1	2-3	1-2	1-3	0-0	*	3-1
18. Wombwell Town	0-2	4-3	2-1	3-0	2-2	3-5	3-2	2-4	1-1	1-0	1-2	1-3	0-1	3-0	1-2	1-1	1-1	*

PREMIER DIVISION NORTH RESULT CHART 1991/92

HOME TEAM	1	2	3	4	5	6	7	8	9	10	11	12	13	14
1. Biwater	*	4-2	1-2	0-2	3-1	1-2	1-0	1-1	1-3	4-2	2-1	1-2	6-1	0-1
2. Blackwell M.W.	1-0	*	1-4	0-1	2-2	0-0	1-3	2-4	0-0	2-1	1-0	2-1	0-1	1-0
3. Fryston Colliery	3-2	7-0	*	1-1	0-3	2-1	1-0	1-0	5-3	5-2	5-0	1-1	7-1	2-1
4. Holbrook M.W.	1-0	1-1	1-3	*	2-2	0-4	2-1	2-3	2-2	3-4	5-2	2-2	0-0	0-2
5. Kilburn M.W.	5-2	1-3	2-6	1-0	*	1-5	7-3	2-2	0-0	3-4	5-0	3-0	1-1	1-3
6. Kiveton Park	0-2	4-2	2-1	3-1	5-0	*	1-1	3-2	0-1	4-1	3-0	6-0	2-1	2-2
7. Lincoln M'lands	2-0	3-1	1-2	3-0	3-2	2-3	*	0-0	0-1	4-3	2-2	1-2	1-1	3-0
8. Mexborough Town	1-0	2-2	1-3	0-1	4-1	3-0	2-1	*	1-1	2-1	1-1	3-1	2-1	0-2
9. Norton Woodseats	2-1	0-3	2-1	4-1	3-4	2-2	2-0	1-2	*	7-0	2-0	6-1	3-1	1-3
10. Nuthall	2-2	1-3	0-2	0-1	1-6	1-4	1-2	1-1	0-4	*	4-1	1-4	0-2	1-2
11. Retford Rail	1-1	2-3	2-3	2-2	2-1	0-2	0-4	1-1	2-3	1-1	*	1-3	4-1	1-6
12. Rossington	2-1	1-1	1-3	1-1	3-0	0-2	2-1	1-5	1-2	2-0	4-3	*	1-2	0-1
13. Selston	0-6	1-2	2-4	1-1	2-1	2-3	1-1	0-3	0-3	5-0	2-0	1-2	*	1-3
14. Sth Normanton Ath.	1-1	0-2	2-1	0-2	1-1	1-0	2-2	1-0	0-0	1-2	3-4	0-4	4-0	*

PREMIER DIVISION SOUTH RESULT CHART 1991/92

HOME TEAM	1	2	3	4	5	6	7	8	9	10	11	12	13	14	15	16
1. Alvaston & Boulton	*	4-0	2-0	6-1	0-1	1-0	2-2	0-2	1-0	0-3	1-1	0-0	1-3	1-0	2-5	3-0
2. Attenborough	0-1	*	3-3	4-1	1-3	3-0	2-2	1-3	1-2	2-3	1-3	2-3	2-1	0-3	0-3	1-3
3. Brailsford	3-4	3-0	*	1-1	0-2	3-0	2-2	1-1	3-2	1-0	4-1	1-5	4-1	2-1	0-5	2-0
4. Bulwell United	1-5	0-1	2-0	*	3-4	4-6	0-2	0-2	0-3	2-3	0-6	4-2	3-2	0-3	1-1	2-3
5. Derby C & W Reckitts	2-1	3-1	6-0	0-5	*	1-1	1-3	0-0	2-4	1-0	4-2	2-3	3-0	1-0	1-2	3-0
6. Derby Rolls Royce	1-0	1-0	4-3	2-1	1-0	*	1-4	1-1	0-4	3-0	2-2	0-2	1-1	1-0	1-3	6-2
7. Gedling Town	2-1	3-2	3-0	5-1	2-0	2-2	*	1-1	3-1	3-1	4-3	3-2	11-0	5-1	1-3	6-1
8. Highfield Rangers	0-0	3-0	3-2	4-0	1-0	1-3	0-0	*	0-2	3-0	0-1	4-1	1-2	2-0	0-2	3-2
9. Kimberley Town	1-1	1-1	2-2	5-3	2-1	3-1	1-4	0-2	*	5-1	3-1	5-0	5-1	2-0	1-1	4-1
10. Leicester Nirvana	1-2	2-1	2-0	2-0	1-0	4-1	0-3	1-5	1-1	*	0-3	1-5	2-1	2-1	0-2	3-2
11. Long Eaton United	5-1	4-0	5-0	2-2	0-2	6-2	1-3	0-0	1-2	3-0	*	1-2	5-3	2-2	0-2	0-2
12. Newhall United	1-2	2-1	3-2	1-3	3-2	1-1	2-1	3-0	0-1	6-0	1-4	*	4-1	0-1	2-3	3-1
13. Radford	3-2	1-3	3-0	1-1	2-1	4-1	4-3	1-0	0-2	2-1	3-2	0-4	*	1-2	1-3	5-2
14. Shardlow St James	2-1	2-2	3-1	4-1	1-0	3-3	2-1	1-1	3-1	1-0	0-1	3-0	2-0	*	1-3	5-0
15. Slack & Parr	4-0	4-0	6-0	4-1	3-0	2-0	1-4	1-2	4-0	3-2	3-1	0-1	0-0	4-0	*	1-0
16. West Hallam	0-0	3-2	2-0	1-3	0-1	1-2	4-3	2-3	1-1	3-1	0-2	0-1	1-2	0-2	1-3	*

Arnold Town FC. Back Row (L/R): Mark Corbett (Players' & Manager's Player of the Year), David Charlesworth, Tony Kellam, Neil Waters, Lee Farmery (Sportsman of the Season), Sean Ingram, Kevin Ping, Chris Mee. Front: Richard Atkin, Nick Whitehurst, Richard Johnson, Darren Stevenson, Chris Shaw (Supporters' Player of the Year). Photo - Gavin Ellis.

RESERVE PREMIER DIVISION RESULT CHART 1991/92

HOME TEAM	1	2	3	4	5	6	7	8	9	10	11	12	13	14	15	16
1. Alvaston & Boulton Res	*	0-1	2-2	0-4	2-0	3-0	1-1	2-2	2-0	4-4	1-0	2-4	1-3	0-0	0-2	2-1
2. Arnold Town Res	0-1	*	0-0	1-1	3-2	2-1	1-1	1-1	1-2	6-1	0-2	0-1	1-2	1-0	3-2	1-1
3. Blidworth Welfare Res	0-0	1-2	*	0-3	3-0	3-1	4-2	2-4	0-3	2-0	2-1	2-3	3-4	1-2	1-8	3-1
4. Borrowash V. Res	1-0	1-2	5-1	*	4-0	3-1	3-2	2-0	2-3	6-2	2-0	0-1	2-0	1-0	0-1	4-1
5. Bulwell United Res	4-3	1-6	6-2	1-3	*	1-0	6-2	3-1	0-3	2-3	1-1	2-2	1-3	4-2	0-3	1-1
6. Derby C & W Rec. Res	2-2	0-4	2-0	0-2	1-0	*	0-1	3-3	1-2	2-1	2-1	2-0	2-3	1-1	1-3	1-4
7. Derby Rolls Royce Res	3-0	1-1	4-2	0-1	3-3	0-0	*	2-0	1-5	0-2	2-1	1-6	1-1	2-2	2-3	0-2
8. Highfield Rangers Res	3-0	0-0	2-1	1-1	3-0	1-1	4-0	*	0-1	2-3	2-1	3-1	1-2	2-0	2-1	2-1
9. Hucknall Town Res	4-1	5-1	7-0	2-2	3-1	3-1	1-1	5-1	*	3-1	2-2	3-0	8-1	1-1	3-1	4-2
10. Melton Town Res	0-3	1-0	2-3	2-2	1-2	1-2	4-2	0-5	1-4	*	0-1	1-3	2-2	1-1	2-5	1-0
11. Mickleover RBL Res	2-0	0-2	2-3	1-1	2-3	2-3	2-2	0-1	2-3	1-3	*	1-0	0-0	3-0	0-0	
12. Oakham United Res	1-1	0-2	1-1	1-1	2-5	4-2	1-3	2-0	0-4	0-3	2-2	*	5-1	3-0	3-5	2-2
13. Priory Eastwood Res	2-0	4-3	3-0	2-0	1-1	3-1	0-1	3-2	2-2	3-0	2-2	1-0	*	1-0	1-0	2-0
14. Rossington Res	2-2	0-1	4-1	0-1	1-1	2-0	1-1	2-2	0-3	2-0	1-1	1-0	2-2	*	3-2	1-2
15. Shirebrook Col. Res	5-0	3-2	4-1	2-0	5-3	2-0	4-1	1-3	0-2	0-0	3-0	1-1	0-3	1-1	*	1-2
16. Wombwell Town Res	2-1	1-1	2-0	2-3	2-1	5-1	0-1	1-0	0-1	5-0	1-3	2-1	2-0	6-1	2-3	*

RESERVE DIVISION ONE RESULT CHART 1991/92

HOME TEAM	1	2	3	4	5	6	7	8	9	10	11	12	13	14	15	16	17
1. Arnold Town 'A'	*	7-1	1-1	1-0	2-2	1-0	3-2	1-1	1-1	0-2	0-2	4-1	2-3	2-1	2-1	1-3	1-4
2. Attenborough Res	2-4	*	1-4	2-0	4-0	2-2	1-1	0-4	3-2	0-2	1-2	6-1	1-1	6-1	1-2	2-1	
3. Biwater Res	3-1	4-1	*	3-1	0-0	6-0	3-3	3-0	5-1	2-1	0-0	3-0	4-0	5-1	2-1	1-1	2-1
4. Borrowash V. 'A'	2-0	3-1	0-3	*	1-2	3-1	1-2	0-2	2-2	6-0	0-1	5-2	3-4	4-0	11-3	1-4	2-3
5. Brailsford Res	2-1	8-2	0-3	2-2	*	6-0	1-5	2-0	1-2	1-2	1-5	3-0	0-0	2-1	2-0	2-1	3-4
6. Derby Rolls Royce 'A'	1-3	2-5	1-11	2-2	3-3	*	1-2	5-2	0-4	1-1	1-4	4-1	2-0	2-1	1-4	0-3	0-9
7. Harworth C.I. Res	5-0	2-2	3-0	1-1	7-1	1-3	*	1-0	2-1	3-2	0-2	2-1	7-1	3-0	3-1	5-4	1-1
8. Hilbrook M.W. Res	1-0	3-2	1-2	3-2	1-3	2-0	0-4	*	2-0	1-1	1-2	2-1	2-2	2-1	3-1	1-0	0-3
9. Kilburn M.W. Res	1-1	0-1	1-1	2-1	1-1	1-1	5-0	0-0	*	1-2	3-1	1-8	1-4	3-2	1-3	1-3	2-1
10. Kimberley Town Res	3-2	0-0	4-4	2-1	0-0	0-0	2-0	6-3	4-3	*	2-3	5-1	3-2	2-3	1-0	3-2	5-2
11. Norton Woodseats Res	4-2	1-0	1-1	4-2	8-1	9-1	1-4	2-1	1-0	5-0	*	7-1	5-0	5-1	6-0	7-1	1-0
12. Nuthall Res	2-0	0-3	0-2	1-2	1-6	1-2	2-4	2-1	1-1	1-3	1-0	*	4-1	2-1	3-1	4-3	2-4
13. Radford Res	2-0	3-1	2-2	4-2	1-2	1-1	2-0	2-4	3-1	2-2	3-2		*	3-3	4-2	3-2	3-3
14. Selston Res	2-2	4-2	1-10	3-3	2-1	0-1	0-2	1-0	0-0	2-4	4-1	3-0	3-1	*	0-1	2-2	1-1
15. Shardlow St James Res	0-0	3-4	0-3	2-1	0-1	1-2	0-4	3-1	0-1	0-7	2-8	4-2	5-1	1-0	*	0-3	2-4
16. Slack & Parr Res	3-1	1-4	1-4	5-0	4-0	7-1	5-1	0-1	4-0	2-2	4-5	4-0	6-0	5-1	3-1	*	6-1
17. Stanton Ilkeston Res	4-4	7-1	0-1	3-1	1-3	4-3	1-1	1-2	3-2	1-5	2-4	6-2	0-0	4-3	2-1	1-1	*

LEAGUE CUP 1991-92

First Round

Kimberley Town v Radford	1-2	Gedling Town v Derby Carriage & Wagon (Reckitts)	0-1

Second Round

Alvaston & Boulton v Derby Rolls Royce	5-1	Biwater v Lincoln Moorlands	7-0
Blackwell Miners Welfare v Attenborough	1-0	Derby C. & W. (Reckitts) v Norton Woodseats	1-4
Holbrook Miners Welfare v Rossington	1-1,2-0	Kilburn Miners Welfare v Selston	1-2
Kiveton Park v Highfield Rangers	5-6	Leicester Nirvana v Nuthall	2-1
Long Eaton United v Fryston Colliery Welfare	0-3	Mexborough Town v Radford	3-1
Newhall United v Brailsford	3-2	Retford Rail v Shardlow St James	0-3
Slack & Parr v Bulwell United	3-3,3-2	West Hallam v South Normanton Athletic	1-0

Third Round

Alvaston & Boulton v Lincoln United	1-4	Blackwell Miners Welfare v Harworth Colliery Inst.	0-3
Borrowash Victoria v Selston	7-3	Brailsford v Nettleham	1-1,0-2
Fryston Colliery Welfare v Hucknall Town	1-3	Glapwell v Blidworth Welfare	0-3
Heanor Town v Shirebrook Colliery	0-1	Holbrook M.W. v Mickleover Royal British Legion	2-5
Leicester Nirvana v West Hallam	5-2	Melton Town v Arnold Town	1-3
Norton Woodseats v Sheffield Aurora	2-3	Oakham United v Highfield Rangers	4-3
Priory (Eastwood) v Biwater	3-4	Slack & Parr v Mexborough Town	6-1
Stanton Ilkeston v Shardlow St James	1-1,1-2	Wombwell Town v Louth United	1-3

Fourth Round

Hucknall Town v Slack & Parr	2-0	Blidworth Welfare v Harworth Colliery Institute	6-0
Lincoln United v Borrowash Victoria	0-1	Nettleham v Leicester Nirvana	4-1
Sheffield Aurora v Arnold Town	1-0	Oakham Utd v Mickleover Royal British Legion	0-5
Shirebrook Colliery v Louth United	1-2	Shardlow St James v Biwater	3-2

Quarter Finals

Hucknall Town v Borrowash Victoria	4-1	Mickleover Royal British Legion v Sheffield Aurora	2-3
Nettleham v Blidworth Miners Welfare	2-1	Shardlow St James v Louth United	0-2

Semi-Finals

Louth United v Hucknall Town	2-2,4-4	Nettleham v Sheffield Aurora	1-0

(both matches at Lincoln Utd, 4-2 to Nettlham on pens) *(at Hucknall Town)*

Final *(at The Baseball Ground, Derby County):* Hucknall Town 1, Nettleham 0.

WAKEFIELD CHALLENGE CUP 1991-92

First Round
Nettleham v Glapwell   5-1,1-4

Second Round

Arnold Town v Sheffield Aurora	1-1,0-1	Borrowash Victoria v Blidworth Welfare	3-0,3-3
Harworth Col. Inst. v Wombwell Town	4-2,3-1	Heanor Town v Lincoln United	2-2,3-6
Louth United v Shirebrook Colliery	1-0,2-0	Melton Town v Priory (Eastwood)	3-4,1-4
Mickleover R.B.L. v Nettleham	3-2,2-4	Oakham United v Hucknall Town	1-1,0-3

Third Round

Hucknall Town v Lincoln United	1-1,0-2	Harworth Colliery Institute v Sheffield Aurora	4-1,2-1
Nettleham v Borrowash Victoria	2-1,4-1	Priory (Eastwood) v Louth United	0-4,1-2

Semi-Finals

Louth United v Lincoln United	4-2,0-0	Harworth Colliery Institute v Nettleham	1-1,3-2

Final (at Sincil Bank, Lincoln City FC): Harworth Colliery Institute 3, Louth United 0

MAVIS MARSLAND BOWL (INVITATION COMPETITION)

First Round

Fryston Colliery Welfare v Radford	5-0,2-1	Kiburn Miners Welfare v Sth Normanton Ath.	3-2,0-3
Retford Rail v Norton Woodseats	1-1,0-8	Rossington v Nuthall	2-1,2-1
Biwater v Kimberley	2-2,1-1 *(KT away g/s)*	Slack & Parr v Gedling Town	1-1,2-1

Second Round

Kimberley Town v Kiveton Park	2-1	Sth Normanton Athletic v Rossington	1-1 *(4-3 pens)*
Fryston Colliery Welfare v Slack & Parr	0-2		

Semi-Finals

Newhall United v Kimberley Town	6-1	South Normanton Athletic v Slack & Parr	0-1

Final (at Priory (Eastwood) FC): Slack & Parr 3, Newhall United 0

RESERVE CHALLENGE CUP 1991-92

First Round
Kilburn M.W. Res v Shardlow St James Res   0-2

Second Round

Alvaston & Boulton Res v Arnold Town 'A'	2-1	Borrowash Victoria Res v Selston Res	4-1
Brailsford Res v Arnold Town Res	0-3	Derby C & W Res v Rossington Res	2-0
Derby Rolls R. 'A' v Bulwell Utd Res	2-8	Harworth Cl Res v Holbrook MW Res	4-1
Highfield R. Res v Biwater Res	3-2	Hucknall Town Res v Melton Town Res	2-0
Kimberley Res v Borrowash Vic. 'A'	1-0	Mickleover RBL Res v Stanton Ilkeston Res	3-2
Nuthall Res v Shardlow St James Res	1-3	Priory (Eastwood) Res v Blidworth Res	6-0
Radford v Attenborough Res	0-1	Shirebrook Colliery Res v Derby Rolls Royce Res	3-1
Slack & Parr Res v N. Woodseats Res	1-1,3-0	Wombwell Town Res v Oakham United Res	4-1

Third Round

Arnold Town Res v Wombwell Res	0-1	Borrowash Victoria Res v Kimberley Town Res	2-0
Bulwell Utd Res v Alvaston & Boulton Res	3-2	Derby C & W Res v Attenborough Res	5-3
Highfield Rgrs Res v Priory Res	0-2	Mickleover RBL Res v Shardlow St James Res	2-1
Shirebrook Res v Harworth Cl Res	3-0	Slack & Parr Res v Hucknall Town Res	1-3

Quarter-Finals

Bulwell Utd Res v Derby C & W Res	7-1	Priory (Eastwood) Res v Borrowash Victoria Res	3-2
Shirebrook Colliery Res v Hucknall Town Res	3-2	Wombwell Town Res v Mickleover RBL Res	4-1

Semi-Finals

Bulwell Res v Shirebrook Res *(at Blidworth)*	1-2	Wombwell Res v Priory (E'wood) Res *(at Glapwell)*	1-0

Final (at Harworth Colliery Institute FC): Shirebrook Colliery Res 1, Wombwell Town Res 0

Mickleover R.B.L., pictured at their adopted home of Gresley Rovers F.C.

SUPREME DIVISION CLUBS 1992-93

ARNOLD TOWN

President: J Brace **Vice President:** D Elvin. **Chairman:** A Croome
Vice Chairman: D Law. **Secretary:** G S Barlow, 95 Plains Rd, Nottm NG3 5QD (0602 2636601).
Manager: R O'Brien **Asst Mgr:** P Moody. **Press Officer:** K Armstrong.
Ground: King George V Playing Fields, Gedling Rd, Arnold, Nottm (0602 263660). **Directions:** From Nth
M1 jct 26, B6004, A614, A60 St Albans Rd, opp. Arnold Market. Five miles from Nottingham Central (BR).
Capacity: 3,500 **Seats:** 150 **Covered:** 700 **Floodlights:** Yes **Clubhouse:** Yes
Midweek matches: Tuesday **Previous Ground:** Calverton Road Rec. 1928-57.
Colours: Yellow/blue/yellow **Change Colours:** All white
Programme: 56 pages, 50p **Programme Editor:** Simon Matters.
Previous Names: Arnold St Marys (founded 1928), Arnold FC, merged with Arnold Kingswell in 1988.
Prev. Lges: Central Alliance 55-63/ Midland 63-82 *Kingswell: 75-82*/ Northern Co's East 82-87.
Record Gate: 3,390 v Bristol Rovers, FA Cup 1st Rd, December 1967.
Hons: Central Mids Lg R-up 88-89 (Lg Cup 87-88 (R-up 90-91)); Northern Co's East Lg 85-86; Notts Snr Cup 60-61 64-
65 65-66 68-69 70-71; FA Cup 1st Rd 66-67 76-77; FA Tphy 2nd Rd 71-72; Midland Co's Lg R-up 70-71 (Lg Cup 74-75).
Arnold Kingswell: Midland Co's Lg Div 1 79-80 (R-up 75-76 78-79 81-82).

BLIDWORTH WELFARE

Secretary: W C Deakin, 220 Brick Kiln Lane, Mansfield, Notts NG19 6LR (0623 29033).
Manager: Andy Brown. **Ground:** Welfare Ground, Mansfield Rd, Blidworth, Mansfield (0623 798724).
Directions: On B6020, Rainworth side of Blidworth. Served by Mansfield-Nottingham buses.
Capacity: 5,000 **Seats:** 250 **Cover:** 400 **Floodlights:** Yes **Programme:** Yes
Colours: White/blue/blue **Change Colours:** Red/black/black
Clubhouse: Matchdays **Record Gate:** 400 v Shirebrook Colliery 1989-90.

BORROWASH VICTORIA

President: I Anderson **Chairman:** G Foweler **Manager:** Martin Rowe.
Secretary: W I Collins, 30 Margreave Road, Chaddesden, Derby DE2 6JD (0332 678016).
Ground: Asterdale Club, Borrowash Road, Spondon, Derby (0332 668656). **Directions:** M1 jct 25,
A52 towards Derby, 3rd left past BP Ockbrook garage. Ground left 100 yds. 1 mile from Spondon (BR).
Capacity: 5,000 **Seats:** No **Covered:** 450 **Floodlights:** Yes **Founded:** 1911
Midweek matches: Tuesday **Previous Ground:** Dean Drive 63-84 **Reformed:** 1963.
Colours: Red & white/red/black **Change Colours:** All yellow **Clubhouse:** Yes
Programme: 16 pages, 50p **Record Gate:** 2,000 v Nottingham Forest, floodlight opening 22/10/85.
Previous Leagues: Derby Sunday School & Welfare 52-57/ Derby Comb./ Midland 79-82/ Northern Counties East.
Hons: Northern Co's East Lg Div 1 Sth 83-84 (R-up 84-85, Div 2 Sth R-up 82-83), Derby Comb. 77-78 (R-up(10) 65-66
68-74 75-77 78-79, Lg Cup 68-69 75-76 (R-up 63-64 66-67), Midland Co's Lg Div 80-81 (Div 1 Cup 80-81), Derbys Snr
Cup R-up 90-91, Derbys Div. Cup 73-74 (R-up 70-71 72-73), B E Webbe Cup R-up 88-89, FA Cup 3rd Qual. Rd 91-92.

GEDLING TOWN

Chairman: Roland Ash **Manager:** Dave Wheat.
Secretary: Roland Ash, 80 Portland Road, Carlton, Nottingham NG4 3PZ (0602 670047).
Ground: 'Stoke Ferry Ground', rear Ferry Boat Inn, Stoke Biddulph, Gedling, Nottm (0602 770258, club-8711932).
Directions: From Carlton Road, under rail bridge, right, follow lane to ground.
Colours: Yellow/blue/yellow **Change colours:** Red/black/red. **Floodlights:** Yes

GLAPWELL

Secretary: Stephen Taylor Brown, 2 Carter Lane West, Shirebrook, Mansfield NG20 8NA (0623 743661).
Manager: Roger Caton **Ground:** Hall Corner, Park Ave., Glapwell, Chesterfield (0860 233934).
Directions: A617 towards Mansfield from M1 jct 29, left at Young Vanish Inn after 2 miles, ground 100yds on right.
From Mansfield on A617, right at Glapwell crossroads after 5 miles, ground 100 yds on right.
Colours: Blue/white/blue **Change colours:** Red/black/black.

HARWORTH COLLIERY INSTITUTE

Secretary: T A Brogan, 30 Lidnsey Road, Harworth, Doncaster, Sth Yorkshire DN11 8QH (0302 750132).
Manager: Graham Gladwin **Ground:** Recreation Ground, Scrooby Rd, Bircotes, Doncaster (0302 750614).
Directions: From Blyth take A614 for approx 2 miles, turn left at top of hill.
Capacity: 2,000 **Seats:** None **Cover:** 150 **Founded:** 1931 **Floodlights:** Yes
Midweek matches: Wednesday **Programme:** 16 pages, 30p
Colours: All red **Change Colours:** All blue **Clubhouse:** Matchdays. Darts, pool, food
Record Gate: 350 v Congleton, 1989. **Prev. Lges:** Yorks 46-50 77-82/ Northern Co's East
Hons: Wharncliffe Cup; Webbe Cup 87-88; Central Mids Lg 87-88 (R-up 86-87, F'lit Cup 91-92); Snr Cup SF 87-88

HEANOR TOWN

Secretary: C K Costello, 45 Stainsby Avenue, Heanor, Derbyshire DE7 7EL (0773 713742).
Manager: Bill Brindley. **Ground:** The Town Ground, Mayfield Avenue, Heanor (0773 713742).
Ground Directions: North: M1 (J27), A608. South: M1 (J26), A610-A608
Capacity: 3,500 **Seats:** 200 **Cover:** 800 **Founded:** 1883 **Floodlights:** Yes
Midweek matches: Wednesday **Programme:** 8 pages, 15p **Clubhouse:** Yes
Colours: White/black/white **Change Colours:** All red
Previous League: Midland Co's 1894-97 98-1900 26-28 61-72 74-82/ Central Alliance 21-25 47-61/ West Mids
Regional 72-74/ Northern Co's Lg East 82-86. **Record Gate:** 6,411 v Carlisle, FA Cup 1958.
Hons: Central Mids Lg Cup R-up 86-87; B E Webbe Removals Cup 88-89; West Mids Reg. Lg R-up 72-73; Midland Co's
Lg R-up 65-66 67-68; Derbys Snr Cup(9) 1892-94 1946-47 65-69 70-71 78-79; FA Cup 1st Rd 58-59 63-64.

KIMBERLEY TOWN

Secretary: Horace Hibbert, 62 Eastwood Road, Kimberley, Nottingham NG16 2HZ (0602 383382).
Manager: Graham Walker. **Ground:** Stag Ground, Nottingham Road, Kimberley (0602 382788).
Directions: Through Nuthall from M1 jct 26, ground signposted 150 yds after Stag Inn. 6 miles from Nottingham (BR).
Buses 357 358 231 332 333 to ground.
Seats: None **Cover:** 200 **Capacity:** 3,000 **Floodlights:** Yes **Founded:** 1948
Colours: All royal **Change colours:** All white. **Prev. Name:** Kimberley YMCA, 1948-56.
Programme: 16 pages, 25p **Clubhouse:** Normal licensing hours & matchdays. Snacks, darts, pool.
Record Gate: 1,122 v Eastwood, Mids Lg April 76. **Prev. League:** Midland Co's 71-82/ Northern Counties East.

LOUTH UNITED

Secretary: P Smith, 84 Scartho Road, Grimsby, South Humberside DN33 2BG (0472 79356).
Manager: Jim Bloomer   **Ground:** Park Avenue, Louth, Lincs (0507 607351).
Directions: A16 To Louth Market Place, exit via Eastgate/Eastfield Rd, to 1st junction, past Fire Station.
Capacity: 3,000   **Seats:** 30   **Cover:** 300   **Founded:** 1947   **Floodlights:** Yes
Midweek matches: Tuesday   **Programme:** 10 pages, 20p   **Clubhouse:** Yes
Colours: Royal/white/royal   **Change Colours:** White/white/royal
Record Gate: Unknown.   **Previous Names:** Merger of Louth Nats & Louth Town.
Previous Leagues: Midland Co's Lg 74-79/ Lincs.
Hons: Lincs Prem. Div 86-87 85-86; Lincs Challenge Cup 86-87; Lincs Lg Cup 85-86, Central Mids Lg F'lit Cup R-up 91-92, Lincs Snr 'B' Cup 91-92.

MICKLEOVER ROYAL BRITISH LEGION

President: A N Waplington   **Chairman:** N L Appleby
Secretary: D Hewitt, 1 Milton Close, Mickleover, Derby DE3 5QN (0332 515295).
Manager: Tony Shaw   **Assistant Manager:** Richard Walshe.
Ground & Directions: Belper Town FC (see page 818).   **Founded:** 1945
Colours: Royal/white/royal   **Change Colours:** All red
Previous Leagues: Derbys Sunday/ East Mids/ Derby Premier.
Previous Grounds: Ypres Lodge, Western Rd, Mickleover (pre-1991)/ Gresley Rovers FC 91-92.
Hons: Centrals Mids Lg Premier Div 89-90 90-91 (R-up 88-89, Lg Cup 88-89 89-90), East Mids Lg 80-81, Derbys Divisional Cup South 80-81.

NETTLEHAM

Secretary: S W Timms, 5 Ash Tree Ave, Nettleham, Lincoln LN2 2TQ (0522 751140).
Manager: Paul Tittcomb   **Ground:** Mulsanne Park, Field Close, Nettleham (0522 750007).
Directions: A46 approx. 3 miles north of Lincoln, right at Brown Cow Pub, proceed past Church 2nd turning on right.
Colours: Blue (white trim)/blue/blue   **Change Colours:** Red (white trim)/red/red
Hons: Central Mids Lg Premier Division Cup R-up 87-88, Village Tphy, Nursing Cup, Kelly Read Cup, Blankney Hunt Cup, Lincoln & Dist. Amtr Cup R-up, Joe Miller Tphy(2).

OAKHAM UNITED

Manager: Steve Giles.
Secretary: S M Brown, 22 Crosby Close, Forest Town, Mansfield, Notts NG19 0PN (0623 643574).
Ground: Mansfield Hosiery Mills, Mansfield Rd, Sutton-in-Ashfield, Notts (0623 552376).
Directions: From M1 junction 28, A38 for Mansfield, ground half mile past Sutton on left. A617 from Mansfield towards M1. 3 miles from Alfreton/Mansfield Parkway (BR).
Capacity: 2,000   **Seats:** None   **Cover:** 350   **Founded:** 1969   **Floodlights:** Yes
Midweek matches: Tuesday   **Previous Lges:** Midland Co's/ Northern Co's East
Clubhouse: Every evening and weekend lunchtimes. Darts, pool, meals and hot snacks on matchdays.
Colours: White/navy/white   **Change Colours:** Yellow/green/yellow
Programme: 28 pages, 30p   **Programme Editor:** J Vazson
Record Gate: 500 v Sutton Town, Midland Counties League 79-80.
Hons: Midland Co's Div 1 Lg Cup 79-80 (Div 1 R-up 79-80)

PRIORY (EASTWOOD)

Secretary: Mr S Wadsley, 41 Stamford Street, Newthorpe, Nottm NG16 2DR (0602 389749).
Manager: Kevin Smith   **Ground:** Tinsley Park, Eastwood, Nottingham (0836 749883).
Directions: M1 junction 26 to Langley Mill, ground on left
Capacity: 2,000   **Seats:** 200   **Cover:** 200   **Founded:** 1967   **Floodlights:** Yes
Midweek matches: Wednesday   **Programme:** 8 pages, 25p   **Clubhouse:** No.
Colours: Red/black/black   **Change Colours:** Yellow/white/white
Previous League: Notts Amtr/ Central Alliance/ East Mids Regional Alliance.
Club honours: Central Mids Lg Prem. Div 88-89 (Div 1 R-up 87-88), East Mids Regional Alliance Div 1, Notts Intermediate Cup 90-91(reserves).

SHEFFIELD AURORA

President: Eric Brightmore   **Chairman:** Peter Wilson.
Secretary: Peter Cresswell, 113 Lopham Street, Sheffield S3 9JR (0742 759115).
Manager: Danny Hague.
Ground: Aurora Sports & Social Club, Bawtry Rd, Brinsworth, Rotherham S60 5ND (0709 372613).
Directions: M1 jct 34 south, round island to A631 Bawtry Rd, 1 mile on right.
Clubhouse: Yes   **Programme:** Yes   **Floodlights:** Yes   **Prev. Name:** Crookes **Founded:** 1964.
Colours: All white   **Change Colours:** Sky/royal/sky
Previous Leagues: Matchard/ Whitbread County Senior.
Hons: Sheffield Snr Cup R-up 85-86, Hatchard Lg Div 1 83-83, Whitbread Co. Snr Lg 83-84 (Lg Cup 85-86).

SHIREBROOK COLLIERY

Secretary: S Wall, 26 Carter Lane West, Shirebrook, Mansfield, Notts NG20 8NA (0623 747638).
Manager: Paul Elrick/ Neil McAllister.   **Ground:** BRSA Ground, Langwith Rd, Mansfield (0623 742535).
Directions: M1 jct 29, A617 to Mansfield, 2.5 miles, B6407 Shirebrook, through town to Langwith Rd. Bus 81 from Chesterfield or 23 from Mansfield.
Capacity: 2,000   **Seats:** 120   **Cover:** 200   **Floodlights:** Yes   **Founded:** 1985
Colours: All blue   **Change Colours:** White/white/black
Programme: 12 pages, 25p   **Clubhouse:** Normal licensing hours.

WOMBWELL TOWN

Secretary: Kevin Byron, 37 Hoyland Street, Wombwell, Barnsley South Yorks S73 8HF. (0226) 340636
Manager: Mick Gabbitas   **Ground:** The Stadium, Station Rd, Wombwell, Barnsley (0226 752128)
Directions: M1 jct 36, Doncaster A1(M) road, groun on left after 4 miles.
Colours: Yellow/blue/white   **Change Colours:** All red

PREMIER DIVISION CLUBS 1992-93

ASKERN MINERS WELFARE (New Club, no details available)

BIWATER (CLAY CROSS)
Secretary: Alan Kilcline, 4 Deerpark Crescent, Wingerworth, Chesterfield S42 6XF (0246 276707).
Manager: Phil Tingay   **Ground:** John's Street, off Market Street, Clay Cross.
Colours: Red/white/red   **Change colours:** Blue/black/black.

BLACKWELL MINERS WELFARE
Secretary: Mrs S M Burnham, 42 Poplar Rd, South Normanton, Derbys DE55 2EQ (0773 861312).
Ground & Directions: Welfare Ground, Primrose Hill, Blackwell, Derbys DE55 5JE. (0773 811295). A38 towards Mansfield from M1 jct 38, left onto B6406 after half a mile, left after a mile, ground on left.
Colours: Red & white stripes/red/red   **Change colours:** All silver grey.

BULWELL UNITED
Secretary: Tom Tattersall, 11 Oakwood Drive, Aspley Hall, Nottingham NG8 3LZ (0602 292197).
Ground & Directions: John Player Sports & Social Club, Aspley Lane, Aspley, Nottingham (0602 294244). Turn off Nottingham ringroad near Raleigh Works r'bout.
Manager: Steve Walker   **Colours:** Red/white/red   **Change colours:** White/red/black.

DERBY CARRIAGE & WAGON (RECKITTS)
Secretary: David Wright, 6 Athol Close, Sinfin, Derby DE2 9LZ (0332 765833).
Ground: Carriage & Wagon Welfare, Longbridge Lane, off Ascot Drive, Derby (0332 571376).
Directions: M1 jct 25, A5111 Raynesway, right at 1st island, left at 2nd island into Ascot Drive, 1st right to ground.
Manager: Stewart Woodings   **Colours:** All yellow   **Change colours:** All white.

DERBY ROLLS ROYCE
Secretary: Michael Lomax, 47 Cleveland Avenue, Caddesden, Derby DE2 6SB (0332 664183).
Manager: D Tice   **Ground:** Rolls Royce Rec. Society, Moor Lane, Derby (0332 249167).
Directions: Derby ringroad, Osmaston Park Road, Moor Lane; ground adjacent to Swimming Baths.
Colours: Royal blue/white/royal blue   **Change:** Black & white stripes/black/black

FRYSTON COLLIERY WELFARE
Secretary: B Bennett, School House, Holyrood Road, Ledsham, South Milford, Leeds LS25 5LL (0977 682593).
Manager: J Kenyon   **Ground:** Askham Rd, Ferry Fryston, Castleford (0977 553413 - messages).
Directions: M62 exit 32, right onto B6136, left at Airedale Hotel into Fryston Drive, Elizabeth Drive, Watling Road, Borrowdale Drive and Askham Drive.
Colours: White/black/black (white tops)   **Change colours:** Red & white stripes/red/red
Previous Leagues: Yorks 76-82/ Northern Co's East 82-91.
Hons: Central Mids Lg Prem. Div (Nth) 91-92.

KILBURN MINERS WELFARE
Secretary: Michael Turner, 68 Warmwell Lane, Ripley, Derby DE5 8JB (0773 746851).
Manager: Mark O'Kane   **Asst Mgr:** Paul Baxter   **Coach:** John Watson
Founded: 1952   **Ground:** Chapel Street, Kilburn (0332 781014).
Directions: A38 North Derby, B6179 to Kilburn village, left into Chapel Street.
Colours: Red/black/red   **Change colours:** All white.
Prev. Leagues: Sth Derbys/ Derbys Prem.**Hons:** Central Mids Lg Prem. Div Cup 90-91 (Div 1 85-86, Div 1 Cup R-up 85-86), Derbyshire Divisional Cup, Belper Nursing Cup.

KIVETON PARK
Secretary: John Holden, 184 Wales Road, Kiveton Park, Sheffield S31 8RE (0909 779558).
Manager: Brian Mellon   **Ground:** Hard Lane, Kiveton Park, Sheffield.
Directions: Follow Worksop signs from M1 exit 31, left down Goosecar Lane after a quarter mile, over crossroads and ground is 200 yds on the right before rail bridge.
Capacity: 2,000   **Seats:** 200   **Founded:** Early 1900s
Colours: All red   **Change colours:** Black & white stripes/black/black
Hons: Yorks Lg Div 2 77-78   **Prev. Lges:** Yorks 63-82/ Northern Co's East 82-91.

LONG EATON UNITED
Secretary: Ernie Mills, 5 Maxwell Street, Long Eaton, Nottingham NG10 1FE (0602 735013).
Manager: Geoff Dodsworth   **Ground:** Grange Park, Station Road, Long Eaton, Nottingham (0602 735700).
Directions: Signposted on left opposite Speedway Stadium. 2 miles from Long Eaton (BR).
Seats: None   **Cover:** 500   **Capacity:** 5,000   **Floodlights:** No   **Founded:** 1956
Colours: All blue   **Change colours:** Yellow/green/black.
Previous Name: Long Eaton Town.   **Record Gate:** 2,000 - 1973 FA Cup.
Previous Leagues: Central Alliance 49-61/ Midland Co's 61-82/ Northern Co's East 82-89.
Hons: Derbys Snr Cup 64-65 75-76, Midland Co's Lg R-up 76-77, Central Alliance Div South 58-59.

MEXBOROUGH TOWN
Secretary: Nigel Hyde, 33 Grosvenor Crescent, Arksey, Doncaster DN5 0SX (0302 820115).
Manager: Gary Taylor   **Ground:** Mexborough Athletic Club, Hampden Rd, Mexborough (0709 586479).
Directions: Just off A6023 Conisborough/Mexborough road, opposite Police station. Half mile from Mexborough (BR).
Seats: 150   **Cover:** 150   **Capacity:** 1,500   **Floodlights:** No   **Founded:** 1890
Colours: Blue & white hoops/blue/blue   **Change colours:** Red & black hoops/red/red.
Previous Name: Mexborough Town Athletic   **Record Gate:** 1,800 v Scarborough, FA Trophy 1973
Honours: Midland Lg 1897-98 25-26, Yorks Lg 72-73 (Lg Cup 72-73), Montague Cup 1898-99 03-04 04-05 33-34 63-64 76-77, Sheffield Senior Cup 1885-86 93-94 95-96 30-31 33-34 63-64 74-75 76-77 82-83.

NEWHALL UNITED
Secretary: David Wain, 26 Willow Drive, Newhall, Swadlincote, Derbys DE11 0NW (0283 225188).
Manager: Sid Gutteridge **Ground:** Hewfields Ground, St Johns Drive, Newhall, Swadlincote (0283 551029).
Directions: A150 into Newhall at Chesterfield Arms, to bottom and turn right. Left after 100 yds, 2nd right at Lamb Inn, 1st left into St Johns Drive.
Colours: Blue & white/white/blue.   **Change:** Green & white hoops/white/white.
Hons: Derbys Premier Lg 73-74 78-79 (Lg 72-73), Mavis Marsland Bowl R-up 91-92.

NORTON WOODSEATS

Secretary: David Taylor, 75 Gleadless, Sheffield S12 2QG (0742 649754).
Manager: Brian Thackeray/ Kevin Murphy. **Ground & Directions:** Coach & Horses
Ground, Stubley Hollow, Sheffield Road, Dronfield (0246 413269-matchdays). Turn for Dronfield off A61
Chesterfield/Sheffield road, ground on way out of Dronfield opposite Coach & Horse pub.
Colours: All blue **Change:** Yellow/blue/yellow. **Prev. Names:** Norton Woodseats Amtr/ Dronfield Utd.
Previous Leagues: Yorks 49-82/ Northern Co's East 82-91.

NUTHALL

Secretary: Tony Benniston, 117 Broad Lane, Brinsley, Nottm NG16 5BU (0773 712350).
Manager: Brian Harrison **Asst Mgr:** Mark Saunders **Coach:** Bob Limb.
Ground & Directions: Basil Russell Playing Fields, Maple Drive, Nuthall, Nottingham (0602 384765). M1 jct 26/
A610 southbound left southbound, right northbound.
Colours: Sky/navy/sky **Change colours:** All yellow.

RADFORD

Secretary: Christopher Michael Daykin, 66 Oakfield Road, Stapleford, Nottingham NG9 8FF (0602 390547).
Manager: Brian Mantle **Ground:** Radford Road, Radford, Nottm (0602 423250).
Directions: A610 Alfreton Road, left just into Bobbersmill Road, ground at top on right.
Colours: Claret & blue/sky/sky. **Change colours:** White/black/black
Previous name: Radford Olympic. **Hons:** Derbys Prem. Lg Div 1 R-up 84-85.

ROSSINGTON

Secretary: Ian Wilson, The Wickets, 3 Hollin Close, Rossington, Doncaster DN11 0XX (0302 867221).
Manager: Ian Wilson/ Gary Mountfield. **Ground & Directions:** Welfare Ground, West End Lane, Rossington,
Doncaster (0302 868272). M18 jct 1, A631 to Bawtry via Maltby/Tickhill. One mile out of Tickhill take B6463 to
Rossington. In Rossington quarter mile on right towards colliery.
Colours: Red/navy/red **Change colours:** White/navy/navy.

SANDIACRE TOWN

Secretary: M S Williams, 38 Pasture Road, Stapleford NG9 8GL (0602 392415). **Manager:** M Cordon
Ground: St Giles Park, Stanton Road, Sandiacre, Nottingham (0602 392880).
Colours: All red **Change colours:** Sky & white stripes/sky/sky

SHARDLOW ST. JAMES

Secretary: Reg Symcox, 22 West End Drive, Shardlow, Derby DE7 2GY (0332 792733).
Manager: Graham Proudler **Ground:** The Wharf, Shardlow, Derby.
Directions: A6 Derby/Leicester, left at shop on corner of The Wharf, follow to Village Hall, ground adjacent.
Colours: All red **Change colours:** Sky/royal/sky. **Prev. Lge:** Midland Regional Alliance.
Hons: Mids Reg. All. 90-91 (Lg Cup 90-91)

SOUTH NORMANTON ATHLETIC

Chairman: Terry Ball **President:** Monsieur A Thibaudeau. **Manager:** Trevor Wasp.
Secretary: Peter Kane, 3 Mansfield Road, South Normanton, Derby De55 2ER (0773 580637).
Asst Mgr: Chris Lee **Coach:** Jim McGowan. **Physio:** Terry Hodson.
Ground & Directions: South Normanton Miners Welfare, Lees Lane, South Normanton, Derby (0773 581491,
club-811396). B6109 from from M1 exit 28, right after 1 mile at Texaco garage, left at The Clock pub, ground at
bottom of Lees Lane.
Colours: All royal blue **Change colours:** Yellow/blue/blue.
Programme: 40 pages **Programme Editor:** Kevin Miles.
Hons: Alfreton & Dist. Sunday Lg 86-87 (Div 2 83-84, Div 3 R-up 80-81, Suppl. Shield 84-85, W L Screen Bowl 86-
87), Mansfield Sunday Lg Prem. Div Cup 88-89 (Div 1 R-up 87-88).

STANTON (ILKESTON)

Secretary: Mick Andrews, 6 Carrfield Avenue, Long Eaton, Nottm NG10 2GW (0602 733159).
Manager: Martin Cooper. **Ground & Directions:** Hallam Fields Sports Ground, Stanton Club,
Hallam Fields, Nr Ilkeston, Derbys (0602 323244). From South, M1 (J25) to Nottm, 1st r-about turn left. From North,
M1 (J26), Ilkeston, through to to Hallam Fields.
Capacity: 2,000 **Seats:** None **Cover:** 300 **Founded:** 1921.
Colours: Blue & white stripes/blue/blue **Change Colours:** Yellow/black/blue
Previous Leagues: Central Alliance 55-58/ Derbyshire Premier/ East Mids Regional Alliance.
Previous Name: Stanton Works. **Hons:** Central Mids Lg Prem. Div 85-86 86-87 (Prem. Div Cup 85-86).

Nettleham FC. Back Row (L/R): Paul Buckthorpe (Asst Mgr), Darren Crookes, Stuart Phillipson, Ian Wheatley (Capt), Lee Cooper, Steve Dolby, Robin Smith, Fred McDonnel, Dennis Thacker (Physio), Paul Titcomb. Front: Garry Wells, Steve Ross, Peter Wilkinson, Craig Frecklington, Ian Darby, John Rainey. Photo - T Sandell-Codd.

NETZ MIDLAND REGIONAL ALLIANCE

Premier Division	P	W	D	L	F	A	PTS
Mackworth United	26	19	6	1	77	32	63
Sandiacre Town	26	19	2	5	85	32	59
Normanton Athletic	26	16	4	6	57	27	52
Matlock United	26	13	6	7	54	36	45
Alfreton T. Res	26	11	7	8	53	38	40
Ripley Town	26	10	9	7	51	38	39
Eastwood T. Res	26	10	7	9	47	39	37
Belper United	26	10	3	13	55	64	33
Butterley Brick	26	9	5	12	42	48	32
Belper Town Res	26	8	5	13	34	55	29
Ruddington Village	26	6	6	14	39	62	24
Ilkeston T. Res	26	6	5	15	47	87	23
Hykeham United	26	6	4	16	38	63	22
Littleover Ivanhoe	26	3	3	20	27	85	12

Division One	P	W	D	L	F	A	PTS
Rowsley '86	26	21	3	2	97	25	66
Ridding St James	26	18	4	4	75	35	58
Pinxton	26	17	5	4	72	33	56
Royal Crown '86	26	16	4	6	101	48	52
Mackworth Utd Res	26	13	2	11	50	63	41
Swanwick Pentrich	26	12	2	12	56	58	38
Holbrook St Mich.	26	11	3	12	43	54	36
Draycott	26	10	6	10	48	63	36
New Eastwood	26	10	4	12	60	54	34
Gotham United	26	7	9	10	53	44	30
Kirk Hallam Castle	26	7	5	14	34	48	26
Chesterfield 'A'	26	6	5	15	37	52	23
Ruddington V. Res	26	4	2	20	33	87	14
Littleover I. Res	26	2	2	22	28	123	8

PREMIER DIVISION CLUBS 1991-92

ALFRETON TOWN RESERVES (See page 759 for other details)

BELPER TOWN RESERVES
Manager: S Watson   (See page 818 for other details)

BELPER UNITED
Secretary/Manager: I Sinclair, 7 Culworth Close, Belper DE6 0EW (0773 821864).
Ground: Whitemoor Hall, Whitemoor Lane, Belper.
Colours: Green & black stripes/black/black   **Change Colours:** Silver/black/black.

BRAILSFORD
Secretary: George Smith, The Folly, Brailsford, Derby DE6 3BD (0335 60831).
Ground & Directions: Osmaston Polo Ground, Osmaston, nr Ashbourne. A52 from Derby, 2 miles before Ashbourne turn left into Osmaston, left at church, past Shoulder of Mutton pub, ground on left past pond.
Colours: Blue & white stripes/blue/blue   **Change colours:** Red/black/black

BUTTERLEY BRICK
Secretary: M Boam, 5 Valley Drive, Newthorpe, Notts NG16 2DT (0773 715277).
Ground: Waingroves Brickworks, Peasehill Road, Ripley, Derbys (Ripley 742287).
Colours: White/red/red   **Change:** Sky/navy/navy   **Manager:** K Jackson.

EASTWOOD TOWN RESERVES   **Manager:** K Shaw   (See page 765 for other details)

HOLBROOK MINERS WELFARE
Secretary: Roy Wainwright, 93 Belper Road, Bargate, Derby DE5 0SU (0773 826300).
Ground & Directions: Shaw Lane, Holbrook, Derby (0332 880259). From Derby, left at Venture Garage into Shaw Lane. From Belper, right into Shaw Lane at Venture Garage.
Colours: White (black pin stripes)/black/black   **Change colours:** Blue/black/blue or blue.

ILKESTON TOWN RESERVES
Manager: Chris Eveson   (See page 543 for other details)

MACKWORTH UNITED
Sec: P E Spray, 5 Embankment Close, Mackworth, Derby DE3 4Hf (0332 517321)   **Manager:** S Slater.
Ground: Mackworth Tertiary College, Prince Charles Avenue, Mackworth, Derby.
Colours: White/black/black   **Change colours:** Red & white/white/red

MATLOCK UNITED
Secretary: B Jamieson, 9 Mais Close, Tansley, Matlock DE4 5GZ (0629 56414).   **Manager:** M Kelly.
Ground: Playing Fields, Cavendish Road, Cavendish Park, Matlock (formerly Matlock College Playing Fields).
Colours: Blue/white/red   **Change colours:** Green & white hoops/white/green

NORMANTON ATHLETIC
Sec: W G Williamson, 103 Balfour Road, Pear Tree, Derby DE3 8UP (0332 270240)   **Manager:** L Ford
Ground: Alvaston Park, Meadow Lane, Alvaston, Derby (571221).
Colours: White/black/black   **Change colours:** Red/white/black.

RIPLEY TOWN
Secretary: Mrs S E Inglesant, 54b Norman Road, Ripley DE5 3GN (0773 748528).   **Manager:** R Yeomans
Ground: Derbys Police HQ, Coach Road, Nottingham Road, Ripley, Derbys.
Colours: Green & white stripes/green/green   **Change colours:** Gold/green/green.

RUDDINGTON VILLAGE
Secretary: W Turton, 14 Samson, Court, Ruddington, Notts NG11 6AP (0602 847405). **Manager:** S Attewell
Ground: Elms Park, Loughborough Road, Ruddington, Notts (0602 844976).
Colours: All red   **Change colours:** All blue.

RIDDINGS ST. JAMES
Secretary: Mrs Vicky Newey, 21 Spanker Lane, Nether Heage, Derby DE5 2AT (0773 853358).
Ground: The Park, West Street, Riddings, Derbys (Leabrooks 607907).   **Manager:** P Robinson.
Colours: Red & black/black/black   **Change colours:** Red & white stripes/red/red.

ROWSLEY 66
Sec: B L Ash, Springwood, 66 Hackney Road, Matlock DE4 2PX (0629 55543).   **Manager:** H W Fletcher
Ground: Rowsley Recreation Ground.
Change colours: Blue & white hoops/black/blue & white.   **Colours:** Red & black hoops/black/red

SELSTON
Secretary: Mike Giles, 90 Main Street, Newton, Derbys DE55 5TE (0773 872244).
Ground & Directions: Selston Parish Hall, Mansfield Road, Selston, Notts (0773 810411). From Alfreton left just after garages in Selston village centre. From M1 right at garages. Ground 150 yds on left.
Colours: All white   **Change colours:** All green.

ROGER SMITH INSURANCE
NOTTS FOOTBALL ALLIANCE

President: R J Leafe.
Chairman: A Wright.
Hon. Secretary: E R Rudd, 18 Whitegate Vale,
Clifton Estate, Nottingham (Nottm 216382).

PLESSEY WIN FIRST TITLE IN FIFTEEN YEARS

The Notts Football Alliance Senior Division championship went to G.P.T. Plessey, who over the past seasons have always been in the running but have slipped back dropping points in the last few matches. The last and only time they won the title was back in 1966-67 when they were known as Erricson's FC.

Notts Police finished as runners-up two points behind Plessey, and also reached the Notts Senior Cup final, losing 2-0 to Eastwood Town.

'Team of the Season' must be Boots Athletic who won the Notts Alliance Senior Cup beating Senior Division Pelican FC who were the holders. Boots have made a great recovery. Two years ago they withdrew their senior status and dropped to Division Two struggling for players, but they have fought back to gain promotion to the Senior Division. They also reached the final of the Notts Intermediate Cup, but lost to Notts Alliance rivals Sneinton.

Congratulations are due to Sneinton who, in addition to winning the Notts Intermediate Cup, finished as joint runners-up level on goal difference with Bulwell Forest Villa. A play-off at Bulwell was necessary, and the home side won 2-0 to earn promotion to the Senior Division.

Division Two was dominated by newcomers Wollaton who led the table all season and were twelve points clear at one stage, finally finishing eight points ahead to clinch promotion to Division One. Wollaton also reached the League Intermediate Cup final, losing 1-0 to Rainworth Miners Welfare Reserves. With a late challenge, Hucknall Rolls Royce finished as runners-up in Division Two.

E R Rudd, League Secretary

SENIOR DIVISION	P	W	D	L	F	A	PTS
GPT Plessey	30	23	3	4	77	25	49
Notts Police	30	23	1	6	75	32	47
Rainworth MW	30	18	8	4	60	21	44
Clipstone MW	30	21	2	7	62	31	44
Worthington Simp.	30	16	4	10	62	45	36
Radcliffe Olympic	30	12	10	8	49	43	34
Pelican	30	13	6	11	64	66	32
Hucknall RR Wf.	30	12	6	12	49	51	30
Dunkirk	30	11	6	13	59	52	28
John Player	30	10	7	13	45	44	27
Greenwood Mead.	30	9	7	14	40	50	25
Cotgrave MW	30	9	6	15	39	58	24
Ruddington	30	9	4	17	45	63	22
Thoresby CW	30	7	6	17	33	61	20
Basford United	30	2	6	22	31	95	10
Clifton All Whites	30	2	2	25	23	77	8

Manager of the year: Ian McCulloch (GPT)
Player of the year: Graham Wright (Huck. RR)

DIVISION ONE	P	W	D	L	F	A	PTS
Boots Athletic	30	24	2	4	93	28	50
Bulwell Forest V.	30	21	4	5	71	27	46
Sneinton	30	21	4	5	73	29	46
Awsorth Villa	30	15	5	10	71	44	35
Keyworth United	30	14	7	9	50	37	35
Worthington S. Res	30	12	6	12	73	74	30
Gedling CW	30	10	8	12	49	48	28
Carlton Athletic	30	12	4	14	47	52	28
Southwell City	30	10	7	13	48	62	27
Clipstone MW Res	30	10	4	16	43	58	24
Rainworth MW Res	30	7	10	13	41	53	24
Bilsthorpe CW	30	10	5	15	44	50	*23
Stapleford Villa	30	9	5	16	33	49	23
City S'wood Hosp.	30	8	7	15	41	70	23
British Rail	30	9	4	17	39	77	22
GPT Plessey Res	30	4	6	20	42	100	14

* - 2 points deducted
Play-off: Bulwell Forest V. 2, Sneinton 0
Manager of the year: Dick Durrant (Boots)
Player of the year: Kevin McMenamin (Stapleford)

DIVISION TWO	P	W	D	L	F	A	PTS
Wollaton	32	28	1	3	100	30	57
Hucknall RR Res	32	21	7	4	83	28	49
Ollerton Bevercotes	32	20	8	4	91	42	48
Bestwood MW	32	20	7	5	89	44	47
Retford United	32	18	5	9	83	48	41
Calverton CW	32	16	8	8	64	44	40
Teversal Grange	32	17	6	9	66	52	40
Linby CW	32	16	5	11	88	45	37
Dunkirk Reserves	32	12	8	12	82	77	32
Fairham	32	9	11	12	60	50	29
John Player Res	32	12	5	15	62	66	29
Basford Utd Res	32	10	6	16	62	69	26
Greenwood M. Res	32	9	8	16	45	69	26
Ruddington Res	32	3	6	23	43	106	12
Ryecroft	32	4	4	24	47	133	12
Carlton Ath. Res	32	4	3	25	30	93	11
Southwell City Res	32	3	2	27	40	139	8

Manager of the year: Dave Cotton (Wollaton)
Player of the year: Gary Kelly (Ryecroft)

TOP SCORERS:

Senior Division:
Mark Gore (Worthington) - 28 (+ 1 Lg Cup)
Tony Heydon (Notts Police) - 27 (2 Lg Cup)

Division One:
Phil Spencer (Boots Ath.) - 23 (+ 3 Lg Cup)
Mick Walsh (Bulwell F.V.) - 24

Division Two:
Andy Powell (Retford Utd) - 40 (+ 2 Lg Cup)
Tim Orme (Bestwood CW) - 28

Referee of the season: Mr Les Howie
Linesmen of the season:
Mr Nick Elderkin, Nr Ian Kirk

NOTTS ALLIANCE SENIOR CUP 1991-92

First Round

Stapleford Villa v Boots Athletic	0-5
Bulwell Forest Villa v John Player	0-1
Hucknall RR Welfare v British Rail Newark	3-1
Rainworth Miners Welfare v Thoresby CW	5-1
Gedling MW v City & Sherwood Hosp.	3-2(aet)
Southwell City v Cotgrave Colliery Welf.	2-1

Bilsthorpe Colliery Welfare v Basford Utd	4-2
Sneinton v Awsworth Villa	0-3
GPT Plessey v Carlton Athletic	2-2(aet),1-0
Clipstone Welf. v Radcliffe Olympic	2-2(aet),0-2
Clifton All Whites v Ruddington	0-3
Dunkirk v Pelican	0-4

Second Round

Worthington Simpson v Boots Ath.	2-2(aet),1-4
Greenwood Meadows v Awsworth Villa	4-2
Rainworth Miners Welfare v Keyworth United	5-0
Gedling Miners Welfare v Ruddington	3-1

John Player v Bilsthorpe Colliery Welfare	2-0
Hucknall Rolls Royce Welfare v GPT Plessey	0-1
Radcliffe Olympic v Notts Police	3-5(aet)
Pelican v Southwell City	3-0

Quarter Finals

Boots Athletic v John Player	5-1
Rainworth Miners Welfare v Notts Police	2-0

Greenwood Meadows v G.P.T. Plessey	1-4
Gedling Miners Welfare v Pelican	0-1

Semi-Finals

Boots Athletic v G.P.T. Plessey	2-1

Rainworth Miners Welfare v Pelican	0-2

Final: Boots Athletic 2, Pelican 0

NOTTS ALLIANCE INTERMEDIATE CUP 1991-92

First Round

Fairham v Rainworth Miners Welfare Res	0-2
Clipstone W. Res v Greenwood Meadows Res	1-2
Southwell City Reserves v Ryecroft	1-3

Dunkirk Reserves v John Player Reserves	3-0
Worthington Simpson Reserves v Teversal Grange	1-0

Second Round

Rainworth MW Res v Basford United Res	5-3
G'wood Meadows Res v Hucknall RR Res	0-1
Ollerton & Bevercotes MW v Worthington Res	5-0
GPT Plessey Reserves v Ryecroft	4-1

Bestwood Miners Welfare v Dunkirk Reserves	2-1
Carlton Athletic Reserves v Retford United	0-3
Linby Colliery Welfare v Calverton Colliery W.	2-1
Wollaton v Ruddington Reserves	5-1

Quarter Finals

Bestwood MW v Rainworth MW Reserves	0-2
Ollerton & Bevercotes MW v Linby Col. W.	3-1

Retford United v Hucknall Rolls Royce W. Res	2-1
GPT Plessey Reserves v Wollaton	1-11

Semi-Finals

Ollerton & Bevercotes MW v Wollaton	2-3(aet)

Rainworth Miners Welfare Reserves v Retford Utd	2-0

Final: Rainworth Miners Welfare Reserves 1, Wollaton 0

SENIOR DIVISION CLUBS 1992-93

BOOTS ATHLETIC
Secretary: Ian Whitehead, 55 Longmoor Lane, Breaston, Derbys DE1 3RB (0331 74203).
Ground: Lady Bay, West Bridgford, Nottingham (0602 822392). **Colours:** Blue & white stipes/navy
Hons: Notts Alliance Div 1 91-92 (Lg Cup 91-92), Notts I'mediate Cup R-up 91-92.

BULWELL FOREST VILLA
Secretary: W Matthews, 322 St.Albans Road, Bulwell, Nottm (0602 278010).
Ground: Haywood Clinic, Arnold Road, Bestwood Estate, Nottingham. **Colours:** All Red
Hons: Notts Alliance Div 1 R-up 91-92

CLIPSTONE WELFARE
Secretary: Barry Clarke, 40 Church Road, Clipstone, Mansfield, NG21 9OG (0632 655674).
Ground & Directions: Clipstone Lido Ground (0632 655674). B6030 from Mansfield, on left entering Clipstone.
Cols: All White **Hons:** Notts Snr Cup 85-86, Notts Lge Cup Double 73 74 75, Notts I'mediate Cup 56

COTGRAVE COLLIERY WELFARE
Secretary: David Southern, 185 Ringleas, Cotgrave, Nottm NG12 3PQ (0602 894940).
Ground: Cotgrave Miners Welfare. **Colours:** Yellow/Blue

DUNKIRK
Secretary: Mr J G Peck, 5 Thistledown Rd, Clifton, Nottm NG11 9DP (0602 842147).
Ground & Directions: The Ron Steel Sports Ground, Trentside Farm, Clifton Bridge, Nottingham. Ring Road -
Clifton Bridge (North End), Industrial Estate, Lenton Lane.
Colours: Red/Black
Hons: Notts Alliance Div 1 84-85 (Div 2 82-83, Lg Cup R-up 84-85), Notts I'mediate Cup 83-84.

GREENWOOD MEADOWS
Secretary: Barry Hall, 34 Sullivan Close, Marmion Estate, Nottm NG3 2HX (0602 582459).
Ground: Lenton Lane, Clifton Bridge, Nottingham. **Colours:** All Green

G.P.T. (PLESSEY)
Secretary: Roger Marshall, Sports Office, G.P.T., Beeston, Nottm (0602 433669). **Colours:** All sky.
Ground: Trent Vale Road, Beeston, Nottm (0602 258320) **Hons:** Notts Alliance 66-67 91-92

HUCKNALL ROLLS ROYCE WELFARE
Secretary: Peter Williams, 38 Tiverton Close, Hucknall, Nottm NG15 6JT.
Ground: Sports and Social Club, Entrance Watnall Road. **Colours:** All Blue.

JOHN PLAYERS
Secretary: Ron Walton, 6 Watson Avenue, Bakersfield, Nottm NG3 7BL (0602 504631).
Ground & Directions: Asplay Lane, Nottm (0602 294244). Corner of Nottingham ring road B690 turn towards City
Centre.
Colours: Yellow/green
Hons: Notts Alliance 21-22 22-23 23-24 24-25 25-26 26-27 67-68 68-69 69-70 85-86 89-90.

NOTTINGHAMSHIRE POLICE
Secretary: Bob Fawcett, 19 Bracken Hill, Mansfield NG18 3NT (0632 636911).
Ground & Directions: Force Training School, Epperstone Manor, Notts. On A60 Mansfield Road, on right from City Centre (2 miles).
Colours: White/Black
Hons: Notts Snr R-up 91-92, Notts All. Div 1 & Lge Snr Cup R-up 85-86, PAAN Nat. K-O Comp 63- 64.

PELICAN
Secretary: Paul Asher, 14 Tahxted Close, Bilborough, Nottm NG8 4NG (0602 288625).
Ground: John Pearson Sports Ground, Lenton Lane, Nottingham.   **Colours:** All Blue.
Hons: Notts Alliance Lg Cup 90-91 (R-up 91-92).

RAINWORTH MINERS WELFARE
Secretary: Alan Wright, 10 Faraday Road, Mansfield NG18 4ES (0632 24379).
Ground & Directions: Kirklington Road, Rainworth. On A617 Mansfield - Newark Road.
Colours: All White
Hons: Notts Alliance 77-78 78-79 79-80 80-81 81-82 82-83 (Lg Cup 81-82), Notts Snr Cup 80-81 81-82 (R-up 82-83), FA Vase R-up 82-82, Thorn EMI F'lit Cup R-up 82-83 83-84 84-85.

RADCLIFFE OLYMPIC
Secretary: C Johnson, 2 The Firs, Holme Pierrepont, Radcliffe-on-Trent (333791).
Ground: Wharf Lane, Radcliffe-on-Trent.   **Colours:** Black & White/White/White

RUDDINGTON
Secretary: John Fisk, 3 Savages Road, Ruddington, Nottm NG11 6EW (0602 842552).
Ground & Directions: The Elms Park Ground, Loughborough Road, Ruddington (0602 844976. On A60 Nottm to Loughborough, 5 miles out of Nottingham.
Colours: Amber/Blue   **Honours:** Notts Comb. Lg 79-80 (Lg Cup 70-71 76-77 80-81)

THORESBY COLLIERY WELFARE
Secretary: Keith Moore, 9 Rufford Road, Edwinstowe, Nr Mansfield, NG21 9HX (0632 822264).
Ground: Thoresby Colliery, Fourth Avenue, Edwinstowe, Nr Mansfield.   **Colours:** Blue/black

WORTHINGTON SIMPSONS
Secretary: Anthony Hopkinson, 109 Hawton Lane, Balderton, Newark, Notts NG24 3EH (0636 79883).
Ground & Directions: Lowfields, off Hawton Lane, New Baldeton, Newark, Notts (0636 702672). From Newark, A6065 to Newark Hospital, right into Bowbridge Road, cont. 1 mile, left by timber yard, over bridge then right. From A1 (By-pass) A6065 Newark to lights. Ahead then left into Hawton Lane.
Colours: Burgundy/Blue   **Hons:** Notts Alliance Lg Cup

NOTTS ALLIANCE DIVISION ONE CLUBS 1992-93

AWSWORTH VILLA
Secretary: Keith Slaney, 24 Attewell Road, Awsworth, Nottm NG16 2SY (0602 302514).
Ground: Attewell Road, Awsworth.   **Colours:** All Blue

BASFORD UNITED
Secretary: Paul Dobson, 26 Chevin Gardens, Top Valley, Nottm NG5 9ES (0602 274790).
Ground & Directions: Greenwich Ave., Sports Ground, Bagnall Road, Basford, Nottm (0602 423918). M1 (J26) follow signs 'A610 Nottingham' then 'B6004 Arnold' into Mill Street.
Colours: Yellow/Black   **Hons:** Notts Snr Cup 46-47 87-88, Notts Alliance Div 1 R-up 71-72 84-85.

BILSTHORPE COLLIERY WELFARE
Secretary: Mr Les Lee, 42 Chaple Lane, Ravenshead, Nottm NG2 6DM (0602 816096).
Ground: Bilsthorpe C.W. Ground, Eakring Road, Bilsthorpe.   **Colours:** All Red

CARLTON ATHLETIC
Secretary: Ron H Pickering, 17 Woodsend Close, Burton Joyce, Nottm NG14 4DY (0602 313392).
Ground: Carlton Hill, Recreation Ground, Carlton (0602 615689).   **Colours:** White/Black

CITY & SHERWOOD HOSPITALS
Secretary: Mr Peter Donohoe, 2 Campden Green, Clifton Est., Nottm NG11 8BN.
Ground: C.O.D. Military Ground, Chilwell (0602 254811).   **Colours:** All Royal Blue

CLIFTON ALL WHITES
Secretary: Keith Elliott, 61 Greencroft, Clifton Est., Nottm NG11 8GT (0602 215401).
Ground & Directions: Green Lane, Clifton Est., Nottm (0602 844903). Off A6005 Nottingham - Long Eaton Road.
Colours: All white   **Hons:** Notts Alliance Div 1

CLIPSTONE WELFARE RESERVES (See preceding page)

GEDLING COLLIERY WELFARE
Secretary: Mrs Maureen Chambers, 8 Fraser Road, Carlton, Nottm NG4 1NJ (0602 612994).
Ground: Gedling Colliery Welfare, Plains Road, Mapperley. Tel: 266300   **Colours:** Yellow/Blue

HUCKNALL ROLLS ROYCE RESERVES
Colours: Yellow/Red   *(Other details as per preceding page)*

KEYWORTH UNITED
Secretary: Maurice G Simpson, 25 Waddington Drive, Wilford Hill, West Bridgford, Nottm NG2 7GT (0602 232921).
Ground: Platt Lane, Keyworth (0607 75998).   **Colours:** Green/Black

RAINWORTH MINERS WELFARE RESERVES (As Senior Div., above)

SNEINTON
Secretary: John W Stokeld, 4 Baker Avenue, Arnold, Nottm NG5 8FU (0602 263681).
Ground: Stoke Lane, Gedling, Nottingham.   **Colours:** All White
Hons: Notts Intermediate Cup 91-92.

SOUTHWELL CITY
Secretary: Pat Johnson, 63 The Ropewalk, Southwell, Notts NG25 0AL (0636 812594).
Ground: Moor Lane Leisure Centre, Southwell.   **Colours:** White pin stripes/Black

STAPLEFORD VILLA
Secretary: Mr Clyde Davis, 33 Molton Rd, Sherwood, Nottm.
Ground: Bramcote Park, Ilkeston Rd Entrance.   **Colours:** White/Blue

WOLLATON
Secretary: Glyn Brewer, 15 Renfrew Drive, Wollaton, Nottm NG8 2FX (0602 281471).
Ground: Wollaton Sports Club, Wollaton Village, Nottm (0602 289748).
Colours: Maroon/sky/maroon   **Hons:** Notts All. Div 2 91-92 (I'mediate Cup R-up 91-92).

WORTHINGTON SIMPSONS RESERVES
Colours: White/black   *(Other details as per preceding page)*

NOTTS ALLIANCE DIVISION TWO CLUBS 1992-93

ABACUS
Previous League: Notts Amateur.

ATTENBOROUGH
Secretary: Terry Allen, 78 Gleneagles Drive, Arnold, Nottingham NG5 8QR (0602 200698).
Ground & Directions: The Village Green, The Strand, Attenborough, Beeston, Nottingham. Midway between Beeston & Long Eaton on A6005 - adjacent to Nature Reserve (via Attenborough Lane).
Colours: All blue   **Change cols:** White/black/black.   **Previous Lge:** Central Mids (pre-1992)

BASFORD UNITED RESERVES (As preceding page)

BESTWOOD MINERS WELFARE
Secretary: Mrs Karen Robinson, 34 Broomhill Rd, Bulwell, Nottm NG6 9GW (0602 763135).
Ground: Bestwood Workshops. Tel: 27377   **Colours:** Red/white

BRITISH RAIL (NEWARK)
Secretary: Mr J Todd, 15 Lamb Close, Newark, Notts (0636 72709).
Ground: The Stadium, Elm Avenue, Newark, Notts.   **Colours:** All red

CALVERTON MINERS WELFARE
Secretary: David Richards, 23 Grimesmoor Road, Calverton, Nottm NG14 (0602 655027).
Ground: Calverton Colliery   **Colours:** Yellow/black

CARLTON ATHLETIC RESERVES (As preceding page)

DUNKIRK RESERVES (As Senior Division)

FAIRHAM
Secretary: Graham Deakin, 18 Vernon Avenue, Wilford, Nottm NG11 7AE (0602 816984).
Ground: Rigley Sports Ground, Cotgrave Colliery, Cotgrave.   **Cols:** Blue & white hoops/white

G.P.T. (PLESSEY), GREENWOOD MEADOWS, JOHN PLAYER RES. (As Senior Div.)

LINBY COLLIERY MINERS WELFARE
Secretary: D G Dickens, 4 Old Mill Close, Bestwood, Nottingham, NG6 8TA. Tel: 276598.
Ground: Church Lane, Linby
Colours: Red/White

OLLERTON & BEVERCOTES MINERS WELFARE
Secretary: A R Ilett, Ashdale Cottage, Eakring Wellow, Newark. Tel: (0632) 835397
Ground: Wallsby Lane, New Ollerton.   **Colours:** Amber/white

RETFORD UNITED
Secretary: Jeff Lamb, 18 Northumbria Drive, Retford, Notts, DN22 7PR (Retford 705833).
Ground: Oaklands Lane (Off London Road), Retford, (enter via Caledonian Road).
Colours: Black & white stripes/black

RUDDINGTON RESERVES
Colours: Blue & white/Blue   *(Other details as per Senior Division)*

RYECROFT
Secretary: S R Withers, 19 Moorfield Str., Stapleford, Nottm NG9 8LA (0602 393578).
Ground: Hickings Lane, Stapleford.   **Colours:** Black & white stripes/black

TEVERSAL GRANGE
Secretary: Kevin Newton, 8 Vere Ave., Sutton in Ashfield, Notts NG17 2ES (0623 511402).
Ground: Carnarvon Street, Sutton in Ashfield.   **Colours:** Yellow/blue/blue

WESTMORLAND LEAGUE

DIVISION ONE	P	W	D	L	F	A	PTS
Coniston	26	18	7	1	84	25	43
Staveley	26	17	5	4	66	33	39
Ambleside	26	16	5	5	88	37	37
Keswick	26	15	5	6	77	35	35
Kirkby Stephen	26	14	6	6	86	55	34
Kendal United	26	12	9	5	73	40	33
Kendal County	26	12	8	6	56	43	32
Wetheriggs	28	11	5	10	58	52	27
Burneside	26	8	4	14	42	63	20
Appleby	26	6	5	15	30	57	17
Greystoke	26	7	3	16	46	80	17
Kirkoswald	26	6	4	16	51	86	16
Sedburgh	26	3	3	20	40	97	9
Victoria Sporting C.	26	1	3	22	32	126	5

DIVISION TWO	P	W	D	L	F	A	PTS
Netherfield Res	26	19	3	4	80	34	41
Windermere	26	18	3	5	104	42	39
Penrith United	26	15	6	5	68	41	36
Keswick Reserves	26	16	3	7	78	44	35
Shap	26	13	9	4	64	36	35
Kirkby Stephen Res	26	12	6	8	78	47	30
Wetheriggs Res	26	13	2	11	62	61	28
Braithewaite	26	9	6	11	58	48	24
Coniston Res	26	11	2	13	47	72	24
Lunesdale	26	7	7	12	58	69	21
Ambleside Res	26	7	4	15	54	64	18
Ibis	26	4	9	13	36	58	17
Kendal Co. Res	26	4	3	19	24	88	11
Esthwaite Vale	26	1	3	11	33	140	5

EVERARDS BREWERY
LEICESTERSHIRE SENIOR LEAGUE

Hon. Secretary: P Henwood,
450 London Road, Leicester LE2 2PP (0533 704121).

HOLWELL CHAMPIONS

Holwell became Premier Division champions for the second time in five seasons finishing eight points clear of their nearest rivals, St Andrews S.C. St Andrews had topped the table from 26th October until they completed their league programme at the end of March, and were finally overtaken by Holwell, who took 39 points from a possible 45 in their last fifteen games, at the beginning of April. Congratulations to Holwell - very well done indeed! Some consolation came for St Andrews by virtue of reaching the Tebbutt Brown Cup final, but again success was elusive as they lost to Barwell Athletic who thus recorded their first ever win in the prestigious competition.

Birstall United, who finished third, made a great improvement on last season and were in the top four most of the season - a good performance. Anstey Nomads had a great run in the FA Vase, finally losing narrowly to Diss Town, but fell behind with their league fixtures; despite having games in hand it came to naught and they came fourth. Last season's champions Lutterworth Town had a moderate campaign by their standards, but did reach the final of the Leicestershire Senior Cup only to lose to Friar Lane by the only goal. It had been seventeen years since Friars last won the Senior Cup, and to celebrate they beat St Andrews in the Rolleston Cup Final to complete their season in great style. It had been a mixed season for the Old Boys as they were looking relegation bound until February, but then put together several wins to move into a comfortable position. Manager Peter Dowsing, who came in for a fair amount of criticism for most of the season, kept his head and faith in his team, and deserves credit for this success.

Houghton Rangers, promoted from Division One as champions last season, started very well but lost their two main strikers Harriman and Battison who became contracted to clubs at a higher grade early in the season. This clearly had quite an effect on the team as from being divisional leaders in mid-October they slipped to a final sixth place. The other newcomers, Ibstock Welfare and Leicestershire Constabulary, also finished in comfortable places and can be well satisfied. The former in fact lost less games than any team other than Holwell, but they also had the most draws; fifteen.

At the bottom, Syston St Peters, who had challenged for the title last term, found what it is like at the other end of the table, and only a great effort at the close (ten points from four games) gave them the chance to dodge relegation. Narborough & Littlethorpe and Hillcroft were the unlucky ones to occupy the final two places after struggling for most of the season.

In Division One, League newcomers Burbage Old Boys had a wonderful season losing only two of 34 games and finishing six points ahead of their nearest rivals North Kilworth. Last season North Kilworth came bottom and had to seek re-election, but this season they were undefeated until their 21st game. Losing this game, at Thringstone, had an unsettling effect as they managed only 22 points out of the next 39 allowing Burbage, who performed consistently all season, to take the title. Downes Sports and Barrow Town also had strong teams, and were breathing bown the necks of the top two for most of the season.

Ravenstone, newly elected to the League, finished in fifth place and can be well pleased with their efforts. Asfordby Amateurs, who also joined this season, can feel quite satisfied with their season's work, but unfortunately the other new member, Huncote S & S, occupied the bottom spot and now seek re-election along with Whetstone Athletic who were edged into the bottom but one place by Leicester YMCA. The latter had to take a point from their last game against a strong Sileby Town, and defending between the odds they managed to save themselves from the threat of losing their Senior League status.

P Henwood, Hon. Secretary

Holwell Sports FC, League Champions. Back Row: Trevor Harbin (Trainer), Greg Woods, Anthony Dawson, Mark Spencer, Paul Humphreys, Chris Newton, Mark Cramp, Andy Bone, Geoff Gibbon (Manager). Front: Steve Kee, Ian Hunter (League top-scorer), Joe Mogg, Jarrad Collington (Captain), Terry Kee, Simon Hill, Stuart Robinson.

LEAGUE TABLES 1991-92

Premier Division	P	W	D	L	F	A	PTS
Holwell Sports	30	21	6	3	97	30	69
St Andrews Soc. C.	30	19	4	7	65	49	61
Birstall United	30	15	8	7	57	44	53
Anstey Nomads	30	15	6	9	64	38	51
Barwell Athletic	30	12	11	7	56	48	47
Houghton Rangers	30	14	4	12	65	51	46
Lutterworth Town	30	12	10	8	46	39	46
Ibstock Welfare	30	9	15	6	45	39	42
Friar Lane OB	30	10	8	12	63	62	38
Newfoundpool WMC	30	10	8	12	48	50	38
Leics Constab.	30	9	9	12	48	52	36
Oadby Town	30	9	8	13	47	60	35
Pedigree Petfoods	30	7	7	16	43	61	28
Syston St Peters	30	8	4	18	49	78	28
Narborough/L'thorpe	30	5	7	18	38	86	22
Hillcroft	30	3	9	18	30	74	18

Division One	P	W	D	L	F	A	PTS
Burbage Old Boys	34	24	8	2	87	31	80
North Kilworth	34	23	5	6	109	41	74
Downes Sports	34	22	3	9	72	55	69
Barrow Town	34	18	11	5	87	49	65
Ravenstone	34	16	9	9	62	51	57
Kirby Muxloe SC	34	15	10	9	62	52	55
Harborough Town	34	15	8	11	75	64	53
Thringstone	34	14	6	14	51	70	48
Quorn	34	11	11	12	51	54	44
Sileby Town	34	12	5	17	51	53	41
Asfordby Amtrs	34	11	8	15	58	61	41
Earl Shilton Albion	34	9	11	14	52	75	38
Aylestone Pk OB	34	10	7	17	49	82	37
Loughborough Dyn.	34	9	8	17	60	66	35
Anstey Town	34	9	5	20	45	72	32
Leicester YMCA	34	6	10	18	42	72	28
Whetstone Ath,	34	5	12	17	54	74	27
Huncote Spts & S.	34	5	7	22	34	79	22

PREMIER DIVISION RESULTS 1991/92

HOME TEAM	1	2	3	4	5	6	7	8	9	10	11	12	13	14	15	16
1. Anstey Nomads	*	1-2	0-0	4-1	4-0	1-3	1-1	1-1	5-1	1-1	0-4	3-0	3-0	3-1	1-2	5-2
2. Barwell Athletic	2-1	*	0-0	1-6	1-1	1-5	0-2	0-0	2-2	3-1	4-1	2-2	2-2	3-1	3-0	2-2
3. Birstall United	1-0	4-2	*	2-0	3-1	2-0	5-1	2-1	2-0	1-4	6-4	1-1	1-2	4-0	1-7	1-1
4. Friar Lane O.B.	2-3	1-5	1-3	*	3-1	1-3	0-5	0-0	1-1	3-2	3-0	6-1	2-0	3-4	2-2	2-3
5. Hillcroft	0-4	1-6	1-1	1-6	*	0-5	1-3	2-3	0-1	1-2	1-1	0-4	1-0	3-2	2-3	2-1
6. Holwell Sports	1-2	0-0	6-1	1-1	4-1	*	2-1	1-1	2-2	1-1	2-2	1-1	4-0	1-1	6-2	4-0
7. Houghton Rangers	5-1	1-2	1-1	5-1	2-2	0-3	*	1-0	0-3	0-1	6-1	3-1	2-3	3-1	1-2	0-5
8. Ibstock Welfare	3-2	1-1	3-3	1-1	1-0	0-2	0-1	*	2-2	2-2	0-0	1-0	3-3	0-1	1-0	4-1
9. Leics Constabulary	0-4	4-1	1-3	1-1	0-0	1-2	3-1	2-2	*	1-1	4-3	1-3	1-3	1-1	0-2	7-1
10. Lutterworth Town	0-0	1-2	1-0	4-1	2-0	0-5	0-2	1-1	1-0	*	0-0	2-1	1-2	1-1	1-2	3-1
11. Narboro. & Littlethorpe	0-4	1-1	0-3	2-5	1-1	1-5	1-6	1-5	1-4	1-2	*	2-1	0-0	3-2	1-4	4-2
12. Newfoundpool WMC	0-1	2-1	2-0	1-3	1-1	0-4	2-3	1-1	2-1	0-0	5-1	*	2-2	2-0	3-1	4-0
13. Oadby Town	0-3	1-1	3-1	2-1	1-1	2-3	0-3	2-2	4-1	2-5	4-1	1-1	*	3-1	0-2	1-4
14. Pedigree Petfoods	1-1	1-2	0-3	2-2	4-4	4-2	2-2	0-1	0-1	1-1	0-1	1-4	2-1	*	2-0	0-0
15. St Andrews SC	4-3	2-1	1-1	2-2	1-0	2-6	3-2	4-1	2-1	3-1	3-1	2-0	3-1	2-1	*	2-3
16. Syston St Peters	0-2	1-2	0-1	0-2	4-1	1-4	4-2	2-4	0-1	0-4	1-1	5-1	1-0	1-4	2-2	*

DIVISION ONE RESULTS 1991/92

HOME TEAM	1	2	3	4	5	6	7	8	9	10	11	12	13	14	15	16	17	18
1. Anstey Town	*	2-3	2-2	1-2	1-5	0-3	3-1	2-4	1-0	2-1	0-1	3-2	0-4	2-4	0-1	0-5	5-0	1-1
2. Asfordby Amateurs	1-2	*	6-1	2-3	0-6	3-4	1-2	1-1	7-0	0-2	1-1	3-0	1-2	0-0	2-1	5-0	0-3	2-3
3. Aylestone Park OB	3-2	1-0	*	2-3	1-1	0-3	0-2	0-2	2-1	2-4	3-2	1-3	0-3	1-1	1-3	1-3	3-2	
4. Barrow Town	2-2	2-2	3-0	*	0-3	1-4	2-2	5-2	3-0	1-2	3-3	3-0	2-1	0-0	2-4	3-2	2-0	3-1
5. Burbage Old Boys	2-1	4-0	2-2	3-1	*	3-1	3-3	2-2	3-2	1-1	3-1	2-0	2-1	5-0	3-0	3-1	4-0	1-1
6. Downes Sports	2-0	7-0	3-1	0-5	1-0	*	3-3	1-1	2-1	0-2	4-3	2-0	0-1	4-0	2-1	2-1	5-0	1-0
7. Earl Shilton Albion	1-1	1-2	4-2	3-2	0-3	0-1	*	0-2	3-0	2-2	2-2	1-1	2-8	2-1	2-0	3-1	1-1	4-2
8. Harborough Town	1-0	0-2	6-2	2-0	2-3	8-3	1-1	*	4-0	1-2	6-1	2-2	0-4	3-1	1-2	2-4	0-1	4-3
9. Huncote Spts & Social	0-1	1-0	0-5	1-1	1-2	0-2	1-1	3-4	*	2-3	0-0	2-0	1-6	0-1	1-1	0-5	2-2	1-1
10. Kirby Muxloe S.C.	3-1	1-1	0-1	1-1	2-3	3-0	2-1	4-4	0-3	*	1-1	2-2	0-3	0-0	0-3	2-0	1-2	2-2
11. Leicester YMCA	1-2	3-0	2-2	3-3	2-3	1-2	1-2	0-2	1-0	2-2	*	1-7	0-5	2-1	1-1	0-0	2-2	
12. Loughborough Dynamo	4-2	1-1	6-0	2-4	0-0	0-2	4-0	0-3	1-1	1-2	3-0	*	1-1	1-2	3-5	3-0	1-2	2-0
13. North Kilworth	4-1	5-1	7-2	3-4	0-0	4-0	0-1	4-1	8-3	5-4	2-1	7-1	*	2-0	3-2	3-1	4-0	2-2
14. Quorn	0-0	1-0	2-1	0-3	2-0	3-3	2-2	1-2	1-2	2-1	3-1	3-3	1-1	*	0-2	2-0	2-2	5-2
15. Ravenstone	3-1	1-1	2-0	0-0	1-2	2-4	3-0	4-0	2-0	2-2	1-0	4-2	1-2	1-0	*	2-1	2-1	1-6
16. Sileby Town	3-0	1-1	0-0	0-3	1-2	0-1	4-0	1-1	2-0	1-2	2-1	2-1	0-2	4-0	3-3	*	0-4	2-0
17. Thringstone	2-1	1-3	5-1	0-9	0-5	2-3	3-1	1-2	2-1	0-2	2-1	3-2	2-1	3-3	4-0	0-1	*	1-1
18. Whetstone Athletic	1-3	1-3	1-1	2-2	1-2	2-3	7-2	1-1	1-3	1-4	0-1	0-1	3-1	0-7	2-2	2-1	0-0	*

LEADING SCORERS 1991-92: I Hunter (Holwell Sports) 34, A Warner (Friar Lane Old Boys) 29, T Kee (Holwell Sports) 28, R Smith (Asfordby Amateurs) 26, J Steane (Burbage Old Boys) 25, I Munroe (Harborough Town) 24, D Culpin (Anstey Nomads) 23, K Williams (Thringstone) 22.

PREMIER DIVISION CLUBS 1992-93

ANSTEY NOMADS
Secretary: D Marston, 115 Tewkesbury Street, Leicester LE3 5HR (0533 628218).
Ground: Cropston Road, Anstey, Leicester (0533 364868).
Directions: Anstey Lane from Leicester to Anstey, right at r'bout into Cropston Rd. 1 mile from London Road (BR).
Seats: None **Cover:** 100 **Capacity:** 2,500 **Floodlights:** No **Founded:** 1945.
Colours: All red **Record Gate:** 4,500 v Hayes, FA Amtr Cup 53-54.
Programme: 12-14 pages, 25p **Hons:** Leics Snr Lg 51-52 53-54 81-82 82-83 (Div 2 73-74).

BIRSTALL UNITED
Secretary: J Noble, 43 Havencrest Drive, Leicester LE5 2AJ (0533 760431).
Ground: Meadow Lane, Birstall (671230) **Directions:** Off Wanlip Lane, Birstall.
Colours: White/navy/navy **Hons:** Leics Snr Lg Div 2 76-77.

BURBAGE OLD BOYS
Secretary: Mrs S Taylor, 8 Brockhurst Avenue, Burbage, Leics LE10 2HG (0455 633916).
Colours: All royal blue **Ground:** Britannia Rd, Burbage, Leics.
Hons: Leics Snr Lg Div 1 91-92.

DOWNES SPORTS
Secretary: G C Higginson, 5 Cleveland Rd, Hinckley, Leics LE10 0AJ (0455 615457).
Colours: All tangerine **Ground:** 259 Coventry Rd, Hinckley (0455 635186).

FRIAR LANE OLD BOYS

Secretary: T J Knibbs, 75 Brighton Avenue, Wigston Fields, Leicester LE18 1JB (0533 888928).
Ground: Knighton Lane East, Leicester (0533 833629).
Directions: Between A50 Welford Rd and Saffron Lane near Sports Centre.
Seats: None   **Cover:** 250   **Capacity:** 3,500   **Floodlights:** No   **Founded:** 1961.
Colours: Black & white stripes/black/red
Record Gate: 1,325 v Stamford, FA Vase Semi Final April 1975.
Hons: FA Vase SF(2) 74-76, Leics Snr Lg(7) 70-72 73-78 (Div 2 69-70), Leics Snr Cup(3) 73-75 91-92

HIGHFIELD RANGERS

Secretary: M Christian, 18 Blanklyn Avenue, Leicester LE5 5FA (0533 734002).
Ground: Gleneagles Ave, Rushey Mead, Leicester (0533 66009)
Directions: A6 to Leicester, 2nd left at Birstall r'bout into Watermead/Troon Way, right at 2nd lights, 1st left.
Colours: Yellow/black/yellow   **Previous League:** Central Mids (until 1992).

HOLWELL SPORTS

Secretary: Mrs C W Warner, 40 Klondyke Way, Asfordby, Melton Mowbray, Leics LE14 3TW (0664 812010).
Ground: Welby Road, Asfordby Hill, Melton Mowbray, Leics (0664 812663)
Directions: One and a half miles out of Melton Mowbray on A607 to Loughborough.
Previous Name: Holwell Works   **Colours:** Green & gold/green/green & gold
Hons: Leics Snr Lg 11-12 86-87 91-92 (Div 1 84-85), Leics Snr Cup 54-55 56-57 57-58.

HOUGHTON RANGERS

Secretary: J P Silver, Red Roofs, 41 Main Street, Houghton-on-the-Hill, Leics LE7 9GE (0533 433951).
Ground: Weir Lane, Houghton-on-the-Hill, Leics (0533 419551).
Colours: Blue/white/blue   **Hons:** Leics Snr Lg Div 2 90-91.

IBSTOCK WELFARE

Secretary: R A Wilkinson, 6 Valley Rd, Ibstock, Leicester LE67 6NY (0530 60744).
Ground: The Welfare, Leicester Road, Ibstock (0530 60656).   **Colours:** Red/black/red.

LEICESTERSHIRE CONSTABULARY

Secretary: Mrs S Martin, 57 Richardsons Close, Broughton Astley, Leics LE9 6NU (0455 284071).
Colours: Yellow/black/yellow   **Ground:** Police WQ, St Johns, Enderby (0533 482198).

LUTTERWORTH TOWN

Secretary: B J Davies, 20 Riverside Rd, Lutterworth, Leics LE17 4BP (0455 554652).
Ground: Hall Lane, Bitteswell, Lutterworth, Leics (0455 554046)
Directions: M6 jct 1 or M1 jct 20, follow A426 through Lutterworth; Bitteswell signposted one and a half miles on beyond town.
Seats: None   **Cover:** None   **Capacity:** 3,000   **Floodlights:** Yes   **Founded:** 1890.
Previous Ground: Dunley Way (pre-1991) **Programme:** 24 pages with admission.
Colours: All red   **Clubhouse:** Normal licensing hours   **Hons:** Leics Snr Lg 90-91 (Div 2 80-81).

NARBOROUGH & LITTLETHORPE

Secretary: B Garner, 78 Sycamore Way, Littlethorpe, Leics LE9 5HU (0533 862191).
Ground: Leicester Road, Narborough (Near M1 bridge) (0533 751855).
Directions: M1 jct 21, follow signs to Narborough (2 miles).
Colours: All sky blue   **Hons:** Leics Snr Lg Div 2 81-82.

NEWFOUNDPOOL W.M.C.

Secretary: D Hunt, 2a Kingston Avenue, Wigston Fields, Leicester LE18 1JB (0533 885052).
Colours: Green & yellow stripes/green/green   **Ground:** Meadow Lane, Birstall (0533 673965).
Directions: Off Wanlip Lane, Birstall. First of two ground in Meadow Lane.
Hons: Leics Snr Lg 65-66 69-70 (Div 2 82-83), Leics Snr Cup 68-69.

NORTH KILWORTH

Secretary: R Bell, High Street, North Kilworth, Lutterworth, Leics LE17 6ET (0858 464048)(Steve Bell).
Ground: Rugby Road, North Kilworth, Lutterworth, Leics (0858 880890).
Colours: All blue   **Hons:** Leics Snr Lg Div 2 R-up 91-92.

OADBY TOWN

Secretary: D P Collins, 26 Hill Way, Oadby, Leics LE2 5YG (0533 713557).
Ground: Invicta Park, Wigston Road, Oadby, Leics (0533 715728)
Directions: Oadby is four miles south of Leicester on A6. From Oadby church in town centre follow signs for Wigston; ground three quarters of a mile on left.
Seats: None   **Cover:** 200   **Capacity:** 2,000   **Prog:** 20 pages   **Founded:** 1939.
Colours: All red   **Clubhouse:** Matchdays only
Hons: Leics Snr Lg 63-64 67-68 68-69 72-73 (Div 2 51-52), Leics Snr Cup 62-63 63-64 75-76 76-77 80-81.

PEDIGREE PETFOODS

Secretary: Mrs L Kidney, 12 Galsworthy Crescent, Melton Mowbray, Leics LE13 1JD (0664 61295).
Ground: Saxby Road, Melton Mowbray, Leics.   **Colours:** All red
Directions: Saxby road out of Melton Mowbray - ground on right just after Pedigree Petfoods factory.

ST ANDREWS SOCIAL CLUB

Secretary: C Smyth, 18 Elston Fields, Saffron Lane, Leicester LE2 6NF (0533 834521).
Ground: Canal Street, Old Aylestone, Leicester (0533 839298).
Directions: Aylestone Rd at rear of Granby Street School.
Colours: Black & white/white/black   **Hons:** Leics Snr Lg 89-90.

SYSTON ST PETERS

Secretary: M Hill, 18 Orchard Way, Syston, Leics LE7 8AL (0533 607468).
Ground: Memorial Ground, Necton Street, Syston, Leics (0533 695922).
Directions: A607 Leicester-Melton Mowbray road, on entering Syston take 1st fork left into Broad Street after railway bridge. Necton Street is third left.
Colours: Red & black stripes/white/white   **Hons:** Leics Snr Lg 61-62 (Div 2 60-61).

DIVISION ONE CLUBS 1992-93

ANSTEY TOWN
Secretary: G Ford, Hollow Rd, Anstey, Leics LE7 7FR (0533 364170).
Ground: Leicester Road, Thurcaston (0533 368231) **Colours:** All blue

ASFORDBY AMATEURS
Secretary: E W Smith, 13 Blakeney Crescent, Melton Mowbray, Leics LE13 0QP (0664 60263).
Ground: Hoby Road Sports Ground, Asfordby, Melton Mowbray,, Leics (0664 434545).
Colours: Yellow & green/green/yellow

AYLESTONE PARK OLD BOYS
Secretary: K Sharp, 1 Kent Crescent, South Wigston, Leicester LE8 2XQ (0533 812010).
Ground: Dorset Avenue, Fairfield Estate, Wigston, Leics (0533 775307)
Colours: Red & white stripes/red/red.

BARROW TOWN
Secretary: N J Freeman, 1 Beacon Drive, Loughborough, Leics LE11 2BD (0509 212853).
Ground: Riverside Park, Meynell Road, Quorn, Leics (0509 620650).
Colours: Red/white/red

COTTESMORE AMATEURS
Secretary: K Nimmons, 17 Redwing Close, Oakham, Rutland LE15 6DA (0572 724582).
Ground: Main Street, Cottesmore, Rutland (0572 813486). **Colours:** Green/white/green.

EARL SHILTON ALBION
Secretary: I C Dawkins, 28 Hillside Rd, Burbage, Leics LE10 2LX (0455 239727).
Ground: Stoneycroft Park, New Street, Earl Shilton, Leics (0455 842056).
Colours: Green & white/green/green & white
Hons: Leics Snr Lg Div 2 68-69 79-80 88-89, Leics Snr Cup 72-73.

FOSSE IMPS
Secretary: I V Colbourne, 55 Harrowgate Drive, Birstall, Leics LE4 3GQ (0533 671424).
Ground: Co-op Grnd, Birstall, Leicester (0533 674059) **Colours:** Red/black/red

HARBOROUGH TOWN IMPERIAL
Secretary: P Dougan, 26 Patrick Street, Market Harborough, Leics (0858 434546).
Ground: Northampton Road Sports Ground, Market Harborough, Leics.
Directions: M1 jct 21, follow signs to Narborough (2 miles).
Colours: Red & black stripes/black/black **Hons:** Leics Snr Lg Div 1 83-84.
Previous Ground: St Mary's Road (until 1992).

HILLCROFT
Secretary: Mrs J A Davies, 4 Kinsdale Drive, Leicester LE5 2PR (0533 415659).
Ground: Lawrence Park, Gipsey Lane, Leicester. **Colours:** Gold/black/gold.

HUNCOTE SPORTS & SOCIAL
Secretary: D Russell, 72 Sycamore Way, Littlethorpe, Leics LE9 5HU (0533 841952).
Ground: Enderby Lane, Thurlaston, Leics (0455 24430). **Colours:** Blue/white/white.

KIRBY MUXLOE S.C.
Secretary: R Pallett, 184 Blackbird Road, Leicester LE4 0AF (0533 626020).
Ground: Ratby Lane, Kirby Muxloe (0533 393201) **Colours:** All blue.

LEICESTER Y.M.C.A.
Secretary: C W Chappell, 132 South Knighton Road, Leicester LE2 3LQ (0533 702721).
Ground: Belvoir Drive, Aylestone, Leicester (0533 440740) **Colours:** Red/white/red

LOUGHBOROUGH DYNAMO
Secretary: R M Hutchinson, 3 Wythburn Close, Loughborough, Leics LE11 3SZ (0509 266092).
Ground: Nanpanton Sport Ground, Loughborough (0509 612144). **Colours:** Gold/black/gold.

QUORN
Secretary: L Caunt, 1 Highfields Road, Mountsorrel, Leics LE12 7HH (0533 303568).
Ground: Warwick Avenue, Quorn, Leics (0509 620490).
Directions: A607 Leicester-Melton Mowbray road, on entering Syston take 1st fork left into Broad Street after railway bridge. Necton Street is third left.
Colours: Red/white/red **Hons:** Leics Snr Cup 53-54.

SILEBY TOWN
Secretary: G Clarke, 123 Highgate Road, Sileby, Leics LE12 7PW (0509 813503).
Ground: Memorial Park, Seagrave Road, Sileby, Leics (0509 816104) **Colours:** All blue.

RAVENSTONE
Secretary: R Brooks, 17 Ashland Drive, Coalville, Leics LE67 3NH (0530 833269).
Ground: Ravenslea Estate, Ravenstone, Leics
Colours: Yellow & royal blue/royal blue/yellow

THRINGSTONE M.W.
Secretary: P Nelson, 29 Scotlands Drive, Coalville, Leics LE6 2SU (0530 837867).
Ground: Homestead Road, Thringstone (0530 223367).
Colours: Gold/black/gold. **Hons:** Leics Snr Lg 84-85 (Div 2 71-72).

WHETSTONE ATHLETIC
Secretary: Mrs S C Morris, 10 Winchester Road, Blaby, Leics LE8 3HJ (0533 773208).
Ground: Warwick Road, Whetstone. **Colours:** Red & white stripes/black/red

TEBBUTT BROWN (LEICS SENIOR LEAGUE) CUP 1991-92

Preliminary Round

Aylestone Park OB v Whetstone Athletic   3-1

Sileby Town v Asfordby Amateurs   3-0

First Round

Premier Division

Anstey Nomads v Barwell Athletic   2-4
Friar Lane OB v Narborough & Littlethorpe   0-4
Hillcroft v Holwell Sports   1-4
Leics Constabulary v Newfoundpool 1-1,3-3.1-1,4-1
Oadbt Town v Lutterworth Town   2-0
Pedigree Petfoods v Houghton Rangers1-1,0-0,3-4
St Andrews Social Club v Birstall United   3-1
Syston St Peters v Ibstock Welfare   2-0

Division One

Anstey Town v Ravenstone   5-0
Burbage Old Boys v Huncote Sports & Social   4-0
Downes Sports v North Kilworth   0-4
Kirby Muxloe SC v Earl Shilton Albion   2-2,2-1
Harborough Town v Aylestone Park OB   1-1,1-1,0-2
Sileby Town v Quorn   2-2,2-0
Thringstone M.W. v Barrow Town   0-4
Leicester YMCA v Loughborough Dynamo   1-3

Second Round

Premier Division

Barwell Athletic v Leicestershire Constabulary 3-0
Narborough & Littlethorpe v Houghton Rangers -2
Oadby Town v Syston St Peters   0-1
St Andrews Social Club v Holwell Sports   2-0

Division One

Burbage Old Boys v Barrow Town   2-1
North Kilworth v Kirby Muxloe SC   3-3,3-1
Loughborough Dynamo v Aylestone Park OB   2-1
Anstey Town v Sileby Town   0-2

Quarter Finals

Barwell Athletic v Burbage Old Boys   1-0
North Kilworth v Aylestone Park OB   1-1,4-6

Houghton Rangers v Syston St Peters   2-0
Sileby Town v Loughborough Dynamo   1-1,1-1,2-0

Semi-Finals

St Andrews v Houghton *(match replayed)* 2-3,2-1

Sileby Town v Barwell Athletic   0-2

Final: Barwell Athletic 3, St Andrews Social Club 0

Holwell Sports celebrate their League Championship success. Photo - Leicester Mercury.

Campbell Curtis, of Division One runners-up North Kilworth, proudly grasps the Harborough Charity Cup after another success for his club. Photo - Leo Heonig.

WEST RIDING COUNTY AMATEUR LEAGUE

Premier Division	P	W	D	L	F	A	PTS
Field FC	26	19	4	3	73	27	42
Halifax Irish	26	16	5	5	70	38	37
Ferrybridge Amtrs	26	14	8	4	46	26	36
Ovenden W. Riding	26	15	4	7	56	41	34
Aberford Albion	26	12	6	8	40	35	30
Brighouse Town	26	13	2	11	51	44	28
Altofts AFC	26	10	6	10	44	38	26
Crag Road Utd	26	9	6	11	47	42	24
Rawdon Old Boys	26	8	7	11	45	48	23
Salts	26	6	9	11	30	54	21
Marsden A.F.C.	26	7	4	15	33	53	18
Gascoigne United	26	6	5	15	34	46	17
Dudley Hill Ath.	26	6	2	18	43	78	14
Littletown	26	4	6	16	29	71	14

League Cup Winners: Crag Road United
League Cup R-up: Halifax Irish

Division One	P	W	D	L	F	A	PTS
Tyersal	30	22	3	5	86	45	47
Wibsey	30	21	4	5	82	41	46
Campion	30	21	3	6	103	43	45
Lower Hopton	30	14	7	9	60	44	35
Farnley W.M.C.	30	14	7	9	61	54	35
Steeton	30	15	4	11	75	59	34
Ventus/Yeadon C.	30	14	4	12	57	52	32
Ardsley Celtic	30	13	3	14	50	56	29
Hall Green Utd	30	11	6	13	55	58	28
T.S. Harrison	30	12	3	15	47	56	27
Morley Town	30	10	7	13	53	66	27
I.C.I. (Huddersfield)	30	12	2	16	54	65	26
Springfield Y.C.	30	9	5	16	56	76	23
Bowling Celtic	30	8	4	18	59	70	20
Brook Motors	30	7	4	19	52	94	18
Eastmoor Albion	30	2	4	24	41	112	8

League Cup Winners: Wibsey
League Cup R-up: Ventus/Yeadon Celtic

Division Two	P	W	D	L	F	A	PTS
Otley Town	28	20	5	3	116	40	45
Allerton Bywater	28	17	4	7	81	47	38
Pontefract	28	17	4	7	89	67	38
Greetland United	28	17	3	8	95	60	37
Dynamoes	28	13	8	7	91	60	34
Westbrook Wdrs	28	13	6	9	65	54	32
Ovenden W.R. Res	28	12	5	11	58	65	29
Morley Minors	28	12	4	12	66	63	28
Trinity Athletic	28	11	3	14	55	74	25
Green Lane	28	10	4	14	55	76	24
Black Horse	28	9	5	14	60	84	23
Altofts Res	28	8	4	16	40	83	18
Vesper Gate	28	6	6	16	40	83	18
Ferrybridge A. Res	28	7	3	18	35	73	17
Queensbury '72	28	4	4	20	55	87	12

League Cup Winners: Allerton Bywater
League Cup R-up: Otley Town

Division Three	P	W	D	L	F	A	PTS
Field Res	28	20	5	3	91	45	45
Brighouse T. Res	28	17	6	5	92	55	40
Crag Rd Utd Res	28	17	4	7	86	46	38
Aberford Albion Res	28	16	6	6	89	52	38
Bowling FC	28	15	4	9	85	53	34
Salt G.S.O.B.	28	13	6	9	67	57	32
Eccleshill Utd	28	13	4	11	67	60	30
Phoenix FC	28	11	3	14	73	65	25
Pudsey Liberal	28	9	7	12	70	68	25
Saville	28	9	6	13	63	81	24
Farnley WMC Res	28	10	3	15	56	82	23
Lucas	28	9	3	16	61	79	21
Dubrovnic	28	9	2	17	48	89	20
Skipton L.M.S.	28	6	1	21	61	112	13
Littletown Res	28	4	4	20	38	103	12

League Cup Winners: Field Reserves
League Cup R-up: Eccleshill Utd

Reserve Division	P	W	D	L	F	A	PTS
Wibsey Res	30	21	3	6	102	56	45
ICI Hud'field Res	30	18	7	5	70	37	43
Tyersal Res	30	16	7	7	87	55	39
Salts Res	30	16	6	8	86	49	38
Lower Hopton Res	30	15	4	11	88	55	34
Steeton Res	30	14	6	10	69	57	34
Ventus/Yeadon Res	30	13	7	10	75	67	33
Rawdon OB Res	30	13	7	10	68	70	33
Westbrook W. Res	30	13	4	13	58	74	30
Marsden Res	30	10	7	13	64	76	27
Ardsley Celtic Res	30	11	5	15	65	82	26
Bowling Celtic Res	30	9	7	14	72	80	25
Campion Res	30	10	5	15	81	96	25
Otley Town Res	30	8	4	18	68	75	20
Hall Green U. Res	30	4	7	19	37	94	15
Trinity Ath. Res	30	5	3	22	49	116	13

League Cup Winners: ICI Hudd. Reserves
League Cup R-up: Rawdon OB Res

Brighouse Town, West Riding County Amateur League Runners-up 1991-92. The picture was taken before the West Riding County F.A. Challenge Cup final at Thackley FC, which Brighouse won with a 2-1 victory over Beeston St Antony's.

PREMIER DIVISION RESULT CHART 1991/92

HOME TEAM	1	2	3	4	5	6	7	8	9	10	11	12	13	14
1. Aberfield Albion	*	1-1	3-0	2-0	3-1	1-1	3-0	1-0	0-2	0-0	3-1	1-0	0-1	0-1
2. Altofts	0-1	*	1-6	3-0	1-1	2-1	2-2	1-2	4-0	3-2	3-0	0-1	1-2	2-2
3. Brighouse Town	1-2	2-0	*	2-0	2-0	1-1	0-2	1-1	0-3	6-0	3-2	2-3	3-1	1-0
4. Crag Road United	3-1	1-1	7-0	*	2-1	0-0	0-1	2-0	1-2	2-1	1-2	1-2	5-3	1-1
5. Dudley Hill Ath.	1-2	3-2	2-1	1-4	*	1-2	1-5	5-0	2-1[0]	2-1	1-2	1-5	1-3	5-3
6. Ferrybridge Amtrs	4-1	0-1	2-2	3-1	3-0	*	1-1	1-0	3-2	2-1	2-0	2-1	2-0	1-2
7. Field	6-0	2-1	1-3	4-2	1-1		*	5-2	2-1	2-2	5-0	5-1	2-1	5-0
8. Gascoigne United	4-2	0-1	0-4	2-0	6-0	1-2	0-2	*	1-3	4-2	0-1	3-0	0-0	0-0
9. Halifax Irish	1-1	3-0	4-1	3-2	1-1	0-3	1-4	2-2	*	4-0	1-1	1-1	4-2	4-0
10. Littletown	0-6	1-5	1-7	1-1	1-3	1-4	1-4	0-0	1-2	*	1-1	1-4	0-4	2-1
11. Marsden	4-2	1-2	0-1	4-6	4-3	0-4	0-1	2-1	1-2	0-3	*	0-2	1-0	0-2
12. Ovenden West Riding	1-2	3-2	5-1	2-2	6-1	4-1	0-4	3-2	1-4	2-2	2-0	*	2-0	5-3
13. Rawdon Old Boys	1-1	1-1	1-2	3-1	3-1	1-1	4-2	4-2	3-5	1-2	1-1	0-0	*	2-2
14. Salts	1-1	0-4	3-2	1-1	3-2	0-0	2-2	1-5	2-1	1-1	0-2	2-3		*

DIVISION ONE RESULT CHART 1991/92

HOME TEAM	1	2	3	4	5	6	7	8	9	10	11	12	13	14	15	16
1. Ardsley Celtic	*	4-2	2-4	1-3	3-3	0-1	2-2	1-4	1-3	2-5	2-0	3-1	1-0	0-1	3-1	1-4
2. Bowling Celtic	1-3	*	2-3	3-5	4-1	1-3	1-2	7-0	2-0	2-4	2-2	4-6	0-2	1-2	0-3	2-2
3. Brook Motors	3-2	2-3	*	3-4	3-3	1-1	4-1	2-2	0-6	3-5	2-1	3-2	0-4	2-4	2-4	0-1
4. Campion	0-1	3-1	6-2	*	1-1[1]	3-0	3-1	4-0	2-2	7-0	3-2	0-1	3-2	3-0	4-3	2-2
5. Eastmoor Albion	1-2	2-4	2-4	0-5	*	3-3	0-0	2-1	0-4	0-1	3-5	0-2	3-0	1-5	0-4	2-4
6. Farnley W.M.C.	1-2	2-0	4-1	3-3	3-1	*	2-2	4-0	4-1	2-1	3-1	1-2	2-6	2-1	0-2	
7. Hall Green United	0-0	2-0	3-0	1-3	6-0	3-1	*	2-4	0-4	1-6	1-1	4-2	2-0	1-3	1-3	1-2
8. ICI Huddersfield	2-1	4-3	1-0	0-2	7-2	3-2	2-0	*	1-2	2-0	1-4	0-2	0-2	1-2	2-3	3-0
9. Lower Horton	2-1	3-0	3-1	0-3	3-0	0-1	2-5	3-1	*	1-2	3-2	0-1	2-1	2-1	1-1	1-2
10. Morley Town	0-1	0-0	3-0	1-7	5-2	2-2	1-0	1-1	2-2	*	2-1	3-4	2-5	1-3	0-1	1-5
11. Springfield	1-2	4-1	4-2	4-3	3-1	1-1	2-4	2-1	1-1	3-0	*	0-2	3-0	1-7	1-2	1-6
12. Steeton	4-0	2-3	5-1	4-3	9-3	5-1	1-2	2-1	2-2	2-2	3-3	*	2-2	2-1	2-0	1-2
13. T.S. Harrison	2-1	0-2	1-1	1-3	2-1	1-3	3-0	1-3	0-2	2-1	1-3	2-2	*	0-2	1-2	5-1
14. Tyersal	1-3	3-2	4-0	1-0	3-2	1-3	2-1	4-3	3-3	2-2	6-1	4-2	3-3	*	3-2	3-0
15. Ventus/Yeadon Celtic	2-4	0-5	3-1	0-4	4-1	1-1	1-4	2-3	1-1	0-6	0-2	0-3	0-0	0-3	*	2-1
16. Wibsey	2-1	1-1	8-2	3-1	2-1	4-1	3-3	3-1	3-0	1-0	5-1	4-1	6-0	1-3	2-0	*

DIVISION TWO RESULT CHART 1991/92

HOME TEAM	1	2	3	4	5	6	7	8	9	10	11	12	13	14	15
1. Allerton Bywater	*	6-0	3-1	1-1	2-0	2-0	1-4	4-1	3-3	3-1	1-5	5-0	1-3	3-1	4-0
2. Altofts Res	0-7	*	2-4	3-3	0-5	3-2	0-2	4-6	1-2	0-1	3-0	1-0	3-0	0-2	3-3
3. Black Horse	2-2	2-3	*	0-4	3-2	0-1	1-5	3-3	3-6	2-1	4-3	3-0	3-4	5-3	1-0
4. Dynamoes	6-0	3-0	2-1	*	3-4	3-4	5-5	2-0	3-3	4-1	5-2	2-2	10-1	3-2	0-2
5. Ferrybridge Res	0-4	1-0	4-1	2-1	*	0-3	0-6	1-2	1-4	1-1	1-2	3-1	0-1	0-5	1-1
6. Green Hall	2-6	4-0	3-0	2-2	2-2	*	1-4	1-3	1-4	2-2	0-2	0-7	2-5	4-1	1-2
7. Greetland	1-0	1-3	3-4	3-4	8-2	3-4	*	6-4	3-1	2-1	3-3	2-1	7-1	2-1	2-1
8. Morley Minors	3-4	2-4	5-6	0-2	2-0	5-1	1-0	*	1-5	2-1	6-3	5-1	3-1	2-0	1-2
9. Otley Town	4-1	5-2	5-1	2-1	8-1	7-0	7-0	1-1	*	8-0	2-3	4-1	2-0	10-1	2-2
10. Ovenden W.R. Reserves	1-1	3-2	3-3	5-3	3-1	2-0	4-0	2-0	5-4	*	3-4	5-1	2-1	2-2	4-2
11. Pontefract	4-3	3-2	2-0	2-5	4-0	4-0	2-7	3-3	2-2	4-1	*	5-1	2-2	4-0	5-3
12. Queensbury	2-4	1-2	4-4	5-5	0-1	2-3	3-3	0-1	2-4	3-0	4-5	*	2-1	2-3	3-6
13. Trinity Athletic	0-2	1-0	5-0	4-4	2-0	2-2	6-3	2-1	0-2	2-4	4-3	2-4	*	3-1	0-4
14. Vesper Gate	0-5	1-1	2-2	1-4	2-1	1-7	0-4	1-1	0-5	1-4	0-5	3-1	4-1	*	2-2
15. Westbrook Wanderers	2-3	2-2	4-1	3-1	2-1	4-1	3-3	3-1	2-3	1-4	1-2	2-3	5-2	3-1	0-0

DIVISION THREE RESULT CHART 1991/92

HOME TEAM	1	2	3	4	5	6	7	8	9	10	11	12	13	14	15
1. Aberford Albion Res	*	1-3	3-1	3-1	4-0	4-3	2-3	2-4	7-0	6-3	2-1	2-1	2-3	2-2	7-3
2. Bowling FC	4-2	*	7-1	4-3	4-1	2-0	6-0	3-4	1-2	0-0	4-2	1-1	2-2	2-3	5-0
3. Brighouse Town Res	1-1	4-1	*	2-2	4-2	5-2	1-0	1-4	4-0	5-2	3-2	5-2	6-0		
4. Crag Road Reserves	1-1	2-1	6-2	*	3-1	2-1	4-1	1-1	7-1	5-1	0-3	3-1	3-2	4-0	5-1
5. Dubrovnic	1-1	3-2	3-2	1-6	*	0-1	3-2	0-2	3-2	0-1	5-4	1-3	2-1	5-2	1-2
6. Eccleshill Utd	2-2	1-0	2-2	3-4	5-0	*	4-1	1-4	1-2	4-1	2-2	3-2	3-1	4-1	3-1
7. Farnley Reserves	3-7	2-4	3-3	3-1	4-4	2-1	*	0-3	8-1	1-1	3-2	2-1	1-3	2-1	2-1
8. Field Reserves	2-2	2-0	3-3	0-1	3-0	1-0	2-3	*	4-2	5-0	3-1	4-3	3-0	2-3	3-1
9. Littletown Reserves	1-3	1-7	1-8	1-3	1-2	1-2	2-3	0-3	*	3-2	1-1	3-3	0-1	1-3	5-1
10. Lucas	2-4	4-2	2-4	1-2	3-1	6-4	4-0	2-5	2-2	*	1-6	6-2	2-3	8-2	3-1
11. Phoenix	0-4	2-2	0-4	2-1	8-3	1-3	3-2	2-4	7-0	4-0	*	1-0	1-3	2-1	5-2
12. Pudsey Liberals	1-2	2-5	3-2	3-6	6-2	3-3	4-1	6-3	4-2	2-0	4-0	*	2-2	4-4	3-2
13. Salts G.S.O.B.	5-4	2-4	2-4	2-1	1-2	2-3	3-1	4-4	5-0	3-2	4-2	1-1	*	3-3	2-2
14. Saville	1-4	2-3	0-3	2-2	4-1	1-7	3-3	2-2	3-0	0-7	2-1	0-3		*	1-4
15. Skipton L.M.S.	0-5	4-6	1-7	1-7	8-1	4-5	6-3	1-8	6-1	0-2	4-2	3-5	0-2	3-7	*

DIVISION THREE RESULT CHART 1991/92

HOME TEAM	1	2	3	4	5	6	7	8	9	10	11	12	13	14	15	16
1. Ardsley Celtic Res	*	2-4	0-3	3-1	2-0	2-2	3-3	3-2	1-6	1-4	0-1	3-1	4-1	4-1	4-0	1-7
2. Bowling Celtic Res	4-3	*	1-1	4-2	1-1	3-2	5-4	1-4	5-1	2-2	2-2	2-3	3-7	0-0	7-0	3-5
3. Campion Reserves	2-0	8-4	*	3-4	2-4	0-6	1-2[2]	5-1[0]	1-2	1-6	1-1	6-2	3-3	4-4	4-2	2-3
4. Hall Green Utd Res	3-4	1-1	0-3	*	0-4	1-4	1-1	2-1	3-5	2-6	0-6	2-1	1-1	2-6	1-1	2-7
5. ICI Huddersfield Res	2-2	3-1	2-1	4-0	*	2-1	4-0	1-0	3-1	2-1	1-1	7-2	2-1	4-3	0-2	1-1
6. Lower Hopton Res	4-2	1-3	6-1	4-2	0-4	*	2-0	3-1	1-3	1-1	6-0	7-0	2-3	2-3	8-0	1-3
7. Marsden Reserves	1-4	2-1	6-3	0-0	4-0	0-3	*	1-1	2-2	3-2	2-3	7-0	1-5	3-3	1-0	2-1
8. Otley Town Reserves	5-7	2-0	2-4	0-2	0-6	3-4	3-0	*	1-3	0-1	6-2	8-2	1-3	4-1	2-3	3-3
9. Rawdon Old Boys	4-2	1-0	6-1	1-2	1-1	4-3	1-1	1-1	*	2-0	3-2	2-2	1-2	2-2	1-2	0-6
10. Salts Reserves	4-0	3-2	2-2	2-1	0-0	3-0	5-3	5-0	5-1	*	1-3	6-1	1-1	5-1	2-4	2-2
11. Steeton Reserves	4-2	5-0	1-0	1-1	0-1	1-3	2-3	2-2	3-0	4-1	*	6-3	0-4	4-1	3-3	3-0
12. Trinity Athletic Res	0-3	2-4	1-3	4-0	2-1	2-2	3-7	2-0	3-5	1-4	0-3	*	0-6	1-2	2-3	3-2
13. Tyersal Reserves	1-1	5-4	7-2	4-1	1-3	3-3	2-3	2-1	2-2	2-4	3-1	3-0	*	2-2	4-1	5-0
14. Ventus/Yeadon C. Res	3-2	4-2	4-0	6-1	3-3	1-3	2-1	1-3	2-3	1-0	2-1	3-3	0-3	*	5-0	1-3
15. Westbrook W. Reserves	3-0	1-1	4-3	1-1	0-2	0-4	3-3	3-3	0-2	5-2	5-1	2-4	5-0	2-0	*	2-0
16. Wibsey Reserves	6-0	3-2	4-1	6-1	4-2	4-0	1-0	3-2	6-2	1-7	4-0	3-2	6-1	1-3	5-2	*

PREMIER DIVISION CLUBS 1992-93

ABERFORD ALBION
Secretary: J L Robson, 85 Derwent Ave., Garforth, Leeds LS25 1HS (Leeds 863421. Club 813248).
Ground & Directions: A1 bypass, Aberford (Adjacent to Sewage Works). From Leeds on A64 and join A1 southbound, left into Yorkshire Water premises 1/4 mile past Aberford turn off.   All others proceed North through Aberford village and join A1 south. (NB. All vehicles must turn left on leaving ground)
Colours: Yellow/yellow/red

ALTOFTS AFC
Secretary: M Bell, 67 Churchfield Croft, Altofts, Normanton WF6 2QB (Wakefield 893507).
Ground & Directions: Altofts Sports Club, Lock Lane, Altofts (Wakefield 892708). M62, exit 31 (Normanton), along A655 towards Castleford for 1/2 mile turn left at Rising Sun and follow road 1 1/2 miles into Altofts.   Lock Lane is 2nd right after 'the Popular' and ground 300 yards on right. **Colours:** Red/black/red

BRIGHOUSE TOWN
Secretary: N Wilson, Lundy House, Limes Ave., Halifax HX3 0NT (Halifax 345057).
Ground & Directions: St Giles Road, Hove Edge, Brighouse **Colours:** Gold/black/black

CRAG ROAD UNITED
Secretary: R Knight, 23 Easthorpe Court, Eccleshill, Bradford BD2 2PB (635889).
Ground & Directions: Apperley Bridge, Greengates, Bradford.   To Greengates traffic lights, 500 yards down Harrogate Road, ground on right after canal bridge. **Colours:** White/red/red

FERRYBRIDGE AMATEURS
Secretary: M Gilbert, 67 Manor Park Avenue, Nevison, Pontefract WF8 2PX (Pontefract 709142).
Ground & Directions: Castleford Lane, Ferrybridge. Leave M62 at J32 and turn left towards Castleford. After 1/2 mile turn right on B6136 towards Ferrybridge. Ground on right opposite Power Station and before a bridge.
Colours: Amber/black

FIELD A.F.C.
Secretary: C Clough, 8 Hospital Rd, Riddlesden Keighley, BD20 5EP (Keighley 603782).
Ground & Directions: Hollingwood Lane, Bradford. Clayton bus from city centre, alight at Works Ground behind new warehouse opposite works. By car leave Bradford on Thornton Road, first left into Listerhills Road, and continue forward to left turn into Hollingwood Lane, in front of Fields Printers.
Colours: Green & white/green/green

GASCOIGNE UNITED
Secretary: J Baron, Greystone Cott., 26 Church St., Boston Spa LS23 6DN (Boston Spa 844476, Leeds 868231).
Ground & Directions: Welfare Ground, Micklefield. AlongA63 Selby Road out of Leeds Town Centre, through Garforth, left to Micklefield just before A1, left into ground after Railway Bridge.
Colours: Black & silver stripes/black/black

HALIFAX IRISH CLUB
Secretary: R Stephenson, 10 Marldon Rd, N'ram, Halifax HX3 7BP (Hx 201594).
Ground & Directions: Natty Lane, Illingworth, Halifax (Halifax 360134). Keighley Rd out of Halifax for 3 miles. Fire station on left, turn right down Natty Lane. **Colours:** Green/white/gold

MARSDEN
Secretary: D Warwick, 44 Western Rd, Cowlersley, Hudds. HD45TH (Huddersfield 647807).
Ground & Directions: Fall Lane, Marsden, Huddersfield (Huddersfield 844191). A62 Huddersfield Ring Road (sign posted Oldham) for 7 miles out of Huddersfd to Marsden, take first turn left after Fire Station into Fall Lane, left at r/about into car park **Colours:** Black & white stripes/black

OVENDEN WEST RIDING
Secretary: S Smith, 192 Illingworth Road, Bradshaw, Halifax HX2 9XH (Halifax 248753).
Ground & Directions: Natty Lane, Illingworth. Keighley Rd out of Halifax for 3 miles, Fire Station on left, right down Natty Lane. From direction of Keighley and Thornton, Natty Lane is 2nd left after Sportsmans Inn.
Colours: Green & white stripes/black/black

RAWDON OLD BOYS
Secretary: D Saynor, 10 West Lea Grove, Yeadon, Leeds LS19 7EF (0532 506037).
Ground & Directions: Hanson Field, Rawdon. A658 from Bradford to Rawdon traffic lights, right towards Leeds, then 100 yards left up Over Lane to Emmott Arms, left to ground. A65 from Leeds and before Rawdon traffic lights turn right opposite Airedale Air Conditioning onto Layton Lane, at top turn left onto Town Street and right immediately before Emmott Arms. **Colours:** Maroon & light blue stripes/dark blue/dark blue

SALTS
Secretary: A Griggs, 17 Longwood Ave, Bingley BD16 2RX (0274 569090). **Colours:** All navy blue
Ground & Directions: Salts Playing Fields, Hirst Lane, Shipley (0274 587427). From Bradford A650, from Leeds A657 to Saltaire, right at roundabout via Clarence Road and Hirst Lane, cross canal bridge.

TYERSAL
Secretary: H Foster, 5 Norwood House, Sticker Lane, Bradford BD4 8DR (666060).
Ground & Directions: Arkwright Street, off Dick Lane, Bradford 4. Leave Bradford on Leeds Road to large Phoenix Park roundabout and turn right onto Dick Lane. Changing accommodation at Quarry Gap PH 1 mile on left.
Colours: Red & white flecks/red/red

WIBSEY AFC
Secretary: D Nolan, 21 Glendale Drive, Bradford BD6 2LT (602934).
Ground & Directions: Horsfall Playing Fields, Centre Pitch. From Odsal Top, Bradford, on Halifax Road towards Shelf. After 1 mile turn left down Cemetery Road and ground on left. **Colours:** Blue/blue/white

FIRST DIVISION CLUBS 1992-93

ALLERTON BYWATER
Secretary: M Bednall, 49 Edward Avenue, Allerton Bywater, Castleford WF10 2HA (Leeds 867048).
Ground & Directions: Ninevah Lane, Leeds Rd, Allerton Bywater.   M62 exit 30, then on A642 to Rothwell for 2 miles, left at roundabout, right at next on A642 towards Garforth for 2 miles, at Pelican Crossing, right towards Allerton Bywater. Right after 2 miles at 'T' junction and Ninevah Lane is 1/10th mile on right.
Colours: Yellow/white/white

ARDSLEY CELTIC
Secretary: N J Crosby, 40 Forsythia Avenue, East Ardsley, WF3 2HT (0924 824389).
Ground & Directions: Recreation Ground, East Ardsley. From Tingley roundabout take A650 towards Wakefield for approx. 1 1/2 miles, turn right into East Ardsley Cricket Club which is opposite Ardsley Bay Horse PH.
Colours: Green & white/white/green

BOWLING CELTIC
Secretary: M Sweeney, 28 Newton St., Bfd BD5 7DP (Bradford 737362).
Ground & Directions: Avenue Rd P.F., Bowling Park, West Bowling, Bradford. From Bradford via Manchester Road, after 1 mile turn left on Parkside Road, (opposite Admiral Nelson Pub) continue forward to Junction of Avenue Road.   **Colours:** Red & black stripes/black/black

BROOK MOTORS
Secretary: W Kaye, 31 Northwood Park, Kirkburton, Huddersfield HD8 0PY (Hudds 604122).
Ground & Directions: New Mill Rd, Brockholes, near Honley, Huddersfield. Leave Huddersfield centre on A616 Sheffield Road after 4 miles, fork left on New Mill Road, ground on right, entrance to Brook Crompton Ltd, Honley Works.   **Colours:** White/navy blue/navy blue

CAMPION
Sec: A Shepherd, 13 Hedge Way, Bradford BD8 0AJ (545193).   **Cols:** Black & white stripes/black/black
Ground & Directions: Manningham Mills CC, Scotchman Rd, Heaton, Bradford (546726). Manningham Lane, at corner of Park turn left up Oak Lane. At first traffic lights, right into Heaton Road, then left up Scotchman Road.

DUDLEY HILL ATHLETIC
Secretary: C Cook, 12 Richardson Street, Oakenshaw, Bradford BD12 7EH (394524).
Ground & Directions: Hunsworth Lane, East Bierley. From Bradford to Tong Cemetery, right to South View Road, then down Hunsworth Lane, ground on left past the childrens play area/swings.
Colours: Red & white stripes/black

FARNLEY
Secretary: P Walker, 7 Water Lane, Farnley, Leeds LS12 5LX (637306).
Ground & Directions: Lawns Lane, Farnley (638826). Leeds-Bradford Ring Road, A6110 to Butt Lane roundabout (by Reservoir) travel up Butt Lane, cross Tong Road to Club on right, left at top of hill, and Chapel Lane is first on right, which becomes Lawns Lane after the Church.   **Colours:** Royal & white hoops/royal/royal.

HALL GREEN UNITED
Secretary: S Marsden, 28 Church View, Crigglestone, Wakefield WF4 3PF (Wakefield 253095).
Ground & Directions: Haslegrove Sports Ground, Criggleston (254544). M1 to Wakefield exit 39, left to Wakefield, 1st right to Crigglestone, 1st right again to Crigglestone, past Empire Stores, 1st right after last house on right, to Haverold Lane, onto end to Painthorpe Country Club, left onto Painthorpe Lane, ground 300 yards on left
Colours: Black & white stripes/black/black

T. S. HARRISON
Secretary: R Fisher, 32 Berwick Ave, Heckmondwike WF16 9AE (Heckmondwike 402206).
Ground & Directions: T S Harrison Sports & Social Club, Healey Lane, Batley. From Heckmondwike Market Place travel up High Street signed to Batley, to Junction PH, turn left past Craven Heifer PH, take left hand fork, and ground on left hand side opposite Healey Junior School   **Colours:** Jade/grey

LITTLETOWN
Secretary: D Knight, 2 Norwood Drive, Moor Lane, Birkenshaw, Bfd BD11 2NS (Cleckheaton 874915).
Ground & Directions: Beck Lane, Heckmondwyke. From Bradford, through Cleckheaton on A638 past Spenborough Baths, forward through 'Swan' traffic lights. Approx 1/4 mile past NEGAS Service Centre turn right down Wormald Street, to end, then Cross Union Road, through tunnel turn left, ground at end of road
Colours: Red, white & blue stripes/blue

LOWER HOPTON
Secretary: R Smith, 5 Bright St., Mirfield WF14 0NJ (Mirfield 492780).   **Colours:** Gold/black/black
Ground & Directions: Woodend Rd, Lower Hopton, Mirfield (Mirfield 492048). To Mirfield Town Centre, A644, turn down right for 150 yards, turn right again along Woodend Rd Newgate, under railway bridge, over river.

MORLEY TOWN
Secretary: S Chippendale, 28 Church St., Morley, Leeds LS27 8LU (Leeds 521429).
Ground & Directions: Brookes PF, Nepshaw Lane, Morley (Leeds 526460). A650 Bradford-Wakefield Road to Angel Pub, Bruntcliffe, turn left down Bruntcliffe Lane, and the Snooker Club is 1/2 mile on left. To ground across carpark   **Colours:** Light blue/navy blue/navy blue

OTLEY TOWN
Secretary: G & C Jones, 3 Swain Hile St., Yeadon, Leeds LS19 7HF (0532 500208).
Ground & Directions: Old Show Field, Pool Rd, Otley (Otley 461025). Harrogate road out of Otley, ground on right after Garden centre.   **Colours:** Tangerine & white/black/tangerine

SPRINGFIELD Y.C.
Sec: A Smith, 58 Wightman St, Bradford BD3 0LD (B'ford 630862).   **Cols:** Green/yellow/yellow
Ground & Directions: Rear of Springfield Boys Club, Idlethorpe Way, Thorpe Edge, Bradford (Bradford 611976). Idlethorpe Way is via Cavendish Road, off Bradford Road, Idle, from Five Lane Ends

STEETON FC
Secretary: A Bates, 14 Aireworth Close, Keighley BD21 4DS (0535 663397).
Ground & Directions: Summer Hill Lane, Steeton. A650 from Keighley towards Skipton, turn right at Steeton traffic lights, after 200 yards turn right opposite Steeton Hall Hotel.   **Colours:** All green

VENTUS & YEADON CELTIC
Sec: A Vento, 1 Delius Av., Ravenscliffe, Bradford BD10 0HY (631690).   **Cols:** Black & white stripes/black
Ground & Directions: Dam Lane, Yeadon. Yeadon Centre to White Swan, turn left on Dam Lane, ground on right.

SECOND DIVISION CLUBS 1992-93

ABERFORD ALBION RES, ALTOFTS RES (See page 852)

BLACK HORSE AFC
Secretary: W Wright, 21 School St., Moorbottom, Cleckheaton BD19 6AF (Bfd 879702).
Ground & Directions: Heckmondwyke Secondary School, Leeds Old Road, Heckmondwyke (0924 474543). A62 Leeds/Huddersfield Rd., at Half Way PH turn into White Lee Rd., and school car park 200 yards on left
Colours: Sky blue/navy/sky blue

BOWLING

Secretary: A Green, 28 Moorside Ave., Bfd BD2 3HG (635706).   **Cols:** Black & white stripes/black/black
Ground & Directions: Fairfax Upper School, Lister Avenue, West Bowling, Bradford 4 (734913). A655 Wakefield/Bradford Rd., towards Bfd, 1/4 mile on Bfd side of Dudley Hill (Ring Rd) flyover, left into Lister Ave., and school is on left.

BRADFORD ROVERS

Secretary: Z Simic, 47 Oaks Lane, Allerton, Bfd BD15 7RT (499537).   **Colours:** Sky/white/sky
Ground: As Campion FC (See page 853).   **Previous Name:** Dubrovnic (pre-'92).

BRIGHOUSE TOWN RESERVES (See page 852)

DYNAMOES

Secretary: A Brotherhead, 4 St. Margarets Avenue, Holmewood, Bradford BD4 9AJ (687323).
Ground & Directions: Broomwood School, Dawson Lane, off Tong Street, Bradford.   A650 Wakefield-Bradford Road, Tong Street, turn down Dawson Lane near CD Bramalls or approach down Burnham Avenue from Bierley roundabout on ring road.   **Colours:** All white

EASTMOOR ALBION

Secretary: E Sykes, 3 Lee Moor Road, Stanley, Wakefield WF3 4EF (827214).   **Colours:** All blue
Ground & Directions: Eastmoor School, Warmfield View, Eastmoor Estate, Wakefield (Wakefield 364756). Leave M62 exit 30 and travel towards Wakefield.   Continue past Pinderfields Hospital and Stanley Royd Hospital. At traffic lights turn left and follow road to Eastmoor High School

FERRYBRIDGE AMATEURS RES, FIELD RES (See page 852)

GREEN LANE

Sec: G Corriett, 31 Harrogate Terrace, Bradford BD3 0LF (0274 641474).   **Cols:** Blue/white/blue
Ground & Directions: Clock House Recreation, off Queens Rd, Bradford   (726563). Out of Bradford on Manningham Lane, right down Queens Road, 1st left North Ave., continue to playing fields at end.

GREETLAND AFC

Secretary: P Walker, 15 Sunnybank Dve, Greetland, Halifax HX4 8NB (Halifax 378203).
Ground & Directions: Goldfields, Rochdale Road, Greetland. M62 to J64, A629 towards Halifax, after 1/2 mile slip road signed Greetland, left on A6024, right at r'bout, after 400 yards bear left following Greetland signs along Saddleworth Rd for 1 mile, left at lights, at next lights turn right after one mile at St. Thomas's Church.
Colours: Green & white stripes/white

OVENDEN WEST RIDING RESERVES (See page 852)

PONTEFRACT

Secretary: M Scott, 6 Avenue, Terrace, Halfpenny Lane, Pontefract WF8 4BE (0977 703141).
Ground & Directions: Pontefract Park (0977 702228). Adjacent to racecourse. M62 to exit 32, turn towards Pontefract, right 1st lights, immediately right again into Park. Follow road over racecourse to car park and changing rooms within the perimeter of the racecourse   **Colours:** Grey, black & white/black

TRINITY ATHLETIC

Secretary: M Ford-Powell, 40 Kingston Road, Thackley, Bradford BD10 8PD (Bfd 621606).
Ground & Directions: The Dell, Cliffe Lane West, Baildon. From Shipley traffic lights along Otley Road turn left up Baildon Road at 2nd set of traffic lights, left at Threshfield Bakery along Cliffe Avenue, left on Cliffe Lane West and ground on left.   **Colours:** White/black/black

WESTBROOK WANDERERS

Secretary: S Waite, 4 Sunnybank Court, Yeadon, Leeds LS19 7UF (0532 507383).
Ground & Directions: Horsforth School, Lee Lane East, Horsforth. From Leeds Ring Rd turn up Fink Hill (adjacent to Eleventh Earl Pub) and signed to Horsforth Centre, continue for 600 yards and turn left on St. Margarets Avenue, 1st left on Lee Lane East, school is 1st left.   **Colours:** Green/black/black

THIRD DIVISION CLUBS 1992-93

ALLERTON

Secretary: Barry Sutcliffe, 178 Main Street, Wilsden, Bradford BD15 0HX (0535 233307).
Ground & Directions: Rhodesway School. From top of M606 second left on Mayo Avenue to r'bout, straight across, thru 4 sets of lights, you are now on Allerton Rd, keep on up dual-c'way following road round to left, 1st left after sharp bend is Rhodesway - school on right.
Colours: Grey/blue/blue   **Change colours:** Red/white/white

BAILIFF BRIDGE

Secretary: Stephen Chapman, 24 Natty Hall Rd, Wibsey, Bradford BD6 3AP (Bfd 600348).
Ground & Directions: Firth's Carpets Spts Field, Victoria Rd, Bailiff Bridge. Manchester/Huddersfield Rd from Bradford thru Red Lion crossroads at Wyke, down to lights at Bailiff Bridge and right again at Punch Bowl PH, up Victoria Rd, ground on right.   **Colours:** Red & white/white   **Change colours:** Silver/black.

CRAG ROAD UNITED RESERVES (See page 852), ECCLESHILL UTD (Details as page 820), FARNLEY RESERVES (See page 853)

HAWORTH

Sec: N A Barnes, 19 North View Terrace, Mytholmes Lane, Haworth, Keighley BD22 8HJ (Keighley 642731).
Ground & Directions: Marley Stadium, Keighley. From Bradford towards Keighley, at Magnet showrooms, Crossflatts turn left onto new Dual Carriageway.   Approaching second roundabout ground can be seen on right. Turn right at the roundabout for access.   **Colours:** Black & white/black/black

HUNSWORTH

Secretary: A Hepworth, 217 Moor Lane, Birkenshaw, Bradford BD11 2NX (Cleckheaton 862693).
Ground & Directions: Birkenshaw Middle School. A651 Bradford-Heckmondwyke Road, 200 yards on Heckmondwyke side of Birkenshaw roundabout (Junction with A58).
Colours: All blue   **Previous Name:** Savile (pre'92).

LITTLETOWN RESERVES (See page 853)

LUCAS

Secretary: R Gamble, 190 Carr Bottom Road, Bankfoot, Bfd BD5 9AQ (572202).
Ground & Directions: Broomwood Middle School, Dawson Lane, off Tong Street, Bradford. A650 Wakefield-Bradford Road, Tong Street, turn down Dawson Lane near CD Bramalls Garage, or approach down Burnham Avenue from Bierley roundabout on ring road.   **Colours:** Maroon & royal blue stripes/blue/blue

OLD MODERNIANS
Secretary: Robert Johnson, 8 Grangwood Court, West Park, Leeds LS16 6ED (0532 612211).
Ground & Directions: Abbey Grange School. Leeds ringroad from Bradford thru lights at Horsforth to r'bout next to Woodside Tavern, right on Hawksworth Rd then left opp. Bridge PH, up Butcher Hill, school 200yds left.
Colours: Red & black   **Change colours:** Yellow

PHOENIX
Secretary: M Breeze, 17 Green Ave., Silsden, Keighley BD20 9LD (0535 669940).
Ground & Directions: Beckfoot Grammar School, Wagon Lane, Bingley. A650 Bradford/Keighley Road, after crossing River Aire at Cottingley Bridge, take second right into Wagon Lane and School immediately on left.
Colours: Silver grey/green/green

PUDSEY LIBERAL
Secretary: R Brook, 44 Brunswick Road, Pudsey LS28 7NA (Leeds 569059).
Ground & Directions: Travel from Thornbury Barracks along Galloway Lane towards Pudsey, fork left into Owlcotes Rd. and after 1/2 mile turn right into Victoria Rd., where car park is immediately on left.   **Colours:** Amber/black/black

SALTHORN
Secretary: Lawrence Barraclough, 7 Richardson Ave., Wibsey, Bradford BD6 1HF (Bfd 603286).
Ground & Directions: Victoria Park, Cleckheaton Rd, Oakenshaw, Bradford. From Odsal Top, Bradford, left down Cleckheaton Rd signed Dewsbury, ground 1 mile on right.
Colours: Red & white diamonds/red/red   **Change colours:** Blue & white checks/blue/blue

SALTS GRAMMAR SCHOOL OLD BOYS
Secretary: P Hellewell, "Stonelands", 28 Belmont Rise, Baildon BD17 5AW (0274 583742).
Ground & Directions: Salts Grammar School, Higher Coach Road, Baildon. From Shipley take A6038 Otley Road, and after 1/2 mile turn left into Green Lane. Continue straight ahead for 1 mile, and after Cup & Ring PH, Salts Grammar School is on right.   **Colours:** White/black

WIBSEY RESERVES   (see page 852)

The Old Show Field, home of Otley Town FC. Photo - James Wright.

Notts Alliance action as Worthington Simpson (dark shirts) lose 1-2 to visting Hucknall Rolls Royce Welfare on 18th April. Photo - Martin Wray.

WHITBREAD COUNTY
SENIOR LEAGUE

Hon. Secretary: John Hamer,
3 Ian's Way, Ashgate, Chesterfield S40 4PY.

PHOENIX RISE ABOVE ASH HOUSE

What a season it proved for Phoenix! After clinching promotion to the top flight for the first time they had an oustanding campaign to sweep powerfully to the Premier Division tile, holding top place throughout.

The Rotherham based side had indeed risen from the ashes having been promoted for the previous two seasons. Finishing third in 1991 behind the two Wath teams had given no indication of what was to follow. They took the League's leading teams by surprise as they marked their bebut by setting a hot pace winning twelve out of thirteen games up to Christmas. The challengers must have been expecting the bubble to burst as the season wore on, but by the beginning of April Phoenix were still sitting proudly at the top with an eight point lead and matches in hand on their rivals.

Ash House, who had won the title for the previous four seasons, were the only serious contenders but needed Phoenix to slip drastically. Ash put together a great late run, winning their last eight, and even beat Phoenix 1-0, but still finished six points adrift.

At the foot of the table were Caribbean Sports whose miserable season was confirmed by February when they knew they would be wooden-spoonists. Their problems lay in defence, conceding 86 goals after some heavy defeats, but they did have the satisfaction of beating Phoenix for one of their three successes. It was a real dog-fight as the other strugglers tried to claw their way to safety. Ecclesfield Red Rose joined Caribbean after their mid-season form deserted them and they lost the last four. While victory for Wath St James in their final game would have saved them and sent White Rose down the Saints were beaten and return to the First Division after one season.

Division One was contested by just three clubs for most of the term, and Frecheville CA, who led almost throughout, remained undefeated to clinch the title. Waiting for any slip were Worsborough Bridge and RES Parkgate who finished second and third respectively to claim promotion.

High Green Villa won their second title in two seasons since joining the League when they lifted the Second Division championship, while Rawmarsh Star, who did the double over Villa (their only defeats), were runners-up. Also promoted were Davy who return to Division One after just a season.

Staveley MW in their first season in the League lost their opening Third Division game but then went nineteen unbeaten to race to the title by twelve points. Early leaders Throstles faltered after Christmas and allowed consistent Clifton Rovers to take runners-up from them.

John Hamer

Action from the top-of-the table clash between Phoenix and Ash House. Phoenix's Andy Kissack goes round the Ash House defence.

FINAL LEAGUE TABLES 1992-93

PREM. DIVISION	P	W	D	L	F	A	PTS
Phoenix	26	20	3	3	50	18	63
Ash House	26	17	6	3	67	30	57
Mexboro Main Str.	26	13	7	6	63	32	46
Goldthorpe Col.	26	11	7	8	34	32	40
Oughtibridge	26	10	7	9	46	37	37
A.B.M.	26	11	3	12	39	47	36
Hallam Res.	26	10	5	11	51	43	35
Denaby & Cadeby	26	8	11	7	51	43	35
Wath Saracens Ath	26	9	6	11	44	45	33
Parramores Spts	26	9	4	13	41	56	31
White Rose Thr.	26	8	6	12	41	43	30
Wath St James	26	7	7	12	32	48	28
Ecclesfield Red R.	26	7	3	16	36	53	24
Caribbean Sports	26	3	3	20	18	86	12

DIVISION ONE	P	W	D	L	F	A	PTS
Frecheville CA	20	14	6	0	54	13	48
Worsboro BMW Res	20	13	5	2	42	23	44
RES Parkgate Res	20	9	8	3	39	21	35
Yorkshire Main	20	9	3	8	34	39	30
Treeton Welfare	20	7	5	8	39	38	26
St Patricks	20	7	5	8	30	37	26
Thurcoft Ivanhoe	20	6	7	7	30	34	25
Swinton Ath.	20	7	2	11	38	50	23
Brunsmeer Ath.	20	5	7	8	38	38	22
Loxley College	20	2	6	12	28	48	12
Woodsetts Welf.	20	2	4	14	28	59	10

DIVISION TWO	P	W	D	L	F	A	PTS
High Green Villa	18	15	1	2	51	23	46
Rawmarsh Star	18	12	3	3	46	22	39
Davy	18	10	3	5	41	30	33
British Gas	18	9	2	7	42	44	29
Penistone Church	18	7	4	7	44	32	25
Industry	18	7	1	10	35	42	22
Sheff. Oakhouse	18	5	5	8	32	52	20
Stocksbridge PS Res	18	4	4	10	32	39	16
Sheff. Centralians	18	3	4	11	23	44	13

DIVISION THREE	P	W	D	L	F	A	PTS
Staveley MW	20	17	2	1	71	15	53
Clifton Rovers	20	13	2	5	54	27	41
Throstles Ridgeway	20	12	4	4	54	24	40
Sheffield PO	20	11	1	8	45	33	34
Sheffield Gas	20	10	3	7	48	31	33
Kiveton Park Res	20	8	7	5	43	33	31
Tinsley Wire	20	9	5	6	40	30	31
P'stone Chur. Res	20	4	5	11	35	53	17
Old Edwardians	20	4	4	12	33	49	16
Abbeydale	20	1	6	13	21	58	8
Brit. Stainless S.	20	0	3	17	14	105	2

Abbeydale, British Stainless Steels and Tinsley Wire all deducted one point for breach of rules.

WHITBREAD TROPHY 1992

SEMI FINALS

Ash House 1, Frecheville CA 0

Phoenix 0, Mexborough Main Street 0
Phoenix 0, Mexboro. M.S. 0 (Phoenix won on pens)

FINAL : ASH HOUSE 1, PHOENIX 0

(at Stocksbridge Park Steels F.C.)

Referee: Ian Pearce (Worksop)
Linesmen: Hughie Cahill (Doncaster), Martyn Mitchell (Sheffield)
Attendance: 335

The remarkable run of success of Ash House continued when they lifted the Whitbread Trophy with a 1-0 victory over eventual champions Phoenix in the final at Bracken Moor.

The well appointed facilities and excellent playing surface of Stocksbridge Park Steels provided the ideal venue for the clash of the League's leading pair in the Premier Division. For Ash it was the first time they had taken the Trophy which had eluded them despite a domination of the League which had seen them take the title for the past four seasons.

Title favourites in their first season in the Premier, Phoenix, with an eight point lead at the top, looked nervous in the opening stages and the more experienced Ash House gained the initiative.

The goal that was to decide the League's showpiece arrived after 23 minutes when Richard Bainbridge's left wing corner was played to the far post for Steve Leary who swivelled round to send the ball goalwards, and despite Ledger's full length dive he could not keep it out.

Phoenix had to wait until the hour before putting in their first serious effort, when Andy Collins drove a 20 yard free-kick just over. This sparked a flurry of activity with Neil Poulton hitting a snap-shot at the keeper, then outpacing Clarkson to the ball causing Brown to sprint from his goal to hack it behind. From the flag-kick player-manager Gary Ward headed over.

Leary, prominent as Ash attacked, saw Ledger smother another the ball at his feet and then hit a shot straight at the keeper. Yearsley opened up the Phoenix defence and drilled a low centre across goal which Leary stabbed over.

Rowlands surged down the right forcing Brown to go down at his feet, then at the other end full-back Gledstone poked the ball inches the wrong side following a real scramble. The game saw defences holding the upper hand with Andy Lockett and Paul Myles snuffing out the threat of Phoenix leading scorers Marren Rankine and Dean Walker, while Andy Clayton showed why the Rotherham side had conceded only fifteen league goals by keeping a close rein on the dangerous Richard Bainbridge who had been outstanding in the Ash semi-final with Frecheville.

In the closing stages Poulton hit a fierce drive inches over, and Chris Savage nearly found a way through when his curling shot towards the far post forced Ledger to leap to his right to grab the ball.

But it was Ash who deservedly took the Trophy to give manager Tony Pierpoint tangible reward in his first campaign since taking over following the success of brother Mick who had stepped down in the close season.

PREMIER DIVISION RESULT CHART 1991/92

HOME TEAM		1	2	3	4	5	6	7	8	9	10	11	12	13	14
1.	A.A.B.M.	*	0-3	1-0	2-1	0-1	1-2	2-3	2-2	3-2	3-0	0-4	2-1	3-1	2-3
2.	Ash House	1-1	*	4-3	2-2	5-0	2-0	4-1	2-6	3-1	4-2	1-0	2-1	1-0	2-0
3.	Caribbean Sports	1-0	0-7	*	2-1	0-5	0-0	0-1	0-1	1-1	1-4	1-2	0-2	1-3	1-2
4.	Denaby & Cadeby MW	2-2	1-1	9-0	*	2-1	2-2	3-1	2-2	0-0	2-1	1-4	1-1	3-3	1-1
5.	Ecclesfield Red Rose	1-2	1-6	7-0	2-1	*	1-2	0-3	0-0	0-2	0-1	1-3	3-2	0-1	1-0
6.	Goldthorpe Colliery	0-1	2-1	0-0	3-1	2-2	*	2-1	2-0	1-1	2-2	1-2	3-1	1-1	1-3
7.	Hallam Reserves	1-2	0-4	10-0	4-1	0-0	2-1	*	3-1	1-1	2-3	1-1		0-0	0-2
8.	Mexborough Main Street	4-1	3-3	7-1	1-2	4-0	2-1	5-2	*	3-0	0-1	1-1	1-2	4-1	0-0
9.	Oughtibridge WMSC	4-0	1-2	5-1	4-1	3-2	4-0	0-1	1-5	*	1-1	0-2	4-2	5-0	1-0
10.	Parramores Sports	1-3	2-2	4-3	0-5	1-0	0-2	1-3	1-5	0-0	*	0-1	3-4	2-0	2-1
11.	Pheonix	4-2	1-0	0-1	1-1	2-0	1-0	2-0	3-1	2-0	3-1	*	1-0	1-2	3-1
12.	Wath Saracens Athletic	2-1	0-1	3-0	1-1	6-1	0-1	1-6	0-3	3-0	3-5	1-1	*	2-1	2-0
13.	Wath St James	3-0	0-2	3-1	1-3	1-5	0-1	2-1	1-1	1-1	4-2	0-1	1-1	*	2-2
14.	White Rose Throstles	0-3	2-2	4-0	1-2	4-2	1-2	3-3	0-1	2-4	3-2	0-2	2-2	4-0	*

DIVISION ONE RESULT CHART 1991/92

HOME TEAM		1	2	3	4	5	6	7	8	9	10	11
1.	Brunsmeer Athletic	*	0-2	2-2	0-2	5-0	0-1	3-3	1-3	5-3	2-2	2-3
2.	Frecheville C.A.	5-1	*	2-1	0-0	3-1	6-1	3-1	4-0	7-1	4-1	0-0
3.	Loxley College	1-3	0-3	*	2-2	2-3	0-3	5-3	1-1	3-3	1-3	1-2
4.	RES Parkgate Reserves	0-0	1-1	1-0	*	2-0	3-1	1-1	2-5	4-0	2-2	5-0
5.	St Patricks	0-4	2-2	2-2	1-0	*	4-2	3-1	3-1	2-2	0-1	2-0
6.	Swinton Athletic	2-2	0-3	3-1	3-3	2-0	*	1-4	1-2	2-3	1-3	1-2
7.	Thurcroft Ivanhoe	2-1	1-1	0-0	0-1	2-1	2-5	*	0-0	2-2	2-1	1-2
8.	Treeton Welfare	2-2	0-3	4-0	1-3	2-2	2-3	1-2	*	4-3	3-3	3-0
9.	Woodsetts Welfare	2-2	0-1	2-3	0-5	2-1	1-2	0-1	2-4	*	0-3	1-3
10.	Worsbrough BMW Reserves	2-1	1-1	2-0	2-0	2-2	4-0	1-0	2-1	2-0	*	2-1
11.	Yorkshire Main	1-2	1-3	4-3	2-2	0-1	5-4	2-2	1-0	3-1	2-3	*

DIVISION TWO RESULT CHART 1991/92

HOME TEAM		1	2	3	4	5	6	7	8	9	10
1.	British Gas	*	1-4	0-4	4-1	2-1	2-2	3-1	3-1	3-3	1-0
2.	Davy	0-2	*	2-4	1-2	2-1	3-1	5-2	5-2	0-5	2-1
3.	High Green Villa	4-1	1-0	*	4-2	2-0	0-2	2-1	4-1	5-1	3-1
4.	Industry	4-2	1-2	0-2	*	5-3	1-5	6-2	1-2	1-2	4-2
5.	Penistone Church	4-3	3-3	1-2	6-3	*	4-2	1-1	2-0	6-1	1-2
6.	Rawmarsh Welfare	4-1	0-1	2-1	3-0	1-1	*	4-2	3-0	4-1	4-4
7.	Sheffield Bankers	1-2	1-1	1-3	0-1	1-0	0-3	*	1-1	1-2	3-1
8.	Sheffield Centralians	4-5	1-3	2-3	0-0	1-4	0-2	1-1	*	3-2	1-4
9.	Sheffield Oakhouse	5-2	0-5	3-3	2-1	1-6	0-2	2-1	1-1	*	0-6
10.	Stocksbridge PS Res	1-5	2-2	3-4	0-2	0-0	1-2	3-2	0-2	1-1	*

DIVISION THREE RESULT CHART 1991/92

HOME TEAM		1	2	3	4	5	6	7	8	9	10	11
1.	Abbeydale	*	1-1	1-4	2-2	1-2	2-2	1-6	2-4	1-2	1-4	0-4
2.	British Steel Stainless	1-2	*	1-4	0-3	3-3	0-6	1-1	1-8	1-6	0-7	0-4
3.	Clifton Rovers	2-1	7-1	*	3-1	3-2	4-1	1-4	1-0	0-1	5-1	2-2
4.	Kiveton Park Reserves	3-2	10-0	3-0	*	1-1	4-1	1-1	4-1	0-4	3-0	1-1
5.	Old Edwardians	1-1	7-1	0-4	2-2	*	0-1	2-4	0-1	1-3	3-8	2-1
6.	Penistone Church Res.	1-1	8-1	1-5	1-1	1-4	*	1-2	0-2	4-3	1-2	1-1
7.	Sheffield Gas	3-0	6-1	4-2	3-4	3-1	3-1	*	1-3	0-1	0-3	2-3
8.	Sheffield Post Office	3-0	8-1	0-3	2-0	3-2	4-2	0-0	*	1-3	0-2	0-2
9.	Staveley Miners Welfare	6-0	9-0	1-0	0-0	3-0	9-0	2-1	5-2	*	2-2	3-0
10.	Throstles Ridgeway	5-0	1-0	1-1	5-0	4-0	1-1	3-1	1-2	1-2	*	1-0
11.	Tinsley Wire	2-2	4-0	1-3	4-0	1-0	4-1	0-3	3-1	1-6	2-2	*

PREMIER DIVISION CLUBS 1992-93

A.B.M.

Secretary: L M Newton, 1 Skelton Way, Sheffield S13 7QW (0742 697900)   **Ground:** Swallowsnest M.W.
Directions: From Sheffield centre; Parkway to Handsworth, A57 to Woodhouse Mill, left at lights opposite the Westerby, ground on left.

ASH HOUSE

Secretary: T Cottam, 41 Pleasant Rd, Sheffield S12 2BD (0742 390897).
Ground: Sheffield Transport, Meadowhead, Sheffield.
Directions: Sheffield A61 Chesterfield road, 4 miles to r'bout, right off Greenhill Main Road on left.

DENABY & CADEBY MINERS WELFARE

Secretary: A Randall, 37 Craganour Place, Denaby Main, Doncaster DN12 4AS (0709 860963).
Ground & Directions: Denaby United FC (see Northern Counties East League section).

FRECHEVILLE C.A.

Secretary: TBA.   **Ground:** Silkstone Road, Frecheville, Sheffield.
Directions: From city A616 for 4 miles on Newark Road, left opposite shopping precinct into Silkstone Road.

GOLDTHORPE COLLIERY

Secretary: D Taverner, 50 East Avenue, Wombwell, Barnsley S73 8QQ (0226 757304).
Ground: Dearne C.M.W., Furlong Road, Goldthorpe.
Directions: From Rotherham A633 to Wath, left at r'bout to Goldthorpe. At Angel turn left under bridge; ground 600 yards on left.

HALLAM RESERVES

Secretary: G L Holland, 34 Standon Crescent, Sheffield S9 1PP.
Ground & Directions: As Hallam FC (Northern Counties East League section).

MEXBOROUGH MAIN STREET

Secretary: A A Hough, 4 Cranswick Way, Conisborough, Doncaster DN12 3AY (0709 866479).
Ground & Directions: As Mexborough Town (see Websters Central Midlands League section).

OUGHTIBRIDGE W.M.S.C.

Secretary: M Dewsbury, 11 Footgate Close, Oughtibridge, Sheffield S30 3JA (0742 862948).
Ground: Station Lane, Oughtibridge, Sheffield.
Directions: From Sheffield A616 to pedestrian crossing in village, right at Cock Inn, river by river.

PARRAMORES SPORTS

Secretary: G Pickering, 31 Medlock Way, Handsworth, Sheffield S13 9BE (0742 697828).
Ground: Armroyd Lane, Elsecar, Barnsley.
Directions: From junction 36, M1 take Barnsley road to second r'bout, right to Chapeltown, left under bridge, second right Armroyd Lane ground on right.

PHOENIX

Secretary: D M Taylor, 22 Widling Way, Kimberworth, Rotherham S61 1PQ (0709 555451).
Ground: Phoenix Sports Ground, Pavilion Lane, Bawtry Road, Brinsworth, Rotherham.
Directions: M1 jct 34, A631 to Rotherham - turn left after British Oxygen.

R.E.S. PARKGATE RESERVES

Secretary: R Goodwin, 6 Cardew Close, Rawmarsh, Rotherham S62 6LB (0709 525117).
Ground & Directions: As RES Parkgate (see Northern Counties East League section).

WATH SARACENS

Secretary: P Henry, 11 Elm Way, Wath-upon-Dearne, Rotherham S63 7PF (0709 874200).
Ground: Wath Sports Centre, Moor Road, Wath-upon-Dearne.
Directions: Rotherham, A633 through Rawmarsh, left at r'bout, left at next r'bout, Moor Road 400 yds on right.

WHITE ROSE THROSTLES

Secretary: M Green, 107 Watson Rd, Kimberworth, Rotherham S61 1JS (0709 554123).
Ground & Directions: Sheffield Transport, Meadowhead, Sheffield (as Ash House - above).

WORSBROUGH BRIDGE M.W. RESERVES

Secretary: D Smith, 18 Shield Avenue, Worsbrough Bridge, Barnsley S70 5BQ (0226 243418).
Ground: As Worsbrough Bridge MW (see Northern Counties East League section).

Exciting action from the First Division fixture between RES Parkgate and Loxley College (stripes).

THE NORTHERN LEAGUE

President: The Rt. Hon. Ernest Armstrong, PC
Vice President: Gordon Nicholson.
Chairman: Arthur Clark.
Hon. Secretary: A Golightly,
85 Par Road North, Chester-le-Street, DH3 3SA Tel: 091 3382056.

GRETNA CLINCH SECOND SUCCESS

The 1991-92 season resulted in Gretna taking the Northern League Division One championship for the second year running, but they were pressed very hard all the way by eventual runners-up Murton, Whitby Town and Guisborough Town. Gretna also became the first Scottish club to reach the First Round Proper of the F.A. Cup.

Two of the three clubs who had been promoted to Division One in 1991, Langley Park and Whickham, went straight back down to the lower tier, along with Shildon who were relegated on goal difference having forty points, the same as three other clubs.

In the Second Division, three clubs fought for the championship almost all season. Eventually promoted were Stockton as champions, Durham City as runners-up, and Chester-le-Street Town in third place.

The Northern League also enjoyed a profitable season in the F.A. Vase with Chester-le-Street Town and Dunston Federation Breweries both reaching the Fourth Round after many good wins. Chester ultimately lost to Knowsley United after extra-time, whilst Dunston bowed out to the holders, and eventual finalists, Guiseley. In the F.A. Trophy, Northern League clubs produced many eye-catching results. Star performers were Northallerton Town who beat a string of H.F.S. Loans League clubs before losing at Telford United in the Second Round Proper.

A Golightly, League Secretary

The all-conquering Gretna side, Northern League Champions for the second successive year, pictured before their 1-1 at already relegated Langley Park on Easter Monday afternoon. Back Row (L/R): James Mullhand, Mike McCartney, Paul Leeming, Kenny Goodrick, Paul O'Hagan, Marc Irwin, Geoffrey Ball, Tony Nelson. Front: David Pratt, Ian Wilson, Paul Gorman, Mark Eagling, Chris Pickford, Gary Bell. Photo - Dave West.

FIRST DIVISION

	P	W	D	L	F	A	Pts
Gretna	38	25	10	3	81	33	85
Murton	38	23	9	6	83	36	78
Whitby Town	38	23	9	6	74	41	78
Guisborough T.	38	22	10	6	81	36	76
Billingham Syn.	38	21	6	11	70	44	69
Blyth Spartans	38	19	8	11	63	44	65
South Bank	38	18	9	11	68	50	63
Northallerton T.	38	18	8	12	63	53	62
Consett	38	15	5	18	59	59	50
Tow Law Town	38	13	11	14	60	73	50
Seaham Red Star	38	13	9	16	50	57	48
Peterlee Newtown	38	14	3	21	47	70	45
Newcastle Blue S.	38	14	5	19	49	52	*44
West Auckland T.	38	11	8	19	45	68	41
Brandon United	38	10	10	18	61	75	40
Ferryhill Athletic	38	10	10	18	45	60	40
Easington Colliery	38	11	7	20	42	61	40
Shildon	38	11	7	20	47	83	40
Langley Park	38	7	7	24	51	89	28
Whickham	38	4	5	29	38	93	17

* - denotes 3 points deducted

SECOND DIVISION

	P	W	D	L	F	A	Pts
Stockton	38	27	7	4	102	35	88
Durham City	38	26	9	3	82	24	87
Chester-le-Street	38	26	8	4	80	36	86
Hebburn	38	27	4	7	101	44	85
Dunston Feds	38	26	6	6	104	33	84
Prudhoe East End	38	22	4	12	61	36	70
Billingham Town	38	18	7	13	60	47	51
Crook Town	38	16	9	13	54	53	57
Alnwick Town	38	15	12	11	54	60	57
Ryhope C.A.	38	17	5	16	77	59	56
Esh Winning	38	13	9	16	76	74	48
Ashington	38	13	9	16	50	69	48
Norton & S. Anc.	38	11	10	17	61	69	43
Shotton Comrades	38	11	6	21	52	66	39
Horden Colliery Wf.	38	10	6	22	52	76	33
Washington	38	8	9	21	36	63	33
Evenwood Town	38	8	7	23	42	105	31
Darlington C.B.	38	7	4	27	47	97	25
Bedlington Terr.	38	7	2	29	38	97	*20
Willington	38	4	3	31	33	119	15

* - denotes 3 points deducted

Gary Cowley gets Consett's first goal in their 2-3 home defeat against Billingham Synthonia on April 18th. Photo - Gavin Ellis.

Player-manager Mike McCartney puts Gretna 2-1 up in a 3-1 home win over South Bank on January 25th. Photo - Alan Watson.

HOME TEAM	1	2	3	4	5	6	7	8	9	10	11	12	13	14	15	16	17	18	19	20
1. Billingham S.	*	2-1	0-2	1-0	5-0	2-1	1-3	2-2	2-3	1-1	1-0	0-2	1-0	3-0	2-0	1-0	5-0	2-2	1-0	1-3
2. Blyth Spart.	3-2	*	4-3	0-2	1-2	2-0	1-2	0-2	2-2	2-0	2-1	1-1	3-1	1-2	4-3	0-0	2-1	3-0	1-1	0-1
3. Brandon Utd	1-1	0-4	*	0-4	0-0	2-3	1-2	0-1	2-1	2-2	1-2	1-1	6-1	1-3	5-0	2-3	2-0	3-1	3-3	0-0
4. Consett	2-3	0-1	4-0	*	1-0	1-1	0-1	0-0	2-1	1-3	0-3	2-0	2-1	0-0	3-4	0-1	1-1	2-3	0-3	2-3
5. Easington	0-1	0-2	1-2	0-0	*	0-5	1-1	1-3	3-0	0-1	2-0	2-2	1-0	0-1	1-2	2-3	0-1	3-1	1-0	1-1
6. Ferryhill	1-2	1-1	1-1	2-3	1-1	*	0-1	0-0	1-3	1-3	2-1	0-3	4-0	2-0	3-1	0-2	0-0	0-3	1-0	2-0
7. Gretna	0-0	3-2	2-0	1-0	4-2	3-0	*	1-1	1-2	0-1	3-0	2-2	5-0	0-0	1-1	3-1	4-1	2-2	4-0	0-2
8. Guisborough	2-2	0-2	0-0	2-1	4-0	2-0	1-2	*	6-1	2-1	2-0	2-1	1-0	4-2	4-1	4-1	1-2	3-1	6-0	0-0
9. Langley Pk	1-4	0-1	0-3	2-4	0-3	2-2	1-1	1-7	*	3-4	1-2	3-4	0-2	1-2	1-2	1-4	0-0	1-2	3-0	2-3
10. Murton	1-1	0-0	2-0	2-3	2-0	5-0	1-1	2-0	3-0	*	3-1	2-0	1-0	1-1	5-1	2-3	1-1	4-1	4-0	2-0
11. N'castle BS	2-1	0-0	6-1	1-0	1-0	0-0	0-1	1-1	0-0	0-1	*	0-1	3-0	2-3	4-0	0-2	2-2	3-2	2-1	2-0
12. Northallerton	1-0	4-1	6-1	3-1	2-5	2-1	0-2	1-3	1-2	0-4	4-2	*	2-2	2-1	2-1	0-1	2-0	1-1	1-0	1-1
13. Peterlee N.	3-2	0-2	0-2	1-4	1-2	4-1	0-1	2-1	4-0	0-2	2-1	2-1	*	3-3	0-0	1-5	3-0	1-1	2-1	1-3
14. Seaham RS	2-1	1-2	3-1	0-1	0-2	2-1	1-4	0-3	2-2	0-2	4-1	0-0	1-2	*	1-1	0-0	2-0	2-0	1-1	1-2
15. Shildon	0-7	2-1	0-0	1-4	0-2	1-1	4-3	0-2	2-1	2-1	1-2	2-0	1-0		*	2-2	0-1	1-1	1-2	1-2
16. South Bank	1-2	0-1	1-1	5-1	3-0	0-0	2-3	1-1	3-2	2-2	1-0	0-1	1-2	2-4	2-0	*	1-1	2-1	4-2	0-2
17. Tow Law T.	1-5	1-0	5-3	2-1	4-0	1-2	3-3	2-2	3-0	1-6	3-1	3-1	2-1	1-2	3-5	1-4	*	1-0	3-1	3-3
18. W Auckland	0-2	1-4	3-2	3-5	1-0	1-1	0-5	0-2	0-0	1-1	1-2	0-2	2-0	2-1	1-1	2-0	2-1	*	2-1	0-2
19. Whickham	0-1	1-5	2-5	0-1	1-3	1-2	1-3	1-2	1-5	3-4	1-2	1-4	2-3	1-0	3-2	1-1	1-1	1-2	*	0-5
20. Whitby T.	4-0	1-1	3-2	4-1	3-3	1-0	1-2	3-1	2-1	2-1	1-0	2-0	0-1	4-2	4-1	0-2	3-3	1-1	2-0	*

SECOND DIVISION RESULT CHART 1991-92

HOME TEAM	1	2	3	4	5	6	7	8	9	10	11	12	13	14	15	16	17	18	19	20
1. Alnwick T.	*	1-1	1-0	3-2	0-0	0-0	4-1	0-3	0-1	1-1	1-0	1-3	4-2	2-1	1-1	1-5	2-1	2-2	1-0	3-2
2. Ashington	3-0	*	2-3	0-0	1-2	3-2	4-2	0-3	0-3	4-3	0-0	0-0	4-2	2-1	1-0	0-4	1-1	0-2	0-2	2-0
3. Bedlington	1-2	0-3	*	2-3	0-4	1-4	0-4	0-3	3-3	0-4	5-2	3-2	2-3	1-3	0-1	1-2	0-3	1-3	1-0	2-1
4. Billingham T.	2-2	1-1	2-0	*	0-1	2-1	3-1	0-2	1-1	2-2	2-1	0-2	1-0	3-1	1-2	3-2	2-0	1-2	3-0	6-1
5. Chester-le-S.	4-1	2-0	2-0	2-0	*	2-0	4-2	2-1	1-1	3-1	3-2	2-3	2-0	2-2	3-1	4-1	3-2	2-2	1-0	3-0
6. Crook Town	1-1	0-0	0-1	1-0	0-2	*	3-0	0-3	0-4	3-2	5-1	0-1	3-2	2-2	1-2	0-3	0-0	1-0	2-1	2-0
7. Darlington CB	1-3	1-1	1-0	1-3	1-2	0-2	*	0-4	0-3	1-2	2-0	0-1	3-0	0-3	0-4	1-2	0-1	1-3	4-2	4-1
8. Dunston F.	1-0	2-0	5-1	4-1	0-0	3-2	3-0	*	3-2	5-1	8-0	3-1	5-1	8-1	2-3	4-1	1-2	0-0	1-0	2-1
9. Durham City	2-2	4-1	1-0	0-0	2-0	1-1	2-0	1-0	*	3-0	2-0	1-1	3-0	1-0	3-1	0-1	2-0	2-1	2-0	4-0
10. Esh Winning	3-0	3-3	1-0	1-2	1-2	1-1	4-0	2-2	0-3	*	4-0	2-3	2-1	2-2	0-2	1-3	0-0	1-5	2-2	4-1
11. Evenwood T.	1-0	5-1	1-0	1-1	0-3	1-2	3-3	1-4	1-2	1-1	*	0-6	0-5	2-2	1-2	2-1	1-1	1-3	0-3	2-1
12. Hebburn	4-1	4-0	4-1	1-0	4-0	5-2	3-0	3-2	1-5	5-1	4-1	*	1-1	4-1	1-0	2-2	3-1	0-1	4-0	7-0
13. Horden CW	1-2	1-4	3-1	2-0	2-2	1-2	6-3	1-1	0-3	2-0	2-2	0-3	*	0-1	2-1	1-2	2-1	1-2	1-1	1-0
14. Norton S.A.	1-2	3-0	2-2	0-2	1-1	1-1	4-2	0-1	1-1	2-4	7-3	0-5	0-0	*	0-1	3-3	5-0	1-2	2-0	3-1
15. Prudhoe EE	2-0	3-0	5-2	0-2	0-1	1-2	3-1	2-2	0-1	0-5	4-0	4-0	1-0	3-0	*	1-0	1-0	1-2	1-0	2-0
16. Ryhope CA	1-2	1-2	2-1	3-0	0-3	0-1	9-0	1-4	4-2	4-1	1-2	1-3	2-1	0-1	0-0	*	2-1	1-3	6-0	3-3
17. Shotton C.	1-3	1-3	8-0	2-1	2-2	1-2	0-0	0-1	0-3	2-5	4-2	0-1	0-4	2-1	1-2	2-0	*	0-2	3-4	2-1
18. Stockton	2-2	3-0	3-0	1-2	3-0	2-3	5-3	2-1	1-1	3-2	10-0	4-1	7-0	2-1	1-0	2-1	3-1	*	0-0	1-1
19. Washington	1-1	3-0	3-1	0-2	0-4	0-0	0-0	1-1	0-1	1-2	0-1	2-4	3-0	1-0	0-0	1-1	0-2	0-4	*	3-2
20. Willington	2-2	1-3	1-2	1-4	0-4	3-2	0-4	0-6	0-6	0-5	0-1	2-1	2-1	1-2	0-4	0-2	1-4	0-8	3-2	*

Gretna's Les Armstrong, watched by team-mate John Wilson, heads for goal during the champions' goalless draw at home to Seaham Red Star on February 8th. Photo - Alan Watson.

NORTHERN LEAGUE CUP 1991-92

First Round

Whickham v Consett	0-4	Peterlee Newtown v Prudhoe East End	4-3
Shotton Comrades v Easington Colliery	0-1	Seaham Red Star v Brandon United	2-3
Ashington v Langley Park	2-1	Stockton v Ryhope C.A.	1-2
Esh Winning v West Auckland Town	2-1		

Second Round

Willington v Alnwick Town	1-6	Peterlee Newtown v Darlington C.B.	1-0
Easington Colliery v Esh Winning	1-2	Gretna v Murton	2-1
Newcastle Blue Star v Hebburn	1-0	Crook Town v Shildon	0-1
Ferryhill Athletic v Consett	1-2	Evenwood Town v Tow Law Town	1-4
South Bank v Horden Colliery Welfare	4-0	Blyth Spartans v Brandon United	1-0
Dunston Federation Breweries v Ashington	2-1	Chester-le-Street v Norton & Stockton Anc.	3-2
Bedlington Terriers v Guisborough Town	0-3	Ryhope CA v Billingham Town	1-4
Billingham Synthonia v Durham City	3-1	Whitby Town v Washington	4-0

Third Round

Alnwick Town v Peterlee Newtown	1-2	Esh Winning v Gretna	0-7
Newcastle Blue Star v Shildon	3-0	Consett v Tow Law Town	4-3
South Bank v Blyth Spartans	2-3	Dunston Fed. v Chester-le-Street Town	3-1
Guisborough Town v Billingham Town	1-3	Billingham Synthonia v Whitby Town	3-2

Quarter Finals

Peterlee Newtown v Gretna	1-0	Newcastle Blue Star v Consett	0-3
Blyth Spartans v Dunston Federation Brew.	5-2	Billingham Town v Billingham Synthonia	1-3

Semi-Finals

Peterlee Newtown v Consett	1-5	Blyth Spartans v Billingham Synthonia	3-0

Final: Blyth Spartans 1, Consett 0

Durham City are caught offside in their vital promotion fixture at Hebburn on February 1st. Durham still ran out comprehensive 5-1 victors. Photo - John Diamond.

Langley Park 'keeper Peter Gardner under pressure at home to Gretna on Easter Monday. Photo - Dave West.

Northern League Division One Ten Year Record

	82/3	83/4	84/5	85/6	86/7	87/8	88/9	89/90	90/1	91/2
Alnwick Town								8	19	
Ashington	16	17								
Bedlington Terriers				2	20					
Billingham Synthonia	6	7	12	19		3	1	1	4	5
Billingham Town				20			5	19		
Bishops Auckland	4	5	1	1	2	6				
Blyth Spartans	1	1	2	4	1	1	9	9	3	6
Brandon United				8	12	10	7	18	17	15
Chester-le-Street Town			8	7	16	18	19			
Consett	9	12	15	13	13	20		6	5	9
Crook Town	10	14	16	9	17	17	20			
Durham City	17						14	17	20	
Easington Colliery					10	15	13	20		17
Evenwood Town	15	18								
Ferryhill Athletic	12	16	14	18	18	14	8	13	8	16
Gretna		8	6	11	7	7	3	2	1	1
Guisborough Town						5	4	7	2	4
Hartlepool United Reserves				10	15					
Horden Colliery Welfare	3	10	17							
Langley Park										19
Murton									13	2
Newcastle Blue Star					4	2	6	4	10	13
Northallerton Town									9	8
North Shields	7	2	5	12	6	9	18			
Peterlee Newtown		13	9	6	19				16	12
Ryhope Community			10	15	14	19				
Seaham Red Star							16	10	11	11
Shildon	14	15	18			12	17	14	14	18
South Bank	11	6	3	3	8	16	15	16	12	7
Spennymoor United	5	11	11	14	3	11	11	11		
Stockton							10	5	18	
Tow Law Town	8	4	4	5	9	8	2	3	7	10
West Auckland Town	18									14
Whickham								15	15	20
Whitby Town	2	3	7	16	11	13	12	12	6	3
Whitley Bay	13	9	13	17	5	4				
Willington	19									
No. of Clubs	19	18	18	20	20	20	20	20	20	20

Division Two Ten Year Record

	82/3	83/4	84/5	85/6	86/7	87/8	88/9	89/90	90/1	91/2
Alnwick Town	11	14	14	10	7	6	2			9
Ashington			10	8	10	15	5	13	12	12
Bedlington Terriers	10	8	2			7	7	9	11	19
Billingham Sythonia					1					
Billingham Town	7	10	4		4	4			5	7
Brandon United		4	1							
Chester-Le-Street Town		1						5	16	3
Consett						1				
Crook Town								6	13	8
Darlington Cleveland Bridge		6	8	18	16	14	16	12	10	18
Darlington Reserves	3	11	16	15						
Dunston Federation Breweries										5
Durham City		5	5	4	13	3				2
Easington Colliery				2					3	
Esh Winning	6	9	11	20	17	5	15	20	7	11
Evenwood Town			15	17	14	16	17	7	6	17
Gretna	2									
Guisborough Town				3	2					
Hartlepool United Reserves	4	7	3							
Hebburn								15	4	4
Horden Colliery Welfare				13	18	11	8	16	19	15
Langley Park Welfare		13	9	12	19	12	13	4	2	
Murton Colliery Welfare							11	1		
Newcasite Blue Star				1						
Northallerton Town	8	12	12	16	12	9	9	2		
Norton & Stockton Ancients	9	16	13	9	8	10	14	18	9	13
Peterlee Newtown	1					8	6	3		
Prudhoe East End							4	8	8	6
Ryhope Community Assoc.	5	2					10	11	14	10
Seaham C.W. Red Star		3	6	6	9	2				
Shildon				19	3					
Shotton Comrades		15	18	14	15	18	20	17	15	14
Stockton				7	6	1				1
Washington							18	10	17	16
West Auckland Town		17	17	5	5	17	12	19	1	
Whickham							3			
Willington		18	7	11	11	13	19	14	18	20
No. of Clubs	11	18	18	20	19	18	20	20	19	20

BILLINGHAM SYNTHONIA

Chairman: Harry Davies   **Press Officer:** Secretary
Secretary: Graham Craggs, 2 Ribble Close, Billingham, Cleveland TS22 5NT. (0642) 535856
Manager: Stuart Coleby   **Physio:** Tony Hetherington   **Coach:** Lenny Gunn
Ground: The Stadium, Central Avenue, Billingham, Cleveland. (0642) 552358
Directions: Turn off A19 onto A1027, continue along Belasis Avenue approx 1 mile, ground on left.
Seats: 370   **Cover:** 370   **Capacity:** 1,970   **Floodlights:** Yes   **Founded:** 1923
Club colours: Green with white trim/white/green.   **Change colours:** Red & white/black/black.
Midweek Matches: Wednesday   **Previous leagues:** Teesside.
Programme: 8 pages, 20p   **Programme Editor:** G Craggs   **Souvenir Shop:** Yes
Clubhouse: Normal club hours.   **Record Gate:** 4,200 v Bishop Auckland 6/9/58.
Best F.A. Cup season: 1st Rd 48-49 51-52 56-57 57-58 87-88 89-90.
Previous Ground: Belasis Avenue 23-58   **Previous Name:** Billingham Synthonia Recreation
Players progressing to Football League: Peter Atkinson & Ken Harrison (Hull 1947), Ernie Wardle & John Murray (M'boro 1948 & 49), Richard Mulvaney (Blackburn 1964), Mike Hodgson (Hartlepool 1964), David Hockaday (Blackpool 1975), Terry Gaffney (Hartlepool 1977), Aidan Davidson (Notts County 1988).
Honours: Northern Lg 56-57 88-89 89-90 (R-up 49-50 50-51 *(No goals conceded at home; P 13, W 12, D 1, L 0; F 44, A 0)* 51-52, Lg Cup 51-52 87-88, Div 2 86-87), Teesside Lg Cup 34-35 38-39, Durham Challenge Cup 88-89, North Riding Snr Cup 66-67 71-72 78-79, FA Amateur Cup 4th Rd 48-49, FA Tphy 1st Rd replay 90-91.

BLYTH SPARTANS

President: M Johnson   **Manager:** Nigel Walker
Chairman: Andrew Fairholm-Little   **Physio:** D Robertson.
Secretary: R Cotterill, 34 Solingen Estate, Blyth, Northumberland NE24 3ER (0670 361057).
Ground: Croft Park, Blyth, Northumberland. (0670) 354818
Directions: Through Tyne tunnel heading north on A19, take Cramlington turn, follow signs for Newsham/Blyth. Right fork at railway gates in Newsham, down Plessey Rd, ground can be seen on left before Masons Arms. Buses X24, X25, X26, X1 from Newcastle.
Seats: 300   **Cover:** 2,500   **Capacity:** 6,000   **Floodlights:** Yes   **Founded:** 1899
Colours: Green & white stripes/black/green   **Change colours:** All yellow or red
Previous leagues: Northumberland 01-07/ Northern Alliance 07-13/ 46-47/ North Eastern 13-14 19-39 47-58 62-64/ Northern Combination 45-46/ Midland 58-60/ Northern Counties 60-62.   **Sponsors:** Viz Magazine.
Programme: 20 pages, 20p   **Programme Editor:** R R Clark   **Souvenir Shop:** Yes
Clubhouse details: Open every night plus Saturday & Sunday lunch & matchdays.
Best F.A. Cup season: 5th Rd replay 77-78 (lost to Wrexham). Competition Proper on 25 occasions.
League Clubs defeated in F.A. Cup: Ashington, Gillingham 22-23/ Hartlepool United 71-72/ Crewe Alexandra, Stockport County 71-72/ Chesterfield, Stoke City 77-78.
Players progressing to Football League: William McGlen (Manchester United 1946), Joe Roddom (Chesterfield 1948), Henry Mills (Huddersfield 1948), John Allison (Reading 1949), James Kelly (Watford 1949), Robert Millard (Reading 1949), Jim Kerr (Lincoln 1952), James Milner (Burnley 1952), John Hogg (Portsmouth 1954), John Allison (Chesterfield 1955), John Inglis (Gateshead 1957), John Longland (Hartlepool 1958).
Hons: Northern Lg(10) 72-73 74-76 79-84 86-88 (R-up 71-72 73-74 77-78 84-85, Lg Cup(5) 72-73 77-79 81-82 91-92), Nth Eastern Lg 35-36 (R-up 22-23, Lg Cup 49-50 54-55), Northumberland Lg 03-04, Northern All. 08-09 12-13 (R-up 46-47), Northumberland Snr Cup(18) 13-15 31-32 33-37 51-52 54-55 58-59 62-63 71-72 73-75 77-78 80-82 84-85, FA Tphy QF rep. 79-80 82-83, FA Amtr Cup SF 71-72.
Local Newspapers: Newcastle Journal & Evening Chronicle.   **Midweek Matches:** Tuesday

BRANDON UNITED

Chairman: Neil Scott   **Press Officer:** Secretary   **Manager:** Peter Feenan
Secretary: Brian Richardson, 109 Braunespath Estate, New Brancepeth, Durham DH7 7JF. (091-373 1304)
Ground: Welfare Ground, rear of Commercial Street, Brandon. (091 378 2957
Directions: A690 - 3 miles west of Durham City. Buses 49 & 49A from Durham.
Seats: 60   **Cover:** 300   **Capacity:** 4,060   **Floodlights:** Yes   **Founded:** 1970.
Colours: All blue (white trim)   **Change colours:** All red with white trim
Previous Lges: Durham & Dist. Sunday 72-77/ Northern XI. 77-80/ Northern Amtr 80-81/ Wearside 81-83.
Programme: 36 pages, 20p   **Programme Editor:** K Nellis   **Souvenir Shop:** No
Clubhouse: Open every day, lunch & evening. Pool & entertainment at weekends.
Best F.A. Cup season: 1st Rd replay 88-89 (lost to Doncaster). Also 1st Rd 79-80.
League Clubs defeated in F.A. Cup: None.   **Record Gate:** 2,500, FA Sunday Cup SF.
Previous Name: Rostrons 72-74.
Players progressing to Football League: Bryan Liddle & Dean Gibbs & Dean Gibb (Hartlepool 1984 & 86 & 87), Paul Dalton (Manchester Utd 1988).
Hons: FA Sunday Cup 75-76, FA Vase QF 82-83 83-84, Northern Lg Div 2 84-85, Northern All.(2) 77-79 (R-up 79-80, Lg Cup 77-78 79-80 (R-up 78-79)), Sunderland Shipowners Cup 81-82, Durham Co. Sunday Cup 73-74 75-76 76-77, FA Tphy 3rd Qual. Rd 87-88 89-90, Durham & Dist Sunday Lg(4) 73-77.
Local Newspapers: Newcastle Journal, Northern Echo.   **Midweek Matches:** Wednesday

CHESTER-LE STREET TOWN

Chairman: John Tomlinson   **President:** J Holden
Secretary: John Watson, 30 Hadrian Avenue, Chester-le-Street, Co Durham DH3 3RS. (091-3887307)
Manager: J Lang   **Coach:** P Stronach   **Press Officer/Programme Ed.:** Jack Thornback (091-3883554)
Ground: Moor Park, Chester Moor, Chester-le Street, Co Durham (091-3883363)
Directions: Ground lies approx 2 miles south of off town on A167 (C-le-S to Durham road).
No. of seats: 200   **Covered Accom:** Yes   **Capacity:** 2,000   **Floodlights:** Yes
Year Formed: 1972   **Midweek Matches:** Tuesday
Club colours: Blue & white hoops/white/white   **Change colours:** Yellow/green/green
Programme: 14 pages, 20p   **Programme Editor:** J Thornback.   **Souvenir Shop:** No
Clubhouse details: Open Wed,Thur,Fri & Sun 7-10.30pm & Sat 1-10.30pm.
Previous Names: Garden Farm 1972-78.   **Nickname:** Cestrians.
Previous Leagues: Newcastle City Amtr 72-75/ Washington 75/ Wearside 77-83.
Previous Grounds: Ravensworth Welfare, Low Fell 72-73/ Riverside Pk 73-78/ Sacriston Welfare 78-79.
Record Gate: 473 v Barrow, FA Cup 83-84 (3,000 for Bradford City v Newcastle, Bradford appeal match 1985).
Hons: Northern Lg Div 2 83-84, Wearside Lg 80-81 (R-up 82-83), Monkwearmouth Cup 80-81 81-82, FA Vase 4th Rd 91-92, Washington Lg, Durham Minor Cup, Washington AM Cup.

Billingham Synthonia. Back Row (L/R): David Golden, Peter McMullen, Andrew Banks, Mark Mullen, Richard Allen, Paul O'Brien, Chris Rooney. Front: Tommy Connor, Craig Blyth, Stephen Corkain, Stuart Coleby (Manager), Sean O'Brien, David Shearer. Photo - Gavin Ellis.

Brandon Utd. Back Row (L/R): Peter Feenan (Mgr), Andy Cunningham, Darren Thompson, Keith Muckle, John White, Neil Mouncher, Martin Spragg, Dave Martin, Ian Mutrie, Bev Dougherty, Darren Bevis. Front: Paul Robertson, Stephen Ross, Darren Palmer, Steve Houlden, Phil Sowerby, Mark Dunn, Rob Dunbar. Photo - Dave West.

Chester-le-Street Town. Back Row (L/R): Ian Steel, Derek McRae, Scott Bone, John Dunn, Tony Hopkins, Gary Todd, Doug Pettit. Front: Roger Wicks, Steven Carter, Joe Calvert, Paul Johnson, Chad Bone, Kevin Taylor, Steven Smith. Photo - Dave West.

CONSETT

Chairman: F Lemon   **Vice Chairman:** I Hamilton.   **President:** D McVickers
Secretary: Peter McClean, 11 Cohort Close, Ebchester, Consett, Co. Durham DH8 0PG (0207 562712).
Manager: Colin Carr **Physio:** Joe Darroch   **Press Officer:** Colin French (0207 580899)
Ground: Belle Vue Park, Ashdale Road, Consett, County Durham (0207 503788)
Directions: Quarter of mile north of town centre - along Medomsley Rd, left down Ashdale Rd, ground 100m yards on left. Follow signs for Sports Centre and Baths. Buses 745, 711 & 772 from Newcastle, 719, 765 from Durham. w signs for Sports Centre and Baths, about 800 yds from town centre.
Seats: 400   **Cover:** 1,000   **Capacity:** 4,000   **Floodlights:** Yes   **Founded:** 1899
Colours: Red/black/red   **Change colours:** Sky blue/dark blue/sky blue
Previous Leagues: Northern Alliance 19-26 35-37/ North Eastern 26-35 37-58 62-64/ Midland 58-60/ Northern Counties 60-62/ Wearside 64-70.
Programme: 16 pages, 30p   **Programme Editor:** Colin French   **Souvenir Shop:** No
Record Gate: 7,000 v Sunderland Reserves, first match at Belle Vue, 1950.   **Nickname:** Steelmen
Clubhouse: Matchdays, and evenings on request. Darts & pool.
Best F.A. Cup season: 1st Rd 58-59 (lost 0-5 at Doncaster Rovers).
Previous Grounds: Vicarage Field (pre-1948)/ Leadgates Eden Colliery 48-50.
Players progressing to Football League: Tommy Lumley (Charlton), Alan Ellison (Reading), Laurie Cunningham (Barnsley), Jimmy Moir (Carlisle), Jackie Boyd (West Bromwich Albion).
Hons: North Eastern Lg 39-40 (Div 2 26-27, Lg Cup 50-51 (jt) 53-54), Durham Challenge 47-48 49-50 58-59 60-61 68-69 (R-up 76-77 89-90), Northern Lg R-up 76-77 (Div 2 88-89, Lg Cup 78-79 80-81), Northern Counties Lg 61-62, Sunderland Shipowners Cup 67-68, Monkwearmouth Charity Cup 67-68, Wearside Lg R-up 68-69 69-70, FA Trophy 2nd Rd 78-79.
Local Newspapers: Journal, Northern Echo, Consett Advertiser.   **Midweek Matches:** Wednesday

DURHAM CITY

Chairman: Dennis Kerry   **Press Officer:** Secretary
Secretary: Graham Lilley, 108 High Street, Carrville, Durham DH1 1BQ. (091-3845924)
Address & Tel No. of ground: 'Ferens Park', The Sands, Durham DH1 1JY. (091-3869616
Simple ground directions: Down Post Office Bank, right at the bottom, 200 yds along The Sands.
Seats: 400   **Cover:** 400   **Capacity:** 6,000   **Floodlights:** Yes   **Reformed:** 1949
Colours: White/blue/gold   **Change colours:** Blue/black/blue.
Nickname: Citizens
Programme: 36 pages, 25p   **Programme Editor:** Graham Lilley   **Souvenir Shop:** No
Clubhouse details: Mon - Fri 7-11pm & Sat 12-6 & 7-11pm.
Previous Leagues: Victory 18-19/ North Eastern 19-21 28-38/ Football League 21-28/ Wearside 38-39 50-52.
Previous Grounds: Garden House Park/ Holliday Park (until 1938).
Record Attendance: 6,000 v Tranmere Rovers, FA Cup 2nd Rd 56-57.
Best F.A. Cup season: 2nd Rd 25-26 57-58 (Also 1st Rd 27-28 55-56).
Players progressing to Football League: Harry Houlahan (Newcastle 1951), Derek Clark (Lincoln 1951), Leo Dale & David Adamson (Doncaster 1954 & 70), Stan Johnstone (Gateshead 1954), Dennis Coughlan (Barnsley 1957), John Wile (Sunderland 1966), Brian Taylor (Coventry 1968), Paul Malcolm (Rochdale 1984).
Hons: Northern Lg R-up 70-71 (Div 2 R-up 30-31 91-92), FA Vase QF 87-88, Durham Benevolent Bowl 55-56, FA Amtr Cup 2nd Rd rep. 57-58, FA Tphy 1st Rd 83-84, Durham Challenge Cup R-up(2).
Local Newspapers: Northern Echo, Sunderland Echo, Evening Chronicle.
Midweek Matches: Wednesday.

EASINGTON COLLIERY

Chairman: F Wellburn   **Press Officer:** Secretary
Secretary: Tom Goodrum, 8 Oswald Terrace, Easington Colliery, Peterlee, Co Durham SR8 3LB (091 527 0737)
Manager: J Maddison   **Asst Manager:** Wilf Constantine.   **Physio:** D Smith.
Ground: Easington Colliery Welfare Ground, C.W. Park, Easington, Co Durham. (091-5273047)
Directions: From A19 take Easington turn-off, through Easington village, on to Easington Colliery, turning right after zebra crossing.
No. of seats: 50   **Covered Accom:** 300   **Capacity:** 2,000   **Floodlights:** Yes
Year Formed: 1914   **Midweek Matches:** Tuesday
Club colours: White/green/green   **Change colours:** Yellow/black/yellow
Programme: 12 pages, 10p   **Programme Editor:** D Elliot   **Souvenir Shop:** No
Clubhouse details: Bar seating 70, pen matchdays only
Previous Leagues: Wearside 13-37 39-64 73-88.
Record Attendance: 4,500 v Tranmere Rovers, FA Cup 1955.
Previous Name: Easington Colliery Welfare.   **Best F.A. Cup season:** 1st Round Proper 1955-56.
Players progressing to Football League: Ron Greener (Newcastle 1951), Frank Wayman (Darlington 1957), John Langridge (Hartlepool 1982).
Honours: Northern Lg Div 2 R-up 85-86, Wearside League 29-30 31-32 32-33 47-48 48-49 (R-up 28-29 46-47 73-74, Lg Cup 32-33 45-46 61-62), Monkwearmouth Cup(3), Sunderland Shipowners Cup(2), FA Trophy 2nd Qualifying Rd replay 88-89, FA Vase 4th Rd replay 82-83.

FERRYHILL ATHLETIC

Chairman: Ken Banks   **Manager:** Ken Banks.
Secretary: Ralph Carr, 23 Morrison Terrace, Ferryhill Station, Co. Durham DL17 9DQ. (0740) 652437
Press Officer: Ken Banks (0388) 815105
Ground: Darlington Road, Ferryhill, County Durham (0740 651937).
Seats: 400   **Cover:** 400   **Capacity:** 6,000   **Floodlights:** Yes   **Founded:** 1921.
Club colours: Amber/black/amber   **Change colours:** red/white/black
Midweek Matches: Tuesday   **Previous Leagues:** Palatine 21-23.
Record Attendance: 13,000 v Bishop Auckland, FA Amateur Cup.
Previous Name: Dean Bank Villa.   **Best F.A. Cup season:** 1st Rd 35-36 53-54.
Players progressing to Football League: William Marsh (Barsley 1947), Richard Steel (Bristol City 1953), Alex Greenwood (Chelsea 1953), John Edgar & John Peverell (Darlington 1954 & 59), Roland Horney (Blackburn 1963), John Pearson (Hartlepool 1967).
Honours: Northern Lg 37-38 47-48 57-58 (R-up 23-24), Durham Challenge Cup 23-24 70-71, Durham Amateur Cup 21-22, FA Amateur Cup 4th Rd 25-26 63-64, FA Trophy 2nd Qualifying Rd replay 81-82 89-90 90-91.
Local Newspapers: Northern Echo

Consett keeper Chris Teasdale punches clear a Billingham Synthonia corner. The Steelmen went down 2-3 in this exciting home match on 18th April. Photo - Dave West.

Durham City. Back Row (L/R): D Maddocks, R Holden, W Irwin, J Bottenschein, C Howey, I Hindmarsh, D Lawson. Front: J Reach, D Holden, B Yovern, P Bragan, N Hixon, D Ord. Photo - Dave West.

Durham's Colin Howey burst through the Chester-le-Street defence during an important top-of-the-table Second Division derby that finished one apiece. Photo. Photo - Dave West.

GUISBOROUGH TOWN

Chairman: John Newton   **Vice Chairman:** F Dadd   **President:** L Bell.
Secretary: Keith Smeltzer, 55 Thames Ave., Guisborough, Cleveland TS14 8AR (0287 638993).
Manager: Mike Hodgson   **Press Officer:** John Newton (0287 636914)   **Coach:** A Smith
Ground: King George V Playing Fields, Howlbeck Rd, Guisborough (0287 636925).
Directions: From West: turn left at 2nd set of lights, left again after 400yds. From East: Through town, turn right at 1st set of lights, then left after 400 yds.
No. of seats: 20   **Covered Accom:** 300   **Capacity:** 3,000
Floodlights: Yes   **Year Formed:** 1973   **Midweek Matches:** Wednesday
Club colours: Red & white stripes/black/red with white trim   **Change colours:** All yellow
Previous leagues: Middlesbrough & District/ South Bank/ Northern Alliance 77-80/ Midland Counties 80-82/ Northern Counties (East) 82-85.
Programme: 32 pages, 30p   **Programme Editor:** John Newton   **Souvenir Shop:** No
Clubhouse details: Evenings plus weekends. Darts & pool.
Record Attendance: 3,112 v Hungerford, FA Vase 1980.   **Nickname:** Priorymen.
Best F.A. Cup season: 1st Round Proper 1988-89 (lost 0-1 to Bury, at Middlesbrough).
Players progressing to Football League: Frank Harrison (Middlesbrough 1982), Mark Foster (Leicester 1983).
Honours: FA Vase R-up 79-80, Northern Lg Cup 88-89 (Div 2 R-up 86-87), Northern Alliance 79-80 (R-up 78-79, Lg Cup 78-79), FA Trophy 1st Rd replay 90-91.
Local Newspapers: M'boro Evening Gazette, N'castle Sunday Cup, Northern Echo.

MURTON

Chairman: Tommy Pratt   **President:** K Nightingale   **Treasuer:** R Storey
Press Officer: George Elliott (091-5260410)
Secretary: John Gardner, 74 Winns Lonnen, Murton, Seaham, Co.Durham SR7 9TG. (091-5263449)
Manager: Jeff Cranson   **Assistant Manager:** Brian Burlinson   **Coach:** Richie Madden
Physio: Vinny Simmonds   **Press Officer:** George Elliott (091-5260410)   **Sponsors:** Hellens.
Ground: Murton Welfare, Church Lane, Murton, County Durham (091 517 0814).
Directions: A19 to Murton slip road. Ground approx 1 mile along, turning left opposite Catholic church.
Seats: 200   **Cover:** 200   **Capacity:** 2,000   **Floodlights:** Yes   **Founded:** 1904
Colours: All white (red trim)   **Change colours:** All red with white trim
Previous Leagues: Wearside 13-46 51-88/ North Eastern Counties 46-51.
Programme: 8 pages, 20p   **Programme Editor:**   **Souvenir Shop:** No
Clubhouse details: Open evry day - 11-3 & 6-11pm. Restuarant and bar meals.
Previous Name: Murton Red Star 04-28/ Murton Colliery Welfare 28-88.
Previous Ground: Fatten Pasture 04-28.   **Record Attendance:** 3,500 v Spennymoor United.
Past players progressing to Football League: Numerous.
Hons: Northern Lg Div 2 89-90, Wearside Lg 28-29 36-37 59-60 (Lg Cup 58-59 70-71), Sunderland Shipowners Cup 59-60 69-70 70-71, Monkwearmouth Charity Cup 21-22 28-29 34-35 35-36 63-64 70-71 87-88, Durham Jnr Cup 50-51.
Club Record Appearances: 'Pop' Welch 500, 1962-78.   **Record Scorer:** David Campbell.
Local Newspapers: Northern Echo, Sunderland Echo.   **Midweek Matches:** Wednesday

NEWCASTLE BLUE STAR

Chairman: Tom Derrick   **Press Officer:** Tom Derrick (091-4696935)
Secretary: J Anderson, 5 Whickham View, Newcastle-upon-Tyne NE15 6TB (091 274 2830).
Manager: Rob Carney.
Ground: Wheatsheaf Sports Ground, Woolsington, Newcastle-upon-Tyne (091 286 0425).
Directions: From Central station follow Airport signs for 7 miles. Ground is next to Wheatsheaf Hotel on left, approx 800 yds before Airport. Metro station 400 yards from ground.
No. of seats: 300   **Covered Accom:** 300   **Capacity:** 2,000
Floodlights: Yes   **Year Formed:** 1930   **Souvenir Shop:** No, but souvenirs are available.
Club colours: Blue/blue/blue & white   **Change colours:** Red/white/red
Previous leagues: Newcastle Business Houses 32-38/ North East Amateur. Tyneside Amateur 46-62/ Northern Combination 62-73/ Vaux Wearside 73-85.
Programme: 20 pages   **Programme Editor:** Tommy Clements.
Clubhouse details: Open match days only.   **Previous Name:** Blue Star FC.
Record Attendance: 1,800 v Almondsbury Greenway, FA Vase SF 77-78.
Previous Name: Blue Star.   **Best F.A. Cup season:** 1st Rd 84-85.
Players progressing to Football League: Ian Crumplin & Tony Robinson (Hartlepool 1978 & 86), Barry Dunn (Darlington 1979), Ian McInerney (Huddersfield 1988).
Honours: FA Vase 77-78 (SF 81-82), FA Tphy QF 88-89, Northern Lg R-up 87-88 (Lg Cup 85-86 (R-up(1)), Div 2 85-86), Wearside Lg 73-74 75-76 82-83 83-84 84-85 (R-up 74-75 77-78 79-80, Lg Cup 76-77 79-80 80-81 82-83 83-84), Northern Combination 62-63 68-69 (Lg Cup 66-67 71-72), Northumberland Snr Cup 76-77 82-83 83-84 85-86 87-88 (R-up 74-75 78-79 80-81), Northumberland Minor Cup 64-65), Sunderland Shipowners Cup 82-83 84-85, Monkwearmouth Charity Cup 74-75 79-80 82-83 88-89, J R Cleator Cup 86-87.
Local Press: Newcastle Journal, Evening Chronicle, Northern Echo, Sunday Sun.   **Midweek Matches:** Monday

NORTHALLERTON TOWN

Chairman: Les Hood   **Press Officer:** Secretary
Secretary: Peter Livingstone, 5 Guisborough Road, Thornaby, Stockton-on-Tees, Cleveland TS17 8EE (0642 614019)
Ground: Ainderby Road, Romanby, Northallerton, N. Yorks (0609 772418).
Directions: Leave A1 at Leeming Bar (signposted Northallerton & Bedale). Floodlights are visible on left on approach to Northallerton; turn left immediately before 'Northallerton' sign; ground on left.
No. of seats: 150   **Covered Accom:** 200   **Capacity:** 4,500
Floodlights: 120 lux   **Year Formed:** 1891   **Midweek Matches:** Wednesday.
Club colours: Black & white stripes/black/black   **Change colours:** All yellow.
Previous Leagues: Allerton, Darlington & District, Claro, Harrogate & District
Clubhouse: Open normal licensing hours 7 all day Sunday
Record Attendance: 503 v Newcastle XI, pre-season 1989.
Previous Name: Northallerton Alliance.   **Previous Ground:** Blue Stone.
Hons: Harrogate & District Lg, Richmond Cup, Bedale Cup, Millbank Cup, FA Tphy 2nd Rd 91-92.
Local Newspapers: Northern Echo, Darlington & Stockton Times, N. Yorks News

Peterlee Newtown 3, Seaham Red Star 3 - Division One 17/4/92. Seaham goalkeeper David Campbell shows a great pair of hands. Photo - Dave West.

Murton AFC. Back Row (L/R): Richie Madden (Coach), Brian Burlinson (Asst Manager), Micky Larkin, Mark Linigan, Barry Corfield, Colin Watson, Tony Holborg, Dave Evans, Gary Hargrave, Jeff Cranson (Manager), Colin Haggie. Front: Dave Laws, Gary Lormor, Keith Hargrave, Kevin Young, Nigel Stewart, Dave Robson, Ian Kerr, Lee Adamson, Nigel Robson. Photo - Dave West.

West Auckland Town 2, South Bank 0 - Division One 19/4/92. West Auckland's Andy Burgess effects an overhead kick watched by South Bank's Andrew Doddy. Photo - Dave West.

PETERLEE NEWTOWN

Chairman: Brian Hall   **Press Officer:** Secretary
Secretary: Danny Cassidy, 23 Melbury Street, Seaham, County Durham SR7 7NF (091 581 4591).
Manager: Bobby Huntington   **Assistant Manager:** Gordon Huntington
Ground: Eden Lane, Peterlee, County Durham (091 586 3004).
Directions: From town centre Fire Station, turn left into Edenhill Rd, then right into Robson Ave. Left at the next junction and ground is on the right.
No. of seats: 50   **Covered Accom:** 200   **Capacity:** 6,000
Floodlights: Yes   **Year Formed:** 1976
Club colours: Sky blue/white/sky blue   **Change colours:** Yellow/black/yellow
Previous leagues: Northern Alliance 76-79/ Wearside 79-82.
Clubhouse details: Open normal licensing hours.
Record Attendance: 2,350 v Northern, Hillsborough Fund match 1989.
Nickame: Newtowners.   **Best F.A. Cup season:** 4th Qualifying Rd.
Honours: Northern Lg Div 2 82-83, North Eastern F'lit League, 4th Qual Rd FA Cup
Local Newspapers: Hartlepool Mail, Sunderland Echo, Northern Echo. **Midweek Matches:** Wednesday.

SEAHAM RED STAR

Chairman: Bryan C Mayhew   **Press Officer:** John Campbell (091-5814308)
Secretary: John McBeth, 29 Frederick Street, Seaham, County Durham SR7 7HX (091 581 5712).
Manager: Chris Copeland   **Coach:** Paul Walker.
Ground: Seaham Town Park, Stockton Road, Seaham, County Durham (091 581 2540).
Directions: From Tyne Tunnel: A19 Teeside approx 8 miles; B1404 Seaham slip road, left at top of slip road. Right at traffic lights & first left past school into ground.
No. of seats: 100   **Covered Accom:** 100   **Capacity:** 4,000
Floodlights: Yes   **Year Formed:** 1973   **Midweek Matches:** Wednesday
Club colours: Red & white stripes/red/red   **Change colours:** All blue
Previous Leagues: Sunday football/ Houghton & District 73-74/ Northern Alliance 74-79/ Wearside 79-83.
Programme: 40 pages, 20p   **Programme Editor:** D Copeland   **Nickname:** The Star.
Clubhouse details: New clubhouse. Mon-Sat 11am-11pm, Sun 12-2, 7-10.30pm. Large function room, snooker, pool, Restuarant & Bars.
Record Attendance: 1,500 v Guisborough, Wearside Lg/ v Sunderland, floodlight opener 1979.
Previous Name: Seaham Colliery Welfare Red Star 78-87.
Previous Grounds: Deneside Recreation Recreation Park 73-75/ Vane Tempest Welfare 75-78.
Players progressing to Football League: Bobby Davison (Huddersfield 1980), Nigel Gleghorn (Ipswich 1985), Billy Stubbs (Nottm Forest 1987), Paul Nixon (Bristol Rovers (1989), Mick Smith (Hartlepool).
Honours: Phillips Floodlit Trophy 78-79, Durham Challenge Cup 79-80, Wearside 81-82 (Lg Cup 81-82), Northern Lg Div 2 R-up 87-88, Monkwearmouth Charity Cup R-up 79-80, FA Vase 5th Rd 78-79, FA Trophy 2nd Rd 89-90.
Local Newspapers: Sunderland Echo, Journal, Northern Echo, Football Echo, Washington Times.

SOUTH BANK

Chairman: Joe Blackmore   **Press Officer:** Les Crossman (0642 473478).
Secretary: Ron Robinson, 182 Normanby Rd, South Bank, Middlesborough TS6 6SW (0642 454088).
Manager: Jimmy Watts   **Assistant Manager:** Colin Ross   **Physio:** Bob Cain
Coach: Maurice Gormley.
Ground: Normanby Road, South Bank, Middlesbrough, Cleveland (0642 453193).
Directions: Follow directions to South Bank, Football Club is major landmark in town.
No. of seats: 500   **Covered Accom:** 500   **Capacity:** 4,500
Floodlights: Yes   **Year Formed:** 1868
Club colours: Red & white stripes/black/red   **Change colours:** All yellow
Previous Leagues: None
Programme: 34 pages, 25p   **Programme Editor:** Les Crossman   **Souvenir Shop:** Not yet.
Clubhouse details: Open normal licensing hours. New development plans under negotiations.
Record Attendance: 10,000 v Bishop Auckland, Northern Lg, pre-war.
Nickame: Bankers.   **Best F.A. Cup season:** 1st Rd 25-26 33-34.
Players progressing to Football League: Gerry Forrest (Rotherham United).
Hons: FA Amateur Cup 12-13 (R-up 09-10), Northern Lg 07-08 19-20 21-22 (R-up 1894-95 95-96 96-97 1906-07 08-09 09-10 10-11 11-12 13-14 26-27 35-36 45-46, Lg Cup 55-56 47-48, North Riding Snr Cup 1897-98 1907-08 09-10 10-11 23-24 31-32 35-36.
Midweek Matches: Wednesday

STOCKTON

Chairman: Keith Wren   **Press Officer:** Secretary
Secretary: John Smith, 71 Rimswell Road, Fairfield, Stockton-on-Tees, Cleveland TS19 7LE (0642 584593).
Ground: Teesdale Park, Acklam Road, Thornaby (0642 606803).
Directions: A19 to Thornaby turn off, ground approx 3/4 mile on right.
No. of seats: 20   **Covered Accom:** 1,000   **Capacity:** 4,000
Floodlights: Yes   **Year Formed:** 1980
Club colours: Red & black stripes/black/red   **Change colours:** All light blue
Previous leagues: Stockton & District, Vaux Wearside.
Programme: 32 pages, 30p   **Programme Editor:** John Smith   **Souvenir Shop:**
Clubhouse: Open every evening plus Fri, Sat & Sun lunchtimes
Previous Leagues: Stockton & District/ Wearside 80-85.
Record Attendance: 3,000 v Middlebrough, pre-season friendly August 1986.
Previous Names: Stockton Cricket Club 1965-80.
Previous Grounds: Grangefield Community Centre 80-82/ Tilery Centre 82-83.
Hons: Northern Lg Div 2 91-92, FA Vase 2nd Round, FA Trophy 1st Round.
Local Newspapers: Northern Echo, Evening Gazette.   **Midweek Matches:** Tuesday.

Peterlee Newtown. Back Row (L/R): Jason Lennox, Colin Chapman, John Graham, Stuart Brown, Stephen Routledge, Tommy Fenwick, Dave Fishburn, John Holvey, Bobby Huntington (Manager), Stephen Fairless, Andy Strong, Eddie Cairns. Front: Gary Clarkson, Lee Collings, Tommy Garside, Chris Hall, Chris Kirby, Wayne Scholick, Gordon Huntington (Coach), Graham Peart (Mascot). Photo - Dave West.

Seaham Red Star. Back Row (L/R): K Mitchell (Player-manager), L Howey, J Gamble, J Todd, S Wilson, P Coxall, D Robinson. Front: T Mahan, P Arthur, C McBeth (Mascot), A Dormand, N Johnson. Photo - Dave West.

South Bank keeper David Campbell pulls off a great save to thwart the West Auckland attack. Photo - Dave West.

TOW LAW TOWN

Chairman: Harry Hodgson   **Press Officer:** Secretary
Secretary: Bernard Fairbairn, 3 Coppice Walk, Mowden Park, Darlington, County Durham DL3 9DP (0325 350743).
Manager: Stuart Leeming   **Assistant Manager:** Michael Haley
Ground: Ironworks Road, Tow Law, Bishop Auckland (0388 731443).
Directions: Just of High Street in Tow Law town centre.
Seats: 200   **Cover:** 300   **Capacity:** 6,000   **Floodlights:** Due   **Founded:** 1890
Colours: Black & white stripes/black/black & white   **Change colours:** Red & white
Previous leagues: None   **Programme:** None   **Club Shop:** Yes
Clubhouse: Every evening 8.30 -10.30.   **Record Gate:** 5,500 v Mansfield Town, FA Cup 1967.
Best F.A. Cup season: 2nd Rd replay 67-68. Also Competition Proper 68-69 84-85 89-90.
League Clubs defeated in F.A. Cup: Mansfield Town 67-68.   **Nickname:** Lawyers.
Players progressing to Football League: Reuben Cook & Ralph Guthrie (Arsenal 1951 & 53), Gordon Hughes & Terry Melling & Chris Waddle (Newcastle 1956 & 65 & 80), Eric Johnstone & Kevin Dixon (Carlisle 1963 & 83), Keith Adamson (Barnsley 1966), Tom Henderson (Bradford PA 1969), Vincent Chapman (Huddersfield 1988).
Hons: Rothmans National Cup 1977, Northern Lg 23-24 24-25 (R-up 28-29 88-89, Lg Cup 73-74, Rothmans Overseas Cup 76-77), Durham Chal. Cup 1895-96, Durham Amtr Cup 1892-93, FA Amtr Cup 3rd Rd rep. 70-71, FA Tphy 2nd Rd rep. 82-83.
Local Newspapers: Northern Echo   **Midweek Matches:** Tuesday

WEST AUCKLAND TOWN

Chairman: Norman Ayton   **President:** R Tomlinson
Secretary: Allen Bayles, 11 Edith Terrace, West Auckland, County Durham DL14 9JD (0388 833783).
Treasurer: Stuart Alderson   **Press Officer:** Brian Hudson
Manager: E Sharp   **Assistant Manager:** B Hudson   **Coach:** P Storey
Commercial Managers: B Hudson, J Nichols.
Ground: Darlington Road, West Auckland, County Durham (0388 834403).
Directions: Take A68 and turn left on entering the village.
Seats: 200   **Cover:** 400   **Capacity:** 4,000   **Floodlights:** Yes   **Founded:** 1893
Midweek Matches: Tuesday   **Previous Name:** St Helens Utd (1919 only).
Colours: White (black & amber trim)/white/white   **Change colours:** All amber
Programme: 24 pages, 50p   **Souvenir Shop:** No
Previous League: Auckland & District.   **Clubhouse:** None (use local Working Men's Club).
Record Attendance: 6,500 v Dulwich Hamlet, FA Amateur Cup.   **Nickname:** West.
Best FA Cup season: 1st Rd 58-59 61-62   **Players progressing to Football League:** None.
Hons: FA Amtr Cup R-up 60-61 (QF 59-60), Northern Lg 59-60 60-61 (Div 2 90-91, Lg Cup 58-59 62-63 (R-up 48-49 61-62 63-64)), Durham Challenge Cup 64-65, Durham Benevolent Cup 62-63, FA Trophy 3rd Rd 77-78, Sir Thomas Lipton Trophy (First World Cup!) 1909 1911.

WHITBY TOWN

Chairman: Bob Scaife   **President:** Don Dunwell.   **Press Officer:** Secretary
Secretary: TBA
Ground: Turnbull Ground, Upgang Lane, Whitby (0947 604847).
Directions: Take West Cliff signs when entering town, ground on main A174 road.
Seats: 200   **Cover:** 500   **Capacity:** 3,500   **Floodlights:** Yes   **Founded:** 1896
Club colours: All royal blue   **Change colours:** All white   **Previous leagues:** None
Programme: 32 pages, 25p   **Programme Editor:** Secretary & B Murfield   **Souvenir Shop:** Yes
Clubhouse details: None   **Record Attendance:** 5,000.   **Nickname:** Seasiders.
Previous Name: Whitby United.   **Best F.A. Cup season:** 2nd Rd 83-84.
Football League Clubs defeated in F.A. Cup: Halifax Town 83-84.
Players progressing to Football League: Malcolm Poskett (Hartlepool, Brighton, Watford, Sammy Kemp (Huddersfield), Jimmy Mulvaney (Hartlepool, Barrow, Stockport), Bobby Veart (Hartlepool), Derek Hampton & Trevor Smith & John Linacre & Phil Linacre (Hartlepool), Mark Hine (Grimsby).
Honours: FA Amtr Cup R-up 64-65, FA Tphy QF 83-84, Northern Lg R-up 27-28 33-34 67-68 81-82 82-83 (Lg Cup 28-29 63-64 69-70 76-77 84-85, Rothmans Overseas Cup 75-76 77-78), Nth Riding Snr Cup(3).
Local Newspapers: Whitby Gazette, Northern Echo.   **Midweek Matches:** Wednesday

Tow Law Town: Back Row (L/R): Darren Darwent, Neil Sant, Mark Wearmouth, Gary Powell, Warren Pearson, Mark Gardiner, Michael Bailey, Keith Knox (Capt). Front: Tony Higgs, Frank Deverdics, Trevor Laidler, David Thompson, Iain Scott, Mark Hayes. Photo - Dave West.

West Auckland Town. Back Row (L/R): Ian Mohan, Ray Stanger, David Race, David Bayles, Andy Burgess, David Clarke. Front: Kelvin Robinson, Paul Jarps, Michael Swainston (Mascot), Geoff Young, Kevin McKimm, Simon Old. Photo - Dave West.

Billingham Town before their 0-2 Division Two defeat at home to Hebburn on Good Friday. Photo - Dave West.

Brandon United 2, Langley Park 1 - Division One 18/4/92. Langley Park's Colin Woodward clears the ball under pressure from Keith Muckle. Photo - Dave West.

SECOND DIVISION 1992-93

ALNWICK TOWN

Chairman: Judith Draycott   **Press Officer:** Secretary
Secretary: Stewart Leason, 19 Stakeford Road, Bedlington, Northumberland NE22 JU (0670 824549).
Manager: Mick Dagless   **Assistant Manager:** Brian Penfold
Coach: Dave Clarke   **Physiotherapist:** Mac Belsize.
Ground: St James' Park, Alnwick, Northumberland (0665 603162).
Directions: 35 miles north of Newcastle on A1, take the slip road to Alnwick, then first left. At roundabout turn left, ground is then on your left.
Seats: 100   **Cover:** 200   **Capacity:** 2,500   **Floodlights:** Yes   **Founded:** 1879
Colours: Black & white stripes/black/black   **Change colours:** All yellow
Reserve Team's League: North Northumberland   **Sponsors:** Schat Davit.
Previous Leagues: North Northumberland/ East Northumberland/ Northern Alliance 36-39 46-64 65-82/ Durham Central 64-65.
Programme: 20 pages, 25p   **Programme Editor:** Stu Leason   **Souvenir Shop:**
Previous Leagues: Wearside 13-37 39-64 73-88.
Record Attendance: 600 v Bedlington Terriers, Northern Alliance 1971.
Previous Names: Alnwick United Services/ Alnwick United.
Best F.A. Cup season:
Players progressing to Football League: George Turnbull (Grimsby 1950), Brian Pringle (1973).
Honours: Northern Lg Div 2 R-up 88-89, Northern Alliance 37-38 62-63 63-64 65-66 67-68 68-69 69-70 70-71 71-72 (R-up 59-60 61-62 66-67 72-73, Lg Cup 61-62 65-66 67-68 68-69 70-71, Subsidiary Cup 80-81), Durham Central Lg Cup 64-65, Northumberland Benevolent Bowl 86-87, Northumberland SNR Cup R-up 61-62, Northumberland Amtr Cup 71-72, FA Trophy 3rd Qualifying Rd 90-91.
Local Newspapers: Northumberland Gazette, Alnwick Advertiser.   **Midweek Matches:** Tuesday

ASHINGTON

Chairman: Ray Graham   **Press Officer:** Brian Bennett (0670 856606)
Secretary: Chris Sanderson, 10 Rydal Mount, Newbiggin-by-the-Sea, Northumberland NE64 6JT (0670 855271).
Ground: Portland Park, Ashington NE63 9XG. (0670) 812240
Directions: 200 yds north at traffic lights in centre of town.
No. of seats: 350   **Covered Accom:** 2,200   **Capacity:** 4,000   **Floodlights:** Yes
Year Formed: 1883   **Midweek Matches:** Wednesday
Club colours: Black & white stripes/black/black   **Change colours:** All red
Programme: Yes, 20p   **Programme Editor:** C Sanderson
Clubhouse details: Open normal licensing hours.
Previous Leagues: Northern Alliance 1892-93 1902-14 69-70/ Football League/ North Eastern 14-21 29-58 62-64/ Midland 58-60/ Northern Counties 60-62/ Wearside 64-65/ Northern Premier 68-69.
Record Attendance: 13,199 v Rochdale, FA Cup 2nd Rd 9/12/50.
Best F.A. Cup season: 3rd Rd 26-27.   **Nickname:** The Colliers.
League Clubs defeated in F.A. Cup: Halifax Town 50-51.
Past players progressing to Football League: Tony Lowery (Mansfield), Les Mutrie (Colchester), R Cummins (Aberdeen, Newcastle).
Hons: FA Amateur Cup SF 73-74, Northumberland Snr 20-21 32-33 38-39 49-50 55-56 56-57 61-62 66-67 79-80, Northumberland Challenge Bowl 12-13 21-22 22-23 23-24 25-26 33-34, Midland Lg 58-59, North Eastern Lg Cup 33-34(jt with Sunderland Reserves) 39-40 (Div 2 26-27(Res)), Northern Alliance 13-14 24-25(Res) 39-40(Res) 55-56(Res) (R-up 05-06 10-11 11-12 22-23(Res) 55-56 56-57(Res), Lg Cup 47-48(Res)).

BEDLINGTON TERRIERS

Chairman: William Ward   **Press Officer:** Eric Young (0670 829196)
Secretary: Allan J Douglas, 26 Terrier Close, Bedlington, Northumberland NE22 5JP (0670 827206).
Ground: Welfare Park, Park Rd., Bedlington, Northumberland (0670 825485).
Directions: Into Bedlington, turn left at 'Northumberland Arms' on Front St., then 2nd Right, ground on right 100 yds.
No. of seats: 40   **Covered Accom:** Yes   **Capacity:** 600   **Floodlights:** No
Year Formed: 1949   **Midweek Matches:** Wednesday
Colours: All red   **Change colours:** All blue   **Souvenir Shop:** No
Clubhouse details: Open every evening, 11-11pm Sat. & Sun lunch. Pool, darts etc.
Record Attendance: 1,013 v Blyth Spartans, Northern Lg 85-86.
Previous Leagues: Northern Alliance.
Previous Names: Bedlington Mechanics 49-53/ Colliery Welfare 53-56/ Mechanics 56-61/ Bedlington United 61-65/ Bedlington Colliery 65-68/ Bedlington Town 68-74.
Hons: Northern League Div 2 R-up 84-85, Northern Alliance 66-67 (R-up 67-68 69-70 71-72, Lg Cup 57-58 66-67 69-70 81-82.

BILLINGHAM TOWN

Chairman: Mr G A Maxwell   **President:** Mr F Cook, MP
Secretary: Tommy Donnelly, 36 Cumberland Crescent, Billingham, Cleveland (0642 555332).
Manager: R Halliday   **Assistant Manager:** A Boynton   **Physio:** T Cushley
Ground: Bedford Terrace, Billingham, Cleveland. (0642 560043)
Directions: Leave A19 on A1027 (signed Billingham). Turn left at 3rd roundabout, over bridge 1st left, then 1st left again to ground.
Seats: 250   **Cover:** 250   **Capacity:** 3,000   **Floodlights:** Yes   **Founded:** 1967
Club colours: All royal blue with white trim   **Change colours:** All red
Programme: 28 pages, 30p.   **Programme Editor:** A Matthews   **Souvenir Shop:** No
Clubhouse: Matchdays only.   **Previous Lges:** Stockton & Dist. 68-74/ Teesside 74-82.
Record Attendance: 1,500 v Manchester City, FA Youth Cup 1985.
Midweek Matches: Tuesday   **Previous Ground:** Mill Lane (pre-1974).
Previous Name: Billingham Social Club (pre-1982).
Nickname: The Social.   **Best F.A. Cup season:** 1st Round Proper 1955-56.
Players progressing to Football League: Gary Pallister (M'boro & Manchester Utd), Gerry Forrest (Southampton), Dave Robinson (Halifax), Tony Barratt (Hartlepool), Mark Hine (Grimsby & Darlington), Tony Hall (M'boro).
Honours: Durham Amateur Cup 76-77 77-78, Teesside Lg 77-78 81-82, Nth Riding Snr Cup R-up 76-77 81-82, Stockton & Dist. Lg(3).

CROOK TOWN

Chairman: B M Humphreys   **Press Officer:** Secretary   **Manager:** Paul Adams.
Secretary: Eric Burton, 12 West End Villas, Crook, County Durham DL15 9PF (0388 762026).
Ground: Millfield Ground, West Road, Crook, County Durham (0388 762959).
Directions: 400 yds from town centre on Wolsingham Road.
No. of seats: 400   **Covered Accom:** 1,150   **Capacity:** 9,500   **Floodlights:** Yes
Year Formed: 1889   **Midweek Matches:** Wednesday
Club colours: Amber with black trim/black/black   **Change colours:** All white
Clubhouse details: Open 7-11 each evening plus matchdays.
Previous Leagues: **Record Attendance:** 17,500, FA Amateur Cup.
Previous Name: Crook Colliery Welfare.   **Nickname:** Black Ambers
Best F.A. Cup season: 3rd Rd (v Leicester) 31-32.
Past players progressing to Football League: None.
Honours: FA Amtr Cup 00-01 53-54 58-59 61-62 63-64 (SF 48-49 57-58 59-60), Northern Lg 14-15 26-27 52-53 58-59 62-63 (R-up 24-25 46-47 53-54 54-55 55-5663-64 64-65, Lg Cup 36-37 45-46 60-61), Durham Challenge Cup 26-27 31-32 54-55 59-60, Durham Benevolent Bowl 13-14 19-20 20-21 21-22 25-26 54-55, FA Trophy 2nd Rd 76-77.

DARLINGTON CLEVELAND BRIDGE

Chairman: Bill Shevels   **Press Officer:** Secretary
Secretary: David Shevels, 202 North Road, Darlington, County Durham DL1 2EL (0325 384256).
Ground: Neasham Road, Darlington (0325 469735).
Seats: 25   **Cover:** 250   **Capacity:** 1,500   **Floodlights:** Yes   **Founded:** 1903
Club colours: All yellow with red pin stripe   **Change colours:** All white
Programme: No   **Midweek Matches:** Tuesday   **Souvenir Shop:** No
Clubhouse details: Open Mon-Fri. 7.30-11pm & Sat. 12-11pm
Previous Leagues: Darlington & District/ Northern Alliance 81-83.
Record Gate: 520 v Darlington, friendly.   **Nickname:** The Bridge.
Players progressing to Football League: Jeff Wealands (Birmingham City, Manchester United).
Honours: Northern Alliance 82-83, North Riding County Cup.

DUNSTON FEDERATION BREWERY

Chairman: John Thompson   **Press Officer:** John McKenna (091-460 9726)
Secretary: Bill Montague, 12 Dundee Close, Chapel House, Newcastle-upon-Tyne NE5 1JJ (091 2672250).
Ground: Federation Park, Wellington Road, Dunston, Gateshead (091 493 2935).
Directions: Dunston/Whickham exit off A1(M), ground 400 yds north along Dunston Rd. 1 mile from Dunston or Metrocentre stations. Numerous buses from Gateshead & Metrocentre stop outside ground.
Seats: 50   **Cover:** 300   **Capacity:** 2,000   **Floodlights:** Yes   **Founded:** 1975
Colours: All blue   **Change colours:** All sky
Programme: 24 pages, 30p   **Midweek Matches:**   **Souvenir Shop:** No
Clubhouse: Matchdays only. Hot & cold snacks, darts, pool.   **Nickname:** The Fed
Previous Ground: Dunston public park 75-80
Previous Leagues: Northrn Amtr 75-80/ Northern Combination 80-87/ Wearside 87-91.
Record Attendance: 1,500 - Sunderland Shipowners Cup Final 1/4/88.
Previous Names: Whickham Sports/ Dunston Mechanics Sports.
Best F.A. Cup season: 2nd Qualifying Rd 2nd replay 91-92 (lost 1-2 at Penrith).
Hons: Northern Amtr Lg 77-78 (R-up 76-77 78-79, Lg Cup 77-78 78-79 (R-up 75-76), Lg Shields 78-79 79-80), Wearside Lg 88-89 89-90 (R-up 90-91, Lg Cup 90-91), Northern Comb. 80-81 85-86 86-87 (R-up 83-84, Lg Cup 83-84 (R-up 84-85 85-86)), Sunderland Shipowners Cup 87-88, Durham County Tphy 81-82 (R-up 83-84 85-86), Gateshead Charity Cup 77-78 80-81, FA Vase 4th Rd 91-92.

EPPLETON COLLIERY WELFARE

Chairman: J Storey   **Press Officer:** Chris Dinning (091 5652651).
Secretary: Fred Barry, 4 Henry Street, Houghton-le-Spring DH5 8AS (091 584 1452).
Manager: Stuart Sherwood   **Coach:** Ernie Harrison.
Ground: Eppleton Welfare Park, Hetton-le-Hole (Wearside 5261048).
Directions: Situated between Front Street Post Office & swimming baths, Hetton le Hole on A182. Buses 192, 193 & 194 stop at Front Street & Library. 8 miles from Durham (BR).
Seats: None   **Cover:** None   **Capacity:** 2,500   **Floodlights:** No   **Founded:** 1929.
Colours: All blue   **Change colours:** All red.
Record Attendance: 1,250 - Monkwearmouth Charity Cup Final 1987-88.
Previous Names: None (merged with Natcobos, early 70's).
Previous Leagues: Wearside 51-65 74-92/ Houghton & District 65-74.
Past players progressing to Football League:
Hons: Wearside Lg 90-91 91-92 (Lg Cup 74-75 78-79 87-88, Sunderland Shipowners Cup 47-48 85-86 90-91 (R-up 91-92), Monkwearmouth Charity Charity Cup 89-90 90-91 91-92).

ESH WINNING

Chairman: Charles Allen Ryan   **Press Officer:** Harold Wharton (091-3734860)
Secretary: Allan Morton, 20 Durham Road, Esh Winning, Durham DH7 9NP (091 373 3611).
Ground: West Terrace, Waterhouses, Durham (091 373 3872).
Directions: Durham to Ushaw Moor, to Esh Winning; ground 1 mile further at Waterhouses.
No. of seats: 180   **Covered Accom:** 180   **Capacity:** 3,000   **Floodlights:** Yes
Year Formed: 1967   **Midweek Matches:** Tuesday
Club colours: Green & yellow stripes/green/green.   **Change colours:** All green
Programme: 15 pages, 20p   **Programme Editor:** Harold Wharton   **Souvenir Shop:** No
Clubhouse details: Open 7-11pm every day, plus 12-3 Sun & 1-7pm Sat matchdays.
Previous Leagues: Durham & District Sunday, Northern Alliance 81-82.
Record Attendance: 900 v Liverpool Fantail, FA Sunday Cup 1982.
Best F.A. Cup season: 2nd Qualifying Rd 90-91 (lost 1-3 at home to Spennymoor).
Players progressing to Football League:
Nickname: 'Esh'   **Previous Names:** Esh Winning Pineapple (pre-1982).
Honours: Durham & District Sunday Lg 78-79 79-80, Durham County Sunday Cup R-up 78-79, Staffieri Cup 74-75, Guards Cup 72-73, FA Vase 2nd Rd 83-84.

EVENWOOD TOWN

Chairman: Gordon Nicholson **Press Officer:** Secretary **Manager:** Dr Graeme Forster.
Secretary: Jim Coates, 19 Wellgarth, Evenwood, Bishop Auckland, Co Durham DL14 9QU (0388 833035).
Ground: Welfare Ground, Stones End, Evenwood, County Durham (0388 832281).
Directions: In village centre by Sports & Social club in Stones Rd.
Seats: None **Cover:** 200 **Capacity:** 3,500 **Floodlights:** No **Founded:** 1890
Previous Leagues: None. **Midweek Matches:** Wednesday **Programme:** None
Club colours: All blue **Change colours:** Green (yellow sleeves)/green/green
Nickname: None **Clubhouse:** Open lunch & evening every day.
Record Gate: 9,000 v Bishop Auckland, FA Amtr Cup 1931. **Best F.A. Cup season:** 1st Rd 1936.
Previous Names: None **Players progressing to Football League:** None.
Hons: Northern Lg 48-49 69-70 70-71 (Lg Cup 35-36), Durham Challenge Cup 69-70.

STOP PRESS # HEBBURN *PROMOTED - DIVISION ONE*

Chairman: Gene Devlin **Press Officer:** Secretary
Secretary: R Hodgson, 23 Redhouse Road, Hebburn, Tyne & Wear (091 430 1098).
Ground: Hebburn S & S Club Ground, Victoria Rd. West, Hebburn (091 483 5101).
Directions: On the main road through the town about 1 mile from railway station.
Seats: 20 **Cover:** Yes **Capacity:** 2,000 **Floodlights:** No **Founded:** 1912
Club colours: Yellow/black/yellow **Change colours:** Red/red/blue
Programme: 16 pages with admission. **Programme Editor:** G Cadsby **Souvenir Shop:** No
Clubhouse details: Open 7-11pm every evening. Pool, darts etc.
Midweek Matches: Wednesday **Previous Leagues:** Wearside 39-40 60-89.
Record Attendance: Unknown. **Previous Names:** Reyrolles/ Hebburn Reyrolle (pre-'88)
Best F.A. Cup season: 2nd Qualifying Rd replay 89-90 (lost 0-3 at South Bank).
Players progressing to Football League:
Hons: Shields Gazette Cup 91-92, FA Vase 2nd Rd 91-92, Wearside Lg 66-67 (Monkwearmouth Charity Cup 68-69), Durham Challenge Cup 42-43.

HORDEN COLLIERY WELFARE

Chairman: J McCoy **Press Officer:** Secretary
Secretary: Ray Matthews, 11 Hudson Avenue, Horden, Peterlee, County Durham SR8 4QL (091 587 0727).
Ground: Welfare Park Ground, Park Road, Horden, Peterlee, County Durham (091 518 0248)
Directions: A19 to Peterlee, signposted from there.
Seats: 300 **Cover:** 400 **Capacity:** 4,500 **Floodlights:** Yes **Reformed:** 1980
Midweek Matches: Tuesday **Programme:** 10 pages, 20p **Nickname:** Colliers
Colours: Red (white trim)/red/red **Change colours:** Blue/black/blue
Clubhouse: Normal licensing hours. Hot & cold snacks, darts, pool.
Previous Lges: Wearside 07-35 63-75/ N. Eastern 35-58 62-64/ Midland (Co's) 58-60/ Northern Co's 60-62.
Best FA Cup year: 2nd Rd 38-39 (2-3 at home to Newport Co.). Also 1st Rd 25-26 52-53 53-54 54-55 81-82.
Previous Names: Horden Athletic. **Record Attendance:** 8,000 - FA Cup 1937.
Players progressing to Football League: Paul Dobson (Hartlepool United).
Hons: Durham Challenge Cup 35-36 63-64 80-81 81-82, Durham Benevolent Cup 33-34, Wearside Lg 11-12 12-13 13-14 33-34 64-65 67-68 69-70 70-71 71-72 72-73 (Lg Cup 33-34 49-50, Monkwearmouth Charity Cup 12-13 23-24 32-33 69-70 72-73, Sunderland Shipowners Cup 65-66 72-73), North Eastern Lg 37-38 63-64 ('Non-Reserve' Medal 50-51).

LANGLEY PARK

Chairman: C Fairless **President:** Bobby Robson.
Secretary: John Ritchie, 17 Nestonton Close, Langley Park, Durham DH7 9FB (091 373 2612).
Manager: Vic Hillier **Press Officer:** Secretary
Ground: Welfare Ground, Low Moor Road, Langley Park, Durham (091 373 1526).
Directions: A691 Durham to Consett. First left after Witton Gilbert, signed Langley Park. Turn right in town centre, ground quarter of a mile on right. Frequent buses from Durham.
No. of seats: 30 **Covered Accom:** 500 **Capacity:** 3,000 **Floodlights:** No
Reformed: 1973 **Midweek Matches:** Tuesday
Club colours: All blue **Change colours:** White/navy/navy OR All yellow
Programme: 30+ pages, 20p. **Programme Editor:** Jeff Dover **Souvenir Shop:** No
Clubhouse details: Open every evening, plus Sat & Sun lunch & directly after match on matchdays.
Previous Leagues: Durham & District Sunday/ Durham City & District.
Previous Name: Rams Head (pre-1983) as Sunday side.
Best F.A. Cup season: 2nd Qualifying Rd replay 90-91 (lost 0-1 at home to Easington Colliery).
Hons: FA Sunday Cup 76-77, Northern Lg Div 2 R-up 90-91, Staffieri Cup 74-75 76-77 77-78 78-79 80-81, Durham & Dist Lg JW Morgan Mem. Cup 82-83, Durham & Dist. Sunday Lg 78-79 (Lg Cup 76-77 78-78 79-80), FA Vase 2nd Rd 85-86 90-91.

NORTON & STOCKTON ANCIENTS

Chairman: Richard Scott **President:** Dennis Swales.
Secretary: Steve Clarkson, 4 South Way, Norton, Stockton-on-Tees, Cleveland TS20 2TQ (0642 534524)
Press Officer: Brian Symons (0642 585836).
Ground: Station Road, Norton, Stockton-on-Tees, Cleveland (0642 530203).
Directions: Norton village 2 miles from Stockton centre, turn into Station Road on outskirts of village.
No. of seats: 200 **Covered Accom:** Yes **Capacity:** 2,000 **Floodlights:** No
Year Formed: 1959 **Midweek Matches:** Wednesday
Club colours: Amber with black trim/black/amber **Change colours:** White with amber trim
Programme: 12 pages, with admission. **Programme Editor:** Richard Scott
Clubhouse details: Full bar facilities, 150 yds from ground.
Previous Leagues: Teesside (pre-1982).
Record Attendance: 1,430 v Middlesbrough, Friendly 1988.
Best F.A. Cup season:
Players progressing to Football League:
Nickname: Ancients
Previous Names: Norton & Stockton Cricket Club Trust.
Hons: Northern Lg Cup 81-82.

Hebburn's Steven Golightly shields the ball from Mike Kirton in a 2-0 win at Billingham Town on Good Friday. Photo - Dave West.

Hebburn before their 6-4 win over Boldon C.A. in the Shields Gazette Cup final on 11th May. Back Row (L/R): Gary Boyce, Steve Power, Justin Perry, Paul Basham, Chris Pearson, Tony Robinson, Scott Oliver. Front: Mark Brown, Paul Tinmouth, Keith Cummins, Stuart Wright, Kevin Bulmer, Steve Brewis, Vic McIntosh. Photo - Mark Webb, Shields Gazette.

Lamgley Park. Back Row (L/R): Graham Ash, Paul Brown, Peter Gardiner, Paul Sheekey, John Gauden, Kevin Berry, Paul Cooper. Front: Kevin McElwee, Kevin Gibson, Graham McDonald, Neil Wilson, Gary Steadman, Bruce Foster. Photo - James Wright.

PRUDHOE EAST END

Chairman: Cecil Allen   **Press Officer:** Gerald Wallace.
Secretary: John Smith, 6 Dene Street, Prudhoe, Northumberland NE42 5JB (0661 32140).
Ground: Kimberley Park, Broomhouse Road, Prudhoe, Northumberland (0661 35900).
Directions: Approach Prudhoe along A695, turn right at 'Falcon' Inn, 200 yds down Eastwood Rd., turn left into Broomhouse Rd., ground on right.
Seats: 150   **Cover:** Yes   **Capacity:** 5,000   **Floodlights:** Yes   **Founded:** 1959
Colours: Sky blue with navy stripes/navy/sky   **Change colours:** All yellow
Programme: 8 pages, 20p   **Editor:** J Smith   **Midweek Matches:** Wednesday
Clubhouse details: Open every evening plus Sat/Sun lunchtimes
Previous Leagues: Hexham & District 59-69/ Newcastle & District 69-71/ Northern Combination/ Northern Amateur/ Northern Alliance 84-88.
Previous Grounds: Farm field, Ovington 59-68/ Mickley Welfare 68-69.
Record Attendance: 2,500 v Blyth Spartans, Northumberland Senior Cup 1981.
Nickname: Citizens   **Previous Names:** Ovington 1969-75.
Hons: Hexham & Dist. Lg 68-69 (Lg Cup 68-69), Newcastle & Dist. Lg 69-70 70-71 (Lg Cup 69-70, Charity Shield 69-70 70-71), Northern Comb. 79-80, Northerm Amtr Lg 71-72, Clayton Charity Cup 68-69, Northumberland Minor Cup 78-79, Northumberland Benevolent Bowl 79-80, Heddon Homes Charity Cup 81-82.

RYHOPE COMMUNITY ASSOCIATION

Chairman: Mark Taylor   **Press Officer:** Mark Taylor (091 374 5423).
Secretary: Robert Lewins, 7 Belsay Gdns, St Gabriels Est., Sunderland, Tyne & Wear SR6 9PJ (091 514 5818).
Ground: Meadow Park, Ryhope, Sunderland (091 523 6555).
Directions: Off Stockton Road, Ryhope, near to Ryhope Hospitals.
Seats: 200   **Cover:** 200   **Capacity:** 2,000   **Floodlights:** Yes   **Founded:** 1961
Midweek Matches: Wednesday   **Record Gate:** 1,018 v Newcastle, friendly 1982.
Colours: Red & white stripes/black/red   **Change colours:** All blue
Programme: 8 page insert,30p   **Club Shop:** No
Clubhouse: Open matchdays only, licensed bar & hot & cold refreshments - no licensed bar.
Previous Leagues: Seaham & District/ Houghton & District/ Northern Alliance 78-82.
Players progressing to Football League: Kevin Todd (now Berwick, to Newcastle for £20,000).
Nickname: None   **Previous Names:** None.
Hons: Northern Alliance Lg Cup 80-81, Northern Lg Div 2 R-up 83-84.

SHILDON

Chairman: Bill Aisbitt   **Manager:** Ray Gowan.   **Press Officer:** Secretary
Secretary: Mike Armitage, 22 Hambleton Ct, Byerley Park, Newton Aycliffe, Co. Durham DL5 7HR (0325 316322).
Ground: Dean Street, Shildon, County Durham (0388 773877).
Diirections: Ground is in the town centre.
Seats: 400   **Cover:** 400   **Capacity:** 4,000   **Fioodlights:** Yes   **Founded:** 1890
Club colours: All red   **Change colours:** All white or Yellow/green/yellow
Programme: 24 pages, 20p   **Programme Editor:** Neil Bennett   **Souvenir Shop:** No
Clubhouse details: Open every evening from 7.30 plus 1.30-6.30 on matchdays. Bar, pool & darts.
Record Attendance: 13,000 - Schoolboys game, 1920s.
Previous Name: Shildon Town 1890-94/ Shildon Utd 94-1900/ Shildon Athletic 00-23.
Best F.A. Cup season: 2nd Rd 36-37. Also 1st Rd 27-28 29-30 34-35 36-37 55-56 59-60 61-62.
Players progressing to Football League: Ken Whitfield (Wolves 1947), James Smith (Chelsea 1951), Mike Peacock & Philip Shute (Darlington 1960 & 84), Kevin Stonehouse (Blackburn 1979).
Honours: Northern Lg 33-34 34-35 35-36 36-37 39-40 (R-up 32-33 38-39, Lg Cup 33-34 34-35 37-38 38-39 39-40 52-53), Durham Challenge Cup 07-08 25-26 71-72, Durham Amateur Cup 01-02 02-03, Durham Benevelopment Bowl(2), FA Trophy 3rd Qualifying Rd 74-75, FA Amateur Cup 4th Rd 58-59, FA Vase 1st Rd 86-87.
Local Newspapers: Northern Echo   **Midweek Matches:** Wednesday

SHOTTON COMRADES

Chairman: Ian Riley   **Press Officer:** Ian Riley (0429 8619239)
Secretary: Billy Banks, 6 Syston Close, Abingdon Grange, Chilton Moor, Fencehouses, Houghton-le-Spring, Tyne & Wear. DH4 6TB (091 385 5361).
Manager: John Oliver   **Assistant Manager:** Colin White   **Coach:**
Ground: Shotton Recreational Ground, Station Road, Shotton Colliery, Co. Durham (091 526 2859).
Directions: From A19, into Shotton Colliery, turn right at War Memorial & follow road round for 600 yds, ground on right.
No. of seats: 60   **Covered Accom:** 460   **Capacity:** 1,700   **Floodlights:** No
Year Formed: 1973   **Midweek Matches:** Wednesday
Club colours: Red & white/black/red & white tops   **Change colours:** All blue
Programme: 60 pages, 25p   **Programme Editor:** Mr A E Jones   **Souvenir Shop:** No
Clubhouse details: Normal licensing hours.
Previous Leagues: Peterlee Sunday 74-76/ Houghton & District 76-80/ Northern Alliance 80-83.
Record Attendance: 1,726 v Dennis Waterman XI.
Best F.A. Cup season: 2nd Qualifying Rd 85-86 (lost 0-2 at home to Wingate).
Nickname: Comrades   **Previous Names:** None.
Hons: Houghton & District Lg 78-79 (Lg Cup(2)), Northern Alliance Lg Cup SF, Hetton Charity Cup R-up, FA Vase 1st Rd 86-87 90-91.

WASHINGTON

Chairman: Billy Blevins   **Press Officer:** John Hurst (091 438 4513).
Secretary: George Abbott, 14 Grosvenor Street, Southwick, Sunderland SR5 2DG (091 549 1384).
Ground: Albany Park, Spout Lane, Concord, Washington (091 417 7779).
Directions: Ground situated behind the cinema opposite bus station.
Seats: 25   **Cover:** Yes   **Capacity:** 3,000   **Floodlights:** No   **Founded:** 1949
Colours: All red   **Change colours:** All blue   **Midweek Matches:** Wednesday
Programme: 8 pages, 10p   **Programme Editor:** Mr Bull (091 4164618)   **Club Shop:** No
Clubhouse: Open normal licensing hours, with live entertainment, pool etc.
Previous Leagues: Washington Amateur/ Northern Alliance 67-68/ Wearside 68-88.
Record Attendance: 3,800 v Bradford Park Avenue, FA Cup 1970.
Nickname: Mechanics   **Previous Ground:** Usworth Welfare Park

WHICKHAM

Chairman: Robert Ferriday   **Manager:** Billy Hodgson   **Press Officer:** Secretary
Secretary: Albert Hutchinson, 6 Fellside Ave., Sunniside, Newcastle upon Tyne NE16 5NL (091 488 7011).
Ground: Glebe Ground, Rectory Lane, Whickham (091 488 3054).
Directions: A692 (Consett) from A69. Left at r'bout signed Consett/Whickham. Up hill and right at mini-r'bout.
Continue along & turn left into Rectory Lane (by Lloyds Bank) for about 500 yds, clubhouse on right.
Seats: 100   **Cover:** Yes   **Capacity:** 4,000   **Floodlights:** Due   **Founded:** 1944
Colours: Black & white stripes/black/black   **Change colours:** All white
Previous Leagues: Derwent Valley -55/ Northern Comb. 55-57 59-74/ Tyneside Amtr 57-59/ Wearside 74-88.
Programme: pages, 20p   **Souvenir Shop:** No   **Midweek Matches:** Wednesday
Clubhouse: Open Mon-Fri. 12-3 & 7-11, Sat.11-11, Sun. 12-2, 7.30-11
Record Attendance: 3,165 v Windsor & Eton, FA Vase SF 1981.
Previous Ground: Rectory Recreation Field.   **Best F.A. Cup season:**.
Players progressing to Football League: Nigel Walker (Newcastle 1977), David Norton (Hartlepool 1981), Mike
Carroll (Chesterfield 1981).
Honours: FA Vase 80-81, Wearside Lg 77-78 87-88 (R-up 80-81 84-85, Lg Cup 86-87, Minkwearmouth Charity Cup 76-
77, Sunderland Shipowners Cup 77-78 80-81), Northern Comb. 69-70 72-73 73-74 (Lg Cup 60-61 73-74).
Local Newspapers: Newcastle Journal, Sunday Sun, Evening Chronicle

WILLINGTON

Chairman: Desmond Ayre   **Press Officer:** Secretary
Secretary: Jim Armstrong, 6 Hollyhock Terrace, Park Hill, Coxhoe, Co Durham DH6 4JD. (091-3771375)
Address & Tel No. of ground: Hall Lane, Willington, Co Durham. (0388) 746221
Directions: Off Commercial Str. (A690 from Durham) at 'The Black Horse Tavern' corner - ground 150yds on right.
Seats: 350   **Cover:** 400   **Capacity:** 7,000   **Floodlights:** Yes   **Founded:** 1906
Colours: Blue & white stripes/blue/blue   **Change colours:** Yellow/green/yellow.
Programme: 16-20 pages, 20p   **Programme Editor:** Bob Nichols   **Souvenir shop:** No
Clubhouse details: Open every evening 7-11pm and from 1pm Saturday matchdays. Pool, darts etc.
Previous Leagues: None.   **Midweek Matches:** Wednesday
Record Attendance: 10,000 v Bromley, FA Amateur Cup 2nd Rd 24/1/53/   **Nickname:** None
Best F.A. Cup season: 1st Rd replay 73-74 (lost 1-6 at Blackburn after 0-0 draw). Also 1st Rd 45-46 50-51.
Previous Ground: West End Ground 1906-11.   **Previous Names:** Willington Temperance 1906-11.
Hons: FA Amtr Cup 49-50 (R-up 38-39, SF 27-28), Northern Lg 13-14 25-26 29-30 (R-up 12-13 57-58 75-76, Lg Cup 24-
25 25-26 27-28 56-57 30-31 31-32 48-49 74-75), FA Trophy 3rd Rd 75-76, Durham Benevolent Cup 48-49 50-51 57-58.

Tow Law Town 3, Gretna 3 - First Division, April 25th 1992. Gretna's Paul Gorman blasts home the first of his two goals in an incident packed match which saw Gretna clinch the point they required to retain the championship. Gretna showed true character by playing the last half hour with ten men and without a recognised goalkeeper, custodian Paul Leeming having been sent off for a professional foul. Gretna's championship success means they are the first club to win promotion from the Northern League under the Pyramid system. Photo - Alan Watson.

T.S.B. HEXHAM & NORTH TYNE LEAGUE

	P	W	D	L	F	A	PTS
Otterburn	18	16	0	2	58	15	32
Haltwhistle CP 'A'	18	13	3	2	54	19	29
Hexham Town	18	9	2	7	45	40	20
Corbridge United	18	8	4	6	30	32	20
Whitfield	18	6	6	6	40	40	18
Bellingham	18	6	5	7	43	33	17
Rochester	18	4	6	8	39	44	14
Haydon Bridge	18	4	3	11	21	49	11
Haltwhistle Red Star	18	1	8	9	29	45	10
Hexhamshire	18	4	2	12	28	66	10

SEASON'S REVIEW

As the season reached its climax there were very serious doubts about the future of the T.S.B. Hexham & North Tyne League. The membership for 91-92 was only ten clubs following the withdrawal of Prudhoe Kimberley Clark and the shock demise of Stocksfield who were runners-up in 1990-91 but lost most of their players to Hexham Swinton and the newly formed Prudhoe Hunting; a week after lifting the League Cup it was announced the the Hexham League champions as recently as 1988 were to disband due to lack of players and the resignation of manager and long-serving player Dickie Purvis. Although a public meeting was called to see what could be done to relaunch the club that was formed just after the last war, the club folded. There were also doubts about Corbridge United after the resignation of manager Eddie Henderson.

Champions were Otterburn who retained the title in style with a 5-1 win over Bellingham at home where they had a 100% record. In fact they did not lose in the league until February when they went down 0-1 at nearest rivals Haltwhistle Crown Paints 'A'. Otterburn stated their intention to quit the league at the end of the season to try their luck in the North East Amateur League, and at this point League Secretary Dave Tiffin appealed for new clubs to join.

The League Cup was won by Hexhamshire with a shock 2-1 win over Haltwhistle Crown Paints 'A' in the final at Haydon Bridge. Nigel Robson scored twice for 'Shire' with Chris Bowerbank pulling back a late goal for the Haltwhistle side. Corbridge gained revenge over Otterburn in the Claydon Charity Cup with a 2-1 win, Swinburn opening the scoring with Wilson taking the match into extra-time before Robert Noble put Corbridge back in front heading in a cross from his father Michael. Victory was sweet for Corbridge who had been beaten by Otterburn in the Sudsidiary Cup final the previous week.

Crown Berger Paints from Haltwhistle sponsored the League K.O. Cup which saw Hexham Town beat Haydon Bridge 4-1 in a penalty shoot-out after a 3-3. Hexham made things hard for themselves. Having led 3-1 with just eight minutes left they let Haydon Bridge take the match into extra-time with goals from Kevin Marshall and Jonathan Clark, but there was no further scoring. The League introduced the Subsidiary Cup to create more fixtures in the latter part of the season, and Otterburn became first winners beating Corbridge 4-3 in an entertaining game of end to end football which drew Corbridge's largest attendance of the season.

Bellingham were the League's last survivors in the Northumberland F.A. Minor Cup, losing 0-1 in the Quarter Finals at Walker Lordwood of the Newcastle & District Welfare League.

David Walton

LEAGUE CUP 1991-92

SF: Hexhamshire v Whitfield   4-0   **SF:** Halthwhistle C.P. 'A' v Corbridge United   3-2
Final (at Haydon Bridge): Hexhamshire 2 *(Robson 30 85)*, Halthwhistle C.P. 'A' 1 *(Bowerbank)*

LEAGUE CUP 1991-92

SF: Whitfield v Otterburn   0-2   **SF:** Halthwhistle C.P. 'A' v Corbridge United   3-4
Final (at Newbrough): Corbridge 2 *(Swinburn 21, R Noble 106)*, Otterburn 1 *(Wilson 47)*

CROWN BERGER K.O. CUP 1991-92

SF: Halthwhistle Red Star v Haydon Bridge 1-2   **SF:** Bellingham v Hexham Town   2-3
Final (at Haltwhistle): Hexham 3 *(Carruthers 16, Marshall 82, J Clark 89)*, Haydon B. 3 *(Harnet 44, Nixon 60 65)* AET 4-1 pens.

SUDSIDIARY CUP 1991-92

SF: Corbridge United v Bellingham   3-2   **SF:** Otterburn v Halthwhistle Crown Paints 'A'   2-1
Final (at Corbridge United): Otterburn 4 *(R Noble 3, Franklin 67, Howdon 84(pen))*, Corbridge 3 *(Gary Rogerson 1 75, Shaw 27, Wilson 80)*

SAVA CENTRE WASHINGHTON LEAGUE

	P	W	D	L	F	A	PTS
Seaham Deneside	30	22	3	5	80	37	69
Hartlepool T. Res	30	20	5	5	103	29	65
Rolls Royce	30	19	6	5	77	31	63
Whitehill	30	17	5	8	63	39	56
Washington Glebe	30	17	4	9	66	33	55
Throston Wanderers	30	16	6	8	63	46	54
Hepworth & Gran.	30	16	4	10	75	47	*49
Wearmouth C.W.	30	13	6	11	66	57	45
Boldon Tedco Rossi	30	13	6	11	54	50	45
Birtley	30	12	5	13	50	56	41
Northern Counties	30	11	4	15	67	76	*34
Belford House	30	10	3	17	58	74	33
Springwell	30	8	5	17	47	67	29
Quarrymans Arms	30	4	5	21	48	90	17
Dawdon CW Mech.	30	2	7	21	32	86	13
Wrekenton B.B.	30	2	2	26	23	154	5

* - 3 points deducted

League Challenge Cup Final:
Hepworth & Grandage 2, Hartlepool Town Res 1

HYPER U.K. TEESSIDE LEAGUE

	P	W	D	L	F	A	PTS
Cassel Mall	30	19	6	5	86	38	63
Rowntree Mack.	30	18	8	4	88	39	62
Redcar Wks BSC	30	19	5	6	70	41	62
Acklam Steelworks	30	20	4	6	61	36	*61
I.C.I. Wilton	30	17	6	7	68	44	57
Dorman Athletic	30	15	6	9	63	53	51
Nunthorpe Athletic	30	16	3	11	44	37	51
New Marske S.C.	30	12	7	11	50	54	43
Tees Components	30	12	4	14	63	69	40
Richmond Town	30	10	7	13	39	53	37
Stockton Supporters	30	8	6	16	44	48	30
B.E.A.D.S.	30	8	6	16	48	70	30
Guisborough Quoits	30	9	2	19	39	65	29
Thornaby Youth C.	30	6	6	18	43	55	24
Fishburn Park	30	5	5	20	39	80	*17
Darlington GSOB	30	4	3	23	40	103	15

* - 3 points deducted

MacMillan Bowl:
SF: B.E.A.D.S. 2, Thornaby Youth Club 2 *(aet)*
rep: Thornaby Youth Club 2, B.E.A.D.S. 1
SF: Cassel Mall v Acklam Steelworks 2
F:(at Guisborough T.): Acklam v Thornaby 2-2*(aet)*,2-1

VAUX WEARSIDE LEAGUE

President: J.C. Thomas.

Hon. Secretary: Bill Robson,
12 Deneside, Howden - Le - Wear, Crook, County Durham DL15 8JR
(0388 762034).

SECRETARY'S REPORT

Season 1991-2 produced what was the closest finish in both divisions of the league for the last four years with the respective championships only being decided in the very last week of the season.

Eppleton C.W. came with a late run to pip long time leaders Hartlepool Town by two points and in so doing retained the Division One title to qualify for promotion, via the Pyramid, to Division Two of the Northern League.

In Division Two the final outcome of the championship race was decided on goal difference with Silksworth winning their final fixture by the lone goal to push newcomers to the league Jarrow Roofing Bolden C.A. into second place. Both clubs were subsequently promoted to Division One to take the places of Usworth Village and Newcastle Bohemians. Unfortunately Bohemians due to financial restraints were forced to offer their resignation from the league at the Annual Meeting.

With the departure of Eppleton C.W. to the Northern League the vacancy caused in the senior section was filled by the promotion of third placed Windscale.

On the domestic cup front teams from Division Two again proved successful with Nissan and Esh Winning Albion qualifying for the Finals of the League and Monkwearmouth Cups respectively. However, they were unable to capture either trophy with I.F.G.Roker defeating Nissan 3-1 and Eppleton C.W. retaining the Monkwearmouth Cup by a 2-0 scoreline.

The Sunderland Shipowners Cup saw the two leading sides from Division One, Hartlepool Town and Eppleton C.W., contesting the Final at Hartlepool's Mayfair Centre Ground. After taking an early lead Eppleton found themselves on the receiving end of a spirited Hartlepool fightback with the Town finally running out comfortable 4-1 winners.

Silksworth completed a Division Two League and Cup double rounding off their season with a 4-1 defeat of Hebburn Colliery in the Final of the divisional cup compeition.

Clubs from the league were unable to repeat last season's sussesses in the County Cup competitions with Marchon reaching the Semi Final stages in the defence of the Cumbria Cup before going out to eventual winners Gretna while Hebburn Colliery lost in the Final of the Durham Trophy.

Next season will see four new clubs joining the league following the election via the Pyramid of Birtley and Washington Glebe from the Washington League along with Murton International and Northallerton Town Supporters. It had been expected that a fifth club, Billingham Cassell Mall, would also be included but following reservations with regard to the standard of their present ground a merger between themselves and Wingate has taken place with the newly formed club to be known as Wingate Mall.

On the question of the Pyramid the league is now actively involved with the Northern and Alliance Leagues in the North East Section of the System following the formation of the N.L.J.L.C. while a Vaux Wearside League Section of the Pyramid is in the course of being established between ourselves and the Teesside and Washington Leagues.

Due to certain anomalies and further clarification being required from the Northern League regarding the application of their Rules covering the registration and retention of players the league have not to date agreed to the signing of the formal Charter covering the Pyramid but it is fully expected that these problems will be overcome and the acceptance of the Charter should be achieved before the start of next season.

With the league celebrating its Centenary this season it is expected that following a highly successful Centenary Dinner that we will be able to arrange a series of representative games against Football League clubs in the area as well as against teams from the respective leagues making up the North East Section of the National Pyramid of Football and the County Association covering the leagues area.

Bill Robson.

LEAGUE TABLES 1991-92

Division One	P	W	D	L	F	A	PTS
Eppleton C.W.	30	22	3	5	79	34	69
Hartlepool Town	30	20	7	3	60	30	67
South Shields	30	21	3	6	90	34	66
Marske United	30	20	4	6	85	37	*58
Annfield Plain	30	17	3	10	57	48	54
Boldon C.A.	30	12	9	9	48	41	45
Wolverton	30	13	5	12	59	55	44
Cleadon S.C.	30	12	7	11	45	43	43
Newton Aycliffe	30	13	3	14	44	45	42
Vaux Ryhope	30	11	8	11	56	65	41
S'land IFG Roker	30	12	4	14	43	46	40
Cleator Moor Celtic	30	8	6	16	43	64	30
Herrington C.W.	30	7	3	20	32	65	24
Darlington R.A.	30	4	9	17	36	66	+18
Usworth Village	30	4	5	21	22	72	17
N'castle Bohemians	30	3	3	24	27	81	12

* - 6 pts, + - 3 pts deducted

Division Two	P	W	D	L	F	A	PTS
Silksworth	22	15	3	4	70	35	48
Jarrow Roofing	22	15	3	4	53	29	48
Windscale	22	15	0	7	45	39	45
Hebburn Colliery	22	13	2	7	45	31	41
Hartlepool BWOB	22	12	1	9	46	29	37
Stanley United	22	9	3	10	29	37	30
Marchon	22	8	4	10	37	41	28
Nissan	22	7	7	8	32	43	28
Esh Winning Alb.	22	7	3	12	33	46	24
Wingate	22	6	5	11	28	32	23
Jarrow	22	5	1	16	32	53	16
Flo-Gas Fulwell	22	3	2	17	26	61	11

DIVISION ONE RESULTS 1991/92

HOME TEAM	1	2	3	4	5	6	7	8	9	10	11	12	13	14	15	16
1. Annfield Plain	*	1-2	0-1	2-0	3-2	4-1	3-1	1-3	2-1	1-5	2-0	2-1	3-1	4-1	1-5	3-3
2. Boldon C.A.	1-1	*	0-0	4-2	3-0	1-2	5-2	0-3	1-3	0-2	1-0	2-1	0-3	2-0	0-1	1-1
3. Cleadon S.C.	0-1	1-1	*	2-0	2-0	3-1	0-1	0-1	1-1	1-6	5-1	3-2	0-3	0-1	4-2	0-1
4. Cleator Moor C.	0-2	1-4	0-4	*	4-1	0-1	4-3	0-1	1-0	3-2	5-1	3-0	1-2	2-2	1-1	3-1
5. Darlington R.A.	0-2	2-2	2-2	2-5	*	1-2	0-2	0-0	0-0	0-0	5-2	1-1	1-3	1-0	3-6	2-5
6. Eppleton C.W.	5-0	2-0	5-2	4-0	3-0	*	2-0	1-1	2-1	3-1	6-1	4-1	1-6	3-1	2-3	2-1
7. Herrington C.W.	1-3	1-4	1-2	1-1	4-1	0-5	*	2-3	0-1	0-3	0-3	0-2	1-3	0-0	1-1	2-0
8. Hartlepool Town	2-1	1-1	1-1	2-0	2-1	0-1	1-0	*	1-0	2-2	4-1	1-0	2-0	3-2	2-2	1-1
9. I.F.G. Roker	1-2	2-2	1-2	3-0	4-2	0-3	3-1	0-3	*	2-0	1-0	2-3	1-2	4-2	1-2	3-1
10. Marske United	4-2	1-0	4-3	4-1	1-4	3-3	2-0	2-0	6-0	*	3-0	3-1	2-0	4-0	3-3	1-3
11. Newcastle Bohemians	2-3	1-3	1-2	2-2	0-0	0-4	1-2	0-4	0-3	0-7	*	0-1	1-4	4-0	1-3	2-1
12. Newton Aycliffe	1-0	0-1	2-1	1-0	0-0	0-1	3-0	2-4	3-0	1-2	1-0	*	3-1	2-0	2-3	2-2
13. South Shields	2-1	3-3	2-2	4-1	2-0	0-1	4-0	8-1	1-1	1-2	5-1	4-1	*	5-1	3-0	8-1
14. Usworth Village	0-4	0-3	2-0	1-1	1-1	0-6	2-0	1-2	3-2	1-1	0-3	0-2	*	1-3	0-4	
15. Vaux Ryhope	1-2	1-1	0-0	1-1	0-3	2-2	1-3	1-7	0-1	0-3	2-1	2-4	2-5	2-0	*	5-2
16. Wolviston	1-1	3-0	0-1	6-1	5-1	2-1	2-3	0-2	0-1	5-0	1-0	3-0	0-3	2-0	5-1	*

DIVISION TWO RESULTS 1991/92

HOME TEAM	1	2	3	4	5	6	7	8	9	10	11	12
1. +sh Winning Albion	*	1-4	5-1	3-2	5-2	2-0	0-1	0-1	0-2	2-3	4-2	
2. Hartlepool Boys WOB	2-0	*	1-2	1-2	1-2	0-1	1-1	2-1	1-0	4-0	5-0	2-0
3. Hebburn Colliery	2-1	0-3	*	3-0	1-3	5-1	3-1	2-0	3-1	2-0	3-0	3-2
4. Jarrow	1-2	3-0	2-4	*	0-3	4-3	1-2	6-2	1-2	0-1	2-3	0-0
5. Jarrow Roofing	4-0	1-2	1-0	1-0	*	5-1	3-3	5-1	0-5	5-0	2-1	1-0
6. Marchon	2-1	1-4	1-1	2-0	0-1	*	6-1	3-0	2-4	1-4	0-1	3-0
7. Nissan	1-1	0-1	0-2	2-1	1-3	3-1	*	2-1	2-2	2-1	3-0	3-1
8. Sunderland Flo-Gas	0-1	4-3	0-3	3-2	1-4	1-4	2-2	*	3-7	1-2	0-1	1-1
9. Silksworth	8-0	4-3	4-3	7-2	2-1	1-1	6-1	3-1	*	1-1	3-0	1-0
10. Stanley United	1-0	1-3	1-0	4-0	1-1	1-2	1-2	1-3	*	2-4	2-1	
11. Windscale	2-1	4-3	3-1	4-1	2-3	2-0	5-1	5-2	2-1	*	0-3	
12. Wingate	3-2	1-0	1-1	1-2	2-2	0-1	0-0	3-0	4-3	3-0	0-1	*

LEAGUE CUP 1991-92

Preliminary Round

Hartlepool Town v Boldon Comm. Assn	3-0	Stanley United v Usworth Village	2-1
Silksworth v Windscale	7-1	Esh Winning Albion v Wingate	1-2
Newton Aylcliffe v Wolviston	4-3(aet)	Herrington Colliery Welfare v Annfield Plain	1-2
Newcastle Bohemians v Jarrow Roofing	2-5	Eppleton Colliery Welfare v Marchon	8-0
Cleadon S.C. v Sunderland I.F.G. Roker	0-3	Darlington Railway Athletic v Sunderland Flo-Gas	0-2
Jarrow v Sunderland Vaux Ryhope	2-1(aet)	South Shields v Marske United	3-2

First Round

Hebburn Colliery v Hartlepool Town	1-4	Stanley United Silksworth	1-5
Wingate v Nissan	1-3	Newton Aycliffe v Annfield Plain	2-1
Cleator Moor Celtic v Hartlepool B.W.O.B.	2-1	Jarrow Roofing v Eppleton Colliery Welfare	0-7
Sunderland I.F.G. Roker v Sunderland Flo-Gas	3-1	Jarrow v South Shields	0-4

Second Round

Hartlepool Town v Silksworth	3-1	Nissan v Newton Aycliffe	1-0(aet)
Cleator Moor Celtic v Eppleton Colliery Wf.	0-1	Sunderland I.F.G. Roker v South Shields	3-0

Semi-Finals

Hartlepool Town v Nissan	0-1	Eppleton Colliery W. v Sunderland I.F.G. Roker	1-2

Final: Nissan 1, Sunderland I.F.G. Roker 2

DIVISION TWO CUP 1991-92

First Round

Silksworth v Hartlepool Boys WOB	2-2,4-1	Wingate (bye)	
Windscale v Sunderland Flo-Gas	5-0,3-4	Nissan v Jarrow	1-1,3-4
Marchon v Stanley United	3-1,1,1	Hebburn Colliery Welfare W/O Blackhall Colliery Welfare	

Quarter-Finals

Silksworth v Wingate	1-1,4-2	Jarrow Roofing v Windscale	5-1,0-3
Jarrow v Marchon	1-0,1-0	Hebburn Colliery Welfare (bye)	

Semi-Finals

Jarrow v Hebburn Colliery Welfare	2-2,0-1	Silksworth v Jarrow Roofing	2-1,0-1(4-3 pens)

Final: Silksworth 4, Hebburn Colliery 1

MONKWEARMOUTH CHARITY CUP 1991-92

Preliminary Round

Silksworth v Herrington Colliery Welfare	2-0	Boldon Community Association v Marske United	1-2
Usworth Village v Stanley United	2-3	Jarrow v Hebburn Colliery	4-1
Cleator Moor Celtic v Newton Aylcliffe	1-0	Nissan v Windscale	2-0
Blackhall C.W. v Sunderland I.F.G. Roker	0-2	Hartlepool Town v Darlington Railway Athletic	1-0
Annfield Plain v South Shields	3-1	Vaux Ryhope v Wingate 4-4*(Wingate won on pens)*	
Wolviston v Hartlepool Boys Welfare O.B.	6-3	Cleadon S.C. v Jarrow Roofing	2-2,2-0
Sunderland Flo-Gas v Marchon	0-1		

First Round

Silksworth v Marske United	0-2	Newcastle Bohemians v Stanley United	2-3
Jarrow v Esh Winning Albion	0-3	Cleator Moor Celtic v Nissan	0-0,1-6
Eppleton C.W. v Sunderland I.F.G. Roker	2-1	Annfield Plain *(bye)*	
Wingate v Wolviston	2-1	Cleadon S.C. v Marchon	3-1

Quarter-Finals

Marske United v Stanley United	3-0	Esh Winning Albion v Nissan	2-2,3-2
Eppleton Col. Wf. v Annfield Plain	2-2,3-0	Wingate v Cleadon S.C.	1-1,0-1

Semi-Finals

Marske United v Esh Winning Albion	2-3	Eppleton Colliery W. v Cleadon S.C.	3-0

Final: Esh Winning Albion 0, Eppleton Colliery Welfare 2

SUNDERLAND SHIPOWNERS' CUP 1991-92

Preliminary Round

Eppleton Colliery Welfare v Silksworth	2-1	South Shields v Sunderland I.F.G. Roker	3-2
Jarrow Roofing v Newcastle Bohemians	3-2	Stanley United v Sunderland Flo-Gas	2-1
Darlington Railway Athletic v Hebburn C.	1-1,1-3	Herrington Colliery Welfare v Newton Aycliffe	2-5
Wolviston v Vaux Ryhope	1-2	Usworth Village v Annfield Plain	0-3
Wingate v Esh Winning Albion	0-1	Nissan v Hartlepool Town	3-4
Marske United v Windscale	3-0	Cleadon S.C. v Marchon	1-2

First Round

Jarrow Roofing v Stanley United	4-1	Eppleton Colliery Roofing v South Shields	2-2,1-0
Hebburn Colliery v Cleator Moor Celtic	0-1	Newton Aycliffe v Vaux Ryhope	3-3,1-2
Annfield Plain v Esh Winning Albion	1-0	Hartlepool Town v Marske United	2-1
Marchon v Hartlepool Boys Welfare O.B.	2-0	Boldon Community Association v Jarrow	1-2

Quarter-Finals

Cleator Moor Celtic v Vaux Ryhope	1-3	Annfield Plain v Hartlepool Town	0-3
Eppleton Col. Wf. v Jarrow Roofing	2-0	Jarrow v Marchon	1-4

Semi-Finals

Hartlepool Town v Marchon	4-1	Eppleton Colliery Welfare v Vaux Ryhope	2-1

Final: Hartlepool Town 4, Eppleton Colliery Welfare 1

VAUX WEARSIDE LEAGUE DIVISION ONE TEN YEAR RECORD

	82/3	83/4	84/5	85/6	86/7	87/8	88/9	89/90	90/1	91/2
Annfield Plain	15	7	9	4	1	18	13	7	3	5
Blackhall Colliery Welfare	-	-	-	-	-	12	17	-	-	-
Boldon Community Association	14	9	13	16	13	15	8	4	4	6
Brandon United	3	-	-	-	-	-	-	-	-	-
Chester-le-Street Town	2	-	-	-	-	-	-	-	-	-
Clarke Champions	-	-	16	15	18	16	16	-	-	-
Cleadon S.C.	-	-	-	-	-	-	-	-	-	8
Cleator Moor Celtic	-	-	-	-	-	-	11	12	8	12
Coundon Three Tuns	5	2	3	1	8	2	15	6	14	-
Darlington Railway Athletic	-	-	-	-	-	-	-	-	-	14
Dawdon Colliery Welfare	-	12	18	17	10	8	14	13	10	-
Dunston Federation Brewery	-	-	-	-	-	9	1	1	2	-
Easington Colliery	4	3	8	-	-	-	-	-	-	-
Eppleton Colliery Welfare	11	10	5	10	6	3	2	2	1	1
Gateshead Reserves	-	15	14	8	20	-	-	-	-	-
Greatham Mayfair Centre				(See Hartlepool Town)						
Hartlepool Boys Welfare Old Boys	-	-	-	-	5	17	9	9	17	-
Hartlepool Town	-	-	-	-	-	-	-	-	12	2
Hebburn (formerly Reyrolles)	17	16	19	13	15	7	5	-	-	-
Herrington Colliery Welfare	-	-	-	-	17	19	10	14	16	13
Marske United	-	-	-	7	7	6	6	8	6	4
Murton Colliery Welfare	12	13	12	2	2	4	-	-	-	-
Newcastle Blue Star	1	1	1	-	-	-	-	-	-	-
Newcastle (ex-NEI) Bohemians	-	-	-	-	-	-	-	15	13	16
Newton Aycliffe	-	-	17	11	16	13	7	3	9	9
Nissan	-	-	-	-	-	-	-	-	18	-
Roker				(See Sunderland IFG Roker)						
Ryhope Colliery Welfare	7	14	6	18	14	20	-	-	-	-
Sporting Club Vaux				(See Sunderland Vaux Ryhope)						
Seaham Colliery Welfare Red Star	9	-	-	-	-	-	-	-	-	-
South Hetton	-	18	-	-	-	-	-	-	-	-
South Shields	10	6	4	12	9	5	4	5	5	3
Stockton E.D.C.	6	11	20	-	-	-	-	-	-	-
Sunderland I.F.G. Roker	18	17	15	14	12	14	12	10	7	11
Sunderland Vaux Ryhope	-	-	11	5	3	10	3	11	11	10
Usworth Village	-	-	-	-	-	-	-	-	-	15
Washington	13	8	10	6	11	11	-	-	-	-
Whickham	8	5	2	3	4	1	-	-	-	-
Wingate	16	4	7	9	19	-	-	-	-	-
Wolviston	-	-	-	-	-	-	-	-	15	7
No. of clubs competing	18	18	20	18	20	20	17	15	18	16

ANNFIELD PLAIN

Chairman: J H Barrett   **Press Officer/Treasurer:** M Cole.
Secretary: Marshall Lawson, 24 Northgate, Anfield Plain, Stanley, County Durham (0207 235879).
Manager: D Longstaff   **Ground:** Derwent Park, Annfield Plain.
Directions: On A693 road to Consett, 200 yds west of junction with A6067. Ground behind new housing estate. 6 miles from Durham (BR). Buses from Sunderland, Newcastle & Durham.
Seats: 20   **Cover:** 200   **Capacity:** 6,000   **Floodlights:** No   **Founded:** 1890.
Colours: Claret/sky/claret   **Change colours:** Navy/sky/white & sky.
Programme: 16 pages, 20p   **Record Attendance:** 7,200 v Southport, FA Cup 28-29.
Previous Names: Annfield Plain Celtic.   **Local Press:** Newcastle Journal.
Previous Leagues: North Eastern 25-58 62-64/ Northern Alliance 02-25 58-60.
Past players progressing to Football League: A Graver (Lincoln), N Wilkinson (York), K Smith (Blackpool), J Hather (Aberdeen).   **Honours:** Wearside Lg 84-85, FA Cup 1st Rd 26-27 28-29 64-65, Durham Chal. Cup 52-53, Northern All. 19-20, Harelaw Snr Cup 35-36, North Eastern Lg Cup 46-47.

BOLDON COMMUNITY ASSOCIATION

Chairman: R A O Shepherd.   **Press Officer:** Secretary   **Treasurer:** A Bell
Secretary: George Pollard, 126 Horsley Hill Road, South Shields (091 4546821).
Ground: Boldon Community Association, New Road, Boldon Colliery.
Directions: A19 to junction with A184 Sunderland/Newcastle. Follow signs to Boldon Asda stores, then to North Road Social Club (SHACK). Ground behind. 800 yds from East Boldon (BR). Buses 533, 531, 319, 528.
Seats: 0   **Cover:** 0   **Capacity:** 2,000   **Floodlights:** No   **Founded:** 1892.
Colours: Red (white sleeves)/black/red (black hoop)   **Change colours:** Blue/blue/black.
Record Attendance: 1,550 v Stockton, Durham Challenge Cup 1934.   **Nickname:** Villa.
Previous Names: Boldon Villa (reformed in 1946)/ Boldon Colliery Welfare 50-76.
Previous Ground: Station Road.   **Prev. Lges:** None (Boldon Villa: Sth Tyne Alliance)
Hons: Wearside Lg 52-53 54-55 74-75 (Lg Cup 67-68 72-73 75-76, Monkwearmouth Charity Cup 57-58 71-72, Shipowners Cup 62-63 71-72 75-76 76-77 78-79 88-89).

CLEATOR MOOR CELTIC

Chairman: R Doyle   **Press Officer:** Secretary
Secretary: Pat McGrath, 105 Birks Road, Cleator Moor, Cumbria (0946 811488).
Ground: Birks Field, Birks Road, Cleator Moor, Cumbria (0946 812476).
Directions: A66 to Bridgefoot, A595 for Barrow at Hensingham, left to Cleator Moor after 2 miles, left approaching town centre to Birks Road, club 200 yds on left. 5 miles from Whitehaven (BR).
Seats: No   **Cover:** 500   **Capacity:** 2,000   **Floodlights:** No   **Founded:** 1908.
Colours: Green & white/white/green   **Change:** Green & white halves/green/green
Record Attendance: 3,100 v Penrith 1950 (12,212 v Tranmere at Workington, FA Cup 1st Rd 1950).
Previous Ground: The Celtic Field 08-59   **Prev. Lges:** West Cumberland/ Carlisle & Dist. (pre'88).
Past players progressing to Football League: Billy Elliott & Pat Fitzsimmons (Preston), Joe Kennedy (West Bromwich Albion), Charlie Woods & Paul Tynan (Ipswich Town)
Honours: FA Cup 1st Rd 50-51, West Cumberland Lg 58-59.

HARTLEPOOL TOWN

Chairman: Robert Lupton   **Press Officer:** Secretary
Secretary: Gerry Watson, 10 Queensway, Greatham, Hartlepool TS25 2HL (0429 871415).
Ground: Mayfair Park, Mayfair Centre, Tees Road, Seaton Carew (0429 861230).
Directions: Just south of Seaton Carew (Hartlepool) on Tees Road before Nuclear Power Station.
Colours: Navy/white/navy   **Change colours:** Red & white/black/black.
Prev. Names: Greatham Mayfair (pre-1991) **Previous Leagues:** Hartlepool/ Teesside (pre-1988).
Honours: Wearside Lg R-up 91-92 (Shipowners Cup 91-92).

HERRINGTON COLLIERY WELFARE

Chairman: Paul Forster   **Press Officer:** Secretary
Secretary: Mel Speding, 12 Lodore Court, Doxford Park, Sunderland (091 5200881).
Treasurer: Bill Oxenham (091 5841730)   **Ground:** Welfare Park, New Herrington.
Directions: Situated on B1286 between the Board Inn and Herrington Burn. Behind New Herrington W.M.C.
Colours: Black & white/black/black & white   **Change colours:** All grey.
Previous Leagues: Washington Amateur 76-89.   **Founded:** 1920   **Reformed:** 1976.
Hons: Monkwearmouth Charity Cup 09-10 10-11 31-32, Shipowners Cup R-up 89-90, NCB National 5-aside 1975.

JARROW ROOFING BOLDON C.A.

Chairman: Brian Marshall   **Press Off.:** Kevin Oliver (091 5373923)   **Treasurer:** Ray Ryan
Secretary: Mrs R McLoughlin, 8 Kitchener Terrace, Jarrow (091 4899825).
Ground: As Boldon C.A. (above).   **Previous Leagues:** Mid-Tyne/ Tyneside Amtr 88-91.
Colours: Claret & blue/sky/maroon   **Change colours:** Blue/yellow/maroon
Hons: Vaux Wearside Lg Div 2 R-up 91-92, Tyneside Amtr Lg R-up 90-91 (Chal. Shield 90-91 (R-up 89-90), Bill Dixon Cup 90-91), Mid-Tyne Lg 87-88, Fred Giles Cup R-up 87-88, Gateshead Charity Cup SF 90-91.

MARSKE UNITED

President: Raymond Jarvis   **Chairman:** John Hodgson   **Press Officer:** Secretary
Secretary: Norman Coleby, 32 Topcliffe Drive, Brookfield, Middlesbrough TS5 8HZ (0642 597963).
Treasurer: Mrs Pat Hodgson.   **Ground:** Mount Pleasant, Marske (0642 471091).
Directions: From A19 take A174 exit marked Yarm, Teesport, Redcar, Whitby and head east towards Teesport and Redcar, continue on A174 and enter Marske by A1040 or A1084. In town square right into Southfield Road, and right again to ground. 200 yds from Marske Holt (BR).
Seats: No   **Cover:** None   **Capacity:** 2,500   **Floodlights:** No   **Founded:** 1956.
Colours: Yellow/blue/yellow   **Change:** Blue/white/blue.
Previous Ground: None.   **Record Gate:** 950 v Sunderland, friendly 1983.
Previous Leagues: Cleveland/ South Bank & District/ Teesside 76-85.
Past players progressing to Football League: Peter Beagrie (Middlesbrough, Stoke City, Sheffield United, Everton, England 'B'), Dave Logan (Mansfield Town, Scarborough), Tony Butles (Gillingham).
Local Press: Sunday Sun/ Northern Echo/ Middlesbrough Evening Gazette.
Honours: North Riding County Cup 84-85, Teesside Lg 80-81 84-85, Wearside Lg Cup R-up 88-89.

Sean Robson heads Vaux Ryhope's second in a 5-1 win at Annfield Plain on 18th April. Photo - Gavin Ellis.

Hartlepool Town, League Runners-up and Sunderland Shipowners Cup Winners 1991-92. Photo - Kerry Miller.

Hebburn Colliery 2, Blackhall 0 - Div. Two 31/8/91. Brian McHugh scores with a freekick. Photo - John Diamond.

NEWTON AYCLIFFE

Chairman: Luke Raine   **Treasurer:** Andrew Coulthard (0325 313416).
Press Officer/Secretary: Luke Raine, 31 Bede Crescent, Newton Aycliffe (0325 314844).
Ground: Moore Lane Sports Club, Newton Aycliffe, County Durham (0325 300324).
Directions: Turn in at Approved School A167, then left at r'bout. Third left, first right, ground at bottom on right. 2 miles from Newton Aycliffe (BR), served by Durham-Darlington buses.
Seats: None   **Cover:** None   **Capacity:** 2,000   **Floodlights:** No   **Founded:** 1968.
Colours: White/blue/blue   **Change colours:** Red/white/red.
Record Attendance: 500 - Vaux Wearside League Cup Final 1987-88.
Previous Names: Newton Aycliffe Sports Club Rangers   **Nickname:** Acorns
Previous Leagues: Auckland District 68-80/ Teesside 80-84.
Players progressing to Football League: Eric Gates (Ipswich Town & England).
Honours: Auckland & District Lg 75-76 (Div 2 68-69, Lg Cup), Brancepeth Aged Miners Cup, Bishop Auckland Charity Cup, Weardale Cup, Wearside Lg Cup R-up 88-89 (Monkwearmouth Charity Cup R-up 86-87).

SILKSWORTH

Chairman: Jeff Eltringham   **Press Officer:** Secretary
Secretary: John Cumiskey, 21 Symington Gdns, Silksworth (091 5283098).
Treasurer: Anthony Stubbs   **Ground:** Silksworth Welfare Park
Directions: Behind Lord Seaham Public House, Blind Lane, Silksworth. 3 miles from Sunderland (BR), bus 133 to Vicarage Court from Sunderland centre.
Seats: No   **Cover:** None   **Capacity:** 1,600   **Floodlights:** No   **Founded:** Yes
Colours: All white   **Change colours:** Red/red/white.   **Reformed:** 1988.
Players progressing to Football League: Bobby Gurney (Sunderland).
Hons: Wearside Lg 26-27 57-58 (Div 2 91-92, Lg Cup 51-52 59-60, Monkwearmouth Charity Cup 19-20 51-52, Shipowners Cup 53-54, Div 2 Cup 91-92).

SOUTH SHIELDS

Chairman: John Rundle   **Press Officer:** Secretary   **Treasurer:** Paul Honeyman.
Secretary: David Fall, 50 Basil Way, Holder Hose Estate, South Shields (091 5366809).
Ground: Filtrona Park, Shaftesbury Avenue, Simonside Industrial Estate.
Directions: From A1(M) take A194(M) to South Shields, town centre road, ignore A1300 to coact and turn left at next lights beside Co-op store, ground at bottom on right.
Seats: None   **Cover:** None   **Capacity:** 2,000   **Floodlights:** No   **Founded:** 1974
Colours: Claret/sky/sky   **Change colours:** Orange/black/black.
Prev. Ground: Jack Clarke Park 74-92.   **Record Attendance:** 1,500 v Brigg Town, FA Vase 1975.
Prev. Lge: Northern Alliance 74-76.   **Local Press:** Shields Gazette/ Newcastle Journal.
Honours: FA Vase QF 75-76, Northern Alliance 74-75 75-76, Wearside Lg 76-77 (Monkwearmouth Charity Cup 87-88, Lg Cup R-up 82-83 83-84, Shipowners Cup R-up 83-84), Durham Chal. Cup 76-77.

SOUTH SHIELDS CLEADON SOCIAL CLUB

Chairman: John Morris   **Press Officer:** David Wood (091 4554607).
Secretary: Peter Spencer, 15 Longfield Close, South Shields NE34 0YJ (091 4559766).
Treasurer: Mrs Joan Wood   **Ground:** Jack Clarke Park, South Shields.
Directions: Enter South Shields on A194 to r'bout taking you onto John Reid Rd. 2nd left at 3rd r'bout into King George Rd, then Sunderland Road. Follow on right into Grosvenor Rd then then left into Horsly Hill Rd. Ground on right behind bowling alley. Three quarters of a mile from Chichester Metro station.
Cols: Black & white stripes/black/black   **Change colours:** All white   **Founded:** Early 60s
Previous Leagues: Shields & Dist./ Washington Amtr (pre'89).
Hons: Wearside Lg Div 2 90-91, Shields & Dist. Lg, Washington Amtr(2), Durham Cup.

SUNDERLAND I.F.G. ROKER

Chairman: J Broadbent   **Press Officer:** Secretary   **Treasurer:** Les Dodd.
Secretary: Tom W Clark, 55 Vicarage Close, New Silksworth SR3 1BQ (091 5211242).
Ground: As Silksworth (see above).   **Record Attendance:** Unknown.   **Founded:** 1940.
Colours: Red & white stripes/red/red   **Change:** All white.
Prev. Names: Roker Methodists/ Roker/ Roker Zanussi/ Sunderland Roker.
Local Press: Sunderland Echo.
Players progressing to Football League: Paul Rutherford (Newcastle).
Hons: Wearside Lg Cup 91-92 (Shipowners Cup 89-90 (R-up 80-81), Monkwearmouth Charity Cup R-up 80-81).

SUNDERLAND VAUX RYHOPE COLLIERY WELFARE

Chairman: R E Forster   **Press Officer:** Secretary   **Treasurer:** I Mankin.
Secretary: Bob E Forster, 43 Beechwood Terrace, Sunderlad (091 5658939).
Ground: Ryhope Recreation Park, Ryhope Street, Ryhope, Sunderland (091 521 2843).
Directions: Take A19 (3 miles south of Sunderland centre) to Ryhope village, at Village Green turn into Evelyn Terrace/Ryhope Street and carry on up bank past Presto's for 600 yds - ground appears on left. 3 miles from Sunderland Central (BR), bus every 10 minutes from Sunderland centre.
Seats: No   **Cover:** No   **Capacity:** 1,000   **Floodlights:** Yes   **Founded:** 1988.
Colours: All blue   **Change colours:** Red & white/black/red.
Prev. Name: Ryhope Colliery Welfare (founded 1898, previously Ryhope Villa) merged with Sporting Club Vaux (founded in 1968 at Monkwearmouth, later Bishopwearmouth, South Hetton) in 1988.
Previous Grounds: Sporting Club Vaux: Glenesk Road (pre-1988).
Previous Leagues: Sporting Club Vaux: Tyne & Wear/ North Eastern Amateur.
Record Gate: 2,000; Ryhope Colliery Welfare v Workington, FA Cup 1967.
Players progressing to Football League: Alan Harding (Lincoln, Darlington, Hartlepool), Kenny Ellis (Hartlepool, Darlington, Belgian clubs), Kenny Mitchell (prof. Icelandic club), Robert Malt (Leeds), Brian Smiles (Chelsea), Ron Robinson (Leeds), Nigel Staddington (Doncaster, Scunthorpe).
Honours *(Sporting Club Vaux hons italicised)* Wearside Lg 61-62 62-63 63-64 65-66 (Lg Cup 63-64 77-78), Durham Challenge Cup 77-78, Monkwearmouth Charity Cup 09-10 65-66 66-67, Sunderland Shipowners Cup 61-62 *86-87*, FA Cup 1st Rd Proper 67-68, FA Vase 1st Rd 81-82.

Newton Aycliffe survive a penalty at home to Burscough in the F.A. Vase, but still lose, 2-4. Photo - Leo Heonig.

Action as Cleadon S.C. (hoops) lose 0-3 at home to Sunderland Roker on 14th September. Photo - John Diamond.

Steve Harkus hits a shot for Wolviston as they capitulate 1-8 at South Shields on 21th September. John Diamond.

WINDSCALE

Chairman: R Napier   **Press Officer:** Secretary   **Treasurer:** A Barwise
Secretary: Geoff Turrell, 65 Leathwaite, Loop Road South, Whitehaven, Cumbria CA28 7UG (0936 62229)
Ground: Falcon Field, Egremont.   **Directions:** A66 to Bridgefoot. A595 for Barrow, right at bottom of hill
approaching Egremont. Ground in centre of housing estate
Cols: Blue & white hoops/royal/royal   **Change:** Claret & blue/white/white   **Founded:** 1950
Previous Leagues: West Cumberland Snr/ Derwent Valley/ Furness Premier.
Hons: Furness Snr Cup 85-86   **Previous Names:** Windscale Rovers/ Windscale United.

WOLVISTON

Chairman: Eddie Poole   **Press Officer:** Secretary
Secretary: Keith Simpson, 14 Lodore Grove, Acklam, Middlesbrough, Cleveland TS5 8PB (0642 823734).
Treasurer: Brian Jones.   **Ground:** Metcalfe Way, Wynyard Road, Wolviston.
Directions: Situated on Wynyard Road between Thorpe Thewles and Wolviston. From A19 onto A689 into
Wolviston village. Take Wynyard Road heading towards Thorpe Thewles. Or, from A1(M) to Stockton direction,
turn left at Thorpe Thewles along Wynyard Road.
Colours: Royal/white/royal   **Change:** Scarlet/white/scarlet   **Founded:** 1910.
Prev. Name: Wolviston St Peters 10-46   **Prev. Lges:** Stockton & Dist. 46-82/ Teesside 82-88.
Players progressing to Football League: Peter (Pike) Atkinson (Grimsby), David Hockaday (Blackpool,
Swindon), Ken McCue (Blackpool), Kenny Lowe (Hartlepool), Laurie Duff (Leicester).
Hons: Wearside Lg Div 2 89-90, Teesside Lg R-up 84-85, Stockton & District Lg(3).

SECOND DIVISION CLUBS 1992-93

BIRTLEY

Chairman: John Kelly   **Press Officer:** Secretary
Secretary: Kevin Finnigan, 6 Elm Terrace, Birtley (091 4104824).
Treasurer: Richard Barrett   **Ground:** Birtley Welfare.
Directions: (From Durham) Along Birtley High Street past Red Lion, Fire Station first left at junction on bottom of
the bank, 1st left again through gates to childrens park, ground adjacent.
Colours: Green & white/white/white   **Change colours:** All blue.
Hons: Northern Alliance 23-24 (R-up 13-14).

ESH WINNING ALBION

Chairman: Keith Wardham   **Press Officer:** Secretary
Secretary: Dennis R Fort, 8 Durham Road, Esh Winning, Durham DH7 9NW (091 3734292).
Treasurer: Secretary.   **Ground:** Esh Winning Welfare.
Directions: From Nevilles Cross take A690 (Crook) to bottom of Nevilles Cross Bank (Stone Bridge Inn). Right
onto B6302 through Broom Park and Ushaw Moor, and on to Esh Winning. Ground situated at rear of South
Terrace (first row of houses as you enter Esh.
Colours: Red/red/white   **Change colours:** All blue.   **Founded:** 1986
Prev. Name: Esh Winning Pineapple 86-91 **Prev. League:** Crook & District 86-89.
Hons: Colin Waites Cup 88-89, Monkwearmouth Charity Cup R-up 91-92.

HARTLEPOOL BOYS WELFARE OLD BOYS

Chairman: Glen Thompson   **Press Officer:** Secretary
Secretary: Tom Harvey, 59 Wansbeck Gdns, Hartlepool TS26 9JH (0429 264753).
Treasurer: George Lester   **Ground:** Grayfields Enclosure.
Directions: Leave A19 on A179 to Hart Village, over two roundabouts, right at next large r'bout, travel half a mile,
Grayfields is 50 yds to right of next r'bout.
Seats: No   **Cover:** No   **Capacity:** 1,500   **Floodlights:** No   **Founded:** 1953.
Colours: All white   **Change colours:** All yellow.   **Local Press:** Hartlepool Mail.
Previous Leagues: Hartlepool Church/ Hartlepool & Dist./ Teesside.
Players progressing to Football League: A Walsh (Middlesbrough, Darlington, Bristol City).
Hons: FA Vase 3rd Rd, Hartlepool Church Lg(2)(Lg Cup(3)), Hartlepool Mem. Shield, Durham Minor Cup 60-61
(R-up 64-65), Hartlepool & Dist. Lg(3)(Lg Cup(3)), Horden Aged Miners Cup, Wingate Aged Miners Cup, Durham
Amtr Cup 64-65 73-74, Teesside Lg 73-74 85-86(R-up(3)).

HEBBURN COLLIERY

Chairman: I Gray   **Press Officer:** Mr J Burns (091 4384405).
Secretary: J H Telford, 46 Woodvale Drive, Hebburn, NE31 1RA (091 4838372).
Treasurer: D Porter.   **Ground:** Monkton Stadium, Jarrow.
Directions: A1(M) along Newcastle then White Mare Pool take A194 for South Shields, pass r'bout, after half mile take
B1516 for Jarrow along Fork Avenue. At end of dual c'way turn left and follow signs to Monkton Stadium. From
A19 take second slip road after Tescos onto A194 for Gateshead. Monkton Stadium signed.
Colours: Blue & red stripes/blue/blue   **Change colours:** All blue.
Previous Leagues: Shields & Dist. 1899-1900/ Gateshead & Dist. 00-09/ Wallsend Amtr 09-13/ Newcastle & Dist.
13-18/ Northern Alliance 18-25/ Mid-Tyne 25-39/ Tyneside/ Business Houses/ Washington Amtr.
Players progressing to Football League: Ned Barkas (Huddersfield), John Wigham (Hartlepool), Jack McQuillam
(Hull), David Wilson (Hamilton Academicals).
Prev. Name: Victoria Park (reformed club) **Hons:** Tyneside Lg(3) 28-31, Mid-Tyne Lg(2) 25-27.

JARROW

Chairman: Dave Wiscombe   **Press Officer:** Secretary
Secretary: Calum McAuley, 109 Bamburgh Avenue, South Shields (091 4555924).
Treasurer: George Cook.   **Ground:** Perth Green Community Centre.
Directions: From A19 or A1(M) follow directions to South Shields, right onto John Reid Road. First slip road onto
Brockley Whinns Estate, follow road past Red Hackle pub, third left left onto Inverness Road, then right into Perth
Community Centre.
Colours: Blue/white/blue & white.   **Change:** Red & white/red/red.   **Founded:** 1980.
Prev. Names: Unionist FC/ Benson Perth Green.   **Prev. Lges:** Sth Tyne 80-87/ Washington 87-91.
Hons: Sth Tyne Lg & Lg Cup, Washington Lg R-up 89-90 (Lg Cup 90-91, Aged Peoples Tphy R-up 90-91),
Gateshead Charity Cup 90-91, Durham Tphy R-up 90-91.

MARCHON

Chairman: Neil Fennel **Press Officer:** Secretary
Secretary: Harry Upton, 14 Foxhouses Road, Whitehaven CA28 8AF (0946 61750)
Treasurer: Steve Gibbons **Ground:** Albright & Wilson, Whitehaven Works
Directions: From Cockermouth turn off A66 onto A595 and enter Whitehaven. Follow 'Town Centre' A5094 then zig zag through one way system following 'St Bees' B5345. Fork right up hill at junction signed 'Sandwith and Marchon Works'. Ground on right or main road beyond works at top of hill. Two miles from Bransty (BR).
Seats: None **Cover:** 50 **Capacity:** **Floodlights:** No **Founded:**
Colours: White/red/red **Change colours:** Red/white/white
Previous Leagues: West Cumberland/ Carlisle & District/ Cumberland
Previous Name: Haig Colliery **Clubhouse:** Works Social Club. Normal hours.

MURTON INTERNATIONAL

Chairman: Tom Pratt **Press Officer:** Secretary
Secretary: John Collings, 7 Station Rd South, Murton, Seaham SR7 9RS (091 526 4906).
Treasurer: Tom Dixon **Ground:** As Murton FC (see page 870)
Colours: All white **Change colours:** Red & white/black/red

NORTHALLERTON TOWN SUPPORTERS

Chairman: Dennis Cope **Press Officer:** Secretary
Secretary: Simon Egan, 11 Lambourne Drive, Denepark, Marton, Middlesbrough (0642 313235).
Treasurer: Martin Gibb **Ground:** As Northallerton Town (see page 870)/
Colours: Black & white stripes/black/black **Change colours:** All yellow

STANLEY UNITED

Chairman: W Westgarth **Press Officer:** Secretary
Secretary: J Vince Kirkup, 71 Scripton Gill, Brandon, Durham DH7 8BQ (091 3780921)
Treasurer: Chairman **Ground:** High Road, Stanley, near Crook.
Directions: From Teeside on A689 to Bishop Auckland and onto Crook, turn left at Market Place then first right for Tow Law to Billey Row and Stanley. Turn right at top of bank then first left. Ground is 250 yards on left. From Tyneside and Sunderland, from Durham take A698 and carry on through Brancepeth Village, turn right onto Oakenshaw/Tow Law road for approx. 3 miles. Ground is 250 yards on left
Seats: None **Cover:** 200 **Capacity:** 3,000 **Floodlights:** No **Founded:** 1890.
Colours: Red & white stripes/black/red **Change colours:** Sky blue/navy/navy
Record Gate: 4,000 v Yorkshire Amateur, FA Amateur Cup 31/1/48.
Previous Leagues: Northern 10-74/ Durham City & Dist. 74-88.
Players progressing to Football League: Geoff Strong (Liverpool, Arsenal), Tommy Cummins (Burnley), Dickie Dale & Eli Ashurst (Birmingham), Jackie Brown & John Wilkinson (York), Gordon Bradley & Fred Batty (Bradford PA), Archie Brown (Sunderland), Jackie Howarth (Chelsea, Aldershot), John Birbeck (Norwich), Alan Ball (Queen of the South).
Hons: Northern Lg 45-46 61-62 63-64 (Lg Cup 46-47 57-58), FA Cup 1st Rd 53-54, FA Amtr Cup 19-20, Durham Amtr Cup 00-01 05-06.

SUNDERLAND FLO-GAS FULWELL

Chairman: John V Holtan **Vice Chairman:** Rob Craggs **Treasurer:** Philip Burdis
Press Off./Secretary: Colin Dagg, 12 Stainton Grove, Seaburn Drive, Sunderland SR6 8PB (091 5487802)
Manager: N Jackson **Ground:** Northumbria Centre.
Directions: From A19 take A1231 to Washington, A195 for District 12, right at 3rd r'bout, ground on left.
Colours: Royal blue **Change colours:** Black & white/black/black
Programme: 24 pages, 25p **Previous League:** Wearside Combination 87-91.
Founded: 1985. **Previous Name:** R & J Carpets.
Hons: Wearside Comb. 90-91 (Div 2 R-up 89-90, Div 3 R-up 88-89), Jollies Cup 88-89, J S Pears Mem. Tphy 89-90.

USWORTH VILLAGE

Chairman: TBA **Press Officer:** Ray Middleton (091 5286077).
Secretary: Steven Cullen, 302 Leechmere Road, Tunstall, Sunderland SR2 9DF (091 5226164).
Ground & Directions: As Sunderland Flo-Gas Fulwell (above).
Colours: Black & gold/black/black & gold **Change colours:** All sky.
Previous Names: David Brown FC/ Mountain Daisy 85-87/ Castle View 87-90.
Previous Leagues: Wearside Apprentices/ Wearside Comb. 72-79/ North Eastern Amtr 79-88/ Washington 88-90.
Hons: Wearside Comb. R-up 78-79, GHB Eltringham Tphy 85-86, North Eastern Amtr Lg 87-88.

WASHINGTON GLEBE

Chairman: Frank Lanaghan **Press Officer:** Secretary
Secretary: Robert Robson, 24 Talbot Close, Glebe, Washington NE38 7RH (091 4151893).
Treasurer: Graham Thirlaway **Ground:** Washington Glebe Welfare.
Directions: A1 them A19, A1231 into Washington, 3rd exit road (signed Gateshead A195), turn for District 9 at r'bout, right for Washington Village at next r'bout, right at 1st T-jnct., pitch 200 yds on right.
Colours: Yellow/green/yellow **Change colours:** All red.

WASHINGTON NISSAN

Chairman: Brian Carolin **Press Officer:** Secretary
Secretary: Harry English, 159 Alston Crescent, Seaburn Dene, Sunderland SR6 8NF (091 5487194)
Treasurer: Tom Dixon **Ground** (To be confirmed): Nissan Spts & Social Club
Directions: Northwards along A1 (M) use A690 (sign post Sunderland) to connect with A19, travel north on A19, after passing the A1231 turn off the plant on the left. Go past plant and follow signs for 'Nissan Offices'. Southwards along A19 and leave A19 at signpost for 'Nissan Offices'.
Cols: Black & blue stripes/black/black **Change colours:** Red & black stripes/black/black
Founded: 1988 **Hons:** Wearside Lg Cup R-up 91-92, Nissan European Tphy 88-89.

WINGATE MALL

Chairman: John Malcolm
Press Officer: Ray Morton
Secretary: Richard Hayes, 40 Tyrone Road, Fairfield, Stockton on Tees TS19 7JW (0642 588900).
Treasurer: John Malcolm
Ground: Welfare Park, Wingate
Directions: From North A19 to A181 junct, South A19 to A179 junct. From Durham A181; to B1280, Front Street, Wingate turn right at Queens Head Public House. Ground 400 yards ahead through Market Crescent.
Colours: Sky/navy/sky
Change colours: Red/white/red.
Previous Names: Wingate St Marys, Wingate Wanderers merged in 1967 to form Wingate FC. This club then merged with Billingham Cassel Mall in 1992.
Previous Leagues: Hartlepool & Dist. *(St Marys & Wanderers)/* Wearside 67-87/ Auckland & Dist. 87-88. *Billingham Cassel Mall: Teesside (pre-1992).*
Hons: Wearside Lg R-up 78-79 (Lg Cup 69-70 (R-up 78-79), Monkwearmouth Charity Cup 77-78 83-84, Shipowners Cup R-up 67-68 78-79), Durham Chal. Cup R-up 73-74, FA Cup 3rd Qual. Rd. *Cassel Mall: Teesside Lg 91-92.*

South Shields Cleadon Social Club: Back Row (L/R): J Morriss (Chairman), D Wood (Manager), D Dixon, D Appleby, P Carr, N Pearce, M Reay, D Bewick, D Bone (now Boldon Tedco), I Grieves, G Henderson, A Race (Assistant Manager). Front: G Boyce, D Bell, D Black, M Harrison (Captain), G Goodwin, J Pease, M Ahmed.

Hebburn Colliery FC, Durham Trophy Finalists 1991-92.

McEWANS NORTHERN ALLIANCE

President: Stan Seymour, Esq.
Chairman: R M Griffiths, Esq.
Press Officer: Bill Gardner, 12 Coronation Road,
Sunniside, Newcastle-upon-Tyne NE16 5NR. Tel: 091 4883422.

Premier Division	P	W	D	L	F	A	PTS
West Allotment C.	30	20	4	6	77	26	64
Walker	30	18	4	8	63	35	58
Gilford Park	30	17	5	8	77	35	56
Seaton Delaval A.	30	15	9	6	62	35	54
Spittal Rovers	30	16	4	10	56	32	52
Seaton Terrace	30	15	6	9	65	45	51
Westerhope	30	13	6	11	48	46	45
Wark	30	12	7	11	62	65	58
Haltwhistle C.P.	30	13	5	12	39	38	*41
Ponteland United	30	11	7	12	55	46	40
Blyth Kitty B.	30	11	7	12	48	54	40
Forest Hall	30	9	8	13	38	55	35
Morpeth	30	8	8	14	38	61	32
Heaton Stann'ton	30	7	10	13	42	39	31
Swalwell	30	3	7	20	33	72	16
Newbiggin	30	2	3	25	31	157	*6

* - 3 pts deducted

Leading Scorers:
M Chilton (West Allotment) 25
I Crumplin (Ponteland Utd) 24
J Moses (Seaton Delaval A.) 20

First Division	P	W	D	L	F	A	PTS
Carlisle City	30	24	3	3	121	32	75
Winlaton H'garth	30	19	8	3	75	38	65
Longbenton	30	18	7	5	69	49	61
Benfield Park	30	15	8	7	69	44	53
Percy Main	30	14	5	11	60	53	47
NEI Reyrolle	30	12	7	11	61	56	43
Wylam H.S.	30	11	9	10	58	56	42
Ryton	30	11	9	10	56	57	42
Proctor & Gamble	30	12	5	13	71	71	41
Northern Electric	30	10	6	14	53	69	36
Northern Counties	30	9	8	13	51	66	35
New York	30	8	9	13	48	63	33
Dudley Welfare	30	7	9	14	52	72	30
Hexham Swinton	30	10	2	18	46	68	*29
N'castle Univ.	30	5	6	19	33	69	21
Wallsend R. Sun	30	3	3	24	34	95	12

* - 3 pts deducted

Leading Scorers:
A Walker (Carlisle City) 32
S Dodds (Northern Co's) 25
V Bollardo (Longbenton) 22

Second Division	P	W	D	L	F	A	PTS
St Columba	28	22	4	2	64	25	70
Percy Rovers	28	20	4	4	76	32	64
C.K. Brinkburn	28	16	7	5	103	50	52
Shankhouse	28	14	9	5	82	42	51
Ashington Hirst	28	15	6	7	74	54	51
Amble	28	15	5	8	75	49	50
Marden	28	12	7	9	57	57	43
Bohemians	28	11	6	11	63	54	39
Swalwell C.C.	28	9	8	11	69	70	35
Norgas	28	9	4	15	62	65	31
KOSA	28	7	9	15	40	77	27
Highfields	28	6	4	18	53	90	22
Stobswood Welf.	28	4	9	15	48	72	21
Heddon Institute	28	5	4	19	34	79	19
Spartan	28	3	1	24	48	132	10

Leading Scorers:
K Henderson (Amble Town) 26
K J Bruce (Swalwell CC) 25
P Jennings (Shankhouse) 23

McEWANS NORTHERN ALLIANCE LEAGUE CUP

First Round

Morpeth Town v Ashington H.P.	1-2
Wark v Newbiggin C.W.	1-0
Amble Town v Haltwhistle Crown Paints	1-2
Carlisle City v Berwick H.F.	6-2
Northern Electric v Dudley Welfare	0-4
Ryton v Winlaton Hallgarth	2-3
Spartan Blyth v Wallsend Rising Sun	0-1
Stobswood Welfare v Swalwell C.C.	2-0

Heaton Stannington v Seaton Delaval Amtrs	1-4 *(aet)*
Benfield Park v Seaton Terrace	1-5
Blyth Kitty Brewster v St Columbas	1-2
Heddon Institute v Percy Main	2-7
N.E.I. Reyrolle v Proctor & Gamble	1-2
Shankhouse v New York	2-3
Wylam H.S. v Hexham Swinton	0-1

Second Round

Swalwell C.C. v Walker	3-4
Forest Hall v Gillford Park	1-2
Wark v Hexham Swinton	3-0
C.K. Brinkburn v Northern Counties	5-1
Marden Athletic v Proctor & Gamble	0-2
Seaton Terrace v Bohemians	6-1
Longbenton v Kosa	2-1
Winlaton Hallgarth v Dudley Welfare	2-1

Ponteland United v Percy Main	2-1
Carlisle City v Seaton Delaval Amateurs	2-1 *(aet)*
Percy Rovers v Newcastle University	2-1
Haltwhistle Crown Paints v West Allotment Celtic	2-3
Spittal Rovers v Norgas	2-1 *(aet)*
New York v Westerhope	0-2
Stobswood Welfare v St Columbas	1-2
Ashington H.P. v Wallsend Rising Sun	4-3

Third Round

Walker v Ponteland United	2-3
Wark v Percy Rovers	4-1 *(aet)*
Proctor Gamble v Spittal Rovers	2-4
Longbenton v St Columbas	4-2

Gillford Park v Carlisle City	2-0
C.K. Brinkburn v West Allotment Celtic	3-5
Seaton Terrace v Westerhope	4-2
Winlaton Hallgarth v Ashington HP	2-2 *(aet)*,3-2

Fourth Round

Wark v Longbenton	2-5
Seaton Terrace v Gillpark Park	1-1 *(aet)*,1-3

Winlaton Hallgarth v Spittal Rovers	1-0
West Allotment Celtic v Ponteland United	0-1

Semi Finals

Winlaton Hallgarth v Longbenton	1-0

Ponteland United v Gillford Park	2-1

Final (at Benfield Park FC, Monday 6th May 1992)
Winlaton Hallgarth v Ponteland United 2-1

PREMIER DIVISION CUP 1991-92

First Round

Blyth Kitty Brewster v Ponteland United	0-1	Newbiggin Colliery Welfare v Seaton Terrace	0-6
Heaton Stannington v Gillford Park	2-3	Seaton Delaval Amateurs v West Allotment Celtic	2-2*(aet)*
Wark v Walker	0-2	Forest S.C. v Spittal Rovers	3-4
Westerhope v Morpeth Town	1-3*(aet)*	Swalwell C.C. v Haltwhistle Crown Paints	0-4

Second Round

Spittal Rovers v Gillford Park	6-4*(aet)*	Haltwhistle Crown Paints v West Allotment Celtic	0-2
Morpeth Town v Seaton Terrace	0-1	Ponteland United v Walker	1-0

Semi-Finals

Spittal Rovers v Ponteland United	4-2	West Allotment Celtic v Seaton Terrace	1-1*(aet)*,0-3

Final (at Newcastle Utd FC, Saturday 11th April 1992): Seaton Terrace 3, Spittal Rovers 0

DIVISION ONE COMBINATION CUP 1991-92

First Round

Ryton v Hexham Swinton	3-0	Dudley Welfare v Wallsend Rising Sun	6-1
Proctor & Gamble v Northern Electric	1-0	New York v Newcastle University	2-1
Winlaton Hallgarth v Northern Counties	2-1	Longbenton v N.E.I. Ryeyrolle	2-2,6-6*(aet 0-2 pens)*
Carlisle City v Percy Main	3-2	Wylam H.S. v Benfield Park	5-3*(aet)*

Second Round

Winlaton Hallgarth v Dudley Welfare	4-1	Wylam H.S. v Proctor & Gamble	2-3
Ryton v Carlisle City	1-7	N.E.I. Reyrolle v New York	0-0*(aet)*,5-0

Semi-Finals

Proctor & Gamble v Carlisle City	1-7	N.E.I. Reyrolle v Winlaton Hallgarth	1-1*(aet)*,0-1

Final (at Newcastle Utd FC, Saturday 11th April 1992): Carlisle City 1, Winlaton Hallgarth 0

DIVISION TWO AMATEUR CUP 1991-92

First Round

Bohemian v Ashington Hirst Progressive	2-5	Norgas v KOSA	2-1
Heddon Institute v Amble Town	1-2*(aet)*	Swalwell C.C. v Spartan Blyth	4-2
Berwick H.F. v Shankhouse	4-3	Percy Rovers v St Columbas	1-3
Stobswood Welfare v Marden Athletic	0-3		

Second Round

Swalwell C.C. v St Columbas	1-4	Marden Athletic v Berwick H.F.	4-1
Norgas v C.K. Brinkburn	3-2	Ashington Hirst Progressive v Amble Town	3-2

Semi-Finals

C.K. Brinkburn v Marden Athletic	4-1	St Columbas v Ashington Hirst Progressive	1-4

Final (at Northern Electric FC, Monday 27th April 1992): Ashington H.P. 4, C.K. Brinkburn 2

SEYMOUR CUP 1991-92

Final (at Dudley Welfare FC, Thursday 7th May 1992): Seaton Delaval Amateurs 2, Amble Town 1

NORTHERN ALLIANCE PREMIER DIVISION TEN YEAR RECORD

	82/3	83/4	84/5	85/6	86/7	87/8	88/9	89/90	90/1	91/2
Blyth Kitty Brewster	-	-	-	-	-	-	-	-	-	11
Carlisle City	10	14	13	9	16	-	-	-	-	-
Carlisle Gillford Park	-	-	-	-	-	-	-	-	11	3
Darlington Cleveland Bridge	1	-	-	-	-	-	-	-	-	-
Dudley Welfare	3	2	1	11	12	6	12	15	-	-
Dunston Tyne Sports	-	-	-	1	2	15	4	13	-	-
Forest Hall	12	12	8	12	8	5	10	3	5	12
Gateshead Tyne					(see Dunston Tyne)					
Gorforth St Nicholas	-	-	14	14	4	3	-	-	-	-
Haltwhistle Crown Paints	-	11	15	-	-	-	-	12	13	9
Heaton Stannington	-	-	-	-	13	7	6	8	3	14
Morpeth Town	11	1	2	3	3	9	9	10	12	13
Newbiggin Colliery Welfare	-	-	-	-	-	12	5	4	8	16
Percy Main	2	13	12	13	11	11	13	6	15	-
Ponteland United	-	9	4	10	5	13	8	5	9	10
Prudhoe East End	7	6	3	2	7	2	-	-	-	-
Seaton Delaval Amateurs	-	8	5	8	15	8	3	1	4	4
Seaton Terrace	4	4	7	7	10	1	1	9	2	6
Shotton Comrades	8	-	-	-	-	-	-	-	-	-
Spittal Rovers	-	-	-	-	-	-	-	-	-	5
Stobswood Welfare	5	3	10	16	-	-	15	-	-	-
Stockton Town	13	-	-	-	-	-	-	-	-	-
Swalwell C.C.	-	-	-	-	14	14	7	11	6	15
Walker	-	-	-	-	-	-	-	-	7	2
Wallsend Town	6	10	9	15	-	-	-	-	-	-
Wark	-	-	-	-	-	-	11	14	14	8
West Allotment Celtic	-	5	6	5	1	4	2	2	1	1
Westerhope Hillheads	-	-	-	-	-	-	-	-	10	7
Wigton	9	7	11	6	9	10	14	7	-	-
Winlaton Queens Head	-	-	-	4	6	-	-	-	-	-
No. of clubs competing	13	14	15	16	16	15	15	15	15	16

PREMIER DIVISION CLUBS 1992-93

BLYTH KITTY BREWSTER

Chairman: A Hall **Manager/Coach:** T Lee.
Secretary: J Norris, 28 Dene, View Drive, Cowpen Estate, Blyth (0670 352940).
Press Officer: Secretary. **Ground:** Tynedale High School, Blyth.
Directions: Coming north on Spine Road, take slip road signposted Kitty Brewster Industrial Estate, take right exit and follow signs. 1st left after mini-roundabout - School on right hand side approximately half a mile along road.
Colours: Grey & maroon/maroon/maroon **Change colours:** Royal/white/royal.
Hons: Northern All. Div 1 90-91 (Div 2 88-89, Lg Cup R-up 90-91).

CARLISLE CITY

Chairman: G Walker **Manager:** D Iveson. **Coach:** D Iveson.
Secretary/Press Off.: J Ewbanks, 16 Landsdown Cres., Stanwix, Carlisle (0228 34623).
Ground: The Sheep Mount. **Directions:** Take B6264 Brampton Carlisle road (not A69) direct to Hardwick Circus. On approach to r'bout keep in righthand lane and take far (Workington) exit, follow dual c'way (Carlisle Castle on right) till dual c'way intersects and come back on yourselves to turning before Castle. Left, and follow down hill, bear left as road divides, over to sports field.
Colours: Sky **Change colours:** White/red.
Hons: Northern All. R-up 75-76 76-77 77-78 79-80 (Div 1 91-92, Chal. Cup 75-76 (R-up 76-77), Comb. Cup 91-92).

CARLISLE GILLFORD PARK

Chairman: R Wilson **Manager:** R Rutherford **Coach:** D Kenyon.
Secretary/Press Off.: I Robinson, 27 Harraby Green Rd, Carlisle (0228 21715).
Ground: Gillford Park, Carlisle. (0228) 26649.
Directions: Take A69 to Rose Hill r'bout, straight over and 2nd left into Eastern Way, 1 mil to lights and turn left, 1st right Petrill Bank Rd, turn right at bridge and ground is 200 yds up this road.
Colours: All red. **Change colours:** White (black pin-stripe)/black.

FOREST HALL S.C.

Chairman: E K Douthwaite **Manager/Coach:** R H Lofthouse **Press Off.:** C Towns
Secretary: R Thompson, 57 Glebe Cres., Forest Hall, Newcastle (091 268 3753).
Ground: Proctor & Gamble Spts Ground, Great Lime Road, Forest Hall.
Directions: From West Moor head east towards Whitley Bay along Great Lime Rd. Ground situated on North side of road approximately 150 yds past Musketeer pub. From Tyne Tunnel take A1 (Morpeth road), until reaching Whitley Bay A191 Insection. Left at r'bout towards Newcastle, right onto Great Lime Road, ground three quarters of a mile along on north side.
Colours: All red. **Change colours:** Black & white stripes. **Hons:** Northern All. Chal. Cup R-up 89-90

HALTWHISTLE CROWN PAINTS

Chairman: J Jackson **Manager/Coach:** David Murray.
Press Officer/Secretary: R Skeet, 14 Westgate, Haltwhistle (0434 320703/ 321271).
Ground: South Tyne Park, Haltwhistle. **Directions:** A69 to Haltwhistle, turn off Main Road at sign for Hadrian Works (on left), under railway bridge. Parking available in Crown Paints car park.
Club colours: All royal blue **Change colours:** Black & white stripes/black.

HEATON STANNINGTON

Chairman: W Pitt **Manager/Press Off./Coach:** E Temple (091 270 0739).
Secretary: J R Groundsell, 73 Cleveland Gardens, High Heaton, Newcastle (091 266 7464).
Ground: Newton Park, Newton Road, High Heaton, Newcastle.
Directions: (a) From Newcastle turn left at 'Corner House' PH traffic lights into Newton Road. Bear left at r'bout for 30 yds and ground is on right behind shops. (b) From South Gosforth into Freeman Road. Pass the Freeman Hospital then turn left at the next r'bout, ground on left after 250 yds.
Colours: White/black/white **Change colours:** All yellow.
Hons: Northern All. Chal. Cup R-up 88-89

MORPETH TOWN

Chairman: K B Beattie **Press Officer:** M Crosby/R Griffiths.
Secretary: W Holian, 7 North Leech, Lancaster Park, Morpeth (0670 511086).
Manager/Coach: J Burley. **Ground Address:** Storey Park, Morpeth.
Directions: From south - Take Morpeth A197 sign off A1. Left at 'Sun Inn', ground on left behind Church.
Colours: Black & amber stripes/black **Change colours:** Red (white trim).
Hons: Northern All. 83-84 (R-up 37-38 65-66 73-74 81-82 84-85, Chal. Cup 38-39 85-86 (R-up 36-37 62-63 73-74)).

PONTELAND UNITED

Chairman: F W Smith **Manager:** P Lowery **Coach:** W Charlton
Secretary/Press Officer: L McMahon, 1 Wardle Drive, Annitsford, Cramlingham (091 250 0463).
Ground: Ponteland Leisure Centre, Ponteland (0661 25441). **Directions:** Enter Ponteland from Newcastle and turn left at traffic lights. Ground is situated 100 metres on left at Castle Ward Sports Centre.
Seats: None **Cover:** None **Capacity:** 3,500 **Floodlights:** No **Founded:** 1900.
Colours: Black & white stripes/black **Change colours:** Blue & red stripes.
Record Attendance: 3,500 v Blyth Spartans, 1982-83.
Hons: Northern Alliance Lg Cup R-up 91-92 (Chal. Cup R-up 84-85 90-91).

SEATON DELAVAL AMATEURS

Chairman: R Westwood **Manager/Coach:** K Scott.
Secretary: W Fellows, 52 Hastings Street, Klondyke, Cramlington (0670 731833).
Press Officer: B Swan (091 236 6165). **Ground:** Wheatridge Park, Seaton Delaval.
Directions: A189 from Newcastle, at Annitsford roundabout take A190 to Seaton Delaval. Entering Seaton Delaval on A190 turn left at roundabout. Ground is 450 yds on right next to Dale Garage and behind Market Garden. 3 miles from Cramlington (BR). Bus 363 from Newcastle passes ground.
Seats: None **Cover:** 200 **Capacity:** 6,000 **Floodlights:** No **Founded:**
Cols: White/red **Change colours:** All blue **Record Attendance:** 6,000 in 1926.
Hons: Northern All. 89-90 (R-up 20-21, Chal. Cup 88-89).

SEATON DELAVAL SEATON TERRACE

Chairman: K Thompson   **Manager/Coach:** I Watts
Secretary: J Mitchell, 7 Turnberry Way, Cramlington (0670 712577).
Press Officer: Secretary   **Ground:** Bates Welfare, Seaton Delaval.
Directions: Entering Seaton Delaval on A190 from Annitsford & Newcastle, turn right at roundabout. Ground approx 800 yds on right.
Club colours: Red/blue/red   **Change colours:** Blue/white/blue.
Hons: Northern All. 87-88 88-89 (Lg Cup 90-91, Chal. Cup 86-87 91-92).

SPITTAL ROVERS

Chairman: C Mole   **Manager/Coach/Press Off.:** I Holloway (0289 305864).
Secretary: D J Moir, 11 Bell Tower Place, Berwick-on-Tweed (0289 302002).
Press Officer: B Cordery (0289 302750).   **Ground:** Shieldfield Park, Berwick-on-Tweed.
Directions: A1 to r'bout signposting Berwick, follow to r'bout at Sports Centre, straight over, left immediately after after railway bridge up Shieldfield Terrace, ground 200yds on right.
Colours: Black & white stripes/black/red   **Change colours:** Red/white/red.

WALKER

Chairman: R T McClellan   **Manager/Coach/Press Off.:** R Mulroy (091 263 4237).
Secretary: Miss S Davidson, 8 Stanmore Road, Heaton, Newcastle (091 276 1095).
Ground: Monkchester Recreation Ground.   **Directions:** From City: Shields Rd to Union Rd, to Welbeck Rd, into Monkchester Rd, left into pitch (between houses) opposite Norbury Grove.
Club colours: White/black/black.   **Change colours:** Green/green/black.
Hons: Northern Alliance Div 1 R-up 89-90.

WARK

Chairman: D Chrisholm   **Manager/Coach:** S Calf
Secretary: J Armstrong, 12 St Michaels Mount, Wark, Hexham (0434 230382).
Press Officer: R Bell (0434 230641).   **Ground:** Wark Spts Field, Wark, Hexham (0434 230359).
Directions: Enter Wark, right at filling station over river bridge, turn right and ground is on right.
Club colours: Royal/white/blue   **Change colours:** Yellow/white.

WEST ALLOTMENT CELTIC

Chairman: J Mather   **Manager/Coach:** D Ridley.
Secretary: J T Jackson, 4 Rosewood Crescent, Seaton Sluice, Whitley Bay (091 237 0416).
Press Officer: A Smailes (091 253 2172). **Ground:** Backworth Miners Welfare (091 268 1048).
Directions: From Newcastle, Old Coast Road (A189) to South Gosforth then A191 to Holystone r'bout, A186 to mini r'bout at Shiremoor, left (B1322), ground on left after 1 mile, entrance opp. Backworth Social Club. 2 miles Shiremoor Metro.
Seats: None   **Cover:** None   **Capacity:** 800   **Floodlights:** No   **Founded:** 1928.
Club colours: All white   **Change colours:** Black & white/black/white.
Previous Ground: Farm Ground 1928-68.
Hons: Northern Alliance 86-87 90-91 91-92 (R-up 88-89 89-90, Chal. Cup 84-85 90-91).

WESTERHOPE

Chairman/Press Off.: J Loan (091 267 9132)   **Manager/Coach:** I Weatherburn
Secretary: B Patterson, 16 Burnstone, West Denton, Newcastle NE5 2EW (091 264 5211).
Ground: Riverside Park, Newburn.
Directions: From A69 follow signs for Lemington, right at bottom of bank to Newburn. On entering Newburn follow signs for Blaydon. At bridge traffic lights (do not cross bridge) carry straight on, ground 300 yds on left.
Colours: White/white/blue   **Change colours:** Sky & navy.
Hons: Northern Alliance Div 1 89-90.

WINLATON HALLGARTH

Chairman: F Parker   **Manager/Coach:** K Rides.
Secretary/Press Officer: G S Batey, 6 Wylam View, Winlaton (091 414 7970).
Ground: Shiblon Park, Blaydon.   **Directions:** From north, over new A1 bridge to 1st slip road, take Swalwell and Consett road to r'bour, Blaydon Baths car park and ground 400yds on right.
Colours: All red.   **Change colours:** Yellow/black/yellow.
Hons: Northern All. Lg Cup 91-92 (Div 1 R-up 91-92, Comb. Cup R-up 91-92).

FIRST DIVISION CLUBS 1992-93

DUDLEY WELFARE

Chairman: K Wake   **Manager/Coach:** P Rutherford
Press Off./Sec.: C Hilliary, 68 Alexandra Way, Hall Cross Chase, Cramlingham NE23 6EB (0670 719604).
Ground: Duldley Welfare.
Directions: From Tyne Tunnel follow A1 to Moor Farm r'bout, A1 Morpeth road then 1st slip road, left at junction, ground on left opp. Owen Pugh. From Newcastle follow main Morpeth road as far as Seaton Burn flyover, take A1 in southerly direction (signed Tyne Tunnel), 1st slip road to r'bout then follow signs to Dudley and as above.
Colours: Royal blue/white   **Change colours:** Red/black.
Hons: Northern Alliance 84-85 (R-up 83-84, Chal. Cup 83-84 (R-up 82-83)).

GATESHEAD NORTHERN COUNTIES

Chairman: C Long   **Press Officer:** Secretary
Secretary: J M Bramley, 9 Fern Gardens, Low Fell, Gateshead (091 487 2494).
Manager/Coach: T Miller
Ground: Wardley Welfare, Felling.
Directions: From Gateshead International Stadium to Heworth r'bout, across, left at slip road at Wardley Black Bull after 1km. A194, left at top of slip road, second right after 250m, ground 800m on right.
Colours: Blue & white/navy   **Change colours:** Yellow & navy

HEBBURN N.E.I. REYROLLE

Chairman: F Hopkins **Manager/Coach:** J Trotter.
Secretary: G Taylor, 29 Crawley Ave., Hebburn NE31 2LT (091 483 4537).
Press Officer: A Graham. **Ground:** Hebburn Sports Ground, Victoria Road West, Hebburn.
Alternative ground: South Tyneside College, Mill Lane, Hebburn.
Directions: From Newcastle along Felling by-pass, Heworth r'bout take Hebburn/Jarrow road, ground two and a half miles on left. College ground as above, but from Newcastle ground approx. 2 miles on right. From Tunnel ground approx. two and a half miles on left.
Colours: Maroon/blue/maroon **Change colours:** Yellow/black/yellow.

HEXHAM SWINTON

Chairman/Press Officer: D Tiffin (0434 604573)
Secretary: A Breen, 59 Adderdale Rd, Prudhoe (0661 834456).
Coach: M Lowes **Ground:** Wentworth Park, Hexham.
Directions: A69 to Hexham r'bout, left towards Hexham, follow to mini-r'bout, straight over and 1st left into car park. Ground opposite Hexham BR station (Carlisle-Newcastle line).
Colours: White/black/red **Change colours:** Blue/maroon/maroon.

LONGBENTON

Chairman: J Fawcett **Manager/Coach:** A Bollado.
Press Officer/Secretary: G Minto, 43 Elizabeth Cres., Dudley, Cramlingham NE23 7AJ (091 250 1581).
Ground: Burradon Recreation Centre. **Directions:** From south: from r'bout at Sth Gosforth to r'bout at Killingworth on A189, left to Cramlingham, right at next r'bout, left at mini-r'bout into Burradon. From north: A189 to Annitsford, left to Burradon, ground behing houses.
Colours: Gold/black **Change colours:** All grey
Hons: Northern All. Div 2 R-up 89-90.

NEWBIGGIN CENTRAL WELFARE

Chairman: H Callan **Manager/Coach:** W Robson.
Press Officer/Secretary: W Cooper, 33 Spital Crescent, Newbiggin (0670 854941).
Ground: Newbiggin Central Welfare, Newbiggin. **Directions:** Enter Newbiggin from Spine Road towards town centre. After 2nd zebra crossing ground on right after 200 yds just before school entrance.
Colours: Red/black/black **Change colours:** Blue & black stripes
Hons: Northern Alliance Chai. Cup R-up 46-47 88-89.

NEWCASTLE BENFIELD PARK

Chairman: R Allan **Press Officer:** R Allan (091 236 6980).
Secretary: D Gates, 5 Winship Terrace, Byker, Newcastle (091 276 3049).
Manager/Coach: C Chambers **Ground:** Benfield Park.
Directions: From Newcastle take 2nd exit after Corner House pub, right into Benfield Rd, ground on left in school grounds.
Colours: Sky/navy/sky **Change colours:** White/red/red.

NEW YORK UNITED

Chairman: R C Robson **Manager/Coach:** D Swinyard
Press Officer/Secretary: R C Robson, 36 Adderstone Gdns, New York (091 257 3396).
Ground: Collingwood View, North Shields.
Directions: Come off coast road at Formica turn, right down Norham Rd North to r'bout at Percy Main, 2nd left down Waterville Rd, 1st left at Toyota Garage, ground on right.
Colours: Tangerine & white

NORTHERN ELECTRIC (WALLSEND)

Chairman: R Veale **Manager/Coach:** T Cornfoot.
Press Off./Secretary: I Thompson, 3 Frenton Close, Chapel House, Newcastle-upon-Tyne (091 264 4855).
Ground: Kings Park, Kings Rd South, Wallsend.
Directions: Coast road from Newcastle, 1st exit past Wills factory, across bridge over motorway, left along slip road to Monitor Eng., right down Kings Rd South, ground 150 yds on left. From coast; Wallsend turn off, bear left to T-junction facing Monitor Eng., then as above.
Colours: Sky & navy **Change colours:** Orange & black.

NORTH SHIELDS ST COLUMBAS

Chairman: N Hooper **Manager/Coach:** J Wall.
Secretary: A J Baird, 8 Beanley Crescent, Tynemouth (091 258 2375).
Press Off.: D Dent (091 259 0100) **Ground:** Appletree Pk, Preston Ave., North Shields.
Directions: Coast road to Tynemouth swimming baths, right to North Shields, 2nd left after school into Preston Ave., ground on left after Rugby Club.
Colours: All white **Change colours:** Green & yellow stripes/green.

PERCY MAIN AMATEURS

Chairman: Mr A Purvis **Mgr/Coach/Press Off.:** R McCullough (091 295 0017)
Secretary: C Willis, 287 Simonside Terrace, Heaton, Newcastle-upon-Tyne NE6 5DS (091 276 2570/ 257 0009).
Ground: St John's Green, Percy Main.
Directions: Nth Shield road from Tyne Tunnel past Duke of Wellington, 2nd left after half mile, ground on right. From North and West turn off coast road at Formica factory, right down Norham Rd to Percy Main Social Club, road to Percy Main Village at r'bout, after half mile left at St John's Terrace. Ground on left past church.
Colours: Claret & blue/blue **Change colours:** Green/red.
Hons: Northern Alliance 80-81 81-82 (R-up 82-83, Lg Cup 71-72, Chal. Cup R-up 79-80 86-87).

PERCY ROVERS ALNWICK

Chairman: P Davies **Manager/Coach:** T Miller
Press Officer/Secretary: I Arkle, 5 Tanners Garth, Alnwick (0665 510105)
Ground: Duchess High School Cricket Field, Alnwside, Alnwick.
Colours: Black & blue stripes/black/black. **Change colours:** White/black/black.
Hons: Northern Alliance Div 2 R-up 91-92.

PROCTOR & GAMBLE (NEWCASTLE)

Chairman: W J Darby **Manager/Coach/Press Secretary:** B Hudson (091 2668239).
Secretary: M Tweddle, 18 Ryedale, Hadrian Lodge, West, Wallsend (091 234 4924/ 268 5918).
Ground: Longbenton Community High School.
Directions: From Newcastle, Benton Rd to Four Lane Ends metro station, continue to 2nd r'bout, right into Goathland Ave., ground and school at end.
Colours: All red **Change colours:** White/red/red. **Hons:** Northern All. Div 2 90-91.

RYTON

Chairman: H Taylor **Manager/Coach:** A Patterson.
Press Off./Secretary: L Robson, 31 Park View Gdns, Runhead, Ryton (091 413 7628).
Ground: Clara Vale Recreation Ground. **Directions:** Thru Ryton to Crawcock crossroads, right 50yds down road, right at T-junction, entering Clara Vale ground is signposted.
Colours: Orange/black/orange **Change colours:** All blue

SWALWELL

Chairman: T Todd **Manager/Coach:** M Falcus.
Secretary: R J Robinson, 6 Brinkburn Avenue, Swalwell (091 488 8279).
Press Officer: S Boe (091 482 4824). **Ground:** Avenue Ground, Hexham Road, Swalwell.
Directions: From Newcastle cross river by Redbeugh Bridge, take A69 (Western bypass) for 3 miles, 1st left after Metro Centre. Right at r'bout, after half mile ground on right just past Fewsters and opposite Blaydon Rugby Club.
Colours: Red & white/red & black **Change colours:** All blue

WYLAM

Chairman: I Slowther **Manager/Coach:** C Dixon.
Secretary: J O'Brien, 17 St Agnes Gdns, Crawcock (091 413 6885).
Press Officer: G Bowmer (0661 852035). **Ground:** Wylam Playing Fields.
Directions: From Newcastle, A69 Hexham road to Wylam turn, into village, left opp. bus shelter by Black Bull heading towards Fox & Hounds. Pitch opposite.
Colours: Yellow/white/white **Change colours:** Green/black/white.
Hons: Div 2 R-up 90-91.

SECOND DIVISION CLUBS 1992-1993

AMBLE TOWN

Chairman: J Coxford **Press Officer:** F Young (0665 712 820).
Secretary: R Henderson, 11 Gordon Street, Amble, Morpeth NE6 5OA (0665 710929).
Manager/Coach: R Gibbard. **Ground:** Amble Welfare Park, Acklington Rd, Amble
Directions: From Ashington or Morpeth; north on A1068 entering Amble past industrial est. on right, over zebra crossing 100yds turn left before Masons Arms, follow as if you are going out of Amble. New Hassal Housing estate on right, turn left opp. Coquet High School car park. Pitch adjacent.
Colours: All tangerine **Change colours:** Red & white stripes/red/red.
Hons: Northern Alliance 54-55 56-57 58-59 59-60 60-61 (Chal. Cup 54-55 60-61 (R-up 37-38 59-60).

ASHINGTON HIRST PROGRESSIVE

Chairman: J S Evans **Press Officer:** A Johnson (0670 816464).
Secretary: G Gibbons, 41 Hawthorn Road, Ashington (0670 815218).
Manager/Coach: G Gibbons/ O O'Neill.
Ground: Ashington High School, Green Lane, Ashington.
Directions: From Spine Rd, Ashington turn off at Woodhorn, A197 at next 2 r'bouts, left at next r'bout, at end turn right, then left down Park Rd, school 500yds on right.
Colours: Red/white **Change colours:** Claret & blue/blue
Hons: Northern Alliance Amateur Cup 91-92.

COUNTY KITCHENS BRINKBURN

Chairman: B Raper **Press Officer:** S Hobson (091 455 5704).
Secretary: M Lynn, 261 Sunderland Rd, South Shields (091 455 5145)
Manager/Coach: G Charlton
Ground: Brinkburn Comprehensive School, Harton Lane, South Shields.
Directions: John Reid Rd (A1300) to 3rd r'bout passing General Hospital on left taking 1st exit left after Hosp. down Temple Park Rd, proceed to Grey Hen pub, left into Harton Lane, ground 150yds on left - concealed entrance.
Colours: Red/navy/red **Change colours:** All blue
Hons: Northern Alliance Amateur Cup R-up 91-92.

GOSFORTH BOHEMIAN

Chairman/Press Officer: J Bell (091 268 3306) **Manager/Coach:** P Robinson.
Secretary: B Dale, 118 Newton Road, Newcastle (091 281 1403)
Ground: Benson Park, Brunton Park Estate, Gosforth
Directions: Turn off Great North Road after passing Gosforth Rugby Club into Polwarth Drive. 2nd left into Layfield Road then 1st right into South Ridge Ground 50 yards on left (concealed entrance between houses)
Colours: Red & white/black **Change colours:** Blue/black

HEDDON INSTITUTE

Chairman: A Smith **Press Officer/Mgr/Coach:** B Tailford (0661 853314).
Secretary: N A D Anderson, 14 Aquila Drive, Heddon on the Wall (0661 853136)
Ground: Throckley Welfare, Throckley
Directions: A69 Newcastle take Throckley exit, turn left at roundabout approx. quarter mile, right into Poplar Street, ground at end. Bus No. X82 and X83 from Eldon Centre, Newcastle to Throckley.
Colours: Maroon & blue **Change colours:** Green

HIGHFIELDS UNITED

Chairman: B Weatherburn   **Press Officer:** N Dudgeon
Secretary: B Dytor, 43 Newfields, Berwick-on-Tweed (0289 305342).
Manager/Coach: S Roughead   **Ground:** Pier Field, Berwick-on-Tweed.
Directions: A1 to Berwick centre, right down High Str., keep right of Town Hall, right into Hide Hill, left at bottom into Silver Str., straight over staggered crossroads, follow road along river bank to clifftops carpark.
Colours: Blue/white/red   **Change colours:** Red/white/red.

MARDEN ATHLETIC

Chairman: G Clark   **Manager/Coach:** D Laidler
Secretary: A Pattison, 74 Bamborough Terrace, North Shields (091 259 2389)
Ground: Churchill Playing Fields, Whitley Bay
Directions: From Coast Road follow signs Whitley Bay, along Seatonville Road, turn right at Cannon Cinema r'bout, 3rd left after Monkseaton Arms Pub into Hartley Ave., ground at end.
Colours: Blue & white/blue/blue   **Change colours:** Red/white/red.

MONKSEATON K.O.S.A. ROBIN HOOD

Chairman: D Meadows   **Press Officer:** O Alston (0661 833933).
Secretary: R A Woods, 15 Rayleigh Drive, Wideopen, Newcastle-upon-Tyne (091 236 2988).
Manager/Coach: R A Woods   **Ground:** Monkseaton High School
Directions: From Newcastle Coast Road to Tynemouth Swimmming Baths, left at r'bout and proceed to r'bout at Foxhunters Pub, turn right at this roundabout and left at next r'bout. School ground is 150 yards on left
Colours: Green/black   **Change colours:** White/blue

NEWCASTLE D.H.S.S.

Chairman/Press Officer: R Blenkinsopp (091 416 5469).
Secretary: L Procter, 4 Alcombe Crescent, Red House Farm Estate, Newcastle-upon-Tyne (091 285 3320).
Manager/Coach: S Lakey   **Ground:** Darsley Park, Longbenton.
Directions: Bus or Metro to Four Lane Ends, Benton. Grounds half mile along Old Whitley Rd towards coast.
Colours: Sky/navy   **Change colours:** All red.
Previous League: Tyneside Amateur (pre-1992).

NEWCASTLE NORGAS UNITED

Chairman: T Watson   **Press Officer:** P Benson (091 268 5100).
Secretary: C R Hogg, 43 Falkirk, Highfields, Killingworth (091 268 3935)
Manager/Coach: T Waugh   **Ground:** Whitley Park, Whitley Road, Benton.
Directions: Bus or Metro to Four Lane Ends, Benton. Grounds situated 1/2 mile along Old Whitley Road on right hand side (towards Coast)
Colours: Green/white   **Change colours:** Yellow/blue

NEWCASTLE UNIVERSITY

Chairman/Press Officer/Manager/Coach: A Brown (091 274 5053).
Secretary: A Bull, 59 Normanton Terrace, Elswick, Newcastle-upon-Tyne (091 273 9329).
Ground: Cochrane Park, Newcastle-upon-Tyne.   **Directions:** From Newcastle, left off coast road at 1st slip road after Corner House pub, right at next r'bout into Etherstone Ave., ground 400yds on left.
Colours: Royal blue/black   **Change colours:** Red/black.

NEW WINNING (WALLSEND)

Chairman: S Pattinson   **Manager/Coach:** D Prest.
Press Officer/Secretary: A Gilroy, 67 South Terrace, Wallsend (091 263 1123).
Ground: Wallsend Sports Centre.
Directions: A1058 Newcastle coast road, Station Rd exit and follow signs for Wallsend Golf Course & Spts Centre.
Cols: All green   **Change colours:** Red/white   **Prev. Lge:** S.E. Northumberland (pre'92)

SHANKHOUSE

Chairman: F Dobson   **Manager/Coach:** K Schooling
Press Officer/Secretary: S Ramsey, 6 Brinkburn Avenue, Cramlington (0670 715943).
Ground: East Hartford Welfare
Directions: Take A189 out of Newcastle to 3rd slip road after Moor Farm r'bout marked Cramlington Ind. Est. Morpeth A192 turn 1st left at r'bout at the top of the slip road. Approx. 1/2 mile down road turn right into East Hartford. The ground is situated on the left.
Colours: Black & yellow stripes/black/yellow   **Change:** Red/white/white
Hons: Northern All. 1892-93 (R-up 95-96), Northumberland Snr Cup 1885-86(jt) 86-87 90-91 92-93 93-94 94-95.

STOBSWOOD WELFARE

Chairman/Press Officer: J W Rutherford (0670 790110).
Secretary: K Wilson, 40 Elizabeth Street, Widdrington, Morpeth (0670 790192).
Manager/Coach: D Brown   **Ground:** Stobswood Welfare (0670 790609).
Directions: A1 to Morpeth, turn right over bridge and follow road to Widdrington, left at Karva Woodcraft, right after 300 yds, ground at bottom.
Colours: Green/black   **Change colours:** Yellow/blue
Hons: Northern All. Div 2 R-up 88-89 (Chal. Cup 82-83 (R-up 83-84)).

SWALWELL CROWLEY CLUB

Chairman: W Burke   **Manager/Coach:** D Collins
Press Officer/Secretary: Ian Pygall, 9 Axwell Terrace, Swalwell, Newcastle (091 488 9580).
Cols: Sky/navy   **Change colours:** Red/white   **Ground:** Dunston Park
Directions: Dunston turn off from Western by-pass onto Dunston road. Ground 200yds from by-pass on right. From Scotswood bridge past Metro Centre take Whickham/Dunston turn, turn left, ground 50yds on right.

WALLSEND RISING SUN

Chairman: T Wonfor, MBE.   **Press Officer:** P Healey (091 263 1829).
Manager/Coach/Secretary: G Tubman, 43 Regent Court, Wallsend (091 263 1829).
Ground: Rising Sun Welfare, Wallsend.
Directions: At top of Kings Road North. Right Swallow Spts Club. Buses 308 306 309 to Rising Sun Hotel.
Colours: Yellow/blue/blue   **Change colours:** White/blue/blue.
Hons: Northern Alliance Chal. Cup R-up 58-59.

WIRRAL PROGRAMME CLUB
The non profit making club formed in March 1967

All programmes donated
to the club are issued
free to members.

3 Tansley Close,
Newton, West Kirby,
Wirral, L48 9XH
051 625 9554

Secretary   Ian Runham

17th NON LEAGUE PROGRAMME SURVEY, 1991-1992

I am pleased to say that, as last season, the overall winner is to receive a shield, and the winners in each league a certificate. These have once again been donated by British Telecom Supercall Sports. This season's survey had programmes from 1,001 clubs, down 46 on last season, with reserve and youth team programmes taking the total to 1,071, 60 down on last year. Yet again I know of several entries that were lost in the post, some almost certainly due to inadequate packaging; over 60 entries arrived in P.O. polythene bags because the original packet had split. As far as I know all entries sent by Recorded Delivery reached us.

The standards are again very high with many clubs showing a big improvement on last season's efforts. Also it is pleasing to see several clubs issuing for the first time. All clubs that issue are to be congratulated, a single sheet being better than nothing. Again many reserve and youth team programmes were received, and in some cases these were better than the first team effort, there being a seperate editor etc. Special thanks are due to all the hard working editors and there helpers. I am sure most supporters and many collectors do not realise just how much time and effort is needed for a programme to be issued. I also thank all those who sent us programmes for the survey and who helped spread the word, the clubs themselves, their supporters, our members, the Football Association, all League secretaries, the Non-League Club Directory, 'Team Talk', 'Non-League Traveller', 'Pyramid', 'Programme Monthly', those who lent us programmes. Sincere apologies to anyone inadvertently omitted.

Some clubs only issue for special games, some only on Saturdays. Some change their style, format, editor etc. Usually we are not aware of most of these circumstances so naturally we can only survey the programmes we receive. Some are from early in the season, some from just prior to the closing date, others from in between. I am sure there are many excellent issues we have not seen, hopefully they will be included next season. The results always create a lot of interest for the various points being expressed, a number we hear second or third hand, but most miss our ears. If you have any comments on the survey please let us know. I am sure the day will come when there is complete agreement on the results, however the more discussion there is over the survey the better - it will keep programmes to the forefront and hopefully maintain or even improve the standards. Better still it may encourage more clubs to issue next season.

Please note programmes have surveyed, **not** voted on. Marks were awarded to each programme as follows:- Cover 15 (design 10, match details 5), Page size 10, Team layout and position within programme 10, Results 10, League table 10, Price 15, Pictures 15, Printing quality and paper 20, Frequency of issue 20, Value for money (accounting for league status and ratio of adverts to articles) 20, Contents (over than above) 10 (accounting for relevance to club, league, environs etc, the size of print and margins, and if oringinal or reproduced (from league bulletins etc) 105. To gain full marks for frequency of issue, section programmes from ten different matches per team were required (allowances being made if fewer matches had beem played by the closing, but all programmes for matches played were received). As many altered from issue to issue, all programmes were surveyed with an average established for each category. A new standard is set each season, so marks should not be compared with previous years as comparison almost certainly be inaccurate: a programme identical to last's season's would almost certainly have gained different marks.

To receive a copy of the results (for the Specials section (for one-offs, big cup ties, friendlies, testimonials etc), please send an SAE to the above address, thank you.

Ian Runham

BEST NON LEAGUE PROGRAMME NATIONALLY 1991-1992

POTTON UNITED	182 points
2nd Raunds Town	173 points
3rd= Barrow & Lincoln Moorlands	165 points

THE NATIONAL TOP 30. 1, Potton 182. 2, Raunds 173. 3=, Barrow, Lincoln Moorlands 165. 5, Yarnfield College 152. 6=, Wycombe Wdrs, Biggleswade Town 151. 8=, Arnold Town, Dynamics, Sutton Utd 148. 11, Corinthian Casuals 147. 12=, Lancing, Hanley Town 146. 14=, Gt Yarmouth, Rocester, Cobblers Mounties 145. 17, Baldock Town 143. 18, Chelmsford City 142. 19=, Wealdstone, Hinckley 141. 21, Hoddesdon Town 140. 22=, Kidderminster Harriers, Inverness Caledonian 139. 24=, Somersham, Bideford, Newton Abbot Spurs, Oadby Town 138. 28, King's Lynn 137. 29=, Colchester Utd, St Albans City 136.

INDIVIDUAL LEAGUE RESULTS, TOP 3 (The first number after the clubs name is the number of programmes received, the next number is the number of points scored).

LEAGUE & No. of entries		First		Second		Third	
GMV CONFERENCE	22	Barrow 10	165	Wycombe 11	151	Kidderminster 12	139
BEAZER HOMES Overall	64	Baldock 12	143	Chelmsford 10	142	Wealdstone 10	141
Prem. Div.	22	Chelmsford 10	142	Wealdstone 10	141	Corby 10	127
Div.1M	21	King's Lynn 10	137	Sutton C'field 10	121	Newport AFC 1	117
Div.1S	21	Baldock 12	143	Newport IW 12	125	Weymouth 11	117
HFS LOANS Overall	42	Colwyn Bay 10	131	Morecambe 10	124	Caernarfon= 12	120
						Southport= 10	120
Prem.Div	20	Morecambe 10	124	Southport 10	120	Leek 12	116
Div.1.	22	Colwyn Bay 10	131	Caernarfon 12	120	Congleton 14	110
DIADORA Overall	67	Sutton Utd 15	148	St Albans 12	136	Wivenhoe 1	131
Prem.Div.	22	Sutton Utd 15	148	St Albans 12	136	Wivenhoe 1	131
Div.1.	15	Stevenage 10	130	Dorking 10	120	Molesey 10	111
Div.2.	15	Met. Police 13	124	Barton Rvrs 18	116	Berkhamsted 13	105
Div.3.	15	Camberley 10	111	Chertsey 12	110	Bracknell 10	103
Bass NWC Overall	34	Chadderton 10	118	Atherton LR= 1	107	Bradford PA= 2	107
Div.1.	18	Atherton LR= 1	107	Bradford PA 2	107	Eastwood Han. 10	104
Div.2.	16	Chadderton 10	118	Salford City 12	106	Newcastle T. 14	100
NC East Overall	30	Sutton Town 10	119	Liversedge 10	109	Immingham 12	106
Prem.Div.	17	Sutton Town 10	119	Liversedge 10	109	Ossett Town 11	99
Div.1.	13	Immingham 12	106	Stocksbridge 10	90	Ross. Main 1	86

900

Other Leagues 6	Unisys 7 86	Jeanfield Sw. 1 85	Easthouses LWM 6 80
WELSH Overall 78	Conna's Quay N. 10 26	Lex X1 10 114	Risca United 10 103
Abacus Overrall 32	Risca United 10 103	Aberystwyth 6 99	Cwmbran T. 12 98
Abacus Nat.Div. 12	Aberystwyth 6 99	Cwmbran T. 12 98	Pembroke 1 63
Abacus Div.1. 15	Risca United 10 103	Cardiff Corries= 12 76	Pontypridd-Yny.= 10 76
Abacus Div.2.	Goytre Utd 2 64	Caerau= 1 59	AFC Porth= 2 59
Manweb Alliance 13	Connah's Quay 10 126	Lex X1 10 114	Welshpool 10 100
Sealink Alliance 8	Cemaes Bay 2 79	Y Felinheli 1 78	Llandudno 2 72
Read National	Overton A. 5 98	Overton A. Res. 5 82	Brit. Aerospace 5 81
Mid Wales 4	Morda United 10 89	Knighton T. 1 64	Berriew 1 60
Universal S.Wales 3	Grange A. 6 74	Tongwynlais 2 65	Llwydcoad Welf. 49
S.Wales Amateur 3	Llantwit Major 11 86	Barry A. 1 56	Caerau Res. 1 54
Gwent 3	Chepstow T. 3 62	SW Switchgear 2 60	Albion Rvrs 1 42
Gwynedd 3	Penrhosgarnedd 10 62	Blaenau A. 1 75	Nefyn U. 1 59
Other Leagues 53	Llansanfraid 1 51	Bailey Arms 1 44	
OTHER LEAGUES 53	N. Abbot Spurs 7 138	Ifield Res. 8 121	Crown Royals 6 115
RESERVES	Colden Comm. 10 133	Eltham Town 1 125	Ifield 8 121
CAPITAL LEAGUE 4	Wycombe Res. 6 88	Slough Res. 1 69	Sutton Utd Res. 5 56
YOUTH 13	Horsham YMCA 10 107	Wycombe Lions 2 106	Merstham 4 93
F.A. YTH CUP 13	St Albans C. 1 86	Horsham YMCA 1 82	Wycombe Wdrs 1 67
SUNDAY LGES Overall 90	Yarnfield Col. 8 152	Cobblers Mou. 10 145	Flying Dutchman 7 118
Festival League 3	Ansells S. Star= 1 58	Hundred Acre= 1 58	Slade Celtic 1 55
Telford League 3	Shrop. FA 10 92	Bird in Hand 1 76	Shifnal WMA 1 58
FA SUNDAY CUP 56	AD Bulwell 1 107	Carnforth 1 87	Blue Union 1 77
IRISH 'B' DIV. 5	Armagh City 11 88	R.U.C. 1 88	Loughall 1 80

(Other Leagues section is for clubs in leagues with less than three entries)

The clubs so far listed plus all the following were represented in the 91-92 survey:-

Altrincham, Bath, Cheltenham, Farnborough, Gateshead, Kettering, Macclesfield, Merthyr, Northwich, Redbridge, Runcorn, Slough, Stafford, Welling, Witton, Yeovil, Bashley, Atherstone, Bromsgrove, Burton, Cambridge City, Dartford, Dorchester, Dover, Fisher, Gloucester, Gravesend, Halesowen Town, Moor Green, Poole, Trowbridge, VS Rugby, Waterlooville, Worcester, Barry, Bedworth, Bilston, Bridgnorth, Dudley, Grantham, Hednesford, Hinckley Town, Leicester Utd, Nuneaton, RC Warwick, Redditch, Rushden, Solihull, Stourbridge, Stroud, Tamworth, Yate, Andover, Ashford (Kent), Braintree, Buckingham Town, Burnham, Bury Town, Canterbury, Erith, Fareham, Gosport, Hastings, Havant, Hythe, Margate, Salisbury, Sittingbourne, Sudbury, Witney, Binfield, Letcombe, Penn & Tylers Green, Prestwood, Stocklake, Broomwade, Eton Wick, Aylesbury Utd, Basingstoke Town, Bishop's S'ford, Bognor Regis, Bromley, Carshalton Athletic, Chesham, Dagenham, Enfield, Grays, Harrow, Kingstonian, Marlow, Staines, Windsor, Woking, Wokingham, Abingdon Town, Boreham Wood, Chalfont St Peter, Croydon, Dulwich, Harlow, Heybridge, Hitchin, Maidenhead, Tooting, Walton & Hersham, Yeading, Billericay, Hemel Hempstead, Leatherhead, Lewes, Malden Vale, Newbury, Purfleet, Ruislip Mnr, Ware, Worthing, Witham, Collier Row, Cove, Eastbourne Utd, Edgware, Feltham & H'low, Flackwell, Hertford, Hampton, Petersfield, Thame, Tilbury, Ashford Middx, Bedfont, Ditton, Farnham, Frimley, Godalming, Horley, Sandhurst, Viking, Accrington, Bangor, Bishop Auckland, Buxton, Chorley, Emley, Fleetwood, Frickley, Gainsborough, Horwich, Hyde, Marine, Matlock, Mossley, Shepshed, Stalybridge, Whitley Bay, Alfreton, Bridlington, Curzon Ashton, Eastwood, Farsley, Guiseley, Harrogate Town, Irlam Town, Knowsley, Lancaster, Netherfield, Newtown, Radcliffe, Rhyl, Rossendale, Warrington, Winsford, Workington, Worksop, Ashton Utd, Bacup, B'pool Rvrs, Bootle, Clitheroe, Darwen, Flixton, Gt Harwood, Maine Rd, Nantwich, Penrith, Prescot, St Helens, Skelmersdale, Vauxhall GM, Ashton Town, Atherton Collieries, Bamber Bridge, B'pool Mechanics, Burscough, Cheadle, Formby, Glossop, Holker, Maghull, Kidsgrove, Oldham Town, Squires Gate, Anstey Nomads, Barwell Athletic, Holwell Sports, Houghton Rgrs, Ibstock Welfare, Leics Constabulary, Narborough & Littlethorpe, St Andrews SC, Nth Kilworth, Belper Town, Brigg Town, Denaby Utd, Glasshoughton, Harrogate RA, Maltby MW, Nth Ferriby, Nth Shields, Ossett Albion, Pontefract, Sheffield, Spennymoor, Thackley, Winterton, Brodsworth, Hall Rd, Hallam, Pickering, RES Parkgate, Tadcaster, Worsborough Bridge, Yrk Rl, Yorks Amtr, Gretna, Guisborough, Northallerton, Shildon, West Auckland, Esh Winning, Hebburn, Cleator Moor Celtic, Darlington RA, Sunderland IFG Roker, Usworth Village, Hartlepool BWOB, Jarrow Roofing, Boldon CA, Nissan, Whitgate, Brantham Athletic, Brightlingsea Utd, Chatteris, Clacton, Cornard Utd, Felixstowe, Gorleston, Halstead, Harwich, Lowestoft, March, Newmarket, Norwich Utd, Thetford, Witham, Wisbech, Wroxham, Downham, Ely, Hadleigh, Ipswich Wdrs, Mildenhall, Soham, Sudbury Wdrs, Swaffham, Warboys, Woodbridge, Arundel, Bexhill, Burgess Hill, Eastbourne Town, Hailsham, Newhaven, Langney, Ringmer, Shoreham, Three Bridges, Bosham, Broadbridge Hth, Crowborough, E Grinstead, Portfield, Little Common, Redhill, Saltdean, Selsey, Sidley, Stamco, Buxted, Lindfield Rgrs, Sidlesham, Withdean, Beckenham, Chatham, Corinthian, Danson Furness Utd, Deal, Faversham, Folkestone Invicta, Ramsgate, Sheppey, Slade Green, Tonbridge, Tunbridge, Audley, Brocton, Congleton Hornets, Goldenhill, Hanford, Hth Hayes, Redgate Clayton, Rists Utd, Alton Town Bass, Alresford, Awbridge, Blackfield & Langley, Fleetlands, Broughton, Compton, Ringwood, Paulsgrove, Almondsbury Picksons, Banbury Utd, Bicester, Carterton, Didcot, Fairford, Kintbury, Milton Utd, Moreton, Pegasus Jnrs, Shortwood, Chipping Norton, Clanfield, Nth Leigh, Tuffley, Yarnton, Bristol MF, Chard, Chippenham, Clevedon Town, Dawlish, Elmore, Frome, Mangotsfield, Minehead, Ottery, Paulton, Saltash, Taunton, Weston-SM, Bridport, Backwell, Bishop Sutton, Clandown, Devizes, Glastonbury, Heavitree, Ilfracombe, Larkhall, Melksham, Radstock, Warminster, Westbury, Falmouth, St Austell, St Blazey, Torpoint, Dungannon Swifts, Moyala Park, Aerostructures, AFC Totton, Bemerton, Brockenhurst, Christchurch, E Cowes Vics, Ryde, Sholing, Thatcham, APV P'borough, Arlesey, Bourne, Brackley, Daventry, Desborough, Eynesbury, Holbeach, Irthlingborough, Kempston, Long Buckby, Mirrlees B'stone, Stamford, Stotfold, Wootton BC, British Timken, Bugbrooke SM, Harrowby Utd, Ramsey, Newton Flotman, Stapleton, Dowty Dynamoes, Attleborough Town, Amersham Town, Barkingside, Beaconsfield, Brimdown, Brook House, Cockfosters, Croydon Athletic, Nth Greenford, Waltham Abbey, Walthamstow Pennant, Brache Sparta, Buckingham Athletic, Harpenden, Leighton, Letchworth, Leverstock, MK Borough, New Bradwell SP, Oxford City, Pirton, Pitstone & Ivinghoe, Potters Bar Town, Shillington, 61FC, Welwyn GC, Wingate & F'ley, Wolverton, Bedford Town/Utd, Luton OB, Risborough, Shenley & L'ton, Bowling, Tyersal, Field, Chasetown, Gresley, H'owen Harriers, Lye, Malvern, Oldswinsford, Paget, Stourport, Wednesfield, Westfields, Willenhall, Darlaston, Donnington Wd, Ettingshall HT, Hill Top Rgrs, Lichfield, Moxley, Wolverhampton Utd, Alcester, Barlestone SG, Bolehall, Chelmsley, Coleshill, Evesham, Highgate, Mile Oak Rvrs & Yth, Northfield, Pershore, Sandwell Borough, Stratford, Walsall Wd, W Mids Police, Studley BKL, Triplex, Thimblemill, Blidworth, Borrowash, Heanor, Lincoln Utd, Louth, Melton, Mickleover, Oakham, Priory, S. Aurora, Shirebrook, Blwater, Fryston, Glapwell, Kiveton Pk, Norton W'seats, Selston, Attenborough, Derby RR, Gedling, Kimberley, Leicester Nirvana, Long Eaton, Wath Saracens, Bacton Utd 89, Framlingham Town, Halesworth, Melton St Audrey, Old Newton Utd, Walsham-le-Willows, Basildon Utd, Concord, Stambridge, Sherborne Town, Hamble, Ladies: Knowsley, Ipswich, Notts Rgrs, Abbeydale, Broadbridge Hth, Hassocks Beacon, Bangor City, Leasowe Pacific, Runcorn, Saltdean, Worcester, Harlow, Pye. Dunkirk, Hucknall RR, Radcliffe Olimpic, Teversal Grange, Bassingbourn, Chevy Hinton, Fulbourn, Chorlton Town, Beechams, Croxley Guild, Blackrod, Eagley, Beith Jnrs, Saltcoats, Armadale, Bailieston, Larkhall, Shettleston, Shotts Bon Accord, Lochgelly Albert, Insch, Manor Town, Brora Rgrs, Peterhead, Afan Lido, Brecon, Bridgend, Briton Ferry, Ebbw Vale, Ferndale, Haverfordwest, Maesteg Pk, Ton Pentre, Ammanford, Aberaman, Blaenrhondda, C'diff CS, Garw, Llanwern, Morriston, Newport YMCA, Pontllanfraith, Seven Sisters, Pt Talbot, Taffs Well, Pontlottyn, S Wales Police, Marchwiel Villa, Penparcau, Porthcawl, Ynysddu, Llangefni, Llanwst, Loco Llanberis, Llanfairpwl, Rhydymyn, Brymbo, Caersws, Conwy, Flint, Gresford, Llanidloes, LLansantffraid, Mostyn, Penrhyncoch, Porthmadog, Birchover, Bridgwater, Burnham Utd, Buckfastleigh, Callington, Peterbridge, Gt Manchester Police, Halton-R, Hayling Utd, Lewes Rvrs, Longwell Green, Leyland Daf, Moulton, Mousehole, Mow Cop, Netherne, Newton St Cyres, Porstewart, Pofton Utd Lions, Pewsey Vale, Quarry Nomads, Richmond Town, Robin Hood, St Agnes, Seaton Delaval, Shrewton, Smith Athletic, Technicolor, Tibberton, Topsham, Wellington Amtrs, Whitecroft & Barton, Southend Mnr, Altone Steels, Avenue Victoria Lodge, Baildon Athletic, B&A Scaffolding, AFC Bishopstoke, Bolton Wds, Boreham Wd Royals, Bricklayers Spts, BFNESC, Broad Plain House, Chapel Utd, Chequers, Collier Row Supporters, Coachman, Continental, Dereham Hobbies, Dock, Dudley & Weetslade, E Bowling, E Levenshulme, Ford-B'don, Framwellgate Moor & Pity Me, Girton Eagles, Hanham Sunday, Hare, H'pool Lion Hotel, Humbledon Plain, Inter Royalle, Jolly Farmers, Littlewoods Athletic, Lodge Cottrell, Lynemouth, Marston Spts, Mayfield Utd, Netherley RBL, Oakenshaw, Old Paludians, Ouzavich, Pheonix, St Albans, Priory Spts, Queens Arms, Radford Pk, Raneleigh, Reading Borough, St Josephs, Sandwell, Sartan Utd, Sawston Rvrs, Seymour, Theale, Watford Labour Club, Western, Bourneville Warriors, Bradford FA 1975, Brinsworth, Birkenshaw, Clifton Athletic, Dye Rections, GWP Aviation, Harrowby Amtrs, Haymakers, ICL Utd, Lord Nelson, Never Say Dai, Northward Utd, Preston 81, Rossett Villa, Royal A., St Anslems, Trentham Romans, Upminster All Stars, Bar Hill, Berridge 'Spts, Dial M for Merthyr.

Apologies to any club inadvertently omitted. The closing date for next season's survey is 31st January 1993 (May 31st for special issues). To gain full marks for frequency please send at least ten issues (to address at start of article), though the minimum entry is one programme.

POLICE ATHLETIC ASSOCIATION
FOOTBALL CUP 1992-93

Preliminary Round

Greater Manchester v Cleveland	2-0	Humberside *W/O* Durham *(Withdrew)*	
Lincolnshire v Leicestershire	2-1	Warwickshire *(Withdrew)* v Derbyshire *(W/O)*	
West Yorkshire v South Yorkshire	1-2		

First Round

Cumbria v Northern	0-2	Derbyshire v Northants	0-0,0-0,5-4
Devon & Cornwall v Avon & Somerset	0-0,0-1	Gloucestershire v South Wales	1-10
Hertforshire v Norfolk	4-2	Humberside v South Yorkshire	3-1
Kent v Suffolk	4-0	North Wales v Dyfed/Powys	2-1
North Yorkshire v Greater Manchester	0-2	Nottmshire v Lincolnshire	1-1,1-1 *(4-3 pens)*
Surrey v City of London	0-0,0-0 *(7-8 pens)*	Tayside v Strathclyde	0-4
Thames Valley v Hampshire	4-2	West Mercia v Staffordshire	3-0
Wiltshire v Dorset	2-5		

Second Round

Essex v Bedfordshire	3-2	Gwent v Avon & Somerset	2-3
Humberside v Greater Manchester	0-2	Kent v Hertfordshire	0-0,2-5
Merseyside v Cheshire	4-1	Northern v Lothian & Borders	1-0
Nottinghamshire v Derbyshire	2-0	South Wales v Dorset	3-2
Strathclyde v Northumbria	6-0	Thames Valley v City of London	1-0
West Mercia v Merseyside	2-0		

Third Round

Avon & Somerset v South Wales	0-4	Essex v Hertfordshire	3-1
Lancashire v Greater Manchester	1-2	Northern v Strathclyde	1-2
Nottinghamshire v West Midlands	1-2	Thames Valley v Metropolitan	2-0
West Mercia v Merseyside	0-4		

Quarter Finals

Greater Manchester v Merseyside	2-3	South Wales v Essex	1-1,1-3
Strathclyde v West Midlands	2-5	Thames Valley v Royal Ulster	0-3

Semi Finals

Essex v West Midlands	1-3	Merseyside v Royal Ulster	0-1

FINAL:
WEST MIDS POLICE (2)5 *(Grimshaw 5,Hussey 31 63 65,Powney 70)*, **R.U.C.** (0)2 *(Love 81,Miller 86)*
WM Police: Darren Carmell, Matthew Wearing, Peter Grimshaw, Darren Powney, Stephen Hopcroft, Adam West, Gary Ingram, Noel McMenamin, David Scriven (capt), Graham Hussey, Sean Small. Subs: Robert Bradford, Philip Keen. Mgr: Colin Brooks.
RUC: George Dunlop, Jim Millar, Ken Whiteside, Nigel Robinson, Joe Crawford (capt), Alan Tosh, Harry Love, Neil Morrow, Earl Aitken, Colin Young, Darrin Coyle. Subs: John Donald, Scott Lucas. Mgr: C McFall.

West Midlands Police captain Dave Scriven receives the National Police Cup from Chief Constable Ron Hadfield. Photo - Keith Clayton.

HUSSEY HAT-TRICK HERO

The RUC team, appearing in its ninth final of the past fourteen years, currently play in the B Division, Section One, of the Irish League. They narrowly missed out on a place in the ECWC in 1981 when they were beaten 0-3 by Crusaders in the Semi Final of the Irish Cup. West Midlands Police are a force in the Influence Combination. They won the title last year, but missed promotion to the Beazer League through lack of floodlights, Solihull Borough taking their place.

The star of this National Police final was striker Graham Hussey who found he was playing only an hour before kick off when Gary Davison was ruled out through back injury. Otherwise the team consisted of the players that lost to Sudbury in the FA Vase Quarter Final, with the addition of substitute Philip Keen. The RUC team included goalkeeper George Dunlop who has League experience with Linfield and full caps for Northern Ireland.

The match exploded into life in the 5th minute when Peter Grimshaw side-footed home a cross to give West Midlands the lead. The RUC countered when Jim Millar put over a cross which Earl Aitken just failed to connect with. Sean Small was causing the all sorts of problems for the RUC down the left, culminating in a superb left-footed shot against the post.

The next 34 minutes belonged to Hussey. His hat-trick began with a perfect header in the 31st minute. After the interval he converted two crosses into goals with a simple tap-in and another superb header, in the 63rd and 65th minutes. During this purple patch Dave Scriven hit a post, and Darren Powney completed the RUC misery with yet another headed goal, in the 70th minute. Because of an injury in the back four, Graham Hussey completed the rest of the game playning at centre half.

The last ten minutes of the game saw the RUC play some of their best football. Harry Love scored in the 81st minute, and came very close with a header soon afterwards, before Millar scored the second in the 86th minute. Substitute Keen came close with a diving header for West Midlands, and RUC sub John Donald had a header saved at the near post in the dying seconds.

West Midlands Police captain Dave Scriven received the Cup from Chief Constable Ron Hadfield QPM, and completed one of the most successful season's in his side's history. If the 28 players who were on show were to form the nucleus of the British Police Football team, I have no doubt they will retain the European Police Cup, won in 1989 with a final victory over Italy, in 1993.

I would like to thank Dave Taylor (West Midlands Police), Eric Downey (Royal Ulster Constabulary) and Dennis Dixon (Officer in Charge on the day) for their help before, during and after the game. **Keith Clayton**

FINALS 1948-1991

1948: Southampton 2, Sheffield 2 *(Cup shared)*
1949: Met.2 District 4, Liverpool City 0
1950: Southampton 1, Grimsby Boro. 0
1951: Met.2 District 4, Lincolnshire 2
1952: Grimsby Borough 2, Met.2 Dist 1
1953: Grimsby Borough 1, Hertfordshire 0
1954: Stafforshire 3, Derbyshire 1 *(aet)*
1955: Edinburgh 2, Cambridge 1
1956: Durham 1, Staffordshire 0
1957: Grimsby Boro. 1, Kent 1 *(Cup shared)*
1958: Grimsby Borough 2, Berkshire 1 *(aet)*
1959: Grimsby Borough 4, Staffordshire 1
1960: Hampshire & IOW 4, Edinburgh City 1
1961: Manchester City 4, Hampshire 2
1962: Birmingham 2, Grimsby Borough 1
1963: Birmingham 1, Lancashire 0 *(aet)*
1964: Birmingham 6, Edinburgh 0
1965: Birmingham 1, Grimsby Boro. 0
1966: Met.4 District 1, Liverpool 0
1967: Birmingham 4, Glasgow 0
1968: Grimsby Borough 1, Birmingham 0
1969: Nottingham 1, Staffordshire 0 *(replay)*

1970: Birmingham 3, Manchester & Salford 0
1971: Bedford & Luton 1, Birmingham 0 *(replay)*
1972: Bedford & Luton 2, Birmingham 0 *(aet)*
1973: Kent 1, Liverpool 0
1974: Birmingham 3, Nottingham 2 *(aet)*
1975: West Midlands 2, Nottingham 1
1976: West Midlands 3, Kent 2
1977: Greater Manchester 3, West Midlands 0
1978: Metropolitan 2, West Midlands 1
1979: Metropolitan 2, Royal Ulster 1
1980: Metropolitan 1, Staffordshire 0
1981: West Midlands 2, Cleveland 1
1982: Royal Ulster 2, Metropolitan 1
1983: Royal Ulster 2, Metropolitan 0 *(aet)*
1984: Merseyside 2, Royal Ulster 0
1985: Metropolitan 3, Royal U. 3 *(4-3 on pens)*
1986: Metropolitan 4, Strathclyde 3 *(aet)*
1987: Royal Ul. 3, Merseyside 3 *(4-3 on pens)*
1988: West Mids 1, Royal Ulster 1 *(4-2 on pens)*
1989: Strathclyde 3, West Midlands 1
1990: Lancashire 2, Hertfordshire 1
1991: Lancashire 3, Royal Ulster 1

Dave Scriven and Joe Crawford, with match officials, exchange pennants before kick off. Photo - Keith Clayton.

COUNTY ASSOCIATION CUPS
SEASON 1991-92

The following section is devoted to a round-up of County Senior Cups. We are again indebted to Leo Heonig and Mike Ford for their tireless work in making this section possible.

Mike Ford's 'Bureau of Non-League Football' magazine is currently the only publication providing round-by-round results from County Cups throughout the season, and full subscription details are provided overleaf.

Bedfordshire

Beds has always had a straightforward KO Cup format, and in recent times the cup has been dominated by Beazer Homes League sides. In 1991 Dunstable's domination, and that of their biggest rivals, Diadora clubs Barton and Vauxhall, was broken by a victory for Electrolux of the South Midlands League. This season the competition had to withstand the blow that the holders had folded and Vauxhall had made a late withdrawal. Barton had to play in the Preliminary Round, defeating Stotfold, but then made a surprising exit in extra-time at Wootton Blue Cross. So would it be easy for Dunstable? Certainly at Biggleswade in the Round One, but then at Totternhoe they surprisingly went down 0-3. Both Semi-Finals were played on neutral grounds. Totternhoe came through against South Midlands League rivals Shillington 1-0, but for goals you needed to be at the other tie which Kempston and Arlesey, both of the the United Counties League, drew 3-3 after extra-time. Kempston won the replay 6-2, but could not repeat this sort of feat in the Final and had to settle for a single goal victory to secure the cup for the first time in fifteen years.

Beds Senior Cup Preliminary Round

Potton United v Leighton Town	2-5	The 61 FC v Biggleswade Town	1-2
Barton Rovers v Stotfold	3-1	Ampthill Town v Ashcroft	2-0

First Round

Wootton Blue Cross v Barton Rovers	3-2	Shefford Town v Kempston Rovers	0-3
Shillington v Delco Products	4-3	Caddington v Arlesey Town	1-2
Leighton Town v Brache Sparta	3-0	Langford W/O Vauxhall Motors *(withdrew)*	
Totternhoe v Ampthill Town	1-0	Dunstable v Biggleswade Town	3-1

Second Round

Totternhoe v Dunstable	3-0	Arlesey Town v Leighton Town	3-2
Kempston Rovers v Wootton Blue Cross	3-2 *(aet)*	Shillington v Totternhoe	2-1

Semi-Finals

Kempston v Arlesey *(Langford, March 10th)*	3-3,6-2	Totternhoe v Shillington *(at Barton R., March 11th)*	1-0

Final *(at Stotfold FC, 5th May)*: Kempston Rovers 1, Totternhoe 0

Dunstable's Chris Campbell evades a lunging tackle during the first half of his side's shock 0-3 defeat at Totternhoe in the Quarter Finals of the Bedfordshire Senior Cup. Photo - Gavin Ellis.

Berkshire & Buckinghamshire

Big scores in the qualifying rounds saw Maidenhead United and Burnham hit seven in their respective victories over Beaconsfield and Wantage respectively. Neither pair had it quite so easy in the next round when both had visits to Abingdon. Burnham were at Town and lost 1-2, whilst Maidenhead were a goal down at United when their match was abandoned in extra-time. They made best use of the replay, going through 2-1. The big scorers of the round were Flackwell Heath who hit seven against Amersham, whilst the area's sole Wessex side, Thatcham, made the best of their second visit to South Midlands League opposition following a 5-1 win at Winslow with 4-1 victory at New Bradwell St Peter. Beyond this point things get serious with the entry of the eight exempt sides. The sides that qualified were guaranteed two survivors who turned out to be Kintbury and and Thatcham, but all those turning out against exempt opposition fell. The lack of home draws may have hindered. In 'all exempt' clashes, holders Marlow beat Diadora Premier Division rivals Wokingham, and a weakened Wycombe side lost 1-2 at home to Reading's reserves. The Second Round produced four home wins, the most notable being Slough's visit to Chesham. Reading lost 0-3 at Windsor & Eton, and with Marlow and Aylesbury winning, the Diadora League Premier Division had a monopoly of Semi-Final places. In the first tie Windsor won 2-1 at Marlow, while later Chesham repeated that scoreline at Aylesbury and then clinched the Cup with a 3-1 win in the Final. A welcome win for Chesham after losing in the Semis in each of the last two seasons.

Berks & Bucks Senior Cup First Qualifying Round

Wolverton AFC v Flackwell Heath	2-4*(aet)*		Maidenhead United v Beaconsfield United	7-0
Sandhurst Town v Abingdon United	1-3		Winslow United v Thatcham Town	1-5
Newbury Town v New Bradwell St Peter	2-3		Burnham v Wantage Town	7-1

Second Qualifying Round

Abingdon Utd v Maidenhead Utd	1-0*(aband.)*,1-2		Flackwell Heath v Amersham Town	7-1
New Bradwell St Peter v Thatcham Town	1-4		Milton Keynes Borough v Bracknell Town	3-2
Abingdon Town v Burnham	2-1		Buckingham Town v Didcot Town	3-1
Kintbury Rangers v Hungerford Town	2-1		Milton United v Chalfont St Peter	4-3

First Round

Milton Keynes Borough v Kintbury Rangers	0-2		Marlow v Wokingham Town	3-1
Chesham United v Buckingham Town	4-2		Wycombe Wanderers v Reading Reserves	1-2
Slough Town v Flackwell Heath	5-2		Windsor & Eton v Milton United	2-1
Abingdon Town v Thatcham Town	0-1		Aylesbury United v Maidenhead United	5-1

Quarter-Finals

Marlow v Kintbury Rangers	4-1		Chesham United v Slough Town	3-1
Windsor & Eton v Reading Reserves	3-0		Aylesbury United v Thatcham Town	1-0

Semi-Finals

Marlow v Windsor & Eton *(28th March)*	1-2		Aylesbury United v Chesham United	1-2

Final *(at Abingdon Town FC, 25th May)*: Chesham United 3, Windsor & Eton 1

Birmingham

A number of Beazer clubs had to play in the First Round, but none were surprised by 'lower' opposition with only Tamworth and Atherstone going out, both to teams from their own level. One fancied side to make an early exit was Evesham who fell at Rocester. The Second Round sees the entry of those fortunate enough to have been exempt earlier, and of course the 'Big Six' as the area's Football League sides are sometimes referred. Of the six, three fell immediately, Walsall to another of the six, Coventry by 1-3, whilst Aston Villa went down 0-1 at VS Rugby after a 0-0 draw, and Wolves fared worst of all drawing at Oldbury before crashing 3-5 at home. In other matches, Willenhall, just relegated from the Beazer League, beat Dudley Town 3-0, whilst Bolehall Swifts, despite relinquishing home advantage, drew 1-1 with Solihull Borough before going down 0-8 in the replay when genuine home advantage told. In the Third Round Coventry lost 1-2 at Willenhall while Birmingham and West Bromwich Albion moved to the Quarter Finals at the expense of Solihull and Hednesford, and West Midlands League Rocester surprisingly beat Beazer League Redditch. West Bromwich broke their five year run as holders when they lost in the last eight at Nuneaton, Willenhall's successes were ended by Birmingham, but the surprise was at Moor Green where Rocester won 4-2. Midland Combination outfit Highgate continued to be a thorn in the flesh of the higher sides; having beaten Worcester on penalties in the previous round they achieved a draw at VS Rugby before going down in the replay. The Semi-Finals produced two home wins, Birmingham ending Rocester's fine run and VS Rugby defeating Nuneaton. The latter won 3-0 at the Hawthorns in the Final, but only 628 saw the game; maybe it is time to reconsider the holding of this Final on a League ground?

Birmingham Senior Cup First Round

Paget Rangers v Wednesfield	1-0		Northfield Town v Redditch United	2-4
Dudley Town v Knowle	2-0		Halesowen Harriers v Stratford Town	1-1,2-0
Solihull Borough v Mile Oak Rovers & Youth	5-1		Tamworth v Sutton Coldfield Town	1-3
Racing Club Warwick v Tividale	2-0		Stourbridge v Sandwell Borough	1-1,2-1
Bolehall Swifts v Banbury United	4-1		Atherstone United v Worcester City	1-1,2-3
Alvechurch v Coleshill Town	7-2		West Midlands Police v Halesowen Town	1-2
Rocester v Evesham United	2-1		Lye Town v Oldbury United	1-2

Second Round

West Bromwich Albion v Paget Rangers	3-0		Redditch United v Boldmere St Michaels	5-2
Olbury Utd v Wolverhampton Wanderers	2-2,5-3		Willenhall Town v Dudley Town	3-0
Hednesford Town v Burton Albion	2-0		Birmingham City v Kings Heath	3-1
Bedworth v Highgate	1-1*(aet)*,1-1*(aet, 5-6 pens)*		Stourbridge v Halesowen Town	1-1,0-2
Sutton Coldfield Town v Alvechurch	2-4		Racing Club Warwick v Worcester City	1-1,0-2
Nuneaton Borough v Halesowen Harriers	3-1		Oldswinford F & SC v Rocester	1-1,0-1
Walsall v Coventry City	1-3		Moor Green v West Bromwich Town	1-0
Aston Villa v V.S. Rugby	0-0,0-1		Bolehall Sw. v Solihull Borough	1-1*(at Solihull)*,0-8

Third Round

Rocester v Redditch United	2-0		Oldbury United v Moor Green	1-4
Highgate Utd v Worcester City	0-0,3-3*(4-1 pens)*		V.S. Rugby v Alvechurch	4-0
Birmingham City v Solihull Borough	2-0		Hednesford Town v West Bromwich Albion	0-3
Nuneaton Borough v Halesowen Town	2-0		Willenhall Town v Coventry City	2-1

Quarter-Finals

V.S. Rugby v Highgate United	1-1,2-1		Moor Green v Rocester	2-4
Birmingham City v Willenhall Town	3-0		Nuneaton Borough v West Bromwich Albion	2-1

Semi-Finals

Birmingham City v Rocester	3-2		V.S. Rugby v Nuneaton Borough	3-1

Final *(at West Bromwich Albion FC, 13th April)*: V.S. Rugby 3, Birmingham City 1

Cambridgeshire

No surprises in the First Round of the Invitation Cup where the odd team, Philips UK of the Cambridgeshire League, lost 0-2 at home to Soham of the Jewson League. In two all Jewson League ties, Wisbech and March scored 3-0 home wins over Ely and Chatteris. Histon then held Beazer League Cambridge City to a draw before going out in a replay. Wisbech beat March in their Semi Final, and with home advantage went on to win the Final.

Cambs Invitation Cup First Round

Philips UK v Soham Town Rangers	0-2	Wisbech Town v Ely City	3-0
Histon v Cambridge City	3-3,1-3	March Town United v Chatteris Town	3-0

Semi-Finals

Wisbech Town v March Town United	1-0	Cambridge City v Soham Town Rangers	4-1

Final *(at Wisbech Town FC, 28th April)*: Wisbech Town 2, Cambridge City 0

Having failed against the first team, Philips, again holding home advantage, may have hoped to have done better against Soham Reserves in the Challenge Cup, but they had to settle for a 3-3 draw. The result was repeated in the return, but a third meeting produced a 4-0 victory for the Soham side. The Challenge Cup is the almost exclusive preserve of Cambridgeshire League sides - the most notable other results in the First Round saw Premier 'B' side TSB Rangers beating Bassingbourn (Premier 'A'), and Whittlesey United of the Peterborough & District League begin their defence of the Cup with a 4-0 win at Willingham. In the Second Round, Whittlesey were unseated, going down by a single goal to West Wratting. Godmanchester Rovers provided a success for Premier 'B' sides with a single goal victory over Steeple Bumstead. The other survivor from their division to the Quarter-Finals was TSB Rangers, while in the absence of Whittlesey, the Peterborough League was represented by the Reserves of Wisbech. The latter won an all-reserve match at Soham to reach the Semis and meet TSB who had won at West Wratting. Successes for Godmanchester at Over Sports, and for Linton Granta at Great Shelford, meant that all Quarter-Final matches ended in away wins. The Semis went the same way with neither home side managing a goal, and the Final, at Chatteris, saw Godmanchester beat Wisbech Reserves to prevent the Fenland club from completing a double of local trophies.

Cambs 'Hereward Sports' Challenge Preliminary Round

Histon Reserves v Bassingbourn	2-2,1-2	Manea United v Steeple Bumstead	3-3,0-1
Levrington Spts v Newmarket Town Reserves	1-3	Great Shelford v Haddenham Rovers	2-1

First Round

St Ives Town Reserves v Linton Granta	0-4	Whittlesford United v Newmarket Town Reserves	3-1
Cottenham United v Over Sports	1-3	Chatteris Town Reserves v Earith United	3-2(aet)
Great Shelford W/O Bottisham		Longstanton v Fulbourn Institute	1-2
Philips UK v Soham TR Res.	3-3(aet),3-3(aet),0-4	Cherry Hinton v Orwell	1-3
Schering v Steeple Bumpstead	1-1,2-4	Godmanchester Rovers v Haslingfield	3-2
Sawston Rovers v Wisbech Town Reserves	3-4	Waterbeach v Gamlingay	1-2(aet)
Purbeck v Camden United	4-0	TSB Rangers v Bassingbourn	3-1
West Wratting v March Town United Reserves	5-1	Willingham v Whittlesey United	0-4

Second Round

Linton Granta v Fulbourn Institute	5-2	Great Shelford v Gamlingay	2-0
Whittlesey United v West Wratting	0-1	Purbeck v TSB Rangers	1-3
Orwell v Soham Town Rangers Reserves	1-3	Chatteris Reserves v Over	0-5(aband.),3-3(aet),2-3
Whittlesford v Wisbech T. Reserves	2-2(aet),0-1	Steeple Bumpstead v Godmanchester Rovers	0-1

Quarter-Finals

Over Sports v Godmanchester Rovers	0-1	Soham Town Rgrs Reserves v Wisbech Town Res	0-3
West Wratting v TSB Rangers	1-2	Great Shelford v Linton Granta	2-3

Semi-Finals

Linton Granta v Godmanchester Rovers	0-1	TSB Rangers v Wisbech Town Reserves	0-2

Final *(at Chatteris Town FC, 29th May)*: Godmanchester Rovers 2, Wisbech Town Reserves 1

Cheshire

With no less than five Conference clubs involved, the Cheshire Senior Cup is perhaps the strongest County competition in England. This claim will be reinforced by the addition of a sixth GMVC club, Stalybridge Celtic, in 1992-93. Last year's competition had thirteen entries, ten of whom contested the First Round. The three exempt sides were 1991 finalists Witton and Macclesfield, and West Cheshire League minnows General Chemicals. All First Round encounters went to form, though Hyde scraped home by the only goal at home to Vauxhall and three GMVC sides could manage only single goal margins against supposedly inferior opposition. Troubled Altrincham were the lucky side to play General Chemicals in the Second Round, and won 3-0, whilst the matches between Macclesfield and Hyde, and Winsford and Runcorn produced five goal thrillers. The Silkmen needing to come from two behing to dispose of Cliff Roberts' men, and at the Barton Stadium, Mike McKenzie's impressive Winsford showed their potential by knocking out the Linnets. The other match was an all-Northwich affair at Wincham Park, and the home side won 3-1 to avenge their 0-3 reverse at the Drill Field a month earlier. The Semi-Finals were virtually decided after the first legs. Witton decisively beat Altrincham 4-1 at Wincham Park in one of their most impressive displays of the season, whilst Peter Wragg's Macclesfield won 3-1 at Winsford. The formality of the second legs saw 3-1 wins for Witton and Macclesfield to set up a repeat of the 1991 Final. Strangely the event was staged at Tranmere's Prenton Park and only just over a thousand turned. A close affair produced no winner, and the replay, a fortnight later was staged at the Drill Field, never a lucky ground for Macc. A healthier crowd turned up, but Witton's performance was clearly afected by their Wembley exertions five days earlier, They were a shadow of the side that had given Colchester such a good run for their money, and the Silkmen won at canter with second half goals from Askey and Hanlon to complete an eighteenth Senior Cup success. Finally, a new new name could appear on the Trophy in 1993 as Colwyn Bay's groundshare arrangement at Northwich's Drill Field has prompted them to enter for the first time.

Cheshire Senior Cup First Round

Congleton Town v Winsford United *(att: 257)*	0-4	Hyde United v Vauxhall G.M. *(att: 350)*	1-0
Nantwich Town v Altrincham *(att: 280)*	1-2	Northwich Victoria v Stalybridge Celtic *(att: 380)*	2-1
Runcorn v Warrington Town *(att: 275)*	2-1		

Quarter-Finals

General Chemicals v Altrincham *(att: 306)*	0-3	Macclesfield Town v Hyde United *(att: 256)*	3-2
Winsford United v Runcorn *(att: 335)*	3-2	Witton Albion v Northwich Victoria *(att: 1,152)*	3-1

Semi-Finals

Altrincham v Witton Albion *(att: 730)*	1-4	Winsford United v Macclesfield Town *(att: 355)*	1-3
Witton Albion v Altrincham *(att: 657)*	3-1	Macclesfield Town v Winsford United *(att: 279)*	3-1

Final *(at Tranmere Rovers FC, 4th May)*: Macclesfield Town 1, Witton Albion 1. AET, att: 1,001.
Replay *(at Northwich Victoria FC, 15th May)*: Macclesfield Town 2, Witton Albion 0., att: 1,449.

Karl Thomas rifles home Witton's equaliser in the 1-1 draw at Prenton Park. Photo - Keith Clayton.

Witton's Carl Alford challenges Macclesfield 'keeper Steve Farrelly at Prenton Park. Photo - Keith Clayton.

Stuart Bimsom, of victorious Macclesfield, proudly exhibits the Cheshire Senior Cup. Photo - Keith Clayton.

The Cheshire Amateur Cup is now sponsored by the Cheshire Building Society. By the Fourth Round stage just three survivors remained from the top division of the Mid-Cheshire League, heavily outnumbered by eight teams from the West Cheshire. Old Stopfordians proved good enough to beat Moreton 2-1, but in the Quarter-Finals fell to the strong Cammell Laird. Two of the surviving Mid-Cheshire clubs met at Grove where holders Bramhall were beaten, while home advantage was not enough to save Knutsford against Heswall. Grove went out to Cammell Laird in the first Semi-Final, at Warrington, but Heswall were made to battle before beating Disley Amateurs after extra-time at Runcorn. Runcorn was again the venue, and extra-time again necessary, for the Final, so the omens were good for Heswall, and they duly obliged, settling the issue with two goals.

Cheshire 'Building Society' Amateur Cup First Round

Moor Celtic v Vauxhall Motors	0-5	Gatley v Metro	1-3
Old Altrinchamians v Blacon Athletic	4-2	Bollington Athletic v Mond Rangers	0-0(aet),3-2(aet)
Atlantic v Middlewich	1-2	Crewe Rolls Royce v Winnington Park	2-3
Ashville v Newton (Wirral)	5-0		

Second Round

Partington Village v Styal	5-6	Stockport Georgians v Mersey Royal	0-2
Vauxhall Motors v Littlemoor	2-0	Manweb v Manor Athletic	1-0
Stork v Poynton	3-1	Newton (Wirral) v Winnington Park	1-2
Mellor v B.I.C.C. Helsby	3-1	General Chemicals v Dukinfield Town	1-0(aet)
Barnton v Cheadle Heath Nomads	2-2,1-0	Bebington Hawks v Disley Amateurs	0-2
Old Stopfordians v Hazel Grove	1-0	Christleton v Broadheath Central	3-0
Lymm v Malpas	4-1	St Werburghs v Willaston	1-1,2-1
I.C.I. Pharmaceuticals v Knutsford	0-2	Poulton Victoria v Kellogs B.A.	2-1
Blacon Youth Club v Ashville	3-1	West Kirby v Dukinfield Amateurs	2-0
Old Altrinchamians v Wilmslow Albion	1-4	Woodley S.C. v Frodsham United	8-1
Metro v Cheadle Hulme	3-1	Linotype v Shell (Wirral)	2-2,1-3
Chester Nomads v Middlewich Athletic	4-1	Bollington Athletic v Upton A.A.	0-3

Third Round

Barnton v General Chemicals	1-3	Styal v West Kirby	0-5
Lymm v Grove United	0-3	Moreton v Chester Nomads	1-1(aet),2-1
Cammell Laird v Manweb	4-1	Vauxhall Motors v Stork	1-2
Blacon Youth Club v St Werburghs	3-4	Old Stocanians v Capenhurst	2-4
Mersey Royal v Disley Amateurs	2-2(aet),1-3	Mellor v Woodley S.C.	2-4
Metro v Heswall	0-2	Upton A.A. v Knutsford	1-1(aet),1-2
Old Stopfordians v Winnington Park	4-1	Wilmslow Albion v Poulton Vitoria	0-2
Shell (Wirral) v Christleton	3-3(aet),2-1	Bromborough Pool v Bramhall	4-4(aet),2-3

Fourth Round

West Kirby v Disley Amateurs	1-1(aet),2-5	Grove United v Woodley S.C.	3-2
Old Stopfordians v Moreton	2-1	Cammell Laird v St Werburghs	6-1
Bramhall v General Chemicals	3-1	Heswall v Shell	2-0
Stork v Capenhurst	4-1	Knutsford v Poulton Victoria	6-3

Quarter-Finals

Cammell Laird v Old Stopfordians	6-2	Grove United v Bramhall	3-1
Knutsford v Heswall	0-1	Stork v Disley Amateurs	0-2

Semi-Finals

Cammell L. v Grove (at Warrington, 4th Mar.) 3-1   Disley A. v Heswall (at Runcorn, 11th March) 1-4(aet)

Final (at Runcorn FC, 24th April): Heswall 2, Cammell Laird 0 (aet)

Cornwall

The Cornwall Senior Cup is very popular among some of the London groundhoppers thanks to the pleasant surroundings and the openness of the draw which allows many small clubs to take on the 'giants' of the Jewson South Western and Great Mills Western Leagues. Giant-killings are however rare, and the only threat to the two GMWL clubs tends to be each other and the top JSWL sides. This season proved no exception as Liskeard and Saltash negotiated Third Round ties before meeting in the Fourth Round. Despite home advantage, holders Saltash went out by a single goal. JSWL sides should have more to fear, but the Quarters were reached without one of their members having lost to a more local team - Penzance, one of the league's weakest sides these days did lose 0-6, but this was to fellow JSWL side Bodmin. Six South Western League clubs joined Liskeard and Bude in the Quarter-Finals. Bude, of the East Cornwall Premier League, were the most junior survivor having disposed of Lostwithiel and Padstow of their own League, and RAF St Mawgan of the Cornwall Combination. There were no surprises in the last eight, though Bude's tie with Millbrook was one of three that needed to be replayed, Liskeard being the only club able to win at the first attempt. Newquay and Millbrook met in one Semi-Final at Liskeard, the latter triumphing 2-1, but the real fireworks were back at Mount Wise where Falmouth took on Liskeard, and beat them 5-3. This meant that for the first time in a decade neither Western League club had reached the Final, and it was the first time a South Western League club had been a Western League side since St Blazey beat both Liskeard and Saltash in 1987. Perhaps appropriately, the Final was played at St Blazey, and perhaps Falmouth's Semi-Final exertions told for it was a Newquay goal that settled this season's Cup.

Cornwall Senior Cup First Round

Camelford v Ludgvan	4-2	Illogan R.B.L. v R.N.A.S. Culdrose	3-2

Second Round

Illogan R.B.L. v Tintagel	4-2	Lostwithiel v Bude	1-1,1-3
Mousehole v St Agnes	0-1	Mullion v Pendeen Rovers	2-1
Nanpean Rovers v Helston Athletic	0-2	St Dennis v Roche	2-4
St Just v St Breward	1-1,1-4		

Third Round

Bodmin Town v Penzance	6-0	Callington v Launceston	0-1
Foxhole Stars v Wadebridge Town	0-2	Helston Athletic v Falmouth Town	1-7
Liskeard Athletic v Bugle	0-0,3-0	Marazion Blues v St Austell	0-2
Millbrook v Roche	4-4,1-1,3-0	Newquay v Perranwell	6-0
Padstow United v Bude	0-1	Penryn Athletic v Saltash United	0-1
Riviera Coasters v Illogan R.B.L.	5-2	St Agnes v R.A.F. St Mawgan	1-2
St Blazey v Porthleven	4-3	St Breward v Torpoint Athletic	2-5
Sticker v Mullion	0-2	Truro City v Camelford	4-0

Fourth Round

Bodmin Town v Truro City	1-1,2-4	Bude v R.A.F. St Mawgan	7-1
Falmouth Town v Torpoint Athletic	0-0,3-1	Millbrook v Mullion	3-1

| Newquay v St Blazey | 3-2 | Saltash United v Liskeard Athletic | 0-1 |
| Wadebridge Town v St Austell | 1-2 | Launceston v Riviera Coasters | 5-0 |

Quarter-Finals

| Falmouth Town v St Austell | 5-0 | Launceston v Liskeard Athletic | 1-3 |
| Millbrook v Bude | 2-2,2-1 | Newquay v Truro City | 0-0,2-1 |

Semi-Finals

| Falmouth v Liskeard *(Newquay, 14th March)* | 5-3 | Newquay v Millbrook *(at Liskeard, 21st March)* | 2-1 |

Final *(at St Blazey FC, 20th April)*: Newquay 1, Falmouth Town 0

Falmouth score during their 2-1 Cornwall Senior Cup Quarter Final win at St Austell. Photo - Elaine Sarjeant.

Sean Hooper scores Newquay's first, from the spot as the Peppermints overcome St Blazey in the Cornwall Senior Cup 4th Round at Mount Wise. Photo - Ray Frith.

A panoramic view of St Blazey FC packed with 1,000 as Newquay defeat Falmouth with a goal seven minutes from time to win the Cornwall Senior Cup. Photo - Barry Lenton.

Cumberland

Workington are supposed to be the County's leading side, but they managed to field a side weak enough to lose 2-6 at home to Keswick of the Westmoreland League on their first outing. Carlisle Gillford Park of the Northern Alliance were the stars of the early rounds, following up a 4-2 win at Cumbria Police with no less than fifteen goals against Langwathby. Their run was ended in the Quarters by local rivals Carlisle City who play in the lower division of the Northern Alliance. The other semi-finalists all came from different leagues; Gretna of the Northern, Marchon from the Wearside and Penrith from the Bass NWC. With Gretna and Penrith kept apart it was little surprise that they progressed to the Final, which was won by an extra-time goal by the Northern League champions.

Cumberland Senior Cup First Round

Kirkoswald v Sporting of Cumbria	4-1	Cumbria Police v Carlisle Gillford Park	2-4
Longtown *(expelled)* Cleator Moor Celtic *(W/O)*		Carlisle United v Carlisle City	1-4
Windscales Barrow v Albert	1-2		

Second Round

Parton United v Cumbria Teachers	4-0	Penrith v Kirkoswald	6-2
Gretna v Greystoke	4-2	Cleator Moor Celtic v Albert	15-0
Marchon Reserves v Whitehaven Miners 'B'	4-1	Marchon v Braithewaite	6-0
Carlisle Gillford Park v Langwathby	15-0	British Steel v Carlisle United	0-9
Wigton v Abbeytown	0-2	Workington v Keswick	2-6
Alston Town v Egremont St Marys	4-2	Penrith United v Museum Inn	0-4
Wetheriggs v Northbank	3-2	Inglewood Forest *(withdrew)* Whitehaven Miners *(W/O)*	
Windscales United v Silloth	4-2	Mirehouse *(W/O)* Hearts of Liddesdale	

Third Round

Museum Inn v Marchon	1-5	Penrith v Cleator Moor Celtic	9-0
Carlisle Gillford Park v Marchon Reserves	3-1	Gretna v Whitehaven Miners	6-0
Carlisle City v Parton United	5-4	Mirehouse v Windscales United	2-5
Keswick v Abbeytown	3-4	Wetheriggs v Alston Town	4-4,5-1

Quarter-Finals

Marchon v Wetheriggs	4-1	Abbeytown v Gretna	0-1
Carlisle Gillford Park v Carlisle City	1-3	Windscales United v Penrith	2-2*(aet)*,0-1

Semi-Finals

Carlisle City v Gretna *(15th February)*	2-4	Marchon v Penrith *(15th February)*	0-1

Final *(at Carlisle United FC, 14th April)*: Gretna 1, Penrith 0 *(aet)*

Stuart Evans heads an equaliser for Gresley against Glossop in the Derbyshire Senior Cup. Photo - Derrick Kinsey.

Buxton's Robert Brown (6) clears a header from Ilkeston's Peter Farrow in the Quarter Finals. Photo - James Wright.

Derbyshire

A complicated cup now - perhaps someone will write in and explain how their exemptions work. Five teams received byes to the Third Round, and three to the Fourth Round. The Third Round placings went to HFS Loans sides Alfreton and Matlock, holders Gresley of the West Midlands League, Belper of the Northern Counties (East) League, and Websters Central Midlands side Borrowash. They were joined by further Central Midland sides Long Eaton United, Stanton Ilkeston and Mickleover, and Glossop of the Bass North West Counties League. All sides defeated in the Second Round were also Central Midlanders, with only Glapwell (Beaten 0-3 at Mickleover) from the Supreme Division. Earlier, nine out of ten sides in the First Round were from the Central Midlands League with two Supreme sides defeated; Heanor at home to Stanton Ilkeston and Shirebrook Colliery by Glossop. As this system leaves nine sides in the Third Round, Glossop, having played in the previous two rounds were exempt. All of the three clubs from Round Two that played in Round Three lost at that stage, while Gresley opened their defence of the Cup with a 2-1 win at Alfreton. Exempt to the Fourth Round were West Midlands Divison One side Ilkeston Town, and Buxton, of the HFS Loans Premier Division, who played each other, and Stapenhill who drew Borrowash. Four home wins were recorded in the Quarter-Finals, and home advantage again told in the Semi-Finals where Matlock crushed Ilkeston and Gresley lost 2-3 at neighbours Stapenhill. Home adavatange counts less in the Final as it is two-legged. Matlock built a 2-1 lead in the home leg, and increaded it by a further goal to secure the Cup in the return at Stapenhill.

Derbyshire Senior Cup First Round

Long Eaton United v Biwater	2-1		Heanor Town v Stanton Ilkeston	1-3
Newhall United v Rolls Royce	3-3,6-1		Glapwell v Kilburn Miners Welfare	2-0
Shirebrook Colliery v Glossop	0-1			

Second Round

Long Eaton United v Newhall United	3-2		Stanton Ilkeston v Derby C. & W. Reckitts	1-0
Mickleover R.B.L. v Glapwell	3-0		West Hallam v Glossop	0-2

Third Round

Alfreton Town v Gresley Rovers	1-2		Borrowash Victoria v Stanton Ilkeston	3-0
Mickleover R.B.L. v Matlock Town	1-2		Long Eaton United v Belper Town	0-3

Quarter-Finals

Ilkeston Town v Buxton	1-0		Stapenhill v Borrowash Victora	3-0
Matlock Town v Belper Town	4-1		Gresley Rovers v Glossop	3-2

Semi-Finals

Stapenhill v Gresley Rovers	3-2		Matlock Town v Ilkeston Town	5-1

Final 1st Leg *(28th April)*: Matlock Town 2, Stapenhill 1
Final 2nd Leg *(4th May)*: Stapenhill 0, Matlock Town 1

Devon

The Devon-based Great Mills Western League clubs play in the St Lukes Challenge Cup leaving the rest of the county's clubs, including five Jewson South Western League sides (Appledore, Devon & Cornwall Police, Clyst Rovers, Holsworthy and Tavistock). Naturally this columnist looks first to see how these five faired - unlike their friends from across the Tamar, Devon South Western League clubs are not known for County Cup succcess. This season started as if it looked to change that with only Appledore falling in the Second Round and only the Police bowing out in the Third. Furthermore, their vanquishers were fellow South Western Leaguers Clyst and Tavistock. The big feature of the Fourth Round was to be the action in Newton Abbot where three sides were all at home. Newton Rangers went down 0-1 to Willand, Newton Abbott beat Buckfstleigh 2-1, whilst Spurs claimed the big result; 4-2 against Clyst. Tavistock scraped through by a single goal at Plymstock, and Holsworthy were held to a 4-4 draw at Coxside, triumphing 7-1 in the replay. So the Quarter-Final line-up boasted two JSWL sides, the two Newton Abbot clubs and Stoke Gabriel and Upton Athletic of the South Devon League, and Willand and Chelston from the Devon & Exeter League. Newton Abbot Spurs sprung the surprise with a 4-1 win over Holsworthy. '66 drew with Stoke Gabriel, but lost the replay and hence the chance of a derby against Spurs in the Semis. Tavistock beat Willand to keep JSWL hopes alive, but in the Semis were drawn against the strong Upton Athletic, and went out. With Stoke Gabriel beating Newton Abbot Spurs, the competition once again had an all South Devon League Final, and Upton won the Cup with a 2-1 victory over Stoke Gabriel at Torquay.

Devon Premier Cup First Round

Budleigh Salterton v Beer Albion	4-1		Exeter St Thomas v Buckland M.C.	0-2
Combe Martin v A.A. Taxis	6-1		Mount Gould Athletic v Topsham Town	3-6
Dolton Rangers v Honiton Town	1-3		Upton Vale v Appledore/B.A.A.C.	1-4
Yealm United v Northam Lions	3-2			

Second Round

Abbot Security v Marjons	0-0,0-2		Alphington v Wessex Rangers	8-1
Braunton v Lynton & Lynmouth	2-0		Brixham Villa v Coxside	1-2
Buckfastleigh Rangers v Bradworthy United	4-1		Chivenor v Dartmouth United	0-1
Combe Martin v Weston Mill Oak Villa	4-1		Clyst Rovers v Appledore/B.A.A.C.	3-1
Dartmouth Y.M.C.A. v Newton St Cyres	3-1		Devon & Cornwall Police v Ivybridge Town	5-1
Exeter Civil Service v Chelston	1-2		Buckland M.C. v Ivybridge United	4-6
Galmpton United v Cullompton Rangers	5-3		Greenwaves v S.T.C. Paignton	1-5
Holsworthy v Yealm United	3-1		Horrabridge Rangers v Chittlehampton	4-4,2-1
Lapford v Kingsteignton Athletic	6-0		Mainstone C.A. v Newton Rangers	1-4
Topsham Town v Plymouth Command	1-2		Newton Abbot '66 v Plymouth United	6-1
Newton Abbot Spurs v Budleigh Salterton	4-2		Okehampton Argyle v Plympton United	2-1
Plymouth Civil Service v Offwell & Widworthy	2-1		Plymstock United v Elburton Villa	2-2,3-0
Prince Rock v Fremington	2-0		S.B. Frankfort v South Molton	2-3
Shamwickshire Rovers v Barnstaple A.A.C.	1-3		Stoke Gabriel v Putford	8-0
Tavistock v Honiton Town	3-0		Teignmouth v Watts Blake Bearne	4-0
Upton Athletic v Dartington United	8-2		Willand Rovers v Exmouth Amateurs	4-1

Third Round

Barnstaple A.A.C. v Holsworthy	0-3		Buckfastleigh Rangers v Ivybridge United	3-1
Chelston v Galmpton United	2-1		Clyst Rovers v Braunton	4-0
Combe Martin v Plymouth Command	0-3		Coxside v Okekampton Argyle	2-1
Dartmouth Y.M.R.C. v South Molton	5-0		Devon & Cornwall Police v Tavistock	1-2
Horrabridge Rangers v Stoke Gabriel	1-2		Marjons v S.T.C. Paignton	3-1
Newton Abbot '66 v Lapford	3-1		Newton Abbot Spurs v Prince Rock	4-1
Plymouth Civil Service v Newton Rangers	0-2		Plymstock United v Teignmouth	5-2
Upton Athletic v Alphington	1-0		Willand Rovers v Dartmouth United	2-0

(Continued overleaf...)

Devon Premier Cup Fourth Round

Coxside v Holsworthy	4-4,1-7	Newton Abbot '66 v Buckfastleigh Rangers	2-1
Newton Rangers v Willand Rovers	0-1	Newton Abbot Spurs v Clyst Rovers	4-2
Plymouth Command v Chelston	1-3	Plymstock United v Tavistock	0-1
Stoke Gabriel v Dartmouth Y.M.R.C.	2-0	Upton Athletic v Marjons	9-0

Quarter-Finals

Newton Abbot '66 v Stoke Gabriel	1-1,1-4	Willand Rovers v Tavistock	1-2
Newton Abbot Spurs v Holsworthy	4-1	Chelston v Upton Athletic	0-1

Semi-Finals

Tavistock v Upton Athletic	1-2	Stoke Gabriel v Newton Abbot Spurs	2-1

Final *(at Torquay United FC, 31st March)*: Upton Athletic 2, Stoke Gabriel 1

Dorset

After a First Round that involves only Dorset Combination sides, the fun starts in Round Two. Two Channel Island clubs were again involved this year, and both were awarded home draws. This is not normally a problem to the visitors, and Weymouth travelled to Guernsey winning 2-1 at Northerners whilst Swanage went to Jersey and won by the same margin at St Pauls. The biggest shock of the round saw Beazer Premier club Poole Town lose at home to Wimborne of the Wessex League. Four all Dorset Combination ties enabled Cranborne, Blandford, Flight Refuelling and Sherborne reach the Quarters, while Bridport beat Shaftesbury in a replay to complete the last eight. There were no surprises in the Quarters with only Flight Refuelling, 1-0 win at Sherborne, surviving from the Combination. Cranborne lost 0-8 at Weymouth while Blandford held up better going down just 0-2 to Wimborne. Bridport completed the Semi-Final line-up with a 2-0 win over Swanage. Wimborne, playing this Cup as their FA Vase run livened up, reached the Final with a 3-0 win over Flight Refuelling, but Weymouth were perhaps distracted by their Beazer Southern Division promotion push. They lost to Bridport, who were subsequently beaten by a Wimborne team that thus adorned their trophy cabinet with silverware even before Wembley.

Dorset Senior Cup First Round

Portland United v Wareham Rangers	0-1	Parley Sports v Blandford United	0-0,1-5
Cranborne v Bournemouth Sports Club	2-1	Holt United v Sturminster Newton	1-0

Second Round

Poole Town v Wimborne Town	0-1	Holt United v Cranborne	1-3
Northerners Athletic v Weymouth	1-2	Blandford United v Hamworthy United	1-0
Shaftesbury v Bridport	1-1,0-4	Gillingham Town v Flight Refuelling	2-4
Sherborne Town v Wareham Rangers	5-2	St Pauls Jersey v Swanage Town & Herston	1-2

Quarter-Finals

Blandford United v Wimborne Town	0-2	Sherborne Town v Flight Refuelling	0-1
Weymouth v Cranborne	8-0	Bridport v Swanage Town & Herston	2-0

Semi-Finals

Flight Refuelling v Wimborne Town	0-3	Bridport v Weymouth	

Final *(at Swanage Town & Herston FC, 14th May)*: Wimborne Town 1, Bridport 0

Durham

The Senior Cup was played as two pre-season groups ech containing four teams. In Group 1, Darlington, despite only drawing with Sunderland and Gateshead, won through by beating Bishop Auckland 4-0. Sunderland finished bottom after losing to Bishop Auckland. Hartlepool United won all three games in their group against Northern League opposition, Billingham Synthonia and Consett, and Wearside League Eppleton. The final was held at Feethams with the home side winning 2-1.

Durham Senior Cup

Darlington v Sunderland	0-0	Billingham Synthonia v Hartlepool United	0-1
Gateshead v Darlington	1-1	Eppleton Colliery Welfare v Billingham Synthonia	2-2
Bishop Auckland v Gateshead	2-2	Eppleton Colliery Welfare v Hartlepool United	1-3
Gateshead v Sunderland	2-2	Billingham Synthonia v Consett	3-0
Darlington v Bishop Auckland	4-0	Consett v Hartlepool United	1-2
Bishop Auckland v Sunderland	2-0	Consett v Eppleton Colliery Welfare	4-0

	P	W	D	L	F	A	Pts		P	W	D	L	F	A	Pts
Darlington	3	1	2	0	5	1	5	Hartlepool United	3	3	0	0	6	2	9
Bishop Auckland	3	1	1	1	4	6	4	Billingham Synthonia	3	1	1	1	5	3	4
Gateshead	3	0	3	0	5	5	3	Consett	3	1	0	2	5	5	3
Sunderland	0	2	1	2	2	4	2	Eppleton Colliery	3	0	1	2	3	9	1

Final *(at Darlington FC, 10th September)*: Darlington 2, Hartlepool United 1

The Durham Challenge Cup has always held more interest for locals, and while traditionally a Northern League preserve, there has always been room for other teams to challenge. More so now with the area having clubs in the HFS Loans and Northern Counties (East) Leagues. Conference club Gateshead still don't enter. Minor shocks started in the First Qualifying Round where Wingate of the Second Division of the Wearside League won at Northern League club Washington. Wingate lost to Darlington Cleveland Bridge in Second Qualifying Round, but here we saw the debut of the season's surprise team, Cockfield of the Auckland & District League, won won 2-0 at Northern League club Horden. Meanwhile, Wearside League teams claimed further scalps at Darlington Railway Athletic where West Auckland Town lost 1-4, at Hartlepool Town where Peterlee Newtown fell 0-1, and finally at Willington where SC Vaux Ryhope won 3-1. All these three lost to Northern League outfits in the First Round Proper, but the Wearside League did manage a couple of victories with Annfield Plain thrashing Northern League Langley Park and South Shields taking Easington in a replay, and of course little Cockfield carried on with a 2-1 win over Dunston Federration Brewery. Spennymoor drew 3-3 with Murton but then scratched, while Bishop Auckland were also held before beating old rivals Crook. The Bishops then had to take on holders Billingham Synthonia, and this proved too much, Synners winning 2-0 away. South Shields tost to Ryhope CA, but Annfield Plain kept the Wearside League flag flying with a replay win over Chester-le-Street. Meanwhile, Cockfield claimed their third scalp, Durham, to reach the Quarter-Finals, but this was the end of the road as they went down 1-2 at home to the holders. Murton joined Synthonia in the Semis by ending Annfield Plain's run, and away wins for Ryhope at Norton & Stockton Ancients and Hebburn at Brandon set up the other Semi-Final. As expected, Synners and Hebburn won their ties, and in the final in-form Hebburn, who won their last twelve leagues matches, upset the odds and took the Cup.

Durham Challenge Cup First Qualifying Round

Silksworth v Swalwell	2-1	Washington v Wingate	0-1
West Auckland Town v Hartlepool B.W.O.B.	4-0		

Second Qualifying Round

Horden Colliery Welfare v Cockfield	0-2	Darlington Railway Ath. v West Auckland Town	4-1
Silksworth v Langley Park	2-6	Tow Law Town v Seaham Red Star	1-2
Ryhope Community Assn v Stanley United	3-0	Billingham Town v Boldon C.A.	2-0
Chester-le-Street Town v Herrington C.W.	2-0	Wingate v Darlington Cleveland Br.	1-3
Sunderland I.F.G. Roker v Wolviston	3-1	Blackhall Colliery Welfare *(Scrat)* South Shields	W/O
Norton & Stockton Ancients v Whickham	3-0	Hartlepool Town v Peterlee Newtown	1-0
Shotton Comrades v Brandon United	1-5	South Shields Cleadon S.C. v Annfield Plain	1-6
Esh Winning Albion v Jarrow Roofing	0-0,3-1	Willington v S.C. Vaux Ryhope	1-3

First Round Proper

Seaham Red Star v Esh Winning	1-0	Darlington Railway Athletic v Billingham Synthonia	1-4
Annfield Plain v Langley Park	5-0	Consett v Chester-le-Street Town	0-1
Ryhope C.A. v Newton Aycliffe	0-0,1-0	Eppleton Colliery Welfare v Hebburn	1-2
Billingham Town v Darlington Cleveland Br.	2-0	Norton & Stockton Anc. v Sunderland V. Ryhope	3-0
Evenwood Town v Hartlepool Town	1-0	Sunderland I.F.G Roker v Durham City	2-6
Spennymoor v Murton	3-3*(Spennymoor scr.)*	Brandon United v Esh Winning Albion	3-1
Shildon v Ferryhill Athletic	2-2,0-1	Bishop Auckland v Crook Town	1-1*(aet)*,1-0
South Shields v Easington Colliery	2-2,3-0	Cockfield v Dunston Federation Brewery	2-1

Second Round

South Shields v Ryhope Community Assn.	0-1	Brandon United v Billingham Town	2-1
Norton & Stockton Anc. v Evenwood Town	2-1	Bishop Auckland v Billingham Synthonia	0-2
Seaham Red Star v Murton	0-1	Annfield Plain v Chester-le-Street Town	2-2,4-3
Hebburn v Ferryhill Athletic	2-1	Cockfield v Durham City	4-2

Quarter-Finals

Brandon United v Hebburn	1-2	Norton & Stockton Anc. v Ryhope Comm. Assn	1-4
Cockfield v Billingham Synthonia	1-2	Annfield Plain v Murton	2-4

Semi-Finals

Ryhope Community v Hebburn	1-3	Billingham Synthonia v Murton	1-0

Final *(at Murton FC, 4th May)*: Hebburn 2, Billingham 1

East Anglia

The East Anglian Cup is played in eight groups in the early rounds, although these are all on a KO basis. The eight winners were Wisbech, Diss and Clacton all of the Jewson Eastern League, Sudbury of the Beazer, Hoddesdon of the South Midlands League, Eynesbury of the United Counties League, and Diadora clubs Bishop's Stortford and Royston. Sudbury beat old rivals Wisbech 7-2, Eynesbury came through against Clacton, Royston beat Diss, and Bishop's Stortford recorded the only away win of the Quarters, at Hoddesdon. In the Semis, Stortford were whipped at Sudbury and Eynesbury won at Royston to earn the right to stage the final, but home advantage did not prevent them losing to an injury time goal.

East Anglian Cup First Round

Long Sutton Athletic v King's Lynn	3-2	Norwich United v Lowestoft Town	1-0
Mirrlees Blackstone v Bourne Town	2-8	Diss Town *(bye)*	
Downham Town v Wisbech Town	0-6	Fakenham Town v Wroxham	1-2
Holbeach United v Stamford	2-5	Gorleston v Watton United	0-1
Stowmarket Town v Harwich & Parkeston	1-0	Heybridge Swifts v Halstead Town	3-0
Witham Town v Brantham Athletic	1-1,1-3	Sudbury Town v Burnham Ramblers	4-0
Clacton Town *(bye)*		Bury Town v Thetford Town	7-0
Colchester United v Woodbridge Town	1-2	Cornard United v Tiptree United	4-1
Hoddesdon Town v Eton Manor	7-0	Hertford Town v Haverhill Rovers	2-1
Rainham Town v Aveley *(at Aveley)*	1-0	Stansted v Bishop's Stortford	1-3
Barkingside *(bye)*		Braintree Town *(bye)*	
East Thurrock United v Woodford Town	2-1	Harlow Town v Ware *(at Ware)*	2-0
Histon v Cranfield United	6-0	Huntingdon United v Eynesbury Rovers	0-2
Letchworth Garden City v Arlesey Town	3-4	March Town United v Biggleswade Town	3-1
Baldock Town v Saffron Walden Town	3-4	Chatteris Town v Somersham Town	0-1
Cambridge City v Royston Town	0-1	Ely City v Soham Town Rangers	3-2

Group Semi-Finals

Long Sutton Athletic v Bourne Town	1-3	Norwich United v Diss Town	1-4
Wisbech Town v Stamford	3-1	Wroxham v Watton United	3-1
Stowmarket Town v Brantham Athletic	1-2	Heybridge Swifts v Sudbury Town	0-3
Clacton Town v Woodbridge Town	1-0	Bury Town v Cornard United	5-4
Hoddesdon Town v Rainham Town	6-1	Hertford Town v Bishop's Stortford	0-1
Barkingside v East Thurrock United	2-1	Braintree Town v Harlow Town	0-2
Histon v Arlesey Town	2-1	Eynesbury Rovers v March Town United	2-1
Saffron Walden Town v Royston Town	0-2	Somersham Town v Ely City	0-0,0-1

Group Finals

Bourne Town v Wisbech Town	4-5	Diss Town v Wroxham	3-2*(aet)*
Brantham Athletic v Clacton Town	1-1,1-3*(aet)*	Sudbury Town v Bury Town	4-2
Hoddesdon Town v Barkingside	4-2	Bishop's Stortford v Harlow Town	2-1
Histon v Royston Town	1-3	Eynesbury Rovers v Ely City	4-1

Quarter-Finals

Sudbury Town v Wisbech Town	7-2	Hoddesdon Town v Bishop's Stortford	2-3
Eynesbury Rovers v Clacton Town	2-0	Royston Town v Diss Town	1-0

Semi-Finals

Sudbury Town v Bishop's Stortford	4-1	Royston Town v Eynesbury Rovers	2-3

Final *(at Eynesbury Rovers FC, 11th May)*: Eynesbury Rovers 0, Sudbury Town 1 *(aet)*

East Riding

It seems almost inevitable that the 'big' sides in East Riding, few as they are, inflict casulties on each other in early rounds, and so it proved this season with Bridlington meeting North Ferriby in Round One when most clubs gained byes. Bridlington won this one, then had no trouble with Hilltop in Round Two. Hull City and Hall Road Rangers also negociated the Second Round, but Bridlington had to go to Hull in the Quarters and won 4-3. Victory at Westella Shopacheck of the East Riding League gave Hall Road a Semi-Final place, while the other matches were won by Reckitts and Schultz YC. Reckitts held Bridlington in the Semis before losing the reply, but Schultz went one better defeating Hall Road before finding Bridlington too strong in the Final.

East Riding Senior Cup First Round

Malet Lambert YC v Solagas	2-1	
Wards Gilberdyke W/O Hull Teachers *(Scr.)*		

Bridlington Town v North Ferriby United	2-0
Calvier v Hedon United	1-0

Second Round

Schultz YC v Wards Gilberdyke	3-1
Hull City v Hull Old Grammarians	2-1
Sculcoates Amateurs v Cavalier	2-1
Haltemprice v Ideal Standard	1-2

Hall Road Rangers v Malet Lambert YC	3-1
Saltshouse Tavern v Reckitts	1-4
Westella Shopacheck v Kelvin Hall	2-4*(ab)*,3-0
Bridlington Town v Hilltop	5-0

Quarter-Finals

Hull City v Bridlington Town	3-4
Schultz YC v Sculcoates Amateurs	3-0

Westella Shopacheck v Hall Road Rangers	1-3
Ideal Standard v Reckitts	2-3

Semi-Finals

Bridlington v Reckitts *(Dene Pk, Dunwell, 14th Apr)*	1-1,2-1
Hall Rd v Schultz *(Northern Foods FC, 15th Apr.)*	1-2

Final *(At Hull City FC, 4th April)*: Bridlington Town 2, Schultz Y.C. 1

Eastern Floodlit Competition

In the Eastern Floodlit Competition there are eight groups on a league basis. The were winners were Beazer Premier club Dover Athletic, East Thurrock of the Essex Senior League, Jewson Eastern side Harwich & Parkeston, Spartan Leaguers Waltham Abbey, and Diadora clubs Heybridge, Barking, Saffron Walden and Stevenage. The Quarter-Finals yielded home wins for Barking, Harwich and Saffron Walden, and a 3-0 away success for Stevenage at Waltham Abbey. Winning away at Barking, Harwich earned the right to stage the Final, against Saffron Walden who came through their tie against Stevenage. At Harwich, Saffron Walden triumphed 3-1 to take the Cup.

Group One

Ashford Town v Dover Athletic	0-4
Dover Athletic v Ashford Town	7-3
Ashford Town v Hythe Town	0-1
Hythe Town v Ashford Town	0-0
Dover Athletic v Hythe Town	4-2
Hythe Town v Dover Athletic	0-1

	P	W	D	L	F	A	Pts
Dover Athletic	4	4	0	0	16	5	12
Hythe Town	4	1	1	2	3	5	4
Ashford Town	4	0	1	3	3	12	1

Group Two

Cornard United v Halstead Town	1-1
Halstead Town v Cornard United	3-2
Cornard United v Saffron Walden Town	1-1
Saffron Walden Town v Cornard United	2-2
Cornard United v Sudbury Town	2-3
Sudbury Town v Cornard United	0-1
Halstead Town v Sudbury Town	0-3
Sudbury Town v Halstead Town	1-4
Halstead Town v Saffron Walden Town	3-3
Saffron Walden Town v Halstead Town	6-2
Sudbury Town v Saffron Walden Town	2-0
Saffron Walden Town v Sudbury Town	2-0

	P	W	D	L	F	A	Pts
Saffron Walden	6	2	3	1	14	10	9
Sudbury Town	6	3	0	3	9	9	9
Halstead Town	6	2	2	2	13	16	8
Cornard United	6	1	3	2	9	10	6

Group Three

Chelmsford City v Harwich & Parkeston	1-4
Harwich Parkeston v Chelmsford City	5-2
Chelmsford City v Tiptree United	2-2
Tiptree United v Chelmsford City	0-5
Harwich & Parkeston v Tiptree United	0-0
Tiptree United v Harwich & Parkeston	0-4

	P	W	D	L	F	A	Pts
Harwich & Parkeston	4	3	1	0	13	3	10
Chelmsford City	4	1	1	2	10	11	4
Tiptree United	4	0	2	2	2	11	2

Group Four

Clacton Town v Heybridge Swifts	0-5
Heybridge Swifts v Clacton Town	2-0
Clacton Town v Witham Town	0-3
Witham Town v Clacton Town	4-3
Heybridge Swifts v Witham Town	0-0
Witham Town v Heybridge Swifts	1-1

	P	W	D	L	F	A	Pts
Heybridge Swifts	4	2	2	0	8	1	8
Witham Town	4	2	2	0	8	4	8
Clacton Town	4	0	0	4	3	14	0

Group Five

Barking v Burnham Ramblers	2-0
Burnham Ramblers v Barking	3-3
Barking v Stambridge	2-0
Stambridge v Barking	3-3
Burnham Ramblers v Stambridge	2-4
Stambridge v Burnham Ramblers	2-1

	P	W	D	L	F	A	Pts
Barking	4	2	2	0	10	6	8
Stambridge	4	2	1	1	9	8	7
Burnham Ramblers	4	0	1	3	6	11	1

Group Six

Baldock Town v Royston Town	2-1
Royston Town v Baldock Town	1-2
Baldock Town v Stevenage Borough	0-1
Stevenage Borough v Baldock Town	3-1
Baldock Town v Welwyn Garden City	1-2
Welwyn Garden City v Baldock Town	0-4
Royston Town v Welwyn Garden City	1-0
Welwyn Garden City v Royston Town	2-1
Royston Town v Stevenage Borough	0-1
Stevenage Borough v Royston Town	2-0
Welwyn Garden City v Stevenage Borough	1-1
Stevenage Borough v Welwyn Garden City	6-1

	P	W	D	L	F	A	Pts
Stevenage Boro.	6	5	1	0	14	3	16
Baldock Town	6	3	0	3	10	8	9
Welwyn Garden City	6	2	1	3	6	14	7
Royston Town	6	1	0	5	4	8	3

Group Seven

Basildon United v Collier Row	2-3
Collier Row v Basildon United	0-1
Basildon United v East Thurrock United	4-2
East Thurrock United v Basildon United	5-2
Collier Row v East Thurrock United	2-4
East Thurrock United v Collier Row	2-3

	P	W	D	L	F	A	Pts
East Thurrock Utd	4	2	0	2	13	11	6
Basildon United	4	2	0	2	9	10	6
Collier Row	4	2	0	2	8	9	6

Group Eight

Harlow Town v Standsted	N/A
Stansted v Harlow Town	N/A
Harlow Town v Waltham Abbey	2-0*(void)*
Waltham Abbey v Harlow Town	2-3*(void)*
Stansted v Waltham Abbey	4-5
Waltham Abbey v Stansted	0-0

	P	W	D	L	F	A	Pts
Waltham Abbey	2	1	1	0	5	4	4
Stansted	4	0	1	1	4	5	1

Harlow failed to fulfill fixtures with Stansted - recorded expunged.

Eastern Floodlit Competition Quarter-Finals

Barking v Heybridge Swifts	2-0	Harwich & Parkeston v Dover Athletic	1-0
Saffron Walden Town v East Thurrock United	4-2	Waltham Abbey v Stevenage Borough	0-3

Semi-Finals

Saffron Walden Town v Stevenage Borough	2-0	Barking v Harwich & Parkeston	1-2

Final *(at Harwich & Parkeston FC, 7th May)*: Harwich & Parkeston 1, Saffron Walden Town 3

Essex

Looking first at the Senior Cup, we see in the First Round that Chelmsford needed extra-time to win at Collier Row by the odd goal in seven. Four First Round ties were all-Diadora affairs, while Braintree of the Beazer League won at Rainham, and Conference side Colchester could only manage a narrow win over Tilbury. Football League side Southend beat Colchester in the Second Round while Orient also went through, against Saffron Walden. Redbridge Forest carried the Conference flag forward beating Barking, and both Beazer League clubs progressed at the expense of Diadora sides. This left three Quarter-Final places for Diadora League sides and they went to Purfleet, Dagenham and Harlow, the latter beating Premier Division Wivenhoe. Harlow's run ended when they lost at home to Southend, Redbridge beat Dagenham in the groundshare derby, Chelmsford set up a Semi-Final against the other Football League club by beating Orient, and Braintree completed the line-up beating Purfleet after a replay. Both Semis were close affairs with the original matches being tied. Redbridge and Chelmsford eventually won through, and, in front of 950 crowd at Braintree, the Conference side secured the Cup with a 3-0 win.

Essex Senior Cup First Round

Saffron Walden Town v Witham Town	5-1	Collier Row v Chelmsford City	3-4*(aet)*
Hornchurch v Harlow Town	0-1	Rainham Town v Braintree Town	0-2
Colchester United v Tilbury	2-1	Purfleet v Clapton	5-3
Barking v Leyton-Wingate	2-0		

Second Round

Heybridge Swifts v Chelmsford City	1-5	Dagenham v Grays Athletic	2-1
Purfleet v Billericay Town	2-1	Colchester United v Southend United	0-1
Wivenhoe Town v Harlow Town	1-4	Barking v Redbridge Forest	0-1
Leyton Orient v Saffron Walden Town	3-2	Braintree Town v Aveley	1-0

Quarter-Finals

Purfleet v Braintree Town	3-3*(aet)*,1-5	Leyton Orient v Chelmsford City	1-3
Harlow Town v Southend United	0-2	Redbridge Forest v Dagenham	3-1

Semi-Finals

Redbridge Forest v Braintree Town	1-1*(aet)*,1-0	Southend United v Colchester United	0-0,2-3

Final *(at Braintree Town FC, 13th April)*: Redbridge Forest 3, Chelmsford City 0

The Challenge Trophy is dominated by the Essex Senior League with sixteen of the twenty five entries last season. The other entrants came from the London Spartan (four clubs) and the Jewson Eastern (five). Mixed league ties in the First Round brought big wins for Spartan Leaguers Waltham Abbey and Walthamstow Pennant against Concord Rangers and Halstead Town. One Spartan side did go down, Beckton at Tiptree, while Eastern League Brightlingsea fell at home to East Thurrock. So on to the Second Round where Pennant won at Waltham Abbey, and Barkingside crushed Maldon to give the Spartan League two Quarter-Finalists. The Jewson Eastern League got only Harwich through as Clacton lost to Southend Manor and Tiptree, after doing the hard part in drawing away, lost a replay against Ford. The three all-Essex Senior affairs yielded wins for Woodford, Bowers and East Thurrock, and the Quarters were a whitewash for the Senior League despite an unpromising draw. Ford then beat Bowers to reach the Final, where East Thurrock, after a single goal win at Woodford were to stand in the way of them retaining the Cup. The resistance offered however was to no avail as the Cup was settled by a 3-0 margin, Ford retaining the Trophy at Burnham Ramblers.

Essex Senior Trophy First Round

Waltham Abbey v Concord Rangers	4-1	Eton Manor v Canvey Island	1-3
Woodford Town v Hullbridge Sports	4-0	Tiptree United v Beckton United	3-1
Brightlingsea United v East Thurrock United	0-2	Maldon Town v East Ham United	4-2
Stambridge v Brentwood	2-1	Basildon United v Harwich & Parkeston	3-5
Walthamstow Pennant v Halstead Town	6-1		

Second Round

Canvey Island v Woodford Town	0-2	Waltham Abbey v Walthamstow Pennant	1-2
Ford United v Tiptree United	0-0,2-1	East Thurrock United v Stambridge	7-4*(aet)*
Harwich & Parkeston v Burnham Ramblers	2-0	Clacton Town v Southend Manor	2-3
Barkingside v Maldon Town	4-0	Stansted v Bowers United	1-2

Quarter-Finals

Harwich & Parkeston v Ford United	1-2	Woodford Town v Southend Manor	1-0
Barkingside v East Thurrock United	1-2	Walthamstow Pennant v Bowers United	0-2

Semi-Finals

Ford Utd v Bowers Utd *(15th February)*	2-1	Woodford T. v East Thurrock U. *(29th February)*	0-1

Final *(at Burnham Ramblers FC, 11th April)*: Ford United 3, East Thurrock United 0

In the Essex Thames-side Trophy, First Round games were generally very even with no real surprises. Purfleet beat Walthamstow Pennant by 3 goals to nil, Tilbury beat Aveley by 2 goals to 0, and Collier Row beat newcomers Southend Manor by 4 goals to 2, in games where goal differences were more than one. The more even games saw Basildon, Leyton-Wingate and Eton Manor progress by the odd goal in three. In the Second Round, Collier Row had a good 1-0 win over Leyton Wingate, Chelmsford City accounted for Tilbury by 2 goals to 1, and Grays Athletic proved too good for Rainham Town winning by 4 goals to 0. Burnham Ramblers beat Barkingside after a marathon tie which finally ended at 10.40pm. With the scores tied at 2 apiece, the match went into penalties. All 22 players featured in this tense finish which finally was decided 8-7. Billericay comfortably made the Quarter Finals as did Dagenham, but two Essex Senior League sides Canvey Island and Ford United had harder games before both also progressed. The tie between Basildon United and Canvey Island had to be abandoned at full time because of adverse ground conditions and the replay was the first match to be played under Canvey's new floodlights. The brilliance of Canvey's lights, however, caused many a problem for this friendly club, as residents protested and embargoes were put on their use in that matches had to be completed by 9.30pm. The fact that the club had a good run right to the Semi Final stage with many of their games played at home did no good to the nerves of the hard working committee as each match ran perilously close to the allotted time. In this run, Canvey eventually accounted for Basildon and beat Grays Athletic - the holders, before falling themselves to Ford in another tight game at the Semi Final stage. En route to the other Semi Final, Dagenham hammered Burnham Ramblers and Billericay Town defeated Collier Row. The Semi Final at Dagenham was very close and was only

(continued from overleaf)

decided in the very last minute of extra time when Billericay Town scored the solitary goal. Ford had a remarkable season culminating in the narrowest of defeats in their first appearance in the Final. After a pulsating match during which they had led for some time, they eventually were defeated by Billericay Town on penalties after they had drawn two goals a piece after extra time. Morris Jeffers (President) assisted by Tony Oliver (Hon Secretary) awarded the trophy and mementoes. Ford United also had their floodlights installed during the season, although they did not have the opportunity to use them in the Essex Thames-side Trophy. However, this did in effect signify that every club in the competition now has floodlights.

Essex Thames-side Trophy First Round

Aveley v Tilbury	0-2	Southend Manor v Collier Row		2-4
Basildon United v East Thurrock United	2-1	Leyton-Wingate v Clapton		2-1
Woodford Town v Eton Manor	1-2	Purfleet v Walthamstow Pennant		3-0

Second Round

Collier Row v Leyton-Wingate	1-0	Barkingside v Burnham R.	2-2*(aet, 7-8 penalties)*	
Hornchurch v Billericay Town	0-3	Eton Manor v Dagenham *(at Dagenham)*		0-5
Purfleet v Ford United	1-2	Basildon v Canvey	1-1*(ab. 90m)*,0-1*(aet, at Canvey)*	
Rainham Town v Grays Athletic *(at Grays)*	0-4	Chelmsford City v Tilbury		3-2

Quarter-Finals

Dagenham v Burnham Ramblers	7-1	Billericay Town v Collier Row		4-2
Canvey Island v Grays Athletic	3-1	Chelmsford City v Ford Utd	1-1*(aet, 1-2 penalties)*	

Semi-Finals

Canvey Island v Ford United	0-1*(aet)*	Dagenham v Billericay Town	0-1*(aet)*

Final *(20th April)*: Billericay Town 2, Ford United 2 *(Billericay won 4-2 on penalties)*

Gloucestershire

Despite having now been expanded to five clubs, the Gloucestershire (Northern) Senior Cup is considered a downbeat competition in the area. The word Northern is no longer accurate as two Southern sides now compete, with Mangotsfield who losing at Stroud in the First Round. In the Semis, Stroud lost at Gloucester and Cheltenham won at Yate to set up a final between the big two. The match was decided in extra-time, Cheltenham putting poor league form behind them to win 4-2.

Gloucestershire (Northern) Senior Cup First Round

Stroud v Mangotsfield United	1-0

Semi-Finals

Gloucester City v Stroud	2-1	Yate Town v Cheltenham Town	0-1

Final *(at Cheltenham Town FC, 7th April)*: Cheltenham Town 4, Gloucester City 2 *(aet)*

In the Senior Trophy, Hellenic teams tend to come to the fore, this year especially as Western League Mangotsfield had switched to the Cup (see above), but this news is little consolation to Moreton who lost 0-6 at home to fellow Hellenic Premier side Cinderford. Bishop's Cleeve lost the other all-Hellenic Premier clash against Cirencester Town, but while Shortwood won convincingly at Dowty, two other sides from their league went down; Almondsbury at Western League Bristol Manor Farm, and Cirencester United at County League sides D.R.G. There were five all-Gloucestershire County League ties in Round One, plus a 5-1 win for Hallen over Longwell Green, the sole Somerset Senior League contenders. The big match in the Second Round saw Shortwood beat Cinderford, while D.R.G. gained their second Hellenic scalp; Fairford. Tuffley, exempt in Round One, won 4-2 at Campden Town, while Cirencester (1-0 v Hambrook), and Manor Farm (2-1 at St Phillips Marsh) beat County opposition. Patchway, Wotton and St Marks CA were also successful, and a freak Quarter-Final draw placed all County League clubs at home. Not that this helped; all bar D.R.G. lost at the first attempt, and they went out to Tuffley in a replay. Shortwood and Cirencester won through from the Semis, and by the time of the Final it was known that one of the two contestants would win the Hellenic League. Shortwood were victorious on both fronts, beating Cirencester 2-1 at Gloucester in the Senior Trophy and winning 2-1 at Almondsbury a week later to snatch the league as well.

Shortwood United with the G.F.A. Trophy after their victory over Cirencester Town at Gloucester. The players holding the Cup are M Williams and T Baycliffe. Photo courtesy of the Gloucester Citizen.

Gloucestershire Challenge Trophy First Round

Moreton Town v Cinderford Town	0-6	Cirencester Town v Bishops Cleeve	2-0
Dowty Dynamos v Shortwood United	0-5	Pucklechurch Sports v Cadbury Heath	3-0
Patchway Town v Ellwood	2-1	St Philips Marsh Adult School v Port of Bristol	4-1
Wotton Rovers v Old Georgians	3-1	Hallen v Longwell Green Abbotonians	5-1
Henbury Old Boys v Campden Town	1-3	Bristol Manor Farm v Almondsbury Picksons	0-0,2-1
Stapleton v Fairford Town	2-2,1-2	D.R.G. (F.P.) v Cirencester United	2-2,2-0

Second Round

Campden Town v Tuffley Rovers	2-4	Harrow Hill v Patchway Town	1-1,1-3
St Philips Marsh A.S. v Bristol Mnr Farm	1-2	Cirencester Town v Hambrook	1-0
Hallen v St Marks C.A.	2-3	Pucklechurch Sports v Wotton Rovers	1-2
Shortwood United v Cinderford Town	2-0	D.R.G. (F.P.) v Fairford Town	1-0

Quarter-Finals

D.R.G. (F.P.) v Tuffley Rovers	1-1,1-3	St Marks C.A. v Shortwood United	1-5
Patchway Town v Cirencester Town	1-3	Wotton Rovers v Bristol Manor Farm	0-1

Semi-Finals

Shortwood Utd v Bristol M.F. *(at Yate Town)*	2-1	Tuffley v Cirencester *(both at Shortwood)*	3-3,1-3

Final *(at Gloucester City FC, 29th April)*: Shortwood United 2, Cirencester Town 1 *(aet)*

Gloucestershire Senior Cup Final *(at Stroud Town FC, 15th April)*: Cheltenham Saracens 6, Vikings (Stroud) 5

Hampshire

With 46 teams of standards varying from two Football League sides and Conference club Farnborough down to the top division of the Hampshire League, and a club each from Guernsey and Jersey, the Hampshire Senior Cup holds the potential to be a very interesting competition. With most byes awarded randomly, this starts in the Preliminary Round where the Wessex League lost three sides to challengers from the Hampshire League. In each tie there was just a single decisive goal; for Downton this was achieved at East Cowes, Whitchurch scored theirs at home to Portsmouth RN, while Colden Common, having gone goalless at Horndean, scored the only goal of the replay. Looking in the other direction, Hants League Fleetlands and Bishops Waltham let in six and five respectively at Bashley and Havant of the Beazer League. There was some joy for the Jewson Wessex with Eastleigh beating Cove and Romsey knocking-out an Andover side that finished with just nine men. Result of the Round however must must to Hants League Blackfield & Langley for a victory over Diadora League Petersfield. In the First Round we see entries from Football League duo AFC Bournemouth (who pasted DCA Basingstoke) and Aldershot (2-0 winners at Basingstoke Town). The Channel Isles pair came in, and as with the Dorset pair, both were draw but had no success, Blackfield & Langley winning at Jersey Wanderers and Fareham getting the only goal at Vale Recreation. There were no further successes for the Hants League bar Malshanger's win over Alresford from the same league. The Beazer Premier sides both had close calls, Bashley against Ryde and Waterlooville against Downton, while pride of place goes to Havant for 4-1 win away to an albeit weakened Farnborough side. In the Second Round the lone Dan-Air side, Hartley Wintney, went down at Gosport, and it was exit time also for the remaining Hants Leaguers. The two Football League sides met at Bournemouth where Aldershot won 1-0, but the only other away wins were for Romsey in an all-Wessex tie at Eastleigh, and and Waterlooville in their replay at Fareham. Wessex League Fleet surprisingly beat Newport I.O.W. 2-1. In the Third Round the Beazer League reigned almost supreme with Bashley defeating Gosport and Waterlooville and Havant both winning on Wessex grounds. The remaing tie saw Aldershot beat Romsey 3-1, but winners folded before the Semis and Romsey were re-instated only to lose 4-1 Havant in the last four. Waterlooville surprised Bashley in the other Semi-Final, and then took the Cup by the same scoreline as part of an end of season run that saw them avoid relegation having struggled for most of the season.

Hampshire Senior Cup Preliminary Round

Alton Town Bass v Hartley Wintney	0-3	Bashley v Fleetlands	6-0
Bournemouth v Newport Isle of Wight	0-1	East Cowes Victoria Athletic v Downton	0-1
Whitchurch United v Portsmouth Royal Navy	1-0	Horndean v Colden Common	0-0,0-1
Eastleigh v Cove	3-2(aet)	Aerostructures Spts & Social v ISL Midanury	2-1
Christchurch v A.C. Delco	2-1	Bemerton Heath Harlequins v A.F.C. Totton	2-0
A.F.C. Lymington v Gosport Borough	1-1,1-2	Havant Town v Bishops Waltham Town	5-1
Petersfield United v Blackfield & Langley	1-2	Romsey Town v Andover	1-0

First Round

Hartley Wintney v Locksheath	3-0	Newport I.O.W. *W/O* Bemerton Heath Harlequins	
Eastleigh v Whitchurch United	4-1	Gosport Borough v Colden Common	4-1
Fleet Town v Christchurch	3-0	AFC Bournemouth v D.C.A. Basingstoke	6-0
Jersey Wanderers v Blackfield & Langley	2-3	Vale Recreation v Fareham Town	0-1
Bashley v Ryde Sports	2-1	Downton v Waterlooville	1-2
Brockenhurst v B.A.T.	2-3	Malshanger v Alresford Town	4-0
Pirelli General v Romsey Town	1-1(aet),2-3	Sholing Sports v Aerostructures Spts & Social	0-1
Farnborough Town v Havant Town	1-4	Basingstoke Town v Aldershot	0-2

Second Round

Havant Town v B.A.T.	2-0	Eastleigh v Romsey Town	0-2
Fleet Town v Newport Isle of Wight	2-1	Aerostructures v Blackfield & Langley	4-1(aet)
Gosport Borough v Hartley Wintney	6-2	Bashley v Malshanger	3-1
Waterlooville v Fareham Town	3-3(aet),2-1	A.F.C. Bournemouth v Aldershot	0-1

Quarter-Finals

Bashley v Gosport Borough	2-1	Fleet Town v Waterlooville	1-2
Aldershot v Romsey Town	3-1	Aerostructures Spts & Social v Havant Town	1-4

Semi-Finals

W'ville v Bashley *(at Eastleigh, 18th March)*	1-0	Havant v Romsey *(at Basingstoke, 25th March)*	4-1

Final *(at Portsmouth FC)*: Waterlooville 1, Havant Town 0

Herefordshire

Hinton have recently pulled out of the West Midlands League, and now play in the Herefordshire League, but this does not prevent them from still having success in the County Cup, as victories over Golden Valley, Thorn Lighting and Woodville (all Herefordshire League) showed, pushing them into the semi-finals. It was Woodville that had won at Ledbury Town, to prove that moving in the other direction (in this case to the Influence Combination) does not guarantee success. The county's 'big' names, Pegasus Juniors (Hellenic-P) and Westfields (W Mids-P) both won through to the Semis as well, where they were joined by a second Herefordshire League side, Bromyard Town. It was Pegasus who ended the Hinton run, while Westfields beat Bromyard 3-0 to join them in the final. Pegasus, four times winners in the last 10 years and former tenants of Hereford United, who staged the final, could not make any of this tell, as Westfields won the final 5-0.

Herefordshire County Challenge Cup First Round

Hinton v Golden Valley	3-0	Ledbury Town '84 W/O Llangarron	

Second Round

Leominster Town v Wellington	2-0	Fownhope v Hereford Lads Club	2-3
Woofferton v Kington Town	3-5	Ross United v Westfields	0-3
Ledbury Town '84 v Woodville	2-3	Putson v Bromyard Town	1-6
Hinton v Thorn Lighting	1-0	Pegasus Juniors v Ewyas Harold	3-0

Quarter-Finals

Leominster Town v Pegasus Juniors	2-7	Bromyard Town v Kington Town	2-0
Hereford Lads Club v Westfields	1-8	Woodville v Hinton	2-5

Semi-Finals

Hinton v Pegasus Juniors	1-2	Westfields v Bromyard Town	3-0

Final (at Hereford United FC, 20th April): Westfields 5, Pegasus Juniors 0

Hertfordshire

This County shows the classic case of split level Cup competitions, the Senior Cup is played by 14 teams, with the two Football League sides exempt from the first round (this year), and the rest all from the Diadora Football League, except Baldock Town. The Senior Centenary Trophy is competed for by 25 clubs, officially below DFL status. Although this arrangement robs the lower clubs of their higher brethren, it ensures that the Senior Cup can always take place mid-week, and tends to produce a higher level of interest.

Looking at the Senior Cup first, and there was a surprise in the first round as St.Albans City (DFL-P) lost 1-0 at home to Boreham Wood (DFL-1). Baldock Town (BHL-S) lost 2-1 at Hertford Town (DFL-3). Both Barnet and Watford had away draws in round two and Watford lost 2-0 at Boreham Wood (DFL-1), but Barnet easily moved through. Hertford fell at home to Bishop's Stortford while the match between Hemel Hempstead and Berkhamsted (both DFL-2) was twice drawn after extra time. Hemel won the penalty contest that followed. Only one period of extra time was needed for Hemel to win their semi-final against Bishop Stortford. Barnet beat Boreham Wood 3-0 and Hemel Hempstead 4-1 to retain the cup.

Herts Senior Cup First Round

St Albans City v Boreham Wood	0-1	Stevenage Borough v Ware	3-1
Bishop's Stortford v Hitchin Town	4-1	Hemel Hempstead v Royston Town	1-0
Hertford Town v Tring Town	2-1(aet)	Tring Town v Berkhamsted Town	0-2

Quarter-Finals

Stevenage Borough v Barnet	0-6	Hertford Town v Bishop's Stortford	2-4
Boreham Wood v Watford	2-0	Hemel H. v Berkhamsted 2-2(aet),1-1(aet, 5-4 pens)	

Semi-Finals

Bishop's Stortford v Hemel Hempstead	1-2(aet)	Boreham Wood v Barnet	0-3

Final (at St Albans City FC, 7th April): Barnet 4, Hemel Hempstead 1

In the first round of the Centenary Trophy, Welwyn Garden City (SML-P) fell 3-2 to Bushey Rangers (Herts-P) and Tring Athletic (SML-1) lost in extra time at St Margaretsbury (Herts-P). In the second round, London Colney (Herts-P) saw out Harpenden (SML-P) and Sawbridgeworth (Essex League) won at Pirton (SML-P). St Margaretsbury were the high scorers, putting seven past Bushey Rangers, while the oddest events occurred in the match between Letchworth GC (SML-P) and Sandridge Rovers (Herts-P). The original match was level (0-0) at half time, when it was called off due to fog. The rearranged fixture included a goal, but it too was called off at half time, this time due to frost. At the third time, the match was completed, including extra time, so a fourth match and extra time were required before Letchworth won through. In the Quarters, the South Midlands League was represented by Letchworth, Leverstock Green and Potters Bar Town; Chesthunt were there from the Spartan, and Sawbridgeworth from the Essex League, the other three places going to the Hertfordshire League, from which only one, London Colney reached the Semis, beating Letchworth 2-0. The holders, Sawbridgeworth, lost in extra time to Potters Bar Town, and Leverstock had the biggest result of the round, beating Elliott Star 4-1. Finally, Cheshunt beat St Margaretsbury to reach the semis. Leverstock Green, with a 2-0 win over Potters Bar Town, while Cheshunt won a replay at London Colney to reach the final. Leverstock Green had already lost 1-0 to Letchworth in the Charity Shield final, and the match made it a double disappointment as they fell 2-1.

Herts Centenary Trophy First Round

Potters Bar Town v Hoddesdon Town	3-2	Pirton v Potters Bar Crusaders	3-2
Bushey Rangers v Welwyn Garden City	3-2	Elliott Star v Oxhey Jets	4-0
Hatfield Town v Kings Langley	3-1	St Margaretsbury v Tring Athletic	4-3(aet)
Sun Sports v Letchworth Garden City	0-2	Colney Heath v Cheshunt	1-3
Bedmond Sports v Park Street	2-0		

Second Round

Elliott Star v Cuffley	2-0	Let. GC v Sandridge 0-0(ab.),1-0(ab.),3-2(aet)	
Bedmond Social v Cheshunt	1-4	Leverstock Green v Chipperfield Corinthians	2-1
St Margaretsbury v Bushey Rangers	7-1	London Colney v Harpenden Town	2-1
Pirton v Sawbridgeworth Town	0-1	Hatfield Town v Potters Bar Town	1-2

Quarter-Finals

London Colney v Letchworth Gdn City	2-0	Cheshunt v St Margaretsbury	3-2
Leverstock Green v Elliott Star	4-1	Sawbridgeworth Town v Potters Bar Town	2-3(aet)

Semi-Finals

Cheshunt v London Colney	1-1,2-1(aet)	Leverstock Green v Potters Bar Town	2-0

Final (at Ware FC, 4th April): Cheshunt 2, Leverstock Green 1

Herts Charity Cup First Round

Boreham Wood v St Albans City	1-0	Hemel Hempstead v Hitchin Town	0-1
Baldock Town v Berkhamsted Town	4-0	Ware v Stevenage Borough	0-1

Semi-Finals

Stevenage Borough v Boreham Wood	1-2	Hitchin Town v Baldock Town 2-2(aet, 3-4 pens)	

Final (at Boreham Wood FC, 2nd May): Boreham Wood 1, Baldock Town 2

Herts Charity Shield First Round

Royston Town v Tring Town	0-1	Hertford Town v Sawbridgeworth Town	2-4(aet)
Cheshunt v Welwyn Garden City	2-0	Leverstock Green v Bedmond Soc.	1-1(aet, 5-4 pens)

Quarter-Finals

Potters Bar Town v London Colney	0-1	Letchworth GC v Harpenden Town	1-1(aet, 4-3 pens)
Tring T. v Leverstock	0-0(aet, 5-6 pens)	Cheshunt v Sawbridgeworth Town	3-1

Semi-Finals

London Colney v Leverstock Green	1-4	Letchworth GC v Cheshunt	2-2(aet, 5-4 pens)

Final (at Hertford Town FC, 25th March): Letchworth Garden City 1, Leverstock Green 0

Westfields celebrate their victory over Pegasus in the Herefordshire Senior Cup. Photo courtesy Hereford Journal.

Action from Baldock Town's triumph at Boreham Wood in the Herts Charity Cup final.

Cheshunt celebrate the win over Leverstock Green that clinched the Herts Senior Trophy. Photo - Gavin Ellis.

The County of Huntindonshire, is, I am glad to say, alive and well and can raise 13 teams for its Senior Cup. The favourites were the holders, Eynesbury Rovers, (UCL-P), and they showed this in style, beating Hotpoint (Peterborough & District League) by 6-0, and Godmanchester Rovers (Cambridgeshire League) 5-1 to reach the semis. Here they met Huntingdon United (UCL-1) who had won two away fixtures at Yaxley (Jewson Eastern-1) and Somersham Town (UCL-1) to get that far. Another UCL side to reach the semis was Ramsey Town, who only had to play Warboys (also UCL-1), while the quartet was made up by LBC Ortonians (Peterborough & District) who followed up a victory at Alconbury with one at St Ives (UCL-1) by 5-0. No surprises at this satge, with Eynesbury gaining a comfortable 4-0 scoreline at Huntingdon, and Ramsey winning by 1-0 at LBC Ortonians. The final was at Somersham, and Eynesbury retained the Cup, beating Ramsey 3-0.

Huntingdonshire Senior Cup First Round

Earith United v Warboys Town	0-3	Clarksteel Yaxley v Huntingdon United	1-2
Eynesbury Rovers v Hotpoint	6-0	Stilton United v Godmanchester Rovers	0-4
Alconbury v L.B.C. Ortonians	2-3		

Quarter-Finals

Somersham Town v Huntingdon United	0-1	St Ives Town v L.B.C. Ortonians	0-5
Ramsey Town v Warboys Town	1-0	Godmanchester Rovers v Eynesbury Rovers	1-5

Semi-Finals

L.B.C. Ortonians v Ramsey Town	0-1	Huntingdon United v Eynesbury Rovers	0-4

Final *(at Somersham Town FC, 4th May)*: Eynesbury Rovers 3, Ramsey Town 0

Isle of Wight

Isle of Wight Senior (Gold) Cup Semi Final

Newport I.O.W. v Cowes Sports	2-0	East Cowes Victoria Athletic v Ryde Sports	0-1

Final: Newport I.O.W. 2, Ryde Sports 0 *(attendance: 500)*

Kent

Kent has two well contested senior competitions. In the Senior Cup, thirteen sides compete. Most of these are from the Beazer Homes League, while the Football League (2), GMVC (1) and Diadora FL (1) are also present. In the First Round, Maidstone (FL) lost the ground-sharers derby match against Dartford (BHL-P): the other Football League side had a bye. Welling (GMVC) surprisingly went down 2-1 at home to Fisher (BHL-P), while there were also wins for Bromley (DFL-P), Ashford and Hythe (both BHL-S). Ashford surprised Gillingham with a 2-1 win in the Second Round, while Hythe won at Fisher to meet Ashford in the semis. Bromley carried on with a good 4-0 win over Gravesend (BHL-P), while Dartford beat another old rival Dover (BHL-P, and holders) at Watling Street. A third home match for Bromley in the semi-finals, and despite letting in their first goals of the competition, they DFL side won by 3-2 to earn, what is for them, a rare final appearance. Hythe beat Ashford 1-0 to join them there, but Bromley stuck firm, to claim the cup for only the second time (previously in 1977) winning 3-1.

Kent Senior Cup First Round

Maidstone United v Dartford	1-2	Hythe Town v Margate	1-0
Ashford Town v Canterbury City	2-0	Bromley v Erith & Belvedere	3-0
Welling United v Fisher Athletic	1-2		

Quarter-Finals

Bromley v Gravesend & Northfleet	3-0	Gillingham v Ashford Town	1-2
Dartford v Dover Athletic	2-0	Fisher Athletic v Hythe Town	0-2

Semi-Finals

Bromley v Dartford	3-2	Hythe Town v Ashford Town	1-0

Final *(at Gillingham FC, 4th May)*: Bromley 3, Hythe Town 1 *(aet)*

Two Southern Amateur League sides are entered in a Kent League dominated Senior Trophy competition, and West Whickham scored a fine 2-0 win at Darenth Heathside. Midland Bank went down 3-1 at Danson Furness United. Swanley Town beat Phoenix 3-0 in an all Spartan (Div.1) match, but the other Spartan sides went down, Catford Wanderers (Div.1) losing 4-0 at home to Tunbridge Wells, and Etham Town (Prem) by 4-1 at home to Greenwich. The only other non-Kent League sides were Stansfield (Kent Amateur - West) who lost 2-0 at home to Tonbridge AFC, and Sittingbourne, who despite elevation to the Beazer Homes League (South), remain in the Trophy, and won at Whitstable after extra time. In the Second Round, Tunbridge Wells took their record against Spartan League sides to eleven goals without reply when they put seven past Swanley. Greenwich claimed their second 4 goal haul against Herne Bay. Sittingbourne (2-1 against Faversham) and West Whickham (1-0 against Cray) provide the non-Kent League sides in the quarter finals. Here West Whickham went down 1-0 to Thames Poly. Tunbridge Wells scored another 4 goals to beat Greenwich, so although two more goals brought the visitors' tally in this season's competition to ten, it didin't matter. Six goals against Sittingbourne brought Deal's Trophy tally to ten as well, but as these were divided between a 3-3 draw and a 4-3 defeat, these also didn't matter. Slade Green won 3-2 at Alma Swanley to challenge Sittingbourne in the semi-finals, and to surprise them with a 2-1 win. Tunbridge Wells won 1-0 at Thames Poly to also reach the final. As in several other finals, defeated semi-finalist Sittingbourne staged the final, and Slade Green earned another victory here - beating Tunbridge Wells 3-1.

Kent Senior Trophy First Round

Darenth Heathside v West Wickham	0-2	Ramsgate v Herne Bay	1-2
Sheppey United v Corinthian	2-1	Stansfield Oxford & Bermondsey v Tonbridge AFC	0-2
Kent Police v Faversham Town	1-3	Catford Wanderers v Tunbridge Wells	0-4
Beckenham Town v Thames Polytechnic	1-2	Swanley Town v Phoenix Sports	3-0
Cray Wanderers v Met Police Hayes	2-0	Danson & Furness United v Midland Bank	3-1
Whitstable Town v Sittingbourne	1-2*(aet)*	Eltham Town v Greenwich Borough	1-4
Slade Green v Chatham Town	1-0		

Second Round

Tunbridge Wells v Swanley Town	7-0	Alma Swanley v Sheppey United	1-0
Thames Polytechnic v Thamesmead Town	4-3	Tonbridge A.F.C. v Deal Town	3-4
Slade Green v Danson & Furness United	2-0	West Wickham v Cray Wanderers	1-0
Sittingbourne v Faversham Town	2-1	Greenwich Borough v Herne Bay	4-0

Quarter-Finals

Deal Town v Sittingbourne	3-3,3-4	Tunbridge Wells v Greenwich Borough	4-2
Alma Swanley v Slade Green	2-3	Thames Polytechnic v West Wickham	1-0

Semi-Finals

Sittingbourne v Slade Green	1-2	Thames Polytechnic v Tunbridge Wells	0-1

Final *(at Sittingbourne FC)*: Slade Green 3, Tunbridge Wells 1

Eynesbury United line-up before their victory in the Huntingdonshire Senior Cup final. Photo - Gavin Ellis.

Bromley celebrate their first Kent Senior Cup success since 1977. Photo - Keith Gillard.

Slade Green, after their triumph in the Kent Senior Trophy final. Photo - Robert Smith.

Lancashire

Atherton L.R. (Bass NWC-1) won 3-1 against Barrow (GMVC) in the first round of the Lancashire ATS Challenge Trophy, while Blackpool Mechanics (B NWC-2) won 4-3 (aet) at Ratcliffe Borough (HFS-1). Things did not go all the way of the Bass North West Counties League, and four of their teams were beaten by Horwich RMI, Southport, Fleetwood Town and Morecambe (all HFS-P). This still left enough from the feeder league to be a thorn in the senior league's side, and while in the second round Blackpool Mechanics went out at Great Harwood (B NWC-1), their neighbours Blackpool Wren Rovers (B NWC-1) won 2-1 at Lancaster City (HFS-1) and Atherton LR beat Marine (HFS-P) by 3-1. So in the third round, there were three members of the North West Counties League, and five from the HFS, with Southport and Chorley playing each other (4-2). The other HFS sides had to play on Bass NWC grounds. Although Atherton LR now bowed out, 1-0 to Accrington Stanley, both Great Harwood Town and Blackpool Wren Rovers made progress with 2-1 wins over Horwich RMI and Morecambe. These two then played each other in the semis, with Great Harwood at home and winning 1-0. Southport won 3-0 at Accrington, but even if this made them favourites, Great Harwood added their scalp to win the final 3-2. This provided consolation to Great Harwood who had finished their league programme 16 days previously with a lead of 12 points, but had found this wittled away as Ashton made up enough points from seven games in hand to take the title.

Lancashire A.T.S. Challenge Trophy First Round

Atherton L.R. v Barrow	3-1	Clitheroe v Southport	1-3
Bacup Borough v Horwich R.M.I.	1-2	Fleetwood Town v Bamber Bridge	1-0
Morecambe v Burscough	3-0	Blackpool Wren Rovers v Atherton Collieries	3-0
Radcliffe Borough v Blackpool Mechanics	3-4(aet)		

Second Round

Southport v Chorley	1-1(aban.),4-2	Horwich R.M.I. v Rossendale United	0-0(aet),3-2
Lancaster City v Blackpool Wren Rovers	1-2	Great Harwood Town v Blackpool Mechanics	3-0
Morecambe v Darwen	2-1	Accrington Stanley v Westhoughton Town	3-0
Atherton L.R. v Marine	3-1	Fleetwood v Skelmersdale United	3-2

Quarter-Finals

Atherton L.R. v Accrington Stanley	0-1	Southport v Fleetwood Town	4-2
Great Harwood Town v Horwich R.M.I.	0-1	Blackpool Wren Rovers v Morecambe	2-1

Semi-Finals

Accrington Stanley v Southport	0-3	Great Harwood Town v Blackpool Wren Rovers	1-0

Final *(at Bolton Wanderers FC, 27th April)*: Great Harwood Town 3, Southport 2

Lancashire Amateur Cup Quarter-Finals

Old Rivingtonians v Garswood United	0-8	Merseyside Police v British Rail North End S.C.	4-2
Old Standians v Rochdale St Clements		Wythenshawe Amateur v R.E.M.Y.A. United	0-0,2-0

Semi-Finals

Garswood United v Rochdale St Clements	0-1	Merseyside Police v Wythenshawe Amateurs	6-5

Final *(at Rochdale FC, 1st May)*: Merseyside Police 3, Rochdale St Clements 1

Leicestershire

The Challenge Cup is known as the 'Westerby' Challenge Cup, while the Senior Cup continues to be sponsored by Jelson Homes. In the First Round of the Challenge Cup, Leicester United (BHL-M) beat Anstey Nomads (Leics), but Holwell Sports (Leics) faired better, twice drawing with Hinckley Town (BHL-M) before winning through on penalties. In the second round, Leicester United were unfortunate; when 3-0 up against Melton Town (CML-S), their match was abandoned. Not to worry, they won the replay 4-0. Shepshed Albion (HFS-P) took time off from their unhappy league campaign to thrash Newfoundpool (Leics) by 7-1. Holwell managed another draw, against football league side Leicester City, but they could not repeat the feat again, losing the replay by 3-0, while Lutterworth Town (Leics) also managed a 0-0 draw at Hinckley Athletic (W Mids-P), winning the replay 3-1. They lost 3-0 at Leicester United in one semi-final while Leicester City defeated Shepshed 3-1 in the other and retained the cup by beating United 3-0.

Leicestershire 'Westerby' Challenge Cup First Round

Leicester United v Anstey Nomads	3-1	Hinckley T. v Holwell	3-3(aet),1-1(aet, 1-4 pens)

Second Round

Hinckley Ath. v Lutterworth T.	0-0,1-3	Shepshed Albion '91 v Newfoundpool W.M.C.	7-1
Holwell Sports v Leicester City	1-1,0-3	Leicester United v Melton Town	3-0(ab.),4-0

Semi-Finals

Leicester City v Shepshed Albion '91	3-1	Leicester United v Lutterworth Town	3-0

Final *(at Leicester City FC, 29th April)*: Leicester City 3, Leicester United 0

The Senior Cup is dominated by Leicestershire League clubs, but there are clubs from both the Central Midlands and Influence Combination League. For the Central Midlands League, Slack & Parr and Highfield Rangers (both Premier Division South) met in the First Round. Highfield won, and then beat Aylestone Park (Leics-1) and Newfoundpool (Leics-P) to reach the quarter finals. Their other representative, Melton Town (Supreme Division) did no prove Supreme at Friar Lane Old Boys (Leics-P), losing 4-2. Frair Lane also reached the quarter-finals, at the expense of Oadby (Leics-P). For the Influence Combination, Hinckley FC (Prem) started well with a 5-1 win at Leicester Nirvana (CML-PS), but then went down by 2-0 at Houghton Rangers (Leics-P). A similar story for Wigston Fields (Div 1), who beat Earl Shilton (Leics-1) but then lost to Barwell (Leics-P). The Combination's representative in the quarter-finals was Barlestone St Giles, who with the advantage of three home draws beat Downes Sports (Leics-1), and Birstall United and Holwell Sports (both Leics-P). Two more Leicestershire Senior League sides, Burbage OB and North Kilworth (both Div 1), made up the quarter-finals - North Kilworth by virtue of two away wins, the first of which (at Leicester Constabulary) was on a higher division ground. Burbage had to play three matches to reach this point, including one Premier Division scalp, Narborough & Littlethorpe. Barlestone, without the advantage of a home draw, fell in the quarter-finals at Friar Lane, by a single goal in extra time. Two other matches were settled by the single goal, both for the home side with Houghton beating Barwell, and Lutterworth overcoming North Kilworth. Highfield won more in style, putting six past poor Burbage. But even Highfield could not stop Lutterworth in the semis, losing in extra time, while Friar Lane won 4-1 against Houghton, within 90 minutes. It was another extra time fixture when Friar Lane took the cup with a single goal.

Leicestershire 'Jelson Homes' Senior Cup First Round

Barlestone St Giles v Downes Sports	2-0	Oadby Town v Donnington Wood	6-1
Barrow Town v Birstall United	1-2(aet)	Pedigree Petfoods v Thringstone M.W.	1-3(aet)
Ravenstone v Loughborough Dynamo	3-1	Earl Shilton Albion v Anstey Town	3-2
Holwell Sports v Hillcroft	1-0	Slack & Parr v Highfield Rangers	1-2
Whetstone Athletic v Burbage Old Boys	2-4	Leicester Y.M.C.A. v Friar Lane Old Boys	1-4

(Continued on page 926)

Garswood United survive an early Ayone attack during their 2-1 win home win in the Fourth Round of the Lancashire Amateur Cup on 16th November. Photo - Rob Ruddock.

Hythe keeper Simon Jolly denies Bromley's Paul McMenemy during the Kent Senior Cup final. Photo - Dave West.

West Wickham's Steve Norris tackles Thames Poly's Archie Dudlin during the Kent Trophy tie. Photo - Mike Floate.

Leicestershire 'Jelson Homes' Senior Cup Second Round

Anstey Nomads v Oadby Town	2-4	Ibstock Welfare v Narborough & Littlethorpe	2-1
Asfordby Amateurs v Barwell Athletic	2-3	Leicester Nirvana v Hinckley FC	1-5
Leicestershire Constabulary v North Kilworth	1-2	Barlestone St Giles v Birstall United	2-1(aet)
Quorn v Lutterworth Town	2-4	Burbage Old Boys v Kirby Muxloe S.C.	2-1
Friar Lane Old Boys v Melton Town	4-1	Sileby Town v Syston St Peters	4-0
St Andrews S.C. v Holwell Sports	0-3	Harborough Town Imperial v Rowenistone	8-1

Third Round

Barlestone St Giles v Holwell Sports	4-3	Highfield Rangers v Newfoundpool W.M.C.	3-2(aet)
Barwell Athletic v Wigston Fields	3-0	Houghton Rangers v Hinckley FC	2-0
Friar Lane Old Boys v Oadby Town	2-0	Ibstock Welfare v Burbage Old Boys	0-1
Sileby Town v Lutterworth Town	0-1	Harborough Town Imperial v North Kilworth	0-1

Quarter-Finals

Houghton Rangers v Barwell Athletic	1-0	Friar Lane Old Boys v Barlestone St Giles	1-0(aet)
Lutterworth Town v North Kilworth	1-0	Highfield Rangers v Burbage Old Boys	6-0

Semi-Finals

Highfield v Lutterworth (at Leicester U.)	1-2(aet)	Houghton v Friar Lane (at Lutterworth)	1-4

Final (at Holmes Park, Whetstone, 27th April): Friar Lane Old Boys 1, Lutterworth Town 0 (aet)

Lincolnshire

Having been relegated from the Beazer Homes League, Spalding United withdrew from their pre-season Lincolnshire Senior 'A' Cup First Round match against Mirrlees Blackstones, one of their new rivals on the United Counties League. The other matches were played as scheduled, with Stamford winning the all UCL clash at Bourne, while single goals settled the two Northern Counties (East) and Central Midlands league clashes with wins for Immingham (NCE-1) at Louth (CML-S) and for Nettleham (CML-S) against Brigg Town (NCE-P). The second round saw the addition of Mirrlees Blackstone, and four clubs with byes in the First Round. Again one all UCL clash with Stamford beating Boston in a replay. Mirrlees Blackstone provided the UCL with a second Semi-Finalists winning 2-1 at Immingham, but Holbeach despite home advantage lost 4-0 to Nettleham. Lincoln United were the second CML-Supreme side through with a 5-1 replay win over Winterton (NCE-P). The Semi-Finals both provided 1-0 wins for CML sides against the UCL, Nettleham requiring extra time at home to Stamford, but Lincoln United needing only 90 minutes at Mirrlees Blackstone. Lincoln City staged the final, where Lincoln United, convincing league champions lost 1-3 to Nettleham.

Lincolnshire Senior Cup 'A' First Round

Bourne Town v Stamford	1-3	Spalding United (withdrew) Mirrlees Blackstone	W/O
Louth United v Immingham Town	0-1	Nettleham v Brigg Town	1-0

Quarter-Finals

Winterton Rangers v Lincoln United	1-1,1-5	Holbeach United v Nettleham	0-4
Boston FC v Stamford	1-1,3-4	Immingham Town v Mirrlees Blackstone	1-2

Semi-Finals

Mirrlees Blackstone v Lincoln United	0-1	Nettleham v Stamford	1-0(aet)

Final (at Lincoln City FC, 16th April): Nettleham 3, Lincoln United 1

The Senior 'B' Cup is mainly the preserve of County League sides, but five other leagues each provided a single club. Deeping Rangers (Peterborough & District) had to start in the only Preliminary Round match where they won 2-1 at Wykerton. They then reached the Quarter-Finals by winning 3-2 at Grimsby Borough. The UCL (Div 1) was represented by holders Harrowby United, who won their first match 3-0 at Immingham Athletic. Hykeham United (Midlands Regional Alliance) lost 1-0 at home to Hykeham Town, while Long Sutton (Eastern - 1) lost 1-2 in the match to Lincoln Moorlands (CML-PN). Strangely enough, while the Preliminary Round match and four First Round clashes that involved non County League sides all ended in away wins, the four all County League clashes were all won by the home sides. This rule did not follow in the quarter-finals where the only away win was in an all County League clash, Hykeham Town's 7-2 win at Skegness. Bottesford won the other all County League clash 1-0 against Grimsby Ross and earned a Semi-Final against Hykeham, with Hykeham again winning away this time by 4-1. Deeping beat Lincoln Moorlands 1-0 and earned a home Semi-Final against Harrowby, 7-0 victors over Sleaford. Another away win followed as Harrowby marched on by 3-0. Another three goals in the final saw Harrowby set up a record of 16 scored, none conceded to win the cup again (the previous season they scored 18 against 4). It will be interesting to see if Harrowby are now 'promoted' to the 'A' Cup. Although they won the League title as well on goal difference from Newport Pagnell, I hear only the latter will be promoted as the UCL-Premier requires floodlights!

Lincolnshire Senior Cup 'A' Preliminary Round

Wyberton v Deeping Rangers	1-2

First Round

Long Sutton Athletic v Lincoln Moorlands	1-2	Grimsby Borough v Deeping Rangers	2-3
Bottesford Town v Appleby Frodingham	3-2	Grimsby Ross Amateurs v Ruston Sports	2-0
Immingham Athletic v Harrowby United	0-3	Skegness Town v Mablethorpe Athletic	3-0
Hykeham Town v Hykeham United	0-1	Sleaford Town v Spilsby Town	2-1

Quarter-Finals

Deeping Rangers v Lincoln Moorlands	1-0	Harrowby United v Sleaford Town	1-0
Skegness Town v Hykeham Town	2-7	Bottesford Town v Grimsby Ross Amateurs	1-0

Semi-Finals

Bottesford Town v Hykeham Town	1-4	Deeping Rangers v Harrowby United	0-3

Final (at Nettleham FC, 17th March): Harrowby United 3, Hykeham Town 0

Liverpool

Three football league reserve sides, and holders Southport (HFS-P) were excempt in the First Round. In the Second Round they were paired together with the Liverpool side collapsing to three extra time goals at Tranmere, Everton farring even worse, losing 4-0 to Southport. These two met in the Semi-Final, with Tranmere winning 2-0. Marine (HFS-P) and Knowsley (HFS-1) had to play two matches apiece to reach the other Semi, which Marine won by 4-0. Marine earlier conquests had been St.Helens Town (BNWC-1) 3-1 (aet) and Skelmersdale United (BNWC-1) by 3-0 while a similar tale saw Knowsley get past Burscough (BNWC-2) 3-1 Prescot (BNWC-1) 4-2. In the final, Marine did puncture the Tranmere defence, unlike Liverpool or Southport, but to no avail, losing 4-1.

Liverpool Senior Cup First Round

Marine v St Helens Town	3-1(aet)	Bootle v Skelmersdale United	1-3
Prescot A.F.C. v Formby	3-0	Knowsley United v Burscough	3-1

(Contunued on page 928)

Friar Lane Old Boys celebrate their triumph in the Leicestershire Senior Cup. Photo - Leicester Mercury.

Tunbridge Wells' Paul Levy is challenged by Thames Polytechnic's Archie Dudblin during his club's 2-1 away win in the Semi Finals of the Kent Senior Trophy. Photo - Francis Short.

Leverstock Green striker Mike Bodger comes away from the challenge of Cheshunt's Dave Robotham during the Herts Senior Trophy final on April 4th. Photo - Francis Short.

Liverpool Senior Cup Quarter-Finals

Knowsley United v Prescot A.F.C.	4-2	Marine v Skelmersdale United	3-0
Southport v Everton Reserves	4-0	Tranmere Rovers v Liverpool Reserves	3-0(aet)

Semi-Finals

Knowsley United v Marine	0-4	Tranmere Rovers v Southport	2-0

Final *(at Everton FC, 5th May)*: Tranmere Rovers 4, Marine 1 *(attendance: 1,380)*

London

Carshalton Athletic (DFL-P), who won the Challenge Cup in the first season since it was returned, declined to defend the Trophy, which is their right as they are a Surrey, not a London club by affiliation. They were not the only club to decline to enter again. Still, with the addition of Kingsbury, and the transfer of three clubs from the Senior Cup, the London F.A. kept the strength of the competition at 16, almost all the clubs being dual-affiliated and playing other competitions as well. Ten of sixteen are DFL clubs, but only Bromley are Premier Division. Their First Round match with Southall was switched to Bromley and they won 3-0. Best result of all the DFL ties gave Hampton (DFL-3) a 3-1 victory over Leyton-Wingate (DFL-1). It was a good round too for two Spartan League clubs; Walthamstow Pennant beat Epsom & Ewell (DFL-3) by 3-1, while Harringey, who had beaten Pennant in last season's Senior Cup final, won 5-4 at Barking (DFL-1). Hoddesdon (S.Mids), also up from the Senior Cup, did well but lost by a single goal to Welling United (GMVC). In the all BHL tie, Fisher beat Erith 2-0. In the Second round, Haringey fell 3-4 at home to Bromley, and Fisher lost 3-2 at Dulwich Hamlet (DFL-1). Pennant carried on by drawing 3-3 at Kingsbury (DFL-3) and then winning the replay 1-0 to earn a Semi-Final against Welling who had beaten Hampton (DFL-3) by 2-1. Welling, however proved a trifle too strong, winning 5-1 while Dulwich won by a single goal at Bromley and 'Leo's theorem' says that Dulwich should then be favourites, as the final was also at Bromley, but this did not work, as Welling, beaten finalists last year, won by 2-0.

London Challenge Cup First Round

Hampton v Leyton-Wingate	2-1	Barking v Haringey Borough	4-5
Kingsbury Town v Clapton	4-2	Fisher Athletic v Erith & Belvedere	2-0
Collier Row v Dulwich Hamlet	1-3	Walthamstow Pennant v Epsom & Ewell	3-1
Southall v Bromley *(at Bromley)*	0-3	Hoddesdon Town v Welling United	0-1

Quarter-Finals

Haringey Borough v Bromley	3-4	Kingsbury Town v Walthamstow Pennant	3-3,0-1
Dulwich Hamlet v Fisher Athletic	3-2	Welling United v Hampton	2-1

Semi-Finals

Bromley v Dulwich Hamlet	0-1	Welling United v Walthamstow Pennant	5-1

Final *(at Bromley FC, 15th April)*: Welling United 2, Dulwich Hamlet 0

The Senior Cup provides an interesting mix of clubs, 9 out of 17 from the Spartan League, 4 from Essex, 2 from Kent plus Wingate & Finchley (S.Mids) and Civil Service (S.Amateur). Two of the Essex League clubs clashed in the only Round One tie, Ford winning 1-0 at Beckton (SL) and Woodford in a second replay to Hanwell (SL). Despite away draws, Cray Wanderers (Kent) won at Cockfosters (SL), but Danson lost at Croydon Athletic (SL). High scoring matches saw home victories for Civil Service and Wingate & Finchley, 6-4 over Eltham Town (SL) and 8-4 against Barkingside respectively. The Civil Servants went down 4-2 at Brimsdown, while Wingate & Finchley, 5-1 winners at Cray, were the only non-Spartan League side in the Semi-Finals. Hanwell won 1-0 at Brimsdown, and Croydon Athletic by 2-1 at Wingate to set up all Spartan Final. Played at Corinthian Casuals, this ended 2-2, and replayed at the same venue, Hanwell won 4-3. Incidently, Corinthian Casuals were earlier beaten by Croydon Athletic the beaten finalists, but this was at Croydon.

London Senior Cup First Round

Eton Manor v Ford United	0-1		

Second Round

Croydon Athletic v Danson Furness United	1-0	Cockfosters v Cray Wanderers	1-2(aet)
Corinthian Casuals v Southgate Athletic	3-0	Civil Service v Eltham Town	6-4
Ford United v Brimsdown Rovers	1-2	Woodford Town v Hanwell Town	4-4,1-1,1-3
Beckton United v East Ham United	1-0	Wingate & Finchley v Barkingside	8-4

Quarter-Finals

Cray Wanderers v Wingate & Finchley	1-5	Croydon Athletic v Corinthian Casuals	3-2
Hanwell Town v Beckton United	4-1	Brimsdown Rovers v Civil Service	4-2

Semi-Finals

Brimsdown Rovers v Hanwell Town	0-1	Wingate & Finchley v Croydon Athletic	1-2

Final *(at Corinthian Casuals FC, 14th March)*: Hanwell Town 2, Croydon Athletic 2
Replay *(at Corinthian Casuals FC)*: Hanwell Town 4, Croydon Athletic 3

Manchester

Another 'Big City' competition, the Manchester Premier Cup has only ten entrants, four from the HFS Loans League and Six from the Bass North West Counties. In the First Round, Chadderton (BNWC-2) surprised Irlam Town (HFS-1) with a 3-1 win. Chadderton then lost to Salford City (BNWC-2) in the next round. The HFS League now lost Droylsden (Prem.Div.), 3-2 at home to Flixton (BNWC-1) and their only representative in the Semi-Finals was holders Mossley (Prem) who beat Curzon Ashton (HFS-1) by 3-2. Mossley then lost 4-1 at home to Ashton United, while Flixton won at Salford to reach the final at Bury FC. Ashton won 2-1. Three weeks later, Ashton United returned to Bury to beat Burscough in the League Cup Final and they completed a fine season by winning the League.

Manchester Premier Cup First Round

Maine Road v Oldham Town	2-1(aet)	Chadderton v Irlam Town	3-1

Quarter-Finals

Chadderton v Salford City	2-3(aet)	Mossley v Curzon Ashton	3-2
Droylsden v Flixton	2-3	Maine Road v Ashton United	0-1

Semi-Finals

Mossley v Ashton United	1-4	Salford City v Flixton	1-2

Final *(at Bury FC, 7th April)*: Ashton United 2, Flixton 1

Mid-Cheshire

Originally a four team tournement introduced in 1982 to replace the old Northwich Senior Cup, the competition has been limited to the Districts' three senior sides since the 1989/90 season. However, due to the commitments of Witton Albion over the past two seasons it has been contested by just Northwich Victoria and Winsford United, and last season the Vics gained their revenge over United for their defeat in 1991 by winning this year's game 3-2 on aggregate. This was Vics' 5th win in the competition during its 10 years history.

Mid-Cheshire Senior Cup Semi-Final: Witton Albion *(withdrew)* Northwich Victoria W/O
Final 1st leg: Winsford United 1 *(Tilley)*, Northwich Victoria 1 *(O'Connor) (Att: 318)*.
Final 2nd leg: Northwich Victoria 2 *(O'Connor, Hancock)*, Winsford United 1 *(Cameron) (Att: 509)*

Ramsey's C Walker gets in a header during the Huntingdonshire Senior Cup final. Photo - Gavin Ellis.

Hanwell keeper Paul Riordan punches a cross off the head of Croydon Athletic's Rodney Prosper during the London Senior Cup final, played at Corinthian Casuals on March 14th. Photo - Dave West.

Billericay Town celebrate their penalties victory in the final of the Essex Thames-side Trophy. Photo - Jon Weaver.

Middlesex

Seven of the eight teams exempt from the two Preliminary Rounds are from the Diadora League, the exception being Wealdstone (BHL-P). Middlesex boast a further eight Diadora sides, but only two made it past the two early rounds - Harrow Borough, who won 6-1 at North Greenford United (Spartan) and Ruislip Manor whose success came at Brimsdown (also Spartan). Fallers in the First Preliminary Round were Harefield United (DFL-2) who went down 2-0 at Rayners Lane (Hellenic), Hampton (DFL-3) by 3-0 at Brook House (Spartan) and Feltham & Hounslow Borough (DFL-3) who lost 5-1 at Cockfosters (Spartan). Cockfosters qualified for the competition proper with a 2-0 replay win at Kingsbury (DFL-3), but Rayners Lane lost at home to Hanwell Town (Spartan), and Brook House to Dan-Air League side Bedfont. Two other Spartan qualifiers were Cheshunt who won 3-2 at Edgware (DFL-3) and Northwood who beat Southall (DFL-2). The remaining side to go through was Wingate & Finchley (S.Mids) who had beaten Southgate Athletic (Spartan) and fellow S.Midlands club Welwyn Garden City. Of the Spartan clubs in the First Round, Hanwell lost 3-0 to Wembley and Cockfosters to the same score at Uxbridge, while Cheshunt lost a home replay against Hayes. With Wingate & Finchley also losing at home in a replay (against Staines), the only non Diadora club to reach Round Two was Northwood, 5-0 victors over Bedfont. Wealdstone lost their replay against Hendon. Northwood continued through to the Semis with a 3-1 win over Uxbridge (DFL-1), while despite home draws Hayes and Hendon (both DCL-P) lost to Yeading and Wembley (both DFL-1). Enfield beat Staines to complete the Semi-Final quartet, but they too succumbed to Yeading. Wembley finally proved too much for Northwood to set up an all Diadora Division One final at Hendon, which Yeading wn by 2-1. Yeading move up to the Diadora Premier for the new season (my theorem fails here as Wembley had earlier won at Hendon!). The Charity Cup was won by Chelsea, in a match played at Yeading - the losing finalists were Edgware, who in turn staged the Premier Cup, won 2-0 by Osterley.

Middlesex Senior Cup Preliminary Round

Southgate Athletic v Wingate & Finchley	0-2	Brimsdown Rovers v Ashord Town (Middx)	2-0
Southall v Haringey Borough	2-2,4-2(aet)	Potters Bar Crusaders v North Greenford United	1-2
Rayners Lane v Harefield United	2-0	Brook House v Hampton	3-0
Viking Sports v Cheshunt	1-4	Kingsbury Town v Hillingdon Borough	2-1
Cockfosters v Feltham & Hounslow B.	5-1		

Preliminary Round Two

Rayners Lane v Hanwell Town	1-2	North Greenford United v Harrow Borough	1-6
Cockfosters v Kingsbury Town	0-0,2-0	Bedfont v Brook House	2-0
Brimsdown Rovers v Ruislip Manor	1-3	Wingate & Finchley v Welwyn Garden City	4-1
Edgware Town v Cheshunt	2-3	Northwood v Southall	2-1

First Round Proper

Northwood v Bedfont	5-0	Enfield v Harrow Borough	1-0
Ruislip Manor v Yeading	0-1	Hendon v Wealdstone	1-1,3-1
Hayes v Cheshunt	2-2,2-0	Cockfosters v Uxbridge	0-3
Staines Town v Wingate & Finchley	2-2,4-2	Hanwell Town v Wembley	0-3

Quarter-Finals

Hayes v Yeading	0-5	Northwood v Uxbridge	3-1
Enfield v Staines Town	2-1	Hendon v Wembley	0-2

Semi-Finals

Yeading v Enfield	2-0	Northwood v Wembley	1-2

Final (at Wembley FC, 20th April): Yeading 2, Wembley 1

Middlesex Senior Charity Cup First Round

Potters Bar Crusaders v Cockfosters	0-5	Wingate & Finchley v North Greenford United	0-3
Welwyn Garden City v Bedfont	1-2	Viking Sports v Harefield United	2-1
Rayners Lane v Brimsdown Rovers	3-6	Ashford Town (Middx) v Northwood	2-4(aet)
Hanwell Town v Feltham & Hounslow Boro.	3-2	Cheshunt v Southall 4-0	2-1

Second Round

Harrow Borough v Cockfosters	0-0(4-3 pens)	Uxbridge v Hanwell Town	3-0
Yeading v Hampton	2-1	Cheshunt v Southgate Athletic	3-0
Kingsbury Town v Northwood	0-4	Hillingdon Borough v North Greenford United	2-3
Brimsdown Rovers v Haringey Borough	1-0	Bedfont v Brook House	0-1
Staines Town v Viking Sports	3-0		

Third Round

Brimsdown Rovers v Edgware Town	1-4	Cheshunt v Wembley	0-3
Staines Town v Harrow Borough	2-1(aet)	Northwood v Chelsea	1-8
Yeading v Brook House	3-2	Uxbridge v North Greenford United	0-1
Hayes v Brentford	1-3	Ruislip Manor v Hendon	1-0

Quarter-Finals

North Greenford United v Ruislip Manor	0-3	Wembley v Brentford	0-1
Edgware Town v Yeading	1-0	Staines Town v Chelsea	0-1

Semi-Finals

Edgware Town v Brentford	3-0	Ruislip Manor v Chelsea	0-3

Final (at Yeading FC, 4th May): Chelsea 3, Edgware Town 1

Midland Floodlit Cup

Previous Winners: 1959-60: Peterborough United, 60-61: Worcester City, 61-62: Peterborough Utd Reserves, 62-63: Peterborough United Reserves, 63-64: Cambridge Utd, 64-65: Worcester City, 65-66: Worcester City, 66-67: Wellington Town, 67-68: Banbury Utd, 68-69: Nuneaton Borough, 69-70: Stafford Rangers, 70-71: Telford Utd, 71-72: Telford Utd, 72-73: Atherstone Town, 73-74: Nuneaton Borough, 74-75: Corby Town, 75-76: Burton Albion, 76-77: Atherstone Town, 77-78: Atherstone Town, 78-79: Atherstone Town, 79-80: Nuneaton Borough, 80-81: Kettering Town, 81-82: Kettering Town, 82-83: Bedworth Utd, 83-84: Bedworth Utd/ Nuneaton Borough, 84-85: V.S. Rugby; 85-86: Cheltenham Town, 86-87: Cheltenham Town, 87-88: Cheltenham Town, 88-89: Hinckley Town, 89-90: V.S. Rugby, 90-91: Moor Green.

Midland Floodlit Cup First Round

Alvechurch v Hinckley Town	0-0,4-5	Corby Town v Dudley Town	1-0,1-0
Leicester United v Moor Green	2-7,1-6	Hinckley Athletic v Racing Club Warwick	0-3,1-3
Redditch United v Bedworth United	0-3,1-0	Nuneaton Borough v Tamworth	1-2,1-2

Quarter-Finals

Bedworth United v Willenhall Town	5-2	Tamworth v Atherstone Utd	2-2(1-4 on penalties)
Hinckley Town v Racing Club Warwick	2-1	Corby Town v Moor Green	0-1

Semi-Finals

Moor Green v Bedworth United	2-0	Hinckley Town v Atherstone United	2-1

Final (at West Bromwich Albion FC): Moor Green 3, Hinckley Town 0

Yeading pictured after winning the Middlesex Senior Cup, beating Wembley at Hendon. Photo - Francis Short.

Chelsea attack on the way to victory in a Middlesex Charity Cup Quarter-Final at Staines. Photo - Ian Morseman.

Tamworth 2, Atherstone United 2 - Midland Floodlit Cup Quarter-Finals 24/3/92. Atherstone's Roy Green (centre) attacks against his former club. Photo - Paul Barber.

Norfolk

Clubs from the Jewson Eastern League's Premier Division were against exempt from the Preliminary Round; with the promotion of Norwich United, the numbers were up to six. This still leaves four Eastern League sides in the First Round among the Anglian Combination clubs. Of these Swaffham Town fell 5-2 at Lakeford Rangers. No less than four of the Eastern League's Premier sides fell in the Second Round, Great Yarmouth by 1-0 at home to Overstrand (Ang. Comb) and Norwich United at Blofield United (also Ang.Comb), while Watton fell 2-1 to King's Lynn reserves (E-1) and Wroxham by 3-2 at Diss Town (E-1). With Mulbarton winning 1-0 at Dereham Town, there were three Anglian Combination clubs in the Quarter Finals with three lower Division Eastern Leaguers, and only two from the Premier. Here Blofield won the all Anglian Combination tie, beating Mulbarton 3-1 while Overstrand beat King's Lynn reserves in a replay. The other Eastern Divison One sides, both challenging for promotion were successful in defeating the remaining Premier Clubs. Thetford being beaten 4-0 at Diss Town, while Fakenham were held somewhat closer, but won 3-2 (aet) against Gorleston. Both Semi-Finals were on the Eastern League grounds with Diss again having easier passage, by 2-1 against Overstrand. Fakenham and Blofield drew 5-5 before Fakenham won through to the final. At Norwich City, another draw was fought out before Fakenham won the cup, reversing the league order where both were promoted but Diss came out on top.

Norfolk Senior Cup Preliminary Round

Hellesdon v Reepham Town	3-2	Mulbarton United v Coltishall H.V.	1-0
Norwich Union v Horsford United	3-2 (at)	Carrow v Wymondham T. (at Wymondham T.)	3-1
Mattishall v Stalham Town	4-3	Wymondham Old Boys v Harleston Town	2-1
Loddon United v Wortwell	4-2		

First Round

Carrow v Blofield United	1-3	Mattishall v St Andrews	2-5
Dereham Town v Hempnall	3-0	Mulbarton United v Downham Town	3-1
Diss Town v Newton Flotman	4-0	Norwich Union v Bradenham Wanderers	0-1
Hellesdon v Fakenham Town	1-4	Overstrand v Loddon United	6-1
Lakeford Rangers v Swaffham Town	5-2 (aet)	Wymondham Old Boys v King's Lynn Reserves	1-4

Second Round

Lakeford Rangers v Gorleston	0-4	Dereham Town v Mulbarton United	0-1
Diss Town v Wroxham	3-2	Bradenham Wanderers v Fakenham Town	1-4
St Andrews v Thetford Town	1-1,0-1	Great Yarmouth Town v Overstrand	0-1
King's Lynn Reserves v Watton United	2-1	Blofield United v Norwich United	2-0

Quarter-Finals

King's Lynn Reserves v Overstrand	3-3 (aet),2-4	Blofield United v Mulbarton United	3-1
Diss Town v Thetford Town	4-0	Fakenham Town v Gorleston	3-2 (aet)

Semi-Finals

Diss Town v Overstrand	2-1	Fakenham Town v Thetford Town	5-5 (aet),1-0

Final (at Norwich City FC, 15th April): Diss Town 2, Fakenham Town 2 (aet)
Replay (at Gorleston FC): Fakenham Town 2, Gorleston 1

Northamptonshire

With Raunds Town as the holders and Rushden as previous beaten finalists, it may seem strange that once again Kettering Town (GMVC) are the Hillier Cup's only exempt side, and that they should be exempt through to the Semi-Finals, but the County F.A. did not see fit to change things. At least neither had to compete in the Preliminary Round. Apart from Kettering, the competition is competed for by 12 members of the United Counties League, and the BHL pair of Corby Town and Rushden Town. Rushden fell in a First Round replay to Rothwell, who in turn lost out to Corby Town. Holders Raunds fell at Cogenhoe in the Second Round, while Northampton Spencer won 4-2 at Desborough to complete the Semi-Final line-up. With Kettering and Corby kept apart, it came as no surprise that they should meet in the final, but not by easy routes; Kettering could only get a single goal against Spencer. Corby put five past Cogenhoe, but that was after extra time as Cogenhoe themselves scored three. The Cup was returned to Kettering thanks to a single goal in the final.

Northamptonshire 'Hillier' Senior Cup Preliminary Round

Cogenhoe United v Daventry Town	3-2	Long Buckby v Hamlet Stewart & Lloyds	3-0

First Round

Rothwell Town v Rushden Town	1-1,2-1	Irthlingborough Diamonds v Corby Town	0-2
Brackley Town v Cogenhoe United	0-5	Raunds Town v A.P.V. Peterborough City	4-2
Northampton Spencer v Long Buckby	5-3	Desborough Town v Wellinborough Town	3-0

Quarter-Finals

Kettering Town (exempt)		Desborough Town v Northampton Spencer	2-4
Corby Town v Rothwell Town	2-1	Cogenhoe United v Raunds Town	4-2

Semi-Finals

Kettering Town v Northampton Spencer	1-0	Corby Town v Cogenhoe Town	5-3 (aet)

Final (at Kettering Town FC): Kettering Town 1, Corby Town 0

North Riding

In the Senior Cup, three Football League sides, and four Northern League Divison One clubs are exempt to the First Round. This leaves one place for the winners of a ten team qualifying competition - most of these clubs are from Teeside Leagues, but also included two members of the Northern Counties (East), Marske United (Wearside) and Stockton (NL-2). York R.I. (NCE-1) lost 2-0 at home to Tees Components in the First Round. Tees Components themselves fell 3-2 at I.C.I. Wilton in the next round. Stockton lost 3-2 at home to Acklam Steelworks and so Marske United, by defeating Pickering Town (NCE-1) by 2-0 were the only non Teeside League club in the Semi-Finals. Victory at Fishburn Park put Marske into the final against Acklam, winners at I.C.I. Wilton. A 3-1 win for Marske in the Qualifying Final earned them a home tie against holders Guisborough Town, a match that Marske only lost in a replay. The Football League had only one Semi-Finalist after Scarborough won 6-2 at Middlesbrough, and York City were beaten 2-0 by Northallerton in a home replay. Both Semi-Finals were home wins, Scarborough beating Northallerton 4-0 with Guisborough beating Whitby Town 3-1. Whitby staged the Final which went to extra time before Scarborough won 3-2.

North Riding Senior Cup First Qualifying Round

I.C.I. Wilton v Nunthorpe Athletic	4-1	York Railway Institute v Tees Components	0-2

Second Qualifying Round

Marske United v Pickering Town	2-0	I.C.I. Wilton v Tees Components	3-2
Stockton v Aclam Steelworks	2-3 (aet)	Fishburn Park v New Marske S.C.	3-2

Qualifying Competition Semi-Finals

I.C.I. Wilton v Acklam Steelworks	1-2	Fishburn Park v Marske United	1-2 (aet)

(continued on page 933)

Qualifying Final

Marske United v Acklam Steelworks	3-1

Quarter-Finals (First Round Proper)

Marske United v Guisborough Town	1-1,1-3	South Bank v Whitby Town	1-3
Middlesbrough v Scarborough	2-6	Northallerton Town v York City	1-1,2-0

Semi-Finals

Scarborough v Northallerton Town	4-0	Guisborough Town v Whitby Town	3-1

Final (at Whitby Town FC): Scarborough 3, Guisborough Town 2 (aet)

Of the sides that try to qualify for the Senior Cup, all but Marske and Stockton also enter the County Cup, and so this competition is even more dominated by the Teeside League. And so it turned out, the two Northern Counties (East) sides could only manage one win between them (by York R.I. at Osbaldwick), and not surprisingly it was two Teeside League sides, Dormans Athletic and ICI Wilton that met in the Final at Guisborough. After a 1-1 draw, ICI Wilton won the replay 1-0.

North Riding County Cup First Round

Pickering Town v Tees Component	3-5	Rowntree Mackintosh v Redcar Works B.S.C.	2-3
I.C.I. Wilton v New Marske S.C.	3-1	Nunthorpe Athletic v B.E.A.D.S.	2-1(aet)

Second Round

Kirbymooreside v Richmond Town	1-0	Osbaldwick v York Railway Institute	0-1
Nunthorpe Athletic v I.C.I. Wilton	1-3	Guisborough Quoits v Fishburn Park	3-1
Redcar Works B.S.C. v Rydale S.C.	10-0	Stockton Supporters v Cayton Corinthians	1-0
Eastfield v Dormans Athletic	0-1	Tees Components v Acklam Steelworks	1-4

Quarter-Finals

I.C.I. Wilton v York Railway Institute	4-2	Stockton Supporters v Kirbymooreside	1-2(aet)
Dormans Ath. v Redcar Works	1-1(aet),2-1(aet)	Guisborough Quoits v Acklam Steelworks	4-4(aet),1-5

Semi-Finals

Acklam v I.C.I. Wilton	0-1	Kirbymooorside v Dormans Athletic	1-1,0-3

Final (at Guisborough Town FC, 21st April): Dormans Athletic 1, I.C.I. Wilton 1 (aet)
Replay: I.C.I. Wilton 1, Dormans Athletic 0

Northumberland

The surprise of the First Round was supplied by Westerhope Hillheads, who had qualified by winning the previous seaon's Benevelent Bowl. Westerhope won 3-2 at Prudhoe East End (NL-2). Another Northern Alliance side, Seaton Delaval Amateurs held Blyth Spartans (NL-1) for 90 minutes but lost 2-0 after extra-time. It was also Blyth that stopped Westerhope in the next round, while holders North Shields (NCE-P) won 2-0 at Seaton Delaval Seaton Terrace (Northern Alliance). Whitley Bay (HFS-P) beat Newcastle reserves and Blue Star (NI-1) beat Alnwick (NI-2) in a replay. In the Semi-Finals, after a replay Blyth beat Whitley Bay, and North Shields beat Blue Star 3-2 to reach the final at St.James Park, but again Blyth stayed on course to win the Cup for the 19th time overall, but after a gap of seven years.

Northumberland Senior Cup First Round

Ashington v Newcastle Blue Star	1-4	Seaton Delaval Amateurs v Blyth Spartans	0-2(aet)
Prudhoe East End v Westerhope	2-3	Seaton Delaval Seaton Terrace v Forest Hall S.C.	5-2

Second Round

Westerhope Hillheads v Blyth Spartans	1-3	Seaton Delaval Seaton Terrace v North Shields	0-2
Whitley Bay v Newcastle United Reserves	4-2	Newcastle Blue Star v Alnwick Town	4-2

Semi-Finals

North Shields v Newcastle Blue Star	3-2	Blyth Spartans v Whitley Bay	1-1,3-1(aet)

Final (at Newcastle United FC, 2nd May): Blyth Spartans 2, North Shields 1

In the Benevolent Bowl, one gets tired of saying it, but again there are single entrants from the Northern League and the Wearside League amongst the North Alliance sides, and again they made early exits, Bedlington Terriers (NL-2) by 3-2 aet at Walker (N.All-P) and Bohemians (Wearside) in a replay at home to Benfield Park (N.All-1). In fact it was Benfield Park who provided the headlines; after ending the chances of Bohemians, they defeated Haltwhistle, Ponteland United and Blyth Kitty Brewster, all from a higher division to take the cup.

Northumberland Benevolent Bowl First Round

Ponteland United v Spittal Rovers	2-1	Newcastle Benfield Pk v Newcastle Bohemians	2-2,2-0
Newbiggin Central Welfare v Wark	1-4	Longbenton v Blyth Kitty Brewster	3-5(aet)
Heaton Stannington v Morpeth Town	1-3	Percy Main Amateurs v Haltwhistle Crown Paints	0-4
Walker v Bedlington Terriers	3-2(aet)	West Allotment Celtic v Dudley Welfare	0-1

Quarter Finals

Morpeth Town v Ponteland United	1-3	Newcastle Benfield Park v Haltwhistle Crown Paints	2-1
Dudley Welfare v Wark	0-3	Blyth Kitty Brewster v Walker	2-1

Semi-Finalists

Blyth Kitty Brewster v Wark	2-1	Newcastle Benfield Park v Ponteland United	2-1

Final (at North Shields FC, 7th April): Newcastle Benfield Park 1, Blyth Kitty Brewster 0

Nottinghamshire

Of five Central Midland Supreme Division clubs, only one made a First Round exit, Arnold Town, who lost 1-3 at home to Sutton Town (NCE-P), but it was bad news for the six CML Premier Division sides who all made their exits. Only Attenborough, who went down 1-0 at home to Blidworth lost out to a CML Supreme side. The worst defeats were for Radford who were hit 10-1 at GPT Plessey (Notts Alliance) and for Kimberley who were beaten 3-1 at home by Bulwell Forest Villa, the only lower Division Notts Alliance club in the Second Round. Eastwood Town (HFS-1) won convincingly over Dunkirk, and scaled the Quarter-Finals with a 3-1 win at Oakham (CML-S). Holders Hucknall Town (CML-S) beat Sutton Town 2-1, while Blidworth and Priory (Both CML-S) won away matches on Notts Alliance grounds to go through. Four Alliance League clubs reached the last eight, but not Bulwell Forest Villa who lost 2-1 at John Player. There was one all Notts Alliance tie at this stage, in which Notts Police won 1-0 at GPT Plessey, while Eastwood Town comfortably won their derby at Priory. The result of the round saw the holders, Hucknall, lose at Rainworth. Rainworth then held Eastwood 0-0 on the Semi-Final but cruelly went down in a penalty shoot out; all the goals being reserved for Notts Police's match, a 6-4 victory over Blidworth. The Police could not upset Eastwood in the Final though, losing 2-0.

Nottinghamshire Senior Cup First Round

G.P.T. Plessey v Radford	10-1	Greenwood Meadows v Ruddington	8-9 on penalties
Thoresby Colliery v Oakham United	0-4	City & Sherwood Hospital v Clifton All Whites	2-3(aet)
Hucknall Town v Nuthall	4-2	Cotgrave Miners Welfare v Worthington Simpson	2-3
			(continued overleaf)

Arnold Town v Sutton Town	1-3	Kimberley Town v Bulwell Forest Villa	1-3*(aet)*
Pelican v Keyworth United	3-0	Nottinghamshire Police v Gedling Town	5-2
Priory (Eastwood) v British Rail Newark	5-0	Basford United v Rainworth Miners Welfare	1-2
Eastwood Town v Dunkirk	7-0	John Player v Clipstone Welfare	5-4
Attenborough v Blidworth Welfare	0-1	Bulwell Utd v Hucknall Rolls Royce Welfare	4-5 *pens*

Second Round

John Player v Bulwell Forest Villa	2-1	Hucknall Rolls Royce Welfare v Notts Police	2-3
Pelican v Blidworth Welfare	2-4	Oakham United v Eastwood Town	1-3
Hucknall Town v Sutton Town	2-1	Ruddington v G.P.T. Plessey	2-6*(aet)*
Worthington Simpson v Priory (Eastwood)	0-1	Clifton All Whites v Rainworth Miners Welfare	0-3

Quarter-Finals

Blidworth Welfare v John Player	1-0	G.P.T. Plessey v Nottinghamshire Police	0-2
Priory (Eastwood) v Eastwood Town	0-4	Rainworth Miners Welfare v Hucknall Town	1-0

Semi-Finals

Eastwood Town v Rainworth	0-0*(7-6 pens)*	Nottinghamshire Police v Blidworth Welfare	6-4

Final *(at Arnold Town FC, 30th April):* Eastwood Town 2, Notts Police 0

Oxfordshire

Oxford United, bidding to win the cup for a fourth successive year, and Witney Town (BHL-S), considered the county's senior non-league side, were both exempt to the Fourth Round again. Once the competition reached this point, the form book was observed, and Witney Town reached the final by putting two goals past each of Oxford City (S.Mids) and Headington Amateurs (Hellenic). Oxford United went to Bletchington (Oxon) and scored five, and then beat Chiltonian leaders Peppard 3-2 after extra-time. Oxford held on to the Cup with a 3-1 home win in the final. In the earlier rounds, there is always plenty of oppurtunity for sides in the Chiltonian and Oxfordshire Leagues to disturb the idea that the Hellenic may be the top dogs in the area. Not however in the First Round, where Chipping Norton (Hell-1) put eleven goals past Blackbird Leys (Oxon). Chipping Norton then beat Banbury United (Hell-P) 2-0, and Audley United (Oxon) 3-1 to reach the Quarter-Finals, and a tie against Headington Amateurs (Hell-P). The Amateurs had achieved this position with two narrow home wins against Oxfordshire League sides Eynsham and Quarry Nomads - Nomads had earlier won 2-1 at Easington Sports (Hell-1). With their elevation to the Diadora League, Thame United may have been expected to do well, and neither Marlborough (Oxon) no Bicester Town (Hell-P) could score a goal to stop them reaching the Fourth Round. Here they met Peppard, who had shown their form in the Second Round with a 7-1 win over Kidlington (Hell-1) and then beaten Garsington (Oxon) by 3-0. In the Quarters, Peppard surprised Thame by winning 1-0 away. Unfortunately, despite the semi-final against Oxford United being at the same venue, they could not repeat this. Oxford City (S.Mids-P) also scored highly in the Second Round when they got eight against Clanfield (Hell-1), they reached the Quarters by then winning at Carterton (Hell-P), before losing to Witney. The only side from the Oxfordshire Senior League to reach the Quarter-Final stage was Bletchington, who achieved this at the expense of Old Woodstock and Woodstock Town, two of their fellows from the Oxfordshire league. Woodstock Town had earlier secured a notable victory, by 4-0 at North Leigh (Hell-1).

First Round

Quarry Nomads *W/O* Oxford Stadium		Worcester College Old Boys v Eynsham	1-3
Chipping Norton Town v Blackbird Leys	11-0		

Second Round

Garsington v Chinnor	8-0	Peppard v Kidlington	7-1
Chipping Norton Town v Banbury United	2-0	Headington Amateurs v Eynsham	3-2
Bicester Town v Watlington	3-1	Easington Sports v Quarry Nomads	1-2
Old Woodstock v Bletchingdon	1-3	Henley Town v Carterton Town	2-4
Thame United v Marlborough	6-0	North Leigh v Woodstock Town	0-4
Yarnton v Ardley United	1-2	Clanfield '85 v Oxford City	0-8

Third Round

Bicester Town v Thame United	0-1	Chipping Norton Town v Ardley United	3-1
Carterton Town v Oxford City	2-3	Headington Amateurs v Quarry Nomads	1-0
Peppard v Garsington	3-0	Woodstock Town v Bletchingdon	0-2

Quarter-Finals

Bletchingdon v Oxford United	0-5	Thame United v Peppard	0-1
Oxford City v Witney Town	0-2*(aet)*	Headington Amateurs v Chipping Norton Town	2-0

Semi-Finals

Witney Town v Headington *(at Thame Utd)*	2-0	Peppard v Oxford United	2-3*(aet)*

Final *(at Oxford United FC, 28th April):* Oxford United 3, Witney Town 1

Bletchington 0, Oxford United Reserves 5 - Oxfordshire Senior Cup Quarter-Final, 14/3/92. Home defender Kevin Willoughby prepares to tackle Oxford United's Matthew McDonnell. Photo - Steve Daniels.

All smiles from Eastwood Town after two goals from Mark Richardson gave them victory over Notts Police in the Nottinghamshire Senior Cup final.

Kevin Drackett (5) salutes the goal that gave Headington victory against Quarry Nomads on 15th February in the Third Round of the Oxfordshire Senior Cup. Photo - Steve Daniels.

Oxford City (hoops) lose at home to Witney in the Oxon Senior Cup Quarter-Finals. Photo - Steve Daniels.

'Evening Post' Reading Senior Cup

First Round

Chalfont Wasps v Fairmile Hospital	3-1	Woodley Arms v Reading Town	3-0
Cotswold v Holmer Green	1-2		

Second Round

IBIS v A.E.R.E. Harwell	1-0	Letcombe Sports v Forest	5-3
Finchampstead v South Reading	1-2	Slough Y.C.O.B. v Binfield	1-5
Mortimer v Sonning	2-1	Hambleton v Harwell	0-0,0-5
Benson v Old Prestonians	0-7	Cookham Dean v Mill End Sports	4-3
Henley Town v West Reading	1-3	Thames Vale v Reading Exiles	2-1
Woodley Arms v Earlbourne United	4-1	Nettlebed United v Prestwood	1-2
Didcot Casuals v Peppard	1-2	Holmer Green v Wraysbury Coopers	0-5
Chalfont Wasps W/O Chinnor withdrew		Faringdon Town v Wallingford United	1-0

Third Round

Thames Vale v IBIS	0-1	Harwell v Cookham Dean	2-0
Faringdon Town v Prestwood	0-4	Peppard v Old Prestonians	5-1
Wraysbury Coopers v Chalfont Wasps	5-1	Letcombe v Mortimer	1-0
South Reading v Binfield	0-6	West Reading v Woodley Arms	2-1

Quarter-Finals

West Reading v Wraysbury-Coopers	0-1	Peppard v Harwell	2-1
Binfield v IBIS	5-2	Letcombe Sports v Prestwood	1-0

Semi-Finals

Wraysbury Coopers v Binfield	1-2	Peppard v Letcombe Sports	2-1

Final (16th May): Peppard 2, Binfield 1

Sheffield & Hallamshire

There are two qualifying rounds before the exempt sides come into the competition, and as always, the clubs from the HFS Loans League and Northern Counties (East) are exempt en bloc. Still there are 20 available places, as reducing numbers in the Northern Counties (East) have reduced the exemptions to nine from this league, and three from the HFS Loans League. The Central Midlands League supplied four of the qualifiers, the rest coming from the Whitbread County Senior League. The qualifying rounds also saw early exits for three CML sides; Norton Woodseats (CML-PN) and Wombwell Town (CML-S) both lost at home to County League sides, Oughtibridge and Clifton Rovers in the First Qualifyer, while Mexborough (CML-PN) fell to Harworth CI (CML-S) in the next Round. In the First Round, Sheffield Aurora (CML-S), Semi-Finalists last season lost 3-2 to County League side High Green Villa, while Rossington (CML-PN) lost 3-1 to Saint James. Surprisingly, none of the qualifiers beat exempt sides in the First Round, but in the Second Round, there were victories for Denaby & Cadeby M.W. and A.B.M. (both County) League. Denaby won 1-0 against Stocksbridge (NCE-1), and A.B.M. by 4-3 at R.E.S. Parkgate (NCE-1). A third County League side to reach the Quarter-Finals was Loxley College, who continued to play only County League sides in going out 6-0, at home to Denaby & Cadeby. All three HFS Loans League sides reached the Quarter-Finals, with Worksop Town (HFS-1) beating A.B.M. 5-1, Emley putting 7 past Rossington Main (NCE-1) and Frickley beating Sheffield (NCE-P) by the narrower score of 2-1. In the two legged Semi-Finals, Emley predictably proved too strong for Denaby & Cadeby, and took an aggregate 9-1 win. The other match was closer, with Worksop and Frickley drawing 2-2 before the Premier side took the honours by the narrowest of margins. Another single goal was all that was seen in the final, taken by Emley.

First Qualifying Round

Dawlish United W/O Harworth C. Institute		Yorkshire Main v Thurcroft Ivanhoe Hoults	4-1
High Green v Villa v Goldthorpe Colliery	3-1	Wath Saracens Athletic v Woodsetts Welfare	3-0
Wombwell Town v Clifton Rovers	1-2	Norton Woodseats v Oughtibridge W.M.S.C.	1-2
Sheffield Bankers v Saint Patricks	0-2	Tinsley Wire v British Steel Stainless	9-1
Sheffield Oakhouse v Staveley Miners W.	1-5	Industry v Loxley College	0-2

Second Round

Clifton Rovers W/O Elsecat Main Colliery		High Green Villa v Old Edwardians	2-2,4-1
Throstles J. v Loxley College	4-4,2-3	Ecclesfield Red Rose v Kiveton Park	0-0,1-2
Abbeydale v Sheffield Gas	1-3	Yorkshire Main v Brunsmeer Athletic	4-2
East Pennine v Staveley Miners Welfare	0-2	British Gas v Davy	2-2,2-8
Caribbean Sports v A.B.M.	2-4	Saint Patricks v Sheffield Post Office	2-3
Penistone Church v Treeton Welfare	3-5	Denaby & Cadeby Miners W. v Swinton Athletic	8-2
Sheffield Aurora v Parramore Sports	8-0	Frecheville Comm. A. v Warth Saracens Athletic	2-1
Phoonix v Ash House	1-3	Mexborough Main Street v Sheffield Centralians	1-2
Saint James v Tinsley Wire	2-0	Rossington v Rawmarsh Star	1-0
Oughtibridge W.M.S.C. (bye)	0-2	Harworth Colliery Institute v Mexborough Town	2-0

First Round Proper

Sheffield Gas v Hallam	0-4	Frecheville Comm. A. v Worsbrough Bridge M.W.	1-2
Sheffield v Davy	5-0	Kiveton Park v Clifton Rovers	1-0
R.E.S. Parkgate v Oughtibridge W.M.S.C.	2-1	Denaby & Cadeby Miners Welfare v Ash House	2-1
Denaby United v Maltby Miners Welfare	2-3	Harworth Colliery Institute v Worksop Town	0-2
Sheffield Post Office v Loxley College	2-3	A.B.M. v Sheffield Centralians	7-3
Saint James v Rossington	3-1	Saint Patricks v Staveley Miners Welfare	5-0
Treeton Welfare v Rossington Main	2-3	Brodsworth Miners Welfare v Frickley Athletic	0-3
Yorkshire Main v Emley	0-8	High Green Villa v Sheffield Aurora	3-2

Second Round Proper

Sheffield v Maltby Miners Welfare	3-1	Hallam v Worksop Town	2-3
Rossington Main v Kiveton Park	4-1	Emley v Worsbrough Bridge W.M.	7-0
Loxley College v Saint James	2-2,3-1	Denaby & Cadeby M.W. v Stocksbridge Pk S.	1-0
R.E.S. Parkgate v A.B.M.	3-4	Frickley Athletic v High Green Villa	2-1

Quarter-Finals

Worksop Town v A.B.M.	5-1	Emley v Rossington Main	7-0
Fricklet Athletic v Sheffield	2-1	Loxley College v Denaby & Cadeby Miners W.	0-6

Semi-Finals

Worksop Town v Frickley Athletic	2-2,0-1	Emley v Denaby & Cadeby Miners W.	4-1,5-0

Final (at Stocksbridge Park Steels FC, 22nd April): Emley 1, Frickley Athletic 0

Peppard 2, Binfield 1 - Reading Senior Cup final, 16/5/92. Binfield forward Mark McLentire heads the ball into the path of Mickey Havermans, but the latter missed the shot. Photo - Dave West.

Peppard celebrate their Reading Senior Cup triumph. Photo - Dave West.

Witney Town captain Kenny Clarke clashes with his Headington Amateurs counterpart Kevin Drackett in the Oxon Senior Cup Semi-Final at Thame. Photo - Steve Daniels.

Shropshire

With the disappearance of Newport Town, three times winners in the last six seasons, the question was whether or not the Cup would be more open, or if the West Midlands clubs could take too tight a grip. Certainly Broseley Athletic and Donnington Wood (both W Mids-1) started strongly with away wins at Snailbeach and Telford Juniors (both Shropshire County League) in the First Round. Donnington Wood went on to the Quarter-Finals with a 4-0 win over Morda United (Mid Wales League), but Broseley lost at home to Bridgnorth Town (M Comb Reserve Division). Ludlow Town and Wem Town (again both W.Mids-1) both reached the last eight with away wins on Shropshire League grounds. Four Shropshire League clubs made up the Quarter-Final line up, with the holders Shifnal Town winning 3-0 away at Albrighton, the side that beat them to the league title last season on goal difference. Meole Brace beat Whitchurch Alport (Mid Cheshire) in a replay, but fell in the Quarter-Finals to Shifnal. Little Drayton Rangers beat Wem Town 2-1 to give the County League a second Semi-Finalist, while Donnington Wood beat Ludlow. The shocks were for the Semi-Finals though, as Shifnal now won at Bridgnorth Reserves, and Little Drayton beat Donnington Wood to set up an all County League league final, won 3-0 by Little Drayton Rangers - a side previously unheralded even within their own County.

Shropshire Senior Cup First Round

Telford Juniors v Donnington Wood	3-5		Snailbeach White Star v Broseley Athletic	1-4

Second Round

Oakengates Town v Admaston	0-3		Meole Brace v Whitchurch Alport	2-2,3-0
Ellesmere Rangers v Ludlow Town	1-4		Little Drayton Rangers v Wellington Amateurs	3-2
Nags Head v Wem Town	1-5		Albrighton S & S v Shifnal Town	0-3
Donnington Wood v Morda United	4-0		Broseley Athletic v Bridgnorth Town Reserves	0-1

Quarter-Finals

Meole Brace v Shifnal Town	1-3		Little Drayton Rangers v Wem Town	2-1
Donnington Wood v Ludlow Town	1-0		Bridgnorth Town Reserves v Admaston	4-2

Semi-Finals

Bridgnorth Town Reserves v Shifnal T.	0-1		Little Drayton Rangers v Donnongton Wood	2-1

Final *(at Telford United FC)*: Little Drayton Rangers 3, Shifnal Town 0

Somerset

Starting with the Premier Cup, where Yeovil Town (GMVC) got off to an explosive start by thrashing Glastonbury (GM West-1) by 6-1; the second successive season that Yeovil had scored six in this round, and also repeating the six Glastonbury conceded (to Bath) in the previous season. Keynsham Town (GM West-1), Yeovil's early victims last season, managed a bye in the First Round before losing 2-1 at Radstock Town (GM West-1). Bath City also came in at the Second Round this time with a 2-1 win at Clevedon Town (GM West-P). Meanwhile the two Bristol Football League sides started with Rovers winning 1-0 at Paulton (GM West-P) and City, the holders, going down 1-0 at Yeovil. The other three Quarter-Finalists were all Western Premier sides, with Minehead winning 7-1 at Clandown (GM West-1) to secure their place. Pity they could not save a few of these goals for the home match against Yeovil, which they lost 2-1. Meanwhile Bristol Rovers won 3-1 at Taunton, but their ground sharing partners, Bath, suffered the round's shock losing 1-0 at Radstock. Mangotsfield beat Weston-Super-Mare 1-0 in the all Western League match, and managed a Semi-Final draw at Yeovil, before losing 4-1 at home. In a similar story, Bristol Rovers and Radstock drew 1-1 before Rovers reached the final. Playing the first leg at Bath, Bristol Rovers lost 2-1, but they then won 2-0 at Huish Park to reverse the scoreline and win the Cup.

Somerset & Avon (South) Premier Round First Round

Yeovil Town v Glastonbury	6-1		Mangotsfield United v Chard Town	1-0
Weston-super-Mare v Welton Rovers	1-0			

Second Round

Clandown v Minehead	1-1,1-7		Chevedon Town v Bath City	1-2
Radstock Town v Keynsham Town	2-1		Paulton Rovers v Bristol Rovers	0-1
Frome Town v Taunton Town	0-2		Yeovil Town v Bristol City	1-0
Larkhall Athletic v Weston-super-Mare	1-1,2-4		Wellington v Mangotsfield United	1-1,0-2

Quarter-Finals

Mangotsfield Utd v Weston-super-Mare	1-0		Radstock Town v Bath City	1-0
Taunton Town v Bristol Rovers	1-3		Minehead v Yeovil Town	1-2

Semi-Finals

Yeovil Town v Mangotsfield United	1-1,4-1		Bristol Rovers v Radstock Town	1-1,5-4

Final *(16th April, 7th May)*: Bristol Rovers 1, Yeovil 2   Yeovil Town 0, Bristol Rovers 2

The Senior Cup is as always dominated by clubs from the Somerset Senior League, but includes a small number of Western League clubs not in the Premier Cup, including newly elevated Brislington, the holders. Backwell, Odd Down and Bishop Sutton also represent the Western League, and this quartet survived the First Round, before Brislington had to travel to fellow new boys Bishop Sutton in the next round, scraping a single goal win. They then drew another all Western League tie in the Third Round, this time being less fortunate, and going down 2-1 at Odd Down. So Odd Down were in the Quarter-Finals, and despite being held up with a 1-1 draw at Long Sutton, a 7-2 win saw them into the Semis. They were also held at this stage by Shepton Mallet before again winning the replay. Backwell United had also made it to the Quarter-Finals, but fell to Clevedon United who in turn fell to Portishead, the leaders of the Somerset Senior League's First Division. With two divisions seperating the finalists, it was no surprise that Odd Down took the Cup.

Somerset & Avon (South) Senior Cup First Round

Brislington v Churchill Club '70	5-0		Bridgwater Town '84 v Teyfant Athletic	9-1
Watchet Town v Winscombe	1-2		Fry Club v Backwell United	0-1
Tunley Athletic v Burnham United	1-2		Clutton v Hengrove Athletic	0-3
Imperial Bristol v Street	3-2		Broad Plain House Old Boys v Castle Cary	0-2
Clevedon United v Wellington Reserves	4-0		Yatton Athletic v Welton Rovers Reserves	0-4
Paulton R. Res v Shepton Mallet Town	0-3		Wrington-Redhill v Timsbury Athletic	1-1,1-3
Blackbrook v P & W United	0-4		Keynsham Cricketers v Long Ashton	1-4
Westland United v Portishead	2-4		Weston-super-Mare v Larkhall Athletic	3-0
T.D.R. Dynamo v Ilminster Town	1-3		Saltford v Clandown Reserves	4-2
Clevedon Town Res v Frome Town Res	2-3		Hartcliffe v Long Sutton	1-4
Hartcliffe Old Boys v Nailsea Town	3-6		Weston St John v Temple Cloud	5-0
Nailsea United v Westland Sports	1-2		St George-Easton-in-Gordano v Highridge Utd	0-1
Odd Down v Congresbury	3-0		Avon & Somerset Police v Bishop Sutton	1-4
Cheddar v Glastonbury Reserves	2-2,4-3(aet)		Stockwood Green v Imperial Utd *(at Imperial)*	1-0
Wells City v Keynsham Town Reserves	0-2		Farleigh Sports v Mendip Hospital	1-3
Dundry Athletic *(bye)*			Peasedown Athletic *W/O* Bristol Spartak	

(continued on page 939)

Somerset & Avon (South) Senior Cup Second Round

Clevedon United v Nailsea Town	2-2,3-2		Burnham United v Weston-super-Mare Reserves	0-2
Highridge United v Portishead	2-3		Shepton Mallet Town v Long Ashton	7-2
Cheddar v Saltford	3-1		Bridgwater Town '84 v Peasedown Athletic	2-3
Dundry Athletic v Westland Sports	2-3		Castle Cary v Tring Athletic	3-2
Welton Rovers Reserves v Winscombe	4-0		Imperial United v Frome Town Reserves	0-2
P & W United v Odd Down	1-2		Bishop Sutton v Brislington	0-1
Ilminster Town v Backwell United	2-4		Hengrove Athletic v Mendip Hospital	2-4
Long Sutton v Weston St John	4-1		Keynsham Town Reserves v Imperial Bristol	0-2

Third Round

Castle Cary v Westland Sports Reserves	1-7		Welton Rovers Reserves v Shepton Mallet Town	1-4
Mendip Hospital v Portishead	1-5		Odd Down v Brislington	2-1
Long Sutton v Frome Town Reserves	7-2		Peasedown Athletic v Weston-super-Mare Reserves	1-4
Clevedon United v Cheddar	1-1,5-2		Backwell United v Imperial Bristol	1-1,2-0

Quarter-Finals

Clevedon United v Backwell United	1-0		Weston-super-Mare Reserves v Shepton Mallet	2-3
Long Sutton v Odd Down	1-1,2-7		Portishead v Westland Sports	2-1

Semi-Finals

Clevedon United v Portishead	1-2		Shepton Mallet Town v Odd Down	0-0,1-3

Final (at Paulton Rovers FC, 4th May): Odd Down 4, Portishead 2

Staffordshire

The Staffordshire Senior Cup now has 32 teams, and they are a mixed bunch, with many of the clubs competing being in the Birmingham FA, and also including Pershore Town (M Comb-P, and Worcestershire FA), while Congleton Town (HFS-1) represented Cheshire, (not for long, as they went down 4-0 at home to Rushall Oylimpic (W.Mids-P) in the First Round). Pershore incidently won 2-0 at Armitage (M Comb-P). The surprise of the First Round was at Chasetown (W.Mids-P) where Port Vale (FL-2) were beaten 3-2. This was the start of a fine run for the Chase, as they followed by beating Stourport Swifts (W Mids-P) by 4-0, and then beat Rushall Olympic 2-0 in a replay to reach the Semis. Rushall had beaten Bilston Town (BHL-M) to reach the Third Round. There was a Third West Midlands League side in the Quarter-Finals, in Oldbury United, who had beaten two other W.Mids sides to get that far. Oldbury followed Boldmere St.Michaels (M.Comb-P) and Stoke City (FL) in being accounted for by Stafford Rangers (GMVC). Another Quarter-Final brought together BHL-M pair Sutton Coldfield Town and Hednesford Town. Sutton, who had earlier beaten Malvern (W.Mids-P) and Pershore, won 2-1. In the last of the Third Round ties, Eastwood Hanley (NWC-1) beat Leek Town (HFS-1) 2-1 in a replay. In the Semi-Finals, Eastwood were beaten 2-0 by Stafford, while Chasetown again provided the shock by beating Sutton Coldfield in a replay. The final has been hled over to the start of the new season.

Staffordshire Senior Cup First Round

Armitage '90 v Pershore Town	0-2		Congleton Town v Rushall Olympic	0-4
Bilston Town v Tamworth	3-1		Halesowen Town v Dudley Town	1-3
Chasetown v Port Vale	3-2		Malvern Town v Sutton Coldfield Town	0-4
Eastwood Hanley W/O Walsall Wood			Mile Oak Rovers & Youth v Stoke City	1-1,2-7
Leek Town v Willenhall Town	3-2		Oldswinford F & SC v Hednesford Town	1-2
Newcastle Town v Paget Rangers	0-1		Stourbridge v Redditch United	4-0
Rocester v Oldbury United	0-1		Wednesfield v Halesowen Harriers	1-1,0-4
Stafford Rangers v Boldmere St Michaels	3-0		Stourport Swifts v Blakenall	3-2

Second Round

Stafford Rangers v Stoke City	2-1		Sutton Coldfield Town v Pershore Town	3-0
Hednesford Town v Dudley Town	2-0		Leek Town v Stourbridge	2-1
Paget Rangers v Oldbury United	0-1		Eastwood Hanley v Kidderminster Harriers	4-3
Chasetown v Stourport Swifts	4-0		Bilston Town v Rushall Olympic	1-1,1-3

Quarter-Finals

Stafford Rangers v Oldbury United	1-0		Eastwood Hanley v Leek Town	1-1,2-1
Chasetown v Rushall Olympic	0-0,2-0		Sutton Coldfield Town v Hednesford Town	2-1

Semi-Finals

Eastwood Hanley v Stafford Rangers	0-2		Sutton Coldfield Town v Chasetown	1-1,0-2

Final: Chasetown v Stafford Rangers (two legs, held over to 1992-93)

Suffolk

Sudbury Town (BHL-S) regained the Suffolk Premier Cup without conceding a goal in their three matches, scoring six at Newmarket, five against Lowestoft, and one more in the final against the holders Stowmarket, thus avenging the previous season's Semi-Final defeat by Stowmarket. This was the first goal that Stowmarket had conceded in this season's competition.

Suffolk Premier Round First Round

Bury Town v Sudbury Town	1-5			

Quarter-Finals

Cornard United v Lowestoft Town	0-2		Brantham Athletic v Felixstowe Town	0-1
Stowmarket Town v Haverhill Rovers	1-0		Newmarket Town v Sudbury Town	0-6

Semi-Finals

Sudbury Town v Lowestoft Town	5-0		Felixstowe Town v Stowmarket Town	0-0(aet),0-2

Final (at Sudbury Town FC, 4th May): Sudbury Town 1, Stowmarket Town 0

While the Eastern League's Premier clubs play in the Premier Cup, those from Division One play in the Senior Cup, with sides from the Suffolk & Ipswich League and the Essex & Suffolk Border League. Four of the seven fell in the First Round. Bury Reserves, who suffered the heaviest reverse, at least had the excuse that their 5-0 defeat came at fellow Eastern Leaguers Sudbury Wanderers. Sudbury Town Reserves however, who in the past have had a fair degree of success as a Border League club in this Cup, have no excusues for the 2-1 home defeat by Long Melford, an old rival from the League. Meanwhile Hadleigh went down 2-1 at B.T. Reserch, and Mildenhall fell at home to Ransomes (both S&I). In the Second Round, Sudbury Wanderers were held up by Melton St.Aubreys (S&I), but they survived to win the replay 4-0. They were not so fortunate in the Quarter-Finals, where they drew at home with Whitton United (S&I) but then fell 4-3 (aet) in the replay, despite a hat-trick from leading goalscorer Adam Crofton. The other two Eastern League sides won through, Ipswich Wanderers beating Lowestoft Reserves (Ang Comb), and Woodbridge beating Framlingham (S&I). Long Melford were the last surviving Border League club, and they reached the Semis by beating Halesworth (S&I). With the two Eastern League sides kept apart in the Semi-Finals, they must have been expected to meet in the final, but both took two goal beatings, Ipswich Wanderers going down 2-0 to Long Melford, and Woodbridge by 3-1 to Whitton United. And so to Ipswich Town for the final, and a well deserved win for Whitton. (Results overleaf).

Suffolk Senior Cup Preliminary Round
B.S. Fonnereau W/O Stowmarket Town Res

First Round

Melton St Audry v Ashlea	1-1,3-1	Walsham-le-Willows v Woodbridge Town	2-4
Sudbury Wanderers v Bury Town Reserves	5-0	Grundisburgh v Bristish Sugar Fonnereau Ath.	0-0,0-2
Old Newton United v Oulton Broad	0-2	Halesworth Town v Haverhill Rovers Reserves	3-0
Framlington Town v Kirkley	2-1	Brandon Town v Felixstowe Town Reserves	0-1
Lowestoft Town Reserves v Leiston Town	2-0	Ipswich Wanderers v Stonham Aspall	2-1
B.T. Research v Hadleigh United	2-1	Haughley United v Beccles Town	2-2,3-2
Stutton v Needham Market	3-1	Sudbury Town Reserves v Long Melford	1-2
Mildenhall Town v R.S.S.C. Ransomes	3-4	Whitton United v Bungay Town	4-0

Second Round

Woodbridge Town v Haughley United	3-1	Oulton Broad v Long Melford	1-3
Flamlington Town v Stutton	2-2	Whitton United v R.S.S.C. Ransomes	4-1
Halesworth Town v B.T. Research	5-0	Melton St Audrys v Sudbury Wanderers	1-1,0-4
B.S. Fonnereau Ath. v Ipswich Wanderers	0-1	Felixstowe Reserves v Lowestoft Reserves	0-2

Quarter-Finals

Long Melford v Halesworth Town	1-0	Woodbridge Town v Framlington Town	4-0
Sudbury Wanderers v Whitton United	1-1,3-4(aet)	Lowestoft Town Reserves v Ipswich Wanderers	1-3

Semi-Finals

Long Melford v Ipswich W. (at Hadleigh Utd)	2-0	Woodbridge Town v Whitton Utd (at Brantham A.)	1-3

Final (at Ipswich Town FC, 14th April): Whitton United 2, Long Melford 0

Whitton United start their victorious run in the Suffolk Senior Cup with a 4-0 win over visting Bungay Town on 26th October. Here the homesters rattle the Bungay bar. Photo - Gavin Ellis.

Surrey

Egham Town (DFL-2) scored no less than 17 goals in the Second and Third Qualifying Rounds, winning 8-0 against Old Suttonians (Old Boys Lge) and 9-2 against Horley Town (Dan-Air). There had been a couple of surprises in the Second Qualifying Round, including a win for Carshalton (S Am Lge) at Frimley Green (Dan-Air) and defeat for Banstead Athletic (DFL-2) at Cobham (Dan-Air). Neither of the victors in these matches made it to the final qualifying round, where the odds do not favour the exempt sides, two out of three defeated. Leatherhead (DFL-2) went down at Egham by 3-2 and Molesey (DFL-1) fell by 3-0 at Farnham Town (Dan-Air). Malden Vale (DFL-2) bucked the trend by winning at Ash United (Dan-Air). After an abandoned match, the final tie saw Corinthian Casuals (Spartan) lose to Farleigh Rovers (Dan-Air). When the draw for the competition proper was seen it was noticed that all four DFL Premier sides were in the same half of the draw, and hence that a lower division side would reach the final. For the Premier Division, there was to be three matches that mattered, and I ended up seeing them all. In the First Round, two goals from Robin Beste gave Carshalton Athletic victory at Sutton United. Meanwhile Kingstonian beat Chertsey (DFL-3) 5-0, and Woking beat Walton & Hersham (DFL-1) by 6-1 to set up a meeting in Round Two. Woking took the lead just before the half-hour, when Graham Pearce put through his own goal, but Kingstonian fought back, and actually led before half time, after Roddy Braithwaite and Francis Vines scored. George Friel levelled the scores just after half-time, and Lawrence Batty, the Woking goalkeeper scored the decisive goal, from the penalty spot. Meanwhile Carshalton won 2-1 at Epsom (DFL-3) to earn the right to visit Woking in the Semi-Final. The match was level at half-time, then Andy Riley moved up from full-back to score a few minutes after the break. Jimmy Bolton added a second, ten minutes later to seal the tie. In the other half of the draw, the story was still about Egham; in the First Round they won 4-3 at Dorking (DFL-1), and they then beat Croydon 4-2, after a 0-0 draw. In the Semi-Final they won 3-1 at Metropolitan Police. Only when they met Carshalton Athletic at Tooting for the final did their goal scoring fade a little, and they went down 3-1.
(results on page 942)

Sudbury Town 1, Stowmarket Town 0 - Suffolk Premier Cup final, 4/5/92. Sudbury's Mervyn Henry (left) is too late to dispossess Dave King of Stowmarket. Photo - Jon Weaver.

Farleigh keeper Phil Gilmore saves a shot from Corinthian-Casual Bruce Martin in a 1-1 Surrey Senior Cup draw.

Croydon 1, Malden Vale 1 - Surrey Senior Cup 1st Round, 30/12/92. Michael Morgan heads the goal that earned Croydon a replay. Photo - Dave West.

Surrey 'Demolition & Excavation' Senior Cup First Qualifying Round

Godalming Town v Cobham	1-3	Ashford Town (Middx) v Farleigh Rovers	2-3
Banstead Athletic v Reigate Priory	3-0	Merstham v Chipstead	3-3(aet),3-0

Second Qualifying Round

Farnham Town v Camberley Town	4-0	Ash United v Malden Town	5-2
Horley Town v Redhill	2-0	Cobham v Banstead Athletic	1-0
Frimley Green v Carshalton	2-4	Merstham v Shene Old Grammarians	3-3(aet),2-1
Ditton F & SC v Farleigh Rovers	0-2	Westfield v Kew Association	4-1
Egham Town v Old Suttonians	8-0	Cranleigh v Corinthian Casuals	1-3

Third Qualifying Round

Egham Town v Horley Town	9-2	Ash United v Merstham	4-4(aet),1-0
Corinthian Casuals v Westfield	2-0	Farleigh Rovers v Cobhan.	0-0(aet),4-1
Carshalton v Farnham Town	2-3		

Fourth Qualifying Round

Egham Town v Leatherhead	3-2	Ash United v Malden Vale	1-4
Farnham Town v Molesey	3-0	Farleigh Rvrs v Corinthian Cas.	-1(aban),3-2

First Round Proper

Kingstonian v Chertsey Town	5-0	Sutton United v Carshalton Athletic	0-2
Dorking v Egham Town	3-4	Tooting & Mitcham v Whyteleafe	1-1,0-0(aet),0-1
Metropolitan Police v Faleigh Rovers	3-0	Woking v Walton & Hersham	6-1
Croydon v Malden Vale	1-1,3-0	Farnham Town v Epsom & Ewell	1-3

Quarter-Finals

Kingstonian v Woking	2-3	Epsom & Ewell v Carshalton Athletic	1-2
Whyteleafe v Metropolitan Police	0-3	Egham Town v Croydon	0-0,4-2

Semi-Finals

Woking v Carshalton Athletic	0-2	Metropolitan Police v Egham Town	1-3

Final *(at Tooting & Mitcham Utd FC, 20th April)*: Carshalton Athletic 3, Egham Town 1

Carshalton Athletic players and supporters celebrate their Surrey Senior Cup final victory over Egham Town at Sandy Lane. Photo - Dennis Nicholson.

Sussex

All the Sussex County League's Division Two sides have to play in the First Round, along with the County's teams in the DFL-Div.3, the Wessex League and some unlucky County League Division One sides, as there are not enough exemptions for them all to excape. Without surprises, all the teams beaten were from Sussex Two, except Haywards Heath Town and Chichester City (both Sx-1). Chichester lost to Bexhill Town (also Sx-1) and Haywards Heath went down 5-1 following an extra time blast in their replay at Eastbourne United (DFL-3). Horsham (the other DFL-3 side) also hit 5, against Saltdean (Sx-2), while Steyning (Wx) managed 6 at Bosham (SX-2). With the addition of exempt teams in Round 2, things began to get more difficult. Horsham lost 3-2 at Littlehampton (Sx-1) and Eastbourne United went down in a replay to Little Common Albion (Sx-2). Another DFL side to fall was Worthing (Div.2) beaten 4-0 at home by Hastings Town (BHL-S). Apart from Little Common, Stamco became the only other Sussex 2 side in the Third Round by beating Shoreham (Sx-1) 5-4. East Preston (Sx-2) suffered the biggest set back, losing by eight clear goals at Burgess Hill Town (Sx-1). Little Common fell to another Burgess Hill onslaught in Round Three, going down 6-1, and Division Two participation was ended with Stamco losing 2-1 at Hailsham Town (Sx-1). Southwick (DFL-1) lost 4-1 in a home replay to Langney Sports (Sx-1) and with Bognor Regis (DFl-P) losing 1-0 at Littlehampton, only Lewes survived to the Quarter-Finals from the DFL camp, by beating Arundel (Sx-1). The classic battle was between Brighton & Hove Albion's Reserve side, and Hastings Town (BHL-S), in which Brighton won the third match by 3-2 (aet). Crawley Town (BHL-P) made the Quarter-Finals with a clear cut 7-0 win, in a replay at Oakwood (Sx-1) after a 3-3 draw. Eastbourne Town (Sx-1) beat Steyning Town by 2-0 to give the County League 5 of the last 8. The County League was therefore guananteed at least one Semi-Finalist, produced by Littlehampton beating Eastbourne Town by 4-1 in a replay, but added a second when Langney Sports won at Crawley Town. Burgess Hill went down 4-2 at Brighton, and Lewes beat Hailsham, to meet in a Semi-Final at Worthing, where Brighton were the single goal winners. In the other Semi, Langney came out on top after extra time, but Brighton had the home advantage in the final and maybe this told in giving them a single goal win.

(results on page 944)

Langney Sports' Matt Jones outumps Wayne Stemp of Brighton & Hove Albion during the Sussex Senior Cup final at the Goldstone Ground. Photo - Roger Turner.

Hailsham defender Neil Thornicroft puts the ball past his own keeper, Gavin Richards, during the Sussex Senior Cup Quarter-Final defeat at Lewes on 15th February. Photo - Colin Stevens.

Langney Sports fans at the Sussex Senior Cup final - the biggest day in the club's history. Photo - Roger Turner.

Sussex Senior Cup First Round

Worthing United v Eastbourne Town	0-2	Haywards Heath Town v Eastbourne United	1-1,1-5
Horsham v Saltdean United	5-0	Chichester City v Bexhill Town	0-4
Portfield v East Preston	0-1	Bosham v Steyning Town	2-6
Lancing v Horsham Y.M.C.A.	2-2,2-1	Little Common Albion v Sidley United	2-2,2-0
Seaford Town v Stamco	2-4	Broadbridge Heath v East Grinstead	0-0,2-0
Newhaven v Crowborough Athletic	5-0	Midhurst & Easebourne v Selsey	3-2

Second Round

Littlehampton Town v Horsham	3-2	Newhaven v Steyning Town	2-2,2-4(aet)
Southwick v Ringmer	4-1	Worthing v Hastings Town	0-4
Lewes v Peacehaven & Telscombe	3-1	Wick v Crawley Town	3-4
Pagham v Bognor Regis Town	2-2(aet),0-2	Eastbourne United v Little Common Albion	2-2,1-2
Three Bridges v Arundel	0-4	Bexhill Town v Hailsham Town	1-1,2-3
Burgess Hill Town v East Preston	8-0	Broadbridge Heath v Oakwood	0-0,2-4
Stamco v Shoreham	5-4	Lancing v Brighton & Hove Albion	1-4
Eastbourne Town v Whitehawk	2-2,1-0	Langney Sports v Midhurst & Easebourne	6-3

Third Round

Crawley Town v Oakwood	3-3,7-0	Burgess Hill Town v Little Common Albion	6-1
Eastbourne Town v Steyning Town	2-0	Littlehampton Town v Bognor Regis Town	1-0
Lewes v Arundel	2-1	Langney Sports v Southwick	1-1,4-1
Hailsham Town v Stamco	2-1	Brighton & Hove A. v Hastings	0-0,2-2(aet),3-2(aet)

Quarter-Finals

Lewes v Hailsham Town	3-1	Brighton & Hove Albion v Burgess Hill Town	4-2
Crawley Town v Langney Sports	2-3	Littlehampton Town v Eastbourne Town	2-2,4-1

Semi-Finals

Langney v Littlehampton (at Lewes)	3-1(aet)	Brighton & Hove A. v Lewes (at Worthing FC)	1-0

Final (at Brighton & Hove Albion, 4th May): Brighton & Hove Albion 1, Langney Sports 0

Sussex Royal Ulster Rifles Charity Cup Preliminary Round

Haywards Heath Town v Newhaven	3-1	Chichester City v Horsham Y.M.C.A.	3-2

First Round

Littlehampton Town v Selsey	7-2	Peacehaven & Telscombe v Sidley United	6-1
Three Bridges v Langney Sports	1-3	Wick v East Grinstead	1-2
Hailsham Town v Haywards Heath Town	4-0	Burgess Hill Town v Chichester City	3-1
Ringmer v Stamco	2-1	Midhurst & Easebourne v Shoreham	1-1(aet),1-4
Worthing United v Portfield	1-2	Whitehawk v Seaford Town	0-2
East Preston v Broadbridge Heath	0-1	Little Common Albion v Eastbourne Town	3-4(aet)
Bexhill Town v Oakwood	2-0	Arundel v Lancing	3-2
Pagham v Bosham	4-0	Saltdean United v Crowborough Athletic	5-1(aet)

Second Round

Pagham v Littlehampton Town	3-0	East Grinstead v Arundel	2-1
Hailsham Town v Ringmer	2-4	Portfield v Broadbridge Heath	4-0
Langney Sports v Bexhill Town	3-2	Saltdean United v Peacehaven & Telscombe	0-3
Seaford Town v Eastbourne Town	6-2	Burgess Hill Town v Shoreham	4-0(aet)

Quarter-Finals

Ringmer v Peacehaven & Telscombe	1-0	Burgess Hill Town v Pagham	4-0
Langney Sports v Portfield	4-2	East Grinstead v Seaford Town	5-1

Semi-Finals

Burgess Hill Town v Langney Spts	1-1,6-0	Ringmer v East Grinstead	6-0

Final (at Lancing FC, 3rd March): Burgess Hill Town 2, Ringmer 1 (after extra-time)

West Riding

In the First Round, Goole Town (HFS-P) required a replay to beat Selby Town (NCE-1), while Guiseley (HFS-1) had a simpler task in winning 2-0 at Yorkshire Amateur (NCE-1). The highlights of the Second Round were two big derby matches. In Ossett, (both sides NCE-P) the Albion won 2-1 at the Town, whereas in Harrogate, the Town side (HFS-1) drew 3-3 with their rivals, Railway Athletic (NCE-P), and then lost 1-0 in the replay. Goole Town again needed a replay, but came through at home against Glasshoughton Welfare (NCE-P); Guiseley won in extra time at Thackley (NCE-P), but Farsley Celtic (HFS-1) were beaten at Bradley Rangers (NCE-1). A second side from the Northern Counties League's lower division made it to the Quarter-Finals, when Garforth (NCE-1) beat Liversedge in a replay. Garforth went out at this stage to the holders Bradford Park Avenue (Bass NWC-1). Bradley Rangers supplied the shock by beating Guiseley 3-2. Goole for once did not need a replay (perhaps it was due to being at home in the first match), and beat Ossett Albion 5-3. Harrogate Railway went down 4-3 at home to Armthorpe Welfare (NCE-P). Goole Town were drawn at home in the Semis, and again scored five, this time against Bradford Park Avenue. In the other Semi-Final, Bradley again provided the surprise by beating Armthorpe. The reward for the finalists was a trip to Leeds United for the last match; but for Bradley it was a disappointment as for the second time in three years they lost the final by the odd goal in five; and so the cup returned to Goole after a two season absence.

West Riding Senior Cup First Round

Liversedge v Eccleshill United	4-0	Garforth Town v Tadcaster Albion	2-1
Yorkshire Amateur v Guiseley	0-2	Selby Town v Goole Town	1-1,0-2

Second Round

Thackley v Guiseley	2-3(aet)	Ossett Town v Ossett Albion	1-2
Hatfield Main v Armthorpe Welfare	2-4	Harrogate T. v Harrogate Railway Athletic	3-3(aet),0-1
Bradley Rangers v Farsley Celtic	3-2	Graforth Town v Liversedge	1-1,4-2
Glasshoughton Welfare v Goole Town	1-1,0-2	Pontefract Collieries v Bradford Park Avenue	1-2

Quarter-Finals

Bradford Park Avenue v Garforth Town	2-0	Goole Town v Ossett Albion	5-3
Bradley Rangers v Garforth Town	3-2	Harrogate Railway Athletic v Armthorpe Welfare	3-4

Semi-Finals

Goole Town v Bradford Park Avenue	5-3	Bradley Rangers v Armthorpe Welfare	2-1

Final (at Leeds United FC): Goole Town 3, Bradley Rangers 2

Langney Sports' diminutive, but effective, goalkeeper Steve Dell makes an unorthodox save during the Sussex Senior Cup final at the Goldstone Ground. Photo - Roger Turner.

Burgess Hill Town celebrate their Sussex R.U.R. Cup triumph against Ringmer at Culver Road, Lancing.

Bradley Rangers' keeper Darrel Rose clears the ball off the head of Mark Tennison during the surprise Third Round elimination of Guiseley in the West Riding Cup. Photo - Barry Lockwood.

Westmoreland

Netherfield (HFS-L), the holders were beaten at home by local rivals Kendal United (Westmoreland Lge) in the Second Round. Kendal United then beat two more Westmoreland League sides, Burneside and Kirkby Stephen to reach the final. Coniston also reached the final, and in some style, putting 8 past Grasmere in the First Round, and then scoring 3 at Ibis, and 4 against Keswick. In the Semi-Finals they beat Kendal County by 3 goals, and still had not conceded one. The final was at Netherfield, and with Coniston's fine form, one could not call Kendal favourites on account of the fact they had earlier won a game on the ground. Kendal did become the first side to put a goal past Coniston in this seasons competition, but to no avail as Coniston won 4-1.

Westmoreland Senior Cup First Round

Kendal County v Wetheriggs	4-2	Ibis v Penrith United	4-0
Ambleside v Greystoke	11-1	Netherfield v Arnside	4-3
Kendal United v Shap	6-0	Esthwaite Vale v Burneside	0-11
Coniston v Grasmere	8-0	Appleby v Keswick	1-2
Corinthians v Endmoor Kgr	8-2	Kirkby Stephen v Kirkby Lonsdale	6-1
Staveley v Braithwaite	4-0	Kirkoswald v Victoria Sports	2-3

Second Round

Burneside v Victoria Sports	2-0	Keswick v Burton Thistle	9-0
Grange v Windermere	1-6	Staveley v Ambleside	0-2
Ibis v Coniston	0-3	Corinthians v Kirkby Stephen	0-4
Netherfield v Kendal United	1-2	Sedburgh v Kendal County	1-4

Quarter-Finals

Coniston v Keswick	4-0	Burneside v Kendal United	1-2
Kirkby Stephen v Windermere	4-2	Kendal County v Ambleside	4-1

Semi-Finals

Kendal County v Coniston	0-3	Kirkby Stephen v Kendal United	0-1

Final (at Netherfield FC, 25th April): Coniston 4, Kendal United 1

Wiltshire

The holders, Pewsey Vale (Wilts) came through a difficult First Round match to win at Bemerton Heath Harlequins (Wessex) in a replay. Generally, the First Round followed form, but Wootton Bassett Town (Hell-1) lost 5-3 at Malmesbury Vics (Wilts). Two more Hellenic sides fell in the Second Round as Supermarine fell 2-1 at Aldbourne Park (Wilts) and Purton lost a home replay to Shrewton United (also Wilts). Newcomers Wollen Sports (Hell-1) won 1-0 at Pewsey Vale, while their Hellenic rivals Highworth Town and Swindon Athletic also made it to the Quarter-Finals, as did Downton (Hants-1). All four of the Quarter-Finals were away victories, with extra time only needed by Highworth at Shrewton. Wollen Sports won 4-1 at Swindon Athletic, and Downton by 2-1 at Walcot (Wilts). In the all County League tie, Wroughton won 3-0 at Aldbourne Park. The Semi-Finals are played on neutral grounds, and sadly without the facility for replays. Wollen Sports beat Wroughton 3-1, while Highworth and Downton drew 1-1 (aet) before the Hampshire League side won by six penalties to five. Naturally the final was held at Swindon Town's County ground, and this provided success at the first attempt for Wollen Sports, who won 3-1.

Wiltshire Senior Cup First Round

Bromham v Wroughton	2-3(ab.),1-4	Pewsey Vale v Bemerton Heath Harlequins	2-2,2-1
Purton v Ferndale Athletic	5-0	Chisledon v Plessey Avebury	2-5
Walcot Athletic v Corsham Town	1-0	Dunbar Wills v Wollen Sports	0-4
Stratton Red Eagles v Burmah Castrol	1-4	Malmesbury Victoria v Wootton Bassett Town	5-3
Shrewton United v West Swindon	4-1	Marlborough Town v Highworth Town	1-3
Sanford Youth Club v Downton	0-1	Supermarine v Biddlestone	1-0
Pinehurst v Amesbury Town	2-0		

Second Round

Burmah Castrol v Swindon Athletic	0-4	Shrewton United v Purton	0-0,0-2
Aldbourne Park v Supermarine	2-1	Downton v Plessey Avebury	3-2
Highworth Town v Dorcan	6-0	Wroughton v Pinehurst	2-0
Pewsey Vale v Wollen Sports	0-2	Malmesbury Victoria v Walcot Athletic	0-2

Quarter-Finals

Shrewton United v Highworth Town	0-1	Aldbourne Park v Wroughton	0-3
Swindon Athletic v Wollen Sports	1-4	Walcot Athletic v Downton	1-2

Semi-Finals

Wollen Spts v Wroughton (at Supermarine)	3-1	Highworth v Downton (at Amesbury)1-1(aet, 5-6 pens)

Final (at Swindon Town FC, 11th April): Wollen Sports 3, Downton 1

Wiltshire Premier Shield (at Salisbury FC, 8th March): Salisbury 1, Trowbridge Town 2

Worcestershire

Sutton Coldfield Town (BHL-M) reached the final, and hence one better than they achieved in the Staffordshire Senior Cup (beaten Semi-Finalist), or in their own native Birmingham Senior Cup (beaten at home in the Second Round). Are Sutton Coldfield gluttons for County Cup action? Certainly their route in this competition was interesting - having gained a bye in the First Round, they then drew 0-0 at home the Worcester City (BHL-P), and so had to travel down to Worcester; another draw followed (1-1) before Sutton triumphed in the third match to earn themselves a visit to Halesowen Town (BHL-P) in the Semi-Finals. Although Sutton lost 2-0, it was found that Halesowen fielded an ineligible player, and so Sutton were re-instated into the final. Redditch United (BHL-M) had beaten Stourbridge (also BHL-M) in the only First Round match, but then went out to Bromsgrove Rovers (BHL-P). Bromsgrove Rovers took time off from their promotion push to give credibility to the GMVC aims, by winning 2-0 at Kidderminster Harriers (GMVC, but struggling) in the Semi-Finals. Sutton Coldfield were at home in the first of the two legs of the final, but a 1-1 draw was never likely to be enough, and the Cup returned to Bromsgrove after three years at Kidderminster (and one at Worcester) when they won the second leg by 3-0.

Worcestershire Senior Cup First Round

Stourbridge v Redditch United	2-2,0-3

Quarter-Finals

Bromsgrove Rovers v Redditch United	3-0	Dudley Town v Halesowen Town	0-2
Moor Green v Kidderminster Harriers	0-4	Sutton Coldfield Town v Worcester City	0-0,1-2

Semi-Finals

Kidderminster Harriers v Bromsgrove R,	0-2	Halesowen Town v Sutton Coldfield Town	2-0
		(Halesowen Town removed for fielding ineligible player)	

Final First Leg: Sutton Coldfield Town 1, Bromsgrove Rovers 1
Final Second Leg: Bromsgrove Rovers 3, Sutton Coldfield Town 0

Action from the Middlesex Senior Cup final: Tony Hedlam (right) of Wembley drives a shot towards goal as Yeading's Lee Charles challenges. Photo - Francis Short.

Hanwell Town captain Phil Player cherishes the London Senior Cup, won with a 4-3 replay victory over Croydon Athletic at Corinthian-Casuals FC. Photo - Dave West.

JUNIOR & INTERMEDIATE COUNTY CUPS 1991-92

INFORMATION PROVIDED BY **ANTHONY DAVIE**

BEDFORDSHIRE
Intermediate Cup
Shambrook v Stotfold Reserves   1-4
Junior Cup
Clapham Sports v Eaton Socon   1-2
Junior Charity Cup
Kempston Town v Marston Shelton Rovers
3-3*(aet, 5-4 pens)*

BERKS & BUCKS
Intermediate Cup
Eton Wick v Lambourn Sports   2-0
Junior Cup
AFC Aldermaston v Wraysbury Coopers   2-1

BIRMINGHAM COUNTY
Junior Cup
Darlaston v Gornal Athletic   1-1*(aet)*,0-1
Minor Challenge Cup
G.P.T. (Coventry) v Sphinx   0-2

CORNWALL
Junior Cup
Winners: Fowey Town   Runners-up: Probus

DEVON
Senior Cup
Falstaff Wanderers v St Martins   0-1
Intermediate Cup
Dartmouth Y.M.R.C. v Hooe St John   2-0

DORSET
Intermediate Cup
Allendale v Littlemoor Spts   1-1*(aet)*,2-2*(aet)*,2-1
Junior Cup
Quayside v Panthers   4-2
Minor Cup
Piddlethrenthide v Weymouth Arms   1-1,3-2*(aet)*

DURHAM
Trophy Cup
Hebburn Colliery v Billingham Cassel Mall   0-3
Minor Cup
Witton Park v Hartlepool Reed Corrugated Cases   3-4

EAST RIDING COUNTY
Intermediate Cup
Bulmans v Youngs   4-0
Junior Cup
Cottingham Trinity v Eureka Club   1-3
Qualifying Cup
Linley Haulage 'A' v Humberside Poly 'A'   1-3

ESSEX COUNTY
Intermediate Cup
Great Wakering Rovers v Kelvedon Hatch
0-0*(aet, 5-4 pens)*
Junior Cup
West Bergholt Reserves v Save & Prosper
2-2*(aet, 4-3 pens)*
Junior Trophy
Tilbury Calcutta v Tate & Lyle 'A'   6-2

GLOUCESTERSHIRE
Amateur Challenge Cup (North)
Cheltenham Saracens v Vikings   6-5
Amateur Challenge Cup (South)
Olveston United v Yate Town Reserves   1-3
Junior Challenge Cup (North)
Ranwick v Tetbury Town   4-1
Junior Challenge Cup (South)
Potterswood v St Philips Marsh A.S. Res.   1-0
Intermediate Cup (North)
Broadwell Sports v Endsleigh Reserves   1-2
Intermediate Cup (South)
Seymour United v Nicholas Wanderers Res.   1-2
Minor Challenge Cup (North)
Endsleigh 'A' v Uley Reserves   5-3
Minor Challenge Cup (South)
London Life v Totterdown Athletic Reserves   0-5
Primary Challenge Cup (North)
Andoversford Reserves v Littledean George   6-1
Primary Challenge Cup (South)
Horfield O B Reserves v Sandringham Sports   0-2

HEREFORDSHIRE
Junior Cup
Colwall Rangers v Leominster United   2-0
Burghill Cup
Great Western v Leominster United   2-0

West Bergholt FC - Essex Junior Cup Winners 1991-92. Photo - Leo Heonig.

HERTFORDSHIRE
Intermediate Cup
Boreham Wood Reserves v Walkern   2-0*(aet)*
Junior Cup
Thundridge United v Hertford Youth Res   3-0

HUNTINGDONSHIRE
Intermediate Scott Getty Cup
Ortonians Reserves v Bluntisham   3-2
Junior Cup
Needingworth Utd v St Neots T. Res   3-2*(aet)*

KENT
Intermediate Challenge Shield
Folkestone Invicta v Gravesend W.I.   3-1
Intermediate Cup
Dover Athletic Res v Thamesmead Town Res   2-1
Junior Cup 'A'
B.I.C.C. v Milton Athletic   0-4
Junior Cup 'B'
Crosskeys v Wellcome Saturday   0-3
Junior Cup 'C'
Staplehurst Monarchs v Strood   2-0

LEICESTERSHIRE & RUTLAND
Intermediate Shield
Saffron Dynamo v Barwell Athletic Reserves   1-0
Page & Moy Junior Cup
Fosse Imps v Parks   1-0
Saturday Medals 'A'
Waltham Athletic v Witherley United Reserves
0-0*(aet)*,0-3
Saturday Medals 'B'
Last Straw v Blaby United Reserves   1-1*(aet)*,0-2
Saturday Medals 'C'
Leicester Fijian v Thurmaston Reserves   1-2

LIVERPOOL COUNTY
Challenge Cup
Stanton Dale v Crawfords U.B.   2-0
Intermediate Cup
Halfie v Red Eagle   1-0
Junior Cup
Aigburgh P.H. v Eagle Sports   2-1

LONDON
Intermediate Cup
Tower Hamlets Tipples v Walthamstow Trojans 1-3
Junior Cup
Broadwater United v Westhill   3-5

MIDDLESEX COUNTY
Premier Cup
Osterley v Northfield Rangers   3-2
Intermediate Cup
British Airway v McDonald Roofing (Saturday)   3-2
Junior Cup
57 Club II v Hillingdon Irish II   3-2
Junior Trophy
Northolt Dynamo v Mill Hill Village IV
1-1*(4-3 on penalties)*

.NORFOLK COUNTY
Junior Cup
Diss Town Reserves v North End United   2-0
Primary Cup
Rangers v Fakenham Town 'A'   2-0

NORTHAMPTONSHIRE
Junior Cup
Raunds Town Res v Peterborough Molins   2-0
Lower Junior Cup
Bugbrooke St Michael v Yardley United   3-2
Area Cup
Oundle Town Res v Peterborough Molins Res   2-1

NOTTINGHAMSHIRE
Intermediate Cup
Boots Athletic v Sneinton   0-1
Junior Cup
Atherton Green v Old Elizabethans II   3-2
Minor Cup
Cotgrave Colliery Welfare v Meden Vale   4-5

OXFORDSHIRE
Intermediate Cup
Thame United Res. v Peppard Res.   2-1*(aet)*

SHROPSHIRE
Junior Cup
Hanwood United v Ludlow Colts   2-3

SOMERSET & AVON (SOUTH)
Junior Cup
Long Sutton Res. v Ace Kitchens/Little Hatch   1-0
Intermediate Cup
Henstridge United v Somerton   2-1

Diss Town Reserves FC - Norfolk Junior Cup Winners 1991-92. Photo - Anthony Davie.

SURREY COUNTY

Intermediate Cup
Banstead Athletic Res v Sutton United Res   1-3
Intermediate Cup
Colliers Wood United v Woking Park Horsell   4-0
Junior Cup
Battersea Pk Rvrs Res v University of Surrey   3-1
Lower Junior Cup
Chessington White Hart Res v Eversley Rgrs   0-1

SUSSEX COUNTY

Intermediate Cup
Hastings Town Res v St Francis Hospital   6-0
Junior Cup
Eastbourne Rose & Crown v Pease Pottage Village   1-0

WESTMORLAND

County Benevolent Cup
Coniston v Kendal County   2-0
County Invitation Trophy
Coniston v Kendal County   2-1
Junior Cup
Corinthians Reserves v Kendal Utd Res   2-1 *(aet)*

WILTSHIRE

Junior Cup
Bradford United v Salisbury Moor   4-0

WORCESTERSHIRE

Senior URN
West Midlands Police v Stourport Swifts   4-1
Junior Cup
County Sports v Bishampton   2-2 *(aet, 3-2 pens)*
Minor Cup
New Lakes v Perrywood   4-1

North Kilworth FC celebrate after winning the 1991-92 Harborough Charity Cup. Photo - Leo Heonig.

Hebburn FC after their historic win in the Durham Challenge Cup. Back Row (L/R): Stuart Wright, Tony Robinson, Lance Jobling (obscured), Chris Pearson, Paul Basham, Les Tatum, Greg Bainbridge. Front: Ian Potts, Paul Tinmouth, Micky Wharton, Kevin Caizley, Brian Hill, Ray Banks, Scott Oliver. Hebburn beat First Division Billingham Synthonia, the holders, in the Final at Murton FC on 4th May. In was their first success in the competition since 1943. Photo - Tim Richardson of the Shields Gazette.

CUP COMPETITION FINALS

A.F.A. SENIOR
West Wickham 2 v 0 Midland Bank

GREENLAND MEMORIAL
Old Ignatians 1 v 0 Lancing Old Boys

ESSEX SENIOR
Old Chigwellians 2 v 1 Old Fairlopians

MIDDLESEX SENIOR
Old Meadowians 2 v 1 Civil Service

SURREY SENIOR
Witan 1*:1 v 1*:0 South Bank Polytechnic

A.F.A. INTERMEDIATE
Old Hamptonians Res. 2 v 0 Old Esthameians Res.

ESSEX INTERMEDIATE
Old Bealonians Res. 2 v 1 Old Westhamians Res.

KENT INTERMEDIATE
Bank of America 1 v 0 Midland Bank Res.

MIDDLESEX INTERMEDIATE
O Hamptonians Res 0*:2* v 0*:1* Winchmore H. Res.

SURREY INTERMEDIATE
Old Tenisonians Res. 4 v 1 Nottsborough Res.

A.F.A. JUNIOR
Hassocks Res. 2 v 0 Old Aloyians 'A'

A.F.A. MINOR
Old Esthameians 'B' 2 v 0 Old SFincheians 'B'

SENIOR NOVETS
National Westminster Bank 'C' 3 v 2 Lloyds Bank 'C'

INTERMEDIATE NOVETS
Civil Service 'C' 2*:1 v 2*:3 Old Salvatorians 'C'

JUNIOR NOVETS
Old Salvatorians 9th 1 v 7 Winchmore Hill 7th

VETERANS'
Winchmore Hill Veterans 1 v 0 Old Salesians Veterans

OPEN VETERANS
O Wulfrunians Vets 1* v 0* Port of London Auth. Vets
(* = After extra-time)

West Wickham captain Neil Linter holds aloft the AFA Senior Cup. Photo - Dennis Nicholson.

West Wickham after their 2-1 Senior Cup Final win over Midland Bank at Cuaco Sports FC. Back Row (L/R): B Quarterman, P Hanifan, D Malone (Manager), G Tanner, G Open, M Norris, S Harding. Front: A Guild, D Hannyngton, N Linter, P Jennings, I Bush, K Clarke. Photo - Dennis Nicholson.

AMATEUR FOOTBALL ALLIANCE SENIOR CUP 1991-92

1st Round Proper

Home		Away	
Chertsey O Salesians	2	Nat West Bank	5
Witan	0	Old Parkonains	2
West Wickham	1	Wake Green	0
Lensbury	0	Old Bealonians	2
Mill Hill Village	1	Cardinal Manning OB	0
Sth Bank Poly.	2	Old Bromleians	0
Old Finchleians	2	Hale End Athletic	1
Norseman	3	Duncombe Sports	1
O Parmiterians	1*:1	O Grammarians	1*:2
Enfield Old Gram.	2	Old Esthameians	1
Old Ignatians	3	Lloyds Bank	1
Royal Bank Scotland	2	British Petrolium	1
Southgate Olympic	0	O Actonians Assn.	7
Wandsworth Borough	0	Winchmore Hill	1
O Latymerians	1+:3	Ulysses	1+:0
Camdenians	2	Carshalton	9
Glyn Old Boys	1*:2	Old Salesians	1*:0
Old Islesworthians	1	Old Stationers	3
Crouch End Vamp.	1*:1	Hassocks	1*:3*
Albanian	6	Latymer Old Boys	1
Old Tiffinians	5	Old Monrovians	0
Economicals	0	Colposa	7
Old Hamptonians	3	Old Owens	2
Old Westminster Cit.	1	Nottsborough	2
Hampstead Heathens	4	Old Southallians	0
St Marys College	1	Old Elizabethans	2
Old Meadonians	2	Midland Bank	3
Old Chigwellians	2	Leyton County OB	1
Old Brentwoods	2	Old Aloysians	6
Old Kingsburians	1*:2*	E Barnet Old Gram.	1*:4*
Old Dorkians	w/o	*Opponents disbarred*	
Civil Service	2	London Airways	0

2nd Round Proper

Home		Away	
Nat West Bank	2*:2	Old Parkonians	2*:3
West Wickham	2	Old Bealonians	1
Mill Hill Village	3	Sth Bank Polytechnic	5
Old Finchleians	1	Norseman	2
Old Grammarians	1	Enfield Old Gramm.	2
Old Ignations	3	Old Esthameians	2
Old Actonians Assn.	3	Winchmore Hill	2
Old Latymerians	3	Carshalton	1
Glyn Old Boys	0	Old Salesias	1
Hassocks	4	Albanian	1
Old Tiffinians	4	Colposa	0
Old Hamptonians	2	Nottsborough	4
Hampstead Heathens	1	Old Elizabethans	3
Midland Bank	3	Old Chigwellians	2
Old Aloysians	3	E Barnet Old Gram.	2
Old Dorkingians	2	Civil Service	5

3rd Round Proper

Home		Away	
Old P	1*:0	West Wickham	1*:1
South Bank Poly	4	Norseman	0
Enfield Old Gram.	1*	Old Ignatians	0*
Old Actonians Assn.	1	Old Latymerians	0
Old Stationers	0	Hassocks	2
Old Tiffinians	0	Nottsborough	1
Old Elizabethans	0	Midland Bank	2
Old Aloysians	2*:2	Civil Service	2*:0

4th Round Proper

Home		Away	
West Wickham	1	South Bank Poly	0
Enfield Old Gram.	2	Old Actonians Assn.	1
Hassocks	1	Nottsborough	2
Midland Bank	2:0x	Old Aloysians	2:0x

Semi-Finals

Home		Away	
West Wickham	2*	Enfield Old Gram.	0*
Nottsborough	0	Midland Bank	4

Final

Home		Away	
West Wickham	2	Midland Bank	1

(*=After extra-time)
(+=Abandoned in extra-time)
(x=Midland Bank won on pens)

West Whickham's captain, Neil Linter, hotly pursues Micky Walker of Midland Bank (right) during the AFA Senior Cup Final at Cuaco Sports. Photo - Dennis Nicholson.

THE ARTHUR DUNN CUP 1991-92

FINAL (at Motspur Park, Saturday 4th April 1992)
Old Chigwellians 3, Old Etonians 1

Old Chigwellians, Arthur Dunn Cup winners 1991-92. Back Row (L/R): F Davis, D Goddard, A Jeffcote, J Connolly, C Sydenham, A Sweet, P Elvin. Front: M Hutchin, P Burbridge, G Bryce (Capt), R Tapper, I Grover. Photo - Dave West.

Old Etonians, Arthur Dunn Cup finalists 1991-92. Back Row (L/R): M Arnander, A Watt, N Matterson, C Yorke, K Angelinitturl, G Granville, N Hurd. Front: G Barnes, D Howell, J Scobie, J Giles (Capt), J Ashmore, R Glanastone, D Lewis. Photo - Dave West.

Richard Tapper is about to score the opening goal of the Arthur Dunn Cup for Old Chigwellians. Photo. Photo - Dave West.

ARTHURIAN LEAGUE

PREM. DIVISION	P	W	D	L	F	A	PTS
Old Chigwellians	16	11	3	2	46	19	25
Old Etonians	16	9	3	4	31	24	21
Old Malvernians	16	8	2	6	27	26	18
Old Cholmeleians	16	6	5	5	30	27	17
Old Reptonians	16	6	4	6	36	25	16
Lancing Old Boys	16	6	2	8	25	28	14
Old Carthusians	16	6	2	8	26	32	14
Old Brentwoods	16	4	4	8	21	31	12
Old Foresters	16	2	3	11	25	55	7

DIVISION ONE	P	W	D	L	F	A	PTS
Old Wellingburians	16	11	3	2	53	18	25
Old Bradfieldians	16	9	3	4	35	26	21
Old Aldenhemians	16	8	4	4	35	20	20
Old Harrovians	16	6	3	7	27	32	15
Old Haileyburians	16	5	4	7	33	38	14
Old Wykehamists	16	4	5	7	28	37	13
Old Ardinians	16	4	5	7	27	42	13
Old Salopians	16	6	0	10	29	32	12
Old Westminsters	16	5	1	10	26	48	11

DIVISION TWO	P	W	D	L	F	A	PTS
Old Witleians	16	11	3	2	53	18	25
Old Cartusians Res	16	9	3	4	35	26	21
Old Cholmel. Res	16	8	4	4	35	20	20
Old Etonians Res	16	6	3	7	27	32	15
Old Chigwel. Res	16	5	4	7	33	38	14
Old Aldenham. Res	16	4	5	7	28	37	13
Old Chigwellians 'A'	16	4	5	7	27	42	13
Old Harrovians Res	16	6	0	10	29	32	12
Lancing OB Res	16	5	1	10	26	48	11

Junior League Cup:
Old Chigwellians 'A' 0, Old Brentwoods Res 0
(Chigwellians on penalties)

DIVISION THREE	P	W	D	L	F	A	PTS
Old Reptonians Res	16	11	2	3	44	15	24
Old Foresters Res	16	10	1	5	50	28	21
Old Malvernians Res	16	9	3	4	43	21	21
Old Brentwoods Res	16	9	2	5	44	24	20
Old Salopians Res	16	7	4	5	38	25	*16
Old Cholmel. 'A'	16	7	1	8	24	29	15
Old Eastbournians	16	3	4	9	22	58	10
Old Chigwellians 'B'	16	4	1	11	25	51	9
Old Foresters 'B'	16	2	2	12	22	61	*4

DIVISION FOUR	P	W	D	L	F	A	PTS
Lancing OB 'A'	16	10	4	2	66	28	24
Old Westminst. Res	16	10	2	4	48	21	22
Old Brentwoods 'A'	16	8	3	5	41	41	19
Old Bradfield. Res	16	7	1	8	50	46	15
Old Carthusians 'A'	16	5	4	7	29	34	14
Old Cholmeleians 'A'	16	4	6	6	31	41	14
Old Haileyburians	16	6	1	9	44	51	13
Old Aldenham. 'A'	16	4	4	8	33	53	12
Old Chigwellians 'C'	16	4	3	9	28	55	11

DIVISION FIVE	P	W	D	L	F	A	PTS
Old Wellingbur. Res	14	11	3	0	50	18	25
Old Cholmel. 'C'	14	8	4	2	27	16	20
Old Ardinians Res	14	7	2	5	34	27	16
Old Brentwoods 'B'	14	5	3	6	41	28	13
Old Wykeham. Res	14	4	4	6	39	37	12
Old Brentwoods 'C'	14	3	3	8	14	40	9
Old Salopians 'A'	14	2	4	8	21	39	8
Old Foresters 'B'	14	3	3	8	24	45	$5

* - 2 points deducted
$ - 4 points deducted

Jim Dixon 6-aside Competition:
Old Chigwellians 2, Old Wellingburians 1

LONDON BANKS F.A.

DIVISION ONE	P	W	D	L	F	A	PTS
Coutts & Co.	16	11	2	3	41	24	24
Citibank	16	8	6	2	48	24	22
Hill Samuel I.M.	16	9	4	3	31	20	22
Allied Irish Bank	16	9	1	6	45	30	19
Kleinworth Benson	16	5	4	7	30	33	14
Credit Suisse	16	5	4	7	31	38	14
Bank of America	16	5	4	7	21	28	14
Chase Manhattan	16	3	2	11	26	47	8
Salomon Bros.	16	2	3	11	27	56	7

DIVISION TWO	P	W	D	L	F	A	PTS
M.I.M.	16	14	0	2	59	12	28
Bank of Scotland	16	9	2	5	35	25	20
Manufact. Hanover	16	9	1	6	43	24	19
Polytechnic	16	6	5	5	25	23	17
Hong Kong Bank	16	7	1	8	38	29	15
Nat West Bank 'A'	16	6	2	8	34	33	14
Coutts & Co. Res	16	5	4	7	29	51	14
Union Bk of Switz.	16	3	7	6	22	40	13
Standard Chartered	16	0	4	12	16	64	4

DIVISION THREE	P	W	D	L	F	A	PTS
Nikko Europe	18	15	3	0	76	18	33
Westpack	18	9	5	4	52	30	23
Chase Manhat. Res	18	11	1	6	53	48	23
C. Hoare & Co Res	18	10	2	6	42	28	22
Morgan Stanley Res	18	8	5	5	40	29	21
Bankers Trust Co.	18	6	2	10	34	43	14
Citibank Res	18	6	1	10	33	44	13
Nat West Bank 'B'	18	4	5	9	27	54	13
Bank of America	18	5	1	12	28	52	11
Nat West Bank 'C'	18	2	3	13	24	63	7

DIVISION FOUR	P	W	D	L	F	A	PTS
Abbey National	14	8	4	2	39	14	20
Morgan Guaranty	14	6	6	2	42	29	17
Scandinavian Bank	14	6	5	3	41	18	16
Australia/NZ Bank	14	7	1	6	25	26	15
Swiss Bank	14	5	4	5	33	37	14
M'fers Hanover Res	14	5	2	7	27	33	12
Nat West Bank 'D'	14	5	1	8	28	38	11
Union Bk Switz. Res	14	2	1	11	24	53	5

DIVISION FIVE (8 teams, won by U.C.B.)

Challenge Cup: Midland Bank 3, Nat West Bank 1
Senior Cup: Barclays 3rd 2, Nat West 3rd 2 *(BB on pens)*
Senior Plate: M.I.M. 2, C. Hoare & Co. 1
Minor Cup: Hong Kong Bk 0, Nat West Bk 5th 1

Junior Cup: Abbey National 2, Morgan Guaranty 1
Junior Plate: Hill Samuel Bk 3, Chase Manhat. Res 1
Sportsmans Cup: Credit Suisse 3, Abbey National 1
Veterans' Cup: Lloyds Bk 4, Royal Bk of Scotland 2

LONDON LEGAL INSURANCE

DIVISION ONE	P	W	D	L	F	A	PTS
Slaughter & May	22	18	1	3	79	16	37
Wilde Sapte	22	13	6	3	59	25	32
Cameron Markby H.	22	15	1	6	52	34	31
Freshfields	22	12	6	4	60	30	30
Pegasus (Inner Tple)	22	14	1	7	68	34	29
Grays Inn	22	10	6	6	59	36	26
Norton Rose	22	7	3	12	27	50	17
Linklers & Paines	22	5	5	12	30	51	15
Clifford Chance	22	6	2	12	30	43	14
Lovell White D.	22	5	3	14	34	83	13
Titmuss Sainer & W.	22	6	1	15	17	69	13
Nabarro Nathanson	22	3	1	18	37	81	7

DIVISION TWO	P	W	D	L	F	A	PTS
Allen & Overy	22	18	1	3	120	31	37
MacFarlanes	22	17	2	3	70	20	36
Herbert Smith	22	14	2	6	48	34	30
Boodle Hatfield	22	12	4	6	38	26	28
D J Freeman & Co.	22	10	4	8	53	37	24
McKenna & Co.	22	10	2	10	52	62	22
Gouldens	22	9	2	11	45	53	20
Stephenson Harwood	22	8	4	10	38	47	20
Beachcroft Stanleys	22	7	4	11	37	77	18
Taylor Joynson G.	22	5	2	15	46	62	12
Denton Hall B & W.	22	5	1	16	46	68	11
Baker & McKenzie	22	2	2	18	25	101	6

League Cup: Grays Inn 0, Freshfields 1

Weavers Arms Cup: Widle Sapte 4, Pegasus 0

SOUTHERN AMATEUR LEAGUE

FIRST DIVISION	P	W	D	L	F	A	PTS
Old Actonians Assn	20	15	2	3	40	13	32
Norsemen	20	9	3	4	31	24	21
Civil Service	20	9	3	8	42	38	21
West Wickham	20	6	9	5	24	20	21
Old Esthameians	20	6	9	5	19	17	21
Nat West Bank	20	7	6	7	31	30	20
Midland Bank	20	5	8	7	34	36	18
Old Parkonians	20	4	9	7	19	31	17
Carshalton	20	5	7	8	25	38	17
Old Bromleians	20	5	4	11	23	34	14
Winchmore Hill	20	3	6	11	20	35	12

SECOND DIVISION	P	W	D	L	F	A	PTS
Crouch End Vamp.	22	16	6	0	54	20	38
South Bank Poly.	22	18	1	3	67	23	37
Lloyds Bank	22	8	7	7	44	38	23
Old Stationers	22	9	5	8	30	27	23
Alexandra Park	22	9	3	10	36	39	21
Polytechnic	22	7	6	9	44	43	20
Barclays Bank	22	8	4	10	39	46	20
Broomfield	22	7	5	10	36	39	19
Southgate Olympic	22	5	7	10	32	34	17
Old Salesians	22	6	4	12	31	52	16
Ibis	22	7	1	14	30	55	15
East Barnet Old Gr.	22	7	1	14	33	60	15

Reserve Section
Div 1: 12 teams, won by Winchmore Hill
Div 2: 11 teams, won by Old Actonians Assn
Div 3: 12 teams, won by Cuaco

3rd Teams Section
Div 1: 12 teams, won by Winchmore Hill
Div 2: 11 teams, won by Lloyds Bank
Div 3: 12 teams, won by Broomfield

THIRD DIVISION	P	W	D	L	F	A	PTS
Lensbury	22	18	2	2	60	21	38
Kew Association	22	16	0	6	66	32	32
Royal Bk of Scotl.	22	14	2	6	55	27	30
Old Latymerians	22	13	3	6	42	30	29
Merton	22	13	2	7	40	29	28
Brentham	22	9	3	10	39	34	21
Alleyn Old Boys	22	9	3	10	39	54	21
Old Westminster C.	22	8	4	10	42	49	20
Cuaco Sports	22	6	4	12	49	64	16
Old Lyonians	22	5	3	14	35	55	13
Bank of England	22	3	5	14	25	46	11
Reigate Prory	22	1	3	18	16	67	5

4th Teams Section
Div 1: 12 teams, won by Winchmore Hill
Div 2: 12 teams, won by Norsemen
Div 3: 11 teams, won by O W'minster Citizens

5th Teams Section
Div 1: 12 teams, won by Nat Westminster Bank
Div 2: 11 teams, won by Old Latymerians
Div 3: 8 teams, won by Alexandra Park

6th Teams Section
Div 1: 11 teams, won by Civil Service
Div 2: 10 teams, won by Norsemen
Div 3: 8 teams, won by E Barnet Old Gramm.

7th Teams Section
Div 1: 10 teams, won by Winchmore Hill
Div 2: 9 teams, won by Carshalton

8th & 9th Teams Sections
Div 1: 12 teams, won by Old Stationers 8th
Div 2: 11 teams, won by Kew Assn 9th

The Southern Amateur League XI that beat Oxford University 1-0 at Old Actonians. Back Row (L/R): Michael Peters & Gareth Shaw (Norsemen), Terry Luther (Alexandra Pk), Neil Backers (Carshalton), Glen Woodcock (O Actonians), Steve Langley (Crouch End Vampires), Gary Tanner & Derek Hannyngton (W Wickham). Front: Cliff McIntosh (O Esthameians), Dave Leach & Chris Hithersay (Capt) (Carshalton), Kevin Clarke (W Wickham), John Frostick (O Esthameians), Peter White (O Bromleians). Photo - James Wright.

Old Salesians: Back Row (L/R): Michael Ayers (Manager), Mick Mallett, William McNamara, Domenic O'Brien, Keith Williams, John Kisz, Lloyd Richards, Michael Brady, Gary Haughey. Front: Gerry McGouch, Neil Bath, Brendan Downton, Danny Rahilly, Peter Sheridan, Pat Nsotea. Photo - Dave West.

SOUTHERN OLYMPIAN LEAGUE

DIVISION ONE	P	W	D	L	F	A	PTS
Old Owens	20	13	4	3	53	33	30
Witan	20	11	7	2	57	32	29
Nottsborough	20	10	4	6	53	38	24
Parkfield	20	7	9	4	39	32	23
Old Parmiterians	20	9	3	8	44	41	21
Old Finchleians	20	10	1	9	38	46	21
Old Bealonians	20	6	8	6	34	32	20
Mill Hill Village	20	8	3	9	43	42	19
Southgate County	20	5	4	11	27	42	14
St Mary's College	20	5	3	12	38	47	13
Colposa	20	2	2	16	35	76	6

DIVISION TWO	P	W	D	L	F	A	PTS
Old Grammarians	18	11	4	3	42	25	26
Old Fairlopians	18	9	5	4	35	26	23
Hadley	18	10	2	6	36	23	22
Hampst'd Heathens	18	6	9	3	39	25	21
Albanian	18	7	4	7	35	34	18
Wandsworth Boro.	18	5	5	8	30	32	15
Academicals	18	4	7	7	29	36	15
Pollygons	18	5	5	8	30	51	15
Old Monovians	18	4	5	9	24	36	13
Hale End Athletic	18	4	4	10	18	30	12

DIVISION THREE	P	W	D	L	F	A	PTS
Duncombe Sports	20	15	4	1	69	25	34
Ealing Association	20	13	2	5	52	31	28
Ulysses	20	12	3	5	53	24	27
Corinthian Cas. 'A'	20	11	5	4	45	23	27
Old Woodhouseians	20	9	6	5	45	32	24
Old Colfeians	20	9	4	7	31	26	22
Electrosport	20	7	3	10	35	67	17
Brent	20	3	6	11	27	40	12
B.B.C.	20	4	3	13	28	43	11
Birkbeck College	20	5	1	14	24	56	11
Inland Revenue	20	2	3	15	17	59	7

Intermediate Section

Div 1: 10 teams, won by O Parmiterians Res
Div 2: 10 teams, won by Nottsborough Res
Div 3: 10 teams, won by Witan Res
Div 1: 9 teams, won by Duncombe Spts Res

DIVISION FOUR	P	W	D	L	F	A	PTS
Westerns	20	17	2	1	79	27	36
Pegasus (Inner T.)	20	13	4	3	81	30	30
London Welsh	20	11	5	4	58	22	27
Fulham Compt. OB	20	11	4	5	50	38	*25
London Airways	20	9	3	8	49	40	21
Mayfield Athletic	20	9	2	9	45	44	20
Centymca	20	8	2	10	50	60	18
Tansley	20	6	2	12	40	61	14
Distillers	20	4	3	13	23	66	11
Economicals	20	3	3	14	32	65	9
Bourneside	20	4	0	16	25	79	8

* - Point deducted - breach of rules

Junior Section

Div 1: 10 teams, won by O Parmiterians 'A'
Div 2: 10 teams, won by Parkfield 'B'
Div 1: 10 teams, won by Witan 'A'
Div 1: 10 teams, won by Mill Hill Vil. 'C'

Minor Section

Div A: 10 teams, won by Old Owens 'A'
Div B: 10 teams, won by O Bealonians 'C'
Div C: 10 teams, won by Witan 'B'
Div D: 9 teams, won by Albanian 8th
Div E: 10 teams, won by Witan 'C'
Div F: 10 teams, won by O Finchleians 8th
Veterans: 8 teams, won by O Parmiterians

Senior Challenge Bowl: Old Parmiterians
Senior Challenge Shield: Nottsborough
Intermediate Challenge Cup: Academicals
Intermediate Challenge Shield: Witan Res
Junior Challenge Cup: Colposa 'A'
Junior Challenge Shield: O Parmiterians 'A'
Mander Cup: Old Finchleians 'B'
Mander Shield: Mill Hill Village 'B'
Burntwood Trophy: Mill Hill Village 'C'
Burntwood Shield: Old Parmiterians 'C'
Thomas Parmiter Cup: Parkfield 'D'
Thomas Parmiter Shield: O Parmiterians 9th
Veterans' Challenge Cup: Colposa Veterans
Veterans' Challenge Shield: Tansley Vets

MIDLAND AMATEUR ALLIANCE

DIVISION ONE	P	W	D	L	F	A	PTS
Brunts Old Boys	22	17	4	1	71	20	38
Magdala Amateurs	22	16	4	2	113	37	36
Sherwood Amateurs	22	15	6	1	86	32	36
Old Elizabethans	22	16	4	3	71	27	36
Derbyshire Amtrs	22	10	5	7	52	47	25
Bassingfield	22	9	3	10	57	59	21
Lady Bay	22	8	2	12	64	70	18
Kirton B.W.	22	5	7	10	32	52	17
Tibshelf Old Boys	22	7	2	13	42	53	16
Nottinghamshire	22	4	3	15	22	63	11
F.C. Toton	22	2	4	16	31	96	8
Beeston OB Assn	22	0	2	20	18	103	2

DIVISION TWO	P	W	D	L	F	A	PTS
O Elizabethans Res	22	18	3	1	75	13	39
Peoples College	22	16	5	1	67	21	37
Magdala Amtrs Res	22	12	4	6	60	30	28
Old Bemrosians	22	12	4	6	69	44	28
Nottm Spartan	22	10	3	9	46	48	23
Brunts OB Res	22	9	2	11	53	51	20
Lady Brown Res	22	9	2	11	43	61	20
Chilwell	22	9	0	13	40	47	18
Nottm Univ P'grads	22	5	7	10	40	56	17
Nottinghamshire Res	22	5	4	13	28	66	14
Derbys Amtrs Res	22	5	2	15	41	82	12
Heanor Amateurs	22	3	2	17	28	71	8

DIVISION THREE	P	W	D	L	F	A	PTS
Sherwood A. Res	18	12	2	4	82	25	26
Tibshelf OB Res	18	11	3	4	43	26	25
O Elizabethans 'A'	18	8	5	5	32	33	21
County Nalgo	18	9	2	7	29	29	20
Peoples College Res	18	8	4	6	36	36	20
Charnos	18	9	2	7	37	37	20
W.B. Casuals	18	8	2	8	36	36	18
Bassingfield Res	18	6	4	8	39	39	16
O Bemrosians Res	18	4	2	12	30	30	10
Beeston OB As. Res	18	2	0	16	23	23	2

DIVISION FOUR	P	W	D	L	F	A	PTS
F.C. Caplan	20	15	3	2	82	28	33
Woodborough Utd	20	14	2	4	63	28	30
Derbys Amtrs 'A'	20	10	8	2	47	27	28
Monty Hind OB	20	10	4	6	62	47	24
O Elizabethans 'B'	20	10	2	8	43	36	22
Magdala Amtrs 'A'	20	9	4	7	43	43	22
Nottmshire 'A'	20	6	5	9	53	63	17
Lady Bay 'A'	20	5	6	9	39	47	16
O Bemrosians 'A'	20	4	5	11	41	65	13
Tibshelf OB 'A'	20	3	5	12	32	65	11
Peoples College 'A'	20	1	2	17	31	87	4

Senior Cup: Sherwood Amateurs
Intermediate Cup: Sherwood Amateurs Res
Minor Cup: Magdala Amateurs 'A'
Challenge Cup: Sherwood Amateurs
Division Two Challenge Cup: O Elizabethans Res
Division Three Cup: Sherwood Amtrs Res
Division Four Challenge Cup: Woodborough Utd
Supplementary Cup 'A': County Nalgo
Supplementary Cup 'B': Woodborough Utd
H.B. Poole Trophy: Old Elizabethans

UNIVERSITY OF LONDON INTER-COLLEGIATE LEAGUE

PREMIER DIVISION	P	W	D	L	F	A	PTS
King's College	16	13	2	1	67	11	28
R H'way/Bedford NC	16	12	1	3	47	21	25
Imperial College	16	8	5	3	36	22	21
University College	16	9	3	4	37	31	21
Goldsmiths College	16	8	2	6	39	23	18
L'don Sch. of Econ.	16	6	0	10	33	47	12
St Georges HMS	16	3	3	10	17	49	9
Qu. Mary W'field Col	16	2	2	12	17	48	6
Sch. of Pharmacy	16	2	0	14	13	54	4

DIVISION ONE	P	W	D	L	F	A	PTS
University Col. Res	18	11	4	3	53	32	26
U.M.D.S.	18	12	1	5	44	29	25
R H'way/B'ford Res	18	11	1	6	58	39	23
St Marys HMS Res	18	9	4	5	66	41	22
Imperial Col. Res	18	8	5	5	51	38	21
King's Col. Res	18	8	3	7	30	26	19
King's Col. HMS	18	6	3	9	42	46	15
Middx/Univ C. HMS	18	6	2	10	25	60	14
Royal Free HSM.	18	4	4	10	37	46	12
QM & W'field C. Res	18	1	1	16	12	61	3

DIVISION TWO	P	W	D	L	F	A	PTS
Char. X & W HMS	18	12	4	2	64	20	28
St Barth'mews HMS	18	12	2	4	38	16	26
Imperial College 'A'	18	11	2	5	39	25	24
Kings College 'A'	18	9	5	4	52	28	23
R Sch of Mines (IC)	18	8	2	8	31	33	18
University Col. 'A'	18	6	4	8	41	49	16
University Col. 'A'	18	6	4	8	41	49	16
Goldsmith Col. 'A'	18	7	1	10	45	34	15
Royal L'don HMC	18	7	1	10	34	53	15
U.M.D.S. Res	18	4	0	14	20	62	8
L'don Sch.Ec. Res	18	3	1	14	22	67	7

Div 3: 9 teams, won by Queen Mary/Westfield 'A'
Div 4: 10 teams, won by Imperial College 'B'
Div 5: 10 teams, won by C. Cross & W'mster HMS Res
Div 6: 8 teams, won by Queen Mary/Wesfield

HMS - Hospital Medical School
HMC - Hospital Medical College
HSM - Hospital School of Medicine

The London University XI that lost to the Old Boys League on 29th October. Back Row (L/R): Kieran Jones, Paul Hales, Mark Loosemore, Mark Dawson, J F Dobson, Den Barnett, G Conroy, Paul Van Dyk. Front: Brendan Herly, Peter Alock, Mazin Abusian, Felix Francis, Derek Stafford, Tim Sharpe. Photo - James Wright.

University of London Representative matches 1991-92: v Ulysses (won 4-2), v Old Boys Lge (lost 0-2), v Royal Navy (lost 0-3), v Southern Amateur Lge (drew 2-2), v Crystal Palace XI (lost 2-6), v Arthurian Lge (won 3-2), v London Legal Lge (won 4-1), v Army XI (drew 0-0), v Oxford University (lost 0-1), v Clapton (lost 0-3), Southern Olympian Lge (lost 0-4), v Cambridge University (won 5-1), v Middx County FA (drew 0-0), v Amateur Football Alliance (lost 0-2), v Crystal Palace XI (lost 1-2), v United Banks (lost 1-4).

28th Amphibious Regiment R.E. (BAOR) - Army Cup winners at Aldershot. Photo - Eric Marsh.

THE OLD BOYS LEAGUE

PREMIER DIVISION	P	W	D	L	F	A	PTS
Old Aloysians	20	11	8	1	34	11	30
Enfield Old Gram.	20	13	3	4	38	27	29
Old Ignatians	20	13	1	6	50	16	27
Old Meadonians	20	10	3	7	40	23	23
Glyn Old Boys	20	9	2	9	32	34	20
Chertsey O Sales.	20	9	1	10	37	38	19
Old Tenisonians	20	9	0	11	30	40	18
Cardinal Mann. OB	20	7	2	11	32	41	16
Old Danes	20	6	3	11	30	44	15
Old Islewortians	20	4	5	11	30	43	13
Latymer Old Boys	20	3	4	13	19	55	10

SENIOR DIV. ONE	P	W	D	L	F	A	PTS
Old Tiffinians	20	12	6	2	72	22	30
Old Wilsonians	20	13	3	4	43	27	29
Pheonix Old Boys	20	12	4	4	46	23	28
Old Wokingians	20	9	4	7	38	31	22
Old Westhamians	20	8	6	6	34	30	22
Old Suttonians	20	10	2	8	38	36	22
O Minchendenians	20	6	5	9	41	44	17
Mill Hill Co. OB	20	7	3	10	31	42	17
Old Salvatorians	20	7	3	10	30	50	17
Old Edmontonians	20	5	3	12	36	64	13
Old Kingsburians	20	1	1	18	25	65	3

SENIOR DIV. TWO	P	W	D	L	F	A	PTS
O Tenisonians Res	22	16	2	4	49	20	34
Old Hamptonians	22	12	4	6	52	39	28
O Tollongtonians	22	9	9	4	41	36	27
John Fisher OB	22	10	6	6	41	47	26
Shene Old Gramm.	22	10	4	8	47	37	24
Clapham Old Xav.	22	10	3	9	45	45	23
Old Southallians	22	7	8	7	29	30	22
Old Greenfordians	22	8	4	10	47	44	20
Old Alpertonians	22	7	5	10	46	49	19
Old Ignatians Res	22	5	7	10	26	37	17
Old Josephians	22	6	4	12	31	42	16
Old Buckwellians	22	3	2	17	36	64	8

SENIOR DIV. 3	P	W	D	L	F	A	PTS
Old Grocers	20	15	2	3	60	19	32
O Meadonians Res	20	11	5	4	44	34	27
Old Dorkinians	20	10	4	6	53	34	24
Old Manorians	20	10	3	7	50	42	23
Old Vaughanians	20	7	7	6	40	30	21
Enfield O Gramm.	20	8	4	8	31	34	20
Letyon Co. OB	20	8	3	9	44	46	19
Ravenscoft OB	20	7	2	11	28	34	16
O Alpertonians Res	20	6	4	10	32	51	16
Old Uffingtonians	20	5	2	13	26	61	12
Chace Old Boys	20	3	4	13	36	59	10

I'mediate Div Nth: 12 teams, won by O Highburians
I'mediate Div Sth: 12 teams, won by O Hampton. Res
Div 1 Nth: 11 teams, won by Old Camdenians Res
Div 1 Sth: 11 teams, won by Old Thorntonias
Div 1 W: 12 teams, won by Chorley Wood Dane OB

Div 2 Nth: 11 teams, won by Old Edmontonians
Div 2 Sth: 11 teams, won by Old Wokinglans 'A'
Div 2 W: 12 teams, won by Old Hamptonians 'A'
Div 3 Nth: 11 teams, won by O Minchendenians 'B'
Div 3 Sth: 11 teams, won by Glyn Old Boys 'B'
Div 3 W: 11 teams, won by Cardinal M. OB 'A'
Div 4 Nth: 11 teams, won by O Edmontonians 'B'
Div 4 Sth: 11 teams, won by Old Tenisonians 'B'
Div 4 W: 11 teams, won by Old Langleyans
Div 5 Nth: 11 teams, won by O Minchendians 'D'
Div 5 Sth: 11 teams, won by Old Dorkinians 'B'
Div 5 W: 11 teams, won by Mill Hill C. OB 'B'
Div 6 Nth: 12 teams, won by O Edmontonians 'D'
Div 6 Sth: 11 teams, won by Clapham O Xav. 'C'
Div 6 W: 10 teams, won by Old Salvatorians 'E'
Div 7 Nth: 12 teams, won by O Edmontonians 'E'
Div 7 Sth: 11 teams, won by Old Sinjuns 'C'
Div 7 W: 11 teams, won by Cardinal M. OB 'C'
Div 8 Sth: 10 teams, won by Glyn Old Boys 'E'
Div 8 W: 10 teams, won by Old Salvatorians 9th

Senior Cup (Semi Finals)
O Parkonians 2, O Tenisonians *(won on pens)* 2
O Wilsonians 3, O Bromleians 4
Final: O Tenisonians 1, O Bromleians 0

Junior Cup (Semi Finals)
O Latymerians 2, Westminster Citizens 1
O Tenisonians Res 4, Stationers 1
Final: O Tenisonians Res 3, O Latymer. Res 1

Minor Cup (Semi Finals)
O Wilsonians 'A' 3, E Barnet Old Gram. 'A' 0
O Stationers 'A' 3, Glyn Old Boys 'A' 2
Final: O Wilsonians 'A' 3, O Stationers 'A' 1

4th Elevens' Cup (Semi Finals)
O Tenisonians 0, O Finchleians 2
O Esthameians 4, O Latymerians 0
Final: O Esthameians 1, O Finceians 0

5th Elevens' Cup (Semi Finals)
O Esthameians 3, O Stationers 5
O Finchleianns 4, O Salesians 0
Final: O Stationers 2, O Finchleians 1

6th Elevens' (Semi Finals)
O Salesians 4, O Suttonians 1
O Wilsonians 6, O Stationers 1
Final: O Salesians 2, O Wilsonians 1

7th & Lower Elevens' Cup (Semi Finals)
O Finchleians 8th 5, O Stationers 7th 0
O Finchleians 9th 4, O Minchendenians 7th 1
Final: O Finchleians 8th 6, O Finchleians 0

Veterans' Cup (Semi Finais)
O Stationers 3, O Colfeians 2
O Wilsonians 2, O Bromleians 0
Final: O Stationers 3, O Wilsonians 2

The Old Boys League XI that beat London University 2-0 at Motspur Park on October 29th. Back Row (L/R): Dennis Day (Manager), Malcolm White (Enfield Old Grammarians), Gary Cusack (Pheonix OB), Rob Carter (Enfield Old Grammarians), John O'Grady (Old Ignatians), Bernard Healy (Old Suttonians), Peter Deadman (Old Tenisons), Neil Sykes (Ravenscroft OB). Front: Kieran Daly (Cardinal Manning OB), Jeff Paterson (Old Tollingtonians), Phil Bray (Pheonix OB), John O'Brien (Old Ignatians), David Harvey (Old Danes, capt). Photo - James Wright.

LONDON INSURANCE F.A.

DIVISION ONE	P	W	D	L	F	A	PTS
Liverpool Victoria	16	14	1	1	69	23	29
Temple Bar	16	12	1	3	69	19	25
Gaflac	16	8	1	7	44	36	17
Colonial Mutual	16	8	1	7	48	45	17
Granby	16	6	3	7	44	47	15
Eagle Star	16	6	3	7	36	48	15
Sun Alliance	20	4	1	11	24	48	9
Bardhill	16	4	1	11	29	61	9
Bowring	16	4	0	12	26	62	8

DIVISION TWO	P	W	D	L	F	A	PTS
Sun Alliance Res	20	11	3	2	58	20	25
Noble Lowndes	16	11	3	2	52	28	22
Temple Bar Res	16	10	2	4	42	27	22
Sedgwick	16	9	1	6	69	37	19
Asphalia	16	9	1	6	47	38	19
Granby Res	16	5	3	8	44	44	13
Norw. Union (L'don)	16	5	3	8	33	40	13
L'pool Victoria Res	16	3	1	12	28	76	7
Eagle Star Res	16	2	0	14	20	83	4

DIVISION THREE	P	W	D	L	F	A	PTS
Temple Bar 'A'	17	15	1	1	72	15	31
Gaflac Res	18	14	1	3	79	39	29
Sun Alliance 'A'	18	11	0	7	48	43	22
Noble Lowndes Res	18	9	2	7	62	48	20
Bowring Res	18	7	3	8	49	51	17
Guard. Royal Exch.	18	7	3	8	40	45	17
Eagle Star 'A'	18	7	0	11	49	51	14
Temple Bar 'B'	18	6	2	10	39	44	14
L'pool Victoria 'A'	17	3	2	12	46	68	8
Gaflac 'A'	18	2	2	14	25	105	6

Charity Cup: Liverpool Vic. 1, Temple Bar 0
Challenge Cup: Cuaco Res 3, Temple Bar 1
Junior Cup: Sedgwick 5, Eagle Star Res 1
Minor Cup: Temple Bar 'A' 4, Bowring Res 1
W A Jewell Mem. Trophy (5-aside): Granby
Sportsmanship Trophy: Colonial Mutual

CIVIL SERVICE LEAGUE (Founded 1907)

FIRST DIVISION	P	W	D	L	F	A	PTS
Mt Pleasant 'A'	18	13	3	2	87	19	29
Vauxhall Ath. 'A'	18	13	3	2	62	18	29
Customs & Ex. 'A'	18	12	3	3	49	11	27
New Scot. Yd 'A'	18	7	1	10	40	43	15
Cabinet Office	18	5	4	9	22	53	14
Dept of Energy 'A'	18	0	6	12	14	63	6
War Office (MOD) 'A'	18	2	2	14	20	87	6

Founders Cup Final (at Kensington Palace):
Mt Pleasant 'A' 4, New Scotland Yard 1

LONDON OLD BOYS CUPS

Senior Cup: O Ignations 1, O Aloysians 0 *(aet)*
I'mediate: O Meadonians Res 2, Enfield OG Res 0
Junior Cup: O Aloysians 'A' 2, Colposa 'A' 1
Minor Cup: O Meadonians 'B' 5, O Greenfordians 0
Novets: Colposa 'C' 4, Enfield OG 'C' 1
Drummond Cup:
O Parmiterians 'D' 0:2, Enfield OG 0:2 *(shared)*
Nemean Cup: Albanian 8th 3, Glyn OB 7th 1
Veterans: O Meadonians Vets 3, O Sinjuns 0

A delighted Mount Pleasant S.S.C. 'A' team celebrate winning the Civil Service Founder Cup at Kensington Palace. They completed the double by winning the Civil Service First Division. Photo - Anthony Davie.

A.F.A. REPRESENTATIVE MATCHES 1991-92

v Cambridge University, won 2-1
v Army F.A., won 1-0
v Royal Air Force, lost 2-3
v London University, won 2-0

v Oxford University, won 3-1
v Royal Navy F.A., lost 1-2
v Sussex County F.A., drew 2-2

THE VARSITY MATCH 1991-92
OXFORD UNIVERSITY 2, CAMBRIDGE UNIVERSITY 1

Cambridge University's Des Anderson clears an Oxford attack in front of a packed terrace at Craven Cottage during the annual Varsity match on Boat Race morning. Photo - Dave West.

Oxford University, winners of the 1992 Varsity match. Photo - Dave West.

Cambridge University pictured before the match. Photo. Photo - Dave West.

SUNDAY FOOTBALL

The Sunday section is yet another part of the directory that seems to get bigger each year. We have again published the top divisions of all Sunday Leagues received, and this season have gone a step further in listing lower division champions. Our thanks again go to Trevor Bailey for supplying the addresses of all League Secretaries.

The F.A. Sunday Cup continues to grow in stature, and this season attracted some large crowds to its latter rounds as Theale's successful run captured the imagination of their Berkshire public.

Theale captain Andy Parr lifts the F.A. Sunday Cup after his side had defeated Marston Sports 3-2 in the Final at Elm Park, Reading. Photo - Paul Dennis.

Theale celebrate their F.A. Sunday Cup win. Photo. Photo - Dave West.

F.A. SUNDAY CUP 1991-92

* denotes extra time played. Venues *italicised*. In latter rounds home clubs play at their previous home venue except where indicated.

First Round. 13-10-91. Replays 20-10-91.   **Res**
Queens Arms v Nenthead *(Cleator Moor Celtic)*   0-4
Dudley & Weetslade v Blyth Waterloo SC
(Dudley Welfare)   3-2
Mayfield Utd v Stanton Dale *(Lancaster City)*   1-4
Lobster v Whetley Lane   *(Croxteth School)*   4-0
Carlisle Utd SC v Iron Bridge
(Mossley Hill Ath Club, Liverpool)   2-4
Lynemouth v Croxteth & Gilmoss RBL
(Ashington FC)   0-4
Framwellgate Moor & Pity Me v Woodlands 84
(St Georges, Framwellgate, Durham)   7-1
Seymour v Hartlepool Lion Hotel
(Edinburgh Park, Liverpool)   3-5*
Western Approaches v Railway Hotel *(Bootle FC)* 2-1
Bolton Woods v Oakenshaw
(King George V, Bradford)   2-2
Oakenshaw v Bolton Wds *(Liversedge FC)*   2-0
Littlewoods v B&A Scaffolding *(Littlewoods Spts)* 2-3
Rob Roy *scr* Chesterfield Park w/o
Eagle Knowsley v Oakenshaw *(Knowsley United)* 2-1
Almithak v AC Sparks   *(Grove Mount, L'pool)* 3-2
Netherley RBL v East Bowling Unity
(Netherley School, Liverpool)   1-1
E Bowling v Netherley *(Crag Rd Utd)*   3-3
E Bowling v Netherley *(Crag Rd Utd)*   3-2
Hare v Clubmoor Nalgo   *(Abbey Hey FC)*   2-2
C'moor Nalgo v Hare   *(Nalgo Spts Club)*   3-2
Carnforth v Britannia VNC *(Cheadle Town FC)*   2-1
BRNESC v Blue Union *(Melling Rd, Aintree)*   1-3
Baildon Ath v FC Coachman *(Thackley FC)*   1-3
Jolly Farmers v Dock   *(Dunkirk FC)*   2-2
Dock v Jolly Farmers   *(Ashville FC)*   1-2
Radford Pk Rgrs v Bricklayers Spts *(Radford)*   *4-5
Altone Steels v Birmingham Celtic
(Sutton Coldfield Town FC)   4-0
Kenwick Dynamo v Brookvale Athletic   4-0
Ansells Stockland Star v AD Bulwell
(Ansells Spts & Social, Perry Bar)   0-2
Dereham Hobbies Sunday v Shouldham Sunday 0-1
Girton Eagles v Watford Labour Club
(Cambridge City FC)   1-4
Sawston Keys v Gamlingay OB *(Histon FC)*   3-0
Inter Volante v Cork & Bottle *(Highgate U)*   3-1
(Above tie awarded to Cork & Bottle)
Boreham Wood Royals v Chequers (Herts)
(Sandridge Rvrs FC)   1-2
Chapel Utd v Evergreen *(Canvey Island FC)*   *2-4
O. Paludians v Broad Plain House *(Burnham FC)* 0-5
Sandwell v Olympic Star *(Oldbury Utd)*   2-0
St Josephs (South Oxhey) v BRSC Aidan   *2-1
Theale v Northfield Rgrs *(Thatcham Town)*   1-0
Hanham Sunday v Bedfont Sunday *(DRG (FP))*   2-1
Pheonix v Lebeq Tavern *(Harpenden Town)*   1-2
Bishopstoke AFC v Santogee 66
(Winchester Castle FC)   *2-3
Sarton Utd v Somerset Ambury V & E
(Brislington FC)   1-0
Inter Royalle v Rolls Royce
(Beckenham Town FC)   0-0
Continental v Concord Rgrs
(Walthamstow Pennant FC)   0-0
Concord v Continental *(Thames Rd, Canvey Is)*   *2-1
Priory Spts v Fryerns Community
(Heybridge Swifts FC)   2-1
Oxford Rd Social v St Clements Hospital
(Cray Wanderers FC)   0-3

Second Round. 10-11-91. Replays 17-10-91.   **Res**
B & A Scaffolding v Green Man 88
(Dene Pk, Dunswell, Hull)   3-0
Almithak v Lobster *(LSFA Grnd, Penny Lane)*   *5-4
Avenue Victoria Lodge v A3 *(Newton FC, Wirral)* 0-1
Eagle-Knowsley v Clubmoor Nalgo *(Nalgo Spts)*   4-1
Nenthead v Northwood *(Sth Tyne Pk, Haltwhistle)* 0-1

Hartlepool Lion Hotel v Carnforth
(Grayfields Enclosure, Hartlepool)   1-0
Jolly Farmers *(removed)* v FC Coachman *(w/o)*

Blue Union v East Levenshulme
(Speke Hall Avenue, Liverpool)   2-2
E L'hulme v Blue U *(Kirkmanshulme Rd, Gorton)* 2-3
F'gate Moor & Pity Me v Dudley & Weetslade   2-0
Western Approaches v Oakenshaw   2-3
Toshiba Sharpies v Stanton Dale *(Kirkby Town)*   1-1
Stanton v Toshiba *(Leisure Time Club, Orrell)*   5-4
Humbledon Plains Farm v Croxteth & Gilmoss RBL
(Silksworth Colliery, Sunderland)   2-0
Iron Bridge v Chesterfield Park
(Edinburgh Park, Liverpool)   3-0
Nicosia v East Bowling Unity   1-1
East Bowling Unity v Nicosia   1-2
Poringland Wanderers v Marston Sports   2-4
AD Bulwell v Brookvale Ath *(Basford Utd)*   *1-2
Sawston Keys v Bourneville Warriors   3-2
Cork & Bottle v Lodge Cottrell *(Paget Rgrs)*   0-1
Slade Celtic v Priory Spts *(Boldmere St M.)*   2-2
Priory Spts v Slade Celtic   2-1
Ford Basildon v Shouldham Sunday *(Ford Spts)*   2-1
St Clements Hospital v Chequers (Herts)
(Willis Faber Dumas, Ipswich)   0-1
Watford Labour Club v Sandwell *(Berk'sted T.)*   1-4
Bricklayers Spts v Brereton Town *(Wem T. FC)*   3-2
Altone Steels v St Josephs (Luton)   0-1
Ranelagh Spts v Evergreen *(Tooting & Mitcham)* 2-2
Sartan Utd v St Josephs (South Oxhey)   1-0
Ouzavich v Leyton Argyle   3-2
Theale v Lebeq Tavern *(Peppard FC)*   3-0
Lee Chapel Nth v Concord Rgrs *(Basildon Bowl)* 2-1
Broad PH v Inter Royalle *(Hengrove Athletic)*   2-0
Reading Borough v Hanham Sunday *(Palmer Pk)* 1-2
Collier Row Supporters v Santogee *(Collier R)*   2-1

Third Round. 8-12-91   **Res**
Stantondale v A3   1-2
Iron Bridge v Humbledon Plains Farm   2-0
FC Coachman v Framwellgate Moor & Pity Me   4-3
Marston Sports v B & A Scaffolding
(Wobaston Rd, Wolverhampton)   *1-0
Hartlepool Lion Hotel v Almithak   3-2
Northwood v Oakenshaw   2-2
Oakenshaw v Northwood   3-2
Nicosia v Bricklayers Sports   0-1
Blue Union v Eagle Knowsley   0-1
Ouzavich v Lodge Cottrell   0-2
Theale v Lee Chapel North   3-2
Sandwell v Ranalegh Sports   1-4
Collier Row Supporters v Brookvale Ath.   *1-2
Chequers v S. Keys *(William Bird PF, St Albans)* *2-1
Ford Basildon v Sartan United   1-0
Broad Plain House v Hanham Sunday   0-3
St Josephs (Luton) v Priory Sports
(Dunstable Town FC)   5-1

Fourth Round. 19-1-92   **Res**
Oakenshaw v FC Coachman   2-1
Marston Spts v Hartlepool Lion Hotel   5-3
Iron Bridge v Bricklayers *(Penny Lane, L'pool)*   0-2
A3 v Eagle-Knowsley *(Waterloo Dock FC)*   2-1
Chequers (Herts) v Theale   2-3
Ranelagh Spts v Hanham Sunday   2-0
St Josephs (Luton) v Brookvale Ath.   *1-0
Lodge Cottrell v Ford Basildon   3-0

Fifth Round. 16-2-92   **Res**
Marston Spts v Bricklayers Sports   Att: 81   2-1
A3 v Oakenshaw   Att: 109   1-1
Oakenshaw v A3 *(23-2-92)*   Att: 250   1-1
A3 v Oakenshaw *(1-3-92)*   Att: 200   0-2
Lodge Cottrell v Ranelagh Spts   3-0
Theale v St Josephs (Luton)   Att: 600   2-0

Semi Finals. 22-3-92. Replay 29-3-92.
Theale v O'shaw *(Wokingham Town)*   Att: 651   *2-2
Oakenshaw v Theale *(Thackley FC)*   Att: 450   0-2
Lodge Cottrell v Marston Spts   Att: 320   0-1
(Moor Green FC)

F.A. SUNDAY CUP FINAL 1991-92

THEALE (1)3 *(Hambridge 85, Eales 80, Parr 32(pen),* **MARSTON SPORTS** (1)2 *(Wells 43(pen), Walker 77)*

(At Elm Park, Reading FC, Sunday 3rd May 1992. Attendance: 2,427)

Theale: Andy Howell, Jamie Murray, Paul Cox, Jamie Ferguson, Mattie Webb, Graham Hambridge, Steve Dale, Andy Parr, Karl Cook (Dave Eales 68), Noel Newton, Paul Mulvaney. Unused sub: John Wylie.

Marston: Kevin Williams, Russell Walton, David Webb, John Horne, Jim Skidmore, Clive Walker, Steve Astley (David Trend 88), Neil Morgan (Roy Green 81), Mick Osborne, Evron Wright, Ian Wells.

Referee: Mr D J Gallagher (Oxfordshire F.A.)

Dave Eales, Theale's substitute (12), scores the second half equaliser with a fine header past Martston Sports goalkeeper. Photo - Paul Dennis.

Theale's scorers in the F.A. Sunday Cup Final at Reading. From left to right: David Eales, Graham Hambridge and Andy Parr. Photo - Paul Dennis.

Oakenshaw's Christoper Shepherd stretches to reach a cross during the 2-2 draw with Theale in the Semi-Finals of the F.A. Sunday Cup. Photo - Paul Dennis.

Despite reading the kick correctly, Marston Sports goalkeeper Kevin Williams cannot stop Andy Parr's penalty putting Theale ahead in the F.A. Sunday Cup Final at Reading. Photo - Dave West.

SUNDAY LEAGUES 1992-93

The following pages are devoted to various Sunday Leagues from around the country. All leagues that replied to our request for a final table are included. If your your league is not featured, then feel free to send us a copy of your final table(s) next Spring and we will do our best to squeeze them into next season's section. Photos are always welcome.

ASHTON & DISTRICT

PREM. DIVISION	P	W	D	L	F	A	PTS
Hare	16	11	5	0	57	26	27
Junction Royton	16	10	4	2	49	22	24
E Levenshulme	16	10	3	3	50	23	23
Bardsley 'A'	16	7	4	5	39	31	18
Copster Villa	16	4	4	8	38	48	12
Hathershaw Junc	16	4	4	8	32	49	12
Butchers Arms	16	4	3	9	35	38	11
Failsworth OB	16	3	3	10	31	59	9
Gardeners Rest	16	2	4	10	30	55	8

Lower Division Champions:
Div. 1: Ridgehill Celtic 'A'
Div. 2: Robin Hood Oldham

Cup Winners:
Presidents Trophy: Robin Hood Oldham
Premier Cup: Hare F.C.
Div.1 Cup: Oldham GPO
Div.2 Cup: Robin Hood Oldham

BANGOR & DISTRICT

PREM. DIVISION	P	W	D	L	F	A	PTS
Bull Valley	14	11	1	2	71	21	34
Waterloo	14	10	3	1	53	25	33
Mermaid	14	9	3	2	53	18	30
Ship Launch	14	7	1	6	37	28	22
Bodedern Ath.	14	4	2	8	38	51	14
Mona	14	4	1	9	29	44	13
U.C.N.W.	14	3	2	9	21	54	11
Kings Head	14	1	1	12	27	88	4

BARKING & DISTRICT

SENIOR DIVISION	P	W	D	L	F	A	PTS
Bancroft Alb.	18	16	2	0	89	13	34
Noakside A.	19	16	2	1	89	30	34
Southchurch Utd	19	11	2	6	47	46	24
Dagenham Ath.	17	11	1	5	53	33	23
Hornchurch W.	17	8	4	5	37	29	20
Blake Hall	19	8	3	8	54	45	19
St.Edwards	18	7	2	9	42	50	16
Bardag	20	4	4	12	31	70	12
Suttons Farm	17	3	3	11	25	49	9
Pondfield P.	16	3	0	13	18	62	6
Thamesview	18	0	1	17	15	73	1
Some matches anulled.							

Lower Division Champions:
Prem.: Lippatarno
Div. 1: Morfdown
Div. 2: Cosmopolitan
Div. 3: Boss Sports

BARNET

PREM. DIVISION	P	W	D	L	F	A	PTS
Elliott Star	18	15	2	1	65	24	32
Prince of Wales	18	11	5	2	44	22	27
Boreham Wood R.	18	10	2	6	39	40	22
Conyers Park	18	8	2	8	53	42	18
Imperial	18	6	6	6	39	34	18
Hendon St.Marys	18	7	3	8	44	40	17
St.Stephens	18	7	2	9	38	44	16
E.Barnet O.G.	18	5	4	9	41	53	14
Fairfield Griffin	18	4	4	10	37	59	12
Old Elizabethans	18	1	2	15	30	72	4

Lower Division Champions:
Div. 1: Leevale
Div. 2: E.Barnet Utd Services Club
Div. 3: Enfield Royal British Legion
Div. 4: Oakleigh Rovers

BASILDON

SENIOR DIVISION	P	W	D	L	F	A	PTS
Ford Basildon	18	15	1	2	77	18	46
Fryerns C.A.	18	14	2	2	60	18	44
Chapel United	18	13	2	3	78	20	41
St.Basils	18	8	3	7	34	57	27
Lee Chapel N.	18	8	2	8	41	15	26
Langdon Hills	18	5	4	9	30	55	19
Barnhall	18	3	6	9	33	52	15
Basildon I.C.	18	3	5	10	17	56	14
Regal	18	3	3	12	29	69	12
Pitsea	18	2	4	12	23	62	10

Lower Division Champions:
Prem. : Beauchamps O.B.
Div. 1: Bata

Div. 2: Cranes Park Rangers
Div. 3: B & C Sports Res.
Div. 4: Haydon Manor

Cup Winners:
Senior Cup: Fryerns C.A.
Div. 1 Cup: York
Div. 4 Cup: Roundacre

BEACON

PREM. DIVISION	P	W	D	L	F	A	PTS
East Park Rangers	18	16	2	0	95	25	34
Bilston Trumpet	18	15	0	3	69	26	30
Sedgley Crown	18	7	8	3	57	23	22
Wall Heath R.	18	7	6	5	58	40	20
S.Beacon Ath. A	18	9	2	7	45	37	20
Oldbury	18	7	5	6	52	35	19
Brittania Inn	18	4	4	10	44	58	12
Wall Heath TFC	18	4	2	12	33	60	10
Battle 87	18	4	2	12	30	72	10
Forge Tavern	18	1	1	16	13	120	3

Lower Division Champions:
Div. 1: Sedgley Red Lion
Div. 2: Bescot United
Div. 3: Belgrade Wanderers

BIRKENHEAD

PREM. DIVISION	P	W	D	L	F	A	PTS
Mitre BS	22	16	3	3	76	32	35
Turleys	22	15	4	3	63	22	34
Dock	22	15	3	4	62	30	33
Queens Park	22	12	2	7	63	43	28
Pelican	22	11	5	6	51	37	27
Kel	22	9	4	9	49	52	22
Pilot	22	8	5	9	32	32	21
Archers Social	22	7	6	9	51	39	20
Avenue V.L.	22	8	2	12	43	61	18
Vale SCA	22	4	2	16	26	60	10
Port Sunlight RBL	22	2	5	15	33	74	9
Comet	22	2	3	17	30	96	7

Lower Division Champions:
Div. 1: Renbad Rovers
Div. 2: Irby Club
Div. 3: Rangers (Breaks)
Div. 4: Sun Valley
Yth Div. : Ashville 'A'

BLACKBURN

DIVISION ONE	P	W	D	L	F	A	PTS
Gibraltar	18	15	3	0	50	9	33
Woodlands *	18	10	4	4	55	30	24
Intack *	18	11	2	5	50	30	24
Old Toll Bar *	18	11	2	5	55	30	24
Darwen Sun L.	18	9	5	4	36	17	23
Clifton	18	7	3	8	36	26	17
Foresters	18	6	4	8	18	36	16
Station	18	4	3	11	18	37	11
Witton Inn	18	3	0	15	29	72	6
West End	18	2	0	16	20	90	4
* - After play off.							

Lower Division Champions:
Div. 2: Gepal
Div. 3: Jubilee

BOSTON & DISTRICT

PREM. DIVISION	P	W	D	L	F	A	PTS
Santos	24	22	2	0	145	26	46
Inter Wyberton	24	20	2	2	93	26	42
Black Bull	24	18	2	4	89	28	38
Boston F.C. Sun	24	14	3	7	61	44	31
Wrangle Sunday	24	9	6	9	59	49	24
Boston F.C. Colts	24	11	2	11	47	55	24
South Kyme	24	10	2	12	43	51	22
Lord Nelson	24	9	3	12	59	68	21
Woodhall Spa Colts	24	7	2	14	37	85	16
Gosberton Sunday	24	7	1	16	46	97	15
King William	24	7	1	16	33	94	15
Billinghay Rovers	24	4	2	18	37	75	10
York Street Utd	24	3	2	19	35	86	8

Lower Division Champions:
Div. 1: Wheatsheaf Wanderers
Div. 2: Poaches

BRADFORD

PREM. DIVISION	P	W	D	L	F	A	PTS
E.Bowling Unity	22	16	6	0	69	30	54
White Horse	22	16	5	1	57	24	53
Ventus United	22	12	5	5	60	42	41
Green Man 88	22	11	4	7	44	31	37
Albion Sports	22	9	4	9	43	53	31
George & Dragon	22	8	6	8	42	39	30
Oakenshaw	22	8	5	9	34	35	29
Woodlands 84	22	8	4	10	46	47	28
Fiddlers 3	22	7	3	12	40	55	24
Victoria Rangers	22	6	2	14	37	53	20
Queens United	22	6	0	16	53	71	18
Lidget Green	22	0	6	16	39	84	6

Lower Division Champions:
Div. 1: Bolton Woods
Div. 1a: Stanley Road
Div. 1b: Manningham Mills
Div. 2a: Brown Cow Wyke
Div. 2b: Cottage Homes FC
Div. 3a: Lord Clyde
Div. 3b: Eccleshill United
Div. 4a: Fagley FC
Div. 4b: Westgate Hill

SPALL SPORTS BRENTWOOD

SENIOR DIVISION	P	W	D	L	F	A	PTS
Cherry Tree W.	20	15	5	0			35
West Horndon	20	12	5	3			29
Harold Hill	20	9	6	5			24
Blackmore	20	10	3	7			23
Prince Albert	20	10	2	8			22
Delma	20	9	3	8			21
Brentwood Sports	20	6	6	8			18
Elm Park Utd	20	5	6	9			16
Mowbrays	20	6	2	12			14
Warley Stars	20	6	1	13			13
Wood United	20	2	1	17			5

Lower Division Champions:
Div. 1: Havering Nalgo
Div. 2: Serpri
Div. 3: Oldchurch Park
Div. 4: Brentwood Eagles

Cup Winners:
Spall Sports knock-out Cup: Cherry Tree Warley
Senior Cup:
Div. 1 Cup: Havering Nalgo
Div. 2: Serpri
Div. 3: Bordeaux
Div. 4: Broxhill

DON BIDGOOD BRIDGWATER & DISTRICT

DIVISION ONE	P	W	D	L	F	A	PTS
Cavaliers	24	19	4	1	74	33	42
Commercial	24	17	2	5	79	29	36
Castlefield	24	16	4	4	72	33	36
Ashcott	24	15	4	5	63	33	34
Hamp	24	13	5	6	82	45	31
Blake Old Boys	24	13	4	7	82	40	30
R.O.Phoenix	24	13	4	7	51	37	30
Berrow Athletic	24	8	2	14	54	87	18
Sedgemoor R.	24	6	3	15	54	71	15
Woolavington	24	6	1	17	38	70	13
Mansion House	24	4	4	16	37	68	12
Bridgewater YMCA	24	3	5	16	33	87	11
North Petherton	24	1	2	21	22	113	4

Lower Division Champions:
Div. 2: Bridgwater YMCA Res.
Div. 3: Brean Coasters

Cup Winners:
Bill Brown K.O. Cup: Blake Old Boys
Dave Hobbs League K.O. Cup: Castlefield
Danny Markall Memorial Bridgwater Referees K.O. Cup: Withycutter
Geoff Harvey K.O. Cup: Fountain Dynamo
Paul Haggett Sporting Trophy: Crown Inn

BRIGHOUSE & DISTRICT

DIVISION ONE	P	W	D	L	F	A	PTS
Star	18	16	1	1	59	16	33
Sun Inn (L)	18	13	3	2	52	28	29
Rastrick C.C.	18	10	3	5	61	26	23
Crown Athletic	18	8	6	4	41	23	22
Windmill	18	7	4	7	33	34	18
Spring Gardens	18	7	1	10	34	35	15
AFC Whitehall *	18	7	1	9	34	51	13
Triangle	18	5	2	11	27	42	12
Pond	18	5	1	12	39	55	11
Eastfield	18	1	0	17	16	83	2

* - 2pts deducted.

Lower Division Champions:
Div. 2: Thornhill Briggs

BRISTOL & DISTRICT

PREM. DIVISION	P	W	D	L	F	A	PTS
Lebeq's Tavern U	22	16	3	3	56	29	35
Broad Plain S.	22	14	4	4	58	30	32
BRSC Aidan	22	12	5	5	39	24	29
Hanham Sunday	20	12	2	6	49	20	26
Beaufort	22	12	2	8	48	42	26
Cabot Towers	22	10	3	9	43	50	23
Sartan United	20	9	3	8	40	36	21
City Alarms	22	6	6	10	30	52	18
Backwell Sunday	22	7	3	12	41	43	17
Little Stoke A.H.	22	5	2	15	27	49	12
London Life A.	22	3	6	13	26	53	12
Stockwood R.	22	4	1	17	29	58	9

Lower Division Champions:
Div. 2: Patchway N.E.
Senior Div: Lebeq's Tavern Res.
Div. 1: George Inn
Div. 3: Bromley Heath
Div. 4: GWP Aviation
Div. 5: Coupland Ins'tion

BURY

DIVISION ONE	P	W	D	L	F	A	PTS
Wattisfield	22	15	3	4	53	19	34
Cockfield	22	14	4	4	85	34	32
M.U.S.Academicals	22	13	4	5	69	32	31
Wickhambrook	22	13	6	3	52	38	29
Red Lion	22	11	8	3	65	56	25
Ixworth	22	9	8	5	35	36	23
Gazeley	22	9	9	4	55	56	22
Greengage	22	6	8	8	66	56	20
Priors United	22	8	10	4	53	54	20
Fornham A S	22	7	12	3	42	53	17
BSSCC	22	2	18	2	21	106	6
Elmswell	22	2	19	1	24	80	5

Lower Division Champions:
Div. 2: Bardwell
Div. 3: Tollgate Rovers
Div. 4: Bury Bowl

CAMBRIDGE & DISTRICT

SENIOR DIVISION	P	W	D	L	F	A	PTS
Swaffham United	20	14	3	3	74	33	31
Sawston Keys	20	13	3	4	62	28	29
Queens Arms	20	12	4	4	48	29	28
Howard Mallett	20	9	5	6	36	30	23
Bar Hill	20	7	7	6	46	38	21
Blades	20	10	1	9	34	37	21
Girton Eagles	20	9	1	10	43	43	19
Nera	20	8	5	7	43	45	19
Italcamb	20	5	1	14	34	67	11
Haddenham R.	20	4	2	14	28	55	10
Exning Utd	20	2	2	16	27	70	2

Lower Division Champions:
Div. 1a: Studlands Park
Div. 1b: Forest Rangers
Div. 2a: Camb Post Office
Div. 2b: Tankard United
Div. 3a: Ely City
Div. 3b: South Cambs Eagles
Div. 4a: Landbeach
Div. 4b: Netherhall
Div. 5: Freshfield United

Oakenshaw FC of the Bradford Sunday Alliance. Back Row (L/R): Warren Fletcher (Manager), Christopher Bushfield, Karl Gray, Christopher Shepherd, Adam Hughes, Timothy Rider, Paul Murphy, Gary Stanley, James Lawler (Asst Manager), Kenneth Wright (Trainer). Front: Michael Lawlor, Paul Smith, Lloyd Simpson, Peter Crowther, Mark Wilkinson, Graham Sykes. Photo - Dave West.

Broad Plain House, Bristol & District Sunday League Runners-up 1991-92. Photo - James Wright.

St Josephs (Luton) 6, Stag Sports 1 - Bedfordshire Sunday Cup final, 3/5/92. Sandor Gyalog of St Josephs kicks the ball forward as Paul Ovenden of Stag Sports tries to intervene. Photo - Paul Dennis.

CAMBRIDGE ALLIANCE

DIVISION ONE

	P	W	D	L	F	A	PTS
Datinton	14	10	1	3	50	31	21
Roct Rovers	14	10	0	4	43	22	20
Chesterton	14	7	2	5	33	33	16
IDA Darwin	14	7	1	6	42	40	15
RAF Ely	14	6	2	6	28	38	14
Reed	14	4	4	6	43	43	12
Fen Ditton	14	3	2	9	39	55	8
Uni Chem Cambs	14	2	2	10	29	45	6

Duraclean withdrawn.

Cup Winners: League Cup: Oatington

CARLISLE CITY

DIVISION ONE

	P	W	D	L	F	A	PTS
Morton	14	8	6	0	34	18	22
Nenthead	14	8	3	3	35	20	19
Magpie	14	7	4	4	25	14	18
Cusc	14	6	5	4	36	36	17
Pirelli	14	7	2	5	37	23	16
Belle Vue	14	2	6	6	24	41	10
Old Harraby	14	2	1	11	28	41	5
Arroyo	14	1	3	10	24	50	5

Lower Division Champions:
Div. 2: Cascade
Div. 3: Joiners

CARR & CARR

DIVISION ONE

	P	W	D	L	F	A	PTS
Tetney Sports	12	11	1	0	64	15	23
AFC Nunsthorpe	12	8	1	3	47	25	17
Albert Darnell	12	8	0	4	40	22	16
Rope Walk	12	8	1	6	41	38	11
S.H. Autos	12	4	0	8	34	61	8
Lloyds Arms	12	2	1	9	19	58	5
Louth Town C.	12	2	0	10	25	50	4

Lower Division Champions:
Div. 2: Louth Park Avenue

CASTLEFORD & DISTRICT

PREM. DIVISION

	P	W	D	L	F	A	PTS
Prince of wales	14	11	2	1	36	18	24
Hemsworth M.W.	14	9	2	3	42	16	20
Weeland W.	14	7	3	4	28	23	17
Sandmartin	14	6	3	5	26	30	15
Methley R.	14	6	2	6	31	24	14
Thorpe Audlin	14	4	3	7	27	31	11
Glass Hougthon	14	2	2	10	17	44	6
Turks Head	14	2	1	11	20	42	5

Cup Winners:
Open Cup: Prince of Wales
Prem. Cup: Hemsworth M.W.

CENTRAL WARWICKSHIRE OVER 35's

	P	W	D	L	F	A	PTS
Baldwin & Williams	22	19	3	0	113	11	41
Kings Heath V.	22	17	2	3	68	29	36
Folly Lane O.B.	22	14	4	4	67	37	32
Co op Tennis	22	13	2	7	64	35	28
Adler Insurance	22	13	2	7	63	47	28
Kynoch	22	11	4	7	51	51	26
Farthings O.B.	22	9	3	10	49	55	21
Edgbaston C.	22	8	5	9	46	58	21
St.Phillips V.	22	8	4	10	43	53	20
Painted Lady	22	7	4	11	38	48	18
Silhill	22	7	4	11	38	51	18
Howcon	22	5	4	13	31	53	14
Saxon	22	4	3	15	24	64	11
Woodpecker O.B.	22	4	2	16	33	75	10
Calthorpe O.B.	22	2	2	18	22	83	6

'POPE & SMITH' CHELMSFORD

PREM. DIVISION

	P	W	D	L	F	A	PTS
Priory Sports	20	16	2	2	55	19	35
Templar	20	12	3	5	59	48	27
Ongar	20	11	3	6	47	27	25
Woodham Town	20	9	3	8	41	41	21
Highfield Victoria	20	9	3	7	41	42	21
Redstones	20	8	5	7	34	35	21
Writtle	20	8	4	8	38	35	20
Cross Keys S.	20	7	3	10	29	36	17
Melbourne Utd	20	6	3	11	36	54	15
O. Chelmsfordians	20	3	4	13	28	52	10
Cherry Tree	20	1	7	12	24	43	9

Lower Division Champions:
Div. 1: Danbury
Div. 2: Cross Keys Dockers
Div. 3: Alma
Div. 4: Good Easter
Div. 5: Great Waltham
Div. 6: Nags Head Wanderers

Cup Winners:
John Coward Challenge Cup: Redstones
Peter Gillott Res Cup: High field Victoria
Prem. Cup: Priory Sports
Div. 1: Danbury
Div. 2: Cross Keys Dockers
Div. 3: Alma
Div. 4: Good Easter
Div. 5: Army & Navy
Div. 6: Margaretting

Redstones FC - Chelmsford Sunday League John Coward Challenge Cup Winners 1991-92.

CHELTENHAM (C & G)

PREM. DIVISION	P	W	D	L	F	A	PTS
Endsleigh	16	9	5	2	42	23	23
Cat & Fiddle	16	9	2	5	51	23	20
Charlton S.B	16	8	4	4	54	32	20
Floormasters	16	8	4	4	43	28	20
Prince of Wales	16	7	4	5	51	37	18
Bishops Cleeve *	16	7	4	5	37	38	17
Newtown Wan.	16	6	2	8	38	48	14
Old Patesians *	16	2	3	11	26	46	6
Whitesmiths	16	2	0	14	16	83	4

* - 1pt deducted.

Lower Division Champions:
Div. 1: Cheltenham Saracens
Div. 2: Hangovers
Div. 3: Charlton Kings
Div. 4: Prestbury Beefeaters
Div. 5: FC Raiders

CHESTERFIELD & DISTRICT

DIVISION ONE	P	W	D	L	F	A	PTS
Grassmoor WMC	26	16	8	2	80	46	40
Brampton Rov.	26	14	7	5	54	28	35
KSPO	26	14	6	6	71	34	34
Staveley MW	26	13	7	6	49	32	33
Woolley Moor	26	10	8	8	56	57	28
Hasland Park R.	26	10	7	9	45	44	27
Wingerworth	26	10	5	11	52	55	25
Killamarsh W.E.	26	8	7	11	61	65	23
Coal Aston	26	6	11	9	54	61	23
Doe Lea	26	7	9	10	35	49	23
Hepthorne L.	26	8	6	12	42	53	22
Clowne MW	26	9	2	15	65	71	20
Park Colts	26	5	10	11	36	46	20
Mastin Moor MW	26	4	3	19	29	88	11

Cup Winners:
League Cup: KSPO

CHICHESTER DISTRICT

DIVISION ONE	P	W	D	L	F	A	PTS
Whyte	18	15	1	2	82	28	31
Pagham S.C.	19	11	4	4	56	33	26
East Preston Y.C.	20	11	3	6	52	41	25
Chich Fernuite	20	11	1	8	45	38	23
Withering RBL	20	9	5	6	39	34	23
W.S.I.H.E.	20	9	4	7	43	37	22
Chich. Fencing	20	6	5	9	36	53	17
Selsey Arms	20	8	0	12	33	4	16
Priory Arms	19	6	3	10	31	48	15
Harrison C.C	20	5	3	12	28	49	12
Tavern Villa	20	2	2	16	18	66	6

Lower Division Champions:
Div. 2: Gem Travel

CORONATION

PREM. DIVISION	P	W	D	L	F	A	PTS
Olton Royale 'A'	20	16	1	3	55	23	33
Bournville W. 'A'	20	12	5	3	40	19	29
Jumbos XI	20	9	6	5	41	29	24
Capricorn	20	10	3	7	41	35	23
Leefal 'A'	20	8	4	8	43	37	20
Sheldon H.S.	20	6	6	8	42	37	18
Kingshurst A.V.T.	20	7	4	9	33	33	18
Kenwick Dynamo	20	6	4	10	31	48	16
Wychall Sports	20	6	2	12	25	39	14
Farthings 'A'	20	6	1	13	30	52	13
Shirley Am.	20	5	2	13	25	54	12

Lower Division Champions:
Prem. Div. 1: The Bell Marston Green
Div. 1: Athletic Centurion
Div. 2: Old Gate
Div. 3: Richmond
Div. 4: Castle Coach & Horses
All. Div. 1: Bradford Arms
All. Div. 2: Damsonwood R.
All. Div. 3: All Points
All. Div. 4: Lakeside 'B'
All. Div. 5: Pelham Arms

Continental 0, Concord Rangers 0 - F.A. Sunday Cup First Round 13/10/91. A fine strike from the homesters in this match at Walthamstow Pennant, but this extra-time effort, like numerous others, went astray. Photo - Gavin Ellis.

CRAMLINGTON

DIVISION ONE

	P	W	D	L	F	A	PTS
New Hartley	22	17	2	3	69	29	36
Dudley & Weetslade	22	14	3	5	73	28	31
Cramlington B.C.S.C	22	14	2	6	66	32	30
Blyth Masons Arms	22	12	4	6	46	47	28
Drift Inn S.B.	22	9	5	8	40	32	23
Seghill S.C.	22	11	1	10	57	53	23
New Fordley	22	7	8	7	39	34	22
Cramlington P.	22	7	4	11	32	49	18
Shankhouse Utd	22	8	1	13	40	55	17
W.Wideopen S.C	22	5	5	12	42	68	15
Melton Constable S.S	22	2	8	12	33	57	12
Cramlington V.C.	22	3	3	16	29	82	9

Lower Division Champions:
Div. 2: Travellers Rest Wideopen
Div. 3: Nelson Village Welfare
Div. 4: Newcastle Shieldfield

CROSBY & DISTRICT

DIVISION ONE

	P	W	D	L	F	A	PTS
Lion Knowsley	20	18	1	1	80	12	37
Eden Vale	20	15	2	3	89	21	32
RNA Kirkby	20	14	3	3	76	18	31
Strand Tavern	20	12	3	5	64	28	27
Star	20	10	2	8	77	52	22
Labour Bootle	20	9	3	8	71	33	21
Chesterfield Park	20	6	7	7	50	33	19
Hawthorne	20	6	2	12	44	73	14
Bootle	20	4	2	14	41	77	10
Stags	20	3	1	16	33	90	7
Alfred Knight	20	0	0	20	14	202	0

Lower Division Champions:
Div. 2: Dominion
Div. 3: Doric Celtic

CROYDON

PREM. DIVISION

	P	W	D	L	F	A	PTS
Holderness United	16	14	1	1	61	16	29
Stafford Athletic	16	11	2	3	50	22	24
South Croydon	15	10	2	3	48	31	22
Kerria Sports	16	9	3	4	51	30	21
Southwood Ath.	15	6	2	7	32	34	14
Mitcham	16	6	2	8	25	43	14
Waddon	16	2	4	10	30	49	8
Thamesford Strikers	16	2	2	12	14	57	6
Stamford United	16	1	2	13	16	45	4

Lower Division Champions:
Div. 1: Addington OB's
Div. 2: Victoria Cross
Div. 3: Newton
Div. 4: AFC Lion Brewery
Div. 5: MFC
Div. 6: Blackhorse
Div. 7: Eversley Rangers Res.
Div. 8: South Croydon Res.
Div. 9: Mitcham Res.
Div. 10: Wolsey

DAGENHAM & DISTRICT

SENIOR DIVISION

	P	W	D	L	F	A	PTS
Cue Ball 'A'	16	8	5	3	40	24	21
Church Elm	16	8	5	3	36	25	21
Thames Water	16	9	1	6	38	21	19
Manor House	16	8	3	5	25	19	19
Mayesbrook	16	7	3	6	37	26	17
Rainham Rangers	16	7	2	7	56	42	16
Thorbridge	16	3	7	6	32	36	13
British Legion	16	4	3	9	27	26	11
Little Heath	16	2	4	16	21	48	8

Lower Division Champions:
Div. 1: Dagenham Trades Hall
Div. 2: Manhattans
Div. 3: Gotham City
Div. 4: S.F.C. Dagenham

DORSET

DIVISION ONE

	P	W	D	L	F	A	PTS
Wareham Legion	20	19	0	1	103	19	38
Poole Town SC	20	15	0	5	82	23	30
Victoria Sports	20	13	2	5	80	28	29
A.F.Transport	20	11	2	7	61	33	24
Colehill Sports	20	11	2	7	62	41	24
Upton W.M.C.	20	11	1	8	57	60	23
Poole Wanderers	20	7	3	10	52	61	17
Longfleet St.Mary	20	7	2	11	55	57	16
Purbeck Insurance	20	4	2	14	28	62	10
AFC Autocolours	20	2	3	15	35	102	7
Grays	20	1	1	18	22	150	3

JUSTSPORT DURHAM & DISTRICT

PREM. DIVISION

	P	W	D	L	F	A	PTS
Sherburn WMC	22	17	2	3	96	30	53
Jasprint Biddick	22	17	1	4	72	23	52
Fram Moor WMC	22	15	3	4	69	24	48
Belmont WMC	22	15	2	5	73	40	47
Relton Tce WMC	22	13	2	7	58	40	41
Peterlee Cath C.	22	11	2	9	71	44	35
Ferryhill WMC	22	6	9	7	46	40	27
Cavalier	22	8	2	12	45	64	26
Wheatley Hill WMC	22	5	4	13	37	64	19
Gilesgate DLI	22	5	.2	15	43	90	17
Fishburn WMC	22	5	1	16	37	89	16
Kelloe WMC	22	0	0	22	29	128	0

Lower Division Champions:
Div. 1: Lumley WMC
Div. 2: Hetton Squashtec
Div. 3: Chester Bridge End
Div. 4: Rixy's Noght Spot
Div. 5: Jovial Monk
Div. 6: Free Gardiners

ESSEX

SENIOR DIVISION

	P	W	D	L	F	A	PTS
Hornchurch Utd	14	10	2	2	41	16	32
Lita Sports	14	9	2	3	33	25	29
Coach & Horses	14	9	3	3	44	38	27
Toby	14	6	2	6	30	30	20
Tow	14	5	4	5	34	32	19
St.Peters	14	5	0	9	19	29	15
Nacanco	14	3	3	8	34	45	12
Manor House	14	1	2	11	10	30	5

Malborough withdrawn.

Lower Division Champions:
Prem. Div: Star Albion
Div. 1: New Beckton
Div. 2: Glenthorne Utd
Div. 3: Romlas
Div. 4: Caterham
Div. 5: Motion Wanderers

Cup Winners:
McDougall Cup: Gidea Park Rangers
Senior Div Cup: Lita Sports
Prem. : Star Albion
Div. 1: Castlerow
Div. 2: Medhurst
Div. 3: Romlas
Div. 4: Caterham
Div. 5: Ever Ready T & P

JEWSON EVESHAM

DIVISION ONE

	P	W	D	L	F	A	PTS
Bear	20	16	3	1	46	15	35
Moreton Youth	20	13	3	4	54	35	29
Bretforton Vic.	20	9	5	6	35	23	23
Evesham WMC	19	11	1	7	39	29	23
Pershore Dyn. **	20	9	4	7	37	39	21
Littleton **	20	7	6	7	35	41	19
Inkberrow *	20	6	5	9	26	31	17
Ashchurch	20	3	7	10	26	46	13
Red Horse	20	5	2	13	29	46	12
Pinvin United	20	4	4	12	27	44	12
Salford R **	19	4	4	11	28	50	10

Salford v Evesham not played & no points awarded.
* Goal(s) deducted
**⁻ Point(s) & goal(s) deducted

Lower Division Champions:
Div. 2: Squirrel
Div. 3: Moreton Fire S C
Div. 4: Hampton United
Div. 5: Robirch Rangers

Action from the Croydon Sunday League Premier Cup final, held at Selhurst Park on 10th May. Kerria Sports defender Mark Dodman heads clear, but his team were beaten 0-1 by Addington Old Boys. Photo - Dave West.

Tony Dunn scores from the spot for A3 in the fifth minute of injury time to take the F.A. Sunday Cup tie against Oakenshaw into extra-time. Photo - Rob Ruddock.

Micky Ratcliffe, of Bristol side Hanham Sunday, is challenged by Ranelagh's Wayne Falana. Photo - Dave West.

FARNHAM & DISTRICT

DIVISION ONE	P	W	D	L	F	A	PTS
Greatham	16	11	3	2	74	23	36
Headley	16	9	4	3	55	37	31
Prince of W. (+3pts)	16	8	3	5	48	36	30
White Horse	16	9	1	5	41	33	28
Morley R.A. (-3)	16	9	2	5	43	36	26
Camelsdale M.	15	6	2	7	29	41	20
Market Inn	16	4	2	10	39	65	14
Alton T B (-3)	16	4	1	11	30	49	10
Havenford (+3)	15	1	2	12	27	66	8

Havenford v Camelsdale M. 1pt to each club.

Lower Division Champions:
Div. 2: White Hart Cranleigh
Div. 3: Royal Oak
Div. 4: Alton Town Bass Res.

THE FESTIVAL LEAGUE

PREMIER LEAGUE

PREM. DIVISION	P	W	D	L	F	A	PTS
Slade Celtic	22	13	6	3	47	28	32
Brookvale Ath.	22	11	6	5	33	21	28
Cork & Bottle	22	8	12	2	34	23	28
Altone Steels	22	10	5	7	39	27	25
Inter Volante	22	10	5	7	36	26	25
Birmingham C.	22	9	7	6	19	19	25
Lodge Cottrell	22	9	5	8	36	34	23
Travellers	22	5	9	8	30	39	19
Hundred Acre	22	7	5	10	27	43	19
Ansells Stockland S	22	4	8	10	31	35	16
Olympic Star	22	5	5	12	30	39	15
Sandwell	22	3	3	16	18	46	9

Lower Division Champions:
Premier League
Div. 1: Regent F.C
Div. 2: Romulus
Festival League
Div. 1: Bartley Green Social
Div. 2: Kings Colts
Div. 3: Anvil
Div. 4: Outer Circle
Combination League
Div. 1: Delta
Div. 2: Alba Vale
Div. 3: Drakes Drum
Div. 4: Kingfisher Masks
Senior Amateur League
Div. 1: Erdington Albion
Div. 2: Stanley Rangers
Div. 3: Baltimore
Junior League
Div. 1: Bristol Street (Shir.)
Div. 2: Royal Vale

GREAT YARMOUTH & DISTRICT

DIVISION ONE	P	W	D	L	F	A	PTS
Wheelwrights	22	14	4	4	78	36	32
Tudor Tavern	22	13	5	4	64	28	31
Arches Utd	22	12	6	4	55	32	30
Gorleston Utd	22	12	4	6	47	26	28
Alleycats	22	11	5	6	60	35	27
Acle	22	11	5	6	55	47	27
Schooners	22	10	5	7	63	26	25
Halvergate	22	10	3	9	58	56	23
St.Cloud	22	5	4	13	37	59	14
Magdalen Arms	22	6	2	14	38	67	14
Ludham	22	5	1	16	32	70	11
Rollesby Vic	22	1	0	21	11	116	2

Lower Division Champions:
Div. 2: G.C. Tigers
Div. 3: Bure Cons.
Div. 4: Acle Res.

GRESHAM ASSURANCE PREMIER & DISTRICT

DIVISION ONE	P	W	D	L	F	A	PTS
Wednesbury Manor	16	11	4	1	46	10	26
Station St WMC	15	11	2	2	36	13	24
Patricks	16	9	4	3	29	22	22
Pelsall RTC	16	6	7	3	39	29	19
Lock Stock	16	6	2	8	26	34	14
Carlton Motors	16	6	1	9	27	41	13
Chuckery WMC	15	3	3	9	27	38	9
Dresden	16	2	4	10	16	37	8
Kwiksave	16	2	3	11	20	42	7

Lower Division Champions:
Div. 2: Tipton Lion
Div. 3: Lion Sports
District League
Div. 1: Sadwica
Div. 2: Cougar
Div. 3: Internazionale
Div. 4: W.B.Trojans
Div. 5: Leathern Bottle
Div. 6: Lagoon Princes End
Div. 7: Happy Wanderer
Div. 8: Coseley Athletic
Div. 9: Central Rovers

Cup Winners:
Premier League
Div. 1 Cup: Station St WMC
Div. 2: Summerhill Social
Div. 3: Lion Sports
District League
Div. 1: Prince of Wales
Div. 2: Hill Top RBL
Div. 3: Waggon & Horses
Div. 4: Gt Bridge Beehive
Div. 5: Green Lane
Div. 6: Lagoon Princes End
Div. 7: Bird in Hand
Div. 8: Duke of York
Div. 9: Ha.Heath Swifts

HARINGEY TOTTENHAM & DISTRICTS

PREM. DIVISION	P	W	D	L	F	A	PTS
S.T. Dutch House	14	12	1	1	62	19	25
Wood Green	14	10	3	1	58	26	23
C.M.B.	14	6	3	5	37	34	15
Risley	14	7	0	7	28	49	14
Black Horse	14	5	1	8	22	29	11
Criterion	14	4	2	8	32	45	10
Highbury Gve	14	3	2	9	26	45	8
Ferry Lane	14	2	2	11	23	41	6

Lower Division Champions:
Div. 1: Albion R.R.
Div. 2: Seaton
Div. 3: Dynamos

GRIMSBY, CLEETHORPES & DISTRICT

DIVISION ONE	P	W	D	L	F	A	PTS
Grimsby College	22	16	4	2	63	20	36
Tetley Utd	22	13	4	5	51	32	30
Blossom Way Spts	22	13	3	6	71	32	29
Youngs Ross	22	10	5	7	45	34	25
Seaware Utd	22	10	5	7	40	35	25
Freetime Sports	22	8	5	9	33	41	21
Kingsway Printers	22	7	6	9	30	50	20
Hainton Inn	22	8	2	12	40	50	18
Bradley Am	22	6	6	10	34	47	18
Athletico	22	7	3	12	34	49	17
Humberston	22	7	2	13	38	59	16
Smugglers Imps	22	4	1	17	35	65	9

Lower Division Champions:
Div. 2: De Rigeur
Div. 3: Axe & Cleaver
Div. 4: Longship 2nd
Div. 5: West Marsh Utd
Div. 6: Harrisons
Div. 7: Wootton
Div. 8: Findus Grimsby
Div. 9: Jazz
Div. 10: Wellow Hotel

HARLOW & DISTRICT

PREM. DIVISION	P	W	D	L	F	A	PTS
Marquis Sports	20	16	3	1	59	20	35
Maypole/Phoenix	20	14	3	3	74	28	31
UG Sports	20	12	2	6	63	30	26
Harlow Rangers	20	10	5	5	57	38	25
Pools United	20	10	4	6	46	32	24
Maypole Sports	20	9	6	5	41	29	24
Lindsey Street	20	6	4	10	44	57	16
Pitney Bowes	20	5	4	11	43	63	14
Northbrooks	20	5	3	12	30	58	13
Staple Tye	20	3	1	16	33	77	7
Whalebone R.	20	2	1	17	31	89	5

Lower Division Champions:
Div. 1: Cossor Swifts
Div. 2: Sol Athletic
Div. 3: Ash Green

Div. 4: Stonards
Div. 5: Sabre
Div. 6: Loughton Swallows

Cup Winners:
Prem. Cup: Maypole/Phoenix
Div. 1: Cossor Swifts
Div. 2: Central Ave.
Div. 3: Ash Green
Div. 4: UG Sports Res.
Div. 5: Harlow Rangers Res.
Div. 6. Loughton Swallows

HASTINGS & EAST SUSSEX

DIVISION ONE	P	W	D	L	F	A	PTS
Hastings Fishermen	18	12	4	2	58	22	28
Oddfellows A	18	13	1	4	65	29	27
Kings Head (Battle)	18	9	5	4	53	38	23
Clarence	18	9	3	6	45	37	21
Kings Head (Ore)	18	8	4	6	42	40	20
Ellerhoop I	18	7	2	9	35	39	16
Viking	18	6	2	10	26	39	14
Harrow I	18	4	3	11	29	50	11
Westfield P I	18	3	5	10	24	55	11
Silverhill Club	18	4	1	13	43	71	9

Lower Division Champions:
Div. 2: Hastings Postal I
Div. 3: Bexhill A.A.C. I
Div. 4: Fire Brigade United
Div. 5: Ellerhoop II

HEAVY WOOLLEN GATE

PREM. DIVISION	P	W	D	L	F	A	PTS
Overthorpe SC	22	18	3	1	68	22	57
Thornhill Lees	22	12	6	4	40	18	42
Battyeford BC	22	12	3	7	61	40	39
Rose & Crown C.	22	9	6	7	38	41	33
Nelson Inn	22	8	7	7	43	39	31
St.John F OB	22	9	3	10	54	47	30
Birstall St.Pats*	22	9	2	11	42	48	28
Birkenshaw	22	8	4	10	48	56	28
Prince of W.*	22	7	5	10	42	56	25
Scholes Ath.	22	7	3	12	40	62	24
Wakefield City	22	6	3	13	38	52	21
Hartshead Moor CC	22	3	3	16	38	71	12
* - 1 point(s) deducted.

Lower Division Champions:
Div. 1: Lay-e-zee
Div. 2: Shaw Cross BC
Div. 3: Drighlington
Div. 4: Nova Colts
Div. 5: Battyeford BC Res.
Div. 6: Gildersome Tavs.

HENDON

PREM. DIVISION	P	W	D	L	F	A	PTS
Red Lion	16	9	7	0	28	15	25
West Hendon ESC	16	8	5	3	37	25	21
Linton	16	7	6	3	41	23	20
Kingfisher Yth	16	7	4	5	31	24	18
West Kilburn	16	6	3	7	27	27	15
Belmont Seniors	16	6	2	8	33	32	14
Moberley	16	4	5	7	31	51	13
Nissan Wembley	16	4	4	8	22	28	12
Maccabi	16	0	6	10	20	45	6

Lower Division Champions:
Intermediate Div.: Park Royals
Div. 1: Pinner Builders
Div. 2: Red Lion II
Div. 3: Espana Div. 4: St.Andrews

HIGH WYCOMBE

PREM. DIVISION	P	W	D	L	F	A	PTS
Hedsor Social	22	21	1	0	116	26	43
Lane End United	22	17	1	4	106	29	35
Pandect	22	14	2	6	68	41	30
The Plough Inn*	22	14	2	6	55	42	28
Chinnor Sports	22	10	3	9	56	56	23
Rose & Crown '82	22	8	3	11	57	68	19
Glory Mill	22	7	4	11	47	76	18
King George V	22	7	3	12	39	55	17
Black & Decker	22	6	3	13	46	65	15
Foresters	22	6	3	13	33	59	15
Hour Glass	22	5	2	15	46	98	12
Chinnor Exiles	22	3	1	18	33	87	7
* - 2pts deducted.

Lower Division Champions:
Div. 1: Hithercroft
Div. 2: White Horse
Div. 3: Blues Club
Div. 4: Flackwell Heath S.C.
Div. 5: Cross Keys

HINCKLEY

PREM. DIVISION	P	W	D	L	F	A	PTS
Scaptoft WMC	22	17	1	4	71	38	35
Whetstone Utd	22	14	3	5	68	24	31
Hillsborough	22	13	5	4	72	46	31
Swan (-2pt)	22	12	6	4	68	32	28
Rutland Rovers	22	10	5	7	53	47	25
Magna 73 Sunday	22	10	1	11	43	37	21
City Arms	22	8	3	11	50	52	19
Vikings Tun.	22	5	7	10	49	54	17
Richmond R.	22	5	6	11	46	73	16
Sharnford (-4)	21	8	3	10	48	73	15
Tudor (-2)	22	5	2	15	40	69	10
Huncote SSC (-4)	22	2	4	16	30	89	4

Lower Division Champions:
Div. 1: Red Lion
Div. 2: Dog Gun
Div. 3: Croft
Div. 4: Seaton Utd
Div. 5: Earl.Shilton WMC

Cup Winners:
Senior Cup: Whetstone United
Junior Cup: Richmond Arms
Les Moore Memorial Cup: Bulls Head

HITCHIN GAZETTE

PREM. DIVISION	P	W	D	L	F	A	PTS
Angles	22	16	4	2	82	22	36
Offley Social	22	16	3	3	91	28	35
Bell	22	16	3	3	61	23	35
Sportsman	22	15	2	5	85	32	32
Westbury C.A.	22	14	3	5	64	26	31
Cricketers Hitchin	22	8	5	9	48	56	21
Wanderers	22	7	6	9	36	42	20
Westbury United	22	7	2	13	34	79	16
Nightingale Utd	22	6	3	13	40	75	15
New Found Out	22	3	4	15	31	66	10
Kings Athletic	22	4	2	16	32	68	10
Pirton Eagles	22	1	1	20	18	105	3

Lower Division Champions:
Div. 1: Walsworth Div. 2: Two Chimneys
Div. 3: Sporting Luton Div. 4: Letchworth Garden City

HUDDERSFIELD & DISTRICT

DIVISION 1	P	W	D	L	F	A	PTS
Sikh Temple	18	14	4	0	65	17	32
Junction	18	9	4	5	36	26	22
Railway Inn	18	8	4	6	34	32	20
Beaumont Arms	18	8	3	7	33	39	19
Bradley R.	18	7	4	7	35	38	18
Wappy Springs	18	8	2	8	32	32	18
Moldgreen Con.	18	7	3	8	37	27	17
Stile Common	18	5	4	9	27	40	14
Rock	18	5	4	9	32	49	14
Freemasons	18	3	0	15	18	49	6

Lower Division Champions:
Div. 2: Black Bull (after play off)
Div. 3: Highgate Oakes
Div. 4: Blacksmiths Arms Div. 5: Black Horse

Cup Winners:
Rollinson Cup: Sikh Temple
Examiner Rosebowl: Highgate Oakes
Challenge Cup: Rock

HULL & DISTRICT

PREM. DIVISION	P	W	D	L	F	A	PTS
Northwood FC	22	16	3	3	65	28	35
Swanfield FC	22	15	3	4	59	24	33
New Inn FC	22	12	6	4	54	27	30
Brighams FC	22	13	3	6	54	29	29
Chalk Lane FC	22	11	6	5	60	32	28
B&A Scaff/ing FC	22	13	1	8	39	20	27
St.Peters FC	22	6	7	9	28	38	19
National Tigers	22	7	4	11	37	53	18
British Gas	22	7	2	13	29	48	16
Viking Malet	22	4	2	16	29	51	10
Fish Trades	22	2	6	14	26	83	10
Roos FC	22	4	1	17	28	75	9

Hull Sunday League continued

Lower Division Champions:
Premier Division
Div. 1: Keyingham
Div. 2: Settingdyke YC
Div. 3: Cholmley FC
Div. 4: Calor Gas
Div. 5: Pint & Pot
Div. 6: West Lee YC
Div. 7: Waterloo Tav
Div. 8: Anlaby Park Rgs
Div. 9: Mill Lane Utd
Div. 10: Gower Rgs
Div. 11: Highway 90
Div. 12: Newport Utd
Div. 13: Royal Oak Rgs
Div. 14: Calvert Rgs
Div. 15: Lanbwath Juventus
Div. 16: Setting Sun Rgs
Div. 17: Viking Malet C
Div. 18: Stadium Develop
Div. 19: Burstwick FC
Div. 20: AFC Lodge

HYDE & DISTRICT

PREM. DIVISION	P	W	D	L	F	A	PTS
Church Inn Failsworth	20	14	5	1	51	22	33
Carters Bridge	20	14	4	2	64	27	32
Royal Oak	20	9	6	5	50	25	24
North Chadderton	20	7	9	4	43	38	23
New Inn	20	7	7	6	35	32	21
Lamb Hotel	20	7	7	6	38	36	21
Haughton Villa	20	6	7	7	23	27	19
Denton Shakespeare	20	6	5	9	32	45	17
Stamford Park	20	5	3	12	34	41	13
Sycamore *	20	5	1	14	30	57	9
Railway	20	2	2	16	28	78	6

* - 2pts deducted

Lower Division Champions:
Div. 1: Old Pack Horse
Div. 2: Grapes Div. 3: Listons
Div. 4: Commercial Div. 5: Crown

IRONBRIDGE

PREM. DIVISION	P	W	D	L	F	A	PTS
Hollinswd	22	19	1	2	82	20	39
Wrekin Vw	22	18	2	2	90	25	38
Beacon	22	15	0	7	61	46	30
Cressage	22	14	2	6	66	39	28
Land Reg	22	12	3	7	58	56	26
Brosley P.	22	10	3	9	40	39	26
Av Social	22	9	4	9	66	67	22
Old Bell	22	8	3	11	64	64	19
Livernall	22	5	4	13	53	71	13
Hills La	22	3	3	16	34	67	9
Royal Oak	22	3	2	17	35	97	9
Talbot	22	3	3	16	27	66	8

Lower Division Champions:
Div. 1: New Inn

Collier Row Supporters 1, Broovale Athletic 2 - F.A. Sunday Cup Third Round, 8/12/92. The Cow clear an attack from the visitors. Photo - Gavin Ellis.

COMBINATION LEAGUE

PREM. DIVISION	P	W	D	L	F	A	PTS
Oldfield Hotel	22	17	2	3			36
Fforde Grene	22	14	5	3			33
Monkbridge	22	14	5	3			33
Holbeck BC	22	11	3	8			25
AFC Cullens	22	9	6	7			24
Horsforth Ex-SC	22	10	3	9			23
Bird in Hand	22	8	6	8			22
Main Line Social	22	7	5	10			19
White Hart	22	4	10	8			18
Prince Philip	22	6	4	12			16
Beulah	22	6	3	13			15
Dewsbury Rd Spts	22	0	0	22			0

Lower Division Champions:
Prem. : Gildersome Tavs
Div. 1: Churwell WMC
Div. 2: Ringway FC
Div. 3: Swillington Hotel
Div. 4: Kippax Band Club
Div. 5: Crown Sports
Div. 6: Horsf Fairweather

LEICESTERSHIRE ALLIANCE

PREM. DIVISION	P	W	D	L	F	A	PTS
Humberstone	20	15	4	1	77	32	49
Hunters	20	15	2	3	88	42	47
Oadby Academicals	20	12	3	5	67	36	39
Star & Garter	20	11	2	7	52	47	35
Huntsman '84	20	9	3	8	71	53	30
Birstall Eagle	20	8	3	9	65	51	27
Wigston Town CC	20	7	4	9	50	58	25
Bulls Head	20	7	2	11	49	67	23
Transbuild	20	5	1	14	45	79	16
New Inn	20	3	4	13	32	91	13
South Wigston	20	2	4	13	26	56	10

Lower Division Champions:
Div. 1: Gearys Bakery
Div. 2: Husbands Bosworth
Div. 3: R F Brooks SSC
Div. 4: Gilmorton

LIVERPOOL BUSINESS HOUSE

PREM. DIVISION	P	W	D	L	F	A	PTS
Nicosia	22	18	2	2	52	18	38
Clubmr Naigo	22	13	5	4	45	32	31
Toshsharples	22	12	4	6	64	48	28
Stantondale	22	10	4	8	46	48	24
B R N E S C	22	8	6	8	48	48	22
A C Sparks	22	10	2	10	44	48	22
A3	22	8	5	9	54	49	21
Permatex	22	6	8	8	43	44	20
Seddons	22	7	5	10	35	40	19
Ford Motors	22	5	7	10	27	44	17
ULT/Joinery	22	3	8	11	34	47	14
Salerno	22	2	4	16	26	66	8

Lower Division Champions:
Div. 1: Napoli
Div. 2: Walford MTME
Div. 3: Norgreen V
Div. 4: Home'rt Bath
Div. 5: Wade Smith

LIVERPOOL & DISTRICT

PREM. DIVISION	P	W	D	L	F	A	PTS
Blue Union	22	14	4	4	59	31	46
Newfield	22	12	5	5	48	36	41
Britannia V.N.C.	22	12	4	6	47	33	40
Eagle Knowsley	22	11	4	6	44	31	37
Lobster	22	11	4	7	40	41	37
Western Approach	22	11	3	8	48	36	36
Croxteth Legion	22	11	2	9	51	36	35
Almithak	22	8	4	10	38	44	28
Halewood Labour	22	6	2	14	42	57	20
Netherley R.B.L.*	22	5	4	12	37	53	22
Seymour *	22	5	3	14	35	57	18
Rob Roy	22	4	3	15	29	63	15
* - Play off.							

Lower Division Champions:
Div. 1: Sandon
Div. 2: Oyster
Div. 3: Breck Turpins
Div. 4: Liverpool Support

LONG EATON

PREM. DIVISION	P	W	D	L	F	A	PTS
Grandstand 83	24	18	4	2	73	18	58
Sandiacre Town	24	17	3	4	64	29	54
Railway	24	16	3	5	53	20	51
Greenwich Albion	24	12	5	7	51	29	41
Sportsman	24	11	4	9	46	33	37
Squires United	24	10	3	11	35	42	33
Stapleford Cons	24	9	2	13	35	56	29
Dovedale	24	7	5	12	24	52	26
Rutland Cottage	24	7	3	14	29	45	24
Ladywood	24	7	3	14	32	54	24
Attenborough Spts	24	6	6	12	30	54	24
Barge	24	7	2	15	35	55	23
Athletica	24	5	5	14	30	52	20

Lower Division Champions:
Div. 1: Jolly Potters
Div. 2: Crown
Div. 3: Beeston Rylands
Div. 4: Trumpet Inn

Cup Winners:
Derbyshire Sunday Senior Cup: Sandiacre Town
Derbyshire Sunday Junior Cup: Wine Vaults

CITY OF MANCHESTER

PREM. DIVISION	P	W	D	L	F	A	PTS
Mauldeth Celtic	22	18	3	1			39
Moss Side BL	22	18	0	4			36
Fallowfield	20	13	5	2			31
Irish Association	22	14	1	7			29
Rusholme LL A	20	11	2	7			24
George & Dragon	22	10	1	11			21
Unicorn Hulme	22	8	5	9			21
Jolson's	22	8	1	13			17
Manchester Wds	22	7	2	13			16
Royal Oak Chorltn	22	5	1	16			11
The Grove	22	5	0	17			10
Claremont Rgrs	22	2	5	14			9

Lower Division Champions:
Div. 2: Charlton
Div. 3: Taymark

MARATHON LEAGUE

PREM. DIVISION	P	W	D	L	F	A	PTS
Bedfont Sunday	16	13	1	2	39	22	27
Belstone	16	10	3	3	45	17	23
Rayners Lane Sun.	16	8	4	4	39	16	20
Northfield Rangers	16	9	1	6	28	23	19
Shamrock Sunday	16	8	1	7	34	31	17
Greenford Park Wds	16	6	4	6	29	22	16
Hanworth Rangers	16	4	3	9	22	49	11
Deane United	16	2	5	9	30	46	9
Harrow Villa	16	1	0	15	17	57	2

Lower Division Champions:
Div. 1: Hatch End
Div. 2: St.Anselms
Div. 3: Brentford Athletic
Div. 4: Ealing Town
Div. 5: Northwick Park H.
Div. 6: Zydeco

Cup Winners:
Challenge Cup: Bedfont Sunday
Charity Cup: Hatch End
Senior Cup: Bedfont Sunday
Intermediate Cup: Capel Arms
Junior Cup: Alma Tavern

MEDWAY AREA

SENIOR DIVISION	P	W	D	L	F	A	PTS
Cavalliers	26	22	2	2	78	21	46
Quested	26	20	5	1	111	32	45
Bly Spartans	26	16	3	7	51	32	35
St.Marys	26	14	5	7	83	60	33
Beach Rovers	26	14	4	8	68	38	32
Earl Social	26	10	6	10	49	52	26
ABC Sports	26	8	8	10	47	44	24
Gills FC Social	26	11	1	14	57	62	23
Gnedland Villa	26	7	7	12	38	56	21
Cecil Arm	26	8	4	14	52	48	20
Spailay	26	7	5	14	40	76	19
Celtic Sports	26	7	3	16	39	101	17
Weedcombe	26	6	1	19	32	90	13
Stevedon Sports	26	3	4	19	45	78	10

METROPOLITAN

PREM. DIVISION	P	W	D	L	F	A	PTS
Brettell Ath.	18	11	4	3	46	24	26
Santogee 66	18	11	3	4	39	22	25
Convoys	18	10	4	4	39	19	24
London Boys	18	8	5	5	35	27	21
Woolwich Postal	18	8	3	7	55	48	19
Fisher Elliots	18	6	5	7	42	37	17
Oxford Road S.	18	7	3	8	27	28	17
Southwark Spts	18	6	4	8	18	31	16
Inter Royalle	18	6	1	11	38	42	13
Lea Bridge	18	0	2	16	14	75	2

Lower Division Champions:
Sen.Div. 1: Lambeth Sportsman
Sen.Div. 2: Coss
Junior Div 1: Catford Invicta
Div. 2: Crofton Albion
Div. 3: Elmstead Strollers
Div. 4: Dulwich Plough
Div. 5: Clydesdale Bank

MEXBOROUGH & DISTRICT

PREM. DIVISION	P	W	D	L	F	A	PTS
Ivanhoe	20	15	1	4	61	19	31
Darfield Station	20	11	8	1	69	24	30
The Gate	20	10	5	5	43	30	25
Dearne C.M.W.	20	9	6	5	30	21	24
Edlington WMC	20	7	5	8	47	46	19
Swinton WMC	20	8	2	10	42	48	18
Wath Saracens	20	7	3	10	34	44	17
Eagle & Child	20	7	3	10	44	65	17
New Masons	20	5	4	11	30	54	14
Queens United	20	5	3	12	40	52	13
Tom Hill	20	4	4	12	23	60	12

Lower Division Champions:
Div. 1: Liner Athletic
Div. 2: Dearne Enterprise
Div. 3: Tavern '91

MID CHESHIRE

PREM. DIVISION	P	W	D	L	F	A	PTS
Lion Ath.	22	16	3	3	77	30	35
Liverpool SC	22	14	4	4	49	25	32
Sandiway	22	13	4	5	43	29	30
Golden Lion	22	13	2	7	61	38	28
FC Coachman	22	9	7	6	50	32	25
Farmers Arms	22	9	4	9	45	53	22
Greenbank	22	8	4	10	36	44	20
Bowling Green	22	7	5	10	36	40	19
FC Salter	22	6	6	10	44	59	18
Roebuck	22	7	1	14	34	58	15
St.Josephs	22	5	4	13	30	46	14
Cuddington	22	2	2	18	20	71	6

Lower Division Champions:
Div. 1: Tesco
Div. 2: Egerton BC **Div. 3:** Volunteer

MORECAMBE & LANCASTER

DIVISION ONE	P	W	D	L	F	A	PTS
Royal Oak Hotel	14	11	3	0	67	18	36
Moorlands Hotel	14	9	2	3	46	23	29
Mayfield United	14	8	1	5	49	29	25
New Inn	14	6	2	6	29	22	20
Skerton Hotel	14	5	2	7	31	36	17
Byrne *	14	5	0	9	37	63	12
Farmers Arms *	14	3	2	9	30	70	8
Longlands Hotel *	14	2	2	10	26	54	5

* - 3pts deducted.

Lower Division Champions:
Div. 2: Upstairs/Downstairs **Div. 3:** Uni-Sports Centre

MORPETH

DIVISION ONE	P	W	D	L	F	A	PTS
Stobswood.W.Res	24	22	1	1	110	20	67
Pegswood Ex/Serv	24	19	3	2	92	32	60
Lynemouth FC	24	17	2	5	72	39	53
Bedlington Ex/Serv.	24	14	3	7	45	38	45
Morpeth St.George's	24	12	4	8	78	42	40
Pegswood S.C.	24	10	5	9	61	67	35
Red Row Brick C.	24	8	4	12	53	62	28
Amble Dock Hotel	24	8	2	14	56	63	26
Ponteland AFI	24	8	2	14	60	80	26
Ashington Comrades	23	7	2	14	64	85	23
Bedlington Gen.Hav.	24	6	1	17	33	76	19
Acklington HM Pris.	24	6	1	17	64	131	19
Morpeth Joiner's A.	24	4	0	20	35	88	12

Lower Division Champions:
Div. 2: Morpeth Comrades
Div. 3: Morpeth Hearts
Cup Winners:
League Cup: Morpeth St.George's
Subsidiary Cup: Red Row Grey Arms
Lewin Cup (Div.1): Amble Dock Hotel
Glaxocham Cup (Div.2): Morpeth Comrades
Welwyn Cup (Div.3): Morpeth Hearts
George Cave Mem.Cup: Bedlington Ex/Serv.

DAND MOTORS NEWBURY

PREM. DIVISION	P	W	D	L	F	A	PTS
New Inn	22	19	1	2	70	30	39
Chieveley	22	14	4	4	62	33	32
New B'ry Hall	22	14	3	5	63	29	31
Westfields	22	11	4	7	46	33	26
Hermitage	22	10	2	10	35	31	22
Leckhampstead	22	8	5	9	47	40	21
Cold Ash	22	8	5	9	42	50	21
Great Bedwyn	22	7	5	10	48	51	19
New Green	22	7	4	11	63	60	18
Donnington	22	8	1	13	42	76	17
TRS College	22	6	1	15	27	43	13
St.Bart's	22	1	3	18	30	99	5

Lower Division Champions:
Div. 1: John O'Gaunt
Div. 2: Nu-Start
Div. 3: Th'm Sunday

REGENCY WINDOWS
NEWCASTLE CENTRAL

DIVISION ONE	P	W	D	L	F	A	PTS
Simonside S&R	18	15	2	1	76	19	47
Birtley Queens Head	18	13	1	4	67	26	40
East Howdon S.C.	18	9	2	7	48	27	29
Backett U.K.	18	8	4	6	52	42	28
Newcastle Ath.	18	9	1	8	31	27	28
Birtley British Legion	18	6	4	8	31	23	22
J&G Landscapes	18	6	3	9	24	34	21
Beaconsfield	18	6	2	10	40	69	20
Heaton C.C.	18	5	4	9	28	53	19
Wallsend S.C.*	18	0	3	15	13	90	0

* - 3pts deducted.

Lower Division Champions:
Div. 2: Fenham

THE NORTH EAST

A. DIVISION	P	W	D	L	F	A	PTS
Wallsend Labour	30	20	1	9	65	33	61
Dunston Social	30	18	4	8	60	34	58
Scotswood Social	30	15	7	8	64	52	52
Balloon	30	15	5	10	48	36	50
Bugle	30	13	9	8	51	46	48
Birds Nest	30	15	5	10	50	37	47
Burradon Social	30	14	5	11	55	44	47
Teams Social	30	12	10	8	42	43	46
Queen Victoria	30	12	8	10	46	37	44
Fusilier	30	12	6	12	50	53	42
Dorset Sports	30	12	5	13	36	46	41
Whickham R & C.	30	12	4	14	50	49	40
Killingworth Arms	30	13	0	17	41	46	36
Lemington Labour	30	9	6	15	47	50	33
West Moor Social	30	5	2	23	30	68	14
Felling Social	30	2	3	25	21	74	9

Lower Division Champions:
B. Div: Halls Elswick
C. Div: Throckley Centurian
D. Div: Springbank Social
E. Div: Gosforth Empire
F. Div: Westerhope Comrades

NORTH HILLINGDON & DISTRICT

PREM. DIVISION	P	W	D	L	F	A	PTS
Black Bull	14	11	2	1	67	21	24
Islip	14	12	0	2	48	18	24
Cyreneans	14	8	2	4	50	24	18
Cowley Packet Boat	14	6	4	4	32	23	15
Hayes Social & S.R.	14	4	3	7	37	39	11
Western United	14	4	1	9	24	45	9
Northholt Rangers	14	4	0	10	22	77	8
The Ickenham	14	1	0	13	19	54	2

Lower Division Champions:
Div. 1: Firefly

PORTSMOUTH

PREM. DIVISION
	P	W	D	L	F	A	PTS
Portsbridge	20	17	3	0	81	28	37
Civil Service	20	16	3	1	80	20	35
Wicor Mill	20	11	5	4	50	38	27
Beehive	20	8	4	8	38	40	20
Harvest Hm	20	6	7	7	58	45	19
J.Taxpayer	20	6	6	8	45	48	18
Havant Rovers	20	7	3	10	50	48	17
Kimber Sp.	20	7	3	10	26	44	17
C Dickens	20	6	4	10	39	49	16
Hillside	20	5	2	13	48	69	12
The Keys	20	1	0	19	18	104	2

Lower Division Champions:
Sen. Div. : Cowplain Soc.
Div. 1: Priory
Div. 2: Southsea Utd
Div. 3: Prospect
Div. 4: B of Minden
Div. 5: Pelham Arms
Div. 6: MTA

READING & DISTRICT

SENIOR DIVISION
	P	W	D	L	F	A	PTS
Theale	20	20	0	0	77	12	40
Reading Borough	20	13	3	4	62	32	29
Caversham Park	20	13	2	5	75	33	28
Quicksilver Ath.	20	10	1	9	41	47	21
Dee Road Rangers	20	9	2	9	38	37	20
FC Richfield	20	8	3	9	43	44	19
Culham Rangers	20	5	7	8	29	40	19
Palmer Park R.	20	6	2	12	39	54	14
Courage Imperial	20	4	5	11	45	63	13
Mowog	20	4	4	12	33	75	12
Cholsey United	20	3	1	16	18	63	7

REDHILL & DISTRICT

DIVISION ONE
	P	W	D	L	F	A	PTS
Iron Horse	18	13	1	4	68	27	27
Meadvale Eagles	18	10	5	3	47	25	25
Woodhatch	18	10	4	4	47	21	24
Caterham Town	18	8	6	4	47	27	22
Tudor Athletic	18	8	2	8	28	46	18
Mid Day Sun	18	7	3	8	35	36	17
Directors	18	6	2	10	37	46	14
Frenches	18	4	6	8	31	48	14
Merstham Orion	18	6	1	11	26	45	13
Grange Park	18	2	2	14	24	69	6

Lower Division Champions:
Div. 2: Mickleham
Div. 3: The Market
Div. 4: Fox Reserves

RHYL & DISTRICT

DIVISION ONE
	P	W	D	L	F	A	PTS
Windsor	20	14	2	4	85	30	32
New Inn	20	14	3	3	90	44	31
Ffrith	20	7	9	4	46	70	18
Railway C.	20	5	10	5	48	85	15
Evadx	20	5	12	3	48	63	13
St.Melyd	20	4	13	3	47	72	11

Lower Division Champions:
Div. 2: Lyons Int.

Cup Winners:
Slaters Shield: New Inn
Sovereign Trophies Consolation Cup: Gronant
John Stanley Jones Memorial Cup: St.Melyd Squash Club

ROTHERHAM & DISTRICT

PREM. DIVISION
	P	W	D	L	F	A	PTS
Thurcroft Hotel	22	16	3	3	70	26	35
Three Magpies 89	22	15	5	2	54	17	35
Drawbridge	22	12	4	6	44	31	28
Rawmarsh Earl G.	22	10	6	6	47	24	26
Joker	22	11	3	8	49	36	25
Brinsworth A.	22	10	5	7	48	46	25
Sportsman *	21	9	6	6	57	25	24
Maltby MW	22	8	6	8	57	51	22
Red Lion	22	8	3	11	40	45	19
Clifton Hotel *	21	3	2	16	27	81	8
Woodman	22	3	2	17	35	90	8
East Dene H.	22	1	5	16	25	84	7

Lower Division Champions:
Div. 1: Aston Rangers
Div. 2: Reresby Rovers
Div. 3: JS New Inn **Div. 4:** Greasboro Crown
Div. 5: Brampton Dynamoes B **Div. 6:** East Dene
Div. 7a : Anston Royals **Div. 7b :** Spartak Rawmarsh

RUNCORN

PREM. DIVISION
	P	W	D	L	F	A	PTS
Cherrysutton	22	18	3	1	88	22	57
Norton Arms	22	18	1	3	68	36	55
Sullivan Express *	22	17	4	1	71	23	54
Old Transporter **	22	12	3	7	45	34	39
Longview L ***	22	7	6	9	50	51	29
Majors	22	8	2	12	40	55	26
Halton Sports	22	7	3	12	39	49	24
Cronton Villa	22	7	3	12	37	51	24
Priestcotte	22	6	5	11	33	50	23
C. C. Speke	22	6	3	13	34	56	21
Tricorn	22	6	1	15	36	67	19
Halefellow	22	2	2	18	37	84	8

* - 1pt deducted
** - 3pts awarded
*** - 1pt awarded

Theale FC, who not only won the F.A. Sunday Cup, but also retained a 100% record throughout the season in the Reading & District Sunday League. Back Row (L/R): Dave Crowdie (Manager), Jamie Murray, Noel Newton, Jamie Ferguson, Andy Howell, Richard Lovegrove, Karl Cooke, Paul Cox. Front: Keith Eatwell (Physio), Andy Parr, John Wylie, Paul Mulvaney, Steve Dale, Graham Hambridge, Mattie Webb. Photo - Dave West.

A quartet of Theale fans clearly enjoying their day out at the F.A. Sunday Cup final. Photo - Eric Marsh.

Reading Borough, Reading & District Sunday League Runners-up 1991-92. Back Row (L/R): Joe Fletcher (Manager), Sean Fletcher, Maurice Somers, John Hicky, Kenny Cox, Craig Rutherford, John Partridge, Mike Kearney, Tony Doherty. Front: Danny Tully (Physio), Gary Stevens, Jim McVey, Rory O'Neill, Pat McCoy, Dave Evans, Jon Sturgess. Photo - Dave West.

Theale's Noel Newton shoots for goal during the F.A. Sunday Cup final. Photo - Paul Dennis.

RUSHDEN

DIVISION ONE

	P	W	D	L	F	A	PTS
Victoria M	22	18	4	0	91	20	40
Valleybrook	22	18	3	1	77	21	39
Finedon Rovers	22	10	3	9	60	64	23
Olympic	22	10	2	10	60	49	22
Raunds Warr'	22	7	7	8	31	31	21
I'boro Horse	22	9	2	11	39	47	20
Grendon H M	22	8	3	11	41	72	19
Irchester	22	7	4	11	38	50	18
Calendar	22	7	2	13	40	45	16
Cannon	22	5	5	12	31	56	15
Ambrook	22	7	1	14	39	74	15
Higham Ferr'	22	6	4	12	36	54	14

Lower Division Champions:
Div. 2: Raunds Wood
Div. 3: Windmill
Div. 4: Rushden K E

DEE JAYS SCUNTHORPE

DIVISION ONE

	P	W	D	L	F	A	PTS
Lions Head	16	12	1	3	52	21	25
Kypros	16	12	0	4	53	23	24
Poachers	16	10	1	5	59	15	21
Park West	16	8	2	6	47	34	18
Keadby & A C.	16	8	1	7	35	28	17
Pied Piper	16	6	2	8	37	40	14
Burringham	16	6	1	9	38	60	13
Comet Wanderers	16	6	0	10	32	45	12
Duffs Dynamoes	16	0	0	16	11	98	0

Lower Division Champions:
Div. 2: Dee Jays
Div. 3: Bridge House
Div. 4: Broughton Clamert
Div. 5: Messingham TOB
Div. 6: Blue Bell
Div. 7: Quebec Rangers

SHREWSBURY

PREM. DIVISION

	P	W	D	L	F	A	PTS
Brick Sports	22	18	2	2	75	30	38
Plough	22	15	5	2	50	27	32
Monkmoor	22	13	5	4	55	31	30
The Apprentice	22	10	6	6	53	37	26
Instones United	22	11	8	3	43	29	25
All Stretton	22	9	10	3	39	49	21
Ford	22	8	11	3	38	44	19
Abbey Hotel	22	7	10	5	37	51	19
Cruckton Rovers	22	7	12	3	50	60	17
Acorn	22	6	13	3	27	51	15
Pontesbury	22	5	15	2	37	65	12
Steam Wagon	22	4	16	2	31	61	10

Lower Division Champions:
Div. 1: Bayston Hill C.
Div. 2: Wroxeter Rovers
Div. 3: Harlescott
Div. 4: Brockton Rovers

SOUTHEND

PREM. DIVISION

	P	W	D	L	F	A	PTS
Catholic United	20	14	3	3	52	17	31
Customs & Exercise	20	12	4	4	62	33	28
Hadleigh Town	20	13	1	6	54	43	27
Mill Sports	20	11	2	7	53	29	24
Rayleigh Town	20	10	4	6	44	27	24
Progress Rovers	20	9	2	9	44	45	20
Milton Athletic	20	7	5	8	46	44	19
Concord Rangers	20	8	0	12	37	47	16
Trinity	20	6	2	12	40	51	14
Hullbridge Sports	20	6	2	12	29	53	14
Rayleigh Avenue	20	1	1	18	16	88	3

Lower Division Champions:
Div. 1: Spartek
Div. 2: Oakwood Sports
Div. 3: Canewdon Anchor
Div. 4: Thundersley Rovers
Div. 5: Olympus
Div. 6: Rochford United
Div. 7: Roche Meadow
Div. 8: Gifford United

SOUTH LONDON

PREM. DIVISION

	P	W	D	L	F	A	PTS
Caribb	14	11	2	1	43	16	24
Lew Way IFC A	14	11	1	2	44	10	23
Masons Sports	14	7	3	4	25	20	17
Salters Hill	14	5	5	4	31	33	15
Cornish Sports	14	4	2	8	22	37	10
Brixton United	14	3	2	9	15	24	8
CWS Wanderers	14	2	4	8	19	43	8
Barracuda A	14	3	1	10	19	35	7

Lower Division Champions:
Div. 1: Riverplate
Div. 2: Tyrrell Rangers
Div. 3: Clifton Casuals
Div. 4: St.John's Wal.
Div. 5: Man On The Moon
Div. 6: Lambeth Social B.

SOUTH THAMESIDE

PREM. DIVISION

	P	W	D	L	F	A	PTS
Drunken Duck **	14	14	0	0	58	8	28
Virginia Water S. *	14	9	1	4	37	30	19
Chessington & H.U.	14	7	0	7	30	31	14
Addlestone Royals	14	7	0	7	28	31	14
Drunken Duck Res.	14	5	3	6	31	28	13
Woking Locals Ath.	14	5	1	8	36	37	11
Hand & Spear *	14	3	2	9	24	48	8
Woburn Park **	14	2	1	11	18	49	5

* - 1pt deducted.
** - 2pts deducted.

Lower Division Champions:
Div. 1: Renegade Royals
Div. 2: Abbey Rangers
Div. 3: Addlestone Wanderers

WATFORD

PREM. DIVISION

	P	W	D	L	F	A	PTS
Evergreen	18	12	2	4	47	16	38
St. Josephs	18	12	2	4	48	19	38
Blues *	18	12	2	4	42	22	35
Rolls Royce	18	9	7	2	38	24	34
Hammer	18	10	2	6	41	27	32
Langleybury O.B.	18	7	1	10	23	52	22
South Ixhey	18	6	3	9	43	48	21
Watford Labour C.	18	6	1	11	31	41	19
Mill End Rangers	18	4	1	13	25	47	13
Croxley Guild of S.	18	1	1	16	20	60	4

* - 3pts deducted.

Lower Division Champions:
Div. 1: Langletbury Cricket Club
Div. 2: Happy Hour
Div. 3: Bedmond Only
Div. 4: Old Parmiterians
Div. 5: Watford Golf Range
Div. 6: Express Communications

STANLEY & DISTRICT

DIVISION ONE

	P	W	D	L	F	A	PTS
Kings Head	22	20	1	1	104	29	62
Duston Utd	22	17	2	3	86	20	53
Murray Park	22	17	1	4	76	27	52
East Stanley	22	13	1	8	69	45	40
Pelton Fell	22	11	5	6	60	48	38
Chopwell	22	7	3	12	53	72	24
Burnhope Ivy	22	7	2	13	46	70	23
Duston Brooms	22	7	2	13	43	73	23
Stanley RAFA	22	5	4	13	51	56	19
Quaking Houses	22	5	3	14	46	90	18
Johns Castle	22	3	6	13	35	80	15
Craghead Soc.	22	2	6	14	39	98	12

Lower Division Champions:
Div. 2: Coach Horses

Cup Winners:
Mooldy Shield: Gateshead Honeysuckle
Richardson Cup: Ouston United
Conroy Cup: Murray Park
G.H.J. Builders Cup: Coach & Horses
Challenge Cup: Murray Park
Bev Haggett Cup: Pelton Fell

Oxford Road Social FC, who are based at Cray Wanderers' Oxford Road ground. Photo - Dave West.

Messrs Slater and Gill appear to be enjoying their visit to Wadham Lodge with Concord Rangers. Photo - Gavin Ellis.

Reading Borough's Pat McCoy takes on Hanham Sunnday's Dave Bayley (stripes). Photo - Dave West.

STEVENAGE & DISTRICT

PREM. DIVISION	P	W	D	L	F	A	PTS
Benington	14	9	3	2	51	24	21
Transpack *	14	8	5	1	52	26	19
Twin Foxes **	14	7	2	5	32	41	18
White Horse	14	6	4	4	45	36	16
Singh Sabha	14	3	5	6	19	24	11
Crooked Billet	14	4	2	8	31	40	10
Dellar Brothers	14	2	5	7	30	52	9
Dynamics	14	2	4	8	23	40	8

* - 2pts deducted.
** - 2pts awarded.

Lower Division Champions:
Div. 1: Pig & Whistle (Stotfold)
Div. 2: The Waggon
Div. 3: Longmeadow Ath. O.B.
Div. 4: J.J. Hunseckers

STOCKPORT & DISTRICT

PREM. DIVISION	P	W	D	L	F	A	PTS
Norris Albion	20	12	6	2	58	26	30
Offerton United	20	12	5	3	63	21	29
Carnforth	20	13	2	5	49	42	28
Hindley Street	20	12	2	6	57	22	26
Rifle Volunteer	20	10	6	4	45	32	26
Mount Villa	20	10	2	8	42	39	22
Medoak	20	9	4	7	48	46	22
Dilke Celtic	20	5	5	10	33	45	15
Bramhall Sunday	20	4	4	12	40	51	12
Adswood United	20	1	3	16	29	74	5
Mile End Albion	20	1	3	16	27	93	5

Lower Division Champions:
Div. 1: Millbrow
Div. 2: Great Moor
Div. 3: Grimond
Div. 4: Fiveways

SUSSEX

PREM. DIVISION	P	W	D	L	F	A	PTS
Snipe	16	14	2	0	59	13	30
Patcham North End	16	8	4	4	32	22	20
Fratsom Rovers	16	7	6	3	35	26	20
Cardinal Newman	16	8	2	6	43	36	18
Hangleton	16	5	4	7	26	37	14
Henfield Mohawks	16	4	4	8	33	43	12
The St.George	16	4	4	8	19	31	12
South Ham United	16	5	1	10	25	31	11
Hove Dynamoes	16	3	1	12	23	56	7

Lower Division Champions:
Int.Div. 1: Preston Dynamos
Int.Div. 2: Bridge Boys
Junior Div. 1: Courthope
Div. 2: Corals
Div. 3: Patcham North End Res.
Div. 4: Admiral Napier Wands.
Div. 5: Red Lion Lindfield Res.
Div. 6: Old Boat Corner.
Div. 7: Windmill Sports
Div. 8: Knoll United
Div. 9: Hangleton Manor
Div. 10: Post Office Sunday
Div. 11: Conway Colts FC
Div. 12: The Coach House Rott.
Div. 13: Worthing Thistle
North Div. 1: Apsley Town
Div. 2: The Ship (Sunday) FC

SUTTON & DISTRICT

PREM. DIVISION	P	W	D	L	F	A	PTS
Queens Park	20	11	8	1	50	26	30
Tile Cross	20	13	3	4	50	35	29
Grimstock Bell	20	13	1	6	63	32	27
Orion	20	8	5	7	51	44	21
Parklands	20	8	3	9	31	36	19
Tame Spts & Soc.	20	7	4	9	36	42	18
Halfway	20	7	3	10	34	38	17
New Anvil Rangers	20	6	5	9	33	51	17
Crown Athletic	20	6	4	10	38	45	16
Springville Whitehorse	20	6	2	12	33	50	15
Crescent	20	3	5	12	28	48	11

Lower Division Champions:
Div. 1: Calthorpe United
Div. 2: St.Mary/St.John Celtic
Div. 3: Aldridge Town

Div. 4: Bella Pais
Div. 5: Coleshill G'Man Res.
Div. 6: Norton Arms

TAUNTON

PREM. DIVISION	P	W	D	L	F	A	PTS
Taunton Rangers	22	20	0	2	91	24	40
Steam Rock	22	18	0	4	90	39	36
Taunton CS	22	14	1	7	64	42	29
Galmington	22	11	4	7	51	37	26
Blackbrook	22	11	1	10	73	61	23
Staplegrove	22	10	3	9	68	62	23
Vivary	22	9	5	8	63	50	23
Rangers 86	22	8	4	10	56	50	20
Bagborough	22	9	1	12	73	70	19
Norton Fitzwarren	22	6	1	15	28	73	13
Kings Royals	22	4	1	17	30	72	9
Alma Spartans	22	1	1	20	19	126	3

TELFORD

PREM. DIVISION	P	W	D	L	F	A	PTS
St.Georges SS	22	15	3	2	69	22	35
Brittania Shakespear	22	14	5	3	49	20	33
Champion Jockey	22	13	3	6	44	37	29
Newport RBL	22	13	2	7	37	19	28
Shifnal Juniors	22	10	3	9	53	42	23
Dun Cow Dynamoes	22	7	9	7	46	53	22
Granville Wood	22	8	5	9	38	46	21
Red Lion Rovers	22	8	3	11	47	49	19
Little Drayton R.	22	7	3	12	42	69	17
Dawley	22	5	4	13	36	57	14
Rose & Crown S.	22	4	4	14	27	48	12
Brossley Rangers	22	3	5	14	31	57	11

Lower Division Champions:
Div. 1: Shif. WM A
Div. 2: Boseley L.
Div. 3: Bird in Hand
Div. 4: Shrews A.
Div. 5: Stormy P
Div. 6: White H U
Div. 7: Bairdwear

THAMES VALLEY

PREM. DIVISION	P	W	D	L	F	A	PTS
Cookham Dean *	18	11	3	4	46	26	39
Farnham Royal M.C	18	11	2	5	46	23	35
Willow Tree	18	10	3	5	40	35	33
South Bucks G.	18	9	4	5	43	23	31
Iver Sports & Social	18	10	4	4	37	18	31
George	18	9	4	5	46	41	31
Jolly Londoner	18	10	0	8	48	27	30
Cippenham Sports	18	6	3	9	48	40	21
Moormede Ramblers	18	2	1	15	25	58	7
Cippenham W.M.C.	18	0	0	18	19	107	0

Foresters (Cox Green), Foresters (Farnham Common)
and Windsor Ex. Services all withdrew from the league.
* - 3pts awarded.
** - 3pts deducted.

Lower Division Champions:
Div. 1: Madigans
Div. 2: S.N.C. F.C.
Div. 3: Proctor & Gamble
Div. 4: Ashby Albion
Div. 5: Rising Sun (Datchet)
Div. 6: Stoke Lions
Div. 7: Brickmakers Arms

AUTOTYPE UPPER THAMES VALLEY

DIVISION ONE	P	W	D	L	F	A	PTS
Hanney R.B.L.	20	18	2	0	88	19	38
The Taverners	20	14	2	4	79	17	30
Five Bells	20	14	2	4	77	35	30
Rutherford Lab.	20	13	3	4	47	21	29
Crown Abingdon	20	11	2	7	57	40	24
East Hendred	20	9	3	8	55	52	21
Athletico Indal"ne	20	6	4	10	41	53	16
Oxford Exiles	20	5	3	12	34	53	13
Uffington Sports	20	3	2	15	22	76	8
A.C.Neilsons	20	3	0	17	32	87	6
Standlake Garage	20	2	1	17	33	114	5

Lower Division Champions:
Div. 2: Drayton
Div. 3: Air Balloon
Div. 4: Didcot Casuals

St Josephs (Luton). Back Row (L/R): Robbie Walsh (Asst Manager), Boyd Skeggs, Richard Priestley, Kirk Standaloft, Anthony McNally, Steve Hunt, Noel Blackwell, John Alder (Manager). Front: Darren Lelliott, Peter Doyle, Sandor Gyalog, Richard Camp, Joe Smith, Pat Walsh, John Darby. Photo - Dave West.

Robbie Singfield of St Josephs heads over, but his team still beat Stag Sports 6-1 in the Bedforshire F.A. Sunday Cup final. Photo - Paul Dennis.

A3's Arthur Dawe launches himself into a diving header, and is unlucky to hit the post. A3 beat Merseyside rivals Eagle-Knowsley 2-1 in this F.A. Sunday Cup tie on 19th January. Photo - Rob Ruddock.

VANGE & DISTRICT

PREM. DIVISION	P	W	D	L	F	A	PTS
C Z 81	18	10	6	2	51	35	36
Winston	18	9	6	3	55	33	33
Greeves	18	9	5	4	43	32	32
Rettendon Ath.	18	9	4	5	46	24	31
Scotia	18	7	6	5	35	30	27
East Tilbury D.	18	7	5	6	45	26	26
North Ockendon	18	7	1	10	45	45	22
Rackets	18	4	7	7	48	38	19
Kent View	18	5	3	10	49	63	18
Beech United	18	0	3	15	15	106	3

Lower Division Champions:
Div. 1: Crouch Nomads
Div. 2: Wickford Dynamoes
Div. 3: Dickens

MERCURY WALTHAM

PREM. DIVISION	P	W	D	L	F	A	PTS
Pengelly	16	12	2	2	52	21	38
Ordance	16	12	1	3	40	21	37
Enfield Royals	16	1	1	5	35	19	21
Newgate Street	16	7	1	8	26	36	22
Abbey	16	5	4	7	29	28	19
Somersett Ambury	16	6	1	9	28	34	19
J.B's	16	5	3	8	30	32	18
Cheshunt Rangers	16	5	3	8	29	33	18
Valencia	16	1	2	13	14	58	5

Lower Division Champions:
Div. 1: Bensons
Div. 2: Northmet Res.
Div. 3: Gladiators
Div. 4: Enfield Supporters
Div. 5: Hollistar
Div. 6: Old Bulls Head
Div. 7: Old Highway
Div. 8: Sparton Rangers

GOBOWEN CELTIC

DIVISION ONE	P	W	D	L	F	A	PTS
Gobowen Celtic	20	17	1	2	137	24	35
Trefonen	20	16	3	1	106	31	35
Hawkstone Arms	20	15	1	4	87	24	31
Oswestry Bell	20	14	1	5	74	36	29
Westin Rhyn Colts	20	10	2	8	77	51	22
Bulls Head	20	8	1	11	53	69	17
Welshamp	20	6	4	10	44	51	16
Banks 88	20	7	2	11	44	62	16
R Park Sts	20	4	3	13	31	107	11
Old Vlts	20	3	0	17	40	127	5
Greyhound	20	1	0	19	23	134	2

Lower Division Champions:
Div. 2: Osw Bell R.

WEST FULHAM

PREM. DIVISION	P	W	D	L	F	A	PTS
Tooting BEC	14	8	4	2	39	27	20
Light Source	14	6	6	2	31	21	18
Deborah	14	6	5	3	25	17	17
Maltese Cat	14	8	1	5	23	31	17
Hammersmith	14	5	4	5	31	27	14
Holderness Utd	14	6	1	7	23	24	13
Barnes Albion	14	4	2	8	23	30	10
Dauntless Ath.	14	1	1	12	20	38	3

Lower Division Champions:
Intermediate: Mortlake
Div. 1: Horseferry
Div. 2: Heidelberg GN
Div. 3: Whitton Alb Res
Div. 4: Barnes Alb Res
Div. 5: Teddington Rgrs

WEYMOUTH

PREM. DIVISION	P	W	D	L	F	A	PTS
Chapelhay	14	9	3	2	47	31	21
Moorings	14	9	1	4	44	16	19
Duke of Albany	14	8	1	5	35	28	17
Market House	14	5	4	5	32	30	14
Mariners	14	6	2	6	40	42	14
Rock	14	5	2	7	32	39	12
Globe	14	3	4	7	20	34	10
Park	14	1	3	10	20	58	5

Lower Division Champions:
Div. 1: Royal Exchange

WHARFEDALE

PREM. DIVISION	P	W	D	L	F	A	PTS
Silsden AFC	14	10	2	2	53	28	32
Druids Arms	14	10	2	2	35	18	32
Wrose Albion	14	8	4	2	42	27	28
Keighley Shamrocks	14	7	1	6	23	25	22
Owlet Hall	14	4	3	7	36	40	15
Whitakers Arms	14	4	2	8	30	39	14
Horsforth C.C.C.	14	3	2	9	24	32	11
Sandy Lane	14	1	2	11	15	49	5

WHARFEDALE TRIANGLE

PREM. DIVISION	P	W	D	L	F	A	PTS
Airedale Magnet	18	15	1	2	82	19	46
Star Athletic	18	12	2	4	74	35	38
Wrose Bull	18	12	0	6	59	34	36
Regent Victoria	18	11	2	5	45	20	35
Keighley Star	18	11	1	6	67	37	34
Silsden Town	18	8	3	7	46	37	27
Tarn Rangers	18	8	1	9	49	54	25
FC Clothiers	18	4	1	13	31	48	13
Yeadon Westfield	18	3	1	14	20	74	10
Hawkhill	18	0	0	18	8	123	0

WOLVERHAMPTON & DISTRICT

PREM. DIVISION	P	W	D	L	F	A	PTS
Wednesfield Alb.	18	18	0	0	92	17	36
Marston Sports	18	10	5	3	58	30	25
W'Ton Retail Market	18	9	4	5	58	26	22
Penn Old Boys	18	10	2	6	43	27	22
Picasso's	18	6	6	6	41	35	18
W'Ton Electricity	18	7	4	7	37	34	18
Pendeford Dovecote	18	5	5	8	31	32	15
Dan O'Connell	18	5	4	9	35	39	14
Harrows	18	3	3	12	30	65	9
Heath Town W.M.C.	18	0	1	17	13	133	1

Lower Division Champions:
Div. 1: Essington St.Johns
Div. 2: Rovers Sports
Div. 3: E.C.C. Transport
Div. 4: Bilston Comm College
Div. 5: Briton Lions
Div. 6: Codsall Crown
Div. 7: Tettenhall Club & Inst.
Div. 8: Heath Town Old Boys
Div. 9: Bagot Wolves

YEOVIL & DISTRICT

DIVISION ONE	P	W	D	L	F	A	PTS
Royal Oak R.	18	14	2	2	79	25	30
Sun Inn	18	13	3	2	89	34	29
Hornets	18	9	3	6	47	48	21
Bradford Sports	18	9	2	7	68	48	20
Westfield Wanderers	18	7	4	7	46	67	18
Brewers Arms	18	7	3	8	60	49	17
Foresters Arms	18	6	1	11	41	56	13
Saracens *	18	6	2	10	41	70	12
Tintnull Forts	18	5	2	11	35	68	12
Barwick & Stofold S.	18	2	2	14	30	71	5

Lower Division Champions:
Div. 2: Royal Oak Rangers Res.
Div. 3: Cathedral Stone
Div. 4: Catnic

Cup Winners:
Dennis Lowe Memorial Cup: Crewkerne Sports
Jon Russell Cup: Crewkerne Sports
Div. 1 Cup: Bradford Sports
Div. 2 Cup: PLS Canaries
Div. 3 Cup: Muntacute W.M.C.
Div. 4 Cup: Crewkerne Sports

North London side Edmonton Rovers. Back Row (L/R): Laurence Hughes, Demitrius Nurse, Gary Southam, Conor McGovern, Russell Mitchell, Kini Ndoko, Stafford Dyer, Kieran McGregor, Trevor Hughes. Centre: Tim Beeden (Asst Secretary), Giuseppe Sarno, Steve Platt, Paul Rebairo, Steve Lewis, Chris Beeden, Steve Beasley, John Dyer. Front: Kevin Young, Mark Howley, Russell Beeden, Francesco Apicella, Aaron Dart, Terry Clark, Lee Finch.

Marston Sports, Runners-up in the Wolverhampton & District Sunday League and the F.A. Sunday Cup. Photo - Eric Marsh.

Ranelagh Sports. Back Row (L/R): P Meredith, S Ward, J Gray, S Shosanya, B Allerdyce, J Egan, W Falana, Front: D Coppin, W Kerrings, C Gartell, C Burck, A Fisher. Photo - Dave West.

Leeming Bar, of the John Smiths Hambleton Sunday Combinatiom (North Yorkshire). Photo - Dave West.

Turf Hotel, of the John Smiths Hambleton Sunday Combinatiom (North Yorkshire). Photo - Dave West.

Roundshaw & District C.A., Surrey Sunday Lower Junior Cup finalists. Photo - Mike Wilson.

Stoke Spartak, Guildford Sunday League winners 1991-92. Photo - Eric Marsh.

B.R. Guildford, Surrey Sunday Cup finalists 1991-92. Photo - Eric Marsh.

Crunching edge-of-the-area action as Collier Row Supporters take on Brookvale Athletic. Photo - Gavin Ellis.

English Schools' Football Association 1991-92

Chief Executive: M R Berry, 4a, Eastgate Street, Stafford St 16 2NQ (0742) 51142

Contributor to Non-League Directory: Mike Simmonds, 19, The Sinney, Bulcote, Burton Joyce, Nottingham NG14 5GX (0602) 313299

The International Season

Pride of place for 1991-92 must go to the Under 18 squad who remained unbeaten in their four matches, including games against the full youth international sides of Holland and Switzerland. Indeed, England recorded their first ever success against Holland with a pulsating second half performance culminating in two goals in the last ten minutes from Alex Sykes and Stephen White. Team Manager, Peter Amos, might class this as one of the most successful substitution decisions of all time as both players did not start the match.

England	2 - 1	Holland	Leicester (Sykes, White)
Wales	1 - 2	England	Cwmbran (Whitmarsh (2))
England	2 - 1	Eire	Yeovil (Johnson, McIntyre)
Switzerland	2 - 2	England	Entlebuch (McIntyre (2))

The games against Wales and Switzerland were in the Centenary Shield which was shared by Switzerland and England, thanks to the latter's fine recovery from a 2-0 half-time deficit with centre back, Ian McIntyre scoring twice in the last eighteen minutes.

England Under 18 Squad 1990-91

Back Row (L-R): Mr. P.Amos (Team Manager), Stephen White, David Johnson, Matthew Lawrence, Jonathan Guppy, Ian McIntyre, Alex Sykes, Dominic Ludden, Mr F.Melia (Physio), Mr P.Brackwell (Assistant Team Manager). Front Row: Paul Terry, Steven Brown, Steven Walker, Neil Hopper, Mr R.L.Eccles (ESFA Chairman), Kevin Pilkington, Simon Butterfield, Andrew Mitchell and Simon Bates. Photo: Peter Rogers (Stafford) Ltd.

Under 18 Appearances

		Holland	Wales	Eire	Switzerland
1	Neil Hooper	1		1	
2	Kevin Pilkington		1		
3	Steven Brown	1	1(c)	1	1
4	Dominic Ludden	1	1	1	1
5	Simon Butterfield	1	1	1	1
6	Ian McIntyre	1(c)		1(c)	1
7	Simon Bates	1	1	1	1
8	Stephen White	S	1	S	1
8	Paul Terry	1		1	
9	Andrew Mitchell	1	1	S	S
10	Jonathan Guppy	S	1	1	
11	Alex Sykes	S	1	S	1
12	Steven Walker	1	S	S	1
13	Paul Whitmarsh	1	1	1	1
14	Matthew Lawrence	1	1	1	1
15	David Johnson	S	S	1	S
16	Adrian Clewlow				1

Key: 1 = Played; S = Substitute

Scorers: McIntyre (3), Whitmarsh (2), Johnson, Sykes, White.

England Schools' Under 15

Although 1991-92 was not an outstanding season for the Under 15 international squad, there can be no doubting the fighting spirit of the sixteen boys who represented England Schools throughout their eight match programme.

Five times in those eight games, they found themselves trailing, but only once did they fail to come back, that in the 4-1 defeat by Germany in Magdeburg. This was the first time an England Schools' team had played in the former East Germany and the defeat, the only one during the season, was no doubt partly a reaction to a magnificent display two days earlier in the Olympic Stadium in Berlin.

In that match, England found themselves behind to a Rottger goal for Germany but the 60,000 crowd certainly admired England's character which was rewarded by Albert Clarke's equaliser.

Against Wales, Clarke equalised in the last minute to gain a vital draw; in France, the team pulled back a 2-0 deficit with goals from Daniel Murphy and Ian Brunskill and in the show-piece finale to the season, it was Steven Goodridge whose late effort prevented Italy's first ever win at this level over England at Wembley.

The 1-0 win over Scotland at Ibrox was the crucial result which brought England the Victory Shield, the home international championship which still survives at Schoolboy level.

Dutch and English players dispute possession in the 0-0 draw between the two countries at Wembley Stadium in March.

Under 15 Results

England	2 - 2	Wales	Burnley (Neville, Clarke)
England	0 - 0	Holland	Wembley Stadium
England	3 - 0	N.Ireland	Brighton (Howell 2, Murphy)
Scotland	0 - 1	England	Ibrox (Neville)
France	2 - 2	England	Laon (Brunskill, Murphy)
Germany	1 - 1	England	Berlin (Clarke)
Germany	4 - 1	England	Magdeburg (Murphy)
England	1 - 1	Italy	Wembley Stadium (Goodridge)

THE VICTORY SHIELD

	P	W	D	L	F	A	Pts
England	3	2	1	0	6	2	5
Wales	3	1	2	0	4	3	4
Scotland	3	1	1	1	5	5	3
N.Ireland	3	0	0	3	3	8	0

UNDER 15 APPEARANCES

	Wales	Holland	N.Ire.	Scot.	France	Germany	Germany	Italy
Neil Cutler	1	1		1	1	1		1
Eric Collins			1				1	
Ian Smith	1	1		S	1		S	S
Iain Brunskill	1	1	1	1	1	1	1	1
Philip Neville	1	1	1	1	1	1	1	1
Ross Taylor	1	1		1	1	1	S	1
Michael Black	1	1	S				1	1
Jamie Howell (C)	1	1	1	1	1	1	1	1
Stephen Hughes	1	1	1	1	1	1	1	1
David Beresford	1	1		S	1	1	1	1
Daniel Murphy	1	1	1	1	1	1	S	1
Albert Clarke	S	S	1	1	1	1	1	S
Steven Goodridge		1	1	1	1		S	S
Graeme Power		S	1				1	1
Stephen Blaney		1	1			1	1	1

Key: 1 = Played; S = Playing substitute; C = Captain

Goalscorers: Murphy (3), Clarke, Howell, Neville (2), Brunskill, Goodridge

England Under 15 Squad. Back Row (L-R): Mike Dickinson (Physio), Philip Neville, Daniel Murphy, Eric Collins, Steve Avory (Team Manager), Neil Cutler, Graeme Power, Stephen Hughes, Ian Brunskill, Phil Naroello (Assistant Team Manager). Front Row: Clinton Ellis, Ian Smith, David Beresford, Steven Goodridge, Ron Eccles (Chairman, E.S.F.A.), Ross Taylor, Michael Black, Jamie Howell, Albert Clarke. Photo: Corporate Images.

The English Schools' F.A. British Gas Trophy 1991-92

First Leg	**Second Leg**
28th April, Elland Road	7th May, Brammall Lane
Leeds 1 - 0 Sheffield	Sheffield 0 - 1 Leeds

Leeds won 2-0 on aggregate

The first year of the British Gas sponsorship of the English Schools' F.A.'s premier competition produced the most disappointing final for many years but not, of course, for Leeds who recored their first ever success in the 97th year of their history.

Sheffield, appearing in their fourth final in a decade, started favourites and in the first 19 minutes looked to be living up to status. Then Leeds unexpectedly took the lead when a header from Howard Smith was not cleared and Scott Jackson was on hand to tap in an easy goal.

This changed the course of the game and although the score remained the same, it was Leeds who came closest to taking a more substantial lead in to the second leg. Scott Jackson, in space, and with only the keeper to beat, hit the advancing Paul Gibson while Leeds went even closer when Sheffield's out-standing player, Richard Naylor nearly headed an own goal.

There was little incident of note during the second leg of this all-Yorkshire affair, particularly during the first half which did not penetrate the memory, let alone remain there.

In the second period, it was the same combination who gave Leeds their first leg win who again combined to ensure that the schools' side joined their professional colleagues in winning a prestigious trophy. The awkward looking Howard Smith set off on a long run down the right which took him clear of the Sheffield defence and his perfectly weighted square pass was met by Scott Jackson who picked his spot.

The same players were involved in most of the memorable incidents, the best of which was Paul Gibson's stunning save after Jackson had again run on to a Smith cross. Smith also had a shot headed off the line by Brett Storey and although Sheffield showed their traditional steel, theirs was a forlorn hope as Leeds deservedly became the first holders of the British Gas Trophy.

Leed's route to the final			**Sheffield's route to the final**		
Round 1	Calderdale	(A) 7-0	Round 1	Harrogate & C.	(A) 10-3
Round 2	York	(H) 4-1	Round 2	Bradford	(A) 3-0
Round 3	North Tyneside	(H) 4-1	Round 3	Chester-le-Street	(A) 3-0
Round 4	Langbaurgh	(H) 3-1	Round 4	Chorley	(H) 7-0
Round 5	Chester	(H) 3-2	Round 5	Barnsley	(H) 2-0
Round 6	Leicester	(A) 2-0	Round 6	Southampton	(A) 4-2
S-Final	Reading	(H) 1-0	S-Final	Bolton	(H) 3-0

Leeds Schools' British Gas Trophy winners 1991-92

Back Row (L-R): Graham Thornton (Team Manager), D.Wade (Hon.Secretary), M.Britton, S.Wooford, H.Smith, P.Kirby, M.Arnot, D.Dunphy, R.Naylor, S.Wright, C.Gilmore, Mr J.Quinn (Assistant Team Manager).
Front Row: P.Singh, C.Walker, P.O'Brien, G.Morin, R.L.Eccles (Chairman, E.S.F.A.), M.Healey (Chairman, Leeds S.F.A.), R.Ward, B.Hird, S.Jackson, S.Portrey. Photo: Mark Rogers.

Leeds captain receives the English Schools' British Gas Trophy from the Chairman of E.S.F.A. Ron Eccles and a representative of British Gas. Photo: Mark Rogers.

Sheffield Schools' British Gas Trophy 1991-92 runners-up

Back Row (L-R): I.H.Rogers (Hon.Secretary), L.Beckett, R.Cadet, B.Cheetham, K.Davies, A.Sollitt, P.Gibson, D.Wright, B.Storey, R.Fidler, C.Ludlam, Mr M.Fidler, Mr D.Johnson.
Front Row: L.Dale, A.Thorpe, R.Davenport, R.L.Eccles (Chairman, E.S.F.A.), Mr J.A.Wilkinson (Sheffield S.F.A. Chairman), B.Dey, R.Stephenson, D.Vine. Photo: Mark Rogers.

The English Schools' F.A.
Individual Schools' Competitions

These competitions entered by over 10,000 schools and colleges, plus hundreds of others at county and local level, provide the 'grass roots' football for an estimated 250,000 players involved in E.S.F.A. activities throughout the season.

E.S.F.A/Barclays Bank U19 Championship

Final

High Pavement College (Notts)   1-0   **John Hampden School (Bucks)**

(Michael Rock (og))

Played at Field Mill, Mansfield Town F.C. May 13th, 1992

An own goal by the unfortunate Michael Rock gave High Pavement their victory in a most exciting final which John Hampden will have been disappointed to lose after missing a succession of good chances. High Pavement's defensive display in the second period, highlighted by Paul Wilson's fine keeping, brought them the Trophy, the last to be played under the Barclays' sponsorship.

Route to the Final

High Pavement College			John Hampden School		
Queen Elizabeths School (Derby)	(H)	5-1	Bye		
Parsons Cross School (S.Yorks)	(A)	2-1	Burford School (Oxfordshire)	(H)	2-0
Barnsley College (S.Yorks)	(H)	1-0	Worcester College (H'ford & Worcs)		1-1, 1-0
St.Cuthberts High School (N.h'land)	(H)	3-0	Taunton's College (Hampshire)	(H)	5-0
Winstanley College (G.Manc)		1-0 (aet)	Southend Highschool	(A)	2-1

High Pavement College Winners of the E.S.F.A/Barclays Bank Under 19 Championship
Back Row (L-R): Graham Castle (Team Manager), B.Sole, A.Miller, P.Davis, R.Derry, C.Cooper, P.Wilson, P.Litchfield, D.Brady, A.Llewellyn, D.Balaguero, Dale Corocran (Assistant Team Manager).
Front Row: G.Cook, A.Wilson, D.Batey, N.Whitehurst, P.Dracott, R.Walmsley, M.Smith, D.Bridgett. Photo: J.Shorland.

E.S.F.A/Diamik Under 16 Individual Schools' Championship

Final

Torquay Boys' Grammar School   2-0   **De La Salle School, Liverpool**

(Devon)   (Merseyside)

Played at Plainmoor, Torquay United F.C. May 4th, 1992

In an unprecedented achievement, holders, De La Salle School reached the final of this competition for the second year running but this time found their opponents too strong. Torquay Grammar School, after a nervous start, fulfilled their potential after the interval with Robert Waldron heading in a corner from James Oliver and then adding a second with another header, this time from Simon Alston. Coincidentally, the two schools met in the 1984 Under 19 final with Torquay winning on that occasion 4-0.

Squads
Torquay Grammar: Jon Purdy, Matthew Armitage, Craig Radford, Stephen Corline, Robert Waldron, James Oliver, Mark Evans, Mark Brudenell, Nicholas Edwards, Simon Alston, Ian Chalk, Carl Edwards, Andy Larmour, James Harkin, Leigh Kayley, Matthew Wise, Gareth Brocklehurst.

De La Salle School: Benn Lang, Simon Bovill, Stephen Farrell, Ian McGarhon, Russell Burke, Lee Chiocchi, Francis Tierney, Matthew Carragher, John Geraghty, Joseph Donnelly, Vincent O'Brien, Danny Fenny, Chris Richards, Stephen McArther.

Paul Wilson of High Pavement College stretches to gather the ball from John Hampden's Michael Rock. Graham Cook looks in danger sandwiched between them. Photo: Bucks Free Press.

E.S.F.A. Smiths Crisps 6-A-Side Championship

The four sides which met at Wembley Stadium on June 6th in the Semi-Finals, third place play-off and final of the Smiths Championship were the survivors from over 8,000 teams at Under 11 level who set out on the road to Wembley in September.

Final: Inglewood Junior School (Carlisle) 2 - 0 Ixworth Middle School (Bury St.Edmunds)

Third Place play-off: Harmans Water School 3 - 2 Meadowhall Junior School

The County Championship

E.S.F.A/Adidas Under 19 Championship

Merseyside 2 - 0 Cornwall
Played at Anfield, Liverpool. Saturday, May 2nd, 1992

Cornwall were making their first ever appearance in an English Schools' final and the occassion plus the venue seemed slightly to overawe the West Country side. Although fully commited throughout the eighty minutes, Cornwall were rarely dangerous and with the home side controlling the midfield, goals always looked likely.

That it took until five minutes before the interval was a credit to Cornwall's determination. A fine run and cross from Mike Riley saw captain Jake Collin put Merseyside ahead with a close range header.

Throughout the second half, Merseyside remained in command but, as in the first period, missed several good chances. It was not until five minutes from the end that a well taken individual goal by Robert Povey made the score more representative of the game.

Routes to the Final

Merseyside			Cornwall		
G.Manchester	(A)	1-2	H'ford & Worcs.	(A)	1-0
Cheshire	(H)	4-1	Devon	(A)	1-0
Lancashire	(H)	1-0	Hampshire	(H)	4-1
Warwickshire	(H)	1-0	**Semi-Final:** Essex	(H)	2-1
Shropshire	(H)	3-1			
S.Yorkshire	(A)	3-2			
Semi-Final: Nottinghamshire	(A)	2-0			

The Squad		The Squad	
A Warner	(Sir Francis Xaviers)	M Gue	(Saltash)
M McDonald	(Cardinal Heenan)	D Sweet	(Duchy College of F.E.)
M Atkinson	(St.Mary's)	N Hartigan	(Newquay Tretherras)
S Carberry	(De La Salle)	N Richards	(St.Austell SFC)
M Reynods	(Sir Francis Xaviers)	L Rushby	(Penwith SFC)
G Connor	(De La Salle)	K Rule	(Camborne)
T Meekin	(St.Wilfrid's)	N Crawford	(Saltash College of F.E.)
J Collin	(Cardinal Heenan)	N Trudgen	(Truro VIth form College)
M Riley	(Knowlsley Tech.College)	S Hore	(St.Austell SFC)
M Lyons	(Millbrook College)	C Twiddy	(Mullion)
R Povey	(Bluecoat)	R Tongue	(Camborne Tech)
P Wilde	(De La Salle)	S Firth	(Callington Community)
N Williams	(De La Salle)	D Clatworth	(Saltash)
L Nolan	(Hugh Baird)	M George	(Penwith S.F.C)
S Bailey	(New Heys)		
S Brough	(St.Wilfrird's)		
L Burgess	(Savio High)		
N Mathieson	(Birkenhead SFC)		
Team Manager	(Tony Brookman)		

E.S.F.A/Adidas Under 16 Championship

Essex 0 - 2 Cheshire
Played at Roots Hall, Southend November 11th, 1991

Cheshire deservedly won their first national title upsetting the odds by defeating Essex 2-0. After some desultory early play, the deadlock was broken in the 28th minute. Essex attempted to defend in numbers at a Cheshire free-kick but two successive mistakes allowed Shaun Fraser to put the visitors ahead.

The goal that confirmed Cheshire's victory was worthy of any final. The Cheshire strikers always looked to have the pace to trouble the Essex back-four and Matthew Nicholls' strong run ended with a perfect cross enabling Mark Rivers to sell a 'dummy' to Rainbow in the Essex goal and slot the ball home.

The Teams

Essex

J Rainbow	Thurrock
R Bird	Barking & Dagenham
J Bates	Havering
D.Scott	Barking & Dagenham
L Townley	Harlow & West Essex
S Woollard	Havering
D Stone	Chelmsford
R Lawrence	Colchester
V Carbon	Barking & Dagenham
K Skinner	Newham
Wai Kit Ho	Chelmsford

Subs:

M Peat	Waltham Forest
C Taylor	Colchester
G Wedlock	N.W.Essex

Cheshire

D Turner	Halton
L Byrne	Warrington
L Millington	Halton
M McDonnell	Warrington
S Iddon	Halton
J Rogers	Halton
A Brown	South Cheshire
W Antrobus	Warrington
M Rivers	South Cheshire
M Nicholls	South Cheshire
S Fraser	Halton

Sub:

C Hancox	Mid Cheshire
M Rigby	Halton
P Lagar	Warrington
S Carter	Chester
L Hughes	Warrington
D Murphy	Chester
D Hawtin	South Cheshire

The English Schools' Festivals of Football

Easter Festivals of Football are a growth area of the English Schools' F.A.'s programme and this year over 2500 players were at six venues. No Cups or Trophies are on offer, just the enjoyment of meeting new faces and making new fiends. The E.S.F.A./Gillette Under 19 Festival, now in its 28th year was the forerunner of a successful formula which has spread to Jersey, North Tynside, the Isle of Wight, Durham and Lowestoft. The Morecambe Under 19 event and the Isle of Wight Under 14 Festival are organised directly by the Council of the English Schools' F.A., the others by Local and County Associations and the Individual Schools' event by the E.S.F.A. in association with Pontins.

Under 19 Playing Records

	P	W	D	L	F	A			P	W	D	L	F	A
Independent Sch.	5	2	2	1	7	8		Derbyshire B	5	2	1	2	7	4
Donegal	5	1	0	4	6	12		Lincolnshire A	5	3	0	2	5	6
USA (East)	5	1	1	3	6	10		Lincolbshire B	5	0	1	4	4	18
USA (North)	5	2	0	3	10	9		Hunberside A	5	4	0	1	8	4
Northumberland A	5	1	2	2	7	6		Humberside B	5	2	0	3	10	15
Northumberland B	5	1	1	3	6	8		Hertfordshire	4	2	1	1	9	5
Cumbria	5	3	1	1	15	7		Essex A	5	2	2	1	13	12
Durham	5	1	0	4	5	12		Essex B	5	2	1	2	10	11
North Yorkshire	5	0	1	4	2	15		Middlesex	5	4	1	0	12	4
South Yorkshire	5	3	1	1	17	7		Kent A	5	1	2	2	5	14
West Yorkshire	5	2	0	3	7	7		Kent B	5	2	1	2	8	12
Isle of Man	5	3	2	0	12	6		Kent C	5	3	1	1	11	8
Cheshire	5	1	1	3	5	11		Inner London	5	3	1	1	14	9
Lancashire	5	3	1	1	16	9		Avon	5	0	1	4	6	11
Merseyside A	5	2	3	0	8	6		Cornwall	4	1	2	1	7	6
Merseyside B	5	2	1	2	9	4		Hampshire A	5	3	0	2	10	5
G.Manchester	5	4	1	0	16	5		Hampshire B	5	4	0	1	16	4
Shropshire A	5	4	0	1	11	6		Dorset	5	3	0	2	12	7
Shropshire B	5	0	2	3	8	16		Somerset A	5	1	0	4	4	10
Warwickshire	5	4	1	0	9	4		Somerset B	5	3	1	1	10	6
Derbyshire A	5	2	1	2	12	8		Hereford & Worcs	5	0	0	5	9	27

THE CAPITAL LEAGUE

Hon. Secretary: P B Braxton, Vicarage Road Stadium,
Watford, Herts WD1 8WR. Tel: 081 866 7959 (B: 0923 212916, FAX 0923 212916).

	P	W	D	L	F	A	PTS
Cambridge United	22	16	4	2	59	23	52
Barnet	22	15	4	3	70	29	49
Wycombe Wdrs	22	12	3	7	45	28	39
Southend United	22	11	2	9	43	29	35
Leyton Orient	22	11	1	10	54	41	34
Crystal Palace	22	9	3	10	33	30	30
Brenrford	22	8	5	9	32	31	29
Sutton United	22	9	2	11	28	33	29
Wealdstone	22	5	9	8	35	50	24
Colchester United	22	7	3	12	25	48	24
Wokingham Town	22	5	3	14	24	66	18
Slough Town	22	3	3	16	29	66	12

* - Aldershot's playing record expunged.

Proposed 92-93 Constitution
Barnet
Brentford
Cambridge United
Crystal Palace
Farnborough Town
Gillingham
Leyton Orient
Reading
Southend United
Sutton United
Wealdstone
Wokingham Town
Wycombe Wanderers

HOME TEAM		1	2	3	4	5	6	7	8	9	10	11	12
1.	Barnet	*	0-2	1-0	2-2	3-1	3-2	2-2	2-1	2-0	5-0	9-0	2-3
2.	Brentford	1-3	*	0-2	0-1	4-2	0-2	1-1	2-0	1-1	1-1	3-2	1-1
3.	Cambridge Utd	2-2	4-1	*	2-0	3-2	2-1	5-1	2-0	2-1	2-2	6-0	1-0
4.	Colchester Utd	1-3	2-1	3-3	*	0-3	0-2	1-0	3-2	2-1	2-2	2-0	0-5
5.	Crystal Palace	0-1	2-0	1-1	1-0	*	1-0	2-3	2-3	3-3	0-0	5-0	0-1
6.	Leyton Orient	1-2	1-0	1-4	3-2	3-1	*	3-5	1-0	7-0	3-4	4-0	4-3
7.	Slough Town	0-7	0-3	1-3	1-3	0-1	2-3	*	0-2	3-1	1-3	3-7	1-3
8.	Southend United	3-3	2-1	0-2	5-0	0-2	4-3	3-0	*	2-0	2-2	0-2	3-0
9.	Sutton United	2-3	0-1	1-2	1-0	0-1	3-0	5-0	1-0	*	2-0	2-1	1-0
10.	Wealdstone	2-5	3-6	1-4	2-0	3-0	2-2	2-2	1-4	3-1	*	0-2	0-4
11.	Wokingham Town	1-8	0-0	0-3	3-1	1-3	0-6	3-2	0-4	0-1	1-1	*	1-1
12.	Wycombe Wdrs	3-2	1-3	4-1	6-0	1-0	3-2	3-1	0-3	0-1	1-1	2-0	*

PRESIDENT'S CUP 1991-92

First Round
Wokingham Town v Slough Town   5-2   Colchester Utd v Wycombe Wdrs   0-1
Brentford v Southend Utd   2-2*(aet, Brentford won 9-8 on pens)*
Sutton Utd v Leyton Orient   5-2   Aldershot v Cambridge United   2-1
Byes: Barnet, Wealdstone, Crystal Palace.

Second Round
Wokingham v Brentford   3-3 *(aet, Brentford won 7-6 on pens)*
Wycombe Wdrs v Crystal Palace   2-3 *(aet; 2-2 after 90 mins)*
Barnet v Aldershot   10-1   Wealdstone v Sutton Utd   1-2

Semi Finals
Barnet v Sutton United   5-1   Crystal Palace v Brentford   1-2

Final
Barnet v Brentford   3-4

Barnet scorers: Mick Bodley 36, Frank Murphy 65, 68(pen)
Brentford scorers: Tony Sealy 42, Paul Buckle 55, Robert Peters 74(pen), Lee Luscombe 89.
Attendance: 507

CAPITAL LEAGUE EIGHT YEAR RECORD (SINCE FORMATION)

	84/5	85/6	86/7	87/8	88/9	89/0	90/1	91/2
Aldershot	-	-	-	-	-	8	7	w/d
Aylesbury United	-	-	-	-	13	-	-	-
Barnet	6	10	6	9	1	5	6	2
Brentford	2	9	-	1	3	3	3	7
Cambridge United	-	-	-	-	4	4	2	1
Colchester United	-	-	-	-	6	6	5	10
Crystal Palace	-	-	-	-	-	-	-	6
Dagenham	3	4	2	8	-	-	-	-
Enfield	4	3	7	10	10	9	w/d	-
Gillingham	7	1	3	6	8	7	-	-
Leyton Orient	8	5	9	3	2	2	4	5
Slough Town	-	-	-	-	-	-	10	12
Southend United	-	8	8	-	5	1	1	4
Sutton United	-	-	-	-	-	-	12	8
Wealdstone	1	2	1	5	7	13	9	9
Welling United	-	-	-	7	11	12	-	-
Wimbledon	5	7	5	4	-	-	-	-
Wokingham Town	-	-	-	-	12	11	8	11
Wycombe Wanderers	-	6	4	2	9	10	11	3
No. of clubs	8	10	9	10	13	13	*13	+13

* - Enfield withdrew after 1 game   + - Aldershot folded in mid-season

Potters Bar Crusaders FC - Campri Leisurewear South Midlands League. Photo - Eric Marsh.

Anstey Nomads FC - Leicestershire Senior League, Coalville Charity Cup winners 1991-92. Back Row (L/R - players' names only): John Metcalf, Bud Roberts, Paul Easom, Drew Wardle, Mark Poulton, Andy Whitehead, Phil Ford. Front: Mark Lint, Daryl Warren, Dave Tansley, Dean Culpin, Darren Warne, Mark Hill, Neil Deeping. Photo - Derrick Kinsey.

SUBURBAN FOOTBALL LEAGUE

Hon. Secretary: M J Bidmead
55 Grange Road, Chessington, Surrey KT9 1EZ. (081-397 4834)

FINAL LEAGUE TABLES 1991-92

SOUTH DIVISION	P	W	D	L	F	A	Pts	League & Cups Leading Scorer	
Sutton United	34	24	4	6	119	35	76	Seagroat	19
Tooting & Mitcham	34	24	3	7	93	42	74	Falana	14
Carshalton Athletic	34	19	6	9	71	43	63	Brown/Gass	13
Bromley	34	18	8	8	73	51	62	Baker	16
Whyteleafe	34	17	5	12	77	57	56	Taylor	18
Walton & Hersham	34	17	3	14	63	60	54	Kilpatrick	11
Metropolitan Police	34	17	3	14	56	61	54	Brace/Hodgson/Scola	13
Leatherhead	34	15	6	13	63	64	51	Browning	15
Epsom & Ewell	34	15	2	17	61	68	47	Sell	11
Woking	34	12	8	14	58	64	44	P Mulvaney	18
Molesey	34	12	7	15	57	68	43	Morgan	9
Three Bridges	34	12	5	17	36	63	41	D Cashman	6
Dorking	34	12	3	19	50	66	39	Lunn	9
Corinthian-Casuals	34	10	8	16	50	73	38	Murray	13
Banstead Athletic	34	20	5	18	57	84	38	Yetzes	15
Kingstonian	34	9	7	18	49	58	34	Martin	10
Malden Vale	34	7	11	16	46	62	32	Major	7
Walton Casuals	34	6	4	24	38	98	22	Valentin/Reps	5

*=3 points deducted

NORTH DIVISION	P	W	D	L	F	A	Pts	League & Cups Leading Scorer	
Hayes	34	25	2	7	81	39	77	Ryder	16
Edgware Town	34	21	7	6	78	40	70	Morris	18
Staines Town	34	21	6	7	64	34	69	K Phillips	13
Wembley	34	19	9	6	70	38	65	Page	8
St Albans City	34	17	10	7	73	36	61	Henstock	19
Fisher Athletic	34	17	7	9	84	51	58	Hynes	28
Uxbridge	34	15	10	8	50	37	55	Wood	11
Yeading	34	13	11	10	64	47	50	V Murphy	9
Ruislip Manor	34	15	5	14	56	53	50	N Whiting	11
Hendon	34	13	9	12	57	41	48	Hendricks/Peterside	7
Harrow Borough	34	13	5	16	54	59	44	Bainbridge/Thomas	9
Northwood	34	10	12	12	44	48	42	Goldsack	7
Hillingdon Borough	34	10	8	16	46	68	38	Pratt	12
Hampton	34	6	12	16	51	73	30	Woods	8
Hanwell Town	34	5	14	15	41	70	29	Thompson	6
Feltham & Hounslow	34	4	11	19	41	68	23	Balding	10
Kingsbury Town	34	3	8	23	35	86	17	Milton	5
Harefield United	34	3	4	27	25	96	13	Hooker	5

Wembley; one point deducted

WEST DIVISION	P	W	D	L	F	A	Pts	League & Cups Leading Scorer	
Thatcham Town	32	23	6	3	89	26	75	Wylie	25
Wokingham Town	32	24	2	6	85	30	74	Pearce	11
Basingstoke Town	32	21	4	7	88	40	67	Worsfold	23
Burnham	32	16	9	7	60	46	57	Bunce	14
Horsham	32	16	9	7	59	57	57	Churchill	14
Farnborough Town	32	16	2	14	77	60	50	Allen	20
Windsor & Eton	32	14	6	12	69	58	48	McDowell	15
Abingdon Town	32	12	9	11	50	47	45	Ward	9
Chalfont St Peter	32	13	8	11	50	41	44	Hawkey	10
Cove	32	13	5	14	57	58	44	Hall	12
Maidenhead United	32	12	4	16	60	70	40	S Doyle	14
Redhill	32	11	2	19	49	65	35	Sestanvich	9
Croydon Athletic	32	9	6	17	62	102	33	Tom	13
Egham Town	32	10	1	21	63	92	31	B Smith	11
Marlow	32	8	6	18	57	61	27	R Jack/Dover	9
Camberley Town	32	4	8	20	29	83	20	Lynch	6
Bracknell Town	32	4	5	23	39	107	17	Jones	7

ALLIED COUNTIES YOUTH LEAGUE

Affiliated with the F.A. direct. For Under-18 sides of senior clubs; midweek floodlit matches.

Central Division	P	W	D	L	F	A	PTS
Wycombe Wdrs	16	15	0	1	88	14	45
Staines Town	16	14	0	2	59	14	42
Slough Town	16	8	3	5	43	43	27
Egham Town	16	7	1	8	27	49	22
Maidenhead Utd	16	6	2	8	28	38	20
Flackwell Heath	16	5	2	9	34	46	17
Bracknell Town	16	5	2	9	27	45	17
Tring Town	16	3	1	12	26	47	10
Chertsey Town	16	3	1	12	22	58	10

West Division	P	W	D	L	F	A	PTS
Reading	16	12	2	2	66	27	38
Hungerford Town	16	11	3	2	46	16	36
Farnborough Town	16	10	2	4	56	27	32
Henley Town	16	7	3	6	23	30	24
Wokingham Town	16	6	4	6	35	24	22
Basingstoke Town	16	6	4	6	30	36	22
Swindon Town	16	4	7	5	25	17	19
Thatcham Town	16	1	2	13	17	62	5
Newbury Town	16	0	3	13	19	78	3

East Division	P	W	D	L	F	A	PTS
Brentford	18	16	2	0	70	17	50
Wembley	18	12	4	2	61	20	40
Ruislip Manor	18	10	4	4	50	34	34
Uxbridge	18	10	3	5	34	28	33
Yeading	18	10	1	7	38	24	31
Southall	18	5	5	8	33	33	20
Harefield United	18	4	3	11	29	40	15
Brook House	18	4	3	11	22	46	15
Hillingdon Borough	18	4	2	12	27	55	14
Feltham & H'low	18	1	1	16	24	91	4

CENTRAL DIVISION RESULTS 1991/92

HOME TEAM		1	2	3	4	5	6	7	8	9
1.	Bracknell Town	*	1-5	0-1	2-1	4-1	1-1	1-2	4-0	0-12
2.	Chertsey Town	2-5	*	0-2	1-6	0-2	1-1	1-5	3-2	0-7
3.	Egham Town	2-4	3-0	*	2-1	2-6	3-1	1-4	2-1	1-6
4.	Flackwell Heath	3-2	4-1	2-2	*	3-3	2-4	0-2	2-3	3-4
5.	Maidenhead United	2-2	2-1	4-0	1-2	*	1-4	0-3	4-2	0-3
6.	Slough Town	2-0	5-2	2-0	5-4	3-1	*	1-5	4-1	1-6
7.	Staines Town	5-0	6-1	5-3	8-0	4-0	4-1	*	1-2	2-1
8.	Tring Town	3-1	1-3	2-3	0-1	0-1	6-6	0-2	*	0-5
9.	Wycombe Wanderers	3-0	6-1	11-0	6-0	5-0	6-2	2-1	5-3	*

EAST DIVISION RESULTS 1991/92

HOME TEAM		1	2	3	4	5	6	7	8	9	10
1.	Brentford	*	10-0	7-0	4-1	4-2	2-1	2-1	4-1	5-2	5-0
2.	Brook House	1-2	*	4-1	0-1	0-2	1-3	2-3	2-2	0-0	0-3
3.	Feltham & Hounslow	2-7	1-2	*	2-2	3-4	0-5	3-5	3-5	0-6	1-4
4.	Harefield United	0-3	1-2	5-0	*	2-1	3-1	1-3	1-3	0-1	0-2
5.	Hillingdon Borough	1-5	4-3	7-2	1-1	*	1-6	0-4	0-3	0-5	0-2
6.	Ruislip Manor	1-1	1-1	6-0	3-2	5-3	*	4-3	1-2	3-3	1-0
7.	Southall	3-4	0-2	1-4	3-3	0-0	3-4	*	0-0	0-0	2-0
8.	Uxbridge	0-2	1-0	2-0	3-2	3-0	0-2	1-1	*	4-3	3-0
9.	Wembley	0-0	5-1	10-0	6-3	3-1	7-1	2-1	5-1	*	1-0
10.	Yeading	1-3	6-1	9-2	2-1	4-0	2-2	1-0	2-0	0-2	*

WEST DIVISION RESULTS 1991/92

HOME TEAM		1	2	3	4	5	6	7	8	9
1.	Basingstoke Town	*	2-1	1-0	0-3	7-0	3-7	2-0	5-1	1-1
2.	Farnborough Town	2-2	*	4-0	1-2	4-0	1-7	0-2	6-5	1-1
3.	Henley Town	2-1	1-4	*	2-5	2-2	1-4	0-0	2-0	2-1
4.	Hungerford Town	4-0	1-3	1-2	*	4-0	4-1	2-1	7-0	2-2
5.	Newbury Town	2-3	0-11	1-3	2-3	*	1-11	0-3	3-6	0-8
6.	Reading	6-2	1-6	3-0	1-1	7-2	*	2-2	3-0	3-0
7.	Swindon Town	0-0	1-2	1-1	0-0	3-3	1-2	*	7-0	1-1
8.	Thatcham Town	1-1	1-8	1-2	0-4	2-2	0-4	0-3	*	1-2
9.	Wokingham Town	6-0	1-2	1-3	1-3	2-1	3-4	2-1	3-0	*

KENT YOUTH LEAGUE

Southern Division	P	W	D	L	F	A	PTS
Dover Athletic	20	14	5	1	60	14	33
Sittingbourne	20	14	3	3	79	28	31
Herne Bay	20	12	5	3	52	28	29
Gillingham	20	12	2	6	55	28	26
Margate	20	10	4	6	45	27	24
Ashford Town	20	8	3	9	34	44	18
Ramsgate	20	8	1	11	28	47	17
Whitstable Town	20	5	5	10	31	42	15
Canterbury City	20	3	4	13	21	54	10
Folkestone Invicta	20	3	3	14	33	73	9
Faversham Town	20	3	2	15	19	71	8

Northern Division	P	W	D	L	F	A	PTS
Vickers-C. D'ford	22	17	4	1	75	23	38
Fisher Athletic	22	15	5	2	61	28	35
Gillingham	22	12	5	5	68	33	29
Phoenix Sports	22	12	1	9	52	50	25
Cray Wanderers	22	11	2	9	47	38	24
Chatham Town	22	7	7	8	26	26	21
Maidstone United	22	9	1	12	45	57	19
Erith & Belvedere	22	8	3	11	30	60	19
Lordswood	22	6	6	10	41	54	18
Tonbridge Angels	22	6	4	12	31	44	16
Dartford	22	3	5	14	23	45	11
Thamesmead Town	22	3	3	16	32	55	9

SOUTHERN DIVISION RESULTS 1991/92

HOME TEAM	1	2	3	4	5	6	7	8	9	10	11
1. Ashford Town	*	4-1	2-2	4-0	1-2	1-3	2-5	2-1	2-1	1-4	3-2
2. Canterbury City	0-3	*	0-2	3-3	4-2	0-3	0-3	1-3	2-1	1-1	1-1
3. Dover Athletic	4-0	1-0	*	6-0	4-0	5-2	2-2	0-0	5-0	2-1	3-1
4. Faversham Town	0-2	W-L	0-3	*	W-L	0-5	1-8	0-1	2-3	1-10	3-3
5. Folkestone Invicta	1-1	4-0	1-9	2-3	*	3-6	2-2	1-3	2-6	2-6	5-3
6. Gillingham	1-0	2-1	1-1	4-1	9-1	*	1-1	1-0	6-0	2-3	2-0
7. Herne Bay	3-0	1-1	0-1	4-1	3-2	2-0	*	3-1	1-0	1-3	4-0
8. Margate	4-1	1-3	1-1	4-3	6-1	3-1	6-1	*	1-2	4-1	3-1
9. Ramsgate	3-2	2-1	1-3	2-1	1-0	2-4	0-2	1-0	*	1-1	1-5
10. Sittingbourne	5-0	14-0	3-2	8-0	6-2	2-1	3-4	2-2	4-1	*	2-0
11. Whitstable Town	2-3	3-2	0-4	1-0	0-0	2-1	2-2	1-1	3-0	1-2	*

NORTHERN DIVISION RESULTS 1991/92

HOME TEAM	1	2	3	4	5	6	7	8	9	10	11	12
1. Chatham Town	*	1-2	1-0	0-2	0-2	0-0	1-1	3-2	0-2	1-1	3-1	0-1
2. Cray Wanderers	1-1	*	2-0	2-4	0-2	1-4	1-0	1-3	6-2	2-0	2-3	2-4
3. Dartford	0-3	0-0	*	2-3	2-2	0-1	4-2	0-2	0-1	1-3	0-3	0-1
4. Erith & Belvedere	4-1	0-3	1-0	*	2-1	0-6	1-1	1-4	1-8	1-0	2-2	0-1
5. Fisher Athletic	2-2	1-0	4-1	6-0	*	1-0	9-3	4-3	3-0	2-0	3-3	3-3
6. Gillingham	0-3	3-0	1-1	3-0	6-1	*	3-3	8-2	5-1	6-3	6-0	0-3
7. Lordswood	1-0	1-3	2-2	2-2	0-1	5-3	*	2-1	1-4	2-4	4-2	0-1
8. Maidstone United	2-0	4-6	3-3	3-2	0-4	4-2	0-3	*	2-4	2-3	2-1	2-3
9. Phoenix Sports	1-3	1-3	3-1	5-1	2-4	1-3	4-2	2-1	*	2-1	2-1	0-2
10. Thamesmead Town	0-2	3-4	0-1	1-2	0-4	1-1	3-4	1-3	5-5	*	0-2	2-3
11. Tonbridge Angels	0-0	0-1	1-3	3-1	1-1	0-4	3-0	W-L	3-4	1-0	*	1-3
12. Vickers C.D. Athletic	1-1	3-1	6-2	5-0	0-1	3-3	4-4	4-0	2-0	9-1	3-0	*

Falmouth Town FC - Jewson South Western League champions.

WOMEN'S NATIONAL LEAGUE

Hon. Secretary: Miss L Whitehead,
448-450 Hanging Ditch, The Corn Exchange, Manchester M4 3ES
(061 8390331).

SEASON'S REPORT

1991/92 will go down as arguably the most historic season in the development of organised women's football in this country. Under the leadership of Chairman Tim Stearn and Secretary Linda Whitehead the women's game demonstrated its ability to sustain a thriving new National League comprising three divisions of eight clubs. Closely following the guidelines established by clubs outside the Football League, women's football now has its own pyramid with promotion from the grass roots through to a Premier Division organised on a national basis.

The Doncaster Belles, who once again formed the nucleus of the England team, completed a unique League and Cup double. The South Yorkshire, club who clinched the League championship with a 100% record, added the Mycil WFA Cup to their list of honours by defeating Red Star Southampton 4-0 in the Final which was televised for the fourth year running by Channel 4.

The success of the new competition has led to an expansion of the League structure to thirty clubs for the coming season as women's football aims to consolidate its position as Britain's fastest growing participation sport.

Doncaster Belles W.F.A. Cup Winners & National League Premier Division champions. Back Row (L-R): M.Jackson, J.Murray, C.Large, L.Hunt, T.Davidson, J.Sherrard, Y.Bagley, G.Borman. Front Row: K.Walker, J.Broadhurst, L.Young, G.Coultard (Capt), S.Edmunds, J.Chipchase. Photo: Dave West.

Premier Division

	P	W	D	L	F	A	Pts
DONCASTER BELLES	14	14	0	0	89	4	28
RS SOUTHAMPTON	14	10	1	3	32	18	21
WIMBLEDON	14	9	2	3	34	27	20
KNOWSLEY UNITED	14	6	5	3	31	30	17
MAIDSTONE T.	14	3	4	7	13	35	10
IPSWICH TOWN	14	2	4	8	15	42	8
MILLWALL L.	14	2	2	10	11	30	6
NOTTS RANGERS	14	1	2	11	17	56	4

Division One North

	P	W	D	L	F	A	Pts
BRONTE	14	12	1	1	49	8	25
SHEFFEILD WED.	14	10	2	2	34	8	22
DAVIES ARGYLE	13	9	1	3	27	19	17
WOLVERHAMPTON	14	5	2	7	23	30	12
SPONDON	14	4	3	7	22	31	11
SUNDERLAND	13	4	1	8	18	40	11
COWGATE KESTRELS	14	5	0	9	19	20	10
VILLA AZTECS	14	1	0	13	8	45	2

DAVIES ARGYLE DEDUCTED 2 POINTS.
SUNDERLAND V DAVIES ARGYLE VOID, POINTS AWARDED TO SUNDERLAND.

Division One South

	P	W	D	L	F	A	Pts
ARSENAL	14	11	3	0	99	11	25
ABBEYDALE	14	11	2	1	62	7	24
HASSOCKS BEACON	14	7	4	3	57	32	18
TOWN & COUNTY	14	7	2	5	52	35	16
REIGATE	14	4	3	7	31	38	11
BRIGHTON & HA	14	4	1	9	22	50	9
BROADBRIDGE HEATH	14	4	1	9	19	52	9
MILTON KEYNES	14	0	0	14	5	119	0

Premier Division Leading goalscorers

36	KAREN WALKER (DONCASTER BELLES)
17	GAIL BORMAN (DONCASTER BELLES)
13	JACKIE SHERRARD (DONCASTER BELLES)
12	MARIEANNE SPACEY (WIMBLEDON)

Division One North Leading goalscorers

12	JULIE GOODMAN (SPONDON)
11	BEV BERTRAM (BRONTE)
	ALI KIRK (ARGYLE)
8	JULIE FOGARTY (BRONTE)
	CLARE TAYLOR (BRONTE)
7	JULIE CALLAGHAN (SHEFF. WED.)
	SARAH QUINTON (WOLVERHAMPTON)
	PAMELA KNOTT (SUNDERLAND)

Division One South Leading goalscorers

27	JO CHURCHMAN (ARSENAL)
24	CAROLINE McGLOIN (ARSENAL)
23	NAZ BALL (ARSENAL)
21	LESLIE SABAN (TOWN & COUNTY)
20	MICHELLE SAUNDERS (HASSOCKS B.)
17	KAREN PRATT (HASSOCKS B.)

NATIONAL LEAGUE CUP

Preliminary Round

Maidstone Tigresses v Town & County	1-2
Milton Keynes v Davies Argyle	1-8

First Round

Abbeydale v Town & County	5-1
Broadbridge Heath v Arsenal	2-12
Ipswich Town v Bronte	2-1
Villa Aztecs v Brighton & Hove Albion	1-3
Davies Argyle v Red Star Southampton	1-0
Hassocks Beacon v Wimbledon(aet)	0-1
Reigate v Sheffield Wednesday	1-0
Wolverhampton v Millwall Lionesses	0-1

Quarter-Finals

Arsenal v Reigate	2-0
Davies Argyle v Abbeydale	2-1
Ipswich Town v Brighton & Hove Albion	2-1
Wimbledon v Millwall Lionesses (aet)	0-0
(Millwall Lionesses win 5-4 on penalties)	

Semi-Finals

Arsenal v Ipswich Town	2-0
Davies Argyle v Millwall Lionesses	2-3

Final

Arsenal v Millwall Lionesses	1-0

Left: Naz Ball scorer of the only goal lifts the League Cup.
Photo: Dave West.

Maidstone Tigresses W.F.C. 1991-92. Back Row (L/R): K Smith, N Inglis, V Jackson, T Gilbert, A Castleton, H Finn, B Frost, C Osborne, B Bowling, H Clancey. Front: L Carpenter, S Price, Mascot, T Proctor, C Summers, K Maincent. Photo - Dave West.

Knowsley United's England International striker Samantha Hayward takes on the Nottingham Rangers defence during a 6-2 home win. Photo - Rob Ruddock.

Arsenal Ladies celebrate after beating Millwall Lionesses 1-0 at Knowsley United to win the first ever Women's National League Cup. Photo - Dave West.

Wimbledon Ladies F.C. - Women's National League Runners-up 1991-92. Back Row (L/R): Marieanne Spacey, Debbie Bampton, Cathy Walsh, Caroline Millar, Terri Wiseman, Jackie Eimermann, Beranadette Kenny, Terry Springett, Brenda Sempare. Front: Fiona Curl, Dee O'Reilly, Sam Wilson, Mal Searle, Livi Hughes, Mandy O'Callaghan, Sue Richman. Photo - Dave West.

Ipswich Town L.F.C. - National League Premier Division. Photo - Dave West.

England 4, Iceland 0 - U.E.F.A. Championship, 17/5/92. Iceland keeper Steindora Steinsdottir palms the ball away under pressure from Karen Walker. Photo - Dave West.

MYCIL WOMEN'S F.A. CUP

FIRST ROUND

Group 1

Bridgwater v Cardiff	0-15	Carterton v Launton	2-8
Cheltenham v Bournemouth	2-3	Cirencester v Frome	0-4
Exeter Rangers v Oxford	0-6	Plymouth v Bristol Blackwell	2-5
Salisbury v Solent	1-3	Swindon v Newbury	3-4
Taunton v Crewkerne	1-8	Torquay United v Amazons	11-0
Truro City v Bristol United	6-1	Warmplas Windows v Swansea	1-3

Group 2

Beccles v Chelmsford	4-6	Leyton Orient v Sporting Kesteven	7-0
Luton Town v Pye	1-2	Newham v Bedford Town Belles	3-1
Romford (wd) v Canary Rangers		Thetford v Suffolk Bluebirds	0-10
Tower Hamlets (wd) v Norwich Falcons		Woodham Wanderers v Southend	0-12
Wanstead v Harlow	0-0, 0-4	Hornchurch	Bye
Milton Keynes	Bye	Town & County	Bye

Group 3

Barnsley v Wakefield	2-5	Bradford City v Hull City	4-1
Middlesborough v Brighouse	3-0	Newcastle v Doncaster Town	2-1
Scarborough v Oakland Rangers	4-1	Bronte	Bye
Cowgate Kestrals	Bye	Sunderland	Bye

Group 4

Sharley Park Spireites v Derby County	6-0	Highfield Rangers v Leicester	0-2
Leyton Linsdale v Calverton	0-6	Millmoor v Gresley Rovers	28-0
Notts County v Nettleham	3-1	Rainworth (wd) v Derby City	
Sheffield Wednesday	Bye	Spondon	Bye

Group 5

Bolton v Nabwood	1-2	Rochdale v Broadoak	1-6
Manchester City v Huddersfield	1-4	Bury v Preston Rangers	0-3
Rossendale v Tranmere Rovers	1-2	Manchester Utd (wd) v St.Martins	
Wigan v Burnley	4-0	Corinthians v Runcorn	1-6
St.Helens v Pilkington	12-0	Liverpool Feds. v Wythenshawe	0-9
Vernon-Carus v Ladyblues	0-1	Blackpool	Bye

Group 6

Palace Eagles v Winchester	5-0	Abbey Rangers v Corematch	1-9
Isle of Wight v Crowborough	25-1	Portsmouth v Hightown	2-5
Farnborough v Saltdean Utd	4-4,1-3	Brighton & Hove Albion	Bye
Hassocks Beacon	Bye	Crystal Palace	Bye
Maidstone United	Bye	Bromley Borough	Bye
Gosport	Bye	Havant	Bye

Group 7

Brentford v Hounslow	4-0	Dunstable v Walton & Hersham	10-0
District Line v Slough	4-0	Hammersmith v Watford	0-24
Reading v Wycombe Wanderers	0-1	Reigate	Bye
Broadbridge Heath	Bye	Binfield	Bye
Bedfont United	Bye	Hemel Hamstead	Bye
Tottenham	Bye		

Group 8

Kidderminster Harriers v Port Vale	20-0	Birmingham City v Crewe	2-4
Worcester City v Bangor	4-1	Leek Town v Telford United	8-2
St.Asaphs v Aston Villa	0-5	Wolverhampton	Bye
Abbeydale	Bye	Villa Aztecs	Bye

SECOND ROUND

Group 1

Swansea v Frome	0-5	Bristol Blackwell v Torquay United	10-1
Solent v Newbury	3-2	Oxford v Truro City	2-2
Crewkerne v Launton	5-3	Bournemouth v Cardiff	5-0

Group 2

Leyton Orient v Chelmsford	6-2	Pye v Newham	5-1
Harlow v Milton Keynes	4-1	Canary Rangers v Suffolk Bluebirds	3-2
Norwich Falcons v Southend	2-5	Hornchurch v Town & County	3-8

Group 3

Wakefield v Newcastle	0-1	Bradford v Middlesborough	1-3
Scarborough v Bronte	1-4	Sunderland v Cowgate Kestrals	1-4

Group 4

Sheffield Weds. v Notts County	11-0	Spondon v Derby City	7-1
Millmoor v Calverton	4-1	Sharley PS v Leicester	3-2

Group 5

Runcorn v Manchester Utd	1-3	Preston Rangers v Wythenshawe	10-1
Wigan v Nabwood	9-0	Broadoak v Tranmere Rovers	2-4
St.Helens v Blackpool	2-0	Ladyblues v Huddersfield	4-5

Group 6

Saltdean v Gosport	4-1	Crystal Palace v Hassocks Beacon	2-8
Maidstone Utd v Bromley Borough	0-11	Havant v Hightown	0-2
Isle of Wight v Corematch	1-3	Palace Eagles v Brighton & HA	1-5

Group 7

Binfield v Watford	1-0	Hemel Hampstead v District Line	1-4
Broadbridge Heath v Reigate	3-4	Bradford v Chelsea	2-10
Wycombe Wanderers v Dunstable	0-3	Tottenham v Bedfont United	14-0

Group 8

Worcester City v Aston Villa	2-3	Leek Town v Kidderminster Harriers	3-7
Crewe v Villa Aztecs	5-0	Wolverhampton v Abbeydale	0-3

Crystal Palce Ladies who went out to Division One South side Hassock Beacon in the 2nd Round. Back Row (L-R): B.Pollington, V.Kirkman, C.McFadden, M.Judge, P.Buckley, J.Smithers, K.Stock, J.Lorton. Front Row: L.Kirkman, K.Flew, P.Owens, A.White, T.Brooks, L.Kirkman. Photol. Dave West.

The Ladies who represented England in their International in Iceland in the European Championship.

Iceland, before playing England at Yeovil Town FC. Back Row (L/R): G Saemundsdottir, S Jonsdottir, A Skulangsdottir, R L Stefansdottir, H Gylfudottir, A B Gunnlaugsdottir. Front: J Vieuvnosdottir, S S Ottarsdottir, S Steinsdottir, V Sieurgeirsdottir, A Maenusdottir. Photo - Dave West.

Karen Walker sees her header give England the lead away to Iceland.

THIRD ROUND

Group 1

Bristol Blackwell v Bournemouth	7-0	Solent v Crewekerne	11-0
Oxford v Frome	2-3		

Group 2

Pye v Town & County	5-3	Harlow v Southend	2-0
Canary Rangers v Leyton Orient	0-7		

Group 3

Newcastle v Bronte	2-3	Cowgate Kestrels v Middlesborough	2-4

Group 4

Sheffield Weds. v Millmoor	1-2	Sharley Park S. v Spondon	0-4

Group 5

Preston Rangers v Huddersfield	3-0	Wigan v St.Helens	1-4
Tranmere Rovers v Manchester Utd	3-4		

Group 6

Hassocks Beacon v Brighton & HA	6-2	Bromley Borough v Coremouth	6-0
Hightown v Saltdean	0-2		

Group 7

District Line v Tottenham	7-0	Reigate v Dunstable	2-0
Chelsea v Binfield	1-3		

Group 8

Aston Villa v Crewe	1-3	Abbeydale v Kidderminster Harriers	7-2

FOURTH ROUND

Arsenal v Red Star Southampton (aet)	0-1	Middlesborough v Frome	5-0
Notts Rangers v Davies Argyle	2-0	Bromley Borough v Abbeydale	3-3,1-0
Preston Rangers v Manchester Utd	4-2	Bronte v Maidstone T. (aet)	0-0,1-2
Saltdean v Pye	4-0	Ipswich Town v Millwall L.	3-1
Binfield v Reigate	0-3	Hassocks Beacon v Bristol Blackwell	2-1
Leyton Orient v Doncaster Belles	0-14	Solent v Spondon	1-3
St.Helens v Knowsley Utd	2-6	Crewe v District Line	1-5
Leasowe Pacific v Millmoor	5-0	Harlow v Wimbledon	1-6

FIFTH ROUND

Ipswich Town v Reigate	5-2	Maidstone v Knowsley	3-2
Middlesborough v Leasowe Pacific	2-3	Notts Rangers v Hassocks Beacon	2-4
Preston Rangers v Doncaster Belles	0-6	RS Southampton v Bromley Borough (aet)	5-2
Spondon v Saltdean	4-0	Wimbledon v District Line	1-0

Millwall Lionesses FC, holders of the W.F.A. Cup. Back Row (L-R): J.McGlashan (Manager), S.Ludgrove, G.Maskell, D.Bowring, P.Cope, E.Grieves, C.Lyons, K.Glyde, A.Hinder.
Front Row: P.Jhooti, A.Walsh, K.Savage, T.Wright (Mascot), D.Willis, L.Waller, J.Fletcher. Photo: Dave West.

Leasowe Pacific 2, Preston Rangers 0 - North West Women's League Cup final, 16/5/92. Louise Thomas hits the post prior to scoring Pacific's second in their victory over Preston Rangers at Prescot. Photo - Rob Ruddock.

Pilkingtons 3, Bury 1 - North West Women's League 3rd & 4th Division Cup final, 16/5/92. Annette James (arms raised) scores Bury's second. Photo - Rob Ruddock.

Pilkingtons celebrate success in the above competition. Photo - Rob Ruddock.

QUARTER-FINAL

Leasowe Pacific v Doncaster Belles	1-5	Maidstone T. v Spondon	2-1
Ipswich Town v RS Southampton	1-3	Hassocks Beacon v Wimbledon	1-6

SEMI-FINAL

Doncaster Belles v Maidstone T.	10-1	RS Southampton v Wimbledon	2-0

FINAL

Doncaster Belles v RS Southampton   4-0

Red Star Southampton this years beaten finalists. Back Row (L-R): V.Raynbird, A.Kaile, J.England, G.Williams, S.Buckett, C.Lambert, S.Hayes, S.Stanbury, P.Chapman (Player/Manager).
Front Row: S.Green, L.Lee, E.Connolly, A.Fisher, D.Ingram. Photo: Dave West.

SOUTH EAST COUNTIES
WOMENS FOOTBALL LEAGUE

First Division

	P	W	D	L	F	A	Pts
SALTDEAN UNITED	14	12	1	1	62	14	25
SHOREHAM	14	12	0	2	45	12	24
CRYSTAL PALACE	14	9	0	6	51	36	16
TEYNHAM	14	5	3	6	25	38	13
HASSOCKS RESERVES	14	3	4	7	24	44	10
MAIDSTONE UTD *	14	4	2	8	27	38	9
COREMATCH	14	2	4	8	28	57	8
FARNBOROUGH	14	2	2	10	20	43	6

* - 1PT DEDUCTED.

Second Division

	P	W	D	L	F	A	Pts
TIGRESSES RESERVES	16	11	2	3	92	18	24
ISLE OF WIGHT	16	11	1	4	74	58	23
ASHFORD (KENT)	16	9	3	4	68	49	21
WEST SUSSEX *	15	9	3	3	61	37	20
REIGATE RESERVES	16	7	3	6	46	53	17
MEADOW SPORTS	16	6	2	8	47	69	14
CHELSEA COLLEGE *	15	5	2	8	45	49	11
CHALTON	16	3	0	13	25	91	6
HASTINGS *	16	2	0	14	36	75	3

* - 1PT DEDUCTED.

Third Division

	P	W	D	L	F	A	Pts
C.PALACE RES	22	20	1	1	148	20	41
LEEDS (KENT)	22	16	2	4	133	26	34
TEYNHAM RES.	22	16	1	5	82	34	33
LEWES	22	14	2	6	81	37	30
UPPER BEADING *	22	12	3	7	76	35	26
HASSOCKS 3RDS	22	11	2	9	82	46	24
SUTTON **	22	9	2	11	43	68	17
CROWBOROUGH	22	7	2	13	63	88	16
WORTHING	22	7	1	14	37	100	15
BRAODBRIDGE H RES	22	7	1	14	66	93	15
HANDCROSS	22	3	1	18	31	116	7
WELCOME WILDCATS	22	1	0	21	5	185	2

* - 1PT DEDUCTED
** - 3PTS DEDUCTED

Reigate Ladies celebrate after winning the South East Counties Presidents Cup, beating Farnborough Ladies 3-0. Photo - Dave West.

Saltdean United Ladies after beating Crystal Palace 3-2 to win the South East Counties Cup. Photo - Dave West.

Lesley Shipp - goalkeeper for Arsenal Ladies and England. Photo - Dave West.

A moment of history as Karen Walker of Doncaster Belles heads her third goal in the Women's F.A. Cup final thus becoming the first player to score a hat-trick in every round.

Karen Walker scores her second in the above final, played at Tranmere Rovers FC.

Clare Taylor, of England and Bronte (Div. One North champions) holds off an Iceland forward. Photo - Dave West.

CHANNEL ISLANDS FOOTBALL

From Rex Bennett, Guernsey Evening Express & Star.

GUERNSEY RETAIN MURATTI CUP

JERSEY SCOTTISH WIN THE UPTON

Guernsey successfully defended the Muratti Cup for the first time since 1980 when they followed up their 3-0 home win of 1991 with a 3-2 victory in Jersey in 1992 which squared the series at 37 wins to each island.

It was a battling triumph, achieved after extra-time, because Jersey were at one stage two goals up.

Craig Allen, who spent nine successful years in professional six-a-side indoor soccer in America after making his Muratti debut in 1978, and who was playing in a Muratti at Springfield for the first time in for fourteen years, made a great long run to pave the way for Kevin Le Tissier to score Guernsey's first goal on the stroke of half-time.

And it was another sparkling run by Allen, player/coach of Guernsey Rangers, which set up the match winner for Tony Vance some eight minutes into extra-time - Vance, who spent most of the season with Enfield, having returned to play for his island.

Guernsey's equaliser, scored midway through the second half, was the subject of considerable controversy. It appeared the ball had been headed into his own net by Jersey defender Paul Bouteloup as he was challenged by Kevin Le Tissier, but T.V. videotape later strongly indicated that, in fact, it was Le Tissier's upstretched right arm which had propelled the ball past Jersey keeper Steve Carlyon. Le Tissier would say only that 'If I did handle it, it was unintentional', while, for his part, Bouteloup, who scored an 'o.g.' in the 1991 final, maintained he hadn't touched the ball. *(continued overleaf)...*

Guernsey player-of-the-year Kevin Le Tissier, of Northerners, receives the award from his younger brother Matt (Southampton and England 'B').

(Continued from page 1015)...

Neil Livesey and Andy Barker scored the early goals for Jersey whose manager, Peter Vicenti, later commented: 'We were doing all right until Guernsey started playing basketball'!

Guernsey midfielder Grant Chalmers was voted man-of-the-match for the second year running. In the Semi-Final, Guernsey had routed Alderney 9-1 with Kevin Le Tissier hitting five of their goals.

A replay was needed to decide the islands' top club match of the year, the Upton Park Cup game between the champions of the Jersey and Guernsey Leagues, and the trophy was eventually won by Jersey Scottish who had captured the Jersey title for the first time.

After holding Guernsey's Northerners to a 1-1 draw at The Track, they won the replay at the Springfield 2-0 with first half goals from Dougie Ross (who had been their marksman in Guernsey) and right-back Martin Forbes, who was named man-of-the-match.

It was a second year running that 'North' had finished beaten by a club who had never previously represented Jersey, having lost to Sporting Academics the previous season. They paid the penalty, at Springfield, for having missed match-winning chances during extra-time at The Track: their hopes of victory in the replay being dashed when star striker Kevin Le Tissier failed a late fitness test and withdrew from the team.

It was a memorable season for Scottish who also won Guernsey's Jeremie Cup in which they beat Wanderers 2-0 in an all-Jersey final - only North of the Guernsey clubs having the semi-final stage.

The Scots pipped St Peter for the Jersey championship while North held off a strong challenge from old rivals Rangers to win the Guernsey title for the third year in succession and the 27th time all-told.

While Jersey were the stronger at club level - only North of the three invited Guernsey clubs managed to reach the semi-finals of the Wheway Cup which was won by Wanderers who beat Scottish in the final - Guernsey were superior at representative level and completed a Muratti grand slam with their Under-21s, Under-18 juniors and Under-15 schoolboys also triumphing over the old enemy.

Kevin Le Tissier was Guernsey's official player-of-the-year and, fittingly, received his trophy from younger brother Matthew, the Southampton and England 'B' star, while St Paul's Liverpool-born midfielder Peter Grierson, who made his debut for the ill-fated Jersey Muratti side, was voted his island's top player.

Guernsey and Jersey had contrasting results on their 1992 tours. Guernsey came from 0-2 down to beat the Metropolitan Police 4-3 at Imber Court in Surrey and, the following night, defeated an Army XI 5-1 at Bordon in Hampshire, while Jersey were held 1-1 draw by the R.A.F. Colts at Uxbridge and were beaten 1-0 by Barking.

After competing in the F.A. Challenge Vase for a number of years, Guernsey's Vale Recreation withdrew from the competition and returned to the Hampshire Senior Cup during the 1991-92 season but lost 0-1 to Fareham Town at home in the First Round. Northerners again took part in the Dorset Senior Cup but also suffered a First Round knockout, being beaten 1-2 at home by Weymouth.

Guernsey-born winger Lee Luscombe played a sufficient number of games for Brentford's Third Division side during the 1991-92 season to qualify for a medal when the Bees won the championship and did well enough - he scored some spectacular goals - to be retained for the 1992-93 season. He was on Southampton's books for three years before returning to the island for a year. He was signed by Brentford after manager Phil Holder had seen him playing for the Guernsey representative team on their 1991 mainland tour.

JERSEY 2, GUERNSEY 3 *(After extra-time)*

Jersey: S Carlyon, R Muddyman, P Bouteloup, W Begbie, M Murray, A Lawlor, A Barker, P Grierson, G Lightbody, N Livesey, P Carberry. Subs: S Le Rougetel, C Hamon.

Guernsey: S Ingrou⁔ , M Bisson, D Tapp, C Dyer, G de Carteret, M Marley, C Le Tissier, G Chalmers, A Vance, ʼ /ʼlen, K Le Tissier. Subs: S Polson, A Exall.

'BARCLAYS' GUERNSEY PRIAULX LEAGUE 1991-93

	P	W	D	L	F	A	PTS
Northerners	18	13	2	3	62	26	41
Rangers	18	12	2	4	66	27	38
Vale Recreation	18	10	3	5	49	35	23
St Martin's	18	7	2	9	38	35	23
Belgrave Wanderers	18	6	5	7	33	38	23
Sylvans	18	6	2	10	28	44	20
Rovers	18	1	0	17	13	82	3

Guernsey captain Chris Dyer led his side to victory over Jersey for the second year running. It was his seventeeth Murratti appearance.

Was it the hand of Kevin Le Tissier or the head of Paul Bouteloup that scored Guernsey's second goal in the Muratti? That was the big question after the Green & Whites' 3-2 victory.

Kevin Le Tissier scores Northerners' goal in the drawn Upton Park Cup match at the Track.

Jersey Scottish after beating Northerners in a replay to become the Channel Islands' champion club.

ISLE OF MAN FOOTBALL

From David W Phillips, Manx Sport Information Services.

The Isle of Man Football League had the closest finish for years with only two points separating the top three teams with St Georges winning their first title for over twenty years. That left the season with two trophies each for Old Boys and St Georges with Peel the unlucky ones coming close but without reward.

The season started with success for Old Boys who defeated Gymms in the Railway Cup, the trophy contested by the top four clubs at the halfway stage. Od Boys continued their good run when they ended the challenge of St Georges to retain the Manx F.A. Cup.

In the Hospital Cup, the holders Peel reached the final again only to receive further disappointment losing to the new league champions St Georges. Old Boys, despite losing their title, are to have their third attempt in the F.A. Vase in the coming season.

In the Second Division, it was Ramsey's year with Ramsey Youth Centre taking the divisional title and near neighbours Ramsey the two Cups.

In the Isle of Man Football Festival, the island team lost to eventual winners Stoke City and to FC Cambur from the Dutch First Division. Stoke City defeated Sunderland 2-0 in the final.

BOWRING ISLE OF MAN LEAGUE TABLES 1991-92

DIVISION ONE	P	W	D	L	F	A	PTS
St Georges	22	16	3	3	89	30	35
Douglas HSOB	22	17	1	4	59	19	35
Peel	22	14	5	3	49	29	33
Pulrose United	22	13	3	6	71	31	29
Castletown	22	12	3	7	56	32	27
Gymnasium	22	10	4	8	59	48	24
Rushen United	22	10	3	9	38	32	23
St Mary's	22	8	4	10	43	54	20
Douglas Royal	22	7	2	13	43	53	16
Ayre United	22	4	2	16	27	74	10
Marown	22	2	3	17	20	84	7
Corinthians	22	2	1	19	32	100	5

DIVISION TWO	P	W	D	L	F	A	PTS
Ramsey YC & OB	22	15	5	2	66	28	35
Ramsey	22	13	6	3	85	38	32
Braddan	22	14	4	4	72	36	32
Onchan	22	12	6	4	60	41	30
Colby	22	11	4	7	57	47	26
Laxey	22	10	2	10	58	65	22
Union Mills	22	9	3	10	42	43	21
Ronaldsway	22	9	2	11	59	75	20
St Johns United	22	6	5	11	53	66	17
Malew	22	6	1	15	44	81	13
Police	22	3	4	15	39	79	10
Michael United	22	1	4	17	29	65	6

St Georges FC, League champions and Hospital Cup winners 1991-92. Photo - Manx Independent.

ISLE OF MAN COMBINATION TABLES (RESERVE TEAMS) 1991-92

TNT Parcels Comb.	P	W	D	L	F	A	PTS
Rushen United	22	17	1	4	82	23	35
Douglas HSOB	22	16	2	4	72	33	34
St Georges	22	15	1	6	92	33	31
Douglas Royal	22	14	3	5	79	42	31
Peel	22	12	3	7	55	41	27
Pulrose United	22	12	3	7	68	47	*25
Castletown	22	12	1	9	57	56	25
Gymnasium	22	8	3	11	43	43	19
Marown	22	7	2	13	36	62	16
St Mary's	22	3	2	17	39	95	8
Ayre United	22	3	0	19	27	117	6
Corinthians	22	2	1	19	28	86	5

* - Failed to fulfill fixture
  Two points deducted

Bowring Comb. 2	P	W	D	L	F	A	PTS
Braddan	20	15	1	4	73	30	31
Union Mills	20	12	6	2	54	17	30
Ramsey	20	12	4	4	51	32	28
Colby	20	10	6	4	54	40	26
Laxey	20	8	2	10	45	53	18
Ronaldsway	20	7	4	9	29	42	18
Onchan	20	8	0	12	56	59	16
St Johns United	20	6	3	11	40	51	15
Ramsey YC & OB	20	6	3	11	27	46	*13
Malew	20	5	3	12	29	64	13
Michael United	20	4	2	14	44	71	10

* - Infringement of rules
  2 points & three goals deducted

Douglas High School Old Boys, pictured after winning the 1991-92 Railway Cup. The Old Boys are set to make another foray into the F.A. Challenge Vase in 1992-93 - so what price a Manx invasion of Wembley next May? Photo - Manx Independent.

Barlestone St Giles - Influence Midland Combination. Back Row (L/R players names only): Rob Davis, Matt Wright, Ash Bailey, Carl Pettit, Roger Goddard, Lee Jeffreys, Dave Cox. Front: Alan Hudson, Scott Marley, Carl Aris, Wayne Aris, Mark Jarvis, Dave Foulkes. Photo - Derrick Kinsey.

Welsh Football

COMPETITION	WINNERS	RUNNERS-UP
Allbrights Welsh Cup	Cardiff City	Hednesford Town
Intermediate Cup	Llangefni Town	Caersws
British Gas Wales Yth Cup	Wrexham	Cardiff City
Manweb Cymru Alliance	Caersws	Llansantffraid
Manweb Cymru Alliance Lge Cup	Lex XI	Flint Town United
Abacus League National Div.	Abergavenny Thursdays	Briton Ferry Athletic
Abacus League Division One	Blaenrhondda	Morrison Town
Abacus League Division Two	AFC Porth	Carmarthen Town
Office Interiors League Cup	Brecon Corinthians	Pembroke Borough
Sealink Welsh Alliance	Llangefni Town	Felinheli
R.Con. Welsh Nat.Lge (Wrexham)	Wrexham Reserves	Ruthin Town
Richards The Builders M.Wales Lge	Knighton Town	Morda United
R.Con. Welsh National Lge Cup	Ruthin Town	Rhos Aelwyd
Richards Builders M.Wales Lge Cup	Caersws Reserves	Rhayader Town

ALLBRIGHT BITTER WELSH CUP

FIRST ROUND

Afan v Seven Sisters	3-0	Llanrwst United Rhyl	1-2
Ammanford Town v Carmarthen Town	3-4	Llay Royal British Legion v Rhos Aelwyd	1-0
Bala Town v New Broughton	1-1 0-4	Maesteg Park Ath v Trelewis Welfare	8-0
Bridgend Town v Ebbw Vale	1-0	Marchwiel Villa v Llay Welfare	0-0 4-2
Buckley v Brymbo	2-1	Morriston Town v Pembroke Borough	2-2 2-1
Caerau v Llanwern	0-4	Nefyn United v Llanfairpwll	1-3
Caerleon v Pontlottyn Blast Furnace	2-1	Newcastle Emlyn v Stourbridge	3-5
Cardiff Civil Service v Cardiff Corinthians	3-0	Penrhyncoch v Builth Wells	1-0
Carno v Llansantffraid	1-2	Penycae v Johnstown Ath.	5-1
Cefn Albion v Gresford Athletic	1-2	Pontllanfraith v Aberaman	3-0
Cemaes Bay v Conwy United	1-0	Porthcawl Town v Pontardawe Ath	6-1
Chirk AAA v Lex XI	1-0	Porthmadog v Locomotive Llanberis	2-1
Connah's Quay N. v Pilkingtons' St.Asaph	1-6	Rhydymwyn v Holywell Town	0-2
Cwmbran Town v Newport YMCA	3-2	Risca United v Abercynon Ath	1-3
Ferndale Ath v Cardiff Inst. Higher Educ.	10-2	Rubery Owen Rockwell v Morda United	1-9
Haverfordwest County v B.P. Llandarcy	3-0	Ruthin Town v Birtish Aerospace	0-1
Inter Cardiff v Caldicot Town	3-3 3-0	Skewen Athletic v Briton Ferry Ath	0-3
Kidderminster Harriers v Rhayder Town	5-1	Taffs Well v Pontyclun	4-0
Knighton Town v Llanidloes Town	0-0 2-3	Ton Pentre v Stroud	1-0
Llandrindod Wells v Brecon Corinthians	1-3	Tonyrefail Welfare v S.W. Constabulary	3-0
Llandudno v Pwllheli Borough	5-0	Welshpool Town v Hednesford Town	0-2
Llanelli v Port Talbot Athletic	1-2	(Played at Hednesford)	

SECOND ROUND

Bangor City v Porthmadog	3-1	Holywell Town v Llandudno	2-2 3-0 *
Brecon Corinthians v Caersws	1-4	Inter Cardiff v Ferndale Athletic	2-1
British Aerospace v Chirk A.A.A.	1-2	Kidderminster Harriers v Morda United	7-1
Briton Ferry Ath v Afan Lido	2-1	Llansantffraid v Llanidloes Town	3-1
Buckley v Llay Royal British Legion	0-3	Maesteg Park Athletic v Llanwern	4-2
Caerleon v Ton Pentre	2-1	Morriston Town v Tonyrefail Welfare	3-0
Cardiff Civil Service v Port Talbot Ath	1-0	Mostyn v Rhyl	2-1
Cemaes Bay v Llanfairpwll	3-2	New Broughton v Penycae	1-0
Connah's Quay N v Colwyn Bay	1-1 0-6	Newport AFC v Bridgend Town	3-0
Cwmbran Town v Taffs well	4-1	Newtown v Aberystwyth Town	1-2
Flint Town United v Caernarfon Town	2-2 2-3	Pontllanfraith v Abergavenny Thursdays	0-4
Gresford Athletic v Marchwiel Villa	0-2	Porthcawl Town v Merthyr Tydfil	1-4
Haverfordwest County v Abercynon	3-0	Stourbridge v Carmarthen Town	7-1
Hednesford Town v Penrhyncoch	3-1	* - Replay played at Colwyn Bay FC	

THIRD ROUND

Barry Town v Aberystwyth Town	2-3	Hednesford Town v New Broughton	3-0
Briton Ferry Ath v Abergavenny Thurs.	3-2	Inter Cardiff v Caerleon	1-2
Caersws v Cemaes Bay	1-2	Kidderminster Harriers v Llansantffraid	4-1
Cardiff City v Newport AFC	3-0	Marchwiel Villa v Caernarfon Town	0-3
Chirk A.A.A. v Llay Royal British Legion	2-1	Merthyr Tydfil v Swansea City	0-2
Colwyn Bay v Holywell Town	5-1	Mostyn v Hereford United	1-3
Cwmbran Town v Maesteg Park Athletic	2-5	Stourbridge v Cardiff Civil Services	0-0 3-1
Haverfordwest County v Morriston Town	4-1	Wrexham v Bangor City	3-2
		(Mostyn played Flint Town United)	

FOURTH ROUND

Briton Ferry Athletic v Colwyn Bay	2-4	Hereford United v Maesteg Park	1-2
Caernarfon Town v Aberystwyth Town	0-1	Kidderminster Harriers v Swnasea City	1-3
Cardiff City v Stourbridge	3-3 1-2	L.R. British Legion v Hednesford T	0-0 0-3
Cemaes Bay v Haverfordwest County	1-2	Wrexham v Caerleon	2-0

FIFTH ROUND

Haverfordwest Co. v Hednesford T	0-0 0-4	Maesteg Park Athletic v Aberystwyth Town	2-0
Wrexham v Colwyn Bay	0-1* 1-3	Swansea City v Cardiff City	0-1
* Match abandoned due to fog.			

SEMI-FINALS (2 Legged)

Cardiff City v Maesteg Park Athletic 0-0 4-0*   Hednesford Town v Colwyn Bay   1-0 3-2
* 2nd Leg played at Ninian Park.

FINAL

Cardiff v Hednesford Town 1-0

Peter Donnelly (Colwyn Bay) challenges Connah's Quay keeper Gary Griffiths in the Welsh Cup. Photo - D Fowler.

Stourbridge defend as they win 5-3 at Cardiganshire League side Newcastle Emlyn. Photo - David Collins.

Connah's Quay keeper Gary Griffiths keeps out Colwyn Bay top scorer Mark Williscroft. Photo - D Fowler.

WELSH INTERMEDIATE CUP

FIRST ROUND

Bala Town v Penycae	1-0	Llanrug United v Cemaes Bay	2-2	0-3
Bethesda Athletic v Locomotive Llanberis		Llanrwst United v Ruthin Town		0-2
Bethesda Ath. withdrew.		Llantwit Fardre v Treharris Athletic		0-3
Builth Wells v Llandrindod Wells	1-0	Llantwit Major v Pontyclun	0-0	0-7
Cardiff Corinthinas v Albion Rovers	1-4	Llay Royal British Legion v Druids United	4-0	
Cardiff Inst Higher Ed v Taffs Well	2-0	Llay Welfare v Cefn Albion		4-1
Chirk A.A.A. v Rhostyllen Villa	1-1	3-2	Maltsters Sports v Newcastle Emlyn	3-2
Christchurch v Bryntirion Ath.	1-1	1-4	Mochdre v British Aerospace	2-1
Cilfynydd v Tredomen	2-2	2-3	Nefyn United v Nantle Vale	3-0
Corwen Amateurs v New Broughton	0-1	Newport Corinthians v Croesyceiliog		1-3
Hirwaun Welfare v Risca United	2-2	0-3	Penley v Rhayader Town	2-0
Hoover Sports v Dinas Powys	3-0	Pilkingtons (St.Asaph) v Llandudno		1-0
Johnstown Ath v Rubery Owen R	1-1	3-4	Pwllheli Borough v Felinheli	1-3
Knighton Town v Penparcau	2-0	Ragged School v Goytre United	3-0	2-1
Llandyrnog United v Rhydymwyn	1-0	Rhos Aelwyd v Buckley		2-1
Llanfairpwll v Blaenau Amateurs	8-0	Suburbs v BSC Port Talbot		8-0
llangeinor v Kenfig Hill	7-0	Trelewis v Penrhiwceiber Rangers	2-2	2-1

SECOND ROUND

Afan Lido v Caldicot Town	0-1	Llangeinor v Suburbs	2-3
Babla Town v New Broughton	4-4 1-3 (aet)	Llanidloes Town v Penrhyncoch	1-0
Blaenrhondda v Maltsters	4-1	Llansantffraid v Morda United	2-1
Brymbo v Llay Royal British Legion	2-1	Llay Welfare v Chirk AAA	1-1 1-2
Bryntirion Athletic v Albion Rovers	-1 0-1 (aet)	Marchwiel Villa v Llandyrnog United	3-2
Builth Wells v Welshpool Town	0-2	Mochdre v Penley	1-1 2-1
Caersws v Brecon Corinthians	3-3 1-0	Nefyn United v Llangefni Town	1-3
Connah's Quay Nomads v Holywell T	0-0 0-1	Pilkingtons (St.Asaph) v Rubery Owen R.	4-0
Conwy United v Locomotive Llanberis	3-0	Pontyclun v Risca United	0-3
Croesyceiliog v Morriston Town	1-0	Porthmadog v Cemaes Bay	2-1
Gresford Athletic v Flint Town United	1-1 1-6	Ragged School v Penrhiwceiber R.	3-3 3-1
Hoover Sports v Cardiff Inst H.Ed.	4-4 4-0	Rhos Aelwyd v Lex XI	1-2
Knighton Town v Carno	4-2	Ruthin Town v Mold Alexandra	1-3
Llanfairpwll PG v Felinheli	1-1 3-2 (aet)	Tredomen v Treharris Athletic	0-2

THIRD ROUND

Abergavenny Thurs v Porthcawl Town	4-2	Llanfairpwll v Knighton Town	2-2 2-1
Albion Rovers v Caersws	1-1 0-1	Llangefni Town v Mochdre	2-0
Brymbo v Mostyn	2-4	Llanidloes Town v Aberystwyth Town	2-1
Chirk AAA v Lex XI	1-1 2-3	Llansantffraid v New Broughton	1-0
Croesyceiliog v Caldicot Town	1-3	Marchwiel Villa v Conwy United	0-2
Flint Town United v Pilkingtons (St.Asaph)	5-1	Porthmadog v Mold Alexandra	7-0
Holywell Town v Welshpool Town	1-1 0-4	Ragged School v Blaenrhondda	1-3
Hoover Sports v Treharris Athletic	2-1	Risca United v Suburbs	1-1 1-3 (aet/pens)

FOURTH ROUND

Abergavenny Thurs v Hoover Sports	0-1	Flint Town United v Welshpool Town	2-0
Blaenrhondda v Llanfairpwll	2-0	Lex XI v Mostyn	4-0
Caersws v Llanidloes Town	2-0	Llangefni Town v Suburbs	3-0
Conwy United v Llansantffraid	2-1	Porthmadog v Caldicot Town	5-0

FIFTH ROUND

Porthmadog v Hoover Sports	5-1	Lex XI v Conwy United	1-2
Caersws v Flint Town United	4-2	Blaenrhondda v Llangefni Town	0-2

SEMI-FINALS

Conwy United v Llangefni Town	0-0 0-1	Caersws v Porthmadog	3-1
PLayed at Y.Treaeth, Porthmadog.		Played at Penrhyncoch FC.	

FINAL

Caersws v Llangefni Town 1-1 1-2
Played at the Race course, Wrexham with replay at Y. Traeth, Porthmadog.

Llansantfraid 2, Morda United 1 - Welsh Intermediate Cup. Llansantfraid keeper Howard Jones is stranded, but saved by the post. Photo - Leo Heonig.

Robbie Jones puts in a cross for Bangor Waterloo at Pilkingtons (St Asaph). Photo - A Monument.

Cardiff Civil Service keeper G John shows a clean pair of hands against Morriston in the Abacus League. Photo - James Wright.

Bangor City - the most famous name in the new League of Wales - pictured before their last ever game in the Northern Premier League. Back Row (L/R): A Bell, A Nicholas, E Johnston, S Healey, T Lloyd, P Lunn. Front: I Williams, N Powell, C Tatlock, J Smith, P Evans. Photo - A Monument.

Newtown also bid farewell to the H.F.S. Loans League. Above is 91-92 League Cup action from Latham Park.

With his keeper beaten, Newtown defender Graham Moffat heads clear another Hereford United attack watched by team-mate Mark Williams during a pre-season friendly. Photo - Colin Stevens.

THE LEAGUE OF WALES

Born amidst much controversy, The League of Wales kicks off in 1992-93, and is the Principality's first national league. The twenty club sides contesting the first season are listed below.

ABERGAVENNY THURSDAYS

Chairman: **President:** **Manager:** Ray Warren
Secretary: Mr D J Morris, 48 Richmond Rd, Abergavenny, Gwent (0873 853906).
Ground: Pen-y-pound Stadium, Abergavenny, Gwent (0873 853906).
Directions: Enter town from Crickhowell on A40 and take 1st left into Penypound Road.
Seats: **Cover:** Yes **Capacity:** **Floodlights:** **Founded:** 1927.
Colours: White (red & blue trim)/white/red **Change colours:** Blue (white & red trim)/blue/red.
Previous League: Abacus **Programme:** Yes
Hons: Abacus Lg 59-60 90-91 91-92 (Div 1 74-75, Lg Cup 51-52), Welsh Intermediate Cup 90-91, South Wales Snr Cup 64-65.

ABERYSTWYTH TOWN

Chairman: Mr D Dawson **President:** Mrs D Richards **Manager:** Tommy Morgan
Secretary: Arthur Griffiths, The Boars Head, Queens Rd, Aberystwyth, Dyfed SY23 2ET (0970 626106).
Ground: Park Avenue, Aberystwyth, Dyfed (0970 612122).
Directions: From south: A487, 1st right at Trefachan Bridge to r'bout, 1st right with Park Avenue being 3rd right. From north: A487 and follow one-way system to railway station, at r'bout 1st left with Park Avenue being 3rd right. 5 mins walk from Aberystwyth (BR) - follow as above.
Seats: 250 **Cover:** Yes **Capacity:** 6,000 **Floodlights:** Yes **Founded:** 1884.
Colours: Green & black stripes/black/black **Change colours:** Yellow/blue/blue.
Previous League: Central & Wales/ Welsh/ Cambrian Coast/ Abacus.
Programme: 28 pages, 50p **Programme Editor:** Steve Moore
Clubhouse: 7-11pm every night **Record Gate:** 4,500 v Hereford, Welsh Cup 1971.
Midweek matches: Wednesday **Local Newspapers:** Cambrian News
Hons: Welsh Cup 1899-1900, Welsh I'mediate Cup 85-86 87-88, Mid Wales Lg(11) 22-24 25-28 32-33 48-50 58-59 83-85 (Lg Cup(7) 26-28 31-32 38-39 47-48 84-86), Welsh Amtr Cup 30-31 32-33 69-70, Welsh Lg Div 2 Sth 51-52, Cambrian Coast Lg(8) 32-37 49-50 56-57 58-59 (Lg Cup 35-36 49-50 56-57), Central Wales Chal. Cup(6) 75-76 81-83 84-85 86-88.

AFAN LIDO

Chairman: Andrew Edwards **President:** Jim Mahoney **Manager:** Phil Robinson
Secretary: Mr P Robinson, 56 Abbeyville Avenue, Port Talbot, West Glamorgan (0639 885638).
Ground: Afan Lido Sports Centre, Aberavon Beach, Port Talbot, West Glamorgan.
Directions: Leave M4 into Port Talbot centre then follow signs to Aberavon Beach where ground is at Afan Lido Leisure complex.
Seats: 150 **Cover:** 150 **Capacity:** 1,500 **Floodlights:** Due **Founded:** 1967.
Colours: Red/white/red **Change colours:** All blue.
Previous League: Abacus **Record Gate:** 1,250 v Wrexham, ground opener 1990.
Programme: 24 pages with entry **Programme Editor:** Alun Evans.
Midweek matches: Tuesday. **Clubhouse:** No - use Grove Park Club.
Local Newspapers: Sth Wales Evening Post, Port Talbot Guardian, Port Talbot Tribune, Sth Wales Echo.
Hons: Abacus Lg Div 1 87-88 88-89 (Yth Cup 91-92), Welsh Intermediate Cup 86-87.

BANGOR CITY

President: Lady Pennant **Chairman:** Keith Collier **Manager/Coach:** Ernie Walley
Comm. Manager: G Thomas.
Secretary: Alum Griffiths, 12 Lon-Y-Bryn, Menai Bridge, Anglesey, Gwynedd LL57 5NM (0248 712096).
Ground: The Stadium, Farrar Road, Bangor, Gwynedd (0248 355852).
Directions: Old A5 into Bangor, 1st left before railway station, ground on left by garage.
Seats: 900 **Cover:** 2,000 **Capacity:** 10,000 **Floodlights:** Yes **Founded:** 1876
Colours: All royal blue **Change colours:** All red. **Nickname:** Citizens
Previous Leagues: North Wales Coast 1893-98 1911-12/ The Combination 1898-1910/ North Wales Comb. 30-33/ West Mids (B'gham) 32-38/ Lancs. Comb. 38-39 46-50/ Cheshire Co. 50-68/ Northern Premier 68-79 81-82 84-92/ GMV Conference 79-81 82-84.
Midweek matches: Tuesday. **Record Gate:** 10,000 v Wrexham, Welsh Cup final 78-79.
Programme: 16 pages, 40p **Programme Editor:** Alan Monument/ John Jones.
Clubhouse: City of Bangor All Sports Club, open nightly and matchdays.
Local Press: Bangor Mail, Holyhead & Anglesey Mail, Nth Wales Weekly News, Nth Wales Chronicle, Liverpool Daily Post.
Hons: FA Tphy R-up 83-84, Northern Prem. Lg 81-82 (R-up 86-87, Lg Cup 68-69, Presidents Cup 88-89, Chal. Shield 87-88), Cheshire Co. Lg R-up 53-54 58-59, Lancs Comb. R-up 30-31, Welsh National Lg 27-28 (R-up 26-27), Nth Wales Coast Lg 1895-96, Welsh Cup 1888-89 95-96 1961-62 (R-up 27-28 60-61 63-64 72-73 77-78 84-85), Nth Wales Chal. Cup 26-27 35-36 36-37 37-38 46-47 51-52 57-58 64-65 67-68, Welsh Amtr Cup 1894-95 96-96 97-98 98-99 1900-01 02-03 04-05 05-06 11-12, Welsh Jnr Cup 1995-96 97-98 1919-20, Welsh All. Alves Cup 49-50 59-60 (Cookson Cup 61-62 68-69 84-85 86-87).

BRITON FERRY ATHLETIC

Chairman: Mr G Jenkins **President:** **Manager:** Carl Harris
Secretary: Mr S Jones, 54 Ruskin Street, Briton Ferry, West Glamorgan (0639 813401).
Ground: Old Road, Briton Ferry, West Glamorgan (0639 812458).
Directions: From A48; 1st right at traffic lights - ground half mile on right.
Seats: **Cover:** Yes **Capacity:** **Floodlights:** **Founded:** 1926.
Colours: Green & white quarters/white/white **Change colours:** All blue.
Previous League: Abacus **Programme:** Yes
Local Newspapers: **Midweek matches:** **Clubhouse:** Yes
Hons: Abacus Lg R-up 91-92 (Div 2 71-72), Welsh Lg Div 2 37-38 38-39 39-40 46-47.

CAERSWS

Chairman: Mr D Lewis **President:** **Manager:** Mickey Evans
Secretary: Mr A Rowlands, Fron Hafren Post Office, Caersws, Powys (0686 688201).
Ground: The Recreation Ground, Caersws, Powys.
Directions:
Seats: Yes **Cover:** Yes **Capacity:** **Floodlights:** Yes **Founded:** 1887.
Colours: Blue (white trim)/white/blue **Change colours:** All white.
Previous League: Cymru Alliance **Programme:** Yes
Clubhouse: Yes **Local Newspapers:**
Hons: Welsh Amtr Cup 60-61, Welsh Intermediate Cup 88-89 (R-up 91-92), Mid-Wales Lg 59-60 60-61 62-63 77-78
82-83 85-86 88-89 89-90 (Lg Cup 79-80 82-83 87-88 89-90), Central Wales Chal. Cup 77-78 82-83 87-88 89-90,
Montgomeryshire Chal. Cup 52-53 59-60 62-63 69-70 70-71 71-72 74-75 76-77 77-78 83-84 84-85 85-86 86-87 87-
88 88-89 90-91, Montgomeryshire Lg 77-78, Central Wales Yth Cup 69-70 72-73.

CONNAH'S QUAY NOMADS

Chairman: Mr R Morris **President:** **Manager:** Ray Jones
Secretary: Ray Hunter, 40 Brookdale Ave., Connah's Quay, Deeside, Clywd CH5 4LU (0244 831212).
Ground: Halfway Ground, Connah's Quay, Deeside, Clwyd.
Directions: On main coast road (A548) from Chester to Rhyl west end of Connah's Quay behind Halfway Hotel.
Seats: 105 **Cover:** Yes **Capacity:** 1,500 **Floodlights:** Yes **Founded:** 1946
Colours: White/blue/white **Change colours:** Maroon & blue stripes/blue/maroon.
Previous Leagues: Clywd/ Welsh Alliance/ Cymru Alliance
Record Gate: 1,200 v Grantham, F.A. Trophy.
Programme: 26 pages, 50p **Programme Editor:** Don Fowler.
Midweek matches: Tuesday **Clubhouse:** No, but Halfway Hotel is adjacent.
Local Newspapers: Evening Leader, Deeside Chronicle, Liverpool Daily Post.
Hons: Welsh Amtr Cup 52-53 54-55, Nth Wales Coast Amtr Cup 52-53, Welsh Intermediate Cup 80-81, Welsh
Alliance Cookson Cup 87-88, Welsh Youth Cup 47-48.

CONWY UNITED

Chairman: Mr C R Jones **President:** A Dale **Manager:** Mark Jones
Secretary: Mr Colin Jones, 'Iolyn', Iolyn Park, Conwy, Gwynedd (0492 593496).
Ground: Morfa Ground, Conwy, Gwynedd (0492 593861).
Directions: Leave A55 on 1st slip road after river tunnel and turn left towards Conwy. Sharp left immediately after
overhead railway bridge - ground 400yds on left of Penmaen Rd.
Seats: 120 **Cover:** 120 **Capacity:** 1,500 **Floodlights:** Yes **Founded:** 1977.
Colours: Tangerine/black/black **Change colours:** All blue.
Previous League: Vale of Conwy/ Gwynedd/ Welsh Alliance/ Cymru Alliance.
Record Gate: 600 v Bangor City.
Programme: 28 pages, 50p **Programme Editor:** Michael Fare.
Clubhouse: No **Midweek matches:** Tuesday.
Local Press: Liverpool Daily Post, Nth Wales Weekly News, Nth Wales Pioneer
Hons: Welsh Alliance 84-85 85-86, Barritt Cup 84-85, Welsh Intermediate Cup 81-82.

CWMBRAN TOWN

Chairman: George Thorneycroft **President:** John Colley **Manager:** Tony Wilcox
Secretary: Mr R Langley, 2 Trafalgar Ct, Penylan Rd, Penylan, Cardiff CF2 5RL (0222 483341).
Ground: Cwmbran Stadium, Henllys Way, Cwmbran (0633 66192/3).
Directions: M4 jct 26, follow signns to Cwmbran on A4042 & A4051, bear right after 3rd r'bout on A4051 to
stadium. One and a half miles from Cwmbran (BR).
Seats: 3,200 **Cover:** 4,700 **Capacity:** 13,200 **Floodlights:** Yes **Founded:** 1955.
Colours: White/black/white **Change colours:** Red/blue/red.
Previous Leagues: Gwent Co./ Abacus **Record Gate:** 3,000 v Hereford Utd, 83-84.
Programme: 28 pages, 50p **Programme Editor:** Maurice Salway.
Clubhouse: Pub hours, on ground **Local Press:** South Wales Argus, Cwmbran Free Press.
Midweek matches: Wednesday.
Hons: Abacus Lg Div 1 66-67 (Lg Cup 85-86 90-91).

EBBW VALE

Chairman: Mr C Rogers **President:** **Manager:** Riley Gray
Secretary: Mr D Coughlin, 107 Mount Pleasant Rd, Ebbw Vale, Gwent (0495 305993).
Ground: Eugene Cross Park, Ebbw Vale, Gwent (0495 302995).
Directions: From A465 follow signs to Ebbw Vale, 1st left at next two r'bouts - ground on left.
Seats: Yes **Cover:** Stand **Capacity:** 10,000 **Floodlights:** Yes **Founded:** 1950
Colours: Amber/black/black **Change colours:** Sky/navy/grey.
Previous League: Abacus **Record Gate:**
Programme: Yes **Programme Editor:**
Clubhouse: Yes **Local Newspapers:**
Midweek matches: Wednesday
Hons: Abacus Lg 87-88 (Div I 64-65, Southern Div 52-53, Div 2 East 60-61), Sth Wales Lg 03-04, Welsh Cup 25-26,
South Wales Snr Cup 04-05, Gwent Snr Cup 24-25 26-27 28-29 32-33 45-46 50-51.

FLINT TOWN UNITED

Chairman: Mr K Davies **President:** **Manager:** Tony Martin
Secretary: Mr N Griffiths, 18 Clifton Park Ave., Connah's Quay, Deeside, Clwyd (0244 814020).
Ground: Holywell Road, Flint (0352 733337).
Directions:
Seats: **Cover:** **Capacity:** **Floodlights:** **Founded:** 1886
Colours: Black & white stripes/black/red **Change colours:** Yellow/black/black.
Hons: Cymru Alliance 90-91, Welsh Cup 53-54, Welsh Amtr Cup 47-48, Welsh Alliance 54-55 55-56 56-57 89-90
(Alves Cup 53-54 89-90, Cookson Cup 52-53 88-89), Welsh Championship Cup 90-91, Nth Wales Coast Chal. Cup
90-91, Nth Wales Coast Amtr Cup 09-10 30-31 31-32 32-33 33-34 34-35 35-36 68-69.

HAVERFORDWEST COUNTY

Chairman: Roger Cottrell **President:** Jimmy Evans **Manager:** Ray Davies
Secretary: Mr C Saies, 46 Wesley Place, Trecwn, Haverfordwest, Dyfed (0348 840083).
Ground: The Bridge Meadow, Haverfordwest, Dyfed SA61 2XE (0437 2082).
Directions: A40 from Carmarthen, under walkway, left at 3rd r'bout with Bridge Meadow facing. 5 mins walk from Haverfordwest (BR).
Seats: 1,180 **Cover:** Yes **Capacity:** 5,000 **Floodlights:** Due **Founded:** Pre-1936.
Colours: Blue/white/white **Change colours:** All white.
Previous League: Abacus **Record Gate:** 3,000 v Milford Utd, 48-49.
Programme: 24 pages, 50p **Programme Editor:** Cliff Saies.
Midweek matches: Wednesday **Local Newspapers:** Western Telegraph.
Clubhouse: Every evening 2.30-11pm. Sat 2-11pm, Sun 12-2, 7-10.30pm. **Hons:** Abacus Lg 56-57 80-81 89-90 (Div 1 55-56 79-80, Lg Cup 60-61 88-89), W. Wales Snr Cup 81-82 88-89 91-92.

HOLYWELL TOWN

Chairman: Mr E Moore **President:** **Manager:** Andy Ericsen
Secretary: Mr P Hughes, 14 Brynteg, Wirral View, Holywell, Clwyd (0352 711818).
Ground: Halkyn Road, Holywell. **Founded:** 1906.
Directions: Off coast road at Halkyn Road or Greenfield.
Colours: Red & white stripes/red/red **Change colours:** Blue & white stripes/blue/blue.
Previous League: Cymru Alliance **Hons:** Nth Wales Coast Amtr Cup 13-14 21-22 57-58, Nth Wales Coast Jnr Cup 76-77, Nth Wales Coast Chal. Cup 86-87, Nth Wales Coast Yth Cup 75-76.

INTER-CARDIFF

Chairman: Chris Asprou **President:** Len Carrol **Manager:** Lyn Jones
Secretary: Paul Woollacott, 7 Lloyd Ave., Barry, South Glamorgan (0446 734389).
Ground: Cardiff Ath. Stadium, Leckwith Rd, Cardiff (0222 225345). **Directions:** M4 jct 33 to Barry (A4232) past Culverhouse Cross take right after 2 miles onto Leckwith Rd - stadium on right.
Seats: 2,500 **Cover:** Yes **Capacity:** 5,000 **Floodlights:** Yes **Founded:** 1990.
Colours: White/black/white **Change colours:** Yellow/black/black.
Prev. Ground: Cwrt-yr-Ala, Fairwater (pre-'92). **Prev. Names:** Sully FC, AFC Cardiff (merged '90).
Previous League: Barry & Dist./ Sth Wales Amtr/ Abacus
Record Gate: 1,500 v Cardiff City, Sth Wales Snr Cup 1974.
Programme: 24 pages, 50p **Programme Editor:** Terry Martin.
Clubhouse: Tues/Thurs/Sat 7-11pm at old ground (Cwrt-yr-Ala). **Midweek matches:** Tuesday.
Local Newspapers: Sth Wales Echo, Cardiff Post, Western Mail.
Hons: Abacus Lg Div 1 86-87, Sth Wales Amtr Lg 84-85 85-86. *As Sully: Sth Wales Amtr Lg Coronation Cup 69-70, Corinthian Cup 78-79, Abacus Lg Div 1 83-84 85-86 89-90 (Div 2 80-81), Sth Wales Snr Cup 80-81 81-82.*

LLANELLI

Chairman: John James **President:** **Manager:** Alwyn Mainwaring.
Secretary: Ray Davies, 29 Pemberton Park, Llanelli, Dyfed (0554 756176).
Ground: Strebonheath Park, Llanelli, Dyfed (0554 772973).
Directions: M4 jct 48, follow link road to Llanelli for four miles, right at 1st lights, left after Esso garage (signed Strebonheath), ground 200yds on right. 2 miles from Llanelli (BR).
Seats: 700 **Cover:** 700 **Capacity:** 3,750 **Floodlights:** Yes **Founded:** 1896.
Colours: All red **Change colours:** White/black/black.
Previous League: Southern/ Abacus **Record Gate:** 20,000 (before redevelopment).
Previous Ground: Halfway Park **Previous Name:** Llanelly FC.
Programme: 24 pages, 50p **Programme Editor:** Nigel Richards.
Midweek matches: Wednesday. **Local Newspapers:** Llanelli Star, Llanelli Weekly.
Clubhouse: Every evening 7-11pm, weekend lunchtimes **Hons:** Abacus Lg 29-30 32-33 70-71 76-77 77-78 (Lg Cup 29-30 74-75), West Wales Snr Cup 30-31 47-48 50-51 52-53 63-64 67-68 70-71 76-77.

LLANIDLOES TOWN

Chairman: Byron Hughes **President:** Richard Thomas **Manager:** Peter Canning
Secretary: Mr G E Parry, 22 Llysnant, Llanidloes, Powys SY18 6BD (0551 22550).
Ground: Victoria Park, Victoria Avenue, Llanidloes, Powys (0551 22196).
Directions: Ground alongside B4518 approx half mile from its northern junction with the A470. Travelling south take second exit from town bypass.
Seats: 200 **Cover:** Yes **Capacity:** 3,250 **Floodlights:** Yes **Founded:** 1875.
Colours: Yellow/green/yellow **Change colours:** White or green/yellow/green.
Previous League: Montgomeryshire & Dist./ Mid-Wales/ Cymru Alliance
Record Gate: 2,500 v Swansea, Welsh Cup 1971
Programme: 40p **Programme Editor:** G E Parry.
Midweek matches: Tuesday/Wednesday **Local Newspapers:** County Times/ Shropshire Star.
Clubhouse: Open Tue/Wed/Fri/Sat 7-11pm, Sunday lunchtimes 12-3pm.
Hons: Welsh Amtr Cup 20-21 64-65, Mid-Wales Lg(12) 24-26 30-32 33-34 35-36 38-39 46-47 50-51 71-72 73-74 80-81 (Lg Cup 50-51 53-54 58-59 61-62 80-81), Central Wales Cup 83-84, Montgomeryshire Cup(22) 12-13 19-22 24-25 27-35 38-39 46-47 48-49 53-54 61-62 64-65 72-73 75-76 79-80.

MAESTEG PARK ATHLETIC

Chairman: Bob Chapman **President:** Cedric Evans **Manager:** Gwynn Williams
Secretary: David Griffiths, 3 Padleys Close, Maesteg, Bridgend, Mid-Glamorgan (0656 733000).
Ground: Tudor Park, St Davids Place, Maesteg, Mid-Glamorgan (0656 732092-ground, 732029-club).
Directions: M6 jct 36, A4063 to Maesteg, top road into town past Gills garage, turn left at Royal Oak. At Gran pub turn left up hill to Red Cow pub, then right - ground on left.
Seats: None **Cover:** 200 **Capacity:** 2,000 **Floodlights:** Yes **Founded:** 1945.
Colours: Blue & white stripes/blue/blue **Change:** Yellow & green stripes/green/yellow.
Previous Ground: South Parade 65-70 **Record Gate:** 1,100 v Cardiff, f'light opener 1981
Previous Leagues: Bridgend & Dist./ Port Talbot & Dist./ Abacus.
Programme: 24 pages, with entry **Programme Editor:** David Griffiths.
Local Press: S. Wales Echo, Glamorgan Gazette, S. Wales Eveing Post. **Midweek matches:** Wed.
Clubhouse: 1-4pm, 6-11pm daily (matchdays all day). Meals and snacks available always.
Hons: Welsh Cup SF 91-92, Sth Wales Snr Cup 78-79 90-91, Abacus Lg R-up 79-80 (Div 1 78-79), Sth Wales Cup 78-79 90-91.

MOLD ALEXANDRA

Chairman: **President:**   **Manager:** Vernon Keep
Secretary: Mr K Biggs, 10 Powell Rd, Buckley, Clwyd (0244 545848).
Ground: Alyn Park, Mold (0352 4007).
Directions:
Seats: **Cover:**   **Capacity:**   **Floodlights:**   **Founded:** 1925.
Colours: White/blue/blue   **Change colours:** All blue.
Previous League: Cymru Alliance   **Record Gate:**
Hons: Welsh National Lg (Wrexham Area) 89-90, Nth Wales Coast Chal. Cup 85-86 89-90, Barritt Cup 89-90, N.E. Wales Chal. Cup 89-90, Nth Wales Coast Jnr Cup 30-31.

NEWTOWN

Chairman: Trevor Jones   **President:** M Foulkes.   **Manager:** Brian Coyne.
Secretary/Press Officer: Keith Harding, 7 Tradyddon Terrace, Newtown, Powys SY16 2ER (0686 628523).
Ground: Latham Park, Newtown, Powys (0686 626159).
Directions: A43 to Newtown, right at 1st lights into Back Lane and town centre - 400yds left into Park Street, 500yds right (at Library) into Park Lane - ground at end.
Seats: 200   **Cover:** 700   **Capacity:** 5,000   **Floodlights:** Yes   **Founded:** 1875.
Colours: Red/white/red   **Change colours:** Yellow/black/black.   **Nickname:** Robins
Previous Leagues: The Combination/ Central Wales/ Northern Premier.
Previous Name: Newtown White Star.   **Record Gate:** 5,002 v Swansea City, Welsh Cup 1954.
Best F.A. Cup season: 2nd Rd 1884-85. Also 1st Rd 1885-86.
Sponsors: Development Board for Rural Wales. Powys Printers. Ansells.
Players progressing to Football League: Clive Lloyd (Orient), John Lovent (C Palace & Exeter), Mike Bloor (Stoke & Lincoln), Ian Woan (Nottm Forest), Jonathan Hill (Rochdale), Ray Newlands (Plymouth), Mike Williams (Shrewsbury).
Programme: 72 pages, 30p   **Programme Editor:** Keith Harding.
Clubhouse: Open every evening. Hot & cold snacks, pool, darts.
Midweek matches: Tuesday.   **Local Press:** Shropshire Times, County Times & Express.
Hons: Welsh Lg 78-79 81-83 85-88 89-90, Welsh Cup 89-90, Welsh Cup 1878-79 94-95 (R-up 85-65 87-88 96-97), Welsh Amtr Cup 1954-55, Central Wales Lg 75-76 78-79 81-82 86-87 87-88 (R-up 51-52 52-53 55-56 56-57 74-75 82-83, Lg Cup 54-55 56-57 74-75 75-76 81-82 83-84), Arthur Barritt Cup 86-87, Central Wales Cup 74-75 80-81, Emrys Morgan Cup 80-81.

PORTHMADOG

Chairman: Iwan Jones   **President:** William Pike   **Manager:** Melir Owen
Secretary: Mr R I Griffiths, Llyn-yr-Eryr, Ynys, Cricieth, Gwynedd (0766 810349).
Ground: Y Traeth, Porthmadog (0766 514687).
Directions: At crossroads in town centre (by Woolworths) turn into Snowdon Street, pass Royal British Legion/Craft Centre onto unmade track, over railway line - ground on right.
Seats: 140   **Cover:** Yes   **Capacity:** 4,000   **Floodlights:** Yes   **Founded:** 1884.
Colours: Red & black stripes/black/red   **Change colours:** Yellow & green/sky/white.
Previous League: Welsh Alliance/ Cymru Alliance
Record Gate: 3,500 v Swansea, Welsh Cup 64-65.
Programme: 22 pages, 50p   **Programme Editor:** Dylan Ellis.
Clubhouse: Not on ground, but matchday refreshments available.
Local Newspapers: Caernarfon & Denbigh Herald/ Cambrian News/ Nth Wales Chronicle/ Y Wylan.
Midweek matches: Tuesday.
Hons: Welsh Amtr Cup 55-56 56-57 57-58, Nth Wales Amtr Cup 37-38 56-57 58-59 62-63, Nth Wales Coast Chal. Cup 55-56 73-74 74-75 76-77 77-78, Welsh Alliance 02-03 37-38 66-67 67-68 68-69 74-75 75-76 89-90 (Cookson Cup 75-76 89-90, Barritt Cup 77-78, Alves Cup 65-66 73-74 76-77), Nth Wales Amtr Cup 37-38 56-57 58-59 62-63.

Colwyn Bay's Steve Jones makes his way down the right wing as the H.F.S. Loans League Division One champions-elect win 4-2 away to Abacus League high-flyers Briton Ferry Athletic in the Allbright Bitter Welsh Cup. Photo - David Collins.

Connah's Quay defender Barry Thomas effects a spectacular goal-line clearance from Wrexham's Lee Jones in a Welsh Cup tie won 3-1 by the Fourth Division club. Photo - D Fowler.

Connah's Quay Nomads FC. Photo - D Fowler.

Clun Valley keeper M Rosser misses a cross as his team lose 0-3 at home to leaders Knighton Town in the Mid-Wales League. Photo - James Wright.

THE ABACUS LEAGUE

Hon. Secretary: K.J. Tucker,
16 The Parade, Merthyr Tydfil, Mid Glamorgan CF47 0ET.
(0388 762034).

SECRETARY'S REPORT

Abergavenny Thursdays retained their title without too much difficulty and few who saw them did not accept that they were by some distance the best side. Unlike previous years, the Thursdays did not make an impact on the National scene which was surprising losing to a South Wales Amateur League team Hoover Sports in the Intermediate Cup.

In some ways the team of the season was Briton Ferry Athletic who under the shrewd leadership of Carl Harris (the ex-Leeds and Welsh international) rose from seventh the previous season to finish as runners-up. The two defeats inflicted by Abergavenny were at the end the difference although the home defeat 3-2 in front of a crowd well in excess of 1,000 and the BBC T.V cameras was a marvellous advertisment for Abacus football. Both the promoted clubs Ebbw Vale and Caldicot Town did well to survive in their first season in the top division while Aberystwyth Town will have been disappointed that they did not really trouble the top two.

In Division One, Blaenrhondda were surprising winners with Manager Ronnie Dobbs assembling an experienced team that scored freely although last seasons' winners Morriston Town pushed them hard. At different times Ammanford Town and Port Talbot Athletic both relegated last season had chances to lead the table, but were not totally convincing. The promoted clubs, Cardiff Civil Service, Taffs Well and Risca United all finished comfortably in mid table which was a fine effort by them all. From an early point it looked as if Garw were going to struggle while Seven Sisters will have been very disappointed to drop from the top half of the table to the bottom.

In Division Two, the arrival of newly elected AFC Porth from the South Wales Amateur League took everyone by storm and it seemed that they would be going through the season undefeated, but lost in the penultimate week. Despite this it was still a marvellous introduction and they won the Division by 15 points, although Carmarthen Town were nearly as dominant due to a miserly defence that only conceded 19 goals, one less than the champions. At the other end of the table Trelewis again struggled finishing bottom while AFC Tondu and Abercyon Athletic did not inspire confidence and all will have been glad that re-election did not apply this year.

As with the Cymru Alliance, the season was dominated by the new League of Wales and most clubs realised that promotion/relegation would not apply as usual. In the end 10 clubs were elected into the new League although Ton Pentre many by declining an invitation. After much discussion the format for 1992/93 will be three divisions of 14 teams renamed Division One, Two and Three which will make rather more sense to all concerned. The new clubs are the champions of the South Wales Amateur League, Penrhiwceiber Rangers and the Gwent County League, Treowen Stars, in what will be a new era in Welsh football, and after a decade of support it is gratifying to know that Roger Gambrini and David O'Connor of Abacus Office Supplies are continuing their sponsorship.

NATIONAL DIVISION RESULTS 1991/92

HOME TEAM		1	2	3	4	5	6	7	8	9	10	11	12	13	14	15	16
1.	Abbergavenny Thurs	*	2-2	1-0	2-2	2-2	1-0	2-0	0-2	0-2	3-0	3-1	3-0	2-1	1-0	5-1	4-2
2.	Aberystwyth T.	1-2	*	2-3	3-1	2-0	1-2	2-1	2-0	5-1	3-1	1-0	1-0	1-0	4-0	2-0	1-2
3.	Afan Lido	1-3	0-4	*	4-1	0-1	1-2	3-2	1-1	2-2	4-0	3-3	1-2	2-1	1-1	1-0	4-0
4.	Brecon Corinthians	0-1	1-1	1-3	*	3-1	1-2	1-2	0-3	4-6	3-0	1-1	1-0	2-3	1-1	0-0	0-4
5.	Bridgend Town	0-1	0-1	2-1	2-0	*	0-6	0-0	2-2	0-1	1-1	0-4	1-1	2-2	1-4	0-1	0-2
6.	Briton Ferry A.	2-3	3-2	2-4	2-1	1-0	*	8-3	2-2	2-1	1-0	3-2	4-0	3-2	3-2	2-1	4-0
7.	Caldicot Town	1-1	1-4	2-2	1-3	3-0	1-2	*	0-0	1-3	3-0	3-0	0-0	2-3	0-1	1-0	0-2
8.	Cwmbran Town	1-4	1-3	4-2	1-0	3-0	3-4	2-2	*	3-3	2-1	1-2	1-0	3-1	3-1	5-2	2-2
9.	Ebbw Vale	0-4	0-2	2-2	2-3	0-2	2-1	1-0	0-0	*	2-1	0-4	1-1	1-2	0-3	2-2	0-2
10.	Ferndale Ath.	1-3	2-2	0-2	3-2	0-0	0-4	5-1	1-1	2-1	*	1-3	0-2	1-3	2-2	4-1	0-1
11.	Haverford west Co.	1-1	2-2	2-0	2-1	3-1	0-2	3-2	1-1	3-3	3-2	*	2-0	3-0	1-0	4-2	3-0
12.	Inter Cardiff	0-1	1-2	0-1	2-0	3-1	3-2	0-2	0-0	0-1	1-0	2-3	*	4-1	2-2	0-0	2-2
13.	Llanelli	0-2	2-2	1-5	4-2	3-3	0-2	1-0	3-0	1-0	1-1	1-1	2-1	*	1-2	2-3	1-1
14.	Maesteg Park	1-2	3-2	0-0	4-0	2-0	0-1	2-1	3-1	4-0	4-2	2-1	5-1	4-0	*	2-0	1-2
15.	Pembroke Boro'	1-4	2-2	4-1	1-2	3-2	4-0	5-1	0-2	5-0	3-0	0-1	0-0	5-1	1-1	*	2-0
16.	Ton Pentre	0-2	2-3	1-0	1-0	3-1	3-4	4-0	0-0	1-1	1-0	3-2	5-4	1-0	3-1	1-1	*

ABACUS LEAGUE TABLES 1991/92

PREM. DIVISION	P	W	D	L	F	A	PTS
Abergavenny Thurs.	30	23	5	2	64	24	74
Briton Ferry Ath.	30	23	1	6	76	43	70
Aberystwyth T.	30	18	6	6	65	35	60
Haverfordwest Co.	30	16	7	7	61	41	55
Ton Pentre	30	15	7	8	61	44	52
Maesteg Park Ath.	30	15	6	9	58	37	51
Cwmbran Town	30	11	12	7	50	42	45
Afan Lido	30	12	7	11	54	46	43
Pembroke Borough	30	10	7	13	50	48	37
Llanelli	30	9	7	14	44	61	34
Ebbw Vale	30	8	8	14	38	62	32
Inter Cardiff	30	7	8	15	32	45	28
Caldicot Town	30	6	6	18	35	69	24
Brecon Corinth.	30	6	5	19	36	61	23
Bridgend Town	30	4	8	18	25	58	20
Ferndale Athletic	30	4	6	20	31	63	18

DIVISION ONE	P	W	D	L	F	A	PTS
Blaenrhondda	32	18	8	6	76	47	62
Morriston Town	32	18	3	11	68	38	57
Ammanford Town	32	16	9	7	55	35	57
Port Talbot Ath	32	15	9	8	57	41	54
Caerleon	32	15	8	9	58	42	53
Pontypridd/Ynysybwl	32	15	4	13	57	53	49
Aberaman Ath.	32	14	6	12	52	48	48
Cardiff Civil Ser.	32	13	9	10	51	48	48
Taffs Well	32	13	7	12	42	41	46
Risca United	32	12	6	14	51	52	42
Llanwern	32	10	9	13	40	44	39
B.P.Llandarcy	32	11	5	16	39	54	38
Newport YMCA	32	11	4	17	47	55	37
Cardiff Corinthians	32	9	9	14	48	57	36
Pontllanfraith	32	8	10	14	38	54	34
Seven Sisters	32	8	7	17	39	73	31
Garw	32	6	8	19	30	73	26

DIVISION TWO	P	W	D	L	F	A	PTS
AFC Porth	32	28	3	1	79	20	87
Carmarthen Town	32	22	6	4	71	19	72
Skewen Athletic	32	18	7	7	61	33	61
Tonyrefail Welfare	32	16	8	8	64	36	56
Caerau	32	16	8	8	61	38	56
South Wales Pol.	32	16	8	8	61	38	56
Pontyclun	32	13	9	10	61	39	48
Treharris Ath.	32	12	7	13	61	54	43
Pontardawe	32	12	5	15	42	51	41
Pontlottyn B.F.	32	10	9	13	42	42	39
Goytre United	32	10	8	14	40	47	38
Milford United	32	11	5	16	48	68	38
Panteg	32	8	5	19	37	63	29
Cardiff Institute	32	7	7	18	41	67	28
AFC Tondu	32	6	6	20	38	69	24
Abercynon Athletic	32	6	6	20	38	69	24
Trelewis	32	4	8	20	28	69	20

Morriston Town's A.Payne gets in a first half shot, but his title chasing side lost 1-4 at Cardiff Civil Service in this Abacus fixture above (Photo: James Wright), and below, Pontllanfraith FC 1991/92 Photo: Chris Bedford.

Andy Morris opens the scoring for Berriew in a 3-1 home win over Aberystwyth based side U.C.W. in the Mid-Wales League. Photo - Leo Heonig.

ABACUS LEAGUE NATIONAL DIVISION NINE YEAR RECORD

	83/4	84/5	85/6	86/7	87/8	88/9	89/90	90/1	91/2
Abergavenny Thursdays						7	3	1	1
Aberystwyth Town					5	2	2	2	3
Afan Lido								12	8
Ammanford Town							14	16	
Barry Town	1	1	1	1	2	1			
Blaemrhondda	5	12	12	12	18				
Brecon Corinthians	10	8	4	10	12	5	12	8	14
Bridgend Town	7	2	2	7	15	6	10	11	15
Briton Ferry Athletic	6	10	6	8	9	11	6	7	2
Caerau	11	11	16	17					
Caerleon	2	5	15	14	16	16			
Caldicot Town									13
Cwmbran Town	12	15	5	3	4	14	4	9	7
Ebbw Vale	15	16	3	6	1	4	16		11
Ferndale Athletic								13	16
Haverfordwest County	4	4	9	5	6	3	1	3	4
Inter Cardiff					7	13	7	6	12
Llanelli	8	9	13	13	14		5	14	10
Maesteg Park Athletic	3	6	11	4	10	10	13	5	6
Milford United	16	17	7	11	17	17			
Pembroke Borough	14	14	10	16	8	9	8	10	9
Pontllanfraith	13	13	14	9	13	15	15		
Port Talbot Athletic		3	17	15	11	12	11	15	
Ton Pentre	9	7	8	2	3	8	9	4	5
No. of teams competing	16	17	17	17	18	17	16	16	16

ABACUS WELSH LEAGUE DIVISION ONE CLUBS 1992-93

ABERAMAN ATHLETIC

Secretary: Brian Fear, 28 Mostyn Street, Abercwmboi, Mid-Glamorgan (0443 472858).
Manager: John Herniman
Ground: Aberaman Park.   **Colours:** All royal blue.

AMMANFORD

Secretary: John Thomas, 154 Hendre Rd, Capel Hendre, Ammanford, Dyfed SA18 3TE (0269 643712).
Player: Alan Walters
Ground: Rice Road, Bettws, Ammanford, Dyfed (0269 592407).
Directions: From Quay Street Post Office head towards Bettws, cross railway line, left on sharp bend into Colonel Road, ground down narrow lane opposite Gwalia Stores.
Seats: Yes   **Cover:** Yes   **Floodlights:** No   **Clubhouse:** Yes   **Programme:** Yes
Club colours: Blue & white stripes/blue/blue
Founded: 1991 (Ammanford Town founded 1948 merged with Ammanford Athletic)

BLAENRHONDDA

Secretary: Gwynne Davies, 60 Elizabeth Street, Pentre, Rhondda, Mid Glamorgan (0443 433901).
Manager: Ronnie Dobbs   **Ground:** Blaenrhondda Park (0443 774772).
Founded: 1934   **Colours:** All royal blue.

BRECON CORINTHIANS

Secretary: Terry Harley, 20 Charles Street, The Watton, Brecon, Powys LD3 7HF. (0874 4568)
Manager: Ian Doherty
Ground: The Rich Field, The Watton, Brecon. (0656 55097)
Directions: Head from town centre, turn at Rich Way Road. Hourly bus from Merthyr takes 40 minutes
Cover: Yes   **Colours:** All red   **Floodlights:** Yes   **Clubhouse:** In Town   **Founded:** 1940.

BRIDGEND TOWN

Secretary: John Clanfield, 116 Merlin Crescent, Bridgend, Mid Glam. (0656 57386)
Manager: John Bekker
Ground: Coychurch Rd, Bridgend. (0656 55097)
Directions: M4 to Pencoed, left at Waterton Cross. 2nd right under railway brige.
Cover: Yes   **Floodlights:** Yes   **Clubhouse:** Yes   **Programme:** Yes   **Founded:** 1954.
Colours: Sky/navy/navy   **Change colours:** White/navy/navy

CAERLEON

Secretary: Len Blakemore, 32 Tan House Drive, Caerleon, Gwent NP6 1BS (0633 420367).
Manager: John Watkins
Ground: Cold Bath Road, Caerleon, Gwent (0633 420074).
Colours: Green/white/green   **Founded:** 1889.

CALDICOT TOWN

Secretary: Mr K Trigg, 8 Stone Cottages, Sudbrook, Newport, Gwent (0291 430180)
Manager: Peter Addis   **Ground:** Jubilee Way, Caldicot, Gwent (0291 423519)
Directions: M4 – take Jnt 22 signs to town centre. Ground behind town centre car park.
Seats: No   **Cover:** Yes   **Programme:** Yes   **Floodlights:** No   **Founded:** 1953
Colours: Yellow/black/black   **Club colours:** White/black/black

CARDIFF CIVIL SERVICE

Secretary: Dennis Richards, 55 York Street, Canton, Cardiff CF5 1ND (0222 230387).
Manager: Kevin Parkins.
Ground: Civil Service Sports Ground, Santatorium Rd, Leckwith, Cardiff.
Directions: West side of Cardiff, near Cardiff City FC.
Seats: No   **Cover:** No   **Clubhouse:** Yes   **Floodlights:** Due   **Programme:** Yes
Founded: 1963   **Colours:** Green & white hoops/white/white

FERNDALE ATHLETIC

Secretary: Glyn Lewis, Dan-yr-allt, Brown Street, Ferndale, Rhondda CF43 4SF. (0443 730201)
Manager: John Humphreys
Ground: Darran Park, Ferndale. (0443 731060)
Directions: From Rhondda Hotel in main street go up the hill to the ground
Seats: Yes   **Cover:** Yes   **Programme:** Yes   **Floodlights:** Yes   **Founded:** 1945.
Colours: Amber/black/black   **Club colours:** Blue/black/black

MORRISTON TOWN

Secretary: John Slater, 133 Lone Rd, Clydach, Swansea SA6 5JB (0792 842530).
Manager: John Doyle/ John Dickerson.
Ground: The Dingle, Morriston, Nr Swansea (0792 702033).
Directions: Through Morriston centre and bear right at foot of hill - ground quarter mile on left.
Seats: No   **Cover:** No   **Programme:** Yes   **Floodlights:** No   **Founded:** 1951.
Club colours: Red/black/red.

PEMBROKE BOROUGH

Secretary: Mr P Tallet, 6 Shropshire Rd, Pembroke Dock, Dyfed (0646 682234).
Manager: Peter Fearn
Ground: London Road, Pembroke Dock, Pembroke. (0636 682239)
Directions: Take A477 from St Clears to Pembroke Dock (not Pembroke). Straight on at roundabout, pass rugby ground on right and football ground is also on right.
Cover: Yes   **Programme:** Yes   **Clubhouse:** Yes   **Founded:** 1935.
Colours: Black & white stripes/black/black   **Change colours:** Amber/black/black

PONTYPRIDD TOWN

Secretary: Adrian Dumphy, 1 Wingfield Close, Pontypridd CF37 4AB (0443 405924).
Manager: Joe Gibson   **Ground:** TBA
Colours: All sky   **Previous Ground:** Ynysbwl Rec. (pre-1992).
Previous Names: Ynysbwl 1995-1991/ Pontypridd-Ynysbwl 91-92

PORT TALBOT ATHLETIC

Secretary: Alf Germaine, 1 Bordsfield Cottage, Graig, Pontypridd CF37 1LE (0443 407868).
Manager: Barry Colwill
Ground: Victoria Park, Aberavon, Port Talbot (0639 8832465).
Directions: On left of main road from Port Talbot to Aberavon. 20 mins walk from Port Talbot (BR).
Cover: Yes   **Programme:** Yes   **Floodlights:**   **Clubhouse:** Yes   **Founded:** 1901
Colours: All blue

TON PENTRE

Secretary: Paul Willoughby, 37 Bailey Street, Ton Pentre, Rhondda, Mid Glam CF41 7EN. (0443 438281)
Manager: John Emmanuel
Ground: Ynys Park, Ton Row, Ton Pentre, Rhondda (0443 432813).
Directions: A4058 Pontypridd to Treorchy Plain Road, turn at Thames Rico Garage, station Ton Pentre quarter of a mile from ground. Two minute walk from Ystrad Rhondda railway station
Cover: Yes   **Floodlights:** Yes   **Clubhouse:** Yes   **Programme:** Yes   **Founded:** 1935
Colours: Red & white stripes/red/red   **Change colours:** All blue

ABACUS LEAGUE DIVISION TWO CLUBS 1992-93

A.F.C. PORTH

Secretary: Ray Hacker, 57 High Street, Cymmer, Porth (0443 684580).
Ground: Dinas Park, Dinas (0443 687161)
Founded: 1987 (prev. Beatus Utd)   **Colours:** Maroon & blue stripes/blue/blue

B.P. LLANDARCY

Secretary: David Maddock, 20 Brookfield, Neath Abbey, Neath SA10 7EG (0639 636327).
Ground: B.P. Sports Ground, Llandarcy (0792 813232x2451)
Founded: 1922   **Colours:** White/white/yellow.

CAERAU

Secretary: David Lewis, 19a Hermon Rd, Caerau, Mid-Glamorgan (0656 734388).
Ground: Caerau Football Ground (0656 732471)
Founded: 1901   **Colours:** All red

CARDIFF CORINTHIANS

Secretary: G Thomas, 9 Palace Rd, Llandaff, Cardiff (0222 562624).
Ground: Riverside Ground, Radyr, Cardiff (0222 843407).
Directions: Left out of Radyr station, under railway - ground through gate marked cricket club.
Founded: 1897   **Colours:** Maroon & amber quarters/maroon/maroon

CARMARTHEN TOWN

Secretary: Alan Latham, 3 Maesdolau, Idole, Carmarthen (0267 232432).
Ground: Richmond Park, Carmarthen (0267 232101).
Founded: 1953   **Colours:** Old gold/black/black

FIELDS PARK PONTLLANFRAITH

Secretary: D P Chiplin, 26 Glannant Street, Cwmfelinfach, Ynysddu, Gwent NP1 7HB (0495 200349).
Ground: Islwyn Park (0495 224512)
Founded: 1964   **Colours:** Royal blue/blue/blue

GARW

Secretary: Tecwyn Thomas, Drosglo, 5 Victoria Street, Pontycymmer, Mid-Glamorgan (0656 870411).
Ground: Blandy Park, Pontycymmer
Founded: 1945   **Colours:** Red/black/red

LLANWERN

Secretary: Stephen Donovan, 37 Nash Road, Newport, Gwent (0633 280615).
Ground: British Steel Sports Club, Llanwern, Newport, Gwent (0633 273790).
Founded: 1962 (prev. Spencer Works)   **Colours:** Royal blue/blue/blue

NEWPORT Y.M.C.A.

Secretary: John Lewis, 23 Bredon Close, Trenewydd Park, Risca, Gwent (0633 615417).
Ground: Mendalgief Road, Newport, Gwent (0633 263387)
Founded: 1971   **Colours:** Red/black/black

RISCA UNITED

Secretary: Mrs Ann Luckwell, 137 Ty Isaf Park Ave., Pontyminster, Risca, Gwent (0633 613434).
Ground: Ty Asaf Park, Risca, Gwent
Founded: 1946   **Colours:** Black & white stripes/black/black

SEVEN SISTERS

Secretary: Stephen Parfitt, 59 Main Road, Dyffryn Cellwen, Nr Neath, West Glamorgan (0639 701370).
Ground: Welfare Ground, Church Road, Seven Sisters
Founded: 1946   **Colours:** Green/grey/grey

SKEWEN ATHLETIC

Secretary: T J Harris, 22 Goshen Park, Skewen, Neath SA10 6PT (0792 814632).
Ground: Tennant Park, Skewen, Neath
Founded: 1949   **Colours:** White & sky stripes/white/white

TAFF'S WELL

Secretary: Ray Toghill, 38 Heol Berry, Gwaelod-y-Garth CF4 8HB (0222 811356).
Ground: Rhiw'r Ddar, Taff's Well (0222 811080)
Founded: 1947   **Colours:** Yellow/blue/yellow

TONYREFAIL WELFARE

Secretary: Peter Jones, 13 Rees Street, Treorchy, Mid-Glamorgan (0443 773460).
Ground: Welfare Park, Tonyrefail
Founded: 1926   **Colours:** Red & black stripes/black/red

ABACUS LEAGUE DIVISION THREE CLUBS 1992-93

ABERCYNON ATHLETIC

Secretary: Jeffrey Dudley, 131 Abercynon Rd, Abercynon (0443 741433).
Ground: Parc Abercynon (0443 740238)
Founded: 1933   **Colours:** Black & white/black/black & white.

A.F.C. TONDU

Secretary: Steve Pope, 102 Bryn Road, Tondu, Nr Bridgend (0656 724711).
Ground: Pandy Park, Aberkenfig (0656 720323)
Founded: **Colours:** Yellow & black/black.

CARDIFF INSTITUTE OF HIGHER EDUCATION

Ground: Cardiff Institute of High Education, Cyncoed Rd, Cardiff
Founded: 1957   **Colours:** Maroon & sky/black/maroon

GOYTRE UNITED

Secretary: Boris Suhanski, 20 Goytre Cres., Port Talbot (0639 886826).
Ground: Glenhafod Park, Goytre (0639 898983).
Founded: **Colours:** Blue & white stripes/blue/blue

MILFORD UNITED

Secretary: Ken Lowe, 17 Milton Crescent, Pill, Milford Haven, Dyfed (0646 692194).
Ground: Marble Hall Rd, Milford Park (0646 693691)
Founded: **Colours:** Red/white/red & white

PANTEG

Secretary: Bob Small, 26 Laburnum Drive, New Inn, Pontypool (0495 756280).
Ground: Panteg House, Greenhill Rd, Griffithstown, Pontypool.
Founded: 1940   **Colours:** Black & white/black/black.

PENRHIWCEIBER RANGERS

Secretary: C Kerr (0443 476134)   **Ground:** Glasbrook Field.
Colours: All red.   **Previous League:** Sth Wales Amtr (champs 91-92).

PONTARDAWE ATHLETIC

Secretary: David Jones, 9 Denbigh Close, Morriston, Swansea (0792 798142).
Ground: Recreation Ground, Pontardawe (0792 865538/862228).   **Colours:** White/black/black.

PONTLOTTYN BLAST FURNACE

Secretary: Barry Horsman, Wordesley, Gwerthonor Road, Gilfach, Bargoed CF8 8JS (0443 831606).
Ground: Welfare Ground, Pontlottyn.
Founded: 1968   **Colours:** Yellow/green/yellow.

PONTYCLUN

Secretary: P Shilton, 3 Lilac Drive, Chandlers Beach, Llantwit (0443 217305).
Ground: The Ivor Park, Pontyclun.
Founded: 1896   **Colours:** Blue/yellow/yellow.

SOUTH WALES CONSTABULARY

Secretary: A Davies, 147 Bwlch Road, Falwater, Cardiff (0222 569105).
Ground: Waterton Cross, Bridgend (0656 55555x286/406).
Founded: 1969   **Colours:** Royal/white/royal.

TREHARRIS ATHLETIC

Secretary: Mike Casey, 10 Windsor Rd, Edwardsville, Treharris (0443 411153).
Ground: Commercial Terrace, Treharris.
Founded: 1889   **Colours:** Blue & white stripes/blue/blue

TRELEWIS

Secretary: J T Toner, 12 Willow Rise, Duffryn Park, Hengoed (0443 835078).
Ground: Welfare Ground, Trelewis
Directions: Through Trelewis village heading north and take sharp right after bridge - continue past houses to end of road, across wasteland to ground.
Founded: 1966   **Colours:** White (red trim)/red/red.

TREOWEN STARS

Ground: Bush Park, Treown, Newbridge.
Colours: White/black/black.   **Previous League:** Gwent County.

Llanfairpwllgwyngyllgogerychwyndropell-llantisiliogogococh FC (Llanfairpwll for short) of the Sealink Welsh Alliance. (Any letters suggesting the above has been mis-spelt will be immediately binned -Ed.!). Back Row (L/R): C Parry, G Jones, S Fowler, P McCann, M Davies, R Jones, P Kasparek. Front: D Williams, F Donahue, G Owens, D Gilford, G Critchlow, G Parry. Photo - A Monument.

Builth Wells goalkeeper A Hayler catches a cross despite the challenge of Morda United's Steve Oliver as the two sides draw 1-1 in a Mid-Wales League fixture. Photo - James Wright.

Rhydymwyn FC of the Sealink Welsh Alliance. Back Row (L/R): Sharples, Thomas, Moxon, Hall, McNally, Messham, Allen. Front: M Hughes, J Hughes, Arnold, Wynne, D Williams. Photo - A Monument.

Bangor Waterloo, Carnarfon & District League champions 1991-92. Back Row (L/R): S Jones (Manager), G Jones (Secretary), M Owen, P Lucas, I Davies, L L Jones, A Roberts, S Devlin (club official). Front: D Jones, D Austin, R Jones, P Owens, R Roberts, D Owen, S Evans, M Thomas. Photo - A Monument.

Action from Lex XI's home fixture against Connah's Quay Nomads in the Manweb Cymru Alliance. Lex used Wrexham FC's Racecourse Ground during 1991-92. Photo - D Fowler.

MANWEB CYMRU ALLIANCE

Hon. Secretary: T.G. Hewitt,
30 High Park, Hawarden, Deeside, Clwyd.

SECRETARY'S REPORT

After the inaugural season the Manweb Cymru Alliance was increased to 16 clubs with the addition of Llansantffraid and Brymbo during the close season but despite successfully completing the full programme the season will be remembered for the "shadow" of the League of Wales and the deduction of 66 points from the champions - elect, Welshpool Town.

Everyone had great sympathy with Welshpool Town who had led all season, only in April to discover that one of their players, Billy Morris was the subject of a seven year ban by the Staffordshire FA, so ineligible! There is no doubt that the club were blameless and had no knowledge of the misdeneanour at all with the irresponsible action of the player having far-reaching consequences - a lot of clubs no doubt thought there but the "grace of god go us". So from their deserved place at the top of the table, the Management Committee had little option but to deduct all the points they had won while Morris was in the team to the bottom of the table.

The acrimonious birth of the League of Wales cast a 'shadow' which eventually saw 8 clubs leaving to join the national competition - more than 50%, quite a body blow. Eight new clubs - Cefn/Druids, Ruthin Town, Rhos Aelwyd, Knighton Town, Morda United, Rhayader Town, Wrexham Reserves and Rhyl - have been elected which means 16 clubs for the 1992/93 season.

With regard to the football then Flint Town United could not repeat their success of last season, but the newcomers, Llansantffraid with a late run finished very creditably as runners up. After the "Welshpool affair" Caersws triumph was somewhat tarnished although the mid-Wales club are progressive off the field as well with new changing rooms and stand. With the move to the Racecourse (home of Wrexham AFC) everyone expected Lex XI to challenge but despite success for a second year in the League Cup they flattered to deceive. The other newcomers, Brymbo found life difficult especially before Christmas but with their marvellous playing surface they seemed by the end of the season to come to terms with the level needed.

All in all a quite eventul season which Secretary, Terry Hewitt must have been glad came to an end with a heartful plea that the 1992/93 campaign sees an improvement.

MANWEB CYMRU ALLIANCE RESULTS 1991/92

HOME TEAM	1	2	3	4	5	6	7	8	9	10	11	12	13	14	15	16
1. Brymbo	*	1-0	1-2	1-1	0-6	0-7	2-4	0-3	0-4	3-1	1-2	0-4	0-1	1-4	1-2	0-6
2. Caersws	3-0	*	3-0	0-1	3-6	2-1	1-2	3-1	1-0	3-0	2-2	6-1	9-0	4-0	0-0	1-1
3. Carno	0-4	1-2	*	0-1	1-0	1-2	1-2	0-4	1-1	0-1	4-2	0-3	4-2	1-1	2-4	0-2
4. Connah's Quay C.	6-1	0-0	3-0	*	1-1	2-1	4-0	1-1	2-2	1-1	1-1	2-0	0-0	0-2	0-2	0-2
5. Conwy United	7-1	0-0	3-0	2-3	*	1-4	2-1	4-2	4-1	2-1	0-2	1-1	0-2	3-2	1-3	1-2
6. Flint Town Utd	4-2	1-1	3-1	1-1	4-2	*	1-0	3-2	1-3	3-1	0-2	2-0	3-4	0-0	1-1	2-1
7. Gresford Athletic	0-1	3-1	4-3	1-2	0-1	0-0	*	1-2	0-0	2-1	0-1	0-1	0-2	0-2	1-3	1-2
8. Holywell Town	6-0	0-0	3-1	1-1	2-2	0-3	4-1	*	2-3	1-1	0-5	1-2	1-0	1-1	0-0	1-2
9. Lex XI	2-2	0-6	3-1	0-1	0-3	0-2	2-2	1-0	*	1-0	2-1	2-1	3-1	2-1	1-1	0-3
10. Llanidloes Town	4-1	0-4	0-0	1-0	2-3	1-1	2-2	1-0	3-2	*	0-1	0-1	0-3	2-1	4-2	0-0
11. Llansantffraid	4-0	1-1	3-0	0-0	2-0	2-2	2-1	3-1	1-1	4-1	*	1-2	5-1	3-1	0-0	1-3
12. Mold Alexandra	3-1	1-2	2-1	3-4	1-3	2-1	0-1	1-1	0-1	0-1	2-1	*	0-2	1-1	3-1	1-3
13. Mostyn	5-2	2-2	3-1	2-0	1-2	1-1	0-1	1-1	5-0	3-2	1-4	2-1	*	3-1	1-1	2-2
14. Penrhyncoch	5-1	1-2	4-2	0-0	0-1	1-2	2-2	3-2	1-1	4-4	5-2	3-1	2-0	*	4-1	0-1
15. Porthmadog	7-1	0-2	0-1	3-1	2-0	2-2	1-1	5-4	3-3	2-1	0-0	3-1	5-2	6-0	*	2-0
16. Welshpool Town	5-1	1-1	2-0	4-2	1-1	1-0	8-0	1-1	2-2	7-1	2-0	0-1	3-0	2-0	5-1	*

MANWEB CYMRU ALLIANCE 91-92

	P	W	D	L	F	A	PTS
Caersws	30	15	10	5	65	27	55
Llansantffraid	30	15	8	7	58	34	53
Porthmadog	30	14	10	6	63	43	52
Flint Town United	30	14	9	7	58	37	51
Conwy United	30	15	5	10	62	45	50
Connah's Quay N.	30	11	12	7	41	33	45
Mostyn	30	13	6	11	52	56	45
Lex XI	30	11	10	9	43	50	43
Penrhyncoch	30	11	7	12	53	51	40
Mold Alexandra	30	12	3	15	40	46	*36
Holywell Town	30	7	10	13	48	49	31
Llanidloes Town	30	8	7	15	37	57	31
Gresford Athletic	30	8	6	16	33	54	30
Carno	30	5	2	23	28	69	17
Brymbo	30	4	2	24	29	108	14
Welshpool Town	30	20	7	3	74	23	+1

* - 3 points deducted
+ - 66 points deducted

MANWEB CYMRU ALLIANCE CLUBS 1992-93

BRYMBO
Secretary: Mr C Morris, Brymbo Sports & Social Complex, Tanyfron, Brymbo, Clwyd (978 752577/755209).
Ground: Brymbo Sports Complex, Tanyfron, Brymbo, Clwyd.
Founded: 1943 (As Brymbo Steelworks)   **Colours:** Amber (black trim)/black/black.

CARNO
Secretary: Mrs T Hughes, 32 Maes-y-Dre, Caersws, Powys (0686 688713).
Ground: The Recreation Ground, Carno.
Founded: 1960   **Colours:** Green/black/black.

CEFN DRUIDS
Secretary: Mr T Johnson, 127 Cae Gwilym Lane, Cefn Mawr, Clwyd (0978 823623).
Ground: Ty Mawr   **Previous League:** Welsh National (Wrexham Area).
Founded: 1992 (merger of Cefn Albion (founded 1968) and Druids United (founded 1873).

GRESFORD ATHLETIC
Secretary: Mr D C Rowland, 26 Gorse Cres., Marford, Nr Wrexham (0978 855354).
Ground: Clappers Lane, Gresford.
Founded: 1946   **Colours:** Red/white/red.

KNIGHTON TOWN
Secretary: Mrs C Sutton, 1 Underhill Crescent, Knighton, Powys (0547 528953).
Ground: Bryn-y-Castell (0547 528999).
Floodlights: Yes   **Colours:** All red   **Previous League:** Mid-Wales (pre-1992).

LLANSANTFFRAID
Secretary: Mr G Ellis, Bro Dawal, Llansantffraid, Powys (0691 828583).
Ground: Recreation Field, Llansantffraid.
Founded: 1945   **Colours:** Green/black/green.

LEX XI
Secretary: Mr P Jones, 18 Mayflower Drive, Marford, Wrexham, Clwyd (0978 854028).
Ground: Stansty Park, Wrexham (0978 261351).
Founded: 1965   **Colours:** Amber/black/amber.

MORDA UNITED
Secretary: Mr W M Clarke, 50 Langland Rd, Oswestry, Shropshire (0691 661985).
Ground: Weston Road, Morda, Shropshire (0691 659621).
Founded: 1976   **Colours:** Yellow/blue/blue
Previous League: Mid-Wales (pre-1992)   **Hons:** Mid-Wales Lg R-up 91-92

MOSTYN
Secretary: B Hughes, Kevalyn, Penrhos Estate, Mostyn, Clwyd (0745 560822).
Ground: Maes Pennant Field.
Founded: 1912   **Colours:** Yellow/blue/blue

PENRHYNCOCH
Secretary: Mr R J Ellis, 4 Maes Laura, Aberystwyth, Dyfed (0970 828992).
Ground: Cae Baker, Penrhyncoch (0970 828992).
Founded: 1965   **Colours:** Yellow (blue trim)/blue/yellow.

RHYADER TOWN
Secretary: Mr P Woosnam, Highlands, St Harmons Rd, Rhyader, Powys (0597 811286).
Ground: Y Weirglodd, Rhyader.
Previous League: Mid-Wales   **Colours:** Red & white stripes/red/red

RHYL

Secretary: Mr D Williams, 81a Dyserth Rd, Rhyl, Clwyd (0745 354773).
Ground: Belle Vue, Rhyl, Clwyd (0745 338327).
Founded: 1883   **Colours:** White/black/white   **Previous League:** Northern Prem.

RHOS AELWYD

Secretary: Mr D G Parry, Penrallt, Queen Street, Rhosllanerchugog (0978 845148).
Ground: Ponclau Banks, Rhosllanerchugog.
Founded: 1948   **Cols:** All blue
Previous League: Welsh National (Wrexham Area)

RUTHIN TOWN

Secretary: Mr B Lewis, 40 Maeshafod, Ruthin, Clwyd (0824 22828).
Ground: Memorial Playing Fields, Ruthin (0824 22766).
Previous League: Welsh National (Wrexham Area).
Founded: 1951   **Colours:** Blue & white stripes/blue/blue.

WELSHPOOL TOWN

Secretary: Mr J A Bartley, 24 Brynglas, Welshpool, Powys (0938 554464).
Ground: Maesydre, Welshpool.
Founded: 1878   **Colours:** White/black/black.

WREXHAM RESERVES

Secretary: Mr D L Rhodes, Racecourse Ground, Mold Rd, Wrexham (0978 262129).
Ground: The Racecourse Ground, Mold Road, Wrexham.   **Founded:** 1873.
Colours: Red/white/red   **Previous League:** Welsh National (Wrexham Area).

Llansantffraid FC - Runners-up in their first season in the Manweb Cymru Alliance. Photo - James Wright.

Morda United will join the Manweb Cymru Alliance in 1992-93. Here their F Mottram puts over a cross as the Shropshire side draw 1-1 away to Builth Wells in the Mid-Wales League. Photo - James Wright.

OTHER MAJOR LEAGUES

SEALINK WELSH ALLIANCE

PREM. DIVISION	P	W	D	L	F	A	PTS
Llangefni T.	28	21	3	4	84	27	66
Y Felinheli	28	20	5	3	70	35	65
Bangor Reserves	28	18	4	6	70	37	58
Cemaes Bay	28	16	5	7	58	37	53
Llandudno	28	15	7	6	74	41	52
Llantairpwll	28	12	5	11	60	51	41
Pilkingtons	28	9	8	11	40	44	35
Rhydymwyn	28	8	9	11	40	47	33
Conwy United	28	7	10	11	29	41	31
Connahs QN*	28	9	6	13	35	51	30
Mochdre	28	7	6	15	40	54	27
L.Llanberis	28	7	5	16	29	62	26
Rhyl	28	7	3	18	28	66	24
Nantlle V.	28	5	7	16	41	58	22
Llanrwst U.	28	5	5	18	26	71	20

* - 3pts deducted.

A hard fought battle for the championship saw Llangefni Town overcome the challenge of Y Felinheli and Bangor City to win the title. The Anglesey club's single point margin over Felinheli gave them their second championship in the two years since they left the Gwynedd League. A decisive factor was the 84 goals that the team scored, 14 more than their nearest rivals. Camaes Bay were also in a position to threaten the leaders, with games in hand, but they could only manage 4th spot. Llangefni also completed a notable double by winning the Welsh Intermediate Cup.

At the other end of the table, Mochdre rallied after a poor start to pull comfortably away from bottom spot, leaving Llanwrst with the wooden spoon. Mention should, also be made of Nantlle Vale. Although they only finished just above Llanwrst, their 22 points compared with a nil return in 1990/91.**Tony Higgs.**

READ CONSTRUCTION WELSH NATIONAL LEAGUE (Wrexham area)

PREM. DIVISION	P	W	D	L	F	A	PTS
Wrexham Res	26	18	2	6	63	28	56
Ruthin Town	26	17	3	6	58	29	54
Marchwiel Villa	26	17	3	6	47	29	54
New Broughton	26	16	2	8	48	32	50
Chirk AAA	26	14	5	7	46	28	47
Llay RBL	26	12	5	9	41	33	41
Llay Welfare	26	11	5	10	45	49	38
Corwen	26	10	6	10	38	40	36
Penycae	26	8	5	13	37	43	29
Rhostyllen	26	8	4	14	36	42	28
Rhos Aelwyd	26	7	6	13	36	43	27
Buckley	26	7	4	15	38	66	25
Cefn Albion	26	6	4	16	25	54	22
Druids United	26	2	4	20	19	62	10

DIVISION TWO	P	W	D	L	F	A	PTS
British Aerospace	34	28	3	3	130	39	87
Gresford Res.	34	21	5	8	115	70	68
Johnstown Res	34	22	2	10	82	55	68
Marchwiel Res	34	20	6	8	87	51	66
JCB Transmission	34	21	3	10	75	66	63
Penley Res	34	18	7	9	91	60	61
Ruthin Colts	34	18	5	11	62	58	59
Llangollen	34	18	4	12	95	68	58
Corwen Res	34	15	5	13	74	73	50
Llay Welfare Res	34	14	6	14	59	53	48
Glynceiring	34	11	7	16	61	59	40
Overton Res	34	10	7	17	54	83	37
Castell AC Res	34	9	7	18	60	79	34
Penycae Res	34	8	8	18	63	90	32
OC Fibreglass	34	8	6	20	63	84	30
Druids Res	34	7	7	20	35	98	28
Llanuwchllyn	34	7	5	22	44	95	26
Bala Town Res	34	5	3	26	37	104	18

DIVISION ONE	P	W	D	L	F	A	PTS
Treuddyn Villa	34	23	5	5	99	42	74
Lex XI Res	34	23	4	7	114	47	73
Overton Ath.	34	22	5	7	93	46	71
Penley	34	17	11	5	82	47	62
Castell AC	34	17	5	12	69	56	56
Ruthin Town Res	34	15	8	11	68	58	54
Kelloggs	34	16	6	12	63	61	54
New Brighton	34	15	7	12	71	48	52
Kinnerton	34	13	8	13	73	71	47
Bradley Park Rgs	34	14	6	14	81	76	48
Bala Town	34	11	10	13	58	65	43
Rubery Owen	34	12	5	17	93	98	38
Rhos Aelwyd Res	34	11	5	18	69	96	38
Johnston Ath.	34	12	2	20	63	92	38
Brymbo Res *	34	11	7	16	71	80	37
Cefn Albion Res	34	9	8	17	66	74	35
New Broughton *	34	8	8	21	41	98	20
Mynydd Isa **	34	3	4	27	49	126	7

* - 3pts deducted
** - 6pts deducted

'RICHARDS BUILDERS' MID WALES LEAGUE

	P	W	D	L	F	A	PTS
Knighton Town	30	20	9	1	66	21	69
Morda United	30	21	5	4	110	28	68
Caersws Reserves	30	18	8	4	72	22	62
Berriew	30	17	8	5	53	25	59
Aberystwyth Res.	30	18	3	9	68	44	57
Talgarth	30	15	6	9	65	40	51
Newtown Reserves	30	14	9	7	59	34	51
Builth Wells	30	12	8	10	57	38	44
Rhayader Town	30	13	4	13	76	62	43
Penparcau	30	12	6	12	53	59	42
Llandrindod Wells	30	11	8	11	51	45	41
Kington Town	30	8	3	19	42	68	27
UCW Aberystwyth	30	6	2	22	39	85	20
Crickhowell	30	4	8	18	28	73	20
Llanidloes T Res	30	2	5	23	19	116	11
Clun Valley	30	1	4	25	21	113	7

WELSH LEAGUE CONSTITUTIONS 1992-93

Sealink Welsh Alliance: Bangor City Reserves, Cemaes Bay, Connah's Quay Nomads Reserves, Conwy United Reserves, Llandudno, Landyrnog United, Llanfairpwll, Llangefni Town, Llanrwst United, Locomotive Llanberis, Mochdre, Nantlle Vale Penygroes, Nefyn United, Penmaenmawr Phoenix, Pilkingtons St Asaph, Rhydymwyn, Rhyl Reserves, Y Felinheli.

Richards Builders Mid-Wales League: Aberystwyth Town Reserves, Berriew, Builth Wells, Caersws Reserves, Clun Valley, Kington Town, Knighton Town Reserves, Llandrindod Wells, Llanidloes Town Reserves, Machynlleth, Newtown Reserves, Penparcau, Penrhyncoch Reserves, Presteigne St Andrews, Talgarth, University College Wales, Vale of Arrow, Waterloo Rovers.

Read Construction Welsh National League (Wrexham Area):
Premier Division: Buckley, Castell Alun Colts Hope, Chirk Amateur Athletic Association, Corwen Amateurs, Lex XI Reserves, Llay Royal British Legion, Llay Welfare, Marchwiel Villa, New Broughton, Overton Athletic, Penley, Penycae, Rhostyllen Middle Villa, Treuddyn Villa.
Division One: Bala Town, Bradley Park Rangers, British Aerospace Broughton, Brymbo Reserves, Cefn Druids Reserves, Gresford Athletic Reserves, J.C.B. Transmission, Johnstown Athletic, Kelloggs Wrexham, Kinnerton, Marchwiel Villa Reserves, Mynydd Isa, New Broughton Reserves, New Broughton Villa, Penley Reserves, Rhos Aelwyd Reserves, Rockwell, Ruthin Town Reserves.
  Division Two: British Aerospace Broughton Reserves, Bala Town Reserves, Castell A.C. Reserves, Cefn Colts, Chirk Amateur Athletic Association Reserves, Corwen Amateurs Reserves, Glynceiriog, Johnstown Athletic Reserves, Llangollen, Llanuwchllyn, Llay Royal British Legion Reserves, Llay Welfare Reserves, Rhostyllen & Bersham Royal British Legion.

Richard Jones of Bangor City Reserves prepares to take on two Llangefni Town defenders. Photo - A Monument.

G Hughes of Knighton Town steadies himself to score the first of his sides' three goals at Clun Valley in the Mid-Wales League. Photo - James Wright.

MISCELLANEOUS WELSH LEAGUES

THREEWAYS SUBARU VALE OF CONWY LEAGUE

PREM. DIVISION

	P	W	D	L	F	A	PTS
Machno United	32	25	4	3	127	40	79
CPD Bro Cernyw	32	26	1	5	123	46	79
Cerrigydrudion	32	22	5	5	76	45	71
Rhos United	32	18	7	7	85	53	61
Crosville	32	18	7	7	55	42	61
Llandudno Res.	32	18	6	8	84	47	60
Mochdre Res.	32	17	6	9	81	51	57
Llanrwst Utd Res.	32	11	6	15	53	71	39
Llansannan	32	11	3	18	74	89	36
Llanfairfechan Res.	32	11	3	18	55	80	36
Llansantffraid	32	10	6	16	47	72	36
Glan Conwy	32	9	6	17	61	59	33
Blaenau Ams Res	32	10	3	19	56	85	33
Penmaenmawr Res	32	8	7	17	45	60	31
Dolgarrog	32	9	4	19	54	84	31
Dolwyddelan	32	8	3	21	50	102	27
Betws y Coed	32	0	5	27	30	114	5

SAIN CAERNARFON AND DISTRICT LEAGUE

	P	W	D	L	F	A	PTS
Bangor Waterloo	28	22	5	1	82	23	71
Mountain Rangers	28	21	6	1	95	28	69
Deiniolen	28	19	7	2	71	33	64
Llanrug Utd Res	28	15	5	8	83	50	50
Caernarfon T Res*	28	11	12	5	54	31	43
Nefyn Utd Res	28	11	6	11	74	61	39
Harlech Town	28	12	3	13	56	62	39
Nantlle Vale Res	28	8	9	11	50	64	33
CPD Y Felinheli Rs	28	9	6	13	48	65	33
Porthmadog Res	28	9	5	14	58	48	32
Llanystymdwy	28	9	3	16	44	66	30
UCNW Bangor Res*	28	9	4	15	46	91	29
Porthmadog Jnrs	28	8	3	17	46	73	27
L.Llanberis Res	28	3	4	21	35	93	13
Bethesda Athletic*	28	4	2	22	32	71	12

* - points deducted.

OCS CLWYD FOOTBALL LEAGUE

PREM. DIVISION

	P	W	D	L	F	A	PTS
Llandyrnog United	24	17	4	3	67	28	55
Connahs Quay A	24	17	2	5	66	24	53
St.Asaph City	24	14	4	6	54	27	46
Colwyn Bay Res	24	14	4	6	51	33	46
Abbey Life	24	13	5	6	51	35	44
Flint Town Res	24	10	7	7	47	48	37
Rhuddlan Town	24	8	4	11	34	50	28
Trefnant Village	24	8	4	12	37	60	28
Holywell Town Res	24	8	3	13	53	41	27
Abergele RBL	24	7	5	12	40	45	26
Mold Alex 2000	24	6	4	14	40	53	19
Point of Ayr	24	4	7	12	36	66	19
Bistre	24	2	3	19	31	85	9

GWENT COUNTY FOOTBALL LEAGUE

DIVISION ONE

	P	W	D	L	F	A	PTS
Treowen Stars	30	24	2	4	73	26	50
Albion Rovers	30	21	5	4	81	37	47
Cwmtillery	30	20	6	4	80	28	46
Abergavenny Thurs	30	20	6	4	75	33	46
Civil Service	30	14	7	9	53	35	35
Pill AFC	30	10	10	10	50	48	30
Lliswerry	30	12	6	12	50	53	30
Cefn Fforest	30	12	5	13	63	60	29
Aberbargoed Buds	30	8	9	13	49	67	25
Newport Corinth.	30	8	9	13	34	52	25
Trinant	30	11	2	17	59	71	24
Risca United	30	7	10	13	38	53	24
Cwmbran Celtic	30	8	6	16	47	77	22
Croesyceiliog	30	8	5	17	49	65	21
Undy United	30	6	7	17	47	87	19
Fields Park	30	3	1	26	32	88	7

JAMES WILLIAMS PEMBROKESHIRE

DIVISION ONE

	P	W	D	L	F	A	PTS
Narberth	28	23	3	2	97	31	72
Merlins Bridge	28	20	5	3	90	29	65
Monkton Swifts	28	16	6	6	55	37	54
Carew	28	13	6	9	43	33	45
Fishguard Sports	28	13	6	9	45	44	45
Goodwick United	28	13	4	11	50	49	43
New Hedges S.	28	13	2	13	50	47	41
Manorbier United	28	10	6	12	59	58	36
Pennar Robins	28	10	5	13	53	55	35
Hakin United	28	8	5	15	53	68	29
St.Ishmaels	28	6	10	12	34	45	28
Solva	28	6	9	13	49	87	27
Milford United	28	6	7	15	44	67	25
Johnston	28	7	2	19	38	71	23
Angle	28	5	6	17	32	71	21

SOUTH WALES AMATEUR

DIVISION ONE

	P	W	D	L	F	A	PTS
Penrhiwceiber Rgers	26	20	2	4	69	36	62
Hoover Sports	26	19	4	3	78	37	61
Porthcawl Town	26	18	3	5	68	24	57
Barry Athletic	26	17	4	5	75	38	55
Llangeinor	26	13	3	10	56	46	42
British Steel	26	11	5	10	48	32	38
Hirwaun Welfare	26	10	5	11	40	50	35
Bryntirion Ath.	26	10	3	13	34	50	33
Ely Rangers	26	9	4	13	52	55	31
Cilfynydd	26	8	5	13	37	56	29
Cardiff C Service	26	6	6	14	30	57	24
Llantwit Major	26	5	4	17	40	70	19
Ynysddu Welfare	26	3	8	15	36	60	17
FC Cwmamnam	26	5	0	21	34	83	15

TANNERS WINES MONTGOMERYSHIRE LEAGUE

	P	W	D	L	F	A	PTS
Llansanffraid Res	22	19	3	0	76	78	60
Llanfair C'non	22	14	6	2	64	28	48
Llangedwyn	22	12	4	6	49	35	40
Waterloo Rovers	22	10	7	5	37	29	37
Abermule	22	9	2	11	46	49	29
Berriew Res	22	7	7	8	29	29	28
Llanymynech Rv	22	8	2	12	57	66	26
Llanfair Wdrs	22	6	5	11	36	62	23
Forden United	22	5	6	11	33	46	21
Montgomery Town	22	6	2	14	24	61	20
Llanfechain	22	5	4	13	32	47	19
Guilsfield	22	4	6	12	30	41	18

GWYNEDD LEAGUE

	P	W	D	L	F	A	PTS
Nefyn United	26	20	4	2	93	23	44
Llanrug United	26	20	2	4	61	26	42
Holyhead United	26	15	4	7	64	60	34
CPD Glantraeth	26	15	3	8	63	39	33
Penrhyndeudraeth	26	13	6	7	62	45	32
Llanfairfechan T	26	12	5	9	62	44	29
Penrhos United	26	12	5	9	59	52	29
Llanerchymedd	26	10	6	10	39	36	26
UCNW Bangor(-2pts)	26	11	4	11	41	67	24
Penmaenmawr Ph	26	10	3	13	47	46	23
Blaenau Amtrs	26	6	8	12	48	60	20
Pwllheli Borough	26	6	0	20	34	73	12
Hotpoint	26	3	2	21	28	70	8
Pwilheli & Dist	26	2	2	22	25	88	6

B&M ROOFING ANGLESEY LEAGUE

	P	W	D	L	F	A	PTS
Bodedern	26	19	6	1	101	29	44
Gwalchmai	26	19	3	4	85	30	41
Llangefni Tmn Res	26	19	2	5	97	29	40
Llandegfan	26	14	6	6	67	30	34
Trearddur Bay	26	14	6	6	63	43	34
Holyhead Hotspur	26	12	5	9	51	44	29
Cemaes By Res	26	11	5	10	44	40	27
Llangoed	26	10	5	11	33	39	25
Holyhead MR	26	10	4	12	50	58	24
Amlwch *	26	10	4	12	41	52	22
Gaerwen	26	6	5	15	43	70	15
Moelfre	26	4	3	19	29	85	15
Holyhead Town	26	4	1	21	28	96	9
Bryngwran Bulls	26	1	3	22	14	100	5

* - 2pts deducted.

North Wales Honours 1991/92 Cup Competitions

Competition	Winners	Runners-Up	Score
North Wales Challenge Cup	Colwyn Bay	Rhydymwyn	2-1
Welsh Intermediate Cup	Llangefni T.	Caersws	2-1 (replay)
B&M Roofing Cookson Cup	Cemaes Bay	Llangefni T.	1-0
North Wales Junior Cup	Llangeni T. Res.	Machno U.	2-1 (aet)
Alves Cup	Felinheli	Nantle Vale	3-0
Barritt Cup	Llangeni T.	Llanfair Pwll	4-2 (on pens)
N.E.Wales Prem. Division Cup	Ruthin T.	Rhos Aelwyd	3-2 (aet)
N.E.Wales Challenge Cup	British Aerospace	Gresford Ath.	3-2 (aet)
Gwynedd Cup	Llanrug U.	Grantraeth	1-0
Manweb Cymru Alliance Cup	Lex XI	Flint T.	3-2 (aet)
N.E. Wales Challenge Cup	Saltney C.C.	Penley	3-1
Challenge Cup (Vale of Conway)	Glan Conway	Machno U.	1-0
Mid Wales League Cup	Caersws	Rhyader	1-0
Central Wales Cup	Caersws	Morda U.	3-2 (aet)
Clwyd Premier Div. Cup	Llandyrnog U.	St.Asaph City	1-0 (replay)
Dargi Cup (Anglesey)	Trearddur Bay	Bodedern	3-2
Megan Cup (Anglesey)	Gwalchhai	Holyhead M'tain	4-1
Elias Cup (Anglesey)	Bodedern	Holyhead M'tain	4-1
Caernarfon & District Cup	Bangor Waterloo	Portmadoc Jun.	1-0
Caernarfon & District Cup	Deiniolen	Llarug U.	6-5 (aet)
Deanfield Cup	Llanrug U.	Mountain Rgers	5-4 (on pens)
Eryri Shield	Llanrug U.	Bangor Uni.	5-4
Ron Jones Trophy	Cerrig Ydrudion	Rhos United	3-1
Clwyd Presidents Cup	St.Asaph	Llandryrnog	2-0
Auxiliary Cup	Denbigh T.	Prestatyn T.	4-1
Ansells Floodlit Cup	Brymbo	Flint	3-2 (aet)
Welsh Youth Cup	Wrexham	Cardiff City	2-1
Youth Auxilliary	Connahs Quay	Rhyl	3-2

SCOTTISH FOOTBALL
SENIOR NON-LEAGUE

The Senior section of Scottish non-league football consists
of teams in the following three leagues:
Highland, South of Scotland and the East of Scotland.

SCOTTISH QUALIFYING CUP
The four semi-finalists from each group qualify for the Scottish Cup.

SOUTH

FIRST ROUND

Annan Athletic	1 v 5	Burntisland S.
Spartans	1 v 0	Glasgow Uni.
Newton Stewart	5 v 3	Tarff Rovers

SECOND ROUND

Coldstream	5 v 0	Newton Stewart
Edinburgh Uni.	0 v 0	Threave Rovers
Threave Rovers	3 v 0	Edinburgh Uni.
Girvan	2 v 1	Spartans
Hawick Royal A.	4 v 1	St.Cuthbert W.
Vale of Leithen	3 v 1	Selkirk
Whitehill Welfare	1 v 1	Gala Fairydean
Gala Fairydean	2 v 2	Whitehill Welfare
Gala went through on penalties.		
Wigtown & B'noch	3 v 2	Dalbeattie Star
Civil Service Str	0 v 0	Burntisland S
Burntisland S	0 v 1	Civil Service Str

THIRD ROUND

Civil Service Str	0 v 0	Wigtown & B
Wigtown & B	1 v 2	Civil Service Str
Vale of Leithen	6 v 0	Coldstream
Girvan	2 v 4	Gala Fairydean
Threave Rovers	2 v 4	Hawick Royal A.

SEMI-FINALS

Civil Service Str	4 v 2	Vale of Leithen
Gala Fairydean	2 v 1	Hawick Royal A.

NORTH

FIRST ROUND

Brora Rangers	0 v 1	Keith
Fort William	3 v 6	Buckie Thistle
Golspie Sutherland	1 v 2	Forres Mechanics
Ross County	3 v 3	Elgin City
Elgin City	0 v 5	Ross County

SECOND ROUND

Buckie Thistle	2 v 3	Forres Mechanics
Clachnacuddin	0 v 1	Inverness Thistle
Fraserburgh	1 v 0	Wick Academy
Huntly	4 v 0	Rothes
Keith	0 v 3	Caledonian
Nairn County	0 v 0	Deveronvale
Deveronvale	1 v 1	Nairn County
Nairn County went through on penalties		
Peterhead	4 v 0	Lossiemouth
Ross County	4 v 1	Cove Rangers

THIRD ROUND

Buckie Thistle	0 v 0	Huntly
Huntly	1 v 0	Buckie Thistle
Fraserburgh	0 v 4	Caledonian
Nairn County	0 v 2	Peterhead
Ross County	1 v 0	Inverness Thistle

SEMI-FINALS

Huntly	0 v 1	Peterhead
Ross County	1 v 2	Caledonian

HIGHLAND LEAGUE

	P	W	D	L	F	A	Pts
Ross County	34	24	3	7	95	43	75
Inverness Cals	34	22	6	6	93	34	72
Huntly	34	21	7	6	70	43	70
Cove Rangers	34	18	9	7	62	35	63
Keith	34	18	6	10	67	44	60
Lossiemouth	34	17	7	10	62	42	58
Buckie Thistle	34	17	6	11	58	46	57
Elgin City	34	16	6	12	76	51	54
Peterhead	34	16	6	12	61	59	54
Inverness Thistle	34	14	8	12	54	57	50
Forres	34	13	8	13	66	62	47
Clachnacuddin	34	11	6	17	43	51	39
Deveronvale	34	12	3	19	41	58	39
Brora Rangers	34	11	5	18	52	67	38
Fraserburgh	34	11	3	20	43	67	36
Fort William	34	8	4	22	48	83	28
Rothes	34	4	4	26	38	99	16
Nairn County	34	3	3	28	23	111	12

Press & Journal INVERNESS CUP:
ROSS COUNTY

Tennents LEAGUE CUP:
ROSS COUNTY

McEwans Lager North of Scotland Cup:
ROSS COUNTY

Gray & Adams Aberdeenshire Cup:
HUNTLY

Evening Express Aberdeenshire Shield:
FRASERBURGH

North of Scotland Qualifying Cup:
INVERNESS CALEDONIAN

Highland League Players Association
PLAYER OF THE YEAR:
CHARLIE CHRISTIE (Inverness Cal.)

SCOTTISH JUNIOR CUP 1992-93

First Round

Arthurlie v Petershill	0-0,2-1
Dalkeith Thistle v Irvine Meadow	1-2
Inverurie v Ardeer Thistle	0-2
Pumpherston v Lugar Boswell	1-3
Sunnybank v Saltcoats Vics	0-2
Forres Thistle v Whitletts Vics	0-4
Yoker Athletic v Royal Albert	4-0
Coupar Angus v Scone Thistle	1-3
Forfar Albion v Rutherglen Glencairn	2-3
Luncarty v Bon Accord	0-13
Stonehouse Violet v Inverurie L.W.	1-3
Burghead Thistle v Lanark United	0-4
Maryhill v Cumnock	1-3
Culter v Montrose R'len	3-2
Forfar West End v Daltry Thistle	0-1
Parkvale v Kelty Hearts	2-5
FC Stoneywood v Hall Russell United	1-2
Fochabers v Linlithgow Rose	0-4
St Roch's v Aberdeen L.C.	0-0,2-2,9-1

Blantyre Vics v Renfrew	1-4
Fauldhouse United v Lochee Harp.	2-2,2-2,2-1
Lochee United v Arbroath S.C.	3-3,0-1
Shotts B.A. v Glenrothes	2-1
West Calder United v Deveronside	4-3
Johnstone Burgh v Ellon United	2-1
Auchinleck Talbot v Bathgate Thistle	7-0
East Craigie v Ormiston Primrose	2-1
Irvine Victoria v Downfield	1-5
R.A.F. Lossiemouth v Banks O'Dee	1-2
Thornton Hibs v Cambuslang Rangers	0-2
Clackmannan v Lochore Welfare	2-2,2-0
Benburb v Dundonald Bluebird	2-1
Edinburgh United v Buckie Rovers	5-1
Kello Rovers v New Elgin	3-2
Sauchie v Carnoustie P'mura	0-2
Troon v Thorniewood United	2-0
St Josephs v Baillieston	1-2

Second Round

Aberdeen East End v Scone Thistle	1-0
Banks O'Dee v Inverurie L.W.	1-2
Bon Accord v Arbroath S.C.	1-3
Cumnock v Renfrew	3-0
Elmwood v St Anthony's	2-2,2-2,3-2
Haddington Athletic v Dundee North End	1-2
Irvine Meadow v Shettleston	0-3
Kilwinning Rangers v Mussleburgh	1-1,3-2
Lewis United v Tayport	0-5
Newburgh v Kirlintilloch Rob Roy	2-5
Saltcoats Vics v Carluke Rovers	1-0
Ardeer Thistle v Troon	3-0
Beith v Annbank United	4-1
Cambuslang Rgrs v Arniston Rangers	1-1,4-0
Craigpark Bohemians v Muirkirk	3-1
Fauldhouse United v Bonnyrigg Rose	1-0
Halbeath v Edinburgh United	3-0
Islavale v Preston Athletic	2-1
Kinnoul v Brechin Violets	4-0
Linlithgow Rose v Crossgates Primrose	4-2
Oakley United v Whitletts Vics	3-2
Stonehaven v Blantyre Celtic	3-3,1-4
Balbeggie v Glenafton Athletic	1-7
Blairgowrie Juniors v Vale of Clyde	2-4
Cuminestown v Yoker Athletic	0-4
Dundee Violet v Turriff United	2-2,0-2
Greenock v Tranent	4-0
Insch v Carnoustie	2-2,2-2,0-3
Kilsyth Rgrs v Bishopmill United	7-1
Lesmahagow v Auchinleck Talbot	3-5
Neilston v Dyce	3-1
St Andrews United v Buchanhaven Hearts	3-0

Arthurlie v Scotts B.A.	2-1
Benburb v Dunipace	1-2
Culter v Maybole	0-1
Downfield v Coltness United	3-0
Fraserburgh Utd v Arbroath V.	1-1,1-1,3-2
Hill of Beath Hawthorn v Newtongrange Star	3-1
Kelty Hearts v Bo'ness United	3-4
Largs Thistle v Port Glasgow	1-0
Maud v Lugar Boswell	1-3
R.A.F. Kinloss v Camelon	1-3
Wishaw v Johnstone Burgh	1-2
Baillieston v Darvel	3-0
Blackburn United v Dalry Thistle	2-2,1-1,1-2
Cumbernauld United v Lossiemouth United	3-0
Dunbar United v East Kilbride	0-0,1-1,2-1
Glasgow Perthshire v Ashfield	5-0
Hurlford United v Winton Rovers	1-1,1-1,2-4
Kilburnie Ladeside v Longside	1-0
Larkhall Thistle v Broxburn Athletic	2-0
Nairn St Ninian v Kello Rovers	0-4
Rutherglen Glencairn v Bankfoot Athletic	4-1
Armadale Thistle v Broughty Athletic	1-0
Bellshill Athletic v St Roch's	4-3
Clackmannan v Vale of Leven	1-3
Crombie Sports v Bonnybridge	2-2,0-4
Formartine Utd v Jeanfield Swifts	1-2
Hall Russell United v Whitburn	1-2
Jubilee Athletic v Lanark United	2-2,0-3
Kirrie Thistle v Livingston United	2-5
Lochgelly Albert v Stoneyburn	2-6
Pollok v Forth Wanderers	4-1
West Calder United v East Craigie	2-3

Third Round

Kilsyth Rangers v Baillieston	0-1
Johnstone Burgh v Kinnoul	2-1
Bo'ness United v Cambuslang Rangers	1-1,0-2
Largs Thistle v Camelon	3-2
Turriff United v Shetteleston	0-1
St Andrews Utd v Saltcoats Vics	4-0
Bellshill Athletic v Rutherglen Glencairn	0-5
Bonnybridge v Arbroath S.C.	0-1
Kello Rovers v Carnoustie P'mura	2-1
Fraserburgh United v Dunbar United	1-1,1-5
Dundee North End v Auchinleck Talbot	1-5
Larkhall Thistle v East Craigie	1-2
Livingston United v Kilwinning Rangers	3-0
Dalry Thistle v Yoker Athletic	0-1
Winton Rovers v Armadale Thistle	1-3
Edinburgh United v Dunipace	0-1

Neilston v Whitburn	2-2,1-4
Stoneyburn v Blantyre Celtic	2-1
Glenafton v V. of Clyde	3-3,2-2,3-4 (replayed),1-0
Aberdeen East End v Fauldhouse United	0-3
Hill of Beath Hawthorn v Downfield	3-0
Cumbernauld Utd v Beith	1-2
Lanark United v Jeanfield S.	0-0,0-0,3-2
Craigpark Bohemians v Pollok	2-4
Lugar Boswell Thistle v Ardeer Thistle	2-1
Elmwood v Arthurlie	0-1
Tayport v Cumnock	2-0
Greenock v Vale of Leven	0-2
Linlithgow Rose v Kirkintilloch Rob Roy	2-0
Kilbirnie Lakeside v Glasgow Perthshire	2-4
Inverurie Loco v Maybole	1-1,1-1,0-2
Oakley United v Islavale	2-0

Fourth Round

Arbroath S.C. v St Andrew's Utd	3-2
Linlithgow Rose v Arthurlie	1-2
Vale of Levenn v Oakley United	2-0
Baillieston v Armadale	2-2,0-3
Lugar Boswell Thistle v Maybole	1-2
Whitburn v Kello Rovers	4-1
Largs Thistle v Dunipace	0-0,1-0
Tayport v Livingston United	3-0

Fauldhouse United v Auchinleck Talbot	0-0,0-1
Shettleston v Rutherglen Glencairn	2-3
Glenafton Athletic v Larkhall Thistle	2-1
Lanark United v Hill of Beath Hawthorn	0-1
Stoneyburn v Dunbar	0-0,0-0,3-2
Cambuslang Rangers v Pollok	3-1
Glasgow Perthshire v Yoker Athletic	2-1
Johnstone Burgh v Beith	1-1,3-4

Fifth Round

Armadale Athletic v Auchinlech Talbot	1-3	Glenafton Athletic v Stoneyburn	1-1,W-L
Largs Thistle v Rutherglen Glencairn	L-W	Glasgow Perthshire v Beith	L-W
Tayport v Arthurlie	1-1,W-L	Hill of Beath Hawthorn v Arbroath S.C.	4-0
Whitburn v Cambuslang Rangers	1-1,W-L	Vale of Leven v Maybole	W-L

Quarter-Finals

Glenafton Athletic v Tayport	3-1	Auchinleck Talbot v Hill of Beath Hawthorn	0-0,5-0
Beith v Vale of Leven	3-1	Rutherglen Glencairn v Whitburn	1-2

Semi Finals:

Auchinleck Talbot v Whitburn	1-0	Glenafton Athletic v Hill of Beath Hawthorn	4-1 *(aet)*
(at Motherwell FC, Att: 5,000)		*(at Ayr United FC, Att: 8,000)*	

FINAL

AUCHINLECT TALBOT 4, GLENAFTON ATHLETIC 0

Auchlinleck Talbot underlined their dominance of Scottish non-league football with a crushing 4-0 victory over game, but ultimately outclassed Glenafton, at Firhill home of Partick Thistle.

The hero of the hour with a superbly crafted hat-trick was Gordon Mills who sealed this win with cooly taken goals in the 17th, 48th and 89th minutes, and only brave goalkeeping by Chris Kelly prevented a rout.

Glenafton had high hopes pre-match of exploiting Auchinleck Talbot's ageing back four, three of whom would not see thirty again, but did their hopes no good by leaving Montgomery to battle away up front all alone. The folly of this ploy became apparent as Auchinleck took contol of the match early on, and opened their account with a beautifully taken goal, Mills working a 1-2 with McDonald and thrashing a half-volley into the roof of the net from 10 yards.

As the rain ceased and the sun came out Glenafton, managed by former Scottish International Alan Rough, held on, defending well, but only attacking sporadically.

Lindsay and Doyle were both cautioned by Glenboig referee Jim O'Hare as things warmed up but just three minutes into the second half Mills effectively killed the game with a delicate chip from a Willie Thomson cross.

Auchinleck, playing in their fifth final in seven seasons relaxed and began playing some very attractive attacking football, and were rewarded when substitute Sam Frew made it three with nine minutes left, heading home Pirie's cross.

It was left to Mills to complete his hat-trick and seal a marvellous win lobbing Kelly, the ball just crossing the line before being cleared by a defender.

So Talbot comfortably re-affirm their standing as the top club in Scottish Junior Football.

Kerry Miller

TEAMS

Auchinleck Talbot: *Derek Hoy, George Gemmell, Willie Young, Ross Findlay, Sam McCullough, Tom MacDonald, Alan Pirie, Ian Dick, Gordon Mills, Kenny Paterson, Willie Thomson, Sam Frew, Hugh Lyden.*

Glenafton Athletic: *Chris Kelly, Lenny Lowe, Steve Lindsay, Justin Crowe, Alex Kennedy, Danny Boland, Peter Conlan, Jimmy Doyle, Tommy Brown, Norman Montgomery, David McFarlane, Andy Milligan.*

Referee: *Jim O'Hare (Glenbog).*

Glenafton Athletic and Auchinleck Talbot line up before the O.V.D. Junior Cup Final. Photo: Howard Watts.

Glenafton Athletic 2, Larkhall Thistle 1 - Scottish Junior Cup 4th Round 15/2/92. Larkhall keeper Murray Bowman blocks a shot from Peter Welsh (partly hidden). Photo - Alan Watson.

Willie Thompson of Auchinleck Talbot takes on a Glenafton Athletic defender during the Junior Cup final at Firhill. Photo - Howard Watts.

Gordon Hills fires in a brilliant half-volley for Auchinleck's opener in the Junior Cup final. Photo - Howard Watts.

SCOTTISH JUNIOR FOOTBALL LEAGUES

Central Region Reebox League

PREM. DIVISION	P	W	D	L	F	A	PTS
Lesmahagow	22	14	5	3	41	18	33
Petershill	22	14	3	5	36	23	31
Pollok	22	12	4	6	54	27	28
Ruth'glen Gelncairn	22	12	3	7	28	27	27
Shotts Bon Accord	22	10	5	7	35	30	25
Arthurlie	22	10	4	8	42	29	24
Vale of Clyde	22	8	4	10	30	37	20
Kilsyth Rangers	22	7	5	10	27	37	19
Cambuslang Rgers	22	6	5	11	29	35	17
Glasgow Perthshire	22	6	4	12	29	37	16
Dunipace	22	3	7	12	20	40	13
Vale of Leven	22	3	5	14	14	45	11

DIVISION ONE	P	W	D	L	F	A	PTS
Renfrew	26	18	6	2	48	27	42
Sheetleston	26	15	6	5	44	28	36
Neilston	26	15	5	6	39	23	35
Larknall Thistle	26	12	5	9	44	34	29
Maryhill	26	10	5	11	43	39	25
E.Kilbride Thistle	26	9	7	10	36	39	25
Stonehouse Violet	26	6	12	8	32	31	24
Ashfield	26	7	10	9	35	35	24
Benburb	26	9	5	12	32	45	23
Lamark United	26	8	6	12	26	33	22
Yoker Athletic	26	6	9	11	32	39	21
Blantyre Victoria	26	7	7	12	43	53	21
Baillieston	26	6	8	12	29	37	20
Cumbernauld United	26	4	8	14	22	42	16

DIVISION TWO	P	W	D	L	F	A	PTS
Johnstone Burgh	26	18	5	3	68	32	41
Forth Wanderers	26	14	8	4	48	25	36
Blantyre Celtic	26	15	5	6	60	39	35
St.Roch's	26	12	9	5	56	31	33
Thorniewood Utd	26	14	4	8	42	31	32
Bellshill Athletic	26	12	5	9	46	44	29
Greenock	26	12	5	9	51	38	29
Port Glasgow	26	11	5	10	43	37	27
Kirk'tilloch Rob Roy	26	10	3	13	55	52	23
Carluke Rovers	26	7	8	11	36	42	22
St Anthony's	26	7	7	12	47	59	21
Wishaw	26	5	3	18	36	66	13
Coltness United	26	3	6	17	20	58	12
Royal Albert	26	3	5	18	26	79	11

North Region
Bon Accord Glass League East Section

PREM. DIVISION	P	W	D	L	F	A	PTS
FC Stoneywood	22	15	2	5	55	33	47
Stonehaven	22	11	9	2	53	34	42
Banks O'Dee	22	12	4	6	38	37	40
Inverurie L. Works	22	9	7	6	45	36	34
Turriff United	22	10	3	9	40	40	33
Cuiter	22	8	7	7	45	45	31
Bon Accord	22	9	3	10	44	34	30
Parkvale	22	9	2	11	46	50	29
Sunnybank	22	8	4	10	35	38	28
Crombie Sports	22	5	6	11	28	48	21
Farserburgh United	22	4	7	11	36	48	19
Aberdeen East End	22	3	4	15	30	53	13

DIVISION ONE	P	W	D	L	F	A	PTS
Buchanhaven Hearts	22	15	4	3	63	26	49
Longside	22	15	2	5	44	28	47
Insch	22	13	6	3	51	36	45
Formartine United	22	12	6	4	49	21	42
Lewis United	22	13	3	6	52	27	42
Hall Russell Utd	22	9	5	8	31	32	32
Aberdeen Lads' C	22	9	3	10	44	46	30
Inverurie	22	7	4	11	38	48	25
Dyce	22	6	5	11	30	35	23
Ellon United	22	4	6	12	24	39	18
Maud	22	4	1	17	31	56	13
Cuminestown	22	2	1	19	25	89	7

Dry Cleaning Well League North Section

	P	W	D	L	F	A	PTS
Lossiemouth Utd*	22	14	3	5	50	29	43
Forres Thistle	22	13	3	6	56	30	42
Islavale	22	11	6	5	36	25	39
Fochabers	22	10	4	8	51	32	34
Deveronside	22	10	3	9	49	42	33
Bishopmill United	22	9	5	8	48	42	32
Buckie Rovers	22	8	6	8	33	37	30
New Eglin	22	7	8	7	39	41	29
Nairn St.Ninian	22	7	4	11	33	61	25
RAF Kinloss	22	5	7	10	40	46	25
RAF Lossiemouth	22	5	6	11	41	51	21
Burghead Thistle	22	3	5	14	35	76	14
* 2pts deducted.							

TAYSIDE REGION

DIVISION ONE	P	W	D	L	F	A	PTS
Tayport	26	19	5	2	74	15	43
Downfield	26	16	8	2	70	20	40
Dundee North End	26	15	6	5	53	34	36
Forfar West End	26	12	9	5	67	35	33
Arbroath S C	26	14	5	7	57	31	33
Jeanfield Swifts	26	12	4	10	41	39	28
Dundee Violet	26	10	7	9	54	56	27
Kirrie Thistle	26	8	9	9	42	49	25
Kinnoull	26	9	6	11	32	38	24
Lochee United	26	6	13	6	36	63	20
East Craigie	26	8	3	15	44	70	19
Dundee Elawood	26	6	6	14	37	57	18
Bankfoot Athletic	26	4	3	19	25	74	11
Blairgowrie	26	2	3	21	29	80	7

DIVISION TWO	P	W	D	L	F	A	PTS
Carnoustie Panaure	22	18	1	3	73	20	37
Lochee Harp	22	16	4	2	69	20	36
Forfar Albion	22	16	2	4	72	25	34
Scone Thistle	22	11	5	6	62	38	27
Broughty Ath.	22	11	3	8	43	30	25
Montrose Roselea	22	9	3	10	39	35	21
Brechin Victoria	22	7	5	10	49	45	19
Coupar Angus	22	7	5	10	39	37	19
Balbeggie	22	8	3	11	47	50	19
Arbroath Victoria	22	6	4	12	35	45	16
St. Joseph's	22	4	3	15	23	73	11
Luncarty	22	0	0	22	9	142	0

FIFE REGION
Tennent Caledonian League

	P	W	D	L	F	A	PTS
Kelty Hearts	26	22	1	3	82	25	45
Hill of Beath H.	26	19	5	2	80	27	43
St.Andrews Utd	26	17	5	4	67	22	39
Glenrothes	26	14	5	7	62	34	33
Dundonald Bluebell	26	15	3	8	60	35	33
Oakley United	26	13	2	11	51	44	28
Halbeath	26	10	6	10	39	43	26
Crossgates P.	26	10	3	13	33	60	23
Thornton Hib.	26	8	6	12	32	52	22
Newburgh	26	8	5	13	38	60	21
Clackmannan	26	7	5	14	32	53	19
Jubilee Athletic	26	5	5	16	32	64	15
Lochore Welfare	26	2	6	18	27	53	10
Lochgelly Albert	26	2	3	21	36	99	7

Scottish Amateur Cup
Heathfield (Ayr) v Viewfield R (Lochwinnoch)   2-0
Played at Hampden Park, Glasgow
Att: 2,000

TENNANTS
EAST OF SCOTLAND LEAGUE

PREM. DIVISION	P	W	D	L	F	A	PTS
Easthouses Lily MW	16	13	1	2	44	25	27
Whitehill Welfare	16	11	2	3	50	22	24
Vale of Leithen	16	9	3	4	34	23	21
Gala Fairydean	16	8	1	7	34	30	17
Craigroyston	16	6	4	6	27	23	16
Edinburgh City	16	4	4	8	24	32	12
Coldstream	16	4	4	8	21	45	12
Spartans	16	3	4	9	18	26	10
Annan Athletic	16	1	3	12	17	43	5

DIVISION ONE	P	W	D	L	F	A	PTS
Manor Thistle	20	16	2	2	39	9	34
Tollcross United	20	15	1	4	49	23	31
Selkirk	20	12	2	6	50	36	26
Kelso United	20	8	5	7	37	28	21
Hawick Royal Albert	20	8	5	7	45	40	21
Pencaitland	20	7	5	8	26	31	19
Civil Service S.	20	7	4	9	42	38	18
Peebles Rovers	20	7	3	10	29	47	17
Eyemouth United	20	5	2	13	26	56	12
Heriot Watt Uni.	20	4	3	13	22	44	11
Edinburgh Uni.	20	3	4	13	31	44	10

SOUTH OF SCOTLAND LEAGUE

	P	W	D	L	F	A	PTS
Wigtown & Blad.	16	11	4	1	41	14	26
Maxwell T HSFP	16	11	3	2	46	28	25
Dalbeattie Star	16	7	6	3	39	21	20
Girvan Amateurs	16	8	4	4	45	32	20
Threave Rovers	16	8	1	7	44	33	17
Newton Stewart	16	7	1	8	43	38	15
St.Cuthbert Wand.	16	5	3	8	41	40	13
Tarff Rovers	16	2	4	10	26	44	8
Creetown	16	0	0	16	10	85	0

Maybole 'keeper Stuart McIntosh foils a Vale of Leven attack above, and below , Vale of Leven's Willie Howie tussles for possession with James Miller of Maybole.

SEASON 1992-93 MATCH RECORD

Date	MATCH	Venue	RESULT & SCORERS	Comp.
8.8.92	Sandy v Potters Bar Cruc.	H	0 · 3	SML
15.8.92	Barkingside v Beaconsfield	H	3 · 2	LSL
18.8.92	Cockposters v Barkingside	H	1 · 1	LSL
22.8.92	Bedworth v Bridgnorth	H	3 · 2	BHL
25.8.92	Wingate & Finchley v Pirton	H	4 · 2	SML
29.8.92	Nuneaton v Boldmere SM	H	2 · 1	FAC
1.9.92	Northwood v Royston	H	1 · 1	DFL
5.9.92	Evesham v Sutton Coldfield	H	0 · 3	BHL
12.9.92	RC Warwick v Eastwood Hanley	H	0 · 2	FAC
19.9.92	Redditch v Caernarfon	H	0 · 3	FAT
26.9.92	Weston SM v Clevedon	H	0 · 4	FAC
3.10.92	Rushden & Diamonds v Anstey Nomads	H	3 · 2	FAV
10.10.92	Leighton v Kingsbury	H	0 · 0	DFL
17.10.92	Leicester U v Matlock	H	3 · 1	FAT
24.10.92	Hednesford v Dagenham & Redbridge	H	1 · 3	FAC
31.10.92	Barri v Sutton Coldfield	H	3 · 3	BHL
7.11.92	Tamworth v RC Warwick	H	1 · 0	BHL
14.11.92	Solihull v VS Rugby	H	2 · 2	FAC
21.11.92	Yate v Paulton Rovers	H	1 · 2	FAV
28.11.92	Stourbridge v Leek	H	1 · 4	FAT
5.12.92	Buxton v Waterlooville	H	0 · 2	BHL
12.12.92	Corby v Bashley	H	5 · 2	BHL
19.12.92	Newport AFC v Hinckley	H	3 · 1	BHL
28.12.92	Dulwich v Carshalton	H	1 · 7	DFL
16.1.93	Newbury v Edgware	H	1 · 0	DFL
30.1.93	Trowbridge v Halesowen	H	1 · 1	BHL
13.2.93	Witney v Sudbury	H	1 · 1	BHL

MATCH RECORD

Date	MATCH	Venue	RESULT & SCORERS	Comp.
20.2.93	E.Thurrock v Royston	H	2 · 1	DFL
27.3.93	Kings Lynn v Dudley	H	2 · 2	BHL
2.4.93	Fulham v Huddersfield	H	0 · 1	BL
3.4.93	Flackwell Heath v Petersfield	H	2 · 2	DFL
10.4.93	Aldershot v Thame	H	2 · ⊘1	DFL
12.4.93	Bromsgrove v Kidderminster	H	2 · 2	GMVC
17.4.93	Grantham v Stourbridge	H	3 · 3	BHL
24.4.93	Gresley v Leicester U.	H	2 · 3	BHL
1.5.93	Stalybridge v Welling	H	0 · 0	GMVC
8.5.93	Lincoln v Darlington	H	2 · 0	BL

MATCH RECORD

Date	MATCH	Venue	RESULT & SCORERS	Comp.

MATCH RECORD

Date	MATCH	Venue	RESULT & SCORERS	Comp.

GM VAUXHALL CONFERENCE
FIXTURE DATES 1992/93

1. Altrincham
2. Bath City
3. Boston United
4. Bromsgrove Rovers
5. Dagenham & Redbridge
6. Farnborough Town
7. Gateshead
8. Kettering
9. Kidderminster Harriers
10. Macclesfield
11. Merthyr Tydfil
12. Northwich Victoria
13. Runcorn
14. Slough Town
15. Stafford Rangers
16. Stalybridge Celtic
17. Telford
18. Welling United
19. Witton Albion
20. Woking
21. Wycombe Wanderers
22. Yeovil

H/A	1	2	3	4	5	6	7	8	9	10	11	12	13	14	15	16	17	18	19	20	21	22
1	*	06-02	19-09	24-04	14-11	17-10	25-08	26-12	17-11	12-04	29-08	07-11	10-10	16-01	26-09	30-01	20-02	19-12	03-04	06-03	28-11	20-23
2	21-11	*	13-02	20-03	27-03	07-11	30-01	08-12	26-12	06-03	08-09	10-10	28-11	25-08	24-04	19-12	23-01	13-10	29-08	15-09	29-09	12-04
3	13-03	03-10	*	30-01	02-01	23-01	03-04	14-04	29-03	14-11	01-05	12-12	22-08	26-09	02-09	10-02	17-10	26-12	20-03	28-11	09-09	27-02
4	12-12	02-01	25-08	*	06-02	26-12	20-02	23-01	12-04	15-09	28-11	05-09	03-04	13-02	14-11	06-03	03-11	12-09	16-01	01-05	10-10	26-09
5	27-02	17-04	17-11	29-08	*	25-08	16-01	01-05	13-03	17-10	30-01	03-10	31-10	09-02	13-02	20-02	28-11	12-04	19-12	06-10	03-04	26-12
6	01-05	16-01	21-11	10-04	06-03	*	22-08	10-10	05-09	24-04	06-10	28-11	06-02	23-02	27-03	31-10	12-12	03-11	26-09	28-12	31-08	02-01
7	16-09	31-10	06-02	07-11	05-09	05-12	*	27-03	12-12	26-09	17-04	10-04	31-08	27-02	02-01	28-12	03-10	17-10	17-11	23-01	13-03	01-05
8	10-04	20-02	28-12	21-11	29-09	08-09	28-11	*	24-04	29-03	17-10	13-02	30-01	03-11	06-10	03-04	02-01	13-03	27-02	25-08	26-09	12-12
9	22-08	10-04	16-01	28-12	19-09	27-02	14-11	31-08	*	30-01	27-03	01-05	19-12	05-12	20-03	21-11	17-04	03-10	17-10	12-09	31-10	20-02
10	28-12	05-09	29-09	17-04	10-10	19-09	19-12	31-10	10-11	*	16-01	31-08	13-03	21-11	17-11	10-04	13-02	27-02	05-12	27-03	22-08	23-01
11	05-12	31-08	07-11	19-01	22-08	03-04	13-02	23-02	02-01	03-10	*	13-03	24-04	10-04	05-09	14-11	28-12	26-09	23-01	10-10	12-09	02-02
12	06-10	03-04	06-03	01-12	24-04	19-12	26-12	19-09	25-08	13-10	31-10	*	05-12	29-08	23-01	26-09	21-11	14-11	12-04	06-02	27-02	27-03
13	02-01	01-05	27-03	27-02	23-01	29-08	06-10	07-11	26-09	25-08	20-03	15-09	*	17-10	12-04	13-10	29-09	13-02	26-12	12-12	21-11	12-09
14	05-09	02-02	31-10	03-10	31-08	14-11	20-03	22-08	23-01	12-12	26-12	20-02	06-03	*	03-04	06-02	19-09	10-11	24-04	02-01	12-04	13-10
15	10-11	19-09	23-03	05-12	21-11	03-10	10-10	19-12	15-09	06-02	20-02	17-04	28-12	01-05	*	25-08	10-04	29-08	30-03	13-03	30-01	31-10
16	27-03	22-08	10-10	17-10	12-12	13-03	12-04	17-04	13-02	26-12	19-09	02-01	17-11	07-11	27-02	*	31-08	01-05	02-02	29-08	23-01	28-11
17	31-10	27-02	05-12	09-02	20-03	12-09	06-03	15-09	10-10	07-11	12-04	30-01	16-01	19-12	26-12	01-12	*	03-04	25-08	26-09	24-04	29-08
18	23-01	12-12	10-04	27-03	28-12	17-04	24-04	06-02	07-11	28-11	21-11	20-03	19-09	10-10	06-03	05-09	22-08	*	31-10	08-12	02-01	31-08
19	31-08	13-03	05-09	22-08	07-11	20-02	27-10	03-10	28-11	02-01	06-03	28-12	10-04	27-03	24-11	15-09	01-05	30-01	*	13-02	12-12	10-10
20	03-10	05-12	19-12	31-10	01-12	12-04	21-11	20-03	03-04	20-02	27-02	17-10	05-09	30-01	22-08	24-04	30-03	16-01	19-09	*	26-12	19-01
21	17-04	17-10	09-03	19-09	15-02	20-03	29-08	05-12	06-02	01-05	19-12	16-01	20-02	28-12	07-11	03-10	05-09	25-08	24-10	10-04	*	15-09
22	13-02	28-12	24-04	19-12	10-04	30-01	19-09	05-09	06-03	03-04	25-08	22-08	03-10	17-04	17-10	16-01	13-03	05-12	21-11	07-11	09-02	*

DIADORA PREMIER DIVISION
FIXTURE DATES 1992/93

1. ✓ Aylesbury United
2. ✓ Basingstoke
3. ✓ Bognor Regis
4. ✓ Bromley
5. ✓ Carshalton Athletic
6. ✓ Chesham United
7. ✓ Dulwich Hamlet
8. ✓ Enfield
9. ✓ Grays Athletic
10. ✓ Harrow Borough
11. ✓ Hayes

12. ✓ Hendon
13. ✓ Kingstonian
14. ✓ Marlow
15. ✓ St.Albans
16. ✓ Staines Town
17. ✓ Steveanage Borough
18. ✓ Sutton United
19. ✓ Windsor & Eton
20. ✓ Wivenhoe Town
21. ✓ Wokingham
22. ✓ Yeading

H/A	1	2	3	4	5	6	7	8	9	10	11	12	13	14	15	16	17	18	19	20	21	22
1	*	27-10	20-03	03-10	22-08	24-04	21-11	26-09	06-02	06-03	05-01	10-04	23-01	12-09	26-12	05-12	07-11	19-12	13-10	03-04	20-02	05-09
2	13-03	*	26-12	17-10	26-09	05-12	10-10	25-08	09-01	03-10	23-01	19-12	06-02	22-08	05-09	24-04	21-11	07-11	06-03	10-04	03-04	13-02
3	17-10	12-04	*	28-12	27-03	13-03	16-01	17-04	10-10	31-08	31-10	30-01	12-12	14-11	06-03	13-02	02-01	29-08	15-09	28-11	01-05	03-10
4	27-02	20-03	05-09	*	23-01	21-11	26-12	06-02	22-08	13-02	26-09	07-11	25-08	09-01	24-04	29-09	19-12	03-04	24-10	10-10	10-04	05-12
5	02-01	30-01	07-11	29-08	*	10-04	31-08	29-09	13-02	16-01	17-10	01-05	13-03	27-02	03-04	19-12	05-12	26-12	08-09	21-11	24-04	10-10
6	02-12	02-09	24-10	17-04	14-11	*	01-05	20-02	12-12	28-12	27-03	02-01	31-10	12-04	16-09	20-03	21-10	30-01	03-10	16-01	29-08	06-03
7	17-04	20-02	25-08	12-04	28-12	09-01	*	14-11	05-09	27-03	12-12	03-10	01-12	06-02	22-08	23-01	06-03	17-10	31-10	13-03	13-10	26-09
8	10-10	16-01	21-11	19-09	06-03	17-10	10-04	*	20-10	01-05	13-03	01-09	03-10	13-02	07-11	03-04	26-12	24-04	02-01	29-08	05-12	19-12
9	19-09	01-05	20-02	02-01	13-10	03-04	05-12	20-03	*	29-08	03-10	24-04	06-03	27-10	19-12	10-04	15-09	21-11	30-01	26-12	16-01	07-11
10	29-09	27-02	05-12	13-10	25-08	05-09	07-11	05-01	23-01	*	06-02	26-12	22-08	26-09	24-10	21-11	20-02	10-04	20-03	24-04	19-12	03-04
11	01-05	29-08	19-12	30-01	20-03	07-11	03-04	12-09	27-02	15-09	*	05-12	13-02	10-10	10-04	20-10	24-04	02-01	16-01	08-09	21-11	26-12
12	14-11	31-10	26-09	27-03	09-01	22-08	27-02	28-12	28-11	12-04	05-09	*	17-04	06-10	25-08	06-02	24-10	29-09	12-12	13-02	20-03	23-01
13	29-08	15-09	03-04	16-01	24-10	19-12	24-04	27-02	29-09	02-01	13-10	21-11	*	20-03	20-02	26-12	30-01	19-09	01-05	05-12	07-11	10-04
14	16-01	02-01	10-04	01-05	03-10	26-12	15-09	13-10	13-03	30-01	06-03	20-02	17-10	*	21-11	07-11	03-04	05-12	29-08	19-12	01-09	24-04
15	12-04	28-12	29-09	01-12	12-12	13-02	02-01	27-03	31-10	13-03	14-11	16-01	10-10	17-04	*	27-02	29-08	01-05	01-09	30-01	19-09	20-10
16	01-09	28-11	13-10	06-03	31-10	27-10	29-08	12-12	14-11	17-04	20-02	15-09	12-04	27-03	03-10	*	01-05	16-01	28-12	02-01	30-01	13-03
17	27-03	17-04	22-08	31-10	05-09	06-02	28-09	12-04	28-12	10-10	28-11	13-03	26-09	12-12	23-01	09-01	*	13-02	14-11	26-10	27-02	24-08
18	31-10	27-03	23-01	12-12	12-04	26-09	20-03	01-12	17-04	14-11	22-08	06-03	28-12	05-09	09-01	25-08	01-09	*	20-02	03-10	27-10	06-02
19	13-02	29-09	24-04	13-03	06-02	27-02	19-12	22-08	26-09	17-10	25-08	03-04	09-01	23-01	05-12	05-09	10-04	10-10	*	07-11	26-12	21-11
20	12-12	14-11	06-02	20-02	17-04	26-08	24-10	23-01	12-04	01-12	28-12	17-10	05-09	31-10	26-09	22-08	20-03	27-02	27-03	*	29-09	05-01
21	20-10	12-12	09-01	14-11	01-12	23-01	13-02	05-09	25-08	31-10	17-04	10-10	27-03	28-12	06-02	26-09	03-10	13-03	12-04	06-03	*	22-08
22	28-12	13-10	27-02	01-09	20-02	29-09	30-01	31-10	27-03	12-12	12-04	29-08	14-11	28-11	20-03	24-10	16-01	15-09	17-04	01-05	02-01	*

DIADORA LEAGUE DIVISION ONE
FIXTURE DATES 1992/93

1. ✓ Abingdon Town
2. ✓ Aveley
3. ✓ Barking
4. ✓ Billericay Town
5. ✓ Bishops Stortford
6. ✓ Boreham Wood
7. ✓ Chalfont St.Peter
8. ✓ Croydon
9. ✓ Dorking
10. ~~Harlow Town~~
11. ✓ Heybridge Swifts

12. ✓ Hitchin Town
13. ✓ Lewes
14. ✓ Leyton
15. ✓ Maidenhead United
16. ✓ Molesey
17. ✓ Purfleet
18. ✓ Tooting & Mitcham
19. ✓ Uxbridge
20. ✓ Walton & Hersham
21. ✓ Wembley
22. ✓ Whyteleafe

H/A	1	2	3	4	5	6	7	8	9	10	11	12	13	14	15	16	17	18	19	20	21	22
1	*	03-10	13-03	01-05	13-10	02-01	01-09	24-04	21-11	03-04	05-09	10-04	16-01	05-12	26-12	17-10	19-12	06-03	15-09	07-11	30-01	20-02
2	27-02	*	13-02	01-09	29-09	30-01	05-09	10-10	03-04	05-12	15-09	07-11	02-01	26-12	10-04	13-03	21-11	17-10	24-04	19-12	16-01	01-05
3	24-10	13-10	*	02-01	20-03	01-05	30-01	07-11	19-12	05-09	05-12	20-02	15-09	21-11	03-04	06-03	26-12	03-10	16-01	10-04	01-09	24-04
4	09-01	23-01	22-08	*	06-02	20-03	24-10	05-12	24-04	19-12	26-12	08-09	27-02	03-04	21-11	25-08	10-10	26-09	10-04	29-09	13-02	07-11
5	13-02	06-03	17-10	15-09	*	16-01	02-01	19-12	07-11	26-12	10-04	21-11	30-01	24-04	10-10	03-10	01-09	13-03	05-12	03-04	01-05	05-09
6	22-08	26-09	09-01	17-10	25-08	*	06-03	13-02	12-09	21-11	10-10	26-12	13-03	07-11	05-12	06-02	10-04	23-01	03-04	24-04	03-10	19-12
7	23-01	06-02	26-09	13-03	22-08	29-09	*	21-11	05-12	10-04	19-12	24-04	13-02	10-10	27-02	09-01	07-11	25-08	26-12	12-09	20-10	03-04
8	28-11	20-02	27-03	05-09	31-10	12-10	17-04	*	20-03	16-01	30-01	27-02	28-12	14-09	28-09	14-11	01-05	12-04	02-01	24-10	12-12	31-08
9	17-04	12-12	31-10	01-12	27-03	28-12	19-09	17-10	*	01-09	02-01	20-09	12-04	01-05	13-02	10-10	30-01	14-11	05-09	27-02	13-03	16-01
10	12-12	07-09	28-12	31-10	12-04	17-04	14-11	24-08	23-01	*	28-09	22-08	27-03	13-02	06-02	26-09	19-10	28-11	27-02	09-01	10-10	13-03
11	06-02	28-12	08-09	12-04	14-11	20-02	31-10	26-09	22-08	06-03	*	25-08	17-04	17-10	09-01	28-11	13-03	12-12	13-10	23-01	27-03	03-10
12	14-11	27-03	10-10	28-12	17-04	12-04	28-11	03-10	06-03	02-01	16-01	*	17-10	01-09	13-03	12-12	15-09	31-10	01-05	13-02	05-09	30-01
13	24-08	22-08	06-02	03-10	26-09	24-10	12-10	12-09	26-12	07-11	21-11	20-03	*	19-12	24-04	23-01	03-04	09-01	20-02	05-12	06-03	10-04
14	12-09	12-04	17-04	12-12	28-11	27-03	20-02	06-02	09-01	13-10	20-03	23-01	31-10	*	26-09	28-12	03-10	22-08	24-10	25-08	14-11	06-03
15	12-04	14-11	12-12	17-04	20-02	05-09	03-10	06-03	13-10	29-08	01-05	24-10	28-11	30-01	*	31-10	16-01	27-03	01-09	20-03	28-12	02-01
16	20-03	24-10	30-09	16-01	27-02	16-09	01-05	10-04	20-02	30-01	24-04	03-04	02-09	05-09	19-12	*	05-12	13-10	07-11	26-12	02-01	21-11
17	31-10	19-04	12-04	20-02	23-01	14-11	27-03	09-01	26-09	20-03	24-10	06-02	12-12	27-02	24-08	12-09	*	28-12	28-09	22-08	28-11	12-10
18	29-09	20-03	27-02	30-01	24-10	01-09	16-01	26-12	10-04	24-04	03-04	19-12	01-05	02-01	07-11	13-02	05-09	*	21-11	10-10	15-09	05-12
19	28-12	28-11	25-08	14-11	12-09	12-12	12-04	22-08	06-02	03-10	13-02	09-01	10-10	13-03	23-01	27-03	06-03	17-04	*	26-09	31-10	17-10
20	27-03	31-10	14-11	06-03	12-12	28-11	12-10	13-03	03-10	01-05	02-09	13-10	05-09	16-01	21-10	21-04	02-01	20-02	30-01	*	17-04	15-09
21	26-09	25-08	23-01	13-10	09-01	27-02	20-03	03-04	24-10	20-02	07-11	05-12	29-09	10-04	08-09	22-08	24-04	06-02	19-12	21-11	*	26-12
22	10-10	09-01	28-11	27-03	28-12	31-10	12-12	23-01	25-08	24-10	27-02	26-09	14-11	29-09	22-08	17-04	13-02	08-09	20-03	06-02	12-04	*

DIADORA LEAGUE DIVISION TWO
FIXTURE DATES 1992/93

1. ✓ Banstead Athletic
2. ✓ Barton Rovers
3. ✓ Berkhamstead Town
4. ✓ Chertsey Town
5. ✓ Edgware Town
6. ✓ Egham Town
7. ✓ Hampton
8. ✓ Harefield United
9. ✓ Hemel Hempstead
10. ✓ Hungerford Town
11. ✓ Leatherhead

12. ✓ Malden Vale
13. ✓ Met Police
14. ✓ Newbury Town
15. ✓ Rainham Town
16. ✓ Ruislip Manor
17. ✓ Saffron Walden
18. ✓ Southall
19. ✓ Tilbury
20. ✓ Ware
21. ✓ Witham Town
22. ✓ Worthing

H/A	1	2	3	4	5	6	7	8	9	10	11	12	13	14	15	16	17	18	19	20	21	22
1	*	30-01	06-03	20-02	24-04	01-05	07-11	21-11	10-04	19-09	05-12	06-10	22-12	19-12	20-03	01-09	24-10	13-10	05-09	16-01	03-04	02-01
2	26-09	*	09-01	24-04	03-04	29-09	21-11	10-10	29-08	13-02	19-12	25-08	07-11	05-12	22-08	17-10	23-01	06-02	10-04	26-12	27-02	13-03
3	29-09	01-05	*	03-04	24-11	19-09	10-04	05-09	26-12	01-09	24-04	13-10	05-12	20-02	27-02	02-01	20-03	24-10	30-01	07-11	19-12	16-01
4	10-10	28-11	12-12	*	30-01	12-04	29-08	01-09	13-02	17-10	16-01	31-10	19-09	06-03	17-04	05-09	14-11	27-03	02-01	01-05	13-03	28-12
5	28-11	12-12	17-04	03-10	*	31-10	23-01	30-09	06-02	14-11	27-02	12-09	13-02	26-08	28-12	12-04	10-10	09-01	24-10	20-03	22-08	27-03
6	09-01	06-03	06-02	26-12	19-12	*	13-02	07-11	24-04	13-03	10-10	23-01	10-04	12-09	25-08	06-10	22-08	26-09	21-11	03-04	05-12	17-10
7	27-03	17-04	14-11	27-02	01-09	13-10	*	19-09	24-10	28-12	30-01	12-04	01-05	20-03	31-10	12-12	28-11	20-02	16-01	02-01	29-09	05-09
8	17-04	20-02	28-12	23-01	06-03	27-03	06-02	*	15-09	27-10	20-03	22-08	03-10	09-01	28-11	14-11	12-09	12-04	13-10	24-10	26-09	12-12
9	14-11	28-12	12-04	13-10	19-09	28-11	13-03	16-01	*	05-09	01-09	20-02	02-01	06-10	12-12	17-04	27-03	31-10	01-05	30-01	17-10	06-03
10	06-02	13-10	23-01	20-03	10-04	24-10	15-09	19-12	05-12	*	24-11	09-01	03-04	26-12	26-09	06-03	03-10	22-08	07-11	20-02	24-04	06-10
11	12-09	31-10	28-11	26-08	06-10	20-02	26-09	17-10	23-01	17-04	*	12-12	13-03	22-08	14-11	27-03	06-02	28-12	06-03	14-10	09-01	12-04
12	27-02	16-01	13-02	19-12	05-12	31-08	26-12	02-01	10-10	01-05	03-04	*	05-09	10-04	24-10	19-09	14-09	20-03	24-04	23-11	07-11	30-01
13	13-04	27-03	15-09	06-02	13-10	14-11	09-01	27-02	22-08	12-12	24-10	29-12	*	26-09	23-01	28-11	31-10	17-04	20-03	29-09	25-08	20-02
14	31-10	05-09	10-10	29-09	16-01	28-12	17-10	01-05	27-02	12-04	02-01	14-11	30-01	*	27-03	13-03	17-04	12-12	01-09	19-09	13-02	28-11
15	17-10	02-01	06-10	24-11	05-09	16-01	19-12	24-04	03-04	30-01	19-04	13-03	01-09	07-11	*	01-05	13-02	06-03	26-12	05-12	10-10	19-09
16	23-01	20-03	22-08	05-12	26-12	27-02	03-04	10-04	21-11	28-09	07-11	06-02	24-04	24-10	09-01	*	26-09	24-08	20-02	19-12	12-09	12-10
17	13-03	01-09	17-10	10-04	20-02	02-01	24-04	05-12	07-11	16-01	19-09	06-03	19-12	24-11	13-10	30-01	*	06-10	03-04	05-09	26-17	01-05
18	13-02	19-09	13-03	07-11	01-05	30-01	10-10	26-12	19-12	02-01	05-09	17-10	24-11	03-04	29-09	16-01	27-02	*	05-12	24-04	10-04	01-09
19	28-12	14-11	26-09	22-08	13-03	17-04	27-10	13-02	09-01	27-03	29-09	28-11	17-10	23-01	12-04	10-10	12-12	12-09	*	27-02	06-02	31-10
20	25-08	12-04	27-03	09-01	17-10	12-12	22-08	13-03	26-09	10-10	13-02	17-04	06-03	06-02	12-09	31-10	28-12	28-11	06-10	*	23-01	14-11
21	12-12	06-10	31-10	24-10	02-01	05-09	06-03	30-01	20-03	28-11	01-05	27-03	16-01	13-10	20-02	28-12	12-04	14-11	19-09	01-09	*	17-04
22	22-08	24-10	25-08	15-09	07-11	20-03	05-12	03-04	29-09	27-02	26-12	26-09	10-10	24-04	06-02	13-02	09-01	23-01	19-12	10-04	21-11	*

DIADORA LEAGUE DIVISION THREE
FIXTURE DATES 1992/93

1. ✓ Aldershot Town
2. ✓ Bracknell Town
3. ✓ Camberley Town
4. ✓ Clapton
5. ✓ Collier Row
6. ✓ Cove
7. ✓ East Thurrock United
8. ✓ Epsom & Ewell
9. ~~Farnham Town~~
10. ✓ Feltham & Hounslow
11. ✓ Flackwell Heath

12. ✓ Hertford Town
13. ✓ Hornchurch
14. ✓ Horsham
15. ✓ Kingsbury Town
16. ✓ Leighton Town
17. ✓ Northwood
18. ✓ Petersfield United
19. ✓ Royston Town
20. ✓ Thame United
21. ✓ Tring Town

H/A	1	2	3	4	5	6	7	8	9	10	11	12	13	14	15	16	17	18	19	20	21
1	•	24-10	20-03	22-08	23-01	09-01	19-12	21-11	26-12	06-02	06-03	20-02	05-12	29-08	24-04	26-09	31-10	12-09	13-10	10-04	07-11
2	13-03	•	26-12	26-09	06-02	23-01	07-11	10-10	12-09	09-01	06-10	03-04	24-04	17-10	05-12	25-08	22-08	13-02	06-03	19-12	21-11
3	17-10	12-04	•	27-03	12-12	31-10	01-09	16-01	06-03	10-10	05-09	01-05	13-02	28-12	13-03	17-04	14-11	06-10	28-11	30-01	02-01
4	02-01	30-01	07-11	•	13-03	17-10	26-12	05-09	03-04	13-02	16-01	24-04	19-12	01-09	10-04	17-11	27-02	10-10	19-09	01-05	05-12
5	02-09	19-09	03-04	24-10	•	14-10	05-09	24-04	20-02	30-09	02-01	07-11	26-12	16-01	19-12	27-02	20-03	10-04	01-05	21-11	30-01
6	01-05	01-09	19-12	20-03	13-02	•	02-01	03-04	10-04	27-02	19-09	21-11	10-10	30-01	07-11	24-10	29-09	26-12	16-01	05-12	24-04
7	03-10	27-03	23-01	12-04	28-12	22-08	•	20-03	09-01	17-04	14-11	24-10	25-08	12-12	26-09	28-11	12-09	06-02	20-02	06-03	13-10
8	17-04	20-02	25-08	28-12	28-11	12-12	17-10	•	22-08	12-09	27-03	13-10	23-01	12-04	09-01	14-11	06-02	26-09	31-10	06-10	06-03
9	12-04	28-12	29-09	12-12	10-10	14-11	01-05	02-01	•	31-10	13-03	19-09	27-02	28-11	13-02	27-03	17-04	17-10	15-09	16-01	01-09
10	19-09	01-05	20-02	14-10	06-03	06-10	21-11	05-12	19-12	•	02-09	16-01	10-04	02-01	03-04	20-03	24-10	07-11	30-01	24-04	05-09
11	27-10	27-02	05-12	25-08	22-08	06-02	10-04	07-11	24-10	23-01	•	19-12	21-11	13-10	12-09	09-01	26-09	03-04	20-03	26-12	20-02
12	10-10	12-12	09-01	28-11	27-03	17-04	13-03	13-02	06-02	25-08	31-10	•	26-09	14-11	23-01	15-09	28-12	22-08	12-04	17-10	06-10
13	05-09	28-11	13-10	31-10	12-04	20-02	16-01	01-09	06-10	14-11	17-04	30-01	•	06-03	17-10	12-12	27-03	13-03	28-12	19-09	01-05
14	27-02	20-03	15-09	23-01	25-08	26-09	03-04	26-12	24-04	22-08	13-02	10-04	29-09	•	21-11	06-02	09-01	05-12	24-10	07-11	19-12
15	28-11	05-09	24-10	14-11	31-10	27-03	30-01	01-05	13-10	12-12	28-12	01-09	20-03	17-04	•	20-02	12-04	06-03	06-10	02-01	19-09
16	30-01	16-01	21-11	06-03	06-10	13-03	24-04	10-04	07-11	17-10	01-05	05-12	03-04	19-09	10-10	•	13-02	19-12	02-01	01-09	26-12
17	16-01	02-01	10-04	06-10	17-10	06-03	05-12	19-09	24-11	13-03	30-01	05-09	07-11	01-05	26-17	03-10	•	24-04	01-09	20-02	03-04
18	28-12	13-10	27-02	20-02	14-11	12-04	19-09	30-01	20-03	27-03	12-12	02-01	24-10	10-11	29-09	27-10	28-11	•	17-04	22-09	16-01
19	13-02	30-09	24-04	06-02	09-01	26-08	10-10	19-12	05-12	26-09	17-10	26-12	12-09	13-03	27-02	22-08	23-01	21-11	•	03-04	10-04
20	14-11	31-10	26-09	09-01	17-04	15-09	29-09	27-02	29-08	28-11	12-04	20-03	06-02	27-03	22-08	28-12	12-10	23-01	12-12	•	24-10
21	27-03	17-04	22-08	12-09	26-09	28-11	13-02	28-09	23-01	28-12	10-10	27-02	09-01	31-10	06-02	12-04	12-12	24-08	14-11	13-03	•

BEAZER HOMES LEAGUE PREMIER DIVISION
FIXTURE DATES 1992/93

1. ✓ Atherstone United
2. ✓ Bashley
3. ✓ Burton Albion
4. ✓ Cambridge City
5. ✓ Chelmsford City
6. ✓ Cheltenham Town
7. ✓ Corby Town
8. ✓ Crawley Town
9. ✓ Dartford
10. ✓ Dorchester Town
11. ✓ Dover Athletic

12. ✓ Gloucester City
13. ✓ Halesowen Town
14. ✓ Hastings Town
15. ✓ Hednesford Town
16. ✓ Moor Green
17. ✓ Solihull Borough
18. ✓ Trowbridge Town
19. ✓ V.S.Rugby
20. ✓ Waterlooville
21. ✓ Weymouth
22. ✓ Worcester City

H/A	1	2	3	4	5	6	7	8	9	10	11	12	13	14	15	16	17	18	19	20	21	22
1	•	20-03	01-01	16-01	31-10	03-04	26-12	12-09	10-10	09-01	24-04	19-12	17-11	23-01	21-11	08-09	06-02	13-03	12-04	26-09	29-08	25-08
2	22-08	•	23-01	05-09	14-11	06-02	10-10	27-03	20-01	31-08	13-03	05-12	24-04	05-01	20-02	03-10	27-02	28-10	19-12	26-12	12-04	07-11
3	07-11	29-08	•	13-03	30-01	17-10	12-04	31-10	19-09	27-03	13-02	02-01	08-09	19-12	16-01	25-08	03-04	27-02	26-12	05-12	01-05	17-11
4	12-12	02-01	20-03	•	10-04	30-01	18-11	09-01	28-12	24-04	26-08	23-01	27-03	09-09	07-11	29-08	24-10	17-04	13-02	06-03	10-10	21-11
5	20-02	03-04	2J-04	26-12	•	22-08	19-12	12-04	26-10	28-11	16-11	29-08	13-03	07-11	05-09	10-10	02-01	16-01	27-03	18-01	27-02	06-02
6	19-01	13-02	20-02	19-12	05-12	•	29-08	28-01	24-10	07-11	10-10	28-12	10-04	06-03	19-09	17-11	21-11	27-03	24-04	05-09	25-08	05-01
7	10-04	12-12	28-12	31-08	06-03	03-10	•	14-11	28-11	05-09	24-10	27-03	09-01	31-10	01-01	23-01	18-01	01-05	24-08	06-02	17-04	27-02
8	17-04	21-11	06-02	27-02	28-12	28-11	22-08	•	07-11	27-10	19-01	10-10	04-12	06-03	05-09	13-02	02-01	31-08	16-01	24-04	
9	01-05	08-09	14-11	12-04	25-08	13-03	03-04	05-01	•	19-12	26-12	03-10	29-08	01-12	27-02	05-12	13-02	30-01	17-10	21-11	31-10	23-01
10	30-01	17-11	12-12	03-04	13-02	27-02	05-12	25-08	16-01	•	02-01	24-10	10-10	13-03	17-04	14-11	01-05	08-09	29-08	12-04	26-12	31-10
11	05-09	17-10	22-08	27-10	05-01	17-04	20-02	08-09	10-04	06-02	•	27-02	21-11	28-12	01-05	20-03	07-11	28-11	03-10	23-01	12-12	03-04
12	19-09	06-03	21-11	22-08	17-04	12-04	16-01	20-02	12-12	05-01	14-11	•	06-02	01-05	31-08	30-01	27-10	26-12	31-10	20-03	08-09	17-10
13	31-08	16-01	19-01	14-11	03-10	26-12	20-03	01-05	06-03	20-02	30-01	28-11	•	17-04	27-10	31-10	12-12	02-01	12-09	22-08	05-09	12-04
14	03-10	30-01	24-10	19-01	13-10	16-01	13-02	26-12	31-08	21-11	12-04	05-09	05-12	•	22-08	27-03	24-04	14-11	27-02	03-11	02-01	12-12
15	13-02	24-10	06-03	05-12	09-01	14-11	24-04	29-08	02-01	23-01	31-10	16-11	24-08	03-04	•	12-04	22-02	10-10	07-09	19-12	13-03	26-12
16	02-01	01-05	27-10	28-11	12-12	31-08	13-03	03-04	05-09	22-08	16-01	24-04	27-02	06-02	28-12	•	10-04	07-11	21-11	24-10	13-02	19-01
17	14-11	31-10	10-10	20-02	23-01	20-03	09-09	03-10	17-04	06-03	19-12	26-08	05-01	29-08	30-01	26-12	•	12-04	18-11	09-01	05-12	27-03
18	05-12	25-08	05-09	03-10	24-10	31-10	21-11	19-12	20-02	19-01	06-03	10-04	23-01	09-01	06-02	05-01	28-12	•	03-04	24-04	17-11	13-10
19	28-12	19-09	10-04	01-01	01-05	12-12	27-10	30-01	06-02	20-03	05-12	13-03	07-11	20-02	19-01	17-04	31-08	22-08	•	10-10	14-11	05-09
20	17-10	10-04	17-04	31-10	08-09	01-05	02-01	17-11	27-03	28-12	29-08	07-11	13-02	25-08	03-10	20-02	28-11	12-12	16-01	•	30-01	13-03
21	06-03	28-12	03-10	06-02	21-11	28-10	07-11	17-10	24-04	10-04	27-03	20-01	19-12	28-11	20-03	09-01	22-08	31-08	23-01	01-01	•	20-02
22	26-10	17-04	31-08	01-05	20-03	02-01	30-01	05-12	22-08	03-10	19-09	13-02	28-12	10-10	10-04	19-12	16-01	29-08	06-03	14-11	24-10	•

BEAZER HOMES LEAGUE MIDLAND DIVISION
FIXTURE DATES 1992/93

1. ✓ Barri
2. ✓ Bedworth United
3. ✓ Bilston Town
4. ✓ Bridgnorth Town
5. ✓ Dudley Town
6. ✓ Evesham United
7. ✓ Forest Green Rovers
8. ✓ Grantham Town
9. ✓ Gresley Rovers
10. ✓ Hinckley Town
11. ✓ King's Lynn

12. ✓ Leicester United
13. ✓ Newport A.F.C.
14. ✓ Nuneaton Borough
15. ✓ Racing Club Warwick
16. ✓ Redditch United
17. ✓ Rushden & Diamonds
18. ✓ Stourbridge
19. ✓ Sutton Coldfield Town
20. ✓ Tamworth
21. ✓ Weston-Super-Mare
22. ✓ Yate Town

H/A	1	2	3	4	5	6	7	8	9	10	11	12	13	14	15	16	17	18	19	20	21	22
1	•	26-09	06-02	21-11	01-01	12-04	26-08	17-10	27-02	05-09	24-04	07-11	26-12	23-01	27-03	03-04	13-03	13-01	31-10	20-02	12-12	18-11
2	28-11	•	10-04	22-08	17-11	20-03	06-02	19-01	16-01	01-05	17-04	13-02	31-10	28-12	06-03	05-09	03-04	01-01	27-10	14-11	03-10	12-12
3	05-12	26-12	•	27-03	12-04	30-01	07-11	24-04	13-02	19-09	06-03	08-09	21-11	25-08	19-12	31-08	02-01	13-03	16-01	10-10	24-10	20-02
4	13-02	30-01	09-01	•	26-12	31-08	17-10	07-11	25-08	05-12	23-01	26-09	05-11	03-04	28-11	12-04	20-03	14-11	27-02	24-04	08-09	06-03
5	19-12	31-08	28-12	10-04	•	02-01	28-11	26-09	07-11	26-08	14-11	06-03	16-01	09-09	09-01	13-02	05-12	24-10	01-05	17-03	30-01	17-04
6	28-12	10-10	26-09	18-11	27-02	•	10-04	13-02	12-12	07-11	17-10	31-10	09-09	09-01	23-01	16-01	24-04	27-03	05-09	19-12	26-08	01-01
7	27-10	02-01	27-02	12-12	13-03	26-12	•	16-01	26-09	03-04	22-08	30-01	31-08	13-02	05-12	17-04	24-10	01-05	10-10	08-09	12-04	14-11
8	09-01	08-09	14-11	01-05	23-01	03-10	20-02	•	24-10	20-03	10-04	28-12	06-02	01-01	27-10	06-03	31-08	17-04	12-12	05-12	21-11	22-08
9	03-10	20-02	05-01	27-10	22-08	19-09	09-01	28-11	•	17-10	20-03	24-04	14-11	10-04	13-03	19-01	19-12	30-01	31-08	28-12	06-03	3-10
10	06-03	27-03	12-12	17-04	28-10	20-02	23-01	10-10	06-02	•	31-08	01-01	26-09	24-10	22-08	09-09	28-12	14-11	28-11	24-04	09-01	
11	24-10	09-01	05-09	19-09	27-03	13-03	19-12	26-12	10-10	07-11	•	25-08	30-01	07-11	13-02	28-11	12-04	27-02	19-01	05-01	29-08	01-05
12	01-05	05-12	19-01	06-02	12-12	17-04	05-09	12-04	02-01	13-03	27-10	•	22-08	27-03	17-11	14-11	26-12	10-10	20-02	23-01	09-01	03-10
13	10-04	27-02	03-04	13-03	24-04	13-01	18-11	05-09	23-01	19-12	05-12	28-11	•	03-10	24-10	02-01	10-10	13-02	27-03	26-08	07-11	28-12
14	17-04	12-04	27-10	10-10	19-01	01-05	20-03	31-10	26-12	27-02	12-12	21-11	20-02	•	05-09	06-02	16-01	22-08	02-01	17-11	06-04	19-09
15	22-08	21-11	17-10	16-01	20-02	14-11	19-09	25-08	17-04	26-12	02-01	31-08	01-05	30-01	•	12-12	27-02	31-10	12-04	06-02	20-03	19-10
16	10-10	24-04	17-11	28-12	31-10	24-10	27-03	30-01	08-09	21-11	20-02	19-12	20-03	05-12	29-08	•	25-08	10-04	13-03	09-01	01-01	23-01
17	14-11	23-01	22-08	05-09	06-02	28-11	06-03	17-11	01-05	19-01	28-12	10-04	12-12	26-09	01-01	27-10	•	09-01	17-04	27-03	20-02	17-10
18	08-09	07-11	23-01	20-02	20-03	05-12	03-10	02-01	05-09	12-04	26-09	16-01	06-04	19-12	24-04	26-12	21-11	•	06-02	06-03	17-11	27-10
19	30-01	26-08	20-03	19-12	21-11	06-03	01-01	03-04	18-11	13-02	09-09	24-10	09-01	24-04	28-12	03-10	07-11	19-09	•	10-04	23-01	05-12
20	02-01	13-03	17-04	24-10	03-10	22-08	19-01	27-02	12-04	16-01	21-11	20-03	27-10	01-09	07-11	01-05	30-01	12-12	26-12	•	13-02	05-09
21	16-01	19-12	01-05	19-01	05-09	27-10	28-12	13-03	05-12	02-01	06-02	03-04	17-04	14-11	10-10	27-02	19-09	31-08	22-08	31-10	•	10-04
22	31-08	24-10	28-11	02-01	10-10	06-02	24-04	19-12	27-03	30-01	16-01	27-02	12-04	13-03	09-09	07-11	13-02	26-08	26-09	03-04	26-12	•

BEAZER HOMES LEAGUE SOUTHERN DIVISION
FIXTURE DATES 1992/93

1. ✓ Andover
2. ✓ Ashford Town
3. ✓ Baldock Town
4. ✓ Braintree Town
5. ✓ Buckingham Town
6. ✓ Burnham
7. ✓ Bury Town
8. ✓ Canterbury City
9. ✓ Dunstable
10. ✓ Erith & Belvedere
11. ✓ Fareham Town
12. ✓ Fisher Athletic
13. ✓ Gravesend & Northfleet
14. ✓ Havant Town
15. ✓ Margate
16. ✓ Newport IOW
17. ✓ Poole Town
18. ✓ Salisbury
19. ✓ Sittingbourne
20. ✓ Sudbury Town
21. ✓ Wealdstone
22. ✓ Witney Town

H/A	1	2	3	4	5	6	7	8	9	10	11	12	13	14	15	16	17	18	19	20	21	22
1	•	27-03	17-11	09-01	07-11	05-12	10-10	24-04	22-08	20-03	27-10	05-09	27-02	28-12	06-02	05-01	19-01	10-04	19-12	28-11	26-09	20-02
2	03-10	•	22-08	06-02	28-11	05-09	20-03	28-12	20-02	08-09	09-01	01-01	25-08	19-12	17-11	24-10	24-04	03-04	10-04	07-11	23-01	13-03
3	31-08	12-12	•	10-04	13-02	10-10	28-12	09-01	19-01	30-03	31-10	13-03	23-01	05-12	21-11	17-04	05-09	01-05	27-02	25-08	05-01	14-11
4	13-03	02-01	26-12	•	31-08	19-01	28-11	05-01	27-10	23-01	05-09	24-04	19-12	22-08	03-04	10-10	13-02	20-02	05-12	12-04	14-11	19-09
5	30-01	01-05	19-12	17-11	•	09-01	25-08	05-12	06-02	03-10	17-10	20-02	29-08	13-03	17-04	27-03	31-10	16-01	08-09	14-11	28-12	10-04
6	13-02	16-09	02-01	09-09	27-02	•	30-01	14-11	20-03	12-04	06-01	24-10	26-12	03-04	16-01	07-11	28-11	02-09	26-09	12-12	26-08	17-10
7	03-04	14-11	12-04	06-03	27-10	20-02	•	19-01	24-04	02-01	22-08	19-09	09-01	21-11	05-09	05-12	23-01	06-02	17-10	26-12	31-08	01-05
8	12-12	12-04	16-01	30-01	05-09	22-08	09-09	•	10-10	01-05	21-11	03-04	18-11	26-09	26-12	06-03	02-01	17-04	28-10	24-10	13-02	07-11
9	23-01	26-09	03-04	25-08	24-10	21-11	01-01	27-02	•	17-11	05-12	07-11	08-09	30-01	01-05	12-12	09-01	29-08	13-02	17-04	10-04	28-12
10	16-01	19-01	24-10	12-12	24-04	28-12	17-04	27-03	31-08	•	14-11	10-04	28-11	13-02	27-10	05-09	27-02	30-01	10-10	19-09	13-03	22-08
11	26-08	30-01	29-08	07-11	03-04	01-05	16-01	20-02	02-01	06-03	•	18-11	24-10	09-09	03-10	12-04	26-12	12-12	06-02	13-03	17-04	28-11
12	21-11	27-02	06-03	26-09	02-01	23-01	13-02	31-10	19-12	26-12	31-08	•	12-04	26-10	07-09	01-05	10-10	14-11	09-01	20-03	05-12	17-04
13	31-10	27-10	20-03	21-11	06-03	10-04	12-12	31-08	16-01	10-10	27-03	28-12	•	20-02	01-01	06-02	22-08	19-09	24-04	19-01	30-01	05-09
14	12-04	17-04	06-02	01-05	10-10	19-09	27-03	28-11	14-11	09-01	19-01	25-08	07-11	•	23-01	26-12	31-08	01-01	20-03	27-02	06-03	12-12
15	14-11	31-08	27-03	24-10	12-12	06-03	19-12	10-04	28-11	25-08	13-02	19-01	13-03	24-04	•	02-01	26-09	10-10	28-12	30-01	07-11	09-01
16	15-09	13-02	28-11	20-03	23-01	13-03	27-02	03-10	17-10	19-12	28-12	30-01	14-11	10-04	31-10	•	27-10	08-09	22-08	09-01	24-04	31-08
17	08-09	21-11	30-01	16-01	19-09	06-02	07-11	13-03	27-03	05-12	10-04	12-12	17-04	17-11	20-02	25-08	•	28-12	01-05	03-10	24-10	01-01
18	26-12	05-12	03-10	17-10	22-08	18-11	24-10	19-12	13-03	07-11	24-04	27-03	13-02	05-09	27-02	20-01	12-04	•	23-01	02-01	09-01	26-08
19	24-10	26-12	07-11	17-04	19-01	27-03	13-03	25-08	19-09	03-04	10-10	28-11	02-01	16-01	12-04	20-02	14-11	06-03	•	31-08	12-12	30-01
20	06-03	16-01	27-10	28-12	05-01	24-04	10-04	06-02	05-09	20-02	23-01	22-08	01-05	17-10	05-12	26-09	19-12	31-10	17-11	•	10-10	03-04
21	01-05	31-10	20-02	27-02	12-04	28-10	18-11	19-09	26-12	17-10	19-12	06-02	03-10	02-01	22-08	16-01	20-03	21-11	05-09	27-03	•	20-01
22	02-01	10-10	24-04	27-03	26-12	19-12	26-09	23-01	12-04	06-02	27-02	16-01	05-12	24-10	20-03	17-11	06-03	27-10	21-11	13-02	08-09	•

INDEX OF LEAGUES CONTAINED IN THIS BOOK

PYRAMID CLUB INDEX

This year, for the first time, the index contains all English clubs who are featured in the Directory. This embraces all clubs within the Pyramid, and many more, and is surely the most comprehensive list of Non-League clubs ever published. Page numbers are given in parentheses after the club name. It is my ambition to see the Directory ultimately contact details of all senior clubs in the country.

J.W.

A.

A.B.M (859)
A.C. Delco (632)
A.F.C. Aldermaston (633)
A.F.C. Cowley (575)
A.F.C. Eltham (396)
A.P. Sports & Social (575)
Abacus (844)
Aberford Albion (852)
Abingdon Town (324)
Abingdon United (566)
Accrington Stanley (735)
Aerostructures S & S (622)
Albright & Wilson (548)
Alcester Town (554)
Aldershot Town (371)
Alfreton Town (759)
Allensbury Sports (404)
Allerton (853)
Allerton Bywater (852)
Alma Swanley (716)
Almondsbury Picksons (566)
Alphington (605)
Alresford Colne Rgrs (706)
Alresford Town (632)
Alsager (806)
Altofts (852)
Alton Town Bass (632)
Altrincham (157)
Amble Town (898)
Amersham Town (390)
Ampthill Town (456)
Andover (514)
Annfield Plain (886)
Anstey Nomads (846)
Anstey Town (848)
Appledore/B.A.A.C. (612)
Archdale '73 (560)
Ardley United (575)
Ardsley Celtic (853)
Arlesey Town (452)
Armitage '90 (554)
Armthorpe Welfare (818)
Arnold Town (836)
Arundel (640)
Asfordby Amateurs (848)
Ash House (859)
Ash United (424)
Ashcroft (456)
Ashford Town (515)
Ashford Town Middx (424)
Ashington Hirst P. (898)
Ashlea (702)
Ashtead (439)
Ashton Town (793)
Ashton United (760)
Ashville (811)
Askern Miners Welfare (838)
Atherstone United (466)
Atherton Collieries (793)
Atherton L.R. (786)
Attenborough (844)
Audley (798)
Aveley (325)
Avon & Somerset Police (602)
Awbridge (632)
Awsworth Villa (843)

Aylesbury United (300)
Aylesford Paper Mills (727)
Aylestone Park Old Boys (848)

B.

B.A.C. Preston (801)
B.A.C. Stevenage (402)
B.A.E. Canberry (802)
B.A.E. Warton (802)
B.A.T. (622)
B.T. (439)
B.T. Research (710)
Backwell United (596)
Bacup Borough (786)
Badsey Rangers (558)
Bailiff Bridge (853)
Baldock Town (516)
Ball Haye Green (798)
Bamber Bridge (786)
Banbury United (566)
Banstead Athletic (348)
Banwell (604)
Barking (326)
Barkingside (390)
Barlestone St Giles (554)
Barnstaple Town (596)
Barnton (806)
Barri (488)
Barrow (736)
Barrow Town (848)
Barrow Wanderers (802)
Barton Rovers (348)
Barwell (554)
Basford United (843)
Bashley (467)
Basildon United (414)
Basing Rovers (633)
Basingstoke Town (301)
Bath City (163)
Battersea Park Rovers (443)
Beaconsfield United (390)
Bearsted (730)
Beaufoy (443)
Beccles Town (702)
Beckenham Town (716)
Becketts Sporting Club (558)
Beckton United (390)
Bedfont (424)
Bedford Town (456)
Bedford United (456)
Bedlington Terriers (876)
Bedmond Social (402)
Bedworth United (491)
Beeches (806)
Beer Albion (606)
Belper Town (818)
Belper United (840)
Bemerton Heath Harlequins (622)
Berkeley Town (582)
Berkhamsted Town (350)
Bestwood Miners Welfare (844)
Bexhill Town (640)
Bicester Civil Service (575)
Bicester Town (566)
Bideford (590)

Biggleswade Town (452)
Billericay Town (327)
Billingham Synthonia (866)
Billingham Town (876)
Bilsthorpe Colliery Welfare (843)
Bilston Town (492)
Binfield (433)
Birstall United (846)
Birtley (890)
Bishop Auckland (737)
Bishop Sutton (596)
Bishop's Stortford (328)
Bishops Cleeve (570)
Bishops Waltham Town (632)
Biwater (838)
Black Horse (853)
Blackbird Leys A.S.C. (575)
Blackbrook (603)
Blackfield & Langley (632)
Blackheath & Electrodrives (548)
Blackpool Mechanics (786)
Blackpool Rangers (801)
Blackpool Rovers (786)
Blackrod Town (802)
Blackwell Miners Welfare (838)
Blacon Youth Club (811)
Blakenall (542)
Blakeney (582)
Blandford United (630)
Bletchingdon (575)
Bletchingley (443)
Blidworth Welfare (836)
Blisworth (674)
Blofield United (702)
Bloxwich Strollers (548)
Bloxwich Town (554)
Blyth Kitty Brewster (895)
Blyth Spartans (866)
Bognor Regis Town (302)
Boldmere St Michaels (554)
Boldon Community Assn (886)
Bolehall Swifts (554)
Bollington Athletic (806)
Bookham (443)
Bootle (793)
Boots Athletic (842)
Boreham Wood (329)
Borough United (730)
Borrowash Victoria (836)
Bosham (652)
Boston (666)
Boston United (169)
Bourne Town (666)
Bournemouth (622)
Bournemouth Sports Club (630)
Bovingdon (402)
Bowers United (414)
Bowling (853)
Bowling Celtic (853)
Boxted Lodgers (706)
Brache Sparta (452)
Brackley Town (666)
Bracknell Town (371)
Bradbank Sports (443)
Bradenham Wanderers (702)
Bradford Park Avenue (788)
Bradford Rovers (853)
Brading Town (633)
Bradley Rangers (825)

Brailsford (840)
Braintree Town (517)
Braishfield (633)
Bramhall (808)
Brandon Town (702)
Brandon United (866)
Brantham Athletic (691)
Brentwood (414)
Brereton Social (798)
Bridge Park (409)
Bridgnorth Town (493)
Bridgwater Town '84 (602)
Bridlington Town (761)
Bridon Sports (398)
Bridport (633)
Brigg Town (818)
Brighouse Town (852)
Brightlingsea United (691)
Brill United (433)
Brimscombe & Thrupp (582)
Brimsdown Rovers (390)
Brislington (596)
Bristol Manor Farm (590)
British Rail Newark (444)
British Sugar Fonnereau (710)
British Timken (674)
Broadbridge Heath (646)
Broadheath Central (808)
Broadmoor Staff (434)
Broadwater United (408)
Broadwell (582)
Brockenhurst (622)
Brocton (798)
Brodsworth M. Welfare (825)
Bromborough Pool (811)
Bromley (303)
Bromley Green (728)
Bromsgrove Rovers (175)
Brook House (390)
Brook Motors (853)
Broomfield United (728)
Broughton (633)
Buckfastleigh Rangers (605)
Buckingham Athletic (452)
Buckingham Town (518)
Buckland Athletic (606)
Budleigh Salterton (606)
Bugbrooke St Michaels (676)
Bulwell Forest Villa (842)
Bulwell United (838)
Burbage Old Boys (846)
Burgess Hill Town (640)
Burnham (519)
Burnham Ramblers (414)
Burnham United (602)
Burnley Bank Hall (793)
Burnley United (801)
Burntwood (560)
Burpham (439)
Burscough (788)
Burton Albion (468)
Burton Park Wanderers (676)
Bury Town (520)
Bushey Mead (444)
Bushey Rangers (402)
Butterley Brick (840)
Buxted (652)
Buxton (738)

C.

C.A.V. Northolt (408)
Cadbury Heath (579)
Caddington (456)
Caernarfon Town (762)
Caius (444)
Calne Town (596)
Calverton M.W. (844)
Cam Bulldogs (582)
Cambridge City (469)
Cammell Laird (811)
Campden Town (579)
Campion (853)
Cannock Chase (546)
Canterbury City (521)
Canvey Island (414)

Capenhurst (811)
Carlisle City (895)
Carlisle Gillford Park (895)
Carlton Athletic (843)
Carnforth Rangers (802)
Carrow (702)
Carshalton Athletic (304)
Carterton Town (571)
Castle Cary (602)
Castleton Gabriels (792)
Catford Wanderers (396)
Chadderton (788)
Chagford (605)
Chalfont St Peter (330)
Chalfont Wasps (434)
Chard Town (590)
Charfield (582)
Charlton United (575)
Chasetown (542)
Chatham Town (716)
Chatteris Town (691)
Cheadle Town (793)
Cheam Village Warriors (444)
Cheddar (602)
Chelmsford City (470)
Chelmsley Town (555)
Chelston (606)
Cheltenham Saracens (571)
Cheltenham Town (471)
Chertsey Town (350)
Chesham United (305)
Cheshunt (390)
Cheslyn Hay (548)
Chessington & Hook United (444)
Chester-le-Street Town (866)
Chichester City (640)
Chingford Town Wanderers (396)
Chinnor (434)
Chippenham Town (590)
Chipperfield Corinthians (402)
Chipping Norton Town (571)
Chipstead (424)
Chobham (439)
Chorley (739)
Chorlton Town (808)
Christchurch (622)
Christleton (811)
Churchill Club '70 (604)
Cinderford Town (566)
Cirencester Town (566)
Cirencester United (571)
City & Sherwood Hospitals (843)
Clacton Town (696)
Clancey Dudley (548)
Clandown (598)
Clanfield (571)
Clapton (372)
Clapton Villa (396)
Cleator Moor Celtic (886)
Clevedon Town (590)
Clevedon United (602)
Clifton All Whites (843)
Clipstone Welfare (842)
Clitheroe (788)
Clutton (603)
Clyst Rovers (598)
Clyst Valley (606)
Cobham (424)
Cockfosters (392)
Cogenhoe United (666)
Colden Common (632)
Coleford United (582)
Coleshill Town (555)
Collets Green (562)
Collier Row (374)
Colliers Wood United (444)
Colne British Legion (801)
Colney Heath (402)
Coltishall H.V. (702)
Colts '85 (730)
Colwyn Bay (740)
Compton (633)
Concord Rangers (414)
Coney Hall (444)
Congleton Town (763)
Congresbury (602)
Consett (868)
Corby Town (472)
Corinthian Casuals (392)

Cornard United (691)
Corona (444)
Cotgrave Colliery Welfare (842)
Cottesmore Amateurs (848)
Cottingham (676)
County Kitchens Brinkburn (89)
Cove (374)
Covies (633)
Cowes Sports (632)
Cradley Town (542)
Crag Road United (852)
Cranborne (630)
Cranfield United (456)
Cranleigh (424)
Craven (396)
Crawley Town (473)
Cray Valley (396)
Cray Wanderers (716)
Crediton United (598)
Crescent Rovers (444)
Crockenhill (718)
Crook Town (877)
Crowborough Athletic (646)
Croxley Guild (402)
Croydon (331)
Croydon Athletic (392)
Croydon M.O. (439)
Croydon United (444)
Cuffley (402)
Cullompton Rangers (605)
Curzon Ashton (764)
D.C.A. Basingstoke (424)
D.R.G.F.P. (579)

D.

Dagenham & Redbridge (181)
Dalton United (801)
Danson Furness Utd (718)
Darenth Heathside (718)
Darlaston (546)
Darlington C.B. (877)
Dartford (474)
Darwen (788)
Daventry Town (668)
Dawlish Town (592)
De Havilland (456)
Deal Town (718)
Dedham Old Boys (706)
Delco Products (457)
Denaby & Cadeby M.W. (859)
Denaby United (818)
Denham United (434)
Derby C & W Reckitts (838)
Derby Rolls Royce (838)
Dereham Town (702)
Desborough Town (668)
Devizes Town (598)
Devon & Cornwall Police (612)
Didcot Town (568)
Diss Town (691)
Ditton (424)
Donnington Wood (546)
Dorchester Town (475)
Dorking (332)
Dover Athletic (476)
Downes Sports (846)
Downham Town (696)
Downton (632)
Dowty Dynamos (579)
Drayton Park (633)
Drayton Wanderers (436)
Droylsden (741)
Dudley Hill Athletic (853)
Dudley Sports (558)
Dudley Town (494)
Dudley Welfare (896)
Dulwich Hamlet (306)
Dundry Athletic (603)
Dunkirk (842)
Dunstable (522)
Dunston Fed. Brewery (877)
Durham City (868)
Dursley Town (582)
Dynamics Stevenage (404)
Dynamoes (853)

E.

E.A.F. Plymouth (605)
Eagley (801)
Earl Shilton Albion (848)
Earlswood Town (562)
Easington Colliery (868)
Easington Sports (571)
East Cowes Victoria Athletic (624)
East Grinstead (646)
East Ham United (414)
East Preston (652)
East Thurrock United (375)
Eastbourne Town (640)
Eastbourne United (646)
Eastleigh (624)
Eastmoor Albion (853)
Eastwood Hanley (790)
Eastwood Town (765)
Ecchinswell (633)
Eccleshall (798)
Eccleshill United (820)
Edenstone (730)
Edgware Town (352)
Egham Town (352)
Elburton Villa (605)
Ellesmere Port Town (794)
Elliott Star (402)
Ellwood (580)
Elmore (592)
Eltham Town (392)
Ely City (697)
Emberton (457)
Emley (742)
Endsleigh (582)
Enfield (307)
Enville Athletic (562)
Eppleton C.W. (877)
Epsom & Ewell (375)
Erith & Belvedere (523)
Esh Winning (877)
Esh Winning Albion (890)
Esso Fawley (633)
Eton Manor (416)
Eton Wick (433)
Ettingshall Holy Trinity (546)
Evenwood Town (878)
Evergreen (404)
Evesham United (495)
Ewell (444)
Ex-Blues (730)
Exeter City 'A' (606)
Exeter Civil Service (606)
Exmouth Amateurs (606)
Exmouth Town (592)
Eynesbury Rovers (668)
Eynsham (575)

F.

Fairfield Villa (562)
Fairford Town (568)
Fairham (844)
Fakenham Town (692)
Falmouth Town (612)
Fareham Town (524)
Farleigh Rovers (426)
Farleigh Sports (604)
Farnborough Town (187)
Farnham Town (376)
Farnley (853)
Farsley Celtic (766)
Faversham Town (718)
Felixstowe Town (692)
Feltham & Hounslow Borough (376)
Feniscowles (801)
Ferring (652)
Ferrybridge Amateurs (852)
Ferryhill Athletic (868)
Fetcham (444)
Field (852)
Finchampstead (433)
Fisher Athletic (525)
Flackwell Heath (378)
Flamstead (457)
Fleet Spurs (633)

Fleet Town (624)
Fleetlands (632)
Fleetwood Hesketh (802)
Fleetwood Town (743)
Flight Refuelling (630)
Flixton (790)
Folkestone Invicta (720)
Ford Sports (676)
Ford United (416)
Forest (652)
Forest Green Rovers (496)
Forest Hall S.C. (895)
Formby (794)
Fosse Imps (848)
Framlingham Town (710)
Frampton United (582)
Franklands Village (653)
Frecheville C.A. (859)
Freckleton (801)
Friar Lane Old Boys (847)
Frickley Athletic (744)
Frimley Green (426)
Frinton Rovers (439)
Frome Town (592)
Fry Club (602)
Fryston Colliery Welfare (838)

G.

G.P.T. Plessey (842)
Gainsborough Trinity (745)
Gala Wilton (582)
Garfields (398)
Garforth Town (825)
Garsington (575)
Garswood United (808)
Gas Recreation (706)
Gascoigne United (852)
Gateshead (193)
Gateshead Northern Co's (896)
Gedling Colliery Welfare (843)
Gedling Town (836)
General Chemicals (811)
Gillingham Town (630)
Glapwell (836)
Glasshoughton Welfare (820)
Glastonbury (598)
Glaxco Sports Club (802)
Glossop North End (790)
Gloucester City (477)
Godalming & Guildford (426)
Goldenhill Wanderers (798)
Goldthorpe Colliery (859)
Goole Town (746)
Gorleston (692)
Gornal Athletic (546)
Gornal Sports (546)
Gosforth Bohemian (898)
Gosport Borough (624)
Grantham Rown (497)
Gravesend & Northfleet (526)
Grays Athletic (308)
Great Harwood Town (767)
Great Wakering Rovers (416)
Great Wyrley (546)
Great Yarmouth Town (692)
Green Lane (853)
Greenside (444)
Greenways (727)
Greenwich Borough (720)
Greenwood Meadows (842)
Greetland (853)
Gresley Rovers (498)
Gretna (768)
Grove United (808)
Grundisburgh (710)
Guisborough Town (870)
Guiseley (769)

H.

Hadleigh United (697)
Hailsham Town (642)
Halesowen Harriers (542)

Halesowen Town (478)
Halesworth Town (710)
Halifax Irish Club (852)
Hall Green United (853)
Hall Road Rangers (825)
Hallam (825)
Hallen (580)
Halliford (444)
Halstead Town (692)
Haltwhistle Crown Paints (895)
Hambrook (580)
Hampton (354)
Hams Hall (558)
Hamworthy Engineering (630)
Hamworthy United (630)
Handrahan Timbers (558)
Hanford (798)
Hanley Town (808)
Hanwell Town (392)
Hanworth Villa (408)
Harborough Town Imperial (848)
Hardwicke (582)
Harefield United (354)
Haringey Borough (392)
Harleston Town (702)
Harlow Town (333)
Harpenden Rovers (404)
Harpenden Town (452)
Harrogate Railway Ath. (820)
Harrogate Town (770)
Harrow Borough (309)
Harrow Hill (580)
Harrow St Mary's (409)
Harrowby United (676)
Hartlepool B.W.O.B. (890)
Hartlepool Town (886)
Hartley Wintney (426)
Harwich & Parkeston (694)
Harworth Colliery Inst. (836)
Haslingden (802)
Hassocks (646)
Hastings Town (479)
Hatfield Main (826)
Hatfield Town Athletic (452)
Haughley United (710)
Havant Town (527)
Haverhill Rovers (694)
Haworth (853)
Hayes (310)
Hayling United (633)
Haywards Heath Town (647)
Hazells (436)
Headcorn (728)
Headington Amateurs (568)
Heanor Town (836)
Heath Hayes (798)
Heathrow Club (409)
Heaton Stannington (895)
Heavitree United (598)
Hebburn (878)
Hebburn Colliery (890)
Hebburn NEI Reyrolle (897)
Heddon Institute (898)
Hedge End (633)
Hednesford Town (480)
Hellesdon (702)
Helston Athletic (616)
Hemel Hempstead (356)
Hempnall (702)
Henbury Old Boys (580)
Hendon (311)
Hengrove Athletic (603)
Henley Town (436)
Herne Bay (720)
Herrington C.W. (886)
Hersham R.B.L. (439)
Hertford Town (378)
Hertford Youth (405)
Hesketh Bank (802)
Heswall (811)
Hexham Swinton (897)
Heybridge Swifts (334)
Higham Town (676)
Highfield Rangers (847)
Highfields United (899)
Highgate United (555)
Highworth Town (571)
Hill Top Rangers (546)
Hillcroft (848)

Hilldene Athletic (582)
Hillingdon Borough (392)
Hinckley Athletic (542)
Hinckley Town (499)
Histon (694)
Hitchin Town (335)
Hoddesdon Town (452)
Holbeach United (668)
Holbrook Miners Welfare (840)
Holker Old Boys (794)
Holly Lane (562)
Holmer Green (433)
Holmesdale (444)
Holsworthy (612)
Holt United (630)
Holwell Sports (847)
Honiton (606)
Hook Venturers (444)
Horden C.W. (878)
Horley Town (426)
Hornchurch (388)
Horndean (625)
Horsford United (702)
Horsham (388)
Horsham Y.M.C.A. (647)
Horwich R.M.I. (747)
Houchin Rovers (728)
Houghton Rangers (847)
Hounslow Town '91 (409)
Hucknall R.R. Welfare (842)
Hucknall Town (826)
Hullbridge Sports (416)
Huncote Sports & Social (848)
Hungerford Town (356)
Hunsworth (853)
Hurstpierpoint (653)
Hyde United (748)
Hythe (728)

I.

I.C.I. Fibres (582)
I.C.I. Pharmaceuticals (808)
I.C.I. Thornton (801)
I.C.L. Letchworth (405)
I.S.L. Midanbury (632)
Ibstock Welfare (847)
Ickleford (457)
Ifield (653)
Ilfracombe Town (598)
Ilkeston Town (543)
Illogan R.B.L. (616)
Ilminster Town (603)
Immingham Town (826)
Imperial Bristol (603)
Imperial United (602)
Ipswich Wanderers (697)
Irchester United (678)
Irlam Town (794)
Iver (436)
Ivybridge Town (605)

J.

Jarrow (890)
Jarrow Roofing B.C.A. (886)
John Players (842)
John Radcliffe (575)

K.

K Chell (794)
Kelvedon Social (706)
Kempston Rovers (669)
Kenilworth Town (558)
Kennington (728)
Kennington United (575)
Kent Police (720)
Kettering Town (199)
Keynsham Cricketers (604)
Keynsham Town (599)

Keyworth United (843)
Kidderminster Harriers (205)
Kidlington (572)
Kidsgrove Athletic (790)
Kilburn Miners Welfare (838)
Kimberley Town (836)
Kimpton Rovers (405)
King's Lynn (500)
Kings Heath (558)
Kings Langley (403)
Kings Norton Ex-Servicemen (558)
Kings Stanley (582)
Kingsbury Town (381)
Kingstonian (312)
Kintbury Rangers (568)
Kirby Muxloe S.C. (848)
Kirkham & Wesham (802)
Kirkley (702)
Kiveton Park (838)
Knatchbull (728)
Knebworth (403)
Knockholt (727)
Knowle (555)
Knowsley United (771)
Knutsford (808)
Knypersley Victoria (546)
Kodak Harrow (436)
Kodak Hemel Hempstead (403)

L.

Lakeford Rangers (702)
Lambourn Sports (572)
Lancaster City (772)
Lancing (647)
Langford (453)
Langley Park (878)
Langney Sports (642)
Lansdowne (633)
Lansil Lancaster (802)
Lapford (606)
Larkhall Athletic (599)
Launceston (612)
Launton Sports (575)
Laverstock & Ford (633)
Leatherhead (358)
Ledbury Town '84 (558)
Leek C.S.O.B. (798)
Leek Town (749)
Leicester United (501)
Leicester Y.M.C.A. (848)
Leics Constabulary (847)
Leighton Town (381)
Letchworth Garden City (453)
Letcombe Sports (433)
Leverstock Green (453)
Lewes (336)
Lewisham Elms (396)
Lewisham Town (398)
Leyland (802)
Leyton (337)
Leyton County (396)
Lichfield (547)
Linby Colliery M.W. (844)
Lincoln United (826)
Lindfield Rangers (653)
Linotype (808)
Liskeard Athletic (592)
Liss Athletic (633)
Little Common Albion (647)
Little Gaddesden (405)
Little Oakley (706)
Littlehampton Town (642)
Littletown (853)
Liversedge (820)
Locksheath (632)
Loddon United (702)
London Colney (457)
Long Ashton (603)
Long Buckby (669)
Long Crendon (575)
Long Eaton United (838)
Long Melford (706)
Long Sutton (602)
Long Sutton Athletic (697)
Longbenton (897)

Longford (582)
Longlevens (582)
Longridge United (802)
Longwell Green Abbotonians (602)
Lordswood (727)
Loughborough Dynamo (848)
Loughton (398)
Louth United (837)
Lower Hopton (853)
Lowestoft Town (694)
Lucas (853)
Lucas Sports (403)
Lucas Sports Club (802)
Ludgvan (616)
Ludlow Town (547)
Luton Old Boys (453)
Lutterworth Town (847)
Lydbrook (582)
Lydd Town (728)
Lydney Town (583)
Lye Town (543)
Lymington A.F.C. (625)
Lytham St Annes (801)

M.

Macclesfield Town (211)
Mackworth United (840)
Maghull (794)
Maidenhead United (338)
Maine Road (790)
Malden Town (426)
Malden Vale (358)
Maldon Town (416)
Malpas (808)
Malshanger (632)
Maltby Miners Welfare (820)
Malvern Town (547)
Manders (548)
Mangotsfield United (594)
Manor Athletic (811)
Maple Cross C.S.S.C. (408)
Marazion Blues (616)
March Town United (694)
Marchon (891)
Marden Athletic (899)
Margate (528)
Marine (750)
Marlborough (575)
Marlow (313)
Marsden (852)
Marshalls (398)
Marske United (886)
Marston Green (558)
Marston Saints (575)
Martin Baker Sports (433)
Matlock Town (751)
Matlock United (840)
Mattishall (702)
Meir K.A. (555)
Melksham Town (599)
Melton St Audrys (710)
Mendip Wells (603)
Mersey Royal (811)
Merseyside Police (811)
Merstham (426)
Merthyr Tydfil (217)
Merton Risley (444)
Metpol Chigwell (396)
Metrogas (396)
Metropolitan Police Bushey (405)
Metropolitan Police (360)
Mexborough Main Street (860)
Mexborough Town (838)
Mickleover R.B.L. (837)
Middlewich Athletic (808)
Midhurst & Easebourne (642)
Mildenhall Town (697)
Mile Oak (647)
Mile Oak Rovers & Youth (555)
Mill End Sports (436)
Millbrook (612)
Milton Keynes Borough (453)
Milton United (568)
Milton United (800)
Minehead (594)

Mirrlees Blackstone (669)
Mistley United (706)
Mitcheldean (583)
Mitchells & Butlers (548)
Molesey (339)
Mond Rangers (812)
Monica Star (562)
Monkseaton KOSA Robin Hood (899)
Monotype Sports (444)
Moonshot Athletic (730)
Moor Green (481)
Morecambe (752)
Moreton (812)
Moreton Town (568)
Morfax (444)
Morley Town (853)
Morpeth Town (895)
Mossley (753)
Mousehole (616)
Moxley Rangers (547)
Mulbarton United (702)
Mullion (612)
Multipart Chorley (802)
Murton (870)
Murton International (891)

N.

N.P.L. (445)
Nailsea Town (604)
Nailsea United (603)
Nantwich Town (791)
Narborough & Littlethorpe (847)
Neasden (408)
Needham Market (710)
Nelson (796)
Netherfield (773)
Netherne (439)
Netley Ath. Victoria (633)
Netley Central Sports (633)
Nettleham (837)
New Bradwell St Peter (453)
New Hanford (408)
New Milton (632)
New Romney (727)
New Street (633)
New Winning Wallsend (899)
New York United (897)
Newbiggin Central Welfare (897)
Newbury Town (360)
Newcastle Benfield Park (897)
Newcastle Blue Star (870)
Newcastle D.H.S.S. (899)
Newcastle Norgas Utd (899)
Newcastle Town (791)
Newcastle University (899)
Newent Town (583)
Newfoundpool W.M.C. (847)
Newhall United (838)
Newhaven (642)
Newmarket Town (695)
Newport A.F.C. (502)
Newport I.O.W. (529)
Newport Pagnell Town (669)
Newquay (612)
Newton (812)
Newton Abbot (605)
Newton Aycliffe (888)
Newton Flotman (702)
Newton St Cyres (605)
Norcross & Warbreck (802)
Normanton Athletic (840)
North Ferriby United (822)
North Greenford United (394)
North Kilworth (847)
North Leigh (572)
North Mymms (405)
North Shield St Columbas (897)
North Shields (774)
North Trafford (796)
Northallerton Supporters (891)
Northallerton Town (870)
Northampton O.N. Chenecks (678)
Northampton Spencer (670)
Northern Electric (897)

Northern Telecom Paignton (605)
Northfield Rangers (408)
Northfield Town (556)
Northolt Dynamo (409)
Northolt Saints (409)
Northway United (575)
Northwich Victoria (223)
Northwood (382)
Norton & Stockton A. (878)
Norton United (800)
Norton Woodseats (839)
Norwich Union (703)
Norwich United (695)
Nottinghamshire Police (843)
Nuclear Electric (583)
Nuneaton Borough (503)
Nutfield (633)
Nuthall (839)

O.

Oadby Town (847)
Oakham United (837)
Oakley United (575)
Oakwood (644)
Oakwood (727)
Odd Down (599)
Offwell & Widworthy (606)
Okehampton Argyle (606)
Old Georgians (580)
Old Modernians (853)
Old Newton United (710)
Old Roan (396)
Old Woodstock (575)
Oldbury United (543)
Oldham Town (796)
Oldwinsford (543)
Ollerton & Bevercotes M.W. (844)
Ollerton (398)
Olney Town (678)
Ossett Albion (822)
Ossett Town (822)
Osterley (408)
Otford United (727)
Otley Town (853)
Otterbourne (633)
Ottershaw (439)
Ottery St Mary (599)
Oughtibridge W.M.S.C. (860)
Oulton Broad (703)
Ovenden West Riding (852)
Overstrand (703)
Overton United (632)
Oxford City (453)
Oxford University Press (575)
Oxhey Jets (403)
Oxted & District (445)

P.

Padiham (802)
Paget Rangers (543)
Pagham (644)
Park Rangers (548)
Park Street (403)
Parley Sports (630)
Parramores Sports (860)
Patchway Town (580)
Paulsgrove (633)
Paulton Rovers (594)
Peacehaven & Telscombe (644)
Peasedown Athletic (602)
Pedigree Petfoods (847)
Pegasus Juniors (568)
Pelican (843)
Pelsall Villa (543)
Pendeen Rovers (616)
Penn & Tylers Green (433)
Penrith (791)
Penryn Athletic (616)
Penzance (614)
Peppard (428)
Percy Main Amateurs (897)
Percy Rovers Alnwick (897)

Perranwell (616)
Pershore Town '88 (556)
Peterlee Newtown (872)
Petersfield United (382)
Phoenix (853)
Phoenix (860)
Phoenix Sports (730)
Pickering Town (822)
Pilkington Recreation (809)
Pirelli General (632)
Pirton (453)
Pitshanger (408)
Pitstone & Ivinghoe (455)
Plymouth Argyle Res. (594)
Plymstock Town (605)
Polesworth North Warwick (558)
Pontefract (853)
Pontefract Collieries (822)
Ponteland United (895)
Poole Town (530)
Portfield (644)
Porthleven (614)
Portishead (602)
Portland United (630)
Portsmouth Civil Service (633)
Portsmouth Royal Navy (625)
Potters Bar Crusaders (457)
Potters Bar Town (455)
Potton United (670)
Poulton Town (802)
Poulton Victoria (812)
Poynton (809)
Prescot A.F.C. (791)
Pressed Steel Fisher (575)
Prestwood (434)
Priory Eastwood (837)
Proctor & Gamble Newcastle (898)
Prudhoe East End (880)
Pucklechurch Sports (580)
Pudsey Liberal (853)
Purfleet (340)
Purton (572)

Q.

Quarry Nomads (576)
Quorn (848)

R.

R.A.F. St Mawgan (616)
R.A.S. Knights (445)
R.E.S. Parkgate (826)
R.N.A.S. Culdrose (616)
R.S.S.C. Ransomes (710)
Racing Club Warwick (504)
Radcliffe Borough (775)
Radcliffe Olympic (843)
Radford (839)
Radstock Town (599)
Rainham Town (361)
Rainworth Miners Welfare (843)
Ramsey United (678)
Ramsgate (720)
Raunds Town (670)
Ravenstone (848)
Rawdon Old Boys (852)
Rayners Lane (570)
Raynes Park (439)
Reading Town (434)
Redditch United (505)
Redgate Clayton (800)
Redhill (648)
Reepham Town (703)
Reigate Town (445)
Retford United (844)
Riddings St James (840)
Ringmer (645)
Ringwood Town (633)
Ripley Town (840)
Risborough Rangers (457)
Rists United (800)
Rivacre Rossfield (812)
Robinsons (603)

Rocester (544)
Romford (416)
Romsey Town (625)
Rossendale United (776)
Rossington (839)
Rossington Main (828)
Rothwell Town (670)
Rowsley '66 (840)
Royston Town (384)
Ruddington (843)
Ruddington Village (840)
Ruislip Manor (361)
Runcorn (229)
Rushall Olympic (544)
Rushden & Diamonds (506)
Rusthall (730)
Ryde Sports (627)
Rye United (728)
Ryecroft (844)
Ryhope Community Assoc. (880)
Rylands (809)
Ryton (898)

S.

Saffron Walden Town (362)
Salesians (576)
Salford City (792)
Salisbury (531)
Saltash United (594)
Saltdean United (648)
Saltford (603)
Salthorn (853)
Salts (852)
Salts Grammar S.O.B. (855)
Sandhurst Town (428)
Sandiacre Town (839)
Sandridge Rovers (403)
Sandwell Borough (556)
Sandwich Sports (728)
Sandy Albion (457)
Sarratt (405)
Sawbridgeworth Town (417)
Scolar (409)
Scott Sports & Social (727)
Seaford Town (648)
Seaham Red Star (872)
Seaton Delaval Amateurs (895)
Seaton Terrace (896)
Selby Town (828)
Selsey (648)
Selston (840)
Sevenoaks Town (728)
Shaftesbury (630)
Shamrock (408)
Shankhouse (899)
Shardlow St James (839)
Sharnbrook (678)
Sharpness (583)
Sheerwater (439)
Sheffield (823)
Shefford Town (457)
Shell (812)
Shenley & Loughton (458)
Sheppey United (722)
Shepshed Albion (777)
Shepton Mallet Town (602)
Sherborne Town (631)
Sherwood Celtic (560)
Shildon (880)
Shillington (455)
Shinewater Association (653)
Shirebrook Colliery (837)
Shirehampton (602)
Shirley Town (562)
Sholing Sports (627)
Shoreham (648)
Shortwood United (570)
Shotton Comrades (880)
Sidlesham (654)
Sidley United (650)
Sidmouth Town (606)
Sileby Town (848)
Silksworth (888)
Simba All Stars (408)
Singh Sabha (398)

Sittingbourne (532)
Skelmersdale United (792)
Slade Green (722)
Slough Town (235)
Slough Y.C.O.B. (434)
Smiths Athletic (580)
Sneinton (843)
Snowdown C.W. (728)
Soham Town Rangers (697)
Solihull Borough (482)
Somersett & Ambury V & E (406)
Somersham Town (698)
Soudley (583)
South Bank (872)
South East Olympic (396)
South Godstone (445)
South Normanton Athletic (839)
South Shields (888)
South Shields Cleadon S.C. (888)
Southall (362)
Southam United (560)
Southend Manor (417)
Southgate Athletic (394)
Southport (754)
Southwell City (843)
Southwick (650)
Spalding United (672)
Spelthorne Sports (408)
Spelthorne Sports (445)
Spennymoor United (823)
Spittal Rovers (896)
Springfield Battersea (439)
Springfield Y.C. (853)
Springfields (802)
Squires Gate (796)
St Agnes (617)
St Albans City (314)
St Andrews (394)
St Andrews (703)
St Andrews 'A' (445)
St Andrews Social Club (847)
St Austell (614)
St Blazey (614)
St Clarets Hayes (409)
St Francis Hospital (653)
St George Easton-in-Gordano (603)
St Helens Town (791)
St Ippolyts (405)
St Ives Town (678)
St Johns Clacton (706)
St Just (617)
St Margaretsbury (394)
St Marks C.A.
St Martins (606)
St Peters St Albans (405)
St Philips Marsh A.S. (580)
St Werburghs (812)
Stafford Rangers (241)
Stafford Town (800)
Staffordshire Police (800)
Staines Town (315)
Stalybridge Celtic (247)
Stamco (650)
Stamford (672)
Standon & Puckeridge (406)
Stanley United (891)
Stansfeld O. & B.C. (728)
Stansted (417)
Stanton Dale (796)
Stanton Ilkeston (839)
Stanway Rovers (698)
Stapenhill (556)
Stapleford Villa (844)
Stapleton (581)
Steeton (853)
Stevenage Borough (316)
Stevenage Club & Institute (406)
Stewart & Lloyds (672)
Steyning Town (428)
Stobswood Welfare (899)
Stockbridge (633)
Stockbridge Park Steels (823)
Stocklake Sports (434)
Stockton (872)
Stockwood Green (603)
Stoke Gabriel (605)
Stokenchurch (436)
Stonehouse Freeway (583)
Stonham Aspal (710)

Stony Stratford Town (458)
Stork (812)
Storrington (654)
Stotfold (672)
Stourbridge (507)
Stourport Swifts (544)
Stowmarket Town (695)
Stratford Town (556)
Street (604)
Strenue (445)
Studley B.K.L. (556)
Sturminster Newton (631)
Stutton (710)
Styal (809)
Sudbury Lucas Athletic (706)
Sudbury Town (533)
Sudbury Wanderers (698)
Sun Sports (404)
Sunderland Flo-Gas F. (891)
Sunderland I.F.G. Roker (888)
Sunderland Vaux Ryhope (888)
Surbiton Town (439)
Sutton Athletic (445)
Sutton Athletic (730)
Sutton Coldfield Town (508)
Sutton High (445)
Sutton Town (823)
Sutton United (317)
Swaffham Town (698)
Swalwell (898)
Swalwell Crowley Club (899)
Swanage Town & Herston (627)
Swanley Town (396)
Swanmore (633)
Swift P.P. (562)
Swindon Supermarine (570)
Syston St Peters (847)

T.

T.S. Harrison (853)
Tadcaster Albion (828)
Tamworth (509)
Taunton Town (595)
Tavistock (614)
Technicolor Sports (408)
Teignmouth (605)
Telford United (253)
Tempest (803)
Temple Cloud (603)
Ten Em Bee (730)
Tenterden & St Michaels (728)
Teversal Grange (844)
Teynham & Lynsted (728)
Thackley (824)
Thame United (384)
Thames Polytechnic (728)
Thamesmead Town (722)
Thatcham Town (627)
The 61 FC Luton (455)
Thetford Town (698)
Thimblemill REC (562)
Thoresby Colliery Welfare (843)
Thrapston Venturas (679)
Three Bridges (645)
Thringstone M.W. (848)
Tilbury (364)
Timsbury Athletic (604)
Tipton Town (547)
Tiptree United (695)
Tiverton Town (595)
Tividale (547)
Toddington Rovers (458)
Tonbridge A.F.C. (722)
Tooting & Mitcham United (341)
Topsham Town (605)
Torpoint Athletic (614)
Torquay United Res. (595)
Torrington (595)
Totternhoe (455)
Totton A.F.C. (627)
Tow Law Town (874)
Towcester Town (679)
Tower Hamlets Tipples (394)
Tring Athletic (458)
Tring Town (386)

Trinity Athletic (853)
Triplex (560)
Trowbridge Town (483)
Truro City (614)
Tuffley Rovers (572)
Tunbridge Wells (722)
Tunley Athletic (604)
Turton (802)
Tyersal (852)

U.

United Biscuits Harlesden (409)
University of Kent (730)
Upton Athletic Assoc. (812)
Upton Town (560)
Usworth Village (891)
Uxbridge (342)

V.

V.S. Rugby (484)
Valmar L.R. (406)
Vandyke (439)
Vauxhall Motors (812)
Ventus & Yeadon Celtic (853)
Verdayne (445)
Vernon Carus (802)
Verwood Town (633)
Vickers C.D. Athletic (728)
Vickers Sports Club (802)
Viking Sports (428)
Vikings Stroud (583)
Villacourt Rovers (398)
Viney St Swithins (583)
Virginia Water (439)
Vosper Thorneycroft (633)

W.

Wadebridge Town (614)
Walden Rangers (458)
Walker (896)
Walkern (404)
Wallingford Town (572)
Wallingford United (436)
Wallsend Rising Sun (899)
Walsall Wood (800)
Walsham-le-Willows (710)
Waltham Abbey (394)
Walthamstow Pennant (394)
Walthamstow Trojans (396)
Walton & Hersham (343)
Walton Casuals (439)
Wantage Town (570)
Warboys Town (698)
Ware (364)
Wareham Rangers (631)
Wark (896)
Warlingham (445)
Warminster Town (600)
Warrington Town (778)
Washington (881)
Washington Glebe (891)

Washington Nissan (891)
Watchet Town (603)
Waterlooville (485)
Wath Saracens (860)
Watlington (576)
Watton United (695)
Wealdstone (534)
Wednesfield (544)
Wellcome (404)
Wellesbourne (560)
Welling United (259)
Wellingborough Town (674)
Wellingborough Whitworths (679)
Wellington (600)
Wells City (603)
Welton Rovers (600)
Welwyn (406)
Welwyn Garden City (455)
Wem Town (547)
Wembley (344)
West Allotment Celtic (896)
West Auckland Town (874)
West Bergholt (706)
West Bromwich Town (544)
West Heath United (560)
West Kirby (812)
West Midlands Fire Service (560)
West Midlands Police (557)
West Wight (633)
Westbrook Wanderers (853)
Westbury United (595)
Westerfield United (710)
Westerham (730)
Westerhope (896)
Westfield (428)
Westfields (544)
Westhoughton Town (796)
Westland United (603)
Weston Mill Oak Villa (605)
Weston St John (602)
Weston-super-Mare (510)
Weymouth (486)
Whetstone Athletic (848)
Whickham (881)
Whitby Town (874)
Whitchurch Alport (809)
Whitchurch United (628)
White Lion Cheriton (730)
White Rose Throstles (860)
Whitecroft (583)
Whitehawk (645)
Whitley Bay (755)
Whitstable Town (724)
Whitton United (710)
Whitwell Athletic (406)
Whyteleafe (345)
Wibsey (852)
Wick (645)
Wigan College (802)
Wigan Rovers (803)
Wigston Fields (560)
Willand Rovers (605)
Willaston (812)
Willenhall Town (544)
Willesden Constantine (409)
Willesden Hawkeye (394)
Willington (882)
Willis Corroon (710)
Wilmcote (560)
Wilmslow Albion (809)
Wimborne Town (628)
Winchester Castle (633)

Winchester City (632)
Windscale (890)
Windsor & Eton (318)
Wingate & Finchley (456)
Wingate Mall (892)
Winlaton Hallgarth (896)
Winnington Park (809)
Winscombe (603)
Winsford United (756)
Winterbourne United (581)
Winterton Rangers (824)
Wisbech Town (696)
Witham Town (366)
Withdean (654)
Witney Town (535)
Witton Albion (265)
Wivenhoe Town (319)
Woking (271)
Wokingham Town (320)
Wollaton (844)
Wollen Sports (570)
Wolverhampton Casuals (547)
Wolverhampton United (548)
Wolviston (890)
Wombwell Town (837)
Wooburn Athletic (436)
Woodbridge Town (700)
Woodford Town (417)
Woodmansterne Sports (445)
Woodnesborough (728)
Woodstock Town (576)
Woolwich Town (398)
Wootton Bassett Town (572)
Wootton Blue Cross (674)
Worcester City (487)
Worcester College O.B. (576)
Worcester Park (445)
Workington (779)
Worksop Town (780)
Worle (604)
Wormley Rovers (404)
Worrall Hill (583)
Worsbrough Bridge M.W. (828)
Worthing (366)
Worthing United (650)
Worthington Simpsons (843)
Wortwell (703)
Wotton Rovers (581)
Wraysbury (434)
Wrington-Redhill (604)
Wroxham (696)
Wycombe Wanderers (277)
Wylam (898)
Wymondham Old Boys (703)
Wymondham Town (703)
Wyre Villa (803)
Wythall (562)

Y.

Yarnton (572)
Yate Town (511)
Yatton Athletic (604)
Yeading (321)
Yeovil Town (283)
Yorkley (583)
Yorkshire Amateur (828)

THE END